the Next Exit®
USER
GUIDE

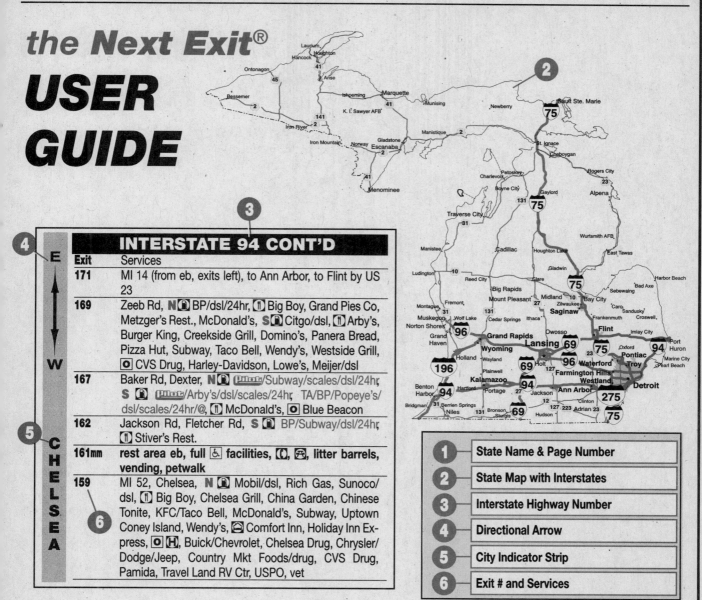

② 2

④ 4 ③ 3

INTERSTATE 94 CONT'D	
Exit	Services
171	MI 14 (from eb, exits left), to Ann Arbor, to Flint by US 23
169	Zeeb Rd, N🅿 BP/dsl/24hr, 🍽 Big Boy, Grand Pies Co, Metzger's Rest., McDonald's, S🅿 Citgo/dsl, 🍽 Arby's, Burger King, Creekside Grill, Domino's, Panera Bread, Pizza Hut, Subway, Taco Bell, Wendy's, Westside Grill, 🅾 CVS Drug, Harley-Davidson, Lowe's, Meijer/dsl
167	Baker Rd, Dexter, N🅿 🚚/Subway/scales/dsl/24hr, S 🅿 🚚/Arby's/dsl/scales/24hr, TA/BP/Popeye's/dsl/scales/24hr/@, 🍽 McDonald's, 🅾 Blue Beacon
162	Jackson Rd, Fletcher Rd, S 🅿 BP/Subway/dsl/24hr, 🍽 Stiver's Rest.
161mm	rest area eb, full ♿ facilities, 🚻, 🅿, litter barrels, vending, petwalk
159	MI 52, Chelsea, N 🅿 Mobil/dsl, Rich Gas, Sunoco/dsl, 🍽 Big Boy, Chelsea Grill, China Garden, Chinese Tonite, KFC/Taco Bell, McDonald's, Subway, Uptown Coney Island, Wendy's, 🏨 Comfort Inn, Holiday Inn Express, 🅾 🅗, Buick/Chevrolet, Chelsea Drug, Chrysler/Dodge/Jeep, Country Mkt Foods/drug, CVS Drug, Pamida, Travel Land RV Ctr, USPO, vet

⑤ 5

E ↑↓ W

C H E L S E A

⑥ 6

① 1	State Name & Page Number
② 2	State Map with Interstates
③ 3	Interstate Highway Number
④ 4	Directional Arrow
⑤ 5	City Indicator Strip
⑥ 6	Exit # and Services

the Next EXIT® USER GUIDE

Exit

Most states number exits by the nearest mile marker(mm). A few states use consecutive numbers, in which case mile markers are given in ( ). Mile markers are the little green vertical signs beside the interstate at one mile intervals which indicate distance from the southern or western border of a state. Odd numbered interstates run north/south, even numbered run east/west.

Services

Services are listed alphabetically by category 🅿=gas 🍽=food 🏨=lodging 🅾=other services including camping. "🅗" indicates an exit from which a hospital may be accessed, but it may not be close to the exit. Services located away from the exit may be referred to by "access to," or "to" and a distance may be given. A directional notation is also given, such as N, S, E or W

Directional Arrows

Follow exits DOWN the page if traveling from North to South or East to West, UP the page if traveling South to North or West to East.

TABLE OF CONTENTS

Abbreviations & Symbols used in *the Next EXIT* ®

AFB	Air Force Base	pk	park
B&B	Bed&Breakfast	pkwy	parkway
Bfd	Battlefield	rest.	restaurant
Ctr	Center	nb	northbound
Coll	College	sb	southbound
Cyn	canyon	eb	eastbound
dsl	diesel	wb	westbound
$	Dollar	SP	state park
Mem	Memorial	SF	state forest
Mkt	Market	Sprs	springs
Mtn	Mountain	st	street, state
mm	mile marker	sta	station
N	north side of exit	TPK	Turnpike
S	south side of exit	USPO	Post Office
E	east side of exit	vet	veterinarian
W	west side of exit	whse.	warehouse
NM	National Monument	@	truckstop (full service)
NHS	Nat Hist Site	red print	RV accessible
NWR	Nat Wildlife Reserve	♿	Handicapped accessible
NF	National Forest	☎	Telephone
H	Hospital	⛽	Gas
✈	Airport	🍴	Food
⛱	Picnic Tables	🏠	Lodging
NP	National Park	▣	Other
NRA	Nat Rec Area		

For Trans Canada Highway (TCH) information and more, please visit us on the web at *www.thenextexit.com*

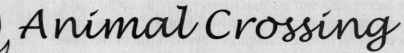

Animal Crossing

by Mark Watson - Winter 2012

I buried the Cat the other night, in the corner of the yard overlooking the valley where he had terrorized the lives of many, many rodents. I made sure he went in near the roots of the young blue rug junipers because of the recycling thing. At the last pat of the shovel I placed a couple of big rocks over his grave because while I advocate back-to-mother earth, I did not want retribution from the other varmints he had so vexed over the last several years. Have you ever noticed how at someone or something's passing we set about to eulogize them into better than they ever were in life? So it is with the Cat. After Debby wept off and on for a good 10 days, we began to wax philosophical about the whole affair, squinting to see the silver lining. No more cat food to buy. No litter box to change. No worry about leaving home for an extended period of time. And no more darn cat hair inexplicably showing up on our Sunday clothes. Just put the sticky mouse pads back out in the garage and move on, right?

The mourning ended, but not before several nettlesome questions surfaced. The most pertinent to me personally is "Why does the dad in the family always have to bury the dead pets?" Before the children were grown we had developed a regular pet cemetery near the borders of our property, complete with small monuments that were erected to commemorate the passing of loved ones. Now, before anyone accuses us of negligence to animals, let me say that most of our pets wandered up and chose us for themselves. They were adopted, fed, immunized, domesticated and loved, all outside the house, except for the cold nights when the weather forecasters recommended they be brought inside. Nevertheless, any number of tragedies can befall an outside animal and so I conducted many little memorial services, usually for dead cats, with only the occasional bird or squirrel, shouldering the responsibility of gravedigger as I went. When I accepted the job of father, perhaps I should have read the fine print.

Other inquiries remain. How do you have a cat for three years and not give him his own permanent name? Does this anticipate brevity in our expected relationship, or is it just because cats never seem to respond to a name anyhow? Moreover, how does a cat get himself killed on a neighborhood street with hardly any traffic? Just luck? His moment in time? I am reluctant to entertain the sinister notion that someone had him in the crosshairs, but who knows…cats make lots of enemies. And what to do post-Cat? Some folks heal by quickly finding another kitty, but too soon seems a little callous and besides, who wants to start over all the way back at the beginning?

What about the grim reaper? Someone must have felt the impact of a 15 pound cat against part of his vehicle. "Just a cat," he might have thought, "so what is the big deal?" I am acquainted with several people who, upon learning of our loss, casually throw out, "well, it's only a cat. Not much good for anything but target practice." Really? I once knew a man whose cat died some eight hundred miles from home. He lovingly wrapped him in plastic, and cryogenically

Continued Next Page

preserved his carcass in a freezer until he could make arrangements for the homeward journey. Some of us actually have tender feelings toward those of the lower species. We would have appreciated knowing from the driver that our cat had been hit, not that it would have changed the outcome.

All of this brings me to a point, in case you were wondering. When the interstate highways were built, fences were also installed along the right-of-way in order to prevent or diminish animal traffic across the freeways. Sometimes they work and sometimes not. One year in western Pennsylvania I counted over a dozen deer lying on and beside Interstate 80 in one 50 mile stretch. Neighborhood fences do not protect streets in any such fashion, so tame critters are left to their own instincts to determine where to cross.

I am fascinated by the signs along the road that proclaim this or that area as a "deer crossing" or "elk herd" habitat. I imagine wildlife management personnel arguing with each other over exactly where to put the warnings. One thing is for certain: if you ever come upon a spot that qualifies as a "cattle drive area"--beware! The nose of a heifer dragged along the side of our VW bus one night, shining a streak the entire length of the vehicle. Another foot and we could have been like the folks who hit that mule, with disastrous results. Or, like our friends, one of whom wrecked her car on the moose while the other totaled hers because of a mouse. As they say out west, "There are two types of drivers…those that have hit a deer and those that are going to." I know one unlucky fellow who collided with two at once.

I recall a lesson learned long ago about misfortunate road kill. Late one Saturday night we were returning home from a trip. I was asleep in the front seat of our Rambler Ambassador as we rolled down a rural highway, my father at the wheel. There was a solid thump as our car smacked a hog that had rooted out onto the asphalt. The damage was severe to the front of our automobile, but nobody was hurt except the hog. Early the next morning, long before church, Dad drove back to the site of the accident, found the owner and helped him dress the pork for curing. Both of them felt there was no need to waste a perfectly good dead hog.

Many accidents are unavoidable and animals, both domesticated and wild, have their own agenda for moving about. Together, these two facts mean that for animal crossings the future probably looks very much like the past. Still, one can hope for a safer world, backed by better caution, good fortune or just plain luck. In the creature world where fences are mostly just a suggestion, we travelers do well to be aware. And remember this: while insurance companies and states require a report to be made when wildlife wanders in the way, only good manners suggest notifying someone that their pet has paid the price.

As for us, the neighbor's cat is desperately trying to fill the void left by his former nemesis, offering to catch our mice in return for the relative comforts of our garage. We are naturally skeptical about his motives, but with winter coming on and the vermin seeking shelter, I am laying out the mouse pads and considering my options.

Boy, do I miss that cat.

🚗 = gas   🍴 = food   🏨 = lodging   ⊙ = other

INTERSTATE 10

Exits	Services
	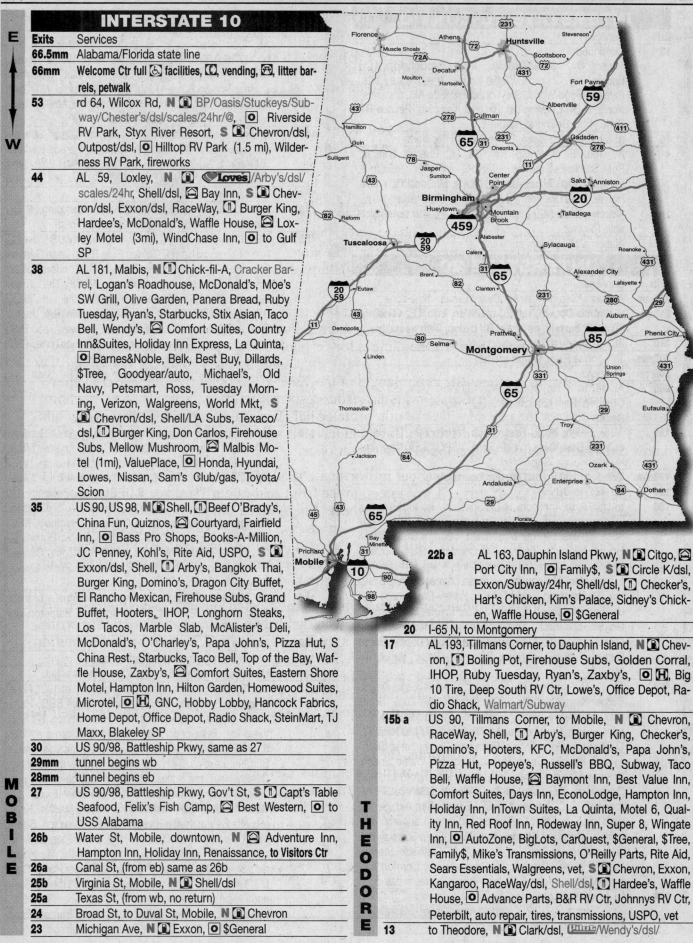
66.5mm	Alabama/Florida state line
66mm	Welcome Ctr full ♿ facilities, 🚰, vending, 🏕, litter barrels, petwalk
53	rd 64, Wilcox Rd, N 🚗 BP/Oasis/Stuckeys/Subway/Chester's/dsl/scales/24hr/@, ⊙ Riverside RV Park, Styx River Resort, S 🚗 Chevron/dsl, Outpost/dsl, ⊙ Hilltop RV Park (1.5 mi), Wilderness RV Park, fireworks
44	AL 59, Loxley, N 🍴 ♥Loves/Arby's/dsl/scales/24hr, Shell/dsl, 🏨 Bay Inn, S 🚗 Chevron/dsl, Exxon/dsl, RaceWay, 🍴 Burger King, Hardee's, McDonald's, Waffle House, 🏨 Loxley Motel (3mi), WindChase Inn, ⊙ to Gulf SP
38	AL 181, Malbis, N 🍴 Chick-fil-A, Cracker Barrel, Logan's Roadhouse, McDonald's, Moe's SW Grill, Olive Garden, Panera Bread, Ruby Tuesday, Ryan's, Starbucks, Stix Asian, Taco Bell, Wendy's, 🏨 Comfort Suites, Country Inn&Suites, Holiday Inn Express, La Quinta, ⊙ Barnes&Noble, Belk, Best Buy, Dillards, $Tree, Goodyear/auto, Michael's, Old Navy, Petsmart, Ross, Tuesday Morning, Verizon, Walgreens, World Mkt, S 🚗 Chevron/dsl, Shell/LA Subs, Texaco/dsl, 🍴 Burger King, Don Carlos, Firehouse Subs, Mellow Mushroom, 🏨 Malbis Motel (1mi), ValuePlace, ⊙ Honda, Hyundai, Lowes, Nissan, Sam's Club/gas, Toyota/Scion
35	US 90, US 98, N 🚗 Shell, 🍴 Beef O'Brady's, China Fun, Quiznos, 🏨 Courtyard, Fairfield Inn, ⊙ Bass Pro Shops, Books-A-Million, JC Penney, Kohl's, Rite Aid, USPO, S 🚗 Exxon/dsl, Shell, 🍴 Arby's, Bangkok Thai, Burger King, Domino's, Dragon City Buffet, El Rancho Mexican, Firehouse Subs, Grand Buffet, Hooters, IHOP, Longhorn Steaks, Los Tacos, Marble Slab, McAlister's Deli, McDonald's, O'Charley's, Papa John's, Pizza Hut, S China Rest., Starbucks, Taco Bell, Top of the Bay, Waffle House, Zaxby's, 🏨 Comfort Suites, Eastern Shore Motel, Hampton Inn, Hilton Garden, Homewood Suites, Microtel, ⊙ 🏥, GNC, Hobby Lobby, Hancock Fabrics, Home Depot, Office Depot, Radio Shack, SteinMart, TJ Maxx, Blakeley SP
30	US 90/98, Battleship Pkwy, same as 27
29mm	tunnel begins wb
28mm	tunnel begins eb
27	US 90/98, Battleship Pkwy, Gov't St, S 🍴 Capt's Table Seafood, Felix's Fish Camp, 🏨 Best Western, ⊙ to USS Alabama
26b	Water St, Mobile, downtown, N 🏨 Adventure Inn, Hampton Inn, Holiday Inn, Renaissance, **to Visitors Ctr**
26a	Canal St, (from eb) same as 26b
25b	Virginia St, Mobile, N 🚗 Shell/dsl
25a	Texas St, (from wb, no return)
24	Broad St, to Duval St, Mobile, N 🚗 Chevron
23	Michigan Ave, N 🚗 Exxon, ⊙ $General

22b a	AL 163, Dauphin Island Pkwy, N 🚗 Citgo, 🏨 Port City Inn, ⊙ Family$, S 🚗 Circle K/dsl, Exxon/Subway/24hr, Shell/dsl, 🍴 Checker's, Hart's Chicken, Kim's Palace, Sidney's Chicken, Waffle House, ⊙ $General
20	I-65 N, to Montgomery
17	AL 193, Tillmans Corner, to Dauphin Island, N 🚗 Chevron, 🍴 Boiling Pot, Firehouse Subs, Golden Corral, IHOP, Ruby Tuesday, Ryan's, Zaxby's, ⊙ 🏥, Big 10 Tire, Deep South RV Ctr, Lowe's, Office Depot, Radio Shack, Walmart/Subway
15b a	US 90, Tillmans Corner, to Mobile, N 🚗 Chevron, RaceWay, Shell, 🍴 Arby's, Burger King, Checker's, Domino's, Hooters, KFC, McDonald's, Papa John's, Pizza Hut, Popeye's, Russell's BBQ, Subway, Taco Bell, Waffle House, 🏨 Baymont Inn, Best Value Inn, Comfort Suites, Days Inn, EconoLodge, Hampton Inn, Holiday Inn, InTown Suites, La Quinta, Motel 6, Quality Inn, Red Roof Inn, Rodeway Inn, Super 8, Wingate Inn, ⊙ AutoZone, BigLots, CarQuest, $General, $Tree, Family$, Mike's Transmissions, O'Reilly Parts, Rite Aid, Sears Essentials, Walgreens, vet, S 🚗 Chevron, Exxon, Kangaroo, RaceWay/dsl, Shell/dsl, 🍴 Hardee's, Waffle House, ⊙ Advance Parts, B&R RV Ctr, Johnnys RV Ctr, Peterbilt, auto repair, tires, transmissions, USPO, vet
13	to Theodore, N 🚗 Clark/dsl, Wendy's/dsl/

Left margin: **E ↕ W**, **M O B I L E**

Right margin: **T H E O D O R E**

AL

INTERSTATE 10 CONT'D

Exit	Services
13	Continued scales/24hr, Shell/Subway, Texaco/McDonald's, 🅕 Burger King, Church's, Waffle House, 🅞 Advance Parts, Family$, Food World, Greyhound Prk, Rite Aid, transmissions, **S** 🅖 Chevron/dsl, 🅞 I-10 Kamping, Paynes RV Park (4mi), Bellingraf Gardens
10	rd 39, Bayou La Batre, Dawes, **N** 🅞 Kenworth
4	AL 188, E to Grand Bay, **N** 🅖 Energize/Blimpie, Shell/Stuckey's/Subway, TA/BP/Buckhorn Rest./dsl/scales/24hr/@, Texaco/dsl, 🅕 Arby's, McDonald's, Waffle House, **S** 🅖 Chevron, 🅕 Hardee's, 🅞 Trav-L-Kamp
1mm	Welcome Ctr eb, full ♿ facilities, info, 🅲, 🗑 litter barrels, petwalk, RV dump
0mm	Alabama/Mississippi state line

INTERSTATE 20

Exits	Services
215mm	Alabama/Georgia state line, Central/Eastern time zone
213mm	**Welcome Ctr wb, full** ♿ **facilities, info,** 🅲**, vending,** 🗑**, litter barrels, petwalk, RV dump, 24hr security**
210	AL 49, Abernathy, **N** fireworks, **S** fireworks
209mm	Tallapoosa River, **weigh sta wb**
208mm	no services
205	AL 46, to Heflin, **N** 🅖 BP/dsl, 🅕 205 Cafe, 🅞 Cane Creek RV Park (2mi), tires, **S** 🅖 Shell/dsl/24hr, 🅞 Truck Repair
199	AL 9, Heflin, **N** 🅖 Texaco/Subway/dsl/24hr, 🅕 Hardee's, 🅐 Best Value Inn, 🅞 Ford, USPO, **S** 🅖 Chevron/Huddle House, SuperMart
198mm	Talladega Nat Forest, eastern boundary
191	US 431, to US 78
188	to US 78, to Anniston, **N** 🅖 Shell/dsl, Texaco/Subway, 🅕 Cracker Barrel, Fuji's Japanese, IHOP, KFC, LoneStar Steaks, Mellow Mushroom, Sonny's BBQ, Waffle House, Wendy's, Zaxby's, 🅐 Comfort Suites, Country Inn&Suites, Courtyard, Fairfield Inn, Hampton Inn, Hilton Garden, Holiday Inn Express, Jameson Inn, Sleep Inn, 🅞 Camping World RV Ctr, Harley-Davidson, Honda, Lowe's, Nissan, O'Reilly Parts, Toyota, **S** 🅕 Arby's, Golden Rule BBQ, Longhorn Steaks, Mexico Lindo Grill, Olive Garden, 🅞 AT&T, Best Buy, Hobby Lobby, Home Depot, Kohl's, Old Navy, Petsmart, Ross, Target, TJ Maxx
185	AL 21, to Anniston, **N** 🅖 Shell, 🅕 Applebee's, Arby's, Burger King, Capt D's, CiCi's Pizza, China Luck, Domino's, Garfield's Rest., Hardee's, Jack's Rest., Krystal, Logan's Roadhouse, McAlister's Deli, McDonald's, O'Charley's, Papa John's, Pizza Hut, Red Lobster, Shoney's, Starbucks, Super Buffet, Taco Bell, Waffle House, Western Sizzlin, 🅐 Days Inn, Liberty Inn, Oxford Inn, Red Carpet Inn, 🅞 BooksAMillion, Dillard's, $General, Firestone/auto, JC Penney, Martin's Foods, Rite Aid, Sears/auto, mall, to Ft McClellan, **S** 🅖 Exxon, Kangaroo/dsl/scales, Murphy USA/dsl, RaceWay, Shell/Subway/dsl, Texaco/Subway/dsl, 🅕 Chick-fil-A, Outback Steaks, Waffle House, Wendy's, 🅐 Baymont Inn, Comfort Inn, EconoLodge, Motel 6, 🅞 H, Walmart, tires/repair
179	to Munford, Coldwater, **N** 🅖 Chevron/dsl, 🅕 China King, Jack's Rest., 🅞 Anniston Army Depot, $General, Rite Aid, Winn Dixie, **S** 🅖 Texaco/dsl

173	AL 5, Eastaboga, **S** 🅖 Shell, 🅕 DQ/Stuckey's, 🅞 to Speedway/Hall of Fame
168	AL 77, to Talladega, **N** 🅖 Citgo/dsl, QV/Domino's, Super 77/KFC/Taco Bell, 🅕 Jack's Rest., Waffle House, **S** 🅖 Chevron/Subway/dsl, Shell/Race City Diner/dsl/scales, Texaco/Burger King, 🅕 McDonald's, MT Grill, Rana's Mexican, 🅐 Comfort Inn, Days Inn, McCaig Motel, 🅞 to Speedway, Hall of Fame
165	Embry Cross Roads, **N** 🅖 Hi-Tech/dsl, ▦/Subway/dsl/scales/24hr, 🅐 McCaig Motel, 🅞 Paradise Island RV Park, **S** 🅖 Chevron/Huddle House/dsl, I-20TrkStp/rest./dsl/scales/24hr, 🅕 JR's BBQ, 🅞 RV Ctr
164mm	Coosa River
162	US 78, Riverside, **N** 🅞 Safe Harbor Camping, **S** 🅖 Marathon, Texaco/dsl, 🅐 Best Value Inn/rest
158	US 231, Pell City, **N** 🅖 Exxon/dsl, Murphy USA/dsl, 🅕 Arby's, Cracker Barrel, Golden Rule BBQ, Jade Garden Chinese, Krystal, Wendy's, Zaxby's, 🅐 Comfort Suites, Hampton Inn, Holiday Inn Express, 🅞 City Tire, $Tree, Home Depot, Radio Shack, Walgreens, Walmart, **S** 🅖 BP, Chevron, Texaco, 🅕 Burger King, Hardee's, Jack's Rest., KFC, McDonald's, Pizza Hut, Subway, Taco Bell, Waffle House, 🅐 Quality Inn, 🅞 H, AutoZone, CVS Drug, Ford/Lincoln/Mercury, Fred's Drug
156	US 78, E to Pell City, **S** 🅖 Chevron/dsl/24hr, Shell
153	US 78, Chula Vista
152	Cook Springs
147	Brompton, **N** 🅖 Citgo, **S** 🅖 Chevron/dsl
144	US 411, Leeds, **N** 🅖 BP/dsl, Raceway, Shell/Subway, 🅕 Arby's, Burger King, Cracker Barrel, Krystal, Milo's Burgers, Pizza Hut, Ruby Tuesday, Waffle House, Wendy's, 🅐 Best Western, Comfort Inn, Super 8, 🅞 $Tree, Food Giant, RV camping, **S** 🅖 Chevron, RaceWay, 🅕 Caney Fork Steaks, Capt D's, Chick-fil-A, El Cazador Mexican, Guadalajara Jalisco Mexican, Hardee's, KFC, McDonald's, Papa John's, Taco Bell, Waffle House, 🅐 Days Inn, 🅞 Advance Parts, AT&T, AutoZone, Curves, $General, Lowe's, NAPA, O'Reilly Parts, Radio Shack, Walgreens, Walmart /Subway
140	US 78, Leeds, **N** 🅞 Distinctive Outlets/famous brands, **S** 🅖 Chevron, Exxon, 🅐 Best Value Inn, Hampton Inn, 🅞 Bass Pro Shop
139mm	Cahaba River
136	I-459, S to Montgomery, Tuscaloosa
135	US 78, Old Leeds Rd, **N** 🅞 B'ham Racetrack
133	US 78, to Kilgore Memorial Dr, (wb return at 132), **N** 🅖 Chevron, Exxon/dsl/24hr, 🅕 Golden Rule BBQ, Hamburger Heaven, Jack's, Krystal, Waffle House, 🅐 Best Value Inn, Eastwood Hotel, Siesta Motel, same as 132, **S** 🅖 BP, Chevron, Texaco/dsl, 🅕 McDonald's, Milo's Burgers, Zaxby's, 🅐 Hampton Inn, Holiday Inn Express, Quality Inn, Rime Suites, 🅞 Sam's Club/gas, Tire Pros
132b a	US 78, Crestwood Blvd, **N** 🅖 Chevron, Exxon, 🅕 Golden Rule BBQ, Hamburger Heaven, Jack's, Krystal, Villa Fiesta, Waffle House, 🅐 Best Value Inn, Siesta Motel, 🅞 Chevrolet, O'Reilly Parts, SuperPetz, same as 133, **S** 🅖 BP, Chevron, Exxon, Crown/24hr, Marathon/dsl, Shell/24hr, Texaco, 🅕 Arby's, Burger King, Capt D's, Chick-fil-A, China Garden, Emperor House, Hacienda Mexican, Hooters, IHOP, KFC, LJ Silver/Taco Bell, Logan's Roadhouse, McDonald's, Milo's Burgers, New China Buffet, Olive Garden, Pizza Hut, Quiznos,

Left margin: ANNISTON

Right margin: PELL CITY · LEEDS

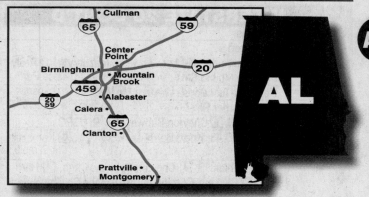

INTERSTATE 20 CONT'D

Exit	Services
132b a	Continued Red Lobster, Ryan's, Starbucks, Wendy's, 🏠 Comfort Inn, Delux Inn, Economy Lodge, Park Inn, USA Lodge, 🄾 H, Advance Parts, Aldi Foods, $General, Home Depot, K-Mart, Office Depot, Old Navy, Radio Shack, Ross, Sears/auto, TJ Maxx, Waldenbooks, Walgreens, Walmart
130b	US 11, 1st Ave, N 📕 Chevron/24hr, Conoco/dsl, Marathon, Petro, Shell, 🄾 AutoZone, Piggly Wiggly, S 📕 Exxon/dsl, 🍴 McDonald's, Pacific Seafood, 🏠 Relax Inn, Sky Inn
130a	I-59 N, to Gadsden
	I-59 S and I-20 W run together from B'ham to Meridian, MS
129	Airport Blvd, N 🏠 Clarion, 🄾 ✈, S 📕 Shell, 🍴 Hardee's, Kabob House, 🏠 Best Inn, Holiday Inn
128	AL 79, Tallapoosa St, N 📕 Kangaroo/Subway/dsl/scales, Exxon/Wings/dsl
126b	31st St, N 📕 Citgo, Shell, 🍴 McDonald's
126a	US 31, US 280, 26th St, Carraway Blvd, N 🍴 Church's, KFC, Rally's
125b	22nd St, N 🏠 Sheraton
125a	17th St, to downtown
124b a	I-65, S to Montgomery, N to Nashville
123	US 78, Arkadelphia Rd, N 📕 Chevron/24hr, Jet-Pep, ⬛⬛⬛/Wendy's/dsl/scales/24hr, Shell/dsl, 🍴 Popeye's, 🏠 Days Inn, S 🄾 H, to Legion Field
121	Bush Blvd, (from wb, no return) Ensley, N 📕 BP, Exxon, 🍴 Wings&Waffles
120	AL 269, 20th St, Ensley Ave, N 📕 Jet-Pep, 🍴 KFC, 🄾 Honda, S 📕 BP, 🄾 H, Toyota
119b	Ave I (from wb)
119a	Scrushy Pkwy, Gary Ave, N 📕 BP, Chevron/dsl, 🍴 Burger King, Fairfield Seafood, McDonald's, Subway, S 📕 Mobil, Texaco, 🄾 H
118	AL 56, Valley Rd, Fairfield, N 🄾 NAPA, S 📕 Shell, 🍴 Papa John's, 🏠 Comfort Inn, Inn At Fairfield, 🄾 Home Depot, Radio Shack
115	Allison-Bonnett Memorial Dr, N 📕 BP/dsl, RaceWay, Shell/dsl, 🍴 Church's, Guadalajara Grill, Jack's, Subway, 🄾 Advance Parts, O'Reilly Parts, USPO
113	18th Ave, to Hueytown, S 📕 Chevron/dsl, Shell, 🍴 McDonald's
112	18th St, 19th St Bessemer, N 📕 RaceWay, Shell, 🍴 Jack's Rest., 🄾 tire/repair, S 📕 BP, Chevron, 🍴 KFC, Krystal (1mi), Rally's, Sykes BBQ, 🄾 Advance Parts, FMS Drug, Lowe's, NAPA, Walgreens
110	AL, Adventure Pkwy, N AL Adventure Funpark, S H
108	US 11, AL 5 N, Academy Dr, N 📕 Exxon, 🍴 Applebee's, Catfish Cabin, Cracker Barrel, Waffle House, 🏠 Best Western, Comfort Inn, Country Inn&Suites, Fairfield Inn, Holiday Inn Express, Jameson Inn, ValuePlace, 🄾 Chevrolet, Chrysler/Dodge/Jeep, Nissan, S 📕 BP, Texaco/Church's/dsl, 🍴 Burger King, Jade Garden, Little Caesar's, McDonald's, Milo's Burgers, Ruby Tuesday, Sonic, Wendy's, Zaxby's, 🏠 Best Value Inn, Economy Inn, Hampton Inn, Motel 6, 🄾 H, Aldi Foods, $Tree, Ford, Radio Shack, Verizon, Walmart /Subway, to civic ctr
106	I-459, N to Montgomery
104	Rock Mt Lakes, S 📕 *FLYING J*/Denny's/dsl/LP/24hr
100	to Abernant, N 📕 Citgo/dsl, 🍴 Plaza Cafe, 🄾 McCalla

Exit	Services
100	Continued Camping, S 📕 BP, Exxon, Petro/Chevron/dsl/rest./scales/24hr/@, 🄾 $General, Tannehill SP (3mi)
97	US 11 S, AL 5, S to, W Blocton, S 📕 BP/KFC/dsl, Exxon/Subway/dsl, Shell/dsl, 🍴 Jack's Rest.
89	Mercedes Dr, N 🏠 Greystone Inn, S 🄾 Mercedes Auto Plant
86	Vance, to Brookwood, N 📕 BP/Huddle House/Subway/dsl, Shell/dsl/rest./24hr
85mm	**rest area both lanes, full ♿ facilities, 📞, ⛽, vending, litter barrels, petwalk, RV dump**
79	US 11, University Blvd Coaling, S 📕 Chevron/dsl, Texaco
77	Cottondale, N 📕 Chevron/McDonald's, TA/BP/Subway/Taco Bell/dsl/scales/@, Wilco/Wendy's/dsl/scales/24hr, 🍴 Arby's, Pizza Hut, Ruby Tuesday, 🏠 Hampton Inn, Microtel, 🄾 Blue Beacon, SpeedCo, USPO, S Chevrolet
76	US 11, E Tuscaloosa, Cottondale, N 📕 Citgo, Exxon, Shell/dsl, 🍴 Burger King, Cracker Barrel, Waffle House, 🏠 Comfort Inn, Howard Johnson, ValuePlace, Western Motel, Wingate Inn, 🄾 transmissions, S 📕 ⬛⬛⬛/Subway/dsl/scales/24hr, Texaco/dsl, 🏠 Sleep Inn
73	US 82, McFarland Blvd, Tuscaloosa, N 📕 BP/dsl, Chevron/dsl, Exxon, RaceWay, Shell/dsl, 🍴 Arby's, Buffalo Wild Wings, Burger King, Capt D's, Chick-fil-A, Jason's Deli, Kobe Japanese, Krystal, Los Calientes, O'Charley's, Olive Garden, Panera Bread, Popeye's, Red Lobster, TCBY, Waffle House, 🏠 Ambassador Inn, Best Western, Best Value Inn, Comfort Suites, Guest Lodge, Masters Inn, 🄾 Aamco, Advance Parts, Barnes&Noble, Belk, Best Buy, Big 10 Tire, Bruno's Foods, $General, Firestone/auto, Goodyear/auto, OK Tire, Rite Aid, Sears, SteinMart, S 📕 Exxon, Jet-Pep, 🍴 Bama Wings, Checker's, Chili's, Church's, Grand Buffet, Guthrie's, Hardee's, Huddle House, KFC, Logan's Roadhouse, McDonald's, Pizza Hut, Sonic, Subway, Taco Bell, Taco Casa, 🏠 Candlewood Suites, Country Inn&Suites, Days Inn, EconoLodge, La Quinta, Motel 6, Quality Inn, Ramada Inn, Super 8, 🄾 BooksAMillion, Chrysler/Dodge/Jeep, $General, $Tree, FoodWorld, Kia, Michael's, NAPA, Office Depot, Sam's Club/gas, TJ Maxx, Walmart
71b	I-359, Al 69, N to Tuscaloosa, N 🄾 H, U of AL, to Stillman Coll
71a	AL 69, S to Moundville, S 📕 Chevron, Citgo, MapCo, Shell/dsl, 🍴 Arby's, Hooters, IHOP, LoneStar Steaks, OutBack Steaks, Pizza Hut, Ryan's, Waffle House, Wendy's, Zaxby's, 🏠 Courtyard, Fairfield Inn, Hilton Garden, Jameson Inn, 🄾 Advance Parts, Big 10 Tire,

◖ = gas   ▥ = food   ◹ = lodging   ▣ = other   Copyright 2012 - The Next Exit®

AL

INTERSTATE 20 CONT'D

Exit	Services
71a	Continued
	Goodyear/auto, K-Mart, Lowe's, Mazda/VW, O'Reilly Parts, to Mound SM
68	Northfort-Tuscaloosa Western Bypass
64mm	Black Warrior River
62	Fosters, N ◖ Chevron/Subway/dsl, ▣ USPO
52	US 11, US 43, Knoxville, N ◖ Exxon/dsl, ▣ Knox Hill Camping
45	AL 37, Union, S ◖ Chevron/Subway, Citgo, ▥ Hardee's, ◹ Best Inn, Comfort Inn, ▣ Greene Co Greyhound Park
40	AL 14, Eutaw, N ▣ to Tom Bevill Lock/Dam, S ◖ BP, Ⓗ
39mm	rest area wb, full ♿ facilities, ◖, 🏕, vending, litter barrels, petwalk, RV dump
38mm	rest area eb, full ♿ facilities, ◖, 🏕, vending, litter barrels, petwalk, RV dump
32	Boligee, N ◖ BP/dsl/rest./24hr, S ◖ Chevron/Subway/24hr
27mm	Tombigbee River, Tenn-Tom Waterway
23	Epes, to Gainesville
17	AL 28, Livingston, S ◖ BP/dsl/24hr, Chevron/Subway/24hr, Texaco/L&B/dsl/24hr, ▥ Burger King, Pizza Hut, ◹ Comfort Inn, Western Inn, ▣ repair/24hr
8	AL 17, York, S ◖ BP/New Orleans Grill/dsl/scales/@, ◹ Days Inn
1	to US 80, E Cuba, N ◖ Rocking Chair Trkstp/Rest./dsl/, S ◖ Chevron
.5mm	Welcome Ctr eb, full ♿ facilities, ◖, vending, 🏕, litter barrels, petwalk, RV dump
	I-20, E and I-59, N run together from Meridian, MS to B'ham
0mm	Alabama/Mississippi state line

INTERSTATE 22 (Future)

Exit	Services
93	rd 77, (I-22 future begins/ends)
91	rd 105, to Brookside
89	rd 65, to Adamsville, Graysville
87	rd 112, to Graysville
85	US 78, Birmingham
81	rd 45, W Jefferson
78	rd 81, Dora, Sumiton, N ◖ TJ's/dsl
72	rd 61, Cordova
70	rd 22, Cordova, Parish
65	Bevill Ind Pkwy, Jasper, N ◹ Hampton Inn (3mi), ▣ Ⓗ, to Walker Co Lake, S ▣ Buick/Cadillac/Chevrolet/GMC
63	AlL 269, Jasper, Parish, N ◖ Chevron/deli/dsl
61	AL 69, Jasper, Tuscaloosa, N ◖ RJ's
57	AL 118, E Jasper, S ◖ Chevron, Exxon, ▥ Panter's Place Rest
52	AL 118, Carbon Hill, S ◹ Shadowbrook Inn
46	rd 11, Carbon Hill, Nauvoo, S ◖ Shell
39	AL 13, Natural Bridge, Eldridge
34	AL 233, Glen Allen, Natural Bridge
30	AL 129, Brilliant, Winfield, S ◖ Shell/deli/dsl, Texaco/deli/dsl, ◹ Hampton Inn
26	AL 44, Brilliant, Guin, S Ⓗ
22	rd 45
16	US 43, US 278, Hamilton, Guin, S ◖ Shell/deli/dsl
14	Hamilton, N ◖ Texaco/dsl, ▥ Huddle House, ◹ Days

Exit	Services
14	Continued
	Inn (1mi), EconoLodge (1mi), Keywest Inn
11	AL 17, Hamilton, Sulligent, N ◖ Citgo/dsl, ▣ Ⓗ
7	Hamilton, Weston, N Ⓗ
3	rd 33
0mm	Alabama/Mississippi State Line

INTERSTATE 59

Exit	Services
241.5mm	Alabama/Georgia state line, Central/Eastern time zone
241mm	Welcome Ctr sb, full ♿ facilities, ◖, vending, 🏕, litter barrels, petwalk, RV dump
239	to US 11, Sulphur Springs Rd, E ▣ camping
231	AL 40, AL 117 Hammondville, Valley Head, E ▣ DeSoto SP, camping (5mi), W ◖ Victory Fuel
224	49th St
222	US 11, to Ft Payne, E ◖ Shell, ▣ Chevrolet, **1 mi** E ▥ Arby's, Hardee's, Jack's Rest., KFC, Krystal, Peking Gourmet, Pizza Hut, Subway, ◹ Country Hearth Inn, ▣ $General, Foodland/gas, W ◖ JetPep/dsl, ▥ Waffle King
218	AL 35, Ft Payne, E ▥ Asian Palace, Capt D's, DQ, Golden Rule BBQ, McDonald's, New China, Papa John's, Quiznos, South End Grill, Taco Bell, Wendy's, Zaxby's, ▣ Advance Parts, AutoZone, BigLots, Buick/GMC, Chrysler/Dodge/Jeep, $General, O'Reilly Parts, W ◖ Kangaroo/dsl, MapCo, Murphy USA/dsl, Victory Fuel, ▥ Burger King, Cracker Barrel, Hardee's, Ryan's, Ruby Tuesday, Santa Fe Steaks, Los Arcos, Subway, Waffle House, ◹ Days Inn, EconoLodge, Hampton Inn, Holiday Inn Express, ▣ Ⓗ, AT&T, $Tree, Ford/Lincoln/Mercury, GNC, K-Mart, Lowe's, Radio Shack, Verizon, Walgreens, Walmart, Will's Creek RV Park
205	AL 68, Collinsville, E ◖ Delta, ▥ Jack's Rest., Smokin' Joe's Rest., ◹ Howard Johnson, ▣ to Little River Canyon, Weiss Lake, W ◖ BP/dsl, Shell
188	AL 211, to US 11, Gadsden, E ◖ Jet-Pep, ▣ Noccalula Falls RV Park, W ◖ Clean Fuels/dsl/E85
183	US 431, US 278, Gadsden, E ◖ Jet-Pep/dsl, Shell, Texaco, ▥ Magic Burger, Waffle House, Wendy's, ◹ Days Inn, Rodeway Inn, Travelodge, ▣ st police, W ◖ Chevron/24hr, Exxon, Jet-Pep, ▥ Krystal, Jumbo Buffet, McDonald's, Pizza Hut, Subway, Taco Bell, ◹ Best Inn
182	I-759 to Gadsden
181	AL 77, Rainbow City, to Gadsden, E ◖ Petro/rest./dsl/scales/24hr/@, ▥ Austin's Rest., ◹ Days Inn, W ◖ Citgo, Kangaroo/dsl, Murphy Express/dsl, Pure/dsl, ▥ Arby's, Cracker Barrel, Dairy Delight, Domino's, Hardee's, Los Arcos, Lucky Wok, Ruby Tuesday, Subway, Waffle House, ◹ Best Western, Comfort Suites, Fairfield Inn, Hampton Inn, Holiday Inn Express, ▣ $General, $Tree, O'Reilly Parts, Radio Shack, Walmart
174	to Steele, E ◖ ⬭Loves/Subway/Chester's/dsl/scales/24hr, W ◖ JetPep/dsl, Shell/rest/dsl
168mm	rest area sb, full ♿ facilities, ◖, 🏕, vending, litter barrels, petwalk, RV dump
166	US 231, Whitney, to Ashville, E ◖ Chevron/dsl, Discount/gas, W ◖ Texaco/dsl, ▥ Jack's Rest., Huddle House, Subway
165mm	rest area nb, full ♿ facilities, ◖, 🏕, vending, litter barrels, petwalk, RV dump
156	AL 23, to US 11, Springville, to St Clair Springs, W ◖ Citgo/dsl, ▥ Azteca's Mexican, China Stix, Waffle House,

Vertical side labels: E ↕ W (left column); N ↕ S, FT PAYNE, GADSDEN (center column)

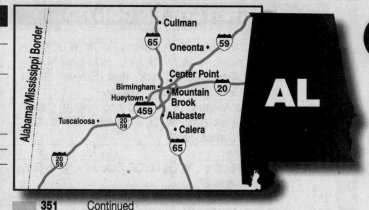

N		

INTERSTATE 59 CONT'D

Exit	Services
156	Continued
	⊡ Curves, $Tree, Walmart /Subway
154	AL 174, Springville, to Odenville, **W** 🅶 Chevron/24hr, Exxon, Shell/dsl, Texaco/Domino's/Subway, 🍴 Big Boulton's BBQ, Jack's Rest., McDonald's, Ms. V's BBQ, Smokin Grill BBQ, ⊡ transmissions, vet
148	to US 11, Argo, **E** 🅶 BP
143	Mt Olive Church Rd, Deerfoot Pkwy
141	to Trussville, Pinson, **E** 🅶 BP/dsl, Chevron/dsl, Shell/Subway/dsl (1mi), Texaco/dsl, 🍴 Applebee's, Cracker Barrel, LoneStar Steaks, McDonald's, Papa John's, Pizza Hut, Taco Bell, Waffle House, Wendy's, 🛏 Comfort Inn, Holiday Inn Express, Jameson Inn, ⊡ Curves, Harley-Davidson, **W** 🅶 Chevron/24hr, Citgo, Exxon, Shell/dsl, 🍴 Arby's, Buffalo Wild Wings, Burger King, Chick-fil-A, Costa's Italian, DQ, Komoni Japanese, Krystal, Milo's Burgers, Moe's SW Grill, Palace Asian, Paul's Hotdogs, Ruby Tuesday, Whataburger, Zaxby's, ⊡ Ace Hardware, Advance Parts, Aldi Foods, CVS Drug, $Tree, GNC, K-Mart, Kohl's, Marshall's, Office Depot, Petsmart, Radio Shack, Sam's Club/gas, Walgreens, Walmart /McDonald's, vet
137	I-459, S to Montgomery, Tuscaloosa
134	to AL 75, Roebuck Pkwy, **W** 🅶 Chevron, Exxon, Mobil, Murphy USA/dsl, Shell, 🍴 Arby's, Azteca Mexican, Chick-fil-A, Krystal, McDonald's, Milo's Burgers, O'Charley's, Ruby Tuesday, Sol Azteca Mexican, Subway, Taco Bell, Waffle House, 🛏 Best Inn, ⊡ 🅷 URGENT CARE, Aldi Foods, CVS Drug, $Tree, Firestone/auto, Honda, NTB, O'Reilly Parts, Rite Aid, Roebuck Tire/repair, V Tires, Walgreens, Walmart
133	4th St, to US 11 (from nb), **W** 🍴 Papa John's, ⊡ $General, Suzuki, USPO, same as 134
132	US 11 N, 1st Ave, **E** same as 131, **W** 🅶 Chevron/24hr, Shell, 🍴 Krispy Kreme, ⊡ city park
131	Oporto-Madrid Blvd (from nb), **E** 🅶 Chevron, 🍴 Church's, Little Caesars, Rally's, ⊡ CVS Drug, Family$, O'Reilly Parts, U-Haul, same as 132, **W** 🅶 Texaco
130	I-20 E, to Atlanta, W to Tuscaloosa
	I-59 S and I-20 W run together from B'ham to Mississippi. See Alabama Interstate 20.

INTERSTATE 65

N		

Exit	Services
366mm	Alabama/Tennessee state line
365	AL 53, to Ardmore, **E** 🅶 Pure, 🛏 Budget Inn 364mm **Welcome Ctr sb, full ♿ facilities, info, 🕿 vending, ☕ litter barrels, petwalk, RV dump**
361	Elkmont, **W** 🅶 BP/dsl, HQ/rest./dsl, 🍴 Momma D's Rest., ⊡ antiques, repair
354	US 31, S to Athens, **W** 🅶 Chevron, Texaco/dsl, 🍴 Capt D's, China Dragon, Domino's, Jack's Rest., Little Caesars, McDonald's, Pizza Hut, Rooster's Cafe, Subway, 🛏 Mark Motel, ⊡ 🅷 Advance Parts, CVS Drug, $General, K-Mart, Northgate RV Park, Piggly Wiggly, Rite Aid, Walgreens, city park
351	US 72, to Athens, Huntsville, **E** 🅶 Exxon, RaceWay, Shell/Subway, Texaco/dsl, 🍴 Burger King, Clark's Rest., Cracker Barrel, Lawler's BBQ, McDonald's/RV Parking, New China Buffet, Pepper's Deli, Waffle House, Wendy's, 🛏 Country

	D E C A T U R	C U L L M A N

Exit	Services
351	Continued
	Hearth Inn, Hampton Inn, Quality Inn, Travel Inn, ⊡ AT&T, Publix, Russell Stover, Verizon, vet, **W** 🅶 BP, Citgo/dsl, Murphy USA, 🍴 Applebee's, Arby's, Bojangles, Burger King, Catfish Cabin, Casa Blanca Mexican, Chick-fil-A, Hardee's, KFC, Krystal, Logan's Roadhouse, Papa John's, Papa Murphy's, Pizza Hut, Ruby Tuesday, Shoney's, Sonic, Starbucks, Steak-Out, Subway, Taco Bell, Zaxby's, 🛏 Best Western, Days Inn, Holiday Inn Express, Sleep Inn, Super 8, ⊡ 🅷, Advance Parts, Big 10 Tire, Chevrolet, Chrysler/Dodge/Jeep, $General, $tree, Ford/Lincoln/Mercury, Goodyear/auto, Lowe's, O'Reilly Parts, Radio Shack, Staples, Verizon, Walmart, to Joe Wheeler SP
347	Brownsferry Rd, Huntsville, **W** Swan Creek RV Park
340b	I-565 ,to Huntsville, to Alabama Space & Rocket Ctr
340a	AL 20, to Decatur, **W** 🅶 Chevron/dsl, RaceWay, **2 mi W** 🛏 Courtyard, Hampton Inn, Holiday Inn
337mm	Tennessee River
334	AL 67, Priceville, to Decatur, **E** 🅶 BP/dsl, RaceWay/dsl, 🍴 JW's Steaks, 🛏 Days Inn, Super 8, ⊡ $General, **W** 🅶 Chevron, 🚛/Subway/Wendy's/dsl/scales/24hr, 🍴 Burger King, DQ, Hardee's, Krystal, McDonald's/playplace, Smokehouse BBQ, Waffle House, 🛏 Comfort Inn, ⊡ 🅷, Hood RV Ctr
328	AL 36, Hartselle, **E** 🍴 Cracker Barrel, **W** 🅶 BP, Cowboys/dsl, Jet-Pep/dsl, Shell, 🍴 Huddle House, 🛏 Country Hearth Inn
325	Thompson Rd, to Hartselle
322	AL 55, to US 31, to Falkville, Eva, **E** 🅶 BP/Chester's/dsl, **W** 🅶 Chevron, Loves/McDonald's/Subway/dsl/scales/24hr, 🍴 Full House Rest., ⊡ $General
318	US 31, to Lacon, **E** 🅶 BP/DQ/Stuckey's, 🛏 Lacon Motel
310	AL 157, Cullman, West Point, **E** 🅶 BP, Conoco/Subway/dsl, Exxon, Shell/dsl, Texaco/Wendy's/dsl, 🍴 Arby's, Backyard Burger, Burger King, Cracker Barrel, Denny's, KFC, McDonald's, New China, Ruby Tuesday, Taco Bell, Waffle House, 🛏 Best Western, Comfort Suites, Hampton Inn, Holiday Inn Express, Quality Inn, Sleep Inn, ⊡ 🅷, Buick/GMC, Ford/Lincoln, Piggly Wiggly, **W** 🅶 BP/dsl, Exxon/dsl, 🛏 Super 8
308	US 278, Cullman, **E** 🛏 Days Inn, **W** 🅶 Chevron, ⊡ flea mkt
304	AL 69, N Good Hope, to Cullman, **E** 🅶 Exxon/dsl, Jet-Pep, Shell/rest/dsl/scales, 🍴 Hardee's, Jack's Rest., Waffle House, 🛏 EconoLodge, ⊡ 🅷, Good Hope Camping, Kountry Mile RV Ctr, dsl/rv repair, **W** 🅶 Jet-Pep, to Smith Lake Camping, ⊡ $General
301mm	**rest area both lanes, full ♿ facilities, 🕿, ☕, vending, litter barrels, petwalk, RV dump**

AL

INTERSTATE 65 CONT'D

Exit	Services
299	AL 69, S to Jasper, **E** 🅾 Millican RV Ctr, **W** 🛢 Dodge City/Conoco/rest./dsl/scales/24hr, HQ, Shell/McDonald's/dsl, Texaco/dsl, 🍴 Jack's Rest., Subway, 🅾 CarQuest, $General, repair/tires
291	AL 91, to Arkadelphia, **E** 🛢 Conoco/dsl, 🅾 Country View RV Park (1mi), **W** 🛢 Shell/rest./dsl/24hr/@, 🍴 Southern Sunrise Cafe
291mm	Warrior River
289	to Blount Springs, **W** 🛢 BP/DQ/Stuckey's, 🅾 to Rickwood Caverns SP
287	US 31, N to Blount Springs, **E** 🛢 Citgo, Conoco/dsl
284	US 31 S, AL 160 E, Hayden Corner, **E** 🛢 Petro, Shell, **W** tires
282	AL 140, Warrior, **E** 🛢 Chevron/Subway/dsl, Exxon/McDonald's, FuelZ/dsl, 🍴 Hardee's, Pizza Hut, Taco Bell, **W** 🛢 BP
281	US 31, to Warrior, **E** 🅾 Chevrolet
280	to US 31, to Warrior, **E** 🅾 Chevrolet
279mm	Warrior River
275	to US 31, Morris
272	Mt Olive Rd, **W** 🛢 Shell/dsl, **W** 🛢 BP/dsl, Chevron/dsl, 🍴 Jack's Rest., 🅾 $General
271	Fieldstown Rd, **E** 🛢 BP/Circle K, Chevron/dsl, Exxon, Murphy USA/dsl, RaceWay/dsl, 🍴 Arby's, Chick-fil-A, China Garden, Guthrie's Diner, Habanero's Mexican, Jim'n Nick's BBQ, KFC, Little Caesars, McDonald's, Milo's Burgers, Pasquales Pizza, Pizza Hut, Ruby Tuesday, Ryan's, Sonic, Subway, Taco Bell, Waffle House, Wendy's, Zaxby's, 🛏 Microtel, 🅾 Advance Parts, AT&T, AutoZone, $General, $Tree, Hobby Lobby, Kia, NAPA, Publix, Radio Shack, Verizon, Walgreens, Walmart/McDonald's, **W** 🛢 Shell/dsl, 🍴 Cracker Barrel, 🛏 Best Western
267	Walkers Chapel Rd, to Fultondale, **E** 🛢 Chevron/dsl, Jet-Pep, Murphy Express/dsl, Shell/Subway/dsl, 🍴 Applebee's, Arby's, Burger King, Casa Fiesta, Chick-fil-A, Chili's, China One, Domino's, Firehouse Subs, 5 Guys Burgers, Fullmoon BBQ, Hardee's, Jack's Rest., Logan's Roadhouse, McDonald's, O'Charley's, Outback Steaks, Stix Asian, Waffle House, Whataburger, Zaxby's, 🛏 Comfort Suites, Fairfield Inn, Hampton Inn, Holiday Inn Express, La Quinta, 🅾 AAA, AT&T, Best Buy, Books-A-Million, CVS Drug, $General, GNC, JC Penney, Lowe's, O'Reilly Parts, Rite Aid, Ross, Target, Verizon, Volvo Trucks, Winn-Dixie, USPO, urgent care, **W** 🛢 Chevron/dsl, 🍴 Porky's Pride BBQ
266	US 31, Fultondale, **E** 🛢 Chevron/dsl, 🛏 Super 8
265	I-22 W, to Memphis
264	41st Ave, **W** 🛢 *FLYING J*/Denny's/dsl/LP/scales/24hr
263	33rd Ave, **E** 🛢 Chevron/dsl, 🛏 Apex Motel, **W** 🛢 Exxon
262b a	16th St, Finley Ave, **E** 🛢 BP, Marathon/dsl, Shell/dsl, 🅾 Kenworth, **W** 🛢 Chevron, Fuel City/dsl, Mobil/dsl/scales, 🍴 Capt D's, McDonald's, Popeye's
261b a	I-20/59, E to Gadsden, W to Tuscaloosa
260b a	6th Ave N, **E** 🛢 BP, Shell, Texaco, 🍴 Mrs Winner's, 🅾 Buick/GMC, Chevrolet, Hyundai, Nissan, **W** 🛢 Chevron/dsl, 🅾 to Legion Field
259b a	University Blvd, 4th Ave, 5th Ave, **E** 🛢 Chevron/dsl, 🍴 Waffle House, 🅾 🏥, **W** 🛢 Chevron/dsl, 🅾 Goodyear

Exit	Services
258	Green Springs Ave, **E** 🛢 Chevron, Shell, 🍴 Exotic Wings
256b a	Oxmoor Rd, **E** 🛢 Exxon, Marathon, Mobil/dsl, Shell, 🍴 Acapulco Grill, Baskits, Burger King, Domino's, Firehouse Subs, KFC, Krystal, McDonald's, Qdoba Mexican, Tai Pei Bistro, Zaxby's, 🛏 Howard Johnson, 🅾 URGENT CARE, Aldi Foods, AutoZone, BigLots, $Tree, Firestone/auto, Food World, K-Mart, Office Depot, Publix, **W** 🛢 Chevron/24hr, Texaco/dsl, 🍴 Hamburger Heaven, Hardee's, Jim'n Nick's BBQ, Waffle House, 🛏 EconoLodge, Comfort Inn, Microtel, Motel 6, Quality Inn, Rodeway Inn, Super 8, 🅾 Batteries+, Valley Tire, vet
255	Lakeshore Dr, **E** 🛢 BP/Circle K, 🅾 🏥, to Samford U, **W** 🛢 Chevron, Shell, 🍴 Aladdin's Grill, Arby's, Chili's, Chick-fil-A, Costas BBQ, Hooters, IHOP, Landry's Seafood, Loco's Deli, LoneStar Steaks, McAlister's Deli, McDonald's, Milo's Burger, Moe's SW Grill, Mr Wang's, O'Charley's, Outback Steaks, Starbucks, Subway, Taco Bell, Taco Casa, Wendy's, 🛏 Best Western, Candlewood Suites, Country Inn&Suites, Drury Inn, Hilton Garden, Holiday Inn, Sun Suites, TownePlace Suites, 🅾 AT&T, Books-A-Million, $Tree, Goodyear/auto, Hobby Lobby, Lowe's, Old Navy, Radio Shack, Sam's Club/gas, Verizon, Walmart /Subway
254	Alford Ave, Shades Crest Rd, **E** 🛢 Chevron, 🅾 vet, **W** 🛢 BP, Shell
252	US 31, Montgomery Hwy, **E** 🛢 BP, Chevron, Shell, Texaco/dsl, 🍴 Arby's, Backyard Burger, Bruster's, Capt D's, ChuckeCheese, Hardee's, Maria Mexican, Mexico Lindo, Milo's Burger, Waffle House, 🛏 Baymont Inn, Quality Inn, 🅾 🏥, Aamco, Big 10 Tire, GMC, Tuesday Morning, NAPA, Volvo, VW, vet, **W** 🛢 BP, Exxon/dsl, Shell, 🍴 Burger King, Chick-fil-A, Dave's Deli, Full Moon BBQ, Golden Rule BBQ, Habanero's Mexican, Krispy Kreme, Krystal, Mandarin House, McDonald's, Outback Steaks, Papa John's, Salvatori's Pizza, Starbucks, Subway, Waffle House, 🛏 Days Inn, 🅾 Acura, Advance Parts, Books-A-Million, Buick, Cadillac, Chevrolet, $Tree, Firestone, Goodyear/auto, Honda, Hyundai, Mr Transmission, Nissan, Publix, Rite Aid, Staples, TJ Maxx
250	I-459, to US 280
247	Al 17, Valleydale Rd, **E** 🛢 BP, **W** 🛢 Mobil/Kangaroo, RaceWay/dsl, Shell, 🍴 Arby's, Backyard Burger, IHOP, Milo's Burgers, Papa John's, RagTime Café, Subway, Waffle House, 🛏 Homewood Suites, La Quinta, Oak Mtn Lodge, 🅾 O'Reilly Parts, Rite Aid, Publix, Walgreens, vet
246	AL 119, Cahaba Valley Rd, **E** 🅾 to Oak Mtn SP, **W** 🛢 Kangaroo/Subway/dsl, Murphy USA/dsl, RaceWay/dsl, Shell, 🍴 Applebee's, Arby's, Burger King, Capt D's, Chick-fil-A, Cracker Barrel, DQ, Dunkin Donuts, Golden Corral, Hooters, KFC, Krystal, Margarita Grill, McAlister's Deli, McDonald's, O'Charley's, Pizza Hut, Purple Onion, Ruby Tuesday, Shoney's, Sonic, Taco Bell, TX Roadhouse, 2 Pesos Mexican, Waffle House, Wendy's, Whataburger, 🛏 Best Western, Comfort Suites, Fairfield Inn, Hampton Inn, Holiday Inn Express, Quality Inn, Ramada Ltd, Sleep Inn, Travelodge, ValuePlace, 🅾 🏥, Advance Parts, AutoZone, Curves, $Tree, Firestone/auto, Harley-Davidson, Kia, Mazda, NAPA, Verizon, Walmart
242	Pelham, **E** 🛢 Chevron/dsl/24hr, Exxon/dsl, Shell/dsl,

BIRMINGHAM

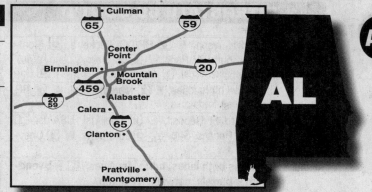

AL

INTERSTATE 65 CONT'D

Exit	Services

N ↕ S

242 Continued
🍴 Subway, 🅞 CVS Drug, Publix, W 🛏 Shelby Motel (2mi), 🅞 Good Sam Camping (1mi)

238 US 31, Alabaster, Saginaw, E 🅖 Murphy USA/dsl, 🍴 Arby's, Buffalo Wild Wings, Chick-fil-A, Coldstone, DQ, Firehouse Subs, Full Moon Cafe, Habanero's Mexican, HoneyBaked Ham, Jim'n Nick's BBQ, Longhorn Steaks, McDonald's, Mizu Japanese, Moe's SW Grill, O'Charley's, Olive Garden, Panda House, Panera Bread, Papa Sala Sports Grille, Ruby Tuesday, Salsarita's Mexican, Starbucks, Taco Bell, 🛏 Candlewood Suites, 🅞 URGENT CARE, AT&T, Belk, Best Buy, Books-A-Million, GNC, JC Penney, Lowe's, Old Navy, Petsmart, Radio Shack, Ross, Target, TJ Maxx, Walmart /Subway, W 🅖 Cannon, Chevron/dsl, Shell/dsl, 🍴 Waffle House, Whataburger, **2 mi** W 🛏 Shelby Motel, 🅞 🅗

234 E 🅖 BP/Subway/dsl, W 🅖 Chevron/dsl/24hr, Shell/dsl, 🅞 GMC, Suncoast RV Ctr

231 US 31, Saginaw, E 🅖 BP/dsl, GasBoy, Murphy USA/dsl, Shell, 🍴 Capt D's, Cracker Barrel, Golden Rule BBQ, McDonald's, Milo's Burgers, Subway, Taco Bell, Tequila Grill, Waffle House, Zaxby's, 🛏 Hampton Inn, Quality Inn, 🅞 Burton RV Ctr, $Tree, Publix, Radio Shack, Rolling Hills RV Park, Walmart, W 🍴 Kristie Rest

228 AL 25, to Calera, E 🅖 Marathon/dsl, Shell/dsl, 🛏 Best Value Inn, Days Inn, W 🅖 Chevron/dsl, 🍴 Hardee's (1mi), Subway, 🅞 $General, Family$, to Brierfield Iron Works SP (15mi)

227mm Buxahatchie Creek

219 Union Grove, Thorsby, E 🅖 Chevron/dsl/24hr, Exxon/Subway/dsl, 🍴 Peach Queen Camping, W 🅖 Shell/dsl, 🍴 Jack's Rest., Smokey Hollow Rest.

213mm rest area both lanes, full ♿ facilities, 🅒, 🖼, vending, litter barrels, petwalk, RV dump

212 AL 145, Clanton, E 🅖 Chevron/dsl, 🅞 Toyota/Scion, W 🅖 Texaco/Subway, Headco/dsl, 🅞 🅗, Buick/Chevrolet/GMC, One Big Peach

208 Clanton, E 🅖 Loves/Arby's/dsl/scales/24hr, 🅞 Higgins Ferry RV Park, W 🅖 Exxon/dsl/24hr, 🍴 Shoney's, 🛏 Guesthouse Inn, 🅞 Dandy RV Park/Ctr, Heaton Pecans, KOA

205 US 31, AL 22, to Clanton, E 🅖 Jet-Pep/dsl/E85, Shell/dsl, Texaco/dsl, 🍴 McDonald's, Waffle House, Whataburger, 🛏 Best Western, Days Inn, Holiday Inn Express, Scottish Inn, 🅞 Peach Park, to Confed Mem Park, **0-2 mi** W 🅖 Chevron/dsl/24hr, Murphy USA/dsl, Shell/dsl, 🍴 Burger King, Capt D's, Jack's Rest., KFC, New China Buffet, Pizza Hut, San Marcos Mexican, Subway, Taco Bell, Wendy's, Zaxby's, 🛏 Key West Inn, 🅞 $General, $Tree, Durbin Farms Mkt, Radio Shack, Walmart

200 to Verbena, E 🅖 Texaco/dsl, W 🅖 Shell/DQ/Stuckey's/dsl

195 Worlds Largest Confederate Flag

186 US 31 Pine Level, E 🅞 Confederate Mem Park (13mi), W 🅖 BP/dsl, Chevron/dsl/24hr, Texaco/Subway/dsl, 🍴 Jose's Mexican, 🛏 Knights Inn, 🅞 🅗

181 AL 14, to Prattville, E 🅖 Chevron/dsl/24hr, Entec/dsl, W 🅖 Exxon, QV, Texaco/DQ/dsl, 🍴 Cracker Barrel, El

CLANTON

---

181 Continued
Torito, Ruby Tuesday, Subway, Waffle House, Wendy's, 🛏 EconoLodge, Hometowne Suites, La Quinta, Quality Inn, Super 8, 🅞 🅗

179 US 82, W Millbrook, E 🅖 Chevron/dsl, 🛏 County Inn&Suites, Key West Inn, Sleep Inn, 🅞 K&K RV Park, **0-2 mi** W 🅖 Jet-Pep, Liberty, RaceWay/dsl, Shell/dsl, USA TC/dsl, 🍴 Applebee's, Beef'O'Brady's, Bruster's, Burger King, Capt. D's, Casitas Mexican, Chick-fil-A, CiCi's Pizza, Hardee's, IHOP, Jim'n Nick's BBQ, KFC, Krystal, Las Casitas Mexican, Logan's Roadhouse, Longhorn Steaks, McAlister's Deli, McDonald's, Mexico Tipico, Moe's SW Grill, O'Charley's, Olive Garden, Outback Steaks, Popeye's, Ryan's, Shoney's, Sonic, Steak'n Shake, Subway, Tokyo Japanese, Waffle House, Zaxby's, 🛏 Courtyard, Days Inn, Hampton Inn, Holiday Inn, Jameson Inn, Rodeway Inn, 🅞 AT&T, AutoZone, Bass Pro Shops, Belk, Best Buy, BigLots, Big 10 Tire, Books-A-Million, Chevrolet, CVS Drug, $General, $Tree, Ford, Hobby Lobby, Home Depot, JC Penney, K-Mart, Kohl's, Lowe's, Michael's, Office Depot, O'Reilly Parts, Petsmart, Publix, Ross, Target, TJ Maxx, Verizon, Walmart, vet

176 AL 143, N (from nb, no return), Millbrook, Coosada

173 AL 152, North Blvd, to US 231

172mm Alabama River

172 Clay St, Herron St, E 🛏 Embassy Suites, Renaissance Hotel, W 🅖 Chevron/dsl

171 I-85 N, Day St

170 Fairview Ave, E 🅖 Citgo/Subway, Gas Depot, 🍴 Church's, McDonald's, Wing Master, 🅞 Advance Parts, AutoZone, CVS Drug, Family$, O'Reilly Parts, Piggly Wiggly, Rite Aid, W 🅖 Exxon, 🅞 Calhoun Foods, Family$

169 Edgemont Ave (from sb), E 🅖 Liberty

168 US 80 E, US 82, South Blvd, E 🅖 BP/dsl, Entec/dsl, Kangaroo/dsl, TA/Marathon/Country Pride/dsl/24hr/@, 🍴 Arby's, Capt D's, KFC, McDonald's, Popeye's, Pizza Hut, Taco Bell, Waffle House, 🛏 Best Inn, Economy Inn, 🅞 🅗, W 🅖 Chevron/dsl, RaceWay/dsl, Shell/Subway/dsl, 🍴 DQ, Hardee's, Wendy's, 🛏 Best Value Inn, Candlelight Inn, Comfort Inn, Days Inn, EconoLodge, Rodeway Inn

167 US 80, W to Selma

164 US 31, Hyundai Blvd, Hope Hull, E 🅖 Liberty, Saveway/dsl/scales/24hr, 🛏 Lakeside Hotel, 🅞 Montgomery Camping, auto repair, W 🅖 BP, Chevron, Liberty, Subway, 🍴 Burger King, Waffle House, 🛏 Best Western, Comfort Suites, Hampton Inn, Holiday Inn, Motel 6, 🅞 auto repair

MILLBROOK

MONTGOMERY

AL

N ↕ **S**

GREENVILLE

EVERGREEN

ATMORE

	INTERSTATE 65 CONT'D
Exit	**Services**
158	to US 31, Tyson, **E** 🅖 BP/DQ/Stuckey's, ⦿ Montgomery South RV Park, **W** 🅖 ⊕FLYING J/Denny's/dsl/scales/24hr
151	AL 97, to Letohatchee, **E** 🅖 Marathon/dsl, **W** 🅖 BP, PaceCar/dsl
142	AL 185, to Ft Deposit, **E** 🅖 Shell/dsl, USA/dsl, 🍴 Priester's Pecans, Subway, ⦿ auto parts, **W** 🅖 Chevron
133mm	**rest areas both lanes, full** 🚻 **facilities,** 🍴, 🛏, **vending, litter barrels, petwalk, RV dump**
130	AL10 E, AL 185, to Greenville, **E** 🅖 Chevron/dsl, Shell, USA/dsl, 🍴 Arby's, Capt D's, Hardee's, KFC, McDonald's, Old Mexico, Pizza&Sub Express, Pizza Hut, Waffle House, Wendy's, 🛏 Days Inn, Quality Inn, ⦿ Advance Parts, CVS Drug, $General, $Tree, Fred's Store, O'Reilly Parts, Super Foods, Walgreens, to Sherling Lake Park, **W** 🅖 Murphy USA/dsl, Phillips 66/Subway/dsl, QV, Texaco/dsl, 🍴 Bates Turkey Rest., Burger King, Cracker Barrel, Krystal, Ruby Tuesday, Shoney's, Sonic, Taco Bell, Vallarta Mexican, 🛏 Best Western, Comfort Inn, Hampton Inn, Holiday Inn Express, Jameson Inn, ⦿ AT&T, Chevrolet, Verizon, Walmart/Subway
128	AL 10, to Greenville, Pine Apple, **E** 🅖 Shell/Smokehouse/dsl, ⦿ 🅷, **W** 🅖 BP
114	AL 106, to Georgiana, **E** ⦿ Hank Williams Museum, **W** 🅖 BP, Chevron, ⦿ auto repair
107	rd 7, to Garland
101	to Owassa, **E** 🅖 BP/dsl, **W** 🅖 Exxon/dsl, ⦿ Owassa RV Park, dsl repair
96	AL 83, to Evergreen, **E** 🅖 Chevron, Shell, 🍴 Burger King, Hardee's, KFC/Taco Bell, McDonald's, ⦿ 🅷, **W** 🅖 Spirit/Subway/dsl, 🍴 Black Angus Rest., Pizza Hut, Waffle House, 🛏 Best Value Inn, Comfort Inn, Days Inn
93	US 84, to Evergreen, **W** 🅖 BP/dsl, ♥Loves/Arby's/dsl/scales/24hr
89mm	**rest area sb, full** 🚻 **facilities,** 🍴, 🛏, **vending, litter barrels, petwalk, RV dump**
85mm	**rest area nb, full** 🚻 **facilities,** 🍴, 🛏, **vending, litter barrels, petwalk, RV dump**
83	AL 6, to Lenox, **E** 🅖 Marathon, ⦿ RV Park (4mi)
77	AL 41, to Range Brewton, Repton, **W** 🅖 Shell/dsl
69	AL 113, to Flomaton, **E** 🅖 Jet-Pep/Subway/dsl, Chevron/dsl, Shell/dsl/scales/24hr, ⦿ dsl repair, **W** 🅖 Minute Stop/dsl, 🍴 Huddle House
57	AL 21, to Atmore, **E** 🅖 Chevron/dsl, Exxon/dsl, 🍴 Hardee's, McDonald's, Wrangler Steaks, 🛏 Hampton Inn, Holiday Inn Express, Muskogee Inn, ⦿ Wind Creek Indian Gaming, **W** 🅖 BP/dsl, ⦿ to Kelley SP
54	Escambia Cty, Rd 1, **E** 🅖 BP/Subway/dsl, ⦿ to Creek Indian Res
45	to Perdido, **W** 🅖 Chevron/dsl
37	AL 287, Gulf Shores Pkwy, to Bay Minette, **E** 🅖 BP, ⦿ 🅷
34	to AL 59, to Bay Minette, Stockton
31	AL 225, to Stockton, **E** ⦿ to Blakeley SP, Confederate Mem Bfd, **W** 🅖 Shell/Subway/dsl, ⦿ Landing RV Park (2mi)
29mm	Tensaw River
28mm	Middle River

MOBILE

25mm	Mobile River
22	Creola, **E** River Delta RV Park (1mi), marine ctr, truck repair
19	US 43, to Satsuma, **E** 🅖 Chevron/dsl/24hr, ▥/Arby's/dsl/scales/24hr, 🍴 McDonald's, Pintoli's Italian (2mi), Waffle House, 🛏 La Quinta, **W** 🅖 Chevron, Shell/dsl, ⦿ I-65 RV Park (1.5mi)
15	AL 41, **E** 🅖 Chevron, Shell/Pizza Inn/dsl, 🍴 China Chef, Church's, Godfather's Pizza, Pizza Hut, ⦿ Family$, Food World, O'Reilly Parts, Rite Aid, Walgreens, **W** 🅖 Circle K, Shell/Subway/dsl, ⦿ $General
13	AL 158, AL 213, to Saraland, **E** 🅖 Murphy USA/dsl, Shell/dsl, 🍴 Krystal, Ruby Tuesday, Waffle House, Wintzell's Oyster House, 🛏 Best Western, Comfort Suites, Days Inn, EconoLodge, Microtel, Quality Inn, ⦿ Radio Shack, Walmart/McDonald's, urgent care, **W** 🅖 Exxon/Subway, 🛏 Hampton Inn, Holiday Inn Express, ⦿ to Chickasabogue Campground
10	W Lee St, **E** 🅖 Kangaroo, Shell/Subway, 🍴 Huddle House, 🛏 Best Inn
9	I-165 S, to Mobile, to I-10 E
8b a	US 45, to Prichard, **E** 🅖 Chevron/Circle K/dsl, Shell/dsl, Texaco/dsl, 🍴 Church's, 🛏 Star Motel, ⦿ $General, tires/repair, **W** 🅖 BP, Citgo/dsl, 1st Stop, Pride Trkstp/dsl/scales, RaceWay/dsl, Texaco/dsl, 🍴 Burger King, Domino's, Golden Egg Café, McDonald's, Pizza Hut, ⦿ CVS Drug, $General, vet
5b	US 98, Moffett Rd, **E** 🅖 Exxon/dsl, Texaco/dsl, 🍴 Burger King, Church's, McDonald's, Saucy Q BBQ, Sub King, ⦿ Big 10 Tire, **W** 🍴 Hardee's, 🛏 Super 8, ⦿ auto repair
5a	Spring Hill Ave, **E** 🅖 Shell/dsl, 🍴 McDonald's, ⦿ 🅷, Big 10 Tire, Mr Transmission, **W** 🅖 Chevron, Shell/dsl, 🍴 Hibachi Express, Starbucks, Subway, Waffle House, Zaxby's, 🛏 Extended Stay America, Wingate Inn
4	Dauphin St, **E** 🅖 BP/Circle K/dsl, Shell/Summit, 🍴 Checker's, Chick-fil-A, Cracker Barrel, Hong Kong Rest., Krystal, McDonald's, Popeye's, Subway, Taco Bell, Waffle House, Wendy's, 🛏 Comfort Inn, Comfort Suites, Red Roof Inn, Rodeway Inn, ⦿ Buick/GMC, $General, FoodWorld, Lowe's, Mercedes, Rite Aid, Tuesday Morning, Walmart/McDonald's, same as 3 & 5a, **W** ⦿ 🅷
3	Airport Blvd, **E** 🅖 Shell, 🍴 Burger King, Cane's, Izume Japanese, Logan's Roadhouse, Macaroni Grill, Morrison's Cafeteria, Piccadilly's, Starbucks, Wendy's, 🛏 Marriott, ⦿ 🅷, Acura/Jaguar/Infiniti, Belk, Best Buy, BigLots, Cadillac, Dillard's, $Tree, Firestone/auto, Ford, Goodyear/auto, Harley-Davidson, Honda, JC Penney, Land Rover, Marshall's, Nissan, Old Navy, Sam's Club, Sears/auto, Staples, Target, mall, **W** 🅖 GasCo/dsl, Shell, 🍴 American Cafe, Arby's, Baumhowers, Big Apple Chinese, Boiling Pot, Burger King, Carrabba's, ChuckeCheese, Denny's, El Chico, Firehouse Subs, GolBerg's Deli, Honeybaked Ham, Hooters, IHOP, Lenny's Subs, Los Rancheros Mexican, Marble Slab, Newk's Cafe, O'Charley's, Olive Garden, Osaka Japanese, Panera Bread, Popeye's, Quiznos, Red Lobster, Ruby Tuesday, Starbucks, Subway, Taco Bell, 🛏 Ashberry Suites, Baymont Inn, Best Value Inn, Courtyard, Days Inn, Drury Inn, EconoLodge, Fairfield Inn, Family Inn, Hampton Inn, Hilton Garden, Holiday Inn, InTowne Suites, La Quinta, Motel 6, Quality Inn, Residence Inn,

◉ = gas   🍴 = food   🛏 = lodging   ⊙ = other

INTERSTATE 65 CONT'D

Exit	Services
3	Continued ValuePlace, ⊙ Books-A-Million, $General, $Tree, Fresh Mkt Foods, Home Depot, Jo-Ann Fabrics, Office Depot, PepBoys, Petsmart, Radio Shack, Ross, SteinMart, TJ Maxx, U-Haul, Walgreens, to USAL
1b a	US 90, Government Blvd, E ◉ Raceway/dsl, 🍴 McAlister's Deli, Steak'n Shake, 🛏 Emerald Palms, ⊙ Audi/Porsche/VW, BMW, Chevrolet, Chrysler/Jeep, Dodge, Kia, Lexus, Lincoln/Volvo, Toyota/Scion, W ◉ Shell/dsl, 🍴 Waffle House, 🛏 Rest Inn
0mm	I-10, E to Pensacola, W to New Orleans, I-65 begins/ends on I-10, exit 20.

INTERSTATE 85

Exit	Services
80mm	Alabama/Georgia state line, Chattahoochee River
79	US 29, to Lanett, E ◉ BP/Circle K, Murphy USA, 🍴 Arby's, Burger King, Capt D's, Chuck's BBQ, KFC, Krystal, Little Caesars, McDonald's, Pizza Hut, San Marcos Mexican, Subway, Taco Bell, Waffle House, Wendy's, Wing Stop, ⊙ Ⓗ, Advance Parts, $General, $Tree, Verizon, Walmart, repair, to West Point Lake, W ◉ JetPep, QV, Raceway/dsl, 🍴 Domino's, Sonic, 🛏 Days Inn, EconoLodge, ⊙ AutoZone, CVS Drug, Kroger, O'Reilly Parts, vet
78.5mm	Welcome Ctr sb, full ♿ facilities, Ⓒ, vending, 🍱 litter barrels, petwalk
77	AL 208, to Huguley, E ◉ Jet Pep/Church's/dsl, Shell/Circle K, 🍴 Waffle House, 🛏 Holiday Inn Express, ⊙ Chevrolet, Chrysler/Dodge/Ford/Lincoln/Mercury, auto repair, W 🛏 Hampton Inn, ⊙ fireworks
76mm	Eastern/Central time zone
70	AL 388, to Cusseta, E ◉ BigCat/dsl, Trvl Plaza/Shell/rest/dsl/scales/24hr/@
66	Andrews Rd, to US 29
64	US 29, to Opelika, E ◉ Sunoco/dsl, W ◉ Tiger/dsl
62	US 280/431, to Opelika, E ◉ Chevron/dsl, Eagle/dsl, Liberty, Shell/Circle K/Church's/dsl, 🍴 Burger King, Durango Mexican, McDonald's, Subway, Wok'n Roll Rest., 🛏 Best Value Inn, Days Inn, EconoLodge, Knights Inn, Quality Inn, Super 8, ⊙ Lakeside RV Park (4.5mi), W ◉ GrubMart, JetPep, 🍴 Capt. D's, Cracker Barrel, Sizzlin Steaks, Waffle House, 🛏 Comfort Inn, Travelodge, ⊙ Buick/Chevrolet/GMC, Chrysler/Dodge/Jeep, Ford, H&W Tire, Harley-Davidson, Jeep, USA Stores/famous brands
60	AL 51, AL 169, to Opelika, E ◉ RaceWay/dsl, 🍴 Hardee's, ⊙ $General, W ◉ Lo-Buck's, ⊙ Ⓗ, auto repair
58	US 280, W to Opelika, E 🛏 Hampton Inn, Holiday Inn Express, ⊙ golf, museum, W ◉ Shell/Subway/dsl, 🍴 Arby's, Brick Oven Pizza, Buffalo Wild Wings, Chick-fil-A, El Patrone Mexican, Huddle House, Jim Bob's, Moe's SW Grill, Logan's Roadhouse, Longhorn Steaks, O'Charley's, Olive Garden, Sonic, Starbucks, Waffle House, Zaxby's, 🛏 Fairfield Inn, Microtel, Motel 6, ⊙ Ⓗ, Best Buy, Books-A-Million, Dick's, Hobby Lobby, Home Depot, Kohl's, Kroger/dsl, Lowe's, Office Depot, Old Navy, PetCo, Ross, Target, TJ Maxx, World Mkt, urgent care
57	Glenn Ave, W ◉ Exxon, QV, 🍴 Provino's Italian,

Exit	Services
57	Continued Shakey's Pizza, Waffle House, Wendy's, 🛏 Hilton Garden, University Motel, ⊙ Sam's Club/gas
51	US 29, to Auburn, E ◉ Shell, 🛏 Hampton Inn, ⊙ Cadillac/Chevrolet, Leisure Time RV Park/Camping, Nissan, Toyota/Scion, to Chewacla SP, W ◉ Chevron/Subway/dsl, Murphy USA, 🍴 Arby's, Burger King, El Dorado Mexican, Firehouse Subs, Hong Kong Buffet, Krystal, Little Caesars, McDonald's, Philly Connection, Pizza Hut, Ruby Tuesday, Sonic, Taco Bell, Waffle House, Wendy's, Zaxby's, 🛏 Catfish Cabin, EconoLodge, Holiday Inn Express, Microtel, Quality Inn, Sleep Inn, ⊙ Advance Parts, $General, Ford/Lincoln/Mercury, Walmart, Winn-Dixie, to Auburn U, tires/repair, urgent care, vet
50	new exit
44mm	rest area both lanes, full ♿ facilities, Ⓒ, 🍱, vending, litter barrels, petwalk, RV dump, 24hr security
42	US 80, AL 186 E, Wire Rd, E ⊙ to Tuskegee NF, dsl repair/tires, W ◉ Torch 85/rest./dsl/24hr
38	AL 81, to Tuskegee, E to Tuskegee NHS, Tuskegee University
32	AL 49, N to Tuskegee, E ◉ BP/dsl
26	AL 229, N to Tallassee, E ◉ Shell/Guthrie's/dsl, W Ⓗ
22	US 80, to Shorter, E ◉ BP/dsl, Marathon/dsl, Petro/Chevron/rest./dsl/scales/24hr, 🛏 Days Inn
16	Waugh, to Cecil, E ◉ BP/Subway/dsl, ⊙ auto repair
11	US 80, AL 110, to Mitylene, to Mt Meigs, E ◉ Exxon/Subway/dsl, Liberty/dsl, 🍴 Anthony's Rest., Bruster's, Burger King, Cracker Barrel, Jose's Grill, McDonald's, Top China, Waffle House, 🛏 Candlewood Suites, Comfort Inn, Country Inn&Suites, Fairfield Inn, Holiday Inn Express, Sleep Inn, ⊙ Home Depot, Walmart/Subway, auto repair, W ◉ Chevron/dsl, 🛏 Microtel
9	AL 271, to AL 110, to Auburn U/Montgomery, E 🍴 Arby's, Boardwalk Burgers, BoneFish Grill, Chick-fil-A, Chili's, 5 Guys Burgers, Guthrie's, Ixtapa Mexican, Mimi's Cafe, Moe's SW Grill, Panera Bread, Red Robin, Ruby Tuesday, Sonic, Starbucks, TX Roadhouse, Wendy's, Zoe's Kitchen, 🛏 Hampton Inn, Staybridge Suites, ⊙ AT&T, Books-A-Million, Costco/gas, Dick's, Dillard's, EarthFare Foods, Jo-Ann Fabrics, Kohl's, Michael's, Old Navy, Petsmart, Radio Shack, Ross, Target, Verizon, World Mkt, urgent care, vet, W Ⓗ
6	US 80, US 231, AL 21, East Blvd, 0-2 mi E ◉ Chevron, Exxon/dsl, RaceWay/dsl, Shell, 🍴 Arby's, Arriba Mexican, Baumhowers, Burger King, Carrabba's, Chick-fil-A, Golden Corral, Hardee's, Jason's Deli, KFC, Longhorn Steaks, Los Cabos, Los Vaqueros Mexican, McDonald's, Ming's Garden, Olive Garden, Panera Bread,

⬆ = gas ⬇ = food ⬆ = lodging ⬆ = other   Copyright 2012 - The Next Exit®

AL

N ← S **MONTGOMERY**

INTERSTATE 85 CONT'D

Exit	Services
6	Continued
	Piccadilly's, Popeye's, Rock Bottom Cafe, Ruby Tuesday, Schlotzsky's, Shogun Japanese, Starbucks, Subway, Sushiyama, Taco Bell, Waffle House, Wendy's, Zaxby's, ⬆ Best Inn, Comfort Inn, Country Inn&Suites, Courtyard, Extended Stay America, La Quinta, Quality Inn, Red Roof Inn, Residence Inn, Rodeway Inn, Sleep Inn, SpringHill Suites, Studio+, ValuePlace, Wingate Inn, ⬆ Acura, Best Buy, Books-A-Million, $General, Family$, Ford/Lincoln, Fresh Mkt Foods, Home Depot, Honda, Hyundai, Lowe's, Office Depot, PetCo, Radio Shack, Subaru, TJ Maxx, Walmart/McDonald's, Winn-Dixie, USPO, **W** ⬆ BP, Chevron, Liberty, Shell, ⬇ Arby's, Buffet City, Capt D's, Guthrie's, Hardee's, Hibaci Buffet, IHOP, Krispy Kreme, Krystal, McDonald's, Outback Steaks, Shoney's, Stevi B's Pizza, Taco Bell, Waffle House, ⬆ Baymont Inn, Budgetel, Comfort Suites, Drury Inn, Express Inn, Motel 6, Ramada Inn, ⬆ Audi/VW, BMW, Buick/Cadillac, Chevrolet, Chrysler/Dodge/Jeep, $General, Firestone/auto, Fred's Store, Infiniti, JC Penney, Kia, Lexus, Mercedes, Nissan, Sam's Club/gas, Sears/auto, Toyota, mall, to Gunter AFB
4	Perry Hill Rd, **E** ⬇ Chappy's Deli, **W** ⬆ Cannon/dsl, Chevron, ⬇ Hardee's, Subway, ⬆ Hilton Garden, Homewood Suites, ⬆ $General, Express Oil Change, Rite Aid, vet
3	Ann St, **E** ⬆ BP/dsl, Chevron, ⬇ Arby's, Capt D's, Country's BBQ, Domino's, KFC, Krystal, McDonald's, Taco Bell, Waffle House, Wendy's, Zaxby's, ⬆ Days Inn, ⬆ Big 10 Tire, **W** ⬆ Entec, Murphy USA/dsl, PaceCar, Ztec, ⬆ Stay Lodge, ⬇ Chick-fil-A, CiCi's Pizza, Hardee's, Popeye's, Subway, ⬆ AT&T, $Tree, Office Depot, Radio Shack, Ross, Verizon, Walmart/Subway
2	Forest Ave, **E** CVS Drug, **W** ⬆
1	Court St, Union St, downtown, **E** ⬆ BP/dsl, Exxon, **W** to Ala St U
0mm	I-85 begins/ends on I-65, exit 171 in Montgomery

INTERSTATE 459 (Birmingham)

N ↑ S

Exit	Services
33b a	I-59, N to Gadsden, S to Birmingham
32	US 11, Trussville, **N** ⬆ BP/24hr, **S** ⬆ BP, Chevron/dsl/24hr, RaceWay/dsl/24hr, Shell/dsl, ⬇ Arby's, Chili's, China Palace, Coldstone, Firehouse Subs, Habanero's Rest., Hooters, Jack's Rest., Jim'n Nick's BBQ, KFC, Lee Garden, Logan's Roadhouse, McDonald's, Red Robin, Starbucks, Subway, Waffle House, Wendy's, ⬆ Courtyard, Hampton Inn, Hilton Garden, ⬆ AT&T, Belk, Best Buy, Big 10 Tires, Books-A-Million, Buick/GMC, Harley-Davidson, Home Depot, JC Penney, Lowe's, Mazda, Michael's, Old Navy, Staples, Target, TJ Maxx, Verizon
31	Derby Parkway, **N** ⬆ B'ham Race Course
29	I-20, E to Atlanta, W to Birmingham
27	Grants Mill Rd, **S** ⬆ Chevron/dsl, ⬆ Audi/Porsche, BMW/Lexus, Chrysler/Dodge/Jeep, Land Rover, Mini
23	Liberty Parkway, **S** ⬇ Billy's Grill, DQ, Tazaki's Greek, ⬆ Hilton Garden
19	US 280, Mt Brook, Childersburg, **N** ⬆ Chevron, ⬇ CA Pizza Kitchen, Cheesecake Factory, Flemings Rest., Macaroni Grill, Panera Bread, PF Chang's, Village Tavern, Barnes&Noble, **0-3 mi S** ⬆ BP/Circle K, Chevron, Exxon, RaceWay.dsl, Shell, ⬇ Arby's, Baha Burger, Burger King, Carrabba's, Chick-fil-A, Chili's, Chipotle Mexican,

B I R M I N G H A M

Exit	Services
19	Continued
	Cracker Barrel, DQ, Edgar's Rest., Fox&Hound Grille, Full Moon BBQ, Hamburger Heaven, Hooters, IHOP, Jade Palace, Jason's Deli, Joe's Crabshack, Kobe Japanese, Logan's Roadhouse, Longhorn Steaks, Lloyd's Rest., Max's Deli, McAlister's Deli, McDonald's, Milo's Burgers, Ming's Chinese, Outback Steaks, Pablo's, Papa John's, Petruccelli's Italian, Pizza Hut, Ralph&Kacoos, Schlotzsky's, Shogun Japanese, Subway, Superior Grill, Suria 280, Taco Bell, Taziki's Greek, TCBY, Tilted Kilt, Wendy's, Zaxby's, ⬆ Best Western, Candlewood Suites, Courtyard, Drury Inn, Fairfield Inn, Hampton Inn, Hilton, Holiday Inn Express, Homestead Suites, Homewood Suites, Hyatt Place, La Quinta, Marriott, Residence Inn, SpringHill Suites, Wingate Inn, ⬆ AT&T, Best Buy, BigLots, Books-A-Million, Curves, CVS Drug, Dick's, Firestone/auto, Fresh Mkt Foods, Goodyear/auto, Hancock Fabrics, Home Depot, Kohl's, Lowe's, Michael's, NTB, PetCo, Petsmart, Ross, Staples, SteinMart, Target, TJMaxx, Verizon, Walgreens, Walmart , vet
17	Acton Rd, **N** ⬆ Shell/dsl/24hr, ⬇ Krystal, McDonald's, **S** ⬆ Comfort Inn
15b a	I-65, N to Birmingham, S to Montgomery
13	US 31, Hoover, Pelham, **N** ⬆ BP, Chevron, Citgo, Exxon, Shell, ⬇ Burger King, Chick-fil-A, Dave's Deli, Fish Mkt Rest., Full Moon Cafe, Golden Rule BBQ, Habanero's, Krispy Kreme, Krystal, McDonald's, Outback Steaks, Papa John's, Quiznos, Salvatori's Pizza, Starbucks, Subway, ⬆ Days Inn, ⬆ URGENT CARE, Acura, AutoZone, Books-A-Million, Buick, Cadillac, Chevrolet, $Tree, Firestone/auto, Goodyear/auto, Honda, Hyundai, Mr Transmission, Nissan, Publix, Rite Aid, Staples, TJ Maxx, vet, **S** ⬆ Jet-Pep, Shell/dsl/24hr, ⬇ Arby's, Bonefish Grill, CA Pizza Kitchen, Carino's, Chipotle Mexican, Guthrie's, J Alexander's Rest., Jason's Deli, Jim'n Nicks BBQ, McDonald's, Michael's Steaks, Moe's SW Grill, Olive Garden, Panera Bread, Pizza Hut, Quiznos, Ruby Tuesday, Shula's Steaks, Starbucks, Subway, Taco Bell, Ted's MT Grill, Top China, Wendy's, ⬆ Courtyard, Days Inn, Embassy Suites, Hampton Inn, Hyatt Place, Microtel, Residence Inn, Wynfrey Hotel, ⬆ Barnes&Noble, Belk, Best Buy, Big 10 Tire, Bruno's Foods, Costco/gas, CVS Drug, Dick's, Hancock Fabrics, Home Depot, Infiniti, JC Penney, Jo-Ann Fabrics, Macy's, Marshall's, Mercedes, Michael's, NTB, Office Depot, Petsmart, Ross, Sam's Club/gas, Sears/auto, Smart Car, Tuesday Morning, Verizon, Walmart (1mi), mall
10	AL 150, Waverly, **N** ⬆ Chevron (1mi), Shell (1mi), ⬇ Frontera Mexican Grill, ⬆ $Tree, Kohl's, PetCo, Target, **S** ⬆ BP/dsl/24hr, Exxon, ⬆ Hampton Inn, Hyatt Place, ⬆ URGENT CARE, Ford, Toyota, Walgreens, Publix/deli
6	AL 52, to Bessemer, **N** ⬆ BP/dsl, **S** ⬆ BP, Jet-Pep, Texaco/Taco Bell, ⬇ Arby's, China Wok, Domino's, Hickory Grill, McDonald's, Pizza Hut, Quiznos, Subway, Waffle House, Wendy's, ⬆ Sleep Inn, ⬆ $General, CVS Drug, TrueValue, Winn-Dixie, RV Camping
1	AL 18, Bessemer, **N** ⬆ Exxon, Shell/dsl, ⬇ Burger King, Chick-fil-A, East Palace, Full Moon BBQ, Habanero's Mexican, Logan's Roadhouse, McAlister's Deli, Taco Bell, ⬆ AT&T, GNC, JC Penney, Publix, Ross, Target, Verizon, **S** ⬆ BP/dsl, ⬇ Bojangles, China King, McDonald's, omma's Rest., San Antonio Grill, Subway, Zaxby's, ⬆ Advance Parts, CVS Drug, Piggly Wiggly, to Tannehill SP
0mm	I-459 begins/ends on I-20/59, exit 106

B E S S E M E R

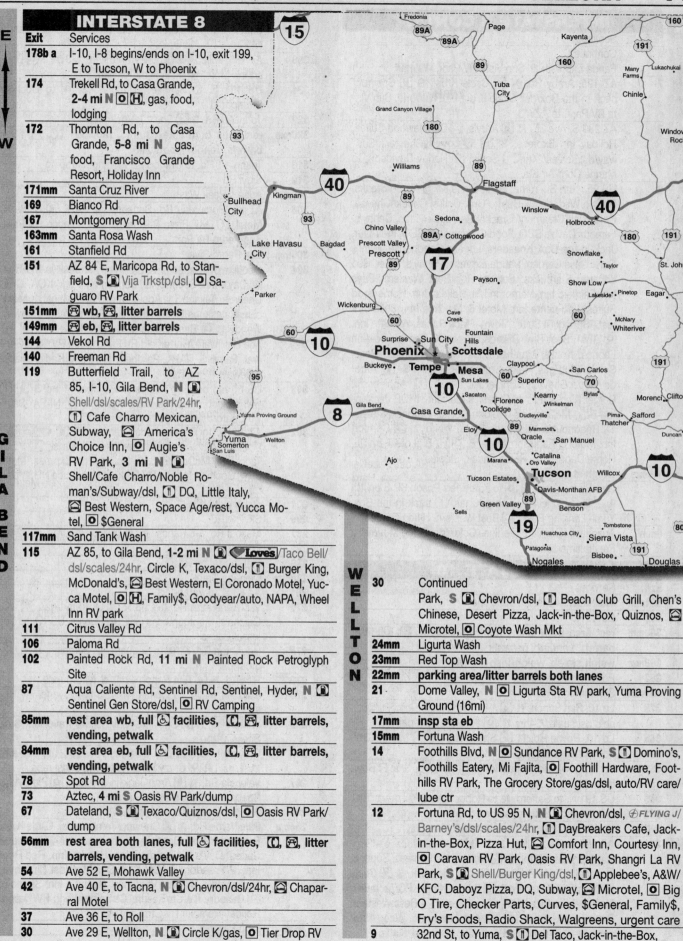

E ↕ W

GILA BEND

INTERSTATE 8		🛡15
Exit	**Services**	
178b a	I-10, I-8 begins/ends on I-10, exit 199, E to Tucson, W to Phoenix	
174	Trekell Rd, to Casa Grande, **2-4 mi** N 🅞🅗, gas, food, lodging	
172	Thornton Rd, to Casa Grande, **5-8 mi** N gas, food, Francisco Grande Resort, Holiday Inn	
171mm	Santa Cruz River	
169	Bianco Rd	
167	Montgomery Rd	
163mm	Santa Rosa Wash	
161	Stanfield Rd	
151	AZ 84 E, Maricopa Rd, to Stanfield, S 🅖 Vija Trkstp/dsl, 🅞 Saguaro RV Park	
151mm	🚻 wb, 🛻, litter barrels	
149mm	🚻 eb, 🛻, litter barrels	
144	Vekol Rd	
140	Freeman Rd	
119	Butterfield Trail, to AZ 85, I-10, Gila Bend, N 🅖 Shell/dsl/scales/RV Park/24hr, 🍴 Cafe Charro Mexican, Subway, 🛏 America's Choice Inn, 🅞 Augie's RV Park, **3 mi** N 🅖 Shell/Cafe Charro/Noble Roman's/Subway/dsl, 🍴 DQ, Little Italy, 🛏 Best Western, Space Age/rest, Yucca Motel, 🅞 $General	
117mm	Sand Tank Wash	
115	AZ 85, to Gila Bend, **1-2 mi** N 🅖 Loves/Taco Bell/dsl/scales/24hr, Circle K, Texaco/dsl, 🍴 Burger King, McDonald's, 🛏 Best Western, El Coronado Motel, Yucca Motel, 🅞🅗, Family$, Goodyear/auto, NAPA, Wheel Inn RV park	
111	Citrus Valley Rd	
106	Paloma Rd	
102	Painted Rock Rd, **11 mi** N Painted Rock Petroglyph Site	
87	Aqua Caliente Rd, Sentinel Rd, Sentinel, Hyder, N 🅖 Sentinel Gen Store/dsl, 🅞 RV Camping	
85mm	rest area wb, full ♿ facilities, 🚻, 🛻, litter barrels, vending, petwalk	
84mm	rest area eb, full ♿ facilities, 🚻, 🛻, litter barrels, vending, petwalk	
78	Spot Rd	
73	Aztec, **4 mi** S Oasis RV Park/dump	
67	Dateland, S 🅖 Texaco/Quiznos/dsl, 🅞 Oasis RV Park/dump	
56mm	rest area both lanes, full ♿ facilities, 🚻, 🛻, litter barrels, vending, petwalk	
54	Ave 52 E, Mohawk Valley	
42	Ave 40 E, to Tacna, N 🅖 Chevron/dsl/24hr, 🛏 Chaparral Motel	
37	Ave 36 E, to Roll	
30	Ave 29 E, Wellton, N 🅖 Circle K/gas, 🅞 Tier Drop RV	

WELLTON

30	**Continued** Park, S 🅖 Chevron/dsl, 🍴 Beach Club Grill, Chen's Chinese, Desert Pizza, Jack-in-the-Box, Quiznos, 🛏 Microtel, 🅞 Coyote Wash Mkt	
24mm	Ligurta Wash	
23mm	Red Top Wash	
22mm	parking area/litter barrels both lanes	
21	Dome Valley, N 🅞 Ligurta Sta RV park, Yuma Proving Ground (16mi)	
17mm	insp sta eb	
15mm	Fortuna Wash	
14	Foothills Blvd, N 🅞 Sundance RV Park, S 🍴 Domino's, Foothills Eatery, Mi Fajita, 🅞 Foothill Hardware, Foothills RV Park, The Grocery Store/gas/dsl, auto/RV care/lube ctr	
12	Fortuna Rd, to US 95 N, N 🅖 Chevron/dsl, ✈FLYING J/Barney's/dsl/scales/24hr, 🍴 DayBreakers Cafe, Jack-in-the-Box, Pizza Hut, 🛏 Comfort Inn, Courtesy Inn, 🅞 Caravan RV Park, Oasis RV Park, Shangri La RV Park, S 🅖 Shell/Burger King/dsl, 🍴 Applebee's, A&W/KFC, Daboyz Pizza, DQ, Subway, 🛏 Microtel, 🅞 Big O Tire, Checker Parts, Curves, $General, Family$, Fry's Foods, Radio Shack, Walgreens, urgent care	
9	32nd St, to Yuma, S 🍴 Del Taco, Jack-in-the-Box,	

AZ

E
↕
W

**Y
U
M
A**

INTERSTATE 8 CONT'D

Exit	Services
9	Continued Panda Express, 🔲 Sun Vista RV Park, Walmart
7	AZ 195, Araby Rd, **N** 🛢 Circle K/dsl, **S** 🛢 Chevron/Jack-in-the-Box/dsl, Circle K/dsl, 🔲 RV World, Sun Vista RV Park, to AZWU
3	AZ 280 S, Ave 3E, **N** 🛢 Arby's, 🛏 Candlewood Suites, Holiday Inn Express, **S** 🛢 **Loves**/Chester's/Subway/dsl/scales/24hr, 🍴 Sonic, 🔲 Harley-Davidson, to Marine Corp Air Sta
2	US 95, 16th St, Yuma, **N** 🛢 Circle K, 🍴 Ah-So Steaks, Buffalo Wild Wings, Burrito Grill, Chili's, ChuckeCheese, Coldstone Creamery, Cracker Barrel, Del Taco, Denny's, Famous Dave's BBQ, Food Ct, Hawaiian BBQ, In-N-Out, Jack-in-the-Box, Kneaders, Logans Roadhouse, Mimi's Cafe, Olive Garden, Panda Express, Penny's, Diner, Red Lobster, Starbucks, Subway, 🛏 Best Western, Days Inn, Fairfield Inn, Hampton Inn, Holiday Inn, Homewood Suites, La Fuente Inn, Motel 6, OakTree Inn, Shilo Inn/rest., SpringHill Suites, TownePlace Suites, Wingate Inn, 🔲 AT&T, Best Buy, Dillards, $Tree, JC Penney, Jo-Ann Fabrics, Kohl's, Marshall's, Old Navy, PetsMart, Ross, Sam's Club/gas, Target, auto/tire repair, **S** 🛢 Arco/dsl/24hr, Chevron/Blimpie/dsl, Shell, 🍴 Applebee's, Burger King, Carl's Jr, Chretin's Mexican, IHOP, Jack-in-the-Box, McDonald's, Golden Corral, Outback Steaks, TX Roadhouse, Village Inn Pizza, Wendy's, 🛏 Comfort Inn, Motel 6, Radisson, Super 8, 🔲🅷, BigLots, Family$, Home Depot, KIA, Radio Shack, Staples
1.5mm	**weigh sta both lanes**
1	Giss Pkwy, Yuma, **N** 🔲 to Yuma Terr Prison SP, **S** on 4th Ave, **E** 🛢 Chevron, Circle K/gas, 🍴 Jack-in-the-Box, Yuma Landing Rest., 🛏 Best Western, Hilton Garden
0mm	Arizona/California state line, Colorado River, Mountain/Pacific time zone

INTERSTATE 10

E
↕
W

W

Exit	Services
391mm	Arizona/New Mexico state line
390	Cavot Rd
389mm	**rest area both lanes, full ♿ facilities, 🔲, 🚻, litter barrels, vending, petwalk**
383mm	**weigh sta eb, weigh/insp sta wb**
382	Portal Rd, San Simon
381mm	San Simon River
378	Lp 10, San Simon, **N** 🛢 4K Trkstp/Noble Romans/Quizno's/dsl/scales/24hrs/@, 🔲 auto/dsl/RV repair
366	Lp 10, Bowie Rd, **N** 🛢 Shell/dsl/24hr, 🍴 Mama Cimino's Pizza, **S** 🔲 Alaskan RV park
362	Lp 10, Bowie Rd, **N** gas, lodging, camping, **S** to Ft Bowie NHS
355	US 191 N, to Safford, **N** to Roper Lake SP
352	US 191 N, to Safford, same as 355
344	Lp 10, to Willcox, **N** 🔲 Lifestyle RV Resort

**W
I
L
C
O
X**

| 340 | AZ 186, to Rex Allen Dr, **N** 🛢 TA/Shell/Popeye's/Subway/dsl/scales/24hr/@, 🛏 Holiday Inn Express, Super 8, 🔲 Magic Circle RV Park, Stout's CiderMill, **S** 🛢 Circle K, Doc's/dsl, Texaco/dsl, 🍴 Burger King, KFC/Taco Bell, McDonald's, Pizza Hut, Plaza Rest., 🛏 Best Western, Day's Inn, Motel 6, 🔲🅷, Ace Hardware, Alco, Autozone, Beall's, Family$, Food City, $General, Radio |

**B
E
N
S
O
N**

340	Continued Shack, Safeway, Grande Vista RV Park, to Chiricahua NM
336	AZ 186, Willcox, **S** 🛢 Chevron/dsl/LP, **1-3 mi S** 🛏 Desert Inn Motel, 🔲 Ft Willcox RV Park
331	US 191 S, to Sunsites, Douglas, **S** 🔲 to Cochise Stronghold
322	Johnson Rd, **S** 🛢 Shell/DQ/dsl/gifts
320mm	**rest area both lanes, full ♿ facilities, 🔲, 🚻, litter barrels, vending, petwalk**
318	Triangle T Rd, to Dragoon, **S** lodging, camping
312	Sibyl Rd
309mm	Adams Peak Wash
306	AZ 80, Pomerene Rd, Benson, **1-2 mi S** 🛢 Circle K, Mobil, 🍴 G&F Pizza Palace, 🔲 Pato Blanco RV Park, San Pedro RV Park
305mm	San Pedro River
304	Ocotillo St, Benson, **N** 🍴 Denny's, Jack-in-the-Box, 🛏 Day's Inn, Super 8, 🔲 Benson RV Park, KOA, **S** 🛢 Chevron, Texaco, 🍴 Apple Farm Rest., Magaly's Mexican, Palatianos Rest, Quizno's, Ruiz's Rest., Subway, Wendy's, 🛏 Best Western, QuarterHorse Inn, 🔲🅷, Ace Hardware, Butterfield RV Park, Dillon RV Ctr, $General, Family$, NAPA, Pardner's RV Park, Radio Shack, Safeway, Walmart
303	US 80 (eb only), to Tombstone, Bisbee, **1 mi S** 🛢 🍴 Reb's Rest., Ruiz Mexican, Wendy's, 🔲 NAPA, Safeway, auto/dsl/repair, to Douglas NHL
302	AZ 90 S, to Ft Huachuca, Benson, **S** 🛢 **Loves**/Chester's/Subway/dsl/scales/24hr, Shell/dsl, 🍴 KFC/Taco Bell, McDonald's, 🛏 Holiday Inn Express, Motel 6, 🔲 Cochise Terrace RV Park, Ft Huachuca NHS, Walmart
301	ranch exit eb
299	Skyline Rd
297	Mescal Rd, J-6 Ranch Rd, **N** 🛢 QuickPic/dsl/deli/24hr
292	Empirita Rd
289	Marsh Station Rd
288mm	Cienega Creek
281	AZ 83 S, to Patagonia
279	Vail/Wentworth Rd, **0-1 mi N** 🛢 QuikMart/gas, 🍴 DQ, Quizno's, Montgomery's Grill, 🔲 Curves, USPO, to Colossal Caves
275	Houghton Rd, **N** 🔲 to Saguaro NP, camping, **S** to fairgrounds
273	Rita Rd, **N** 🛢 Rita Ranch (2mi), **S** fairgrounds
270	Kolb Rd, **N** 🛏 La Quinta (9mi), **S** 🔲 Voyager RV Resort
269	Wilmot Rd, **N** 🛢 Chevron/A&W/dsl, 🛏 Travel Inn, **S** 🛢 Shell/Quizno's
268	Craycroft Rd, **N** 🛢 TTT/dsl/rest./scales/24hr, Circle K, Mr T/dsl/LP, 🔲 Crazy Horse RV Park, **S** dsl repair
267	Valencia Rd, **N** 🛢 Arco/Jack-in-the-Box, 🔲 Pima Air & Space Museum, **S** 🖼
265	Alvernon Way, Davis-Monthan AFB
264b a	Palo Verde Rd, **N** 🛢 Chevron/Wendy's/dsl, Circle K, 🍴 Brooklyn's Grill, Denny's, Waffle House, 🛏 Crossland Suites, Day's Inn, Fairfield Inn, Holiday Inn, Red Roof Inn, 🔲 Freedom RV Ctr, **S** 🛢 QuikMart/dsl, 🍴 Arby's, McDonald's, 🛏 Pelo Verde Inn, Ramada Inn, Studio 6, 🔲 Beaudry RV Ctr/Resort, Camping World RV Resort, Holiday Rambler RV Ctr, La Mesa RV Ctr
263b	Kino Pkwy, **N**

INTERSTATE 10 CONT'D

Exit	Services
263a	Kino Pkwy S, **S** 🖭 Chevron, Shamrock, 🍽 Fry's Foods, ⊙ 🖽 AutoZone, Radio Shack, to Tucson Intn'l ✈
262	Benson Hwy, Park Ave, **S** 🖭 Arco/24hr, Chevron, Shell, 🍽 Carl's Jr., Country Folks, McDonald's, 🛏 Best Value, Motel 6, Quality Inn, Western Inn, ⊙ 7-11, Volvo/Mack Trucks
261	6th/4th Ave, **N** 🖭 GasCo, 🍽 Little Caesar's, Los Portales, 🛏 Econolodge, ⊙ Discount Tire, Food City, 99c Store, **S** 🖭 Circle K/dsl, Shell, 🍽 Church's, El Indio, Jack-in-the-Box, LJ Silver, 🛏 Lazy 8 Motel, ⊙ Big O Tire, El Super Foods, Family$
260	I-19 S, to Nogales
259	22nd St, Starr Pass Blvd, **N** 🖭 Circle K/dsl, **S** 🍽 Kettle, Waffle House, 🛏 La Quinta, Motel 6, Riverpark Inn, Silverbell Inn, Super 8, Travelodge
258	Congress St, Broadway St, **N** 🖭 Circle K/gas, 🍽 Garcia's Rest., 🛏 Inn Suites, **S** 🍽 Carl's Jr, Whataburger, 🛏 Days Inn, Howard Johnson, Motel 6, River Park Inn, Travelodge
257a	St Mary's Rd, **N** 🖭 Union, ⊙ 🖽, **S** 🖭 Arco, Shell/24hr, 🍽 Burger King, Denny's, Furr's Cafeteria, 🛏 Ramada Ltd., ⊙ Pim Comm Coll
257	Speedway Blvd, **N** 🛏 Best Western, ⊙ 🖽, Victory Motorcycles, Old Town Tucson, museum, U of AZ, **S** 🖭 Arco/dsl/24hr
256	Grant Rd, **N** 🍽 Sonic, dsl/transmission repair, **S** 🖭 Circle K, Shamrock, 🍽 Del Taco, IHOP, Las Cazuelita's, Subway, Waffle House, 🛏 Baymont Inn, Comfort Inn, Grant Inn, Hampton Inn, Holiday Inn Express, Super 8, ⊙ dsl/transmission repair
255	AZ 77 N, to Miracle Mile
254	Prince Rd, **N** ⊙ U-Haul, tires, **S** ⊙ Kenworth, Prince of Tucson RV Park, golf
252	El Camino del Cerro, Ruthrauff Rd, **N** 🖭 Arco/24hr, ⊙ Ruthrauff RV Ctr, **S** 🖭 Chevron/Jack-in-the-Box
251	Sunset Rd
250	Orange Grove Rd, **N** 🖭 Arco/24hr, Circle K, 🍽 Domino's, Subway, Wendy's, ⊙ RV Central, **N on Thornydale** 🍽 El Chalito, Little Caesar's, Luke's Sandwiches, Quizno's, ⊙ Big O Tire, Costco/gas, Home Depot, Parts+, PetsMart
248	Ina Rd, **N** 🖭 Chevron/dsl, Circle K, QuikMart/dsl, Shell, 🍽 Carl's Jr, Chuy's, DQ, Eegee's Cafe, Hooters, Jack-in-the-Box, La Parilla Suiza Mexican, LJ Silver, McDonald's, Ms Saigon, Old Father Rest., Peter Piper's Pizza, Starbucks, Taco Bell, Waffle House, 🛏 InTown Suites, Motel 6, ⊙ Ace Hardware, BigLots, CarQuest, CVS Drug, Discount Tire, Fry's Foods, Goodyear/auto, Hancock Fabrics, Lowe's Whse, Michael's, 99c Store, Office Depot, PepBoys, Radio Shack, Target, U-Haul, Walgreens, **S** 🖭 Circle K, 🍽 Denny's, Starbucks, 🛏 Comfort Inn, Red Roof Inn, Travelodge, ⊙ Harley-Davidson
246	Cortaro Rd, **N** 🖭 Circle K/Arby's/dsl, 🍽 IHOP, Wendy's, **S** 🖭 Shell/dsl, 🍽 Boston's Mkt, Burger King, Chili's, Cracker Barrel, Eegee's Rest., In-N-Out, KFC, Magpie's Pizza, McDonald's, Panda Express, Quizno's, Starbucks, Subway, Taco Bell, Texas Roadhouse, 🛏

246	**Continued** Best Western, Day's Inn, Holiday Inn Express, La Quinta, Super 8, ⊙ Ace Hardware, Batteries+, Checker Parts, Curves, Kohl's, USPO, Walmart, access to RV camping
242	Avra Valley Rd, **S** ⊙ Saguaro NP (13mi), RV camping, ✈
240	Tangerine Rd, to Rillito, **N** A-A RV Park, **S** USPO
236	Marana, **S** 🖭 Chevron/dsl/LP, Circle K/gas, ⊙ Sun RV Park, auto repair
232	Pinal Air Park Rd, **S** Pinal Air Park
228mm	wb pulloff, to frontage rd
226	Red Rock, **S** USPO
219	Picacho Peak Rd, **N** 🖭 Mobil/DQ/dsl, Shell/dsl, **S** ⊙ Ostrich Ranch, Pichaco Peak RV Park, to Picacho Peak SP
212	Picacho (from wb), **N** 🖭 Premium Gas/tires, ⊙ USPO, **S** Picacho Camping
211b	AZ 87 N, AZ 84 W, to Coolidge
211a	Picacho (from eb), **S** ⊙ Picacho RV Park, state prison
208	Sunshine Blvd, to Eloy, **N** 🖭 Pilot/Subway/dsl/scales/24hr, dsl repair, **S** 🖭 Flying J/Denny's/dsl/scales/24hr, ⊙ Blue Beacon
203	Toltec Rd, to Eloy, **N** 🖭 Chevron/McDonald's/playplace/24hr, Circle K/dsl, 🍽 Carl's Jr, El Zarape Rojo Mexican, 🛏 Best Value Inn, Red Roof Inn, ⊙ Desert Valley RV Park, dsl/tire repair, **S** 🖭 TA/A&W/Taco Bell/dsl/24hr/@, 🍽 Pizza Hut, ⊙ truckwash
200	Sunland Gin Rd, Arizona City, **N** 🖭 Petro/Iron Skillet/dsl/scales/24hr/@, Pride/Subway/dsl/24hr, 🍽 Burger King, Eva's Mexican, 🛏 Day's Inn, Travelodge, ⊙ Blue Beacon, Eagle Truckwash, Las Colinas RV Park, **S** 🖭 Loves/Arby's/Baskin-Robbins/dsl/24hr, 🍽 Golden 9 Rest., Starbucks, 🛏 Motel 6, ⊙ Speedco Lube
199	I-8 W, to Yuma, San Diego
198	AZ 84, to Eloy, Casa Grande, **N** Robson Ranch Rest./Golf, **S** 🍽 Wendy's, ⊙ Casa Grande Outlets/famous brands, Buena Tierra RV Pk
194	AZ 287, Florence Blvd, to Casa Grande, **N** 🍽 Ah-So Steaks, In-N-Out, Mimi's Cafe, Olive Garden, Red Brick Pizza, Rubio's, Subway, ⊙ Best Buy, Dillards, JC Penney, Kohl's, Marshalls, Michaels, Old Navy, PetsMart, Radio Shack, Staples, Sunscape RV Park (7mi), Target, Walgreens, World Mkt, **0-2 mi S** 🖭 Arco/dsl/24hr, Circle K/gas, Shell/DQ, 🍽 Burger King, Coldstone Creamery, Cracker Barrel, Del Taco, Denny's, Golden Corral, IHOP, LJ Silver, Panda Express, Papa Murphy's, Peter Piper Pizza, Quizno's, Sonic, Starbucks, Subway, Taco Bell, 🛏 Best Western, Comfort Inn, Legacy Suites, Mainstay Suites, Super 8, ⊙ 🖽, AutoZone, CVS Drug,

gas = gas, food = food, lodging = lodging, other = other

AZ

INTERSTATE 10 CONT'D

E ↕ W

Exit	Services
194	Continued Discount Tire, Fry's Food/drug, Home Depot, Lowe's, Palm Creek RV/golf Resort, Tuesday Morning, Walgreens, Walmart /McDonalds
190	McCartney Rd, N other to Central AZ Coll
185	AZ 387, to Coolidge, Florence, S food Eva's Mexican (6mi), other Fry's Food/gas (6mi), Val Vista RV camping (3mi), hwy patrol
183mm	**rest area wb, full ♿ facilities, phone, picnic, litter barrels, vending, petwalk**
181mm	**rest area eb, full ♿ facilities, phone, picnic, litter barrels, vending, petwalk**
175	AZ 587 N, Casa Blanca Rd, Chandler, Gilbert, S gas Shell/dsl
173mm	Gila River
167	Riggs Rd, to Sun Lake, N gas Shell (3mi), other Akimel Smoke Shop
164	AZ 347 S, Queen Creek Rd, to Maricopa, N other to Chandler airport, gas
162b a	Wild Horse Pass Rd, Sundust Rd, N gas Loves/Arby's/dsl/scales/24hr, food McDonald's, other Beaudry RV Ctr, S gas Chevron, lodging Wildhorse Pass Hotel/Casino, other Firebird Sports Park, Gila River Casino
161	Pecos Rd, lp 202, E
160	Chandler Blvd, to Chandler, N gas Chevron/dsl, Circle K, food Burger King, Denny's, Marie Callender's, Villa Pandos Mexican, Whataburger/24hr, lodging Fairfield Inn, Hampton Inn, Homewood Suites, Radisson, Red Roof Inn, Super 8, other Aamco, Firestone/auto, Harley-Davidson, to Compadre Stadium, Williams AFB, S gas Chevron, Circle K/dsl, 7-11, food Applebee's, Arriba Mexican, Carl's Jr, Cracker Barrel, Del Taco, Dunkin Donuts, Hooters, Jersey Mike's, Starbucks, Waffle House, Wendy's, lodging Holiday Inn Express, Extended Stay America, InTown Suites, La Quinta, other H, AutoZone, CVS Drug, Discount Tire, Kohl's
159	Ray Rd, N gas Circle K, Shell/dsl, food Buca Italian, Carrabba's, Charleston's Rest., Chipotle Mexican, El Pollo Loco, 5&Diner, Fleming's Steaks, In-N-Out, Jasons Deli, Jilly's Rest., McDonald's, Outback Steaks, Paradise Cafe, Red Lobster, Roy's Cafe, Rumbi Grill, Starbucks, Tejas, Tomaso's Italian, lodging Courtyard, other BMW, Chevrolet, Ford, Home Depot, Lexus, Lowe's Whse, Mercedes, PetsMart, Sam's Club/gas, S gas Shell, Circle K/dsl, food Boston Mkt, IHOP/24hr, Jack-in-the-Box, Macaroni Grill, Mimi's Café, On-the-Border, Peter Piper Pizza, Pizza Hut, Rock Bottom Rest., Rubio's, Sweet Tomatoes, Wendy's, lodging Extended Stay America, other Barnes&Noble, Best Buy, CVS Drug, JC Penney, Jo-Ann Fabrics, Michael's, Old Navy, PetCo, Ross, SteinMart, Target, urgent care
158	Warner Rd, N gas Circle K/dsl, QT, food Port of Subs, S gas Arco/24hr, Circle K/dsl, food Burger King, ChuckeCheese, DQ, Macayo's Mexican, Malaya Mexican, McDonald's, Nello's Pizza, Panda Garden, Quizno's, Ruffino's Italian, other Ace Hardware, Basha's Foods, Big 10 Tire, Goodyear/auto, vet
157	Elliot Rd, N gas Chevron, Shell/Circle K, food Applebee's, Arby's, Baja Fresh, Burger King, Coco's, Crackers Cafe,
157	Continued Crazy, W Buffet, Dayton's Place, HoneyBear's BBQ, Kabab Palace, Kobe Japanese, Moe's SW Grill, Olive Garden, Panda Express, Quizno's, Red Robin Rest., Souper Salad, Sonic, Starbucks, Subway, Taco Bell, The Groves, Wendy's, YC Mongolian Grill, Yupha's Kitchen, lodging Country Inn&Suites, other Acura, Buick, Cadillac/GMC, Costco/gas, Discount Tire, Dodge, $Tree, Ford/Lincoln/Mercury, Honda, Nissan, PetsMart, Savers, Staples, Toyota/Scion, Walmart, Urgent Care, S gas Shell/Circle K, food Baskin-Robbins, Cactus Jack's, KFC, Mesquite Broiler, McDonald's, Sub Factory, lodging Clarion, Grace Inn, other Checker Parts, Safeway, Walgreens
155	Baseline Rd, Guadalupe, N gas Shell/Circle K/Popeye's/dsl, food Carl's Jr, ClaimJumper, 5& Diner, Joe's Crabshack, KFC, McDonald's, Poliberto's Tacos, Popeye's, Rainforest Cafe, Waffle House, Wendy's, lodging Best Western, Candlewood Studios, Holiday Inn Express, InnSuites, Ramada, Residence Inn, SpringHill Suites, TownePlace Suites, other AutoZone, AZ Mills/Famous Brands, CVS Drug, Food City, Home Depot, JC Penney Outlet, Marshall's, Pro Auto Parts, Ross, Walgreens, S gas Arco, QT, 7-11, lodging Homestead Suites, food Aunt Chilada's Mexican, China Town, Denny's, Sonic, Subway, other Fry's Electronics, Fry's Foods
154	US 60 E, AZ 360, Superstition Frwy, to Mesa, N other to Camping World (off Mesa Dr)
153b	Broadway Rd E, N gas Circle K/gas, food Denny's, lodging Comfort Suites, Courtyard, Fairfield Inn, Hilton, Homestead Suites, La Quinta, Quality Inn, Red Roof Inn, Sheraton, Sleep Inn, other to Diablo Stadium, S gas Chevron, Shell/Circle K/Del Taco/24hr, food Panda Express, Papa John's, Pizza Hut, Port of Subs, Taco Bell, Whataburger, lodging Hampton Inn, Homewood Suites, other Staples
153a	AZ 143 N, N food Denny's, lodging Courtyard, Fairfield Inn, Hilton, La Quinta, Quality Inn, Sheraton, Sleep Inn, other to Diablo Stadium, S same as 153b
152	40th St, N gas Shell/dsl, other U Phoenix, S gas Shell/Circle K, food Burger King
151mm	Salt River
151b a	28th St, 32nd St, University Ave, N food Waffle House, lodging Extended Stay America, Hilton Garden, Holiday Inn Express, Radisson, other AZSU, U Phoenix, S gas Circle K, food McDonald's
150b	24th St, E (from wb), N Air Nat Guard, lodging Motel 6, S lodging Best Western/rest.
150a	I-17 N, to Flagstaff
149	Buckeye Rd, N other Sky Harbor airport
148	Washington St, Jefferson St, N gas Chevron/dsl, Shell, Tiemco/dsl, food Carl's Jr, McDonald's, lodging Motel 6, Sterling Hotel, other to Sky Harbor airport, S gas Circle K, other H
147b a	AZ 51 N, AZ 202 E, to Squaw Peak Pkwy
146	16th St, N gas Shell/Circle K, food Filiberto's Mexican, S gas Circle K, Shamrock/dsl, food Church's, Jack-in-the-Box, Salsita's Mexican, other H, Ranch Mkt
145	7th St, N food McDonald's, Sonic, Starbucks, Subway, Taco Bell, Whataburger, other Safeway Foods, Walgreens, S gas Circle K, Shell, Sinclair/dsl, food Quiznos, lodging Courtyard, Holiday Inn Express, Hyatt, Sheraton, Springhill Suites, other H, to Chase Field
144	7th Ave, N gas Circle K, food Peiwei Asian, Starbucks, S gas Circle K, other central bus dist

CHANDLER

PHOENIX

🅖 = gas 🍽 = food 🏨 = lodging 🅞 = other

INTERSTATE 10 CONT'D

Exit	Services
143c	US 60, 19th Ave, (from wb) downtown
143b a	I-17, N to Flagstaff, S to Phoenix
142	27th Ave (from eb, no return), N 🏨 Comfort Inn
141	35th Ave, N 🍽 Jack-in-the-Box, Rita's Mexican, S 🅖 Shell/Circle K
140	43rd Ave, N 🅖 Circle K/dsl, 7-11, Shell, 🍽 KFC, Filberto's Mexican, Pizza Hut, Salsita's Mexican, Subway, 🏨 ValuePlace Hotel, 🅞 AutoZone, Fry's Mercado/gas, 99c Store, Radio Shack, Walgreens
139	51st Ave, N 🅖 Chevron/dsl, Circle K, 🍽 Burger King, Domino's, El Pollo Loco, McDonald's, Sonic, Waffle House, 🏨 Best Value Inn, Budget Inn, Crossland Suites, Holiday Inn, InTown Suites, La Quinta, Motel 6, Red Roof Inn, Travelodge, 🅞 Discount Tire, Food City, 7-11, S 🅖 QT/dsl/scales, Shell/dsl, 🍽 Carl's Jr, IHOP, Port of Subs, Taco Bell, 🏨 I-10 West Hotel, Super 8, Travelers Inn
138	59th Ave, N 🅖 Circle K, Shamrock, 🍽 Los Armandos Mexican, Subway, 🅞 AutoZone, Checker Parts, Family$, 7-11, Walgreens, S 🅖 Liberty/Chester's/dsl/24hr, 🍽 Waffle House, 🅞 Blue Beacon/scales
137	67th Ave, N 🅖 QT, Circle K/dsl, Shell/dsl, 🍽 Church's, S 🅖 ✈FLYING J/Denny's/dsl/LP/24hr
136	75th Ave, N 🅖 Chevron/dsl, Circle K/dsl, 🍽 A&W/LJ Silver, CiCi's Pizza, Coco's, Denny's, Great China, IHOP, Lin's Buffet, McDonald's, Olive Garden, Red Lobster, Starbucks, Subway, TX Roadhouse, Wendy's, Whataburger, 🅞 AT&T, Big O Tire, Dillards, Home Depot, Lowe's, PetsMart, Radio Shack, Ross, Sears, Staples, Target, Walmart, S 🅖 Arco/24hr
135	83rd Ave, N 🅖 Circle K/dsl, 🍽 Arby's, Burger King, Jack-in-the-Box, Waffle House, 🏨 Comfort Suites, Premier Inn, Victory Inn, 🅞 K-Mart, Sam's Club/gas
134	91st Ave, Tolleson, N 🅖 Circle K/dsl
133b	Lp 101, N
133a	99th Ave, N 🅖 Chevron/dsl, 🍽 Baja Fresh, Carabba's, Chick-fil-A, Chipotle Mexican, ClaimJumper, HoneyBaked Ham, Ichiban Rest., Island's Burgers, McDonald's, Peter Piper Pizza, Red Robin, Rumbi Grill, Starbucks, Subway, Village Inn, 🏨 Courtyard, 🅞 Best Buy, Costco/gas, Discount Tire, GNC, Hobby Lobby, Marshall's, Old Navy, PetCo, Verizon, urgent care, S 🍽 Pilot/Subway/Wendy's/dsl/scales/24hr, 🅞 CarMax, Chevrolet
132	107th Ave, N 🅞 Walgreens, S 🅞 Chrysler/Jeep, Dodge, Dodge, Honda, Hyundai, Kia, Nissan, Subaru, Suzuki, Toyota/Scion, VW
131	Avondale Blvd, to Cashion, N 🅖 Circle K/dsl, S 🍽 Jack-in-the-Box, Panda Express, Ruby Tuesday, 🏨 Hilton Garden, Homewood Suites, 🅞 Fresh&Easy, Staples, to Phoenix Intnl Raceway
129	Dysart Rd, to Avondale, N 🅖 Chevron/dsl, Shell/Circle K/dsl, 🍽 Big Apple Rest., Buffalo Wild Wings, Chick-fil-A, In-N-Out, Jack-in-the-Box/24hr, Mimi's Cafe, NYPD Pizza, Ono Hawaiian BBQ, Palermo's Pizza, Panda Express, Papa Murphy's, Peiwei Asian, Starbucks, Subway, Taco Bell, Tagliani Italian, Tomo Japanese, 🏨 Holiday Inn Express, 🅞 AT&T, AutoZone, Discount Tire, JC Penney, Jo-Ann Fabrics, Fry's Foods, Kohl's, Lowe's, PetsMart, Sprouts Mkt, Tuesday Morning, Verizon,

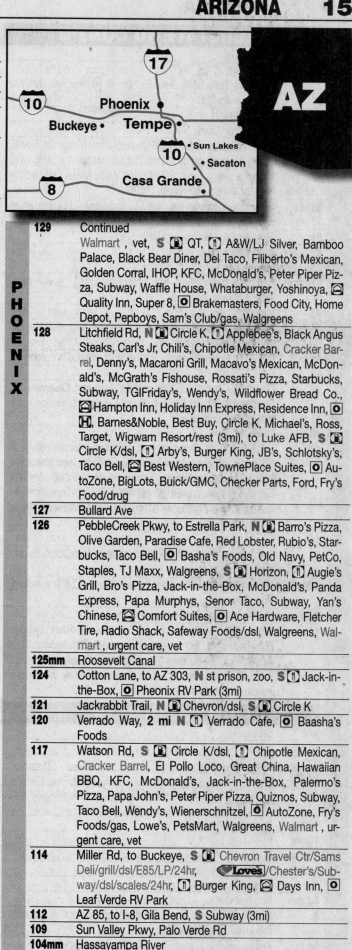

129	Continued
	Walmart , vet, S 🅖 QT, 🍽 A&W/LJ Silver, Bamboo Palace, Black Bear Diner, Del Taco, Filiberto's Mexican, Golden Corral, IHOP, KFC, McDonald's, Peter Piper Pizza, Subway, Waffle House, Whataburger, Yoshinoya, 🏨 Quality Inn, Super 8, 🅞 Brakemasters, Food City, Home Depot, Pepboys, Sam's Club/gas, Walgreens
128	Litchfield Rd, N 🅖 Circle K, 🍽 Applebee's, Black Angus Steaks, Carl's Jr, Chili's, Chipotle Mexican, Cracker Barrel, Denny's, Macaroni Grill, Macavo's Mexican, McDonald's, McGrath's Fishouse, Rossati's Pizza, Starbucks, Subway, TGIFriday's, Wendy's, Wildflower Bread Co., 🏨 Hampton Inn, Holiday Inn Express, Residence Inn, 🅞 🅷, Barnes&Noble, Best Buy, Circle K, Michael's, Ross, Target, Wigwam Resort/rest (3mi), to Luke AFB, S 🅖 Circle K/dsl, 🍽 Arby's, Burger King, JB's, Schlotsky's, Taco Bell, 🏨 Best Western, TownePlace Suites, 🅞 AutoZone, BigLots, Buick/GMC, Checker Parts, Ford, Fry's Food/drug
127	Bullard Ave
126	PebbleCreek Pkwy, to Estrella Park, N 🅖 Barro's Pizza, Olive Garden, Paradise Cafe, Red Lobster, Rubio's, Starbucks, Taco Bell, 🅞 Basha's Foods, Old Navy, PetCo, Staples, TJ Maxx, Walgreens, S 🅖 Horizon, 🍽 Augie's Grill, Bro's Pizza, Jack-in-the-Box, McDonald's, Panda Express, Papa Murphys, Senor Taco, Subway, Yan's Chinese, 🏨 Comfort Suites, 🅞 Ace Hardware, Fletcher Tire, Radio Shack, Safeway Foods/dsl, Walgreens, Walmart, urgent care, vet
125mm	Roosevelt Canal
124	Cotton Lane, to AZ 303, N st prison, zoo, S 🍽 Jack-in-the-Box, 🅞 Pheonix RV Park (3mi)
121	Jackrabbit Trail, N 🅖 Chevron/dsl, S 🅖 Circle K
120	Verrado Way, 2 mi N 🍽 Verrado Cafe, 🅞 Baasha's Foods
117	Watson Rd, S 🅖 Circle K/dsl, 🍽 Chipotle Mexican, Cracker Barrel, El Pollo Loco, Great China, Hawaiian BBQ, KFC, McDonald's, Jack-in-the-Box, Palermo's Pizza, Papa John's, Peter Piper Pizza, Quiznos, Subway, Taco Bell, Wendy's, Wienerschnitzel, 🅞 AutoZone, Fry's Foods/gas, Lowe's, PetsMart, Walgreens, Walmart , urgent care, vet
114	Miller Rd, to Buckeye, S 🅖 Chevron Travel Ctr/Sams Deli/grill/dsl/E85/LP/24hr, Loves/Chester's/Subway/dsl/scales/24hr, 🍽 Burger King, 🏨 Days Inn, 🅞 Leaf Verde RV Park
112	AZ 85, to I-8, Gila Bend, S Subway (3mi)
109	Sun Valley Pkwy, Palo Verde Rd
104mm	Hassayampa River

AZ

E ↕ W

INTERSTATE 10 CONT'D

Exit	Services
103	339th Ave, **S** 🛢 TA/Country Fare/Pizza Hut/Shell/Subway/Taco Bell/dsl/scales/LP/24hr/@, ⊙ truckwash
98	Wintersburg Rd
97mm	Coyote Wash
95.5mm	Old Camp Wash
94	411th Ave, Tonopah, **S** 🛢 Chevron/dsl, Mobil/dsl, Shell/Cafe Charro/Noble Roman's/Subway/dsl/LP/24hr, 🍴 Tonopah Joe's Rest., 🛏 Mineral Wells Motel, ⊙ Saddle Mtn RV Park, tires/repair, USPO
86mm	**rest area both lanes, full** 🦽 **facilities,** 🍴, 🛏, **litter barrels, petwalk, vending**
81	Salome Rd, Harquahala Valley Rd
69	Ave 75E
53	Hovatter Rd
52mm	**rest area both lanes, full** 🦽 **facilities,** 🍴, 🛏, **vending, litter barrels, petwalk**
45	Vicksburg Rd, **N** 🛢 Zip TC/HotStuff/dsl/scales/LP/24hr, 🍴 Cactus Cafe, **S** 🛢 Valero/dsl/rest./scales/24hr, ⊙ Jobski's dsl Repair/towing, Kofa NWR, RV Park, tires
31	US 60 E, to Wickenburg, **12 mi N** ⊙ food, camping
26	Gold Nugget Rd
19	Quartzsite, to US 95, Yuma, **N** 🛢 Arco/dsl, Chevron/dsl, Shell/dsl, 🍴 Taco Mio, ⊙ Beall's, Family$, Roadrunner Foods, RV camping
18mm	Tyson Wash
17	US 95, AZ 95, Quartzsite, **N** 🛢 Mobil/Burger King/LP, 🚚/DQ/Subway/dsl/scales/24hr, 🍴 Best Mexican, Carl's Jr, McDonald's, Quartzsite Yacht Grill, ⊙ RV camping, tires/repair, **S** 🛢 Loves/Chester's/Subway/dsl/24hr, 🛏 Super 8, ⊙ Desert Gardens RV Park, Lifestyles RV Ctr
11	Dome Rock Rd
5	Tom Wells Rd, **N** 🛢 Texaco/SunMart/Quizno's/dsl/scales
4.5mm	**rest area both lanes, full** 🦽 **facilities,** 🍴, 🛏, **vending, litter barrels, petwalk**
3.5mm	eb AZ Port of Entry, wb **weigh sta**
1	Ehrenberg, to Parker, **N** 🛢 Texaco, ⊙ River Lagoon RV Resort, **S** 🛢 FLYING J/Wendy's/Cookery/dsl/LP/scales/lube/repair/tires/24hr, 🛏 Best Western
0mm	Arizona/California state line, Colorado River, Mountain/Pacific time zone

Q U A R T Z S I T E

INTERSTATE 15

N ↕ S

Exit	Services
29.5mm	Arizona/Utah state line
27	Black Rock Rd
21mm	turnout sb
18	Cedar Pocket, **S** ⊙ Virgin River Canyon RA/camping, parking area
16mm	truck parking both lanes
15mm	truck parking nb
14mm	truck parking nb
10mm	truck parking nb
9	Desert Springs
8.5mm	Virgin River
8	Littlefield, Beaver Dam, **E** ⊙ RV park, **1 mi W** gas/dsl, food, lodging, camping
0mm	Arizona/Nevada state line, Pacific/Mountain time zone

N ↕ S FLAGSTAFF / SEDONA

INTERSTATE 17

Exit	Services
341	McConnell Dr, I-17 begins/ends, **N** 🛢 Chevron/dsl, Conoco/dsl, Flag, Gasser/dsl, Giant/dsl, Mobil, Circle K, Shell, Texaco/Wendy's/dsl, 🍴 Arby's, August Moon Chinese, Baskin-Robbins, Buffalo Wild Wings, Burger King, Buster's Rest., Carl's Jr, Casa Bonita, Chili's, China Garden, Coco's, Coldstone, DQ, Del Taco, Denny's, Domino's, Fazoli's, Garcia's Mexican, IHOP, Jack-in-the-Box, KFC, Mandarin Buffet, McDonald's, Olive Garden, Papa John's, Picazzo's Pizza, Peter Piper Pizza, Pizza Hut, Quizno's, Red Lobster, Roma Pizza, Szechuan Chinese, Sizzler, Starbucks, Strombolli's, Subway, Taco Bell, 🛏 AZ Motel, Budget Inn, Canyon Inn, Comfort Inn, Courtyard, Day's Inn, Drury Inn, Econolodge, Embassy Suites, Fairfield Inn, Hampton Inn, Highland Country Inn, Hilton Garden, Knights Inn, La Quinta, Motel 6, Quality Inn, Ramada Ltd, Rodeway Inn, Sleep Inn, SpringHill Suites, Super 8, ⊙ H, Barnes&Noble, Basha's Foods, Discount Tire, Hastings Books, Jo-Ann Crafts, Kohl's, Michael's, Ross, Safeway, Staples, Target, Walgreens, Walmart, auto/RV repair
340b a	I-40, E to Gallup, W to Kingman
339	Lake Mary Rd (from nb), Mormon Lake, **E** 🛢 Circle K/dsl, 🛏 AZ Mtn Inn, access to same as 341
337	AZ 89A S, to Sedona, Ft Tuthill RA, **W** 🍴 camping
333	Kachina Blvd, Mountainaire Rd, **E** 🍴 Mountainaire Rest. (1mi), 🛏 Sled Dog B&B, **W** 🛢 Conoco/Subway/dsl
331	Kelly Canyon Rd
328	Newman Park Rd
326	Willard Springs Rd
322	Pinewood Rd, to Munds Park, **E** 🛢 Shell, Woody's/dsl, 🍴 Lone Pine Rest., ⊙ Motel in the Pines/RV camp, USPO, golf, **W** ⊙ Munds RV Park, auto/RV repair
322mm	Munds Canyon
320	Schnebly Hill Rd
317	Fox Ranch Rd
316mm	Woods Canyon
315	Rocky Park Rd
313mm	scenic view sb, litter barrels
306	Stoneman Lake Rd
300mm	runaway truck ramp sb
298	AZ 179, to Sedona, Oak Creek Canyon, **7-15 mi W** 🍴 Burger King, Cowboy Club Rest., Joey's Bistro, 🛏 Belrock Inn, Hilton, La Quinta, Radisson/cafe, Wildflower Inn, ⊙ Rancho Sedona RV Park
297mm	**rest area both lanes, full** 🦽 **facilities,** 🍴, 🛏, **litter barrels, vending, petwalk**
293mm	Dry Beaver Creek
293	Cornville Rd, McGuireville Rd, to Rimrock, **E** 🛢 ExpressFuel, **W** 🛢 Beaver Hollow/dsl/RV Park, 76/dsl, 🍴 Crusty's Cafe, Las Margaritas Mexican
289	Middle Verde Rd, Camp Verde, **E** 🛢 Mobil/dsl, 🍴 Sonic, The Gathering Rest., 🛏 Cliff Castle Lodge/casino/rest., ⊙ to Montezuma Castle NM, **W** ⊙ Distant Drums RV Park
288mm	Verde River
287	AZ 260, to AZ 89A, Cottonwood, Payson, **E** 🛢 Arco, Chevron, Shell/Noble Roman's/Subway/dsl/RV dump/LP/24hr, 🍴 A&W/KFC, Burger King, DQ, Denny's, Los

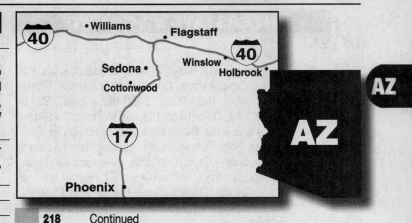

CAMP VERDEN ← → S

INTERSTATE 17 CONT'D

Exit	Services
287	Continued
	Betos Mexican, McDonald's, Quizno's, Starbucks, Taco Bell, 🅻 Comfort Inn, Day's Inn, Super 8, 🅾 Territorial RV Park (1mi), Trails End RV Park, Zane Grane RV Park, **W** 🅖 Chevron/Wendy's/dsl/24hr, 🅾 to Jerome SP, RV camping
285	Camp Verde, Gen Crook Tr, **3 mi E** 🅵 Rio Verde Mexican, 🅻 Territorial Town Inn, 🅾 Zane Gray RV Park (9mi), Trail End RV Park, to Ft Verde SP
281mm	safety pullout area nb
278	AZ 169, Cherry Rd, to Prescott
269mm	Ash Creek
268	Dugas Rd, Orme Rd
265.5mm	Agua Fria River
262b a	AZ 69 N, Cordes Jct Rd, to Prescott, **E** 🅖 Chevron/24hr, Shell/Subway/Noble Roman's/dsl/24hr, 🅵 CJ's Diner, McDonald's, 🅻 Cordes Jct Motel/RV Park
262mm	Big Bug Creek
259	Bloody Basin Rd, to Crown King, Horsethief Basin RA
256	Badger Springs Rd
252	Sunset Point, **W scenic view/rest area both lanes,**
252	Continued
	Sunset full 🅿 facilities, 🅲, 🅰, litter barrels, vending
248	Bumble Bee, **W** 🅾 Horsethief Basin RA
244	Squaw Valley Rd, Black Canyon City, **E** 🅵 Kid Chileean BBQ/Steaks, 🅾 KOA, **W** gas
243.5mm	Agua Fria River
242	Rock Springs, Black Canyon City, **E** KOA (1mi), **W** 🅖 Chevron/dsl/24hr, Shell, 🅵 Byler's Kitchen, Rock Springs Café, 🅻 Bradshaw Mtn RV Resort, Mtn Breeze Motel
239.5mm	Little Squaw Creek
239mm	Moore's Gulch
236	Table Mesa Rd
232	New River, **E** 🅵 RoadRunner Rest., 🅾 Curves, vet
231.5mm	New River
229	Anthem Way, Desert Hills Rd, **E** 🅖 Circle K/gas, 🅵 Asiana, McDonald's, Native NewYorker Rest., Pizza Hut, Quizno's, Rosati's Pizza, Starbucks, Subway, Taco Bell, Taco Del Mar, 🅾 Ace Hardware, CVS Drug, Safeway, **W** 🅖 Chevron/dsl, Circle K/gas, 🅵 Del Taco, Denny's, Papa John's, 🅻 Hampton Inn, 🅾 Anthem Outlets/famous brands/food court, AutoZone, BrakeMasters, Checker Parts, Curves, Discount Tire, $Store, Harley-Davidson, U-Haul, Walmart, vet
227	Daisy Mtn Dr, **E** 🅖 Circle K/dsl, 🅵 Domino's, Jack-in-the-Box, Starbucks, Subway, 🅾 CVS Drug, Fry's Foods
227mm	Dead Man Wash
225	Pioneer Rd, **W** 🅾 Pioneer RV Park, museum
223	AZ 74, Carefree Hwy, to Wickenburg, **E** 🅖 Chevron, 🅵 AZool Grill, Chili's, Denny's, Good Egg Cafe, In-N-Out, Krispy Kreme, McDonald's, Subway, 🅾 Albertson's/Osco, Home Depot, Kohl's, Staples, **W** 🅾 Lake Pleasant Park, camping
220	Dixileta
219	Jomax Rd
218	Happy Valley Rd, **E** 🅖 Shell, 🅵 Applebees, Bajio, Carl's Jr, Chipotle Mexican, Coldstone Creamery, Dickey's BBQ, Jack-in-the-Box, Joey's Hotdogs, Johnny Rocket's,

Exit	Services
218	Continued
	Logan's Roadhouse, L&L Hawaiian BBQ, Olive Garden, Panda Express, PF Chang's, Quizno's, Rays Pizza, Red Robin, Shane's Ribshack, Starbucks, Streets of NY Deli, Subway, TGIFriday's, Tilly's Grill, 🅻 Courtyard, Hampton Inn, Homewood Suites, Residence Inn, 🅾 Barnes&Noble, Best Buy, Checker Parts, Lowe's Whse, Old Navy, PetCo, Staples, TJ Maxx, Walmart , World Mkt
217	Pinnacle Peak Rd, **E** Phoenix RV Park
215a	Rose Garden Ln, same as 215b
215b	Deer Valley Rd, **E** 🅖 Circle K, Shamrock, 🅵 Arby's, Armando's Mexican, Culvers, Jack-in-the-Box, McDonald's, Sonic, Taco Bell, Wendy's, 🅾 Little Dealer RV Ctr, **W** 🅖 Arco, Circle K, 🅵 Cracker Barrel, Denny's, Times Square Italian, Waffle House, 🅻 Days Inn, Country Inn&Suites, Extended Stay America, 🅾 🅷, NAPA, Pinnacle Peak RV Ctr, U-Haul
214c	AZ 101 loop
214b	Yorkshire Dr, **W** 🅵 In-N-Out, Jack-in-the-Box, 🅻 Budget Suites, 🅾 🅷, Costco/gas, **W on 27th Ave** 🅖 7-11, 🅵 El Patron Mexican, 5&Diner, Pizza Hut, Wendy's, 🅾 Michael's, PetsMart, Ross, Target
214a	Union Hills Dr, **E** 🅖 Circle K/dsl, Valero, **W** 🅖 Arco, 🅻 Comfort Inn, Sleep Inn, Studio 6
212b a	Bell Rd, Scottsdale, to Sun City, **E** 🅖 Chevron/dsl, Circle K/gas, QT, 🅵 Big Apple Rest., Black Bear Diner, Burger Mania, Caramba Mexican, IHOP/24hr, Jack-in-the-Box, Lamar's Doughnuts, LJ Silver, McDonald's, Quizno's, Schlotzsky's, Waffle House, 🅻 Bell Hotel, Comfort Inn, Fairfield Inn, Motel 6, 🅾 Big O Tire, Checker Parts, Chevrolet, Chrysler/Jeep/Dodge, Ford, Kohl's, Lincoln/Mercury, Nissan/Infiniti, Buick/GMC, Sam's Club/gas, Toyota, U-Haul, Walmart , **W** 🅖 Chevron, 🅵 Applebee's, Denny's, Good Egg Rest., HomeTown Buffet, Hooters, Kyoto Bowl, 🅻 Red Roof Inn, 🅾 Fry's Foods
211	Greenway Rd, **E** 🅻 Embassy Suites, La Quinta, 🅾 7-11
210	Thunderbird Rd, **E** 🅖 Arco, Circle K/dsl, Valero, 🅵 Asian Cafe, Barro's Pizza, Big Tortas, DQ, Jack-in-the-Box, Macayo's Mexican, Pizza Hut/Taco Bell, Subway, Wendy's, 🅾 CVS Drug, Home Depot, Jiffy Lube, Osco Drug, Walgreens, **W** 🅖 QT, 🅵 Jamba Juice, McDonald's, Quizno's, 🅻 Days Inn, 🅾 Best Buy, Fry's Electronics, Lowe's Whse
209	Cactus Rd, **W** 🅖 Chevron/24hr, 7-11, 🅵 Cousins Subs, China Harvest, Don Pedro's Mexican, 🅻 Ramada Inn, 🅾 Food City
208	Peoria Ave, **E** 🅵 Fajita's, LoneStar Steaks,

SCOTTSDALE

AZ

INTERSTATE 17 CONT'D

N ↑ S

Exit	Services
208	Continued
	Pappadeaux, TGIFriday, ⌂ Candlewood Suites, Comfort Suites, Crowne Plaza, Extended Stay America, Homewood Suites, Hyatt Place, **W** ◨ Black Angus, Burger King, Chili's, China Chan, Chipotle Mexican, Coldstone, Culvers, El Torito, Mimi's Cafe, Old Country Buffet, Olive Garden, Peter Piper Pizza, Red Lobster, Samurai Sam's, Sizzler, Souper Salad, Starbucks, Swenson's Ice Cream, Subway, Wendy's, Whataburger, ⌂ Premier Inn, ⊙ Barnes&Noble, Dillard's, $Tree, Firestone/auto, Macy's, Michael's, Old Navy, PetCo, PetsMart, Ross, Sears/auto, Staples, mall
208.5mm	Arizona Canal
207	Dunlap Ave, **E** ■ Circle K/gas, Shell/dsl, ◨ Big Burrito, Blimpie, Fajitas, Fuddrucker's, Lonestar Steaks, Outback Steaks, Steak'n Burger, Sweet Tomato, ⌂ Budget Lodge, Comfort Suites, Courtyard, Homestead Suites, Mainstay Suites, Sheraton, SpringHill Suites, TownPlace Suites, ⊙ URGENT CARE, Aamco, CVS Drug, Firestone, Sun City RV Ctr, mall, **W** ■ Chevron, ◨ Denny's, Schlotsky's, Subway, ⌂ ValuePlace, ⊙ U-Haul, repair
206	Northern Ave, **E** ■ Circle K, Shell/dsl, ◨ Big Burrito, Boston Mkt, Burger King, Del Taco, Denny's/24hr, Dunkin Donuts, El Pollo Loco, Los Compadres Mexican, Marie Callender's, McDonald's, Mr. Sushi, Papa John's, Pizza Hut, Subway, ⌂ Best Western, ⊙ Albertson's, Checker Parts, Osco, USPO, Walgreens, **W** ■ Arco, QT, ◨ DQ, Village Inn Rest., ⌂ Motel 6, Residence Inn, Super 8, ⊙ $General, K-Mart, 99 Cent Store, vet
205	Glendale Ave, **E** ■ QT, ⊙ Ace Hardware, Circle K, auto repair, transmissions, vet, **W** ■ Circle K/dsl, ◨ Jack-in-the-Box, ⊙ Checker Parts, 7-11, Walgreens, to Luke AFB
204	Bethany Home Rd, **E** ■ Arco/24hr, Shell/Church's/ dsl, ◨ Dunkin Donuts, McDonald's, Subway, Samauri Sam's, Whataburger, ⊙ [H], URGENT CARE, BigLots, Circle K, vet, **W** ■ Shell, Valero, ◨ Burger King, Great Dragon, ⊙ Food City, Jiffy Lube, 99 Cent Store, Savers
203	Camelback Rd, **E** ◨ Blimpie, Buffet Cactus Jack's, Cubano, Church's, Country Boy's Rest., ⊙ Chrysler/Jeep/ Dodge, Discount Tire, Frys' Foods, Hyundai, Kia, **W** ■ QT, ◨ DQ, Jack-in-the-Box, McDonald's, TacoMex, ⌂ Comfort Inn, ⊙ AutoZone, Chevrolet, Circle K, to Grand Canyon U
202	Indian School Rd, **E** ■ Arco/24hr, ◨ Domino's, Federico's Mexican, Pizza Hut, Subway, ⊙ Ace Hardware, CVS Drug, Family$, Food City, Skyline RV Ctr, **W** ■ Circle K, Red Dog/dsl/LP, Shell, Valero/dsl, ◨ Subway, Wendy's, ⌂ Motel 6, ⊙ 7-11, Wide World of Maps, auto repair
201	Thomas Rd, **E** ■ Chevron/McDonald's/playplace, ◨ Arby's, Denny's, Dunkin Donuts, Jack-in-the-Box, Roman's Pizza, Starbucks, ⌂ Day's Inn, La Quinta, ⊙ Circle K, **W** ■ QT, ◨ Carl's Jr, Subway, Taco Factory, ⊙ NAPA
200b	McDowell Rd, Van Buren, **E** ⊙ Purcell's Tire, **W** ⌂ Travelodge
200a	I-10, W to LA, E to Phoenix
199b	Jefferson St (from sb), Adams St (from nb), Van Buren St (from nb), **E** ■ Circle K/gas, ◨ Jack-in-the-Box, ⊙ to st capitol, **W** ■ Circle K/gas, ◨ La Canasta Mexican,

PHOENIX

Exit	Services
199b	Continued
	Salsita's Mexican, ⊙ Penny Pincher Parts, PepBoys
199a	Grant St
198	Buckeye Rd (from nb)
197	US 60, 19th Ave, Durango St, **E** ◨ Jack-in-the-Box, Whataburger/24hr, to St Capitol
196	7th St, Central Ave, **W** ■ DZ/dsl
195b	7th St, Central Ave, **E** ■ Big Tiger/dsl, Circle K/dsl, ◨ Jack-in-the-Box, McDonald's, Taco Bell, ⌂ EZ 8 Motel/ rest., ⊙ [H], NAPA Care
195a	16th St (from sb, no EZ return), **E** ◨ Burger King, ⊙ Food City, to Sky Harbor ✈
194	I-10 W, to AZ 151, to Sky Harbor ✈

I-17 begins/ends on I-10, exit 150a

INTERSTATE 19

N ↑ S

I-19 uses kilometers (km)

Exit	Services
101b a	I-10, E to El Paso, W to Phoenix, I-19 begins/ends on I-10, exit 260
99	AZ 86, Ajo Way, **E** ■ Circle K, ◨ Eegee's Cafe, Hamburger Stand, Peter Piper Pizza, Subway, Taco Bell, ⊙ Fry's Foods, GNC, Goodyear/auto, U-Haul, Walgreens, auto repair, vet, **W** ■ Circle K, Gas City/dsl, Shell, ◨ Burger King, Church's, Domino's, Little Caesars, ⊙ [H], URGENT CARE, Family$, Food City, 99 Cent Store, Jiffy Lube, to Old Tucson, museum
98	Irvington Rd, **E** ⊙ Fry's Foods/drug/dsl, **W** ■ Chevron, Circle K, ◨ Buffalo Wild Wings, China Olive Buffet, McDonald's, Olive Garden, Panda Express, Peter Piper Pizza, Starbucks, Subway, ⊙ Best Buy, Family$, Food City, Home Depot, JC Penney, Marshall's, Michael's, Office Depot, Old Navy, PetsMart, Ross, Target
95b a	Valencia Rd, **E** ◨ Church's, Donut Wheel, Eegee's Cafe, Jack-in-the-Box, McDonald's, Peter Piper Pizza, Sonic, Viva Burrito, Whataburger, Yokohama RiceBowl, ⊙ Aamco, AutoZone, Brake Masters, Checker Parts, $Tree, Food City, Family$, Jiffy Lube, USPO, Walgreens, To ✈, **W** ■ Chevron/dsl, Circle K, ◨ Applebee's, Arby's, Burger King, Carl's Jr, Chili's, Chuey's Cafe, Denny's, Dunkin Donuts/Baskin-Robbins, El Taco Tote, Golden Corral, Grand Buffet, Hamburger Stand, IHOP, Little Caesars, Papa John's, Papa Murphy's, Pizza Hut, Subway, Taco Bell, Wendy's, ⊙ Big O Tire, CVS Drug, Lowe's Whse, 99c Store, Radio Shack, Walgreens, Walmart, repair, transmissions
92	San Xavier Rd, **W** ⊙ to San Xavier Mission
91.5km	Santa Cruz River
87	Papago Rd
80	Pima Mine Rd, **E** ◨ Agave Rest., Diamond Casino
75	Helmut Peak Rd, to Sahuarita, **E** ■ Shell, ⊙ Jerrybob's Rest., McDonald's, Sertino's Cofee/Ice Cream, Starbucks, Subway, ⊙ Fry's Foods/drug, USPO
69	US 89 N, Duval Mine Rd., Green Valley, **E** ◨ Carl's Jr., Denny's, Pollo Feliz, Pizza Hut, Quizno's, Subway, ⊙ Basha's Food, Fletcher's Repair, 99 Cent Store, Radio Shack, Walgreens, Walmart, **W** ■ Circle K/gas, Texaco/dsl, ◨ Burger King, Domino's, DQ, Manuel's Rest., Rigoberto's Mexican, Starbucks, Taco Bell/TCBY, ⌂ Holiday Inn Express, ⊙ Big O Tire, Curves, Ford/Lincoln/Mercury/Hyundai, Green Valley RV Resort, Safeway/gas, Titan Missile Museum, USPO, vet
65	Esperanza Blvd, to Green Valley, **E** ■ Shell/repair/dsl,

TUCSON **GREEN VALLEY**

INTERSTATE 19 CONT'D

N ↕ S

AMADO

65 Continued
W ⓖ Texaco/dsl, ⓕ AZ Family Rest., Dona's Rest., La Placita Mexican, ⓛ Comfort Inn, Quality Inn, ⓞ Ace Hardware, Family$, Walgreens

63 Continental Rd, Green Valley, E ⓕ Quail Valley Rest., ⓞ golf, USPO, **2 mi** E ⓞ San Ignacio Golf Club/rest., W ⓖ Chevron, ⓕ China Vic, HotStuff Pizza, KFC, Mama's Kitchen, McDonald's, Trivettie's Rest., ⓞ CVS Drug, Safeway, TrueValue, Walgreens, tires/repair, to Madera Cyn RA

56 Canoa Rd, W ⓛ San Ignacio Inn

54km **rest area both lanes, full** ⓗ **facilities,** ⓒ**,** ⓐ**, litter barrels, vending, petwalk**

48 Arivaca Rd, Amado **2-3 mi** E ⓛ Amado Inn, ⓞ Mtn View RV Park, Rex Ranch Resort, W ⓖ Amado Plaza, ⓕ Cow Palace Rest., Longhorn Grill, ⓞ Amado Mkt, Jim's Auto Repair

42 Agua Linda Rd, to Amado, E ⓞ Mtn View RV Park

40 Chavez Siding Rd, Tubac, E ⓕ Nob Hill Rest. (3mi), ⓞ Tubac Golf Resort

34 Tubac, E ⓖ Nob Hill Mkt/dsl, ⓕ Artists Palate, Cafe Prisidio, Chef's Table, Elvira's Cafe, ⓞ Anza Mkt, Tubac Golf Resort, USPO, to Tubac Presidio SP

29 Carmen, Tumacacori, E gas, food, lodging, ⓞ to Tumacacori Nat Hist Park

25 Palo Parado Rd

22 Pec Canyon Rd

17 Rio Rico Dr, Calabasas Rd, W ⓖ Gas4Less, Chevron/dsl/LP, ⓕ Hua Mei Chinese, La Placita, Wood Oven Pizza, ⓛ Esplendor Resort, ⓞ IGA Foods, JC Auto Repair/Lube, USPO, vet

12 AZ 289, to Ruby Rd, E ⓖⓕⓦ Wendy's/dsl/scales/24hr, W ⓞ to Pena Blanca Lake RA

8 US 89, AZ 82, (exits left from sb, no return), Nogales, **0-3 mi** E ⓖ Chevron, Circle K/gas, MinniMart, Pronto Fuel/dsl, ⓕ 7 Mares Seafood, ⓞ ⓗ, Mi Casa RV Park

NOGALES

4 AZ 189 S, Mariposa Rd, Nogales, E ⓖ Chevron, FasTrip, Jumpin' Jack Gas, 76, ⓕ Bella Mia Rest., China Buffet, ChinaStar, Denny's, DQ, Jack-in-the-Box, KFC, Little Caesars, McDonald's, Quizno's, Subway, Taco Bell, Yokohama Rest., ⓛ Motel 6, Super 8, ⓞ AutoZone, Batteries+, BigLots, Chevrolet/Cadillac, Buick/GMC, $Tree, Ford/Lincoln/Mercury, GNC, Home Depot, JC Penney, K-Mart, Mexico Insurance, NAPA, Buick/GMC, Radio Shack, Ross, Safeway, Walgreens, Walmart (N Grand Ave), W ⓖ Valero/dsl, ⓕ Carl's Jr, IHOP, ⓛ Best Western, Candlewood Suites, Holiday Inn Express, ⓞ Chrysler/Dodge/Jeep

1b Western Ave, Nogales

1a International St

0km I-19 begins/ends in Nogales, Arizona/Mexico Border, **1/2 mi** ⓕ Circle K/gas, Jr.s Fuel Depot/dsl, Puchi's Gas, ⓕ Burger King, Church's, Domino's, Jack-in-the-Box, McDonald's, Peter Piper Pizza, Pizza Hut, Subway, ⓞ AutoZone, CarQuest, Checker Parts, Family$, Food City, NAPA, Parts+, PepBoys, museum

INTERSTATE 40

Exit	Next
359.5mm	Arizona/New Mexico state line
359	Grants Rd, to Lupton, N Welcome Ctr/rest area both lanes, full ⓗ facilities, ⓒ, ⓐ, litter barrels, petwalk,

---

E ↕ W

CHAMBERS

359 Continued
ⓖ Speedy's/dsl/rest./24hr, ⓞ Tee Pee Trading Post/rest., YellowHorse Indian Gifts

357 AZ 12 N, Lupton, to Window Rock, N ⓞ USPO

354 Hawthorne Rd

351 Allentown Rd, N ⓞ Chee's Indian Store, Indian City Gifts

348 St Anselm Rd, Houck, N ⓞ Ft Courage Food/gifts

347.5mm Black Creek

346 Pine Springs Rd

345mm Box Canyon

344mm Querino Wash

343 Querino Rd

341 Ortega Rd, Cedar Point, N ⓖ Armco/gas/gifts

340.5mm insp/weigh sta both lanes

339 US 191 S, to St Johns, S ⓖ Conoco/dsl, ⓞ Family$, RV Park, USPO

333 US 191 N, Chambers, N ⓖ Rte 66 Gas/dsl, ⓞ to Hubbell Trading Post NHS, USPO, S ⓖ Mobil/dsl, ⓛ Chieftain Inn/rest.

330 McCarrell Rd

325 Navajo, S ⓖ Shell/Subway/Navajo Trading Post/dsl/24hr

323mm Crazy Creek

320 Pinta Rd

316mm Dead River

311 Painted Desert, N ⓖ Chevron, ⓞ Petrified Forest NP, Painted Desert

303 Adamana Rd, N ⓞ Stewarts/gifts, S ⓞ Painted Desert Indian Ctr

302.5mm Big Lithodendron Wash

301mm Little Lithodendron Wash

300 Goodwater

299mm Twin Wash

294 Sun Valley Rd, N Root 66 RV camping, S ⓞ Knife City

292 AZ 77 N, to Keams Canyon, N ⓖ Conoco/Burger King/dsl/24hr, ⓞ dsl repair

HOLBROOK

289 Lp 40, Holbrook, N ⓖ Chevron/dsl, Hatch's/dsl, ⓕ Denny's, Jerry's Rest., Mesa Rest., ⓛ Best Inn, Best Western, Comfort Inn, Days Inn, EconoLodge, Motel 6, Ramada Ltd, Sahara Inn, Travelodge, ⓞ Goodyear

286 Navajo Blvd, Holbrook, N ⓖ Chevron/dsl, Circle K, ⓕ Aliberto's Mexican, Burger King, Hilltop Cafe, KFC, McDonald's, Pizza Hut, Taco Bell, ⓛ Holiday Inn Express, Super 8, 66 Motel, ⓞ Alco, $General, KOA, OK RV Park, O'Reilly Parts, S ⓖ Chevron/dsl, Fuel Express/dsl, Jack's/repair/LP, MiniMart/gas, Speedy Dsl, ⓕ DQ, Rte 66 Cafe, ⓛ Best Value, El Rancho Motel/rest., Knights Inn, ⓞ ⓗ, Dodge/Ford/Lincoln/Mercury, Scotty & Son Repair, SW Transmissions, museum, rockshops

---

[State map showing Arizona with cities: Phoenix, Scottsdale, Tempe, Mesa, Sacaton, Coolidge, Casa Grande, Eloy, Marana, Tucson Estates, Tucson, Green Valley, Nogales, with Interstates 10, 8, 19. Labeled AZ.]

INTERSTATE 40 CONT'D

Exit	Next
285	US 180 E, AZ 77 S, Holbrook, **1 mi S** 🅖 Giant/dsl, 🍴 Butterfield Steaks, Wayside Mexican, 🏨 Best Western, Economy Inn, Globetrotter Hotel, Wigwam Motel, 🅾 Best Hardware, Family$, Safeway, repair, rest area/picnic tables/litter barrels, to Petrified Forest NP
284mm	Leroux Wash
283	Perkins Valley Rd, Golf Course Rd, **S** 🅖 Fuel Express/dsl/rest./scales/24hr/@
280	Hunt Rd, Geronimo Rd, **N** 🅾 Geronimo Trading Post
277	Lp 40, Joseph City, **N** 🅖 Loves/Chester's/Subway/scales/dsl/24hr, **S** 🅾 to Cholla Lake CP, RV camping
274	Lp 40, Joseph City, **N** gas, food, lodging, RV camping
269	Jackrabbit Rd, **S** 🅾 Jackrabbit Trading Post
264	Hibbard Rd
257	AZ 87 N, to Second Mesa, **N** 🅾 to Homolovi Ruins SP, camping, **S** 🅾 trading post
256.5mm	Little Colorado River
255	Lp 40, Winslow, **N** 🅖 Winslow Fuel/dsl, 🅾 Mi Pueblo Mexican, 🏨 Best Western, 🅾 Take-A-Rest RV Park, **S** 🅖 *FLYING J*/Denny's/dsl/LP/scales/RV Dump/24hr, 🍴 Sonic, 🅾 Chrysler/Dodge/Jeep, Nissan, rest area
253	N Park Dr, Winslow, **N** 🅖 Chevron, Maverik/dsl, 🍴 Arby's, Capt Tony's Pizza, Denny's, Pizza Hut, 🅾 $General, Ford, O'Reilly Parts, Walmart /truck parking, tires/lube, **S** 🍴 Alfonso's Mexican, KFC, LJ Silver/Taco Bell, McDonald's, Subway, 🏨 EconoLodge, Motel 6, Quality Inn, 🅾 🏥, Family$, NAPA, Safeway
252	AZ 87 S, Winslow, **S** 🅖 Shell/dsl, 🍴 Entre Chinese, 🏨 Best Value, Rest Inn, Super 8, The Lodge
245	AZ 99, Leupp
239	Meteor City Rd, Red Gap Ranch Rd, **S** 🅾 Meteor City Trading Post, to Meteor Crater
235mm	**rest area both lanes, full** ♿ **facilities, info,** 🚻, 🛢, **litter barrels, petwalk**
233	Meteor Crater Rd, **S** 🅖 Mobil/Meteor Crater RV Park/dump, 🅾 to Meteor Crater NL
230	Two Guns
229.5mm	Canyon Diablo
225	Buffalo Range Rd
219	Twin Arrows
218.5mm	Padre Canyon
211	Winona, **N** 🅖 Shell/dsl/repair
207	Cosnino Rd
204	to Walnut Canyon NM
201	US 89, Flagstaff, to Page, **N** 🅖 Chevron, Express Stop/dsl, Shell, Texaco, 🍴 Arby's, Burger King, Del Taco, Jack-in-the-Box, LJ Silver/Taco Bell, McDonald's, Pizza Hut, Quiznos, Roma Pizza, Ruby Tuesday, Sizzler, Smokehouse BBQ, Village Inn, Wendy's, 🏨 Best Western, Days Inn, Hampton Inn, Howard Johnson, Luxury Inn, Super 8, 🅾 🏥, Best Buy, CVS Drug, Dillard's, Discount Tire, Family$, Flagstaff RV Ctr/LP, Goodyear/auto, Home Depot, JC Penney, KOA, Marshall's, Old Navy, O'Reilly Parts, PetCo, PitStop Lube, Safeway/dsl, Sears/auto, Toyota, World Mkt, auto repair, mall, **S** 🅖 Mobil/dsl, 🏨 Residence Inn
198	Butler Ave, Flagstaff, **N** 🅖 Chevron, Conoco/dsl, Shell, 🍴 Burger King, Country Host Rest., Cracker Barrel,

Exit	Next
198	Continued Denny's, Hogs Rest., McDonald's, Outback Steaks, Sonic, Taco Bell, 🏨 EconoLodge, Holiday Inn Express, Howard Johnson, Motel 6, Quality Inn, Ramada, Rodeway Inn, Super 8, Travelodge, 🅾 Ace Hardware, NAPA, Sam's Club/gas, U-Haul, Walmart , vet, **S** 🅖 Mobil, Sinclair/Little America/dsl/motel/@, 🍴 Black Bart's Steaks/RV Park
197.5mm	Rio de Flag
195b	US 89A N, McConnell Dr, Flagstaff, **N** 🅖 Chevron/Del Taco/dsl, Circle K, Conoco/dsl, Giant/dsl, Mobil/dsl, Shell, Sinclair/dsl, Texaco/Wendy's/dsl, 🍴 Arby's, August Moon Chinese, Baskin-Robbins, Buffalo Wild Wings, Burger King, Buster's Rest., Carl's Jr, Casa Bonita, Chili's, China Garden, Chipotle Mexican, Coco's, Coldstone, Crystal Creek, DQ, Denny's, Domino's, El Capitan, Freddy's Steak Burgers, Garcia's Mexican, Granny's Closet, Jack-in-the-Box, KFC, Mandarin Buffet, McDonald's, Olive Garden, Papa John's, Peter Piper Pizza, Picazzo's Pizza, Pizza Hut, Quiznos, Red Lobster, Sizzler, Starbucks, Strombolli's, Subway, Taco Bell, 🏨 Best Inn, Best Value, Budget Inn, Canyon Inn, Comfort Inn, Courtyard, Days Inn, Drury Inn, EconoLodge, Embassy Suites, Fairfield Inn, Hampton Inn, Highland Country Inn, Hilton Garden, Knights Inn, La Quinta, Motel 6, Quality Inn, Ramada Ltd, Rodeway Inn, Sleep Inn, SpringHill Suites, Super 8, Travel Inn, 🅾 🏥, AT&T, Barnes&Noble, Basha's Foods, Discount Tire, Hastings Books, Jo-Ann Crafts, Kohl's, Michael's, O'Reilly Parts, Ross, Safeway, Staples, Target, Walgreens, Walmart, auto/RV repair
195a	I-17 S, AZ 89A S, to Phoenix
192	Flagstaff Ranch Rd
191	Lp 40, to Grand Canyon, Flagstaff, **5 mi N** 🅖 Chevron, Maverik, Whistle Stop/dsl, 🍴 Galaxy Diner, 🏨 Best Value, Budget Host, Comfort Inn, Days Inn, EconoLodge, Radisson, Super 8, Travelodge, Travel Inn, 🅾 CarQuest, Checker Parts, Chevrolet/Cadillac, Home Depot, Kia, Kit Carson RV Park, vet, Woody Mtn Camping
190	A-1 Mountain Rd
189.5mm	Arizona Divide, elevation 7335
185	Transwestern Rd, Bellemont, **N** 🅖 ⛽/McDonald's/Subway/dsl/scales/24hr/@, 🏨 Motel 6, **S** 🅾 Harley-Davidson/Roadside Grill
183mm	**rest area wb, full** ♿ **facilities,** 🚻, 🛢, **litter barrels, vending, weather info, petwalk**
178	Parks Rd, **N** 🅖 Texaco/dsl/24hr
171	Pittman Valley Rd, Deer Farm Rd, **S** 🏨 Quality Inn/grill
167	Garland Prairie Rd, Circle Pines Rd, **N** 🅾 KOA
165	AZ 64, to Williams, Grand Canyon, **N** 🅖 Texaco (8mi), Shell/dsl (4mi), 🅾 KOA (4mi), **S** 🏨 Super 8 (1mi)
163	Williams, **N** 🅖 Chevron/Subway/dsl, 🏨 Fairfield Inn, 🅾 Canyon Gateway RV Park, to Grand Canyon, **S** 🅖 Circle K, Mobil/dsl, Mustang/dsl, Conoco, 🍴 Jack-in-the-Box, KFC, McDonald's, Pine Country Rest., Pizza Factory, Pizza Hut, Rod's Steaks, Rosa's Cantina, Rte 66 Diner, Taco Bell, Twisters Soda Fountain, 🏨 EconoLodge, El Rancho Motel, Holiday Inn, Howard Johnson, Knights Inn, Mountainside Motel, Rodeway Inn, Rte 66 Inn, Travelodge, 🅾 CarQuest, USPO, same as 161
161	Lp 40, Golf Course Dr, Williams, **N** RV camping, **0-3 mi S** 🅖 Circle K, Conoco/dsl/LP, Shell, 🍴 DQ, Denny's, Jessica's Rest., Pizza Factory, Rolando's Mexican, 🏨 AZ Motel, Best Western, Best Value, Budget Host, Can

(Left margin vertical text: E, W, WINSLOW, FLAGSTAFF)
(Right margin vertical text: FLAGSTAFF, WILLIAMS)
(Far left: AZ)

INTERSTATE 40 CONT'D

E ↑↓ **W**

Exit	Next
161	Continued
	yon Country Inn, Comfort Inn, Days Inn, Grand Canyon Hotel, Highlander Motel, Motel 6, Super 8, Westerner Motel, 🅞 🅗, Family$, Safeway, Railside RV Ranch, to Grand Canyon Railway
157	Devil Dog Rd
155.5mm	safety pullout wb, litter barrels
151	Welch Rd
149	Monte Carlo Rd, N 🅞 dsl repair
148	County Line Rd
146	AZ 89, to Prescott, Ash Fork, N 🅖 Mobil/dsl, Shell/dsl, 🍽 Ranch House Cafe, 🛏 Ash Fork Inn
144	Ash Fork, N 🛏 Ash Fork Inn, 🅞 Grand Canyon RV Park, museum, USPO, S 🅖 Chevron/Piccadilly's/dsl, Texaco/dsl/RV Park, 🅞 auto/RV repair
139	Crookton Rd, to Rte 66
123	Lp 40, to Rte 66, Seligman, N 🅖 Shell, 1 mi N 🅖 Chevron/A&W, Mustang/dsl, 🍽 Copper Cart Cafe, Lilo's Rest., 🛏 Canyon Lodge, Stagecoach 66 Motel/pizza, Supai Motel, 🅞 KOA (1mi), to Grand Canyon Caverns, USPO, repair, (same as 121), S 🅖 Chevron/Subway/dsl/24hr
121	Lp 40, to Rte 66, Seligman, 1 mi N 🅖 Chevron/A&W, Mustang/dsl, 🍽 Copper Cart Cafe, Lilo's Rest., Roadkill Cafe, 🛏 Canyon Lodge, Route 66 Motel/pizza, Supai Motel, 🅞 KOA (1mi), to Grand Canyon Caverns, USPO, repair (same as 123)
109	Anvil Rock Rd
108mm	Markham Wash
103	Jolly Rd
96	Cross Mountain Rd
91	Fort Rock Rd
87	Willows Ranch Rd
86mm	Willow Creek
79	Silver Springs Rd
75.5mm	Big Sandy Wash
73.5mm	Peacock Wash
71	US 93 S, to Wickenburg, Phoenix
66	Blake Ranch Rd, N 🅖 Petro/Mobil/Iron Skillet/dsl/rest./scales/24hr/@, 🅞 Blake Ranch RV Park, Blue Beacon, SpeedCo Lube
60mm	Frees Wash
59	DW Ranch Rd, N 🅖 Loves/Chester's/Subway/dsl/scales/24hr, 🅞 Hualapai Mtn Park, truckwash
57mm	Rattlesnake Wash
53	AZ 66, Andy Devine Ave, to Kingman, N 🅖 Chevron, FLYING J/dsl/LP/scales/24hr, Terrible's/dsl, Texaco, 🍽 Arby's, Burger King, Denny's, Jack-in-the-Box, McDonald's, Pizza Hut, Taco Bell, 🛏 Days Inn, EconoLodge, 1st Value Inn, Motel 6, Silver Queen Motel, Super 8, Travelodge, 🅞 🅗, Basha's Foods, Freightliner, Goodyear, K-Mart, KOA (1mi), Outdoorsman RV Ctr/Service, TireWorld, dsl/tire repair, S 🅖 Mobil/dsl, Shell/repair, 🍽 ABC Chinese, JB's, Lo's Chinese, Oyster's Mexican, Sonic, 🛏 Best Value Inn, Best Western, Comfort Inn, Days Inn, High Desert Inn, Holiday Inn Express, Lido Motel, Rodeway Inn, Rte 66 Motel, SpringHill Suites, 🅞 Chrysler/Dodge/Jeep, Kia, NAPA, Sunrise RV Park, Uptown Drug
51	Stockton Hill Rd, Kingman, N 🅖 Arco/24hr, Chevron, Circle K/dsl, 🍽 Chili's, Cracker Barrel, Del Taco,

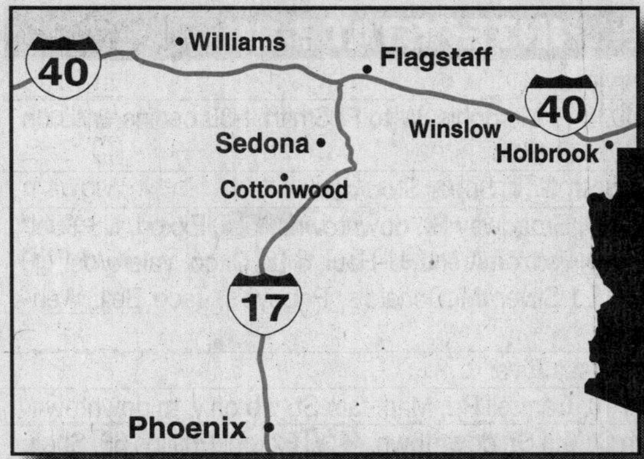

KINGMAN (left margin, vertical)

Exit	Next
51	Continued
	Golden Corral, IHOP, In-N-Out, KFC, Panda Express, Papa John's, Palace Buffet, Papa Murphy, Scotty's Rest., Sonic, Starbucks, Subway, Taco Bell, 🛏 Hampton Inn, 🅞 AT&T, AutoZone, AZ RV Depot/repair, BigLots, BrakeMasters, Buick/Chevrolet, Checker Parts, CVS Drug, $General, $Tree, Ford/Lincoln/Mercury, Home Depot, Honda, Hyundai, Oil Can Henry's, PetCo, Petsmart, Ross, Safeway/gas, Smith's Foods/dsl, Staples, Superior Tire, TrueValue, Walgreens, Walmart, vet, S 🅖 Circle K, 🍽 Alfonso's Mexican, Kingman Co Steaks, Little Caesars, Pizza Hut, 🅞 CarQuest, Family$, Hastings Books, JC Penney, Radio Shack, Safeway/gas, Sears
48	US 93 N, Beale St, Kingman, N 🅖 Chevron/dsl, Express Stop, Mobil/dsl, USA/Subway/dsl/24hr, Shell/dsl/24hr, TA/Country Pride/Popeye's/dsl/scales/24hr/@, Texaco/dsl, Woody's, 🍽 Wendy's, 🛏 Budget Inn, Economy Inn, Tristate Inn, 🅞 URGENT CARE, Best Tire/auto/RV repair, truckwash, S 🅖 Chevron/Quiznos/dsl/24hr, 🍽 Calico's Rest., Carl's Jr, 🛏 AZ Inn, Motel 6, 🅞 Ft Beale RV Park, city park, museum
46.5mm	Holy Moses Wash
44	AZ 66, Oatman Hwy, McConnico, to Rte 66, S 🅖 Crazy Fred's Fuel/dsl/café, 🅞 Canyon West RV Camping (3mi), truckwash
40.5mm	Griffith Wash
37	Griffith Rd
35mm	Black Rock Wash
32mm	Walnut Creek
28	Old Trails Rd
26	Proving Ground Rd, S 🅞 AZ Proving Grounds
25	Alamo Rd, to Yucca, N 🅖 Micromart/dsl/diner, 🍽 Jr Grill, 🅞 USPO, S auto repair, towing
23mm	rest area both lanes, full ♿ facilities, 🅒, 🚻, litter barrels, vending, petwalk
21mm	Flat Top Wash
20	Santa Fe Ranch Rd
18.5mm	Illavar Wash
15mm	Buck Mtn Wash
13.5mm	Franconia Wash
13	Franconia Rd
9	AZ 95 S, to Lake Havasu City, Parker, London Br, S 🅖 Chevron/Burger King/dsl, Loves/Carl's Jr/dsl/scales, Pilot/Wendy's/dsl/scales, 🅞 Prospectors RV Resort
4mm	weigh sta both lanes
2	Needle Mtn Rd
1	Topock Rd, to Bullhead City, Oatman, N gas, food, camping, to Havasu NWR
0mm	Arizona/California state line, Colorado River, Mountain/Pacific time zone

KINGMAN   YUCCA (center margin, vertical)

🅖 = gas 🍴 = food 🏨 = lodging 🄾 = other   Copyright 2012 - The Next Exit®

AR

INTERSTATE 30

Exit	Services
143b a	I-40, E to Memphis, W to Ft Smith, I-30 begins/ends on I-40, exit 153b
142	15th St, S 🅖 Super Stop/dsl
141b	US 70, Broadway St, downtown, N 🅖 Exxon, US Fuel/dsl, 🄾 Verizon Arena, U-Haul, S 🅖 Citgo, Valero/dsl, 🍴 KFC/LJ Silver, McDonald's, Popeye's, Taco Bell, Wendy's
141mm	Arkansas River
141a	AR 10, Cantrell Rd, Markham St, wb only, to downtown
140	9th St, 6th St, downtown, N 🅖 Exxon, Phillips 66, Shell, 🍴 Pizza Hut, 🏨 Holiday Inn, 🄾 USPO, S 🅖 SuperStop, 🏨 Comfort Inn
139b	I-630, downtown
139a	AR 365, Roosevelt Rd, N 🅖 Exxon, 🄾 AutoZone, S 🅖 Shell, 🄾 Family$, Kroger, NAPA
138b	I-530 S, US 167 S, US 65 S, to Pine Bluff
138a	I-440 E, to Memphis 🅡
135	W 65th St, N 🅖 Exxon/dsl, MapCo, Shell/dsl, 🏨 Executive Inn, S 🏨 Rodeway Inn
134	Scott Hamilton Dr, S 🅖 Exxon/dsl, 🍴 Waffle House, 🏨 Best Value Inn, Motel 6
133	Geyer Springs Rd, N 🅖 Exxon, Hess, 🍴 Church's, Sonic, Subway, S 🅖 Exxon, Phillips 66, Shell, 🍴 Arby's, Burger King, El Chico, KFC, Little Caesars, McDonald's, Panda Chinese, Rallys, Shark's Rest., Taco Bell, Waffle House, Wendy's, 🏨 Baymont Inn, Best Western, Comfort Inn, Rest Inn, 🄾 Advance Parts, Family$, Goodyear/auto, Kroger/gas, Radio Shack, Walgreens
132	US 70b, University Ave, N 🅖 RaceWay/dsl, SuperStop, Valero, 🏨 Best Value Inn, 🄾 Chevrolet, S 🍴 Luigi's Pizza
131	McDaniel Dr, N 🄾 U-Haul, S 🏨 Knight's Inn, Super 7 Inn, 🄾 Crain RV Ctr, Firestone
130	AR 338, Baseline Rd, Mabelvale, N 🅖 MapCo/dsl, 🍴 FatBoys Diner, 🏨 Best Value Inn, 🄾 Harley-Davidson, S 🅖 Phillips 66, Shell/Popeye's, 🍴 Applebee's, China Buffet, Dixie Cafe, McDonald's, Sonic, Taco Bueno, Wendy's, 🄾 AT&T, $Tree, GNC, Home Depot, Walmart/Subway
129	I-430, N
128	Otter Creek Rd, Mabelvale West, N 🅖 Loves/Hardee's/Subway/dsl/scales/24hr, S 🅖 Exxon, 🏨 La Quinta, 🄾 🄷, Goodyear
126	AR 111, County Line Rd, Alexander, N 🅖 Phillips 66/dsl, Shell/dsl, S 🅖 Citgo, 🄾 Cherokee RV Park/dump (4mi)
123	AR 183, Reynolds Rd, to Bryant, Bauxite, N 🅖 Murphy USA, Shell, SuperStop, 🍴 Arby's, Backyard Burgers, Burger King, Catfish Barn, Cracker Barrel, D-Light Chinese, Domino's, Firehouse Subs, IHOP, KFC, Papa Murphy's, Pizza Hut, Quizno's, Ruby Tuesday, Subway, TaMolly's, Waffle House, 🏨 Best Value Inn, Comfort Inn, Hampton Inn, Holiday Inn Express, Hometown Hotel, La Quinta, Vista Inn, 🄾 AT&T, AutoZone, $Tree, Radio Shack, Walgreens, Walmart/Subway, S 🅖 Conoco/dsl, Exxon/dsl, 🍴 Chick-fil-A, Little Caesar's, McDonald's, Mi Ranchito, Sonic, Taco Bell, Wendy's, Zaxby's, 🏨 Super 8, 🄾 $General, Lowe's Whse, O'Reilly Parts, USPO
121	Alcoa Rd, N 🅖 Citgo, ⬚/Subway/dsl/scales/24hr/@, 🍴 McDonald's, 🄾 Chrysler/Dodge/Jeep, Firestone, S 🅖 🍴

Exit	Services
121	Continued Chili's, McAlister's Deli, Moe's SW Grill, Sakura Japanese, Starbucks, Subway, 🄾 At&T, Best Buy, Buick/GMC, GNC, Kohls, Old Navy, PetCo, Target
118	Congo Rd, N 🍴 Applebee's, Brown's Rest, CiCi's, Dixie Café, Santa Fe Grill, 🄾 Chevrolet/Hummer, Curves, Home Depot, Williams Tire, S 🅖 Exxon, 🍴 Burger King, 🏨 Days Inn, Ramada Inn, 🄾 Ford/Lincoln/Mercury, RV City, USPO
117	US 64, AR 5, AR 35, N 🅖 Shell, 🍴 Denny's, IHOP, Papa John's, Pizza Hut, Waffle House, 🏨 Best Inn, Best Western, Econolodge, S 🅖 Exxon, Fina, Murphy USA, Shell, 🍴 Arby's, Backyard Burger, Burger King, Capt D's, Colton's Steaks, IHOP, La Hacienda Mexican, McDonald's, Popeye's, Quizno's, Rib Crib, Sonic, Subway, Taco Bell, Wendy's, Western Sizzlin, 🏨 Days Inn, 🄾 🄷, Advance Parts, AutoZone, $Tree, Firestone, GNC, Hastings Books, Kroger, Office Depot, O'Reilly Parts, Radio Shack, TireTown, Tuesday Morning, Walmart, USPO
116	Sevier St, N 🅖 Citgo/dsl, Shell/dsl, 🏨 Troutt Motel, S 🅖 Citgo, 🏨 Capri Inn
114	US 67 S, Benton, S 🅖 Valero/McDonald's/dsl, 🍴 Sonic
113mm	insp sta both lanes
111	US 70 W, Hot Springs, N 🄾 Cloud 9 RV Park, to Hot Springs NP
106	Old Military Rd, N 🅖 Fina/JJ's Rest./dsl/scales/@, S 🄾 JB'S RV Park
99	US 270 E, Malvern, N 🄷
98b a	US 270, Malvern, Hot Springs, N 🏨 Super 8, S 🅖 Fina/dsl, Murphy USA, Shell/dsl, Valero, 🍴 Baskin-Robbins, Burger King, Chile Peppers, El Parian, Great Wall Buffet, Larry's Pizza, McDonald's, Pizza Hut, Pizza Pro, Sonic, Subway, Taco Bell, Waffle House, Wendy's, Western Sizzlin, 🏨 Best Value Inn, Comfort Inn, Holiday Inn Express, 🄾 🄷, AutoZone, Buick/GMC, Chevrolet, Chrysler/Dodge/Jeep, $General, $Tree, Ford, O'Reilly Parts, Radio Shack, Verizon, Walmart/Subway, USPO
97	AR 84, AR 171, N 🄾 Lake Catherine SP, RV camping
93mm	rest area (both lanes exit left), full 🚻 facilities, 🄲, 🄿, litter barrels, vending, petwalk
91	AR 84, Social Hill
83	AR 283, Friendship, S 🅖 Shell/dsl
78	AR 7, Caddo Valley, N 🅖 Fina/dsl/24hr, Valero/dsl, Shell/dsl, 🍴 Cracker Barrel, 🄾 Arkadelphia RV Park, to Hot Springs NP, S 🅖 Exxon/Subway/dsl, Phillips 66/Stuckey's, Shell/dsl, 🍴 McDonald's, Taco Bell, TaMolly's Mexican, Waffle House, Wendy's, 🏨 Best Value Inn, Best Western, Comfort Inn, Days Inn, Hampton Inn, Motel 6, Quality Inn, Super 8, 🄾 De Gray SP
73	AR 8, AR 26, AR 51, Arkadelphia, N 🅖 Citgo/dsl, Shell/Stuckey's, 🍴 Chicken Express, Domino's, Great Wall Buffet, McDonald's, Western Sizzlin, 🄾 AT&T, $Tree, Radio Shack, Verizon, Walmart/Subway, to Crater of Diamond SP, S 🅖 Exxon/dsl, Shell, 🍴 Andy's Rest., Burger King, Mazzio's, Pizza Shack, Subway, Taco Tico, 🄾 🄷, Ace Hardware, AutoZone, Brookshire Foods, $General, Fred's, O'Reilly Parts, USPO, Walgreens, tires/repair, vet
69	AR 26 E, Gum Springs
63	AR 53, Gurdon, N 🅖 Citgo/dsl/rest., 🏨 Best Value Inn, S 🅖 Shell/dsl/rest., 🄾 to White Oak Lake SP

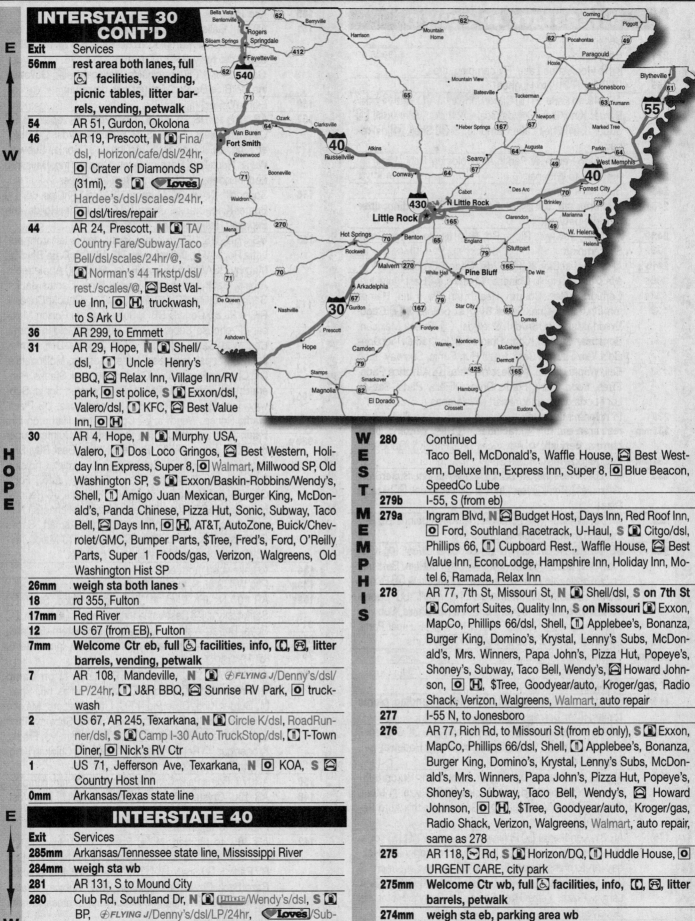

INTERSTATE 30 CONT'D

E ↕ W

Exit	Services
56mm	rest area both lanes, full ♿ facilities, vending, picnic tables, litter barrels, vending, petwalk
54	AR 51, Gurdon, Okolona
46	AR 19, Prescott, **N** 📱 Fina/dsl, Horizon/cafe/dsl/24hr, 🅾 Crater of Diamonds SP (31mi), **S** 📱 Loves/Hardee's/dsl/scales/24hr, 🅾 dsl/tires/repair
44	AR 24, Prescott, **N** 📱 TA/Country Fare/Subway/Taco Bell/dsl/scales/24hr/@, **S** 📱 Norman's 44 Trkstp/dsl/rest./scales/@, 🏨 Best Value Inn, 🅾 H, truckwash, to S Ark U
36	AR 299, to Emmett
31	AR 29, Hope, **N** 📱 Shell/dsl, 🍴 Uncle Henry's BBQ, 🏨 Relax Inn, Village Inn/RV park, 🅾 st police, **S** 📱 Exxon/dsl, Valero/dsl, 🍴 KFC, 🏨 Best Value Inn, 🅾 H

H O P E

Exit	Services
30	AR 4, Hope, **N** 📱 Murphy USA, Valero, 🍴 Dos Loco Gringos, 🏨 Best Western, Holiday Inn Express, Super 8, 🅾 Walmart, Millwood SP, Old Washington SP, **S** 📱 Exxon/Baskin-Robbins/Wendy's, Shell, 🍴 Amigo Juan Mexican, Burger King, McDonald's, Panda Chinese, Pizza Hut, Sonic, Subway, Taco Bell, 🏨 Days Inn, 🅾 H, AT&T, AutoZone, Buick/Chevrolet/GMC, Bumper Parts, $Tree, Fred's, Ford, O'Reilly Parts, Super 1 Foods/gas, Verizon, Walgreens, Old Washington Hist SP
26mm	weigh sta both lanes
18	rd 355, Fulton
17mm	Red River
12	US 67 (from EB), Fulton
7mm	Welcome Ctr eb, full ♿ facilities, info, 🚻, 🏨, litter barrels, vending, petwalk
7	AR 108, Mandeville, **N** 📱 FLYING J/Denny's/dsl/LP/24hr, 🍴 J&R BBQ, 🏨 Sunrise RV Park, 🅾 truckwash
2	US 67, AR 245, Texarkana, **N** 📱 Circle K/dsl, RoadRunner/dsl, **S** 📱 Camp I-30 Auto TruckStop/dsl, 🍴 T-Town Diner, 🅾 Nick's RV Ctr
1	US 71, Jefferson Ave, Texarkana, **N** 🅾 KOA, **S** 🏨 Country Host Inn
0mm	Arkansas/Texas state line

INTERSTATE 40

E ↕ W

Exit	Services
285mm	Arkansas/Tennessee state line, Mississippi River
284mm	weigh sta wb
281	AR 131, S to Mound City
280	Club Rd, Southland Dr, **N** 📱 🅾/Wendy's/dsl, **S** 📱 BP, FLYING J/Denny's/dsl/LP/24hr, Loves/Subway/dsl, Petro/Iron Skillet/dsl/24hr/@, 🍴 KFC/

W E S T   M E M P H I S

Exit	Services
280	*Continued* Taco Bell, McDonald's, Waffle House, 🏨 Best Western, Deluxe Inn, Express Inn, Super 8, 🅾 Blue Beacon, SpeedCo Lube
279b	I-55, S (from eb)
279a	Ingram Blvd, **N** 🏨 Budget Host, Days Inn, Red Roof Inn, 🅾 Ford, Southland Racetrack, U-Haul, **S** 📱 Citgo/dsl, Phillips 66, 🍴 Cupboard Rest., Waffle House, 🏨 Best Value Inn, EconoLodge, Hampshire Inn, Holiday Inn, Motel 6, Ramada, Relax Inn
278	AR 77, 7th St, Missouri St, **N** 📱 Shell/dsl, **S on 7th St** 📱 Comfort Suites, Quality Inn, **S on Missouri** 📱 Exxon, MapCo, Phillips 66/dsl, Shell, 🍴 Applebee's, Bonanza, Burger King, Domino's, Krystal, Lenny's Subs, McDonald's, Mrs. Winners, Papa John's, Pizza Hut, Popeye's, Shoney's, Subway, Taco Bell, Wendy's, 🏨 Howard Johnson, 🅾 H, $Tree, Goodyear/auto, Kroger/gas, Radio Shack, Verizon, Walgreens, Walmart, auto repair
277	I-55 N, to Jonesboro
276	AR 77, Rich Rd, to Missouri St (from eb only), **S** 📱 Exxon, MapCo, Phillips 66/dsl, Shell, 🍴 Applebee's, Bonanza, Burger King, Domino's, Krystal, Lenny's Subs, McDonald's, Mrs. Winners, Papa John's, Pizza Hut, Popeye's, Shoney's, Subway, Taco Bell, Wendy's, 🏨 Howard Johnson, 🅾 H, $Tree, Goodyear/auto, Kroger/gas, Radio Shack, Verizon, Walgreens, Walmart, auto repair, same as 278
275	AR 118, 🚕 Rd, **S** 📱 Horizon/DQ, 🍴 Huddle House, 🅾 URGENT CARE, city park
275mm	Welcome Ctr wb, full ♿ facilities, info, 🚻, 🏨, litter barrels, petwalk
274mm	weigh sta eb, parking area wb
271	AR 147, to Blue Lake, **S** 📱 BP/dsl, Exxon/Chester's,

AR

INTERSTATE 40 CONT'D

Exit	Services
271	Continued
	🅞 to Horseshoe Lake, RV camping, tires
265	US 79, AR 218, to Hughes
260	AR 149, to Earle, N 🅖 Citgo/Subway, TA/Country Pride/ Burger King/Taco Bell/dsl/scales/24hr/@, Valero/dsl, 🛏 Super 8, 🅞 Shell Lake Camping, S 🅖 Shell, 🅞 dsl repair
256	AR 75, to Parkin, N Parkin Archeological Park (12mi)
247	AR 38 E, to Widener
245mm	St Francis River
243mm	**rest area wb, full 🅿 facilities, 🅲, 🅰, vending, litter barrels, petwalk**
242	AR 284, Crowley's Ridge Rd, N 🅞 🅷, to Village Creek SP, camping
241b a	AR 1, Forrest City, N 🅖 BP/dsl, Citgo/DQ/dsl, Shell/Popeye's/dsl, 🍴 HoHo Chinese, Wendy's, 🛏 Best Value Inn, Comfort Suites, Country Hearth Inn, Days Inn, Hampton Inn, Luxury Inn, Super 8, 🅞 st police, S 🅖 Citgo, Exxon, Murphy USA/dsl, Shell/dsl, 🍴 Ameca Mexican, Bonanza, Burger King, Dragon China, KFC, McDonald's, Ole Sawmill Cafe, Pizza Hut, Sonic, Subway, Taco Bell, Waffle House, 🛏 Best Western, 🅞 Advance Parts, $Tree, Food Giant, Fred's Drug, O'Reilly Parts, Sav-A-Lot Foods, Verizon, Walmart , Walgreens
239	to Wynne, Marianna
235mm	**rest area eb, full 🅿 facilities, 🅲, 🅰, vending, litter barrels, petwalk**
234mm	L'Anguille River
233	AR 261, Palestine, N 🅖 Loves/Chester's/Subway/ dsl/scales/24hr, 🛏 Rest Inn, S 🅖 Citgo/dsl, 🍴 Head's Cafe
221	AR 78, Wheatley, N 🅖 SweetPea/dsl/repair, S 🅖 BP/ Pitstop/diner/dsl, MapCo/Subway/dsl
216	US 49, AR 17, Brinkley, N 🅖 Citgo, Shell/dsl, 🅞 KFC/ Taco Bell, Los Piños Mexican, 🛏 Baymont Inn, Best Inn, EconoLodge, Motel 6/RV Park, 🅞 dsl repair, S 🅖 Exxon/ Baskin-Robbins/dsl, MapCo/dsl/24hr, Shell, 🍴 Gene's BBQ, McDonald's, New China, Pizza Hut, Sonic, Subway, Waffle House, 🛏 Heritage Inn/RV Park, 🅞 Bumper Parts, $General, Family$, Fred's, Kroger, O'Reilly Parts
205mm	Cache River
202	AR 33, to Biscoe
200mm	White River
199mm	**rest areas both lanes, full 🅿 facilities, vending, picnic tables, litter barrels, no phones**
193	AR 11, to Hazen, N 🅖 Exxon/Chester's, S 🅖 Citgo/dsl, Shell/dsl/24hr, 🍴 Cocos Dos Mexican, 🛏 Rodeway Inn, Super 8, 🅞 T-rix RV Park,
183	AR 13, Carlisle, S 🅖 Citgo, Conoco/dsl, Exxon/Subway/dsl, Phillips 66/dsl, 🍴 Nick's BBQ, Pizza 'N More, Sonic, 🛏 Best Value Inn, 🅞 $General, Keith's Auto Repair, NAPA
175	AR 31, Lonoke, N 🅖 Phillips 66, Valero/dsl, 🍴 El Torito Mexican, McDonald's, 🛏 Days Inn, Economy Inn, Holiday Inn Express, Super 8, 🅞 AT&T, Verizon, Walmart, S 🅖 Shell/Subway, 🍴 I-40 Catfish Rest., KFC/Taco Bell, Larry's Pizza, Pizza Hut, Sonic, 🛏 Perry's Motel, 🅞 Goodyear/auto
169	AR 15, Remington Rd

Exit	Services
165	Kerr Rd
161	AR 391, Galloway, N 🅖 Loves/Chester's/subs/dsl/ scales/24hr, 🅞 Camping World RV Ctr, S 🅖 Petro/Iron Skillet/dsl/scales/24hr/@, 🍴 Subway/Chester's/dsl/ scales/24hr, IA-80 TruckOMat/dsl/scales, 🛏 Galloway Inn, 🅞 Blue Beacon, Freightliner, dsl repair
159	I-440 W, S ⊟
157	AR 161, to US 70, N 🅖 Exxon/dsl, 🅞 repair, S 🅖 Citgo/dsl, Hess, Super, S Stop/dsl, Shell/dsl, 🍴 Burger King, KFC/Taco Bell, McDonald's, Sonic, Subway, Waffle House, 🛏 Best Value Inn, Comfort Inn, Days Inn, EconoLodge, Red Roof Inn, Rest Inn, Super 8
156	Springhill Dr, N 🅖 Murphy USA/dsl, Phillips 66, 🍴 Burger King, Cracker Barrel, 🛏 Fairfield Inn, Holiday Inn Express, Residence Inn, Walmart
155	US 67 N, US 167, to Jacksonville (exits left from eb), Little Rock AFB, **0-3 mi N on US 167/McCain Blvd** 🅖 Murphy USA/dsl, Phillips 66/dsl, Shell, 🍴 Applebee's, Arby's, Backyard Burger, Burger King, Cactus Jacks, Carino's Italian, Chick-fil-A, Chili's, ChuckeCheese, CiCi's Pizza, Corky's BBQ, Dixie Cafe, El Porton Mexican, Firehouse Subs, 5 Guys Burgers, Golden Corral, Hog Wild Cafe, Hooters, IHOP, Jason's Deli, Jimmy John's, Kanpai Japanese, Little Caesar's, McDonald's, Old Chicago Pizza, Olive Garden, Outback Steaks, Panera Bread, Pizza Hut, Rally's, Red Lobster, Sonic, Subway, Taco Bell, TGIFriday's, TX Roadhouse, US Pizza, Waffle House, Wendy's, 🛏 Comfort Inn, Hampton Inn, Hilton Garden, Holiday Inn Express, La Quinta, Super 8, 🅞 🅷, Aamco, AT&T, Barnes&Noble, Best Buy, BigLots, Books-A-Million, Buick/GMC, Chevrolet, Chrysler/ Dodge/Jeep, Dillard's, $Tree, Firestone/auto, Ford, Gander Mtn, Home Depot, Honda, Hyundai, JC Penney, KIA, Lincoln/Mercury, Lowe's, Mazda, Michael's, Nissan, Office Depot, PepBoys, PetCo, Petsmart, Sam's Club/gas, Sears/auto, Steinmart, Target, TJ Maxx, Toyota/Scion, Verizon, VW, Walmart , mall, vet
154	to Lakewood (from eb)
153b	I-30 W, US 65 S, to Little Rock
153a	AR 107 N, JFK Blvd, N 🅖 Exxon, Mapco, Shell, 🍴 Schlotzsky's, 🛏 Best Value Inn, 🅞 vet, S 🅖 Exxon, 🍴 Royal Buffet, Waffle House, 🛏 Best Western, Bugetel, Country Inn&Suites, Hampton Inn, Holiday Inn, Motel 6, 🅞 🅷, USPO
152	AR 365, AR 176, Camp Pike Rd, Levy, **N on Camp Robinson Rd** 🅖 Exxon, EZ Mart, Phillips 66, Shell, 🍴 Burger King, Dixie Pig, KFC, Little Caesars, Mexico Chiquito, McDonald's, Pizza Hut, Sonic, Subway, Taco Bell, US Pizza, Wendy's, 🅞 AutoZone, Family$, Fred's, Kroger/gas, O'Reilly Parts, S 🅖 Shell, 🍴 Chicken King, 🅞 🅷, Family$, Kroger, Radio Shack
150	AR 176, Burns Park, Camp Robinson, S 🅞 info, camping
148	AR 100, Crystal Hill Rd, N 🅖 Shell, S 🅖 Citgo/dsl, other:KOA
147	I-430 S, to Texarkana
142	AR 365, to Morgan, N 🅖 Phillips 66, Valero/dsl, 🍴 I-40 Rest., 🛏 Days Inn, 🅞 Bumper Parts, Trails End RV Park, S 🅖 Shell/dsl, 🍴 KFC/Taco Bell, McDonald's, Razorback Pizza, Smokeshack BBQ, Subway, Waffle House, 🛏 Best Value Inn, Holiday Inn Express, Quality Inn, 🅞 antiques
135	AR 365, AR 89, Mayflower, N 🅖 Hess/dsl, 🅞 May

Side labels: E W, FORREST CITY, BRINKLEY, LONOKE, LITTLE ROCK

INTERSTATE 40 CONT'D

Exit	Services
135	**Continued**
	flower RV Ctr (1mi), S 🅟 Exxon/dsl, Valero, 🍴 Sonic, Stroud's Country Diner, Tampico Mexican, 🄾 Big Star Food/Drug, $General
134mm	**truck parking both lanes**
129	US 65B, AR 286, Conway, S 🅟 Citgo/dsl, Exxon, Map-Co/dsl, 🍴 Arby's, Subway, 🛏 Budget Inn, Continental Motel, 🄾 🄷, Chrysler/Dodge/Jeep, Honda, Toyota/Scion, st police, to Toad Suck SP
127	US 64, Conway, N 🅟 Exxon, Satterfield, Shell, 🍴 Arby's, Chick-fil-A, Chili's, Denny's, Logan's Roadhouse, Sonic, Starbucks, Subway, TGIFriday's, Waffle House, 🛏 Best Value Inn, Best Western, Country Inn&Suites, Comfort Suites, Days Inn, Economy Inn, Hampton Inn, Hilton Garden, 🄾 AT&T, Belk, Best Buy, Buick/GMC, Chevrolet, $General, Firestone/auto, Ford/Mercury, GNC, Goodyear/auto, Harley-Davidson, Home Depot, Hyundai, Kohl's, Moix RV Ctr, NAPA, Nissan, Old Navy, O'Reilly Parts, Petsmart, Radio Shack, Staples, Target, TJ Maxx, Verizon, repair/transmissions, to Lester Flatt Park, vet, S 🅟 RaceWay, Shell/dsl, Valero/dsl, 🍴 Burger King, Church's, Colton's Steaks, Hardee's, Jimmy John's, Kings Steaks, LJ Silver, McDonald's, New China, Pizza Inn, Rally's, Saigon Rest., Shipley Doughnuts, Sonic, Taco Bell, Tokyo Japanese, Wendy's, Whole Hog Cafe, 🛏 Kings Inn, 🄾 AutoZone, BigLots, Family$, Fred's Drugs, Hancock Fabrics, Hobby Lobby, Kroger/gas, Walgreens, tires
125	US 65, Conway, N 🅟 Conoco/dsl, Exxon/Subway/dsl, Shell/dsl/24hr, 🍴 China Town, Cracker Barrel, El Acapulco Mexican, La Hacienda Mexican, MktPlace Deli, McDonald's, 🛏 Quality Inn, 🄾 $Tree, JC Penney, Office Depot, Sears, S 🅟 Citgo, Mobil/dsl, Murphy USA, Sinclair, 🍴 Backyard Burger, Burger King, CiCi's Pizza, Dixie Cafe, Firehouse Subs, Hart's Seafood, IHOP, McAlister's Deli, Mexico Chiquito, New China, Outback Steaks, Panera Bread, Ruby Tuesday, Sonic, Starbucks, Subway, Waffle House, Wendy's, 🛏 Candlewood Suites, Fairfield Inn, Holiday Inn, Holiday Inn Express, Howard Johnson, La Quinta, Microtel, Motel 6, Stacy Motel, Super 8, 🄾 🄷, Advance Parts, $General, Hastings Books, Lowe's, Walmart, tires
124	AR 25 N, to Conway, 1 mi S 🅟 Shell/dsl, 🍴 Catfish&More, DQ, KFC, Mazzio's, Popeye's, 🄾 🄷, U-Haul
120mm	Cadron River
117	to Menifee
112	AR 92, Plumerville, N 🅟 Exxon/dsl, S 🅟 Country Store/dsl, 🄾 USPO
108	AR 9, Morrilton, S 🅟 Murphy USA, Shell/Pizza Pro/dsl/24hr, Valero, 🍴 Bonanza, Chop Stix, Hardees, McDonald's, Ortega's Mexican, Pizza Hut, Sonic, Subway, Waffle House, Wendy's, 🛏 Super 8, 🄾 🄷, Ace Hardware, AT&T, Chrysler/Dodge/Jeep, $General, Ford/Lincoln, Kroger, NAPA, Verizon, Walmart, to Petit Jean SP (21mi), RV camping
107	AR 95, Morrilton, N 🅟 Shell/dsl, 🛏 Scottish Inn, KOA, S 🅟 Loves/Subway/dsl/24hr, Shell, 🍴 Mom&Pop's Waffles, Morrilton Drive Inn, Yesterdays Rest., 🛏 Days Inn, 🄾 Bumper Parts
101	Blackwell, N 🅟 Blackwell TrkStp/Valero/dsl/diner/scales/24hr, 🄾 Utility Trailer Sales
94	AR 105, Atkins, N 🅟 Exxon/Subway/dsl/24hr, Shell/McDonald's/dsl, 🍴 Berky's Diner, El Parian Mexican, KFC/Taco Bell, Sonic, 🄾 $General, repair, S 🄾 Sexton Foods
88	Pottsville, S 🍴 Pottsville Country Cafe, 🄾 truck repair/wash
84	US 64, AR 331, Russellville, N 🅟 ⚡FLYING J/Denny's/dsl/scales/LP/24hr, Shell/dsl, 🄾 Ivys Cove RV Retreat, trucklube, S 🅟 Phillips 66, ▦/Subway/Wendy's/dsl/scales, 🍴 CiCi's Pizza, Hardee's, Hunan Chinese, McDonald's, Sonic, Waffle House, 🛏 Comfort Inn, Quality Inn, 🄾 🄷, AutoZone, Belk, Buick/Chevrolet/GMC, Chrysler/Dodge/Jeep, $Tree, JC Penney, Hastings Books, Hobby Lobby, Hyundai, K-Mart, Lowe's, Nissan, Petsmart, Staples, TJ Maxx, Toyota, USPO
83	AK 326, Weir Rd, S 🅟 Murphy USA/dsl, Phillips 66, 🍴 DQ, McAlisters Deli, Popeye's, Ryan's, Starbucks, Subway, Taco Bueno, 🛏 Comfort Inn, 🄾 AT&T, AutoZone, Curves, $General, Ford, Mazda, NAPA, O'Reilly Parts, Verizon, Walmart
81	AR 7, Russellville, N 🅟 SuperStop/dsl, 🍴 CJ's Burgers, 7-40 Rest., 🛏 Motel 6, 🄾 Outdoor RV Ctr/Park, S 🅟 Exxon/dsl/24hr, Phillips 66/dsl/24hr, Shell/24hr, 🍴 Arby's, Burger King, Colton's Steaks, Cracker Barrel, Dixie Café, IHOP, La Huerta Mexican, New China, Ruby Tuesday, Subway, Waffle House, 🛏 Best Value, Best Western, Days Inn, Economy Inn, Fairfield Inn, Hampton Inn, Hawthorn Park Inn, La Quinta, Super 8, 🄾 to Lake Dardanelle SP, RV camping
80mm	Dardanelle Reservoir
78	US 64, Russellville, S 🍴 Fat Daddy's BBQ, 🄾 🄷, Darrell's Mkt, Mission RV Park, to Lake Dardanelle SP
74	AR 333, London
72mm	**rest area wb, full ♿ facilities, 🄲, 🄰, litter barrels, vending, petwalk**
70mm	overlook wb lane, litter barrels
68mm	**rest area eb, full ♿ facilities, 🄲, 🄰, litter barrels, vending, petwalk**
67	AR 315, Knoxville, S 🅟 Citgo, Knoxville Mkt, 🄾 USPO
64	US 64, Clarksville, Lamar, S 🅟 Valero/Pizza Pro/dsl, 🄾 Dad's Dream RV Park
58	AR 21, AR 103, Clarksville, N 🅟 Shell/dsl, Valero, 🍴 Emerald Dragon Chinese, KFC, Larry's Pizza, McDonald's, Pasta Grill, Pizza Hut, Sonic, Subway, Taco Bell, Waffle House, 🛏 Best Western, Quality Inn, Super 8, 🄾 🄷, Buick/Chevrolet, $General, S 🅟 Murphy USA/dsl, 🍴 Arby's, South Park Rest., Wendy's, 🄾 Chrysler/

Side markers: E, W (Conway), CONWAY, MORRILTON, RUSSELLVILLE

INTERSTATE 40 CONT'D

Exit	Services
58	Continued Dodge/Jeep, Ford, Walmart /Subway
57	AR 109, Clarksville, **N** ⬛ Fuel Stop/dsl, ⬛ Subway, ⬛ Family$, Harvest Foods/drug, **S** ⬛ Shell/Chester's/dsl, ⬛ repair
55	US 64, AR 109, Clarksville, **N** ⬛ Crosswoods Rest., Hardee's, ⬛ Days Inn, Hampton Inn, Holiday Inn Express, **S** ⬛ Exxon/dsl, ⬛ Jackson Family Steaks, ⬛ Radio Shack, st police
47	AR 164, Coal Hill
41	AR 186, Altus, **S** ⬛ Swiss Family Rest., Wiederkehr Rest., ⬛ Pine Ridge RV Park, winery
37	AR 219, Ozark, **S** ⬛ ⬤Loves/Subway/dsl/scales/24hr, Shell/McDonald's/dsl, ⬛ KFC/Taco Bell, ⬛ Days Inn, ⬛ ⬛
36mm	**rest area both lanes, full** ⬛ **facilities,** ⬛, ⬛, **litter barrels, petwalk**
35	AR 23, Ozark **3 mi S** ⬛ 23 One Stop, ⬛ Hardee's, Subway, ⬛ Ozark Inn, Oxford Inn, ⬛ ⬛, Aux Arc Park (5mi), to Mt Magazine SP (20 mi)
24	AR 215, Mulberry, **S** Vine Prairie Park
20	Dyer, **N** ⬛ Conoco/dsl, ⬛ Freightliner/Western Star, **S** ⬛ Phillips 66/dsl, Shell/dsl, ⬛ Mill Creek Inn
13	US 71 N, Alma, **N** ⬛ Phillips 66, Shell, ⬛ Burger King, Catfish Hole, China Fun, Cracker Barrel, KFC, La Fiesta Mexican, Mazzio's, Pizza Parlor, Subway, Taco Bell, ⬛ Comfort Inn, Meadors Inn, ⬛ Crabtree RV Ctr/Park, Curves, $General, KOA (2mi), O'Reilly Parts, to U of AR, Lake Ft Smith SP, **S** ⬛ Murphy USA/dsl, Shamrock, Valero/dsl, ⬛ Braum's, El Trio, Geno's Pizza, McDonald's, Sonic, ⬛ Days Inn, ⬛ Alma Drug, AT&T, C&H Tires, CV's Foods, Harp's Foods, Walgreens, Walmart
12	I-540 N, to Fayetteville, **N** ⬛ to Lake Ft Smith SP
9mm	**weigh sta both lanes**
7	I-540 S, US 71 S, to Ft Smith, Van Buren, **S** ⬛
5	AR 59, Van Buren, **N** ⬛ Citgo/dsl, Murphy USA/dsl, Phillips 66, ⬛ Arby's, Burger King, Chili's, China Buffet, Domino's, Firehouse Subs, Frank's Italian, Golden Wok, La Fiesta Mexican, McDonald's, Popeye's, Zaxby's, ⬛ Best Western, Hampton Inn, ⬛ Advance Parts, AT&T, Cooley's Tire, $Tree, Radio Shack, Lowe's, NAPA, Verizon, Walmart , USPO, **S** ⬛ Shell/dsl/24hr, ⬛ Braum's, Big Jake's Steaks, Geno's Pizza, Home Run Pizza, KFC/Taco Bell, La Fresas Mexican, Rick's Rib House, Sonic, Subway, Waffle House, Wendy's, ⬛ Holiday Inn Express, Motel 6, Sleep Inn, Super 8, ⬛ CV's Foods, $General, Grizzle Tire, Outdoor RV Ctr, Walgreens, truckwash
3	Lee Creek Rd, **N** ⬛ Shell, ⬛ Park Ridge Camping
2.5mm	**Welcome Ctr eb, full** ⬛ **facilities, info,** ⬛, ⬛, **litter barrels, vending, petwalk**
1	to Ft Smith (from wb), Dora
0mm	Arkansas/Oklahoma state line

INTERSTATE 55

Exit	Services
72mm	Arkansas/Missouri state line
72	State Line Rd, **weigh sta sb**
71	AR 150, Yarbro
68mm	**Welcome Ctr sb, full** ⬛ **facilities,** ⬛, ⬛, **litter barrels, petwalk**

Exit	Services
67	AR 18, Blytheville, **E** ⬛ Murphy USA/dsl, ⬛ Burger King, Capt D's, Subway, Waffle Inn, Zaxby's, ⬛ Days Inn, Travelodge, ⬛ $Tree, Lowe's, Walmart , **W** ⬛ Citgo/dsl, QuikStop/dsl, Shell, ⬛ El Acapulco Mexican, GreatWall Chinese, Grecian Steaks, Hardee's, McDonald's, Olympia Steaks, Perkins, Pizza Inn, Sonic, Subway, Taco Bell, Wendy's, ⬛ Comfort Inn, Fairview Suites, Hampton Inn, Holiday Inn, Quality Inn, Super 8, ⬛ ⬛, Advance Parts, AutoZone, Family$, Ford/Lincoln/Mercury, Fred's Store, JC Penney, Nissan, O'Reilly Parts, Toyota
63	US 61, to Blytheville, **E** ⬛ Shearins RV Park (2mi), **W** ⬛ Dodge's Store/dsl, Exxon/Baskin-Robbins/Chesters/dsl, Shell/McDonald's/dsl/24hr, ⬛ Best Western, Relax Inn, ⬛ truckwash
57	AR 148, Burdette, **E** ⬛ NE AR Coll
53	AR 158, Victoria, Luxora
48	AR 140, to Osceola, **E** ⬛ Mobil/dsl, Shell/dsl, ⬛ Cotton Inn Rest., Huddle House, ⬛ Days Inn, Deerfield Inn, Fairview Inn, Plum Point Inn/rest, **3 mi E** ⬛ McDonald's, Pizza Inn, Sonic, Subway, ⬛ ⬛
45mm	**truck parking nb, litter barrels**
44	AR 181, Keiser
41	AR 14, Marie, **E** ⬛ to Hampson SP/museum
36	AR 181, to Wilson, Bassett
35mm	**truck parking sb, litter barrels**
34	AR 118, Joiner
23b a	US 63, AR 77, to Marked Tree, Jonesboro, ASU, **E** ⬛ Citgo/chicken/pizza
21	AR 42, Turrell, **W** ⬛ Exxon/rest./dsl/scales/24hr
17	AR 50, to Jericho
14	rd 4, to Jericho, **E** ⬛ Citgo/scales/dsl/24hr, ⬛ flea market, **W** ⬛ Citgo/Stuckey's, ⬛ Chevrolet, KOA
10	US 64 W, Marion, **E** ⬛ Citgo/Subway/scales, Phillips 66, Shell/McDonald's, ⬛ KFC/Taco Bell, Tops BBQ, ⬛ Comfort Inn, Hallmarc Inn, ⬛ $General, Market Place Foods, **W** ⬛ BP/dsl, JP Mkt, ⬛ Colton's Steaks, Mi Pueblo, Wendy's, Zaxby's, ⬛ Best Western, Journey Inn, ⬛ AutoZone, to Parkin SP (23mi)
9mm	**truck parking nb, weigh sta sb**
8	I-40 W, to Little Rock
278	AR 77, 7th St, Missouri St, **E** ⬛ Shell/24hr, **W on 7th St** ⬛ Cracker Barrel, KFC, Pizza Inn, ⬛ Quality Inn, ⬛ ⬛, Sawyers RV Park, Sears, **W on Missouri St** ⬛ Exxon, Mapco, Phillips 66/dsl, Shell, ⬛ Bonanza, Burger King, Domino's, Mrs Winner's, Popeye's, Subway, Taco Bell, Wendy's, ⬛ Comfort Suites, Quality Inn, ⬛ $Tree, Goodyear/auto, Walgreens
279b	I-40 E, to Memphis
279b	Ingram Blvd, **E** ⬛ Margaritas Mexican, ⬛ Comfort Inn, Days Inn, Homegate Inn, Red Roof Inn, Rodeway Inn, ⬛ Ford, Southland Racetrack, U-Haul, **W** ⬛ Citgo/dsl, Phillips 66, ⬛ Cupboard Rest., Waffle House, ⬛ Best Value Inn, EconoLodge, Hampshire Inn, Holiday Inn, Motel 6, Ramada, Relax Inn
4	King Dr, Southland Dr, **E** ⬛ ✈FLYING J/Denny's/dsl/LP/scales/RV dump, ⬤Loves/Subway/dsl/scales/@, Petro/Iron Skillet/dsl/rest./24hr/@, ⬛/Subway/Wendy's/dsl/scales/24hr, ⬛ KFC/Taco Bell, McDonald's, ⬛ Best Western, Deluxe Inn, Express Inn, Super 8, ⬛ Blue Beacon, SpeedCo Lube, **W** ⬛ Poncho's Mexican, ⬛ Sunset Inn

INTERSTATE 55 CONT'D

Exit	Services
3b a	US 70, Broadway Blvd, AR 131, Mound City Rd (exits left from nb), **W** 🛏 Budget Inn
2mm	**weigh sta nb**
1	Bridgeport Rd
0mm	Arkansas/Tennessee state line, Mississippi River

INTERSTATE 430 (LITTLE ROCK)

Exit	Services
13b a	I-40. I-430 begins/ends on I-40, exit 147.
12	AR 100, Maumelle, **W** 🅖 Citgo, 🅞 O'Reilly Parts, NAPA, vet
10mm	Arkansas River
9	AR 10, Cantrell Rd., **W** Maumelle Park, Pinnacle Mtn SP
8	Rodney Parham Rd, **E** 🅖 Conoco, Shell, 🍴 Arby's, Baskin-Robbins, El Chico, Firehouse Subs, KFC, McAlister's Grill, McDonald's, Mt Fuji Japanese, New China Buffet, Sonic, Starbucks, Subway, Taco Bell, Terri Lynn's BBQ, US Pizza, 🛏 La Quinta, 🅞 Advance Parts, AutoZone, $Days, $General, Drug Emporium, Kroger, Walgreens, **W** 🅖 Exxon, 🍴 Burger King, Chili's, Chizi's Pizza, ChuckeCheese, Dixie Cafe, Dominos, Franke's Café, Heavenly Ham, LoneStar Steaks, Olive Garden, Shorty Small's Ribs, Wendy's, 🛏 Best Western, 🅞 Firestone/auto, GNC, K-Mart, Radio Shack, USA Drug, Whole Foods Mkt, vet
6	I-630, Kanis Rd, Markham St, to downtown, **E** 🍴 McDonald's, 🛏 Candlewood Suites, Comfort Inn, Motel 6, SpringHill Suites, **W** 🅖 Exxon, 🍴 Cozymel's Grill, Denny's, Famous Dave's BBQ, IHOP, Jason's Deli, Kobe Japanese, Lenny's Subs, Macaroni Grill, McAlister's Deli, Mimi's Cafe, On-the-Border, PF Chang's, Shotgun Dan's Pizza, Starbucks, Taco Bell, Waffle House, Wendy's, 🛏 Courtyard, Crowne Plaza, Embassy Suites, Extended Stay America, Jameson Inn, La Quinta, Ramada Ltd, 🅞 AT&T, Barnes&Noble, Best Buy, PetsMart, Walmart
5	Kanis Rd, Shackleford Rd, **E** 🍴 Cracker Barrel, Panda Garden, Samurai Steaks, TX Roadhouse, 🛏 Candlewood Suites, Comfort Inn, Motel 6, SpringHill Suites, Towneplace Suites, 🅞 Gordman's, JC Penney, **W** 🅖 Shell, 🍴 Krispy Kreme, 🛏 Hampton Inn, Holiday Inn Select, La Quinta, Residence Inn, Studio+, Wingate Inn, 🅞 🅷, Lexus
4	AR 300, Col Glenn Rd, **E** 🍴 Subway, Wendy's, 🛏 Holiday Inn Express, ValuePlace Hotel, 🅞 Toyota/Scion, **W** 🅖 Valero/Burger King/dsl, 🅞 Honda, Hyundai, Jaguar, Land Rover, Mazda, Mercedes, Nissan
1	AR 5, Stagecoach Rd, **E** 🍴 Our Place Grill, **W** 🅖 Phillips 66, Valero, 🍴 Grandpa's Catfish, Jordan's BBQ, Subway, 🅞 Tires
0mm	I-30. I-430 begins/ends on I-30, exit 129.

INTERSTATE 440 (LITTLE ROCK)

Exit	Services
11	I-440 begins/ends on I-40, exit 159.
10	US 70, **W** 🅞 Peterbilt
8	Faulkner Lake Rd, **W** 🅖 Pioneer/dsl
7	US 165, to England, **S** Agricultural Museum, Toltec Mounds SP, Willow Beach SP
6mm	Arkansas River

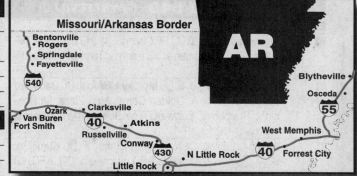

Missouri/Arkansas Border

Bentonville · Rogers · Springdale · Fayetteville — 540

Ozark, Van Buren, Fort Smith — 40 — Clarksville · Atkins, Russellville, Conway — 430 — N Little Rock — 40 — Little Rock

Blytheville, Osceda — 55 — West Memphis, Forrest City

AR

Exit	Services
5	Fourche Dam Pike, LR Riverport, **N** 🅖 Exxon, Shell/Subway, 🍴 McDonald's, 🛏 Travelodge, 🅞 Kenworth, **S** 🅖 Phillips 66/dsl, Valero/dsl
4	Lindsey Rd
3	Bankhead Dr, **N** 🛏 Comfort Inn, 🅞 LR ✈, **S** 🅖 Valero, 🍴 Boston's Rest., Waffle House, 🛏 Days Inn, Holiday Inn, Holiday Inn Express
1	AR 365, Springer Blvd, **S** Little Rock Ntl Cemetery
0mm	I-440 begins/ends on I-30, exit 138.

INTERSTATE 540 (FAYETTEVILLE)

Exit	Services
93	US 71B, Bentonville, I-540 begins/ends on US 71 N.
88	AR 72, Bentonville, Pea Ridge, **E** 🅖 Conoco, 🍴 River Grille, 🛏 Courtyard, Simmon's Suites, **W** 🅖 Shell, 🍴 Smokin' Joe's Ribs, 🅞 Walmart Visitors Ctr
86	US 62, AR 102, Bentonville, Rogers, **E** 🛏 TownePlace Suites, 🅞 Sam's Club/gas, Walmart Mkt, Pea Ridge NMP, **W** 🅖 Phillips 66/McDonald's/dsl, Shell/dsl, 🍴 Arby's, Sonic, Subway, Taco Bell, 🛏 ValuePlace
85	US 71B, AR 12, Bentonville, Rogers, **E** 🅖 Conoco/dsl, 🍴 Abuelo's, Applebee's, Arby's, Atlanta Bread, Carino's Italian, Chick-fil-A, Chili's, Colton's Steaks, Copeland's Rest., Dixie Café, Famous Dave's, IHOP, KFC, Mad Pizza, McDonald's, O'Charley's, On-the-Border, Outback Steaks, Quiznos, Red Robin, Sonic, Starbucks, 🛏 Candlewood Suites, Country Inn&Suites, Fairfield Inn, Hampton Inn, Homewood Suites, Hyatt Place, Mainstay Suites, Residence Inn, 🅞 AT&T, Barnes&Noble, Belk, Firestone/auto, Kohl's, Lowe's, Office Depot, Old Navy, PetCo, Staples, Verizon, Beaver Lake SP, Prairie Creek SP, **W** 🅖 Kum&Go, Murphy Express, Phillips 66/dsl, 🍴 Boston's Grill, Braum's, Buffalo Wild Wings, Denny's, Firehouse Subs, HoneyBaked Ham, Jonny Brusco's Pizza, Krispy Kreme, Lenny's Subs, Lin's Chinese, Mama Asian, McAlister's Deli, Starbucks, Taco Bueno, Village Inn, Waffle House, Zaxby's, 🛏 Best Western, Clarion, Comfort Inn, Comfort Suites, Days Inn, DoubleTree Hotel, Hilton Garden, Holiday Inn Express, La Quinta, Microtel, Quality Inn, Sleep Inn, SpringHill Suites, Suburban Lodge, Super 8, Travelodge, 🅞 🅷, Buick/GMC, Christian Bro's Auto, Honda, Kia, Mazda, Nissan, Toyota/Scion
83	AR 94 E, Pinnacle Hills Pkwy, **E** 🅖 Phillips 66, 🍴 ChuckeCheese, Guido's Pizza, Olive Garden, Red Lobster, Steak'n Shake, Taco Bell, 🅞 🅷, Home Depot, Horse Shoe Bend Park, Walgreens, **W** 🍴 Bonefish Grill, Carrabba's, Crabby's Seafood Grill, Coldstone, Ruth's Chris Steaks, Silver Joe's Coffee, Subway, 🛏 Embassy Suites, Holiday Inn, Staybridge Suites, ALoft

INTERSTATE 540 (FAYETTEVILLE)

Exit	Services
82	Promenade Blvd, **E** [food] PF Changs, [other] [H], Best Buy, Dillard's, GNC, Gordman's, JC Penney, Target, TJMaxx, **W** [other] Walmart Mkt
81	Pleasant Grove Rd, **E** [gas] Murphy USA/dsl, [food] Backyard Burger, Chick-fil-A, Golden Corral, Mad Pizza, McDonald's, Starbucks, Subway, Taco Bueno, [other] Walgreens, Walmart
78	AR 264, Lowell, Cave Sprgs, Rogers, **E** [gas] Kum&Go, Shell, [food] Arby's, Dickey's BBQ, Domino's, DQ, KFC, LJ Silver, Mazzio's Pizza, McDonald's, Sonic, Subway, Taco Bell, [other] Ramada, [other] AT&T, $General, New Hope RV Ctr
76	Wagon Wheel Rd, **E** to Hickory Creek Park
73	Elm Springs Rd, **E** [gas] Kum&Go, Valero/dsl, [food] Patrick's Burgers, [lodging] ValuePlace, [other] Chevrolet, Family$, **W** [gas] Shell/dsl
72mm	weigh sta nb
72	US 412, Springdale, Siloam Springs, **E** [gas] Citgo, Phillips 66/Subway, [food] Applebee's, Braum's, Cancun Mexican, Denny's, Jimmy John's, Joe's Pizza, Mkt Place Rest., McDonald's, Sonic, Taco Bell, TaMolly's Rest., Waffle House, Wendy's, Western Sizzlin, [lodging] Comfort Suites, DoubleTree Hotel, Extended Stay America, Fairfield Inn, Hampton Inn, Holiday Inn, La Quinta, Residence Inn, Royal Inn, Scottish Inn, Sleep Inn, Super 8, [other] AT&T, $General, Kenworth/Volvo Trucks, Lowe's, Office Depot, Radio Shack, Verizon, **W** [gas] [Pilot]/Burger King/dsl/scales/24hr, [food] Arby's, Buffalo Wild Wings, Cracker Barrel, Jose's Mexican, KFC, Taco Bueno, [other] Advance Parts, BigLots, Buick/GMC, Hobby Lobby, vet
71mm	weigh sta sb
69	Johnson, **1-2 mi E** [food] Chick-fil-A, Eureka Pizza, Fire Mtn Grill, Hooters, Inn at the Mill Rest, James Rest, Shogun Japanese, [lodging] Inn at the Mill, TownePlace Suites
67	US 71B, Fayetteville, **E** [H]
66	AR 112, Garland Ave, **E** [gas] Phillips 66, [lodging] Days Inn (2mi), Motel 6, **W** [other] Acura, Chevrolet, Honda, Sam's Club/gas, Toyota/Scion

Exit	Services
65	Porter Rd
64	AR 16 W, AR 112 E, Wedington Dr, **E** [food] AQ Chicken House (3mi), Eureka Pizza (2mi), **W** [gas] Citgo/McDonald's/dsl, Murphy Express/dsl, Phillips 66, [food] Boar's Nest BBQ, IHOP, Sonic, Subway, Taco Bell, [lodging] Country Inn&Suites, Holiday Inn Express, Homewood Suites, Quality Inn, [other] Harp's Food/gas, vet
62	US 62, AR 180, Farmington, **E** [gas] Citgo, Conoco, Shell, [food] Arby's, Braum's, Burger King, Charlie's Chicken, Chick-fil-A, Hardee's, JD China, KFC, McDonald's, Mexico Viejo, Popeye's, Sonic, Subway, Taco Bell, Taiwan Chinese, Waffle House, Wendy's, Zaxby's, [lodging] Best Western, Candlewood Suites, Red Roof Inn, [other] USA Drug, **W** [gas] Murphy USA/dsl, [food] Braum's, Denny's, Firehouse Subs, Papa Murphy's, Pavilion Buffet, Ruby Tuesday, [lodging] Clarion, Comfort Inn, Hampton Inn, Regency 7 Motel, Super 8, Travelodge, ValuePlace, [other] AT&T, AutoZone, $Tree, Lowe's, Verizon, Walgreens, Walmart
61	US 71, to Boston Mtn Scenic Lp, sb only
60	AR 112, AR 265, Razorback Rd, **E** [lodging] Staybridge Suites, [other] South K RV Park, to U of AR
58	Greenland, **W** [gas] Phillips 66/McDonalds/dsl/scales/24hr, [food] Sonic
53	AR 170, West Fork, **E** [other] Winn Creek RV Resort (4mi), **W** to Devils Den SP
45	AR 74, Winslow, **W** to Devils Den SP
41mm	Bobby Hopper Tunnel
34	AR 282, to US 71, Chester, **W** Chester Mercantile/gas, USPO
29	AR 282, to US 71, Mountainburg, **1 mi E** [gas] Silver Bridge Auto/TrkPlaza/dsl/scales/24hr, [other] $General, to Lake Ft Smith SP
24	AR 282, to US 71, Rudy, **E** [gas] Shell/dsl, [food] Red Hog BBQ, [other] KOA, Boston Mtns Scenic Lp
21	Collum Ln
20	to US 71, **E** [gas] Shell, [food] KFC, Taco Bell, [lodging] Comfort Inn, Days Inn

I-540 N begins/ends on I-40, exit 12.

CALIFORNIA

INTERSTATE 5

Exit	Services
797mm	California/Oregon state line
796	Hilt, **W** [gas] State Line Service/café/gas
793	Bailey Hill Rd
791mm	inspection sta sb
790	Hornbrook Hwy, Ditch Creek Rd
789	A28, to Hornbrook, Henley, **E** [gas] Chevron/dsl/LP, [other] Blue Heron RV Park/rest., phone, to Iron Gate RA
786	CA 96, Klamath River Hwy, **W** rest area both lanes, full [handicap] facilities, info, [C], [RV], litter barrels, petwalk, to **Klamath River RA**
782mm	Anderson Summit, elev 3067
780mm	vista point sb
779mm	Shasta River
776	Yreka, Montague, **E** [lodging] Holiday Inn Express, [other] Yreka RV Park, **W** [gas] USA/dsl, [food] Casa Ramos Mexican, Puerto Vallarta, [lodging] Mtn View Inn, Super 8, [other] Ray's Foods

Exit	Services
775	Miner St, Central Yreka, **W** [gas] Chevron, Texaco/dsl, [food] China Dragon, Grandma's House, Purple Plum Rest., RoundTable Pizza, [lodging] Best Western, Budget Inn, EconoLodge, Klamath Motel, Relax Inn, Rodeway Inn, Yreka Motel, [other] [H], Ace Hardware, Baxter Parts, CarQuest, Clayton Tire, Honda, Rite Aid, Shop Smart Foods, USPO, museum
773	CA 3, to Ft Jones, Etna, **E** [gas] CFN/dsl, [other] Schwab Tire, Trailer Haven RV Park, **W** [gas] Shell/dsl, [food] BlackBear Diner, Burger King, Carl's Jr, McDonald's, Papa Murphy's, Subway, Taco Bell, [lodging] Baymont Inn, Comfort Inn, Motel 6, [other] [H], AT&T, $Tree, Ford/Lincoln, JC Penney, Radio Shack, Raley's Foods, Schuck's Parts, Walmart, CHP, **1 mi W** [gas] Valero/dsl, [food] KFC, Pat's BBQ, Yreka Rest.
770	Shamrock Rd, Easy St, **W** [gas] Beacon, Fuel 24/7/dsl, [other] RV camping
766	A12, to Gazelle, Grenada, **E** [gas] 76/dsl, **W** [gas] Texaco/dsl, [other] RV camping

Side tab: **AR CA** / **N S** / **FAYETTEVILLE** / **FARMINGTON** / **N S YREKA**

🅖 = gas 🍽 = food 🛏 = lodging 🅞 = other

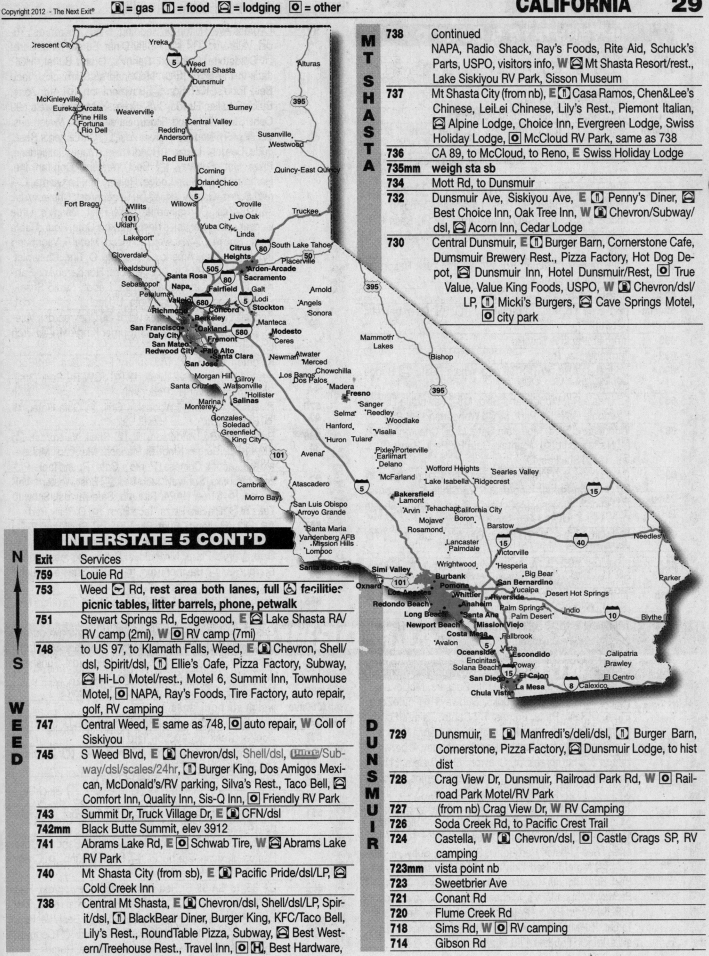

MT SHASTA

738	Continued
	NAPA, Radio Shack, Ray's Foods, Rite Aid, Schuck's Parts, USPO, visitors info, W 🛏 Mt Shasta Resort/rest., Lake Siskiyou RV Park, Sisson Museum
737	Mt Shasta City (from nb), E 🍽 Casa Ramos, Chen&Lee's Chinese, LeiLei Chinese, Lily's Rest., Piemont Italian, 🛏 Alpine Lodge, Choice Inn, Evergreen Lodge, Swiss Holiday Lodge, 🅞 McCloud RV Park, same as 738
736	CA 89, to McCloud, to Reno, E 🛏 Swiss Holiday Lodge
735mm	**weigh sta sb**
734	Mott Rd, to Dunsmuir
732	Dunsmuir Ave, Siskiyou Ave, E 🍽 Penny's Diner, 🛏 Best Choice Inn, Oak Tree Inn, W 🅖 Chevron/Subway/dsl, 🛏 Acorn Inn, Cedar Lodge
730	Central Dunsmuir, E 🍽 Burger Barn, Cornerstone Cafe, Dumsmuir Brewery Rest., Pizza Factory, Hot Dog Depot, 🛏 Dunsmuir Inn, Hotel Dunsmuir/Rest, 🅞 True Value, Value King Foods, USPO, W 🅖 Chevron/dsl/LP, 🍽 Micki's Burgers, 🛏 Cave Springs Motel, 🅞 city park

INTERSTATE 5 CONT'D

N ↕ S   WEED

Exit	Services
759	Louie Rd
753	Weed ✈ Rd, **rest area both lanes, full ♿ facilities, picnic tables, litter barrels, phone, petwalk**
751	Stewart Springs Rd, Edgewood, E 🛏 Lake Shasta RA/RV camp (2mi), W 🅞 RV camp (7mi)
748	to US 97, to Klamath Falls, Weed, E 🅖 Chevron, Shell/dsl, Spirit/dsl, 🍽 Ellie's Cafe, Pizza Factory, Subway, 🛏 Hi-Lo Motel/rest., Motel 6, Summit Inn, Townhouse Motel, 🅞 NAPA, Ray's Foods, Tire Factory, auto repair, golf, RV camping
747	Central Weed, E same as 748, 🅞 auto repair, W Coll of Siskiyou
745	S Weed Blvd, E 🅖 Chevron/dsl, Shell/dsl, 🅖 Subway/dsl/scales/24hr, 🍽 Burger King, Dos Amigos Mexican, McDonald's/RV parking, Silva's Rest., Taco Bell, 🛏 Comfort Inn, Quality Inn, Sis-Q Inn, 🅞 Friendly RV Park
743	Summit Dr, Truck Village Dr, E 🅖 CFN/dsl
742mm	Black Butte Summit, elev 3912
741	Abrams Lake Rd, E 🅞 Schwab Tire, W 🛏 Abrams Lake RV Park
740	Mt Shasta City (from sb), E 🅖 Pacific Pride/dsl/LP, 🛏 Cold Creek Inn
738	Central Mt Shasta, E 🅖 Chevron/dsl, Shell/dsl/LP, Spirit/dsl, 🍽 BlackBear Diner, Burger King, KFC/Taco Bell, Lily's Rest., RoundTable Pizza, Subway, 🛏 Best Western/Treehouse Rest., Travel Inn, 🅞 H, Best Hardware,

DUNSMUIR

729	Dunsmuir, E 🅖 Manfredi's/deli/dsl, 🍽 Burger Barn, Cornerstone, Pizza Factory, 🛏 Dunsmuir Lodge, to hist dist
728	Crag View Dr, Dunsmuir, Railroad Park Rd, W 🅞 Railroad Park Motel/RV Park
727	(from nb) Crag View Dr, W RV Camping
726	Soda Creek Rd, to Pacific Crest Trail
724	Castella, W 🅖 Chevron/dsl, 🅞 Castle Crags SP, RV camping
723mm	vista point nb
723	Sweetbrier Ave
721	Conant Rd
720	Flume Creek Rd
718	Sims Rd, W 🅞 RV camping
714	Gibson Rd

INTERSTATE 5 CONT'D

Exit	Services
712	Pollard Flat, **E** 🅶 Pollard Flat/dsl/LP, ⏹ Pollard Flat Diner
710	Slate Creek Rd, La Moine
707	Delta Rd, Dog Creek Rd, to Vollmers
705mm	**rest area sb, full** 🦽 **facilities,** ⏹, **litter barrels, picnic tables**
704	Riverview Dr, **E** ⏹ Klondike Diner, 🏠 Lakehead Lodge/RV Camping
702	Antlers Rd, Lakeshore Dr, to Lakehead, **E** 🅶 Shell/Subway/dsl, 🏠 Antlers RV Park, Lakehead Camping, Neu Lodge Motel, ⓞ USPO, auto repair, **W** ⏹ Bass Hole Rest., 🏠 Shasta Lake Motel/RV, Lakeshore Villa RV Park
698	Salt Creek Rd, Gilman Rd; **W** 🏠 Salt Creek Resort/RV Park, Trail In RV Park
695	Shasta Caverns Rd, to O'Brien
694mm	**rest area nb, full** 🦽 **facilities,** ⏹, 🛢, **litter barrels, petwalk**
693	(from sb)Packers Bay Rd
692	Turntable Bay Rd
690	Bridge Bay Rd, **W** ⏹ Tail of a Whale Rest., 🏠 Bridge Bay Motel
689	Fawndale Rd, Wonderland Blvd, **E** 🏠 Fawndale Lodge, Fawndale Oaks RV Park, **W** 🏠 Wonderland RV Park
687	Wonderland Blvd, Mountain Gate, **E** 🅶 Chevron/dsl/LP, ⏹ Nellie's Grill, ⓞ Mountain Gate RV Park, Ranger Sta, vet, **W** 🅶 Shell/dsl/LP
685	CA 151, Shasta Dam Blvd, Project City, Central Valley, **W** 🅶 Chevron/Burger King/dsl/LP, 76/Circle K, Valero/dsl, ⏹ Latino's Mexican, McDonald's, Taco Shop, 🏠 Shasta Dam Motel, ⓞ Rite Aid, Sentry Foods, vet
684	Pine Grove Ave, **E** ⓞ Cousin Gary's RV Ctr, **W** 🅶 76/dsl/LP
682	Oasis Rd, **E** ⓞ CA RV Ctr/camping, Peterbilt, **W** 🅶 Arco, Shell/Subway/dsl, ⓞ Redding RV Ctr, U-Haul, CHP
681b	(from sb, no re-entry) CA 273, Market St, Johnson Rd, to Central Redding, **W** 🅷
681a	Twin View Blvd, **E** 🅶 Chevron/dsl, 🏠 Motel 6, Ramada Ltd, ⓞ Harley-Davidson, **W** 🅶 Pacific Pride/dsl, ⏹ Fat Boys, 🏠 Best Western, Fairfield Inn
680	CA 299E, **1/2 mi W** 🅶 Arco, Chevron/dsl, Spirit, ⏹ A&W/KFC, Arby's, Carl's Jr, Little Caesars, McDonald's, RoundTable Pizza, Starbucks, Subway, ⓞ AutoZone, $Tree, O'Reilly Parts, Premier RV Camp, Raley's Foods, Redding RV Park, ShopKO, Walgreens, transmissions
678	CA 299 W, CA 44, to Eureka, Redding, Burney, **E between Hilltop & Churncreek** 🅶 Chevron, Shell, Valero, ⏹ Applebee's, Burger King, Carl's Jr, Casa Ramos, Chevy's Mexican, Chipotle Mexican, ChuckeCheese, Coldstone, 5 Thai's, Hometown Buffet, In-N-Out, Jack-in-the-Box, Jamba Juice, Keva Juice, La Conquista Mexican, Luigi's Pizza, McDonald's, Olive Garden, Outback Steaks, Panda Express, Red Lobster, Red Robin, Starbucks, Subway, Taco Bell, 🏠 Motel 6, Red Lion Inn, ⓞ AT&T, Barnes&Noble, Best Buy, BigLots, Costco, FoodMaxx, Home Depot, JC Penney, Kohl's, Macy's, Michael's, Old Navy, Office Depot, O'Reilly Parts, PetCo, Petsmart, Schwab Tire, Sears/auto, Target, TJ Maxx, Trader Joe's, Verizon, Walmart/McDonald's, WinCo Foods, World Mkt, vet
677	Cypress Ave, Hilltop Dr, Redding, **E** 🅶 Chevron/dsl, 76/dsl, Valero/dsl, ⏹ Black Bear Diner, Burger King, Carl's Jr, Coldstone, Del Taco, Denny's, Grand Buffet, IHOP, Jack-in-the-Box, KFC, McDonald's, Starbucks, Taco Bell, Togo's, Wendy's, 🏠 Baymont Inn, ⓞ AutoZone, Buick/Cadillac/GMC, CVS Drug, K-Mart, Lowe's, 99 Cent Store, Rite Aid, Ross, Safeway/gas, Walgreens, vet, **E on Hilltop** 🅶 Chevron/dsl, ⏹ Cattlemen's Rest., Jade Garden, Logan's Roadhouse, Marie Callender's, Pizza Hut, Subway, 🏠 Best Western, Comfort Inn, Hampton Inn, Hilltop Lodge, Holiday Inn, La Quinta, Oxford Suites, Quality Inn, **W** 🅶 Beacon/dsl, Chevron/dsl, 76, USA/dsl, ⏹ California Cattle Rest, Denny's, Little Caesar's, Lumberjack's Rest., Perko's Cafe, RoundTable Pizza, Subway, 🏠 Howard Johnson, Motel 6, Vagabond Inn, ⓞ Aamco, America's Tire, Big O Tire, Chevrolet, Cousin Gary's RV Ctr, Dodge, Ford, Honda, JoAnn Fabrics, KIA, Lincoln, Nissan, Office Depot, Radio Shack, Raley's Foods, Subaru, Toyota, U-Haul
675	Bechelli Lane, Churn Creek Rd, **E** 🅶 Chevron/dsl, Valero, 🏠 Super 8, **W** 🅶 Texaco/Burger King/dsl, 🏠 Hilton Garden
673	Knighton Rd, **E** 🅶 TA/Country Pride/Pizza Hut/Popeye's/dsl/LP/scales/24hr/@, **W** ⓞ JGW RV Park (3mi), Sacramento River RV Park (3mi)
670	Riverside Ave, **E** ⏹ Woodside Grill, 🏠 Gaia Hotel, **W** ⓞ B&B RV Ctr
668	Balls Ferry Rd, Anderson, **E** 🅶 Shell, Valero/dsl, ⏹ A&W/KFC, Burger King, El Mariachi Mexican, McDonald's, Peacock Chinese, Perko's Cafe, RoundTable Pizza, Starbucks, Subway, Taco Bell, 🏠 Best Western, Valley Inn, ⓞ $Tree, NAPA, Rite Aid, Safeway/dsl, Schwab Tire, **W** ⏹ Players Pizza, Taco Barn, ⓞ O'Reilly Parts
667	CA 273, Factory Outlet Blvd, **W** 🅶 Shell/dsl/LP, ⏹ Arby's, Jack-in-the-Box, LJ Silver, Luigi's Pizza, Marble Slab, Mary's Pizza, Mr Pickles, Panda Express, Sonic, Starbucks, 🏠 Baymont Inn, ⓞ AT&T, Shasta Outlets/famous brands, Verizon, Walmart/Subway
665	(from sb) Cottonwood, **E** 🏠 Alamo Motel, Travelers Motel/RV Park
664	Gas Point Rd, to Balls Ferry, **E** 🅶 Cottonwood/dsl, Chevron/dsl/LP, 🏠 Alamo Motel, Travelers Motel, ⓞ Alamo RV Park, auto repair, **W** 🅶 Holiday/dsl, Sunshine/dsl, ⏹ Subway, ⓞ Ace Hardware, Holiday Foods
662	Bowman Rd, to Cottonwood, **E** 🅶 Texaco/dsl
660mm	**weigh sta both lanes**
659	Snively Rd, Auction Yard Rd, (Sunset Hills Dr from nb)
657	Hooker Creek Rd, Auction Yard Rd
656mm	**rest area both lanes, full** 🦽 **facilities,** ⏹, 🛢, **litter barrels, petwalk**
653	Jellys Ferry Rd, **E** 🏠 Bend RV Park/LP
652	Wilcox Golf Rd
651	CA 36W (from sb), Red Bluff, **W** 🅶 Arco/dsl, Chevron/dsl, ⓞ same as 650
650	Adobe Rd, **W** 🅶 Chevron/dsl, ⏹ Burrito Bandito, Casa Ramos Mexican, Starbucks, 🏠 Hampton Inn, ⓞ Chevrolet/Cadillac, Home Depot, CHP
649	CA 36, to CA 99 S, Red Bluff, **E** 🅶 Chevron/dsl, Red Bluff Gas, Shell/dsl, ⏹ Applebee's, Burger King, Del Taco, Perko's Cafe, KFC, McDonald's, 🏠 Best Western, Comfort Inn, Motel 6, **W** 🅶 USA/dsl, Valero, ⏹ Denny's, Egg Roll King, Los Mariachis, Luigi's Pizza, Ramos

INTERSTATE 5 CONT'D

Exit	Services
649	Continued
	Doughnuts, Riverside Grill, RoundTable Pizza, Shari's, Subway, 🄻 Cinderella Motel, Super 8, Travelodge, 🄾 AT&T, CVS Drug, Durango RV Resort, Foodmaxx, O'Nite RV Park, River's Edge RV Park, Verizon, vet
647a b	S Main St, Red Bluff, **E** 🄰 Valero, 🄻 Days Inn, 🄾 🄷, **W** 🄰 Arco/dsl, Chevron, Shell/dsl, 🄵 Arby's, Baskin-Robbins, Domino's, Jack-in-the-Box, Papa Murphy's, Starbucks, Subway, Wendy's, 🄻 American Inn, Triangle Motel, 🄾 $Tree, GNC, Kragen Parts, Radio Shack, Raley's Food/drug, Staples, Tire Factory, True Value, Verizon, Walgreens, Walmart/McDonald's
642	Flores Ave, to Proberta Gerber, **1 mi E** 🄾 Walmart Dist Ctr
636	rd A11, Gyle Rd, to Tehama, **E** 🄾 RV camping (7mi)
633	Finnell Rd, to Richfield
632mm	**rest area both lanes, full** 🄳 **facilities,** 🄾, 🄰, **litter barrels, petwalk**
631	A9, Corning Rd, Corning, **E** 🄰 Chevron, Shell/dsl/LP, Spirit Gas, 76/dsl, 🄵 Burger King, Casa Ramos Mexican, Marco's Pizza, Olive Pit Rest., Papa Murphy's, Quiznos, Rancho Grande Mexican, RoundTable Pizza, Starbucks, Subway, Taco Bell, 🄻 American Inn, Best Western, Economy Inn, 7 Inn Motel, Super 8, 🄾 Ace Hardware, Buick/Chevrolet, Clark Drug, $Tree, Ford/Mercury, Heritage RV Park, NAPA, O'Reilly Parts, Radio Shack, Rite Aid, Safeway, Verizon, auto repair, **W** 🄵 Giant Burger, 🄻 Corning RV Park
630	South Ave, Corning, **E** 🄰 🄵 Loves/Denny's/dsl/LP/RV dump/scales/24hr, Petro/Iron Skillet/dsl/scales/@,TA/Arby's/Subway/dsl/scales/24hr/@, 🄵 Jack-in-the-Box, McDonald's, 🄻 Days Inn, Holiday Inn Express, 🄾 Ace Hardware, Blue Beacon, Olive Hut/RV Parking, SpeedCo Lube, Woodson Br SRA/RV Park (6mi), truck wash/lube
628	CA 99W, Liberal Ave, **W** 🄰 Chevron/dsl, 🄻 Rolling Hills Hotel/Casino, 🄾 Rolling Hills RV Park
621	CA 7
619	CA 32, Orland, **E** 🄰 Arco, 76/dsl, 🄵 Burger King, Berry Patch Rest., Subway, 🄻 Orlanda Inn, 🄾 CVS Drug, Walgreens, **W** 🄰 Shell/dsl, 🄵 Taco Bell, 🄻 Old Orchard RV Park, Parkway RV Park
618	CA 16, **E** 🄰 Shell/dsl, 🄵 El Potrero Mexican, 🄻 Orland Inn
614	CA 27
610	Artois
608mm	**rest area both lanes, full** 🄳 **facilities,** 🄾, 🄰, **litter barrels, petwalk, RV dump**
607	CA 39, Blue Gum Rd, Bayliss, **2 mi E** 🄻 Blue Gum Motel
603	CA 162, to Oroville, Willows, **E** 🄰 Arco, Chevron, Shell/dsl, 🄵 Burger King, Casa Ramos, Denny's/24hr, KFC, La Cascada Mexican, McDonald's, Papa Murphy's, RoundTable Pizza, Starbucks, Subway, Taco Bell, Wong's Chinese, 🄻 Baymont Inn, Holiday Inn Express, Days Inn/RV parking, Motel 6, Super 8, Travelodge, 🄾 🄷, Radio Shack, CHP, **W** 🄵 Nancy's Café/24hr, 🄾 Walmart, RV Park (8mi), 🄼
601	rd 57, **E** 🄰 76/CFN/dsl
595	Rd 68, to Princeton, **E** to Sacramento NWR
591	Delevan Rd
588	Maxwell (from sb), access to camping
586	Maxwell Rd, **E** 🄾 Delavan NWR, **W** 🄰 CFN, Chevron, 🄻 Maxwell Inn/rest., 🄾 Country Mkt, Maxwell Parts
583	**rest area both lanes, full** 🄳 **facilities,** 🄾, 🄰, **litter barrels, petwalk**
578	CA 20, Colusa, **W** 🄰 Orv's/dsl/rest., Shell/dsl, 🄾 🄷, hwy patrol
577	Williams, **E** 🄰 Shell/Baskin-Robbins/Togo's/dsl, 🄵 Carl's Jr, Subway, Taco Bell, 🄻 Ramada Inn, **W** 🄰 CFN/dsl, Chevron/dsl/24hr, 76, Shell/dsl, 🄵 Burger King, Denny's, Granzella's Rest., Louis Cairo's Steak, McDonald's/RV parking, Straw Hat Pizza, Williams Chinese Rest., 🄻 Granzella's Inn, Motel 6, Quality Inn, StageStop Motel, 🄾 🄷, NAPA, Shop'n Save Foods, USPO, camping, hwy patrol
575	Husted Rd, to Williams
569	Hahn Rd, to Grimes
567	frontage rd (from nb), to Arbuckle, **W** 🄰 CFN, Chevron/dsl/24hr
566	to College City, Arbuckle, **E** 🄾 Ace Hardware, USPO, **W** 🄰 J&J/grill/dsl
559	Yolo/Colusa County Line Rd
557mm	**rest area both lanes, full** 🄳 **facilities,** 🄾, 🄰, **litter barrels, petwalk**
556	E4, Dunnigan, **E** 🄰 Chevron/dsl, 🄵 Jack-in-the-Box, 🄻 Best Value Inn, Motel 6, 🄾 Farmers Mkt Deli, **W** 🄻 Camper's RV Park/golf (1mi)
554	rd 8, **E** 🄰 🄵 Pilot/Wendy's/dsl/scales/24hr, 🄾 Oasis Grill, 🄻 Hacienda Motel, 🄾 HappyTime RV Park, **W** 🄰 United TP/dsl
553	I-505 (from sb), to San Francisco, callboxes begin sb
548	Zamora, **E** 🄰 Shell/dsl
542	Yolo, **1 mi E** gas
541	CA 16W, Esparta, Woodland, **3 mi W** 🄾 🄷
540	West St, **W** 🄰 Arco, 🄵 Denny's
538	CA 113 N, E St, Woodland, **E** 🄻 Valley Oaks Inn, **W** 🄰 Chevron/dsl, 🄵 Denny's, 🄻 Best Western
537	CA 113 S, Main St, to Davis, **E** 🄾 Buick/Cadillac/Chevrolet/GMC, same as 536, **W** 🄰 Chevron/dsl, 🄵 Denny's, McDonald's, Rafael's Rest., Sonic, Taco Bell, Wendy's, 🄻 Days Inn, Motel 6, Quality Inn, 🄾 Food 4 Less
536	rd 102, **E on Main St** 🄰 Arco, Shell, 🄵 Applebee's, Burger King, Jack-in-the-Box, McDonald's, Quiznos, Subway, 🄻 Hampton Inn, Holiday Inn Express, 🄾 America's Tire, Home Depot, Main St Mkt, Staples, Walmart, museum, same as 537, **W** 🄰 Chevron, 🄵 In-N-Out, Panda Express, Red Robin, Starbucks, Subway, 🄾 Best Buy, Costco/gas, Michael's, Target, Verizon

N

S

C O R N I N G

O R O V I L L E

W I L L I A M S

D U N N I G A N

🅖 = gas 🍽 = food 🛏 = lodging 🅞 = other   Copyright 2012 - The Next Exit®

INTERSTATE 5 CONT'D

Exit	Services
531	rd 22, Sacramento
530mm	Sacramento River
529mm	rest area sb, full ♿ facilities, 🚻, 🅟, litter barrels, petwalk
528	Airport Rd, **E** 🅖 Arco, 🅞♻, food
525b	CA 99, to CA 70, to Marysville, Yuba City
525a	Del Paso Rd, **E** 🅖 Chevron, 🍽 A&W/KFC, IHOP, In-N-Out, Jack-in-the-box, Jamba Juice, Malabar Rest., Panera Bread, Panda Express, Sizzler, Starbucks, Straw Hat Pizza, Taco Bell, Wienerschnitzel, 🛏 Hampton Inn, Holiday Inn Express, Homewood Suites, 🅞 Rite Aid, Safeway Foods/dsl, **W** 🍽 Subway, 🛏 Sheraton, 🅞 Walgreens
524	Arena Blvd, **E** 🍽 Subway, 🅞 Power Balance Arena, **W** 🍽 RoundTable Pizza, Starbucks, 🅞 Bel-Air Food/Drug/dsl
522	I-80, E to Reno, W to San Francisco
521b a	Garden Hwy, West El Camino, **W** 🅖:Shell/dsl, 🍽 Baja Fresh, Carl's Jr, Jack-in-the-Box, Starbucks, Subway, Togo's, 🛏 Courtyard, Hilton Garden, Homestead Village, Residence Inn, SpringHill Suites
520	Richards Blvd, **E** 🅖 Chevron/dsl/24hr, 🍽 Memphis BBQ, McDonald's, Monterey Rest., Stonebrooks Rest., 🛏 Governor's Inn, Hawthorn Suites, Ramada Ltd, Super 8, **W** 🅖 Shell, Valero, 🍽 Coyote Jct Mexican, 🛏 Best Western/rest., Comfort Suites, Days Inn, La Quinta, Motel 6, Super 8
519b	J St, Old Sacramento, **E** 🍽 Denny's, 🛏 Holiday Inn, Vagabond Inn, **W** 🛏 Embassy Suites, 🅞 Railroad Museum
519a	Q St , downtown, Sacramento, **W** 🛏 Embassy Suites, to st capitol
518	US 50, CA 99, Broadway, **E** services downtown
516	Sutterville Rd, **E** 🅖 Land Park/dsl, 76/dsl, 🅞 Prime Foods, Wm Land Park, zoo
515	Fruitridge Rd, Seamas Rd
514	43rd Ave, Riverside Blvd (from sb), **E** 🅖 76/repair
513	Florin Rd, **E** 🅖 Arco/24hr, Chevron/24hr, Shell/repair, 🍽 Rosalinda's Mexican, RoundTable Pizza, Sizzling Wok, 🅞 Bel Air Foods, Kragen Parts, Longs Drug, **W** 🍽 Burger King, JimBoy's Tacos, Shari's, Starbucks, Subway, Wings Stop, 🅞 Marshall's, Nugget Foods, Radio Shack, Rite Aid
512	CA 160, Pocket Rd, Meadowview Rd, to Freeport, **E** 🅖 Shell/dsl/24hr, Valero/dsl, 🍽 IHOP, KFC, LJ Silver, McDonald's, Starbucks, Togo's, Wendy's, 🅞 Home Depot, Staples
508	Laguna Blvd, **E** 🅖 Chevron/McDonald's/dsl, 76/Circle K/dsl/LP, Shell, 🍽 A&W/KFC, Starbucks, Subway, Wendy's, 🛏 Extended Stay America, Hampton Inn, 🅞 Jiffy Lube, Laguna Tire/Wheel
506	Elk Grove Blvd, **E** 🅖 Arco/dsl, Chevron/dsl, Shell, 🍽 Carl's Jr, Lyla's Mexican, Pete's Grill, Quizno's, Stone Lake Mexican, 🛏 Comfort Suites
504	Hood Franklin Rd
498	Twin Cities Rd, to Walnut Grove
493	Walnut Grove Rd, Thornton, **E** 🅖 CFN/dsl, Chevron/Subway/dsl
490	Peltier Rd

Exit	Services
487	Turner Rd
485	CA 12, Lodi, **E** 🅖 Arco/Subway/dsl/24hr, Chevron/dsl, 🅕FLYING J/Denny's/dsl/scales/24hr, Shell/Wendy's/dsl, 76/Rocky's Rest./dsl/scales/24hr, 🍽 Burger King, Carl's Jr, McDonald's, Starbucks, Taco Bell, 🛏 Best Western, Microtel, 🅞 Blue Beacon, Flag City RV Resort, Profleet Trucklube, tires/lube, **W** 🅞 Tower Park Marina Camping (5mi)
481	Eight Mile Rd, **W** 🅖 Chevron/dsl, 🍽 Del Taco, Hawaiian BBQ, Jack-in-the-Box, Jamba Juice, MooMoo's Burgers, Panda Express, Panera Bread, Qdoba Mexican, RoundTable Pizza, Sonic, Starbucks, Strings Italian, Subway, Wendy's, 🅞 AAA, Jo-Ann Fabrics, KOA, Kohl's, Lowe's Whse, Office Depot, Petsmart, Ross, Target
478	Hammer Lane, Stockton, **E** 🅖 Arco/24hr, 76/Circle K/dsl, 🍽 Adalberto's Mexican, Carl's Jr, KFC, Little Caesar's, Shirasoni Japanese, Subway, 🅞 AutoZone, Radio Shack, SMart Foods, vet, **W** 🅖 Chevron/dsl, QuikStop, 🍽 Jack-in-the-Box, Mexico Lindo, Taco Bell
477	Benjamin Holt Dr, Stockton, **E** 🅖 Arco, Chevron/dsl/24hr, 🍽 Pizza Guys, 🛏 Motel 6, 🅞 Quikstop, **W** 🍽 Fon Wong Chinese, McDonald's, Lyon's/24hr, Subway/TCBY, 🅞 Ace Hardware, Marina Foods, 7-11, vet
476	March Lane, Stockton, **E** 🅖 7-11, 🍽 Applebee's, Arroyo's Mexican, Black Angus, Carl's Jr, Denny's, El Torito, Jack-in-the-Box, John's Incredible Pizza, McDonald's, Marie Callender's, Olive Garden, Red Lobster, StrawHat Pizza, Taco Bell, Toot Sweets Bakery, Wendy's, 🛏 Comfort Inn, Hilton, 🅞 Longs Drug, Marshall's, SMart Foods, **1/2 mi E** 🍽 Baskin-Robbins, Burger King, Outback Steaks, Quizno's, Subway, Wienerschnitzel, 🅞 Dillard's, $Tree, 99c Store, Office Depot, Target, World Mkt, **W** 🅖 76/dsl/24hr, 🍽 Carrow's Rest., In-N-Out, Italian Cuisine, Jamba Juice, RoundTable Pizza, Old Spaghetti Factory, Starbucks, Subway, Wong's Chinese, 🛏 Courtyard, Extended Stay America, La Quinta, Quality Inn, Residence Inn, 🅞 Home Depot
475	Alpine Ave, Country Club Blvd, same as 474 b
474b	Country Club Blvd (from nb), **E** 🅖 76/dsl, **W** 🅖 7-11, USA/Subway/dsl, Safeway/gas, 🅞 BigLots
474a	Monte Diablo Ave, **W** 🅞 Aamco
473	Pershing Ave (from nb), **W** 🅖 Arco, 🛏 Red Roof Inn
472	CA 4 E, to CA 99, Fresno Ave, downtown
471	CA 4 W, Charter Way, **E** 🅖 Chevron/24hr, Shell/24hr, 🍽 Burger King, Denny's, Little Ceasar's, McDonald's, Quizno's, 🛏 Days Inn, Motel 6, 🅞 Kragen Parts, transmissions, **W** 🅖 76/dsl/rest./scales/24hr, Valero, 🍽 Jack-in-the-Box, Taco Bell, 🛏 Motel 6, 🅞 truck repair
470	8th St, Stockton, **W** 🅖 CA Stop/dsl, Shell/Subway/dsl, 🛏 I-5 Inn
469	Downing Ave, **W** 🍽 China Express, Jalapeños Mexican, Mtn Mike's Pizza, Subway, 🅞 Curves, Food4Less/gas
468	French Camp, **E** 🅖 76/Togo's/dsl, 🅞 Pan Pacific RV Ctr, **W** 🅞 🅷
467b	Mathews Rd, **E** 🅖 Exxon/CFN/dsl, 🅞 RV Ctr, tires/repair, **W** 🅞 🅷
467a	El Dorado St (from nb)
465	Roth Rd, Sharpe Depot, **E** 🅞 Freightliner, Kenworth, truck/rv repair
463	Lathrop Rd, **E** 🅖 Chevron/dsl/24hr, Joe's Trkstp/Subway/dsl/scales, TowerMart/dsl, Valero/dsl, 🍽 Country

INTERSTATE 5 CONT'D

N ↕ S

Exit	Services
463	Continued Kitchen, Little Ceasar's, Starbucks, [lodging] Best Western, Comfort Inn, Days Inn, [other] Harley-Davidson, SaveMart Foods, Walgreens, **W** [other] Dos Reis CP, RV camping
462	Louise Ave, **E** [gas] Arco/24hr, 76, Shell, [food] A&W/KFC, Carl's Jr, Denny's, Jack-in-the-Box, McDonald's, Mtn Mike's Pizza, Quizno's, Taco Bell, Valarta Mexican, [lodging] Hampton Inn, Holiday Inn Express, [other] Mossdale CP, **W** [other] Target
461	CA 120, to Sonora, Manteca, **E** [other] Oakwood Lake Resort Camping, to Yosemite
460	Mossdale Rd, **E** [gas] Arco/dsl, **W** [food] fruit stand/deli
458b	I-205, to Oakland (from sb, no return)
458a	11th St, to Tracy, Defense Depot, **2 mi W** [gas] gas/dsl/food
457	Kasson Rd, to Tracy, **W** [gas] Valley Pacific/dsl
452	CA 33 S, Vernalis
449b a	CA 132, to Modesto, **E** [other] The Orchard Campground
446	I-580 (from nb, exits left, no return)
445mm	**Westley Rest Area both lanes, full [accessible] facilities, picnic tables, litter barrels, phone, RV dump, petwalk**
441	Ingram Creek, Howard Rd, Westley, **E** [gas] Chevron/dsl/24hr, Joe's Trvl Plaza/Perko's/Quizno's/dsl/scales, 76, Stars/dsl, Westley TruckStp/dsl, [food] Antojito's Mexican, Carl's Jr, McDonald's, Subway, [lodging] Best Value Inn, Days Inn, Econolodge, Holiday Inn Express, **W** [gas] Shell/dsl/24hr, [food] Ingram Creek Rest., fruits, [other] truck repair
434	Sperry Ave, Del Puerto, Patterson, **E** [gas] Chevron, 76/Subway/dsl, [food] A&W/KFC, Carl's Jr, Denny's, El Rosal Mexican, Golden Lion Chinese, Jack-in-the-Box, Lamp Post Pizza, Nik's BBQ, Quizno's, Starbucks, [lodging] Best Western, [other] Kit Fox RV Park
430mm	vista point nb
428	Fink Rd, Crow's Landing
423	Stuhr Rd, Newman, **5 mi E** food, lodging, [other] [H], RV camping
422mm	vista point sb
418	CA 140E, Gustine, **E** [gas] 76/dsl, Shell/dsl
409	**weigh sta both lanes**
407	CA 33, Santa Nella, **E** [gas] Arco/24hr, Loves/Del Taco/dsl/scales/24hr, TA/76/Popeye's/dsl/rest./24hr/@, [food] Carl's Jr, Andersen's Rest, Subway, Wendy's, [lodging] Best Western/Andersen's, Holiday Inn Express, **W** [gas] Chevron/24hr, Rotten Robbie/dsl/scales, Shell/Jack-in-the-Box/dsl, Valero/dsl, [food] Denny's, McDonald's, Quizno's, Starbucks, Taco Bell, [lodging] Motel 6, Ramada Inn, [other] Santa Nella RV Park
403b a	CA 152, Los Banos, **6 mi E** [other] [H], **W** [gas] Petro/dsl/24hr (1mi), [other] San Luis RV Park
391	CA 165N, Mercy Springs Rd, **E** [H], **W** [gas] Shell
388mm	vista point (from nb)
386mm	**rest area both lanes, full [accessible] facilities, [phone], [picnic], litter barrels, petwalk**
385	Nees Ave, to Firebaugh, **W** [gas] Chevron/CFN/Subway/dsl/scales
379	Shields Ave, to Mendota
372	Russell Ave
368	Panoche Rd, **W** [gas] Chevron/McDonald's, Mobil/Taco Bell/dsl, 76/dsl, Shell/dsl, [food] Apricot Tree Rest., Fosters

WESTLEY

SANTA NELLA

Exit	Services
368	Continued Freeze, [lodging] Best Western/Apricot Inn, [other] Palms Mkt
365	Manning Ave, to San Joaquin
357	Kamm Ave
349	CA 33 N, Derrick Ave
337	CA 33 S, CA 145 N, to Coalinga
334	CA 198, to Lemoore, Huron, **E** [gas] Shell/Subway/dsl/24hr, [lodging] Harris Ranch Inn/rest., **W** [gas] Chevron, Mobil/dsl, 76/Circle K, [food] Burger King, Carl's Jr, Cazuela's Mexican, Denny's, McDonald's, Oriental Express Chinese, Red Robin, Taco Bell, [lodging] Best Western, Motel 6, Travelodge, [other] [H]
325	Jayne Ave, to Coalinga, **W** [gas] Arco/24hr, Shell/dsl, [lodging] RV Park, [other] [H]
320mm	**rest area both lanes, full [accessible] facilities, [phone], [picnic], litter barrels, petwalk**
319	CA 269, Lassen Ave, to Avenal, **W** [gas] Hillcrest TP/76/dsl/scales/rest.
309	CA 41, Kettleman City, **E** [gas] CFN/dsl, Chevron/McDonald's, Exxon/Subway/dsl, Mobil/Starbucks/dsl/24hr, KwikServ/Quizno's/dsl, Shell/dsl, Valero/dsl, [food] Carl's Jr, In-N-Out, Jack-in-the-Box, Mike's Roadhouse Café, Pizza Hut/Taco Bell, [lodging] Best Western, Super 8, [other] Travelers RV Park
305	Utica Ave
288	Twisselman Rd
278	CA 46, Lost Hills, **E** [gas] Buford Star Mart/dsl, [other] to Kern NWR, **W** [gas] Arco/24hr, Chevron/dsl/24hr, Loves/Arby's/dsl, Mobil/McDonald's/, Pilot/Wendy's/dsl/scales/24hr, 76/Quizno's/24hr, Valero/dsl, [food] Carl's Jr, Denny's, Jack-in-the-Box, McDonald's, [lodging] Days Inn, Motel 6, [other] Lost Hills RV Park
268	Lerdo Hwy, to Shafter
262	7th Standard Rd, Rowlee Rd, to Buttonwillow
259mm	**Buttonwillow Rest Area both lanes, full [accessible] facilities, [phone], [picnic], litter barrels, petwalk**
257	CA 58, to Bakersfield, Buttonwillow, **E** [gas] Arco/dsl/24hr, Bruce's/dsl/wash, Chevron/dsl/24hr, TA/Pizza Hut/Taco Bell/dsl/scales/24hr/@, Shell/dsl, [food] Carl's Jr, Denny's, McDonald's, Starbucks, Subway, Taste of India, Tita's Mexican, Willow Ranch BBQ, [lodging] Homeland Inn, Motel 6, Red Roof Inn, Super 8, [other] Castro's Tire/Truckwash, **W** [gas] Valero/dsl
253	Stockdale Hwy, **E** [gas] Shell/dsl/24hr, [food] IHOP, Jack-in-the-Box, [lodging] Best Western, Rodeway Inn, **W** [other] Tule Elk St Reserve
246	CA 43, to Taft, Maricopa, [other] to Buena Vista RA
244	CA 119, to Pumpkin Center, **E** [gas] Mobil/dsl, **W** [gas] Chevron/dsl/LP

BUTTONWILLOW

🅟 = gas 🍽 = food 🏨 = lodging 🅞 = other   Copyright 2012 - The Next Exit®

INTERSTATE 5 CONT'D

N ↑ ↓ S

Exit	Services
239	CA 223, Bear Mtn Blvd, to Arvin, **E** 🅞 Bear Mtn. RV Resort, **W** 🅞 to Buena Vista RA, RV camping
234	Old River Rd
228	Copus Rd, **E** Murray Farms Mkt
225	CA 166, to Mettler, **2-3 mi E** gas/dsl, food
221	I-5 and CA 99 (from nb, exits left, no return)
219b a	Laval Rd, Wheeler Ridge, **E** 🅟 Chevron/Subway, TA/dsl/rest./scales/@, 🍽 Burger King, Pizza Hut, Taco Bell, 🅞 Blue Beacon, repair, **W** 🅟 Chevron, Petro/Mobil/Iron Skillet/Subway/dsl/scales/24hr/@, 🍽 In-N-Out, McDonald's, Panda Express, Starbucks, Wendy's, 🏨 Best Western
218	**truck weigh sta sb**
215	Grapevine, **E** 🅟 Mobil, 🍽 Denny's, Jack-in-the-Box, **W** 🅟 76/dsl, Shell/dsl, 🍽 Don Perico Cantina, 🏨 Ramda Ltd.
210	Ft Tejon Rd, **W** 🅞 to Ft Tejon Hist SP, towing/repair
209mm	**brake check area nb**
207	Lebec Rd, **W** 🅞 USPO, CHP, antiques, towing
206mm	**rest areas both lanes, full ♿ facilities, phone, vending, picnic tables litter barrels, petwalk**
205	Frazier Mtn Park Rd, **W** 🅟 Arco, Chevron/Subway/dsl/24hr, Ⓕ FLYING J/Denny's/dsl/LP/24hr, Shell/Quizno's/dsl, 🍽 Jack-in-the-Box, Los Pinos Mexican, 🏨 Best Rest Inn, Holiday Inn Select, 🅞 Auto Parts+, towing/repair/radiators/transmissions, to Mt Pinos RA
204	Tejon Pass, elev 4144, **truck brake insp sb**
202	Gorman Rd, to Hungry Valley, **E** 🅟 Chevron/dsl/LP, 76/dsl, 🍽 Carl's Jr, El Grullense, 🏨 EconoLodge, **W** 🅟 Valero, 🍽 McDonald's, 🅞 auto repair
199	CA 138, E (from sb), Lancaster Rd, to Palmdale
198b a	Quail Lake Rd, CA 138, E (from nb)
195	Smokey Bear Rd, Pyramid Lake, **W** 🅞 Pyramid Lake RV Park
191	Vista del Lago Rd, **W** 🅞 **visitors ctr**
186mm	**brake inspection area sb, motorist callboxes begin sb**
183	Templin Hwy, **W** 🅞 Ranger Sta, RV camping
176b a	Lake Hughes Rd, Parker Rd, Castaic, **E** 🅟 7-11, Castaic Trkstp/dsl/rest./24hr, 🍽 ⬛/Wendy's/dsl/24hr/scales, Shell, 🍽 Baskin-Robbins, Burger King, Mike's Diner, Carl's Jr, Casa Lupa Mexican, Denny's, Domino's, El Pollo Loco, Fosters Freeze, Jersey Mikes, McDonald's, Pizza Factory, Popeye's, Quizno's, Starbucks, Subway, Telly's Drive-in, Vinny's Pizza, Wienerschnitzel, Wok's Chinese, 🏨 Castaic Inn, Days Inn, Rodeway Inn, 🅞 Benny's Tire, Castaic Lake RV Park, Kragen Parts, Ralph's Food, Rite Aid, tires, vet, to Castaic Lake, **W** 🅟 Mobil, 76/Circle K/Pizza Hut/Taco Bell/repair, 🍽 Jack-in-the-Box, 🅞 Walgreens, auto repair
173	Hasley Canyon Rd, **W** 🍽 Ameci Pizza/pasta, Coldstone Creamery, Subway, 🅞 Ralph's Foods
172	CA 126 W, to Ventura, **E** 🏨 Courtyard
171mm	**weigh sta nb**
171.	Rye Canyon Rd (from sb), **W** 🅟 Chevron, Shell, 🍽 Del Taco, Jack-in-the-Box, Jimmy Deans, Starbucks, Subway, Tommy's Burgers, 🅞 6 Flags
170	CA 126 E, Magic Mtn Pkwy, Saugus, **E** 🍽 Denny's, Pastamichi Italian, Quizno's, Red Brick Pizza, Starbucks,

Vertical labels (left): FT TEJON / CASTAIC

Exit	Services
170	Continued 🏨 Best Western/rest., Holiday Inn Express, **W** 🅟 Chevron, 🍽 El Torito, Hamburger Hamlet, Marie Callender's, Red Lobster, Rio Rio Grill, Wendy's, 🏨 Hilton Garden, 🅞 Six Flags of CA
169	Valencia Blvd, **W** 🍽 La Salsa, Nick'n Willy's Pizza, Panda Express, Starbucks, Subway, 🅞 Albertson's, SavOn
168	McBean Pkwy, **E** 🅞 🅗, **W** 🍽 Baskin-Robbins, Cabo Cabana, Chili's, ChuckeCheese, ClaimJumper Rest., Jamba Juice, Macaroni Grill, Mamma Mia Italian, Pick up Stix, Starbucks, Subway, Wood Ranch BBQ, 🅞 Marshall's, Michael's, Old Navy, Staples, Vons Foods, WorldMkt
167	Lyons Ave, Pico Canyon Rd, **E** 🅟 Chevron/24hr, 76/Circle K, Shell/dsl, 🍽 Burger King, Wendy's, **W** 🅟 Arco/24hr, Mobil, Shell/dsl, 🍽 Carl's Jr, Chuy's Chinese, Coco's, Del Taco, Denny's, El Pollo Loco, Fortune Express Chinese, IHOP, In-N-Out, Jack-in-the-Box, McDonald's, Outback Steaks, Spumoni Italian, Taco Bell, Yamato Japanese, 🏨 Comfort Suites, Extended Stay America, Fairfield Inn, Hampton Inn, La Quinta, Residence Inn, 🅞 Camping World RV Ctr, GNC, Jiffy Lube, PetsMart, Ralph's Foods, SteinMart, Walmart
166	Calgrove Blvd
162	CA 14 N, to Palmdale
161b	Balboa Blvd (from sb)
160a	I-210, to San Fernando, Pasadena
159	Roxford St, Sylmar, **E** 🅟 Chevron/dsl, Mobil/dsl, 🍽 Denny's/24hr, McDonald's, 🏨 Good Nite Inn, Motel 6
158	I-405, S (from sb, no return)
157b a	SF Mission Blvd, Brand Blvd, **E** 🅟 Arco, Chevron, Mobil/dsl, 76, Shell, 🍽 Carl's Jr, In-N-Out, Little Caesars, New Asia, Pollo Gordo, Popeye's, Subway, Taco Bell, Winchell's, 🅞 🅗, Honda, Rite Aid
156b	CA 118
156a	Paxton St, Brand Ave (from nb), **E** 🅟 Shell/dsl, 🅞 7-11
155b	Van Nuys Blvd (no EZ nb return), **E** 🅟 Eagle, 🍽 Jack-in-the-Box, KFC/LJ Silver, McDonald's, Pizza Hut, Popeye's, 🅞 Discount Parts, USPO, **W** 🍽 Domino's, 🅞 auto repair
155a	Terra Bella St (from nb), **E** 🅟 Arco
154	Osborne St, to Arleta, **E** 🅟 Arco, Chevron/dsl, 🍽 El Pollo Loco, Knight's Pizza, Papa's Tacos, 🅞 AutoZone, BigLots, Food4Less, Superior Grocers, Target, **W** 🅟 Mobil/Burger King, 76, 🅞 7-11
153b	CA 170 (from sb), to Hollywood
152a	Sheldon St, **E** 🍽 Big Jim's Rest., 🅞 Big O Parts, 🅗, auto repair
152	Lankershim Blvd, Tuxford, **E** 🅟 Superfine/dsl/scales
151	Penrose St
150b	Sunland Blvd, Sun Valley, **E** 🅟 Mobil, 76/dsl, 🍽 Acapulco Rest., Carl's Jr, El Pollo Loco, Old Time Burgers, Quiznos, Subway, Town Café, Yoshinoya, 🏨 Economy Inn, 🅞 Ralph's Foods, 7-11, **W** 🅟 76, Shell, 🍽 Big Boy, McDonald's
150a	GlenOaks Blvd (from nb), **E** 🅟 Superior/dsl, 🏨 Willows Motel
149	Hollywood Way, **W** 🅟 Shell/dsl, 🅞 U-Haul, ⬤
148	Buena Vista St, **E** 🏨 Hampton Inn, **W** 🅟 76/dsl, 🍽 Jack-in-the-Box, 🏨 Quality Inn, Ramada Inn
147	Scott Rd, to Burbank, **E** 🅟 Sevan/dsl, **W** 🍽 Home

Vertical labels (right): SANTA CLARITA / SYLMAR / ARLETA / SUN VALLEY

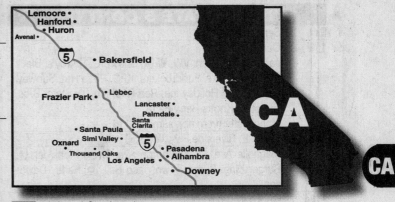

INTERSTATE 5 CONT'D

Exit	Services
147	Continued
	town Buffet, Krispy Kreme, Outback Steaks, Panda Express, Starbucks, Wendy's, 🛏 Courtyard, Extended Stay America, ⊙ Best Buy, Lowe's, Marshall's, Michael's, Staples, Target, Verizon
146b	Burbank Blvd, E 🅿 76/repair, 🍴 Baskin-Robbins, CA Pizza Kitchen, Carl's Jr, Chevy's Mexican, ChuckeCheese, Corner Cafe, Harry's Rest., Hooters, IHOP, In-N-Out, McDonald's, Pizza Hut, Popeye's, Quiznos, Robek's Juice, Shakey's Pizza, Starbucks, Subway, Taco Bell, Tommy's Burgers, Yoshinoya, 🛏 Holiday Inn, ⊙ Barnes&Noble, Curves, CVS Drug, Henry's Mkt, K-Mart, Loehmanns, Macy's, Office Depot, Old Navy, Ralph's Foods, Ross, Sears, W 🍴 McDonald's, Subway, ⊙ Costco/gas, Discount Tire
146a	Olive Ave, Verdugo, E 🍴 Black Angus, BJ's Rest., 🛏 Holiday Inn, ⊙ Radio Shack, USPO, W ⊙ H, Chevrolet, Metro RV Ctr, 7-11
145b	Alameda Ave, E 🅿 Chevron, 🍴 Baskin-Robbins/Togo's, Del Taco, Habit Burgers, Starbucks, ⊙ CarMax, CVS Drug, Home Depot, Ralph's Foods, Trader Joes, Walgreens, W 🅿 Arco, Shell, 🛏 Burbank Inn, ⊙ U-Haul
145a	Western Ave, W ⊙ Gene Autrey Museum
144b a	CA 134, Ventura Fwy, Glendale, Pasadena
142	Colorado St
141a	Los Feliz Blvd, E ⊙ H, W ⊙ Griffith Park, zoo
140b	Glendale Blvd, E 🅿 76, Valero, 🍴 Starbucks, Subway, ⊙ auto repair, W 🅿 Valero
140a	Fletcher Dr (from sb)
139b a	CA 2, Glendale Fwy
138	Stadium Way, Figueroa St, E 🅿 Chevron, Thrifty, Valero, 🍴 IHOP, McDonald's, ⊙ Home Depot, W ⊙ to Dodger Stadium
137b a	CA 2, Glendale Fwy, W 🅿 76
136b	Broadway St (from sb), W 🅿 76
136a	Main St, E 🅿 Chevron/24hr, 76, 🍴 Chinatown Express, Jack-in-the-Box, McDonald's, Mr Pizza, ⊙ H, Parts+
135c	I-10, W (from nb), Mission Rd (from sb), E 🅿 Chevron, 76/dsl, 🍴 Jack-in-the-Box, McDonald's, ⊙ H
135b	Cesar Chavez Ave, W ⊙ H
135a	4th St, Soto St, E 🅿 76/dsl, Shell/Subway/dsl, W 🅿 Arco/dsl, ⊙ city park
134b	Ca 60, E (from sb), Soto St (from nb)
134a	CA 60 W, Santa Monica Fwy
133	Euclid Ave (from sb), Grand Vista (from nb), E 🅿 Arco, USA/dsl, W 🅿 Mobil, Shell, ⊙ H
132	Calzona St, Indiana St, E 🅿 Arco/dsl
131b	Indiana St (from nb), E 🅿 Arco/dsl, Valero/dsl
131a	Olympic Blvd, E 🍴 McDonald's, W 🍴 Jack-in-the-Box, King Taco, ⊙ H
130c b	I-710 (exits left from nb), to Long Beach, Eastern Ave, E 🍴 McDonald's
130a	Triggs St (from sb), E ⊙ outlet mall, W 🍴 Denny's/24hr, 🛏 Destiny Inn
129	Atlantic Blvd N, Eastern Ave (from sb), E 🍴 Carl's Jr, Fresca's Mexican, Panda Express, Ruby's Diner, Starbucks, Subway, 🛏 Doubletree, ⊙ Hyundai, outlets/famous brands, W 🍴 Denny's, Steven's Steaks
128b	Washington Blvd, Commerce, E 🅿 Chevron/dsl/repair/24hr, 🍴 McDonald's, 🛏 Doubletree, Crowne
128b	Continued
	Plaza Hotel/casino, ⊙ Costco, outlets/famous brands, W 🅿 Arco, 🍴 Del Taco, Subway
128a	Garfield Blvd, E 🛏 Commerce/Hotel/casino, ⊙ Home Depot, Office Depot, W 🅿 76
126b	Slauson Ave, Montebello, E 🅿 Shell, Valero/dsl, 🍴 Ozzie's Diner, Quiznos, Starbucks, 🛏 Quality Inn, Super 8, W 🅿 Arco, 🍴 Denny's, 🛏 Budget Inn, Ramada Inn
126a	Paramount Blvd, Downey, E 🅿 Shell/Jack-in-the-Box/dsl
125	CA 19 S, Lakewood Blvd, Rosemead Blvd, E 🅿 Mobil, Thrifty, 🍴 Arthurs Cafe, Foster's Freeze, Sam's Burgers, Starbucks, Taco Bell, 🛏 EconoLodge, W 🍴 China Wok, Chris&Pitt's BBQ, McDonald's, Subway, ⊙ Ralph's Foods
124	I-605
123	Florence Ave, to Downey, E 🅿 Mobil, W ⊙ Honda, repair
122	Imperial Hwy, Pioneer Blvd, E 🅿 Chevron, 🍴 Applebees, Habit Burgers, IHOP, Jack-in-the-Box, McDonald's, Subway, Wendy's, Wood Grill Buffet, ⊙ Firestone/auto, Rite Aid, Target, W 🅿 Chevron, 7-11, 🍴 Alberts Mexican, Denny's, HongKong Express, Panda King, Pizza Hut, Rally's, Shakey's Pizza, Sizzler, Wienerschnitzel, 🛏 Comfort Inn, Keystone Motel, Rodeway Inn, ⊙ Toyota/Scion, Walmart
121	San Antonio Dr, to Norwalk Blvd, E 🍴 IHOP, Jack-in-the-Box, McDonald's, Outback Steaks, Starbucks, Wood Grill Buffet, 🛏 Doubletree Inn, ⊙ Rite Aid, Target, W 🅿 76, ⊙ auto repair
120b	Firestone Blvd (exits left from nb)
120a	Rosecrans Ave, E 🅿 Valero/dsl, 🍴 Jim's Burgers, KFC, Little Caesars, Starbucks, Taco Joe, ⊙ H, Big-Saver Foods, W 🅿 Arco/24hr, 🍴 El Pollo Loco, Fosters Freeze, 🛏 Guesthouse Inn, ⊙ Camping World RV Ctr, El Monte RV Ctr, Tune-Up Masters
119	Carmenita Rd, Buena Park, E 🅿 Arco, 🍴 Burger King, ⊙ Ford Trucks, Lowe's, W 🍴 Galaxy Burgers 🛏 Budget Inn, Dynasty Suites
118	Valley View Blvd, E 🍴 Carl's Jr, Elephant Bar Rest, In-N-Out, Northwoods Rest, Red Robin, Subway, 🛏 Extended Stay America, Holiday Inn Select, Residence Inn, ⊙ Staples, W 🅿 Chevron, 🍴 Burger King, El Pollo Loco, ⊙ Thompson's RV Ctr, to Camping World
117	Artesia Blvd, Knott Ave, E 🅿 Chevron, 76/24hr, 🛏 Extended Stay America, ⊙ CarMax, W ⊙ Chrysler, Knotts Berry Farm, to Camping World RV Ctr
116	CA 39, Beach Blvd, E 🅿 Chevron, ⊙ H, Acura, BMW, Buick/GMC, CarMax, Honda, Hyundai, Mercedes,

🅿 = gas 🍴 = food 🏨 = lodging 🅾 = other   Copyright 2012 - The Next Exit

INTERSTATE 5 CONT'D	

N ↕ S

CA

LOS ANGELES AREA

Exit	Services
116	**Continued** san, Toyota/Scion, VW, **W** 🅿 Chevron, 🍴 Arby's, Black Angus, Denny's, Fuddruckers, KFC, Pizza Hut, Subway, Wendy's, 🏨 Holiday Inn, Red Roof Inn, 🅾 Stater Bros, Target, to Knotts Berry Farm
115	Manchester (from nb), same as 116
114b	CA 91 E, Riverside Fwy, **W** to ♻
114a	Magnolia Ave, Orangethorpe Ave, **E** 🅿 Mobil/dsl, 🍴 Burger King, Burger Town, Taco Bell, 🅾 Harley-Davidson
113c	CA 91, **W** (from nb)
113b a	Brookhurst St, LaPalma, **E** 🅿 Chevron/dsl, 🍴 Subway, **W** 🅿 Arco, Texaco/dsl, 🍴 Carl's Jr., Quiznos, Starbucks, 🅾 Home Depot, Staples
112	Euclid St, **E** 🅿 Arco, 🍴 IHOP, Marie Callender's, McDonald's, Starbucks, Taco Bell, Wendy's, 🅾 AAA, PetCo, Ross, 7-11, TJ Maxx, Walmart, **W** 🅿 Mobil, 76, 🍴 Burger King, Charley's Subs, Denny's, KFC/LJ Silver, Subway, 🅾 Radio Shack, Target, Verizon
111	Lincoln Ave, to Anaheim, **E** 🍴 El Triunfo Mexican, La Casa Garcia Mexican, Ruby's Diner, Starbucks, Subway, 🅾 vet, **W** 🅾 Discount Auto Repair
110b	Ball Rd (from sb), **E** 🅿 Chevron/dsl, 7-11, Shell, 🍴 Burger King, El Pollo Loco, McDonald's, Shakey's Pizza, Starbucks, Taco Bell, Subway, 🏨 Best Inn, Best Value Inn, Days Inn, Hotel Menage, 🅾 Anaheim RV, Traveler's World RV Park, **W** 🅿 Arco/24hr, Shell/dsl, 🏨 Best Western, Budget Inn, Holiday Inn, Rodeway Inn, Sheraton, Travelodge, 🅾 Camping World RV Ctr, Disneyland, USPO
110a	Harbor Blvd, **E** 🅿 Chevron, Shell, 🍴 Carrow's, Shakey's Pizza, Taco Bell, 🏨 Days Inn, EconoLodge, Frontier Harbor Hotel, Hotel Menage, Ramada Ltd, 🅾 Anaheim Harbor RV Park, **0-2 mi W** to Disneyland, 🍴 Acapulco Mexican, Captain Kidd's, Coldstone, Del Sol, Dennys, IHOP, McDonald's, Millie's Rest., Mimi's Cafe, Mortons Steaks, Overland Sage BBQ, Quiznos, Tony Roma's, 🏨 Anaheim Resort, Best Inn, Best Western, Candy Cane Inn, Camelot Inn, Carousel Inn, Castle Inn Suites, Clarion, Courtyard, Desert Inn, Fairfield Inn, Hampton Inn, Hilton Garden, Howard Johnson, ParkVue Inn, Portofino Inn, Ramada Inn, Red Lion, Saga Inn, Sheraton, Travelodge, Tropicana Inn, same as 109
109	Katella Ave, Disney Way, **E** 🅿 Arco, 🍴 Baskin-Robbins, Carl's Jr, Catch Seafood, Denny's, El Torito, McDonald's, Mr Stox Dining, Panda Express, Subway, Togo's, 🏨 Angel Inn, TownePlace Suites, 🅾 Angels Stadium, **W** 🅿 Chevron, 🍴 Bubba Gump Shrimp, CA Pizza Kitchen, Cheesecake Factory, Del Taco, McCormick&Schmick, PF Chang's, Roy Roy's, Subway, 🏨 Arena Inn, Best Value Inn, Comfort Inn, Desert Palms Suites, Extended Stay America, Hilton, Holiday Inn Express, Little Boy Blue, Marriott, Peacock Suites, Ramada Inn, Residence Inn, Riviera Motel, Staybridge Suites, Super 8, Worldmark, 🅾 7-11, to Disneyland
107c	St Coll Blvd, City Drive, **E** 🍴 Del Taco, 🏨 Hilton Suites, **W** 🏨 Doubletree Hotel
107b a	CA 57 N, Chapman Ave, **E** 🍴 Burger King, Del Taco, Denny's, 🏨 Holiday Inn, Motel 6, Quality Inn, **W** 🅿
107b a	**Continued** Chevron, 🍴 Krispy Kreme, Lucille's BBQ, Taco Bell, Wendy's, 🏨 Ayer's Inn, DoubleTree, 🅾 🏥, Best Buy
106	CA 22, **W** (from nb), Garden Grove Fwy, Bristol St
105b	N Broadway, Main St, **E** 🅿 7-11, 🍴 Baskin-Robbins, CA Pizza Kitchen, Carl's Jr, Chili Pepper Mexican, Corner Bakery, El Torito, FoodCourt, Habit Burgers, Jamba Juice, Manhattan Steaks, McCormick&Schmicks, Papa Johns, Pat&Oscars, Polly's Café, Rubio's Grill, Starbucks, Subway, Taco Bell, Togo's, 🏨 Days Inn, Red Roof Inn, 🅾 🏥, Barnes&Noble, CVS Drug, JC Penney, Macy's, Nordstrom's, Staples, Verizon, mall, **W** 🏨 Golden West Motel, Travel Inn, 🅾 Bowers Museum
105a	17th St, **E** 🅿 76/dsl/24hr, 🍴 Hometown Buffet, IHOP, McDonald's, 🅾 Chevrolet, CVS Drug, Food4Less, Walgreens, same as 104b, **W** 🅿 Chevron, 🍴 YumYum Donuts, 🅾 7-11
104b	Santa Ana Blvd, Grand Ave, **E on Grand** 🍴 Denny's, Hometown Buffet, IHOP, KFC/LJ Silver, Marie Callender, McDonald's, Pizza Hut/Taco Bell, Popeye's, Starbucks, Subway, Taco Sinaloa, 🅾 Big O Tire, CVS Drug, $Tree, Goodyear, Kragen Parts, Target, Walgreens, vet, **W** 🅾 KIA, Suzuki
104a	(103c from nb), 4th St, 1st St, to CA 55 N, **E** 🅿 Chevron, Shell, 76, 🍴 Del Taco
103b	CA 55 S, to Newport Beach
103a	CA 55, N (from nb), to Riverside
102	Newport Ave (from sb), **W** 🅿 Arco
101b	Red Hill Ave, **E** 🅿 Mobil/dsl, Shell/repair, 🍴 Del Taco, Denny's, Starbucks, Subway, Wendy's, 🏨 Key Inn, 🅾 BigLots, U-Haul, **W** 🅿 Arco/24hr, Chevron/24hr, 76, 🍴 Pizza Shack, Taco Bell, 🅾 7-11, Stater Bros
101a	Tustin Ranch Rd, **E** 🍴 McDonald's, 🅾 Acura, Buick/GMC, Cadillac, Chrysler/Dodge/Jeep, Costco, Ford, Lincoln/Mercury, Hyundai, Infiniti, Lexus, Mazda, Nissan, Toyota/Scion
100	Jamboree Rd, **E** 🅿 Shell, 🍴 Baja Fresh, BJ's Rest., Buca Italian, Burger King, CA Pizza, Carl's Jr, Chick-fil-A, Corner Bakery, Daphne's Greek, DQ, El Pollo Loco, IHOP, In-N-Out, Jamba Juice, JinJin Asian, Lazy Dog Cafe, Macaroni Grill, On the Border, Panda Express, Panera Bread, Pick-up Stix, Quiznos, Red Robin, Rubio's, Starbucks, Subway, Taco Bell, Taco Rosa, 🅾 AAA, AT&T, Barnes&Noble, Best Buy, Costco, Dick's, Henry's Mkt, Home Depot, Loehmann's, Lowe's, Old Navy, Petsmart, Radio Shack, Ralph's Foods, Rite Aid, Ross, Target, TJ Maxx, Verizon
99	Culver Dr, **E** 🅿 Shell/24hr, 🅾 vet
97	Jeffrey Rd, **E** 🅿 Arco, 🍴 Baskin-Robbins, Juice-it-Up, La Salsa, Starbucks, Subway, 🅾 Albertson's, Kohl's, **W** 🅿 76/dsl, 🍴 Thai Cafe, 🅾 Ranch Mkt Foods, Verizon, vet
96	Sand Canyon Ave, Old Towne, **W** 🅿 76/dsl, 🍴 Denny's, Jack-in-the-Box, Knowlwood Burgers, Tiajuana's Rest., 🏨 La Quinta, 🅾 🏥, Traveland USA RV Park
95	CA 133 (toll), Laguna Fwy, N to Riverside, S Laguna Beach
94b	Alton Pkwy, **E** 🅿 Shell/Subway/dsl, 🍴 Cabo Grill, Carl's Jr, Quiznos, Starbucks, 🏨 Homestead Suites, **W** 🍴 CA Pizza, Cheesecake Factory, Chipotle Mexican, Dave&Buster's, Johnny Rockets, Panda Express, PF Chang's, Wahoo's Fish Tacos, Wood Ranch, Yardhouse Rest., 🏨 Doubletree Inn, 🅾 Barnes&Noble, Macy's,

N		

INTERSTATE 5 CONT'D

Exit	Services
94b	Continued
	Nordstrom, Old Navy, Target
94a	I-405, N (from nb)
92b	Bake Pkwy, same as 92a
92a	Lake Forest Dr, Laguna Hills, E 🅿 Chevron/24hr, Shell/dsl, 🍴 Buffalo Wild Wings, Del Taco, Jack-in-the-Box, McDonald's, Panera Bread, Pizza Hut, RoundTable Pizza, Subway, Taco Bell, The Hat, 🛏 Best Value Inn, Holiday Inn, Irvine Suites Hotel, Quality Inn, ⊙ America's Tire, Buick/GMC, Chrysler/Dodge/Jeep, Ford/Lincoln/Mercury, Honda, Hyundai, Mazda, Nissan, Subaru, Volvo, VW, W 🅿 Chevron/24hr, Shell, 🍴 Carl's Jr, Coco's, Del Taco, McDonald's, Quiznos, Subway, 🛏 Comfort Inn, Courtyard, ⊙ AZ Leather, Best Buy, BMW/Mini
91	El Toro Rd, E 🅿 Chevron/dsl, USA, 🍴 Arby's, Asia Buffet, Baskin-Robbins, Cafe Rio, Chipotle Mexican, Chronic Tacos, Denny's, El Pollo Loco, Flamebroiler, Fuddrucker's, Hooters, Jack-in-the-Box, Lucille's BBQ, McDonald's, Mr Wok, Panda Express, PeiWei Asian, Quiznos, Scarantino's Rest., Sizzler, Starbucks, Subway, Tommy's Burgers, Wendy's, ⊙ CVS Drug, Firestone/auto, Home Depot, 99c Store, PetCo, PetsMart, Ralph's Foods, Ross, Staples, W 🅿 Chevron/dsl/24hr, Shell/24hr, 76/Circle K, 🍴 BJ's Rest., Carrow's, El Torito, In-N-Out, King's Fishhouse, LoneStar Steaks, Nami Seafood, Starbucks, Woody's Diner, 🛏 Laguna Hills Lodge, ⊙ H, CVS Drug, Firestone/auto, JC Penney, Just Tires, Macy's, Marshall's, Sears/auto, Trader Joe's, Walgreens, USPO, mall
90	Alicia Pkwy, Mission Viejo, E 🍴 Del Taco, Denny's, Subway, ⊙ Albertson's, America's Tire, CVS Drug, $Tree, Kragen Parts, Target, W 🅿 Chevron, 76/dsl, 🍴 Carl's Jr, It's a Grind, Togo's, Wendy's, ⊙ AAA, BigLots, Mazda, vet
89	La Paz Rd, Mission Viejo, E 🅿 Arco/24hr, Shell, 🍴 Chronic Tacos, Pizza Hut, Starbucks, Taco Bell, TK Burgers, ⊙ Albertson's/Sav-On, vet, W 🅿 76, 🍴 Claim Jumper Rest., DQ, Flamingos Mexican, Hot Off the Grill, Jack-in-the-Box, Krispy Kreme, La Salsa, McDonald's, Outback Steaks, Spasso's Italian, Starbucks, Subway, Villa Roma, Wienerschnitzel, Yamato Japanese, 🛏 Hills Hotel, ⊙ Best Buy, Curves, Goodyear/auto, Jo-Ann Fabrics, PetCo, 7-11, urgent care, to Laguna Niguel Pk
87	Oso Pkwy, Pacific Park Dr, E 🅿 Chevron/repair, 76/dsl/repair, 🍴 Carl's Jr, Starbucks, Subway, 🛏 Fairfield Inn, ⊙ golf
86	Crown Valley Pkwy, E 🅿 Arco, Chevron, 76, 🍴 Buffalo Wild Wings, Chili's, Coco's, Islands Grill, ⊙ H, Macy's, mall, vet, W 🅿 Chevron/dsl, ⊙ Aamco, Costco/gas
85b	Avery Pkwy, E 🅿 Shell/dsl, 🍴 Alberto's Mexican, Carrow's, Del Taco, Jack-in-the-Box, Mongolian BBQ, Papa John's, Starbucks, Subway, ⊙ Acura, America's Tire/auto, Audi/Infiniti, Jaguar/Land Rover, Lexus, Parts+, World Mkt, W 🅿 Chevron, Shell/dsl/24hr, 🍴 A's Burgers, Carl's Jr, In-N-Out, 🛏 Best Value Laguna Inn, ⊙ Aamco, Cadillac/GMC, Costco/gas, Firestone/auto, Hyundai, Mercedes
85a	CA 73, N (toll)
83	Junipero Serra Rd, to San Juan Capistrano, W 🅿 Shell, Spirit/service/dsl

Exit	Services
82	CA 74, Ortego Hwy, E 🅿 Chevron/dsl, 76, Shell, 🍴 Bad to the Bone BBQ, Ballpark Pizza, Bravo Burgers, Denny's, Subway, 🛏 Best Western, ⊙ vet, W 🅿 Chevron/24hr, 🍴 Arby's, Carl's Jr, Del Taco, Jack-in-the-Box, KFC, Marie Callender's, McDonald's, Oeeshi Japanese, Pedro's Tacos, Quiznos, RoundTable Pizza, Ruby's Cafe, Starbucks, Taco Bell, 🛏 Cedar Creek Inn, Mission Inn, ⊙ Capistrano Trading Post, GNC, Marshall's, Ralph's Foods, Ross, TrueValue, San Juan Capistrano Mission
81	Camino Capistrano, E ⊙ VW, W on Capistrano 🅿 Chevron, 🍴 El Adobe Rest., El Pollo Loco, Eng's Chinese, KFC, Papa John's, Pizza Hut, Ricardo's Mexican, Starbucks, ⊙ Aamco, BigLots, Costco, Ford, Goodyear/auto, Honda, KIA, Nissan, PetCo, PetsMart, Radio Shack, Rite Aid, Ross, Staples, Toyota/Scion, Vons Foods, San Juan Capistrano SP (1mi), CHP, urgent care
79	CA 1, Pacific Coast Hwy, Capistrano Bch, Capistrano, 1 mi W 🅿 Arco/24hr, 76/dsl, 🍴 A's Burgers, Carl's Jr, Del Taco, Denny's, Jack-in-the-Box, JuiceSpot, McDonald's, Rib Joint, Subway, 🛏 DoubleTree, Harbor Inn, Holiday Inn Express, ⊙ Ralph's Foods, Rite Aid, USPO, vet
78	Camino de Estrella, San Clemente, E 🅿 76/dsl, 🍴 Carl's Jr, China Well, Coldstone, Crispins, Flame Broiler, Jamba Juice, Melting Pot, Papa Murphy's, RoundTable Pizza, Rubio's, Starbucks, Subway, Wahoo's Fish Taco, ⊙ H, AT&T, CVS Drug, Ralph's Foods, Stater Bros Foods, Trader Joe's, vet, W 🅿 Arco/dsl, 🍴 Las Golondrinas, ⊙ BigLots, Kragen Parts, Sears Essentials
77	Ave Vista Hermosa
76	Ave Pico, E 🅿 Mobil, 🍴 Buono Pizza, Carrow's, Golden Spoon, Juice it Up, McDonald's, Panda Express, ⊙ Albertson's/Sav-On, GNC, W 🅿 Chevron, Shell/dsl, 🍴 Bad to the Bone BBQ, BurgerStop, Del Taco, Denny's/24hr, Pick-up-Stix, Pizza Hut, Stuft Pizza, Subway, 🛏 Holiday Inn Express, ⊙ Curves, 99c Store, Staples, Tuesday Morning, USPO, tires/repair, vet
75	Ave Palizada, Ave Presidio, W 🅿 Valero, 🍴 Baskin-Robbins, Coffee Bean, Mr. Pete's Burgers, Sonny's Pizza, Subway, Starbucks, Taka-O Japanese, 🛏 Holiday Inn, ⊙ 7-11, TrueValue
74	El Camino Real, E 🅿 Chevron/dsl/24hr, 🍴 El Mariachi Rest., Pipes Cafe, 🛏 Budget Lodge, San Clemente Inn, Tradewinds Motel, ⊙ vet, same as 75, W 🅿 Exxon, 76/dsl, 🍴 FatBurger, KFC, Pizza Hut/Taco Bell, Subway, Taste Of China, Tommy's Rest./24hr, ⊙ Kragen Parts, Radio Shack, Ralph's Foods, 7-11
73	Ave Calafia, Ave Magdalena, E 🅿 76/dsl, Shell, 🍴

Side labels (left margin, top to bottom): N · S · LAGUNA HILLS · MISSION VIEJO

Side labels (center column margin, top to bottom): CAPISTRANO · SAN CLEMENTE

INTERSTATE 5 CONT'D

Exit	Services

73 Continued
Jack-in-the-Box, Molly Bloom's Cafe, Pedro's Tacos, Sugar Shack Cafe, 🏠 Budget Inn, Calafia Beach Motel, C-Vu Inn, Hampton Inn, LaVista Inn, San Clemente Motel, Travelodge, 🄾 San-O Tire, 7-11, repair, **W** to San Clemente SP

72 Cristianitios Ave, **E** 🍴 Cafe Del Sol, Carl's Jr., 🏠 Comfort Suites, Carmelo Motel, 🄾 San Mateo RV Park/dump, **W** 🄾 to San Clemente SP

71 Basilone Rd, **W** 🄾 San Onofre St Beach

67mm **weigh sta both lanes**

66mm viewpoint sb

62 Las Pulgas Rd

59mm **Aliso Creek rest area both lanes, full ♿ facilities, 🍴, 🅿, vending, litter barrels, petwalk, RV dump**

54c Oceanside Harbor Dr, **W** 📖 Chevron, Mobil, 🍴 Burger King (1mi), Del Taco, Denny's/24hr, 🏠 GuestHouse Inn, Holiday Inn Express, Sandman Hotel, Travelodge, The Bridge Motel, 🄾 to Camp Pendleton

54b Hill St (from sb), to Oceanside, **W** 📖 Chevron, Mobil, 🍴 Carrow's Rest., Denny's, 🏠 GuestHouse Inn, Holiday Inn Express, Travelodge

54a CA 76 E, Coast Hwy

53 Mission Ave, Oceanside, **E** 📖 Arco/24hr, Mobil/dsl, 🍴 Alberto's Mexican, Arby's, Armando's Tacos, Burger King, China Star, Jack-in-the-Box, KFC, McDonald's, Mission Donuts, 🏠 Quality Inn, Ramada, 🄾 CarQuest, NAPA, PepBoys, Valu+ Foods, **W** 🍴 El Pollo Loco, Panda Express, Subway, Wendy's, 🄾 99¢ Store, Office Depot, Radio Shack

52 Oceanside Blvd, **E** 🍴 Alberto's Mexican, Domino's, IHOP, McDonald's, Papa John's, Pizza Hut, Starbucks, Subway, Taco Bell, Wienerschnitzel, 🄾 Boney's Foods, CVS Drug, Ralph's Foods, CHP, **W** 📖 Oceanside/dsl, 🏠 Best Western Oceanside

51c Cassidy St (from sb), **W** 📖 7-11, Mobil, 76, 🄾 🄷

51b CA 78, Vista Way, Escondido, **E** 📖 Chevron/dsl/24hr, 76/Circle K, Shell, 🍴 Applebee's, Boston Mkt, Burger King, Carl's Jr, Chili's, ChuckeCheese, Fuddrucker's, Golden Taipei, Hooters, Macaroni Grill, McDonald's, Mimi's Café, Olive Garden, Outback Steaks, QuikWok, Rubio's, Starbucks, Subway, Wendy's, 🏠 Holiday Inn Express, 🄾 Best Buy, CVS Drug, $Tree, Firestone, Henry's Mkt, JC Penney, Macy's, Marshall's, Michael's, PetCo, Sears/auto, Staples, Stater Bros Foods, Target, Tuesday Morning, Vons Foods, Walmart/auto, World Mkt, **W** 🍴 Hunter Steaks

51a Las Flores Dr

50 Elm Ave, Carlsbad Village Dr, **E** 📖 Shell/24hr, 🍴 Lotus Thai Bistro, **W** 📖 Carlsbad/dsl/LP, Valero, 🍴 Al's Cafe, Carl's Jr, Denny's/24hr, Jack-in-the-Box, KFC/Taco Bell, Mikko Japanese, 🏠 Extended Stay America, Motel 6, 🄾 Albertson's, TrueValue

49 Tamarack Ave, **E** 📖 Chevron/24hr, 76/dsl, 🍴 Village Kitchen, 🏠 Comfort Inn, Rodeway Inn, Travel Inn, 🄾 GNC, Rite Aid, Vons Foods, **W** 📖 Arco, 🍴 Hensley's Grill

48 Cannon Rd, Car Country Carlsbad, **E** 🄾 Acura, Buick, Cadillac/Chevrolet, Ford, Honda, Lexus, Lincoln/Mercury, Mazda, Mercedes, Toyota, VW

47 Carlsbad Blvd, Palomar 🅰 Rd, **E** 📖 Chevron, Mobil/dsl, 7-11, 🍴 BJ's Rest., Carl's Jr, Islands Burgers, Panda Express, Pat&Oscar's Rest., PF Chang's, Subway, Strauss Brewery Rest., Taco Bell, TGIFriday's, 🏠 Holiday Inn, Motel 6, 🄾 Carlsbad Ranch/Flower Fields, Chrysler/Dodge/Jeep, Costco/gas, Ford, outlet mall, **W** 📖 Shell/dsl, 🍴 ClaimJumper Rest., Marie Callender's, McDonald's, 🏠 Hilton Garden, 🄾 S Carlsbad St Bch

45 Poinsettia Lane, **W** 📖 Chevron, 🍴 Benihana, El Pollo Loco, Golden Spoon, Jack-in-the-Box, Pick-Up Stix, Starbucks, Subway, 🏠 La Quinta, Motel 6, Quality Inn, Ramada, 🄾 Ace Hardware, Porsche/Volvo, Ralph's Foods, Rite Aid

44 La Costa Ave, **E** vista point, **W** 📖 Chevron/dsl

43 Leucadia Blvd, **E** 🏠 Howard Johnson, **W** 📖 Shell/service

41b Encinitas Blvd, **E** 📖 Chevron/dsl, O'Brien Sta., Valero, 🍴 Coco's Cafe, Del Taco, Gusto Trattoria, HoneyBaked Ham, Oggi's Pizza, 🄾 CVS Drug, NAPA, to Quail Botanical Gardens, vet, **W** 📖 Shell, 🍴 Denny's, Little Caesar's, Subway, Wendy's, 🏠 Best Western/rest., Days Inn, 🄾 PetCo

41a Santa Fe Dr, to Encinitas, **E** 📖 Shell, 🍴 Carl's Jr, El Nopalito, Papa Toni's Pizza, 🄾 7-11, **W** 🍴 Today's Pizza, 🄾 🄷, Rite Aid, Vons Foods, vet

40 Birmingham Dr, **E** 📖 Chevron, Valero, 🍴 Mandarin City, 🏠 Holiday Inn Express, **W** 📖 Arco/24hr

39mm viewpoint sb

39 Manchester Ave, **E** 📖 76, 🄾 to MiraCosta College

37 Lomas Santa Fe Dr, Solana Bch, **E** 🍴 Baskin-Robbins, Pizza Nova, Samurai Rest., Starbucks, 🄾 Ross, Vons Foods, We-R-Fabrics, **W** 📖 Mobil, 🍴 Carl's Jr, Golden Spoon, Jamba Juice, Panda Express, Panera Bread, RoundTable Pizza, Starbucks, Togo's, 🄾 CVS Drug, Discount Tire, GNC, Henry's Foods, Marshall's, Staples

36 Via de La Valle, Del Mar, **E** 📖 Chevron, Mobil, 🍴 Chevy's Mexican, Coffee Bean, McDonald's, Milton's Deli, Pappachino's Italian, Paradise Grille, Pasta Pronto, Pick-Up Stix, Taste of Thai, 🄾 Albertson's/SavOn, PetCo, Radio Shack, **W** 📖 Arco/24hr, Shell/dsl, 🍴 Denny's, FishMkt Rest., Red Tracton's Rest., 🏠 Hilton, 🄾 racetrack

34 Del Mar Heights Rd, **E** 📖 Shell/dsl, **W** 📖 7-11, 🍴 Elijah's Rest., Jack-in-the-Box, Mexican Grill, 🄾 CVS Drug, Vons Foods, vet

33 Carmel Mtn Rd, **E** 📖 Arco, Shell/repair, 🍴 Taco Bell, Tio Leo's Mexican, 🏠 DoubleTree Hotel, Hampton Inn, Marriott

32 CA 56 E, Carmel Valley Rd

31 I-805 (from sb)

30 Sorrento Valley Rd, new exit

29 Genesee Ave, **E** 🄾 🄷

28b La Jolla Village Dr, **E** 🍴 Italian Bistro, 🏠 Embassy Suites, Hyatt, Marriott, 🄾 🄷, to LDS Temple, **W** 📖 Mobil/dsl, 🍴 BJ's Grill, CA Pizza Kitchen, Chipotle Mexican, Dominos, Elijah's Deli, El Torito, Flame Broiler, Islands Burgers, Mrs Gooch's, Pick-Up Stix, RockBottom Café, Rubio's, TGIFriday's, 🏠 Sheraton, 🄾 🄷, AT&T, Best Buy, CVS Drug, Marshall's, PetsMart, Radio Shack, Ralph's Foods, Ross, Staples, Whole Foods Mkt, Trader Joe's

Left margin: N ↕ S | CA | OCEANSIDE | ESCONDIDO

Right margin: ENCINATAS

INTERSTATE 5 CONT'D

Exit	Services
28a	Nobel Dr (from nb), **E** 🛏 Hyatt, 🔵 LDS Temple, **W** same as 28b
27	Gilman Dr, La Jolla Colony Dr
26b	CA 52, E
26a	La Jolla Rd (from nb)
23b	CA 274, Balboa Ave, **1 mi E** 🅖 Shell, 🍴 Del Taco, 🔵 Albertson's, **W** 🅖 Mobil, 76/repair, 7-11, 🍴 McDonald's, In-N-Out, Rubio's, Wienerschnitzel, 🛏 Days Inn, Holiday Inn Express, Mission Bay Inn, San Diego Motel, 🔵 🄷 Discount Tire, Express Tire, Ford, Nissan, Toyota/Scion, Mission Bay Pk
23a	Grand Ave, Garnet Ave, same as 23b
22	Clairemont Dr, Mission Bay Dr, **E** 🅖 Arco, Shell, 🛏 Best Western, 🔵 Chevrolet/VW, **W** to Sea World Dr
21	Sea World Dr, Tecolote Dr, **E** 🅖 Shell, 🛏 Seaside Inn, 🔵 Aamco, CarQuest, Circle K, PetCo, **W** 🛏 Hilton, 🔵 Old Town SP, Seaworld
20	I-8, W to Nimitz Blvd, E to El Centro, CA 209, S (from sb), to Rosecrans St
19	Old Town Ave, **E** 🅖 Arco/24hr, Shell, 🛏 Courtyard, La Quinta
18b	Washington St, **E** 🛏 Comfort Inn
18a	Pacific Hwy Viaduct, Kettner St
17b	India St, Front St, Sassafras St, **E** 🅖 Mobil, Rte 66 Gas, **W** 🔵 ♿, civic ctr
17a	Hawthorn St, Front St, **W** 🅖 Exxon/dsl, 🛏 Holiday Inn, Motel 6, Radisson, 🔵 🄷
16b	6th Ave, downtown
16a	CA 163 N, 10th St, **E** 🔵 AeroSpace Museum, **W** 🅖 Shell, 🍴 Del Taco, Jack-in-the-Box, McDonald's, 🛏 Days Inn, Downtown Lodge, El Cortez Motel, Holiday Inn, Marriott, 🔵 🄷
15c b	CA 94, E (from nb), Pershing Dr, B St, civic ctr
15a	CA 94 E, J St, Imperial Ave (from sb),
14b	Cesar Chavez Pkwy
14a	CA 75, to Coronado, **W** toll rd to Coronado
13b	National Ave SD, 28th St, **E** 🍴 Little Caesar's, Starbucks, Subway, 🔵 AutoZone, **W** 🅖 Shell, 🍴 Burger King, Del Taco, El Pollo Loco
13a	CA 15 N, to Riverside
12	Main St, National City
11b	8th St, National City, **E** 🅖 Arco, Shell/24hr, 🍴 Jack-in-the-Box, 🛏 Holiday Inn, Howard Johnson, Ramada Inn, Super 8, Value Inn, **W** 🅖 Chevron/dsl
11a	Harbor Dr, Civic Center Dr
10	Bay Marina, 24th St, Mile of Cars Way, **1/2 mi E** 🍴 Denny's, In-N-Out
9	CA 54, E
8b	E St, Chula Vista, **E** 🛏 Motel 6, **W** 🍴 Anthony's Fish Grotto, 🛏 GoodNite Inn
8a	H St
7b	J St (from sb)
7a	L St, **E** 🅖 7-11, 76, Shell/dsl, 🍴 Mandarin Chinese, 🛏 Best Western, 🔵 AutoZone, NAPA, Parts+, Office Depot
6	Palomar St, **E** 🅖 Arco, 🍴 China King, Del Taco, DQ, HomeTown Buffet, KFC, Little Caesar's, McDonald's, Subway, 🛏 Palomar Inn, 🔵 Food4Less, Office Depot, 7-11, **E on Broadway** 🍴 Jack-in-the-Box, KFC, Panda Express, Quizno's, Yoshinoya, 🔵 Costco/gas, Michael's, Ross, Target, Walmart

Exit	Services
5b	Main St, to Imperial Beach, **E** 🅖 Arco, 🍴 AZ Chinese
5a	CA 75 (from sb), Palm Ave, to Imperial Beach, **E** 🅖 Arco, 🍴 Armando's Mexican, Papa John's, Wahshing Chinese, 🔵 Discount Tire, 7-11, Soto's Transmissions, **W** 🅖 Arco, 7-11, Shell/repair/24hr, Thrifty, 🍴 Boll Weevil Diner, Burger King, Carl's Jr, Carrow's, Coldstone Creamery, El Chile Mexican, Los Pancho's Tacos, McDonald's, Rally's, Red Hawk Steaks, Roberto's Mexican, Subway, Taco Bell, Wienerschnitzel, 🛏 Super 8, Travelodge, 🔵 AutoZone, CVS Drug, Home Depot, Jiffy Lube, 99¢ Store, Von's Foods
4	Coronado Ave (from sb), **E** 🅖 Chevron/service, Shell/service, 🍴 Denny's, Taco Bell, 🛏 EZ 8 Motel, 🔵 7-11, **W** 🅖 Shell/dsl, 🛏 Day's Inn, 🔵 to Border Field SP
3	CA 905, Tocayo Ave, **W** 🅖 7-11
2	Dairy Mart Rd, **E** 🅖 Arco/24hr, Circle K, 🍴 Burger King, Carl's Jr, Coco's, KFC, McDonald's, Roberto's Mexican, 🛏 Americana Inn, Best Value, Super 8, Valli-Hi Motel, 🔵 CarQuest, Radio Shack, Pacifica RV Resort
1b	Via de San Ysidro, **E** 🅖 Chevron, Exxon, Mobil, 76, 🔵 Max's Foods, NAPA, **W** 🅖 Chevron, 🍴 Denny's, KFC, 🛏 Economy Inn, Knights/RV park, Motel 6
1a	I-805, N (from nb), Camino de la Plaza (from sb), **E** 🍴 Burger King, El Pollo Loco, Jack-in-the-Box, KFC, McDonald's, Subway, 🛏 Flamingo Motel, Gateway Inn, Holiday Motel, Travelodge, 🔵 AutoZone, **W** 🍴 Achiato Mexican, Gingling House Chinese, IHOP, Iron Wok, McDonald's, Pizza Hut/Taco Bell, Sunrise Buffet, 🔵 Baja Duty-Free, K-Mart, Ross, Marshall's, factory outlet, border parking
0	US/Mexico Border, California state line, customs, I-5 begins/ends

INTERSTATE 8

Exit	Services
172.5mm	California/Arizona state line, Colorado River, Pacific/Mountain time zone
172	4th Ave, Yuma, **N** Ft Yuma Casino, **S** 🅖 Chevron, Circle K, 🍴 Jack-in-the-Box, Yuma Landing Rest., 🛏 Best Western, Hilton Garden, 🔵 Rivers Edge RV Park, to Yuma SP
170	Winterhaven Dr, **S** Rivers Edge RV Park
166	CA 186, Algodones Rd, Andrade, **S** Cocopah RV
166	Continued Resort/golf, Quechan Hotel/Casino, to Mexico
165mm	**CA Insp/weigh Sta**
164	Sidewinder Rd, **N** st patrol, **S** 🅖 Shell/LP, 🔵 Pilot Knob RV Park
159	CA 34, Ogilby Rd, to Blythe

Left margin (top to bottom): N ↕ S ... SAN DIEGO AREA ... SAN DIEGO AREA ... YUMA E ↕ W

CA

INTERSTATE 8 CONT'D

Exit	Services
156	Grays Well Rd, N Imperial Dunes RA
155mm	**rest area both lanes (exits left), full facilities, Ⓗ, litter barrels, petwalk**
151	Gordons Well
146	Brock Research Ctr Rd
143	CA 98, to Calexico, Midway Well
131	CA 115, VanDerLinden Rd, to Holtville, **5 mi** N gas, food, lodging, RV camping
128	Bonds Corner Rd
125	CA 7 S, Orchard Rd, Holtville, **4 mi** N gas/dsl, food
120	Bowker Rd
118b a	CA 111, to Calexico, **1 mi** N Ⓡ Shell/dsl/café/scales, Ⓞ RV park, tires/truckwash
116	Dogwood Rd, S Ⓡ Arco, Ⓕ Carino's, Chili's, Chuck-eCheese, Denny's, Famous Dave's BBQ, Fortune Garden, Jack-in-the-Box, Sombrero Mexican, Starbucks, Ⓛ Fairfield Inn, TownePlace Suites, Ⓞ Americas Tire, Best Buy, Dillard's, $Tree, JC Penney, Macy's, Marshall's, Michael's, Old Navy, PetCo, Ross, Sears/auto, Staples, mall

EL CENTRO

Exit	Services
115	CA 86, 4th St, El Centro, N Ⓡ Arco/24hr, Chevron/dsl, 7-11/dsl, Shell/dsl, Ⓕ Carl's Jr, China Express, Exotic Thai, Jack-in-the-Box, Manila Lumpia, McDonald's, Mexicali Taco, Ⓛ Holiday Inn Express, Motel 6, Ⓞ El Sol Mkt, U-Haul, S Ⓡ Mobil/dsl/scales, On the Go/Subway, Ⓕ IHOP, In-N-Out, Taco Bell, Ⓛ Best Western, Comfort Inn, Rodeway Inn, Ⓞ AutoZone, Home Depot, Honda/Hyundai, Lucky Foods, Desert Trails RV Park
114	Imperial Ave, El Centro, **0-3 mi** N Ⓡ Arco, Chevron/dsl, 7-11/dsl, Shell, USA/dsl, Ⓕ Applebee's, Burger King, Carl's Jr, Carrow's, Church's, Del Taco, Denny's, Domino's, El Pollo Loco, Farmer Boys, Golden Corral, Jack-in-the-Box, KFC, Little Caesars, McDonald's, Mexicali Grill, Pizza Hut, Quiznos, Rally's, Scribble's Rest, Sizzler, Sonic, Subway, Taco Bell, TasteeFreez Burgers, Wendy's, Ⓛ Clarion, EconoLodge, Howard Johnson, Knights Inn, SuperStar Inn, Vacation Inn/RV Park, Ⓞ Americas Tire, AutoZone, Costco/gas, $Tree, Food4Less, Ford, Goodyear/auto, K-Mart, Kragen Parts, Lowe's, 99c Store, Nissan, PepBoys, Radio Shack, Rite Aid, Staples, Target, Toyota/Scion, Von's Foods, Walgreens, Walmart, st patrol
111	Forrester Rd, to Westmorland
108mm	**Sunbeam Rest Area both lanes, full Ⓗ facilities, Ⓒ, Ⓗ, litter barrels, petwalk, RV dump**
107	Drew Rd, Seeley, N Sunbeam RV Park, to Sunbeam Lake, S Rio Bend RV Park
101	Dunaway Rd, Imperial Valley, elev 0 ft, N st prison
89	Imperial Hwy, CA 98, Ocotillo, N Ⓞ USPO, S Ⓡ Texaco/dsl, Ⓞ RV camping, museum
87	CA 98 (from eb), to Calexico
81mm	**runaway truck ramp, eb**
80	Mountain Springs Rd
77	In-ko-pah Park Rd, N Ⓒ, towing
75mm	**brake insp area eb, Ⓒ**
73	Jacumba, S Ⓡ Chevron/dsl, Shell/Subway/dsl/24hr, Ⓞ RV camping
65	CA 94, Boulevard, to Campo, S Ⓡ MtnTop/dsl, Ⓛ Lux Inn, Ⓞ auto repair, USPO, to McCain Valley RA (7mi)

Exit	Services
63mm	Tecate Divide, elev 4140 ft
62mm	Crestwood Summit, elev 4190 ft
61	Crestwood Rd, Live Oak Springs, S Ⓡ Golden Acorn Trkstp/casino/dsl, Ⓛ Live Oak Sprs Country Inn, Ⓞ Outdoor World RV Camp, info
54	Kitchen Creek Rd, Cameron Station, S food, RV camping
51	rd 1, Buckman Spgs Rd, to Lake Morena, S gas/dsl, LP, food, lodging, RV camping, Lake Morena CP (7mi), Potrero CP (19mi), rest area both lanes, **full Ⓗ facilities, Ⓒ, Ⓗ, litter barrels, petwalk, RV dump**
48	**insp sta, wb**
47	rd 1, Sunrise Hwy, Laguna Summit, elev 4055 ft, N to Laguna Mtn RA
45	Pine Valley, Julian, N Ⓕ Calvin's Rest., Frosty Burger, Major's Diner, Ⓛ Pine Valley Inn, Ⓞ Curves, Mtn Mkt, Pine Valley/gas, to Cuyamaca Rancho SP, city park, USPO, vet
44mm	Pine Valley Creek
42mm	elev 4000 ft
40	CA 79, Japatul Rd, Descanso, N Ⓕ Descanso Rest., Ⓞ to Cuyamaca Rancho SP
37mm	vista point eb, elev 3000 ft
36	E Willows, N Alpine Sprs RV Park, Viejas Indian Res, casino
33	W Willows Rd, to Alpine, N Alpine Sprs RV Park, Viejas Outlets/famous brands, casino, same as 36, S ranger sta
31mm	elev 2000 ft
30	Tavern Rd, to Alpine, N Ⓡ Chevron/dsl, Valero/dsl, S Ⓡ 76/Circle K, Shell, Ⓕ Carl's Jr, La Carreta, Little Caesars, Mediterraneo Grill, Ramon's BBQ, Subway, Ⓛ Ayre's Inn, Ⓞ Ace Hardware, CVS Drug, Daniel's IGA Mkt, Rite Aid, TrueValue, city park
27	Dunbar Lane, Harbison Canyon, N Ⓞ RV camping, Flinn Sprgs CP
25mm	elev 1000 ft, 24mm, phone
23	Lake Jennings Pk Rd, Lakeside, N Ⓡ Arco/Jack-in-the-Box/dsl/24hr, to Lake Jennings CP, Ⓞ RV camping, S Ⓡ 7-11, Ⓕ Burger King, Karla's Mexican, Marechiaro's Pizza
22	Los Coches Rd, Lakeside, N Ⓡ Eagle/dsl/LP, 7-11, Valero, Ⓕ Albert's Mexican, Danny's Pizza, Laposta Mexican, Mike's NY Pizza, Ⓞ RV camping/dump, S Ⓡ Shell/dsl, Ⓕ Denny's, Giant NY Pizza, McDonald's, Panda Express, Subway, Taco Bell, Ⓞ Radio Shack, Vons Foods, Walmart
20b	Greenfield Dr, to Crest, N Ⓡ Chevron/dsl, Valero/dsl, Ⓕ Jack-in-the-Box, Marita's Mexican, McDonald's, Panchos Tacos, Pernicano's Pizza, Subway, Ⓞ Ⓗ, Albertson's, AutoZone, Curves, Ford, 99c Store, RV camping, 7-11, auto repair, st patrol, urgent care, S Ⓡ Mobil/dsl/LP

EL CAJON

Exit	Services
20a	E Main St (from wb, no EZ return), N Ⓡ Budget Inn, Ⓞ Ford, Vacationer RV Park, repair, S Ⓡ Arco, Ⓞ Cadillac
19	2nd St, CA 54, El Cajon, N Ⓡ Arco/24hr, Chevron/dsl, Exxon/dsl, Ⓕ Marechio's Italian, Ⓞ CVS Drug, NAPA, Vons Foods, repair, S Ⓡ On the Go, Shell, Ⓕ Arby's, Burger King, Carl's Jr, Estrada's Mexican, Fred's Burgers, IHOP, Jack-in-the-Box, KFC, McDonald's, Pizza Hut, Popeye's, Quiznos, Subway, Taco Bell, Taco Shop, Ⓛ Best Value Inn, Ⓞ CarQuest, Firestone/

🅖 = gas 🍴 = food 🛏 = lodging 🅞 = other

INTERSTATE 8 CONT'D

Exit	Services
19	Continued auto, Jiffy Lube, PepBoys, PetCo, Ralphs Foods, Radio Shack, Rite Aid, Walgreens
18	Mollison Ave, El Cajon, N 🅖 Chevron, 🍴 Denny's, 🛏 Best Western, Days Inn, S 🅖 Arco/24hr, QuickTrip/dsl, 🍴 Taco Bell, 🛏 Super 8
17c	Magnolia Ave, CA 67 (from wb), to Santee, N 🅖 Arco, 🍴 Black Angus, Del Taco, Jack-in-the-Box, Panda Express, 🅞 Food4Less, Target, mall, S 🅖 Shell/service, 🍴 Panda Express, Perry's Cafe, Red Brick Pizza, Rubio's, 🛏 Motel 6, Rodeway Inn, 🅞 Nudo's Drug, Ross
17b	CA 67 (from eb), same as 17 a&c
17a	Johnson Ave (from eb), N 🍴 Applebee's, Boston Mkt, Burger King, Carl's Jr, Coco's, KFC, LJ Silver, McDonald's, On the Border, Pat&Oscars, Rubio's, Sizzler, Subway, 🅞 Best Buy, Big Boy, Big O Tire, Chevrolet, CVS Drug, $Tree, Goodyear/auto, Home Depot, Honda, JC Penney, Macy's, Marshall's, Office Depot, PetsMart, Sears/auto, Subaru, Toyota/Scion, Walmart, mall, S 🅞 Aamco, KIA, vet
16	Main St, N 🅖 Arco/24hr, 🍴 Denny's/24hr, Sombrero Mexican, 🛏 Relax Inn, 🅞 7-11, S 🅖 Chevron/dsl, Super Star, 🅞 Nissan, brakes/transmissions
15	El Cajon Blvd (from eb), N 🅖 Quality Inn, S 🅖 Exxon/dsl, 🍴 Wrangler BBQ, 🅞 BMW
14c	Severin Dr, Fuerte Dr (from wb), N 🅖 Arco/24hr, 🍴 Anthony's Fish Grotto, Charcoal House Rest., 🛏 Holiday Inn Express, S 🍴 Brigantine Seafood Rest.
14b a	CA 125, to CA 94
13b	Jackson Dr, Grossmont Blvd, N 🅖 Chevron, 🍴 Arby's, Casa de Pico, Chili's, Chipotle Mexican, ChuckeCheese, ClaimJumper, Fuddrucker's, Jamba Juice, McDonald's, Olive Garden, Panda Express, Panera Bread, Red Lobster, Rubio's, Schlotsky's, Starbucks, 🅞 🛏, Barnes&Noble, Best Buy, CVS Drug, $Tree, Kragen Parts, Macy's, 7-11, Staples, Target, Trader Joes, Walmart, mall, USPO, S 🅖 76, 🍴 Honeybaked Ham, Jack-in-the-Box, 🅞 Discount Tire, Ford, Hyundai, Ralph's Foods, VW
13a	Spring St (from eb), El Cajon Blvd (from wb), N 🅞 Chrysler/Jeep, Dodge, S 🍴 La Salsa Mexican, Starbucks, Subway, 🛏 Hitching Post, 🅞 AutoZone, 99c Store
12	Fletcher Pkwy, to La Mesa, N 🅖 Shell, 🍴 Chipotle Mexican, McDonald's, Pick Up Stix, 🛏 Heritage Inn, Holiday Inn, 🅞 Costco, 7-11, S 🍴 El Torito, La Salsa Mexican, Starbucks, 🛏 Motel 6, 🅞 Chevrolet, 99c Store, San Diego RV Resort
11	70th St, Lake Murray Blvd, N 🅖 Shell/dsl, 🍴 Subway, 🅞 truck/RV repair, S 🅖 Shell/7-11/dsl, 🍴 Aiken's Deli, Denny's, Marie Callender's, 🅞 🛏
10	College Ave, N 🅖 Chevron/dsl, 🅞 Windmill Farms Mkt, S 🅞 🛏, to SDSU
9	Waring Rd, N 🍴 Nicolosi's Italian, 🛏 Days Inn, Quality Inn
8	Fairmount Ave (7 from eb), to Mission Gorge Rd, N 🅖 Arco/24hr, Mobil/dsl, 7-11, 🍴 Arby's, Black Angus, Carl's Jr, Chili's, Coco's, El Pollo Loco, Jack-in-the-Box, Jamba Juice, McDonald's, Rally's, Roberto's Tacos, Rubio's, Sombrero Mexican, Starbucks, Subway, Szechuan

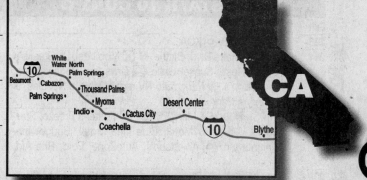

8	Continued Chinese, Togo's, Wendy's, 🛏 Super 8, 🅞 🛏, Aamco, CVS Drug, Discount Tire, Home Depot, Honda, NAPA, Rite Aid, Toyota/Scion, Tuesday Morning, Vons Foods
7b a	I-15 N, CA 15 S, to 40th St
6b	I-805, N to LA, S to Chula Vista
6a	Texas St, Qualcomm Way, N 🍴 Dave&Buster's, same as 5
5	Mission Ctr Rd, N 🅖 Chevron, 🍴 Carl's Jr, Chevy's Mexican, Chipotle Mexican, Fuddrucker's, Hooters, In-N-Out, Jack-in-the-Box, King's Fishouse, Maggie Moo's, Mimi's Cafe, On The Border, Outback Steaks, Panda Express, Pick-Up Stix, Peiwei Asian, Robex Juice, Subway, Taco Bell, 🛏 Marriott, Sheraton, 🅞 Best Buy, Chevrolet, Lincoln/Mercury, Macy's, Marshall's, Michael's, Nordstrom Rack, Old Navy, Staples, Target, mall, S 🅖 Arco/24hr, 🍴 Benihana, Denny's, El Torito, Wendy's, 🛏 Comfort Suites, Hilton, La Quinta, Sheraton, 🅞 Mazda, Suzuki
4c b	CA 163, Cabrillo Frwy, S to downtown, zoo
4a	Hotel Circle Dr (from eb), CA 163 (from wb)
3a	Hotel Circle, Taylor St, N 🍴 Hunter Steaks, Kelly's Steaks, 🛏 Comfort Suites, Crowne Plaza, Handlery Hotel, Motel 6, Town&Country Motel, 🅞 golf, S 🅖 Arco, 🍴 Adam's Cafe, Albie's Rest., Ricky's Rest., Tickled Trout, Valley Kitchen, 🛏 Best Western, Comfort Inn, Courtyard, Days Hotel, DoubleTree Inn, Extended Stay America, Hawthorn Suites, Hilton, Howard Johnson, King's Inn/rest., Mission Valley Hotel, Ramada Inn, Residence Inn, Super 8, Travelodge, Vagabond Inn, 🅞 Chrysler/Jeep, vet
2c	Morena Blvd (from wb)
2b	I-5, N to LA, S to San Diego
2a	Rosecrans St (from wb), CA 209, S 🅖 Chevron, 🍴 Burger King, Chipotle Mexican, Del Taco, In-N-Out, Jack-in-the-Box, McDonald's, Panda Express, Starbucks, 🛏 Super 8, 🅞 BigLots, PetsMart, Staples
1	W Mission Bay Blvd, Sports Arena Blvd (from wb), N to SeaWorld, S 🅖 Arco, 🍴 Arby's, Chick-fil-A, Denny's, Jack-in-the-Box, McDonald's, Phil's BBQ, Red Lobster, Taco Bell, Wendy's, 🛏 Heritage Inn, Holiday Inn Express, Ramada Ltd, 🅞 CVS Drug, Home Depot, U-Haul
0mm	I-8 begins/ends on Sunset Cliffs Blvd, N Mission Bay Park, 1/4 mi W 🅖 Exxon, Shell, 🍴 Jack-in-the-Box, Kaiserhof Cafe

INTERSTATE 10

Exit	Services
245mm	California/Arizona state line, Colorado River, Pacific/Mountain time zone
244mm	inspection sta wb

(Side label, left margin: E ↕ W, EL CAJON)

(Side label, right column: SAN DIEGO AREA)

INTERSTATE 10 CONT'D

E W BLYTHE

Exit	Services
243	Riviera Dr, **S** ⊙ KOA
241	US 95, Intake Blvd, Blythe, **N** ⛽ Mobil/dsl, 🍴 Steaks'n Cakes Rest., Sunset Grille, 🛏 Days Inn, Rodeway Inn, ⊙ Burton's RV Park, auto/RV repair/24hr, to Needles, **S** McIntyre Park
240	7th St, **N** ⛽ EZ Mart, 76/dsl, 🍴 Foster's Freeze, Starbucks, 🛏 Astro Motel, Blue Line Motel, Budget Inn, Knights Inn, ⊙ Albertson's, AutoZone, Ford, Rite Aid, repair
239	Lovekin Blvd, Blythe, **N** ⛽ Mobil/Subs/dsl, Shell/Quiznos, 🍴 Carl's Jr, Del Taco, Domino's, Jack-in-the-Box, La Casita Dos, McDonald's, Pizza Hut, Popeye's, Rosita's Mexican, Sizzler, Starbucks, Wang's Chinese, 🛏 Best Value Inn, Best Western, Budget Host, Hampton Inn, Regency Inn, Willow Inn, ⊙ H, Ace Hardware, Checker Parts, $Tree, Goodyear/auto, K-Mart/Little Caesars, Radio Shack, Verizon, **S** ⛽ Chevron/dsl/24hr, 76/dsl, Shell/DQ/dsl, Valero, 🍴 Burger King, Casa de Maria Mexican, Denny's, KFC, Subway, Taco Bell, 🛏 Comfort Suites, Holiday Inn Express, Motel 6, Super 8, ⊙ Buick/Chevrolet, city park
236	CA 78, Neighbours Blvd, to Ripley, **N** ⛽ Valero/dsl, **S** to Cibola NWR
232	Mesa Dr, **N** ⛽ 76/dsl/rest./scales/24hr/@, Valero/Subway/dsl, ⊙ ⛑
231	weigh sta wb
222mm	Wileys Well Rd, **N** rest area both lanes, full ♿ facilities, 🚻, 🛏, litter barrels, petwalk, **S** to st prison
217	Ford Dry Lake Rd
201	Corn Springs Rd
192	CA 177, Rice Rd, to Lake Tamarisk, **N** 🍴 Desert Ctr Cafe, ⊙ camping
189	Eagle Mtn Rd
182	Red Cloud Rd
177	Hayfield Rd
173	Chiriaco Summit, **N** ⛽ Chevron/Foster's Freeze/dsl/24hr, 🍴 Chiriaco Rest., ⊙ Patton Museum, truck/tire repair
168	to Twentynine Palms, to Mecca, Joshua Tree NM
162	frontage rd
159mm	**Cactus City Rest Area both lanes, full ♿ facilities, 🚻, litter barrels, petwalk**
147mm	0 ft elevation
146	Dillon Rd, to CA 86, to CA 111 S, Coachella, **N** ⛽ Chevron/24hr, Loves/Carl's Jr/dsl/24hr, 🍴 Del Taco, **S** ⛽ Chevron/Jack-in-the-Box, TA/Arco/Arby's/Taco Bell/dsl/24hr/@, ⊙ Spotlight Casino
145	(from eb), CA 86, **S**

I N D I O

Exit	Services
144	CA 111 N, CA 86 S, Indio, **N** 🛏 Holiday Inn Express, ⊙ Classic RV Park, Fantasy Sprgs Casino/Hotel/Cafe
143	Jackson St, Indio, **N** 🍴 Jack-in-the-Box, KFC, McDonald's, Panda Express, Subway, Taco Bell, ⊙ BigLots, CVS Drug, $Tree, Fletcher's Tire, Home Depot, Marshall's, PetCo, Ross, Target, Walgreens, WinCo Foods, **S** ⊙ Circle K
142	Monroe St, Central Indio, **N** ⊙ RV camping, **S** ⛽ Circle K, 76, Shell/dsl/LP, 🍴 Mexicali Cafe, Taco Jalisco, 🛏 Quality Inn
139	Jefferson St, Indio Blvd, **N** ⊙ Shadow Hills RV Resort, hwy patrol

PALM SPRINGS

Exit	Services
137	Washington St, Country Club Dr, to Indian Wells, **N** ⛽ Arco/24hr, Chevron, 🍴 Burger King, Burger Time, Coco's, Del Taco, Mario's Italian, Popeye's, Starbucks, Winchell's, 🛏 Comfort Suites, Motel 6, ⊙ Buick/GMC, Ford/Lincoln/Mercury, Honda, McMahon's RV Ctr, 1000 Trails RV Park, Rite Aid, Stater Bros, Toyota/Scion, VW, Walgreens, **S** ⛽ Mobil/dsl, 76/Circle K, 🍴 Baskin-Robbins/Togo's, Carl's Jr, Chicken Pie Factory, China Wok, Domino's, Goody's Cafe, Lili's Chinese, Pizza Hut, Quiznos, Subway, Taco Shop, Wendy's, 🛏 Embassy Suites, ⊙ Firestone/auto, Goodyear/auto
134	Cook St, to Indian Wells, **S** ⛽ Arco, Mobil, 🍴 Applebees, Carl's Jr, Dogo's Hot Dogs, Firehouse Grill, Jack-in-the-Box, Starbucks, Subway, 🛏 Courtyard, Hampton Inn, Hilton/Homewood Suites, Residence Inn
131	Monterey Ave, Thousand Palms, **N** ⛽ Arco/24hr, 🍴 Jack-in-the-Box, **S** 🍴 Clark's Cafe/Food Mkt, Del Taco, El Pollo Loco, IHOP, McDonald's, Panda Express, Quiznos, Red Robin, Starbucks, Subway, Taco Bell, Wendy's, ⊙ America's Tire, Costco/gas, Curves, Home Depot, Kohls, PetsMart, Sam's Club/gas, Verizon, Walmart
130	Ramon Rd, Bob Hope Dr, **N** ⛽ Chevron/24hr, ⛟FLYING J/dsl/LP/rest./24hr, Shell/dsl, Valero, 🍴 Carl's Jr, Casa de Pasta, Del Taco, Denny's, Guerro Mexican, In-N-Out, McDonald's, 🛏 Red Roof Inn, ⊙ truckwash, **S** ⊙ H, Agua Caliente Casino/rest.
126	Date Palm Dr, Rancho Mirage, **S** ⛽ Arco/24hr, Mobil, Valero, 🍴 La Palapa Mexican, ⊙ RV Camping
123	Palm Dr, to Desert Hot Sprgs, **N** ⛽ Arco, Chevron/Jack-in-the-Box, ⊙ Caliente Springs Camping, 3 mi, **S** to Gene Autry Trail
120	Indian Ave, to, N Palm Sprgs, **N** ⛽ 76/Circle K, Shell, 🍴 Denny's, 🛏 Motel 6, **S** ⛽ Chevron, ▥/DQ/Wendy's/dsl/scales/24hr, 🍴 Jack-in-the-Box, ⊙ H
117	CA 62, to Yucca Valley, Twentynine Palms, to Joshua Tree NM
114	Whitewater, many windmills
113mm	**rest area both lanes, full ♿ facilities, 🚻, 🛏, litter barrels**
112	CA 111 (from eb), to Palm Springs
110	Haugeen-Lehmann
106	Main St, to Cabazon, **N** ⛽ Shell/dsl, 🍴 Burger King, Wheel Inn Rest., **S** ⛽ Valero/Circle K/dsl
104	Cabazon, same as 103
103	Fields Rd, **N** ⛽ Chevron, TC/A&W/dsl, 🍴 McDonald's, Ruby's Diner, ⊙ Hadley Fruit Orchards, Premium Outlets/famous brands, Morongo Reservation/casino

BANNING

Exit	Services
102.5mm	**Banning weigh sta both lanes**
102	Ramsey St (from wb)
101	Hargrave St, Banning, **N** ⛽ 76/Church's, Shell/dsl/LP, Valero/dsl, 🛏 Country Inn, ⊙ tires
100	CA 243, 8th St, Banning, **N** ⛽ Chevron/dsl, 🍴 Ahloo Chinese, IHOP, Jack-in-the-Box, ⊙ Rite Aid, **S** ⊙ KOA
99	22nd St, to Ramsey St, **N** ⛽ Arco/24hr, Shell, 🍴 Carl's Jr, Carrow's, Chelos Tacos, Del Taco, KFC, McDonald's, Pepe's Mexican, Pizza Hut, Russo's Italian, Sizzler, Starbucks, Subway, Wall Chinese, 🛏 Days Inn, Super 8, Travelodge, ⊙ Banning RV Ctr, Goodyear/auto
98	Sunset Ave, Banning, **N** ⛽ Chevron/dsl, 🍴 Domino's, Gramma's Kitchen, Gus Jr #7 Burger, 🛏 Holiday Inn

 🅖 = gas 🍴 = food 🏠 = lodging 🅞 = other

INTERSTATE 10 CONT'D

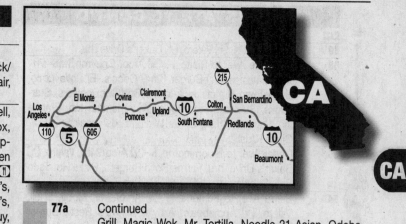

E ↕ W

B E A U M O N T

Exit	Services
98	Continued Express, 🅞 Ace Hardware, AutoZone, BigLots, Buick/Chevrolet/GMC, Ray's RV Ctr, Rio Ranch Mkt, repair, vet
96	Highland Springs Ave, N 🅖 Arco/24hr, Chevron, Shell, 🍴 Applebee's, Burger King, Denny's, Jack-in-the-Box, Orchid Thai, Papa John's, Subway, Wendy's, 🏠 Hampton Inn, 🅞 🏥, Do-It Hardware, Food4Less, Kragen Parts, Stater Bros Foods, Walgreens, S 🍴 Mobil, 🍴 Carl's Jr, Chili's, El Pollo Loco, La Casita, McDonald's, Palermo's Pizza, Panda Express, Quiznos, Rubio's, Starbucks, Wienerschnitzel, 🅞 Albertson's, Best Buy, Curves, GNC, Home Depot, K-Mart, Kohls, PetCo, Rite Aid, Ross, Staples, Walmart/Subway, hwy patrol
95	Pennsylvania Ave, (from wb), Beaumont, N 🍴 Jasmine Thai, 🏠 Rodeway Inn, 🅞 AutoZone, Miller RV Ctr, Tom's RV Ctr
94	CA 79, Beaumont, N 🅖 Arco, 76/dsl, 🍴 Baker's Drive-Thru, Hawaiian BBQ, McDonald's, Popeye's, YumYum Donuts, 🏠 Best Western, Best Value Inn, 🅞 NAPA, S 🍴 Del Taco, Denny's, 🅞 RV camping
93	CA 60 W, to Riverside
92	San Timoteo Canyon Rd, Oak Valley Pkwy, N 🅖 Chevron, 🍴 Figero's Pizza, 🏠 Holiday Inn Express, 🅞 Rite Aid, golf, S golf
91mm	**rest area wb, full ♿ facilities, 🚻, 🏕, litter barrels, petwalk**
90	Cherry Valley Blvd, N 🅞 truck/tire repair
89	Singleton Rd (from wb), to Calimesa
88	Calimesa Blvd, N 🅖 Arco/24hr, Chevron/dsl, Shell, 🍴 Best Wok, Burger King, Carl's Jr, Denny's, Isabella's Italian, McDonald's, Subway, Taco Bell, Tang's Chinese, 🏠 Calimesa Inn, 🅞 Fresh&Easy Foods, Stater Bros Foods, Walgreens, S 🍴 Big Boy, Jack-in-the-Box
87	County Line Rd, to Yucaipa, N 🅖 FasTrip/gas, Shell/dsl, 🍴 Baker's DriveThru, Del Taco, 🅞 auto repair/tires
86mm	**Wildwood Rest Area eb, full ♿ facilities, 🚻, 🏕, litter barrels, petwalk**
85	Live Oak Canyon Rd, Oak Glen
83	Yucaipa Blvd, N 🅖 Arco/dsl/24hr, Chevron, Mobil, 🍴 Baker's DriveThru, Starbucks, S 🍴 Subway
82	Wabash Ave (from wb)
81	Redlands Blvd, Ford St, S 🅖 76
80	Cypress Ave, University St, N 🏥, to U of Redlands
79b a	CA 38, 6th St, Orange St, Redlands, N 🅖 Chevron, Thrifty, 🏠 Budget Inn, Stardust Motel, 🅞 Stater Bros Foods, S 🅖 76, Shell, 🍴 Chipotle Mexican, Denny's, Domino's, Eureka Burger, Open Kitchen Chinese, Phoenicia Greek, Rubio's, Togo's, Sizzler, Starbucks, Subway, 🅞 Kragen Parts, NAPA, Office Depot, Trader Joe's, Von's Foods
77c	(77b from wb)Tennessee St, N 🍴 Shakey's Pizza, 🅞 Home Depot, Toyota/Scion, S 🅖 Shell, 🍴 Arby's, Bakers DriveThru, Carl's Jr, Coco's, El Burrito, El Pollo Loco, Papa John's, Subway, Taco Bell, 🏠 Ayers Hotel, Comfort Suites, Dynasty Suites, Howard Johnson, 🅞 Ford, USPO
77b	(77c from wb) CA 30, to Highlands
77a	Alabama St, N 🅖 76/Circle K, 🍴 Canton Bistro, Chili's, Chick-fil-A, Coldstone Creamery, Denny's, Famous Dave's BBQ, Hawaiian BBQ, Jamba Juice, Macaroni

R E D L A N D S

S A N   B E R N A R D I N O

Exit	Services
77a	Continued Grill, Magic Wok, Mr. Tortilla, Noodle 21 Asian, Qdoba Mexican, Red Robin, Starbucks, Subway, Tom's Charburgers, 🏠 Best Value Inn, Super 8, 🅞 Barnes&Noble, GNC, JC Penney, Jo-Ann Superstore, Kohl's, Marshall's, Michael's, PetCo, Target, Verizon, VW, U-Haul, S 🅖 Chevron, Shell, 🍴 Del Taco, IHOP, Marie Callender's, McDonald's, Mona Lisa Pizza, Nick's Burgers, Old Spaghetti Factory, Quizno's, Slim's BBQ, Starbucks, Zabella's Mexican, 🏠 Country Inn&Suites, GoodNite Inn, 🅞 Aamco, BigLots, Chevrolet, CVS Drug, Discount Tire, $Tree, Goodyear/auto, K-Mart, Lowe's, 99c Store, Nissan, PepBoys, 7-11, Tuesday Morning
76	California St, N 🍴 Mill Creek Rest., 🅞 funpark, museum, S 🅖 Arco/24hr, Shell/LP/24hr, 🍴 Applebee's, Bravo Burger, Jose's Mexican, Panda Express, Subway, Weinerschnitzel, Wendy's, 🅞 AT&T, Food4Less, Just Tires, Mission RV Park, Radio Shack, Verizon, Walmart
75	Mountain View Ave, Loma Linda, N 🅖 Valero/dsl, S 🍴 Domino's, FarmerBoys Burgers, Lupe's Mexican, Subway
74	Tippecanoe Ave, Anderson St, N 🅖 Thrifty, 🍴 CA Pizza Kitchen, Chipotle Mexican, Coldstone Creamery, Denny's, Elephant Bar Rest., El Pollo Loco, Hawaiian BBQ, In-N-Out, Jack-in-the-Box, Jamba Juice, Panera Bread, Pick-Up Stix, Ruby Tuesday, Starbucks, Subway, Tasty Goody, 🏠 American Inn, Fairfield Inn, Residence Inn, 🅞 Costco/gas, Sam's Club, Staples, Verizon, S 🅖 76/dsl, 🍴 Baker's DriveThru, Del Taco, HomeTown Buffet, KFC, Napoli Italian, Wienerschnitzel, 🅞 Harley-Davidson, Honda, Hyundai, transmissions, to Loma Linda U
73b a	Waterman Ave, N 🅖 76, Shell/dsl/24hr, 🍴 Baja Fresh, Black Angus, Chili's, ChuckeCheese, ClaimJumper, Coco's, Crabby Bob's, El Torito, IHOP/24hr, King Buffet, Lotus Garden Chinese, Mimi's Café, Olive Garden, Outback Steaks, Panda Express, Pat&Oscar's, Red Lobster, Sizzler, Souplantation, Starbucks, TGIFriday's, 🏠 Best Western, Days Inn, Hilton, Hilton Garden, La Quinta, Quality Inn, Super 8, 🅞 Best Buy, Home Depot, Office Depot, PetsMart, S 🅖 Arco/24hr, 🍴 Burger King, Carl's Jr, Gus Jr Burger #8, McDonald's, Popeye's, Starbucks, Taco Bell, 🏠 Motel 6, 🅞 Camping World RV Service/supplies, El Monte RV Ctr, repair
72	I-215, CA 91
71	Mt Vernon Ave, Sperry Ave, N 🅖 7-11, Trkstp/dsl/LP, 🏠 Colony Inn, Colton Motel, 🅞 brake/muffler, repair
70b	9th St, N 🅖 Mobil, 🍴 Burger King, Denny's, McDonald's, P&G Burgers, Subway, 🏠 Hampton Inn, 🅞 Bumper Parts, Stater Bros Foods, USPO
70a	Rancho Ave, N 🍴 Del Taco, Jack-in-the-Box, KFC/Taco Bell, Wienerschnitzel

E ← → W

S A N   B E R N A R D I N O   O N T A R I O

CA

INTERSTATE 10 CONT'D

Exit	Services
69	Pepper Dr, N ⛽ Valero, 🍴 Baker's DriveThru
68	Riverside Ave, to Rialto, N ⛽ Arco, Chevron, I-10 Trk-stp/dsl/scales, 🍴 Burger King, Coco's, El Pollo Loco, HomeTown Buffet, Jack-in-the-Box, McDonald's, Starbucks, Subway, Taco Joe's, 🏨 American Inn, Empire Inn, Super 8, ⭕ Big O Tire, Walmart, dsl repair, S ⛽ 76/Circle K/dsl
66	Cedar Ave, to Bloomington, N ⛽ Arco/24hr, Valero, 🍴 Baker's DriveThru, FarmerBoys Burgers, Pizza Hut/Taco Bell, Subway, ⭕ USPO, S ⛽ Citgo/7-11
64	Sierra Ave, to Fontana, N ⛽ Arco/24hr, Mobil, Shell, Valero, 🍴 Applebee's, Arby's, Billy J's Rest., Burger King, China Cook, ChuckeCheese, DQ, Denny's, Del Taco, El Gallo Giro, In-N-Out, Jack-in-the-Box, KFC, Little Caesars, McDonald's, Millie's Kitchen, 1 China, Pancho Villa's, Papa John's, Pizza Hut/Taco Bell, Popeye's, Sizzler, Spire's Rest., Subway, 3 Hermanos, Wendy's, Wienerschnitzel, Yoshinoya, 🏨 Best Value Inn, EconoLodge, Motel 6, Valley Motel, ⭕ H, AT&T, Big-Lots, CVS Drug, $Tree, Fiesta Foods, Food4Less, GNC, Honda, Just Tires, Kia, K-Mart, Kragen Parts, PepBoys, Radio Shack, Rite Aid, Stater Bros Foods, Verizon, S 🍴 Brandon's Diner, China Buffet, Circle K, Del Taco, El Gran Burrito, Shakey's Pizza, Tasty Goody, 🏨 Hilton Garden, ⭕ AutoZone, 99c Store, Ross, Target
63	Citrus Ave, N ⛽ Gasco, 76, 🍴 Baker's DriveThru, Subway, ⭕ Ford, S ⛽ Arco, 7-11/dsl
61	Cherry Ave, N ⛽ Arco, Chevron/dsl, Trucktown Trkstp/dsl/24hr/@, Valero, 🍴 Carl's Jr, Del Taco, Jack-in-the-Box, 🏨 Circle Inn Motel, ⭕ Ford Trucks, S ⛽ North American Trkstp/dsl, 3 Sisters Trkstp/dsl/@, 76/Circle K, 🍴 Farmer Boy's Rest., La Chaquita, Mariscos Mexican, ⭕ Peterbilt 59, Etiwanda Ave, Valley Blvd
58b a	I-15, N to Barstow, S to San Diego
57	Milliken Ave, N ⛽ Arco/24hr, Chevron, Mobil/Albertos Mexican/dsl, 76/dsl, Shell, 🍴 Applebee's, Arby's, Baja Fresh, BJ's Rest., Boston's, Burger King, Carl's Jr, Chevy's Mexican, Chipotle, Coco's, Coldstone, Dave&Buster's, Del Taco, El Pollo Loco, Famous Dave's BBQ, Fat Burger, Fuddruckers, Hooters, IHOP, In-n-Out, Jack-in-the-Box, Jamba Juice, KFC, Krispy Kreme, McDonald's, Mkt Broiler, New City Buffet, NY Grill, Olive Garden, Outback Steaks, Rain Forest Cafe, Red Lobster, Rubio's, Sonic, Starbucks, Subway, Tokyo Tokyo, Wendy's, Wienerschnitzel, Wing Place, 🏨 Ayre's Suites, Country Inn&Suites, Courtyard, Hampton Inn, Hilton Garden, Holiday Inn Express, Homewood Suites, Hyatt, TownePlace Suites, ⭕ America's Tire, Best Buy, Big O Tire, Carmax, Costco/gas, JC Penney, Jo-Ann Fabrics, Kohl's, Marshalls, Ontario Mills Mall, Petsmart, Sam's Club/gas, Staples, Target, Verizon, S 🍴 TA/Shell/Pizza Hut/Subway/Taco Bell/dsl/rest./24hr/@, 🏨 Rodeway Inn
56	Haven Ave, Rancho Cucamonga, N ⛽ Mobil, 🍴 Benihana, Black Angus, Pizza Factory, 🏨 Aloft Hotel, Best Western, Extended Stay America, Hilton, La Quinta, Ontario Grand Suites, S 🍴 Panda Chinese, TGIFriday's, 🏨 Fairfield Inn
55b a	Holt Blvd, to Archibald Ave, N ⛽ Arco, Mobil/dsl, 🍴 Baker's Drive-thru, Burgertown USA, Hawaiian BBQ, Subway, Weinerschnitzel

M O N T C L A I R

Exit	Services
54	Vineyard Ave, N ⛽ 76/Circle K, 🍴 Carl's Jr, Del Taco, El Pollo Loco, Great China, Pizza Hut/Taco Bell, Popeye's, Quiznos, Rocky's Pizza, ⭕ AutoZone, Ralph's Foods, Rite Aid, Stater Bros Foods, S ⛽ Mobil, 76, Valero, 🍴 Basil Rest., Cowboy Bugers, Denny's, Garden Square Rest., In-N-Out, Jack-in-the-Box, Marie Callenders, Quiznos, Rosa's Italian, Spires Rest., Yoshinoya Japanese, Wendy's, 🏨 Ayers Suites, Best Western, Comfort Suites, Countryside Suites, DoubleTree Inn, Holiday Inn, Motel 6, Ontario 🛏 Inn, Quality Inn, Ramada Inn, Red Roof Inn, Residence Inn, Sheraton, ⭕ Buick/Cadillac/Chevrolet/GMC, USPO, to 🛏
53	San Bernardino Ave, 4th St, to Ontario, N ⛽ Arco, 7-11, 76, Shell, 🍴 Burger King, Carl's Jr, Jack-in-the-Box, 🏨 EconoLodge, Motel 6, ⭕ K-Mart, Radio Shack, S ⛽ Arco/24hr, 76, Valero, 🍴 Denny's, Little Caesars, Subway, YumYum Donuts, 🏨 Days Inn, Rodeway Inn, ⭕ Jax Mkt, city park
51	CA 83, Euclid Ave, to Ontario, Upland, N ⭕ H
50	Mountain Ave, to Mt Baldy, N ⛽ Chevron, Mobil/dsl, Shell/dsl, 🍴 Carrow's, Denny's, El Torito, Fresh&Easy, HoneyBaked Ham, Mimi's Café, Mi Taco, Rubio's, Subway, Trader Joe's, Wendy's, 🏨 Super 8, ⭕ AT&T, CVS Drug, $Tree, Home Depot, Kohl's, Michaels, Radio Shack, Staples, S ⛽ 76/dsl, 🍴 Baskin-Robbins, Carl's Jr, Chopstix, Coldstone, Jo-Anne's Cafe, Pizza Hut, Quiznos, Roundtable Pizza, Starbucks, Wingnuts, ⭕ Albertsons, Rite Aid, USPO, vet
49	Central Ave, to Montclair, N 🍴 Carl's Jr., Chipotle Mexican, Del Taco, El Pollo Loco, Hometown Buffet, John's Incredible Pizza, McDonald's, Panda Garden Buffet, Pizza Hut, Quiznos, Starbucks, Subway, Taco Bell, ⭕ America's Tire, AT&T, AutoZone, Barnes&Noble, Best Buy, Firestone/auto, Giant RV Ctr, Goodyear/auto, Harley-Davidson, JC Penney, Just Tires, Macy's, 99c Store, PepBoys, PetCo, Ross, Sears/auto, Target, Tuesday Morning, mall, vet, same as 48, S ⛽ Chevron, Thrifty, 🍴 Alberto's Mexican, Fulin Chinese, Jack-in-the-Box, LJ Silver, Subway, Wienerschnitzel, ⭕ Acura/Honda/Infiniti, Costco/gas, Nissan, 7-11, Stater Bro's
48	Monte Vista, N ⛽ Shell, 🍴 Acapulco Mexican, Applebee's, Chilis, Black Angus, Elephant Bar Rest., Macaroni Grill, Olive Garden, Red Lobster, ⭕ H, Nordstrom's, Macy's, mall, same as 49
47	Indian Hill Blvd, to Claremont, N ⛽ Mobil, 🍴 BC Cafe, Garden Square, 🏨 Claremont Lodge, Howard Johnson, S ⛽ Chevron/McDonald's, 76/dsl, 🍴 Burger King, Carl's Jr, Denny's, In-N-Out, Norm's Rest., RoundTable Pizza, Starbucks, World Famous Grill, ⭕ 7-11, Toyota/Scion
46	Towne Ave, N ⛽ 76/dsl, 7-11, 🍴 Jack-in-the-Box
45b	Garey Ave, to Pomona, N ⛽ Arco, ⭕ H, vet, S ⛽ Chevron, Shell/dsl, 🍴 Del Taco
45	White Ave, Garey Ave, to Pomona
44	(43 from eb) Dudley St, Fairplex Dr, N ⛽ Arco/dsl, 🍴 Denny's, 🏨 LemonTree Motel, Sheraton, S ⛽ Chevron/24hr, 🍴 Jack-in-the-Box, McDonald's, Starbucks, ⭕ 7-11
42b	CA 71, S (from eb), to Corona
42a	I-210 W, CA 57, S
41	Kellogg Dr, S to Cal Poly Inst
40	Via Verde

INTERSTATE 10 CONT'D

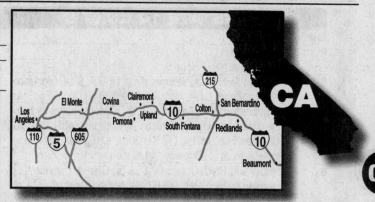

Exit	Services
38b	Holt Ave, to Covina, **N** 🍴 Hamiltons Steaks, 🛏 Radisson
38a	Grand Ave, **N** 🅖 Arco/dsl, United, 🍴 Baily's Rest, Denny's, 🛏 Best Western
37b	Barranca St, Grand Ave, same as 37a, **N** 🅖 76, Shell/dsl, 🍴 BJ's Rest., Carinos, Carl's Jr, Chili's, Chipotle Mexican, Dockside Grill, El Torito, Habit Burgers, Hooters, Islands Burgers, Marie Callender, Mariposa Mexican, Starbucks, 🛏 Best Western, Clarion, Fairfield Inn, Hampton Inn, 🅾 Albertsons, CVS Drug, Dick's, IKEA, Marshalls, Office Depot, Old Navy, Petsmart, Target, Verizon, **S** 🍴 In-N-Out, McDonald's, 🛏 Days Inn, 5 Star Inn
37a	Citrus Ave, to Covina, same as 37b, **N** 🅖 Chevron, 🍴 Buffalo Wild Wings, Burger King, Del Taco, IHOP, Jack-in-the-Box, Millie's Rest., Starbucks, Subway, TGIFriday's, Yum Yum Donuts, 🅾 Acura, Albertsons, Baja Ranch Foods, Buick/GMC, CVS Drug, KIA, Marshall's, Nissan, VW, **S** 🅖 76/autocare, 🍴 Classic Burger, 🅾 🅷, Cadillac
36	CA 39, Azusa Ave, to Covina, **N** 🅖 Arco/24hr, 76/dsl, 🍴 Dennys, Green Field Brazillian, McDonald's, Norm's Rest., Papa John's, Quiznos, Subway, 🅾 BigLots, Chrysler/Dodge/Jeep, CVS Drug, Food4Less, Stater Bros, **S** 🅖 Mobil, Shell/dsl, 🍴 Carrow's, 🅾 Audi, Chevrolet, Ford, Honda, Hummer, Mercedes, Toyota
35	Vincent Ave, Glendora Ave, **N** 🅖 76/dsl/autocare, **S** 🅖 76, 🍴 Applebee's, Baja Fresh, CA Pizza Kitchen, Elephant Bar Rest., Fresh&Easy, Grand Buffet, Jamba Juice, Panera Bread, Pizza Hut, Red Robin, Starbucks, Subway, Weinerschnitzel, 🅾 Best Buy, Big O Tire, Firestone, JC Penney, Macy's, Sears/auto, Verizon, mall, USPO
34	Pacific Ave, **N** 🅖 76, **S** 🅖 Mobil, Valero, 🅾 🅷, Discount Tire, K-Mart, Sears Outlet, mall, same as 35
33	Puente Ave, **N** 🅖 Chevron, 🍴 Denny's, Farmer Boy's, Guadalajara Grill, McDonald's, Panda Express, Sizzler, Starbucks, 🛏 Courtyard, Motel 6, 🅾 AT&T, Home Depot, Verizon, Walmart, **S** 🅖 Valero/dsl, 🛏 Regency Inn, 🍴 Jack-in-the-Box, 🅾 Harley-Davidson, U-Haul
32b	Francisquito Ave, to La Puente, **N** 🅖 V&G, 🅾 hwy patrol, **S** 🅖 76, 🍴 Carl's Jr, In-N-Out, Wienerschnitzel, 🛏 Grand Park Inn
32a	Baldwin Pk Blvd, **N** 🅖 Chevron/McDonald's, 🍴 Burger King, Fronteiras, IHOP, Jack-in-the-Box, Papa Johns, Pizza Hut/Taco Bell, Starbucks, Subway, Wok'n Go, Yum Yum Donuts, 🅾 🅷, CVS Drug, Food4Less, Target, transmissions, **S** 🍴 In-N-Out
31c	(31b from wb) Frazier St, **N** 🅾 7-11
31b a	(31a from wb) I-605 N/S, to Long Beach
30	Garvey Ave, **S** 🅖 Rte 66
29b	Valley Blvd, Peck Rd, **N** 🅖 Chevron, 🍴 Baskin-Robbins, Carl's Jr., Denny's, Hometown Buffet, Jamba Juice, KFC, Papa Johns, Shakey's Pizza, Subway, Taco Bell, Yoshinoya, 🛏 Motel 6, 🅾 Honda, Hyundai, Lexus, Nissan, Radio Shack, Sears Essentials, Staples, Toyota/Scion, Walgreens, **S** 🍴 McDonald's, Pepe's Seafood, Tommy's Burgers
29a	S Peck Rd (from eb)
28	Santa Anita Ave, to El Monte, **S** 🅖 76/dsl, 🅾 7-11, vet
27	Baldwin Avenue, Temple City Blvd, **S** 🅖 Arco/24hr, 🍴 Denny's, same
26b a	no services
26b	CA 19, Rosemead Blvd, Pasadena, **N** 🍴 Coldstone, Denny's, IHOP, Jamba Juice, Mayumba Cuban, Subway, 🛏 Knights Inn, 🅾 $Tree, GNC, Goodyear/auto, Office Depot, Radio Shack, Target, **S** 🍴 Del Taco, Jack-in-the-Box, Quiznos, Starbucks
26a	Walnut Grove Ave
25b	San Gabriel Blvd, **N** 🅖 Shell, 🍴 Carl's Jr, Pizza Hut/Taco Bell, Popeye's, Wienerschnitzel, 🛏 Budget Inn, **S** 🅖 7-11
25a	Del Mar Ave, to San Gabriel, **N** 🅖 76, 🅾 auto repair, **S** 🅖 Arco, Chevron/dsl, 🛏 Rodeway Inn
24	New Ave, to Monterey Park, **N** 🍴 KFC, to Mission San Gabriel
23b	Garfield Ave, to Alhambra, **S** 🅖 Arco, 🛏 Grand Inn, 🅾 🅷
23a	Atlantic Blvd, Monterey Park, **N** 🅖 Mobil, 76, 🍴 Pizza Hut, Popeye's, Starbucks, 🅾 🅷, **S** 🛏 Best Western, 🅾 Ralph's Foods, auto repair
22	Fremont Ave, **N** 🅷, tuneup, **S** 🍴 Papa Johns, 🅾 7-11
21	I-710, Long Beach Fwy, Eastern Ave (from wb)
20b a	Eastern Ave, City Terrace Dr, **S** 🅖 Chevron/service, Mobil, 🍴 Burger King, McDonald's
19c	Soto St (from wb), **N** 🅖 Chevron/dsl, 🍴 Burger King, 🅾 🅷, city park, **S** 🅖 Mobil, 76
19b	I-5 (from wb), US 101 S, N to Burbank, S to San Diego
19a	State St, **N** 🅷
17	I-5 N
16b	I-5 S (from eb)
16a	Santa Fe Ave, San Mateo St, **S** 🅖 76/dsl, 🅾 Penske Trucks, industrial area
15b	Alameda St, **N** 🅖 76/dsl, 🍴 Jack-in-the-Box, to downtown, **S** industrial area
15a	Central Ave, **N** 🅖 Shell/repair
14b	San Pedro Blvd, **S** industrial
14a	LA St, **N** conv ctr, **S** 🍴 El Pollo Loco, McDonald's, 🅾 URGENT CARE, 99c Store, O'Reilly Parts, Radio Shack, Rite Aid
13	I-110, Harbor Fwy
12	Hoover St, Vermont Ave, **N** 🅖 Mobil, 🍴 Burger King, McDonald's, Subway, 🅾 AutoZone, Honda, PepBoys, Rite Aid, **S** 🅖 Arco, Chevron, 76, 🍴 Jack-in-the-Box, Papa Johns, Yoshinoya, 🅾 Ralph's Foods
11	Normandie Ave, Western Ave
10	Arlington Ave, **N** 🅖 Chevron, 76
9	Crenshaw Blvd, **S** 🅖 Chevron, Mobil, 76, Thrifty, 🍴 El Pollo Loco, McDonald's, Pizza Hut/Taco Bell, Subway,

📷 = gas   🍴 = food   🛏 = lodging   ⊙ = other   Copyright 2012 - The Next Exit®

CA

E ↕ W

LOS ANGELES AREA

N ↕ S

BAKER

INTERSTATE 10 CONT'D

Exit	Services
9	Continued
	Yoshinoya, ⊙ U-Haul
8	La Brea Ave, **N** 📷 Valero/dsl, ⊙ USPO, **S** 📷 Chevron, ⊙ AutoZone
7b	Washington Blvd, Fairfax Ave, **S** 📷 Mobil, same as 8
7a	La Cienega Blvd, Venice Ave (from wb), **N** 📷 Chevron/24h, Mobil, 🍴 Carl's Jr., Del Taco, ⊙ Firestone/auto, **S** 🍴 Subway, ⊙ Aamco
6	Robertson Blvd, Culver City, **N** 📷 Chevron, Valero, 🍴 Domino's, Taco Bell, ⊙ EZ Lube, Goodyear, **S** 🍴 Del Taco, ⊙ Albertsons, CVS Drug, Ross
5	National Blvd, **N** 📷 76, United Oil, 🍴 Starbucks, Subway, Taco+, ⊙ Rite Aid, Von's Foods, **S** 📷 Arco
4	Overland Ave, **S** 📷 Mobil/dsl
3b a	I-405, N to Sacramento, S to Long Beach
2c b	Bundy Dr, **N** 📷 Chevron, Shell/dsl, 🍴 Taco Bell, ⊙ Cadillac/GMC, Staples
2a	Centinela Ave, to Santa Monica, **N** 🍴 Taco Bell, **S** 🍴 McDonald's, Trader Joe's, 🛏 Santa Monica Hotel
1c	20th St (from wb), Cloverfield Blvd, 26th St (from wb), **N** 📷 Arco, 76/dsl, Shell/repair, ⊙ 🄷
1b	Lincoln Blvd, CA 1 S, **N** 📷 Mobil, 🍴 Arbys, Denny's, Jack-in-the-Box, McDonald's, Norm's Rest., Starbucks, 🛏 Holiday Inn, ⊙ BrakeMasters, Jo-Ann Fabrics, Sears, Toyota, Tuesday Morning, Vons Foods, USPO, **S** 📷 Chevron/dsl, Mobil, 76, Shell, World Gas, 🍴 Dominos, Hawaiian BBQ, Jack-in-the-Box, Subway, Taco Bell, Tommy's Burgers, loding Doubletree Suites, ⊙ EZ Lube, Firestone/auto, 7-11, U-Haul
1a	4th, 5th, (from wb), **N** ⊙ Sears, mall
0	Santa Monica Blvd, to beaches

I-10 begins/ends on CA 1.

INTERSTATE 15

Exit	Services
298	California/Nevada state line, facilities located at state line, Nevada side
291	Yates Well Rd
286	Nipton Rd, **E** Mojave Nat Preserve, to Searchlight
281	Bailey Rd
276mm	**brake check area for trucks, nb**
272	Cima Rd, **E** 📷 Shell/cafe/dsl/towing
270mm	**Valley Wells Rest Area both lanes, full ♿ facilities, 📷, 🛏, litter barrels, petwalk**
265	Halloran Summit Rd
259	Halloran Springs Rd
248	to Baker (from sb), same as 246
246	CA 127, Kel-Baker Rd, Baker, to Death Valley, **W** 📷 Arco, Chevron/Taco Bell, 76/dsl, Shell/Jack-in-the-Box/dsl, Valero/A&W/Pizza Hut/Subway/TCBY, Valero/DQ/Quiznos/dsl, 🍴 Arby's, Big Boy Rest., Burger King, Carl's Jr, Del Taco, Dennys, IHOP, Mad Greek Café, 🛏 BunBoy Hotel, Will's Fargo Motel, ⊙ Alien Fresh Jerky, Baker Mkt Foods, Country Store, World's Tallest Thermometer, USPO, repair
245	to Baker (from nb), same as 246
239	Zzyzx Rd
233	Rasor Rd, **E** 📷 Shell/Rasor Sta/dsl/towing/24hr
230	Basin Rd
221	Afton Rd, to Dunn, **W** ⊙ Mini Mkt

BARSTOW

217mm	**rest area both lanes, full ♿ facilities, 📷, 🛏, litter barrels, petwalk**
213	Field Rd
206	Harvard Rd, to Newberry Springs
198	Minneola Rd, **W** gas/dsl
197mm	**agricultural insp sta sb**
196	Yermo Rd, Yermo
194	Calico Rd
191	Ghost Town Rd, **E** 📷 Arco/24hr, Mohsen Oil Trkstp/dsl/24hr, 🍴 Jack-in-the-Box, Peggy Sue's 50s Diner, Penny's Diner, 🛏 OakTree Inn, **W** 📷 Shell/dsl/24hr, 76, ⊙ Calico GhostTown (3mi), KOA
189	Ft Irwin Rd
186	CA 58 W, to Bakersfield, **W** 🍴 Idle Spur Steaks
184	E Main, Barstow, Montera Rd (from eb), to I-40, **E** 📷 76/dsl, 🍴 Grill It, Hollywood Subs, McDonald's, Mega Tom's Burgers, Panda Express, Popeye's, Starbucks, Straw Hat Pizza, 🛏 Best Western, Travelodge, **S of I-40** 📷 Arco/24hr, ⊙ Walmart/McDonald's/auto, **W** 📷 Chevron, Circle K, Shell, Thrifty, Valero, 🍴 Burger King, Carl's Jr, Coco's, Del Taco, Denny's, FireHouse Italian, IHOP, Jack-in-the-Box, Jenny's Grill, LJ Silver, Sizzler, Taco Bell, Wienerschnitzel, 🛏 Astrobudget Motel, Best Motel, Budget Inn, California Inn, Days Inn, Desert Inn, EconoLodge, Economy Inn, Motel 6, Quality Inn, Ramada Inn, Rodeway Inn, Super 8, ⊙ AutoZone, $Tree, O'Reilly Parts, Radio Shack, U-Haul/LP, Von's Foods, vet
184a	I-40, E (from nb), I-40 begins/ends
183	CA 247, Barstow Rd, **E** 📷 Circle K, Valero/dsl, 🍴 Pizza Hut, Jimenez Mexican, ⊙ Rite Aid, **W** 📷 Chevron/24hr, ⊙ 🄷, Food4Less, Mojave River Valley Museum, st patrol,
181	L St, W Main, Barstow, **W** 📷 Chevron, Thrifty, Valero/B's Diner/dsl, 🍴 BunBoy Rest., Foster's Freeze, 🛏 Best Value Inn, Holiday Inn Express, ⊙ Home Depot, NAPA, tires/towing
179	CA 58, to Bakersfield
178	Lenwood, to Barstow, **E** 📷 Arco/dsl, Chevron/dsl, ⊕FLYING J/Dennys/dsl/24hr, Shell/24hr, 76/dsl, Valero, 🍴 Arby's, Big Boy, Burger King, Carl's Jr, Chili's, Chipotle Mexican, Coldstone, Del Taco, El Pollo Chile, El Pollo Loco, In-N-Out, Jack-in-the-Box, Panda Express, Quigley's, Starbucks, Subway, Tommy's Burgers, 🛏 Comfort Suites, Country Inn&Suites, Hampton Inn, Holiday Inn Express, ⊙ Blue Beacon, Old Navy, Tanger Outlet/famous brands/food ct, **W** 📷 Love's/Chester's/Godfather's/dsl/scales/24hr, Subway/dsl/scales/24hr, TA/Country Fare/Subway/dsl/scales/24hr/@, 🍴 McDonald's, 🛏 Days Inn, ⊙ Zippy Lube, repair, truckwash
175	Outlet Ctr Dr, Sidewinder Rd, **3 mi E** ⊙ factory outlets
169	Hodge Rd
165	Wild Wash Rd
161	Dale Evans Pkwy, to Apple Valley
157	Stoddard Wells Rd, to Bell Mtn
154	Stoddard Wells Rd, to Bell Mtn, **E** 🍴 Taco Chon, ⊙ Shady Oasis Camping/LP, **W** 📷 Mobil, 76/dsl, 🍴 Frankie's Diner, 🛏 Motel 6, Queens Motel
153.5mm	Mojave River
153b	E St
153a	CA 18 E, D St, to Apple Valley, **E** 📷 Arco, ⊙ 🄷, Cooper Tire, repair, **W** 📷 Arco/24hr
151b	Mojave Dr, Victorville, **E** 📷 Gasmart/dsl/24hr, 🛏 Bud

N ↕ S

V I C T O R V I L L E

H E S P E R I A

INTERSTATE 15 CONT'D

Exit	Services
151b	Continued
	get Inn, **W** 🅟 Valero, 🛏 Economy Inn, Sunset Inn, 🅞 repair
151a	La Paz Dr, Roy Rogers Dr, **E** 🅟 Chevron, Shell/dsl, 🍴 Carl's Jr, El Pollo Loco, HomeTown Buffet, IHOP, Jack-in-the-Box, McDonald's, Wendy's, 🅞 AutoZone, BigLots, Costco/gas, $Tree, Food4Less, Harley-Davidson, Jo-Ann Fabrics, 99c Store, Pepboys, Radio Shack, Rite Aid, Toyota/Scion, same as 144, **W** 🅟 Arco/24hr, 🍴 Carl's Jr, Dominos, Farmer Boys, Golden ChopStix, Hawaiian BBQ, In-N-Out, Panda Express, Papa Johns, Quiznos, Starbucks, Subway, 🅞 Americas Tire, Buick/GMC, Chrysler/Dodge/Jeep, Curves, Home Depot, Honda, Kia, Nissan, Stater Bros, Walgreens, WinCo Foods
150	CA 18 W, Palmdale Rd, Victorville, **E** 🍴 Baker's Drive-Thru, Burger King, Denny's, KFC, Richie's Diner, 🛏 Greentree, Red Roof Inn, **W** 🅟 Arco, Circle K, 🍴 Coco's, Del Taco, La Casita Mexican, McDonald's, Pizza Hut, Starbucks, Subway, Taco Bell, Tom's Rest., 🛏 Ambassador Inn, Budget Inn, Days Inn, 🅞 🅷 Aamco, AutoZone, CVS Drug, Ford, Hyundai, Kamper's Korner RV, Target, Town&Country Tire, vet
147	Bear Valley Rd, to Lucerne Valley, **0-2 mi** **E** 🅟 Arco/24hr, Chevron, Mobil, 76/Circle K, 🍴 Arby's, Baker's Drive-Thru, Burger King, Carl's Jr, Del Taco, Dragon Express, John's Pizza, KFC, Little Caesars, Los Alazanes Mexican, Los Toritos, Marie Callender's, McDonald's, Panda Express, Popeye's, Red Robin, Starbucks, Steer'n Stein, Subs'n Salads, Tacos Mexico, Wienerschnitzel, 🛏 Comfort Suites, Day&Night Inn, EconoLodge, Extended Studio Hotel, Hilton Garden, La Quinta, Super 8, Travelodge, 🅞 Affordable RV Ctr, AutoZone, Firestone/auto, Food4Less, Home Depot, Michael's, O'Reilly Parts, Range RV, Rite Aid, Tire Depot, Vallarta Foods, Walmart/auto, vet, **W** 🅟 Arco, Chevron, 76/Circle K, Valero/dsl, 🍴 Applebee's, Archibald's Drive-Thru, Baja Fresh, Baskin-Robbins, Carino's, Chili's, Chipotle Mexican, ChuckeCheese, Coldstone, Del Taco, El Pollo Loco, El Tio Pepe Mexican, Farmer Boy's Rest., Foster's Freeze, Freddy's Custard, Giuseppe's, Jack-in-the-Box, Little Caesar's, McDonald's, Mimi's Cafe, Olive Garden, Outback Steaks, Red Lobster, RoadHouse Grill, Sonic, Starbucks, Subway, Tokyo Steaks, Wendy's, 🛏 Hawthorn Suites, 🅞 Albertson's, Barnes&Noble, Best Buy, CVS Drug, JC Penney, Kohl's, Lowe's, 99c Store, Petsmart, Rite Aid, Sears/auto, Verizon, Walgreens, mall
143	Main St, to Hesperia, Phelan, **E** 🅟 Chevron, Shell/Popeye's/dsl, Valero/Alberto's, 🍴 Arby's, Burger King, Denny's, IHOP, In-N-Out, Jack-in-the-Box, Quiznos, Starbucks, 🛏 Courtyard, SpringHill Suites, **W** 🅟 Arco/dsl/24hr, 76/dsl, 🍴 Baker's Drive-thru, Farmer Boys, Golden Corral, Subway, 🛏 Holiday Inn Express, Motel 6, 🅞 GNC, Marshall's, Radio Shack, Ross, SuperTarget, Verizon, RV camping, urgent care
141	US 395, Joshua St, Adelanto, **W** 🅟 Arco/dsl, Pilot/Wendy's/dsl/scales/24hr, 🍴 Outpost Café, 🅞 Goodyear, Zippy Lube, repair, truck/RV wash
138	Oak Hill Rd, **E** 🅟 Chevron/dsl, 🍴 Summit Inn Café, **W** 🅞 Oak Hills RV Village/LP

137mm	Cajon Summit, elevation 4260, **brake check sb**
131	CA 138, to Palmdale, Silverwood Lake, **E** 🅟 Chevron/McDonald's/24hr, **W** 🅟 76/Circle K/Del Taco/LP, Shell/Subway/dsl, 🛏 Best Western
130mm	**weigh sta both lanes**, elevation 3000
129	Cleghorn Rd
124	Kenwood Ave
123	I-215 S, to San Bernardino, **E** 🅟 Arco/24hr, to Glen Helen Park
122	Glen Helen Parkway
119	Sierra Ave, **W** 🅟 Arco/dsl/24hr, Chevron/dsl, Shell/Del Taco/dsl, Valero/dsl, 🍴 Jack-in-the-Box, McDonalds, 🅞 to Lytle Creek RA
116	Summit Ave, **E** 🅟 Chevron, 7-11, 🍴 Chili's, Coldstone, Del Taco, El Ranchero, Hawaiian BBQ, Jack-in-the-Box, Panera Bread, Quiznos, Roundtable Pizza, Starbucks, Subway, Taco Bell, Wendy's, 🅞 CVS Drug, GNC, Kohl's, Marshall's, Michael's, Petsmart, Ross, Staples, Stater Bros, Target
115b a	CA 210, Highland Ave, **E** to Lake Arrowhead
113	Base Line Rd, **E** 🅟 USA, 🍴 Denny's, Jack-in-the-Box, Logans Roadhouse, Pizza Hut, Rosa Maria's, Starbucks, 🛏 Comfort Inn
112	CA 66, Foothill Blvd, **E** 🅟 Chevron, 🍴 Asia Buffet, ClaimJumper Rest., Golden Spoon, In-N-Out, Osuna's Mexican, Panda Express, Subway, Wienerschnitzel, 🅞 Food4Less, Walmart/auto, **1-2 mi** **W** 🅟 Chevron/dsl, 76/dsl, 🍴 Buffalo Wild Wings, Carino's, Cheesecake Factory, Chick-fil-A, Chipotle Mexican, Coldstone, Del Taco, Denny's, El Pollo Loco, El Torito, Flemings Steaks, Fresh&Easy, Harry's Grill, The Hat Grill, Islamadora, Joe's Crab Shack, Johnny Rockets, Kings Fishouse, Lucille's BBQ, Old Spagetti Factory, Omaha Jack's Steaks, Paisano's Rest., PF Chang's, Popeyes, Rancho Victoria Food Hall, Red Robin, Richie's Diner, Shakey's Pizza, Starbucks, Wendy's, Yardhouse Rest., 🛏 4 Points, 🅞 AT&T, AutoZone, Bass Pro, Shops, Best Buy, Fresh&Easy Foods, Home Depot, JC Penney, Office Depot, Sears Grand
110	4th St, **E** 🅟 Arco/dsl, 🍴 Baker's Drive-Thru, Subway, **W** 🅟 Arco/24hr, Chevron, Mobil/Albertos Mexican/dsl, 76/dsl, Shell, 🍴 Applebee's, Arby's, Baja Fresh, BJ's Rest., Boston's, Burger King, Carl's Jr, Chevy's Mexican, Chipotle, Coco's, Coldstone, Dave&Buster's, Del Taco, El Pollo Loco, Famous Dave's BBQ, Fat Burger, Fuddruckers, Golden , Hooters, IHOP, In-n-Out, Jack-in-the-Box, Jamba Juice, KFC, Krispy Kreme, McDonald's, Mkt Broiler, New City Buffet, NY Grill, Olive Garden, Outback Steaks, Rain Forest Cafe, Red Lobster, Rubio's, Sonic, Starbucks, Subway, Tokyo Tokyo,

🅖 = gas 🍴 = food 🛏 = lodging 🅞 = other

INTERSTATE 15 CONT'D

Exit	Services
110	Continued
	Wendy's, Wienerschnitzel, Wing Place, 🛏 Ayre's Suites, Country Inn&Suites, Courtyard, Hampton Inn, Hilton Garden, Holiday Inn Express, Homewood Suites, Hyatt, TownePlace Suites, 🅞 America's Tire, Best Buy, Big O Tire, Costco/gas, JC Penney, Jo-Ann Fabrics, Kohl's, Marshalls, Ontario Mills Mall, Petsmart, Sam's Club/gas, Staples, Target, Verizon
109b a	I-10, E to San Bernardino, W to LA
108	Jurupa St, E 🅖 Chevron, 🍴 Del Taco, Starbucks, 🅞 Affordable RV, BMW, Chrysler/Dodge/Jeep, Honda, Hyundai, Lexus, Mazda, Nissan, Toyota/Scion, Volvo, VW, W 🅖 Arco/24hr, 🍴 Carl's Jr, 🅞 Ford, Kia, Lincoln/Mercury, Scandia funpark
106	CA 60, E to Riverside, W to LA
105	Cantu-Galleano Ranch Rd
103	Limonite Ave, E 🍴 Carl's Jr, Charro Chicken, Del Taco, Denny's, Hawaiian BBQ, Jamba Juice, 🅞 Lowe's Whse, Michael's, PetCo, Ross, W 🍴 Applebee's, Carino's, Coldstone Creamery, El Grande Burrito, Farmer Boys, On-the-Border, Quizno's, Red Brick Pizza, Starbucks, Subway, Wendy's, 🅞 Best Buy, Border's Books, Curves, GNC, Home Depot, Kohl's, PetsMart, Ralph's Foods/gas, Staples, Target, TJ Maxx, Vons Foods/gas
100	6th St, Norco Dr, Old Town Norco, E 🅖 Chevron/24hr, Exxon/dsl, 🍴 Jack-in-the-Box, McDonald's, 🅞 Rite Aid, W 🅖 Arco/24hr, Valero, 🍴 Big Boy, Izzy's Mexican, Norco's Burgers, Starbucks, Wienerschnitzel, 🛏 Guesthouse Inn, 🅞 Brake Masters, Jiffy Lube, USPO, vet
98	2nd St, W 🅖 76/dsl, Shell/dsl, Thrifty, 🍴 Arby's, Burger King, Del Taco, Domino's, In-N-Out, Magic Wok, Pizza Hut, Polly's Cafe, Sizzler, 🛏 Hampton Inn, Howard Johnson Express, 🅞 America's Tire, Chrysler/Dodge/Jeep, Ford, Mazda, Mitsubishi, Norco RV, 7-11, Stater Bro's
97	Yuma Dr, Hidden Valley Pkwy, E 🅖 7-11, 🍴 Baja Fresh, Chick-fil-A, Fat Burger, 🅞 Kohl's, Stater Bro's, W 🅖 Chevron, 76/dsl, Shell/dsl, 🍴 Alberto's Mexican, Burger City Grill, Carl's Jr, Chipotle, Denny's, Hickory Joe's BBQ, Jamba Juice, Jack-in-the-Box, KFC, McDonald's, Miguel's, Papa John's, Pizza Hut, Quizno's, Rodrigo's Mexican, Round Table Pizza, Rubio's, Starbucks, Taco Bell, 🅞 Albertson's, AutoZone, Big Lots, GNC, Kragen Parts, Radio Shack, Sears Essentials, Staples, Target, Walgreens
96b a	CA 91, to Riverside beaches
95	Magnolia Ave, E 🅖 Chevron/dsl, 🍴 Blackwoods Grill, Chui's Rest., Islands Grill, Jack-in-the-Box, Lonestar Steaks, 🛏 Residence Inn, 🅞 Lowe's Whse, Office Depot, W 🅖 Mobil, Shell, 🍴 A&W/LJ Silver, Burger King, Carl's Jr, Coco's, McDonald's, Pizza Palace, Sizzler, Subway, Zendejas Mexican, 🛏 Holiday Inn Express, 🅞 CVS Drug, $Tree, El Tapatio, Kragen Parts, Rite Aid, Stater Bros Foods
93	Ontario Ave, to El Cerrito, E 🅖 Shell, 🍴 Starbucks, W 🅖 Arco/24hr, Chevron/24hr, 76, 🍴 Chopstix, Denny's, Eatza Pizza, Hawaiian BBQ, In-N-Out, Jack-in-the-Box, KFC, Magic Wok, McDonald's, Miguel's Mexican, Quizno's, Rubio's, Taco Bell, Tommy's Burgers,

93	Continued
	Wienerschnitzel, 🛏 SpringHill Suites, 🅞 Albertson's/Starbucks, Home Depot, Long's Drug, Radio Shack, Sam's Club/gas, USPO, Walmart/auto, vet
92	El Cerrito Rd
91	Cajalco Rd, E 🍴 BJ's Grill, Chick-fil-A, Chili's, Jamba Juice, King's Fish House, Macaroni Grill, Miguel's, On-the-Border, Panera Bread, Rosine's Grill, Starbucks, Wendy's, 🅞 Barnes&Noble, Best Buy, Kohl's, Marshall's, Michael's, Old Navy, PetCo, Ross, See's Candies, Staples, Target, World Mkt, W 🅖 Mobil/dsl, 🍴 Golden Spoon, Jack-in-the-Box, NY Pizza, Subway, 🅞 Stater Bros
90	Weirick Rd, Dos Lagos Dr, E 🍴 Citrus City Grill, Marble Slab Creamery, Miguel's, Starbucks, Tap's Rest., TGIFriday, Wood Ranch BBQ, 🅞 7 Oaks Gen Store
88	Temescal Cyn Rd, Glen Ivy, E 🅖 Shell, W 🅖 Arco/dsl/24hr, 🍴 Carl's Jr, Tom's Farms/BBQ
85	Indian Truck Trail, W 🍴 Starbucks, Subway, 🅞 Von's Foods/gas, CVS Drug
81	Lake St
78	Nichols Rd, W 🅖 Arco/24hr, 🅞 Outlets/famous brands
77	CA 74, Central Ave, Lake Elsinore, E 🅖 Arco/24hr, Chevron, Mobil/dsl, 🍴 Archibald's, Burger King, Chili's, Coffee Bean, Coldstone Creamery, Del Taco, Douglas Burgers, Hawaiian BBQ, Panda Express, Submarina, Taco Del Mar, Wendy's, 🅞 Costco/gas, $Tree, EZ Lube, Lowes Whse, PetsMart, Staples, W 🍴 El Pollo Loco, Farmer Boys, IHOP, McDonald's, 🅞 Home Depot, 99¢ Store, PetCo, Target, Walgreens
75	Main St, Lake Elsinore, W 🅖 76, 🛏 Elsinore Motel, 🅞 Circle K, tires/repair
73	Railroad Cyn Rd, to Lake Elsinore, E 🅖 Shell/Circle K, 76/Circle K, 🍴 Denny's, El Pollo Loco, In-N-Out, KFC, Peony Chinese, Quizno's, Starbucks, 🛏 Holiday Inn Express, 🅞 GNC, Jiffy Lube, Kragen Parts, Von's Foods, Walmart/auto, W 🅖 Arco, Chevron, Mobil/dsl, 🍴 Cafe China, Carl's Jr, Coco's, Del Taco, Don Jose's Mexican, Don Ruben's Mexican, McDonald's, Pizza Hut, Sizzler, Subway, Taco Bell, 🛏 Best Western Lake View, Quality Inn, Travel Inn, 🅞 Albertson's, AutoZone, BigLots, BrakeMasters, Buick/GMC, Chevrolet, CVS Drug, Do-It Hardware, Express Tire/auto, Ford, NAPA, Radio Shack, Rite Aid, SavOn Drug, 7-11, vet
71	Bundy Cyn Rd, W 🅖 Arco/24hr, 🍴 Jack-in-the-Box
69	Baxter Rd, E 🍴 Pizza Factory
68	Clinton Keith Rd, E 🅖 Chevron/dsl, USA, 🍴 Arby's, Denny's, Golden Spoon, La Cresta Mexican, McDonald's, Panda Express, Starbucks, Subway, 🅞 🏥, Ace Hardware, Albertsons/Sav-on, W 🅖 Arco, 7-11, 🍴 Charro Chicken, China Panda, Del Taco, Jack-in-the-Box, Olivera's Rest., Starbucks, 🅞 Stater Bros
65	California Oaks Rd, Kalmia St, E 🅖 Chevron, Mobil/dsl, 76/Circle K, Shell/dsl, 🍴 Burger King, Cal Oaks Burger, Carl's Jr, Chili's, DQ, Jimenez Mexican, KFC, Little Caesar's, Papa John's, Starbucks, 🛏 Comfort Inn, 🅞 Albertson's/Sav-On, AutoZone, Big O Tire, Express Tire, $Tree, Kragen Parts, Radio Shack, Rite Aid, Ross, Target, Tuesday Morning, Walgreens, vet, W 🅖 Arco/24hr, Chevron, 🍴 Applebee's, Carrow's, Chick-fil-A, Farmer Boys, Jack-in-the-Box, RJ's Grill, Stix Rest., 🅞 Ameri

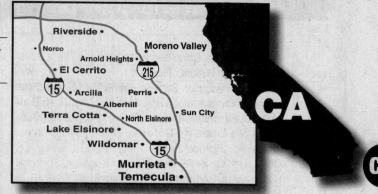

INTERSTATE 15 CONT'D

Exit	Services
65	Continued
	ca's Tire, Giant RV Ctr, Kohl's, Lowe's Whse, Office Depot, PetCo, fun ctr
64	Murrieta Hot Springs Rd, to I-215, **E** 🅟 7-11, Shell/dsl, 🍴 Alberto's Mexican, Baja Grill, Buffalo Wild Wings, Carl's Jr, El Pollo Loco, Gourmet Italian, Richie's Diner, Rubio's, Seafood Grill, Sizzler, Starbucks, Wendy's, 🄾 Ralph's Foods, Rite Aid, Ross, Sam's Club/gas, Walgreens, **W** 🅟 7-11, Shell/Popeyes/dsl, 🍴 Alberto's Mexican, Arby's, Chuy's, Coldstone Creamery, Denny's, IHOP, McDonald's, MegaToms, Panda Express, Quizno's, Starbucks, Subway, Wienerschnitzel, 🄾 Best Buy, Big Lots, Home Depot, 99¢ Store, PetsMart, Staples, Walmart/auto
63	I-215, N (from nb), to Riverside
61	CA 79 N, Winchester Rd, **E** 🅟 Chevron, 76/dsl, 🍴 Alberto's Mexican, Baja Fresh, Baskin-Robbins/Togo's, Bj's Rest., Burger King, Carino's, Carl's Jr, Coldstone Creamery, Del Taco, El Torito, Harry's Grill, Jamba Juice, La Salsa, Lucille's BBQ, Macaroni Grill, McDonald's, Olive Garden, On-the-Border, Outback Steaks, Panda Express, PF Chang's, Red Lobster, Roadhouse Grill, Ruby's Diner, Shogun Chinese, Souplantation, Starbucks, Subway, Taco Bell, TGIFriday, Togo's, Yellow Basket Hamburgers, 🄾 America's Tire, AutoZone, Barnes&Noble, Big O Tire, Costco/gas, Food4Less, Express Tire, JC Penney, Jo-Ann Fabrics, K-Mart, Kragen Parts, Longs Drug, Lowe's Whse, Macy's, Office Depot, PepBoys, PetCo, Sears/auto, See's Candies, TJ Maxx, VW, WinCo Foods, World Mkt, **W** 🅟 Arco/24hr, Chevron/dsl, 🍴 Arby's, Banzai Japanese, Big Boy, Del Taco, El Pollo Loco, Farmer Boys, Hungry Hunter, In-N-Out, Jack-in-the-Box, Sizzler, Starbucks, Subway, Super China, Wendy's, 🛏 Best Western, Extended Stay America, Fairfield Inn, Holiday Inn Express, La Quinta, Quality Inn, 🄾 Hyundai, NAPA, Richardson's RV Ctr, st patrol, tires/repair
59	Rancho California Rd, **E** 🅟 Arco, Mobil/dsl, Shell/dsl, Valero, 🍴 Black Angus, Chili's, ClaimJumper, Del Taco, Daphne's Greek, Marie Callender's, Pat & Oscar's Rest., Pizza Hut, RoundTable Pizza, Rubio's, Texas Loosey's, Starbucks, Subway, 🛏 Embassy Suites, 🄾 Big Lots, CVS Drug, Michael's, Target, Von's Foods, vet, **W** 🅟 Chevron, 76/Circle K/dsl, 🍴 Denny's, KFC, McDonald's, Mexico Chiquito's, Penfold's Cafe, Rosa's Café, 🛏 Hampton Inn, Motel 6, Rancho California Inn, Rodeway Inn, SpringHill Suites, 🄾 USPO
58	CA 79 S, to Indio, Temecula, **E** 🅟 Mobil/dsl, Valero/Circle K/dsl, 🍴 Carl's Jr, Del Taco, Domino's, In-N-Out, Starbucks, other, Ace Hardware, America's Tire, EZ Lube, Longs Drug, 7-11, **W** 🅟 Arco, Shell/dsl/24hr, 🍴 7 Mares Grill, Western Burrito, Wienerschnitzel, 🛏 Ramada Inn, 🄾 Express Tire, Harley-Davidson
55mm	check sta nb
54	Rainbow Valley Blvd, **2 mi E** gas, food, **W** CA Insp Sta
51	Mission Rd, to Fallbrook, **W** 🄷
46	CA 76, to Oceanside, Pala, **E** 🄾 RV camp, **W** 🅟 Mobil, 🛏 Comfort Inn
44mm	San Luis Rey River
43	Old Hwy 395
41	Gopher Canyon Rd, Old Castle Rd, **1 mi**, **E** 🛏 Welk
41	Continued
	Resort, 🄾 RV camping, gas
37	Deer Springs Rd, Mountain Meadow Rd, **W** 🅟 Arco/24hr
34	Centre City Pkwy (from sb)
33	El Norte Pkwy, **E** 🅟 Arco/24hr, Shell/dsl, 🍴 Arby's, IHOP, 🛏 Best Western, 🄾 Express Tire, RV Resort, **W** 🅟 76/dsl, Circle K, 🍴 Jack-in-the-Box, Subway, Wendy's, 🄾 Von's Foods, vet
32	CA 78, to Oceanside
31	Valley Pkwy, **E** 🅟 Arco/24hr, 🍴 Baja Fresh, Chili's, ChuckeCheese, McDonald's, Olive Garden, Panda Express, Quizno's, Starbucks, Subway, Thai Kitchen, 🄾 🄷 Barnes&Noble, Michael's, PetCo, mall, **W** 🅟 Express, 🍴 Applebee's, Burger King, Carl's Jr, Coco's, Del Taco, Jamba Juice, La Salsa Grill, Panera Bread, Wendy's, 🛏 Comfort Inn, Holiday Inn Express, 🄾 Albertson's, Big Lots, Dodge, Home Depot, Long's Drug, 7-11, Staples, Target, TJ Maxx, World Mkt
30	9th Ave, Auto Parkway, **E** 🄾 Infiniti, Mercedes, same as 31
29	Felicita Rd
28	Centre City Pkwy (from nb, no return), **E** 🍴 Center City Café, 🛏 Palms Inn
27	Via Rancho Pkwy, to Escondido, **E** 🅟 Chevron/24hr, Shell, 🍴 Macaroni Grill, On-the-Border, Onami Grill, Panera Bread, Red Robin, 🄾 JC Penney, Macy's, Nordstrom's, Sears/auto, San Diego Animal Park, mall, **W** 🅟 Shell/Subway/dsl, 🍴 McDonald's, Starbucks
26	W Bernardo Dr, to Highland Valley Rd, Palmerado Rd
24	Rancho Bernardo Rd, to Lake Poway, **E** 🅟 Arco/24hr, Mobil, 🍴 Domino's, Soup Plantatino, Stirfresh, 🛏 Hilton Garden, 🄾 Barons, Von's Foods, **W** 🅟 76/Circle K, Shell/repair, 🍴 Elephant Bar Rest., Hooters, Starbucks, 🛏 Holiday Inn, Rodeway Inn
23	Bernardo Ctr Dr, **E** 🅟 Chevron, 🍴 Burger King, Carl's Jr, Coco's, Denny's, El Torito, Rubio's Grill, 🄾 CVS Drug, Express Tire/auto, Firestone/auto, vet
22	Camino del Norte
21	Carmel Mtn Rd, **E** 🅟 Chevron, Shell, 🍴 Baskin-Robbins, Boston Mkt, CA Pizza Kitchen, Carl's Jr, Cheeburger Cheeburger, Chevy's Mexican, ClaimJumper, El Pollo Loco, In-N-Out, Islands Burgers, JambaJuice, Joey's BBQ, Marie Callender's, McDonald's, Olive Garden, Quizno's, Panera Bread, Rubio's Grill, Subway, Taco Bell, TGIFriday, Thigo Rest., Wendy's, 🛏 Residence Inn, 🄾 Barnes&Noble, Costco, EZ Lube, GNC, Home Depot, Marshall's, Michael's, PetCo, Ralph's Foods, Rite Aid, Ross, Sears Essentials, Staples, Trader Joes, USPO, **W** 🅟 Chevron, 🍴 Jack-in-the-Box, Starbucks, 🄾 Albert

N ↕ S   T E M E C U L A

E S C O N D I D O

🅿 = gas ⊞ = food ⌂ = lodging ⊡ = other   Copyright 2012 - The Next Exit®

INTERSTATE 15 CONT'D

Exit	Services
21	Continued
	son's, Big O Tire, Office Depot, 7-11
19	CA 56 W, Ted Williams Pkwy
18	Rancho Penasquitos Blvd, Poway Rd, **E** 🅿 Arco/24hr, **W** 🅿 Exxon/dsl, Mobil/dsl, 76/dsl, ⊞ IHOP, McDonald's, Mi Ranchito Mexican, NY Pizza, Starbucks, Subway, ⌂ La Quinta, ⊡ 7-11
17	Mercy Rd, Scripps Poway Pkwy, **E** 🅿 USA/dsl, ⊞ Chili's, Fish Grille, Wendy's, ⌂ Residence Inn, Springhill Suites, **W** 🅿 Chevron, ⊞ KFC, Starbucks
16	Mira Mesa Blvd, to Lake Miramar, **E** ⊞ Denny's, Filippi's Pizza, Golden Crown Chinese, Lucio's Mexican, Pizza Hut, Shozen BBQ, ⌂ Holiday Inn Express, Quality Suites, ⊡ Curves, USPO, **W** 🅿 Arco/24hr, Shell, ⊞ Applebee's, Arby's, Buca Italian, Café China, Coldstone Creamery, In-N-Out, Islands Burgers, Jack-in-the-Box, Jamba Juice, McDonald's, Mimi's Café, On the Border, Pat & Oscar's Rest., Panera Bread, Pick Up Stix, Popeye's, Rubio's, Santana's Mexican, Starbucks, Togo's, ⊡ Albertson's, AutoZone, Barnes&Noble, Best Buy, Big Lots, Home Depot, Long's Drug, Old Navy, Ralph's Foods, Rite Aid, Ross, USPO
15	Carroll Canyon Rd, to Miramar College, **E** ⊞ Carl's Jr
14	Pomerado Rd, Miramar Rd, **W** 🅿 Arco/dsl, Chevron/dsl, Mobil, Shell/24hr, ⊞ Carl's Jr, Chin's Rest., Keith's Rest., Subway, ⌂ Best Western, Budget Inn, Holiday Inn, ⊡ Audi/Porsche/VW, Land Rover, vet
13	Miramar Way, US Naval Air Station
12	CA 163, S (from sb), to San Diego
11	to CA 52
10	Clairemont Mesa Blvd, **W** ⊞ Boll Weevil Rest., Carl's Jr, Giovanni's Pizza, Jack-in-the-Box, La Salsa, McDonald's, Mr. Chick's Rest., Panda Express, Rubio's, Spice House Cafe, Starbucks, Subway, Sunny Donuts, Taco Bell, Togo's, Wendy's, ⊡ 7-11
9	CA 274, Balboa Ave
8	Aero Dr, **W** 🅿 Arco/24hr, 7-11, Shell, ⊞ Baja Fresh, Baskin Robbins, Jack-in-the-Box, McDonald's, Papa John's, Pick Up Stix, Sizzler, Starbucks, Submarina, Taco Bell, ⌂ Holiday Inn, ⊡ $Tree, Express Tire/auto, Fry's Electronics, PetSmart, Radio Shack, Von's Foods, Walmart/auto
7b	Friars Rd W, **W** ⊞ Coldstone Creamery, Dragon Chinese, IHOP, Islands Burgers, Little Fish Mkt, McDonald's, Mondo's Mexican, Oggi's Pizza, Starbucks, Subway, ⊡ Costco/gas, Lowes Whse, San Diego Stadium
7a	Friars Rd, E
6b	I-8, E to El Centro, W to beaches
6a	Adams Ave, downtown
5b	El Cajon Blvd, **E** 🅿 Pearson, ⊞ Subway, ⊡ Carquest, **W** 🅿 Chevron/dsl, ⊡ Pep Boys
5a	University Ave, **E** 🅿 Chevron/dsl, ⊞ Burger King, Jack-in-the-Box, ⊡ USPO
3	I-805, N to I-5, S to San Ysidro
2b	(2c from nb) CA 94 W, downtown
2a	Market St, downtown
1c	National Ave, Ocean View Blvd
1b	(from sb) I-5 S, to Chula Vista
1a	(from sb) I-5 N. I-15 begins/ends on I-5

INTERSTATE 40

Exit	Services
155	California/Arizona state line, Colorado River, Pacific/Mountain time zone
153	Park Moabi Rd, to Rte 66, **N** boating, camping
149mm	insp both lanes
148	5 Mile Rd, to Topock, Rte 66 (from eb)
144	US 95 S, E Broadway, Needles, **N** 🅿 Chevron/dsl, Mobil, Shell/dsl, ⊞ Domino's, ⊡ Basha's Foods, Laundry, Rite Aid, **S** ⌂ Best Value, ⊡ $Tree, tires/repair
142	J St, Needles, **N** 🅿 76/24hr, Valero, ⊞ Jack-in-the-Box, McDonald's, ⌂ Travelers Inn, ⊡ NAPA, **S** ⊞ Denny's, ⌂ Day's Inn, Motel 6, ⊡ 🅷, st patrol
141	W Broadway, River Rd, Needles, **N** ⊞ KFC, ⌂ Best Motel, Desert Mirage Inn, River Valley Motel, **S** 🅿 Arco/24hr, Chevron/dsl/24hr, Mobil/dsl, Shell/DQ/24hr, ⊞ Carl's Jr, China Garden, River Cafe, Taco Bell, ⌂ Best Western, Budget Inn, Needles Inn, Relax Inn, ⊡ Chevrolet/Cadillac/Buick/GMC, auto/RV/tire/repair
139	River Rd Cutoff (from eb), **N** rec area, Hist Rte 66, ⊡ KOA, Desert View RV Park
133	US 95 N, to Searchlight, to Rte 66
120	Water Rd
115	Mountain Springs Rd, High Springs Summit, elev 2770
107	Goffs Rd, Essex, **N** gas/dsl/food, Hist Rte 66
106mm	rest area both lanes, full ♿ facilities, ⊞, ⌂, litter barrels, petwalk
100	Essex Rd, Essex, **N** to Providence Mtn SP, Mitchell Caverns
78	Kelbaker Rd, to Amboy, E Mojave Nat Preserve, Kelso, **S** Hist Rte 66, ⊡ RV camping (14mi)
50	Ludlow, **N** 🅿 76/DQ/24hr, **S** 🅿 Chevron, ⊞ Ludlow Cafe, ⌂ Ludlow Motel
33	Hector Rd, to Hist Rte 66
28mm	rest area both lanes, full ♿ facilities, ⊞, ⌂, litter barrels, petwalk
23	Ft Cady Rd, to Newberry Spgs, **N** 🅿 Texaco/dsl/24hr, **S** ⊡ Newberry Mtn RV Park, Twins Lake RV Park (8mi)
18	Newberry Springs, **N** ⊡ Spirit/dsl, **S** 🅿 Chevron/Subway/dsl/LP
12	Barstow-Daggett ✈, **N** ✈
7	Daggett, **N** ⊡ RV camping (2mi), to Calico Ghost Town
5	Nebo St (from eb), to Hist Rte 66
2	USMC Logistics Base, **N** ⌂ Pennywise Inn
1	E Main St, Montara Rd, Barstow, **N** 🅿 76/dsl, ⊞ Grill It, Hollywood Subs, McDonald's, Panda Express, Popeye's, Starbucks, Straw Hat Pizza, Tom's Burgers, ⌂ Best Western, Travelodge, **1 mi N** 🅿 Chevron, Circle K/TCBY, Shell, Thrifty, Valero, ⊞ Burger King, Carl's Jr, Coco's, Del Taco, Denny's, FireHouse Italian, IHOP, Jack-in-the-Box, KFC, LJ Silver, Sizzler, Taco Bell, Wienerschnitzel, ⌂ Astrobudget Motel, Best Motel, Budget Inn, California Inn, Days Inn, Desert Inn, EconoLodge, Economy Inn, Quality Inn, Ramada Inn, Rodeway Inn, Super 8, ⊡ AutoZone, $Tree, O'Reilly Parts, Radio Shack, U-Haul/LP, Von's Foods, urgent care, **S** 🅿 Arco/24hr, ⊡ Walmart/McDonald's/auto
0mm	I-40 begins/ends on I-15 in Barstow

INTERSTATE 80

Exit	Services
208	California/Nevada state line

INTERSTATE 80 CONT'D

Exit	Services
201	Farad
199	Floristan
194	Hirschdale Rd, **N** to Boca Dam, Stampede Dam, **S** RV Park
191mm	(from wb), **weigh sta, inspection sta**
190	Overland Trail
188	CA 89 N, CA 267, to, N Shore Lake Tahoe, **N** ⊙ USFS, **S** same as 186
186	Central Truckee (no eb return), **S** 🛢 Beacon, 76, 🍴 Best Pies Pizzeria, Burger Me, Casa Baeza Mexican, El Toro Bravo Mexican, Wagon Train Café, 🏨 Hilltop Lodge, Truckee Hotel
185	CA 89 S, to, N Lake Tahoe, **N** 🍴 DQ, Jiffy's Pizza, Nik'n Willies Pizza, Panda Express, Port of Subs, RoundTable Pizza, Starbucks, Zano's Pizza, ⊙ H, URGENT CARE, Ace Hardware, NAPA, New Moon Natural Foods, Radio Shack, Rite Aid, Safeway Foods, 7-11, hwy patrol, **S** 🛢 Shell/dsl, 🍴 Bill's Rotisseire, KFC, McDonald's, Subway, Village Pizzaria, ⊙ CVS Drug, SaveMart Foods, auto repair, to Squaw Valley, RV camping
184	Donner Pass Rd, Truckee, **N** 🛢 Shell/dsl, 🍴 La Bamba Mexican, Pizza Shack, Truckee Pizza, 🏨 Sunset Inn, **S** 🛢 Chevron/dsl, 76, 🍴 Taco Bell, 🏨 Truckee Donner Lodge, ⊙ chain service, to Donner SP, RV camp/dump
181mm	vista point both lanes
180	Donner Lake (from wb), **S** 🏨 Donner Lake Village Resort
177mm	Donner Summit, elev 7239, **rest area both lanes, full** 🦽 **facilities, view area,** 🚻, 🏕, **litter barrels, petwalk**
176	Castle Park, Boreal Ridge Rd, **S** 🏨 Boreal Inn/rest., ⊙ Pacific Crest Trailhead, skiing
174	Soda Springs, Norden, **S** 🛢 Beacon/dsl, 🍴 Summit Rest., 🏨 Donner Summit Lodge, ⊙ chain services
171	Kingvale, **S** 🛢 Shell
168	Rainbow Rd, to Big Bend, **S** 🏨 Rainbow Lodge/rest., ⊙ RV camping
166	Big Bend (from eb)
165	Cisco Grove, **N** ⊙ RV camp/dump, skiing, snowmobiling, **S** 🛢 Valero/24hr, ⊙ chain services
164	Eagle Lakes Rd
161	CA 20 W, to Nevada City, Grass Valley
160	Yuba Gap, **S** ⊙ **snowpark,** 🚻, 🏕, **boating, camping, skiing**
158	Laing Rd, **S** 🏨 Sierra Woods Lodge/café
157mm	**brake check area, wb**
158a	Emigrant Gap (from eb), **S** 🏨 Sierra Woods Lodge/café
156	Nyack Rd, Emigrant Gap, **S** 🛢 Shell/Burger King/dsl, 🍴 Nyack Café
156mm	**brake check area**
155	Blue Canyon
150	Drum Forebay
148b	Baxter, **N** ⊙ RV camping, chainup services, food, 🚻
148a	Crystal Springs
146	Alta
145	Dutch Flat, **N** 🍴 Monte Vista Rest., **S** 🛢 Tesoro/dsl, ⊙ RV camping, chainup services, hwy patrol
144	Gold Run (from wb), **N** gas/dsl, food, phone, chainup
143mm	**rest area both lanes, full** 🦽 **facilities,** 🚻, 🏕, **litter barrels, petwalk**

143	Magra Rd, Gold Run, **N** chainup services	
140	Magra Rd, Rollins Lake Rd, Secret Town Rd	
139	Rollins Lake Road (from wb), RV camping	
135	CA 174, to Grass Valley, Colfax, **N** 🛢 76/dsl, 🍴 Colfax Max Burgers, McDonald's, Pizza Factory, Starbucks, Taco Bell, TJ's Roadhouse, 🏨 Colfax Motel, ⊙ 1Buck+, Sierra Mkt Foods, NAPA, **S** 🛢 Chevron/dsl, Valero/dsl, 🍴 Shang Garden Chinese, Subway, ⊙ Best Hardware	
133	Canyon Way, to Colfax, **S** 🍴 Dine'n Dash Cafe, ⊙ Chevrolet, Plaza Tire	
131	Cross Rd, to Weimar	
130	W Paoli Lane, to Weimar, **S** 🛢 Weimar Store/dsl	
129	Heather Glen, elev 2000 ft	
128	Applegate, **N** 🛢 Applegate Gas/dsl/LP, ⊙ chainup services	
125	Clipper Gap, Meadow Vista, **N** Oliver's Gas	
124	Dry Creek Rd	
123	Bell Rd	
122	Foresthill Rd, Ravine Rd, Bowman, **N** ⊙ RV camping/dump, **S** 🍴 Burger King, La Bonte's Rest., Sizzler, Starbucks, Subway, TioPepe Mexican, 🏨 Best Western, Quality Inn, same as 121	
121	(from eb) Lincolnway, Auburn, **N** 🛢 Arco, Flyers/dsl, Valero, 🍴 Denny's, JimBoy's Tacos, Maria's Tacos, Taco Bell, Wienerschnitzel, 🏨 Comfort Inn, Foothills Motel, Motel 6, Super 8, **S** 🛢 Arco, Beacon/dsl, Chevron/dsl, Gas&Shop, Shell/dsl, 🍴 Burger King, Burrito Shop, Carl's Jr, Hawaiian BBQ, Jack-in-the-Box, Joe Caribe Bistro, KFC, La Bonte's Rest., McDonald's, Pete's Grill, Sierra Grill, Sizzler, Starbucks, Subway, 🏨 Best Western, Quality Inn, ⊙ Ikeda's Mkt, Raley's Foods, Verizon	
120	Russell Ave (from wb), to Lincolnway from eb, same as 121	
119c	Elm Ave, Auburn, **N** 🛢 76/dsl, Shell, 🍴 Foster's, 🏨 Holiday Inn, ⊙ CVS Drug, Grocery Outlet, Rite Aid, SaveMart Foods, Staples, Verizon	
119b	CA 49, to Grass Valley, Auburn, **N** 🛢 76, Shell, 🍴 In-N-Out, 🏨 Holiday Inn, ⊙ Staples	
119a	Maple St, Nevada St, Old Town Auburn, **S** 🛢 Valero, 🍴 Mary Belle's, Tiopete Mexican	
118	Ophir Rd (from wb)	
116	CA 193, to Lincoln, **S** ⊙ truck repair	
115	Indian Hill Rd, Newcastle, **N** ⊙ transmissions, **S** 🛢 Flyers/dsl, Valero/dsl, 🍴 Denny's, CHP	
112	Penryn, **N** 🛢 76/dsl, Valero/Subway/dsl, 🍴 Cattle Baron's Cafe, Houston's Steaks	
110	Horseshoe Bar Rd, to Loomis, **N** 🍴 Burger King, RoundTable Pizza, Starbucks, Taco Bell, ⊙ Raley's Food	
109	Sierra College Blvd, **N** 🛢 Chevron/McDonald's/dsl, 7-11, 🍴 Carl's Jr, ⊙ Camping World RV Ctr, Eads RV Ctr	

Side labels (vertical): E ↕ W TRUCKEE — COLFAX — AUBURN — NEWCASTLE

INTERSTATE 80 CONT'D

E ↕ W

CA

CITRUS HEIGHTS

Exit	Services
108	Rocklin Rd, **N** 🅖 Valero, 🍽 Adalberto's Mexican, A&W/KFC, Arby's, Baskin-Robbins, Denny's, Golden Dragon, Jack-in-the-Box, Jamba Juice, Papa Murphy's, Quiznos, RoundTable Pizza, Starbucks, Subway, Taco Bell, 🛏 Days Inn, Heritage Inn, Howard Johnson, ⊙ CVS Drug, GNC, Land Rover, Mercedes, Porsche, Radio Shack, Safeway Foods, **S** 🅖 Arco, 🍽 Little Caesar's, 🛏 Rocklin Park Hotel, ⊙ vet
106	CA 65, to Lincoln, Marysville, **1 mi N on Stanford Ranch Rd** 🅖 Arco, Chevron, 76, Shell, 🍽 Applebee's, BJ's Rest, Buca Italian, Carl's Jr, Cheesecake Factory, IHOP, Jack-in-the-Box, KFC, McDonald's, Mimi's Cafe, Olive Garden, On-the-Border, PF Changs, Red Robin, Subway, 🛏 Comfort Suites, Coutyard, Hyatt Place, Homewood Suites, ⊙ AutoZone, Barnes&Noble, Best Buy, Costco, Goodyear/auto, JC Penney, Macy's, Marshall's, Michael's, Nordstrom's, Old Navy, Ross, Staples, Whole Foods Mkt
105b	Taylor Rd, to Rocklin (from eb), **N** 🍽 Cattlemen's Rest., **S** 🅖 Chevron, 76/Burger King/dsl, 🍽 Islands Burgers, Subway, Tahoe Joe's, 🛏 Fairfield Inn, Hilton Garden, Holiday Inn Express, Larkspur Suites, Residence Inn, ⊙ 🅗, SaveMart Foods, funpark
105a	Atlantic St, Eureka Rd, **S** 🅖 76, Shell/Circle K, 🍽 Chicago Fire Rest, In-N-Out, Panda Express, Taco Bell, Wendy's, 🛏 Marriott, ⊙ 🅗, America'sTire, Buick/GMC, Carmax, Chevrolet, Ford, Home Depot, Hyundai, Lexus, Mazda, Nissan, Petsmart, Subaru, Target, Toyota/Scion, VW, Walmart, mall
103b a	Douglas Blvd, **N** 🅖 Arco/dsl, Chevron, 76/dsl, 🍽 Burger King, Carolina's Mexican, McDonald's, Starbucks, 🛏 Extended Stay America, Heritage Inn, Residence Inn, ⊙ 🅗, Ace Hardware, BigLots, Big O Tire, BrakeMasters, $Tree, Firestone, Goodyear, Kragen Parts, Radio Shack, Rite Aid, Sunflower Mkt, Trader Joe's, **S** 🅖 Shell, 🍽 Carl's Jr, Carrow's, Denny's, Outback Steaks, Subway, 🛏 Hampton Inn, Orchid Suites, ⊙ Fry's Electronics, Office Depot, Target
102	Riverside Ave, Auburn Blvd, to Roseville, **N** 🅖 Arco/dsl, Chevron/dsl, 🍽 Starbucks, Subway, ⊙ auto repair, vet, **S** 🅖 76, Shell, Tower, Valero/dsl, 🍽 Baskin-Robbins, CA Burgers, DQ, Grand China, Jack-in-the-Box, ⊙ AutoZone, BMW Motorcycles, $World, K-Mart, NAPA, Schwab Tire, Village RV Ctr, transmissions/auto repair
100	Antelope Rd, to Citrus Heights, **N** 🅖 76, 🍽 Carl's Jr, Giant Pizza, McDonald's, Papa Murphy's, Popeye's, RoundTable Pizza, Subway, Taco Bell, Wendy's, ⊙ $Tree, O'Reilly Parts, Raley's Foods, 7-11, vet
100mm	**weigh sta both lanes**
98	Greenback Lane, Elkhorn Blvd, Orangevale, Citrus Heights, **N** 🍽 Carl's Jr, Little Caesar's, McDonald's, Pizza Hut, Subway, Taco Bell, ⊙ CVS Drug, Radio Shack, Safeway Foods
96	Madison Ave, **N** 🅖 Chevron/dsl, Valero/dsl, 🍽 Brookfield's Rest., Denny's, El Zarape Mexican, Jack-in-the-Box, Mongolian BBQ, Starbucks, 🛏 Motel 6, Super 8, ⊙ funpark, to McClellan AFB, **S** 🅖 Arco, 76, Shell/dsl, 🍽 Boston Mkt, Burger King, Chipotle Mexican, El Pollo Loco, IHOP, In-N-Out, Jack-in-the-Box, McDonald's, Panda Express, Starbucks, Subway, Wienerschnitzel,

SACRAMENTO

DAVIS

Exit	Services
96	Continued 🛏 Holiday Inn, La Quinta, ⊙ Acura, AT&T, Chevrolet, Ford, Office Depot, PepBoys, Schwab Tire, 7-11, Target, Verizon, Walgreens
95	CA 99, S
94b	Auburn Blvd
94a	Watt Ave, **N** 🅖 Arco, 76/dsl, 🍽 Golden Corral, KFC, 🛏 Days Inn, Motel 6, ⊙ Firestone/auto, McClellan AFB, **S** 🅖 Arco, Chevron, Shell, 🍽 CheeseSteak, China Taste, Denny's, Jimboy's Tacos, Starbucks, Subway, Wendy's, 🛏 Great Value Inn
93	Longview Dr
92	Winters St
91	Raley Blvd, Marysville Blvd, to Rio Linda, **N** 🅖 Arco, Chevron, **S** ⊙ Mkt Basket Foods, Valley Tires, USPO
90	Norwood Ave, **N** 🅖 Arco/Jack-in-the-Box, Valero, 🍽 Golden China, McDonald's, RoundTable Pizza, Starbucks, Subway, ⊙ Rite Aid, Viva Foods
89	Northgate Blvd, Sacramento, **N** ⊙ Fry's Electronics, **S** 🅖 Arco, Circle K, Shell, 🍽 Carl's Jr, Classic Burgers, El Pollo Loco, IHOP, KFC, LJ Silver, McDonald's/playplace, Starbucks, Subway, Taco Bell, 🛏 Extended Stay America, Quality Inn, ⊙ BigLots, Foodsco Foods, Kragen Parts, PepBoys, Schwab Tire
88	Truxel Rd, **N** 🅖 Chevron, Shell/dsl, 🍽 Applebee's, BJ's Rest, Canyon Creek Grill, Carino's Italian, Chili's, Chipotle Mexican, Del Taco, Hooters, In-N-Out, Jamba Juice, Logan's Roadhouse, Mongolian BBQ, On the Border, Panera Bread, Qdoba, Rubio's, Starbucks, 🛏 Staybridge Suites, ⊙ Arco Arena, Barnes&Noble, Best Buy, GNC, Home Depot, Michael's, Old Navy, Petsmart, Radio Shack, Raley's Depot, Ross, Staples, Target, Walmart, World Mkt, mall
86	I-5, N to Redding, S to Sacramento, to CA 99, N
85	W El Camino, **N** 🅖 Chevron/Subway/dsl/24hr, 49er Trkstp/Silver Skillet/dsl/scales/24hr/@, 🍽 Burger King, 🛏 Fairfield Inn, Super 8
83	Reed Ave, **N** 🅖 76/dsl, 🍽 Hawaiian BBQ, Jack-in-the-Box, Los Amigo's, Quizno's, Panda Express, Starbucks, Subway, 🛏 Extended Stay America, Hampton Inn, ⊙ dsl repair, **S** 🅖 Arco/24hr, Shell/McDonald's/dsl, 🍽 In-N-Out, Taco Bell, ⊙ Home Depot, Walmart
82	US 50 E, W Sacramento
81	Enterprise Blvd, W Capitol Ave, W Sacramento, **N** 🅖 Chevron/dsl/24hr, Valero/dsl, 🍽 Eppie's Rest/24hr, 🛏 Granada Inn, **S** 🅖 7-11, 🍽 Denny's, JR's BBQ, Starbucks, Subway, ⊙ KOA
78	Rd 32A, E Chiles Rd, **S** Fruit Stand
75	Mace Blvd, **N** 🅖 Arco, **S** 🅖 Chevron/24hr, Valero/dsl, 🍽 Burger King, Cindy's Rest., McDonald's, Mtn Mike's Pizza, Subway, Taco Bell/24hr, 🛏 Howard Johnson, Motel 6, ⊙ Chevrolet, Chrysler/Dodge/Jeep, Ford, Honda, Nissan, Nugget Mkt Foods, Schwab Tire, Toyota/Scion, Tuesday Morning, to Mace Ranch
73	Olive Dr (from wb, no EZ return)
72b a	Richards Blvd, Davis, **N** 🅖 Shell/24hr, 🍽 Caffe Italia, In-N-Out, Redrum Burger, 🛏 University Park Inn, ⊙ NAPA, **S** 🅖 Chevron, 🍽 Applebee's, Del Taco, IHOP, KFC, Wendy's, 🛏 Comfort Suites, Hotel Davis, ⊙ Jiffy Lube, Kragen Parts
71	to UC Davis

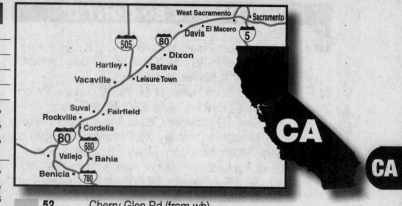

INTERSTATE 80 CONT'D

Exit	Services
70	CA 113 N, to Woodland, N ⊞
69	Kidwell Rd
67	Pedrick Rd, N ☐ Chevron/dsl, 76/LP, ☐ produce
66b	Milk Farm Rd (from wb)
66a	CA 113 S, Currey Rd, to Dixon, S ☐ Arco, CFN/dsl, Shell/dsl, Valero/Popeye's/dsl, ☐ Cattlemen's Rest., Jack-in-the-Box, Papa Murphy's, Subway, Taco Del Mar, Wendy's ☐ Comfort Suites, ☐ Walmart
64	Pitt School Rd, to Dixon, S ☐ Chevron/24hr, Valero/24hr, ☐ Arby's, Asian Garden, Burger King, Chevy's Mexican, Denny's, IHOP, Little Ceasar's, Maria's Mexican, Mary's Pizza, McDonald's, Pizza Guys, Quizno's, Solano Bakery, Starbucks, Subway, Taco Bell, ☐ Best Western, Microtel, ☐ Curves, Ford, Kragen Parts, Safeway/dsl
63	Dixon Ave, Midway Rd, N ☐ Truck Stp/dsl, S ☐ Chevron/LP/lube, USA/24hr, ☐ Carl's Jr, Mr Taco, ☐ Super 8, ☐ Dixon Fruit Mkt, RV Dump
60	Midway Rd, Lewis Rd, Elmya, N Produce Mkt, RV camping
59	Meridian Rd, Weber Rd
57	Leisure Town Rd, N ☐ ⊞, Camping World, S ☐ Arco, Chevron, KwikStop/dsl, 76/McDonald's, ☐ Black Oak Rest., Island Grill, Jack-in-the-Box, King's Buffet, Omlette Bistro, Popeye's, Quizno's, ☐ Best Value, Extended Stay America, Fairfield Inn, Holiday Inn Express, Motel 6, Quality Inn, Residence Inn, ☐ Buick/GMC, Chevrolet, Chrysler/Dodge/Jeep, Harley-Davidson, Home Depot, Honda, Kohl's, Nissan, Toyota, VW
56	I-505 N, to Winters,
55	Nut Tree Pkwy, Monte Vista Dr, Allison Dr, N ☐ 7-11, 76/Circle K, Valero, ☐ Amici Pizza, Arby's, Burger King, Denny's, Elephant Bar Rest., Hisui Japanese, IHOP, Jamba Juice, McDonald's, Murillo's Mexican, Nations Burger, Panera Bread, Pelayo's Mexican, Rubio's, Subway, Taco Bell, Wendy's, ☐ Best Value Inn, Best Western, Super 8, ☐ ⊞, America's Tire, Best Buy, Big O Tire, Firestone/auto, Lowe's Whse, Nugget Foods, Old Navy, Petsmart, See's Candies, U-Haul, transmissions, S ☐ Arco/24hr, Chevron/24hr, ☐ Applebee's, Baja Fresh, BJ's Grill, Black Oak Rest., Carl's Jr, Chevy's Mexican, Chili's, Coldstone Creamery, Fresh Choice Rest., In-N-Out, Jack-in-the-Box, Jamba Juice, KFC, Mel's Diner, Olive Garden, Omlette Bistro, Popeye's, Quizno's, Starbucks, String's Italian, Tahoe Joe's Steaks, TGIFriday, Togo's, ☐ Comfort Suites, Courtyard, Fairfield Inn, Holiday Inn Express, Motel 6, Residence Inn, ☐ GNC, Jo-Ann Fabrics, Marshall's, Michael's, PetCo, GMC, Radio Shack, Ross, Safeway, Sam's Club, Staples, Target, Vacaville Stores/famous brands, Walmart/auto
54b	Mason St, Peabody Rd, N ☐ Chevron, Valero, ☐ A&W/LJ Silver, ☐ Hampton Inn, ☐ NAPA, Schwab Tire, S ☐ USA, ☐ Domino's, Starbucks, Subway, ☐ Costco/gas, 7-11
54a	Davis St, N ☐ Chevron/McDonald's, ☐ Outback Steaks, ☐ Hampton Inn, S ☐ QuikStop, ☐ WinCo Foods, repair
53	Merchant St, Alamo Dr, N ☐ Chevron, Shell/dsl, Valero, ☐ Bakers Square, Baldo's Mexican, Baskin-Robbins, Lyon's/24hr, RoundTable Pizza, Subway, Tin Tin Buffet, ☐ Alamo Inn, ☐ BigLots, vet, S ☐ 76/dsl, ☐ Jack-in-the-Box, KFC, McDonald's, Pizza Hut, Starbucks, ☐ Radio Shack

Exit	Services
52	Cherry Glen Rd (from wb)
51b	Pena Adobe Rd, S ☐ Ranch Hotel
51a	Lagoon Valley Rd, Cherry Glen
48	N Texas St, Fairfield, S ☐ Arco/24hr, Chevron, Shell, ☐ El Pollo Loco, Jim Boy's Tacos, RoundTable Pizza, Panda Express, Starbucks, Subway, Texas Roadhouse, ☐ Longs Drugs, Raley's Foods
47	Waterman Blvd, N ☐ Dynasty Chinese, Loard's Icecream, RoundTable Pizza, Starbucks, Strings Italian, ☐ Chevrolet/Cadillac, Safeway, to Austin's Place, S to Travis AFB, museum
45	Travis Blvd, Fairfield, N ☐ Arco/24hr, Chevron/24hr, ☐ Baskin-Robbins, Burger King, Denny's, In-N-Out, McDonald's, Peking Rest., Subway, Taco Bell, ☐ Courtyard, Motel 6, ☐ Raley's Foods, Harley-Davidson, Ford, Hyundai, Nissan, PetCo, CHP, S ☐ BizWiz Tasty Burgers, Carino's Italian, Chevy's Mexican, Chipotle Mexican, Coldstone Creamery, FreshChoice Rest., Marie Callender's, Mimi's Café, Panda Express, Quizno's, Redbrick Pizza, Red Lobster, Starbucks, ☐ Hilton Garden, ☐ ⊞, Barnes&Noble, Best Buy, Cost+, JC Penney, Macy's, Michael's, Ross, Sears/auto, Trader Joe's, World Mkt, mall
44	W Texas St, same as 45, Fairfield, N ☐ Shell/dsl, Valero/dsl, ☐ ChuckeCheese, Gordito's Mexican, Starbucks, ☐ Extended Stay America, ☐ Staples, S ☐ Valero, ☐ Baldo's Mexican, McDonald's, Paleyo's Mexican, Scenario's Pizza, ☐ Acura/Honda, Chrysler/Jeep/Dodge, FoodMaxx, Home Depot, Hyundai, Infiniti, Mitsubishi, Nissan, Target, Toyota, Volvo, Walgreens
43	CA 12 E, Abernathy Rd, Suisun City, S ☐ Budweiser Plant, Walmart
42mm	weigh sta both lanes, phone
41	Suisan Valley Rd, N ☐ Homewood Suites, Staybridge Suites, S ☐ Arco/24hr, Chevron, 76/dsl/24hr, Shell/dsl, Valero, ☐ Arby's, Bravo's Pizza, Burger King, Carl's Jr, Denny's, Green Bamboo, Jack-in-the-Box, McDonald's, Starbucks, Subway, Taco Bell, Wendy's, ☐ Best Western, Comfort Inn, Days Inn, Fairfield Inn, Holiday Inn Express, ☐ Ray's RV Ctr, Scandia FunCtr
40	I-680 (from wb)
39b	Green Valley Rd, I-680 (from eb), N ☐ Hawaiian BBQ, Peloyas Mexican, RoundTable Pizza, Starbucks, Sticky Rice Bistro, Subway, ☐ Homewood Suites, Staybridge Suites, ☐ Costco/gas, Longs Drug, Safeway, TJ Maxx, S ☐ Arco
39a	Red Top Rd, N ☐ 76/Circle K/24hr, ☐ Jack-in-the-Box
36	American Canyon Rd
34mm	rest area wb, full ☐ facilities, info, ☐, ☐, litter barrels, petwalk, vista parking

🚗 = gas 🍴 = food 🏨 = lodging 🅾 = other   Copyright 2012 - The Next Exit®

INTERSTATE 80 CONT'D

VALLEJO

Exit	Services
33b a	CA 37, to San Rafael, Columbus Pkwy, **N** 🚗 Chevron/dsl, 🍴 Baskin-Robbins, Carl's Jr., 🏨 Best Western, Courtyard, 🅾 funpark **S** same as 32
32	Redwood St, to Vallejo, **N** 🚗 76, 🍴 Denny's, Panda Garden, 🏨 Best Inn, Motel 6, 🅾 H, **S** 🚗 Arco, Bon-Fair, Shell, 🍴 Applebee's, Black Angus, Chevy's Mexican, Coldstone Creamery, IHOP, Jamba Juice, Lyon's Rest., McDonald's, Mtn. Mike's Pizza, Olive Garden, Panda Express, Red Lobster, Rubio's, Starbucks, Subway, Taco Bell, Wendy's, 🏨 Comfort Inn, Ramada Inn, 🅾 AutoZone, Best Buy, Cadillac/Chevrolet, Costco/gas, Hancock Fabrics, Home Depot, Honda, Hyundai, Longs Drug, Marshall's, Mazda, Michael's, Old Navy, PepBoys, PetCo, Radio Shack, Ross, Safeway, Toyota
31b	Tennessee St, to Vallejo, **S** 🚗 Valero/dsl, 🍴 Jack-in-the-Box, Pacifica Pizza, Pizza Guys, 🏨 Great Western Inn, Quality Inn, 🅾 Grocery Outlet
31a	Solano Ave, Springs Rd, **N** 🍴 Burger King, Church's, El Rey Mexican, Taco Bell, 🏨 Deluxe Inn, Relax Inn, 🅾 Rite Aid, U-Haul, **S** 🚗 Chemco, Chevron, Grand Gas, QuikStop, 🍴 DQ, Domino's, Pizza Hut, Starbucks, Subway, Wok, 🏨 Islander Motel, 🅾 Island Pacific Foods, Kragen Parts
30c	Georgia St, Central Vallejo, **N** 🚗 Safeway/gas, **S** 🚗 Shell/Starbucks/dsl, 🍴 McDonald's, 🏨 California Motel
30b	Benicia Rd (from wb), **S** 🚗 Shell/dsl, 🍴 McDonald's, Starbucks
30a	I-780, to Martinez
29b	Magazine St, Vallejo, **N** 🚗 BPG, 🍴 Starbucks, Subway, 🏨 Budget Inn, El Rancho, 7 Motel, 🅾 Tradewinds RV Park, **S** 🍴 McDonald's, 🏨 Travel Inn, 🅾 7-11
29a	CA 29, Maritime Academy Dr, Vallejo, **N** 🚗 Chevron/dsl/24hr, 5 Star Gas, 🍴 Subway, 🏨 Motel 6, Vallejo Inn
28mm	**toll plaza, pay toll from eb**
27	Pomona Rd, Crockett, **N** 🍴 Dead Fish Seafood, vista point
26	Cummings Skyway, to CA 4 (from wb), to Martinez
24	Willow Ave, to Rodeo, **N** 🍴 Straw Hat Pizza, Subway, 🅾 Safeway/24hr, USPO, **S** 🚗 76/Circle K/dsl, 🍴 Burger King, Mazatlan, Starbucks, Willow Garden Chinese
23	CA 4, to Stockton, Hercules, **N** 🚗 Shell, 🍴 Extreme Pizza, Jack-in-the-Box, Starbucks, 🅾 Radio Shack, **S** 🍴 McDonald's, RoundTable Pizza, Subway, Taco Bell, 🅾 BigLots, Curves, Home Depot, Lucky Foods, Rite Aid, USPO
22	Pinole Valley Rd, **S** 🚗 Arco/24hr, Chevron/dsl, 🍴 Jack-in-the-Box, Jamba Juice, NY Pizza, Red Onion Rest., Subway, 🅾 7-11, Trader Joe's, Walgreens
21	Appian Way, **N** 🚗 Pinole Express, 🍴 China Delite, McDonald's, Pizza Hut, 🅾 Kragen Parts, Longs Drug, Safeway, **S** 🚗 Valero/dsl, 🍴 Burger King, Carl's Jr, Coldstone Creamery, Hawaiian BBQ, HomeTown Buffet, HotDog Sta, KFC, Krispy Kreme, In-N-Out, Panda Express, Papa Murphy's, RoundTable Pizza, Sizzler, Starbucks, Subway, Taco Bell, Wendy's, Wing Stop, 🏨 Days Inn, Motel 6, 🅾 AutoZone, Best Buy, $Tree, K-Mart, Lucky Foods, Radio Shack
20	Richmond Pkwy, to I-580 W, **N** 🚗 Chevron, 🍴 Ground Round Rest., IHOP, McDonald's, Me&Ed's Pizza, Subway, 🅾 Barnes&Noble, Chrysler/Dodge/Jeep, Ford,

RICHMOND

Exit	Services
20	Continued 99¢ Store, Petsmart, Ross, **S** 🚗 Chevron, Shell/dsl, 🍴 Applebee's, Chuck Steak, In-N-Out, Krispy Kreme, Outback Steaks, Panda Express, RoundTable Pizza, 🅾 FoodMaxx, Kragen Parts, Old Navy, Michael's, Staples, Target
19b	Hilltop Dr, to Richmond, **N** 🚗 Chevron, 🍴 Chevy's Mexican, Olive Garden, Red Lobster, Tokyo Rest., 🏨 Courtyard, Extended Stay America, 🅾 Firestone, JC Penney, Jo-Ann Fabrics, Macy's, Nissan, Sears/auto, Walmart, mall, **S** 🚗 Hilltop Fuel/dsl
19a	El Portal Dr, to San Pablo, **S** 🚗 SMP, 🍴 McDonalds, Mtn. Mike's Pizza, KFC, Subway, 🅾 Raley's Foods, Walgreens
18	San Pablo Dam Rd, **N** 🚗 Chevron, 🍴 Burger King, Denny's, El Pollo Loco, Empire Buffet, Jack-in-the-Box, Jamba Juice, Nations Burgers, Popeye's, RoundTable Pizza, Starbucks, Subway, Taco Bell, 🏨 Holiday Inn Express, 🅾 H, AutoZone, $Tree, FoodMaxx, Lucky Foods, Walgreens, **S** 🅾 CamperLand RV Ctr
17	Macdonald Ave (from eb), McBryde Ave (from wb), Richmond, **N** 🚗 Arco/24hr, 🍴 Burger King, Church's, **S** 🚗 Chevron/24hr, 🍴 Wendy's, 🅾 Safeway, auto repair
16	San Pablo Ave, to Richmond, San Pablo, **S** 🚗 Chevron, 🍴 KFC, LJ Silver, Subway, Wendy's, 🅾 Safeway
15	Cutting Blvd, Potrero St, to I-580 Br (from wb), to El Cerrito, **N** 🚗 Arco, 🍴 Panda Express, 🅾 Target, **S** 🚗 Chevron, 🍴 Carrow's Rest., Church's, Denny's, IHOP, Jack-in-the-Box, Little Ceasar's, McDonald's, Starbucks, 🅾 $Tree, Home Depot, Honda, Staples, Walgreens
14b	Carlson Blvd, El Cerrito, **N** 🚗 76, 🏨 40 Flags Motel, **S** 🏨 Best Value Inn
14a	Central Ave, El Cerrito, **S** 🚗 76, Valero, 🍴 Burger King, KFC, Nations Burgers
13	to I-580 (from eb), Albany
12	Gilman St, to Berkeley, **N** Golden Gate Fields Racetrack, **S** 🅾 Target
11	University Ave, to Berkeley, **S** 🚗 76, University Gas, 🏨 La Quinta, 🅾 to UC Berkeley
10	CA 13, to Ashby Ave
9	Powell St, Emeryville, **N** 🚗 Shell, 🍴 Chevy's Mexican, 🏨 Hilton Garden, **S** 🚗 76, 🍴 Burger King, CA Pizza Kitchen, Denny's, Elephant Bar/Grill, Jamba Juice, PF Chang's, Starbucks, Togo's, 🏨 Courtyard, Sheraton, Woodfin Suites, 🅾 Barnes&Noble, Old Navy, Ross, Trader Joe's
8c b	Oakland, to I-880, I-580
8a	W Grand Ave, Maritime St
7mm	toll plaza wb
5mm	SF Bay
4a	Treasure Island (exits left)
2c b	Fremont St, Harrison St, Embarcadero (from wb)
2a	4th st (from eb), **S** 🚗 Shell
1	9th st, Civic Ctr, downtown SF
1b a	I-80 begins/ends on US 101 in SF

BERKELEY

INTERSTATE 110 (LOS ANGELES)

Exit	Services
21	I-110 begins/ends on I-10.
20c	Adams Blvd, **E** 🚗 Chevron, 🅾 Audi, Chrysler/Dodge/Jeep, Mercedes, Nissan, Office Depot, VW, LA Convention Ctr.
20b	37th St, Exposition Blvd, **W** 🚗 Chevron/McDonald's, 🏨 Radisson, 🅾 Chevrolet

INTERSTATE 110 CONT'D (LOS ANGELES)

Exit	Services
20a	MLK Blvd, Expo Park, **W** ⓖ Chevron, 🍴 McDonald's, Subway
19b	Vernon Ave, **E** ⓖ Mobil, 🍴 Tacos El Gavilan, **W** ⓖ 76/24hr, Shell, 🍴 Burger King, Jack-in-the-Box, ⓞ Rite Aid, Ross
18b	Slauson Ave, **E** ⓖ Mobil, **W** ⓖ 76
18a	Gage Blvd, **E** ⓖ Arco, 🍴 Church's, Hercules Burgers
17	Florence Ave, **E** ⓖ Shell, 🍴 Jack-in-the-Box, **W** ⓖ Chevron, Valero, 🍴 Burger King, Little Caesars, McDonald's, Pizza Hut, Subway
16	Manchester Ave, **E** ⓖ Arco, 🍴 El Pollo Loco, Little Caesars, McDonald's, Subway, Winchell's, ⓞ AutoZone, **W** ⓖ 76/Circle K, 🍴 Church's, Jack-in-the-Box, Tam's Burgers, Popeye's
15	Century Blvd, **E** ⓖ Arco, Shell/Subway/dsl, 🍴 Burger King, McDonald's, **W** ⓖ 76/dsl
14b	Imperial Hwy, **W** ⓖ Chevron/dsl, 🍴 McDonald's, Jack-in-the-Box
14a	I-105
13	El Segundo Blvd, **E** 🍴 Dominos, Taco Bell, **W** ⓖ Mobil, Shell, 🛏 Executive Inn
12	Rosecrans Ave, **E** ⓖ Arco/24hr, Valero, **W** ⓖ Chevron/McDonald's, Valero, 🍴 Jack-in-the-Box, KFC/LJ Silver, Pizza Hut, Popeye's, Subway, Yoshinoya, ⓞ Chief Parts, 7-11, casino
11	Redondo Beach Blvd, **E** 🍴 McDonald's, **W** ⓖ Mobil, ⓞ ⓗ, casino
10b a	CA 91, 190th St, **W** ⓖ Arco, 🍴 Carl's Jr, Jack-in-the-Box, Krispy Kreme, McDonald's, Pizza Hut/Taco Bell, Subway, ⓞ Food4Less, Ranch Mkt, Sam's Club
9	I-405, San Diego Fwy
8	Torrance Blvd, Del Amo, **E** 🍴 Burger King, Chile Verde, Hawaiian BBQ, Starbucks, ⓞ K-mart, **W** ⓖ Mobil, Shell/Subway/dsl
7b	Carson St, **E** 🍴 KFC, 🛏 Cali Inn, ⓞ vet, **W** ⓖ 76, Shell, 🍴 FatBurger, Hong Kong Deli, In-N-Out, Jack-in-the-Box, Louis Burgers, McDonalds, Pizza Hut, Polly's Pies, Starbucks, Subway, Wienerschnitzel, ⓞ ⓗ, Autozone, Carson Drug, Costsaver Mkt, O'Reilly Parts, Rite Aid
5	Sepulveda Blvd, **E** 🍴 McDonald's, ⓞ Albertson's, Home Depot, Staples, Target, **W** ⓖ Arco/24hr, Chevron, Mobil, 🍴 Burger King, Carl's Jr, McDonald's, Pizza Hut/Taco Bell, Popeye's, Starbucks, Subway, 🛏 Motel 6, ⓞ AT&T, $Tree, Food4Less, 99¢ Store, Rite Aid, Ross
4	CA 1, Pacific Coast Hwy, **E** ⓖ Arco, 76, 🍴 Jack-in-the-Box, Pizza Hut, Wienerschnitzel, **W** ⓖ Circle K, United/dsl, 🍴 Del Taco, Denny's, El Pollo Loco, Subway, 🛏 Best Western, ⓞ ⓗ, Discount Parts, PepBoys, Rite Aid, transmissions
3b	Anaheim St, **W** ⓖ Mobil/dsl, Thrifty, ⓞ radiators, **W** Conoco/Phillips Refinery
3a	C St
1b	Channel St, **W** ⓖ Arco, Chevron, 🍴 Subway, ⓞ Home Depot, 7-11, Target
1a	CA 47, Gaffey Ave
0mm	I-110 begins/ends

INTERSTATE 205 (TRACY)

Exit	Services
12	I-205 begins wb, ends eb, accesses I-5 nb

Exit	Services
9	MacArthur Dr, Tracy, **S** gas Chevron/Jack-in-the-Box/Subway/dsl, ⓞ Prime Outlet Ctr/famous brands
8	Tracy Blvd, Tracy, **N** ⓖ Chevron, Shell/dsl, Tracy Trkstp/Mean Gene's Burger/dsl/24hr, 🍴 Denny's/24hr, 🛏 Holiday Inn Express, Motel 6, **S** ⓖ Arco/24hr, 🍴 American Diner, Arby's, Burger King, In-N-Out, McDonald's, Nations Burgers, Subway, Tracy Buffet, Wendy's, 🛏 Best Western, Microtel, Quality Inn, ⓞ ⓗ, FoodMaxx, Kragen Parts, Longs Drugs, Walgreens, CHP
6	Grant Line Rd, Antioch, **N** ⓖ Chevron, 🍴 Applebee's, Burger King, Chevy's Mexican, Golden Corral, Hometown Buffet, IHOP, Jamba Juice, Olive Garden, Panda Express, Quizno's, Sonic, Starbucks, Strings Italian, Taco Bell, Texas Roadhouse, Wienerschnitzel/TasteeFreeze, 🛏 Extended Stay America, Fairfield Inn, Hampton Inn, ⓞ America's Tire, Barnes&Noble, Chevrolet, Costco/gas, Ford, Home Depot, Hyundai, JC Penney, Michael's, Nissan, Ross, Schwab Tire, Sears/auto, Staples, Target, Toyota, Walmart/McDonald's/auto, World Mkt, mall, **S** ⓖ Arco/24hr, Citgo/7-11, Shell/dsl, Valero, 🍴 Carl's Jr, Chili's, Hawaian BBQ, KFC/A&W, Mtn Mike's Pizza, NYPD Pizza, Orchard Rest., Taco Del Mar, ⓞ Cadillac/GMC, Rite Aid, Tracy Marine
4	11th St (from eb), to Tracy, Defense Depot
2	Mtn House Pkwy, to I-580, E
0mm	I-205 begins eb/ends wb, accesses I-580 wb.

INTERSTATE 210 (PASADENA)

Exit	Services
74	I-215, N to Barstow, S to San Bernardino
73	State St, University Pkwy, **N** ⓖ Thrifty, Valero
71	Riverside Ave, **N** 🍴 Carl's Jr, Del Taco, Starbucks, Subway, ⓞ Fresh&Easy, Ralph's Foods, Rite Aid, Walgreens, **S** ⓖ Arco, 🍴 Jack-in-the-Box, ⓞ 7-11
70	Ayala Dr, **S** ⓞ Target
68	Alder Ave
67	Sierra Ave, **N** 🍴 Applebee's, Carl's Jr, Dickie's BBQ, El Pollo Loco, Hawaiian BBQ, Jamba Juice, Mimi's Cafe, Panda Express, Pizza Hut, Teo's Mexican, Subway, ⓞ Costco/gas, $Tree, Lowe's Whse, **S** ⓞ Chevrolet, Nissan
66	Citrus Ave, **N** 🍴 El Gran Burrito, FarmerBoys Rest., Marble Slab Creamery, Pick Up Stix, Quizno's, Red Brick Pizza, Wienerschnitzel, ⓞ Home Depot, Ralph's Foods, Walgreens
64	Cherry Ave
63	I-15, N to Barstow, S to San Diego
62	Day Creek Blvd, **S** ⓖ Arco/dsl, Shell, 🍴 Chinese Food, Jack-in-the-Box, Marble Slab Creamery, Pizza Factory,

📮 = gas 🍴 = food 🛏 = lodging ⊙ = other   Copyright 2012 - The Next Exit®

CA

INTERSTATE 210 (PASADENA)

Exit	Services
62	Continued Starbucks, Wendy's, ⊙ Ralph's Foods
60	Milliken Ave, **S** 📮 Mobil, 🍴 Taco Bell, ⊙ Albertsons, CVS Drug, Kragen Parts
59	Haven Ave, **N** 📮 Mobil, 76, 7-11, 🍴 Del Taco, Domino's, Jack-in-the-Box, McDonald's, Subway, Teo's Mexican, ⊙ Trader Joe's, Vons Foods, Walgreens
58	Archibald Ave, **S** 🍴 Blimpie, Barboni's Pizza, Carl's Jr, ⊙ Stater Bros, vet
57	Carnelion St, **S** 📮 76, 🍴 Baskin-Robbins, Del Taco, El Ranchero Mexican, Papa John's, Starbucks, ⊙ Radio Shack, Rite Aid, Vons Foods, Walgreens
56	Campus Ave, **S** 🍴 Carl's Jr, Chick-fil-A, Golden Spoon Yogurt, Hawaiian BBQ, IHOP, Jamba Juice, Magic Wok, Qdoba Mexican, Quizno's, Starbucks, Subway, ⊙ Albertsons, Goodyear, Home Depot, Kohl's, Office Depot, Petsmart, Target
54	Mtn Ave, Mount Balde
52	Baseline Rd
50	Towne Ave
48	Fruit St, LaVerne, **S** 📮 Shell, 🍴 El Pollo Loco, Magic Wok, McDonald's, Myiabi, Panda Express, Pizza Hut, Quizno's, Round Table Pizza, Rubio's, Subway, ⊙ Kohl's, Marshall's, Office Depot, Pet Depot, Vons Foods, U of LaVerne, vet
47	Foothill Blvd, LaVerne, **N** 📮 Mobil/Taco Bell, 🍴 Denny's, **S** 📮 Chevron/dsl, Shell, 🍴 IHOP, Starbucks, Togo's, ⊙ GNC, Radio Shack
46	San Dimas Ave, **N** San Dimas Canyon CP
45	CA 57, **S**
44	Lone Hill Ave, Santa Ana, **S** 📮 Chevron, 🍴 Baja Fresh, Chili's, Coco's, In-N-Out, Subway, Wendy's, ⊙ Barnes&Noble, Best Buy, Chevrolet, Chrysler/Dodge/Jeep, Ford, Home Depot, Hyundai, Kohl's, Old Navy, Petsmart, Sam's Club/gas, Staples, Toyota, Walmart/auto
43	Sunflower Ave
42	Grand Ave, to Glendora, **N** 📮 76, Valero/dsl, 🍴 Denny's, ⊙ Ⓗ
41	Citrus Ave, to Covina
40	CA 39, Azusa Ave, **N** 📮 Arco/24hr, Chevron, Mobil, Shell/Del Taco, 🍴 Jack-in-the-Box, 🛏 Rodeway Inn, Super 8, **S** 📮 Chevron, Valero, 🍴 Baskin-Robbins, In-N-Out, Marquez Mexican, 🛏 Best Value, ⊙ Rite Aid, 7-11
39	Vernon Ave (from wb), same as 38
38	Irwindale, **N** 📮 Arco, 🍴 Carl's Jr, Denny's, FarmerBoys Rest., McDonald's, Shanghai Buffet, Taco Bell, ⊙ Costco/gas, NAPA
36b	Mt Olive Dr
36a	I-605 S
35b a	Mountain Ave, **N** 📮 Arco, Chevron 🍴 Denny's, Old Spaghetti Factory, Tommy's Hamburgers, Wienerschnitzel, 🛏 Oak Park Motel, ⊙ Best Buy, BMW/Mini, CarMax, Buick/Chevrolet, Ford, Honda, Infiniti, Nissan, Staples, Subaru, Target, Walgreens, **S** 🍴 IHOP, Panda Express, Roasty Toasty Chicken, Senor Fish, Subway, ⊙ Home Depot, Ross, Walmart
34	Myrtle Ave, **S** 📮 Chevron, 76, 🍴 Jack-in-the-Box
33	Huntington Dr, Monrovia, **N** 📮 Shell/dsl, 🍴 Acapulco Rest., Applebee's, Black Angus, Burger King, Chili's,

MONROVIA

PASADENA

Exit	Services
33	Continued ChuckeCheese, Domino's, LeRoy's Rest., McDonald's, Mimi's Cafe, Panda Express, Popeye's, Quizno's, RoundTable Pizza, Rubio's, Starbucks, 🛏 Courtyard, ⊙ GNC, King Ranch Foods, Marshall's, Office Depot, Pepboy's, Radio Shack, Rite Aid, Trader Joe's, **S** 📮 Chevron, 🍴 Baja Fresh, BJ's Grill, Capistrano's, ClaimJumper, Daphne's Rest., Derby Rest., Fusion Grill, Golden Dragon, Macaroni Grill, Olive Garden, Outback Steaks, Red Lobster, Sesame Grill, Soup Plantation, Starbucks, Subway, Taisho Rest., Togo's, Tokyo Wako, 🛏 Double Tree, Embassy Suites, Extended Stay America, Hampton Inn, Hilton Garden, Homestead Suites, OakTree Inn, Residence Inn, SpringHill Suites
32	Santa Anita Ave, Arcadia, **N** 📮 Arco, 76, 🍴 KFC, McDonald's, Pizza Hut, Subway, ⊙ Ralph's Foods, Rite Aid, **S** 📮 Chevron/dsl, 🍴 In-N-Out, ⊙ carwash
31	Baldwin Ave, to Sierra Madre
30b a	Rosemead Blvd, **N** 📮 Arco, 76/dsl, 🍴 Boston Mkt, ChuckeCheese, Jamba Juice, Starbucks, ⊙ CVS Drug, EZ Lube, Marshall's, Ralph's Foods, Rite Aid, Sears/auto, Whole Foods Mkt, **S** 📮 76, 🍴 Coco's, Jack-in-the-Box, 🛏 Days Inn, ⊙ Big O Tires
29b a	San Gabriel Blvd, Madre St, **N** 📮 76, 🍴 Chipotle Mexican, El Torito, Starbucks, Togo's, ⊙ Best Buy, Old Navy, Petsmart, Ross, **S** 📮 76, 🍴 Jack-in-the-Box, 🛏 Best Western, Holiday Inn Express, Quality Inn, ⊙ Buick/Chevrolet/GMC, Cadillac, Hyundai, Jiffy Lube, Land Rover, Saab, Staples, Target, Toyota
28	Altadena Dr, Sierra Madre, **S** 📮 Chevron, Mobil, ⊙ Just Tires
27 b	Allen
27 a	Hill Ave
26	Lake Ave, **N** 📮 Mobil, ⊙ Jo-Ann Fabrics
25b	CA 134, to Ventura
25a	Del Mar Blvd, CA Blvd, CO Blvd (exits left from eb)
24	Mountain St
23	Lincoln Ave, **S** 🛏 Lincoln Motel, ⊙ auto repair
22b	Arroyo Blvd, **N** 🍴 Jack-in-the-Box, **S** to Rose Bowl
22a	Berkshire Ave, Oak Grove Dr
21	Gould Ave, **S** 📮 Arco, 🍴 Dominos, McDonald's, RoundTable Pizza, Trader Joes, ⊙ Firestone, Just Tires, Ralph's Foods
20	CA 2, Angeles Crest Hwy
19	CA 2, Glendale Fwy, **S** ⊙ Ⓗ
18	Ocean View Blvd, to Montrose
17b a	Pennsylvania Ave, La Crescenta, **N** 📮 76, Shell, Valero, 🍴 Baja Fresh, Burger King, Domino's, Starbucks, Subway, Togo's, Wienerschnitzel, ⊙ GNC, Nissan, Office Depot, Ralph's Foods, Rite Aid, Toyota, Vons Foods, Walgreens, USPO, **S** ⊙ Gardenia Mks/deli, 7-11
16	Lowell Ave
14	La Tuna Cyn Rd
11	Sunland Blvd, Tujunga, **N** 📮 Mobil, 76, Shell, 🍴 Coco's, Jack-in-the-Box, KFC, Sizzler, Yum Yum Donuts, ⊙ Ralph's Foods, Rite Aid, 7-11, city park
9	Wheatland Ave
8	Osborne St, Lakeview Terrace, **N** 🍴 Ranch Side Cafe, ⊙ 7-11
6a	Paxton St
6b	CA 118
5	Maclay St, to San Fernando, **S** 📮 Chevron, 76/dsl, 🍴

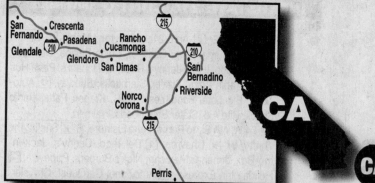

INTERSTATE 210 (PASADENA)

Exit	Services
5	Continued El Pollo Loco, KFC, McDonald's, Quizno's, Subway, Taco Bell, 🅾 Home Depot, Office Depot, Radio Shack, Sam's Club
4	Hubbard St, **N** 🅟 Chevron, 🍴 Denny's, Yum Yum Donuts, 🅾 AutoZone, Radio Shack, Rite Aid, Valley Foods, **S** 🅟 Mobil/dsl, Shell, 🍴 El Caporal Mexican, Jack-in-the-Box, Shakey's Pizza, Subway, 🅾 Vons Foods
3	Polk St, **S** 🅟 Arco, Chevron/24hr, 🍴 KFC, 🅾 🅷, 7-11
2	Roxford St, **N** 🅟 Arco/dsl, 🍴 Topia Pizza/Subs, 🅾 🅷, Jiffy Lube, **S** 🛏 Country Side Inn
1c	Yarnell St
1b a	I-210 begins/ends on I-5, exit 160.

INTERSTATE 215 (RIVERSIDE)

Exit	Services
55	I-215 begins/ends on I-15.
54	Devore, **E** 🅟 Arco/dsl, Shell, **W** 🍴 Tony's Diner
50	Palm Ave, Kendall Dr, **E** 🅟 Arco, 7-11/gas, 🍴 Burger King, Mico Cina Mexican, Popeye's, Starbucks, Subway, **W** 🍴 Denny's
48	University Pkwy, **E** 🅟 Chevron, 76/Circle K, 🍴 Alberto's, Baskin Robbins/Togo's, Carl's Jr, Del Taco, Domino's, IHOP, KFC, Little Ceasars, McDonald's, Papa John's, Starbucks, Wienerschnitzel, 🅾 Curves, EZ Lube, Jiffy Lube, Ralph's Foods, Staples, **W** 🅟 Arco/24hr, Shell/dsl/LP, 🍴 Jack-in-the-Box, Pizza Hut/Taco Bell, Zendejas Mexican, 🛏 Day's Inn, Motel 6, 🅾 Lowe's Whse, Walmart/Subway
46c b	27th St, **E** golf, **W** golf
46a	CA 210 W, Highland Ave
45b	Musciape Dr, **E** 🅟 Shell/dsl, Thrifty, 🍴 Jack-in-the-Box, 🅾 Chevrolet, Home Depot, SavOn Foods, Stater Bros
45a	CA 210 E, Highlands
44b	Baseline Rd
44a	CA 66 W, 5th St, **E** 🛏 Best Value, Econolodge
43	2nd St, Civic Ctr, **E** 🅟 Arco, Chevron/dsl, 🍴 China Hut, Del Taco, In-N-Out, McDonald's, Pizza Hut/Taco Bell, Starbucks, 🛏 Best Value, 🅾 Ford, Food4Less, Marshall's
42b	Mill St, **E** 🍴 Carl's Jr, Del Taco, Jack-in-the-Box, McDonald's, 🅾 AutoZone, **W** 🅟 Shell, 🍴 Yum-yum Donuts
42a	Inland Ctr Dr, **E** 🅟 Chevron/dsl, 🍴 Carl's Jr, Jack-in-the-Box, Wienerschnitzel, 🅾 AutoZone, Kragen Parts, Macy's, Sears/auto, mall
41	Orange Show Rd, **E** 🅟 Arco, Chevron, Exxon, 🍴 Denny's, Pancho Villa Mexican, Subway, 🛏 Knight's Inn, Travelodge, 🅾 BigLots, Chrysler/Dodge/Jeep, Firestone/auto, Kelly Tire, Radio Shack, 99c Store, Target, **W** 🅾 Hyundai, Isuzu, Kia, Mazda, Mitsubishi, Nissan, Scion, Suzuki, Toyota
40b a	I-10, E to Palm Springs, W to LA
39	Washington St, Mt Vernon Ave, **E** 🅟 Arco/24hr, 5 Points, 76, 🍴 Arby's, Baker's Drive-Thru, China Town, DQ, Siquios Mexican, Taco Joe's, Starbucks, 🛏 Colton Inn, 🅾 BigLots, $Tree, Goodyear/auto, Jiffy Lube, **W** 🍴 Burger King, Carl's Jr, Del Taco, Denny's, El Pollo Loco, Jack-in-the-Box, McDonald's, Quizno's, Starbucks, Subway, Taco Bell, Zendejas Mexican, 🛏 Red Tile Inn, 🅾 GNC,

Exit	Services
39	Continued 99¢ Store, Radio Shack, Ross, Walmart/auto, multiple RV dealers
38	Barton Rd, **E** 🅟 Arco, Shell/Circle K, 🍴 Quizno's, 🅾 AutoZone, **W** 🍴 Demetri's Burgers
37	La Cadena Dr, **E** 🅟 Shell/dsl/24hr, 🍴 Jack-in-the-Box, YumYum Rest., 🛏 Holiday Inn Express
36	Center St, to Highgrove, **W** 🅟 Valero/dsl
35	Columbia Ave, **E** 🅟 Arco, **W** 🅾 Circle K
34b a	CA 91, CA 60, Main St, Riverside to beach cities
33	Blaine St, 3rd St, **E** 🅟 76, Shell, Valero, 🍴 Baker's Drive-Thru, Jack-in-the-Box, Starbucks, 🅾 EZ Lube, K-Mart
32	University Ave, Riverside, **W** 🅟 Mobil/dsl, Shell, Thrifty, 🍴 Carl's Jr, Coco's, Del Taco, Denny's, Gus Jr, IHOP, Jack-in-the-Box, Little Ceasars, Mediterranean Palace Cafe, Mongolian BBQ, Pizza Hut, Quizno's, Rubio's, Santana's Mexican, Starbucks, Super Buffet, Subway, Taco Bell, Wienerschnitzel, 🛏 Comfort Inn, Courtyard, Dynasty Suites, Motel 6, 🅾 Food4Less, Kragen Parts, Radio Shack, Rite Aid
31	MLK Blvd, El Cerrito
30b	Central Ave, Watkins Dr
30a	Fair Isle Dr, Box Springs, **W** 🅟 76, 🍴 Jack-in-the-Box, 🅾 Ford
29	CA 60 E, to Indio, **E on Day St** 🅟 Shell/dsl, 🍴 Applebees, Baker's Drive-Thru, Carl's Jr, Chick-fil-A, El Pollo Loco, Golden Chop Stix, Hawaiian BBQ, Home Town Buffet, Hooters, Jamba Juice, Jason's Deli, McDonald's, Mimi's Cafe, Olive Garden, Outback Steaks, Panda Express, Portillo's Hot Dogs, Qdoba Mexican, Quizno's, Red Robin, Starbucks, Subway, Wendy's, Wienerschnitzel, 🛏 Hampton Inn, 🅾 Best Buy, Costco/gas, $Tree, Home Depot, JC Penney, Jo-Ann Fabrics, Lowe's Whse, Macy's, Marshall's, Michael's, Old Navy, PetSmart, Sears/auto, Staples, Target, Walmart, WinCo Foods, mall
28	Eucalyptus Ave, Eastridge Ave, **E** 🍴 Bravo Burgers, Hooters, 🅾 Sam's Club/gas, Target, Walmart, same as 29
27b	Alessandro Blvd, **E** 🅟 Arco/24hr, 76/Circle K/dsl, 🅾 Big O Tire, auto repair, **W** 🅟 Chevron, 🍴 Farmer Boys
27a	Cactus Ave to March ARB, **E** 🅟 Chevron, 76/Circle K/dsl, 🍴 Carl's Jr, Richie's Burgers
25	Van Buren Blvd, **E** 🅾 March Field Museum, **W** 🅾 Riverside Nat Cen.
23	Harley Knox Blvd, **E** 🅾 auto repair
22	Ramona Expswy, **1 mi E on Perris Blvd** 🅟 Chevron, Mobil, Shell, 🍴 Old Chicago Pizza, Subway, **W** 🅟 Arco/dsl/scales/24hr, 76/Circle K/dsl/LP, 🍴 Jack-in-the-Box

🅖 = gas 🍴 = food 🛏 = lodging 🄾 = other   Copyright 2012 - The Next Exit®

INTERSTATE 215 CONT'D (RIVERSIDE)

Exit	Services
19	Nuevo Rd, **E** 🅖 Arco/24hr, Chevron, Mobil, 🍴 Baskin Robbins, Burger King, Carl's Jr, China Palace, Del Taco, El Pollo Loco, IHOP, Jenny's Rest., McDonald's, Pizza Hut, Round Table Pizza, Sizzler, Starbucks, Subway, 🄾 Auto-Zone, Big Lots, Food4Less, GNC, Kragen Parts, Radio Shack, Rite Aid, Stater Bros Foods, Walmart
17	CA 74 W, 4th St, to Perris, Lake Elsinore, **E** 🅖 Shell/24hr, Thrifty, **W** 🅖 Chevron, 🍴 Del Taco, Denny's, Jack-in-the-Box, Jimenez Mexican, Nick's Burgers, Popeye's, 🛏 Holiday Inn Express, 🄾 AutoZone, CarQuest, Chrysler/Dodge/Jeep/Kia, $Mart, vet
15	CA 74 E, Hemet, **E** 🛏 Sun Leisure Motel
14	Ethanac Rd, **E** 🍴 KFC/Taco Bell, 🄾 Richardson's RV, **W** 🅖 Circle K, Exxon/dsl, 🍴 Carl's Jr, Del Taco, Hawaiian BBQ, Subway, 🄾 Just Tires, Home Depot, WinCo Foods
12	McCall Blvd, Sun City, **E** 🅖 Valero/dsl, 🍴 Wendy's, 🛏 Best Value, Super 8, 🄾 🄷, **W** 🅖 Chevron/dsl, Valero, 🍴 Coco's, Domino's, McDonald's, Rong's Chinese, Santana's Mexican, Subway, 🄾 Rite Aid, Stater Bros Foods, Von's Foods, Walgreens
10	Newport Rd, Quail Valley, **E** 🅖 Shell/Del Taco/dsl, 🍴 Cathay Chinese, Coldstone Creamery, Jack-in-the-Box, Papa John's, Subway, Taco Bell, 🄾 AutoZone, GNC, Ralph's Foods, Ross, **W** 🅖 Arco/24hr, 76/Circle K/dsl, 🍴 Chipotle, In-N-Out, Panda Express, Red Robin, Starbucks, Yellow Basket Cafe, 🄾 Best Buy, Kohl's, Lowes Whse, Old Navy, PetCo, Staples, SuperTarget
7	Scott Rd, **E** 🅖 Arco/dsl, 7-11, 🍴 Carl's Jr, Del Taco, Jack-in-the-Box, Subway, 🄾 Albertson's/SavOn
4	Clinton Keith Rd, **W** 🍴 Juice It Up, Subway, 🄾 Marshall's, Target
2	Los Alamos, **E** 🅖 Shell, 🍴 Board'z Grill, In-N-Out, Mama Rose's Pizza, Peony Chinese, Taco Bell, 🄾 USPO, **W** 🅖 Mobil/McDonald's, 🍴 ChuckeCheese, City Deli/bakery, Jack-in-the-Box, Pizza Hut, Starbucks, Subway, TJ's Pizza, 🄾 CVS Drug, Stater Bros Foods
1	Murrieta Hot Springs, **E** 🅖 7-11, Shell/dsl, 🍴 Alberto's Mexican, Baja Grill, Buffalo Wild Wings, Carl's Jr, El Pollo Loco, Gourmet Italian, Richie's Diner, Rubio's, Seafood Grill, Sizzler, Starbucks, Wendy's, 🄾 Ralph's Foods, Rite Aid, Ross, Sam's Club/gas, Walgreens
0mm	I-215 begins/ends on I-15.

INTERSTATE 280 (BAY AREA)

Exit	Services
58	4th St, I-280 begins/ends, **N** 🄾 Whole Foods Mkt, **S** 🅖 Shell
57	7th St, to I-80, downtown
56	Mariposa St, downtown
55	Army St, Port of SF
54	US 101 S, Alemany Blvd, Mission St, **E** 🅖 Shell
52	San Jose Ave, Bosworth St (from nb, no return)
51	Geneva Ave
50	CA 1, 19th Ave, **W** 🅖 Chevron, 🄾 to Bay Bridge, SFSU
49	Daly City, **E** 🅖 76/dsl/LP, 🄾 Toyota, Walgreens, **W** 🅖 Arco, 🍴 Carl's Jr, Domino's, IHOP, In-N-Out, Krispy Kreme, McDonald's, Val's Rest., 🛏 Hampton Inn
47a	Serramonte Blvd, Daly City (from sb), **E** 🅖 Silver Gas, 🄾 Cadillac, Chevrolet, Ford, Home Depot, Honda,

---

Exit	Services
47a	Continued Nissan, Target, **W** 🅖 Olympian, 76, 🍴 Boston Mkt, Elephant Bar Rest., McDonald's, Sizzler, Starbucks, 🄾 Macy's, Longs Drugs, Office Depot, PetsMart, Ross, Target
47b	CA 1, Mission St, (from nb), Pacifica, **E** 🍴 Hawaiian BBQ, RoundTable Pizza, Sizzler, 🄾 🄷, Chrysler/Jeep/Dodge, Drug Barn, Fresh Choice Foods, Home Depot, Infiniti, Isuzu, Jo-Ann Fabrics, Lexus, Mitsubishi, Nordstrom's, PetCo, Target, mall
46	Hickey Blvd, Colma, **E** 🅖 Chevron/dsl/24hr, Shell, **W** 🅖 Shell/dsl/24hr, 🍴 Boston Mkt, Celia's Rest., Koi Palace, Moonstar, Outback Steaks, Sizzler, 🄾 Ross, 7-11
45	Avalon Dr, (from sb), Westborough, **W** 🅖 Arco/24hr, Valero/dsl, 🍴 Denny's, McDonald's, Subway, 🄾 Pak'n Save Foods, Walgreens/24hr, Skyline Coll
44	(from nb)
43b	I-380 E, to US 101, to SF ⮕
43a	San Bruno Ave, Sneath Ave, **E** 🍴 Au's Kitchen, Baskin-Robbins, Carl's Jr, Jamba Juice, Quizno's, Starbucks, Taco Bell, 🄾 GNC, Longs Drugs, Mollie Stones Mkt, Radio Shack, **W** 🅖 Chevron, 76, 🍴 Baker's Square, 🄾 7-11
42	Crystal Springs (from sb), county park
41	CA 35 N, Skyline Blvd (from wb, no EZ return), **to Pacifica 1 mi W** 🅖 Chevron
40	Millbrae Ave, Millbrae, **E** 🅖 Chevron
39	Trousdale Dr, to Burlingame, **E** 🄷
36	Black Mtn Rd, Hayne Rd, **W** golf, vista point
36mm	**Crystal Springs rest area wb, full ♿ facilities, 🍴, 🛏, litter barrels, petwalk**
35	CA 35, CA 92W (from eb), to Half Moon Bay
34	Bunker Hill Dr
33	CA 92, to Half Moon Bay, San Mateo
32mm	vista point both lanes
29	Edgewood Rd, Canada Rd, to San Carlos, **E** 🄾 🄷
27	Farm Hill Blvd, **E** 🄾 Cañada Coll, phone
25	CA 84, Woodside Rd, **Redwood City 1 mi W** 🅖 Chevron/dsl, 🍴 John Bentley's Rest., Buck's Rest., 🄾 Robert's Mkt, USPO
24	Sand Hill Rd, **Menlo Park 1 mi E** 🅖 Shell, 🍴 Starbucks, 🄾 Longs Drug, Safeway
22	Alpine Rd, Portola Valley, **E** 🄾 🄷, **W** 🅖 Shell/autocare, 🍴 Red Lotus Cafe, RoundTable Pizza, 🄾 Curves
20	Page Mill Rd, to Palo Alto, **E** 🄷, to Stanford U
16	El Monte Rd, Moody Rd
15	Magdalena Ave
13	Foothill Expswy, Grant Rd, **E** 🅖 Chevron/24hr, 🍴 Starbucks, Woodpecker Grill, 🄾 Rite Aid, Trader Joe's, **W** 🄾 to Rancho San Antonio CP
12b a	CA 85, N to Mtn View, S to Gilroy
11	Saratoga, Cupertino, Sunnyvale, **E** 🅖 Chevron, 🍴 Carl's Jr, Quizno's, 🛏 Cupertino Inn, 🄾 Goodyear, Michael's, Rite Aid, TJ Maxx, repair, **W** 🅖 Chevron, Dianza Gas, 76, USA, 🍴 BJ's Rest., Outback Steaks, 🛏 Cypress Hotel, 🄾 Apple Computer HQ, PetsMart
10	Wolfe Rd, **E** 🅖 Arco/24hr, 🍴 Teppan Steaks, Starbucks, 🛏 Courtyard, Hilton Garden, 🄾 Ranch Mkt, **W** 🅖 76, 🍴 Alexander Steaks, Benihana, Vallco Dynasty Chinese, 🄾 FreshChoice Foods, JC Penney, Jiffy Lube, Sears/auto, Vallco Fashion Park
9	Lawrence Expswy, Stevens Creek Blvd (from eb), **N** 🍴

INTERSTATE 280 CONT'D (BAY AREA)

SAN JOSE N ↕ S

Exit	Services
9	Continued
	El Pollo Loco, McDonalds, Mtn Mikes Pizza, Panda Express, Quizno's, Starbucks, 🅾 Safeway, Marshalls, 🅾 Land Rover, Nissan, S 📱 Rotten Robbie, 76, 🍴 IHOP, Subway, 🛏 7-11, Woodcrest Hotel
7	Saratoga Ave, N 📱 Arco/24hr, Chevron/24hr, 🍴 Black Angus, Burger King, Garden City Rest., Happi House, Lion Rest., McDonald's, Taco Bell, 🅾 Cadillac, Chevrolet, Ford, Goodyear, Jiffy Lube, PepBoys, 7-11, S 📱 76, Shell, Valero, 🍴 Applebee's, Tony Roma's, 🛏 MoorPark Hotel
5c	Winchester Blvd, Campbell Ave (from eb)
5b	CA 17 S, to Santa Cruz, I-880 N, to San Jose
5a	Leigh Ave, Bascom Ave
4	Meridian St (from eb), N 📱 76, 🅾 Big O Tire, FoodMaxx, S 📱 Chevron, 🍴 KFC, Subway, Wienerschnitzel, 🅾 7-11
3b	Bird Ave, Race St
3a	CA 87, N 🛏 Hilton, Holiday Inn, Hotel Sainte Claire, Marriott
2	7th St, to CA 82, N conv ctr
1	10th St, 11th St, N 🅾 7-11, 🅾 to San Jose St U
0mm	I-280 begins/ends on US 101.

INTERSTATE 405 (LOS ANGELES)

N ↕ S   LOS ANGELES AREA

Exit	Services
73	I-5, N to Sacramento, I-5, S to LA
72	Rinaldi St, Sepulveda, E 📱 Chevron/dsl, 76, 🍴 Arby's, McDonald's, Presidente Mexican, Subway, 🅾 H, Nissan, Toyota, W 📱 Shell, 🛏 Best Value Inn
71	CA 118 W, Simi Valley
70	Devonshire St, Granada Hills, E 📱 Arco, GasMart/dsl, 76, 🍴 Holiday Burger, Millie's Rest., Papa John's, Quiznos, Safari Room Rest., Subway, 🅾 Bare's RV Ctr, Radio Shack, Ralph's Foods, Rite Aid, Verizon, Vons Foods
69	Nordhoff St, E 📱 Mobil/dsl, 🍴 China Wok, Coldstone, Del Taco, KFC, Panda Express, Pollo Campero, 7 Mares, Starbucks, 🛏 Hillcrest Inn, 🅾 Marshalls, 7-11, Vallarta Foods, Walgreens, W 📱 Arco, 76/dsl, 🍴 Jack-in-the-Box, Pizza Hut
68	Roscoe Blvd, to Panorama City, E 📱 76/dsl, Shell, 🍴 Burger King, Country Folks Rest., Denny's, Galpin Rest., Jack-in-the-Box, Little Caesars, McDonald's, Panda Express, Taco Bell, Yoshinoya, 🛏 Holiday Inn Express, 🅾 AutoZone, Ford, Lincoln/Mercury, Jaguar/Volvo, 7-11, U-Haul, W 📱 Chevron/dsl, Shell/dsl, 🍴 Tommy's Burgers, 🛏 Motel 6
66	Sherman Blvd, Reseda, E 📱 Chevron, Mobil/LP, 🍴 Golden Chicken, KFC, McDonald's, Starbucks, 🛏 Motel 6, 🅾 BigLots, CVS Drug, Jon's Foods, W 📱 76/dsl/24hr, 🍴 Taco Bell, 🅾 H, USPO
65	Victory Blvd, Van Nuys, E on Sepulveda 🍴 Carl's Jr, El Pollo Loco, Jack-in-the-Box, Subway, Wendy's, 🅾 CVS Drug, El Monte RV Ctr, Costco/gas, Office Depot, PepBoys, Staples, W on Victory 📱 Arco/24hr, 🅾 H
64	Burbank Blvd, E 📱 Chevron, Shell, 🍴 Denny's, 🛏 Best Western, Hampton Inn, 🅾 Target
63b	US 101, Ventura Fwy
63a	Ventura Blvd (from nb), E 📱 Mobil, 🍴 Cheesecake Factory, El Pollo Loco, 🅾 Whole Foods Mkt, mall, W 📱 76, 🍴 Ameci Pizza, CA Chicken Cafe, Corner Bakery Cafe,

Exit	Services
63a	Continued
	IHOP, McDonald's, 🛏 Courtyard, Valley Inn
63a	Valley Vista Blvd (from sb)
61	Mulholland Dr, Skirvall Dr
59	Sepulveda Blvd, Getty Ctr Dr, W to Getty Ctr
57	Sunset Blvd, Morega Dr, E 📱 Chevron/24hr, 76/dsl, 🅾 to UCLA, W 🛏 Luxe Hotel
56	Waterford St, Montana Ave (from nb)
55c b	Wilshire Blvd, E downtown, W 🅾 H
55a	CA 2, Santa Monica Blvd, E 📱 Chevron, Mobil, Shell, Thrifty, 🍴 Coffee Bean, Jack-in-the-Box, Jamba Juice, Quiznos, Starbucks, Winchell's, Yoshinoya, Zankau Chicken, 🅾 Firestone/auto, 7-11, LDS Temple, Staples, vet, W 📱 Chevron/dsl, 76/24hr, 🍴 Subway, 🛏 Holiday Inn Express
54	Olympic Blvd, Peco Blvd, E 📱 Mobil, 🍴 Islands Burgers, Jack-in-the-Box, La Salsa, Norm's Rest., Stabucks, 🅾 Barnes&Noble, Nordstroms, W 🍴 Big Tomy's Rest., 🅾 Best Buy, Marshall's, USPO
53	I-10, Santa Monica Fwy
52	Venice Blvd, E 📱 Chevron/service, Shell/dsl, 🍴 Carl's Jr, Subway, 🛏 Ramada, 🅾 7-11, services on Sepulveda, W 📱 SP/dsl, 🍴 FatBurger
51	Culver Blvd, Washington Blvd, E 🍴 Dear John's Café, Taco Bell, 🅾 vet, W 📱 76/repair
50b	CA 90, Slauson Ave, to Marina del Rey, E 📱 Arco/24hr, 🍴 Del Taco, El Pollo Loco, HoneyBaked Ham, Shakey's Pizza, Winchell's, 🅾 BigLots, $Tree, Firestone/auto, Goodyear/auto, Just Tires, Office Depot, Old Navy, Staples, transmissions, W 📱 76, 🍴 Denny's, 🅾 Albertson's
50a	Jefferson Blvd (from sb), E 🍴 Coco's, Jack-in-the-Box, 🅾 PetsMart, Rite Aid, Target, W to LA 🖼
49	Howard Hughes Pkwy, to Centinela Ave, E 📱 Chevron/dsl, Mobil/dsl, 🍴 BJ's Brewhouse, Quiznos, Sizzler, 🛏 Courtyard, Sheraton, 🅾 Best Buy, CVS Drug, Ford, Honda, JC Penney, Macy's, Marshall's, Target, mall, W 📱 Chevron, 🍴 Dinah's Rest., Habuki Japanese, Islands Burgers, Marie Callender's, Rubio's, Starbucks, Subway, Wild Thai, 🛏 Extended Stay America, Radisson, 🅾 Howard Hughes Ctr, Nordstrom
48	La Tijera Blvd, E 📱 Mobil/sl, 🍴 Burger King, Chuck-eCheese, El Pollo Loco, Jamba Juice, KFC, McDonald's, Starbucks, Subway, Taco Bell, TGIFriday's, 🛏 Best Western, 🅾 CVS Drug, 99c Store, Ralph's Foods, Ross, Vons Foods, W 📱 Chevron/dsl/24hr, 76/Circle K, 🍴 Buggy Whip Rest., Wendy's, 🅾 USPO
47	CA 42, Manchester Ave, Inglewood, E 📱 76/Circle K/dsl/24hr, 🍴 Carl's Jr, Subway, 🛏 Best Western, Economy Inn, 🅾 7-11, repair, W 📱 Arco, Circle K, Shell, 76,

🅖 = gas 🍴 = food 🛏 = lodging 🅞 = other   Copyright 2012 - The Next Exit®

CA

HAWTHORNE N ↕ S

TORRANCE

CARSON

INTERSTATE 405 CONT'D (LOS ANGELES)

Exit	Services
47	Continued
	Valero, 🍴 Arby's, Burger King, Denny's, El Pollo Loco, Jack-in-the-Box, Louis Burgers, 🛏 Days Inn, 🅞 CarMax, Chrysler/Dodge/Jeep, Home Depot, Hyundai
46	Century Blvd, E 🅖 Chevron/dsl, 🍴 Casa Gamino Mexican, El Pollo Loco, Flower Drum Chinese, Hawaiian BBQ, Little Caesars, Panda Express, Rally's, 🛏 Best Value Inn, Best Western, Comfort Inn, Motel 6, Tivoli Hotel, 🅞 LAX Transmissions, 7-11, W 🅖 Arco/24hr, Chevron/dsl, 76/Circle K, Shell, 🍴 Carl's Jr, Denny's, McDonald's, Pizza Hut/Taco Bell, 🛏 Hampton Inn, Hilton, Holiday Inn, Marriott, La Quinta, Travelodge, Westin Hotel, 🅞 to LAX
45	I-105, Imperial Hwy, E 🅖 76/dsl, Shell, Valero, 🍴 El Pollo Loco, El Tarasco Mexican, KFC/Taco Bell, Jack-in-the-Box, McDonald's, 🛏 Best Value Inn, Candlewood Suites, Holiday Inn Express, 🅞 J&S Transmissions, repair, W 🍴 Wild Goose Rest./Theater (1mi)
44	El Segundo Blvd, to El Segundo, E 🅖 Chevron/24hr, Thrifty, Valero, 🍴 Burger King, Christy's Donuts, Cougars Burgers, Jack-in-the-Box, Jase Burgers, Subway, 🛏 El Segundo Inn, 🅞 transmissions, W 🍴 Denny's, 🛏 Ramada Inn
43b a	Rosecrans Ave, to Manhattan Beach, E 🅖 76, Shell, 🍴 Denny's, El Pollo Loco, Pizza Hut, Starbucks, Subway, 🅞 Best Buy, CVS Drug, Food4Less, Ford/Lincoln/Mercury, Home Depot, Marshall's, Michael's, Office Depot, Ross, W 🅖 Thrifty, 🍴 Cafe Rio, Carl's Jr, Chipotle Mexican, Flemings Rest., Hawaiian BBQ, Houston's, Luigi's Rest., Macaroni Grill, McDonald's, Qdoba Mexican, Robeks Juice, Sansai Japanese, Starbucks, Subway, 🛏 Ayres Hotel, Hyatt, TownePlace Suites, SpringHill Suites, 🅞 AT&T, Barnes&Noble, Costco/gas, CVS Drug, Fresh&Easy, Nissan, Office Depot, Old Navy, Staples, Trader Joe's, VW
42b	Inglewood Ave, E 🅖 Shell, 🍴 Baskin-Robbins, Del Taco, Denny's, Domino's, In-N-Out, Quiznos, 🅞 CVS Drug, Marshall's, PetCo, Vons Foods, W 🅖 76, Shell/dsl/24hr, 🍴 La Salsa Mexican, Subway, 🅞 99¢ Store, repair
42a	CA 107, Hawthorne Blvd, E 🅖 Chevron, 🍴 Carl's Jr, Jack-in-the-Box, Little Caesars, McDonald's, Panda Express, Papa John's, Wendy's, Wienerschnitzel, 🛏 Baymont Inn, Best Western, Days Inn, 🅞 CVS Drug, Kragen Parts, 99¢ Store, PepBoys, Radio Shack, Value+ Foods, vet, W 🅖 Arco/24hr, Chevron/dsl, Thrifty, 🍴 Boston Mkt, Marie Callendar's, Quiznos, Sizzler, Starbucks, Subway, Taco Bell, Yoshinoya, 🅞 AutoZone, Macy's, Nordstom
40b	Redondo Beach Blvd (no EZ sb return), Hermosa Beach, E 🅖 Arco/24hr, 76, 🍴 ChuckeCheese, Jack-in-the-Box, 🅞 golf, W 🍴 RoundTable Pizza, Starbucks, 🅞 AutoZone, Curves, CVS Drug, urgent care
40a	CA 91 E, Artesia Blvd, to Torrance, W 🅖 Chevron, 🍴 Carl's Jr, Starbucks, YumYum Donuts
39	Crenshaw Blvd, to Torrance, E 🅖 Arco/24hr, Shell, 🍴 Burger King, El Pollo Loco, McDonald's, 🅞 Ralph's Foods, USPO, W 🅖 Mobil/dsl, Shell/Subway/dsl, 🅞 Jiffy Lube
38b	Western Ave, to Torrance, E 🅖 Arco, Chevron, 76/dsl, 🍴 Del Taco, Denny's, Hong Kong Express, Local Place, Papa John's, Quiznos, Starbucks, Wendy's, Yorgo's Burgers, 🛏 Dynasty Inn, 🅞 Albertson's/Sav-On, Curves, GNC, Toyota/Scion, W 🅖 Mobil, 🍴 Mill's Rest., 🛏 Courtyard, 🅞 Lexus

Exit	Services
38a	Normandie Ave, to Gardena, E 🛏 Comfort Inn, W 🅖 Shell/dsl, 🍴 Big Island BBQ, Carl's Jr, Chile Verde Mexican, Hong Kong Cafe, Pizza Hut/Taco Bell, Quiznos, Starbucks, Subway, Wienerschnitzel, 🛏 Extended Stay America, 🅞 $Tree, Walmart
37b	Vermont Ave (from sb), W 🛏 Holiday Inn, 🅞 hwy patrol
37a	I-110, Harbor Fwy
36	Main St (from nb)
36mm	**weigh sta both lanes**
35	Avalon Blvd, to Carson, E 🅖 Chevron, Mobil, 🍴 Carson Buffet, Chili's, ChuckeCheese, Denny's, 5 Guys Burgers, FoodCourt, Jack-in-the-Box, Jamba Juice, McDonald's, Panda Express, Panera Bread, Pizza Hut, Quiznos, Sensai Grill, Shakey's Pizza, Sizzler, Starbucks, Tokyo Grill, Tony Roma, WingStop, 🛏 Clarion, 🅞 America's Tire, AT&T, Bestway Foods, Firestone/auto, Goodyear/auto, Ikea, JC Penney, Just Tires, PepBoys, Radio Shack, Sears/auto, Target, Verizon, mall, USPO, W 🅖 Arco/24hr, Mobil, 🍴 Carl's Jr, McDonald's, 🅞 Kia, Kragen Parts, Ralph's Foods
34	Carson St, to Carson, E 🛏 EconoLodge, W 🅖 Mobil, 76/dsl/24hr, 🍴 Carl's Jr, Jack-in-the-Box, Subway, 🛏 DoubleTree Inn
33b	Wilmington Ave, E 🅖 Mobil/dsl, 🍴 Carson Burgers, W 🅖 Chevron/Jack-in-the-Box/dsl, Shell/Subway/dsl, 🍴 Del Taco, Spires Rest., 🅞 Chevrolet/Hyundai, Honda,
33b	Continued
	Nissan, Toyota/Scion
33a	Alameda St
32d	Santa Fe Ave (from nb), E 🅖 Arco/24hr, W 🅖 Chevron/24hr, United/dsl, 🍴 Fantastic Burgers
32c b	I-710, Long Beach Fwy
32a	Pacific Ave (from sb)
30b	Long Beach Blvd, E 🅖 Arco/dsl, 🍴 Subway, 🅞 7-11, W 🅖 Exxon, 🅞 🅷
30a	Atlantic Blvd, E 🅖 Chevron/dsl, 🍴 Arby's, Carl's Jr, Denny's/24hr, El Torito, Jack-in-the-Box, Polly's Cafe, 🅞 CVS Drug, NAPACare, Staples, Target, Walgreens, vet, W 🅞 🅷, $Tree, Home Depot, PetCo, Ross
29c	Orange Ave (from sb), W 🅞 Dodge/GMC/Nissan
29b a	Cherry Ave, to Signal Hill, E 🅖 Mobil/dsl, 🍴 Fantastic Burgers, 🅞 Ford, Lincoln/Mercury, Mazda, auto repair, W 🅖 76, 🅞 America's Tire, Best Buy, BMW/Mini, Buick, Dodge, Firestone, Honda, Mercedes, Nissan
27	CA 19, Lakewood Blvd, E 🛏 Marriott, 🅞 🍽, W 🅖 Chevron, Shell/24hr, 🍴 Spires Rest., 🛏 Extended Stay America, Holiday Inn, Residence Inn, 🅞 🅷, Ford, Goodyear/auto
26b	Bellflower Blvd, E 🅖 76, 🍴 Burger King, Carl's Jr, Denny's, Jamba Juice, KFC, Papa John's, Subway, Togo's, 🅞 Ford, K-Mart, Lowe's, W 🅖 Chevron, Mobil/dsl, Shell, 🍴 Baja Fresh, Hof's Hut, IHOP, McDonald's, Pick-Up Stix, Quiznos, Wendy's, 🅞 🅷, BigLots, CVS Drug, Goodyear/auto, Rite Aid/24hr, Sears, See's Candies, Target, USPO
26a	Woodruff Ave (from nb)
25	Palo Verde Ave, W 🅖 76, 🍴 Dave's Burgers, Del Taco, Domino's, Pizza Hut/Taco Bell, Starbucks, Subway
24b	Studebaker Rd, (from sb)
24a	I-605, N
23	CA 22 W, 7th St, to Long Beach
22	Seal Beach Blvd, Los Alamitos Blvd, E 🅖 Chevron/repair/24hr, Mobil/dsl, 76/dsl, 🍴 Baja Fresh, CA Pizza Kitchen Daphne's Greek, Hot Off the Grill, Islands Burg

INTERSTATE 405 CONT'D (LOS ANGELES)

N
↕
S

Exit	Services
22	**Continued**
	ers, Jamba Juice, KFC, Kobe Japanese, Macaroni Grill, Marie Callenders, Peiwei Asian, Pick-Up Stix, Quiznos, Rubio's, Spaghettini Grill, Starbucks, Z Pizza, 🏨 Ayres Hotel,· 🅾 AT&T, CVS Drug, GNC, Kohl's, Marshall's, Ralph's Foods, Sprouts Mkt, Target, **1 mi** W 🅿 Chevron, 76/dsl, 🍴 Carl's Jr, Del Taco, Domino's, 🏨 Hampton Inn
21	CA 22 E, Garden Grove Fwy, Valley View St, E 🅾 Ford
19	Westminster Ave, to Springdale St, E 🅿 Arco/24hr, Chevron/dsl, 76/Circle K, Thrifty, 🍴 Café Westminster, Carl's Jr, In-N-Out, KFC, McDonald's, 🏨 Knights Inn, Motel 6, Travelodge, 🅾 America's Tire, AutoZone, Big-Lots, Home Depot, Kragen Parts, Radio Shack, Rite Aid, Ross, 7-11, W 🅿 Chevron/dsl/24hr, 🍴 Starbucks, Subway, 🏨 Best Western, Courtyard Inn, 🍴 Ranchito Mkt
18	Bolsa Ave, Golden West St, W 🅿 Mobil/dsl, 76, 🍴 Coco's, El Torito, IHOP, Jack-in-the-Box, Outback Steaks, Rodrigo's Mexican, Starbucks, Wendy's, 🅾 CVS Drug, $Tree, JC Penney, Jo-Ann Fabrics, Jons Foods, Macy's, Sears/auto, Target, mall
16	CA 39, Beach Blvd, to Huntington Bch, E 🅿 Chevron, Shell, 🍴 Jack-in-the-Box, Subway, 🏨 Super 8, 🅾 🄷, PepBoys, Toyota, U-Haul, W 🅿 Mobil/service, 🍴 Arby's, BJ's Rest., Buca Italian, Burger King, CA Pizza Kitchen, Chipotle Mexican, Panera Bread, Islands Burgers, Jack-in-the-Box, Macaroni Grill, Marie Callender's, McDonald's, Popeye's, Quiznos, Starbucks, Subway, 🏨 Comfort Suites, 🅾 AT&T, Barnes&Noble, Big O Tire, Chrysler/Dodge/Jeep, Firestone/auto, Kohl's, Office Depot, See's Candies, Staples, Target, Verizon, Whole Foods Mkt
15b a	Magnolia St, Warner Ave, E 🍴 Del Taco, Sizzler, 🅾 Fresh&Easy, W 🅿 Chevron, Mobil, 🍴 Carrow's, Magnolia Café, Starbucks, Tommy's Burgers, 🏨 Days Inn, 🅾 CVS Drug, Grocery Outlet, 7-11, Tuesday Morning, Winchell's
14	Brookhurst St, Fountain Valley, E 🅿 Arco/24hr, Chevron, Mobil, Shell, 🍴 Alerto's Mexican, Carl's Jr, Coco's, Del Taco, KFC, Taco Bell, 🏨 Courtyard, Residence Inn, 🅾 America's Tire, Sam's Club/gas, Thompson's RV Ctr, W 🅿 Arco, 76/dsl, Shell/dsl, 🍴 Applebee's, Black Angus, Chop Stix, ClaimJumper, Coco's, Coldstone, Corner Bakery Cafe, Islands Burgers, Mandarin, Mimi's Cafe, Quiznos, Rubio's, Starbucks, Subway, Togo's, Wendy's, 🅾 🄷, Albertson's, Office Depot, Ralph's Foods, Rite Aid, TJ Maxx, vet
12	Euclid Ave, E 🍴 Cancun Fresh, Carl's Jr, Coffee Bean, FlameBroiler, Panda Express, Pita Fresh Grill, Quiznos, Souplantation, Starbucks, Subway, Taco Bell, Z Pizza, 🅾 🄷, Big Lots, Costco/gas, $Tree, PetsMart, Staples, Tire Whse
11b	Harbor Blvd, to Costa Mesa, E 🍴 Hooters, 🏨 La Quinta, W 🅿 Arco, Chevron, Mobil, Shell/dsl, 7-11, 🍴 Burger King, Denny's, Domino's, El Pollo Loco, IHOP, Jack-in-the-Box, KFC, LJ Silver, McDonald's, Subway, 🏨 Costa Mesa Inn, Motel 6, Super 8, Vagabond Inn, 🅾 Acura/Dodge, Albertson's, Big O Tire, Buick, Cadillac, Chevrolet, Ford/Lincoln/Mercury, Honda, Infiniti, JustTires, Mazda, Radio Shack, Rite Aid, Target, Vons Foods, Winchell's
11a	Fairview Rd, E 🅾 Barnes&Noble, Best Buy, Marshall's, Nordstrom's, Old Navy, W 🅿 Chevron, 76, Shell, 🍴

C
O
S
T
A

M
E
S
A

IRVINE

11a	Fairview Rd,
	Del Taco, Jack-in-the-Box, Round Table Pizza, Taco Bell, 🅾 CVS Drug, Kragen Parts, Stater Bros
10	CA 73, to CA 55, S (from sb), Corona del Mar, Newport Beach
9b	Bristol St, E 🅿 Chevron/dsl, 🍴 Antonello's Italian, Baja Fresh, Baskin-Robbins, Boudin SF Cafe, Capital Grill, Carrow's, Chick-fil-A, China Olive, Chipotle Mexican, ClaimJumper, Corner Bakery, Darya Persian, In-N-Out, Jack-in-the-Box, Jade Palace, Maggiano's Rest., McDonald's, Morton's Steaks, Pat&Oscar's, Pizza Hut, Quiznos, Red Robin, Sabores Mexican, Scott Seafood, South Coast Rest, Starbucks, Subway, Z Pizza, Ztejas Rest, 🏨 Marriott Suites, Westin Hotel, 🅾 Big-Lots, Bloomingdale's, CVS Drug, Firestone/auto, GNC, Macy's, Michael's, Office Depot, PetCo, Radio Shack, Rite Aid, Ross, Sears/auto, Staples, Target, TJ Maxx, Trader Joe's, Vons Foods, World Mkt, mall, W 🅿 Chevron/dsl, 76/Circle K/dsl, 🍴 Del Taco/24hr, El Pollo Loco, McDonald's, Orchid Rest., Subway, Wahoo's Fish Taco, 🏨 Hanford Hotel, Hilton, 🅾 PepBoys, 7-11, vet
9a	CA 55, Costa Mesa Fwy, to Newport Bch, Riverside
8	MacArthur Blvd, E 🅿 Chevron, Mobil/Subway, 🍴 Carl's Jr, El Torito, McCormick&Schmick's, McDonald's, Quiznos, Starbucks, 🏨 Crowne Plaza, Embassy Suites, 🅾 Pepperdine U, W 🅿 Chevron, 🍴 El Torito, Gulliver's Ribs, IHOP, 🏨 Atrium Hotel, Hilton, to 🛫
7	Jamboree Rd, Irvine, E 🅿 Shell, 🍴 Andrei's Rest., Burger King, Soup Plantation, 🏨 Courtyard, Hyatt, Residence Inn, W 🍴 CA Pizza Kitchen, Daily Grill, FatBurger, Flamebroiler, Houston's, Melting Pot, Ruth's Chris Steaks, Starbucks, Subway, Taleo Mexico, Wahoo's Fish Taco, 🏨 Marriott, 🅾 Office Depot
5	Culver Dr, W 🅿 Alfie's Gas, Chevron/dsl, 🍴 Carl's Jr, Subway, 🅾 Ace Hardware, Rite Aid, Wholesome Foods Mkt
4	Jeffrey Rd, University Dr, E 🅿 Chevron, Circle K/gas, 🍴 Baja Fresh, Coffee Bean, Daphney's Greek, El Cholo Cantina, El Pollo Loco, Golden Spoon, Juice It Up, McDonald's, NY Pizza, Peiwei Asian, Pick-Up Stix, Pomodoro Italian, Starbucks, Togo's, Z Pizza, 🅾 🄷, Ace Hardware, CVS Drug, Gelson's Mkt, Office Depot, Ralph's Foods, Walgreens, W 🅿 Mobil/dsl, 🍴 IHOP, Korean BBQ, Subway, 🅾 Curves, Ralph's Foods, vet
3	Sand Canyon Ave, E🄷, W🅿 Arco/dsl, 🏨 Crystal Jade Asian, Lucca Cafe, Mitsui Grill, Red Brick Pizza, Sharkey's Mexican, Starbucks, Subway, Thai Bamboo, 🅾 Albertson's, Starbucks, CVS Drug
2	CA 133, to Laguna Beach, E 🏨 DoubleTree Inn
1c	Irvine Center Dr, E 🍴 Cheesecake Factory, Chipotle

(map of California, Bay Area region showing:) Danville, San Ramon, San Leandro, Castro Valley, San Ramon Village, San Lorenzo, Hayward, Asco, Livermore, Kilkare Woods, Pleasanton, Hall Station, Union City, Fremont, Newark, with highways 580, 680, 880. **CA**

📷 = gas 🍴 = food 🏨 = lodging ⊙ = other   Copyright 2012 - The Next Exit®

INTERSTATE 405 CONT'D (LOS ANGELES)

N ↑ S

Exit	Services
1c	Continued
	Mexican, Dave&Buster's, Oasis Cafes, Panda Express, PF Chang's, Wahoo's Fish Tacos, ⊙ Barnes&Noble, Macy's, Nordstrom, Target, W 📷 7-11, 🍴 Burger King, La Salsa, NY Deli, ⊙ Big O Tire
1b	Bake Pkwy, W ⊙ Carmax, Toyota
1a	Lake Forest
0mm	I-405 begins/ends on I-5, exit 132.

INTERSTATE 505 (WINTERS)

N ↑ S

CA

Exit	Services
33	I-5. I-505 begins/ends on I-5.
31	CA 12A
28	CA 14, Zamora
24	CA 19
21	CA 16, to Esparto, Woodland, W 📷 Guy's Food/fuel, 🍴 La Plazita
17	CA 27
15	CA 29A
11	CA 128 W, Russell Blvd, W 📷 Chevron/24hr, Interstate/dsl, 🍴 RoundTable Pizza, Subway, ⊙ Lorenzo's Mkt, vet
10	Putah Creek Rd, no crossover, same as 11
6	Allendale Rd
3	Midway Rd, E ⊙ RV camping
1c	Vaca Valley Pkwy
1b	I-80 E. I-505 begins/ends on I-80.

INTERSTATE 580 (BAY AREA)

E ↑ W

LIVERMORE

Exit	Services
79	I-580 begins/ends, accesses I-5 sb.
76b a	CA 132, Chrisman Rd, to Modesto, E 📷 76/dsl, ⊙ RV camping (5mi)
72	Corral Hollow Rd
67	Patterson Pass Rd, W 📷 76/dsl/24hr
65	I-205 (from eb), to Tracy
63	Grant Line Rd, to Byron
59	N Flynn Rd, Altamont Pass, elev 1009, **S Brake Check Area**, many wind-turbines
57	N Greenville Rd, Laughlin Rd, Altamont Pass Rd, to Livermore Lab, S 📷 Chevron/Subway/dsl, 🏨 Best Western, La Quinta, ⊙ Harley-Davidson
56mm	weigh sta both lanes
55	Vasco Rd, to Brentwood, N 📷 Arco, Chevron, Quik-Stop/dsl, 76, Shell/dsl/deli, 🍴 A&W/KFC, McDonald's, S 📷 Citgo/7-11, Valero/dsl, 🍴 Blimpie, Jack-in-the-Box, Taco Bell, 🏨 Quality Inn
54	CA 84, 1st St, Springtown Blvd, Livermore, N 📷 Chevron, 🏨 DoubleTree Hotel, Holiday Inn, Motel 6, Springtown Inn, ⊙ 7-11, S 📷 Shell, 76/24hr, Valero/Circle K, 🍴 Applebee's, Arby's, Burger King, Chevy's Mexican, Chili's, Crazy Buffet, IHOP, Italian Express, McDonald's, Panda Express, Starbucks, Subway, Taco Bell, Togo's, ⊙ America's Tire, Longs Drug, Lowe's Whse, Office Depot, Radio Shack, Ross, Safeway/gas, Target
52	N Livermore Ave, S 📷 Chevron/Jack-in-the-Box, Citgo/7-11, 🍴 Baja Fresh, Coldstone Creamery, In-N-Out, Popeye's, Quizno's, String's Italian, 🏨 Hawthorn Suites, ⊙ Home Depot, Honda, Schwab Tire, Walmart/auto
51	Portola Ave, Livermore (no EZ eb return)
50	Airway Blvd, Collier Canyon Rd, Livermore, N 📷 Shell/

Exit	Services
50	Continued
	dsl, 🍴 Baskin-Robbins, Wendy's, 🏨 Courtyard, Hampton Inn, Hilton Garden, Holiday Inn Express, Residence Inn, ⊙ Costco Whse/gas, S 🍴 Cattlemen's Rest., Chicago Pizza, Starbucks, 🏨 Extended Stay America, ⊙ Chrysler/Jeep, Ford/Lincoln/Mercury, Mazda, 7-11
48	El Charro Rd, O'Fallon Rd
47	Santa Rita Rd, Tassajara Rd, N ⊙ Buick/GMC, Saab, Safeway Foods, S 📷 Shell, 🍴 Bakers Square, Korea Garden, McDonald's, Quizno's, Subway, Taco Bell, TGI Friday, Thai Quisine, ⊙ Acura, BMW, Cadillac, GMC, Hummer, Infiniti, Lexus, Long's Drug, MiniCooper, Mitsubishi, Rose Pavilion, Saab, Trader Joe's, Volvo
46	Hacienda Dr, Pleasanton, N 📷 Shell, 🍴 Applebee's, Black Angus, Fuddruckers, Macaroni Grill, Mimi's Cafe, On-the-Border, Papa John's, Woks Up, 🏨 AmeriSuites, ⊙ Barnes&Noble, Best Buy, Ford, Old Navy, TJ Maxx, S 🍴 Red Robin, ⊙ H, Kohl's, Staples, Walmart/auto
45	Hopyard Rd, Pleasanton, N 📷 76/Circle K, Minimart, Shell/dsl, 🏨 Hilton, Holiday Inn Express, ⊙ America's Tire, Dodge, El Monte RV Ctr, Goodyear, Honda, Nissan, Office Depot, Pak'n Sav, RV Ctr, U-Haul, Toyota, S 📷 Chevron, Shell/dsl, 🍴 Arby's, Burger King, Chef India, Chevy's Mexican, Chili's, Denny's, El Balazo, In-N-Out, Nations Burgers, Pleasant Asian, Starbucks, Taco Bell, 🏨 Candlewood Suites, Courtyard, Hilton, Larkspur Landing, Marriott, Motel 6, Sheraton, Super 8, ⊙ Home Depot, Mercedes
44b	I-680, N to San Ramon, S to San Jose
44a	Foothills Rd, San Ramon Rd, N 📷 CA Fuel, Chevron, Shell, Valero, 🍴 Burger King, Casa Orozco, China Wall, Chipotle Mexican, ChuckeCheese, Country Waffles, Elephant Bar, Frankie's Johnny's & Luigi's Too, Hooters, Korean BBQ, Outback Steaks, Panera Bread, Popeye's, RoundTable Pizza, Starbucks, 🏨 Radisson, ⊙ Big Lots, Curves, $Tree, Kragen Parts, Long's Drug, Marshall's, Michael's, PetCo, PetsMart, Ranch Mkt Foods, Ross, Target, S 🍴 Cheesecake Factory, PF Chang's, 🏨 Marriott, Residence Inn, Sheraton, ⊙ JC Penney, Macy's, Nordstrom's, Sears, mall
39	Eden Canyon Rd, Palomares Rd, S ⊙ rodeo park
37	Center St, Crow Canyon Rd same as 35, S 📷 Arco/24hr, Chevron/dsl/, 76/dsl, Quikstop, 🍴 McDonald's, Starbucks, Subway
35	Redwood Rd (from eb), Castro Valley, N 📷 Chevron, 76/dsl, Shell/dsl, 🍴 Baker's Square, Chipotle Mexican, KFC, McDonald's, Quizno's, RoundTable Pizza, Sizzler, Taco Bell, Wendy's, ⊙ Comfort Suites, Holiday Inn Express, ⊙ Goodyear, Longs Drug, Lucky Foods, NAPA, Radio Shack, Rite Aid, Safeway, Walgreens
34	I-238 W, to I-880, CA 238, W off I-238 🍴 McDonald's, Jack-in-the-Box, ⊙ Chrysler/Jeep, 99c Store
33	164th Ave, Miramar Ave, E 📷 Chevron/dsl, Valero, 🏨 Fairmont Inn
32	150th Ave, Fairmont, E ⊙ H, W 📷 Shell, 76/dsl, 🍴 Arby's, Burger King, Carrows, Chili's, Denny's, McDonald's, RoundTable Pizza, Starbucks, Tito's Cafe, ⊙ Goodyear, Kohl's, Long's Drug, Macy's, Pepboys, Staples, Target
31	Grand Ave (from sb), Dutton Ave, W 📷 Coast, ⊙ Rite Aid
30	106th Ave, Foothill Blvd, MacArthur Blvd, W 📷 Arco, ⊙ Church's
29	98th Ave, Golf Links Rd, E 📷 Shell, ⊙ Oakland Zoo, W 📷 76, Valero

PLEASANTON

INTERSTATE 580 CONT'D (BAY AREA)

Exit	Services
27b	Keller Ave, Mtn Blvd, **E** repair
27a	Edwards Ave (from sb, no EZ return), **E** US Naval 🅗
26a	CA 13, Warren Fwy, to Berkeley (from eb)
26b	Seminary Rd, **E** Observatory/Planetarium, **W** 🅟 Arco/24hr
25b a	High St, to MacArthur Blvd, **E** 🅟 76, 🍴 Subway, Razzo's Pizza, 🅞 Kragen Parts, Lucky Foods, USPO, **W** 🅟 76, 🅞 Walgreens
24	35th Ave (no EZ sb return), **E** 🅟 76, 🍴 Taco Bell, **W** 🅟 Chevron, QuikStop, 76
23	Coolidge Ave, Fruitvale, **E** 🅟 Shell/24hr, 🍴 China Gourmet, McDonald's, Subway, 🅞 Longs Drug, Farmer Joe's, Radio Shack
22	Park Blvd, **E** 🅟 Shell, **W** 🅟 Arco, Quikstop, 🅞 🅗
21b	Grand Ave, Lake Shore, **E** 🅟 Chevron/dsl, 76/24hr, 🍴 KFC, Subway, 🅞 Long's Drug, Trader Joe's, Walgreens, USPO, **W** 🅟 Chevron/dsl/24hr
21a	Harrison St, Oakland Ave, **E** 🅟 Quikstop, **W** 🅞 Honda
19d c	CA 24 E, I-980 W, to Oakland
19b	West St, San Pablo Ave, **E** 🏠 Extended Stay America, 🅞 Best Buy, Home Depot, Jo-Ann Fabrics, Michael's, Office Depot
19a	I-80, W
18c	Market St, to San Pablo Ave, downtown
18b	Powell St, Emeryville, **E** 🅟 76, 🍴 Burger King, CA Pizza Kitchen, Denny's, Elephant Bar/Grill, Jamba Juice, PF Chang's, Starbucks, Togo's, 🏠 Courtyard, Sheraton, Woodfin Suites, 🅞 Barnes&Noble, Old Navy, Ross, Trader Joe's, **W** 🅟 Shell, 🍴 Chevy's Mexican, 🏠 Hilton Garden
18a	CA 13, Ashby Ave, Bay St, same as 18b
17	University Ave, Berkeley, **E** 🅟 76, University Gas, 🏠 La Quinta, 🅞 to UC Berkeley
16	Gilman St, **E** 🅞 Golden Gate Fields Race Track, **W** 🅞 Target
13	Albany St, Buchanan St (from eb)
12	Central Ave (from eb), El Cerrito, **E** 🅟 Shell, Valero, **W** 🅞 Costco/gas
11	Bayview Ave, Carlson Blvd, **E** 🅟 76
10b	Regatta Blvd, **E** 🅟 Golden Gate/dsl
10a	S 23rd St, Marina Bay Pkwy, **E** 🅟 Stop and Save/dsl, 🍴 Subway, **W** 🍴 Cafe Tiatro, El Molchaete, Quizno's, Wing Stop, 🅞 Longs Drugs
9	Harbour Way, Cutting Blvd, **E** 🅟 Arco, **W** 🍴 Burger King
8	Canal Blvd, Garrard Blvd, **W** 🅟 Chevron/dsl, 🏠 Days Inn
7b	Castro St, to I-80 E, Point Richmond, downtown industrial
7a	Western Drive (from wb), Point Molate
5mm	Richmond-San Rafael Toll Bridge
2a	Francis Drake Blvd, to US 101 S, **E** 🏠 Extended Stay Deluxe, 🅞 BMW/Saab, Home Depot
1b	Francisco Blvd; San Rafael, **E** 🅟 Beacon, Circle K, Francisco, 🍴 Burger King, La Croissant, 🏠 Motel 6, Travelodge, 🅞 Mazda, tires, U-Haul, **W** 🍴 Subway, Wendy's, 🅞 Office Depot, USPO, to San Quentin
1a	US 101, N to San Rafael, I-580 begins/ends on US 101.

INTERSTATE 605 (LOS ANGELES)

Exit	Services
27c	Huntington Dr. I-605 begins/ends, 🅟 Mobil, 🍴 Subway,

27c	Continued 🅞 CVS Drug, Fresh&Easy Foods
27	I-210
26	Arrow Hwy, Live Oak, **E** Santa Fe Dam, **W** Irwindale Speedway
24	Lower Azusa Rd, LA St
23	Ramona Blvd, **E** 🅟 Mobil, 🍴 Del Taco/24hr
22	I-10, E to San Bernardino, W to LA
21	Valley Blvd, to Industry, **E** 🅟 Chevron/Chester's/Subway/dsl, 76, 🍴 El Charro, Las Milpas Mexican, 7 Mares Rest., Winchell's Donuts, 🏠 Valley Inn
19	CA 60, Pamona Fwy
18	Peck Rd, **E** 🅟 Shell, **W** 🅞 Ford Trucks
17	RoseHills Rd, **W** Sports Arena
16	Beverly Blvd
15	Whittier Blvd, **E** 🅟 Arco, 76/dsl, 🍴 Carl's Jr, Taco Bell, YumYum Donuts, 🏠 GoodNite Inn, 🅞 7-11, **W** 🅟 Chevron, Shell, 🍴 DQ, Pizza Hut, Shakey's Pizza, Starbucks, Subway, Taco's Mexico, Tommy's Burgers, 🏠 Howard Johnson, 🅞 AutoZone, Rite Aid
14	Washington Blvd, to Pico Rivera, **E** 🅞 Firestone/auto
13	Slauson Ave, **E** 🅟 Arco, Mobil, 🍴 Denny's, 🏠 Motel 6, **W** 🅗
12	Telegraph Rd, to Santa Fe Springs, **E** 🅟 Chevron, 76, 🍴 Del Taco, Jack-in-the-Box, KFC, Subway, Taco Bell, Yoshinoya, 🅞 urgent care, **W** 🅟 Arco/dsl
12mm	I-5
11	Florence Ave, to Downey, **E** 🅟 Mobil, 🅞 Cadillac, Chevrolet, Honda
10	Firestone Blvd, **E** 🅟 76, 🍴 ChuckeCheese, KFC, McDonald's, Norm's Burgers, Sam's Burgers, Subway, 🏠 Best Western, 🅞 Audi/BMW/Porsche, Costco, Food4-Less, 99c Store, Staples, Verizon, Walgreens, **W** 🅟 Chevron/repair, 🍴 Starbucks, 🅞 Chrysler/Dodge/Jeep, Office Depot, Target
8	I-105, Imperial Hwy, **E** 🅟 76, 🍴 Domino's, KFC, LJ Silver, McDonald's, Pizza Hut/Taco Bell, 🅞 CVS Drug, Food4Less, **W** 🅟 Arco
9	Rosecrans Ave, to Norwalk, **E** 🅟 Chevron, Mobil, 🍴 Del Taco, Little Caesars, McDonald's, Subway, 🅞 🅗, Food Basket Foods, Fresh&Easy, Walgreens, vet, **W** 🍴 Carrow's Rest., 🏠 Motel 6
7	Alondra Blvd, **E** 🅟 Chevron, 7-11, 🍴 A&W, Alondra's Mexican, Frantone's Rest., KFC, Red Chili, 🅞 CVS Drug, Home Depot, Staples, **W** 🅟 Shell/Subway/24hr, 🍴 Del Taco
6	CA 91
5	South St, **E** 🍴 BJ's Rest., CA Pizza Kitchen, Carl's Jr, Chick-fil-A, Coco's, Coldstone, 5 Guys, Hometown Buffet, Jamba Juice, Lazy Dog Cafe, Luecille's BBQ,

□ = gas □ = food □ = lodging □ = other Copyright 2012 - The Next Exit®

INTERSTATE 605 CONT'D (LOS ANGELES)

Exit	Services
5	Continued Panda Express, Panera Bread, Quiznos, Red Robin, Starbucks, ▣ AT&T, Firestone, Macy's, Nordstrom's, Sears/auto, Target, Verizon, mall, **W** ▣ Shell/service, Valero, ▣ Acura, Buick/GMC, Chevrolet, Chrysler/Dodge/Jeep, Ford, Honda, Hyundai, Infiniti, KIA, Lexus, Mazda, Nissan, Smartcar, Suzuki, Toyota/Scion, VW
4	Del Amo Blvd, to Cerritos, **E** ▣ Del Taco, Omega Burgers, Starbucks, ▣ Ralph's Foods, **W** ▣ Mobil
3	Carson St, **E** ▣ Price Saver/dsl, 76, ▣ Alberto's Mexican, Jack-in-the-Box, KFC, Little Caesar's, McDonald's, Pizza Hut, Popeye's, Subway, Taco Bell, Wienerschnitzel, ▣ Lakewood Inn, ▣ CVS Drug, Food4Less, O'Reilly Parts, Price Right Foods, 7-11, **W** ▣ Chevron/Subway/dsl, ▣ Carl's Jr, Chick-fil-A, Denny's, Del Taco, El Pollo Loco, El Torito, FoodCourt, In-N-Out, Island's Burgers, Jack-in-the-Box, Leucille's BBQ, Panda Express, Roadhouse Grill, Starbucks, SuperMex, TGIFriday's, Yashi Japanese, ▣ America's Tire, Barnes&Noble, Lowe's, Michael's, Old Navy, Petsmart, Radio Shack, Ross, Staples, Sam's Club, Walmart/auto
1	Katella Ave, Willow St, **E** ▣ Shell, ▣ Madera's Steaks, McDonald's, Polly's Cafe, Starbucks, ▣ ▣, Rite Aid, **W** Eldorado Regional Park
0mm	I-605 begins/ends on I-405.

INTERSTATE 680 (BAY AREA)

Exit	Services
71 b a	I-80 E, to Sacramento, W to Oakland, I-680 begins/ends on I-80.
70	Green Valley Rd (from eb), Cordelia, **N** ▣ Arco am/pm, ▣ Costco/gas, Longs Drug, Safeway
69	Gold Hill Rd, **W** ▣ TowerMart/dsl
65	Marshview Rd
63	Parish Rd
61	Lake Herman Rd, **E** ▣ Arco/Jack-in-the-Box/dsl, **W** ▣ Gas City/dsl, Shell/Carl's Jr/dsl/24hr, ▣ vista point
60	Bayshore Rd, industrial park
58	I-780, to Benicia, **toll plaza**
56	Marina Vista, to Martinez
55mm	Martinez-Benicia Toll Br
54	Pacheco Blvd, Arthur Rd, Concord, **W** ▣ 76, Shell/dsl
53	CA 4, E to Pittsburg, W to Richmond
52	CA 4 E, Concord, Pacheco, **E** ▣ Hometown Buffet, Marie Callender's, Starbucks, Taco Bell, ▣ Crowne Plaza, Holiday Inn, ▣ Chevrolet, Ford, Hyundai, Infiniti/VW, Sam's Club, Toyota, Trader Joe's, USPO, **W** ▣ Grand Gas, Shell/24hr, 76, ▣ Denny's, McDonald's, Wendy's, ▣ AutoZone, Barnes&Noble, Firestone, K-Mart, Kragen Parts, Pepboys, Safeway Foods, Schwab Tire, Target, Toyota
51	Willow Pass Rd, Taylor Blvd, **E** ▣ Benihana Rest., Buffet City, Claim Jumper, Denny's, Elephant Bar Rest., El Torito, Fuddruckers, Grissini Italian, Jamba Juice, Panera Bread, Quizno's, Sizzler, ▣ Hilton, ▣ Cost+, Old Navy, Willows Shopping Ctr, **W** ▣ Baja Fresh, Red Robin, ▣ JC Penney, Macy's, Sears/auto
50	CA 242 (from nb), to Concord
49b	Monument Blvd, Gregory Lane (from sb), **E** ▣ Valero/dsl, ▣ Country Waffles, Panda Express, Rubio's, Starbucks, ▣ Kohl's, Marshall's, **W** ▣ Chevron, ▣ Boston

Exit	Services
49b	Continued Mkt, Jack-in-the-Box, McDonald's, Nations Burgers, Pizza Hut, Red Brick Pizza, Taco Bell, ▣ Courtyard, Hyatt, ▣ Big O Tire, Grocery Outlet, Lucky Foods, Michael's, Radio Shack, Rite Aid, Ross, Safeway Foods, Staples, Tuesday Morning
49a	Contra Costa Blvd (from nb)
48	Treat Blvd, Geary Rd, **E** ▣ Chevron, ▣ Back 40 BBQ, Heavenly Cafe, Subway, ▣ Embassy Suites, Extended Stay America, ▣ Best Buy, Office Depot, 7-11, **W** ▣ Chevron, Shell, ▣ Black Angus, Primavera Pasta, Quizno's, Starbucks, Wendy's, Yan's China Bistro, ▣ Walgreens
47	N Main St, to Walnut Creek, **E** ▣ Chevron, ▣ Fuddrucker's, Jack-in-the-Box, Taco Bell, ▣ Marriott, Motel 6, Walnut Cr Motel, ▣ Cadillac, Chevrolet, Chrysler/Dodge/Jeep, Harley-Davidson, Honda, Jaguar, Land Rover, Mercedes, Nissan, Target, **W** ▣ 76/7-11/dsl/24hr, ▣ Domino's, ▣ NAPA, Porsche
46b	Ygnacio Valley Rd
46a	SR-24, W
45b	Olympic Blvd, Oakland
45a	S Main St, Walnut Creek, **E** ▣
44	Rudgear (from nb)
43	Livorna Rd
42b a	Stone Valley Rd, Alamo, **W** ▣ Chevron, Shell/dsl, ▣ Papa Murphy's, Starbucks, Subway, Taco Bell, Xenia's, ▣ Curves, Longs Drugs, Rite Aid, Safeway, 7-11, vet
41	El Pintado Rd, Danville
40	El Cerro Blvd
39	Diablo Rd, Danville, **E** ▣ 76/24hr, ▣ Chinese Cuisine, Taco Bell, ▣ Walgreens, Mt Diablo SP (12mi), **W** ▣ Diablo
38	Sycamore Valley Rd, **E** ▣ Shell, ▣ Denny's, ▣ Best Western, **W** ▣ 76/dsl, Valero/dsl
36	Crow Canyon Rd, San Ramon, **E** ▣ Shell, ▣ Burger King, Carl's Jr, Chili's, Cheesesteak, El Ballazo, Jamba Juice, Max's Diner, O'Zachary's Rest., Starbucks, Subway, ▣ Extended Stay America, ▣ ▣, Big O Tire, Costco, Lucky Foods, Marshall's, Office Depot, PetCo, Rite Aid, Sea's Candies, USPO, **W** ▣ Chevron/repair/24hr, 76, Shell/autocare, Valero, ▣ Chipotle Mexican, Giuseppe's Italian, In-N-Out, McDonald's, Nation's Burger's, Quizno's, Subway, Taco Bell, Togo's, ▣ Hotel Sierra, ▣ Home Depot, Jo-Ann Fabrics, Longs Drug, Safeway, 7-11, Staples, repair/tires, vet
34	Bollinger Canyon Rd, **E** ▣ Valero, ▣ Baja Fresh, El Ballazo, Izzy's Steaks, Subway, ▣ Marriott, Residence Inn, ▣ Long's Drug, Target, Whole Foods, **W** ▣ Chevron, ▣ Applebee's, Chevy's Mexican, Marie Callender's, ▣ Courtyard, Homestead Village
31	Alcosta Blvd, to Dublin, **E** ▣ 76/7-11, **W** ▣ Chevron, Shell/dsl, ▣ DQ, Mtn Mike's Pizza, McDonalds, Papa John's, Rulu's Cafe, Subway, Taco Bell, ▣ Lucky Foods, Walgreens
30	I-580, W to Oakland, E to Tracy
29	Stoneridge, Dublin, **E** ▣ Hilton, **W** ▣ Cheesecake Factory, PF Chang's, Taco Bell, ▣ JC Penney, Macy's, Nordstrom's, Sears, mall
26	Bernal Ave, Pleasanton, **E** ▣ Shell/Jack-in-the-Box, ▣ Lindo's Mexican
25	Sunol Blvd, Pleasanton
21 b a	CA 84, Calvaras Rd, Sunol, W to Dumbarton Bridge

INTERSTATE 680 CONT'D (BAY AREA)

FREMONT

Exit	Services
20	Andrade Rd, Sheridan Rd (from sb), **E** 🅖 Sunol Super Stp/dsl
19mm	weigh sta nb
19	Sheridan Rd (from nb)
18	Vargas Rd
16	CA 238, Mission Blvd, to Hayward, **E** 🅖 Shell, 🍴 McDonald's, **W** 🅗
15	Washington Blvd, Irvington Dist, **E** 🅖 QuikStop
14	Durham Rd, to Auto Mall Pkwy, **W** 🅖 76/Circle K/Subway/24hr, Shell/Jack-in-the-Box, 🅞 Fry's Electronics, Home Depot, Walmart

SAN JOSE

12	CA 262, Mission Blvd, to I-880, Warm Springs Dist, **W** 🅖 76, Valero, 🍴 Burger King, Carl's Jr, Denny's, KFC, RoundTable Pizza, Starbucks, Subway, Taco Bell, 🛏 Extended Stay America, 🅞 GNC, Longs Drug, Radio Shack, Ross, Safeway, 7-11, Walgreens
10	Scott Creek Rd
9	Jacklin Rd, **E** 🅞 Bonfare Mkt, **W** 🅖 Shell
8	CA 237, Calaveras Blvd, Milpitas, **E** 🅖 Shell/repair, 76, 🍴 Domino's, Flames CoffeeShop, RoadTable Pizza, Sizzler, Subway, 🛏 Exectuive Inn, 🅞 Oceans SuperMkt, 7-11, **W** 🅖 Shell, 🍴 El Torito, Giorgio's Italian, It's a Grind, Lyon's Rest., McDonald's, Red Lobster, 🛏 Embassy Suites, Extended Stay America, 🅞 Longs Drug, Lucky Foods, Safeway, Staples
6	Landess Ave, Montague Expswy, **E** 🅖 Arco, Chevron, 76, 🍴 Burger King, Jack-in-the-Box, McDonald's, Taco Bell, Togo's, Wienerschnitzel, 🅞 Firestone, Lucky Foods, Radio Shack, Rite Aid, Target, Walgreens

N ↑ ↓ S

5	Capitol Ave, Hostetter Ave, **E** 🅖 Shell, 🍴 Carl's Jr, Popeye's, 🅞 SaveMart Foods, **W** 🅖 Valero, 🅞 Jiffy Lube
4	Berryessa Rd, **E** 🅖 Arco/24hr, USA, Valero/repair, 🍴 Denny's, Lee's Sandwiches, McDonald's, Taco Bell, 🅞 AutoZone, Longs Drug, Safeway
2b	McKee Rd, **E** 🅖 76, Chevron, Shell, 🍴 Burger King, HomeTown Buffet, Pizza Hut, Quizno's, Starbucks, Togo's, Wienerschnitzel, 🅞 $Tree, PaknSave Foods, Ross, Target, Walgreens, **W** 🅖 World Gas, 🍴 Baskin-Robbins, Foster's Freeze, Lee's Sandwiches, McDonald's, RoundTable Pizza, Yum Yum Doughnut, Wendy's, 🅞 🅗, Kohl's
2a	Alum Rock Ave, **E** 🅖 Shell/dsl/24hr, 🍴 Jack-in-the-Box, Taco Bell, **W** 🅖 Chevron, 76/24hr, 🍴 Carl's Jr
1d	Capitol Expswy
1c	King Rd, Jackson Ave (from nb), **E** 🅖 L&D Gas, Shell, 🍴 El Gallo Giro, Jamba Juice, Kings Burger, Panda Express, Starbucks, Super Buffet, Taco Bell, 🅞 Target, Walgreens
1b	US 101, to LA, SF
1a	(exits left from sb), I-680 begins/ends on I-280.

INTERSTATE 710 (LOS ANGELES)

E ↑ ↓ W

Exit	Service
23	I-710 begins/ends on Valley Blvd, **E** 🅖 Arco
22b a	I-10
20c	Chavez Ave
20b	CA 60, Pamona Fwy, **W** 🅖 Shell, **E** 🍴 King Taco, Monterrey Hill Rest.
20a	3rd St
19	Whittier Blvd, Olympic Blvd, **W** 🅖 Shell, 🍴 McDonald's
17b	Washington Blvd, Commerce, **W** 🅖 Commerce Trkstp/dsl/rest.

LOS ANGELES AREA

17a	Bandini Blvd, Atlantic Blvd, industrial
15	Florence Ave, **E** 🍴 Alfredo's Mexican, Applebee's, Coldstone, El Pescador Mexican, El Pollo Loco, IHOP, KFC, McDonald's, Panda Express, Quiznos, Red Brick Pizza, Starbucks, Subway, Taco Bell, Yoshinoya, 🛏 Comfort Inn, 🅞 $Tree, Food4Less, Marshall's, Rite Aid, Ross, casino, **W** truck repair
13	CA 42, Firestone Blvd, **E** 🅖 Arco, 🍴 Burger King, Denny's, McDonald's, Panda Express, Subway, 🛏 Guesthouse Inn, 🅞 El Super Foods, Ford, GNC, Radio Shack, Sam's Club, Target
12b a	Imperial Hwy, **E** 🅖 Shell/dsl, 🍴 Abierto's Mexican, Carl's Jr., El Pollo Loco, Subway, **W** 🅖 Chevron/dsl, 76, Shell, 🍴 KFC, McDonald's, Panda Express, Pizza Patron, Starbucks, Subway, Taco Bell, Winchell's, Wienerschnitzel, 🅞 AutoZone, Manny's Repair, Radio Shack, Valu+ Foods, Walgreens
11b a	I-105
10	Rosecrans Ave
9b a	Alondra Ave, **E** 🅖 Chevron/dsl, 🍴 Jack-in-the-Box, 🅞 Home Depot
8b a	CA 91
7b a	Long Beach Blvd, **E** 🅖 Chevron, Mobil, United/dsl, Valero, 🍴 El Ranchito Mexican, McDonald's, Sizzler, 🅞 CVS Drug, **W** 🅖 Arco/24hr, 🍴 Jack-in-the-Box, Mocasalitos, Subway, 🛏 Luxury Inn
6	Del Amo Blvd
4	I-405, San Diego Freeway
3b a	Willow St, **E** 🅖 Arco, Chevron, 🍴 Baskin-Robbins, Chee Chinese, Dominos, Pizza Hut, 🅞 Radio Shack, Walgreens, **W** 🅖 Arco, 76, 🍴 KFC, Little Caesars, Popeye's, 🅞 AutoZone, Big Saver Foods
2	CA 1, Pacific Coast Hwy, **E** 🅖 Arco/mart, Chevron, Mobil, 76/dsll, 🍴 Hong Kong Express, KFC, McDonald's, 🛏 Beacon Inn, Don Chente Tacos, King Taco, La Mirage Inn, Travel Eagle Inn, 🅞 Ranch Mkt, auto repair, **W** 🅖 76/service, Shell/Carl's Jr/dsl, PCH Trkstp/dsl, 🍴 Alberto's Mexican, Golden Star Rest., Jack-in-the-Box, McDonald's, Taco Bell, Tom's Burgers, Winchell's, 🛏 Hiland Motel, SeaBreeze Motel, 🅞 TrueValue, truckwash
1d	Anaheim St, **W** 🅖 Speedy Fuel, 🅞 dsl repair/scales
1c	Ahjoreline Dr, Piers B, C, D, E, Pico Ave
1b	Pico Ave, Piers F-J, Queen Mary
1a	Harbor Scenic Dr, Piers S, T, Terminal Island, **E** 🛏 Hilton
0mm	I-710 begins/ends in Long Beach

INTERSTATE 780 (VALLEJO)

Exit	Services
7	I-780 begins/ends on I-680.
6	E 5th St, Benicia, **N** 🅖 Fast&Easy, **S** 🅖 Citgo/7-11,

CA

B E N I C I A **E** ↕ **W** **N** ↕ **S**

INTERSTATE 780 CONT'D (VALLEJO)

Exit	Services
6	Continued Valero/dsl, 🍴 China Garden, ⭕ Big O Tire, repair, vet
5	E 2nd St, Central Benicia, N ⛽ Valero, 🏨 Best Western, S 🍴 McDonald's, Pappa's Rest.
4	Southampton Rd, Benicia, N 🍴 Asian Bistro, Burger King, Coldstone Creamery, Country Waffles, Jamba Juice, Rickshaw Express, RoundTable Pizza, Starbucks, Subway, ⭕ Ace Hardware, Radio Shack, Raley's Foods, vet
3b	Military West
3a	Columbus Pkwy, N ⛽ Shell, 🍴 Burger King, Napoli Pizza, Subway, ⭕ Jiffy Lube, Longs Drugs, S to Benicia RA
1d	Glen Cove Pkwy, N Hwy Patrol, S 🍴 Baskin-Robbins, Subway, Taco Bell, ⭕ Safeway
1c	Cedar St
1b a	I-780 begins/ends on I-80.

INTERSTATE 805 (SAN DIEGO)

Exit	Services
28mm	I-5 (from nb). I-805 begins/ends on I-5.
27.5	CA 56, E (from nb)
27	Sorrento Valley Rd, Mira Mesa Blvd
26	Vista Sorrento Pkwy, E ⛽ Mobil/dsl, Shell, 🍴 Chili's, Jamba Juice, McDonald's, Starbucks, 🏨 Country Inn, Courtyard, Holiday Inn Express, ⭕ Staples
25b a	La Jolla Village Dr, Miramar Rd, 1 mi E ⛽ 76/dsl, ⭕ Discount Tire, Firestone, W 🍴 Coast Cafe, Cozymel's Cantina, Donovan's Grill, Harry's Grill, Miami Grill, PF Chang's, 🏨 Embassy Suites, Marriott, ⭕ 🏥 Macy's, Nordstom's, Sears, mall
24	Governor Dr
23	CA 52
22	Clairemont Mesa Blvd, E ⛽ Chevron, Mega/Subway/dsl, Shell, 🍴 Arby's, Burger King, Carl's Jr, Coco's, Godfather Rest., McDonald's, Players Grill, Quizno's, Rubio's Grill, Souplantation, Starbucks, Tommy's Burgers, ⭕ Food4-Less, Ford, Jiffy Lube, Ranch Mkt, Sears Essentials, Walmart, W ⛽ Arco/24hr, 🍴 Joe's Pizza, Mr. Bon's Rest, VIP Oriental Buffet, 🏨 Best Western, CA Suites, Motel 6
21	CA 274, Balboa Ave, E ⛽ Arco, Chevron, Exxon/dsl, 76, Shell, 🍴 Applebee's, Islands Burger, Jack-in-the-Box, ⭕ Albertson's/SavOn, Balboa AutoCare, Chevrolet, Dodge
20	CA 163 N, to Escondido
20a	Mesa College Dr, Kearney Villa Rd, W 🏥
18	Murray Ridge Rd, to Phyllis Place
17b	I-8, E to El Centro, W to beaches
16	El Cajon Blvd, E ⛽ Arco/24hr, Ultra, 🍴 ⭕ Pancho Villa Mkt, W ⛽ North Park Gas, 76, 🍴 Carl's Jr, Jack-in-the-Box, Starbucks, Subway, Wendy's
15	University Ave, E ⛽ Chevron, 🍴 Subway, ⭕ Radio Shack, W ⛽ Exxon, Thrifty/dsl, 🍴 Starbucks, ⭕ CVS Drug, Walgreens
14	CA 15 N, 40th St, to I-15
13b	Home Ave, MLK Ave
13a	CA 94
12b	Market St
12a	Imperial Ave, E ⛽ Exxon, Homeland Gas/dsl, W 🍴 Domino's, KFC/LJ Silver, Sizzler, Starbucks, ⭕ Home Depot, 99¢ Store

S A N   D I E G O   A R E A

S A N   D I E G O   A R E A

Exit	Services
11b	47th St
11a	43rd St, W 🍴 Giant Pizza, Jack-in-the-Box, ⭕ Auto-Zone, CVS Drug, Northgate Mkt
10	Plaza Blvd, National City, E 🍴 Chow King, DQ, Dragon Garden Chinese, McDonald's, Pizza Hut, Popeye's, Starbucks, Winchell's, ⭕ 🏥 AutoZone, Firestone/auto, Ralph's Foods, Walgreens, Well's Drug, vet, W ⛽ Thrifty Gas, 🍴 Family House Rest., IHOP, Sizzler, 🏨 Comfort Inn, Stardust Inn, ⭕ Big Lots, CVS Drug, Discount Tire, Jo-Ann Fabrics
9	Sweetwater Rd, E 🍴 Applebee's, Outback Steaks, ⭕ JC Penney, 7-11, W ⛽ Chevron/dsl, 🍴 Ben's Rest., Carl's Jr, Denny's, Hanaoka Japanese, La Placita Mexican, L&L BBQ, Pizza Hut, Starbucks, Subway, Taco Bell, ⭕ Curves, Goodyear, Longs Drug, Staples
8	CA 54
7c	E St, Bonita Rd, E on Bonita Plaza Rd 🍴 Applebee's, 🍴 Outback Steaks, Pat&Oscar's Rest., ⭕ JC Penney, Macy's, mall, W ⛽ Chevron, Shell, 🍴 Burger King, Denny's, Love's Rest., 🏨 La Quinta, Ramada Inn, ⭕ RV Park
7b a	H St, E ⛽ Carmalor Gas, 🍴 China China, Coldstone Creamery, Jack-in-the-Box, Subway, Taco Bell, ⭕ Longs Drug, Marshall's, Vons Foods, mall, RV camping
6	L St, Telegraph Canyon Rd, E ⛽ Canyon Fuel/dsl, 🍴 Mandarin Canyon, McDonald's, Starbucks, Subway, ⭕ 🏥, Rite Aid, Olympic Training Ctr, RV camping, W ⛽ Thrifty, ⭕ 7-11
4	Orange Ave, E Olympic Training Ctr
3	Main St, Otay Valley Rd, E ⛽ Shell, 🍴 Panda Express, Souplantation, ⭕ Chevrolet, Chrysler/Jeep/Dodge, Ford, Kohl's, PetsMart, Scion, Staples, Toyota, W 🏨 Holiday Inn Express
2	Palm Ave, E ⛽ Arco/24hr, Chevron/24hr, 🍴 Carl's Jr, Hometown Buffet, Starbucks, Subway, Taco Bell, ⭕ Big O Tires, Home Depot, Radio Shack, USPO, Von's Foods, Walmart, W ⛽ 76/dsl, 🍴 KFC, McDonald's
1b	CA 905, E Brown Field ✈, Otay Mesa Border Crossing
1a	San Ysidro Blvd, E ⛽ Arco, Shell, 🏨 Travelodge, Factory2U, Kragen Parts, Longs Drug, 99c Store, U-Haul, W ⛽ Chevron, Exxon, Mobil, 76, 🍴 Denny's, McDonald's, Si Senor Mexican, 🏨 Motel 6

I-805 begins/ends on I-5.

INTERSTATE 880 (BAY AREA)

Exit	Services
46b a	I-80, W (exits left). I-80 E/580 W.
44	7th St, Grand Ave, downtown
42b a	Broadway St, E 🍴 KFC, 🏨 Marriott, W 🏨 Jack London Inn, ⭕ to Jack London Square
41a	Oak St, Lakeside Dr, downtown
40	5th Ave, Embarcadero, E 🍴 Burger King, W 🍴 Quizno's, Starbucks, 🏨 Executive Inn, Homewood Suites, Motel 6
39b a	29th Ave, 23rd Ave, to Fruitvale, E ⛽ Shell, 🍴 Boston Mkt, Burger King, DonutStar, Popeye's, Starbucks, ⭕ AutoZone, Lucky Foods, Office Depot, Radio Shack, W ⛽ 7-11
38	High St, to Alameda, E 🏨 Bay Breeze Inn, Coliseum Motel, ⭕ El Monte RV Ctr, W ⛽ Shell/dsl, 🍴 McDonald's, ⭕ Home Depot
37	66th Ave, Zhone Way, E coliseum
36	Hegenberger Rd, E ⛽ Arco/24hr, Shell/dsl, 🍴 Burger King, Chubby Freeze, Denny's, Jack-in-the-Box/24hr,

N ↕ **S**

INTERSTATE 880 CONT'D (BAY AREA)

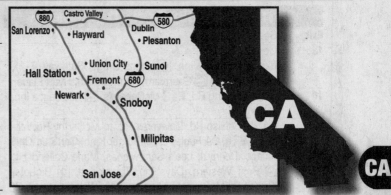

N ↕ S

OAKLAND AREA

Exit	Services
36	Continued
	McDonald's, Taco Bell, 🏨 Day's Hotel, Fairfield Inn, La Quinta, Motel 6, Quality Inn, ⊙ Pak'n Save Foods, GMC/Volvo, Freightliner, **W** ⛽ 76/Circle K/dsl, Shell, 🍴 Carrows Rest., Francesco's Rest., Hegen Burger, In-N-Out, Jamba Juice, Panda Express, Quizno's, Red Barn Pizza, Starbucks, Subway, Wing Stop, 🏨 Best Western, Courtyard, Econolodge, Hilton, Holiday Inn, Holiday Inn Express, Marriott, Park Plaza Motel, ⊙ Harley-Davidson, Infiniti, Lexus, Walmart/auto, to Oakland ⛵
35	98th Ave, **W** ⛵
34	Davis St, **W** ⛽ Shell/Burger King, 🍴 Hawaiian BBQ, Jamba Juice, Starbucks, Togo's, ⊙ Costco/gas, Home Depot, Office Depot, See's Candy, Walmart/McDonald's
33b a	Marina Blvd, **E** ⛽ Valero, 🍴 Jack-in-the-Box, La Salsa Mexican, Panda Express, Starbucks, Taco Bell, ⊙ Buick/GMC, Chevrolet, Ford, Honda, Hyundai, Kia, Marshall's, Nissan, Nordstrom's, Radio Shack, Volvo, **W** ⛽ Flyers/dsl, 🍴 A&W/KFC, DairyBelle, Denny's
32	Washington Ave (from nb), Lewelling Blvd (from sb), **W** ⛽ Arco, 76, TechCo, 🍴 Hometown Buffet, Jack-in-the-Box, McDonald's, Papa Murphy's, Subway, 🏨 Nimitz Motel, ⊙ Big Lots, Big O Tire, Food Maxx, GNC, Home Depot, Longs Drugs, 99c Store, Radio Shack, Safeway/24hr, Walgreens/24hr, same as 30
31	I-238 (from sb), to I-580, Castro Valley
30	Hesperian Blvd, **E** ⛽ 76, 🍴 KFC, In-N-Out, Quizno's, Starbucks, ⊙ Kragen Parts, Walmart, Wheelworks Repair, **W** ⛽ Arco, Chevron, 76, 🍴 Black Angus, Hometown Buffet, 🏨 Hilton Garden, Nimitz Inn, ⊙ BigLots, Food Maxx, Longs Drugs, Lucky Foods, 99¢ Store, Radio Shack, USPO, vet, same as 32
29	A St, San Lorenzo, **E** ⛽ 76/Circle K, 🍴 McDonald's, 🏨 Best Western, ⊙ Costco, tires/repair, **W** ⛽ KB/dsl, 76/Circle K, Valero, 🍴 Burger King, Carrow's, Chef Ming, Hawaiian BBQ, Jamba Juice, Pizza Hut, Starbucks, Subway, 🏨 Days Inn, Heritage Inn, La Quinta, MainStay Suites, Phoenix Lodge, ⊙ $Tree, Home Depot, Mi Pueblo Foods, Target
28	Winton Ave, **W** ⛽ Chevron, Valero/dsl, 🍴 Applebee's, Coldstone Creamery, Elephant Bar/Grill, Hawaiian BBQ, Hometown Buffet, Marie Callendar's, Mimi's Cafe, Olive Garden, Panda Express, Panera Bread, Sizzler, Subway, ⊙ Firestone/auto, Goodyear/auto, JC Penney, Kragen Parts, Macy's, Ross, Sears/auto, mall
27	CA 92, Jackson St, **E** ⛽ Beacon, 76, Valero/24hr, 🍴 Asian Wok, Baskin-Robbins, Hawaiian BBQ, Mnt Mike's Pizza, Nations Burgers, Papa Murphy's, Popeye's, Starbucks, Subway, Taco Bell, ⊙ Grocery Outlet, Longs Drug, Lucky Foods, Radio Shack, Safeway, 7-11, Walgreens, **W** San Mateo Br
26	Tennyson Rd, **E** ⛽ All American/dsl, 76, 🍴 Jack-in-the-Box, KFC, RoundTable Pizza, ⊙ Kragen Parts, Walgreens, **W** ⛽ 76, ⊙ 🄷
25	Industrial Pkwy (from sb), **E** ⛽ Industrial/dsl, 🍴 Lite Wok, Quizno's, Starbucks, **W** 🏨 Pheonix Lodge
24	Whipple Rd, Dyer St, **E** ⛽ Chevron/dsl/24hr, 76, 🍴 Country Waffles, Del Taco, Denny's, McDonald's, Panda Express, Taco Bell, Wing Stop, 🏨 Best Value Inn, Motel 6, ⊙ FoodMaxx, Home Depot, PepBoys, Target, **W** ⛽ Shell, 🍴 Applebee's, Baskin-Robbins, Burger King,

FREMONT

Exit	Services
24	Continued
	Chili's, FreshChoice, Fuddrucker's, In-N-Out, IHOP, Jamba Juice, Jollibee, Krispy Kreme, La Salsa Mexican, Pasta Pormadora, Starbucks, Texas Roadhouse, TGIFriday, Togo's, Tony Roma's, 🏨 Extended Stay America, Holiday Inn Express, ⊙ Best Buy, Lowe's Whse, Lucky Foods, Michael's, PetCo, Radio Shack, Walmart/auto
23	Alvarado-Niles Rd, (same as 24), **E** ⛽ Shell, 🏨 Crowne Plaza, ⊙ 7-11, **W** ⛽ Shell, ⊙ Walmart/auto
22	Alvarado Blvd, Fremont Blvd, **E** 🍴 Phoenix Garden Chinese, Subway, 🏨 Motel 6, ⊙ Lucky Foods
21	CA 84 W, Decoto Rd to Dumbarton Br, **E** ⛽ 7-11, 🍴 McDonald's, ⊙ Walgreens
19	CA 84 E, Thornton Ave, Newark, **E** ⊙ U-Haul, **W** ⛽ Chevron/dsl/24hr, Shell, 🍴 Carl's Jr, KFC, Mtn Mike's Pizza, Taco Bell, ⊙ BigLots, Home Depot, 7-11
17	Mowry Ave, Fremont, **E** ⛽ Chevron/dsl, QuikStop, 76/Circle K, Valero, 🍴 Applebee's, Burger King, Chinese Buffet, Denny's, HoneyBaked Ham, KFC, Olive Garden, Starbucks, Subway, T&D Sandwiches, 🏨 Best Western, Extended Stay Deluxe, Residence Inn, ⊙ 🄷, Lucky Foods, **W** ⛽ 76, 🍴 Arby's, BJ's Rest., Bombay Garden, El Burro Mexican, Jack-in-the-Box, McDonald's, Red Robin, Subway, Taco Bell, TK Noodles, 🏨 Chase Suites, Comfort Inn, EZ 8 Motel, Homewood Suites, Motel 6, Towneplace Suites, ⊙ Firestone, Goodyear/auto, JC Penney, Jiffy Lube, Lion Mkt., Macy's, Mazda, Sears/auto, Target, TJ Maxx, mall
16	Stevenson Blvd, **E** ⛽ Arco/dsl, Shell, 🍴 Jack-in-the-Box, Outback Steaks, **W** ⛽ Chevron, 🍴 Chevy's Mexican, ChuckeCheese, Palm Gardens Rest., Starbucks, Togo's, 🏨 Hilton, ⊙ FoodMaxx, Ford, Harley-Davidson, Nissan, Tuesday Morning, Walmart
15	Auto Mall Pkwy, **E** ⛽ Arco, Chevron, 🍴 Subway, **W** ⛽ Shell/dsl, 🍴 Applebee's, Asian Pearl, Carino's, Chipotle Mexican, ClaimJumper, Coldstone Creamery, Dickey's BBQ, Hawaiian BBQ, In-N-Out, Jamba Juice, Panda Express, Panera Bread, PF Chang's, Quizno's, Rubio's, Starbucks, Subway, Tandoori Grill, Wendy's, Wing Stop, ⊙ BMW, Chrysler/Dodge/Jeep, Costco/gas, Honda, Jo-Ann Fabrics, Jaguar, Kia, Kohl's, Land Rover, Lexus, Lowes Whse, Mercedes, Office Depot, Old Navy, Porsche, Radio Shack, Staples, Toyota, Volvo
14mm	weigh sta both lanes
13	Fremont Blvd, Irving Dist, **W** ⛽ Valero/Subway, 🍴 McDonald's, SmartBrew, 🏨 GoodNite Inn, Homestead Suites, La Quinta, Marriott
13a	Gateway Blvd (from nb), **E** 🏨 Holiday Inn Express
12	Mission Blvd, **E** to I-680, ⛽ 76, Valero, 🍴 Carl's Jr, Denny's, Jack-in-the-Box, KFC, Togo's, 🏨 Holiday Inn

INTERSTATE 880 CONT'D (BAY AREA)

Exit	Services
12	Continued
	Express, Quality Inn, ⊙ Longs Drugs, Safeway, 7-11, Walgreens, **W** 🛏 Courtyard, Hampton Inn, Hyatt Place
10	Dixon Landing Rd, **E** 🍽 McDonald's, 🛏 Residence Inn, ⊙ 7-11
8b	CA 237, Alviso Rd, Calaveras Rd, to McCarthy Rd, Milpitas, **E** 🛢 CA Fuel, 76, 🍽 Burger King, Carl's Jr, Chili Palace, Denny's, Lee's Sandwiches, Marie Callender's, 🛏 Best Western, Days Inn, Travelodge, ⊙ BigLots, Kragen Parts, SaveMart Foods, 7-11, Walgreens, vet, **W on McCarthy Rd** 🛢 Chevron, 🍽 Applebee's, Black Angus, HomeTown Buffet, Happi House, In-N-Out, Jamba Juice, Macaroni Grill, McDonald's, On the Border, Pasta Pomodoro, RedBrick Pizza, Starbucks, Subway, Taco Bell, 🛏 Crowne Plaza, Hampton Inn, Hilton Garden, Homestead Suites, Larkspur Landing Hotel, Staybridge Suites, ⊙ Best Buy, GNC, Michael's, Petsmart, RanchMkt Foods, Ross, Walmart/McDonald's/auto
8a	Great Mall Parkway, Tasman Dr, **E** ⊙ Toyota
7	Montague Expswy, **E** 🛢 Shell/dsl, Valero, 🍽 Jack-in-the-Box, 🛏 Sleep Inn, ⊙ U-Haul, **W** 🛢 Chevron/dsl, 🍽 Dave&Buster's, 🛏 Beverly Heritage Hotel, Sheraton

Exit	Services
5	Brokaw Rd, **E** ⊙ Lowe's Whse, **W** ⊙ Ford Trucks, Fry's Electronics, CHP
4d	Gish Rd (nb only), **W** ⊙ auto/dsl repair/transmissions
4c b	US 101, N to San Francisco, S to LA
4a	1st St, **E** 🛢 76, Shell/repair, 🍽 Subway, **W** 🛢 76, 🍽 Cathay Chinese, Denny's/24hr, Empire Buffet, Genji Japanese, 🛏 Clarion, Comfort Suites, Days Inn, Executive Inn, EZ 8 Motel, Holiday Inn Express, Homestead Suites, Radisson, Red Roof Inn, Vagabond Inn, Wyndham Garden, ⊙ 7-11
3	Coleman St, **E** 🛢 Valero/dsl, 🍽 Quizno's, **W** ▷
2	CA 82, The Alameda, **W** 🛢 Shell/repair, 🍽 Starbucks, Subway, Taco Bell, 🛏 Best Western, Santa Clara Inn, St. Francis Hotel, Sterling Motel, Valley Inn, ⊙ Safeway, Santa Clara U
1d	Bascom Ave, to Santa Clara, **W** 🛢 Rotten Robbie/dsl, Valero, 🍽 Burger King
1c	Stevens Creek Blvd, San Carlos St, **E** 🛢 Valero/dsl, Valley/dsl, 🛏 Valley Park Hotel, ⊙ 🅗, **W** 🛢 76, 🍽 Arby's, CheeseCake Factory, Jack-in-the-Box, RoundTable Pizza, ⊙ Audi/VW, Best Buy, Ford, Goodyear/auto, Lexus, Longs Drugs, Macy's, Nordstrom's, Old Navy, Safeway, 7-11, Subaru, mall
1b	I-280. I-880 begins/ends on I-280
1a	Ca 17 to Santa Cruz.

COLORADO

INTERSTATE 25

Exit	Services
299	Colorado/Wyoming state line
296	point of interest both lanes
293	to Carr, Norfolk
288	Buckeye Rd
281	Owl Canyon Rd, **E** KOA Campground
278	CO 1 S, to Wellington, **W** 🛢 Kum&Go, Loaf'N Jug/Blimpie, Shell, 🍽 Burger King, Subway, Taco Bell, 🛏 Days Inn, ⊙ Main St Mkt/drugs, USPO
271	Mountain Vista Dr, **W** Budweiser Brewery
269b a	CO 14, to US 87, Ft Collins, **E** 🍽 Gambler's Steaks, McDonald's, 🛏 Mulberry Inn, **W** 🛢 Conoco, Phillips 66/dsl, 🍽 Denny's, Waffle House, 🛏 Comfort Inn, Day's Inn, Econolodge, La Quinta, Motel 6, Plaza Inn, Ramada Inn, Sleep Inn, Super 8, ⊙ RV Service, U-Haul, truck repair, vet, to CO St U, **2mi W** 🛢 Shamrock, 🍽 DQ, Papa John's, Qdoba Mexican, ⊙ Home Depot, Radio Shack, Walmart
268	Prospect Rd, to Ft Collins, **W** ⊙ 🅗, **Welcome Ctr, rest area both lanes, full** ♿ **facilities, litter barrels,** 🚮, **petwalk**
267mm	**weigh sta both lanes**
266mm	st patrol
265	CO 68 W, Timnath, **E** Walmart, **W** 🛢 Shell/dsl, **2-3 mi W** 🍽 Austin's Grill, Carrabba's, Golden Corral, Hunan Chinese, IHOP, Macaroni Grill, Outback Steaks, Papa John's, Quizno's, Subway, Texas Roadhouse, Village Inn Rest., 🛏 Courtyard, Hampton Inn, Marriott, Residence Inn, Safeway/gas, Sam's Club
262	CO 392 E, to Windsor, **E** 🛢 Conoco/dsl, Phillips 66/Subway/dsl, 🍽 Arby's, GoodTimes Burgers, Taco John's, 🛏 AmericInn, Super 8, **W** ⊙ Powder River RV Ctr

Exit	Services
259	Crossroads Blvd, **E** 🛢 Phillips 66/dsl, 🍽 Carl's Jr, Qdoba Mexican, Subway, 🛏 Candlewood Suites, Embassy Suites, Holiday Inn Express, **W** 🍽 Hooters, ⊙ BMW, Chevrolet, Chrysler/Dodge/Jeep, GMC, Harley-Davidson, Subaru, to ▷
257b a	US 34, to Loveland, **E** 🛢 gas/deli, 🍽 Biaggi Italian, BoneFish Grill, Costa Vida, Culver's, On-the-Border, PF Chang's, Red Robin, Rock Bottom Rest., Spicy Pickle, Starbucks, ⊙ Barnes&Noble, Best Buy, Macy's, **W** 🛢 Conoco/dsl, 🍽 Arby's (2mi), Blackeyed Pea, Carino's Italian, Chick-fil-A, Chili's, Chipotle Mexican, Cracker Barrel, Hooters, IHOP, KFC/Taco Bell, LoneStar Steaks, McDonald's, Mimi's Cafe, Noodles&Co, Old Chicago, Panera Bread, Quizno's, Subway, Taco John's, Waffle House, Wendy's, 🛏 Best Western, Comfort Inn, Fairfield Inn, Hampton Inn, Holiday Inn Express, Residence Inn, Super 8 (2mi), ⊙ 🅗, JoAnn Fabrics, Loveland Outlets/famous brands, Marshall's, PetsMart, Ross, Sportsman's Whse, Staples, Target, RV camping, museum, to Rocky Mtn NP
255	CO 402 W, to Loveland
254	to CO 60 W, to Campion, **E** 🛢 Johnson's Corner/Sinclair/dsl/café/motel/24hr, 🛏 Budget Host, ⊙ RV camping/service
252	CO 60 E, to Johnstown, Milliken, **W** 🛢 Loaf'n Jug/Subway
250	CO 56 W, to Berthoud, **W** Berthoud B&B, to Carter Lake
245	to Mead
243	CO 66, to Longmont, Platteville, **E** 🛢 Conoco/dsl, Boulder Gas/Gyros/dsl, 🍽 Red Rooster Rest., ⊙ Big John's RV Ctr, Camping World/K&C RV Ctr, tires, **W** to Rocky Mtn NP, to Estes Park
241mm	St Vrain River

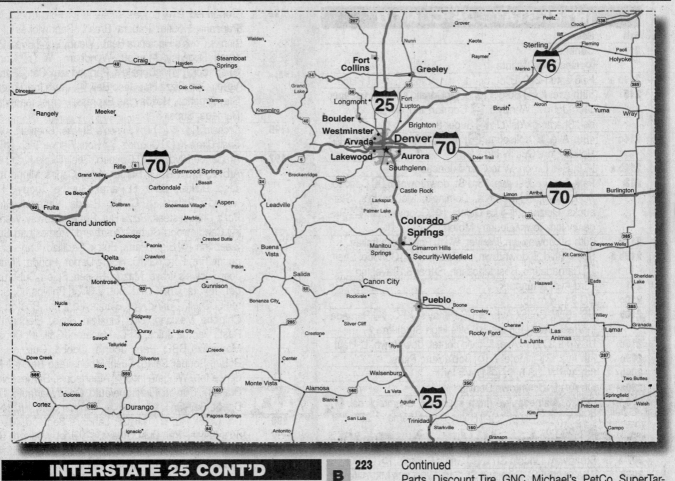

INTERSTATE 25 CONT'D

Exit	Services
240	CO 119, to Longmont, **E** 🛢 Phillips 66/dsl, 🍴 Carl's Jr, Del Taco, Qdoba, Quizno's, Starbucks, Wendy's, 🏠 Best Western, Value Place Inn, 🄾 Kia, Lexus, Toyota/Scion, **W** 🛢 Conoco/Subway/dsl/scales/24hr, Shell/dsl, 🍴 Arby's, Burger King, McDonald's, Taco Bell, Waffle House, 🏠 Best Value Inn, Comfort Inn, Day's Inn, 1st Inn, Super 8, 🄾 🅷, Del Camino RV Ctr, Valley Camper RV Ctr, museum, to Barbour Ponds SP
237	new exit
235	CO 52, Dacono, **E** 🄾 Ford, **W** 🛢 Conoco/McDonald's/dsl/LP, 🍴 Pepper Jacks, 🄾 Harley-Davidson, to Eldora Ski Area
232	to Erie
229	CO 7, to Lafayette, Brighton, **E** 🍴 Chick-fil-A, Famous Dave's BBQ, Goodtimes Burgers, Gunther Toody's, Heidi's, La Fogata, Starbucks, Village Inn, 🄾 Costco/gas, Home Depot, PetsMart, Sears Grand
228	E-470, tollway, to Limon
226	**W** 🍴 Mimi's Cafe, Red Robin, Starbucks, 🄾 JC Penney, Macy's, SuperTarget
225	136th Ave, **W** 🍴 Big Burrito, Carl's Jr, Starbucks, Subway, 🄾 Lowes Whse, Walmart /McDonald's
223	CO 128, 120th Ave, to Broomfield, **E** 🛢 Conoco, Shamrock/dsl, 🍴 Applebee's, Burger King, Chipotle Mexican, Chick-fil-A, Coldstone Creamery, Damon's, Fazoli's, Fuddrucker's, Krispy Kreme, LoneStar Steaks, McDonald's, Panda Express, Pizza Hut, Olive Garden, Outback Steaks, Sonic, TGI Friday, 🏠 Hampton Inn, Radisson, Ramada Inn, Sleep Inn, 🄾 Albertson's, Barnes&Noble, Big Lots, Big O Tire, Brakes+, CarQuest, Checker's

Exit	Services
223	**Continued** Parts, Discount Tire, GNC, Michael's, PetCo, SuperTarget, Tires+, Walgreens, vet, **W** 🛢 Conoco/dsl, Shell/Circle K/Popeye's/dsl, Shamrock, 🍴 Chili's, Cracker Barrel, DQ, Hooters, Jade City Chinese, Laguna's Mexican, Perkins, Starbucks, Subway, Village Inn Rest., Wendy's, 🏠 Comfort Suites, Extended Stay America, Fairfield Inn, La Quinta, Savannah Suites, Super 8
221	104th Ave, to Northglenn, **E** 🛢 Conoco, Phillips 66, 🍴 Burger King, DQ, Denny's, IHOP, Old Chicago, Sonic, Subway, Taco Bell/Pizza Hut, Texas Roadhouse, 🄾 🅷, AutoZone, Gander Mtn, Gordman's, Home Depot, King's Soopers, **W** 🛢 Conoco, 7-11, Shell/dsl, 🍴 Applebee's, Blackeyed Pea, Cinzinetti's Italian, GoodTimes Burger, Gunther Toody's, Hop's Grill, Mandarin Garden, McDonald's, Quizno's, Red Lobster, Taco Bell, 🏠 Best Value Inn, 🄾 Best Buy, Dodge, Firestone/auto, Ford, Goodyear/auto, Jo-Ann Fabrics, Lowe's Whse, Marshall's, Office Depot, Old Navy, Ross, Subaru, mall
220	Thornton Pkwy, **E** 🍴 Golden Corral, Starbucks, Taco Del Mar, 🄾 🅷, GNC, Sam's Club/gas, Tires+, Walmart, Thornton Civic Ctr, **W** 🛢 Conoco, Shamrock, Western/gas
219	84th Ave, to Federal Way, **E** 🛢 Conoco, Shamrock, 🍴 Arby's, Goodtimes Grill, Quizno's, Starbucks, Subway, Taco Bell, Waffle House, 🏠 Crossland Suites, 🄾 Walgreens, **W** 🛢 Econogas, Shamrock/dsl, 🍴 Burger King, DQ, El Jimador, Pizza Hut, Popeye's, Santiago's Mexican, Village Inn Rest., 🏠 Motel 6, 🄾 🅷, AutoZone, CarQuest, Discount Tire, Sav-A-Lot, vet
217	US 36, **W** (exits left from nb) to Boulder, **W** 🍴 Subway,

🅰 = gas   🍴 = food   🛏 = lodging   ⊙ = other

Copyright 2012 - The Next Ex

CO

INTERSTATE 25 CONT'D

Exit	Services
217	Continued
	⊙ Chevrolet, Toyota
216b a	I-76 E, to I-270, E
215	58th Ave, **E** 🍴 Burger King, McDonald's, Steak Escape, Taco John's, Wendy's, 🛏 Comfort Inn, **W** 🅰 Conoco/dsl, Shamrock/dsl/LP, 🛏 Super 8
214c	48th Ave, **E** coliseum, 🍴, **W** 🍴 Village Inn Rest., 🛏 Holiday Inn, Quality Inn
214b a	I-70, E to Limon, W to Grand Junction
213	Park Ave, W 38th Ave, 23rd St, downtown, **E** 🅰 Conoco, 7-11, Shell, 🍴 Denny's, Domino's, McDonald's, Starbucks, Quizno's, 🛏 La Quinta, ⊙ Goodyear, **W** 🛏 Regency Inn, Town&Country Motel
212c	20th St, downtown, Denver, **W** 🍴 Pagliacci's Italian
212b a	Speer Blvd, **E** downtown, museum, **W** 🅰 Conoco, Shell, 🛏 Ramada Inn, Residence Inn, Super 8, Travel Inn
211	23rd Ave, **E** funpark
210c	CO 33 (from nb)
210b	US 40 W, Colfax Ave, **W** 🍴 Denny's, KFC, 🛏 Ramada Inn/rest., Red Lion Inn, ⊙ Mile High Stadium
210a	US 40 E, Colfax Ave, **E** civic center, downtown, U-Haul
209c	8th Ave, **E** 🛏 Motel 7, ⊙ Bob's Auto Parts
209b	6th Ave W, US 6, **W** 🛏 Day's Inn
209a	6th Ave E, downtown Denver
208	CO 26, Alameda Ave (from sb), **E** 🅰 Shamrock/dsl, 🍴 Burger King, Denny's, ⊙ Home Depot, same as 207b, **W** 🅰 Conoco
207b	US 85 S, Santa Fe Dr, same as 208
207 a	Broadway, Lincoln St, **E** 🍴 Griff's Burgers, ⊙ USPO
206b	Washington St, Emerson St, **E** ⊙ WildOats Mkt/café, **W** ⊙ 🅷
206a	Downing St (from nb)
205b a	University Blvd, **W** to U of Denver
204	CO 2, Colorado Blvd, **E** 🅰 Conoco, Shamrock, 7-11, Shell, Sinclair, 🍴 Arby's, Asian Grill, Black Eyed Pea, Boston Mkt, GoodTimes Grill, Hooters, KFC, Lazy Dog Café, McDonald's, Noodles&Co, Pizza Hut, Starbucks, Subway, Taco Bell, Village Inn Rest., Wild Oats Cafe, 🛏 Cherry Creek, Day's Inn, Fairfield Inn, Hampton Inn, Lowes Denver, Ramada, ⊙ AAA, Barnes&Noble, Best Buy, Chevrolet/Buick, Mercedes/BMW, Ross, Safeway Foods, VW, Walgreens, **W** 🅰 Conoco, 🍴 A&W/KFC, Dave&Buster's, Denny's, McDonald's, Perkins, 🛏 La Quinta
203	Evans Ave, **E** 🅰 Conoco, 🍴 Big Papa's BBQ, Breakfast Inn, McDonald's, Palace Chinese, Quiznos, 🛏 Rockies Inn, ⊙ AutoZone, Discount Tire, NAPA, Walgreens, **W** 🛏 Cameron Motel, ⊙ Ford
202	Yale Ave, **W** 🅰 Shamrock
201	US 285, CO 30, Hampden Ave, to Englewood, Aurora, **E** 🅰 Conoco/Circle K/LP, Phillips 66, Shamrock, Sinclair, 🍴 Ajuuai Rest, Applebee's, Boston Mkt, Chicago Grill, Chili's, Domino's, Einstein Bros, McDonald's, Mexican Grill, Noodles&Co, NY Deli, Old Chicago, On-the-Border, Qdoba, Starbucks, Subway, 🛏 Embassy Suites, Marriott, Sheraton, TownePlace Suites, ⊙ Discount Tire, King's Sooper Foods, Walgreens, Whole Food Mkt, vet, **W** 🅰 Conoco, 🍴 Aurelio's Pizza, Burger King, Starbucks, ⊙ Safeway
200	I-225 N, to I-70
199	CO 88, Belleview Ave, to Littleton, **E** 🅰 Sinclair, 🍴 Chipotle Mexican, Harvest Rest., Off Belleview Grill,

N   ↕   **S**   **DENVER AREA**   **CHERRY HILLS**

Exit	Services
199	Continued
	Pancake House, Panera Bread, Sandwiches+, Starbucks, Tosh's Hacienda Rest., Wendy's, 🛏 Hyatt Place, Hyatt Regency, Marriott, Wyndham, **W** 🅰 Conoco, Shamrock, 🍴 McDonald's, Pappadeaux Café, Paradise Valley Grill, Pizza Hut, Taco Bell, 🛏 Day's Inn, Extended Stay America, Holiday Inn Express, HomeStead Village, Ramada, Super 8
198	Orchard Rd, **E** 🍴 Del Frisco's Steaks, Shepler's, **W** 🅰 Shell/Circle K, 🍴 Quizno's, 🛏 Hotel Denver Tech, ⊙ 🅷
197	Arapahoe Blvd, **E** 🅰 Conoco, Shell/Circle K, 🍴 A&W, Arby's, Bro's BBQ, Burger King, Carlos Miguel's, Del Taco, Dickie's BBQ, El Parral, Gunther Toody's Rest., Hoong's Palace, KFC, Mr. Panda, Outback Steaks, Pat's Cheesesteak, Pizza Hut, Sonic, Subway, Wendy's, 🛏 Candlewood Suites, Courtyard, Homestead Suites, Sleep Inn, ⊙ Big A Parts, Buick, Cadillac, Chrysler, Discount Tire, Ford, GMC, Home Depot, Honda, Hyundai, Jeep, Lowe's Whse, Mazda, Nissan, Scion, Subaru, Target, Toyota, USPO, Walmart , **W** 🅰 Phillips 66, Shamrock, Shell, 🍴 Arby's, Blackeyed Pea, Boston Mkt, Chipotle Mexican, DQ, Einstein Bro's, Elephant Bar Rest., Jamba Juice, KFC, Macaroni Grill, McDonald's, Mongolian BBQ, Papa John's, Qdoba, Quizno's, Red Robin, Souper Salad, Sushi Moon, Taco Bell, 🛏 Residence Inn, Wingate Inn, ⊙ Albertson's, Barnes&Noble, Brakes+, Curves, Firestone/auto, Goodyear/auto, Office Depot, Sav-On
196	Dry Creek Rd, **E** 🍴 IHOP, Landry's Seafood, Maggiano's Italian, Trail Dust Steaks, 🛏 Best Western, Bradford Suites, Country Inn Suites, Days Inn, Holiday Inn Express, Homestead Suites, La Quinta, Quality Inn, Ramada Ltd, Studio+, **W** 🛏 Drury Inn
195	County Line Rd, **E** 🛏 Courtyard, Residence Inn, **W** 🅰 Conoco, 🍴 Buffalo Wild Wings, Burger King, California Pizza Kitchen, Champ's Rest., Chick-fil-A, Fleming's Rest., PF Changs, Red Robin, Rock Bottom Brewery/Cafe, Starbucks, Thai Basil, 🛏 Hyatt Place, ⊙ Barnes&Noble, Best Buy, Costco/gas, Dillard's, Home Depot, JC Penney, JoAnn Fabrics, Michaels, Nordstrom's, PetsMart
194	CO 470 W, CO 470, E (tollway), **1 exit W on Quebec** 🍴 Arby's, ClaimJumper, Country Buffet, LoneStar Steaks, McDonald's, TGIFriday, 🛏 Comfort Suites, Fairfield Inn, Hyatt Place, ⊙ Barnes&Noble, Firestone, Home Depot, PepBoys, Sam's Club, Walmart/gas
193	Lincoln Ave, to Parker, **E** 🅰 Shamrock, 🍴 Carraba's, PanAsia Bistro, Hacienda Colorado, 🛏 Candlewood Suites, Extended Stay America, Hilton Garden, **W** 🅰 Conoco/dsl, 🍴 Chipotle Grill, Chili's, Heidi's, McDonald's, Pizza Hut/Taco Bell, Starbucks, Subway, 🛏 Marriott, ⊙ 🅷, Discount Tire, Safeway
192	no services
191	no services
190	Surrey Ridge
188	Castle Pines Pkwy, **W** 🅰 Conoco, Shell/Circle K/Popeye's/24hr, 🍴 Cafe De France, La Dolce Vita, Little Italy, Starbucks, Subway, Wendy's, ⊙ Big O Tires, Discount Tire, King's Sooper/dsl, Safeway, vet
187	Happy Canyon Rd, services **2 mi W**
184	Founders Pkwy, Meadows Pkwy, to Castle Rock, **E** 🅰 Conoco/Cirlce K/dsl, Shell/Circle K/dsl, 🍴 A&W/KFC, Applebee's, Baskin-Robbins, Chick-fil-A, Chipotle Mexican, Goodtimes Grill, Italian Eatery, Jimmy

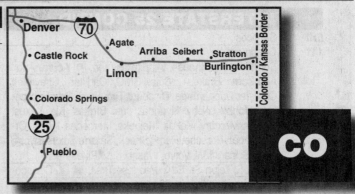

INTERSTATE 25 CONT'D

CASTLE ROCK N S **LARKSPUR**

Exit	Services
184	Continued
	John's, LePeep, Little Caesar's, Qdoba, Quizno's, Outback Steaks, Red Robin, Sonic, Starbucks, Subway, Taco Bell, Wendy's, ▣ URGENT CARE, AT&T, Checker Parts, Discount Tire, GNC, Goodyear/auto, Grease Monkey, Home Depot, King's Sooper/24hr, Kohl's, Michael's, Natural Grocers, Office Depot, Petsmart, Radio Shack, Target, Walgreens, Walmart, W ▣ Conoco/Blimpie/dsl, ▥ Arby's, Blackeyed Pea, Chili's, Food Court, IHOP, McDonald's, Rockyard Grill, ⌂ Best Western, Comfort Suites, Days Inn, Hampton Inn, ▣ Castle Rock Outlet/famous brands, Lowe's, Midas
182	CO 86, Castle Rock, Franktown, E ▣ Conoco/dsl, Phillips 66/dsl, 7-11/dsl, ▥ Augustine Grill, Castle Rock BBQ, El Meson Mexican, ▣ Castle Pines Motel, st patrol, vet, W ▣ Shell/Circle K/dsl, Valero/dsl, ▥ Burger King, Guadalajara Mexican, McDonald's, Old West BBQ, Santiago's Mexican, Village Inn, Waffle House, Wendy's, ⌂ Holiday Inn Express, Quality Inn, Super 8, ▣ NAPA, vet
181	CO 86, Wilcox St, Plum Creek Pkwy, Castle Rock, E ▣ Conoco, Valero/dsl, Western/dsl, ▥ DQ, Papa Murphy's, Pizza Hut, Starbucks, Subway, Taco Bell, ⌂ Castle Rock Motel, ▣ AutoZone, Big O Tire, Buick, Chevrolet, Ford/Mercury, Safeway/gas, Tuesday Morning, Walgreens, USPO
174	Tomah Rd, W ▣ Castle Rock RV Park/camping
173	Larkspur (from sb, no return), **1 mi** W ▣ Conoco/Larkspur Cafe/dsl/phone
172	South Lake Gulch Rd, Larkspur, **2 mi** W ▣ Conoco/dsl/phone, ▥ Larkspur Pizza Cafe
167	Greenland
163	County Line Rd
162.5mm	Monument Hill, elev 7352
162mm	**weigh sta both lanes**
161	CO 105, Woodmoor Dr, E ▣ Conoco, ▥ Margarita's Mexican, ▣ CO Hts RV Park (2mi), vet, W ▣ Conoco/Circle K/dsl, 7-11, ▥ Arby's, Chinese Rest., Domino's, McDonald's, Pizza Hut, Rosie's Diner, Starbucks, Subway, Taco Bell, Village Inn, ▣ Big O Tire, Curves, Natural Grocers, Radio Shack, Safeway/dsl, Walgreens, USPO
158	Baptist Rd, E ▣ Shell/Circle K/Popeye's/dsl/24hr, ▥ Carl's Jr, Chili's, Coldstone Creamery, Fusion Cuisine, McDonald's, Nick&Willy's, Papa Murphy's, Subway, TX Roadhouse, ⌂ Fairfield Inn, ▣ URGENT CARE, Checker Parts, Home Depot, King's Sooper/24hr, Kohl's, Petsmart, Staples, Walgreens, Walmart, vet, W ▣ Shamrock/dsl/scales
156b	N Entrance to USAF Academy, **W visitors center**
156a	Gleneagle Dr, **E** mining museum
153	InterQuest Pkwy, E ⌂ Hampton Inn, Residence Inn
152	scenic overlook on sb
151	Briargate Pkwy, E ▣ 7-11, ▥ Biaggi's, California Pizza Kitchen, Champp's, Maggie Moo's, Panera Bread, PF Changs, Qdoba, Starbucks, Ted's MT Grill, ⌂ Hilton Garden, Homewood Suites, ▣ to Black Forest
150b a	CO 83, Academy Blvd, E ▣ Conoco, Shamrock/dsl, Shell/Circle K/dsl, ▥ Applebee's, A&W, Baskin-Robbins, Boston Mkt, Buffalo Wild Wings, Burger King, Chick-fil-A, Chipotle Mexican, Cici's Pizza, Culver's, Cracker Barrel, Denny's, Egg&I Café, Elephant Bar Rest., Famous

COLORADO SPRINGS

Exit	Services
150b a	Continued
	Dave's, Fat Burger, Five Guys Burgers, GoodTimes Grill, IHOP, Jason's Deli, KFC, McDonald's, Mimi's Café, Olive Garden, On-the-Border, Panera Bread, Pei Wei, Pizza Hut, Qdoba, Quizno's, Red Robin, Rumbi Island Grill, Salt Grass Steaks, Schlotzsky's, Sonic, Souper Salad, Starbucks, Subway, Taco Bell, Thai Basil, Wahoo's, Wendy's, ⌂ Best Western, Comfort Suites, Days Inn, Drury Inn, Howard Johnson, Super 8, ▣ Advance Parts, AT&T, Barnes&Noble, Best Buy, Checker Parts, Dillard's, $Tree, Firestone/auto, Ford, Hobby Lobby, Home Depot, Hyundai, JC Penney, King's Sooper, Macy's, Marshall's, Michael's, Natural Grocers, Office Depot, Old Navy, PepBoys, Petsmart, Radio Shack, Sam's Club/gas, Sears/auto, Steinmart, USPO, Walmart, Whole Foods Mkt, mall, to Peterson AFB, **W** S Entrance to USAF Academy
149	Woodmen Rd, E ▥ Carl's Jr, Carraba's, ▣ Nissan, W ▣ Shell/Circle K, ▥ Old Chicago Pizza, Hooters, Outback Steaks, TGIFriday's, Zio's Italian, ⌂ Comfort Inn, Embassy Suites, Fairfield Inn, Hampton Inn, Holiday Inn Express, Microtel, Staybridge Suites
148	Corporate Ctr Dr (exits left from sb), Nevada Ave, E ▥ Chipotle Mexican, Panera Bread, Smash Burger, ▣ Costco/gas, Harley-Davidson, Kohl's, Lowe's, vet, W ▣ Shell/Circle K, ▥ Mason Jar Rest., ⌂ Crestwood Suites, Extended Stay America, Hyatt Summerfield Suites, Marriott, ▣ to Rodeo Hall of Fame
146	Garden of the Gods Rd, E ▣ Conoco, Shell/Circle K/dsl, ▥ Antonio's Italian, Carl's Jr, Drifter's Burgers, McDonald's, ⌂ Best Value Inn, La Quinta, ▣ Aamco, Carquest, W ▣ Conoco/Circle K, 7-11, Shamrock/dsl, Shell/dsl, ▥ Applebee's, Arceo's Mexican, A&W, Blackeyed Pea, Chick-fil-A, Jimmy John's, Mollica's Italian, Panda Express, Quizno's, Scholtzsky's, Souper Salad, Sonic, Starbucks, Subway, Taco Bell, Village Inn, Wendy's, ⌂ Days Inn, Hyatt Place, Quality Inn, Super 8, ▣ Discount Tire, Staples, to Garden of Gods, vet
145	CO 38 E, Fillmore St, E ▣ 7-11, Shamrock/dsl, ▥ Arby's, DQ, Lucky Dragon, McDonald's, Subway, ⌂ Budget Host, ▣ Ⓗ Advance Parts, W ▣ Conoco/dsl, Shell/Circle K/dsl, ▥ Waffle House, ⌂ Motel 6, Super 8
144	Fontanero St
143	Uintah St, E ▣ 7-11, ▣ Uintah Fine Arts Ctr
142	Bijou St, Bus Dist, E ⌂ Hilton, ▣ Firestone/auto, visitor info, W ▥ Denny's, ⌂ Clarion, Quality Inn, ▣ Family$, 7-11
141	US 24 W, Cimarron St, to Manitou Springs, W ▣ Conoco/dsl, Shell/dsl, ▥ Arby's, Borriello's Bros Pizza, Capt D's, La Castia Mexican, McDonald's, Popeye's,

= gas   = food   = lodging   = other   Copyright 2012 - The Next Exi

COLORADO SPRINGS N ← → S

INTERSTATE 25 CONT'D

Exit	Services
141	Continued Sonic, TX Roadhouse, Express Inn, Acura, Audi, AutoZone, Brakes+, Buick/GMC, Cadillac, Chevrolet, Chrysler/Dodge/Jeep, Discount Tire, Ford, Grease Monkey, Hobby Lobby, Hyundai, Just Brakes, Kia, Lexus, Lincoln/Mercury, Mazda, Meineke, Mercedes, NAPA, Office Depot, Porsche, Radio Shack, Saturn, Scion/Toyota, 7-11, Subaru/VW, Volvo, Walmart , to Pikes Peak
140b	US 85 S, Tejon St, **E** Peerless Tires, **W** Conoco/dsl, access to same as 141
140a	Nevada Ave, **E** Chateau Motel, Howard Johnson, Tire King, **W** 7-11, Shamrock, Arceo's Mexican, Burger King, China Kitchen, KFC, McDonald's, Mollica's Italian, Noodles&Co, Panera Bread, Schlotzsky's, Starbucks, Subway, Taco Bell, Taco Express, Wendy's, Chief Motel, Rodeway Inn, Sunsprings Motel, Travelodge, Big O Tire, Checker Parts, $Tree, Midas, Natural Grocers, Office Depot, Safeway, Sears, Tuesday Morning, Walgreens, tires/repair, USPO, access to auto dealers at 141
139	US 24 E, to Lyman, Peterson AFB
138	CO 29, Circle Dr, **E** Conoco, Shell/Circle K/dsl, McDonald's, Crowne Plaza, Days Inn, Super 8, Kohl's, , zoo, **W** 7-11, Arby's, Baskin-Robbins, Burger King, Carrabba's, Carl's Jr, Chili's, ChuckeCheese, Culver's, Denny's, Fazoli's, Macaroni Grill, Outback Steaks, Village Inn, Subway, Best Western, Comfort Inn, Courtyard, DoubleTree Hotel, Fairfield Inn, Hampton Inn, La Quinta, Residence Inn, AT&T, Batteries+, GNC, PetCo, Target
135	CO 83, Academy Blvd, **E** to Cheyenne Mtn SP, to , **W** Ft Carson
132	CO 16, Wide Field Security, **E** Loves/Subway/dsl, Camping World RV , KOA
128	to US 85 N, Fountain, Security, **E** Loaf'n Jug/Subway/dsl, 7-11, Grand China, USPO, **W** Tomahawk/Shell/dsl/rest./24hr/@, Fountain Inn, Super 8
125	Ray Nixon Rd
123	no services
122	to Pikes Peak Meadows, **W** Pikes Peak Intn'l Raceway
119	Rancho Colorado Blvd
116	county line rd
115mm	**rest area nb, full facilities, picnic tables, litter barrels, petwalk**
114	Young Hollow
112mm	**rest area sb, full facilities, picnic tables, litter barrels, petwalk**
110	Pinon, **W** Sinclair/dsl/repair/motel
108	Purcell Blvd, Bragdon, **E** racetrack, **W** KOA
106	Porter Draw
104	Eden
102	Eagleridge Blvd, **E** Loaf'n Jug/dsl, Burger King, TX Roadhouse, Holiday Inn, Big O Tire, Home Depot, Sam's Club/gas, **W** Shell/Blimpie/dsl, Buffalo Wild Wings, Cactus Flower Mexican, Carino's, Chili's, Cracker Barrel, IHOP, Starbucks, Taco Star, Village Inn, Best Western, Comfort Inn, EconoLodge, Hampton Inn, La Quinta, Ramada, Wingate Inn, Best Buy, Kohl's, Old Navy, PetCo, Harley-Davidson, frontage rds access 101
101	US 50 W, Pueblo, **E** Conoco/dsl, Capt D's, Coldstone Creamery, Country Buffet, Denny's, 3 Margarita's

PUEBLO

101	Continued Mexican, Souper Salad, Subway, Ruby Tuesday, Sleep Inn, Barnes&Noble, Dillard's, JC Penney, Petsmart, Ross, Sears/auto, Target, Walmart , U-Haul, mall, **W** Loaf'n Jug/dsl, 7-11, Shamrock/dsl, Shell/dsl, Valero, Applebee's, Arby's, Blackeyed Pea, Boston Mkt, Carl's Jr, Casa de Burrito, China Rest., Chipotle Mexican, Country Kitchen, Del Taco, DJ Steaks, DQ, Domino's, Fazoli's, Giacomo's Rest., Golden Corral, McDonald's, Olive Garden, Papa John's, Papa Murphy's, Pass Key Rest., Pizza Hut, Popeye's, Quizno's, Red Lobster, Starbucks, Subway, SW Grill, Taco Bell, Wendy's, Clarion, Days Inn, Howard Johnson, Motel 6, Rodeway Inn, Super 8, Aamco, Advance Parts, Albertson's, AT&T, AutoZone, Batteries+, Brakes+, Checker Parts, Chevrolet, Chrysler/Jeep, Discount Tire, EmergiCare, Ford, Goodyear/auto, Hyundai, KIA, K-Mart, Lowe's, Mazda, NAPA, Nissan, Staples, Subaru, Topper RV Ctr, Toyota, Walgreens, vet, frontage rds access 102
100b	29th St, Pueblo, **E** Country Buffet, KFC, Mongolian Grill, Ruby Buffet, $Tree, Hobby Lobby, King's Sooper Foods, Natural Grocers, Peerless Tires, mall, **W** Conoco, Sonic, USA Motel, Grease Monkey, Safeway
100a	US 50 E, to La Junta, **E** Loaf'n Jug, Shell, Little Caesar's, McDonald's, Pizza Hut, Wendy's, AutoZone, Big R Foods, Goodyear, Sav-A-Lot Foods, Walgreens
99b a	Santa Fe Ave, 13th St, downtown, **W** Subway, Taco Bell, Wendy's, Guesthouse Inn, Travelers Motel, , Buick/Cadillac/GMC, Chevrolet, Honda, VW
98b	CO 96, 1st St, Union Ave Hist Dist, Pueblo, **W** Loaf'n Jug, Carl's Jr, Cambria Suites, Marriott
98a	US 50E bus, to La Junta, **W** Phillips 66/dsl, Sonic
97b	Abriendo Ave, **W** Spirit, Pass Key Rest., Subway, Taco Bell
97a	Central Ave, **W** Shamrock, McDonald's
96	Indiana Ave, **W**
95	Illinois Ave (from sb), **W** to dogtrack
94	CO 45 N, Pueblo Blvd, **W** Loaf'n Jug, Western/dsl, Felice's Pizza, Pizza Hut/Taco Bell, Hampton Inn, Microtel, Lowe's, RV camping, fairgrounds/racetrack, to Lake Pueblo SP
91	Stem Beach
88	Burnt Mill Rd
87	Verde Rd
83	no services
77	Hatchet Ranch Rd, Abbey Rd
74	CO 165 W, Colo City, **E** Shamrock/deli/dsl/24hr, KOA, **W** Shell/Subway/Noble Roman's/dsl, Max's Rest., Days Inn/rest., **rest area both lanes, full facilities, , , vending, litter barrels, petwalk**

WALSENBURG

71	Graneros Rd
67	to Apache
64	Lascar Rd
60	Huerfano
59	Butte Rd
56	Redrock Rd
55	Airport Rd
52	CO 69 W, to Alamosa, Walsenburg, **W** Loaf'n Jug/dsl (2mi), Phillips 66/A&W/dsl/24hr, Western, Carl's Jr (2mi), George's Rest., KFC, Pizza Hut, Rambler Rest., Subway (2mi), Taco Bell, Best Western, Budget Host, Country Host RV Park, Family$ (2mi), to Great Sand

🔳 = gas 🍴 = food 🛏 = lodging 🔲 = other

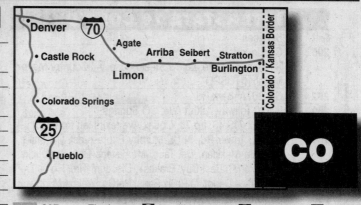

CO

INTERSTATE 25 CONT'D

Exit	Services
N ↕ S	
52	Continued Dunes NM, San Luis Valley
50	CO 10 E, to La Junta, **W** 🅷, tourist info
49	Lp 25, to US 160 W, Walsenburg, **1 mi W** 🔳 Loaf'n Jug, 🍴 Carl's Jr., 🔲 Lathrop SP, to Cuchara Ski Valley
42	Rouse Rd, to Pryor
41	Rugby Rd
34	Aguilar, **E** 🔳 Cenex/dsl/rest.
30	Aguilar Rd, **W** rv park, truck/tire repair
27	Ludlow, **W** Ludlow Memorial
23	Hoehne Rd
18	El Moro Rd, **W rest area both lanes, full** ♿ **facilities, picnic tables, litter barrels, petwalk**
15	US 350 E, Goddard Ave, **E** 🍴 Burger King, 🛏 Super 8, 🔲 🅷, Big R Ranch Store, Family$, **W** 🔳 Shell, 🛏 Frontier Motel/café
14b a	CO 12 W, Trinidad, **E CO Welcome Ctr,** 🔳 Shamrock, Shell/Subway, 🍴 KFC/Taco Bell, McDonald's, Sonic, 🔲 Trinidad Motor Inn, **W** 🔳 Shamrock, 🍴 Domino's, DQ, Wonderful House Chinese, 🛏 Prospect Plaza Motel, 🔲 Parts+, RV camping, to Trinidad Lake, Monument Lake
13b	Main St, Trinidad, **E** 🔳 Shamrock/dsl, Shell, 🍴 McDon- ald's, Sonic, 🛏 Trinidad Hotel, 🔲 CarQuest, Safeway Foods/gas
13a	Santa Fe Trail, Trinidad, **E** 🛏 Best Western, 🔲 RV camp- ing
11	Starkville, **E** 🔳 Shell/Wendy's/dsl/24hr, weigh/check sta, 🍴 Taquila's Mexican, 🛏 Budget Host, Budget Summit Inn/RV Park, Holiday Inn, 🔲 Bigg's RV Park, to Santa Fe Trail, **W** 🔳 Miristar, 🍴 Country Kitchen, 🛏 La Quinta, Quality Inn, 🔲 Big O Tire, Checker Parts, Grease Monkey, Toyota, Walmart
8	Springcreek
6	Gallinas
2	Wootten
1mm	scenic area pulloff nb
0mm	Colorado/New Mexico state line, Raton Pass, elev 7834, **weigh sta sb**

INTERSTATE 70

Exit	Services
450mm	Colorado/Kansas state line
438	US 24, Rose Ave, Burlington, **N** 🔳 Conoco/dsl, 🛏 Sloan's Motel, 🔲 🅷, Buick/Chevrolet/GMC, CarQuest, $General, Family$, Ford/Lincoln/Mercury, NAPA, Safe- way Foods, **S** 🔳 Shell/Reynaldo's Mexican/dsl/24hr, 🔲 Bonny SRA, RV Camping, truck repair
437.5mm	**Welcome Ctr wb, full** ♿ **facilities, info,** 🔳, 🛏, **litter barrels, petwalk, historical site**
437	US 385, Burlington, **N** 🔳 Conoco/dsl/24hr, Western/dsl, 🍴 Arby's, Burger King, McDonald's, Pizza Hut, Route Steaks, Subway, 🛏 Best Value Inn, Best Western/rest., Burlington Inn, Chaparral Motel, Comfort Inn, Western Motel, 🔲 🅷, Alco, to Bonny St RA
429	Bethune
419	CO 57, Stratton, **N** 🔳 Cenex/dsl, Conoco/dsl, 🍴 Burg- er Delight, 🛏 Best Western/rest., Claremont Inn/café, 🔲 Marshall Ash Village Camping, auto museum
412	Vona, **1/2 mi N** 🔳, 🔳
405	CO 59, Seibert, **N** Shady Grove Camping, **S** 🔳 Conoco/ dsl, 🔲 tire repair

Exit	Services
E ↕ W	
395	Flagler, **N** 🔳 Loaf'N Jug/dsl, 🍴 I-70 Diner, 🛏 Little England Motel, 🔲 Flagler SWA, NAPA, RV camping, **S** 🔳 Cenex/dsl 🔲 golf
383	Arriba, **N** 🔳 DJ/dsl/café, motel, **S rest area both lanes full** ♿ **facilities,** 🛏, **litter barrels, point of interest, petwalk, RV camping**
376	Bovina
371	Genoa, **N** point of interest, gas, food, 🔳, **S** 🅷
363	US 24, US 40, US 287, to CO 71, to Hugo, Limon, **13 mi** **S** 🅷
361	CO 71, Limon, **N** 🔲 Ace Hardware, Chrysler/Dodge/ Jeep, **S** 🔳 Conoco/dsl/24hr, Shell/Wendy's/dsl/24hr, 🍴 Golden China, Pizza Hut, 🛏 1st Inn Gold, Knights Inn, 🔲 Alco, KOA, st patrol, RV camping
360.5mm	weigh/check sta both lanes
359	to US 24, CO 71, Limon, **N** 🔳 ✈FLYING J/IHOP/dsl/ scales/LP/24hr, 🔲 dsl repair, RV camping, **S** 🔳 Phil- lips 66, Qwest, TA/Shell/Subway/Country Pride/dsl/ scales/24hr/@, 🍴 Arby's, Denny's, McDonald's, Oscar's Grill, 🛏 Comfort Inn, EconoLodge, Holiday Inn Express, Super 8, TS Inn, Quality Inn, 🔲 camping
354	no services
352	CO 86 W, to Kiowa
348	to Cedar Point
340	Agate, **1/4 mi S** gas/dsl, 🔳
336	to Lowland
332mm	**rest area wb, full** ♿ **facilities, info,** 🔳, 🛏, **litter bar- rels, vending, petwalk**
328	to Deer Trail, **N** 🔳 Phillips/dsl, **S** 🔳 Shell/dsl, 🔲 USPO
325mm	East Bijou Creek
323.5mm	Middle Bijou Creek
322	to Peoria
316	US 36 E, Byers, **N** 🔳 Sinclair, 🛏 Budget Host, 🔲 Thrift- way Foods/Drug, **S** 🔳 Tri Valley/gas, 🍴 Country Burger Rest., 🛏 Lazy 8 Motel (1mi), 🔲 USPO
310	Strasburg, **N** 🔳 Conoco/dsl/24hr, Ray's gas/24hr, 🍴 Patio Cafe, 🛏 Strasburg Inn, 🔲 Country Gardens RV Camping (3mi), KOA, NAPA, Western Hardware, dsl/ auto repair, USPO
306mm	Kiowa , Bennett, **N rest area both lanes, full** ♿ **facili- ties,** 🔳, 🛏, **litter barrels, petwalk**
305	Kiowa (from eb)
304	CO 79 N, Bennett, **N** 🔳 Conoco/Hotstuff Pizza/dsl, ❤Loves/Chester's/McDonald's/dsl/scales/24hr, 🍴 China Kitchen, High Plains Diner, Starbucks, Subway, 🔲 King Soopers Foods/dsl, USPO, **S** 🔲 Ace Hard- ware
299	CO 36, Manila Rd, **S** 🔳 Shamrock/dsl
295	Lp 70, Watkins, **N** 🔳 Shell/Tomahawk/dsl/rest./24hr/@,

CO

INTERSTATE 70 CONT'D

E ↕ W

Exit	Services
295	**Continued** 🍴 Biscuit's Cafe, Lulu's Steakhouse, 🛏 Country Manor Motel, 🅾 USPO
292	CO 36, Airpark Rd
289	E-470 Tollway, 120th Ave, CO Springs
288	US 287, US 40, Lp 70, Colfax Ave (exits left from wb)
286	CO 32, Tower Rd, **N** 🅿 Murphy Express/dsl, 🍴 Chili's, Chipotle Mexican, Del Taco, McAlister's Deli, Starbucks, Wendy's, 🅾 Best Buy, Brakes+, Discount Tire, Home Depot, Office Depot, O'Reilly Parts, PetCo, Walmart/Subway
285	Airport Blvd, **N** Denver Int ✈, **S** 🅿 ⊕FLYING J/Denny's/dsl/scales/24hr, Shell/McDonald's/dsl, 🍴 Denny's, 🛏 Comfort Inn, Crystal Inn, 🅾 Harley-Davidson
284	I-225, N (from eb)
283	Chambers Rd, **N** 🅿 Conoco, Shell/Circle K/Popeye's, 🍴 A&W/KFC, Anthony's Pizza, Applebees, Chicago Grill, Jimmy John's, LJ Silver/Taco Bell, Outback Steaks, Pizza Hut, Qdoba, Sonic, Subway, Ted's MT Grill, Urban Sombrero, Wendy's, 🛏 A Loft, Cambria Suites, Country Inn&Suites, Crowne Plaza, Hampton Inn, Hilton Garden, Homewood Suites, Hyatt Place, Marriott, Residence Inn, Sleep Inn, 🅾 Tires+, U-haul, **S** 🅿 Shamrock, 🍴 Burger King, 🛏 Crossland Suites, 🅾 America East RV Ctr
282	I-225 S, to Colorado Springs
281	Peoria St, **N** 🅿 Conoco, 7-11, Shell/dsl, 🍴 Burger King, Del Taco, Domino's, El Patron Mexican, GoodTimes Burgers, McDonald's, Peoria Grill, Subway, 🛏 Drury Inn, La Quinta, Timbers Motel, 🅾 Big O Tire, Family$, **S** 🅿 Conoco/dsl, Shamrock/dsl, 🍴 Bennett's BBQ, Chester's Grill, Church's, Denny's, Ho Mei Chinese, Pizza Hut/Taco Bell, Real Deminas Mexican, Subway, Waffle House, Wendy's, 🛏 Motel 6, Quality Inn, Star Hotel, Stay Inn, 🅾 Curves, Goodyear/auto, Tires For Less, auto/RV repair, vet
280	Havana St, **N** 🛏 Embassy Suites
279	I-270 W, US 36, W (from wb), to Ft Collins, Boulder
278	CO 35, Quebec St, **N** 🅿 Sapp Bros/Sinclair/Subway/dsl/@, TA/dsl/rest./24hr/@, 🍴 Coldstone, Del Taco, Jim'n Nick's BBQ, Marco's Pizza, Olive Garden, Qdoba, Red Lobster, Starbucks, TGIFriday's, Wahoo's, 🛏 Best Inn, Comfort Inn, Studio Suites, 🅾 AT&T, Bass Pro Shops, JC Penney, Macys, Old Navy, Super Target, Verizon, mall, **S** 🍴 Arby's, Buffalo Wild Wings, Country Buffet, Famous Dave's BBQ, Jimmy John's, IHOP, McDonald's, Panda Express, Panera Bread, Papa John's, Red Robin, Sonic, Subway, 🛏 Courtyard, DoubleTree Hotel, Holiday Inn, Red Lion Inn, Renaissance Inn, Super 8, 🅾 AT&T, GNC, Home Depot, Office Depot, Radio Shack, Ross, Sam's Club/gas, Tires+, Walgreens, Walmart/Subway
277	to Dahlia St, Holly St, Monaco St, frontage rd
276b	US 6 E, US 85 N, CO 2, Colorado Blvd, **S** 🅿 Conoco/Subway/dsl, 🍴 Carl's Jr, Domino's, KT'S BBQ, Starbucks
276a	Vasquez Ave, **N** 🅿 ▱▱/Wendy's/dsl/scales/24hr, 🛏 Colonial Motel, Western Inn, 🅾 Blue Beacon, Ford/Mack Trucks, **S** 🅿 7-11, 🍴 Burger King
275c	York St (from eb), **N** 🛏 Colonial Motel
275b	CO 265, Brighton Blvd, Coliseum, **N** 🅿 7-11
275a	Washington St, **N** 🍴 Pizza Hut, **S** 🅿 Conoco, 🍴 McDonald's, Quiznos, Subway
274b a	I-25, N to Cheyenne, S to Colorado Springs

DENVER AREA

Exit	Services
273	Pecos St, **N** 🅾 CO Ranch Mkt, Family$, True Value, **S** 🅿 7-11, 🍴 Quiznos, 🅾 transmissions
272	US 287, Federal Blvd, **N** 🅿 Conoco/dsl, Sinclair, 🍴 Burger King, Goodtimes Burgers, Little Caesar's, McCoy's Rest., McDonald's, Pizza Hut, Rico Pollo, Subway, Taco Bell, Village Inn, Winchell's, Wendy's, 🛏 Motel 6, 🅾 Advance Parts, $Tree, tires, **S** 🅿 Conoco/Circle K, 🍴 El Padrino Mexican, Popeye's, Starbucks, 🛏 Howard Johnson
271b	Lowell Blvd, Tennyson St (from wb)
271a	CO 95, **S** funpark
270	Sheridan Blvd, **N** 🅿 Shell/dsl, **S** 🍴 El Paraiso Mexican, 🅾 Family$, Firestone/auto, Radio Shack, fun park, repair
269b	I-76, E (from eb), to Ft Morgan, Ft Collins
269a	CO 121, Wadsworth Blvd, **N** 🅿 Conoco, 7-11, Shell, 🍴 Alamos Verdes Mexican, Anthony's Pizza, Applebee's, Bennet's BBQ, Burger King, Chipotle Mexican, Coldstone, El Tapatio, Fazoli's, Gunther Toody's Diner, IHOP, Kukoro Japanese, LoneStar Steaks, McDonald's/playplace, Red Robin, Ruby Tuesday, Smiling Moose Deli, Starbucks, Subway, Taco Bell, TX Roadhouse, 🅾 Advance Parts, Brakes+, Costco/gas, Discount Tire, $Tree, Goodyear/auto, Home Depot, Lowe's, Office Depot, Petsmart, Radio Shack, Sam's Club, Tires+, city park, mall, urgent care
267	CO 391, Kipling St, Wheat Ridge, **N** 🅿 Conoco, Shell/Carl's Jr/Circle K/dsl, 🍴 Burger King, Einstein Bros, Furr's Dining, Jack-in-the-Box, Lil Nick's Pizza, Margarita's Mexican, Panda Express, Qdoba, Quiznos, Starbucks, Subway, 🛏 American Inn, Motel 6, 🅾 Cadillac/Chevrolet, Chrysler/Jeep, GNC, NAPA, 7-11, Target, Verizon, repair, vet, **S** 🅿 Conoco/Circle K, Phillips 66, Shell, 🍴 Pizza Hut/Taco Bell, Smokin' Joe's Grill, Village Inn, Winchell's, 🛏 Affordable Inn, Best Value Inn, Comfort Inn, Holiday Inn Express, Ramada, 🅾 Ketelesen RV Ctr
266	CO 72, W 44th Ave, Ward Rd, Wheat Ridge, **N** 🅿 Conoco/dsl, 🅾 transmissions, **S** 🅿 Shamrock/dsl, TA/rest./scales/dsl/24hr/@, 🛏 Howard Johnson, 🅾 RV America
265	CO 58, W (from wb), to Golden, Central City
264	Youngfield St, W 32nd Ave, **N** 🅿 Conoco/Circle K, 🍴 Denny's, GoodTimes Burgers, 🛏 La Quinta, **S** 🍴 Abrusci's Italian, Chili's, DQ, McDonald's, Old Chicago Pizza, Pizza Hut/Taco Bell, Qdoba, SmashBurger, Starbucks, Subway, 🅾 Camping World RV Ctr, King's Sooper/24hr, Petsmart, Tuesday Morning, Walgreens, Walmart
263	Denver West Blvd, **N** 🛏 Marriott/rest., **S** 🍴 Coldstone, Jamba Juice, Keg Steaks, Macaroni Grill, McGrath's Fishouse, Mimi's Cafe, Qdoba, 🅾 Barnes&Noble, Best Buy, Office Depot, Old Navy, Whole Foods Mkt, same as 262
262	US 40 E, W Colfax, Lakewood, **N** 🅿 Sinclair/dsl, 🍴 Jack-in-the-Box, Little Ricky's Cafe, Subway, 🛏 Hampton Inn, 🅾 Buick/GMC, Camping World RV Ctr, Chrysler/Jeep, Dodge, Home Depot, Honda, Hyundai, Kohl's, NAPA, PetCo, Staples, Subaru, U-Haul, transmissions, vet, **S** 🅿 Shell/Circle K/dsl/LP, 🍴 Chipotle Mexican, Hops Brewery, Jamba Juice, Mimi's Cafe, On-the-Border, Outback Steaks, Pei Wei Asian, Quiznos, Wendy's, 🛏 Courtyard, Days Inn/rest., Holiday Inn, Mtn View Inn, Residence Inn, 🅾 Chevrolet, Lexus, Old Navy, Target, Toyota, mall, same as 263

WHEAT RIDGE

LAKEWOOD

Copyright 2012 - The Next Exit®

INTERSTATE 70 CONT'D

E

W

Exit	Services
261	US 6, E (from eb), W 6th Ave, to Denver
260	CO 470, to Colo Springs
259	CO 26, Golden, **N** ⓖ Conoco, ⌂ Hampton Inn (2mi), ⊙ Heritage Sq Funpark, **S** Music Hall, to Red Rocks SP
257mm	**runaway truck ramp eb**
256	Lookout Mtn, **N** to Buffalo Bill's Grave
254	Genesee, Lookout Mtn, **N** to Buffalo Bill's Grave, **S** ⓖ Conoco/Genesee Store, LP, ⑪ Chart House Rest., Christie's Rest., Genesee Towne Cafe, Guido's Pizza, ⊙ vet
253	Chief Hosa, **S** RV Camping, phone
252	(251 from eb), CO 74, Evergreen Pkwy, **S** ⓖ Conoco, ⑪ Burger King, El Rancho Rest., McDonald's, Qdoba, Smiling Moose Deli, Subway, ⌂ Quality Suites, ⊙ Big O Tire, Home Depot, King's Sooper, Walmart, Echo Mtn Ski Area
248	(247 from eb), Beaver Brook, Floyd Hill, **S** antiques
244	US 6, to CO 119, to Golden, Central City, Eldora Ski Area
243	Hidden Valley
242mm	tunnel
241b a	rd 314, Idaho Springs West, **N** ⓖ Conoco/McDonald's/dsl, Sinclair, Shell/dsl, Western/dsl/e85, ⑪ Carl's Jr, Cherry Blossom Chinese, Marion's Rest., Quiznos, Smokin' Yards BBQ, Starbucks, Subway, Wildfire Rest., ⌂ Argo Inn, Columbine Inn, H&H Motel, Idaho Springs Hotel, JC Motel, Marion's Rest., 6&40 Motel, ⊙ CarQuest, Safeway Foods/Drug, USPO
240	CO 103, Mt Evans, **N** ⓖ Kum&Go/dsl, Shell, Sinclair/dsl, ⑪ Azteca Mexican, Beaujo's Pizza, Buffalo Rest., Jiggie's Cafe, Main St Rest., Mangia Italian, Picci Pizza, Tommy Knocker Grill, 2 Bros Deli, West Winds Cafe, same as 241, **S** to Mt Evans
239	Idaho Springs, **S** ⊙ camping
238	Fall River Rd, to St Mary's Glacier
235	Dumont (from wb)
234	Downeyville, Dumont, **N** ⓖ Conoco/Subway/dsl, ⑪ Burger King, Starbucks, ⊙ ski rentals, **weigh sta both lanes**
233	Lawson (from eb)
232	US 40 W, to Empire, **N** to Berthoud Pass, Rocky Mtn NP, Winterpark/Sol Vista ski areas
228	Georgetown, **S** ⓖ Conoco/Subway/dsl, Shell/dsl, Valero, ⑪ Mountain Buzz Cafe, ⌂ Chateau Chamonix, Super 8, ⊙ **visitors ctr**
226.5mm	scenic overlook eb
226	Georgetown, Silver Plume Hist Dist, **N** ⊙ Buckley Bros Mkt, repair
221	Bakerville
220mm	Arapahoe NF eastern boundary
219mm	parking area (eb only)
218	no services
216	US 6 W, Loveland Valley, Loveland Basin, ski areas
214mm	Eisenhower/Johnson Tunnel, elev 11013
213mm	parking area eb
205	US 6 E, CO 9 N, Dillon, Silverthorne, **N** ⓖ Conoco/dsl, 7-11, Shell/7-11/dsl, ⑪ Asian Oven, China Gourmet, Chipotle Mexican, Dominos, Mint Cafe, Mtn Lyon Café, Murphy's Cafe, Quiznos, Village Inn, Wendy's, ⌂ Days Inn, 1st Interstate Inn, La Quinta, Luxury Suites, Quality Inn, Silver Inn, ⊙ Buick/Cadillac/Chevrolet/GMC,

IDAHO SPRINGS

205	Continued CarQuest, Chrysler/Dodge/Jeep, Ford, Old Navy, Outlets/famous brands, Subaru, Target, TrueValue, **S** ⓖ Shamrock, Shell/dsl, ⑪ Arby's, Bamboo Garden, Blue Moon Deli, Burger King, Dam Brewery/Rest., DQ, Fiesta Mexican, Jimmy John's, McDonald's, Nick'n Willy's Pizza, Noodles&Co, Pizza Hut, Qdoba, Red Mtn Grill, Ruby Tuesday, SmashBurger, Smiling Moose Cafe, Starbucks, Subway, Sunshine Cafe, ⌂ Comfort Suites, Dillon Inn, Super 8, ⊙ City Mkt Foods/gas, Outlets/famous brands, Natural Grocery, Tuesday Morning, Verizon, Walgreens, vet
203.5mm	scenic overlook both lanes
203	CO 9 S, to Breckenridge, Frisco, **S** ⓖ Conoco/Wendy's/dsl, 7-11, Shell, Valero/dsl, ⑪ A&W, KFC, Carlos Miguel's Mexican, Hacienda Real Mexican, Q4U BBQ, Starbucks, Subway, Szechuan Chinese, Taco Bell, ⌂ Alpine Inn, Best Western, Holiday Inn, Ramada Ltd, Summit Inn, ⊙ Big O Tire, NAPA, Radio Shack, Safeway Foods, Walmart/McDonald's, vet, to Breckenridge Ski Area, RV Resort (6mi)
201	Main St, Frisco, **S** ⓖ Loaf N' Jug, ⑪ Alpine Deli, Backcountry Brew Pub, Boatyard Pizzaria, Butterhorn Cafe, Cowboy Pizza, Log Cabin Cafe, Lost Cajun Rest., Rainbow Ct Rest., ⌂ Blue Spruce Inn, Frisco Lodge, Hotel Frisco, Snowshoe Motel, ⊙ Bighorn Reservations, RV camping, museum/visitor info, USPO, to Breckenridge Ski Area
198	Officers Gulch, emergency callbox
196mm	scenic area (wb only)
195	CO 91 S, to Leadville, **1 mi S** ⓖ Conoco/dsl, ⑪ Quiznos, ⌂ Copper Lodging, ⊙ to Copper Mtn Ski Resort, 190, **S rest area both lanes, full ♿ facilities,** ⑪, ⊼, **litter barrels**
189mm	Vail Pass Summit, elev 10662 ft, parking area both lanes
180	Vail East Entrance, phone, **services 3-4 mi S**
176	Vail, **S** ⊙ Ⓗ, ski info/lodging
173	Vail Ski Area, **N** ⓖ Phillips 66, Shell/dsl, ⑪ Bearfish Grill, Gohanya Chinese, McDonald's, Qdoba, Subway, Taco Bell, Wendy's, ⌂ Holiday Inn, Roost Lodge, ⊙ Ace Hardware, City Mkt Foods/deli, Safeway Food/Drug, 7-11, USPO, **S** ⓖ Conoco/dsl/LP, ⌂ Black Bear Inn, Marriott/Streamside Hotel
171	US 6 W, US 24 E, to Minturn, Leadville, **N** ⊙ Ski Cooper ski area, **2 mi S** ⓖ Shell, ⑪ Magusto's Italian, Minturn Steaks, ⌂ Minturn Inn, ⊙ RV Camping, USPO
169	Eaglevale, (from wb), no return
168	William J. Post Blvd, **S** ⑪ Zaccazai Cafe, ⊙ Home Depot, Walmart/McDonald's

FRISCO

🅖 = gas 🍴 = food 🛌 = lodging 🅞 = other Copyright 2012 - The Next Exit®

INTERSTATE 70 CONT'D

Exit	Services
167	Avon, **N** 🅖 Conoco/7-11/dsl, Shell, 🍴 Pizza Hut, 🅞 Goodyear, vet, **S** 🍴 Burger King, Denny's, Domino's, Fiesta Jalisco Mexican, Panda City, Pazzo's Pizza, Starbucks, Subway, 🛌 Avon Ctr Lodge, Christie Lodge, Comfort Inn, Sheraton, Westin, 🅞 City Mkt/drugs, GNC, Office Depot, to Beaver Creek/Arrowhead Ski, ski info, urgent care, USPO
163	Edwards, **S rest area both lanes, full** 🅰 **facilities,** 🅰, **litter barrel, RV dump,** 🅖 Conoco/dsl, Shell/Wendy's/dsl, 🍴 Cafe Milano, Cosmos BBQ, Dish Cafe, Gashouse Rest., Gore Range Brewery, Marble Slab Creamery, Marko's Pizza, Old Forge Pizza, Smiling Moose, Subway, Zino's Italian, 🛌 Riverwalk Inn, 🅞 Villiage Mkt, to Arrowhead Ski Area, USPO
162mm	scenic area eb
159mm	Eagle River
157	CO 131 N, Wolcott, **N** to Steamboat Ski Area
147	Eagle, **N** 🅖 Kum&Go/pizza/dsl, 🍴 Burger King, Starbucks, 🛌 AmericInn, Comfort Inn, Holiday Inn Express, 🅞 City Mkt Foods, **S** 🅖 Conoco/dsl, Sinclair/Subway/dsl, 🍴 Eagle Diner, El Pariente, Gourmet China, Grand Ave Grill, Moe's Original BBQ, Pazzo's Pizzaria, Taco Bell, Wendy's, 🛌 Eagle Lodge&Suites, Silverleaf Suites, 🅞 Costco/gas (3mi), USPO, **rest area both lanes, full** 🅰 **facilities, info**
140	Gypsum, **S** 🅖 Kum&Go, Shell, 🍴 Columbine Mkt Deli, Ritten House Rest., Salsa's Mexican, 🅞 auto/truck repair, 🅰, USPO, **3 mi S** River Dance Resort camping
134mm	Colorado River
133	Dotsero, **N** 🅞 River Dance RV Camping (3mi)
129	Bair Ranch, **S rest area both lanes, full** 🅰 **facilities, picnic tables, litter barrels, petwalk**
128.5mm	parking area eb
127mm	tunnel wb
125mm	tunnel
125	to Hanging Lake (no return eb)
123	Shoshone (no return eb)
122.5mm	exit to river (no return eb)
121	to Hanging Lake, Grizzly Creek, **S rest area both lanes, full** 🅰 **facilities, picnic tables, litter barrels**
119	**No Name, rest area both lanes, full** 🅰 **facilities), RV camping, rafting**
118mm	tunnel
116	CO 82 E, to Aspen, Glenwood Springs, **N** 🅖 Conoco/dsl, Shell/dsl, 🍴 Chomp's Rest., Fiesta Guadalajara, KFC, Qdoba, Subway, Tequilas Rest., Village Inn, 🛌 Best Western, Glenwood Springs Inn, Hampton Inn, Holiday Inn Express, Hotel Colorado, Ramada Inn, Silver Spruce Motel, Starlight Motel, 🅞 Land Rover, NAPA, Toyota, Hot Springs Bath, funpark, **0-2 mi S** 🅖 Conoco, Phillips 66/dsl, Shamrock/dsl, Shell, Sinclair, 🍴 Arby's, Bears Loft Rest., China Town, Domino's, Little Ceasar's, McDonald's, 19th St Diner, Pizza Hut, Rib City Grill, Starbucks, Subway, Taco Bell, Taipei Japanese, Wendy's, 🛌 Caravan Inn, Cedar Lodge, Frontier Lodge, Hotel Denver, 🅞 🅷, Alpine Tire, AutoZone, B.Thornal DDS, City Mkt Foods, Curves, NAPA, Office Depot, Rite Aid, Safeway Foods, 7-11, Walmart, USPO, city park, to Ski Sunlight
115mm	**rest area eb, full** 🅰 **facilities,** 🅰, **litter barrels**
114	W Glenwood Springs, **N** 🅖 Phillips 66/dsl, 7-11, Shell, 🍴 Burger King, Jilbirtito's Mexican, Porker's BBQ, Rte

Exit	Services
114	Continued 6 Grill House, Vicco's Charcoal Burger, 🛌 Affordable Inn, Best Value Inn, Ponderosa Motel, Red Mtn Inn, Rodeway Inn, 🅞 AT&T, Big O Tire, Checker Parts, Ford, JC Penney, K-Mart, Radio Shack, Staples, Subaru, Verizon, mall, **S** 🅖 Conoco/DQ/dsl, 🍴 Chili's, Moe's SW Grill, Russo's Pizza, Starbucks, 🛌 Courtyard, Glenwood Suites, Quality Inn, Residence Inn, 🅞 Audi/VW, Harley-Davidson, Lowe's, PetCo, Target, urgent care
111	South Canyon
109	Canyon Creek
108mm	parking area both lanes
105	New Castle, **N** 🅖 Conoco/dsl, Kum&Go/dsl, 🍴 McDonald's, New Castle Diner, Subway, 🛌 Rodeway Inn, 🅞 City Mkt Foods/deli, Elk Creek Campground (4mi), **S** 🅞 Best Hardware
97	Silt, **N** 🅖 Conoco/dsl/24hr, Kum&Go, Phillips 66/dsl, 🛌 Red River Inn, 🅞 auto repair, to Harvey Gap SP, **S** 🍴 Red Brick BBQ, 🛌 Holiday Inn Express, Ruby River Cabins, 🅞 Heron's Nest RV Park
94	Garfield County 🅰 Rd
90	CO 13 N, Rifle, **N rest area both lanes, full** 🅰 **facilities,** 🅰, **litter barrels, RV dump, NF Info,** 🅖 Conoco, Kum&Go, Phillips 66/dsl, Shell, 🍴 KFC, 🛌 Winchester Motel (1mi), 🅞 USPO, Rifle Gap SP, **S** 🅖 Kum&Go, Phillips 66/Subway/dsl, Shell, 🍴 Burger King, Domino's, Little Caesar's, McDonald's/playplace, Rib City Grill, Sonic, Starbucks, Taco Bell, 🛌 Comfort Inn, Hampton Inn, La Quinta, Red River Inn/rest., Rusty Cannon Motel, 🅞 🅷, Checker Parts, Radio Shack, Walmart/Subway
87	to CO 13, West Rifle
81	Rulison
75	Parachute, **N rest area both lanes, full** 🅰 **facilities, info,** 🅲, 🅰, **litter barrels, petwalk,** 🅖 Sinclair/dsl, Shell/dsl/24hr, 🍴 El Tapatio Mexican, Hong's Garden Chinese, Outlaws Rest., Subway, 🛌 Comfort Inn, Parachute Inn, 🅞 NAPA, Radio Shack, Verizon, USPO, vet, **S** 🅖 Phillips 66/Domino's/dsl, Shell/Wendy's, Sinclair, 🛌 Candlewood Suites, Holiday Inn Express, 🅞 Family$, RV Park (4mi), True Value
63mm	Colorado River
62	De Beque, **N** 🅖 CFN Fuel, Kum&Go/Subway/dsl, 🅞 food, phone, auto repair
50mm	parking area eastbound, Colorado River, tunnel begins eastbound
49mm	Plateau Creek
49	CO 65 S, to CO 330 E, to Grand Mesa, Powderhorn Ski Area
47	Island Acres St RA, **N** CO River SP, RV camping, **S** 🅖 Conoco/rest./dsl
46	Cameo
44	Lp 70 W, to Palisade, **3 mi S** gas, food, lodging
43.5mm	Colorado River
42	US 6, Palisade, **1 mi S** Fruitstand/store, gas, 🛌 Wine Country Inn, 🅞 wineries
37	to US 6, to US 50 S, Clifton, Grand Jct, **0-1 mi S** 🅖 Conoco/dsl, Maverik/dsl, Shamrock/dsl, Sinclair, 🍴 Burger King, Cactus Canyon, Chin Chin Oriental, Dos Hombres, Jimmy Johns, KFC, Little Caesar's, McDonald's/playplace, Papa Johns, Papa Murphy's, Pizza Hut, Qdoba, Sonic, Starbucks, Subway, Taco Bell, Wendy's, 🛌 Best Western, 🅞 Ace Hardware, AutoZone, Checker Parts, City Mkt Food/gas, Curves, Family$, Murdoch's Store, USPO, Walgreens,

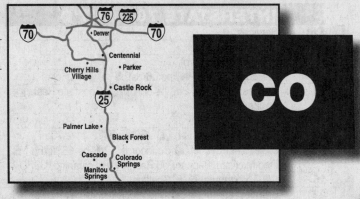

INTERSTATE 70 CONT'D

Exit	Services
37	Continued Walmart (2mi), repair
31	Horizon Dr, Grand Jct, **N** 📯 Shell/dsl, 🍴 Enzo's Pizza, Las Palmas Mexican, Pepper's Rest., Village Inn, Wendy's, 🏨 Best Value Inn, Clarion, Comfort Inn, Courtyard, Grand Vista Hotel, Holiday Inn, La Quinta, Motel 6, Ramada Inn, Residence Inn, ◯ Harley-Davidson, USPO, Zarlingo's Repair, ⟳, **S** 📯 Conoco/Subway/dsl, Shell/dsl, 🍴 Applebee's, Burger King/playland, Denny's, Good Pastures Rest., Herford Steaks, Nick'n Willy's Pizza, Pizza Hut, Sang Garden, Starbucks, Taco Bell, 🏨 Affordable Inn, Best Western, Country Inn, Doubletree Hotel, Mesa Inn, Quality Inn, Super 8, ◯ ⊞ Safeway Food/drug/gas, golf, visitors ctr, to Mesa St Coll, CO NM
28	Redlands Pkwy, 24 Rd, **N** Kenworth, 0-2 mi **S** 🏨 Candlewood Suites, city park, same as 26
26	US 6, US 50, Grand Jct, **N** ◯ Hyundai, Jct, W RV Park, 0-4 mi **S** 📯 Conoco/A&W/dsl, 🍴 Boston's Grill, Burger King, Cafe Rio, Carino's Italian, Carl's Jr, Chick-fil-A, Chili's, Chipotle Mexican, Coldstone, Famous Dave's BBQ, Genghis Grill, Golden Corral, Grand Buffet, IHOP, Jimmy John's, McDonald's/playplace, Olive Garden, Outback Steaks, Papa Murphys, Qdoba, Red Lobster, Red Robin, Schlotzky's, Sonic, Starbucks, Subway, Taco Bell, Wendy's, 🏨 Holiday Inn Express, West Gate Inn, ◯ AutoZone, Barnes&Noble, Best Buy, Big O Tire, Buick/Chevrolet, Cabela's, Chrysler/Dodge/Jeep, City Mkt, $Tree, Ford, Freightliner, Hobby Lobby, Home Depot, Honda, JC Penney, Kohl's, Lowe's, Michael's, Mobile City RV Park, Nissan, Office Depot, Old Navy, PetCo, Petsmart, Rite Aid, Ross, Sam's Club/gas, Scott RV Ctr, Sears/auto, Subaru, Suzuki, Target, Toyota, Verizon, Walmart/McDonald's, mall
19	US 6, CO 340, Fruita, **N** 📯 Conoco/dsl, 🍴 Burger King, Munchie's Burgers/Pizza, 🏨 Balanced Rock Motel, ◯ ⊞ City Mkt Foods/deli/24hr, USPO, Walgreens, **S** Welcome Ctr, **full** ♿ **facilities**, 🚻, 🛒, litter barrels, RV dump, petwalk, 📯 Conoco/Subway/dsl/24hr, Shell/Wendy's/dsl/24hr, 🍴 Dragon Treasure Chinese, El Tapatio Mexican, McDonald's/playplace, Rib City Grill, Taco Bell, 🏨 Comfort Inn, La Quinta, Super 8, ◯ Monument RV Park, Peterbilt/Volvo, Verizon, dinosaur museum, to CO NM, vet
17mm	Colorado River
15	CO 139 N, to Loma, Rangely, **N** to Highline Lake SP, gas/dsl, 🛒
14.5mm	**weigh/check sta both lanes, phones**
11	Mack, 2-3 mi **N** gas/dsl, food
2	Rabbit Valley, to Dinosaur Quarry Trail
0mm	Colorado/Utah state line

INTERSTATE 76

Exit	Services
185mm	I-76 begins/ends on NE I-80, Exit 102
184mm	Colorado/Nebraska state line
180	US 385, Julesburg, **N** 📯 *FLYING J*/dsl/LP/rest./24hr, Shell, 🍴 Subway, 🏨 Budget Host, ◯ ⊞ **Welcome Ctr/rest area both lanes, full** ♿ **facilities, info, RV dump, S** 📯 Conoco/dsl
172	Ovid, 2 mi **N** food
165	CO 59, to Haxtun, Sedgwick, **N** Lucy's Cafe
155	Red Lion Rd
149	CO 55, to Fleming, Crook, **S** 📯 Sinclair/dsl/café
141	Proctor
134	Iliff
125	US 6, Sterling, 0-3 mi **N** 📯 Cenex/dsl, Mirastar, Sinclair, 🍴 Arby's, Bamboo Garden, Burger King, Domino's, DQ, KFC/LJ Silver, McDonald's, Papa Murphy's, Pizza Hut, River City Grill, Sonic, Subway, Taco Bell, Taco John's, Village Inn, Wendy's, 🏨 Best Western, 1st Interstate Inn, ◯ ⊞ Big O Tire, Chrysler/Dodge/Jeep, $General, $Tree, Ford/Lincoln/Mercury, Home Depot, NAPA, Sun Mart Foods, Walgreens, Walmart, N Sterling SP, museum, st patrol, **rest area both lanes (full handicapped) facilities, picnic tables, litter barrels, petwalk, vending, RV dump, S** 📯 Reata/Quiznos/dsl, 🍴 Country Kitchen, 🏨 Comfort Inn, Ramada Inn, Super 8, Travelodge, ◯ RV Camping
115	CO 63, Atwood, **N** 📯 Sinclair/dsl, ◯ ⊞, **S** 🍴 Steakhouse
102	Merino
95	Hillrose
92	to US 6 E, to US 34, CO 71 S
90b a	CO 71 N, to US 34, Brush, **N** 📯 Tomahawk Trkstp/Shell/rest./dsl/24hr, 🍴 China Buffet, Pizza Hut, Wendy's, 🏨 Econolodge, **S** 📯 Conoco/dsl, 🍴 McDonald's, 🏨 Microtel
89	Hospital Rd, **S** ⊞, golf
86	Dodd Bridge Rd
82	Barlow Rd, **N** 📯 Conoco/dsl, 🍴 Maverick's Grill, 🏨 Comfort Inn, Rodeway Inn, **S** 📯 Mirastar/dsl, Reata/Quiznos/dsl/scales, 🍴 Burger King, ◯ $Tree, Walmart/Subway
80	CO 52, Ft Morgan, **N** ◯ City Park, Golf, RV Camping, **S** 📯 Conoco/dsl/24hr, Shell/dsl, Sinclair/dsl, Western/dsl, 🍴 Arby's, DQ, McDonald's, Sonic, Subway, Taco John's, Wonderful House Chinese, 🏨 Best Western/rest., Central Motel, Days Inn, Super 8, ◯ ⊞ AutoZone, Toyota, Walgreens
79	CO 144, to Weldona, (no wb return)
75	US 34 E, to Ft Morgan, **S** 📯 Shell/Chester's/dsl, 🏨 Clarion, ◯ st patrol
74.5mm	**weigh sta both lanes**
73	Long Bridge Rd
66b	US 34, W (from wb), to Greeley
66a	CO 39, CO 52, to Goodrich, **N** 📯 Phillips 66/dsl, ◯ RV Camping, to Jackson Lake SP, **S** 📯 Sinclair/cafe/dsl/e-85, ◯ **rest area both lanes, full** ♿ **facilities**, 🚻, **litter barrels, petwalk, vending**
64	Wiggins (from eb)
60	to CO 144 E, to Orchard

INTERSTATE 76 CONT'D

Exit	Services
57	rd 91
49	Painter Rd (from wb)
48	to Roggen, **N** ⛽ Phillips 66/dsl, **S** ⊙ USPO
39	Keenesburg, **S** ⛽ Phillips 66/dsl, 🍴 Rooster's Rest., 🛏 Keene Motel
34	Kersey Rd
31	CO 52, Hudson, **N** ⛽ Loves/Subway/Carl's Jr/scales/24hr/dsl, **S** ⛽ Conoco/dsl, Phillips 66/dsl, 🍴 El Faro Mexican, Pepper Pod Rest., ⊙ RV camping, USPO
25	CO 7, Lochbuie, **N** ⛽ Shell/dsl
22	Bromley Lane, **N** ⛽ Shamrock/dsl, 🍴 Wendy's, ⊙ Lowe's, ⊙ 🄷, **S** Barr Lake SP
21	144th Ave, **N** 🍴 Buffalo Wild Wings, Chick-fil-A, Chili's, Heidi's Deli, McDonald's, Quiznos, Subway, 🄷, $Tree, GNC, Home Depot, JC Penney, Kohl's, Michael's, Office Depot, PetsMart, Super Target, Verizon
20	136th Ave, **N** Barr Lake RV Park, same as 21
18	E-470 tollway, to Limon (from wb)
16	CO 2 W, Sable Blvd, Commerce City, **N** ⛽ Shell/diner/dsl/24hr/@, to Denver ✈
12	US 85 N, to Brighton (exits left from eb), Greeley
11	96th Ave, **N** dsl repair, **S** GMC Trucks
10	88th Ave, **N** ⛽ Shell/Blimpie/dsl, 🛏 Holiday Inn Express, Super 8, **S** flea mkt
9	US 6 W, US 85 S, Commerce City, **S** ⛽ Shell/dsl, ⊙ Freightliner, transmissions, st patrol
8	CO 224, 74th Ave (no EZ eb return) **1 mi N** NAPA, **S** ⛽ Shamrock/dsl
6b a	I-270 E, to Limon, to I-25 N, to ✈
5	I-25, N to Ft Collins, S to Colo Springs
4	Pecos St
3	US 287, Federal Blvd, **N** ⛽ Shamrock/dsl, **S** 🍴 Taco House
1b	CO 95, Sheridan Blvd
1a	CO 121, Wadsworth Blvd, **N** ⛽ Conoco, Phillips 66, 7-11/gas, 🍴 Alamos Verdes Mexican, Applebee's, Bennet's BBQ, Burger King, Chipotle Mexican, Coldstone Creamery, Fazoli's, Gunther Toody's Diner, IHOP, Koro Japanese, LoneStar Steaks, McDonald's/playplace, Red Robin, Ruby Tuesday, Starbucks, Subway, Taco Bell, ⊙ Advance Parts, Brakes+, Costco/gas, Discount Tire, $Tree, Goodyear/auto, Home Depot, Lowe's Whse, Office Depot, Petsmart, Radio Shack, Sam's Club, Tires+, mall
0mm	I-76 begins/ends on I-70, exit 269b.

INTERSTATE 225 (DENVER)

Exit	Services
12b a	I-70, W to Denver, E to Limon
10	US 40, US 287, Colfax Ave, **E** ⛽ Conoco/dsl, Phillips 66, 7-11, Shell, Sinclair, 🍴 Arby's, Burger King, Del Taco, DQ, KFC, McDonald's, Pizza Hut/Taco Bell, Popeye's, Starbucks, Subway, Wendy's, Village Inn, ⊙ Aamco, Advance Parts, Chevrolet, Family$, King's Sooper/gas, K-Mart, NAPA, RV camping, Walgreens, **W** ⛽ Conoco/dsl, 🍴 Anthony's, Caribou Coffee, Chipotle Mexican, Noodles&Co, Spicy Pickle, ⊙ 🄷, Curves, U-Haul
9	Co 30, 6th Ave, **E** ⛽ Conoco/dsl, 🍴 Denny's, 🛏 Super 8, ValuePlace Inn, ⊙ Hobby Lobby, **W** ⛽ Phillips 66/dsl, ⊙ 🄷
8	Alameda Ave, **E** ⛽ Conoco, Shamrock, 🍴 Atlanta

Exit	Services
8	Continued Bread, Baja Fresh, Benny's Cafe, BJ's Rest., Chili's, FatBurger, Jamba Juice, L&L BBQ, Macaroni Grill, Mimi's Cafe, Panda Express, Starbucks, TGIFriday, Wingstop, ⊙ Barnes&Noble, Dillards, Gordman's, JC Penney, Macys, Old Navy, Petsmart, Ross, Sears/auto, Super Target, **W** ⛽ Conoco/dsl, Shell/Circle K, ⊙ $Tree
7	Mississippi Ave, Alameda Ave, **E** 🍴 Arby's, Bono's BBQ, Burger King, CiCi's, Chubby's Mexican, ChuckeCheese, Fazoli's, Guadalajara Mexican, Schlotsky's, Sonic, Subway, Village Inn, 🛏 Best Western, Holiday Inn Express, La Quinta, ⊙ Best Buy, Burlington Coats, Home Depot, JoAnn Fabrics, Sam's Club/gas, Tires +, Walmart, **W** 🍴 IHOP, McDonald's, Senor Ric's, Waffle House, ⊙ AutoZone, 7-11, Office Depot, Pepboys, PetCo
5	Iliff Ave, **E** ⛽ 7-11, 🍴 Applebee's, Boston Mkt, Carrabba's, Fuddrucker's, Hibachi Japanese, Joe's Crabshack, Outback Steaks, Rosie's Diner, Ruby Tuesday, Sweet Tomatoes, TX Roadhouse, 🛏 Comfort Inn, Crestwood Suites, Extended Stay Deluxe, Fairfield Inn, Homestead Suites, Motel 6, **W** ⛽ Phillips 66, 🍴 Dragon's Boat, Subway, 🛏 DoubleTree
4	CO 83, Parker Rd, **E** 🛏 Red Lion, ⊙ Cherry Creek SP, **W** ⛽ Phillips 66/dsl, 🍴 Big Burrito, Bent Noodle, DQ, Little Caesars, Popeyes, Starbucks, Subway, Table Steaks, Taco Bell, Wendy's, ⊙ $Tree, Firestone/auto, King Sooper/dsl, 7-11
2b	no services
2	DTC Blvd, Tamarac St, **W** ⛽ Conoco, 🍴 La Fogata Mexican, Quizno's, Sonic, ⊙ Curves, Goodyear, 7-11, vet
1b a	I-25, I-225 begins/ends on I-25, exit 200

INTERSTATE 270 (DENVER)

Exit	Services
4	I-70
3	**N** ⛽ TA/Burger King/Country Pride/Popeye's/Pizza Hut/dsl/24hr/@, **S** ⛽ Sapp Bros/Sinclair/Subway/dsl/@
2b a	US 85, CO 2, Vasquez Ave, **N** 🍴 Arby's, Carls Jr, Chipotle Mexican, GoodTimes Grill, KFC/LJ Silver, McDonald's, Taco John's, Wendy's ⊙ TDS, Walgreens, Walmart
1b	York St
1a	I-76 E, to Ft Morgan
1c	I-25 S, to Denver

CONNECTICUT

INTERSTATE 84

Exit	Services
98mm	Connecticut/Massachusetts state line
74 (97)	CT 171, Holland, **S** 🍴 Traveler's Book Rest., ⊙ RV camping
95mm	weigh sta wb
73 (95)	CT 190, Stafford Springs, **N** ⊙ camping (seasonal), motor speedway, st police
72 (93)	CT 89, Westford, **N** 🛏 Ashford Motel, camping (seasonal)
71 (88)	Ruby Rd, **S** ⛽ TA/Shell/Burger King/Country Fried/dsl/scales/24hr/@, 🛏 Rodeway Inn
70 (86)	CT 32, Willington, **N** ⊙ 🄷, **S** ⛽ Mobil/dsl, Sunoco/dsl, ⊙ RV Camping
85mm	rest area both lanes, full ♿ facilities, info, ⊙, 🏞,

CT

INTERSTATE 84 CONT'D

Exit	Services
85mm	**Continued** **vending, litter barrels, petwalk, campers**
69 (83)	CT 74, to US 44, Willington, **S** gas, food, phone, RV camping, st police
68 (81)	CT 195, Tolland, **N** 🅰 Gulf/dsl, Mobil, 🍴 Dunkin Donuts, Papa T's Rest., Subway, 🅾 NAPA, RV camping, **S** 🅰 Citgo, 🅾 Big Y Foods, Radio Shack
67 (77)	CT 31, Rockville, **N** 🅰 Mobil, Shell, 🍴 Burger King, China Taste, McDonald's, Subway, Theo's Rest., Tim Horton, 🅾 🏥, RV Camping, **S** Nathan Hale Mon
66 (76)	Tunnel Rd, Vernon
65 (75)	CT 30, Vernon Ctr, **N** 🅰 Mobil/24hr, Shell, 🍴 Brick Oven Pizza, Burger King, KFC, Lotus Rest., Rein's Deli, Top Fuji, Vernon Diner, 🛏 Comfort Inn, Howard Johnson, 🅾 CarQuest, Firestone, K-Mart, Stop&Shop/gas, Vernon Drug
64 (74)	Vernon Ctr, **N** 🅰 Mobil/24hr, Sunoco, 🍴 Angellino's Italian, Anthony's Pizza, Denny's, Dunkin Donuts, Friendly's, McDonald's, 99 Rest., Rita's Custard, Taco Bell, Wood'n Tap, 🛏 Holiday Inn Express, 🅾 AutoZone, CVS Drug, $Tree, Goodyear/auto, PriceChopper, Staples, TJ Maxx, vet, **S** 🛏 Quality Inn
63 (72)	CT 30, CT 83, Manchester, S Windsor, **N** 🍴 Applebee's, Azteca Mexican, Dunkin Donuts, McDonald's, HomeTown Buffet, Longhorn Steaks, Outback Steaks, Panera Bread, Red Robin, Starbucks, TGIFriday's, 🛏 Courtyard, Residence Inn, 🅾 AT&T, Best Buy, Dick's, JC Penney, Macy's, Marshall's, Michael's, Sears/auto, Walgreens, Walmart, same as 62, **S** 🅰 BP, Shell/24hr, Sunoco, Xtra, 🍴 Shea's Grill, 🛏 Best Value Inn, Extended Stay America, Super 8, 🅾 🏥, Big Y Mkt, Hyundai, Kohl's, Toyota/Scion
62 (71)	Buckland St, **N** 🅰 Mobil/Dunkin Donuts/dsl, 🍴 Boston Mkt, Bugaboo Creek Steaks, Chili's, Friendly's, Hooters, John Harvard's Brewhouse, KFC, Olive Garden, Pizza Hut/Taco Bell, 🛏 Fairfield Inn, 🅾 Home Depot, Jo-Ann Fabrics, Lowe's, Michael's, PetsMart, Sam's Club, Target, mall, same as 63, **S** 🅰 Citgo/repair, Xtra, 🍴 Burger King, Carraba's, ChuckeCheese, Golden Dragon, McDonald's, Randy's Pizza, Subway, TX Roadhouse, Wendy's, 🅾 BJ's Whse/gas, Firestone/auto, GNC, Honda, USPO
61 (70)	I-291 W, to Windsor
60 (69)	US 6, US 44, Burnside Ave (from eb)
59 (68)	I-384 E, Manchester
58 (67)	Roberts St, Burnside Ave, **N** 🍴 Margarita's Grill, 🛏 Comfort Inn, Holiday Inn, **S** 🅰 Sunoco, 🍴 Dunkin Donuts, 🅾 Cabelas
57 (66)	CT 15 S, to I-91 S, Charter Oak Br
56 (65)	Governor St, E Hartford, **S** 🔄
55 (64)	CT 2 E, New London, downtown
54 (63)	Old State House, **N** 🅾 Ford, Lincoln/Mercury
53 (62)	CT Blvd (from eb), **S** 🛏 Sheraton
52 (61)	W Main St (from eb), downtown
51 (60)	I-91 N, to Springfield
50 (59.8)	to I-91, S (from wb), **N** 🛏 Crowne Plaza, **S** 🛏 Hilton, Residence Inn
48 (59.5)	Asylum St , downtown, **N** 🛏 Crowne Plaza, **S** 🛏 Holiday Inn Express, 🅾 🏥
47 (59)	Sigourney St, downtown, **N** Hartford Seminary, Mark Twain House
46 (58)	Sisson St, downtown, UConn Law School
45 (57)	Flatbush Ave (exits left from wb)
44 (56.5)	Prospect Ave, **N** 🅰 Mobil, Shell/dsl, 🍴 Burger King, D'angelo's, Gold Roc Diner/24hr, HomeTown Buffet, McDonald's, Prospect Pizza, Wendy's, 🅾 ShopRite Foods
43 (56)	Park Rd, W Hartford, **N** to St Joseph Coll
42 (55)	Trout Brk Dr (exits left from wb), to Elmwood
41 (54)	S Main St American School for the Deaf
40 (53)	CT 71, New Britain Ave, **S** 🅰 Shell, Sunoco, 🍴 Brio Grill, Burger King, CA Pizza, China Pan, Dunkin Donuts,

E ↑↓ **W** **VERNON CTR** **WINDSOR**

HARTFORD

CT

INTERSTATE 84 CONT'D

E ↕ W

Exit	Services
40 (53)	Continued McDonald's, Olive Garden, Red Robin, Pf Chang's, Starbucks, Subway, Wendy's, 🛏 Courtyard, 🅞 Barnes&Noble, Best Buy, JC Penney, Macy's, Nordstrom, Office Depot, Old Navy, PetCo, Radio Shack, Sears/auto, Target, TJ Maxx, Trader Joe's, mall
39a (52)	CT 9 S, to New Britain, Newington, S 🅷
39 (51.5)	CT 4, Farmington, N 🅷
38 (51)	US 6, W (from wb), Bristol, N 🅗 same as 37
37 (50)	Fienemann Rd, to US 6 W, N 🅖 Shell, 🍴 Dunkin Donuts, Stonewell Rest., Subway, 🛏 Hampton Inn, Marriott, S 🛏 Extended Stay Deluxe
36 (49)	Slater Rd (exits left from eb), S 🅷
35 (48)	CT 72, to CT 9 (exits left from both lanes), New Britain, S 🅷
34 (47)	CT 372, Crooked St, N 🅖 Citgo/dsl, Sunoco, 🍴 Applebee's, Friendly's, McDonald's, Starbucks, 🛏 Fairfield Inn, 🅞 Big Y Mkt, Ford/Lincoln/Mercury, Kohl's, Lowe's, Marshall's, Old Navy, Petsmart, VW
33 (46)	CT 72 W, to Bristol (exits left from eb)
32 (45)	Ct 10, Queen St, Southington, N 🅖 Citgo, Cumberland Farms, Shell/dsl, 🍴 Beijing Chinese, Bertucci's, Burger King, Chili's, D'angelo's, Denny's, Dunkin Donuts, JD's Rest., KFC, McDonald's, Outback Steaks, Puerto Vallarta, Randy's Pizza, Ruby Tuesday, Starbucks, Subway, Taco Bell, 🛏 Motel 6, 🅞 🅷, CVS Drug, $Tree, GNC, PetCo, Radio Shack, ShopRite Foods, Staples, TJ Maxx, TownFair Tire, S 🅖 Hess, Mobil, Sunoco, 🍴 Aziagos Italian, Brannigan's Ribs, Fish&Chops, Friendly's, Rita's Custard, Subway, TD Homer's Grill, Wendy's, Wood'n Tap Grill, 🛏 Holiday Inn Express, Knights Inn, Red Carpet Inn, 🅞 Advance Parts, Firestone, PriceChopper Foods, Rite Aid, Walmart
31 (44)	CT 229, West St, N 🅖 Mobil, Sunoco/dsl/24hr, 🅞 Lowe's, Target, S 🅖 Citgo, Quick Fuel, 🍴 Dunkin Donuts, Giovanni's Pizza, Mack's Pizza, Subway, 🛏 Residence Inn
30 (43)	Marion Ave, W Main, Southington, N ski area, S 🅖 Mobil, 🅞 🅷
29 (42)	CT 10, Milldale (exits left from wb)
41.5mm	rest area eb, full ♿ facilities, info, 🍴, 🚻, litter barrels, petwalk
28 (41)	CT 322, Marion, S 🅖 Mobil, Sam's Gas, TA/Pizza Hut/Popeye's/Taco Bell/dsl/scales/24hr/@, 🍴 Anna's Diner, Blimpie, Burger King, DQ, Dunkin Donuts, Manor Inn Rest., Young Young Chinese, 🛏 Comfort Suites, EconoLodge, 🅞 Home Depot, repair
27 (40)	I-691 E, to Meriden
26 (38)	CT 70, to Cheshire, N 🍴 Blackie's Cafe
25a (37)	Austin Rd (from eb), N 🅖 Winzz/dsl, 🛏 Holiday Inn, 🅞 Costco/gas, Kohl's, funpark
25 (36)	Harper's Ferry Rd, Reed Dr, Scott Rd, E Main St, N 🅖 Gulf/dsl, Mobil/dsl, 🍴 Dunkin Donuts, S 🅖 Gulf, 🍴 Burger King, Friendly's, McDonald's, Nino's Rest., Subway, 🛏 Ramada Inn, Super 8, 🅞 Aldi Foods, BJ's Whse/gas, Cadillac/Chevrolet, CVS Drug, Super Stop&Shop/gas
23 (33.5)	CT 69, Hamilton Ave, N 🍴 Bertucci's, Chili's, HomeTown Buffet, McDonald's, Olive Garden, TGIFriday's, 🅞 🅷, Barnes&Noble, JC Penney, Macy's, Michael's, Sears/auto, Walgreens, mall, S 🅖 Shell, 🍴 Dunkin Donuts

Exit	Services
22 (33)	Baldwin St, Waterbury, N 🅖 Gulf, 🛏 Courtyard, 🅞 🅷 same as 23
21 (33)	Meadow St, Banks St, N 🅖 Citgo, 7-11, S 🅖 Sunoco, dsl/24hr, 🅞 Home Depot, PetsMart
20 (32)	CT 8, N (exits left from eb), to Torrington
19 (32)	CT 8, S (exits left from wb), to Bridgeport
18 (32)	W Main, Highland Ave, N 🍴 Lena's Deli, 🛏 Hampton Inn, 🅞 🅷, CVS Drug
17 (30)	CT 63, CT 64, to Watertown, Naugatuck, N 🍴 Maggie McFly's Rest., S 🅖 Mobil/dsl, 🍴 Leo's Rest., Maples Rest., Subway
16 (25)	CT 188, to Middlebury, N 🅖 Mobil, 🍴 Patty's Pantry Deli, 🛏 Crowne Plaza
15 (22)	US 6 E, CT 67, Southbury, N 🅖 Mobil, Shell/repair, 🍴 Dunkin Donuts, Friendly's (1mi), McDonald's, 🛏 Heritage Hotel, 🅞 K-Mart, Stop&Shop, S 🅞 to Kettletown SP
14 (20)	CT 172, to, S Britain, N 🅖 Mobil/24hr, 🍴 Dunkin Donuts, Maggie McFly's, Miranda's Pizza, S 🅞 st police
20mm	motorist callboxes begin eb, end wb
13 (19)	River Rd (from eb), to Southbury
11 (16)	CT 34, to New Haven
10 (15)	US 6 W, Newtown, N 🍴 Iron Bridge Rest., Katherine's Kitchen, Subway, S 🅖 Mobil/dsl, 🍴 Blue Colony Diner, Pizza Palace, Starbucks, 🅞 🅷
9 (11)	CT 25, to Hawleyville, S gas Citgo/dsl, loding Howard Johnson, Microtel, Stony Hill Inn, 🅞 vet
8 (8)	Newtown Rd, N 🅖 Global, Mobil/dsl, 🍴 Outback Steaks, 🛏 La Quinta, 🅞 Best Buy, Harley-Davidson, Lowe's, Volvo, S 🅖 Shell, Sunoco, 🍴 Bangkok Thai, Bertucci's Italian, Boston Mkt, Burger King, Chili's, Denny's, Dunkin Donuts, Friendly's, Ichiro Steaks, McDonald's, Subway, Taco Bell, 🛏 Best Western, Hampton Inn, Holiday Inn/rest., Quality Inn, 🅞 Buick, Chrysler/Jeep, Goodyear/auto, Marshall's, Radio Shack, Staples, Stop&Shop, Target, Town Fair Tire, Walmart
7 (7)	US 7N/202E, to Brookfield, (exits left from eb), New Milford, 1 exit N on Federal Rd 🅖 Mobil, Sunoco, 🍴 Arby's, 5 Guys Burgers, KFC, Pizza Hut, Starbucks, Subway, Wendy's, 🅞 CVS Drug, Ford, GNC, Harley-Davidson, Home Depot, Kohl's, Michael's, Stew Leonards, Subaru, Town Fair Tire, Toyota/Scion, Walgreens, mall
6 (6)	CT 37 (from wb), New Fairfield, N 🅖 Gulf, 🍴 Burger King, Castello's Italian, Dunkin Donuts, Elmer's Diner, KFC, McDonald's, Moon Star Chinese, 🅞 A&P Foods, $Tree, Radio Shack, Rite Aid, S 🅖 Citgo, Valero, 🍴 KFC
5 (5)	CT 37, CT 39, CT 53, Danbury, N 🅖 Gulf/dsl, Shell, 🛏 Best Value Inn, S 🅖 Mobil, 🍴 Dunkin Donuts, Taco Bell, 🅞 🅷, to Putnam SP
4 (4)	US 6 W/202 W, Lake Ave, N 🅖 Gulf/dsl, Shell/dsl, Xtra, 🍴 Dunkin Donuts, McDonald's, 🛏 Ethan Allen Hotel, Maron Hotel, Super 8, 🅞 CVS Drug, Stop&Shop Foods, S 🅖 Sunoco, 🛏 Residence Inn, to mall
3 (3)	US 7, S (exits left from wb), to Norwalk, S 🅖 Mobil, 🍴 Buffalo Wild Wings, ChuckeCheese, Coldstone, Olive Garden, Red Lobster, 🅞 Barnes&Noble, JC Penney, Macy's, Sears/auto, mall
2b a (1)	US 6, US 202, Mill Plain Rd, N 🍴 Desert Moon Café, Starbucks, Tuscanero's Pizza, 🛏 Comfort Suites, Hilton Garden, Super 8, 🅞 Rite Aid, Staples, Trader Joe's, S Welcome Ctr/weigh sta, full ♿ facilities, info, 🚻, litter barrels, petwalk, to Old Ridgebury, 🛏 SpringHill Suites

SOUTHINGTON

MARION

SOUTHBURY

INTERSTATE 84 CONT'D

Exit	Services
1 (0)	Saw Mill Rd, **N** 🛏 Comfort Suites (2mi), Hilton Garden, Maron Hotel
0mm	Connecticut/New York state line

INTERSTATE 91

Exit	Services
58mm	Connecticut/Massachusetts state line
49 (57)	US 5, to Longmeadow, MA, **E** 🚗 Pride, Valero, 🍽 McDonald's, 🛏 Holiday Inn, 🅾 repair, **W** 🚗 Sunoco, 🍽 Baco's Pizza, Cloverleaf Café, DQ, Dunkin Donuts, Pizza Palace, 🅾 Dodge
48 (56)	CT 220, Elm St, **E** 🚗 Mobil, 🍽 Arby's, Burger King, Denny's, Dunkin Donuts, Friendly's, McDonald's, Oyama Japanese, Outback Steaks, Panera Bread, Ruby Tuesday, TGIFriday's, Wendy's, 🅾 AAA, AutoZone, Best Buy, Costco/gas, Dick's, $Tree, Macy's, Home Depot, Honda, Hyundai, Kohl's, Nissan, Radio Shack, Sears/auto, Target, TownFair Tire, Toyota, VW, same as 47
47 (55)	CT 190, to Hazardville, **E** 🚗 Mobil, 🍽 D'angelo, Dunkin Donuts, Hazard Grille, McDonald's, 99 Rest., Olive Garden, Pizza Hut, Red Robin, Starbucks, Taco Bell, 🛏 Hampton Inn, Motel 6, Red Roof Inn, 🅾 H, Advance Parts, Aldi Foods, AutoZone, Barnes&Noble, Big Y Foods, CVS Drug, Ford, Goodyear, Marshall's, Michael's, NAPA, Office Depot, PetCo, Rite Aid, ShopRite, Staples, Stop&Shop Foods, Walgreens, mall, same as 48
46 (53)	US 5, King St, to Enfield, **E** 🚗 Mobil, 🍽 Astro's Rest., **W** 🍽 Hacienda Del Sol, 🛏 Super 8
45 (51)	CT 140, Warehouse Point, **E** 🚗 Shell, 🍽 Blimpie, Burger King, Cracker Barrel, Dunkin Donuts, Friendly's, Jake's Burgers, Jimmy Chen's Chinese, Sofia's Rest., 🛏 Comfort Inn, 🅾 Big Y Foods, Walmart/Subway, to Trolley Museum, **W** 🚗 Sunoco/dsl/24hr, 🛏 Clarion, 🅾 Advance Parts
44 (50)	US 5 S, to E Windsor, **E** 🚗 Sunoco/dsl, 🍽 Dunkin Donuts, E Windsor Diner, KFC, Taco Bell, Tj's Rest., Wendy's, 🛏 Holiday Inn Express
49mm	Connecticut River
42 (48)	CT 159, Windsor Locks, **E** Longview RV Ctr, **W** same as 41
41 (47)	Center St (exits with 39), **W** 🍽 Ad's Pizzaria, 🛏 Bradley Hotel
40 (46.5)	CT 20, **W** Old New-Gate Prison, 🛬
39 (46)	Kennedy Rd (exits with 41), Community Rd, **W** 🚗 Shell/dsl/24hr, 🍽 Charkoon, Chili's, 🅾 $Tree, GNC, PetCo, Radio Shack, Stop&Shop Foods, Target
38 (45)	CT 75, to Poquonock, Windsor Area, **E** 🚗 Mobil/dsl, 🍽 Buffalo Wild Wings, China Sea, Dunkin Donuts, Pizzarama, Subway, 🅾 to Ellsworth Homestead, AT&T, PriceChopper Foods, Verizon, **W** 🍽 River City Grill, 🛏 Courtyard, Hilton Garden, Hyatt Summerfield Suites, Marriott
37 (44)	CT 305, Bloomfield Ave, Windsor Ctr, **E** 🚗 Mobil/dsl, 🍽 McDonald's, **W** 🚗 Sunoco, 🛏 Residence Inn
36 (43)	CT 178, Park Ave, to, W Hartford
35b (41)	CT 218, to Bloomfield, to, S Windsor, **E** gas/dsl, food
35a	I-291 E, to Manchester
34 (40)	CT 159, Windsor Ave, **E** 🚗 Shell/dsl, **W** 🚗 Citgo/dsl, 🛏 Flamingo Inn, RanchHouse Rest., 🅾 H
33 (39)	Jennings Rd, Weston St, **E** 🅾 Cadillac, Jaguar, VW, **W** 🚗 Mobil, Sunoco/dsl, 🍽 Burger King, Dunkin Donuts, McDonald's, Subway, 🛏 Best Value Inn, Super 8, 🅾 CarMax, Honda, Hyundai, Infiniti/Toyota/Scion, Mazda,

Exit	Services
33 (39)	Continued Mercedes, Mini, Nissan, Subaru
32b (38)	Trumbull St (exits left from nb), **W** to downtown, 🛏 Crowne Plaza, Hilton, 🅾 H, Goodyear
32a	(exit 30 from sb), I-84, **W**
29b (37)	I-84 E, Hartford
29a (36.5)	US 5 N, CT 15, N (exits left from nb), **W** downtown, 🅾 H, capitol, civic ctr
28 (36)	US 5, CT 15, S (from nb), **W** 🚗 Citgo, 🍽 Burger King, Wendy's
27 (35)	Brainerd Rd, 🛬 Rd, **E** 🚗 Mercury/Dunkin Donuts/Subway/dsl, Shell/dsl, 🍽 McDonald's, 🛏 Days Inn, Holiday Inn Express, 🅾 Ford Trucks, to Regional Mkt
26 (33.5)	Marsh St, **E** Silas Deane House, Webb House, CT MVD
25 (33)	CT 3, Glastonbury, Wethersfield
24 (32)	CT 99, Rocky Hill, Wethersfield, **E** 🚗 Phillips 66/dsl, Sunoco, 🍽 Angry Olive, Chuck's Steaks, Dakota Steaks, Dunkin Donuts, McDonald's, On-the-Border, Rockyhill Pizza, Saybrook Seafood, Subway, 🛏 Hampton Inn, Howard Johnson, Super 8, 🅾 Aldi Foods, Kohl's, **W** 🚗 Mobil, Shell, Valero/dsl, 🍽 Burger King, D'angelo's, Denny's, Dunkin Donuts, Friendly's, Ginza Cuisine, HomeTown Buffet, Humphrey's Grill, KFC, Red Lobster, Sake Japanese, Sapporo Japanese, Sophia's Pizzaria, Starbucks, Townline Diner, Wendy's, Wood-n-Tap Grill, 🛏 Comfort Inn, Motel 6, 🅾 CVS Drug, $Tree, Goodyear/auto, Marshalls, Office Depot, Radio Shack, Stop&Shop, TJMaxx, TownFair Tire, TrueValue, Walgreens, Walmart/Subway
23 (29)	to CT 3, West St, Rocky Hill, Vet Home, **E** 🛏 Marriott, 🅾 H, to Dinosaur SP, **W** 🚗 Mobil, Valero/dsl, 🍽 D'angelo's, Dunkin Donuts, Michelangeo's Pizza, Papa John's, Subway, 🛏 Residence Inn, 🅾 IGA Foods, vet
22 (27)	CT 9, to New Britain, Middletown
21 (26)	CT 372, to Berlin, Cromwell, **E** 🚗 Sunoco/dsl/repair, 🛏 Comfort Inn, Crowne Plaza, 🅾 Krauszer's Foods, Lowe's, **W** 🚗 Citgo/Subway/dsl, Mobil/dsl, 🍽 Baci Grill, Burger King, Chili's, Cromwell Diner, Dunkin Donuts, McDonald's, Oyama Japanese, 🛏 Courtyard, Super 8, 🅾 Firestone/auto, Price Rite Foods, Walmart, vet
20 (23)	Country Club Rd, Middle St
22mm	**rest area/weigh sta nb, full ♿ facilities, info, 🅿, 🛢, litter barrels, vending, RV dump, petwalk**
19 (21)	Baldwin Ave (from sb)
18 (20.5)	I-691 W, to Marion, access to same as 16 & 17, ski area
17 (20)	CT 15, N (from sb), to I-691, CT 66 E, Meriden
16 (19)	CT 15, E Main St, **E** 🚗 Gulf/dsl, Mobil, Valero, 🍽 American Steaks, Gianni's Rest., NY Pizza, Olympos Diner, Subway, Zorba's Rest., 🛏 Candlewood Suites, Hampton Inn,

N   **S** (left margin)

WINDSOR AREA (left margin)

ROCKY HILL (center margin)

CT (right tab)

INTERSTATE 91 CONT'D

N ↕ S   **WALLINGFORD**   **NEW HAVEN N ↕ S**

CT

Exit	Services
16 (19)	Continued
	Sheraton, The Meridan Inn, 🅞 Family$, Lowe's, Verizon, Volvo, urgent care, **W** 🅖 BP/dsl, Getty/dsl, Gulf/repair, 🍴 Boston Mkt, Burger King, Dominos, Dunkin Donuts, Friendly's, KFC, Les' Dairy Bar, McDonald's, Ramini Pizza, Subway, Taco Bell, Wendy's, 🛏 Comfort Inn, 🅞 🏥, CarQuest, CVS Drug, Hancock's Drug, Walgreens, vet
15 (16)	CT 68, to Durham, **E** golf, **W** 🛏 Courtyard, Fairfield Inn, Homewood Suites
15mm	**rest area sb, full ♿ facilities, info, 🚻, 🛒, litter barrels, petwalk**
14 (12)	CT 150 (no EZ return), Woodhouse Ave, Wallingford
13 (10)	US 5 (exits left from nb), Wallingford, **2 mi W on US 5** services, to Wharton Brook SP
12 (9)	US 5, Washington Ave, **E** 🅖 Shell, Sunoco, Valero, 🍴 Boston Mkt, Burger King, D'angelo's, DQ, Droogie's Pizza, Dunkin Donuts, Friendly's, Jade City Chinese, KFC, McDonald's, Rustic Oak Rest., Starbucks, Subway, Taco Bell, Wendy's, 🅞 CVS Drug, Stop&Shop Food, Walgreens, USPO, **W** 🅖 Gulf/dsl, Mobil, 🍴 Arby's, Athena II Diner, Dunkin Donuts, Greatwall Chinese, Outback Steaks, Thai Cuisine, 🛏 Holiday Inn/Harry's Grill, 🅞 Advance Parts, BigY Foods/drug, CarQuest, vet
11 (7)	CT 22 (from nb), North Haven, same as 12
10 (6)	CT 40, to Cheshire, Hamden
9 (5)	Montowese Ave, **W** 🅖 Berkshire/dsl, Sunoco, 🍴 Dunkin Donuts, Dynasty Chinese, Friendly's, Longhorn Steaks, McDonald's, Olive Garden, Panera Bread, Red Lobster, Ruby Tuesday, Subway, Wendy's, 🅞 AT&T, Barnes&Noble, Best Buy, BigLots, BJ's Whse/gas, $Tree, GNC, Home Depot, Michael's, PetCo, Petsmart, Radio Shack, Staples, Target, TJMaxx, Verizon, urgent care
8 (4)	CT 17, CT 80, Middletown Ave, **E** 🅖 Citgo, Global/dsl, Mercury/dsl, 7-11, Shell, Sunoco/24hr, 🍴 Burger King, Country House Rest., Dominos, Dunkin Donuts, Exit 8 Diner, KFC, McDonald's, Pizza Hut/Taco Bell, 🛏 Days Inn, 🅞 Advance Parts, Aldi Foods, AT&T, AutoZone, Lowe's, Walgreens, Walmart/Subway, vet
7 (3)	Ferry St (from sb), Fair Haven, **W** 🅖 Hess/dsl, 🅞 NAPA
6 (2.5)	Willow St (exits left from nb), Blatchley Ave, **E** repair
5 (2)	US 5 (from nb), State St, Fair Haven, **E** 🍴 New Star Diner
4 (1.5)	State St (from sb), downtown
3 (1)	Trumbull St, downtown, **W** Peabody Museum
2 (.5)	Hamilton St, downtown, New Haven
1 (.3)	CT 34W (from sb), New Haven, **W** 🏥, downtown
0mm	I-91 begins/ends on I-95, exit 48.

INTERSTATE 95

Exit	Services
94mm	Connecticut/Rhode Island state line
93 (111)	CT 216, Clarks Falls, **E** 🅖 Shell/dsl/repair, 🍴 Dunkin Donuts, Subway, to Burlingame SP, **W** 🅖 Mobil/Dunkin Donuts/dsl, 🚚Shell/Stuckey's/Roy Rogers/Sbarro's/dsl/scales/24hr, 🍴 McDonald's, 🛏 Budget Inn, Stardust Motel
92 (107)	CT 2, CT 49 (no EZ nb return), Pawcatuck, **E** 🅖 Shell, 🍴 Dunkin Donuts, 🛏 La Quinta, 🅞 🏥, Stop&Shop, **W** 🛏 Cedar Park Suites, 🅞 FoxWoods (8mi), KOA
91 (103)	CT 234, N Main St, to Stonington, **E** 🅞 🏥

MYSTIC   **GROTON**

Exit	Services
90 (101)	CT 27, Mystic, **E** 🅖 Mobil/Domino's/Dunkin Donuts/dsl, 🍴 Boathouse Rest., Equinox Diner, 5 Guys Burgers, Friendly's, Go Fish, McDonald's, Starbucks, Steak Loft, Ten Clams, 🛏 EconoLodge, Hilton, Holiday Inn Express, Howard Johnson, Hyatt Place, 🅞 Curves, Mystic Outlet Shops, Verizon, aquarium, **W** 🅖 Shell/Subway/dsl, 🍴 Dunkin Donuts, Jakes Burgers, Pizza Grille, Thai 1, 🛏 Comfort Inn, Days Inn, Hampton Inn, Ramada Inn, Residence Inn, 🅞 Chevrolet, Chrysler/Dodge/Jeep, Ford, RV camping, TrueValue, VW
89 (99)	CT 215, Allyn St, **W** camping (seasonal)
89mm	scenic overlook
88 (98)	CT 117, to Noank, **E** 🔁, **W** 🍴 Octagon Steaks, Starbucks, 🛏 Marriott
87 (97)	Sharp Hwy (exits left from sb), Groton, **E** 🛏 Hampton Inn, 🅞 to Griswold SP, 🔁
86 (96)	rd 184 (exits left from nb), Groton, **E** 🍴 Applebees, 99 Rest., 🛏 Hampton Inn, Knights Inn, 🅞 Walgreens, **W** 🅖 Cory's/dsl, Hess, Mobil, Shell/dsl, 🍴 Chinese Kitchen, Dunkin Donuts, Flanagan's Diner, Groton Rest., KFC, NY Pizza, Russell's Ribs, Subway, Taco Bell, 🛏 Best Western, Groton Inn, Super 8, 🅞 Advance Parts, $Tree, GNC, Honda, Kia, Kohl's, Midas, Stop&Shop, Verizon, to US Sub Base
85 (95)	US 1 N, Groton, downtown, **E** 🅞 NAPA
84 (94)	CT 32 (from sb), New London downtown
83 (92)	CT 32, New London, **E** to Long Island Ferry
82a (90.5)	frontage rd, New London, **E** 🅖 Mobil, 🍴 Panda Buffet, Pizza Hut, 🅞 AutoZone, NSA Foods, Radio Shack, Staples, TownFair Tire, Verizon, same as 82, **W** 🍴 Chili's, ChuckeCheese, Outback Steaks, 🛏 Clarion, SpringHill Suites, 🅞 Marshall's, Petsmart, ShopRite Foods, same as 82
82 (90)	CT 85, to I-395 N, New London, **W** 🅖 Mobil/Dunkin Donuts, 🍴 Coldstone, FoodCourt, Longhorn Steaks, Olive Garden, Panera Bread, Ruby Tuesday, Subway, Wendy's, 🅞 Best Buy, Dick's, Home Depot, JC Penney, Macy's, Michael's, PetCo, Sears/auto, Target, Verizon, mall
90mm	**weigh sta both directions**
81 (89.5)	Cross Road, **W** 🛏 Rodeway Inn, 🅞 BJ's Whse/gas, Lowe's, Walmart/McDonald's
80 (89.3)	Oil Mill Rd (from sb), **W** 🛏 Rodeway Inn
76 (89)	I-395, N (from nb, exits left), to Norwich
75 (88)	US 1, to Waterford
74 (87)	rd 161, to Flanders, Niantic, **E** 🅖 Cory's/repair, Citgo/dsl, Mobil, 🍴 Burger King, Country Gourmet, Dunkin Donuts, Illiano's Grill, Quiznos, Shoreline Rest., Starbucks, 🛏 Best Value Inn, Hilltop Inn, Motel 6, Sleep Inn, 🅞 Ford, Stop&Shop, Tires+, **W** 🅖 Shell, 🍴 5 Guys Burgers, Flanders Pizza, Flanders Seafood, Kings Garden Chinese, McDonald's, Nanami Japanese, Shack Rest., Smokey O'Grady's BBQ, Yummy Yummy Pizza, 🅞 Curves, CVS Drug, IGA Foods, Rite Aid, TrueValue, RV camping, vet
74mm	**rest area sb, full ♿ facilities, st police**
73 (86)	Society Rd
72 (84)	to Rocky Neck SP, **2 mi E** food, lodging, RV camping, to Rocky Neck SP
71 (83)	4 Mile Rd, River Rd, to Rocky Neck SP beaches, **1 mi E** camping (seasonal)
70 (80)	US 1, CT 156, Old Lyme, **W** 🅖 Shell/dsl, 🍴 Morning Glory Cafe, Subway, 🛏 Old Lyme Inn/dining, 🅞 Big Y Foods, Rite Aid, Griswold Museum, USPO, vet

INTERSTATE 95 CONT'D

Exit	Services
69 (77)	US 1, CT 9 N, to Hartford, **W** 🍴 Bangkok Sushi, 🛏 Comfort Inn, ⊙ antiques, vet
68 (76.5)	US 1 S, Old Saybrook, **E** 📦 Irving/dsl, Mobil, 🍴 Cloud 9 Deli, Pat's Country Kitchen, **W** ⊙ Buick/GMC, Chevrolet/Nissan, Chrysler/Dodge/Jeep, Kia, Mazda, NAPA, VW
67 (76)	CT 154, Elm St (no EZ sb return), Old Saybrook, **E** 🍴 Pasta Vita Itaian, same as 68
66 (75)	to US 1, Spencer Plain Rd, **E** 📦 Citgo/dsl, 🍴 Blue Crab Steaks, Brick Oven Pizza, Cuckoo's Nest Mexican, DQ, Dunkin Donuts, Fogo Grill, Luigi's Italian, Mike's Deli, Pizza Palace, Sal's Pizza, Samurai Japanese, Siagon City, Tiberio's Italian, 🛏 Days Inn, EconoLodge, Saybrook Motel, Super 8, ⊙ Benny's Mkt, transmissions, vet
65 (73)	rd 153, Westbrook, **E** 📦 Mobil/Dunkin Donuts, Valero, 🍴 Cafe Rotier, Cristy's Rest., Denny's, Subway, Westbook Deli, ⊙ Honda, Old Navy, Tanger Factory Stores/famous brands, Toyota/Scion, Walgreens, USPO
64 (70)	rd 145, Horse Hill Rd, Clinton
63 (68)	CT 81, Clinton, **E** 📦 Shell, **1 mi E on US 1** 📦 Shell/dsl/LP, Sunoco/dsl, 🍴 Chips Rest., Friendly's, McDonald's, Piccadeli Sta., ⊙ CVS Drug, USPO, vet, **W** 🍴 Coldstone, Dunkin Donuts, ⊙ AT&T, Clinton Crossing Premium Outlets/famous brands, PetCo
62 (67)	**E** to Hammonasset SP, RV camping, beaches
66mm	service area both lanes, Mobil/dsl, McDonald's, atm
61 (64)	CT 79, Madison, **E** 📦 Gulf, Shell, Sunoco, 🍴 Cafe Allegre, Starbucks, Subway, Village Pizza, ⊙ CVS Drug, Stop&Shop, USPO
61mm	East River
60 (63.5)	Mungertown Rd (from sb, no return), **E** food, lodging
59 (60)	rd 146, Goose Lane, Guilford, **E** 📦 Citgo, Mobil/24hr, Shell/DQ/dsl, 🍴 Avest Pizza, Dunkin Donuts, First Garden Chinese, Nick&Tony's Pizza, McDonald's, Shoreline Diner, Splash American Grill, The Whole Enchilada, Wendy's, 🛏 Comfort Inn, Tower Motel, ⊙ NAPA, transmissions, **W** URGENT CARE, st police
58 (59)	CT 77, Guilford, **on US 1** **E** 🍴 BP, Hess, Mobil, Sunoco/dsl, ⊙ CVS Drug, Walgreens, to Henry Whitfield Museum, **W** st police
57 (58)	US 1, Guilford, **E** ⊙ Extra/Dunkin Donuts/dsl, **W** ⊙ Land Rover, Saab
56 (55)	rd 146, to Stony Creek, **E** 🛏 Rodeway Inn, **W** 📦 Mobil, Shell/dsl, TA/Popeye's/Starbucks/Subway/dsl/scales/24hr/@, 🍴 Dunkin Donuts, Friendly's, USS Chowderpot, 🛏 Baymont Inn, Best Value Inn, ⊙ Freightliner, Stop&Shop Foods, Verizon
55 (54)	US 1, **E** 📦 Branford/repair, Cumberland, Global, 🍴 Hornet's Nest Deli, Lynn's Rest, Marco Pizzaria, Rita's Custard, Sapori d'Italia, TNT Seafood Grill, 🛏 Holiday Inn Express, Motel 6, ⊙ Ford, Walgreens, vet, **W** 📦 Gulf, Mobil/Dunkin Donuts/dsl, 🍴 Brother's Deli, Chuck's Margarita Grill, Gourmet Wok, Parthenon Diner, Su Casa Mexican, 🛏 Days Inn
54 (53)	Cedar St, Branford, **E** 📦 Citgo/repair, Mobil, 🍴 Dragon East Chinese, Dunkin Donuts, La Luna Ristorante, ⊙ AAA, Hyundai, Staples, Subaru, **W** Krauszer's Foods
52mm	**service area both lanes**, Mobil/dsl/24hr, McDonald's, pizza, atm
52 (50)	rd 100, North High St, **E** ⊙ to Trolley Museum, **W** st police
51 (49.5)	US 1, Easthaven, **E** 📦 Hess/dsl, Sunoco, Valero/dsl, 🍴 Boston Mkt, Chili's, 🛏 Quality Inn, ⊙ Chevrolet, Lexus, TJ Maxx, Verizon, **W** 🍴 Dunkin Donuts, Wendy's, ⊙ AutoZone, CarMax, Home Depot, USPO
50 (49)	Woodward Ave (from nb), **E** ⊙ US Naval/Marine Reserve, Ft Nathan Hale
49 (48.5)	Stiles St (from nb)
48 (48)	I-91 N, to Hartford
47 (47.5)	CT 34, New Haven, **W** 📦 Mobil/Dunkin Donuts/dsl, 🍴 Brazi's Italian, Greek Olive Diner, 🛏 La Quinta, ⊙ Ikea, Long Warf Theater, same as 46
46 (47)	Long Wharf Dr, Sargent Dr, **E** 🍴 Leon's Rest., **W** 📦 Mobil/Dunkin Donuts/dsl, 🍴 Brazi's Italian, Greek Olive Diner, 🛏 La Quinta, ⊙ Ikea, Long Warf Theater
45 (46.5)	CT 10 (from sb), Blvd, **W** 📦 BP, 🍴 Dunkin Donuts, McDonald's, same as 44
44 (46)	CT 10 (from nb), Kimberly Ave, **E** 🛏 Super 8, **W** 📦 BP, 🍴 Dunkin Donuts, McDonald's, same as 45
43 (45)	CT 122, 1st Ave (no EZ return), West Haven, **W** 📦 1st Fuel/dsl, 🍴 China Sea, ⊙ H, to U of New Haven
42 (44)	CT 162, Saw Mill Rd, **E** 🍴 Pizza Hut, 🛏 EconoLodge, **W** 📦 Mobil, Shell, 🍴 American Steaks, Dan's Dog House, Denny's, Dunkin Donuts, Friendly's, Starbucks, Subway, TX Roadhouse, 🛏 Best Western, Hampton Inn, ⊙ Aldi Foods, Walmart
41 (42)	Marsh Hill Rd, to Orange
41mm	**service area both lanes**, 📦 Mobil/dsl, 🍴 McDonald's
40 (40)	Old Gate Lane, Woodmont Rd, **E** 📦 Citgo/dsl, Pilot/Wendy's/dsl/scales/24hr, Shell, Sunoco, 🍴 Cracker Barrel, Duchess Rest., Dunkin Donuts, Gipper's Rest., Presto's Rest., 🛏 Hilton Garden, Mayflower Motel, Quality Inn, ⊙ Blue Beacon, Lowe's, 7-11
39 (39)	US 1, to Milford, **E** 📦 BP, Cumberland Farms/dsl, 🍴 Athenian Diner, Chicago Grill, Friendly's, Hooters, 🛏 Howard Johnson, Super 8, ⊙ CVS Drug, Firestone/auto, Mazda/Volvo, ShopRite Foods, Walgreens, **W on US 1** gas Mobil, 🍴 Arby's, Boston Mkt, Buffalo Wild Wings, Burger King, Chili's, Chipotle Mexican, Dunkin Donuts, Hometown Buffet, HoneyBaked Ham, KFC, McDonald's, Michelangelo Pizza, Panera Bread, Red Robin, Subway, Taco Bell, ⊙ Acura, Advance Parts, AT&T, Barnes&Noble, BigLots, Costco/gas, Dick's, JC Penney, Jeep, Jo-Ann Fabrics, Macy's, Marshall's, Michael's, Old Navy, PetCo, Rite Aid, Sears/auto, Staples, Target, TownFair Tire, USPO, Walmart/Subway, Whole Foods Mkt, mall
38 (38)	CT 15, Merritt Pkwy, Cross Pkwy
37 (37.5)	High St (no ez nb return), **E** 📦 Gulf, Sunoco, USA, 🍴 Kimberly Diner, ⊙ 7-11, Toyota/Scion
36	Plains Rd, **E** 📦 Mobil, 🛏 Hampton Inn
35 (37)	Bic Dr, School House Rd, **E** 📦 Citgo, 🍴 Armellino's

Map of Connecticut showing Interstate 95 route with cities: New Haven, Westbrook, Clinton, Sachem Head, Stratford, Milford, Wildermere Beach, Lordship, Bridgeport, Southport, Westport, Norwalk, Harborview, Stamford, Port Chester. **CT**

INTERSTATE 95 CONT'D

N↕S **MILFORD** **CT**

Exit	Services
35 (37)	Continued
	Italian, Wendy's, 🛏 Fairfield Inn, 🔵 AutoZone, Buick/GMC, Chevrolet/Saab, Chrysler/Dodge/Jeep, Dennis' Parts, Ford/Lincoln/Mercury, Honda, Kia, K-Mart, Land Rover, Nissan, Stop&Shop Foods/gas, Subaru, Walgreens, **W** 🛏 Red Roof Inn, SpringHill Suites
34 (34)	US 1, Milford, **E on US 1** 🍴 Dunkin Donuts, Gourmet Buffet, McDonald's, Pizza Hut, Subway, Taco Bell, 🛏 Devon Motel, 🔵 $Tree, Hyundai,Radio Shack, Walgreens
33 (33.5)	US 1 (from nb, no EZ return), CT 110, Ferry Blvd, **E** 🅖 Shell/dsl, Sunoco, 🍴 Brazilian Steaks, Bridgehouse Rest., Danny's Drive-In, Savin Rock Grill, Subway, 🔵 BJ's Whse, PetCo, Staples, **W** 🍴 McDonalds, 99 Rest., 🔵 Home Depot, Marshall's, Shaw's Foods, ShopRite Foods, Stop&Shop Foods, Walmart/Subway
32 (33)	W Broad St, Stratford, **E** 🅖 USA/Subway/dsl, **W** 🅖 Gulf, 🍴 Dunkin Donuts
31 (32)	South Ave, Honeyspot Rd, **E** 🅖 Gulf/Dunkin Donuts, 🛏 Comfort Inn, **W** 🅖 Citgo/dsl, 🔵 NAPA, TownFair Tire, VIP Service Ctr
30 (31.5)	Lordship Blvd, Surf Ave, **E** 🅖 Shell, Sunoco/dsl, 🍴 Dunkin Donuts, 🛏 Ramada/rest., **W** 🅖 Massey/dsl
29 (31)	rd 130, Stratford Ave, Seaview Ave, **W** 🄷
28 (30)	CT 113, E Main St, Pembrook St
27 (29.5)	Lafayette Blvd, downtown, **W** 🍴 Dunkin Donuts, Subway, 🔵 🄷, Barnum Museum
27a (29)	CT 25, CT 8, to Waterbury
26 (28)	Wordin Ave
25 (27)	CT 130 (from sb, no EZ return), State St, Commerce Dr, Fairfield Ave, **E** 🅖 BP, Santa/dsl/repair, 🍴 Wendy's, 🔵 Audi, Buick, Infiniti, Mercedes, Porsche, Smart Car, Stop&Shop, USPO, **W** 🅖 Prime, 🍴 McDonald's, 🔵 transmissions
24 (26.5)	Black Rock Tpk, **E** 🍴 Blackrock Oyster Bar, Fairfield Pizza, Sweet Basil, 🛏 Best Western, 🔵 BJ's Whse/Subway, Lexus, Porsche, Staples, USPO, Verizon, **W** 🅖 Gulf, 🔵 Firestone/auto, Nissan
23 (26)	US 1, Kings Hwy, **E** 🅖 Sunoco/dsl, 🔵 CVS Drug, Home Depot, Whole Foods Mkt
22 (24)	Round Hill Rd, N Benson Rd
23.5mm	**service area both lanes** 🅖 Mobil/dsl, 🍴 FoodCourt (sb), McDonald's
21 (23)	Mill Plain Rd, **E** 🅖 Citgo/dsl, Mobil, 🍴 Avellino's Italian, DQ, Rawley's Drive-In, Starbucks, Subway, The Shack Grill, Wilson's BBQ, 🔵 Hemlock Hardware, Rite Aid
20 (22)	Bronson Rd (from sb)
19 (21)	US 1, Center St, **W** 🅖 BP, Shell/dsl, 🍴 Athena Diner, Baskin-Robbins/Dunkin Donuts, Friendly's, Subway, 🛏 Westport Inn, 🔵 Balducci's Mkt, Curves, Honda, Stop&Shop, TownFair Tire, Verizon, Walgreens
18 (20)	to Westport, **E** Sherwood Island SP, beaches, **W 1 mi on US 1** 🅖 Citgo, Gulf, Mobil, 🍴 Angelina's Trattoria, Arby's, Arcudi's Rest., Bertucci's Italian, McDonald's, Sherwood Diner, Starbucks, Subway, 🔵 Barnes&Noble, Marshall's, Radio Shack, Toyota/Scion, Walgreens, st police, vet
17 (18)	CT 33, rd 136, Westport, **W** 🔵 FastStop Mart
16 (17)	E Norwalk, **E** 🅖 Citgo, Mobil, Shell/dsl, Sunoco, 🍴 Baskin-Robbins/Dunkin Donuts, Eastside Café, Penny's Diner, Subway, 🔵 Rite Aid, **W** 🅖 Stew Leonard's Mkt
15 (16)	US 7, to Danbury, Norwalk, **E** 🅖 Shell, 🔵 Walgreens, **W** 🅖 Getty

N **O** **R** **W** **A** **L** **K**

Exit	Services
14 (15)	US 1, CT Ave, S Norwalk, **E** st police, **W** 🅖 Shell, Dunkin Donuts, 🍴 Burger King, Driftwood Diner, Post Road Diner, Rowley's Tavern, Sierra Grill, Silver Star Diner, Wendy's, 🔵 🄷, Barnes&Noble, Best Buy, Kohl's, Old Navy, Petsmart, Radio Shack, ShopRite Foods, Stop&Shop, TJ Maxx, TownFair Tire, same as 13
13 (13)	US 1 (no EZ return), Post Rd, Norwalk, **W** 🅖 Mobil, Shell, Sunoco, 🍴 American Steaks, Bertucci's, Chipotle Mexican, Darien Diner, Friendly's, John's Rest., KFC, McDonald's, 🛏 DoubleTree Hotel, 🔵 AT&T, Costco, Home Depot, Land Rover, Staples, Walmart, vet, same as 14
12.5mm	**service area nb**, Mobil/dsl, McDonald's
12 (12)	rd 136, Tokeneke Rd (from nb, no return), **W** 🍴 deli
11 (11)	US 1, Darien, **E** 🅖 BP, 🍴 Chuck's Steaks, 🔵 Chevrolet, Nissan, vet, **W** 🅖 Gulf, 🍴 Panera Bread, 🔵 BMW, Whole Foods Mkt
10 (10)	Noroton, **W** 🅖 BP, Shell, 🔵 vet
9.5mm	**service area sb**, 🅖 Mobil/dsl, 🍴 McDonald's
9 (9)	US 1, rd 106, Glenbrook, **E** 🛏 Best Value Inn, 🔵 Mini, **W** 🅖 Gulf, 🍴 Chin's Chinese, Dunkin Donuts, McDonald's, Subway, 🔵 cat vet
8 (8)	Atlantic Ave, Elm St, **E** U-Haul, **W** 🅖 Sunoco, 🛏 Marriott, 🔵 🄷
7 (7)	CT 137, Atlantic Ave, **W** 🛏 Hampton Inn, Marriott, 🍴 PF Chang's, 🔵 Barnes&Noble, USPO, same as 8
6 (6)	Harvard Ave, West Ave, **E** 🅖 Gulf, 🍴 City Limits Diner, Starbucks, 🛏 La Quinta, 🔵 Advance Parts, Petsmart, Subaru, USPO, **W** 🅖 Shell, 🛏 Super 8, 🔵 🄷
5 (5)	US 1, Riverside, Old Greenwich, **W** 🅖 A&P, BP, Shell, 🍴 Boston Mkt, Corner Deli, Hunan Cafe, McDonald's, Mo's Burger Joint, Starbucks, Subway, Taco Bell, 🛏 Hyatt Regency, 🔵 CVS Drug, GNC, Staples, Walgreens, USPO
4 (4)	Indian Field Rd, Cos Cob, **W** 🔵 Bush-Holley House Museum
3 (3)	Arch St, Greenwich, **E** Bruce Museum, **W** 🅖 Shell, 🔵 🄷, Lexus, Saab
2mm	**weigh sta nb**
2 (1)	Delavan Ave, Byram
0mm	Connecticut/New York state line

G **R** **E** **E** **N** **W** **I** **C** **H**

INTERSTATE 395

N↕S **PUTNAM**

Exit	Services
55.5mm	Connecticut/Massachusetts state line
100 (54)	E Thompson, to Wilsonville
99 (50)	rd 200, N Grosvenor Dale, **E**, **W** Thompson Lake Camping (seasonal)
98 (49)	to CT 12 (from nb, exits left), Grosvenor Dale, same as 99
97 (47)	US 44, to, E Putnam, **E** 🍴 Dunkin Donuts, Empire Buffet, McDonald's/playplace, Subway, Wendy's, 🔵 Advance Parts, BigLots, CVS Drug, $Tree, Giant Pizza, GNC, Radio Shack, Sears Essentials, Stop&Shop/gas, **W** 🅖 Shell/dsl/repair, Sunoco, 🔵 Walmart/Subway
96 (46)	to CT 12, Putnam, **W** 🍴 Casa Mariachi, 🛏 King's Inn, 🔵 🄷
95 (45)	Kennedy Dr, to Putnam, **E** Ford, **W** 🄷
94 (43)	Ballouville, **W** 🍴 Gold Eagle Rest., 🛏 Comfort Inn, 🔵 truck parts
93 (41)	CT 101, to Dayville, **E** 🅖 Shell/dsl, 🍴 Burger King, China Garden, Domino's, Dunkin Donuts, Nuccio's Pizza, Subway, Yamoto Japanese, Zip's Diner, 🔵 Aldi Foods, $Tree, Walgreens, Wibberley Tire/repair, **W** 🅖 Mobil/

INTERSTATE 395 CONT'D

Exit	Services
93 (41)	Continued dsl, Xtra/dsl, 🍴 Dunkin Donuts, McDonald's, Mozzarella's Grill, 99 Rest., 🄾 AT&T, GNC, Lowe's, Michael's, PetCo, Target, TJ Maxx, Staples, Stop&Shop, Verizon, city park
92 (39)	to, S Killingly, **W** 🍴 Dunkin Donuts, Giant Pizza, 🄾 Bonneville Drug, st police
91 (38)	US 6 W, to Danielson, to Quinebaug Valley Coll
90 (36)	to US 6, E (from nb), to Providence
35mm	**rest area both lanes, full (handicapped) facilities**, 🅿 Mobil/dsl
89 (32)	CT 14, to Sterling, Central Village, **E** 🅿 Best Way, Gulf/repair, 🍴 Johnny's Rest., Pizza Pizzaz, 🄾 Rite Aid, RV camping, USPO, **W** 🅿 7-11/dsl, Shell/Dunkin Donuts/dsl, 🍴 Music Lady Cafe, Subway, 🛏 Knights Inn, 🄾 transmissions
88 (30)	CT 14A to Plainfield, **E** RV camping (seasonal), **W** 🅿 Mobil
87 (28)	Lathrop Rd, to Plainfield, **E** 🅿 Shell/Domino's/dsl, 🍴 Dunkin Donuts, HongKong Star Chinese, Subway, Wendy's, 🛏 Holiday Inn Express, Quality Inn, 🄾 Big Y Foods, Ford, Hyundai, Mazda, Mercedes, Radio Shack, **W** 🅿 Gulf, Sunoco/dsl, 🍴 Bakers Dozen Cafe, Eli's Steaks, McDonald's, 🄾 Advance Parts, Curves, CVS Drug
86 (24)	rd 201, Hopeville, **E** Hopeville Pond SP, RV camping
85 (23)	CT 164, CT 138, to Pachaug, Preston, **E** 🅿 Petro Max/Dunkin Donuts/dsl, 🄾 Curves, $Tree, RV camping, **W** 🛏 AmericInn
84 (21)	CT 12, Jewett City, **E** 🍴 Chili's, Panera Bread, Ruby Tuesday, 🄾 Aldi Foods, AT&T, Dick's, GNC, Home Depot, Kohl's, Lowe's, PetCo, Target, Verizon, Walmart/Dunkin Donuts, **W** 🅿 Gulf/dsl, Mobil/dsl, Shell/dsl, 🍴 McDonald's, 🄾 Val-U Foods
83a (20)	CT 169 (from nb), Lisbon, **E** RV camping
83 (18)	rd 97, Taftville, **E** 🅿 BP/dsl, **W** 🅿 7-11
82 (14)	to CT 2 W, CT 32 N, Norwichtown, **E** 🍴 Friendly's, 🄾 tires, **W** 🅿 BP/Dunkin Donuts/dsl, Mobil/dsl, Shell/dsl, 🍴 Buddy's Dugout, Illiano's Grill, Prime Rest., Subway, 🛏 Courtyard, Rosemont Suites, 🄾 Ace Hardware
81 (14)	CT 2 E, CT 32 S, Norwich, **E** 🄷, to Mohegan Coll
80 (12)	CT 82, Norwich, **E** 🅿 Mobil, Shell, Xtra/dsl, 🍴 Burger King, Chinese Buffet, Dunkin Donuts, Friendly's, KFC/Taco Bell, McDonald's, Mr Pizza, 99 Rest., Papa Gino's, Subway, Wendy's, 🄾 Jo-Ann Fabrics, Rite Aid, ShopRite Foods, Staples, TJ Maxx, TownFair Tire, Verizon, **W** 🛏 Holiday Inn, 🄾 Big Y Foods, Walmart, RV Camping

Exit	Services
79a (10)	CT 2A E, to Ledyard, **E** to Pequot Res
8.5mm	**nb** st police, 🄲, **sb** Mobil/dsl, **rest area, full facilities**
79 (6)	rd 163, to Uncasville, Montville, **1 mi E** 🅿 Mobil/dsl, 🍴 Dunkin Donuts, Friendly Pizza, McDonald's, Subway, 🄾 Rite Aid, Tri-Town Foods, repair
78 (5)	CT 32 (from sb, exits left), to New London, RI Beaches
77 (2)	CT 85, to I-95 N, Colchester **1/2 mi E** 🅿 Shell/dsl, Dunkin Donuts, 🛏 Oakdell Motel
0mm	I-95. I-395 begins/ends on I-95, exit 76.

INTERSTATE 691

Exit	Services
I-691 begins/ends on I-91	
12 (12)	Preston Ave
11 (11)	I-91 N, to Hartford
10 (11)	I-91 S, to New Haven, CT 15 S, W Cross Pkwy
9	Berlin Tpk
8 (10)	US 5, Broad St, **N** 🅿 Citgo, Cumberland, Irving, Shell/dsl, 🍴 Broad St Pizza, Chinese Gourmet, DQ
7 (9)	downtown (no ez wb return), Meriden, **S** 🅿 Citgo
6 (8)	Lewis Ave (from wb, no EZ return), to CT 71, **N** 🍴 Ruby Tuesday, 🄾 🄷, Best Buy, Dick's, Macy's, JC Penney, Macy's, Old Navy, Sears/auto, Target, mall, **S** 🅿 7-11, 🍴 Subway
5 (7)	CT 71, to Chamberlain Hill (from eb, no EZ return), **N** 🄾 🄷, Best Buy, Target, mall, **S** 🅿 7-11/gas, 🍴 McDonald's, Subway
4 (4)	CT 322, W Main St (no re-entry from eb), **N** 🅿 Sunoco, 🍴 Dunkin Donuts, Hubbard Park Pizza, 🄾 🄷
3mm	Quinnipiac River
3 (1)	CT 10, to Cheshire, Southington, **N** 🍴 Sam's Clams Rest., Tony's Rest.
2 (0)	I-84 E, to Hartford
1 (0)	I-84 W, to Waterbury
I-691 begins/ends on I-84	

DELAWARE

INTERSTATE 95

Exit	Services
23mm	Delaware/Pennsylvania state line, motorist callboxes for 23 miles sb
11 (22)	to I-495 S, DE 92, Naamans Rd, **E** 🍴 China Star, 🄾 Burlington Coats, $General, Jo-Ann Fabrics, K-Mart, WaWa, **W** 🅿 Gulf/dsl, 🍴 KFC/Taco Bell, Quiznos, 🛏 Holiday Inn Select, 🄾 Home Depot, Radio Shack, Rite Aid
10 (21)	Harvey Rd (no nb return)
9 (19)	DE 3, to Marsh Rd, **E** 🍴 Dunkin Donuts, Lamberti's Italian, Starbucks, 🄾 Rockwood Museum, to Bellevue SP,
9 (19)	Continued st police
8b a (17)	US 202, Concord Pike, to Wilmington, **E** 🄾 Home Depot, to Brandywine Park
7b a (16)	DE 52, Delaware Ave
6 (15)	DE 4, MLK Blvd, **E** 🍴 Joe's Crabshack, McDonald's, 🄾 AAA, Fresh Grocer Foods, Rite Aid, **W** 🅿 Gulf, 🄾 Family$
5c (12)	I-495 N, to Wilmington, to DE Mem Bridge
5b a (11)	DE 141, to US 202, to New Castle, Newport, **E** 🛏 Quality Inn (3mi)

◉ = gas　🍴 = food　🛏 = lodging　◎ = other　Copyright 2012 - The Next Exit

INTERSTATE 95 CONT'D

Exit	Services
4b a (8)	DE 1, DE 7, to Christiana, **E** 🍴 Brio Tuscan Grille, CA Pizza Kitchen, Cheesecake Factory, Don Pablo, Food-Court, JB Dawson's Rest., Panera Bread, Ruby Tuesday, ◎ Barnes&Noble, Costco, Dick's, JC Penney, Macy's, Michael's, Nordstrom, PetCo, Target, mall, **W** 🍴 Applebee's, Bugaboo Creek Steaks, Cheeseburger Paradise, Chili's, Dunkin Donuts, Firebird's Grill, Marble Slab Creamery, Michael's Rest., Old Country Buffet, Olive Garden, Quiznos, Red Lobster, 🛏 Country Inn&Suites, Courtyard, Days Inn, Fairfield Inn, Hilton, Homestead Suites, Red Roof Inn, ◎ Ⓗ, AAA, Best Buy, Home Depot, Office Depot, Petsmart, TJ Maxx, Verizon, casino/racetrack
3b a (6)	DE 273, to Newark, Dover, **E** ◉ BP, Exxon/dsl, 🍴 Bertucci's, Bob Evans, Boston Mkt, Ciao Pizza, Famous Dave's BBQ, Red Robin, Olive Grill Italian, Shell Hammer's Grille, Wendy's, 🛏 Ramada Inn, Residence Inn, Staybridge Suites, TownePlace Suites, ◎ Acme Foods, Boscov's, Jo-Ann Fabrics, Old Navy, Staples, Walgreens, **W** ◉ Getty, Shell/dsl, 🍴 Denny's, Dunkin Donuts, Pizza Hut, 🛏 Comfort Inn, EconoLodge, Holiday Inn Express, ◎ 7-11
5mm	**service area both lanes (exits left from both lanes), info,** ◉ Sunoco/dsl, 🍴 Baja Fresh, Burger King, Famiglia, Popeye's, Starbucks, Z-Mkt
1b a (3)	DE 896, to Newark, to U of DE, Middletown, **W** ◉ Exxon, Gulf/dsl, Shell/dsl, Sunoco, 🍴 Boston Mkt, China Garden, Dunkin Donuts, 896 Diner, Friendly's, Mario's Pizza, Matilda's Rest., McDonald's, TGIFriday's, 🛏 Best Value Inn, Courtyard (3mi), Embassy Suites, Homewood Suites, Howard Johnson, Sleep Inn, ◎ DE Tire Ctr
1mm	toll booth, st police
0mm	Delaware/Maryland state line, motorist callboxes for 23 miles nb

INTERSTATE 295　(WILMINGTON)

Exit	Services
15mm	Delaware/New Jersey state line, Delaware River, Delaware Memorial Bridge
14.5mm	toll plaza
14	DE 9, New Castle Ave, to Wilmington, **E** ◉ BP, Citgo, 🍴 Giovanni's Cafe, ◎ Advance Parts, Family$, Firestone/auto, Harley-Davidson/rest., Rite Aid, SuperFresh Foods, **W** ◉ Shell, Super/dsl, 🍴 Dunkin Donuts, McDonald's, 🛏 Budget Inn, Motel 6, SuperLodge
13	US 13, US 40, to New Castle, **E** ◉ BP, Hess, Sunoco/dsl, Shell/dsl, WaWa, 🍴 Applebee's, Arby's, Arner's Rest, Burger King, DogHouse, Dove Diner, Dunkin Donuts, Hadfield's Seafood, Hooters, IHOP, KFC, Lonestar Steaks, McDonald's, Pizza Hut, Popeye's, Season's Pizza, Subway, Taco Bell, TGIFriday's, Wendy's, 🛏 EconoLodge, Quality Inn, Super 8, ◎ Acura, AutoZone, BJ's Whse/gas, Chevrolet, Chrysler/Jeep/Dodge, Cottman Transmissions, $Tree, Fiat, Ford, Home Depot, Hyundai, Lincoln, Mazda, Nissan, PathMark Foods, PepBoys, Radio Shack, Ross, Save-a-Lot, 7-11, Staples, Toyota/Scion, Walgreens, Walmart, repair, **W** ◉ WaWa/dsl, 🍴 Dunkin Donuts, 🛏 Clarion, ◎ Ford Trucks, Freightliner, Lowe's
12	I-495, US 202, N to Wilmington
15mm	Delaware
	I-295 begins/ends on I-95

INTERSTATE 495

Exit	Services
11mm	I-95 N. I-495 begins/ends on I-95.
5 (10)	US 13, Phila Pike, Claymont, **W** ◉ BP, Exxon/dsl, Sunoco/dsl, 🍴 Arby's, Boston Mkt, Dunkin Donuts, McDonald's, 🛏 Milan Motel, ◎ Family$, Food Lion, USPO
4 (5)	US 13, rd 3, Edgemoor Rd, to Fox Point Park
3 (4)	12th St
2 (3)	rd 9A, Terminal Ave, Port of Wilmington
1 (1)	US 13, **E** 🛏 WaWa/dsl, 🍴 Dunkin Donuts, 🛏 Clarion, ◎ Ford Trucks, Lowe's
0mm	I-95 S. I-495 begins/ends on I-95.

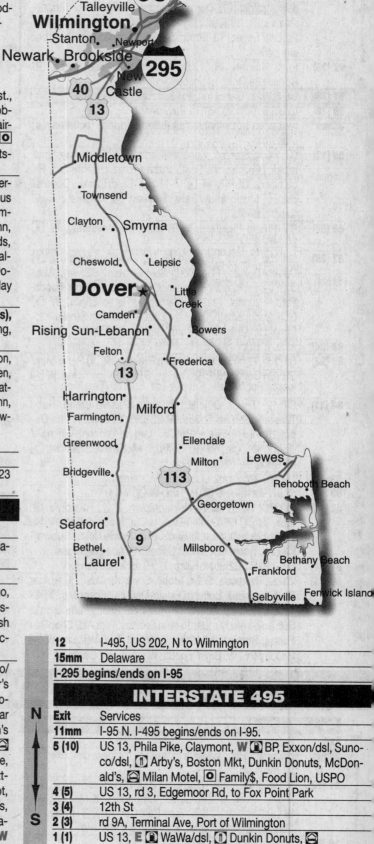

opyright 2012 - The Next Exit®

INTERSTATE 4

E ↕ **W**

Exit	Services
132	I-95, S to Miami, N to Jacksonville, FL 400. I-4 begins/ends on I-95, exit 260b
129	to US 92 (from eb, exits left)
126mm	rest area eb, 🏠, litter barrels, no services, no security
118	FL 44, to DeLand, N 🔲 BP/dsl 🏠 Howard Johnson, 🔲 Ⓗ
116	Orange Camp Rd, Lake Helen
114	FL 472, to DeLand, Orange City, N 🔲 Clark Campground (1mi), to Blue Sprgs SP
111b a	Deltona, N 🔲 Hess/dsl, RaceTrac/dsl, Shell/Circle K, 🍴 Baskin-Robbins/Dunkin Donuts, Bob Evans, Chick-fil-A, Chili's, Denny's, Jimmy John's, KFC, Papa John's, Perkins, Pizza Hut, Quiznos, Ruby Tuesday, Sonic, Sonny's BBQ, Steak'n Shake, Subway, Taco Bell, Tijuana Flats, Zaxby's, 🏠 Holiday Inn Express, 🔲 Ⓗ, URGENT CARE, $General, Firestone/auto, Home Depot, Lowe's, Office Depot, Publix/deli, Save-A-Lot Foods, Tire Kingdom, Tires+, Verizon, Walgreens, Walmart, S 🔲 Chevron/repair, 🍴 Wendy's, 🔲 Family$, Publix, Walgreens
108	Dirksen Dr, DeBary, Deltona, N 🔲 Chevron, 🍴 Burger King, IHOP, 🏠 Hampton Inn, S 🔲 Kangaroo, 🍴 McDonald's, Subway, Waffle House, 🏠 Best Western, 🔲 Publix (2mi)
104	US 17, US 92, Sanford, N 🍴 Captains Cove Rest., 🔲 La Mesa RV Ctr, S 🔲 Citgo/Subway
101c	rd 46, to Mt Dora, Sanford, N 🔲 7-11, 🍴 Tijuana Flats, 🔲 Ace Hardware, Ford, S 🔲 Chevron/dsl, Mobil, Murphy USA/dsl, RaceTrac, 7-11, 🍴 Baskin-Robbins/Dunkin Donuts, Big Boy, Burger King, Cracker Barrel, Denny's, Don Pablo, Firehouse Subs, Hooters, Joe's Crabshack, LJ Silver/Taco Bell, Logan's Roadhouse, McDonald's, Olive Garden, Outback Steaks, Panda Express, Panera Bread, Red Brick Pizza, Red Lobster, Rte 46 Smokehouse, Smokey Bones BBQ, Steak'n Shake, Subway, Wendy's, 🏠 Comfort Inn, Days Inn, SpringHill Suites, Super 8, 🔲 Ⓗ, URGENT CARE, Aldi Foods, Beall's, Belk, Best Buy, Big 10 Tire, BJ's Whse/gas, Books-A-Million, CVS Drug, Dillard's, $Tree, GNC, Goodyear/auto, Harley-Davidson, JC Penney, Jo-Ann Fabrics, Macy's, Marshall's, Michael's, Old Navy, PetCo, Ross, Sears/auto, Target, Tire Kingdom, Tuffy Auto, Verizon, Walmart, World Mkt, mall
101a b	rd 46a, FL 417 (toll), FL 46, Sanford, Heathrow, N 🍴 Applebee's, Carlos'n Charley's, Crisper's, FishBones, Moe's SW Grill, Papa Joe's Pizza, Rikka Asian Bistro, Ruth's Chris Steaks, Shula's 347 Grill, Subway, Vamonos, 🏠 Hampton Inn, Marriott, Residence Inn, Westin, 🔲 URGENT CARE, Publix, Walgreens, S 🔲 Acura, CarMax, CVS Drug, Honda, Kohl's, Sam's Club/gas, 7-11, Toyota/Scion

SANFORD

HEATHROW

98	Lake Mary Blvd, Heathrow, N 🔲 Shell, 🍴 Luigino's Italian, Panera Bread, Peach Valley Cafe, Stonewood Grill, Subway, 🏠 Courtyard, Hyatt Place, 🔲 CVS Drug, Verizon, Walgreens, Winn-Dixie, S 🔲 BP/24hr, Chevron/24hr, Citgo, Mobil/dsl, 7-11, 🍴 Arby's, Baskin-Robbins/Dunkin Donuts, Bob Evans, Boston Mkt, Burger King, Checkers, Chick-fil-A, Chili's, Chipotle Mexican, Chop Stix, Domino's, Firehouse Subs, Frank&Naomi's, KFC, Krystal, Longhorn Steaks, Macaroni Grill, McDonald's, Panera Bread, Papa John's, Papa Joe's Pizza, Pizza Hut/Taco Bell, Quiznos, Starbucks, Steak'n Shake, Subway, Taste of China, Uno, Wendy's, WingZone, 🏠 Candlewood Suites, Extended Stay America, Hilton Garden, Homestead Suites, Homewood Suites, La Quinta, 🔲 Advance Parts, Albertsons, AT&T, Family$, Gander Mtn, Goodyear, Home Depot, K-Mart, Office Depot, Petsmart, Publix, Radio Shack, Staples, Target, Tires+, TJ Maxx, Walgreens, USPO, mall, vet
95mm	rest areas both lanes, full ♿ facilities, 🔲, 🏠, vending, litter barrels, petwalk, 24hr security
94	FL 434, to Winter Springs, Longwood, N 🔲 Hess/dsl, Mobil/dsl, 7-11, 🍴 Burger King, East Buffet, Imperial Dynasty, Kobe Japanese, Melting Pot Rest., Miami Subs,

🅖 = gas   🍴 = food   🛏 = lodging   🅞 = other   Copyright 2012 - The Next E

INTERSTATE 4 CONT'D

E ← → W

ALTAMONTE SPRINGS

Exit	Services
94	Continued Panera Bread, Papa Joe's Pizza, Starbucks, Tijuana Flats, Wendy's, 🛏 Comfort Inn, 🅞 CVS Drug, Publix, **S** 🍴 Bonefish Grill, Boston Mkt, Carmela's Rest., Crisper's, Pickle's NY, 🛏 Candlewood Suites, 🅞 🅗
92	FL 436, Altamonte Springs, **N** 🅖 7-11, Shell/Circle K/dsl, 🍴 Bojangles, Boston Mkt, Checkers, Chick-fil-A, Chipotle Mexican, ChuckeCheese, Cracker Barrel, Kobe Japanese, Little Caesars, Longhorn Steaks, McDonald's, Olive Garden, Perkins, Pollo Tropical, Popeye's, Red Lobster, Sweet Tomatoes, Taco Bell, TGIFriday's, Waffle House, WingHouse, 🛏 Days Inn, Hampton Inn, Hotel Altamonte, Quality Suites, Remington Inn, Residence Inn, SpringHill Suites, 🅞 URGENT CARE, Best Buy, CVS Drug, Family$, Firestone/auto, Goodyear/auto, Tire Kingdom, U-Haul, Walgreens, **S** 🅖 BP, Citgo, Hess/dsl, Mobil/dsl, 🍴 Bahama Breeze, Burger King, Chili's, Denny's, Dunkin Donuts, Elephant Bar, 5 Guys Burgers, Jason's Deli, Mimi's Cafe, Moe's SW Grill, Orlando Alehouse, Panda Express, Pizza Hut, Starbucks, Steak'n Shake, Subway, Wendy's, 🛏 Embassy Suites, Hilton, Homestead Suites, 🅞 🅗, Advance Parts, Albertsons, Barnes&Noble, CVS Drug, Dillard's, JC Penney, Marshall's, Michael's, Office Depot, PetCo, Publix, Ross, Sears/auto, TJMaxx, vet
90b a	FL 414, Maitland Blvd, **N** 🅖 7-11, 🍴 Applebee's, Chick-fil-A, Oak Grill, Wendy's, 🛏 Extended Stay America, Extended Stay Deluxe, Homewood Suites, Sheraton, **S** Maitland Art Ctr
88	FL 423, Lee Rd, **N** 🅖 7-11, 🍴 Arby's, Burger King, Del Frisco, IHOP, Little Caesars, LJ Silver/Taco Bell, McDonald's, Nick&Glna's Italian, Popeye's, Quiznos, 🛏 Countryside Inn, InTown Suites, La Quinta, Motel 6, 🅞 Aamco, Family$, Firestone/auto, Home Depot, Land Rover, Mini, Ross, Save-A-Lot Foods, Tires+, VW, **S** 🅖 Chevron/dsl, Sunoco, 🍴 Denny's, 🅞 BMW
87	FL 426, Fairbanks Ave (no eb re-entry), **N** 🅖 Hess/Blimpie/Dunkin Donuts/Godfather's/dsl, **1mi S** 🍴 Burger King, Chick-fil-A, Chipotle Mexican, Pizza Hut/Taco Bell, Popeye's, Steak'n Shake, Subway, Wendy's, 🅞 Walgreens
86	Par St (from eb, no re-entry), **S** 🅖 Shell/Circle K
85	Princeton St, **S** 🅖 Chevron, 7-11, 🅞 🅗
84	FL 50, Colonial Dr, Ivanhoe Blvd, **N** 🛏 Crowne Plaza
83b	US 17, US 92, FL 50, Amelia St (from eb), **N** 🛏 Crowne Plaza
83a	FL 526 (from eb), Robinson St, **N** 🛏 Sheraton
83	South St (from wb), downtown
82c	Anderson St E, Church St Sta Hist Dist, downtown
82b	Gore Ave (from wb), **S** 🅗, downtown
82a	FL 408 (toll), to FL 526
81b c	Kaley Ave, **S** 🅖 Mobil, 🅞 🅗
81a	Michigan St (from wb), **N** 🅖 Citgo/dsl
80b a	US 17, US 441 S, US 92 W, **S** 🅖 Citgo, Chevron, RaceTrac, Shell, Sunoco, 🍴 Checkers, Gyros, McDonald's, Subway, 🛏 Days Inn, 🅞 Aldi Foods, AutoZone, Goodyear/auto, Save-A-Lot Foods, Walgreens
79	FL 423, 33rd St, John Young Pkwy, **N** 🛏 Ramada Inn, 🅞 Harley-Davidson, **S** 🅖 RaceTrac/dsl, 🍴 IHOP, 🛏 Days Inn
78	Conroy Rd, **N** 🅖 7-11, **S** 🍴 BJ's Rest.,

ORLANDO

Exit	Services
78	Continued Bloomingdale's, Elephant Bar Rest., Green's Grill, Krispy Kreme, McDonald's, Mimi's Cafe, Moe's SW Grill, Olive Garden, Panda Express, Pollo Tropical, Subway, TGIFriday's, Village Tavern, Waffle Shop, Wendy's, Zaxby's, 🅞 AT&T, Best Buy, BJ's Whse, Dick's, $Tree, Home Depot, Infiniti/Smart, Macy's, Marshall's, Mercedes, Old Navy, PetCo, Super Target, mall
77	FL 527, FL TPK (toll)
75b a	FL 435, International Dr (exits left from both lanes), **N** 🅖 Mobil, 🍴 Cracker Barrel, Denny's, TGIFriday's, 🛏 Days Inn, DoubleTree Motel, Fairfield Inn, Holiday Inn, Hyatt Place, 🅞 to Universal Studios, **S** 🅖 Chevron, 7-11, 🍴 Bamboo Rest., Black Angus Steaks, Denny's, Great Western Steaks, IHOP, Ponderosa, Red Lobster, Sizzler, Sweet Tomatoes, 🛏 Best Western, Clarion, Court of Flags Hotel, EconoLodge, Hampton Inn, Hilton Garden, Holiday Inn Express, Homewood Suites, Howard Johnson, International Gateway Inn, Lakefront Inn, Las Palmas Hotel, Motel 6, Rodeway Inn, Sheraton, Super 8, multiple hotels & resorts, 🅞 Bass Pro Shops, Belz Outlet/famous Brands, Books A Million, Office Depot, Walgreens
74b	Universal Studios (from wb)
74a	FL 482, Sand Lake Rd, **N** 🅖 Chevron, 7-11, 🍴 Alexander's Rest., Chick-fil-A, McDonald's, Timpano Italian, Wendy's, multiple restaurants, 🛏 Comfort Suites, 🅞 K-Mart, Publix, Whole Food Mkt, Walgreens, Walmart, **S** 🅖 BP, Chevron, Mobil, 7-11, Shell/Circle K/dsl, 🍴 Asian Buffet, Bahama Breeze, Buffalo Wild Wings, Burger King, Cattleman's Steaks, Charley's Steaks, Checkers, Chili's, CiCi's Pizza, China Jade, Crabhouse, Denny's, Fish Bones Rest., Friendly's, Golden Corral, Houlihan's, IHOP, Italianni's, Kobe Japanese, Lobster Feast, McDonald's, Miller's Alehouse, Ming Court, Olive Garden, Perkins, Pizza Hut, Ponderosa, Popeye's, Sizzler, TGIFriday's, Tony Roma, Uno, Vito's Chophouse, Wendy's, Wild Bean Cafe, 🛏 Best Western, Castle Hotel, Courtyard, Comfort Inn, Crowne Plaza, EconoLodge, Embassy Suites, Fairfield Inn, Hampton Inn, Holiday Inn, Homewood Suites, Howard Johnson, Hyatt Place, La Quinta, Marriott, Masters Inn, Microtel, Peabody Hotel, Quality Inn, Radisson Inn, Ramada Inn, Red Roof Inn, Residence Inn, Rodeway Inn, Rosen Suites, Staybridge Suites, Wyndham Garden, 🅞 🅗, Harley-Davidson, Ripley's Believe-it-or-not!, Stouffer Resort, Walgreens, RV Park
72	FL 528 E (toll, no eb re-entry), to Cape Canaveral, **N** USPO, **S** to 🚲
71	Central FL Pkwy (from eb no re-entry), **S** 🅖 Chevron, 🍴 Wendy's, 🛏 Hilton Garden, Renaissance Resort, Residence Inn, to SeaWorld
68	FL 535, Lake Buena Vista, **N** 🅖 Mobil/dsl, 7-11, Shell/Circle K/dsl, 🍴 AleHouse, Amici Italian, Black Angus Steaks, Buffalo Wild Wings, Burger King, Chevy's Mexican, Chili's, China Buffet, CiCi's Pizza, Denny's, Dragon Super Buffet, El Patron, Flipper's Pizzaria, Fuddrucker's, Giordano's, Havana's Cuisine, Hooters, IHOP, Joe's Crabshack, Johnnie's Rest., Kobe Japanese, Macaroni Grill, McDonald's, Olive Garden, Perkins, Pizza Hut, Qdoba, Quiznos, Red Lobster, Shoney's, Sizzler, Steak'n Shake, Subway, Sweet Tomatoes, Taco Bell, The Crabhouse, TGIFriday's, Uno, 🛏 Comfort Inn, Country Inn&Suites, Courtyard, DoubleTree, Embassy Suites, Extended Stay Deluxe, Hampton Inn, Hawthorn

INTERSTATE 4 CONT'D

E
W
ORLANDO

Exit	Services
68	Continued Suites, Hilton, Hilton Gargen, Holiday Inn, Holiday Inn Express, Homewood Suites, Hyatt Hotel, Orlando Vista Hotel, Quality Inn, Radisson, Residence Inn, Sheraton, StayBridge Suites, 🔲 Gooding's Foods/drug, Walgreens, USPO, **S** 🔲 Chevron, 7-11, Shell/dsl, 🍴 Applebee's, Bahama Breeze, Carrabba's, Chick-fil-A, CiCi's Pizza, Dunkin Donuts, Golden Corral, Landry's Seafood, LoneStar Steaks, Panera Bread, Santa Fe Steaks, Starbucks, Wendy's, 🛏 Blue Heron Resort, Buena Vista Suites, Courtyard, Fairfield Inn, Holiday Inn Resort, Marriott Village, Residence Inn, Sheraton, SpringHill Suites, 🔲 CVS Drug, Orlando Premium Outlets, Verizon, Walgreens
67	Fl 536, to Epcot, **N** DisneyWorld, **1 mi S** 🔲 7-11, 🍴 Asian Harbor, 🛏 Buena Vista, Marriott, 🔲 CVS Drug, to ✈, multiple resorts
65	Osceola Pkwy, to FL 417 (toll), **N** to DisneyWorld, Epcot, Animal Kingdom, and Wide World of Sports
64b a	US 192, FL 536, to FL 417 (toll), to Kissimmee, **N** 🔲 7-11, to DisneyWorld, MGM, **0-3 mi S** 🔲 Mobil/dsl, RaceTrac/dsl, 7-11, 🍴 Applebee's, Arby's, Bob Evans, Boston Lobster Feast, Burger King, Charley's Steakhouse, Checkers, Chick-fil-A, Chili's, Chinese Buffet, CiCi's Pizza, Cracker Barrel, Denny's, Domino's, Dunkin Donuts, Golden Corral, IHOP, Joe's Crabshack, Kabuki Oriental, KFC, Kobe Japanese, Krispy Kreme, Logan's Roadhouse, Longhorn Steaks, Macaroni Grill, McDonald's, Ocean 11 Rest., Olive Garden, Pacino's Italian, Panda Express, Papa John's, Perkins, Pizza Hut, Ponderosa, Quiznos, Red Lobster, Rio Mexican Grill, Ruby Tuesday, Sizzlin Grill, Smokey Bones BBQ, Starbucks, Subway, Taco Bell, TGIFriday's, Uno, Waffle House, Wendy's, 🛏 Best Inn, Celebration Suites, Comfort Suites, Days Inn, Holiday Inn, Howard Johnson, Knight Inn, Masters Inn, Mona Lisa Hotel, Motel 6, Orlando Palms, Parkway Resort, Quality Suites, Ramada, Radisson, Red Roof Inn, Rodeway Inn, Sun Inn, Super 8, Seralago Hotel, Travelodge, 🔲 🅷, AT&T, Camping World RV Ctr, CVS Drug, $General, Harley-Davidson, Jo-Ann Fabrics, Marshall's, Publix, Target, Walgreens, USPO, factory outlet/famous brands
62	FL 417 (toll, from eb), World Dr, **N** to DisneyWorld, **S** Celebration, to ✈
60	Fl 429, N (toll), Apopka
58	FL 532, to Kissimmee, **N** 🔲 BP, 7-11, 🍴 Chili's, China One, McDonald's, Pizzaria, Subway, 🛏 Championship Gate Resort, 🔲 Publix, Walgreens, **S** 🍴 Dunkin Donuts (1mi), 🛏 Reunion Resort (2mi)
55	US 27, to Haines City, **N** 🔲 7-11, Sunoco/dsl, 🍴 Burger King, Cracker Barrel, Denny's, McDonald's, Waffle House, Wendy's, 🛏 Comfort Inn, Hampton Inn, Holiday Inn Express, Super 8, 🔲 Ford, FL Camp Inn (5mi), **S** 🔲 BP/dsl, Marathon, RaceWay/dsl, 7-11, Shell/dsl/service, 🍴 Bob Evans, CiCi's Pizza, Grand China, Perkins, Sake Steaks, Subway, 🛏 Days Inn, Microtel, Quality Inn, Southgate Inn, 🔲 🅷, Belk, Best Buy, Books-A-Million, Deer Creek RV Resort, Dick's, $Tree, GNC, JC Penney, KOA, Michael's, Petsmart, Ross, Staples, Target, Theme World RV Park, Verizon, to Cypress Gardens, tourist info

ORLANDO

LAKELAND

Exit	Services
48	rd 557, to Winter Haven, Lake Alfred, **S** 🔲 BP/dsl
46mm	**rest area both lanes, full** ♿ **facilities,** 🔲, 🚻, **vending, litter barrels, petwalk, 24hr security**
44	FL 559, to Auburndale, **S** 🔲 BP/dsl/scales/24hr, 🔷Loves/Arby's/dsl/scales/24hr
41	FL 570, W toll, Auburndale, Lakeland
38	FL 33, to Lakeland, Polk City
33	rd 582, to FL 33, Lakeland, **N** 🔲 BP, Exxon/24hr, 7-11, 🍴 Applebee's, Cracker Barrel, 5 Guys Burger, McDonald's, Starbucks, Wendy's, 🛏 Crestwood Suites, Country Inn&Suites, Days Inn, Jameson Inn, Hampton Inn, La Quinta, Quality Inn, Ramada, Sleep Inn, 🔲 BMW, CVS Drug, GNC, Publix, **S** 🔲 BP/dsl, 🍴 Waffle House, 🛏 ValuePlace, 🔲 🅷, Harley-Davidson, Lakeland RV Resort, Nissan
32	US 98, Lakeland, **N** 🔲 BP, Mobil, Murphy USA/dsl, 7-11, 🍴 Asian Buffet, Checkers, Chili's, ChuckeCheese, CiCi's Pizza, DQ, Domino's, Dunkin Donuts, Golden Corral, Hooters, IHOP, KFC, Ling's Buffet, LJ Silver, McDonald's, Moe's SW Grill, Olive Garden, Outback Steaks, Panera Bread, Papa John's, Place Garden, Red Lobster, Smokey Bones BBQ, Sonny's BBQ, Starbucks, Steak'n Shake, Subway, Taco Bell, TGIFriday's, Wendy's, Zaxby's, 🛏 Comfort Inn, La Quinta, Royalty Inn, 🔲 Advance Parts, Aldi Foods, AT&T, AutoZone, Barnes&Noble, Beall's, Belk, Best Buy, CVS Drug, Dillard's, $General, Firestone/auto, Goodyear/auto, JC Penney, JoAnn Fabrics, Lowe's, Macy's, PepBoys, PetCo, Publix, Sam's Club/gas, Sears/auto, Staples, Sweetbay Foods, Target, Tire Kingdom, Tires+, Verizon, Walgreens, Walmart (2mi), vet, **S** 🔲 Coastal, RaceTrac/dsl, 7-11, Sunoco/dsl, 🍴 Bob Evans, Burger King, Denny's, LJ Silver, McDonald's, Popeye's, Waffle House, 🛏 Howard Johnson, Motel 6, 🔲 🅷, AutoZone, Beall's, Chrysler/Dodge, Family$, Home Depot, NAPA, U-Haul
31	FL 539, to Kathleen, Lakeland, **N** 🔲 Shell/Circle K, 🍴 Romeo's Pizza, Suwbay, Wendy's, 🔲 Publix/dsl, Walgreens, **S** hist dist
28	FL 546, to US 92, Memorial Blvd, Lakeland, **S** 🔲 Shell/Circle K/dsl, Sunoco, 🍴 Hardee's
27	FL 570, E toll, Lakeland
25	County Line Rd, **S** 🔲 Citgo/dsl, Shell/Circle K/Subway, 🍴 McDonald's, Wendy's, 🛏 Fairfield Inn, 🔲 FL Air Museum
22	FL 553, Park Rd, Plant City, **N** 🔲 Chevrolet, **S** 🔲 Shell/Circle K/Subway, 🍴 Arby's, Burger King, Denny's, Popeye's, 🛏 Comfort Inn, Holiday Inn Express
21	FL 39, Alexander St, to Zephyrhills, Plant City, **S on FL 39** 🔲 BP/dsl, Shell/dsl, 🛏 Days Inn, Red Rose Inn/rest.
19	FL 566, to Thonotosassa, **N** 🔲 BP, **S** 🔲 RaceTrac/dsl,

◉ = gas ⑪ = food ⌂ = lodging ◎ = other   Copyright 2012 - The Next Exit®

Exit	Services

INTERSTATE 4 CONT'D

Exit	Services
19	Continued
	⑪ Applebee's, BuddyFreddy's Rest., Carraba's, Lin's Chinese, Little Caesars, McDonald's, Mi Casa, OutBack Steaks, Pizza Hut/Taco Bell, Sonny's BBQ, Starbucks, Subway, Waffle House, ◎ Ⓗ, AT&T, $General, Publix, Walgreens
17	Branch Forbes Rd, **N** ◉ Marathon, Sunoco, ◎ Dinosaur World, **S** ◉ BP, Shell/Circle K/Subway/dsl, ◎ Advance Parts, AutoZone
14	McIntosh Rd, **N** ◉ BP/dsl, ◎ Longview RV Ctr, Windward RV Park (2mi), **S** ◉ RaceWay/dsl, 7-11/dsl, ⑪ Burger King, McDonald's/playplace, ◎ Bates RV Ctr, East Tampa RV Park
12mm	**weigh sta, both lanes**
10	rd 579, Mango, Thonotosassa, **N** ◉ ⊕FLYING J/Denny's/dsl/LP/scales/24hr, Sunoco, TA/Arby's/Popeye's/dsl/scales/24hr/@, ⑪ Bob Evans, Cracker Barrel, ⌂ Country Inn&Suites, Hampton Inn, ◎ Camping World RV Ctr, Ford/Lincoln/Mercury, Hillsboro River SP, Lazy Day's RV Ctr, Rally RV Park, **S** ◉ Shell/Circle K/dsl, ⑪ Hardee's, Subway, Wendy's, ⌂ Masters Inn
9	I-75, N to Ocala, S to Naples
7	US 92W, to US 301, Hillsborough Ave, **N** ◉ Chevron/dsl, ⑪ Waffle House, ◎ Motel 6, ◎ Hard Rock Hotel/casino, **S** ◉ BP, Hess, ⑪ 5 Guys Burgers, WingHouse, ⌂ Comofort Suites, Holiday Inn Express, La Quinta, Red Roof Inn, ◎ FL Expo Fair
6	Orient Rd (from eb)
5	FL 574, MLK Blvd, **N** ⑪ McDonald's, **S** ◉ BP, Mobil/Subway, Sunoco, ⑪ Wendy's, ⌂ Fairfield Inn, Masters Inn, ◎ Kenworth
3	US 41, 50th St, Columbus Dr (exits left from eb), **N** ◉ Chevron/dsl, Shell, ⌂ Days Inn, Quality Inn, USA Inn, ◎ to Busch Gardens, **S** ◉ Marathon/dsl, Sunoco/dsl, ⑪ Checker's, Church's, KFC, McDonald's, Salem's Subs, Subway, Taco Bell, ⌂ Howard Johnson, ◎ Advance Parts, Family$, Save-A-Lot Foods, Sweetbay Foods
1	FL 585, 22nd, 21st St, Port of Tampa, **S** ◉ Sunoco, ⑪ Burger King, McDonald's, ◎ museum
0mm	I-4 begins/ends on I-275, exit 45b.

INTERSTATE 10

Exit	Services
363mm	I-10 begins/ends on I-95, exit 351b.
362	Stockton St, to Riverside, **S** ◉ BP, Gate, ◎ Ⓗ
361	US 17, S (from wb), downtown
360	FL 129, McDuff Ave, **S** ◉ BP, ⑪ Popeye's
359	Lenox Ave, Edgewood Ave (from wb)
358	FL 111, Cassat Ave, **N** ◉ Hess/Blimpie/Godfather's/dsl, Shell/Subway/dsl, ⑪ Burger King, McDonald's, Popeye's, Wendy's, ◎ AutoZone, Mr Transmission, **S** ◉ BP, RaceWay/dsl, ⑪ Baskin-Robbins/Dunkin Donuts, Domino's, Gorgi's BBQ, Pizza Hut, Taco Bell, Wendy's, ◎ Advance Parts, Discount Tire, Lowe's, Walgreens
357	FL 103, Lane Ave, **N** ◉ Hess/dsl, ⑪ Andy's Sandwiches, ⌂ Knights Inn, Stars Rest Inn, **S** ◉ BP, Shell/dsl, ⑪ Applebee's, Bono's BBQ, Cross Creek Steaks, Hardee's, KFC, Lee's Dragon, Linda's Seafood, McDonald's, Monty's Pizza, Piccadilly's, ⌂ Diamond Inn, Executive Inn, Sleep Inn, ◎ Home Depot, Office Depot, PepBoys

Exit	Services
356	I-295, N to Savannah, S to St Augustine
355	Marietta, **N** ◉ Gate/dsl/24hr, Exxon, **S** ◉ Hess/Blimpie/Dunkin Donuts/Godfather's/dsl, Shell/dsl, ⑪ Domino's
351	FL 115, Chaffee Rd, to Cecil Fields, **N** ◉ Kangaroo/dsl/24hr, ◎ Rivers RV Ctr, **S** ◉ Chevron, KwikChek, Shell/Subway/dsl/24hr, ⑪ Cracker Barrel, King Wok, McDonald's, Perard's Italian, Quiznos, Wendy's, ⌂ Best Western, Fairfield Inn, Hampton Inn, Holiday Inn Express, ◎ Family$, Winn-Dixie
350	FL 23, Cecil Commerce Ctr Pkwy
343	US 301, to Starke, Baldwin, **S** ◉ Chevron, ▦/Subway/dsl/scales/24hr, TA/Shell/Arby's/dsl/scales/24hr/@, ⑪ Burger King, McDonald's, Waffle House, ⌂ Best Western, ◎ NAPA
336	FL 228, to Maxville, Macclenny, **N** ◉ Murphy USA/dsl, ⑪ Starbucks, ◎ Ⓗ, Walmart /Subway, fireworks
335	FL 121, to Lake Butler, Macclenny, **N** ◉ BP/dsl, Citgo, Kangaroo, ⑪ China Dragon, Domino's, Hardee's, KFC, Krystal River Seafood, McDonald's, Pizza Hut, Subway, Taco Bell, Waffle House, Wendy's, Woody's BBQ, Zaxby's, ⌂ American Inn, ◎ Ⓗ, Advance Parts, AutoZone, $General, $Tree, Food Lion, Walgreens, Winn-Dixie, USPO, **S** ◉ RaceWay/dsl, Exxon/dsl, ⑪ Burger King, China Buffet, El San Jose, ⌂ EconoLodge, Travelodge
333	rd 125, Glen Saint Mary, **N** ◉ Citgo/dsl/24hr
327	rd 229, to Raiford, Sanderson, **1 mi N** gas
324	US 90, to Olustee, Sanderson, **S** ◉ Citgo/dsl, to Olustee Bfd
318mm	**rest area both lanes, full ♿ facilities, ▢, ▤, vending, litter barrels, petwalk, 24hr security**
303	US 441, to Fargo, Lake City, **N** ◉ Chevron/dsl/24hr, ◎ Lake City Camping (1mi), Oaks'n Pines RV Park, **S** ◉ Shell/dsl, Sunoco/dsl, ⑪ Huddle House, ⌂ Days Inn, ◎ Ⓗ
301	US 41, to Lake City, **N** ◉ Exxon/dsl, ◎ to Stephen Foster Ctr, **S** ◎ Ⓗ
296b a	I-75, N to Valdosta, S to Tampa
294mm	**rest area both lanes, full ♿ facilities, ▢, ▤, vending, litter barrels, petwalk, 24hr security**
292	rd 137, to Wellborn
283	US 129, to Live Oak, **N** ◉ Penn/dsl, to Boys Ranch, **S** ◉ BP, Chevron/dsl, Exxon, Murphy USA/dsl, Shell/dsl, ⑪ China Buffet, Huddle House, Krystal, McDonald's, Subway, Taco Bell, Waffle House, Wendy's, ⌂ Best Western, EconoLodge, Holiday Inn Express, ◎ Ⓗ, $Tree, Lowe's, Verizon, Walmart
275	US 90, Live Oak, **N** to Suwannee River SP, **S** ◎ Ⓗ
271mm	**truck insp sta both lanes**
269mm	Suwannee River
265mm	**rest areas both lanes, full ♿ facilities, ▢, ▤, vending, litter barrels, petwalk, 24hr security**
264mm	**weigh sta both lanes**
262	rd 255, Lee, **N** ◉ Exxon/dsl, ◎ to Suwannee River SP, **S** ◉ Jimmy's/Chevron/rest./dsl/24hr, ⬭Loves/Arby's/dsl/scales/24hr
258	FL 53, **N** ◉ Chevron/McDonald's/dsl, Mobil/DQ/Subway/Wendy's/dsl/scales/24hr, Shell/Burger King/dsl/24hr, ⑪ Denny's, Waffle House, ⌂ Days Inn, Holiday Inn Express, Super 8, ◎ Ⓗ, **S** ⌂ Deerwood Inn, ◎ Jellystone Camping, Madison Camping
251	FL 14, to Madison, **N** ◉ Mobil/Arby's/24hr, ◎ Ⓗ
241	US 221, Greenville, **N** ◉ Mobil/DQ

INTERSTATE 10 CONT'D

Exit	Services
234mm	rest area both lanes, full ♿ facilities, 🅲, 🛢, litter barrels, petwalk, 24hr security
233	rd 257, Aucilla, **N** 🅿 Shell/dsl
225	US 19, to Monticello, **N** 🅾 Camper's World Camping, **S** 🅿 BP, Chevron/McDonald's, Mobil/Arby's/dsl, Sunoco/dsl, 🍴 Huddle House, 🛏 Days Inn, Super 8, 🅾 KOA, dogtrack
217	FL 59, Lloyd, **S** 🅿 BP/dsl/rest./scales/24hr, Shell/Subway/dsl, 🛏 Quality Inn, 🅾 truckwash
209b a	US 90, Tallahassee, **S** 🅿 Circle K/dsl, Shell/Subway/dsl, 🍴 Eastern Chinese, Waffle House, 🛏 Best Western, Country Inn&Suites, 🅾 Publix, Tallahassee RV Park, auto museum
203	FL 61, US 319, Tallahassee, **N** 🅿 BP/dsl, Shell/Circle K, USA Gas, 🍴 Applebee's, Bonefish Grill, Firehouse Subs, Georgio's Rest., Great Wall Chinese, Marble Slab, McDonald's, Moe's SW Grill, Morelia Mexican, Panda Buffet, Popeye's, Sonny's BBQ, Starbucks, Subway, Taco Bell, Village Pizza, Waffle House, Wendy's, 🛏 Motel 6, 🅾 AT&T, Books-A-Million, CVS Drug, Discount Tire, $Tree, Fresh Mkt Foods, GNC, Publix, Radio Shack, SteinMart, SuperLube, TJ Maxx, Walgreens, Walmart (3mi), **S** 🅿 BP, Citgo, 🍴 Boston Mkt, Carraba's, Chick-fil-A, Los Amigos, McDonald's, Osaka Japanese, Outback Steaks, Steak'n Shake, Subway, Ted's MT Grill, TGIFriday's, Village Inn, Zaxby's, 🛏 Cabot Lodge, Courtyard, Hampton Inn, Hilton Garden, Residence Inn, Studio+, 🅾 🏥, URGENT CARE, Advance Parts, Goodyear/auto, Home Depot, Infiniti, Office Depot, Petsmart, Tire Kingdom, vet
199	US 27, Tallahassee, **N** 🅿 BP/dsl, Chevron/dsl, McKenzie/dsl, 🍴 Burger King, Dominos, Papa John's, Pizza Hut, Taco Bell, Waffle House, 🛏 Comfort Inn, Country Inn&Suites, Days Inn, Fairfield Inn, Holiday Inn, Microtel, Quality Inn, 🅾 Big Oak RV Park (2mi), $General, USPO, Walmart, **S** 🅿 Chevron/dsl, Shell/Circle K, USA/dsl, 🍴 Acapulco Mexican, Arby's, Boston Mkt, Burger King, Chick-fil-A, China Buffet, ChuckeCheese, Cracker Barrel, Crystal River Seafood, DQ, El Jalisco, Firehouse Subs, Golden Corral, Hooters, Julie's Rest., Kacey's Rest., KFC, Krispy Kreme, Krystal River Seafood, Lindy's Chicken, Little Caesars, Longhorn Steaks, McDonald's, On-the-Border, Papa John's, Quiznos, Red Lobster, Seminole Wind, Shoney's, Sonic, Sonny's BBQ, Subway, TCBY, Whataburger, Wendy's, Zaxby's, 🛏 Best Value Inn, Capital Inn, EconoLodge, Guesthouse Inn, Howard Johnson, La Quinta, Motel 6, Super 8, 🅾 AT&T, AutoZone, Barnes&Noble, Belk, Big 10 Tire, CVS Drug, $Tree, Publix, Ross, Staples, Sun Tire, Tire Kingdom, Tuffy Auto, Verizon, Walgreens, city park, mall, vet
196	FL 263, Tallahassee, **S** 🅿 Chevron/dsl, Shell/dsl, Stop'n Save Gas, 🍴 Applebee's, Checker's, Firehouse Subs, KFC, Sonic, Steak'n Shake, Subway, Waffle House, Wendy's, Zaxby's, 🛏 Sleep Inn, 🅾 Aamco, Advance Parts, Chrysler/Dodge/Jeep, Harley-Davidson, Home Depot, Lowe's, Mazda, Stop'n Save, Toyota, VW, Walgreens, Walmart, ➡
194mm	rest area both lanes, full ♿ facilities, 🅲, 🛢, vending, litter barrels, petwalk, 24hr security
192	US 90, to Tallahassee, Quincy, **N** 🅿 BP, ⚡FLYING J/Denny's/dsl/LP/scales/24hr, 🛏 Comfort Inn, Howard

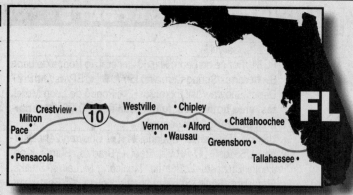

Q**U****I****N****C****Y**	**192**	Continued Johnson, 🅾 Camping World RV Ctr (2mi), **S** 🅿 ⬛/Subway/dsl/scales/24hr, 🍴 Waffle House, 🛏 Best Western, 🅾 RV Camping (4mi)
	181	FL 267, Quincy, **N** 🅿 Murphy USA, 🍴 Dominos, Mayflower Chinese, 🅾 🏥, Walmart, **S** 🅿 BP/dsl, Pure, 🛏 Hampton Inn, Holiday Inn Express, Parkway Inn, to Lake Talquin SF
	174	FL 12, to Greensboro, **N** 🅿 BP, Shell/Burger King/dsl, 🅾 Beaver Lake RV Park
	166	rd 270A, Chattahoochee, **N** to Lake Seminole, to Torreya SP, **S** 🅿 Shell/dsl, 🅾 KOA (1mi)
	161mm	rest area both lanes, full ♿ facilities, 🅲, 🛢, vending, litter barrels, petwalk, 24hr security
	160mm	Apalachicola River, central/eastern time zone
	158	rd 286, Sneads, **N** Lake Seminole, to Three Rivers SP
	155mm	weigh sta both lanes
	152	FL 69, to Grand Ridge, Blountstown, **N** 🅿 BP, Exxon
	142	FL 71, to Marianna, Oakdale, **N** 🅿 87 Depot, Murphy USA, ⬛/Arby's/dsl/scales/24hr, 🍴 Beef O'Brady's, Burger King, Firehouse Subs, KFC/LJ Silver, Pizza Hut, PoFolks, Ruby Tuesday, San Marco's Mexican, Sonny's BBQ, Waffle House, 🛏 Comfort Inn, Country Inn&Suites, Days Inn, Fairfield Inn, Marianna Inn, Microtel, Quality Inn, Super 8, 🅾 🏥, AT&T, Lowe's, Walmart/Subway, Arrowhead Camping (2mi), to FL Caverns SP (8mi), **S** 🅿 Chevron/dsl, Sunoco/dsl, TA/Taco Bell/Popeye's/dsl/scales/24hr/@, 🍴 McDonald's, 🛏 Best Value Inn, 🅾 camping
	136	FL 276, to Marianna, **N** 🅾 to FL Caverns SP (8mi)
	133mm	rest area both lanes, full ♿ facilities, 🅲, 🛢, litter barrels, petwalk, 24hr security
C**H****I****P****L****E****Y**	**130**	US 231, Cottondale, **N** 🅿 BP/dsl, Chevron, 🍴 Hardee's, Subway, 🅾 Big Rig RV Park, **S** 🅿 RaceWay
	120	FL 77, to Panama City, Chipley, **N** 🅿 BP/dsl, Exxon/Burger King/Stuckey's, Murphy USA, Shell/Dominos/dsl, 🍴 Arby's, Cancun Mexican, Hardee's, Hungry Howie's, JinJin Chinese, KFC, McDonald's, Pizza Hut, Skins&Bubba's, Sonic, Subway, Waffle House, Wendy's, 🛏 Comfort Inn, Days Inn/rest., Executive Inn, Holiday Inn Express, Super 8, 🅾 🏥, Advance Parts, CVS Drug, $General, $Tree, NAPA, O'Reilly Parts, Save-a-Lot Foods, Verizon, Walmart, **S** Falling Water SP
	112	FL 79, Bonifay, **N** 🅿 Chevron, Citgo/Tom Thumb/dsl, Exxon/dsl, 🍴 Burger King, Hardee's, Hungry Howie, McDonald's, Pizza Hut, Simbo's Rest., Subway, Waffle House, 🛏 Best Western, Bonifay Inn, Tivoli Inn, 🅾 🏥, FL Springs RV Camping, Fred's Drug, repair, **S** Panama City Beach

📇 = gas 🍴 = food 🛏 = lodging ⊡ = other   Copyright 2012 - The Next Exit®

INTERSTATE 10 CONT'D

Exit	Services
104	rd 279, Caryville
96	FL 81, Ponce de Leon, **N** ⊡ $General, to Ponce de Leon SRA, Vortex Spring Camping (5mi), **S** 📇 BP/dsl/24hr, 87 Depot/Subway/dsl, Exxon/dsl, ⊡ Ponce de Leon Motel, **rest area both lanes, full ♿ facilities, ⊡, 🚻, litter barrels, petwalk, 24hr security**
85	US 331, De Funiak Springs, **N** 📇 Chevron/24hr, Murphy USA/dsl, 🍴 Arby's, Beef O'Brady's, Burger King, JinJin Chinese, LaRumba Mexican, McLain's Steaks, Pizza Hut, Sonic, Subway, Waffle House, 🛏 Best Value Inn, Sundown Inn, Super 8, Travelodge, ⊡ Ⓗ, $General, Lowe's, Walgreens, Walmart, Winn-Dixie, winery, **S** 📇 BP, 87 Depot/dsl, Emerald Express/dsl, 🍴 KFC, McDonald's, Whataburger, 🛏 Best Western, Comfort Inn, ⊡ Ⓗ, camping (3mi)
70	FL 285, to Ft Walton Bch, Eglin AFB, **N** 📇 RaceWay, **S** 🛏 Rodeway Inn, ⊡ Dixie RV Ctr, repair
60mm	**rest area both lanes, full ♿ facilities, ⊡, 🚻, vending, litter barrels, petwalk, 24hr security**
56	FL 85, Crestview, Eglin AFB, **N** 📇 BP/dsl, Mobil/Chester's/dsl, 🍴 Applebee's, Asian Garden, Bamboo Chinese, Beef O'Brady's, Burger King, Capt D's, China 1, Golden Asian, Hungry Howie's, McDonald's, Mia's Italian, Ryan's, Sonic, Starbucks, Taco Bell, 🛏 Country Inn&Suites, EconoLodge, ⊡ Ⓗ, Advance Parts, AT&T, AutoZone, BigLots, $General, Lowe's, Publix, Staples, Walgreens, Walmart , **S** 📇 Citgo/Tom Thumb/dsl, Exxon, 🍴 Arby's, Coach-n-Four Steaks, Cracker Barrel, Hardee's, Hooters, LaRumba Mexican, Waffle House, Wendy's, Whataburger, 🛏 Baymont Inn, Comfort Inn, Hampton Inn, Holiday Inn Express, Jameson Inn, Quality Inn, Super 8, ⊡ Buick/GMC, Chevrolet, Ford, museum, RV camping
45	rd 189, to US 90, Holt, **N** 📇 Chevron (1mi), 🍴 Gartz Pizza, ⊡ to Blackwater River SP, Eagle's Landing RV Park, **S** River's Edge RV Park (1mi)
31	FL 87, to Ft Walton Beach, Milton, **N** 📇 Exxon/dsl, 🍴 Waffle House, 🛏 Holiday Inn Express, ⊡ Blackwater River SP, Gulf Pines KOA, **S** 📇 BP, Shell/dsl, 🛏 Comfort Inn, Red Carpet Inn
31mm	**rest area both lanes, full ♿ facilities, ⊡, 🚻, litter barrels, petwalk, 24hr security**
28	rd 89, Milton, **N** Ⓗ
27mm	Blackwater River
26	rd 191, Bagdad, Milton, **N** 📇 Shell/Circle K/dsl, ⊡ Ⓗ, **S** 📇 Chevron/DQ/Stuckey's, ⊡ Pelican Palms RV Park
22	N FL 281, Avalon Blvd, **N** 📇 Tom Thumb, 🍴 McDonald's, **S** 📇 Shell/Circle K/Subway/dsl, 🍴 Waffle House, 🛏 Red Roof Inn, ⊡ RV Park (3mi)
18mm	Escambia Bay
17	US 90, Pensacola, **N** 📇 BP/dsl, **S** 📇 Exxon, 🍴 DQ, 🛏 Ramada Inn/rest.
14mm	**truck inspection sta**
13	FL 291, to US 90, Pensacola, **N** 📇 BP, Exxon, Shell/dsl, 🍴 Arby's, Capt D's, Denny's, DQ, La Hacienda Mexican, McDonald's, Monterrey Mexican, Santino's Cafe, Subway, Taco Bell, Waffle House, 🛏 Comfort Inn, Holiday Inn, La Quinta, Motel 6, ⊡ CVS Drug, Food World/24hr, Ross, U-Haul, Walgreens, **S** 🍴 ChuckeCheese, Fazoli's, Honeybaked Ham, Los Rancheros Mexican,
13	Continued Waffle House, Wendy's, Whataburger, 🛏 Baymont Inn, Best Value Inn, Courtyard, Extended Stay America, Fairfield Inn, Hampton Inn, Motel 6, Red Roof Inn, TownePlace Suites, University Inn, ⊡ Ⓗ, Belk, Firestone/auto, JC Penney, Jo-Ann Fabrics, Mr Transmission, Radio Shack, Sears/auto, TJ Maxx, Tuesday Morning, U-Haul, mall
12	I-110, to Pensacola, Hist Dist, Islands Nat Seashore
10b a	US 29, Pensacola, **N** 📇 BP, Kangaroo/dsl/scales, Murphy USA/dsl, 🍴 Church's, Hardee's, Ryan's, Sonic, Vallarta Mexican, Waffle House, ⊡ Advance Parts, AutoZone, Carpenter's RV Ctr, $Tree, GNC, Office Depot, O'Reilly Parts, Radio Shack, Tires+, Walmart, **0-2 mi S** 📇 Citgo, RaceWay/dsl, Shell/Circle K, 🍴 Burger King, Capt D's, Founaris Bro's Rest., IHOP, McDonald's, Pizza Hut, Ruby Tuesday, Smokey's BBQ, Wendy's, Whataburger, 🛏 Best Value Inn, Days Inn, Executive Inn, Howard Johnson, Key West Inn, Luxury Suites, Motel 6, Palm Court, Pensacola Inn, Quality Inn, Ramada Inn, Travelodge, ⊡ Buick/Cadillac/GMC, Chevrolet, Dodge/Jeep, Ford, Harley-Davidson, Honda, Hyundai, Kia, LeisureTyme RV Ctr, Lincoln/Mercury, Mazda, NAPA, Nissan, Subaru, Suzuki/Toyota
7b a	FI 297, Pine Forest Rd, **N** 📇 Chevron, 🍴 McDonald's, Starbucks, Wendy's, 🛏 Best Western, Comfort Inn, Garden Inn, Value Place, ⊡ Publix, Tall Oaks Camping, transmissions, **S** 📇 BP, Citgo, Raceway/dsl, 🍴 Burger King, Cracker Barrel, Hardee's, McDonald's, Ruby Tuesday, Sonny's BBQ, Subway, Waffle House, Wayne's Diner, 🛏 Country Inn&Suites, Holiday Inn Express, Microtel, Quality Inn, Red Roof Inn, ⊡ Food World/24hr, Big Lagoon SRA (12mi), museum
5	US 90 A, **N** 📇 BP, Shell/Kangaroo/dsl, 🍴 Beef'O Brady's, Hershey's Ice Cream, Starbucks, Wendy's, ⊡ Publix/gas, Walgreens, **S** Leisure Lakes Camping
4mm	**Welcome Ctr eb, full ♿ facilities, info, ⊡, 🚻, vending, litter barrels, petwalk, 24hr security**
3mm	**weigh sta both lanes**
1mm	**inspection sta eb**
0mm	Florida/Alabama state line, Perdido River

INTERSTATE 75

Exit	Services
471mm	Florida/Georgia state line. Motorist callboxes begin sb.
469mm	**Welcome Ctr sb, full ♿ facilities, info, ⊡, 🚻, vending, litter barrels, petwalk**
467	FL 143, Jennings, **E** ⊡ Budget Lodge, **W** 📇 Exxon/dsl, 🛏 N Florida Inn, Scottish Inn, ⊡ Jennings Camping, fireworks
460	FL 6, Jasper, **E** 📇 BP/Burger King, Indian River Fruit/gas, Penn Oil/Huddle House/dsl, 🛏 7 Oaks Inn, **W** 📇 Shell/dsl, Sunoco/dsl, 🍴 Sheffield's Country Kitchen, 🛏 Scottish Inn, ⊡ Suwanee River SP
451	US 129, Jasper, Live Oak, **E** 📇 Mobil/DQ/Subway/dsl, **W** 📇 BP/Lester's Grill/dsl, ⊡ Suwanee Music Park (4mi), to FL Boys Ranch
448mm	**weigh sta both lanes**
446mm	**insp sta both lanes**
443mm	Historic Suwanee River
439	to FL 136, White Springs, Live Oak, **E** 📇 Gate/dsl, Shell/dsl, 🍴 Ann's Country Kitchen, McDonald's, ⊡ Kelly RV Park (5mi), Lee's Camping (3mi), Suwanee RV Camping (4mi), to, S Foster Ctr, **W** 🛏 Best Value Inn

FL

E W CRESTVIEW PENSACOLA

N S PENSACOLA

N ↕ S

LAKE CITY

INTERSTATE 75 CONT'D

Exit	Services
435	I-10, E to Jacksonville, W to Tallahassee
427	US 90, to Live Oak, Lake City, E BP/dsl, Chevron/dsl/24hr, Gas'n Go, Murphy USA/dsl, Shell, Applebee's, Arby's, Burger King, Cedar River Seafood, Cracker Barrel, Domino's, Elliano's Coffee, El Potro, Hardee's, Gondolier Italian, IHOP, Kazbor's Grille, Ken's BBQ, Krystal, McAlister's Deli, McDonald's, Moe's SW Grill, Ole Times Buffet, Papa John's, Pizza Hut, Red Lobster, Ruby Tuesday, Sonny's BBQ, Starbucks, Steak'n Shake, Subway, Taco Bell, TX Roadhouse, Waffle House, Wendy's, Zaxby's, Best Inn, Cypress Inn, Days Inn, Driftwood Inn, Holiday Inn, Howard Johnson, Jameson Inn, Piney Woods Motel, Ramada Ltd, Rodeway Inn, Scottish Inn, H, Advance Parts, AT&T, AutoZone, Belk, BigLots, CVS Drug, Ford/Lincoln/Mercury, Home Depot, In&Out RV Park, JC Penney, Lowe's, Publix, Radio Shack, Tire Kingdom, TireMart, TJ Maxx, Toyota/Scion, Verizon, Walgreens, Walmart, mall, W BP, Chevron/dsl, Shell, Bob Evans, China One, Waffle House, Best Western, Cabot Lodge, Comfort Suites, Country Inn&Suites, EconoLodge, Fairfield Inn, Gateway Inn, Hampton Inn, Quality Inn, Red Roof Inn, Travelodge, Cadillac/Chevrolet, Chrysler/Dodge/Jeep, Family$, FoodLion, Nissan, vet
423	FL 47, to Ft White, Lake City, E Shell/dsl, Mack/Volvo Trucks, W BP/dsl, Exxon/dsl, Stop-N-Go/USPO, Little Caesars, Subway, Motel 8, Super 8, Casey Jones RV Park, $General, Freightliner
414	US 41, US 441, to Lake City, High Springs, E Chevron/dsl/24hr, Exxon, Pitstop, Traveler's Inn, Travelodge, W BP/dsl, Shell/dsl, Huddle House, Subway, Red Carpet Inn, antiques, tires/repair, to O'Leno SP
413mm	**rest areas both lanes, full facilities, vending, litter barrels, petwalk**
409mm	Santa Fe River
404	rd 236, to High Springs, E Chevron/fruits/gifts, Citgo/dsl, Sunoco, W High Springs Camping
399	US 441, to High Sprs, Alachua, E BP, Kangaroo, Domino's, El Toro Mexican, McDonald's, Moe's SW Grill, Pizza Hut, Sonny's BBQ, Subway, Taco Bell, Waffle House, EconoLodge, Quality Inn, Advance Parts, $General, Family$, FoodLion, Hitchcock's Foods, Traveler's Campground (1mi), Walgreens, vet, W Chevron, Citgo/PizzaVito/dsl, Exxon/Wendy's, Kazbor's Grille, KFC, Days Inn, Royal Inn
390	FL 222, to Gainesville, E Chevron/dsl, Exxon/McDonald's/dsl, Kangaroo/Subway/dsl, Burger King, La Fiesta Mexican, Pomodoro Cafe, Sonnys BBQ, Wendy's, Publix, Walgreens, W BP/DQ/dsl, Chophouse Rest., Best Western, Harley-Davidson, vet
387	FL 26, to Newberry, Gainesville, E BP, Chevron/dsl, Sunoco, Shell/dsl, BJ's Rest., Bono's BBQ, Boston Mkt, Burger King, Dunkin Donuts, FoodCourt, HoneyBaked Ham, LJ Silver, Macaroni Grill, McAlister's Deli, McDonald's, New Century Buffet, Perkins, Red Lobster, Ruby Tuesday, Starbucks, Subway, Wendy's, La Quinta, H, Belk, Books-A-Million, Dillard's, JC Penney, Macy's, Office Depot, PetCo, Sears/auto, SteinMart, to UFL, mall, W BP, Chevron/dsl, Exxon/dsl, Mobil/dsl/LP, El Nortino's Mexican, KFC, Krystal,

GAINESVILLE

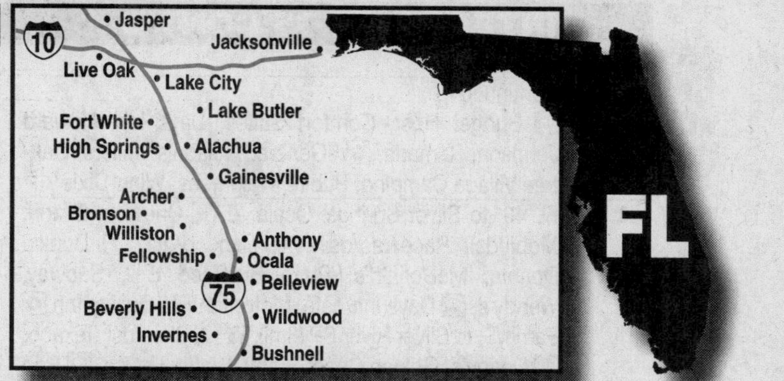

GAINESVILLE

Exit	Services
387	Continued Moe's SW Grill, Napolatanos Rest., PizzaVito, Taco Bell, Waffle House, Days Inn, EconoLodge, Fairfield Inn, Gainesville Hotel, Advance Parts, $Tree, Goodyear/auto, Home Depot, Jo-Ann Fabrics, K-Mart, PepBoys, Publix, TJ Maxx, Walgreens, Winn-Dixie, tires/repair, vet
384	FL 24, to Archer, Gainesville, E BP, Chevron/dsl/24hr, Exxon/dsl, Kangaroo, Shell, Arby's, Backyard Burger, BoneFish Grill, Burger King, Capt D's, Checkers, Chick-fil-A, Chili's, China King, Chipotle Mexican, CiCi's Pizza, Cody's Roadhouse, Coldstone, Crisper's, DQ, Dunkin Donuts, Firehouse Subs, 5 Guys Burgers, Gainesville Alehouse, Hooters, KFC, McAlister's Deli, McDonald's, Michael's Rest., Moe's SW Grill, Olive Garden, Outback Steaks, Panera Bread, Papa John's, Pizza Hut, Sonny's BBQ, Starbucks, Steak'n Shake, Subway, Taco Bell, TX Roadhouse, TGIFriday's, Waffle House, Zaxby's, Cabot Lodge, Comfort Inn, Courtyard, Extended Stay America, Hampton Inn, Hilton Garden, Homewood Suites, Motel 6, Red Roof Inn, Residence Inn, Sleep Inn, SpringHill Suites, Super 8, Barnes&Noble, Best Buy, CarQuest, CVS Drug, $Tree, Firestone/auto, GNC, Kohl's, Lowe's, Michael's, Old Navy, Petsmart, Publix, Radio Shack, Ross, Target, Tuffy Auto, Verizon, Walgreens, Walmart, W Mobil/dsl, Cracker Barrel, Country Inn&Suites, Holiday Inn Express, Sunshine RV Park, to Bear Museum
382	FL 121, to Williston, Gainesville, E Marathon/dsl, Mobil/Subway/dsl, 1st Wok, Green Plantain, Little Caesars, McDonalds, Subway, Travelodge, Publix, USPO, W BP/dsl, Chevron/dsl/24hr, Kangaroo/dsl, 43rd St Deli, Quality Inn, Rodeway Inn, ValuePlace, Fred Bear Museum
381mm	**rest areas both lanes, full facilities, vending, litter barrels, petwalk, 24hr security**
374	rd 234, Micanopy, E BP, Chevron/dsl, antiques, fruit, to Paynes Prairie SP, W Micanopy/repair, Knights Inn
368	rd 318, Orange Lake, E Chevron, Jim's/BBQ, Petro/Iron Skillet/dsl/scales/24hr/@, Wendy's, Grand Lake RV Park (3mi), W Ocala, N RV Camping
358	FL 326, E BP/FL Citrus Ctr/dsl, Mobil/McDonald's/dsl, Pilot/Arby's/dsl/scales/24hr, Pilot/Wendy's/dsl/24hr, Freightliner, auto/truck repair, W Chevron/dsl, DQ, auto repair/tires
354	US 27, to Silver Springs, Ocala, E BP/dsl/24hr, RaceTrac/dsl, Suvnr/gas, Burger King, Rascal's BBQ, Golden Palms Inn, W BP/dsl, Chevron/dsl, Shell/dsl, Blanca's Cafe, China Taste, McDonald's, Subway,

FL

FL

S I L V E R   S P R I N G S   N
↕
S   O C A L A
I N V E R N E S S

INTERSTATE 75 CONT'D

Exit	Services
354	Continued
	🏨 Budget Host, Comfort Suites, Days Inn, Howard Johnson, Ramada, 🄾 $General, Nelson's Trailers, Oaktree Village Camping, Publix, Walgreens, Winn-Dixie
352	FL 40, to Silver Springs, Ocala, E 🅖 Chevron, Exxon, Mobil/dsl, RaceTrac/dsl/24hr, Sunoco/dsl, 🍴 Dunkin Donuts, McDonald's, Pizza Hut/Taco Bell, Subway, Wendy's, 🏨 Days Inn/café, Motor Inn/RV, Quality Inn 🄾 Family$, to Silver River SP (8mi), W 🅖 Shell/dsl, Texaco, 🍴 Denny's, Golden Coast Buffet, Waffle House, 🏨 Red Roof Inn, Super 8, Travelodge, 🄾 Gander Mtn, Holiday Trav-L Park
350	FL 200, to Hernando, Ocala, 0-2 mi E 🅖 BP/dsl, Chevron/dsl, Citgo/repair, Texaco/dsl, 🍴 Applebee's, Arby's, Bob Evans, Boston Mkt, Burger King, Carrabba's, Checkers, Chick-fil-A, Chili's, ChuckeCheese, Cody's Roadhouse, Coldstone, Domino's, El Toreo Mexican, Golden Corral, Grand Buffet, Hardee's, Hooters, Krystal, Lee's Chicken, Logan's Roadhouse, McDonald's, Olive Garden, Outback Steaks, Papa John's, Panera Bread, Perkins, Pizza Hut, Red Lobster, Ruby Tuesday, Smoothie King, Starbucks, Sonic, Sonny's BBQ, Stevi B's Pizza, Subway, Taco Bell, Wendy's, Zaxby's, 🏨 Country Inn&Suites, Hampton Inn, Hilton, La Quinta, 🄾 🏥, Acura, Advance Parts, Aldi Foods, AT&T, Belk, Best Buy, Books-A-Million, Chevrolet/Nissan, CVS Drug, Discount Tire, $Tree, Goodyear/auto, Hobby Lobby, Home Depot, Honda, Hyundai, JC Penney, Kia, K-Mart, Lowe's, Macy's, Mazda, Michael's, Office Depot, PepBoys, Petsmart, Publix, Ross, Sears/auto, Staples, SteinMart, Subaru, Suzuki, Target, Tire Kingdom, TJ Maxx, Toyota, Tuffy Auto, Verizon, Walgreens, Walmart, W 🅖 BP/24hr, Chevron/24hr, 🍴 Bonefish Grill, Burger King, Cracker Barrel, Dunkin Donuts, KFC, McDonald's, Mimi's Cafe, Panera Bread, Starbucks, Steak'n Shake, Tijuana Flats, Waffle House, Yamoto Japanese, 🏨 Best Western, Courtyard, Fairfield Inn, Holiday Inn, Homewood Suites, Residence Inn, 🄾 🏥, Barnes&Noble, BMW, Buick/GMC, Cadillac, Camper Village RV Park, Dick's, Dillard's, Kohl's, Ocala RV Park, Old Navy, PetCo, Porsche, Sam's Club/gas, Tires+, VW, Walgreens, vet
346mm	rest area both lanes, full ♿ facilities, 🅲, 🄿, vending, litter barrels, petwalk, 24hr security
341	FL 484, to Belleview, E 🅖 Chevron/fruit/24hr, Citgo/Baskin-Robbins/Dunkin Donuts, Exxon/dsl, Shell/dsl, 🍴 Cracker Barrel, KFC/Taco Bell, Sonny's BBQ, Zaxby's, 🏨 Microtel, Sleep Inn, 🄾 FL Citrus Ctr, drag racing museum, W 🅖 🚚/Arby's/DQ/dsl/scales/24hr, 🍴 McDonald's, Subway, Waffle House, 🏨 Hampton Inn, 🄾 Ocala Sun RV Resort, outlets
338mm	weigh sta both lanes
329	FL 44, to Inverness, Wildwood, E 🅖 Gate/Steak'n Shake/dsl, Mobil/dsl, Sunoco, 🍴 Burger King, DQ, Denny's, McDonald's, Waffle House, Wendy's, 🄾 other FL Citrus Ctr, Three Flags RV Resort (1mi), KOA, W 🅖 Citgo/dsl/repair/24hr, 🚚/dsl/scales/24hr, TA/BP/Pizza Hut/Popeye's/Subway/dsl/scales/24hr/@, 🍴 IHOP, KFC, 🏨 Best Value Inn, Days Inn/rest., Economy Inn, Super 8, 🄾 truckwash, truck repair

D A D E   C I T Y   T A M P A

Exit	Services
328	FL TPK (from sb), to Orlando
321	rd 470, to Sumterville, Lake Panasoffkee, E 🅖 Spirit/deli/dsl/scales/24hr, 🄾 Coleman Correctional, W 🅖 Chevron/7-11/dsl, Mobil/Hardee's/Subway/dsl, 🄾 Countryside RV Park (1mi), Turtleback RV Resort (1mi)
314	FL 48, to Bushnell, E 🅖 BP/dsl, Citgo, Murphy USA/dsl, Shell/Circle K/Subway, 🍴 4 Season Chinese, KFC/Taco Bell, Little Caesars, McDonald's, Wendy's, 🏨 Rodeway Inn, 🄾 AutoZone, BlueBerry Hill RV Camp, $Tree, Red Barn RV Camp, The Oaks Camp (1mi), Walmart, vet, to Dade Bfd HS, W 🅖 Shell/dsl, Sunoco/dsl, 🍴 Beef'O'Brady's, Sonny's BBQ, Waffle House, 🏨 Microtel, 🄾 Flagship RV Ctr
309	rd 476, to Webster, E Breezy Oaks RV Park (1mi), Sumter Oaks RV Park (1mi)
307mm	rest areas both lanes, full ♿ facilities, 🅲, coffee, vending, 🄿, litter barrels, petwalk, 24hr security
301	US 98, FL 50, to Dade City, E 🅖 RaceTrac/dsl, Sunoco, 🍴 Beef'O'Brady's, Cracker Barrel, Denny's, McDonald's, Quinzos, Waffle House, Wendy's, 🏨 Days Inn, Holiday Inn Express, 🄾 Advance Parts, Curves, $General, Tall Pines RV Park, Winn-Dixie, W 🅖 Chevron/Subway/dsl, 🍴 Burger King, 🏨 Hampton Inn, Microtel, Quality Inn, 🄾 🏥
293	rd 41, to Dade City, E 🅖 Citgo (2mi), 🄾 to Sertoma Youth Ranch, W 🄾 Travelers Rest Resort RV Park
285	FL 52, to Dade City, New Port Richey, E 🅖 🛩FLYING J/Denny's/dsl/LP/scales/24hr, 🄾 🏥, W 🅖 Citgo/dsl/scales/24hr, 🍴 Waffle House
279	FL 54, to Land O' Lakes, Zephyrhills, E 🅖 Hess/Blimpie/Dunkin Donuts/Godfather's/dsl, 🍴 Applebee's, Burger King, Gonna China, Papa's John's, Pizza Hut/Taco Bell, Sonny's BBQ, Subway, Super Buffet, Waffle House, Wendy's, 🄾 Ace Hardware, Advance Parts, Beall's, Ford, Happy Days RV Camping (9mi), Kia, Leasure Days RV Park (7mi), Nissan, Publix, Ralph's RV Camping (7mi), Toyota/Scion, Walgreens, W 🅖 Marathon, Mobil/Dunkin Donuts, 7-11, Shell/Circle K/dsl, 🍴 Beef'O'Brady's, Buffalo's, Cracker Barrel, DQ, Hungry Howie's, McDonald's, Outback Steaks, Remington's Steaks, Shanghai Chinese, 🏨 Best Western, Comfort Inn, Holiday Inn Express, Sleep Inn, 🄾 URGENT CARE, Best Buy, CVS Drug, Dick's, $General, $Tree, Encore RV Camping, GNC, Goodyear/auto, Honda, Hyundai, Mazda, Michael's, Petsmart, Quail Run RV Camping, Ross, SweetBay Foods, Tire Kingdom, TJ Maxx, Tuffy Auto, Verizon
277mm	rest areas both lanes, full ♿ facilities, 🅲, 🄿, vending, litter barrels, petwalk, 24hr security
275	FL 56, Land O Lakes, Tarpon Springs, E 🍴 TX Roadhouse, 🏨 Hampton Inn, 🄾 Publix
274	I-275 (from sb), to Tampa, St Petersburg
270	rd 581, Bruce B Downs Blvd, E 🅖 Hess/dsl, Mobil, 7-11, Shell/Circle K/Taco Bell/dsl, 🍴 Baskin-Robbins/Dunkin Donuts, Chick-fil-A, Chili's, Coldstone, DQ, Golden China, KFC, Liang's Asian Bistro, Macaroni Grill, McDonald's, Panera Bread, Papa John's, Quiznos, Ruby Tuesday, Selmon's Cafe, Starbucks, Steak'n Shake, Subway, TGIFriday's, Wasabi Japanese, Wendy's, 🏨 Holiday Inn Express, Wingate Inn, 🄾 URGENT CARE, Best Buy, CVS Drug, GNC, Home Depot, Kauffman Tire, Michael's, Publix, Radio Shack, SweetBay Foods,

INTERSTATE 75 CONT'D

Exit	Services

270 Continued
Tires+, Verizon, Walgreens, Walmart, W 🅿 7-11, 🍴 McDonald's, Olive Garden, Panda Buffet, Red Lobster, Stonewood Grill, 🅾 BJ's Whse/gas, CVS Drug, Jo-Ann Fabrics, Lowe's, Petsmart, Ross, Staples, USPO

266 rd 582A, Fletcher Ave, W 🅿 Shell/Circle K/dsl, 🍴 Baskin-Robbins/Dunkin Donuts, Bob Evans, Lenny's Subs, Starbucks, Wendy's, 🛏 Courtyard, Extended Stay America, Fairfield Inn, Hampton Inn, Hilton Garden, La Quinta, Residence Inn, Sleep Inn, 🅾 🏥

265 FL 582, Fowler Ave, Temple Terrace, E 🅾 Happy Traveler RV Park, flea mkt, W 🅿 BP, Chevron/dsl, 🍴 IHOP, 🛏 Ramada Inn, 🅾 NAPA Care, U-Haul, to USF, to Busch Gardens

261 I-4, W to Tampa, E to Orlando

260b a FL 574, to Mango, Tampa, E 🅿 Chevron/24hr, Shell/Circle K/Subway/24hr, 🍴 Baskin-Robbins/Dunkin Donuts, China Wok, Waffle House, 🅾 SweetBay Foods, Walgreens, W 🅿 BP, Mobil, 🛏 Crowne Plaza Hotel, Hilton Garden, Residence Inn

257 FL 60, Brandon, E 🅿 Chevron, Citgo, Mobil/dsl, Shell/Circle K, 🍴 Anthony's Pizza, Arby's, Brandon Ale House, Boston Mkt, Burger King, Cheescake Factory, Chili's, China Buffet, ChuckeCheese, DQ, Denny's, Dunkin Donuts, Firehouse Subs, 5 Guys Burgers, Grill Smith Grill, Jesse's Steaks, Kobe Japanese, LJ Silver, Macaroni Grill, McDonald's, Moe's SW Grill, Olive Garden, Outback Steaks, Panda Express, Panera Bread, Papa John's, Qdoba, Red Lobster, Smokey Bones BBQ, Steak'n Shake, Subway, Tops China, Tres Amigos Mexican, Waffle House, Wendy's, 🛏 Holiday Inn Express, HomeStead Suites, La Quinta, 🅾 🏥, Aamco, Advance Parts, AutoZone, Barnes&Noble, Best Buy, Books-A-Million, CVS Drug, Dick's, Dillard's, $Tree, Firestone/auto, JC Penney, Kia, Kohl's, K-Mart, Macy's, Marshall's, Michael's, Office Depot, PepBoys, PetCo, Petsmart, Publix, Radio Shack, Ross, Sam's Club/gas, Sears/auto, Staples, Target, Tires+, TJ Maxx, Tuffy Auto, U-Haul, Walgreens, mall, **E on Causeway Blvd** 🅿 Mobil, 🍴 Buca Italian, Cheddars, Chick-fil-A, Crisper's Rest., Giordano's Italian, Longhorn Steaks, McDonald's, Quiznos, Starbucks, Steak'n Shake, 🅾 Cadillac, Costco/gas, Jo-Ann Fabrics, Kohl's, Publix, Walmart, W 🅿 Citgo/dsl, Marathon, Shell, 🍴 Beef O'Brady's, Bob Evans, Burger King, Hooters, McDonald's, Sonny's BBQ, Sweet Tomatoes, Wendy's, 🛏 Best Western, Comfort Suites, Country Inn&Suites, Courtyard, Days Inn, Embassy Suites, Fairfield Inn, Homewood Suites, La Quinta, Red Roof Inn, SpringHill Suites, 🅾 Buick/GMC, Chevrolet, Chrysler/Dodge/Jeep, Ford, Harley-Davidson, Home Depot, Honda, Hyundai, Mazda, Nissan, Office Depot, Toyota/Scion, VW

256 FL 618, W (toll), to Tampa

254 US 301, Riverview, E 🅿 RaceTrac/dsl, 🍴 Panda Express, Steak'n Shake, 🅾 CVS Drug, Home Depot, Super Target, W 🅿 Marathon, 7-11/dsl, Shell/Circle K, 🍴 Subway, 🛏 Hilton Garden

250 Gibsonton Dr, Riverview, E 🅿 RaceWay/dsl, 7-11, 🍴 Beef'O'Brady's, Burger King, DQ, Lucky Buffet, McDonald's, New China, Ruby Tuesday, Subway, Taco Bell, Wendy's, 🅾 Alafia River RV Resort, Beall's, CVS Drug,

250 Continued
$Tree, Family$, Hidden River RV Resort (4mi), Lowe's, Walgreens, Winn-Dixie, USPO, W 🅿 BP, Murphy USA/dsl, 🅾 Walmart

246 rd 672, Big Bend Rd, Apollo Bch, E 🅿 Hess/dsl, 7-11, 🍴 Applebee's, Beef'O'Brady's, Buffalo Wild Wings, Burger King, China Taste, CiCi's Pizza, East Coast Pizza, East Coast Pizza, 5 Guys Burgers, Little Caesar's, McDonald's, Panera Bread, Papa John's, Rita's Custard, Sonic, Starbucks, Subway, Qdoba, Village Inn, 🅾 Ace Hardware, Advance Parts, AT&T, AutoZone, Beall's, Goodyear/auto, Publix, Sam's Club/gas, Sweetbay Foods, Tuffy, Verizon, Walgreens, W 🅿 7-11, Shell/Dunkin Donuts/dsl

240b a FL 674, Sun City Ctr, Ruskin, E 🅿 Shell, 🍴 Beef'O'Brady's, Bob Evans, Burger King, Denny's, Pizza Hut, Sonny's BBQ, Subway, Taco Bell, Wendy's, 🛏 Comfort Inn, 🅾 🏥, Beall's, GNC, Home Depot, Radio Shack, SunLake RV Resort (1mi), to Little Manatee River SP, W 🅿 Circle K/dsl, Hess/dsl, RaceTrac/dsl, 🍴 China Wok, Domino's, KFC, McDonald's, Ozzie's Buffet, 🛏 Holiday Inn Express, 🅾 BigLots, NAPA, auto repair

237mm **rest area both lanes, full ♿ facilities, 🚻, 🛏, vending, litter barrels, petwalk, 24hr security**

229 rd 6, Moccasin Wallow Rd, to Parrish, E Little Manatee Sprs SRA (10mi), W 🅾 Circle K, Fiesta Grove RV Park (3mi), Frog Creek RV Park (3mi), Terra Ceia RV Village (2mi), Winterset RV Park (3mi)

228 I-275 N, to St Petersburg

224 US 301, to Bradenton, Ellenton, E 🅿 Mobil, RaceWay, Shell/dsl, 🍴 Applebee's, Checker's, Gio's Pizza, Hungry Howie's, Kings Wok, McDonald's, Peach' Rest., Ruby Tuesday, Sonic, Subway, Wendy's, 🛏 Hampton Inn, Sleep Inn, 🅾 Ace Hardware, Beall's, $General, $Tree, Just Brakes, K-Mart, Publix, Walgreens, Prime Outlets/famous brands, USPO, W 🅿 🏧/dsl, 🍴 Anna Maria's, Crabtrap Seafood, Waffle House, 🛏 GuestHouse Inn, Ramada Ltd

220b a FL 64, to Zolfo Springs, Bradenton, E Lake Manatee SRA, W 🅿 BP/dsl, Citgo/dsl/24hr, RaceTrac/dsl, Shell/Circle K/dsl, 🍴 Burger King, Cracker Barrel, D. Americo's Pizza, Dunkin Donuts, Friendly's, KFC/LJ Silver, McDonald's, Sonny's BBQ, Subway, Waffle House, Wendy's, 🛏 Comfort Inn, Days Inn, EconoLodge, Holiday Inn Express, Motel 6, 🅾 🏥, Dream RV Ctr, Encore RV Resort (1mi), Harley-Davidson, Walmart

217b a FL 70, to Arcadia, E 🅿 Hess/Blimpie/Godfather's/dsl/24hr, 🍴 Burger King, Crisper's Salads, 🛏 Wingate Inn, 🅾 Goodyear/auto, Sweetbay Foods, W 🅿 BP/dsl/

Left margin (top to bottom): **TAMPA N ↕ S**, **BRANDON**, **RIVERVIEW**

Right margin: **FL**, **BRADENTON**

Map labels: Largo, Tampa, Brandon, Lealman, Gibsonton, Memphis, Bradenton, Myakka City, Bee Ridge, Laurel, 75, Port Charlotte, Harbour Heights, Grove City, Fort Myers Shores, Fort Myers, I-4, **FL**

INTERSTATE 75 CONT'D

Exit	Services
217b a	Continued LP, 7-11/dsl, Shell/Circle K, [food] Applebee's, Arby's, Bob Evans, Bogey's Rest., Chick-fil-A, DQ, Hungry Howie's, LJ Silver/Taco Bell, McDonald's, Papa John's, Starbucks, Subway, [lodging] Country Inn&Suites, [other] Beall's, CVS Drug, Lowe's, Pleasant Lake RV Resort, Publix, Tire Kingdom, Tires+, vet
213	University Parkway, to Sarasota, E [gas] Mobil/dsl, [food] Broken Egg Rest., Chili's, Pizza Hut, Quiznos, [lodging] Fairfield Inn, Holiday Inn, [other] H, GNC, Publix, Walgreens, W [food] Bellacino's, BoneFish Grill, Carrabba's, Chipotle Mexican, 5 Guys Burgers, Jason's Deli, Onesti's Italian, Pei Wei, Red Elephant Pizza, Ruby Tuesday, Selmon's Rest., Starbucks, Stonewood Grill, Sweet Tomatoes, Wendy's, [lodging] Comfort Suites, Hampton Inn, [other] Beall's, Best Buy, BJ's Whse/gas, CVS Drug, $Tree, Fresh Mkt Foods, Home Depot, Kohl's, Marshall's, Michael's, Ringling Museum, Staples, SteinMart, Super Target, Verizon
210	FL 780, Fruitville Rd, Sarasota, W [gas] BP/dsl/LP, Mobil/dsl, RaceTrac/dsl, Shell, [food] Applebee's, Baskin-Robbins/Dunkin Donuts, Bob Evans, Burger King, Checker's, Chick-fil-A, KFC, La Tropicana, Longhorn Steaks, McDonald's, Perkins, Quiznos, Subway, Taco Bell, Trader Vic's, [lodging] AmericInn, Homewood Suites (2mi), [other] Advance Parts, $Tree, CVS Drug, GNC, Lowe's, Publix, Radio Shack, Sam's Club, Sav-On/dsl, Target, Tire Kingdom, Tuffy, Winn-Dixie
207	FL 758, Sarasota, W [gas] BP/Subway, Marathon/Subway, [food] Arby's, Chili's, Domino's, Grand China Buffet, MadFish Grill, McDonald's, Panera Bread, Pizza Hut, Sarasota Alehouse, Steak'n Shake, Subway, Sugar&Spice, Taco Bell, [lodging] Hampton Inn, [other] H, Beall's, Goodyear/auto, Home Depot, Publix, Selby Botanical Gardens (8mi), Tuesday Morning, Verizon, Walgreens, Walmart, vet
205	FL 72, to Arcadia, Sarasota, E Myakka River SP (9mi), W [gas] BP/dsl, Mobil/dsl, 7-11/dsl, Shell/Circle K, [food] Applebee's, Burger King, Chick-fil-A, Dunkin Donuts, Gecko's Grill, Just Pizza, KFC, McDonald's, Quiznos, Starbucks, Subway, Waffle House, Wendy's, Wings&Weenies, [lodging] Comfort Inn, Country Inn&Suites, Days Inn, [other] Acura, AT&T, Beall's, BMW, CVS Drug, Jaguar/Smart, Land Rover, Lexus, Mercedes, Publix, Tire Choice/auto, Tire Kingdom, Turtle Beach Camping (8mi), Walgreens, Windward Isle RV Park, UPSO, vet
200	FL 681S (from sb), to Venice, Osprey, Gulf Bchs
195	Laurel Rd, Nokomis, E [gas] BP/USPO/dsl, [food] Subway, [other] CVS Drug, W [other] Encore RV Park (2mi), Scherer SP (6mi)
193	Jaracanda Blvd, Venice, W [gas] Citgo/Subway/dsl/24hr, Hess/Blimpie/Godfather's/dsl, RaceTrac/dsl, [food] China Taste, Cracker Barrel, McDonald's, [lodging] Best Western, Fairfield Inn, Holiday Inn Express, [other] H, CVS Drug, Publix
191	rd 777, Venice Rd, to Inglewood, W [other] KOA (6mi), to Myakka SF (9mi)
182	Sumter Blvd, to North Port
179	Toledo Blade Blvd, North Port, **1-2 mi** W [gas] Mobil/Subway/dsl, Shell/Quizno's, [other] H, Publix
170	rd 769, to Arcadia, Port Charlotte, E [gas] Murphy USA/

Exit	Services
170	Continued dsl, RaceTrac/dsl, 7-11/dsl, [food] Applebee's, [lodging] Hampton Inn, Holiday Inn Express, [other] Lettuce Lake Camping (7mi), Riverside Camping (5mi), Walmart, W [gas] Hess/dsl, Mobil/7-11/dsl, Shell/Circle K, [food] Burger King, Cracker Barrel, DQ, Domino's, Dunkin Donuts, McDonald's, Peach House Pizza, Quizno's, Starbucks, Subway, Taco Bell, Top China, Waffle House, Wendy's, [lodging] Country Inn&Suites, La Quinta, Sleep Inn, [other] H, Ace Hardware, Advance Parts, Beall's, Curves, CVS Drug, $General, $Tree, GNC, Publix, Walgreens, Winn-Dixie, USPO, vet
167	rd 776, Port Charlotte
164	US 17, Punta Gorda, Arcadia, E [gas] Chevron/dsl, RaceWay/dsl, Shell/Circle K/dsl/24hr, [food] King House Chinese, Subway, [other] $General, Winn-Dixie, RV camping (2mi), W [gas] Shell/Circle K, [food] Fisherman's Village Rest. (2mi), [other] H, vet
161	rd 768, Punta Gorda, E **rest area both lanes, full [&] facilities, [C], [phone], vending, litter barrels, petwalk, 24hr security,** W [gas] BP/DQ/Subway, Murphy USA/dsl, [truck] Arby's/dsl/scales/24hr, Sunoco/Quiznos, [food] Burger King, McDonald's, Pizza Hut, Waffle House, Wendy's, [lodging] Days Inn, Motel 6, [other] Encore RV Park (2mi), Walmart
160mm	**weigh sta both lanes**
158	rd 762, Tropical Gulf Acres, E Babcock-Wells Wildlife Mgt Area
143	FL 78, to Cape Coral, N Ft Myers, E [gas] Marathon/dsl, [other] Seminole Camping (1mi), Up the River Camping, W [lodging] Encore RV Camping
141	FL 80, Palm Bch Blvd, Ft Myers, E [gas] Marathon, Sunoco/dsl, [food] Cracker Barrel, Waffle House, [lodging] Comfort Inn, ValuePlace, W [gas] Hess/dsl, Mobil, 7-11, [food] Country Kitchen, Domino's, Hardee's, Papa John's, Pizza Hut, Sonny's BBQ, Subway, Taco Bell, [other] Beall's, BigLots, CVS Drug, $General, Martin's Tire/auto, North Trail RV Ctr, Radio Shack, USPO
139	Luckett Rd, Ft Myers, E [other] Camping World RV Service/supplies, Cypress Woods RV Resort, W [gas] [truck] Subway/dsl/scales/24hr/@
138	FL 82, to Lehigh Acre, Ft Myers, E [gas] Coastal/dsl, [lodging] Hyatt Place, W [gas] Mobil/dsl, Sunoco/dsl
136	FL 884, Colonial Blvd, Ft Myers, E [lodging] Candlewood Suites, Holiday Inn Express, [food] Bajio, 5 Guys Burgers, Starbucks, Subway, [other] Best Buy, Books-A-Million, GNC, Home Depot, PetCo, Ross, Staples, Target, W [gas] BP, Marathon/Subway/dsl, Murphy USA/dsl, 7-11, Shell/Circle K/dsl, [food] Applebee's, Bob Evans, Burger King, Chick-fil-A, Chili's, China King, Golden Corral, LJ Silver/Taco Bell, McDonald's, Panda Express, Steak'n Shake, Subway, [lodging] ValuePlace, [other] H, AT&T, Beall's, BJ's Whse/gas, $Tree, Kohl's, Lowe's, Petsmart, Publix, Tire Choice/auto, Verizon, Walmart
131	Daniels Pkwy, to Cape Coral, E **rest area both lanes, full [&] facilities, [C], [phone], vending, litter barrels, petwalk, 24hr security,** [gas] BP/Dunkin Donuts/Subway/dsl, RaceTrac/dsl, [food] Cracker Barrel, [lodging] AmericInn, Comfort Inn, WynStar Inn, [other] CVS Drug, [X], W [gas] Chevron/dsl, Hess/dsl, RaceWay/24hr, 7-11/24hr, Shell/Circle K/24hr, [food] Arby's, Beef'O'Brady's, BoatHouse Grill, Burger King, DQ, Denny's, McDonald's, New China, Sam Sneed's

CAPE CORAL · ESTERO · N ← → S · NAPLES

INTERSTATE 75 CONT'D

Exit	Services
131	Continued
	Grill, Slice of Chicago, Subway, Taco Bell, Uno, Waffle House, Wendy's, 🏨 ✈ Hotel, Best Western, Comfort Suites, Hampton Inn, La Quinta, SpringHill Suites, Travelodge, 🅾 H, American RV Ctr, CVS Drug, Publix, Tire Choice/auto, Tuffy, Walgreens
128	Alico Rd, San Carlos Park, E 🅟 7-11, 🍴 Carrabba's, Chick-fil-A, Coldstone, Firepit Grill, Foster's Grill, Miller's Alehouse, McDonald's, Moe's SW Grill, Outback Steaks, PF Chang's, Pincher's Crabshack, Red Robin, Rita's Custard, Vapaino Italian, 🏨 Courtyard, Hilton Garden, Holiday Inn, Homewood Suites, Residence Inn, 🅾 AT&T, Bass Pro Shop, Belk, Best Buy, Costco/gas, Dick's, $Tree, JC Penney, JoAnn Fabrics, Marshall's, PetCo, Ross, Staples, Super Target, Verizon, W 🅟 Hess/Dunkin Donuts/dsl, 7-11/dsl
123	rd 850, Corkscrew Rd, Estero, E 🅟 BP/dsl, Chevron/dsl, 🍴 Beef'O'Brady's, China Gourmet, Marsala's Italian, McDonald's, Perkins, Subway, 🅾 CVS Drug, Germaine Arena, Johnson Tire/auto, Miramar Outlet/famous brands, Publix, W 🅟 7-11, Shell/Blimpie/dsl, Sunoco/Dunkin Donuts/Subway, 🍴 Applebee's, Arby's, Ruby Tuesday, 🏨 Embassy Suites, Hampton Inn, 🅾 URGENT CARE, Chevrolet, Lowe's, Tire Choice/auto, Koreshan St HS (2mi), Woodsmoke RV Park (4mi)
116	Bonita Bch Rd, Bonita Springs, E 🅟 Chevron/dsl, Mobil, 🍴 Subway, 🅾 Advance Parts, AT&T, Publix, Tire Choice, W 🅟 BP/McDonald's/24hr, Hess/Blimpie/dsl/24hr, 🍴 Waffle House, 🏨 Best Western, 🅾 CVS Drug, Home Depot, Imperial Bonita RV Park, Walgreens, to Lovers Key SP (11mi)
111	rd 846, Immokalee Rd, Naples Park, E 🅟 Mobil, 7-11, 🍴 Bob Evans, Burger King, Chili's, L'Appetite, Panera Bread, 🏨 Hampton Inn, 🅾 Staples, Super Target, World Mkt, W 🅟 Shell/Circle K/dsl, 🍴 Bella's Pizza, McDonald's, Subway, 🅾 H, Publix, Walmart, to Delnor-Wiggins SP
107	rd 896, Pinebridge Rd, Naples, E 🅟 BP/McDonald's/dsl/24hr, 🍴 Alice Sweetwaters, China Garden, Coldstone, Giovanni Ristorante, Starbucks, Subway, 🅾 H, Publix, Walgreens, vet, W 🅟 Chevron/dsl/24hr, RaceTrac, Shell/Circle K/dsl/24hr, 🍴 Bajio Grill, Burger King, 5 Guys Burgers, Hooters, IHOP, Perkins, Sophia's Rest., Starbucks, Waffle House, 🏨 Best Western, Hawthorn Suites, Spinnaker Inn, 🅾 Harley-Davidson, Johnson Tire/auto, Tire Choice, Nissan, vet
105	rd 886, to Golden Gate Pkwy, Golden Gate, E 🍴 Subway, W 🅟 to ✈, zoo
101	rd 951, to FL 84, to Naples, E 🅟 BP/Subway, 🏨 Fairfield Inn, SpringHill Suites, 🅾 H, W 🅟 BP/dsl, Circle K, Mobil/dsl, Shell/dsl/24hr, 🍴 Buddy's Burgers, Cracker Barrel, McDonald's, Rodeo BBQ, Subway, Taco Bell, Waffle House, 🏨 Comfort Inn, Holiday Inn Express, La Quinta, Super 8, 🅾 AT&T, Club Naples RV Ctr, Endless Summer RV Park (3mi), KOA
100mm	toll plaza eb
80	FL 29, to Everglade City, Immokalee, W 🅾 Big Cypress NR, Everglades NP, Smallwoods Store
71mm	Big Cypress Nat Preserve, hiking, no security
63mm	W rest area both lanes, full ♿ facilities, 🚻, 🏕, vending, litter barrels, petwalk, 24hr security

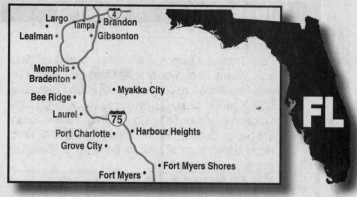

49	rd 833, Snake Rd, Big Cypress Indian Reservation, E 🅟 Miccosukee Service Plaza/deli/dsl, 🅾 museum, swamp safari
41mm	rec area eb, 🏕, litter barrels
38mm	rec area wb, 🏕, litter barrels
35mm	W rest area both lanes, full ♿ facilities, 🚻, 🏕, vending, litter barrels, petwalk, 24hr security
32mm	rec area both lanes, 🏕, litter barrels
26mm	toll plaza wb, motorist callboxes begin/end
23	US 27, FL 25, Miami, South Bay
22	NW 196th, Glades Pkwy, W 🅾 Publix, same as 21
21	FL 84, W (from nb), Indian Trace, W 🅟 Citgo/dsl, 🍴 Mamma Nostra, Papa John's
19	I-595 E, FL 869 (toll), Sawgrass Expswy
15	Royal Palm Blvd, Weston, Bonaventure, W 🅟 Chevron, Mobil, 🍴 Carolina Ale House, El Mariachi, Flanigan's Rest., Il Toscano Rest., La Granja, Lucille's Cafe, Offerdahl's Grill, Wendy's, Yogurt Cafe, 🏨 Courtyard, Hawthorn Suites, Residence Inn, 🅾 H, Tires+, USPO
13b a	Griffin Rd, E 🅟 Shell/dsl, 🍴 Burger King, DQ, Donato's Rest., Outback Steaks, Waffle House/24hr, 🅾 Goodyear/auto, Publix, vet, W 🅟 Tom Thumb/dsl, 🍴 Bone Fish Grill, Chili's, Domino's, Mayor's Rest., McDonald's, Pei Wei, Pizza Heaven, Starbucks, Ultimate Burrito, 🅾 Home Depot, Honda, Hyundai, Nissan/Volvo, Office Depot, Publix, Radio Shack, Smart Car, Toyota/Scion, Walgreens, vet
11b a	Sheridan St, E 🅟 Chevron, 🍴 Cracker Barrel, Wendy's, 🏨 Hampton Inn, Holiday Inn Express, 🅾 H (3mi), Audi, BMW, Piccolo Park, W 🅟 Shell/dsl, 🍴 Applebee's, Bistro 555, China One, Coldstone, El Mariachi, Little Caesar's, McDonald's, Original Pancake House, Roasters'n Toasters, Starbucks, Subway, TGIFriday's, 🅾 URGENT CARE, GNC, Lowe's, Publix, Walgreens, vet
9b a	FL 820, Pine Blvd, Hollywood Blvd, E 🅟 BP, Shell, 🍴 Boston Mkt, Brio Italian, Brimstone Woodfire Grill, Chili's, Fuddrucker's, HoneyBaked Ham, Jason's Deli, Latin-American Grill, Macaroni Grill, McDonald's, On-the-Border, Sal's Italian, Village Tavern, Wendys, 🅾 H, Barnes&Noble, BJ's Whse/gas, Dick's, Dodge, Mercedes, Petsmart, Walgreens, USPO, W 🅟 BP, Chevron, Citgo/dsl, Shell, 🍴 Burger King, Chipotle Mexican, KFC/Taco Bell, Las Vegas Cuban, McDonald's, Panda Express, Starbucks, Sweet Tomatoes, Wendy's, 🅾 Acura, Advance Parts, AutoZone, Costco/gas, CVS Drug, GNC, Lexus, Publix, Sedano's Foods, Tires+, USPO, Walgreens, Winn-Dixie
7b a	Miramar Pkwy, E 🅟 Chevron, 🍴 Baskin-Robbins/Dunkin Donuts, Cancun Grill, La Carreta, McDonald's,

WESTON

FL

INTERSTATE 75 CONT'D

Exit	Services
7b a	Continued
	Pollo Tropical, Quiznos, Sal's Italian, Starbucks, Subway, Tijuana Flats, Wendy's, Courtyard, Hilton Garden, Residence Inn, Wingate Inn, Publix, Walgreens, USPO, **W** Shell, Benihana, Chick-fil-A, Chili's, Coldstone, McDonald's, Orient Chef, Panera Bread, Starbucks, Subway, Yummy Asian, , CVS Drug, Home Depot, Marshall's, Office Depot, Ross, SuperTarget, Winn-Dixie, city park
5	to FL 821 (from sb), FL TPK (toll)
4	FL 860, NW 186th, Miami Gardens Dr, **E** BP/24hr, Chevron/24hr, Carrabba's, Dunkin Donuts, McDonald's, Starbucks, Subway, CVS Drug, GNC, Publix/deli, Sedanos Foods, vet
2	NW 138th, Graham Dairy Rd, **W** Mobil, Shell/dsl, China Casa, Little Caesar's, McDonald's, Starbucks, Subway, Wendy's, , GNC, Publix, Walgreens
1b a	I-75 begins/ends on FL 826, Palmetto Expswy, multiple services on FL 826.

INTERSTATE 95

Exit	Services
382mm	Florida/Georgia state line, St Marys River, motorist callboxes begin/end.
381mm	**inspection sta both lanes**
380	US 17, to Yulee, Kingsland, **E** Osprey RV Park, **W** Shell/24hr, Best Value Inn, Days Inn
378mm	**Welcome Ctr sb, full facilities, , , vending, litter barrels, petwalk, 24hr security**
376mm	**weigh sta both lanes**
373	FL 200, FL A1A, to Yulee, Callahan, Fernandina Bch, **E** Flash/Krystal, Sunoco, Burger King, KFC/Pizza Hut, DQ, McDonald's, Wendy's, Comfort Inn, Country Inn&Suites, Holiday Inn Express, Nassau Holiday Motel (3mi), RV Camping (3mi), to Ft Clinch SP (16mi), **W** BP/Subway/dsl, Exxon/dsl
366	Pecan Park Rd, **W** Flea&Farmer's Mkt, Pecan Park RV Camping
363b a	Duval Rd, **E** Mobil, Arby's, Boston's, Buffalo Wild Wings, Chick-fil-A, Chili's, Coldstone, Cracker Barrel, 5 Guys Burgers, Green Papaya, Hardee's, McDonald's, Olive Garden, Panda Express, Panera Bread, Red Lobster, Starbucks, Sticky Fingers, Subway, Taco Bell, A Loft, URGENT CARE, AT&T, AutoZone, Best Buy, Discount Tire, $Tree, Gander Mtn, GNC, Goodyear/auto, Lowe's, Michael's, Old Navy, Petsmart, Ross, Walgreens, Walmart, **W** BP, Chevron, Exxon/dsl, Sunoco/Subway, Denny's, Longhorn Steaks, Millhouse Steaks, Ruby Tuesday, Waffle House, Zaxby's, Best Western, Comfort Suites, Country Hearth Inn, Courtyard, Crowne Plaza, Days Inn, Fairfield Inn, Hampton Inn, Hilton Garden, Hyatt Place, Jacksonville Hotel, Microtel, Quality Inn, Red Roof Inn, Residence Inn, Springhill Suites, Travelodge, Wingate Inn, , , RV Ctr
362b a	I-295 S, FL 9A, to Blount Island, Jacksonville
360	FL 104, Dunn Ave, Busch Dr, **E** Gate/dsl, Hardee's, Waffle House, Executive Inn, Sam's Club/gas, USPO, **W** BP, Chevron, Hess, RaceTrac/dsl, Shell, Arby's, Burger King, Capt D's, Checkers, China Buffet, Country Cabin Rest., KFC, Krystal, McDonald's,

Exit	Services
360	Continued
	New Century Buffet, New China, Pizza Hut, Popeye's, Sonny's BBQ, Starbucks, Subway, Taco Bell, Wendy's, Best Value Inn, La Quinta, Motel 6, Aamco, Advance Parts, BigLots, CVS Drug, $Tree, Family$, Office Depot, PepBoys, Publix, Tires+, Walgreens
358b a	FL 105, Broward Rd, Heckscher Dr, **E** zoo, **W** USA Inn
357mm	Trout River
357	FL 111, Edgewood Ave, **W** BP/dsl, Gas Express
356b a	FI 115, FL 117, Lem Turner Rd, Norwood Ave, **E** Hardee's, **W** BP/24hr, Hess/Dunkin Donuts, Shell, Burger King, Checker's, Golden EggRoll, Krystal, Popeye's, Subway, Taco Bell, Advance Parts, NAPACare, Save-a-Lot Foods, Tires+, Walgreens, flea mkt
355	Golfair Blvd, **E** Shell, **W** Chevron/dsl, RaceWay/dsl
354b a	US 1, 20th St, to Jacksonville, to AmTrak, MLK Pkwy
353d	FL 114, to 8th St, **E** McDonald's, , Walgreens
353c	US 23 N, Kings Rd, downtown
353b	US 90A, Union St, Sports Complex, downtown
353a	Church St, Myrtle Ave, Forsythe St, downtown
352d	I-10 W, Stockton St (from sb), Lake City
352c	Monroe St (from nb), downtown
352b a	Myrtle Ave (from nb), downtown
351d	Stockton St, , downtown
351c	Margaret St, downtown
351b	I-10 W, to Tallahassee
351a	Park St, College St, , to downtown
351mm	St Johns River
350b	FL 13, San Marco Blvd, **E**
350a	Prudential Dr, Main St, Riverside Ave (from nb), to downtown, **E** BP, Extended Stay America, Hampton Inn, Wyndham, **W** Panera Bread, Hilton Garden
349	US 90, E (from sb), to beaches, downtown, **W** Super 8
348	US 1, S (from sb), Philips Hwy, **W** Scottish Inn, Super 8, Volvo
347	US 1A, FL 126, Emerson St, **E** Chevron/dsl, Shell, Hot Wok, Advance Parts, Family$, O'Reilly Parts, **W** BP/dsl, Gate/dsl, Hess/dsl, McDonald's, Taco Bell, Emerson Inn, Chevrolet, Goodyear/auto
346b a	FL 109, University Blvd, **E** Exxon/dsl, Hess/dsl, Shell, Capt D's, Checkers, DQ, El Potro Mexican, Firehouse Subs, Happy Garden Chinese, Huddle House, Korean BBQ, Krystal, Pizza Hut, Popeye's, Ying's Chinese, , Ace Hardware, CarQuest, CVS Drug, Family$, Firestone/auto, NAPA, Tire Kingdom, Tires+, Sun Tire, Winn-Dixie, **W** BP/dsl, Chevron, RaceTrac, Arby's, Baskin-Robbins/Dunkin Donuts, Burger King, Famous Amos, KFC, McDonald's, Papa John's, Sonny's BBQ, Taco Bell, Wendy's, Whataburger, Woody's BBQ, Days Inn, Ramada Inn, Super 8, Family$, U-Haul, auto repair
345	FL 109, University Blvd (from nb), **E** Chevron, Gate/dsl/24hr, Hess/Blimpie/Godfather's Pizza/dsl, Bono's BBQ, Schnitzel House, ,
344	FL 202, Butler Blvd, **E** Gate/dsl, Dave&Buster's, Best Western, Candlewood Suites, EconoLodge, Holiday Inn Express, Homestead Suites, Howard Johnson, Marriott, Radisson, , , USPO, **W** BP/dsl, Shell, Applebee's, Baskin-Robbins/Dunkin Donuts, Chick-fil-A, Cracker Barrel, Hardee's, McDonald's,

N ↑ S MIAMI

N ↑ S JACKSONVILLE

JACKSONVILLE

INTERSTATE 95 CONT'D

N ← → S

JACKSONVILLE

Exit	Services

344 Continued
Quiznos, Sonic, Starbucks, Waffle House, Wendy's, Whataburger/24hr, Zaxby's, Courtyard, Extended Stay Deluxe, Fairfield Inn, Jameson Inn, La Quinta, Microtel, Red Roof Inn, Wingate Inn

341 FL 152, Baymeadows Rd, E BP/dsl, Gate/dsl, Shell/dsl, Arby's, Chili's, CiCi's Pizza, Hardee's, Krystal, Omaha Steaks, Panda Express, Quiznos, Subway, Bay Meadows Inn, Comfort Suites, Embassy Suites, Holiday Inn, HomeStead Suites, Advance Parts, Tires+, Walgreens, Winn-Dixie, W Kangaroo, Shell, Al's Pizza, Bamboo Creek, Chicago Pizzaria, Denny's, Gator's Seafood, IHOP, KFC, Larry's Subs, Little Caesars, McDonald's, Pagoda Chinese, Red Lobster, Taco Bell, Wendy's, Woody's BBQ, Best Inn, Homewood Suites, La Quinta, Motel 6, Quality Inn, Residence Inn, Sheraton, Studio 6, Sun Suites, BJ's Whse/gas, CVS Drug, Discount Tire, $Tree, Goodyear/auto, Harley-Davidson, Lowe's, Office Depot

340 FL 115, Southside Blvd (from nb), E on FL 115 Kangaroo/dsl, 5 Guys Burgers, Longhorn Steaks, AT&T, Home Depot, Michael's, Petsmart, Target, same as 339

339 US 1, Philips Hwy, E Kangaroo/dsl, RaceTrac, Arby's, Bono's BBQ, Buca Italian, Burger King, Chick-fil-A, Coldstone, McDonald's, Mikado, Moe's SW Grill, Olive Garden, Ruby Tuesday, Starbucks, Taco Bell, Belk, Best Buy, Chevrolet, Dillard's, $Tree, Ford, JC Penney, Mazda, Nissan, Sears/auto, Tire Kingdom, Toyota, Walmart, mall, W BP/dsl, Benito's Italian, Steak&Shake, Subway

337 I-295 N, to rd 9a, Orange Park, Jax Beaches

335 Old St Augustine Rd, E Applebee's, Starbucks, Courtyard, H, W Chevron, Gate/dsl, Shell, Bono's BBQ, Brookland Pizza, Chili's, Daruma Steaks, McDonald's, Panera Bread, Subway, Zaxby's, Hampton Inn, Kohl's, Publix, Walgreens, vet

331mm rest area both lanes, full facilities, , , vending, litter barrels, petwalk, 24hr security

329 rd 210, Green Cove Springs, Ponte Vedra Beach, E McDonald's/dsl/scales/24hr, Sunoco/fruit, TA/Shell/Subway/dsl/scales/@, Waffle House, W BP/dsl, Mobil/dsl, Shell, Burger King, China Wok, Domino's, Firehouse Subs, Jenk's Pizza, Starbucks, Subway, Tropical Smoothie, CVS Drug, Winn-Dixie, USPO, fireworks, vet

ST AUGUSTINE

323 International Golf Pkwy, E BP/dsl/USPO, Shell/Subway/dsl, Comfort Suites, W Cino's Pizza, King Wok, Village Grill/Subs, Renaissance Resort, Publix, World Golf Village, vet

318 FL 16, Green Cove Sprgs, St Augustine, E BP/DQ/dsl, Gate/dsl/fruit, Kangaroo/dsl, Shell, Burger King, McDonald's, NY Diner, Subway, Comfort Inn, Courtyard, Fairfield Inn, Holiday Inn Express, La Quinta, Quality Inn, Travelodge, Camping World RV Ctr, Cadillac, Ford/Lincoln/Mercury, Gander Mtn, Prime Outlets/Famous Brands, W Exxon, RaceTrac/dsl, Cracker Barrel, Denny's, Giovanni's Italian, IHOP, KFC, Lemon-Grass Asian, Ruby Tuesday, Sonny's BBQ, Taco Bell,

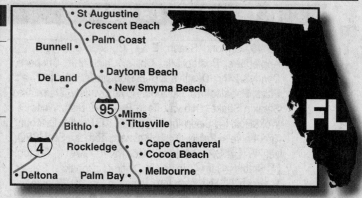

PALM COAST

318 Continued
Wendy's, Best Western, Days Inn, Hampton Inn, Ramada Ltd, Super 8, Wingate Inn, Harley-Davidson, St Augustine Premium Outlets Ctr, RV camping, funpark

311 FL 207, St Augustine, E Chevron/24hr, Hess/Subway/dsl, RaceTrac, H, Indian Forest RV Park (2mi), Indian River Fruit, KOA (7mi), St Johns RV Park, flea mkt/fireworks, to Anastasia SP, W Mobil/dsl, Quality Inn

305 FL 206, to Hastings, Crescent Beach, E FLYING J/Denny's/Subway/dsl/LP/scales/24hr, to Ft Matanzas NM, truck repair, W other:truck repair

302mm rest areas both lanes, full facilities, , , vending, litter barrels, petwalk, 24hr security

298 US 1, to St Augustine, E BP/dsl, Indian River Fruit/gas, Sunoco, to Faver-Dykes SP, W Mobil/DQ/dsl, Sunrise/dsl

289 to FL A1A (toll br), to Palm Coast, E Kangaroo/dsl, RaceTrac, Shell, Colletti's Italian, Cracker Barrel, Denny's, Dunkin Donuts, Grand Hong Kong, KFC, McDonald's, Starbucks, Wendy's, Best Western, Fairfield Inn, Microtel, Sleep Inn, Beall's, CVS Drug, Publix, Staples, Walgreens, W Chevron, Shell, Kangaroo/dsl, Baskin-Robbins/Dunkin Donuts, Bob Evans, Brusters, Golden Corral, HoneyBaked Ham, Nathan's Cafe, Outback Steaks, Perkins, Ruby Tuesday, Sakura Japanese, Sonny's BBQ, Steak'n Shake/24hr, Taco Bell, Wendy's, Days Inn, Advance Parts, AutoZone, Beall's, Belk, CVS Drug, $General, Ford, Home Depot, Kohl's, Lowe's, Publix, Tire Kingdom, Tuffy, Walmart, Winn-Dixie, USPO

286mm weigh sta both lanes,

284 FL 100, to Bunnell, Flagler Beach, E Chevron/dsl/24hr, Mobil/dsl, Burger King, Domino's, McDonald's, Oriental Garden, Subway, Woody's BBQ, Hampton Inn, Holiday Inn Express, Ace Hardware, Curves, Russell Stover's, Winn-Dixie, vet, W BP/dsl, Hilton Garden, H, Chevrolet, Chrysler/Dodge/Jeep

278 Old Dixie Hwy, E 7-11, King Chinese, Bulow RV Park (3mi), Publix, to Tomoka SP, W BP/dsl, Joe's Pizza, Country Hearth Inn, Holiday Travel Park

273 US 1, E Chevron, RaceTrac, Sunoco, McDonald's, Saddle Jack's Grill, Waffle House, Comfort Suites, Econo Inn, fruit/fireworks, RV Ctr, W Exxon/Burger King, Loves/Arby's/dsl/scales/24hr, Daytona Pig Stand BBQ, DQ, Houligan's, Days Inn, Daytona Hotel, Quality Inn, Scottish Inn, Super 8, Encore RV Park, Harley-Davidson

◐ = gas ⑪ = food ◪ = lodging ⊡ = other   Copyright 2012 - The Next Exit®

INTERSTATE 95 CONT'D

O R M O N D   B E A C H

D A Y T O N A

N ↑ S

Exit	Services
268	FL 40, Ormond Beach, **E** ◐ Chevron/dsl, Hess, ⑪ Applebee's, Boston Mkt, Chili's, Chick-fil-A, Crisper's, Denny's/24hr, Dustin's BBQ, Houligan's, Mama Mia's Pizza, Papa John's, Quiznos, Royal Dynasty, Starbucks, Steak'n Shake, Subway, Taco Bell, The Dish, Wendy's, Wok&Roll, ◪ Sleep Inn, ⊡ ⊞ AT&T, Beall's, Discount Tire, Lowe's, Publix, Ross, Walmart, Tomoka SP, USPO, vet, **W** ◐ BP, Mobil/dsl, RaceTrac/dsl, 7-11, Texaco, ⑪ Cracker Barrel, Joe's NY Diner, McDonald's, Salsa's Mexican, ◪ Hampton Inn, Jameson Inn, ⊡ Walgreens
265	LPGA Blvd, Holly Hill, Daytona Beach, **E** ◐ 7-11, Shell/dsl, ⑪ Wendy's, Subway (2mi), ⊡ CVS Drug, **W** ◪ Holiday Inn, ⊡ BMW, Chrysler/Dodge/Jeep, Ford/Lincoln/Mercury, Mazda, Nissan, VW
261b a	US 92, to DeLand, Daytona Bch, **E** ◐ Hess/Blimpie/dsl, RaceWay/dsl, 7-11, Shell/dsl, ⑪ Applebee's, BJ's Rest., Bob Evans, Burger King, Carrabba's, Checkers, Chicago Grill, Chick-fil-A, Chili's, China Buffet, Chipotle Mexican, Cracker Barrel, Daytona Ale House, Denny's, 5 Guys Burgers, Friendly's, Gators, Hooters, Jimmy John's, KFC, Krystal, Longhorn Steaks, McDonald's, Olive Garden, Outback Steaks, Panera Bread, Piccadilly, Quiznos, Red Lobster, Ruby Tuesday, Smoothie King, Subway, Taco Bell, Tijuana Flats, Waffle House, Winghouse, ◪ Comfort Suites, Courtyard, Extended Stay Deluxe, Hampton Inn, Hilton Garden, Holiday Inn Express, Homewood Suites, La Quinta, Quality Inn, Ramada Inn, Residence Inn, ⊡ ⊞, Barnes&Noble, Beall's, Best Buy, BigLots, Books-A-Million, Dick's, Dillard's, $Tree, Firestone/auto, Hobby Lobby, Home Depot, JC Penney, Jo-Ann Fabrics, K-Mart, Macy's, Marshall's, Michael's, Old Navy, PepBoys, PetCo, Petsmart, Sears/auto, Staples, SteinMart, Target, TJMaxx, Tuesday Morning, Verizon, mall, to Daytona Racetrack, **W** ◐ BP/dsl, Sunoco, ⑪ IHOP, McDonald's, ◪ Days Inn, Super 8, ⊡ KOA, flea mkt
260b a	I-4, to Orlando, FL 400 E, to, S Daytona, **E** ◐ Chevron/dsl
256	FL 421, to Port Orange, **E** ◐ BP, Circle K/gas, Shell, ⑪ Applebee's, Bob Evans, Chick-fil-A, Chili's, Daily Grind Burgers, Denny's/24hr, Dustin's BBQ, Marble Slab Creamery, Monterrey Grill, Panera Bread, Papa John's, Quiznos, Smoothie King, Sonny's BBQ, Tijuana Flats, ◪ La Quinta, ⊡ Daytona Beach RV Park, Home Depot, Lowe's, Super Target, Tuffy, Walgreens, Walmart (1mi), vet, **W** ◐ Hess, 7-11, Texaco, ⑪ Luigi's Pizza, McDonald's, Olive Garden, Red Robin, Subway, Takara Steaks, Wendy's, ⊡ AT&T, Belk, GNC, Kohls, Marshall's, Michael's, PetCo, Publix, Walgreens
249b a	FL 44, to De Land, New Smyrna Beach, **E** ◐ Shell/dsl/fruit, ⊡ New Smyrna RV Camp (3mi), **W** ◐ Chevron/dsl
244	FL 442, to Edgewater, **E** ◐ BP/dsl/24hr, ⑪ truck repair
231	rd 5A, Scottsmoor, **E** ◐ BP/Stuckey's/dsl, ⊡ Crystal Lake RV Park
227mm	**rest area sb, full** ♿ **facilities,** ☏, ♨, **vending, litter barrels, petwalk, 24hr security**
225mm	**rest area nb, full** ♿ **facilities,** ☏, ♨, **vending, litter barrels, petwalk, 24hr security**
223	FL 46, Mims, **E** ◐ Chevron (2mi), ⑪ McDonald's, ⊡ Willow Lakes Camping (2mi), **W** ◐ BP, Shell, ⊡ KOA/LP, Seasons RV Park

T I T U S V I L L E

M E L B O U R N E

Exit	Services
220	FL 406, Titusville, **E** ◐ BP/dsl, Shell/dsl, ⑪ Beef o'Brady's, 1st Wok, Kelsey's Pizza, McDonald's, Subway, Wendy's, ◪ Super 8, ⊡ ⊞, Advance Parts, Beall's, $General, Publix, Tires+, Walgreens, to Canaveral Nt'l Seashore, **W** ◐ Chevron/dsl
215	FL 50, to Orlando, Titusville, **E** ◐ BP/KFC/Pizza Hut/dsl, Circle K, Mobil/Subway/dsl, Murphy USA/dsl, Shell/DQ/dsl, ⑪ Burger King, Denny's, Durango Steaks, McDonald's, Panda Express, Quiznos, Sonny's BBQ, Taco Bell, Waffle House, Wendy's, Whistle Jct, ◪ Best Western, Ramada Inn, ⊡ Aldi Foods, Ford/Mercury, GNC, Home Depot, Lowe's, Marshall's, PetCo, Radio Shack, Staples, Target, Tire Kingdom, Walmart, to Kennedy Space Ctr, **W** ⑪ Cracker Barrel, IHOP, ◪ Days Inn, Fairfield Inn, Hampton Inn, Holiday Inn, Quality Inn, ⊡ Christmas RV Park (8mi), Great Outdoors RV/golf Resort
212	FL 407, to FL 528 toll (no re-entry sb)
208	Port St John
205	FL 528 (toll 528), to Cape Canaveral & Cape Port AFS
202	FL 524, Cocoa, **E** ◐ Shell/dsl, ⊡ Museum of History & Science, **W** ◐ BP/dsl, ◪ Days Inn, Ramada Inn/rest., Super 8
201	FL 520, to Cocoa Bch, Cocoa, **E** ◐ BP/dsl, Chevron, [Pilot]/Subway/dsl/scales/24hr, ⑪ IHOP, Waffle House, ◪ Best Western, Motel 6, ⊡ ⊞, Sams Club/gas, fireworks, **W** ◐ Chevron/dsl, Shell/Burger King, Sunoco/dsl, ⑪ McDonald's, ◪ Holiday Inn Express, ⊡ Sun Coast RV Ctr
195	FL 519, Fiske Blvd, **E** ◐ Mobil/dsl (1mi), 7-11, ⑪ Dominico Italian, Ruby Tuesday, ◪ Swiss Inn, ⊡ ⊞, Lowe's, Space Coast RV Park
191	rd 509, to Satellite Beach, **E** ◐ BP, Hess/dsl, 7-11, Sunoco, ⑪ Bob Evans, Chick-fil-A, Denny's, McDonald's, Papa John's, Perkins, Sonny's BBQ, Tropical Smoothie, Uno, Wendy's, ◪ Hampton Inn, Holiday Inn, ⊡ URGENT CARE, CVS Drug, Tires+, Tuffy, Walgreens, to Patrick AFB, **W** ◐ Chevron/dsl, Murphy USA, ⑪ Asian Too, Asian Wok, Burger King, Chili's, Cracker Barrel, 5 Guys Burgers, Longhorn Steaks, Mimi's Cafe, Moe's SW Grill, Panera Bread, Pizza Gallery, Starbucks, Steak&Shake, Subway, ◪ La Quinta, ⊡ Belk, Books-A-Million, $Tree, Hobby Lobby, Kohl's, Lexus, Michael's, Office Depot, Old Navy, PetCo, Ross, SuperTarget, Verizon, Walmart/McDonald's, World Mkt
188	new exit
183	FL 518, Melbourne, Indian Harbour Beach, **E** ◐ BP, Chevron/Baskin Robbins/Dunkin Donuts/dsl, RaceTrac/dsl, 7-11, ⊡ AT&T, art museum, **W** ⊡ Flea Mkt
180	US 192, to Melbourne, **E** ◐ BP/dsl, Circle K, Mobil/dsl, RaceTrac, 7-11, Sunoco/dsl, ⑪ Denny's, IHOP, Waffle House, ◪ Best Value Inn, Budget Inn, Days Inn, EconoLodge, Fairfield Inn, Holiday Inn Express, Rodeway Inn, ⊡ ⊞, Ace Hardware, Lowe's, Sam's Club/gas, fireworks, vet
176	rd 516, to Palm Bay, **E** ◐ BP/dsl, Citgo, Murphy USA/dsl, 7-11, ⑪ Baskin Robbins/Dunkin Donuts, Bob Evans, Chick-fil-A, Cracker Barrel, Denny's, Golden Corral, Starbucks, ◪ Jameson Inn, ⊡ Aldi Foods, BJ's Whse/gas, $Tree, GNC, Harley-Davidson, Office Depot, Walmart, Walgreens, vet, **W** ◐ RaceTrac, 7-11, Shell, ⑪ Burger King, El Japones, 5 Guys Burgers, Long Doggers, McDonald's, Moe's SW Grill, Panera Bread,

FL

INTERSTATE 95 CONT'D

N ← → S

P A L M B A Y

O K E E C H O B E E

Exit	Services
176	Continued
	Ranchero's Mexican, Subway, Thai Thai House, Wendy's, ⊡ AT&T, Curves, CVS Drug, Discount Tire, Kohl's, Marshall's, Michaels, PetCo, Publix, Ross, Target, Walgreens
173	FL 514, to Palm Bay, **E** ☐ Shell, Sunoco/dsl, 🛏 Holiday Inn Express, ⊡ Ⓗ, Firestone/auto, Ford, truck/RV repair, **W** ☐ BP/dsl, Hess, Sunoco, 🍴 Arby's, Burger King, IHOP, McDonald's/playplace, Panda Express, Sonny's BBQ, Subway, Taco Bell, TX Roadhouse, Waffle House, Wendy's, Woody's BBQ, 🛏 Comfort Suites, Motel 6, ⊡ URGENT CARE, Advance Parts, BigLots, CVS Drug, $General, Home Depot, Lowe's, Publix, Tire Kingdom, Walgreens, Walmart, USPO
168mm	rest areas both lanes, full ♿ facilities, 🍴, 🛏, vending, litter barrels, petwalk, 24hr security
156	rd 512, to Sebastian, Fellsmere, **E** ☐ BP/DQ/Stuckey's/dsl, Chevron/McDonald's, RaceWay/dsl, ⊡ Ⓗ, Encore RV Park, Sebastian Inlet SRA, Vero Bch RV Park (8mi), **W** ⊡ Marsh Landing Camping, St Sebastian SP
147	FL 60, Osceola Blvd, **E** ☐ BP, Citgo/dsl/24hr, Mobil/dsl, 7-11, Sunoco, TA/BP/Popeye's/Subway/dsl/scales/24hr/@, Texaco/dsl, Valero/dsl, 🍴 IHOP, Sloane's Rest., Wendy's, 🛏 Best Western, Comfort Suites, Howard Johnson, Vero Beach Resort, ⊡ Ⓗ, Hyundai, NAPA, USPO, vet, **W** ☐ Shell, 🍴 Cracker Barrel, McDonald's, Steak'n Shake, 🛏 Country Inn&Suites, Hampton Inn, Holiday Inn Express, ⊡ Vero Beach Outlets/famous brands
138	FL 614, Indrio Rd, **3 mi E** ⊡ Oceanographic Institute
133mm	rest areas both lanes, full ♿ facilities, 🍴, 🛏, vending, litter barrels, petwalk, 24hr security
131b a	FL 68, Orange Ave, **E** ⊡ Ⓗ, to Ft Pierce SP, **W** ☐ /🚩FLYING J/Denny's/Subway/dsl/LP/scales/24hr, ⊡ Blue Beacon
129	FL 70, to Okeechobee, **E** ☐ Citgo, Hess/dsl, Murphy USA, RaceTrac/dsl, Shell/Circle K, Sunoco, 🍴 Applebee's, Cowboys BBQ, Golden Corral, Sonic, Waffle House, ⊡ Ⓗ, Advance Parts, $General, $Tree, Firestone/auto, Home Depot, Radio Shack, Walgreens, Walmart, truck tires, **W** ☐ BP/scales/dsl, Chevron, ♥Loves/Arby's/dsl/24hr/@, Mobil/Dunkin Donuts/Subway, ☐/McDonald's/dsl/scales/24hr, 🍴 Burger King, Cracker Barrel, LJ Silver, KFC, McDonald's, Red Lobster, Steak'n Shake, Waffle House, Wendy's, 🛏 Best Western, Comfort Suites, Days Inn, Fairfield Inn, Hampton Inn, Holiday Inn Express, La Quinta, Motel 6, Quality Inn, Rodeway Inn, Sleep Inn, Treasure Coast Inn, ⊡ Indian River Fruit, Treasure Coast RV Park, to FL TPK, UF R&E Ctr
126	rd 712, Midway Rd, services 3-5 mi **E**
121	St Lucie West Blvd, **E** ☐ BP/Dunkin Donuts, Mobil, Murphy USA/dsl, 7-11, Shell/Subway/dsl, 🍴 Arbys, Burger King, Carrabba's, Chili's, Chipotle Mexican, Coldstone, Dairy Fresh Cafe, Duffy's Grill, Friendly's, Hokaido, KFC, Little Caesars, McDonald's, Outback Steaks, PA BBQ, Panda Express, Panera Bread, Quiznos, Red Ginger Asian, Ruby Tuesday, Starbucks, Taco Bell, TGIFriday's, Wendy's, 🛏 Hampton Inn, Holiday Inn Express, Residence Inn, SpringHill Suites, ⊡ Ⓗ, URGENT CARE, Beall's, Curves, $Tree, Outdoor Resorts Camping (2mi),

Exit	Services
121	Continued
	PetCo, Publix/deli, Sears Essentials, Staples, SteinMart, Radio Shack, Tires+, Tire Kingdom, Verizon, Walgreens, Walmart, USPO, **W** ☐ Mobil/dsl, 🛏 Hilton Garden, MainStay Suites, Sheraton Resort, ⊡ PGA Village
120	Crosstown Pkwy
118	Gatlin Blvd, to Port St Lucie, **E** ☐ BP/dsl/LP, Chevron/Subway/dsl, Shell/Dunkin Donuts, Sunoco/e-85, 🍴 McDonald's, Taco Bell, ⊡ AutoZone, Home Depot, Sam's Club/gas, Tires+, Walgreens, Walmart, vet, **W** 🍴 Longhorn Steaks, McDonald's, Olive Garden, 🛏 Homewood Suites, ⊡ Michaels, Old Navy, Petsmart, Publix, Target, TJ Maxx
114	Becker Rd
112mm	weigh sta sb
110	FL 714, to Martin Hwy, Palm City, Stuart, **E** Ⓗ
106mm	rest areas both lanes, full ♿ facilities, 🍴, 🛏, vending, litter barrels, petwalk, 24hr security
102	Rd 713, High Meadow Ave, Palm City, Stuart
101	FL 76, to Stuart, Indiantown, **E** ☐ Chevron/24hr, Sunoco/dsl, 🍴 Baskin-Robbins/Dunkin Donuts, Cracker Barrel, McDonald's, Wendy's, 🛏 Courtyard, Holiday Inn Express, ⊡ Ⓗ, RV camping, **W** ☐ Shell/DQ/Stuckey's/deli/dsl, Valero/dsl
96	rd 708, to Hobe Sound, **E** Dickinson SP (11mi), RV camping
92mm	weigh sta nb
87b a	FL 706, to Okeechobee, Jupiter, **E** ☐ Citgo, Mobil/dsl, Shell, Sunoco, 🍴 Applebee's, Cheeseburgers & More, Domino's, Duffy's Rest., Dunkin Donuts, IHOP, KFC, McDonald's, Panera Bread, Pollo Tropical, Rancho Chico, Subway, Taco Bell, Tomato Pie, 🛏 Comfort Inn, Fairfield Inn, ⊡ Ⓗ, URGENT CARE, Advance Parts, BMW, Books-A-Million, GNC, Goodyear/auto, Home Depot, PepBoys, Publix, Tire Kingdom, Walgreens, Walmart, Winn-Dixie, to Dickinson SP, hist sites, museum, vet, **W** ☐ Sunoco, ⊡ RV camping, to FL TPK
83	Donald Ross Rd, **E** ☐ Shell, 🛏 Hampton Inn, Holiday Inn Express, Homewood Suites, ⊡ Ⓗ, Walgreens, stadium
79c	FL 809, S (from sb), Military Tr, **W** to FL TPK, same services as 79b
79a b	FL 786, PGA Blvd, **E** ☐ Shell, 🍴 Chili's, TGIFriday's, 🛏 Hilton Garden, Marriott, ⊡ Ⓗ, Best Buy, Michael's, PetCo, Publix, **W** ☐ Shell/dsl/24hr, 🍴 Cantina Laredo, Field Of Greens Cafe, J Alexanders, Outback Steaks, 3 Forks, 🛏 DoubleTree Hotel, Embassy Suites, ⊡ CVS Drug, Publix
77	Northlake Blvd, to, W Palm Bch, **E** ☐ Hess, Shell/dsl,

INTERSTATE 95 CONT'D

Exit	Services
77	Continued Texaco, 🍴 Applebee's, Arby's, Burger King, Checkers, Chick-fil-A, KFC, McDonald's, Panera Bread, Pollo Tropical, Quarter Deck Rest., Taco Bell, ⊙ [H], Buick/Chevrolet/GMC, Chrysler/Dodge/Jeep, Costco, CVS Drug, $Tree, Ford, Gander Mtn, Home Depot, Hyundai, K-Mart, Lincoln/Mercury, Lowe's, PepBoys, Ross, Staples, Target, VW, Walgreens, **W** 🛢 Chevron/dsl, Mobil/dsl, Shell, Sunoco/dsl, Valero, 🍴 Duffy's Grill, Original Pancakes, Papa John's, Pizza Hut, Uncle Joe's Chinese, Wendy's, 🛏 Inn of America, ⊙ Advance Parts, CVS Drug, Radio Shack, Publix, Verizon, Winn-Dixie, vet
76	FL 708, Blue Heron Blvd, **E** 🛢 BP/dsl, Shell/dsl, 🍴 Wendy's, 🛏 Travelodge, ⊙ Honda, Kia, Nissan, Walgreens, **W** 🛢 BP, Cumberland Farms, RaceTrac/dsl, Texaco/dsl, 🍴 Burger King, Denny's, McDonald's, Quiznos, 🛏 Super 8
74	FL 702, 45th St, **E** 🍴 Burger King, Hong Kong Cafe, IHOP, 🛏 Days Inn, ⊙ [H], Cadillac, Walgreens, **W** 🛢 RaceTrac, 🍴 Cracker Barrel, McDonald's, Pollo Tropical, Subway, Taco Bell, Wendy's, 🛏 Courtyard, Extended Stay Deluxe, Holiday Inn Express, Homewood Suites, Red Roof Inn, Residence Inn, Springhill Suites, ⊙ Goodyear/auto, Harley-Davidson, Sams Club/gas, Walmart
71	Lake Blvd, Palm Beach, **E** 🛢 BP, 🍴 McDonald's, 🛏 Best Western, Hawthorn Suites, ⊙ [H], Best Buy, Dillard's, Firestone/auto, Home Depot, JC Penney, Target, **W** 🛢 Texaco/dsl, Valero, 🍴 Carrabba's, Chick-fil-A, Chipotle Mexican, Hooters, Manzo Italian, PA BBQ, Rain Dancer Steaks, Red Lobster, Sweet Tomatoes, 🛏 Comfort Inn, La Quinta, ⊙ URGENT CARE, Walgreens, vet
70b a	FL 704, Okeechobee Blvd, **E** 🍴 Ruth's Chris Steaks, 🛏 Marriott, ⊙ McCormick&Schmicks, museum, **W** 🛢 Chevron/dsl, Exxon/dsl, Hess, Shell, Texaco, 🍴 Aleyda's Mexican, Checkers, Denny's, IHOP, McDonald's, Miami Subs, Nick's Diner, Pizza Hut, Pollo Tropical, Starbucks, ⊙ AT&T, Audi/Porsche, BMW/Mini, Chevrolet, $Tree, GNC, Hyundai, Michael's, Office Depot, Old Navy, Petsmart, Staples, Verizon
69b	**W** to ✈
69a	Belvedere Rd, **W** 🛢 BP, Shell, 🍴 Burger King, IHOP, Wendy's, 🛏 Best Western, Courtyard, Crowne Plaza, Doubletree, Hampton Inn, Hilton Garden, Holiday Inn/rest., Studio 6
68	US 98, Southern Blvd, **E** 🛢 Texaco, ⊙ CVS Drug, Publix, **W** 🛏 Hilton
66	Forest Hill Blvd, **E** 🍴 Havana Cuban Cafe, **W** 🛢 Chevron/dsl, Sunoco, 🍴 Bellante's Pizza, ⊙ Advance Parts
64	10th Ave N, **W** 🛢 BP, Citgo, Shell/dsl/24hr, 🍴 China Empire, Dunkin Donuts, Flanigans Grill, Wendy's, ⊙ CarQuest, CVS Drug, Family$, Ford, Goodyear, President Foods, Tires+, Walgreens, vet
63	6th Ave S, **W** [H]
61	FL 812, Lantana Rd, **E** 🛢 Shell, 🍴 Domino's, Dunkin Donuts, KFC, McDonald's, Quiznos, Riggin's Crabhouse, Subway, 🛏 Motel 6, ⊙ Ace Hardware, CVS Drug, $General, Publix, 7-11, **W** 🍴 Rosalita's Café, ⊙ [H], Costco/gas
60	Hypoluxo Rd, **E** 🛢 BP, Mobil/dsl, Shell/dsl, 🍴 IHOP, Popeye's, Subway, Taco Bell, Wendy's, 🛏 Best Western, Comfort Inn, Super 8, ⊙ Sam's Club, Tires+, Tire

Exit	Services
60	Continued Kingdom, Winn-Dixie, **W** 🛢 Fuel Stop/dsl, ⊙ Advance Parts
59	Gateway Blvd, **W** 🛢 Mobil/dsl, 🍴 Bonefish Grill, Boynton Cafe, Carrabba's, Chili's, Firehouse Subs, Friendlys, Golden Phoenix Chinese, McDonald's, Starbucks, Subway, Tropical Smoothie, 🛏 Hampton Inn, ⊙ CarMax, CVS Drug, Kohl's, Publix, Ross, Tuesday Morning, vet
57	FL 804, Boynton Bch Blvd, **E** 🛢 Marathon/dsl, 🍴 KFC, 🛏 Holiday Inn Express, ⊙ [H], USPO, **0-2 mi W** 🛢 BP, Mobil, Shell, 🍴 Applebee's, Burger King, Checker's, Chick-Fil-A, ChuckeCheese, Dennys, Ginza Japanese, Golden Corral, HoneyBaked Ham, KFC, Little Caesars, Starbucks, Steak'n Shake, Subway, TGIFriday's, Wendy's, ⊙ Barnes&Noble, BJ's Whse/gas, CVS Drug, Dick's, Dillards, GNC, JC Penney, Macy's, Office Depot, Old Navy, Petsmart, Publix, Radio Shack, Sears, Steinmart, TJ Maxx, Walmart, USPO, vet
56	Woolbright Rd, **E** 🛢 Shell/24hr, Valero, 🍴 McDonald's, Subway, Wendy's, ⊙ [H], $Tree, 7-11, Walgreens, Winn-Dixie, vet, **W** 🛢 Mobil, RaceTrac/dsl, 🍴 Burger King, Cracker Barrel, Dunkin Donuts, ⊙ Advance Parts, Home Depot, Lowe's, Staples, Walgreens
52b a	FL 806, Atlantic Ave, **W** 🛢 Chevron/dsl, Shell/dsl, 🍴 La Bamba Mexican, Sandwich Man, Subway, ⊙ [H], Tires+, Verizon, Walgreens, transmissions, vet
51	rd 782, Linton Blvd, **E** 🛢 Shell, 🍴 Applebee's, Arby's, Chipotle Mexican, Duffy's Grill, KFC, King's Diner, McDonald's, Outback Steaks, Pollo Tropical, Steak'n Shake, Subway, Taco Bell, Wendy's, ⊙ AT&T, Chevrolet, Ford, Home Depot, Marshalls, Mercedes, Petsmart, Publix, Ross, Staples, Target, Tire Kingdom, Verizon, **W** 🛢 Shell, 🍴 Little Caesars, ⊙ [H], Family$, NAPA, Winn-Dixie, auto repair
50	Congress Ave, **W** 🛏 Hilton Garden, Homestead Motel
48b a	FL 794, Yamato Rd, **E** 🛢 Mobil, 🍴 Panera Bread, ⊙ CVS Drug, vet, **W** 🛢 Chevron/dsl, 🍴 Blue Fin, Dunkin Donuts, Jimmy John's, McDonald's, Quiznos, Sal's Italian, Starbucks, Subway, Wendy's, 🛏 DoubleTree, Embassy Suites, Hampton Inn, SpringHill Suites, TownePlace Suites
45	FL 808, Glades Rd, **E** 🍴 J Alexander's Rest, Jamba Juice, PF Changs, 🛏 Fairfield Inn, ⊙ Barnes&Noble, McCormick&Schmick's, Whole Foods Mkt, museum, **W** 🛢 BP, 🍴 Abe&Louie's, Brewzzi Cafe, Capital Grille, Cheesecake Factory, Chili's, Chipotle Mexican, Coldstone, Copper Canyon Grill, Duffy's Grill, Grand Lux Cafe, Houston Rest., Maggiano's Italian, Moe's SW Grill, Quiznos, Starbucks, Subway, Wendy's, 🛏 Courtyard, Holiday Inn, Marriott, Wyndham Garden, ⊙ Macy's, Nordstrom, Sears/auto
44	Palmetto Park Rd, **E** 🛢 Sunoco, 🍴 Denny's, Dunkin Donuts, Subway, Taco Bell, Tomasso's Pizza, ⊙ K-Mart, Publix, museums, **W** 🍴 McDonald's (2mi)
42b a	FL 810, Hillsboro Blvd, **E** 🛢 BP, Shell/dsl, 🍴 Hook Fish&Chicken, McDonald's, Popeye's, Wendy's, 🛏 Hampton Inn, Hilton, La Quinta, ⊙ Advance Parts, **W** 🛢 Chevron, Mobil/dsl, 🍴 Boston Mkt, Checker's, Dunkin Donuts, Subway, 🛏 Holiday Park Hotel, La Quinta, ⊙ CVS Drug, Home Depot, Walgreens
41	FL 869 (toll), SW 10th, to I-75, **E** 🛢 Mobil, 🍴 Cracker Barrel, 🛏 Extended Stay America, **W** 🛏 Best Western,

N ↕ S

P O M P A N O   B E A C H

F T   L A U D E R D A L E

INTERSTATE 95 CONT'D

Exit	Services
41	Continued Comfort Suites
39	FL 834, Sample Rd, **E** 🅖 BP, Hess, Marathon/dsl, Shell/dsl, 🍴 Taco Bell, 🅞 🅷, $General, Save-a-Lot, 7-11, U-Haul, **W** 🅖 Chevron, Citgo, Mobil, Solo/dsl, Sunoco/dsl, 🍴 Burger King, Checker's, IHOP, McDonald's, Miami Subs, Subway, 🅞 CarMax, Costco/gas, CVS Drug, Family$, Seabra Foods, 7-11, vet
38b a	Copans Rd, **E** 🅖 BP, 🍴 McDonald's, Subway, 🅞 Land Rover, Mercedes, PepBoys, Porche/Audi, Walmart, **W** 🅖 BP, Chevron, 🅞 Home Depot, NAPA
36b a	FL 814, Atlantic Blvd, to Pompano Beach, **E** 🅖 RaceTrac/dsl, 🍴 KFC/Pizza Hut/Taco Bell, Miami Subs, **1 mi W** 🅖 BP, Chevron, Mobil/dsl, Murphy USA/dsl, Shell, 🍴 Baskin-Robbins/Dunkin Donuts, Burger King, Golden Corral, KFC/LJ Silver, McDonald's, Pollo Tropical, Popeye's, Ruby Tuesday, Subway, Wendy's, 🅞 Chevrolet/Mazda, CVS Drug, $Tree, Radio Shack, Walgreens, Walmart, Winn-Dixie, USPO, to FL TPK, Power Line Rd has many services
33b a	Cypress Creek Rd, **E** 🅖 BP, Hess, 🍴 Duffy's Diner, 🛏 Extended Stay America, Hampton Inn, Westin Hotel, **W** 🅖 Hess, Shell/repair, 🍴 Arby's, Burger King, Canun Mexican, Carlucci's Italian, Champp's Grill, Chili's, Hooters, Jamba Juice, Lenny's Subs, Longhorn Steaks, McDonald's, Moonlite Diner, Subway, Sweet Tomatoes, Wendy's, 🛏 Courtyard, Extended Stay Deluxe, La Quinta, Marriott, Sheraton Suites, 🅞 URGENT CARE, GNC, Jaguar, Office Depot, Tires+
32	FL 870, Commercial Blvd, Lauderdale by the Sea, Lauderhill, **E** 🍴 Subway, **W** 🅖 BP, Circle K, Exxon, Mobil, Shell, Sunoco/dsl, 🍴 Burger King, Dunkin Donuts, KFC, McDonald's, Miami Subs, Waffle House, 🛏 El Palacio, Holiday Inn Express, Red Roof Inn, 🅞 Advance Parts, BJ's Whse/gas, auto repair
31b a	FL 816, Oakland Park Blvd, **E** 🅖 Chevron, Mobil/dsl/24hr, Petro America/dsl, 🍴 BBQ Jacks, Big Louie's Pizza, Burger King, Checker's, Denny's, Domino's, Dunkin Donuts, Little Caesar's, McDonald's, Miami Subs, Primanti Bros, Subway, Taco Bell, 24 Diner, Wendy's, 🅞 Advance Parts, K-Mart, Lowe's, Publix, Radio Shack, 7-11, Walgreens, **W** 🅖 BP/dsl, RaceTrac/dsl, Shell, Texaco, 🍴 Burger King, Checker's, Dunkin Donuts/Baskin-Robbins, IHOP, KFC, 🛏 Days Inn, 🅞 $General, Home Depot, Toyota/Scion, Walgreens, USPO, vet
29b a	FL 838, Sunrise Blvd, **E** 🅖 BP, Shell, Sunoco/dsl, 🍴 Burger King, Krystal, Miami Subs, Popeye's, 🅞 Advance Parts, Family$, Winn-Dixie, auto repair/tires, to Birch SP, **W** 🅖 Exxon/dsl, Marathon, Shell, Sunoco, 🍴 China Bowl, Church's, KFC, McDonald's, Snapper's Fish&Chicken, Subway, 🅞 🅷, Family$
27	FL 842, Broward Blvd, Ft Lauderdale, **E** 🅷
26	I-595 (from sb), FL 736, Davie Blvd, **W** to ✈
25	FL 84, **E** 🅖 Marathon/dsl, RaceTrac/dsl/24hr, 7-11, Shell/dsl, Sunoco/dsl, Texaco, Valero, 🍴 Dunkin Donuts, Li'l Red's BBQ, McDonald's, Subway, Wendy's, 🛏 Best Western, Candlewood Suites, Hampton Inn, Holiday Inn Express, Motel 6, Sky Motel, 🅞 BigLots, $Tree, Firestone/auto, Radio Shack, U-Haul, Winn-Dixie, **W** 🛏 Ramada Inn, Red Carpet Inn, Rodeway Inn

H O L L Y W O O D

Exit	Services
24	I-595 (from nb), to I-75, **E** to ✈
23	FL 818, Griffin Rd, **E** 🛏 Hilton, Sheraton, **W** 🅖 Citgo/dsl, 🍴 Subway, Tropical Acres, 🛏 Courtyard, Fairfield Inn, Homewood Suites, 🅞 Bass Pro Shops, N Trail RV Ctr, Publix
22	FL 848, Stirling Rd, Cooper City, **E** 🍴 AleHouse Grill, Burger King, Dave&Buster's, Chipotle Mexican, McDonald's, Moonlite Diner, Quiznos, Red Lobster, Sweet Tomatoes, Taco Bell, TGIFriday's, Wendy's, 🛏 Comfort Inn, Hampton Inn, Hilton Garden, Hyatt Place, Hyatt Summerfield, La Quinta, SpringHill Suites, 🅞 Advance Parts, Barnes&Noble, BJ's Whse, GNC, Home Depot, K-Mart, Marshall's, Michael's, Old Navy, Petsmart, Radio Shack, Ross, Verizon, to Lloyd SP, **W** 🍴 DiSalvos Rest., Las Vegas Cuban, Mr M's Sandwiches, Subway, 🛏 Best Western, 🅞 CVS Drug, PepBoys, Tire Kingdom, Walgreens, Winn-Dixie, vet
21	FL 822, Sheridan St, **E** 🅖 BP, Citgo, Cumberland Farms/gas, same as 22, **W** 🅖 Shell, 🍴 Denny's, 🛏 Days Inn, Holiday Inn
20	FL 820, Hollywood Blvd, **E** 🅖 Shell, 🍴 IHOP, Miami Subs, 🛏 Hollywood Gateway Inn, 🅞 Goodyear/auto, Office Depot, U-Haul, vet, **W** 🅖 BP, Chevron, 🍴 Boston Mkt, Coldstone, Firehouse Subs, Mama Fu's Asian, McDonald's, Offerdahl's Grill, Quiznos, Taco Bell, Starbucks, Subway, Waffle Works, Wendy's, 🅞 🅷, Publix, Radio Shack, Target, Verizon, Walgreens
19	FL 824, Pembroke Rd, **E** 🅖 Shell, **W** 🅖 Shell
18	FL 858, Hallandale Bch Blvd, **E** 🅖 Chevron, Exxon, Mobil, 7-11, Shell, Ugas/E85, 🍴 Baskin-Robbins/Dunkin Donuts, Burger King, Denny's, IHOP, KFC, Little Caesar's, McDonald's, Miami Subs, Pollo Tropical, Subway, Wendy's, Won Ton Garden, 🛏 Best Western, 🅞 🅷, Family$, Firestone/auto, Goodyear/auto, Office Depot, Tire Kingdom, Walgreens, Winn-Dixie, vet, **W** 🅖 BP/dsl, RaceTrac/dsl, Sunoco, 🅞 Advance Parts
16	Ives Dairy Rd, **E** 🅷, mall, **W** 🅖 7-11, 🍴 Subway
14	FL 860, Miami Gardens Dr, N Miami Beach, **E** 🅷, Oleta River SRA, **W** 🅖 BP, Chevron, Citgo, Marathon/dsl, 🍴 Subway
12c	US 441, FL 826, FL TPK, FL 9, **E** 🅖 BP, Chevron, Hess, 7-11, Ugas/dsl, Valero, 🍴 Baskin-Robbins/Dunkin Donuts, Burger King, Wendy's 🛏 Holiday Inn, 🅞 🅷
12b	US 441 (from nb), same as 12c
12a	FL 868 (from nb), FL TPK, N
11	NW 151st, (from nb), **W** 🅖 Sunoco, 🍴 McDonald's, 🅞 Advance Parts, Winn-Dixie, services on US 441 N
10b	FL 916, NW 135th, Opa-Locka Blvd, **W** 🅖 Chevron, Liberty, Mobil, 🍴 Checker's, Subway

🅖 = gas   🍴 = food   🛏 = lodging   🅞 = other   Copyright 2012 - The Next Exit®

INTERSTATE 95 CONT'D

N ↕ **S** **MIAMI**

Exit	Services
10a	NW 125th, N Miami, Bal Harbour, **W** 🅖 Shell, 🍴 Burger King, Wendy's
9	NW 119th (from nb), **W** 🅖 BP/McDonald's, 🍴 KFC, 🅞 Advance Parts, AutoZone, Family$, Walgreens, Winn-Dixie
8b	FL 932, NW 103rd, **E** 🅖 Shell, Texaco, 🅞 7-11, **W** 🅖 BP, Sunoco, 🍴 Baskin-Robbins/Dunkin Donuts, Bravo Foods
8a	NW 95th, **E** 🅖 BP, **W** 🅖 CR/dsl, Mobil/dsl, 🍴 McDonald's, 🅞 Ⓗ, Advance Parts, Walgreens
7	FL 934, NW 81st, NW 79th, **E** 🅖 BP/dsl, Chevron/dsl, **W** 🅖 Sunoco, 🍴 Checker's
6b	NW 69th (from sb)
6a	FL 944, NW 62nd, NW 54th, **W** 🍴 McDonald's, Subway, 🅞 Family$, Presidente Mkt, Walgreens
4b a	I-195 E, FL 112, W (toll), Miami Beach, **E** downtown, **W** ✈
3b	NW 8th St (from sb)
3a	FL 836, W (toll) (exits left from nb), **W** Ⓗ, to ✈
2d	I-395, E (exits left from sb), to Miami Beach
2c	NW 8th, NW 14th (from sb), Miami Ave, **E** Port of Miami
2b	NW 2nd (from nb), downtown Miami
2a	US 1 (exits left from sb), Biscayne Blvd, downtown Miami
1b	US 41, SW 7th, SW 8th, Brickell Ave, **E** 🅖 BP, Chevron, Citgo, 🍴 Casa Roma, McDonald's, Moe's SW Gril, Subway, Wendy's, 🛏 Extended Stay America, 🅞 CVS Drug, GNC, Publix, Walgreens, **W** 🅖 Shell, 🍴 Papa John's
1a	SW 25th (from sb), downtown, to Rickenbacker Causeway, **E** 🅞 museum, to Baggs SRA
0mm	I-95 begins/ends on US 1. **1 mi S** 🅖 BP, 🍴 Quiznos

INTERSTATE 275 (TAMPA)

N ↕ **S** **TAMPA**

Exit	Services
59mm	I-275 begins/ends on I-75, exit 274.
53	Bearss Ave, **E** 🅖 Citgo/dsl, 🅞 Carmax, **W** 🅖 BP, Chevron/dsl, Marathon/Dunkin Donuts, RaceTrac/dsl, Shell, 🍴 Burger King, Domino's, McDonald's, Perkins, Popeye's, Quiznos, Subway, 🛏 Quality Inn, 🅞 Aldi Foods, BigLots, GNC, Ross
52	Fletcher Ave, **E** 🅖 BP, Citgo/dsl, Hess, RaceTrac/dsl, Shell, Sunoco, 🍴 Arby's, Church's, DQ, Domino's, Hoho Chinese, Krystal, Little Caesars, McDonald's, Popeye's, Subway, 🛏 Days Inn, 🅞 Ⓗ, Aldi Foods, AutoZone, Office Depot, Target, Tire Kingdom, Toyota/Scion, Walmart, auto repair, to USF, **W** 🅖 BP, Citgo, Mobil, 🍴 Dunkin Donuts, 🛏 Super 8, 🅞 Beall's, Cadillac, Family$, Jaguar, Sweetbay Foods
51	FL 582, Fowler Ave, **E** 🅖 BP, Citgo/dsl, GK, Mobil/dsl, Shell/Circle K, 🍴 A&W/LJ Silver, Baskin-Robbins/Dunkin Donuts, Burger King, Checkers, Chili's, China Buffet, Chipotle Mexican, Denny's, Firehouse Subs, 5 Guys Burgers, Jason's Deli, Jimmy John's, KFC, Longhorn Steaks, McAlister's Deli, McDonald's, Pizza Hut, Quiznos, Sonic, Steak'n Shake, Subway, Taco Bell, TGIFriday's, Tia's TexMex, Waffle House, Wendy's, 🛏 Clarion, Embassy Suites, Howard Johnson, Hyatt Place, La Quinta, Wingate Inn, 🅞 Advance parts, AT&T, CarQuest, CVS Drug, $General, $Tree, Family$, Firestone/auto, Macy's, Sears/auto, 7-11, Sweetbay Foods, Walgreens, **W** 🛏 Economy Inn, Motel 6, Rodeway Inn, 🅞 BMW

TAMPA

Exit	Services
50	FL 580, Busch Blvd, **E** 🅖 BP, Chevron, Citgo, 🍴 Arby's, Sonny's BBQ, Subway, Taco Bell, 🛏 Comfort Inn, Days Inn, EconoLodge, Red Roof Inn, 🅞 AutoZone, Busch Gardens, Family$, Walgreens, **W** 🅖 Chevron/dsl, 🍴 Burger King, Pizza Hut, 🅞 Advance Parts, CVS Drug, Family$, Firestone/auto, Home Depot, Radio Shack, Walmart Mkt
49	Bird Ave (from nb), **W** 🅖 Shell, 🍴 Checkers, KFC, McDonald's, Wendy's, 🅞 K-Mart, Save-A-Lot Foods
48	Sligh Ave, **E** 🅖 BP, Sunoco, 🅞 USPO, **W** 🅞 zoo
47b a	US 92, to US 41 S, Hillsborough Ave, **E** 🅖 Circle K, Marathon, Mobil/dsl, 🍴 Burger King, Checkers, McDonald's, Popeye's, Subway, Wendy's, 🅞 Advance Parts, Ross, Walgreens, **W** 🅖 BP, Shell/Circle K, 🍴 Starbucks, 🛏 Dutch Motel
46b	FL 574, MLK Blvd, **E** 🅖 BP, 🅞 Advance Parts, Sweetbay Foods, Walgreens, **W** 🅖 Chevron/dsl, 🍴 McDonald's, 🅞 Ⓗ
46a	Floribraska Ave (from sb, no return)
45b	I-4, E to Orlando, I-75
45a	Jefferson St, downtown E
44	Ashley Dr, Tampa St, downtown W
42	Howard Ave, Armenia Ave, **W** 🅖 Texaco/dsl, 🍴 Popeye's
41c	Himes Ave (from sb), **W** RJ Stadium
41b a	US 92, Dale Mabry Blvd, **E** 🅖 BP, Marathon, Shell, Circle K, 🍴 Brickhouse Grill, Burger King, Carrabba's, Chick-Fil-A, Don Pan Cuban, Donatello Italian, Giordano's Italian, Grill Smith, Honey Baked Ham, IHOP, J.Alexander's Rest., Pei Wei, Pizza Hut, Quiznos, Ruby Tuesday, Shells Rest., Starbucks, Subway, Village Inn, 🛏 Best Western, Courtyard, Quality Inn, Tahitian Inn/cafe, 🅞 Barnes&Noble, CVS Drug, Hancock Fabrics, Office Depot, Tire Kingdom, Verizon, to MacDill AFB, **W** 🅖 Marathon, 🍴 Burger King, Chili's, China 1, Crazy Buffet, Denny's, Fleming's, Jimmy John's, Joe's Pizza, Kona Grill, Longhorn Steaks, Macaroni Grill, McDonald's, Moe's SW Grill, Selmon's, Sonic, Sonny's BBQ, Subway, Sweet Tomatoes, Wendy's, 🛏 Days Inn, Hilton, Howard Johnson, Residence Inn, 🅞 Best Buy, Chrysler/Dodge/Jeep, Family$, Home Depot, International Plaza, K-Mart, Petsmart, Staples, SweetBay Foods, Target, Walmart, Whole Foods Mkt, to RJ Stadium
40b	Lois Ave, **W** 🅖 Marathon/dsl, 🍴 Charlies Rest., 🛏 DoubleTree Hotel, Sheraton
40a	FL 587, Westshore Blvd, **E** 🅖 BP, Chevron/dsl, Citgo/Subway, 🍴 Burger King, Chipotle Mexican, Gogo's Greek, Maggiano's Rest., McDonald's, Panera Bread, PF Chang's, Season's Grill, Starbucks, Taco Bell, Waffle House, 🛏 Crowne Plaza, Embassy Suites, 🅞 Goodyear, JC Penney, Macy's, Old Navy, PetCo, Sears/auto, Walgreens, **W** 🅖 Shell/Subway, 🍴 Blue Water Grill, 🛏 Marriott, Ramada Inn, SpringHill Suites, Wyndham
39b a	FL 60 W, **W** 🍴 Outback Steaks, 🅞 to ✈
32	Fl 687 S, 4th St N, to US 92 (no sb re-entry)
31b a	9th St N, MLK St, N (exits left from sb), info, ✈
30	FL 686, Roosevelt Blvd, **0-2mi W** 🍴 Bascom's Chophouse, Bob Evans, Burger King, Chil-fil-A, Cracker Barrel, McDonald's, Panchero's Mexican, Taco Bell, 🛏 Best Western, Courtyard, Days Inn, Extended Stay America, Fairfield Inn, Hampton Inn, La Quinta, Marriott, Sleep Inn, SpringHill Suites, Super 8, 🅞 CVS Drug

FL

INTERSTATE 275 CONT'D (TAMPA)

Exit	Services
28	FL 694 W, Gandy Blvd, Indian Shores, **0-2mi** W 🍴 Applebee's, BJ's Brewhouse, Bob Evans, Cracker Barrel, Dunkin Donuts, Godfather's, McDonald's, 🛏 La Quinta, ⊙ Cadillac, Marshall's, Michael's, Office Depot, Target
26b a	54th Ave N, **E** 🍴 Cracker Barrel, 🛏 Comfort Inn, Holiday Inn Express, **W** 🛢 RaceTrac/dsl, 🍴 Waffle House, 🛏 Days Inn, La Quinta, ⊙ ℍ, Harley-Davidson, NAPA
25	38th Ave N, to beaches, **E** 🍴 McDonald's, **W** 🛢 Citgo/dsl, 🍴 Burger King, Hardee's
24	22nd Ave N, **E** 🛢 7-11, Shell, ⊙ Sunken Gardens, **W** 🛢 Citgo/dsl, RaceTrac/dsl, 🍴 Panchero's Mexican, ⊙ Home Depot, Lowe's, Tommy's Auto Service
23b	FL 595, 5th Ave N, **E** ℍ
23a	I-375, **E** The Pier, Waterfront, downtown
22	I-175 E, Tropicana Field, **W** ℍ
21	28th St S, downtown
20	31st Ave (from nb), downtown
19	22nd Ave S, Gulfport, **W** 🛢 Chevron, Citgo, Shell, 🍴 Church's, KFC, Quiznos, ⊙ Family$, PriceBuster Foods
18	26th Ave, S (from nb)
17	FL 682 W, 54th Ave S, Pinellas Bayway, services, **W on US 19 (34th St)** 🛢 7-11, Sunoco, 🍴 Bob Evans, Burger King, Denny's, Domino's, IHOP, McDonald's, Pizza Hut, Portofino Italian, Subway, Taco Bell, Wendy's, 🛏 Bayway Inn, Crystal Inn, ⊙ Beall's, CVS Drug, GNC, Publix, Radio Shack, Walmart, to Ft DeSoto Pk, St Pete Beach
16	Pinellas Point Dr, Skyway Lane, to Maximo Park, **E** 🛏 Holiday Inn resort, **W** marina
16mm	toll plaza sb
13mm	N Skyway Fishing Pier, **W** rest area both lanes, full ♿ facilities, 🚻, 🅿, vending, litter barrels, petwalk
10mm	Tampa Bay
7mm	S Skyway Fishing Pier, **E** rest area both lanes, full ♿ facilities, 🚻, 🅿, vending, litter barrels, petwalk
6mm	toll plaza nb
5	US 19, Palmetto, Bradenton
2	US 41, (last nb exit before toll), Palmetto, Bradenton, **E** ⊙ Terra Ceia Village Campground, Circle K, Fiesta Grove RV Resort, Frog Creek Campground, Winterset RV Resort, **W** 🛢 BP/DQ/Subway/dsl
0mm	I-275 begins/ends on I-75, exit 228.

INTERSTATE 295 (JACKSONVILLE)

Exit	Services
35b a	I-95, S to Jacksonville, N to Savannah. I-295 begins/ends on I-95, exit 362b.
33	Duval Rd, **W** ⊙
32	FL 115, Lem Turner Rd, **E** 🍴 China Wok, Cross Creek Steak, Larry's Subs, McDonald's (1mi), Subway, Wendy's, ⊙ Home Depot, Radio Shack, Walmart, **W** ⊙ Flamingo Lake RV Resort, Lakeside Cabins/RV Park
30	FL 104, Dunn Ave, **E** 🛢 Gate/dsl, Shell/24hr (1mi), 🍴 McDonald's (1mi), Wendy's (4mi), **W** ⊙ Big Tree RV Park
28b a	US 1, US 23, to Callahan, Jacksonville, **E** 🛢 Kangaroo/gas, **W** 🛢 BP/DQ/dsl, Chevron/Subway/dsl, RaceTrac/dsl/24hr, auto repair
25	Pritchard Rd, **W** 🛢 Kangaroo/Subway/deli/dsl/24hr
22	Commonwealth Ave, **E** 🛢 BP/dsl, 🍴 Burger King, Hardee's, Waffle House, 🛏 Holiday Inn, ⊙ dogtrack, **W** 🍴 Wendy's, 🛏 Comfort Suites, Country Inn&Suites

Exit	Services
21b a	I-10, W to Tallahassee, E to Jacksonville
19	FL 228, Normandy Blvd, **E** 🛢 BP/dsl/24hr, Murphy USA/dsl, 🍴 Arby's, Burger King, El Potro, Firehouse Subs, Golden Corral, Hot Wok, McDonald's, Panda Express, Papa John's, Sonic, Wendy's, ⊙ CVS Drug, $Tree, Food Lion, Radio Shack, Walgreens, Walmart, st patrol, **W** 🛢 BP, Hess/dsl, RaceTrac/dsl, Shell, 🍴 Famous Amos, Golden China, Hardee's, KFC, McDonald's, Pizza Hut, Popeye's, Whataburger, ⊙ Advance Parts, Curves, CVS Drug, Family$, K-Mart, Publix, Walgreens, Winn-Dixie
17	FL 208, Wilson Blvd, **E** 🛢 BP/Subway/dsl, Hess/Dunkin Donuts/dsl, 🍴 China Wok, Hardee's, McDonald's (1mi), ⊙ Advance Parts, $General, FL RV Ctr, Food Lion, **W** 🛢 Kangaroo
16	FL 134, 103rd St, Cecil Field, **E** 🛢 BP, Gate/dsl, Hess, Shell/dsl, 🍴 Applebee's, Arby's, Capt D's, Firehouse Subs, Krystal, Papa John's, Popeye's, Red Apple Asian, Sonic, Wendy's, Ying's Chinese, 🛏 ℍity Inn, ⊙ Advance Parts, CVS Drug, $General, Food Lion, Goodyear/auto, NAPA, Radio Shack, Save-A-Lot Foods, Tires+, U-Haul, Walmart/McDonald's, **W** 🛢 BP, Chevron, Exxon/dsl, Kangaroo, Shell, 🍴 Burger King, DQ, Dunkin Donuts, IHOP, KFC, Little Caesars, McDonald's, Pizza Hut, Rosy's Mexican, Subway, Taco Bell, ⊙ Aamco, AutoZone, Family$, Food Lion, Goodyear/auto, O'Reilly Parts, Publix, SavRite Foods, Sun Tires, Walgreens, vet
12	FL 21, Blanding Blvd, **E** 🛢 BP, Hess/Blimpie/Dunkin Donuts/Godfather's/dsl, RaceWay/dsl, Texaco, 🍴 Burger King, Larry's Subs, McDonald's, Pizza Hut, Subway, Sunrise Cafe, ⊙ Acura, Audi, Best Buy, Buick/GMC, Cadillac, Chrysler/Dodge/Jeep, CVS Drug, $General, Ford, Honda, Hyundai, Lincoln/Mercury, Lexus, Mazda, Mercedes, Nissan, Office Depot, Petsmart, Subaru, U-Haul, VW, Walgreens, USPO, **W** 🛢 BP, Kangaroo/dsl, Shell, 🍴 Applebee's, Arby's, Buffalo's, Burger King, Carrabba's, Chick-fil-A, Chili's, China Buffet, Chipotle Mexican, ChuckeCheese, Denny's, El Potro, 5 Guys Burgers, HoneyBaked Ham, Hooters, KFC, Kyodai Steaks, Longhorn Steaks, Olive Garden, Orange Park Ale House, Outback Steaks, Panda Express, Panera Bread, Papa John's, Red Lobster, Ruby Tuesday, Smokey Bones, Sonic, Starbucks, Steak'n Shake, Sweet Tomatoes, Taco Bell, Ted's MT Grill, TGIFriday's, Thai Garden, 🛏 Country Inn&Suites, Hampton Inn, La Quinta, Motel 6, Red Roof Inn, Suburban Lodge, Super 8, ⊙ ℍ, Advance Parts, AT&T, Belk, Books-A-Million, Dick's, Dillard's, Discount Tire, $Tree, Food Lion, Goodyear/auto, Home Depot, JC Penney, Jo-Ann Fabrics, Michael's, Old Navy, O'Reilly Parts, PepBoys, Publix, Sam's Club/gas, Sears/auto,

[gas] = gas [food] = food [lodging] = lodging [O] = other

INTERSTATE 295 CONT'D (JACKSONVILLE)

N ↕ S

Exit	Services
12	Continued Target, Tire Kingdom, Tires+, TJMaxx, Toyota, Verizon, Walgreens, mall
10	US 17, FL 15, Roosevelt Blvd, Orange Park, E [lodging] Best Western, W [gas] BP, Chevron/dsl/24hr, Hess, RaceTrac/dsl, [food] Aron's Pizza, Cracker Barrel, Krystal, McDonald's, Ramirez Rest., Subway, Waffle House, Wendy's, [lodging] Comfort Inn, Days Inn, Fairfield Inn, Hilton Garden, Holiday Inn, Rodeway Inn, [O] [H], CVS Drug, $General, General RV Ctr, Harley-Davidson, Save-A-Lot Foods, Sun Tire, Winn-Dixie, vet
7mm	St Johns River, Buckman Br
5b a	FL 13, San Jose Blvd, E [gas] Chevron/DQ/dsl, Hess, [food] Arby's, Bob Evans, Bono's BBQ, Carrabba's, Domino's, Famous Amos, Firehouse Subs, 5 Guys Burgers, Honey-Baked Ham, Krystal, McDonald's, Outback Steaks, Popeye's, Red Elephant Pizza, Smoothie King, Starbucks, Steak'n Shake, Subway, Tijuana Flats, Village Inn, Wendy's, [lodging] La Quinta, Ramada Inn, [O] URGENT CARE, Aamco, Advance Parts, BigLots, CVS Drug, Firestone/

JACKSONVILLE

Exit	Services
5b a	Continued auto, K-Mart, Office Depot, PepBoys, Publix, Sun Tire, Target, Tire Kingdom, Tires+, Verizon, Walgreens, Whole Foods Mkt, auto repair, vet, W [gas] BP, Citgo, Shell (1mi), [food] Al's Pizza, Brooklyn Pizza, Bruster's, Chili's, Chipotle Mexican, Golden China, Golden Corral, Hardee's, Krispy Kreme, Lee's Chicken, Mama Fu's, Mandarin Ale House, McDonald's, Moe's SW Grill, Osaka Grill, Panera Bread, Papa John's, Papa Murphy's, Pizza Hut, Subway, Taco Bell, [O] Ace Hardware, Advance Parts, AT&T, AutoZone, Barnes&Noble, Books-A-Million, $Tree, Goodyear/auto, Marshall's, Michael's, NAPA, PetCo, Publix, Radio Shack, Staples, SteinMart, Tire Kingdom, TJMaxx, U-Haul, Walmart, Winn-Dixie, World Mkt
3	Old St Augustine Rd, E [gas] BP, Shell, [food] Burger King, Little Caesars, Little China, McDonald's, Taco Bell, Wendy's, [lodging] Holiday Inn Express, [O] CVS Drug, $General, $Tree, Family$, GNC, Hobby Lobby, Publix/deli, Winn-Dixie, W [gas] Gate/dsl, Kangaroo/dsl, [food] Firehouse Subs, KFC, Rosy's Mexican, Subway, Vino's Pizza, [O] Lowe's, Walgreens, vet
61 a b	I-295 begins/ends on I-95, exit 337.

FL GA

GEORGIA

INTERSTATE 16

E ↕ W

Exit	Services
167b a	W Broad, Montgomery St, Savannah, **0-1 mi** N [gas] Chevron, Enmark, Parker's, [lodging] Doubletree, Country Inn Suites, Courtyard, Hampton Inn, Hilton Garden, Quality Inn, Residence Inn, Sheraton, [O] S [food] Burger King, Popeye's, Wendy's, I-16 begins/ends in Savannah.
166	US 17, Gwinnet St, Savannah, Savannah Visitors Ctr
165	GA 204, 37th St (from eb), to Ft Pulaski NM, Savannah College
164b a	I-516, US 80, US 17, GA 21
162	Chatham Pkwy, S [gas] Shell/dsl, [food] Kan Pai Japanese, Larry's Subs, Sunrise Rest., [O] Kia, Lexus, Toyota
160	GA 307, Dean Forest Rd, N [gas] Shell/dsl, Pilot/Subway/dsl/scales, [food] Ronnie's Rest., Waffle House
157b a	I-95, S to Jacksonville, N to Florence
155	Pooler Pkwy, S [gas] BP/dsl, to [airport]
152	GA 17, to Bloomingdale
148	Old River Rd, to US 80
144mm	**weigh sta both lanes**
143	US 280, to US 80, S [gas] El Cheapo/dsl/café, Zip'N Go/Subway
137	GA 119, to Pembroke, Ft Stewart
132	Ash Branch Church Rd
127	GA 67, to Pembroke, Ft Stewart, N [gas] El Cheapo/dsl, Shell/dsl, [food] Morgan Creek Rest., [O] antiques, S [gas] Chevron/dsl/24hr
116	US 25/301, to Statesboro, N [gas] Chevron/dsl/rest/scales/24hr, [food] Magnolia Springs SP (45 mi), to GA, S U, S [gas] Sunoco/dsl, [lodging] Scottish Inn
111	Pulaski-Excelsior Rd, S [gas] Citgo/Grady's Grill/dsl, [O] tires/repair
104	GA 22, GA 121, Metter, N [gas] BP/dsl/scales/24hr, Chevron/dsl, Exxon, Pure, Shell/dsl, [food] Bevrick's Grill, Burger King, Crabby Joes, DQ, Hardee's, Huddle House, Jomax BBQ, KFC/Taco Bell, Krispy Chic, McDonald's,

METTER

Exit	Services
104	Continued Señor Luis, Subway, Village Pizza, Waffle House, Zaxby's, [lodging] American Inn, Econolodge, Scottish Inn, Holiday Inn Express, [O] [H], Chevrolet, Rite Aid, to Smith SP, RV camping, S [gas] Marathon/dsl, Phillips 66/dsl, [O] Ford
101mm	Canoochee River
98	GA 57, to Stillmore, S [gas] BP/dsl/24hr, Chevron/dsl, [O] to Altahama SP
90	US 1, to Swainsboro, N [gas] Marathon/dsl, [O] tires
88mm	Ohoopee River
84	GA 297, to Vidalia, N truck sales
78	US 221, GA 56, to Swainsboro, N [gas] BP/dsl (1mi)
71	GA 15, GA 78, to Soperton, N [gas] Chevron/dsl
67	GA 29, to Soperton, S [gas] Chevron/dsl, Marathon/dsl, [food] Huddle House
58	GA 199, Old River Rd, East Dublin
56mm	Oconee River
54	GA 19, to Dublin, S [gas] Chevron
51	US 441, US 319, to Dublin, N [gas] BP/Stuckey's/Subway/dsl, Flash/gas, Neighbor's/dsl, Pilot/dsl/scales, Shell/24hr, [food] Arby's, Buffalo's Café, Burger King, KFC, McDonald's, Ruby Tuesday, Shoney's, Taco Bell, Waffle House/24hr, Wendy's, [lodging] Comfort Inn, Day's Inn, Econolodge, Hampton Inn, Holiday Inn Express, Jameson Inn, Super 8, Travelodge, [O] [H], Ace Hardware, Chrysler/Jeep/Dodge, Steve's RV, S [gas] Chevron, [food] Cracker Barrel, Longhorn Steaks, Zaxby's, [lodging] La Quinta, [O] Pinetucky Camping (2mi), to Little Ocmulgee SP
49	GA 257, to Dublin, Dexter, N [gas] Chevron, [O] [H], S [gas] Loves/Subway/dsl/scales/24hr, [O] auto/dsl repair
46mm	**rest area wb, full [handicapped] facilities, [phone], [picnic], litter barrels, vending, petwalk, RV dump**
44mm	**rest area eb, full [handicapped] facilities, [phone], [picnic], litter barrels, vending, petwalk, RV dump**
42	GA 338, to Dudley

DUBLIN

INTERSTATE 16 CONT'D

Exit	Services
39	GA 26, to Cochran, Montrose
32	GA 112, Allentown, S 📱 Chevron/dsl
27	GA 358, to Danville
24	GA 96, to Jeffersonville, N 📱 Marathon/dsl, S 📱 BP/dsl/24hr, 🍴 Huddle House/24hr, 🛏 Best Value, ⊙ to Robins AFB, museum
18	Bullard Rd, to Jeffersonville, Bullard
12	Sgoda Rd, Huber, N 📱 Marathon/dsl
6	US 23, US 129A, East Blvd, Ocmulgee, N 📱 BP/Circle K/DQ, 🛏 Day's Inn (2mi), ⊙ to ✈, GA Forestry Ctr, S 📱 Chevron/Huddle House/dsl, Friendly Gus, 🍴 Subway
2	US 80, GA 87, MLK Jr Blvd, N ⊙ Ⓗ, Ocmulgee NM, conv ctr, S 📱 Marathon/dsl, ⊙ to Hist Dist
1b	GA 22, to US 129, GA 49, 2nd St (from wb), N ⊙ coliseum, S 🛏 Ramada, ⊙ Ⓗ
1a	US 23, Gray Hwy (from eb), N 📱 BP, Citgo, Flash/dsl, Marathon, Shell, 🍴 Arby's, Burger King, Chen's Wok, DQ, El Sombrero Mexican, Fincher's BBQ, Krispy Kreme, Krystal, Little Caesars, McDonald's, Papa John's, Subway, Taco Bell, Wendy's, ⊙ Ⓗ, Kroger, O'Reilly Parts, Radio Shack, Tire Planet, U-Haul, Walgreens, transmissions, S 📱 Exxon, Spectrum, 🍴 Burger King, Checker's, Krystal, Pizza Hut, Waffle House, Zaxby's, 🛏 Ramada, Scottish Inn
0mm	I-75, S to Valdosta, N to Atlanta. I-16 begins/ends on I-75, exit 165 in Macon.

INTERSTATE 20

Exit	Services
202mm	Georgia/South Carolina state line, Savannah River
201mm	**Welcome Ctr wb, full ♿ facilities, 🚻, 🚮, vending, litter barrels, petwalk**
200	GA 104, Riverwatch Pkwy, Augusta, N 📱 Pilot/Wendy's/dsl/24hr, 🍴 Waffle House, 🛏 Baymont Inn, Candlewood Suites, Comfort Suites, Jameson Inn, Microtel, Quality Inn, Sleep Inn, Value Place
199	GA 28, Washington Rd, Augusta, **0-3 mi** N 📱 BP, RaceWay/24hr, Shell/Circle K, Sprint, 🍴 Applebee's, Baskin-Robbins/Dunkin Donuts, Burger King, CA Dreaming, Capt D's, Checker's, Chick-fil-A, DQ, Domino's, Denny's, Firehouse Subs, Fujiyama Japanese, Krystal, Longhorn Steaks, McDonald's, Mi Rancho Mexican, Omakase Japanese, Piccadilly, Pizza Hut, Quiznos, Rhinehart's Seafood, Starbucks, Steakout, Vera Cruz Mexican, Waffle House, Wild Wing Cafe, 🛏 Augusta Inn, Best Value Inn, Clarion, Courtyard, Days

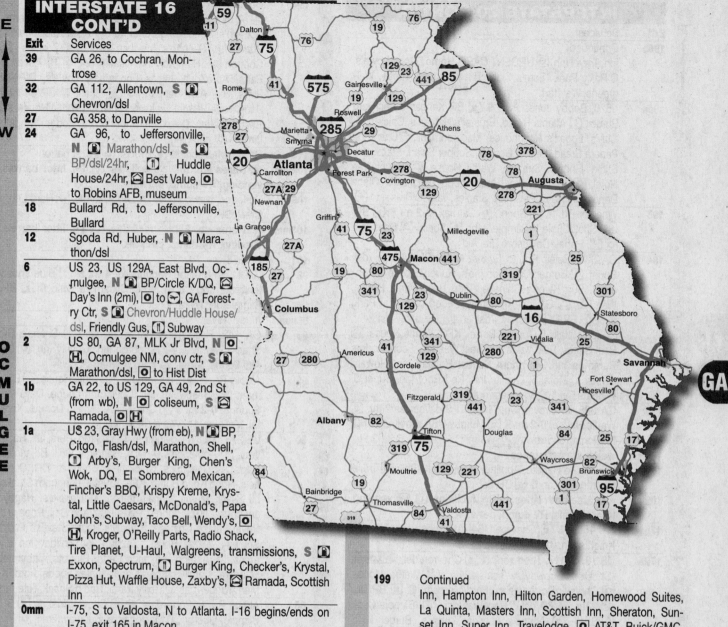

Exit	Services
199	**Continued** Inn, Hampton Inn, Hilton Garden, Homewood Suites, La Quinta, Masters Inn, Scottish Inn, Sheraton, Sunset Inn, Super Inn, Travelodge, ⊙ AT&T, Buick/GMC, Chrysler/Jeep, Chevrolet, CVS Drug, $Tree, Goodyear/auto, Hancock Fabrics, Hyundai, Infiniti, K-Mart, Lexus, Mazda, Mercedes, NAPA, Nissan, Radio Shack, Scion/Toyota, Suzuki, Tuesday Morning, S 📱 BP, 76/Circle K, Shell/Circle K/dsl, 🍴 Arby's, BoneFish Grill, Carrabba's, Church's, 5 Guys Burgers, Flyin Cowboy BBQ, HoneyBaked Ham, Hooters, IHOP, Krispy Kreme, McDonald's, Moe's SW Grill, New Peking, Olive Garden, Outback Steaks, Quizno's, Red Lobster, Shangri La, Subway, Taco Bell, T-Bonz Steaks, TGIFriday's, Thai Jong Rest., Vallarta Mexican, Waffle House, Wendy's, Zaxby's, 🛏 Best Western, Country Inn&Suites, Guest Inn, Knights Inn, Motel 6, Parkway Inn, Ramada Inn, Staybridge Suites, Westbank Inn, ⊙ Aamco, BooksAMillion, CVS Drug, $Tree, Firestone/auto, Fred's Drug, Fresh Mkt Foods, Goodyear/auto, Kroger/gas, PepBoys, Publix, Rite Aid, SteinMart, Tire Kingdom, Verizon, Walgreens, vet
196b	GA 232 W, N 📱 Enmark, Murphy USA/dsl, 🍴 Checker's, Golden Corral, Krispy Kreme, Krystal, Ruby Tuesday, Ryan's, Salsa's Grill, Stevi B's Pizza, 🛏 Baymont

INTERSTATE 20 CONT'D

Exit	Services
196b	Continued Inn, Travel Inn, [o] URGENT CARE, Home Depot, Lowe's, O'Reilly Parts, Sam's Club, Tire Kingdom, Tires+, Walgreens, Walmart
196a	I-520, Bobby Jones Fwy, S [gas] BP, Kangaroo/Backyard Burger, [food] Atlanta Bread, Bruster's/Nathan's, Chick-fil-A, Chili's, Logan's Roadhouse, Macaroni Grill, O'Charley's, Panera Bread, Peking Gormet, Souper Salad, Starbucks, Sticky Fingers, Subway, Waffle House, [lodging] DoubleTree Hotel, [o] [H], Best Buy, Hobby Lobby, Michael's, Office Depot, Old Navy, Petsmart, Staples, Target, Tires+, to [icon]
195	Wheeler Rd, N [gas] Sprint, [o] Carmax, 0-2 mi S [gas] BP/dsl, Shell/Circle K/Blimpie/24hr, [food] Sonic, [lodging] Days Inn, [o] [H], Harley-Davidson, Rite Aid
194	GA 383, Belair Rd, to Evans, N [gas] Shell/Circle /dsl, Sprint, [food] Burger King, Domino's, Hungry Howie's, Popeye's, Sun Kwong Chinese, Taco Bell, Waffle House, Wendy's, [lodging] GA Inn, [o] Family$, Food Lion, Fun Park, S [gas] BP/DQ/Stuckey's/dsl, [icon]/Subway/dsl/24hr, [food] Amici Italian, Cracker Barrel, KFC, Waffle House, [lodging] Best Suites, Best Value Inn, Best Western, EconoLodge, Hampton Inn, Hawthorn Suites, Holiday Inn, Howard Johnson, Motel 6, Quality Inn, Red Roof Inn, Super 8, Wingate Inn, [o] Goodyear/auto
190	GA 388, to Grovetown, N [gas] TPS/dsl/scales/24hr, [food] Waffle House, 0-2 mi S [gas] Murphy USA, Shell, [food] KFC, McDonald's, Subway, [o] Walmart
189mm	weigh sta both lanes
183	US 221, to Harlem, Appling, N [gas] Shell (2mi), [o] Travel Country RV Ctr, S [gas] BP/dsl
182mm	rest area both lanes, full [icon] facilities, [icon], [icon], vending, litter barrels, RV dump, petwalk
175	GA 150, N [gas] Chevron/USA Trkstp/dsl/rest./24hr, [lodging] Knights Inn, [o] to Mistletoe SP
172	US 78, GA 17, Thomson, N [gas] Chevron/dsl, [Loves]/Chester's/Subway/dsl/scales/24hr, [food] Waffle House, [o] Chrysler/Dodge/Jeep, Ford/Mercury, S [gas] BP/DQ/dsl/24hr, M&A/dsl, RaceWay/dsl, 76/Blimpie/Circle K, Shell, [food] Amigo's Mexican, Arby's, Burger King, Checker's, Domino's, Krystal, LJ Silver, Lucky Chinese, McDonald's, Mingwah Chinese, Pizza Hut, Popeye's, Ryan's, Taco Bell, Waffle House, Wendy's, Zaxby's, [lodging] Best Western, EconoLodge, Holiday Inn Express, Scottish Inn, [o] [H], AutoZone, Bi-Lo, Walgreens
165	GA 80, Camak
160	E Cadley Rd, Norwood
154	US 278, GA 12, Barnett
148	GA 22, Crawfordville, N [gas] BP/dsl, [o] to Stephens SP
138	GA 77, GA 15, Siloam, N [gas] FLYING J/Denny's/dsl/LP/scales/24hr, S [gas] BP/dsl, Metro/dsl, [o] [H]
130	GA 44, Greensboro, weigh sta, N [gas] BP/dsl/24hr, Exxon, [food] DQ, McDonald's, Pizza Hut, Subway, Waffle House, Wendy's, Zaxby's, [lodging] Jameson Inn, Microtel, [o] [H], Buick/Chevrolet, $General, Tire Pros, S [gas] Chevron/dsl/24hr, [food] Arby's, [o] Home Depot/gas
121	to Lake Oconee, Buckhead, S [gas] Chevron, [o] Museum of Art (3mi)
114	US 441, US 129, to Madison, N [gas] Chevron/Subway, Citgo/dsl, [icon]/Denny's/dsl/scales/24hr, RaceTrac,

Exit	Services
114	Continued [food] Arby's, Burger King, Chick-fil-A, Cracker Barrel, Domino's, Hong Kong Buffet, KFC, Krystal, McDonald's, Pizza Hut, Sancho's Mexican, Wendy's, Zaxby's, [lodging] Comfort Inn, Hampton Inn, Quality Inn, [o] [H], Advance Parts, AutoZone, Ingles Foods/gas, Lowe's, O'Reilly Parts, Rite Aid, Walmart, S [gas] Flash, TA/BP/Country Pride/Popeye's/dsl/scales/@, Shell, [food] Waffle House, [lodging] Best Value Inn, Delux Inn, Super 8, Travelodge, Wingate Inn, [o] RV camping
113	GA 83, Madison, N [gas] BP/dsl, [o] [H], st patrol
108mm	rest area wb, full [icon] facilities, [icon], [icon], litter barrels, vending, RV dump, petwalk
105	Rutledge, Newborn, N [gas] BP/pizza/dsl, [o] Hard Labor Creek SP
103mm	rest area eb, full [icon] facilities, [icon], [icon], litter barrels, vending, RV dump, petwalk
101	US 278
98	GA 11, to Monroe, Monticello, 4 mi N [food] Blue Willow Inn/rest., Log Cabin Rest., Sycamore Grill, S [gas] BP/Blimpie/dsl, Marathon
95mm	Alcovy River
93	GA 142, Hazelbrand Rd, S [gas] QT, [food] Shane's Rib Shack, Wendy's, [lodging] Hampton Inn, Quality Inn, [o] [H], Aldi Foods, $Tree, Verizon, Walmart/Subway
92	Alcovy Rd, N [gas] Chevron/dsl, [food] Waffle House, [lodging] Baymont Inn, Best Value Inn, Covington Lodge, Days Inn, Super 8, 0-2 mi S [food] Chick-fil-A, Dunkin Donuts, Krystal, McDonald's, Wendy's, [o] [H]
90	US 278, GA 81, Covington, S [gas] Citgo, Pure, QT, RaceWay, [food] Applebee's, Arby's, Bangkok Grill, Bojangles, Capt D's, Checker's, Chick-fil-A, Church's, DQ, Domino's, Hong Kong Buffet, KFC, Krystal, Longhorn Steaks, LJ Silver, Mama Maria's Italian, McDonald's, Nagoya Japanese, Papa John's, Pizza Hut/Taco Bell, Popeye's, Royal Palace Chinese, Stalvey's Rest., SteviB's Pizza, Subway, Waffle House, Zaxby's, [lodging] Holiday Inn Express, [o] Aamco, Advance Parts, BigLots, Chevrolet, $General, Family$, Food Depot, Ingles Foods, Ford, K-Mart, Kroger/gas, O'Reilly Parts, Radio Shack, Rite Aid
88	Almon Rd, to Porterdale, N [gas] Chevron/dsl, S [gas] BP/Blimpie, Liberty, [food] McDonald's, Subway (2mi), [o] Riverside Estates RV Camp, transmissions/repair
84	GA 162, Salem Rd, to Pace, N [gas] BJ's Whse/gas, QuickSpot/dsl, S [gas] Chevron/dsl/24hr, Citgo, QT, RaceWay, [food] Baskin-Robbins, Burger King, Dunkin Donuts, Hardee's, Los Bravos Mexican, McDonald's, Subway, Taco Bell, Waffle House, Wendy's, [o] Advance Parts, $General, Family$, Food Depot, Ingles/gas, Rite Aid
83mm	parking area wb
82	GA 138, GA 20, Conyers, N [gas] BJ's Gas, QT, [food] Applebee's, Bruster's, Chili's, ChuckeCheese, Cracker Barrel, Don Tello's, Golden Corral, IHOP, O'Charley's, Outback Steaks, Red Lobster, Sonic, Subway, [lodging] Country Inn&Suites, Days Inn, Hampton Inn, Holiday Inn Express, Jameson Inn, La Quinta, Super 8, [o] AT&T, Belk, Chevrolet, Ford, Home Depot, Kohl's, Michael's, NAPA, Office Depot, Old Navy, Petsmart, Staples, Tires+, U-Haul, Walmart, S [gas] Chevron/24hr, Shell/dsl, [food] Arby's, Baskin-Robbins, Blimpie, Burger King, Capt D's, Checker's, Chianti Italian, Chick-fil-A, CiCi's, Daruma Japanese, Dunkin Donuts, Folk's Rest., Frontera

Side markers: E / W, GA, THOMSON, MADISON, COVINGTON, CONYERS

E	**INTERSTATE 20 CONT'D**

Exit	Services
82	Continued
	Mexican, Gable's Rest, Glenn's BBQ, Grand Buffet, Hooters, KFC, Krystal/24hr, LJ Silver, McDonald's, Mellow Mushroom, Milano Cafe, Moe's SW Grill, Oaks Family Rest., Piccadilly's, Popeye's, Ruby Tuesday, Silver Dragon, Sonny's BBQ, Starbucks, Subway, Taco Bell, Waffle House, Wendy's, Zaxby's, ⌂ Suburban Lodge, ⊙ Aldi Foods, AutoZone, BigLots, Big 10 Tire, Dodge, $General, $Tree, Goodyear/auto, Hobby Lobby, Honda, Jo-Ann Fabrics, Kia, Kroger/gas/24hr, Lowe's, NTB, PepBoys, Publix, Radio Shack, Rite Aid, Target, TJ Maxx, Toyota, Walgreens, USPO, mall
80	West Ave, Conyers, **N** ⓡ Chevron, Shell/dsl, ⑪ DQ, Domino's, Mrs Winner's, Subway, Waffle House, ⌂ Best Value Inn, Ramada, ⊙ Conyers Drug, Family$, Harley-Davidson, Piggly Wiggly, **S** ⓡ Exxon/dsl/24hr, QT, Texaco, ⑪ Longhorn Steaks, McDonald's, ⌂ Comfort Inn, ⊙ Chrysler/Dodge/Jeep, JustBrakes, Nissan, vet
79mm	parking area eb
78	Sigman Rd, **N** ⓡ Shell/dsl, Texaco, ⑪ Waffle House, **S** ⊙ Crown RV Ctr, st police
75	US 278, GA 124, Turner Hill Rd, **N** ⓡ BP/dsl, Citgo/dsl/24hr, **S** ⑪ Applebee's, Arizona's, Bruster's, Buffalo Wild Wings, Bugaboo Steaks, Chick-fil-A, Chicken&Waffles, Chili's, Firehouse Subs, Grand China, Kampa's Steaks, IHOP, LJ Silver/Taco Bell, McDonald's, Olive Garden, Panera Bread, Ruby Tuesday, Smokey Bones BBQ, Steak n'Shake, Subway, Wendy's, Supreme Fish Delight, Zaxby's, ⌂ Comfort Inn, Comfort Suites, Fairfield Inn, Hilton Garden, Holiday Inn Express, Hyatt Place, ⊙ AT&T, Best Buy, Curves, Dillard's, $Tree, JC Penney, Kohl's, Macy's, Marshall's, PetCo, Rite Aid, Ross, Sam's Club/gas, Sears/auto, Staples, Target, Tires+, Toyota, Verizon, mall
74	GA 124, Lithonia, **N** ⓡ Chevron/24hr, Shell/24, ⑪ Capt D's, KFC/Taco Bell, McDonald's, Pizza Hut, SoulFood Rest., Wendy's, ⊙ Advance Parts, CVS Drug, O'Reilly Parts, **S** ⓡ Citgo/dsl/24hr, ⑪ Da-Bomb Wings/Seafood, DQ, Dudley's Rest., Golden Palace Chinese, Krystal/24hr, Waffle House, ⌂ EconoLodge, Microtel, ⊙ $General
71	Hillandale Dr, Farrington Rd, Panola Rd, **N** ⓡ QT/dsl, Shell, ⑪ Burger King, Checker's, KFC, McDonald's, Mrs. Winner's, Waffle House, ⌂ Budgetel, Holiday Inn Express, Super 8, ⊙ Family$, **S** ⓡ BP/dsl/24hr, Citgo, Murphy USA/dsl, Shell, ⑪ IHOP, New China, Popeye's, Ruby Tuesday, Subway, Taco Bell/LJ Silver, Wendy's, ⌂ Red Roof Inn, ⊙ Lowe's, Publix, Radio Shack, Tires+, Walgreens, Walmart
68	Wesley Chapel Rd, Snapfinger Rd, **N** ⑪ Capt D's, Checker's, Chick-fil-A, Church's, KFC, New China, Taco Bell, Waffle House, ⌂ Economy Inn, Rite4Us, ⊙ CVS Drug, $General, Ford, Home Depot, Kroger, **S** ⓡ Chevron/dsl/24hr, Mobil, QT, Shell/dsl, ⑪ Dragon Chinese, JJ's Fish& Chicken, McDonald's, Popeye's, ⌂ Super Inn
67b a	I-285, S to Macon, N to Greenville
66	Columbia Dr (from eb, no return), **N** ⓡ Chevron
65	GA 155, Candler Rd, to Decatur, **N** ⓡ Chevron, Citgo, Marathon, ⑪ DunDee's Cafe, Pizza Hut, Popeye's,
65	Continued
	Red Lobster, Wendy's, ⌂ Best Value Inn, Motel 6, ⊙ CVS Drug, U-Haul, **S** ⓡ BP, Chevron/24hr, Marathon/dsl, Shell/dsl, Stop&Go, ⑪ Baskin-Robbins/Dunkin Donuts, Burger King, Checker's, China Express, Church's, DQ, Homebox Rest., KFC, McDonald's, Picadilly's, Taco Bell, Waffle King, ⌂ Budget Lodge, Candler Inn, Country Hearth Inn, Sunset Lodge, ⊙ BigLots, Firestone/auto, Jiffy Lube, Kroger, Macy's, Maxway, mall
63	Gresham Rd, **N** ⓡ Chevron, Citgo/dsl, ⊙ Walmart/Subway, **S** ⓡ BP/dsl/24hr, Citgo, Marathon, Shell, ⑪ Church's, ⊙ auto repair
62	Flat Shoals Rd (from eb, no return), **N** ⓡ Exxon
61b	GA 260, Glenwood Ave, **N** ⓡ BP, Chevron, Texaco/dsl, ⑪ KFC, Wild Bean Cafe
61a	Maynard Terrace (from eb, no return)
60b a	US 23, Moreland Ave, **N** ⓡ Exxon, ⌂ Atlanta Motel, ⊙ Advance Parts, **S** ⓡ Citgo/dsl, Shell, ⑪ Checker's, Krystal, LJ Silver, McDonald's, Mrs Winner's, Wendy's
59b	Memorial Dr, Glenwood Ave (from eb)
59a	Cyclorama, **N** ⓡ Chevron/Blimpie/dsl, ⊙ Confederate Ave Complex, MLK Site, **S** ⓡ BP
58b	Hill St (from wb, no return), **N** ⓡ Shell, ⑪ Mrs. Winners
58a	Capitol St (from wb, no return), downtown, **N** to GA Dome, **S** Holiday Inn
57	I-75/85
56b	Windsor St (from eb) to Turner Field
56a	US 19, US 29, McDaniel St (eb only), **N** ⓡ Chevron/dsl
55b	Lee St (from wb), Ft McPherson, **S** ⓡ Exxon/dsl, Shell, ⑪ Church's, Popeye's, Taco Bell, West Inn Food Court, ⊙ Family$, Maxway, Sav-A-Lot
55a	Lowery Blvd, **S** ⓡ Exxon/dsl, Shell, ⑪ Church's, Popeye's, Taco Bell, West Inn Food Court, ⊙ Family$, Maxway, Sav-A-Lot
54	Langhorn St (from wb), to Cascade Rd
53	MLK Dr, to GA 139, **N** ⓡ Chevron/24hr, Shell/dsl/24hr, **S** ⓡ Texaco/dsl, ⊙ auto repair
52b a	GA 280, Holmes Dr, High Tower Rd, **S** ⓡ Chevron, Exxon/dsl, ⑪ American Deli, McDonald's, Wendy's, ⊙ AutoZone, CVS Drug, Family$
51b a	I-285, S to Montgomery, N to Chattanooga
49	GA 70, Fulton Ind Blvd, **N** ⓡ Citgo/dsl/24hr, Shell, ⑪ Subway, Wendy's, ⌂ Days Inn, Fulton Inn, Mosley Motel, ⊙ ♿, **S** ⓡ BP/dsl, Chevron/dsl, Citgo/dsl, Shell, ⑪ Grand Buffet, McDonald's, Waffle House, ⌂ Best Value Inn, Rodeway Inn, Travel Inn, ⊙ U-Haul
48mm	Chattahoochee River
47	Six Flags Pkwy (from wb), **N** ⓡ BP, ⌂ EconoLodge,

Side bar (left): E ↑↓ W C O N Y E R S / L I T H O N I A

Side bar (right): A T L A N T A   A R E A / GA

INTERSTATE 20 CONT'D

E ↑ W

Exit	Services
47	Continued S 🏨 Howard Johnson, Sleep Inn, Wingate Inn, 🅞 Six Flags Funpark
46b a	Riverside Parkway, N 🅖 Citgo/Church's, Marathon, QT, 🍴 Hong Kong Buffet, Waffle House, 🏨 Austell Inn, 🅞 Family$, S 🅖 Pure, 🍴 Wendy's, 🏨 Howard Johnson, Sleep Inn, Wingate Inn, 🅞 Six Flags Funpark
44	GA 6, Thornton Rd, to Lithia Springs, N 🅖 BP/24hr, QT, RaceTrac, Shell, 🍴 Applebee's, Burger King, Chick-fil-A, Domino's, El Pollo Loco, Golden Dragon Chinese, IHOP, KFC, Krystal, McDonald's, New China, Olive Tree Rest., Ruby Tuesday, Shoney's, Sonic, Subway, Taco Bell, Waffle House, Wendy's, Zaxby's, 🏨 Budget Inn, Comfort Inn, $General, Knight's Inn, Quality Inn, Suburban Lodge, 🅞 🏥, Atlanta West Camping (2mi), Carmax, Chevrolet, $General, Ford, Goodyear/auto, Harley-Davidson, Home Depot, Honda, Kroger/gas, Nissan, Office Depot, Tires+, Verizon, VW, Walgreens, S 🅖 Phillips 66, 🍴 Cracker Barrel, Fiesta Mexican, Wendy's, 🏨 Country Inn&Suites, Courtyard, Fairfield Inn, Hampton Inn, Hilton Garden, SpringHill Suites, 🅞 Chrysler/Dodge/Jeep, Toyota, Walmart, to Sweetwater Creek SP
42mm	**weigh sta eb**
41	Lee Rd, to Lithia Springs, N 🅖 Citgo/dsl, S 🅖 Chevron/dsl, Shell/Blimpie/dsl
37	GA 92, to Douglasville, N 🅖 Marathon, RaceTrac, Shell/dsl/24hr, 🍴 Blimpie, Checker's, Chick-fil-A, Church's, DQ, Kenny's Rest., Krystal, Longhorn Steaks, Martin's Rest., McDonald's, Monterrey Mexican, Mrs Winner's, Pizza Hut, Subway, Waffle House, Wendy's, 🏨 Best Value Inn, Best Western, Comfort Inn, Days Inn, Quality Inn, Ramada Ltd, Royal Inn, 🅞 🏥, AutoZone, BigLots, CVS Drug, Family$, Fred's Drug, Kroger/gas, NAPA, O'Reilly Parts, Tires+, Walgreens, S 🅖 Chevron, QT, 🍴 Waffle House, 🅞 Aamco
36	Chapel Hill Rd, N 🏥, S 🅖 BP, QT/24hr, Shell/dsl 🍴 Applebee's, Arby's, Asia Buffet, Carraba's, China Garden, Coldstone Creamery, 5 Guys Burgers, Joe's Crabshack, Johnny's Subs, King Buffet, Logan's Roadhouse, McDonald's, O'Charley's, Olive Garden, Outback Steaks, Panda Express, Provino's Italian, Quizno's, Starbucks, Taste Of Thai, TX Roadhouse, TGIFriday's, Waffle House, 🏨 Hampton Inn, 🅞 Aldi Foods, AT&T, Belk, Dillard's, Discount Tire, Firestone/auto, Hobby Lobby, JC Penney, Kohl's, Macy's, Marshall's, Michael's, Old Navy, Petsmart, Rite Aid, Ross, Sears/auto, Target, Verizon, mall
34	GA 5, to Douglasville, N 🅖 RaceTrac, Texaco, 🍴 Cracker Barrel, Hibachi Cafe, Hooters, Stevie B's Pizza, Waffle House, Williamson Bro's BBQ, Zaxby's, 🏨 Holiday Inn Express, La Quinta, Sleep Inn, 🅞 URGENT CARE, $Tree, Honda, Kauffman Tires, Sam's Club, Walmart, S 🅖 Chevron/dsl, Circle K, Shell, 🍴 Applebee's, Bruster's, Buffalo Wild Wings, Burger King, Chick-fil-A, Chili's, ChuckeCheese, CiCi's Pizza, DQ, Dunkin Donuts, El Rodeo Mexican, Fiesta Mexican, Folk's Rest., Golden Buddah, Golden Corral, IHOP, KFC, Krystal, LJ Silver, McDonald's, Mellow Mushroom, Moe's SW Grill, New China, Papa John's, Pizza Hut, Quizno's, Red Lobster, Ruby Tuesday, Seabreeze Seafood, Sonic,

D O U G L A S V I L L E

GA

Exit	Services
34	Continued Sonny's BBQ, Subway, Taco Bell, Taco Mac, Torero's, Wendy's, 🏨 InTown Suites, 🅞 Advance Parts, AT&T, Best Buy, Big 10 Tire, GNC, Goodyear/auto, Home Depot, Jo-Ann Crafts, K-Mart, Kroger, Lowe's, Office Depot, PetCo, Publix, Radio Shack, Tuesday Morning, U-Haul, Walgreens, USPO, vet
30	Post Rd, S 🅖 Shell/dsl
26	Liberty Rd, Villa Rica, N 🅖 Shell/dsl, Swifty/dsl, 🍴 China Wok, Johnny's Pizza, McDonald's, Mex-Grill, Olive Tree Rest., Subway, Sumo Japanese, Waffle House, 🅞 🏥, $General, Publix, Walgreens, S 🅖 Chevron, Wilco/Hess/Godfather's Pizza/Subway/dsl/scales/24hr, 🏨 American Inn
24	GA 101, GA 61, Villa Rica, N 🅖 Citgo, RaceTrac, Shell/dsl, 🍴 Arby's, Chick-fil-A, Hardee's, KFC/Taco Bell, Krystal, McDonald's, Pizza Hut, Romero's Italian, Sonic, Stix Grill, Subway, Waffle House, Wendy's, 🏨 Comfort Inn, Days Inn, Hometowne Lodge, Super 8, 🅞 🏥, Advance Parts, AutoZone, CVS Drug, Ingles Foods, Piggly Wiggly, Rite Aid, Walgreens, S 🅖 QT, Shell/dsl, 🍴 Burger King, Capt D's, Domino's, El Ranchito Mexican, O'Charley's, Papa John's, Philly Connection, Waffle House, Zaxby's, 🅞 AT&T, Chevrolet, Curves, $Tree, Home Depot, GNC, Radio Shack, Walmart/Subway, to W GA Coll
21mm	Little Tallapoosa River
19	GA 113, Temple, N 🅖 ⊛FLYING J/Denny's/dsl/scales/24hr, ▣Subway/Wendy's/dsl/scales/24hr/@, 🍴 Fortune Star Chinese, Hardee's, McDonald's, Waffle House, 🅞 Ingles Foods/gas, Truck-o-Mat/scales
15mm	**weigh sta wb**
11	US 27, Bremen, Bowdon, N 🅖 Chevron/dsl, Murphy USA, Shell, Texaco, 🍴 Arby's, Checker's, Chopsticks Chinese, Cracker Barrel, Domino's, Juanito's, KFC, McDonald's, Papa John's, Pizza Hut, Subway, Waffle House, Wendy's, Zaxby's, 🏨 Days Inn, Holiday Inn Express, Hampton Inn, Microtel, Quality Inn, 🅞 🏥, Advance Parts, $General, Ford/Mercury, Ingles Foods/gas, Walmart (1mi), S 🅖 BP/dsl, Kangaroo, 🍴 Waffle House, John Tanner SP
9	Waco Rd, N ♥Loves/Chester's/Subway/dsl/scales/24hr, 🅞 Jellystone RV Park (2mi)
5	GA 100, Tallapoosa, N 🅖 Citgo/dsl/24hr, Exxon/dsl/24hr, 🍴 Waffle House 🅞 Big Oak RV park, S 🅖 Newborn TrkStp/rest/dsl/24hr/@, ▣/KFC/Taco Bell/dsl/scales/24hr, Robinson/Subway, 🍴 DQ, GA Diner, 🏨 Comfort Inn, 🅞 to John Tanner SP
1mm	**Welcome Ctr eb, full ♿ facilities, 🚻, 🏪, vending, litter barrels, petwalk**
0mm	Georgia/Alabama state line, Eastern/Central time zone

V I L L A   R I C A

B R E M E N

INTERSTATE 59

N ↕ S

Exit	Services
	I-59 begins/ends on I-24, exit 167. For I-24, turn to Tennessee Interstate 24.
20mm	I-24, W to Nashville, E to Chattanooga
17	Slygo Rd, to New England, W 🅖 Midnite/dsl, 🅞 KOA (2mi)
11	GA 136, Trenton, E 🅖 Chevron/dsl, Citgo, Exxon/dsl, 🍴 Asian Garden, Hardee's, McDonald's, Pizza Hut, Subway, 🏨 Days Inn, 🅞 Advance Parts, CVS Drug,

INTERSTATE 59 CONT'D

Exit	Services
11	Continued Family$, Ingles, O'Reilly Parts, to Cloudland Canyon SP, **W** 📓 BP, Citgo, 🍴 Huddle House, Krystal, Little Caesars, Taco Bell, Wendy's, 🅾 BiLo, $General, Food Lion
4	Rising Fawn, **E** 📓 Citgo/24hr, **W** 📓 BP/dsl/24hr, 📓/Subway/dsl/24hr, 🅾 camping
0mm	Georgia/Alabama state line, eastern/central time zone

INTERSTATE 75

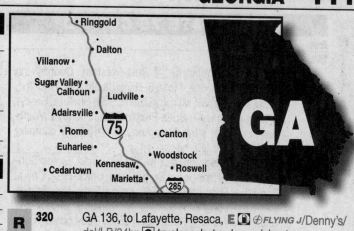

Exit	Services
355mm	Georgia/Tennessee state line
354mm	Chickamauga Creek
353	GA 146, Rossville, **E** 📓 BP/24hr, 🛏 Cloud Springs Lodge, **W** 📓 BP/Subway/dsl, Shell, 🅾 antiques
352mm	Welcome Ctr sb, full ♿ facilities, info, 🚻, 🏤, vending, litter barrels, petwalk
350	GA 2, Bfd Pkwy, to Ft Oglethorpe, **E** 📓 BP/dsl, Kangaroo, 🛏 Hampton Inn, Hometown Inn, **W** 📓 Murphy USA, RaceTrac/dsl/24hr, Shell, 🍴 BBQ Corral, 🅾 🅷, KOA, **1-4 mi W** 🍴 Fazoli's, O'Charly's, Panera Bread, Taco Bell, Zaxby's, 🅾 Walmart, to Chickamauga NP
348	GA 151, Ringgold, **E** 📓 BP/dsl, Shell/dsl, 🍴 Cracker Barrel, Hardee's, Krystal/24hr, KFC, McDonald's, Pizza Hut, Ruby Tuesday, Subway, Taco Bell, Waffle House, 🛏 Day's Inn, Holiday Inn Express, Red Roof Inn, Super 8, 🅾 Advance Parts, Curves, CVS Drug, Chevrolet, Chrysler/Jeep, Family$, Ingles, RV camping, Walgreens, **W** 📓 BP, Exxon, Shell, 🍴 Domino's, New China, Wendy's, 🛏 Comfort Inn, 🅾 Food Lion, Peterbilt
345	US 41, US 76, Ringgold, **E** 📓 BP, **W** 📓 Chevron, Cochran's/Midnite/rest./scales/dsl/24hr/@, Kangaroo/Subway/scales/dsl, 🍴 Waffle House
343mm	weigh sta both lanes
341	GA 201, to Varnell, Tunnel Hill, **W** 📓 Chevron, Shell, 🅾 carpet outlets
336	US 41, US 76, Dalton, Rocky Face, **E** 📓 Murphy USA, RaceTrac, Shell, 🍴 Waffle House, 🛏 Econolodge, Stay Lodge, 🅾 🅷, Checker Parts, Ford/Lincoln/Mercury, Home Depot, Walmart, **W** 📓 BP/dsl, Exxon, 🍴 Bryson's Grill, Cornerstone Grill, Tijuana's Mexican, Wendy's, 🛏 Best Western, Guest Inn, Motel 6, Staylodge, Super 8, carpet outlets
333	GA 52, Dalton, **E** 📓 BP/dsl, Citgo, Exxon/dsl, RaceTrac/dsl, 🍴 Amici's Italian, Applebee's, Burger King, Capt D's, Chick-fil-A, CiCi's, Cracker Barrel, DQ, Five Guys Burgers, Fuji Japanese, IHOP, KFC, Los Pablos Mexican, LJ Silver, Longhorn Steaks, McDonald's, O'Charley's, Outback Steaks, Panera Bread, Pizza Hut, Schlotsky's, Shoney's, Sonic, Starbucks, Steak'n Shake, Taco Bell, Waffle House, Wendy's, 🛏 Best Inn, Days Inn, Hampton Inn, Travelodge, 🅾 BigLots, Chevrolet, Chrysler/Jeep, Harley-Davidson, Isuzu, K-Mart, Kroger/gas, Tanger Outlets/famous brands, TJ Maxx, Walgreens, **W** 🍴 Chili's, Red Lobster, 🛏 Comfort Inn, Courtyard, Country Inn Suites, Holiday Inn, Jameson Inn, La Quinta, Quality Inn, Ramada, 🅾 NW GA Trade/Conv Ctr
328	GA 3, to US 41, **E** 📓 BP/dsl, 📓/Arby's/dsl/scales/24hr, 🍴 Waffle House, Wendy's, 🛏 Super Motel, **W** carpet outlets
326	Carbondale Rd, **E** 📓 Chevron/dsl, 📓/McDonalds/Subway/dsl/scales, **W** 📓 BP, Exxon

Exit	Services
320	GA 136, to Lafayette, Resaca, **E** 📓 FLYING J/Denny's/dsl/LP/24hr, 🅾 truckwash, truck repair/parts
319mm	Oostanaula River, **rest area sb, full ♿ facilities**, 🚻, 🏤, **vending, litter barrels, petwalk**
318	US 41, Resaca, **E** 📓 Hess/Wilco/DQ/Wendy's/scales/dsl/24hr, 🍴 Hardee's, 🛏 Relax Inn, **W** 📓 Pure, Shell/dsl, 🍴 Chuckwagon Rest., 🛏 Best Inn, Super 8
317	GA 225, to Chatsworth, **E** New Echota HS, Vann House HS, **W** 📓 BP (1mi), 🛏 Express Inn
315	GA 156, Redbud Rd, to Calhoun, **E** 📓 Citgo/dsl, Kangaroo, 🍴 Waffle House, 🛏 Oglethorpe Inn, 🅾 Food Lion, KOA (2mi), **W** 📓 BP/dsl, Liberty/Subway/dsl, Shell, 🍴 Arby's, Shoney's, 🛏 Ramada Ltd, 🅾 🅷, Rite Aid
312	GA 53, to Calhoun, **E** 📓 Shell/dsl, 🍴 Cracker Barrel, Longhorn Steaks, 🛏 Budget Host, Days Inn, Country Inn, La Quinta, 🅾 Prime Outlets/famous brands, **W** 📓 BP/Arby's, Chevron/dsl, Kangaroo, Murphy USA, 🍴 Big John's Rest., Bojangles, Burger King, Capt D's, Checker's, Chick-fil-A, China Palace, DQ, Domino's, Eastern Cafe, El Nopal Mexican, Gondolier Pizza, Huddle House, IHOP, KFC, Krystal/24hr, Little Caesar's, Los Reyes Mexican, LJ Silver, McDonald's, Papa's Pizza, Pizza Hut, Ryan's, Ruby Tuesday, Starbucks, Subway, Taco Bell, Tokyo Steaks, Wendy's, Zaxby's, 🛏 Guest Inn, Hampton Inn, Holiday Inn Express, Jameson Inn, Motel 6, Royal Inn, 🅾 Advance Parts, AutoZone, $General, GNC, Goodyear/auto, Home Depot, Ingles, Kroger/gas, Office Depot, Walmart, vet
308mm	**rest area nb, full ♿ facilities**, 🚻, 🏤, **litter barrels, vending, petwalk**
306	GA 140, Adairsville, **E** 📓 Cowboy's/dsl, Patty's/Citgo/dsl/24hr/@, QT/dsl/scales/24hrs, Shell, 🍴 Cracker Barrel, Huddle House, Wendy's, **W** 📓 All American/dsl/scales, BP/dsl, Chevron, Exxon/dsl, 🍴 Burger King, Hardee's, McDonald's, Taco Bell, Waffle House, Zaxby's, 🛏 Best Western, Comfort Inn, Ramada Ltd, 🅾 Harvest Moon RV Park
296	Cassville-White Rd, **E** 📓 📓/McDonald's/Subway/dsl/scales, Pure, TA/Exxon/Burger King/Pizza Hut/Popeye's/Taco Bell/dsl/scales/24hr/@, Texaco/24hr, 🛏 Sleep Inn, 🅾 truckwash, **W** 📓 Chevron, Citgo/dsl, Shell, 🍴 Second Half Grill, 🛏 Best Inn, Budget Host/rest., Howard Johnson, Red Carpet Inn, 🅾 KOA
293	US 411, to White, **E** 📓 BP/dsl, Sunoco/dsl, 🛏 Quality Inn, **W** 📓 Chevron/dsl, Citgo/dsl/24hr, 🍴 AJ's Cafe, Waffle House, 🛏 Courtesy Inn, Holiday Inn, 🅾 Harley-Davidson, RV camping, mineral museum, st patrol
290	GA 20, to Rome, **E** 📓 Chevron/Subway/dsl, Exxon/dsl, Kangaroo/dsl, 🍴 Arby's, Fruit Jar Cafe,

Left margin (top to bottom): N S / N S / DALTON

Right margin (top to bottom): RESACA · CALHOUN · ADAIRSVILLE

GA

INTERSTATE 75 CONT'D

N ↕ S

ACWORTH

GA

Exit	Services
290	**Continued** McDonald's, Wendy's, 🏠 Best Western, Country Inn Suites, Econolodge, Motel 6, Ramada Ltd, Red Roof Inn, Super 8, **W** ⬛ BP, Murphy USA (1.5mi), Shell, 🍴 Cracker Barrel, Michael's BBQ, Pruitt's BBQ, Shoney's, Waffle House, 🏠 Day's Inn, Hampton Inn, ⊙ 🅗, RV camping (7mi), Walmart (1.5mi)
288	GA 113, Cartersville, **0-2 mi W** ⬛ BP/dsl, Exxon/Subway/dsl, 🍴 Applebee's, Burger King, Chick-Fil-A, Chili's, Gondolier Pizza, IHOP, KFC, Krystal/24hr, Las Palmas Mexican, Longhorn Steaks, McDonald's, Moe's SW Grill, Mrs Winner's, Pizza Hut, Publix, Red Lobster, Starbucks, Taco Bell, Waffle House, Wing Moon, 🏠 Fairfield Inn, Knight's Inn, Quality Inn, ⊙ Belk, Chrysler/Jeep/Dodge, K-Mart, Kohl's, Kroger, Rite Aid, Staples, Target, to Etowah Indian Mounds (6mi)
286mm	Etowah River
285	Emerson, **E** ⬛ Texaco/24hr, 🏠 Red Top Mtn Lodge, ⊙ to Allatoona Dam, to Red Top Mtn SP
283	Allatoona Rd, Emerson, **2 mi E** Allatoona Landing Resort, camping, **W** ⬛ Sunoco (1mi)
280mm	Allatoona Lake
278	Glade Rd, to Acworth, **E** ⬛ BP/dsl, Shell, 🏠 Best Value, ⊙ McKinney Camping (3mi), to Glade Marina, **W** ⬛ Chevron, 🍴 Bojangles, Hong Kong Chinese, KFC, Krystal, Papa John's, Pizza Hut, Subway, Taco Bell, Waffle House, 🏠 Best Inn, ⊙ AutoZone, BigLots, Ingles/cafe, Rite Aid
277	GA 92, Acworth, **E** ⬛ BP, RaceTrac, 🍴 Hardee's, Shoney's, Waffle House, 🏠 Comfort Suites, La Quinta, Ramada Ltd, **W** ⬛ Chevron/dsl, Shell/DQ/dsl, 🍴 Bamboo Garden, China Chef, Domino's, McDonald's, Ricardo's Mexican, Sonic, Subway, Taco 2 Go, Waffle House, Wendy's, Zaxby's, 🏠 Best Western, Day's Inn, Econolodge, Motel 6, Super 8, ⊙ Advance Parts, CVS Drug, Goodyear/auto, Publix, Walgreens
273	Wade Green Rd, **E** ⬛ BP, Pure, RaceTrac, 🍴 Arby's, Burger King, Dunkin Donuts, Las Palmas Mexican, McDonald's, Mrs Winners, Papa John's, Pizza Hut/Taco Bell, Subway, Waffle House, 🏠 Sleep Inn, Travelodge, ⊙ BigLots, GNC, Goodyear/auto, Publix, Rite Aid, **W** ⬛ Shell, Texaco/dsl, 🍴 BBQ Street, Coldstone Creamery, Johnny's Pizza/Subs, Quizno's, Starbucks, Wendy's, Wing Zone, ⊙ Home Depot, Kroger/gas, Walgreens
271	Chastain Rd, to I-575 N, **E** ⬛ Chevron, 🍴 CA Dreaming, Brewsters, Chick-Fil-A, Chilito's Mexican, Cracker Barrel, Dunkin Donuts, Firehouse Subs, Five Guys Burgers, Kayson's Grill, Little Zio, Los Reyes, McAlister's Deli, O'Charley's, Panda Express, Panera Bread, Sidelines Grille, Starbucks, Taco Mac, ToGo's/Baskin Robbins, Zaxby's, Zucca Pizza, 🏠 Best Western, Comfort Inn, Embassy Suites, Extended Stay America, Fairfield Inn, La Quinta, Residence Inn, Suburban Lodge, Super 8, ⊙ Goodyear/auto, Outlets Ltd Mall, **W** ⬛ Citgo, Swifty Save Gas/Blimpie, Shell/dsl, 🍴 Arby's, Mrs Winners, Waffle House/24hr, Wendy's, 🏠 Country Inn Suites, SpringHill Suites, Sun Suites, ⊙ museum
269	to US 41, to Marietta, **E** ⬛ Chevron/24hr, Shell, Texaco/dsl, 🍴 Applebee's, Burger King, Fuddrucker's, Highlands Grill, Honey Baked Ham, Longhorn Steaks,

MARIETTA

SMYRNA

Exit	Services
269	**Continued** McDonald's, New China, Olive Garden, Pizza Hut, Provino's, Red Lobster, Shogun Japanese, Smoothie King, Smokey Bones, Starbucks, Subway, Twisted Taco, Waffle House, 🏠 Comfort Inn, Econolodge, Holiday Inn Express, La Quinta, Red Roof Inn, Super 8, ⊙ Barnes&Noble, Big 10 Tire, Firestone/auto, Home Depot, JC Penney, Macy's, Marshall's, Publix, Sears/auto, TJ Maxx, mall, **W** ⬛ BP, Exxon, 🍴 Bahama Breeze, Bailey's Grill, Bugaboo, Carrabbas, Copelands Grill, Creek Steaks, Chick-fil-A, Chili's, ChuckeCheese, Coldstone, Golden Corral, Joe's Crabshack, Macaroni Grill, On-the-Border, Outback Steaks, Rafferty's, Starbucks, Steak'n Shake, Sweet Tomato, TGIFriday, Willy's Mexican, 🏠 Day's Inn, Hampton Inn, Hilton Garden, Quality Inn, Wingate Inn, ⊙ Best Buy, Buick/GMC, CarMax, Chevrolet, Costco/gas, Ford/Lincoln/Mercury, Goodyear/auto, Jo-Anne Fabrics, Kia/Toyota, Nissan, Mitsubishi, NTB, Office Depot, Old Navy, PetsMart, Target, mall, to Kennesaw Mtn NP
268	I-575 N, GA 5 N, to Canton
267b a	GA 5 N, to US 41, Marietta
265	GA120, N Marietta Pkwy, **W** ⬛ Chevron, Shell/dsl, 🍴 Arbys, Bojangles, Chick-fil-A, KFC, 🏠 Days Inn, Sun Inn, Suburban Lodge, Travelers Motel
263	GA 120, to Roswell, **E** ⬛ Chevron/dsl/24hr, QT, Texaco/24hr, **W** ⬛ Exxon/dsl, RaceTrac, 🍴 Applebee's, Capt D's, China Kitchen, DQ, Hardee's, Haveli Rest., Piccadilly's, Subway, 🏠 Best Western, Crowne Plaza, Fairfield Inn, Hampton Inn, Marietta Motel, Ramada Ltd, Regency Inn, Super 8, Wyndham Garden, ⊙ U-Haul, Atl-Marietta RV Resort
261	GA 280, Delk Rd, to Dobbins AFB, **E** ⬛ Exxon, RaceTrac, Shell/McDonald's/24hr, 🍴 CC Cafeteria, China Wok, Hardee's, KFC/Taco Bell, Murphy's Deli, Ruby Tuesday, Spaghetti Whse, 🏠 Budget Inn, Courtyard, Drury Inn, Motel 6, Scottish Inn, Sleep Inn, Super 8, Travelers Inn, ⊙ Publix, **W** ⬛ BP, Chevron/24hr, 🍴 Cracker Barrel, D&B Rest., Waffle House, 🏠 Best Inn, Comfort Inn, Days Inn, Fairfield Inn, Holiday Inn, La Quinta, Quality Inn, Wingate Inn
260	Windy Hill Rd, to Smyrna, **E** ⬛ BP, 🍴 Boston Mkt, Famous Dave's, Fuddrucker's, Houston's Rest., Jersey Mike's Subs, NY Pizza, Pappasito's Cantina, Pappadeaux Seafood, Philly Cafe, Salgrosso Brazilian, , Schlotsky's, Starbucks, Subway, TGIFriday, 🏠 Econolodge, Extended Stay Deluxe, Hilton Garden, Hyatt, Marriott, Studio Lodge, ⊙ CVS Drug, **W** ⬛ Chevron, Citgo, Shell, 🍴 Arby's, Chick-fil-A, Fatburger, Halftime Grill, McDonald's, Panda Express, Popeye's, Starbucks, Waffle House, Wendy's, 🏠 Best Western, Country Inn Suites, Courtyard, Day's Inn, DoubleTree, Hilton, Masters Inn, Red Roof Inn, ⊙ 🅗, Target
259b a	I-285, W to Birmingham, E to Greenville
258	Cumberland Pkwy, **W** 🍴 Doc Green's Rest., Hooters, Moe's SW Grill, Shane's Ribshack, Subway
257mm	Chattahoochee River
256	to US 41, Northside Pkwy
255	US 41, W Paces Ferry Rd, **E** ⬛ Chevron, Shell/dsl, 🍴 Blue Ridge Grill, Caribou Coffee, Chick-fil-A, Houston's Rest., McDonald's/playplace, OK Café/24hr, Pero's Pizza, Starbucks, Steak'n Shake, Taco Bell,

INTERSTATE 75 CONT'D

Exit	Services
255	Continued
	Willy's Rest., ⊡ Ⓗ, Ace Hardware, CVS Drug, Publix, **W** ⓡ Exxon/24hr
254	Moores Mill Rd
252b	Howell Mill Rd, **E** ⓡ Shell, ⑪ Chick-fil-A, Domino's, McDonald's, Willy's Grill, ⊡ Goodyear, Publix, Rite Aid, USPO, **W** ⓡ Shell, ⑪ Arby's, Arthur's Italian, Chin Chin Chinese, Einstein Bro's, Kayson's, KFC/Pizza Hut, Mexican, Rest., Piccadilly, Sensational Subs, Starbucks, Subway, Taco Bell, US BBQ, Waffle House, Wendy's, ⌂ Budget Inn, Holiday Inn, ⊡ Ace Hardware, Firestrone/auto, GNC, Just Brakes, Kroger, Office Depot, PetsMart, Ross, TJ Maxx, Walmart
252a	US 41, Northside Dr, **E** ⓡ Ⓗ, **W** ⓡ Shell, ⑪ Krystal/24hr, Little Zio's, McDonald's, Waffle House, ⌂ Day's Inn
251	I-85 N, to Greenville
250	Techwood Dr (from sb), 10th St, 14th St, **E** ⌂ Travelodge
249d	10th St, Spring St (from nb), **E** ⓡ BP, Chevron/24hr, ⑪ Checker's, Domino's, Pizza Hut, The Varsity, ⌂ Fairfield Inn, Regency Suites, Renaissance Hotel, Residence Inn, **W** ⑪ McDonald's, ⌂ Courtyard, Comfort Inn, ⊡ Ⓗ, to GA Tech
249c	Williams St (from sb), downtown, to GA Dome
249b	Pine St, Peachtree St (from nb), downtown, **W** ⌂ Hilton, Marriott
249a	Courtland St (from sb), downtown, **W** ⌂ Hilton, Marriott, ⊡ GA St U
248d	Piedmont Ave, Butler St (from sb), downtown, **W** ⌂ Courtyard, Fairfield Inn, Radisson, ⊡ Ⓗ, Ford, MLK NHS
248c	GA 10 E, Intn'l Blvd, downtown, **W** ⌂ Hilton, Holiday Inn, Marriott Marquis, Radisson
248b	Edgewood Ave (from nb), **W** ⊡ Ⓗ, downtown, hotels
248a	MLK Dr (from sb), **W** st capitol, to Underground Atlanta
247	I-20, E to Augusta, W to Birmingham
246	Georgia Ave, Fulton St, **E** ⌂ Comfort Inn, Country Inn& Suites, Holiday Inn, ⊡ stadium, **W** ⓡ BP, ⑪ KFC, ⊡ to Coliseum, GSU
245	Ormond St, Abernathy Blvd, **E** ⌂ Comfort Inn, Country Inn& Suites, ⊡ stadium, **W** st capitol
244	University Ave, **E** ⓡ Chevron, Exxon, ⊡ NAPA, **W** ⑪ Mrs Winner's
243	GA 166, Lakewood Fwy, to East Point
242	I-85 S, to ✈
241	Cleveland Ave, **E** ⓡ BP, Chevron, ⑪ Checker's, Church's, McDonald's, Subway, ⌂ Palace Inn, ⊡ Advance Parts, K-Mart, **W** ⓡ Shell, Marathon, Phillips 66, Texaco, ⑪ Blimpie, Burger King, Krystal/24hr, Mrs Winners, ⌂ American Inn, Day's Inn, ⊡ CVS Drug, Kroger
239	US 19, US 41, **E** ⓡ Chevron/dsl, ⑪ Waffle House, ⊡ USPO, **W** ⓡ Texaco, ⑪ IHOP, McDonald's, Wendy's, ⌂ Best Western, to ✈
238b a	I-285 around Atlanta
237a	GA 85, S (from sb), **W** ⑪ Denny's, ⌂ Burger King, McDonald's, Waffle House, ⌂ Day's Inn, Day's Lodge
237	GA 331, Forest Parkway, **E** ⓡ BP, Chevron/dsl, Shell/McDonald's, ⑪ Burger King, Mr Taco, Subway, Waffle House, ⌂ Econolodge, ⊡ Farmer's Mkt, **W** ⓡ BP, ⑪ Denny's, ⌂ Day's Inn, Ramada Ltd
235	US 19, US 41, GA 3, Jonesboro, **E** ⓡ Chevron/dsl, Exxon/Subway/dsl, Phillips 66, Valero, ⑪ Waffle House, ⌂ Travelodge, **W** ⓡ BP, Shell, Texaco/dsl, ⑪ Applebee's, Burger King, Checker's, ChuckeCheese, Dunkin Donuts, Folk's Rest., Hooters, Krystal, Popeye's, Red Lobster, Tokyo Buffet, Waffle House, Zaxby's, ⌂ Best Value, Econolodge, Holiday Inn, Motel 6, ⊡ Ⓗ, Office Depot, O'Reilly Parts
233	GA 54, Morrow, **E** ⓡ BP, Citgo, Marathon, ⑪ Cracker Barrel, IHOP, Krystal/24hr, Mrs Winner's, Papa Buffet, Taco Bell, Waffle House, Wendy's, ⌂ Best Western, Days Inn, Drury Inn, Red Roof Inn, ⊡ Walmart, **W** ⓡ Circle K, Exxon/24hr, ⑪ China Café, KFC, Lenny's Subs, McDonald's, Quizno's, Subway, Waffle House, ⌂ Hampton Inn, Quality Inn, ⊡ Acura, Best Buy, Costco/gas, Harley-Davidson, Macy's, Nissan, TJ Maxx, Toyota, Tuesday Morning
231	Mt Zion Blvd, **E** ⓡ QT, ⊡ Chrysler/Dodge/Jeep, Ford/Lincoln/Mercury, Honda, **W** ⓡ Chevron, Exxon/dsl, Texaco/dsl, ⑪ Arby's, Boston's Rest., Brewster's, Burger Shack, Burger King, Chick-fil-A, Chili's, Joe's Crabshack, Longhorn Steaks, McDonald's, Mo-Joe's, Panda Express, Papa John's, Pizza Hut, Steak'n Shake, Subway, Truett's Rest., Waffle House, Wendy's, Wok Asian, ⌂ Country Inn&Suites, Extended Stay America, Sleep Inn, Sun Suites, ⊡ Barnes & Noble, Best Buy, Home Depot, Michael's, NTB, Old Navy, PetsMart, Publix, Ross, Target
228	GA 54, GA 138, Jonesboro, **E** ⓡ Exxon, Raceway/24hr, ⑪ Applebee's, Arby's, Broadway Diner, Burger King, Chick-fil-A, ChinChin Chinese, CiCi's, DQ, Frontera Mexican, Golden Corral, Honeybaked Ham, IHOP, KFC, Krystal, McDonald's, O'Charlie's, Piccadilly's, Subway, Taco Mac, Tokyo Seafood, Waffle House, Wendy's, ⌂ Best Western, Day's Inn, Comfort Inn, Holiday Inn, Howard Johnson, La Quinta, Hampton Inn, Holiday Inn, Motel 6, Red Roof Inn, ⊡ Ⓗ, GNC, Goodyear, K-Mart, Kroger/dsl, Lowes Whse, Office Depot, Tires+, **W** ⓡ BP/24hr, Marathon, Sunoco/Wendy's, ⑪ Dragon Garden Chinese, Ranchero's Mexican, ⊡ CarMax, CVS Drug, Kohl's
227	I-675 N, to I-285, E (from nb)
224	Hudson Bridge Rd, **E** ⓡ Shell, Texaco/dsl, ⑪ Chick-fil-A, China Wok, DQ, KFC, La Hacienda, Outback Steaks, Pizza Hut, Starbucks, Subway, Waffle House, Wendy's, ⌂ Baymont Inn, ⊡ Ⓗ, Publix, Rite Aid, Walgreens, **W** ⓡ Murphy USA/dsl, QT, ⑪ Arby's, China Cafe, Firehouse Subs, McDonald's, Mellow Mushroom, Subway, Taco Bell, Zaxby's, ⌂ Super 8, ⊡ Discount

N ↕ **S**

ATLANTA AREA

MORROW

JONESBORO

GA

INTERSTATE 75 CONT'D

N ↕ S

Exit	Services
224	Continued Tire, $Tree, Walmart
222	Jodeco Rd, **E** 🅖 BP, Citgo/24hr, Texaco, 🍴 Hardee's, Waffle House, **W** 🅖 BP, Chevron/dsl, Citgo, 🄾 Atlanta So. RV Camping
221	Jonesboro Rd, **E** 🅖 QT, 🄾 Kroger/gas, Kauffman Tire, **W** 🍴 Arby's, Burger King, Chili's, Cici's Pizza, Golden Corral, Hooter's, Logan's Roadhouse, Longhorn Steaks, Marble Slab Creamery, McDonald's, O'Charley's, Olive Garden, Quizno's, Red Lobster, Rocky's Pizza, Starbucks, Subway, Truett's Grill, Wendy's, 🏨 Fairfield Inn, 🄾 Belk, Best Buy, Books-A-Million, BJ's Whse/gas, Home Depot, Marshall's, Michael's, PetsMart, Radio Shack, Ross, Sam's Club/gas, Staples, Target
218	GA 20, GA 81, McDonough, **E** 🅖 BP, Murphy USA, QT, Texaco, 🍴 Applebee's, Arby's, Blimpie, Burger King, China Star, Cracker Barrel, DQ, KFC, IHOP, McDonald's, Moe's SW Grill, Mrs Winner's, OB's BBQ, Pizza Hut, Quizno's, Ruby Tuesday, Taco Bell, 3 Dollar Cafe, Tokyo Japanese, Waffle House, Wendy's, Zaxby's, 🏨 Best Inn, Best Western, Economy Inn, Hampton Inn, Motel 6, 🄾 Aamco, $General, Goodyear, Lowe's Whse, Office Depot, Rite Aid, Walmart, **W** 🅖 Citgo/dsl, RaceTrac, Shell/24hr, 🍴 Chick-fil-A, El Agade Mexican, Firehouse Subs, Fuddruckers, Starbucks, Subway, Waffle House, 🏨 Comfort Inn, Econolodge, Hilton Garden, Holiday Inn Express, Super 8, 🄾 JC Penney, Kohl's, Toyota
216	GA 155, McDonough, Blacksville, **E** 🅖 Shell, Sunoco/Backyard Burger, Texaco/dsl, 🍴 Blimpie, 🏨 Best Value, Budget Inn, Day's Inn, Roadway Inn, 🄾 Chevrolet, Buick, Lincoln/Mercury, GMC, **W** 🅖 BP/dsl, Chevron, Citgo, Citgo/dsl/24hr, Mystik/dsl, QT, 🍴 Da Vinci's Pizza, Krystal, Kuma Japanese, Legends Grill, Subway, Waffle House, 🏨 Country Inn&Suites, Quality Inn
212	to US 23, Locust Grove, **E** 🅖 BP/McDonald's/dsl, Chevron/Burger King, Citgo/dsl, JP, Marathon/Subway, Shell/dsl, 🍴 Capt D's, Country Steaks, Denny's, Gabino's Mexican, Huddle House, KFC/Pizza Hut/Taco Bell, Shane's Ribshack, Sunrise China, Waffle House, Wendy's, Zaxby's, 🏨 Economy Inn, Executive Inn, La Quinta, Ramada Ltd, Red Roof Inn, 🄾 Ingles/gas, NapaCare, Tanger Outlet/famous brands, **W** 🅖 Citgo/DQ/dsl, Exxon/dsl, 🏨 Comfort Suites, Scottish Inn, Sundown Lodge, Super 8, 🄾 Bumper Parts
205	GA 16, to Griffin, Jackson, **E** 🅖 BP, **W** 🅖 BP, Chevron/dsl, 🄾 Forest Glen RV Park, auto repair
201	GA 36, to Jackson, Barnesville, **E** 🅖 ❤Love's/McDonald's/dsl/grill/scales/24hr, TA/Subway/Taco Bell/dsl/scales/24hr/@, Wilco/Hess/DQ/Stuckey's/Wendy's/dsl/scales/24hr/@, 🄾 Blue Beacon, **W** 🅖 BP/dsl, ⊕FLYING J/Denny's/dsl/LP/24hr, 🄾 Sagon RV Ctr, Speedco Lube, truckwash
198	Highfalls Rd, **E** 🅖 Exxon (1mi), 🍴 High Falls BBQ, Ken's Cafe, 🏨 High Falls Lodge, 🄾 High Falls SP, **W** High Falls RV Park
193	Johnstonville Rd, **E** 🅖 BP
190mm	weigh sta both lanes
188	GA 42, **E** 🅖 Shell/24hr, 🏨 Best Western, Budget Inn, 🄾 to Indian Springs SP, RV camping

Exit	Services
187	GA 83, Forsyth, **E** 🏨 Econolodge, New Forsyth Inn, Regency Inn, **W** 🅖 BP/Circle K, Citgo/dsl, Marathon, Shell, 🍴 Burger King, Capt D's, China Inn, DQ, Hardee's, McDonald's, Pizza Hut, Subway, Taco Bell, Waffle House, Wendy's, 🏨 Day's Inn, Tradewinds Motel, 🄾 Advance Parts, Freshway Foods, O'Reilly Parts, Walmart
186	Tift College Dr, Juliette Rd, Forsyth, **E** Jarrell Plantation HS (18mi), KOA, **W** 🅖 BP/dsl, Chevron, Marathon, 🍴 Waffle House, 🏨 Holiday Inn/rest., Holiday Inn Express, Super 8, 🄾 🅷, CVS Drug, Ingles/Deli
185	GA 18, **E** L&D RV Park (2mi), **W** 🅖 BP/Circle K/24hr, Shell/dsl, 🍴 Shoney's, 🏨 Comfort Inn, 🄾 Ford, repair, st patrol
181	Rumble Rd, to Smarr, **E** 🅖 BP/dsl/24hr, Shell/dsl/24hr
179mm	**rest area sb, full 🅥 facilities, 🄲, 🄵, vending, litter barrels, petwalk**
177	I-475, S around Macon (from sb)
175	Pate Rd, Bolingbroke (from nb, no re-entry)
172	Bass Rd, **E** 🍴 Pig in a Pit BBQ, McDonald's, Quizno's, Zaxby's, 🄾 Bass Pro Shop, **W** 🅖 Citgo/dsl/24hr, 🍴 Magarita's Mexican, Mellow Mushroom, 🍴 Homewood Suites, 🄾 Publix, to Museum of Arts&Sciences
171	US 23, to GA 87, Riverside Dr, **E** 🅖 BP, Marathon/dsl, 🍴 Bonefish Grill, Chili's, Jock&Jill's Grill, Mandarin Express, Sticky Fingers, 🄾 Acura, Barnes & Noble, Belk, Dillards, KIA, Mercedes, Subaru, Volvo, **W** 🍴 Cracker Barrel, 🄾 Lexus, Toyota/Scion, same as 169 W
169	to US 23, Arkwright Dr, **E** 🅖 Shell/Circle K/24hr, 🍴 Carrabba's, Logan's Roadhouse, Outback Steaks, Waffle House, Wager's Grill, 🏨 Candlewood Suites, Comfort Inn, Country Inn & Suites, Courtyard, Fairfield Inn, Hampton Inn, Holiday Inn, La Quinta, Red Roof Inn, Residence Inn, Sleep Inn, Super 8, 🄾 Buick/Cadillac/GMC, **W** 🅖 BP/dsl, Chevron/24hr, Marathon/dsl, 🍴 Arby's, Burger King, Cheddar's, Cheng's Kitchen, Chick-fil-A, Corky Bells, Cracker Barrel, Dunkin Donuts, El Azteca Mexican, 5 Guys Burgers, Guiseppi's Italian, Hooters, KFC, Krystal, Longhorn Steaks, Mandarin Chinese, McDonald's, Papa John's, Papoulis' Gyros, Panera Bread, Pizza Hut, Shoki Japanese, Starbucks, Steak'n Shake, Steve B's Pizza, Subway, Taco Bell, Waffle House, 🏨 Baymont Inn, Best Inn, Extended Stay Deluxe, Quality Inn, Travelodge, Wingate Inn, 🄾 🅷, Ace Hardware, Chrysler/Jeep/Dodge, $Tree, Hyundai, K-Mart, Kroger, Mazda, Publix, Radio Shack, same as 167
167	GA 247, Pierce Ave, **E** 🏨 Days Inn, **W** 🅖 BP/Circle K/dsl, Chevron, Conoco, Exxon, LoBucks Gas, Marathon/Subway/dsl, Shell, 🍴 Applebee's, Loco's Grill, Pier 97 Seafood, Pizza Hut, Red Lobster, San Marcos Mexican, Shogun Japanese, SteakOut Rest., Waffle House, 🏨 Best Western/rest., Comfort Inn, Holiday Inn Express, Howard Johnson, Motel 6, 🄾 ExperTire, Rite Aid
165	I-16 E, to Savannah
164	US 41, GA 19, Forsyth Ave, Macon, **E** 🍴 Sid's Rest., 🄾 hist dist, **W** 🅖 BP, Citgo, 🄾 🅷, museum
163	GA 74 W, Mercer U Dr, **E** 🏨 Hilton Garden, 🄾 to Mercer U, **W** 🅖 Citgo, Marathon/dsl
162	US 80, GA 22, Eisenhower Pkwy, **W** 🅖 BP, Chevron/24hr, Lo-lo Gas, 🍴 Burger King, Capt D's, Checker's, IHOP, Krispy Kreme, Krystal, LJ Silver, McDonald's, Mrs Winners, Subway, Taco Bell, Wendy's, 🄾 $Tree, Office Depot, O'Reilly Parts, PepBoys, SavAlot Foods, Walgreens

MC DONOUGH

GA

FORSYTH

MACON

MACON

INTERSTATE 75 CONT'D

Exit	Services
160	US 41, GA 247, Pio Nono Ave, **E** 📱 Flash/dsl, RaceWay/Dunkin Donuts, 🍴 Waffle House, 🛏 Best Inn, **W** 📱 BP, Enmark/dsl, 🍴 Advance Parts, Arby's, DQ, KFC, King Buffet, McDonald's, Subway, Waffle House, ⊙ Advance Parts, $General, Goodyear/auto, NAPA, O'Reilly Parts, Roses, USPO, same as 162
156	I-475, N around Macon (from nb)
155	Hartley Br Rd, **E** 📱 BP/KFC/dsl/24hr, 🍴 Subway, Wendy's, ⊙ Kroger/dsl, **W** 📱 Citgo/dsl, Exxon, Flash/DQ/dsl, 🍴 McDonald's, Zaxby's, 🛏 Best Value Inn, ⊙ Advance Parts, CVS Drug
152	new exit
149	GA 49, Byron, **E** 📱 Chevron/dsl, Marathon/dsl, Shell/dsl, 🍴 Burger King, Denny's, Krystal, McDonald's, Pizza Hut, Subway, Waffle House, Wendy's, Zaxby's, 🛏 Best Western, Comfort Suites, Holiday Inn Express, Super 8, ⊙ Campers Inn RV Ctr, Mid-State RV Ctr, Peach Stores/famous brands, antiques, **W** 📱 Citgo/dsl/24hr, Exxon, Flash/dsl, Marathon, RaceWay, Texaco/dsl, 🍴 Country Cupboard, DQ, Huddle House, Waffle House, 🛏 Days Inn, EconoLodge, Passport Inn, Quality Inn, ⊙ Ace Hardware, Advance Parts, Bumper Parts, Camping World RV Ctr, Chevrolet, $General, Family$, Ford, Freshway Mkt, Suncoast RV Ctr, Verizon, USPO
146	GA 247, to Centerville, **E** 📱 Exxon, Flash/dsl, Shell, 🍴 Subway, Waffle House, 🛏 EconoLodge, Knights Inn, ⊙ Ⓗ, to Robins AFB, museum, **W** 📱 Pilot/Arby's/dsl/24hr
144	Russel Pkwy, **E** Robins AFB, aviation museum
142	GA 96, Housers Mill Rd, **E** 📱 Chevron/dsl, ⊙ Ponderosa RV Park
138	Thompson Rd, **E** ⊙ Ⓗ, **W** ✈
136	US 341, Perry, **E** 📱 BP, Flash/dsl, Shell/dsl, 🍴 Arby's, Burger King, Capt D's, Chick-fil-A, China House, Hong Kong Buffet, KFC, Krystal, Longhorn Steaks, McDonald's, Pizza Hut, Red Lobster, Sonny's BBQ, Subway, Taco Bell, Waffle House, Wendy's, Zaxby's, 🛏 Best Inn, Great Inn, Hampton Inn, Howard Johnson, Jameson Inn, Super 8, ⊙ Ⓗ, Ace Hardware, Advance Parts, $Tree, GNC, Kroger, NAPA, Radio Shack, Walmart, **W** 📱 Chevron/dsl, Marathon/dsl, RaceWay/24hr, 🍴 Applebee's, Green Derby Rest., Grill Master BBQ, 🛏 Ashburn Inn, EconoLodge, Holiday Inn, Knights Inn, Passport Inn, Quality Inn, Rodeway Inn, ⊙ Ford, Crossroads Camping
135	US 41, GA 127, Perry, **E** 📱 BP/dsl, Exxon, Flash/dsl, Marathon, Shell, 🍴 Cracker Barrel, Subway, Waffle House, 🛏 Best Western, Comfort Inn, Red Carpet Inn, Relax Inn, Travelodge, ⊙ Chrysler/Dodge/Jeep, Kia, GA Nat Fair, **W** ⊙ Fair Harbor RV Park, st patrol
134	South Perry Pkwy, **W** 🛏 Microtel, ⊙ Buick/Chevrolet/GMC, Priester's Pecans
127	GA 26, Henderson, **E** ⊙ Twin Oaks Camping, **W** 📱 Chevron
122	GA 230, Unadilla, **E** 📱 Chevron/dsl, ⊙ Chevrolet/Ford, **W** 🛏 Red Carpet Inn, ⊙ Bleakley RV Ctr
121	US 41, Unadilla, **E** 📱 Borum/repair, Danfair, Flash/DQ/Stuckey's/dsl, Shell, 🍴 Country Boys BBQ, Don Ponchos Mexican, Subway, 🛏 Economy Inn, Scottish Inn, ⊙ Carquest, $General, Firestone, Piggly Wiggly, Southern Trails RV Resort, **W** 📱 Citgo/dsl/rest./scales/24hr

Exit	Services
118mm	rest area sb, full ♿ facilities, 📞, 🛒, vending, litter barrels, petwalk, RV dump
117	to US 41, Pinehurst, **W** 📱 Pinehurst TC/dsl/scales/24hr, ⊙ truckwash
112	GA 27, Vienna, **W** 📱 Citgo/dsl
109	GA 215, Vienna, **E** 📱 Pilot/McDonalds/dsl/scales/24hrs, **W** 📱 Citgo/dsl, PigJig, Shell/Subway/dsl/e85, 🍴 Huddle House, Popeye's, 🛏 Executive Inn, ⊙ Ⓗ, antiques, Cotton Museum
108mm	rest area nb, full ♿ facilities, 📞, 🛒, vending, litter barrels, petwalk, RV dump
104	Farmers Mkt Rd, Cordele
102	GA 257, Cordele, **W** 🍴 Pecan House, ⊙ Ⓗ
101	US 280, GA 90, Cordele, **E** 📱 Chevron, Exxon/dsl, Pilot/Arby's/dsl/scales/24hr, Shell, 🍴 Denny's, Golden Corral, Waffle House, 🛏 Days Inn, Fairfield Inn, Holiday Inn Express, Ramada Inn, ⊙ Ford/Lincoln/Mercury, st patrol, **W** 📱 BP/dsl, Gas'n Go, Sunoco, 🍴 Burger King, Capt D's, Compadres Mexican, Cracker Barrel, Cutter's Steaks, Dominos, DQ, Hardee's, KFC/Pizza Hut, Krystal/24hr, Los Compadres, McDonald's, New China, Sonic, Subway, Taco Bell, Wendy's, Zaxby's, 🛏 Ashburn Inn, Athens 8 Motel, Best Western, Comfort Inn, Deluxe Inn, Express Inn, Hampton Inn, Quality Inn, Travelodge, ⊙ URGENT CARE, Ace Hardware, Advance Parts, AT&T, AutoZone, Belk, $General, $Tree, Harvey's Foods, Home Depot, NAPA, O'Reilly Parts, Radio Shack, Verizon, Walgreens, Walmart, to Veterans Mem SP, J Carter HS
99	GA 300, GA/FL Pkwy, **E** 🍴 Horizon/DQ, **W** 🍴 Waffle House, 🛏 Country Inn&Suites, ⊙ to Chehaw SP
97	to GA 33, Wenona, **E** ⊙ Cordele RV Park, dsl repair, **W** ⊙ KOA, truckwash
92	Arabi, **E** 📱 Shell/Plantation House, **W** 📱 BP/dsl, ⊙ Southern Gates RV Park
85mm	rest area nb, full ♿ facilities, 📞, 🛒, vending, litter barrels, petwalk
84	GA 159, Ashburn, **E** 📱 Shell/dsl, **W** 📱 Chevron/dsl/24hr, 🍴 DQ, Subway, 🛏 Ashburn Inn/RV Park
82	GA 107, GA 112, Ashburn, **W** 📱 BP, Shell, TC, 🍴 KFC, McDonald's, Pizza Hut, Shoney's, Waffle House, Zaxby's, 🛏 Best Western, Days Inn, Super 8, ⊙ Buick/Chevrolet/GMC, $General, Fred's Drugs, O'Reilly Parts, Piggly Wiggly, Rite Aid, to Chehaw SP
80	Bussey Rd, Sycamore, **E** 📱 Shell, 🛏 Budget Inn, **W** ⊙ Allen's Tires
78	GA 32, Sycamore, **E** to Jefferson Davis Mem Pk (14mi)
76mm	rest area sb, full ♿ facilities, 📞, 🛒, vending, litter barrels, petwalk

(side column, top to bottom) **N ↕ S** · **PERRY** · **CORDELE** · **WENONA** · **ASHBURN** · **GA**

GA

INTERSTATE 75 CONT'D

N ↕ S   T I F T O N   A D E L

Exit	Services
75	Inaha Rd, W 🅖 Citgo/Stuckey's
71	Willis Still Rd, Sunsweet, W 🅖 BP/dsl
69	Chula-Brookfield Rd, E 🅖 Homeland/dsl, 🛏 Carpet Inn, ⊙ antiques
66	Brighton Rd
64	US 41, Tifton, E 🅖 BP/dsl, ⊙ 🄷, $General, Harvey's Foods, W 🅖 Shell
63b	8th St, Tifton, E 🅖 Bob's, Flash, 🍴 KFC, Los Compadres, 🛏 Budget Inn, W 🍴 Pit Stop BBQ, ⊙ GA Museum of Agriculture
63a	2nd St, Tifton, E 🅖 BP, Chevron, 🍴 Asahi Xpress, Arby's, Checker's, El Cazador Mexican, Krystal, McDonald's, Pizza Hut, Red Lobster, Subway, Taco Bell, Waffle House, 🛏 EconoLodge, Super 8, ⊙ Belk, Buick/Cadillac/GMC, $General, $Tree, JC Penney, K-Mart, W 🅖 West Side/Cafe/dsl, 🍴 El Chile Verde, 🛏 Quality Inn, Travelodge
62	US 82, to US 319, Tifton, E 🅖 BP, Citgo, Flash/dsl, 🍴 Applebee's, Charles Seafood, Chili's, Country Buffet, Cracker Barrel, DQ, Golden Corral, King Buffet, Sonic, Tokyo Japanese, Waffle House, Zaxby's, 🛏 Comfort Inn, Courtyard, Country Inn&Suites, Fairfield Inn, Hampton Inn, Microtel, ⊙ Advance Parts, AutoZone, BigLots, Bumper Parts, $Tree, Family$, Ford/Lincoln/Mercury, NAPACare, O'Reilly Parts, Pecan Outlet, Staples, W 🅖 BP, Exxon/Burger King, EZ Mart, Murphy USA/dsl, RaceWay/dsl, Shell/dsl, 🍴 Capt D's, Chick-fil-A, Cici's Pizza, HogBones BBQ, Little Caesars, Loco's Grill, Longhorn Steaks, McDonald's, Old Mexico, Quiznos, Ruby Tuesday, Shoney's, Subway, Waffle House, Wendy's, 🛏 Days Inn, Hilton Garden, Ramada Ltd, Rodeway Inn, ⊙ URGENT CARE, AT&T, Chevrolet, Chrysler/Dodge, Honda, Lowe's, Radio Shack, Toyota, Verizon, Walmart
61	Omega Rd, W 🅖 Shell/Stuckey's/Country Diner/pizza/dsl/24hr, 🛏 Motel 6, ⊙ Harley-Davidson, Pines RV Park, E Nissan
60	Central Ave, Tifton, E 🅖 Chevron, 🍴 Dragon 1 Chinese, W 🅖 🄿/Subway/Steak'n Shake/dsl/scales/24hr, ⊙ Blue Beacon, KOA
59	Southwell Blvd, to US 41, Tifton, E 🅖 ♥Loves/Hardees/dsl/24hr
55	to Eldorado, Omega, E 🅖 Shell/Magnolia Plantation
49	Kinard Br Rd, Lenox, E 🅖 Dixie/dsl, 🛏 Knights Inn, W 🅖 BP/dsl/24hr, ⊙ repair
47mm	**rest area both lanes, full ♿ facilities, ☎, 🚻, vending, litter barrels, petwalk**
45	Barneyville Rd, E 🛏 Economy Inn
41	Rountree Br Rd, E 🅖 Citgo, W to Reed Bingham SP
39	GA 37, Adel, Moultrie, E 🅖 Citgo/dsl, Dixie Gas, Quick Gas, Shell/McDonald's/dsl, 🍴 DQ, Hardee's, Old Mexico Mexican, Subway, Waffle House, 🛏 Budget Lodge, Scottish Inn, Super 8, ⊙ 🄷, Advance Parts, CarQuest, $General, Family$, Harvey's Foods, Piggly Wiggly, Rite Aid, W 🅖 BP, Citgo/Huddle House/dsl/scales, 🍴 Burger King, Capt D's, IHOP, Taco Bell, Wendy's, Western Sizzlin, 🛏 Days Inn, Hampton Inn, ⊙ Factory Stores/famous brands, to Reed Bingham SP
37	Adel
32	Old Coffee Rd, Cecil, E 🅖 Citgo, 🛏 Family World Motel, Stagecoach Inn, ⊙ repair, W 🅖 Chevron, ⊙ Cecil Bay RV Park

V A L D O S T A

Exit	Services
29	US 41 N, GA 122, Hahira, Sheriff's Boys Ranch, E 🍴 Subway, ⊙ NAPA, W 🅖 Big Foot TC/Apple Valley/dsl, Stuckey's/Blimpie/TCBY/dsl, 🛏 Knights Inn
23mm	**weigh sta both lanes**
22	US 41 S, to Valdosta, E 🅖 BP, Shell/Subway/dsl, 🍴 Waffle House, 🛏 Hawthorn Suites, ⊙ 🄷, Chevrolet/Mazda, golf, W 🅖 Citgo/Stuckey's, 🍴 Burger King, DQ, 🛏 Days Inn
18	GA 133, Valdosta, E 🅖 Flash, Mobil, 🍴 Applebee's, Arby's, Atl. Bread Co, Brusters, Buffalo Wild Wings, Burger King, Chick-fil-A, Chili's, Cracker Barrel, Cici's Pizza, Crystal River Seafood, Denny's, El Potro Mexican, El Toreo, Fazoli's, Hibachi Grill, Honeybaked Ham, Hooters, KFC, Krystal, Little Caesar's, Longhorn Steaks, Marble Slab, McAlister's Deli, McDonald's, Outback Steaks, Quiznos, Red Lobster, Ruby Tuesday, Sonny's BBQ, Starbucks, Steak'n Shake, Subway, Taco Bell, TX Roadhouse, Waffle House, Wendy's, 🛏 Best Western, Comfort Suites, Country Inn&Suites, Courtyard, Hilton Garden, Holiday Inn Express, InTown Suites, Jameson Inn, Jolly Inn, La Quinta, Quality Inn, Red Roof Inn, Rodeway Inn, Scottish Inn, ⊙ AT&T, Belk, Best Buy, Books-A-Million, $Tree, Family$, Hobby Lobby, Home Depot, JC Penney, Kohl's, Lowe's, Michaels, Office Depot, Old Navy, Petsmart, Publix, Ross, Sears/auto, Target, TJ Maxx, Verizon, Walgreens, mall, repair, W 🅖 BP/dsl, RaceWay, Shell, 🍴 Steamhouse Seafood, 🛏 EconoLodge, Magnuson Hotel, Sleep Inn, ⊙ RiverPark Camping, Toyota/Scion
16	US 84, US 221, GA 94, Valdosta, E 🅖 Big Foot/dsl, BP/dsl, Citgo/dsl, Danfair Express, Murphy Express/dsl, Mystik/Blimpie/Stuckey's/dsl, Shell/dsl, 🍴 Aligatou Japanese, Bojangles, Burger King, Cheddar's, McDonald's, Old South BBQ, Pizza Hut, Shoney's, Sonic, Waffle House, Wendy's, 🛏 Days Inn, Guesthouse Inn, Hampton Inn, Holiday Inn, Motel 6, New Valdosta Inn, Quality Inn, Super 8, Wingate Inn, ⊙ NAPA, Sam's Club/gas, Walmart/Subway, repair, to Okefenokee SP, W 🅖 Shell/dsl/24hr, 🍴 Austin's Steaks, 🛏 Briarwood Hotel, Clarion, Knights Inn
13	Old Clyattville Rd, Valdosta, W Wild Adventures Park
11	GA 31, Valdosta, E 🅖 🄿/Subway/dsl/24hr/@, Wilco/Hess/Stuckey's/dsl/scales/24hr, 🍴 Waffle House, 🛏 Travelers Inn, W 🅖 BP, ⊙ $Tree
5	GA 376, to Lake Park, E 🅖 Citgo, Flash/Krystal/dsl, RaceWay, Shell, 🍴 Chick-fil-A, Domino's, Farmhouse Rest., Lin's Garden Chinese, Rodeo Mexican, Shoney's, Sonny's BBQ, Subway, Waffle House, 🛏 Guesthouse Inn, Quality Inn, ⊙ $Tree, Eagles Roost Camping, Family$, Preferred Outlets/famous brands, Travel Country RV Ctr, Winn-Dixie, antiques, USPO, W 🅖 Citgo/dsl, Shell/dsl, 🍴 Cracker Barrel, McDonald's, Pizza Hut, Taco Bell, Wendy's, 🛏 Days Inn, Hampton Inn, Super 8, Travelodge, ⊙ KOA, SunCoast RV Ctr
3mm	**Welcome Ctr nb, full ♿ facilities, ☎, 🚻, vending, litter barrels, petwalk**
2	Lake Park, Bellville, E 🅖 Mobil/DQ, SpeedCo, Shell/dsl, TA/BP/Arby's/dsl/scales/24hr/@, W 🅖 ⓕFLYING J/Denny's/Subway/dsl/LP/scales/24hr, 🛏 Motel 6, ⊙ lube/tires/wash
0mm	Georgia/Florida state line

Copyright 2012 - The Next Exit®

INTERSTATE 85

Exit	Services
179mm	Georgia/South Carolina state line, Lake Hartwell, Tugaloo River
177	GA 77 S, to Hartwell, **E** ⬛ BP/gifts/dsl, 🍴 Dad's Grill, ◉ to Hart SP, Tugaloo SP
176mm	Welcome Ctr sb, full ♿ facilities, info, ℂ, 🚻, litter barrels, vending, petwalk
173	GA 17, to Lavonia, **E** ⬛ RaceTrac/dsl, 🍴 Blimpie, La Cabana Mexican, McDonald's, Subway, Taco Bell, Waffle House, 🛏 EconoLodge, Sleep Inn, ◉ $General, Lavonia Foods, Rite Aid, **W** ⬛ Chevron/dsl, Exxon/dsl, 🍴 Burger King, Hardee's, Pizza Hut, Shoney's, Wendy's, Zaxby's, 🛏 Holiday Inn Express, Super 8, ◉ Chrysler/Dodge/Jeep, Ford, to Tugaloo SP
171mm	weigh sta nb
169mm	weigh sta sb
166	GA 106, to Carnesville, Toccoa, **E** ⬛ Wilco/Hess/DQ/Wendy's/dsl/scales/24hr, **W** ⬛ Echo Trkstp/Chevron/Echo Rest./dsl/scales/24hr, ◉ truck repair
164	GA 320, to Carnesville, **E** ⬛ Chevron/dsl
160	GA 51, to Homer, **E** ⬛ Shell/Subway/dsl/24hr, ◉ Ty Cobb Museum, to Russell SP, Victoria Bryant SP, **W** ⬛ ✈FLYING J/dsl/24hr, Carnsville TrvlPlaza/dsl/scales/24hr, ◉ Blue Beacon
154	GA 63, Martin Br Rd
149	US 441, GA 15, to Commerce, Homer, **E** ⬛ Murphy USA, QT/dsl, TA/Buckhorn Rest/dsl/scales/24hr/@, 🍴 Capt D's, Denny's, El Azteca, Grand Buffet, Krispy Kreme, Longhorn Steaks, Outback Steaks, Pizza Hut/Taco Bell, Sonny's BBQ, Zaxby's, 🛏 Best Value Inn, Dandelion Inn, Hampton Inn, Scottish Inn, ◉ Ⓗ, $General, $Tree, Funopolis, GNC, O'Reilly Parts, Radio Shack, Walmart, **W** ⬛ BP/Krystal/dsl, Citgo, RaceTrac/dsl, 🍴 Applebee's, Arby's, Burger King, Checker's, Chick-fil-A, Cracker Barrel, DQ, 5 Guys Burgers, La Fiesta, La Hacienda, McDonald's, Pizza Hut, Ruby Tuesday, Ryan's, Sonic, Starbucks, Subway, Wendy's, 🛏 Best Inn, Best Western, Comfort Suites, Fairfield Inn, Holiday Inn Express, Howard Johnson, Jameson Inn, Motel 6, Quality Inn, Super 8, ◉ Home Depot, Pritchett Tires, Tanger Outlet/famous brands
147	GA 98, to Commerce, **E** ⬛ ✈FLYING J/Dunkin Donuts/dsl/24hr, FuelMart/dsl, Valero, ◉ Ⓗ, **W** ◉ Gulf
140	GA 82, Dry Pond Rd, **E** Freightliner, **W** RV & Truck Repair
137	US 129, GA 11 to Jefferson, **E** ⬛ RaceTrac/dsl, 🍴 Arby's, El Jinete Mexican, KFC/Taco Bell, McDonald's, Waffle House, Zaxby's, 🛏 Comfort Inn, ◉ museum, **W** ⬛ QT/dsl/scales/24hr, 🍴 Burger King, Waffle House, Wendy's, ◉ flea mkt
129	GA 53, to Braselton, **E** ⬛ Chevron/dsl, Shell/Golden Pantry/dsl, 🍴 La Hacienda Mexican, Waffle House, 🛏 Best Western, ◉ USPO, **W** ⬛ 🛢/McDonald's/dsl/scales/24hr, 🍴 Cracker Barrel, Domino's, El Centinela, Stonewall's, Subway, Tea Garden Chinese, Wendy's, Zaxby's
126	GA 211, to Chestnut Mtn, **E** ⬛ Shell/dsl, 🍴 Subway, Waffle House, 🛏 Country Inn&Suites, **W** ⬛ BP/dsl, 🍴 Blimpie, Chateau Elan Winery/rest., China Garden, Papa John's, 🛏 Holiday Inn Express, ◉ Publix, vet

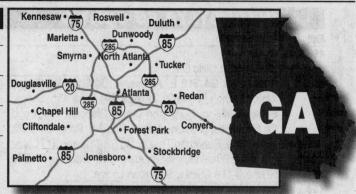

Exit	Services
120	to GA 124, Hamilton Mill Rd, **E** ⬛ BP, QT/dsl, 🍴 Arby's, Buffalo's Café, Burger King, Caprese Rest., Dos Copas Mexican, 5 Guys Burgers, McDonald's, Moe's SW Grill, Shane's Rib Shack, Starbucks, Subway, Wendy's, Zaxby's, ◉ AT&T, Home Depot, Kohl's, Publix/Deli, RV World of GA (1mi), auto repair, vet, **W** ⬛ Chevron, Murphy USA/dsl, Shell/dsl, 🍴 Barbarito's, Chick-fil-A, Chili's, El Molcajete, Hardee's, Italy's Pizza, Little Caesars, ◉ CVS Drug, O'Reilly Parts, Tires+, Walmart
115	GA 20, to Buford Dam, **E** ⬛ QT, **W** ⬛ QT/dsl, 🍴 Arby's, Bonefish Grill, Bruster's, Buck Head Pizza, Buffalo's Cafe, Burger King, Chick-fil-A, Chili's, Chipotle, ChuckeCheese, Einstein's Bagels, Firehouse Subs, 5 Guy's Burgers, Genghis Grill, Kani House, Krispy Kreme, Longhorn Steaks, Liu's Buffet, Macaroni Grill, McDonald's, Mimi's Cafe, Moe's SW Grill, O'Charley's, Olive Garden, On-the-Border, Panda Express, PF Chang's, Provino's Italian, Red Lobster, Shogun Japanese, Sonny's BBQ, Starbucks, Steak n' Shake, Subway, Taco Mac, Ted's MT Grill, TGIFriday's, Waffle House, Wendy's, 🛏 Country Inn&Suites, Courtyard, Hampton Inn, SpringHill Suites, Wingate Inn, ◉ AT&T, Belk, Best Buy, Costco/gas, Dick's, Dillard's, Discount Tire, $Tree, Fiat, Firestone, Honda, Hyundai, JC Penney, Lowe's, Macy's, Mazda, Michael's, Nissan, Nordstrom's, PetCo, Petsmart, Radio Shack, Ross, Sam's Club/gas, Staples, Target, TJ Maxx, Toyota/Scion, Verizon, VW, Walmart, Mall of GA, to Lake Lanier Islands
113	I-985, N (from nb), to Gainesville
111	GA 317, to Suwanee, **E** ⬛ BP, Sims/dsl, 🍴 Applebee's, Arby's, Checker's, Chick-fil-A, Cracker Barrel, Dunkin Donuts, Oriental Garden, Outback Steaks, Philly Connection, Pizza Hut/Taco Bell, Subway, Waffle House, Wendy's, 🛏 Comfort Inn, Comfort Suites, Courtyard, Fairfield Inn, Mayqueen Hotel, Motel 6, Sun Suites, ◉ CVS Drug, GNC, **W** ⬛ Chevron/dsl, Murphy USA/dsl, RaceTrac/dsl, Shell, 🍴 Atlanta Bread, CiCi's Pizza, HoneyBaked Ham, IHOP, KFC, McDonald's, Moe's SW Grill, Sonic, Subway, Taco Mac, 🛏 Budgetel, Super 8, ◉ AT&T, $Tree, Lowe's, Office Depot, Tires&More, Walmart
109	Old Peachtree Rd, **E** ⬛ QT/dsl/24hr, 🍴 McDonald's, Mi Casa Mexican, 🛏 Hampton Inn, ◉ Bass Pro Shops, $World, Publix, **W** 🍴 Califonia Dreaming, Chick-fil-A, China Delight, Firehouse Subs, 5 Guys Burgers, Jim&Nicks BBQ, Magnolia Bakery Cafe, Starbucks, Subway, Waffle House, 🛏 Hilton Garden, Holiday Inn, ◉ Home Depot
108	Sugarloaf Pkwy (from nb), **E** ⬛ Hampton Inn, **W** 🍴 Carrabba's, Chick-fil-A, 🛏 Hilton Garden, Holiday Inn,

Left margin (top to bottom): **L A V O N I A N ↕ S C O M M E R C E J E F F E R S O N**

Right margin of second column (top to bottom): **S U W A N E E D U L U T H**

Side tab: **GA**

🅖 = gas 🍴 = food 🛏 = lodging ⊙ = other   Copyright 2012 - The Next Exit

INTERSTATE 85 CONT'D

N ↑ S

ATLANTA AREA

GA

Exit	Services
108	Continued ⊙ Gwinnett Civic Ctr
107	GA 120, to GA 316 E, Athens, **E** 🅖 Shell, 🍴 Burger King, Carino's, Jillian's, Zaxby's, ⊙ Bass Pro Shops, Books-a-Million, Burlington Coats, Discount Tire, Food Ct, Mercedes, Nieman-Marcus, Rite Aid, Ross, Saks 5th Ave, Sears, Suburban Tire, **W** 🅖 BP, Chevron, 🍴 China Gate, McDonald's, Roadhouse Grill, Subway, Waffle House, 🛏 La Quinta, Suburban Lodge
106	Boggs Rd (from sb, no return), Duluth, **W** 🅖 QT/dsl/24hr
104	Pleasant Hill Rd, **E** 🅖 Chevron/24hr, QT, Shell, Sim's/dsl, 🍴 Arby's, Bahama Breeze, Burger King, Chick-fil-A, East Pearl, Fung Mi Chinese, GA Diner, Golden House, Grand Buffet, Ida's Pizza Kitchen, Joe's Crabshack, Krispy Kreme, Lobster House, McDonald's, Moe's SW Grill, Popeye's, Quiznos, Starbucks, Stevie B's Pizza, Subway, TGIFriday's, Waffle House, Wendy's, 🛏 Candlewood Suites, Comfort Suites, Hampton Inn Suites, Holiday Inn Express, Marriott, Residence Inn, ⊙ Advance Parts, Best Buy, $General, $Tree, Family$, Home Depot, Publix, Walgreens, urgent care, **W** 🅖 BP/dsl, Chevron, Sim's/dsl, 🍴 Applebee's, Arby's, Bruster's, Burger King, Checker's, Chili's, Chipotle Mexican, Hooters, IHOP, Jimmy John's, KFC, McDonald's, Olive Garden, On the Border, Panda Express, Red Lobster, Ryan's, Starbucks, Steak'n Shake, Subway, Sweet Tomatoes, Taco Bell, Wendy's, 🛏 Courtyard, Days Inn, Extended Stay America, Holiday Inn, Hyatt Place, Quality Inn, Wingate Inn, ⊙ AT&T, Audi, Barnes&Noble, Batteries+, Belk, BMW, Buick/GMC, Firestone/auto, Fry's Electronics, Goodyear/auto, Honda, JC Penney, Jo-Ann Fabrics, KIA, Macy's, Marshall's, Nissan, Old Navy, PetCo, Rite Aid, Sears/auto, Staples, TJ Maxx, Toyota/Scion, Tuesday Morning, Verizon, mall
103	Steve Reynolds Blvd (from nb, no return), **W** 🅖 QT, Shell, 🍴 Dave&Buster's, Waffle House, 🛏 InTown Suites, ⊙ Costco/gas, Kohl's, Petsmart, Sam's Club, Target, same as 104
102	GA 378, Beaver Ruin Rd, **E** 🅖 Shell/dsl, QT, **W** 🅖 Citgo
101	Lilburn Rd, **E** 🅖 QT/dsl, Shell/dsl/24hr, 🍴 Blimpie, Bruster's, Burger King, Hong Kong Buffet, Krystal, KFC, Manhattan Pizza, McDonald's/playplace, Quiznos, Starbucks, Taco Bell, Waffle House, 🛏 Guesthouse Inn, InTown Suites, ⊙ Jones RV Park, **W** 🅖 Chevron, Marathon, QT, 🍴 Arby's, El Indo Mexican, El Taco Veloz, Grand Buffet, Papa John's, Pizza Plaza, Subway, Waffle House, Wendy's, 🛏 Knights Inn, Red Roof Inn, ⊙ CarMax, Lowe's
99	GA 140, Jimmy Carter Blvd, **E** 🅖 Phillips 66/dsl, Shell, 🍴 Checker's, Chick-fil-A, Cracker Barrel, Denny's, Dunkin Donuts, El Nortino Mexican, KFC, McDonald's, Papa John's, Pizza Hut/Taco Bell, Pollo Campero, Wendy's, 🛏 Best Inn, Courtyard, Horizon Inn, La Quinta, Motel 6, Ramada, Rite4Us Suites, ⊙ Advance Parts, Aldi Foods, Family$, U-Haul, Walgreens, **W** 🅖 Chevron/24hr, Citgo/dsl, QT/dsl, 🍴 Barnacle's Grill, 5 Guys Burgers, Hong Kong Buffet, Pappadeaux Steak/seafood, Quiznos, Sonic, Waffle House, Wendy's, 🛏 Days Inn, Drury Inn,

ATLANTA AREA

Exit	Services
99	Continued Country Inn&Suites, Microtel, ⊙ AutoZone, CarQuest, NTB, O'Reilly Parts, PepBoys
96	Pleasantdale Rd, Northcrest Rd, **E** 🍴 Burger King, 🛏 Peachtree Inn, **W** 🅖 Exxon/dsl, QT/dsl, 🍴 Subway, Waffle House, 🛏 Atlanta Lodge
95	I-285
94	Chamblee-Tucker Rd, **E** 🅖 Chevron/dsl, Shell, **W** 🅖 QT/dsl, Shell, 🍴 DQ, Waffle House, 🛏 Motel 6, Super 8, ⊙ to Mercer U
93	Shallowford Rd, to Doraville, **E** 🅖 Shell, 🍴 Blimpie, Hop Shing Chinese, ⊙ Publix, U-Haul, **W** 🅖 Shell/dsl, 🛏 Quality Inn
91	US 23, GA 155, Clairmont Rd, **E** 🅖 Chevron, Shell, 🍴 IHOP, Mo's Pizza, Popeye's, ⊙ IGA Foods, repair, **W** 🅖 BP, 🍴 McDonald's, Mykonos Greek, Waffle House, 🛏 Marriott, Wingate Inn, ⊙ NTB, Sam's Club/dsl
89	GA 42, N Druid Hills, **E** 🅖 Chevron/Subway/dsl, QT/dsl/24hr, Shell, 🍴 Arby's, Boston Mkt, Burger King, Chick-fil-A, Einstein Bro's, El Torero, Fortune Cookie, Jersey Mike's, Lettuce Souperise You, McDonald's, Moe's SW Grill, Piccadilly's, Starbucks, Taco Bell, Tin Roof Cantina, 🛏 Courtyard, ⊙ $Tree, Firestone/auto, GNC, Target, Walgreens, **W** 🅖 Chevron/dsl, Exxon, Shell, 🍴 Atlanta Diner, HoneyBaked Ham, Krystal, Waffle House, 🛏 DoubleTree, Hampton Inn, Red Roof Inn, ⊙ CVS Drug, Just Brakes, vet
88	Lenox Rd, GA 400 N, Cheshire Br Rd (from sb), **E** 🅖 Shell, 🛏 La Quinta
87	GA 400 N (from nb)
86	GA 13 S, Peachtree St, **E** 🅖 BP, 🍴 Denny's, Wendy's, 🛏 Intown Inn, La Quinta, ⊙ Brake-O
85	I-75 N, to Marietta, Chattanooga
84	Techwood Dr, 14th St, **E** 🅖 BP, Shell, 🍴 CheeseSteaks, La Bamba Mexican, Thai Cuisine, VVV Ristorante Italiano, 🛏 Best Western, Hampton Inn, Marriott, Sheraton, Travelodge, ⊙ Woodruff Arts Ctr, **W** 🍴 Blimpie, 🛏 Courtyard, Knights Inn, ⊙ CVS Drug, Dillard's, Office Depot, to Georgia Tech
249d	10th St, Spring St (from nb), **E** 🅖 BP, Chevron/24hr, Shell, 🍴 Checker's, Domino's, Pizza Hut, Varsity Drive-In, 🛏 Fairfield Inn, Marriott, Regency Suites, Renaissance Hotel, Residence Inn, Wyndham Hotel, ⊙ Publix, to Mitchell House, **W** 🍴 McDonald's, 🛏 Courtyard, ⊙ 🏥, CVS Drug, to GA Tech
249c	Williams St (from sb), downtown, to GA Dome
249b	Pine St, Peachtree St (from nb), downtown, **E** 🛏 Reniassance Inn, ⊙ 🏥, to midtown, **W** downtown, hotels
249a	Courtland St (from sb), downtown, **W** 🛏 Hilton, Marriott, ⊙ GA St U
248d	Piedmont Ave, Butler St (from sb), downtown, **W** 🛏 Courtyard, Fairfield Inn, Radisson, ⊙ 🏥, Ford, MLK NHS
248c	GA 10 E, Intn'l Blvd, downtown, **W** 🛏 Hilton, Holiday Inn, Marriott Marquis, Radisson
248b	Edgewood Ave (from nb), **W** ⊙ 🏥, downtown, hotels
248a	MLK Dr (from sb), **W** st capitol, to Underground Atlanta
247	I-20, E to Augusta, W to Birmingham
246	Georgia Ave, Fulton St, **E** 🛏 Hampton Inn, Holiday Inn Express, ⊙ to Turner Stadium, **W** 🍴 KFC, ⊙ to Coliseum, GSU

INTERSTATE 85 CONT'D

N

S

ATLANTA AREA

Exit	Services
245	Ormond St, Abernathy Blvd, **E** 🛏 Comfort Inn, Country Inn Suites, Hampton Inn, Holiday Inn Express, 🅾 Turner Stadium, **W** st capitol
244	University Ave, **E** 🛢 Chevron/dsl, Exxon/dsl, 🍴 Subway, Wendy's, 🅾 NAPA
243	GA 166, Lakewood Fwy, to East Point
77	I-75 S
76	Cleveland Ave, **E** 🛢 Citgo/dsl, Marathon, 🍴 Burger King, Krystal, Papa John's, 🅾 Ⓗ, AutoZone, BigLots, CVS Drug, $Tree, Family$, Kroger, Radio Shack, Walgreens, **W** 🛢 Shell/dsl, Texaco/dsl, 🍴 Chick-fil-A, Church's
75	Sylvan Rd, **E** 🛢 Phillips 66, Shell/dsl, 🍴 Chick-fil-A
74	Loop Rd, Aviation Commercial Center
73b a	Virginia Ave, **E** 🛢 Citgo/dsl, 🍴 Jonny's Pizza, Malone's Grill, McDonald's, Pizza Hut, Quiznos, Ruby Tuesday, Schlotsky's, Spondivit's Rest., Waffle House, Wendy's, Willy's Mexican, 🛏 Courtyard, Drury Inn, Hilton, Motel 6, Renaissance Hotel, Residence Inn, **W** 🛢 Chevron/Subway, Shell, 🍴 Arby's, Blimpie, Giovanna's Italian, Happy Buddah Chinese, KFC, La Fiesta Mexican, Waffle House, 🛏 Comfort Inn, Country Inn&Suites, Crowne Plaza, DoubleTree, EconoLodge, Fairfield Inn, Hampton Inn, Hilton Garden, Holiday Inn, Hyatt Place, Ramada Inn, Wellesley Inn
72	Camp Creek Pkwy
71	Riverdale Rd, Atlanta ✈, **E** 🍴 Ruby Tuesday, 🛏 Courtyard, Fairfield Inn, Microtel, Hampton Inn, Holiday Inn, Hyatt Place, La Quinta, Sheraton/grill, Sleep Inn, Springhill Suites, Super 8, **W** 🛢 Chevron, 🍴 Joe's Rest., 🛏 Days Inn, Embassy Suites, Hilton Garden, Holiday Inn Express, Marriott, Westin Hotel
70	I-85 (from sb)
69	GA 14, GA 279, **E** 🛢 Chevron/dsl, Exxon/dsl, 🍴 Blimpie, Bojangles, Burger King, Checker's, China Cafe, Church's, KFC, Krystal, McDonald's, Taco Bell, Wendy's, 🛏 Baymont Inn, Comfort Inn, Quality Inn, Super 8, Travelodge, Wyndham Garden, 🅾 CVS Drug, Goodyear/auto, U-Haul, urgent care, **W** 🛢 Chevron/dsl, Texaco, 🍴 Waffle House, 🛏 EconoLodge
68	I-285 Atlanta Perimeter (from nb)
66	Flat Shoals Rd, **W** 🛢 BP, Chevron/dsl, Shell/Blimpie, 🍴 Supreme Fish Delight, Waffle House, 🛏 Motel 6
64	GA 138, to Union City, **E** 🛢 BP/dsl, RaceTrac/dsl, 🍴 Waffle House, 🛏 EconoLodge, Western Inn, 🅾 BMW/Mini, Buick/GMC, Chevrolet, Chrysler/Dodge/Jeep, CVS Drug, Ford/Lincoln, Honda, Infiniti, Kia/Nissan, Lexus, Lincoln/Mercury, Subaru, Toyota/Scion, **W** 🛢 Chevron/dsl, QT, Shell/dsl, 🍴 Arby's, Burger King, Capt D's, China Garden, Corner Cafe, IHOP, KFC, Krystal, McDonald's, Papa John's, Pizza Hut, Sonic, Subway, Taco Bell, Wendy's, Zaxby's, 🛏 Best Western, Comfort Inn, Country Hearth Inn, Days Inn, Garden Inn, La Quinta, Microtel, 🅾 Advance Parts, BigLots, $Tree, Firestone, Goodyear/auto, Kroger/dsl, NTB, O'Reilly Parts, PepBoys, Radio Shack, Sears/auto, Walgreens, Walmart/Subway, vet
61	GA 74, to Fairburn, **E** 🛢 BP/Huddle House/dsl/scales/24hr, Citgo/dsl, RaceTrac/dsl, Shell, 🍴 Chick-fil-A, Dunkin Donuts, McDonald's, Waffle House,

FAIRBURN

NEWNAN

61	Continued Wendy's, Zaxby's, 🛏 Country Inn&Suites, Hampton Inn, Holiday Inn Express, Sleep Inn, Wingate Inn, 🅾 Tire Depot, vet, **W** 🛢 Chevron/dsl, Citgo/Blimpie/dsl, 🛏 Efficiency Motel
56	Collinsworth Rd, **W** 🛢 Marathon/dsl, Shell, 🍴 Frank's Rest., 🅾 South Oaks Camping
51	GA 154, to Sharpsburg, **E** 🛢 Phillips 66/dsl, Texaco/Blimpie, **W** 🛢 Chevron/dsl, Shell/Subway/dsl, 🍴 Waffle House
47	GA 34, to Newnan, **E** 🛢 BP, Chevron/dsl, Marathon/Subway/dsl, QT, Shell, 🍴 Applebee's, Arby's, Asian Chef, Capt D's, Chin Chin, Dunkin Donuts, Hooters, La Hacienda, Longhorn Steaks, Marco's Pizza, Me'n Ed's Pizza, Moe's SW Grill, Panda Express, Papa's Smokehouse, Red Lobster, Ruby Tuesday, Sprayberry's BBQ, Steak'n Shake, Stevie B's Pizza, TX Roadhouse, Waffle House, Wendy's, 🛏 Country Inn&Suites, Hampton Inn, Springhill Suites, 🅾 GNC, Goodyear, Hobby Lobby, Home Depot, Kauffman Tire, Kohl's, Lowe's, Petsmart, Ross, Walmart/McDonald's, **W** 🛢 Exxon, Phillips 66, RaceTrac, 🍴 Burger King, Chick-fil-A, Coldstone, Cracker Barrel, 5 Guys Burgers, Goldberg's Deli, Golden Corral, HoneyBaked Ham, IHOP, KFC, Krystal, Logli Mogli, Mama Lucia's, O'Charley's, Olive Garden, Panera Bread, Red Robin, Rockback Pizza, Shane's BBQ, Shoney's, Taco Bell, Taco Mac, Thai Heaven, Zaxby's, 🛏 Best Western, Comfort Inn, La Quinta, Motel 6, Ramada, 🅾 Ⓗ, AT&T, Barnes&Noble, Belk, Best Buy, BigLots, BJ's Whse, Buick/Cadillac/GMC, Chevrolet, Dick's, Dillards, &General, $Tree, Ford/Lincoln/Mercury, Hyundai, JC Penney, Just Brakes, Michael's, Office Depot, Old Navy, Publix, Radio Shack, Target, Tires+, TJ Maxx, Toyota/Scion, Verizon, Walgreens, USPO, vet
41	US 27/29, Newnan, **E** 🛢 🛢/Subway/Wendy's/dsl/scales/24hr, 🅾 Little White House NHS, Roosevelt SP, **W** 🛢 BP/dsl, Chevron, Phillips 66/dsl, 🍴 Huddle House, McDonald's, Waffle House, 🛏 Best Value Inn, Howard Johnson, Super 8, 🅾 $General
35	US 29, to Grantville, **W** 🛢 BP/dsl, Phillips 66/dsl
28	GA 54, GA 100, to Hogansville, **W** 🛢 Chevron/dsl, Loves/Arby's/dsl/scales/24hr, Shell/dsl, 🍴 China Cafe, Intnat'l Cafe, McDonald's, Roger's BBQ, Subway, Waffle House, Wendy's, 🛏 Garden Inn, Wood Stream Inn, 🅾 Ingles
23mm	Beech Creek
22mm	**weigh sta both lanes**
21	I-185 S, to Columbus
18	GA 109, to Mountville, **E** 🛢 Marathon/Domino's,

GA

INTERSTATE 85 CONT'D

N S

L A G R A N G E

Exit	Services
18	Continued
	🛏 Red Roof Inn, Wingate Inn, 🔲 to FDR SP, Little White House HS, **W** 🚗 BP/dsl, Circle K/dsl, RaceTrac/dsl, Shell/dsl, Texaco/dsl, 🍴 Applebee's, Banzai Japanese, Burger King, Chick-fil-A, Cracker Barrel, IHOP, Juanito's Mexican, Longhorn Steaks, Los Nopales, McDonald's, Mi Casa Mexican, Moe's SW Grill, Ryan's, Starbucks, Subway, Waffle House, Wendy's, Zaxby's, 🛏 Baymont Inn, Best Western, Comfort Inn, Country Inn&Suites, Holiday Inn Express, Jameson Inn, Super 8, 🔲 AT&T, Belk, Chrysler/Dodge/Jeep, Ford/Lincoln, Home Depot, Honda, Hyundai, JC Penney, Verizon, RV Park (3mi), mall
14	US 27, to La Grange, **W** 🚗 Pure, Shell, Summit/dsl, 🛏 Hampton Inn
13	GA 219, to La Grange, **E** 🍴 Waffle House, 🛏 Days Inn, **W** 🚗 ▦/Subway/dsl/scales/24hr, Shell/dsl, 🍴 Arbys, McDonald's, 🔲 🅗
10mm	Long Cane Creek
6	Kia Blvd, **W** Kia Plant
2	GA 18, to West Point, **E** 🚗 Shell/dsl, Summit/dsl, 🛏 Travelers Inn, **W** 🍴 Subway (1.5), 🔲 to West Point Lake, camping
.5mm	**Welcome Ctr nb, full ♿ facilities, ☎, ▣, litter barrels, vending, petwalk**
0mm	Georgia/Alabama state line, Chattahoochee River

INTERSTATE 95

N S

S A V A N N A H

Exit	Services
113mm	Georgia/South Carolina state line, Savannah River
111mm	**Welcome Ctr/weigh sta sb, full ♿ facilities, info, ☎, ▣, vending, litter barrels, petwalk**
109	GA 21, to Savannah, Pt Wentworth, Rincon, **E** 🚗 Enmark/dsl, ▦/McDonald's/Subway/dsl/scales/24hr, 🍴 Waffle House, 🛏 Country Inn&Suites, Hampton Inn, Mulberry Grove Inn, Wingate Inn, 🔲 Peterbilt, **W** 🚗 Flash/dsl, Shell/Circle K/Quizno's/dsl, 🍴 Island Grill, Sea Grill, Wendy's, Zaxby's, 🛏 Comfort Suites, Day's Inn, Holiday Inn Express, Quality Inn, Ramada Ltd, Sleep Inn, Super 8, 🔲 CVS Drug, Family$, FoodLion, Green Piece RV Park (5mi), Whispering Pines RV Park (3mi)
107mm	Augustine Creek
106	Jimmy DeLoach Pkwy
104	Savannah ✈, **E** 🚗 BP, Shell/dsl, 🍴 Sneed's Tavern, Waffle House, 🛏 Cambria Suites, Candlewood Suites, Comfort Suites, Country Inn&Suites, Fairfield Inn, Hampton Inn, Hawthorn Suites, Hilton Garden, Sheraton, Springhill Suites, Staybridge Suites, Towneplace Suites, Wingate Inn, 🔲 to ✈, **W** 🚗 Murphy USA, Shell/Subway, 🍴 Arby's, Cheddar's, Chick-fil-A, Hilliard's Rest., Lemongrass Grill, Longhorn Steaks, Ruby Tuesday, Sonic, Zaxby's Café, 🛏 Embassy Suites, Red Roof Inn, 🔲 Home Depot, Sam's Club/gas, Walmart/McDonald's
102	US 80, to Garden City, **E** 🚗 BP, Enmark/dsl, Flash/dsl, 🍴 Busy Dean's, Cracker Barrel, Huddle House, KFC, Krystal, Larry's Subs, Masato Japanese, McDonald's, Okyama Japanese, Peking Chinese, Pizza Hut/Taco Bell, Quizno's, Waffle House, 🛏 Best Western, Jameson Inn, Microtel, Ramada Ltd, Travelodge, 🔲 Camping World RV Ctr, Food Lion, Family$, to Ft Pulaski NM, museum,

---

S A V A N N A H

Exit	Services
102	Continued
	W 🚗 BP, Gate/Subway/dsl, Shell, Texaco, 🍴 Burger King, Domino's, Don's BBQ, El Potro Mexican, Hardee's, Italian Pizza, Mihn Xing Chinese, Wendy's, Western Sizzlin, 🛏 EconoLodge, Holiday Inn, La Quinta, Magnolia Inn, Quality Inn, Sleep Inn, 🔲 NAPA, auto repair
99b a	I-16, W to Macon, E to Savannah
94	GA 204, to Savannah, Pembroke, **E** 🚗 BP/dsl, El Cheapo, Exxon, Murphy USA/dsl (2mi), 76/Circle K, Shell/dsl, 🍴 Applebees, Cracker Barrel, Denny's, Hardee's, Hoolihan's, McDonald's, Perkins, Ruby Tuesday, Shoney's, Sonic, 🛏 Baymont Inn, Best Value Inn, Best Western, Clarion, Comfort Suites, Days Inn, EconoLodge, Fairfield Inn, Hampton Inn, Holiday Inn Express, Howard Johnson, La Quinta, Ramada Inn, Red Roof Inn, Scottish Inn, Sleep Inn, SpringHill Suites, Wingate Inn, 🔲 🅗, Factory Stores/Famous Brands, GNC, Walmart (2mi), **W** 🚗 Chevron/dsl/24hr (2mi), Shell, 🍴 El Potro Mexican, Hooters, JT's Grill, Shellhouse Rest, Subway, Waffle House, 🛏 Country Hearth Inn, Knights Inn, Microtel, Travelodge, 🔲 Harley-Davidson, Savannah Oaks RV Park (2mi)
91mm	Ogeechee River
90	GA 144, Old Clyde Rd, to Ft Stewart, Richmond Hill SP, **E** 🚗 Exxon/dsl, Parkers, 🍴 DQ, Jalapeno's, Subway, 🔲 URGENT CARE, AT&T, Kroger/deli/dsl, **W** 🚗 Loves/McDonald's/dsl/scales/24hr, Shell/dsl, 🔲 Gore's RV Ctr
87	US 17, to Coastal Hwy, Richmond Hill, **E** 🚗 BP, Chevron/dsl/24hr, Citgo, RaceWay/dsl, 🍴 China 1, Denny's/24hr, Domino's, Fuji Japanese, Gianni's, Southern Image Rest., Steamer's Rest., Subway, Waffle House, 🛏 Days Inn, Motel 6, Royal Inn, Scottish Inn, Travelodge, 🔲 URGENT CARE, Food Lion, **W** 🚗 El Cheapo, Exxon/McDonald's/dsl, TA/BP/Popeye's/dsl/24hr/@, Shell/dsl, 🍴 Arby's, KFC/Taco Bell, Waffle House, Wendy's, 🛏 Best Western, Comfort Suites, EconoLodge, Hampton Inn, Quality Inn, Savannah South Inn, 🔲 KOA
85mm	Elbow Swamp
80mm	Jerico River
76	US 84, GA 38, to Midway, Sunbury, **E** hist sites, **W** 🚗 El Cheapo/dsl/scales, Parker's/dsl, 🍴 Holton's Seafood, Huddle House, 🔲 🅗, museum
67	US 17, Coastal Hwy, to, S Newport, **E** 🚗 Chevron/Subway/dsl, Citgo/dsl, El Cheapo, Shell/McDonald's, 🍴 Jones BBQ, 🔲 Harris Neck NWR, S Newport Camping (2mi), **W** 🚗 Texaco
58	GA 99, GA 57, Townsend Rd, Eulonia, **E** 🚗 BP/dsl, Citgo, 🔲 $General, USPO, **W** 🚗 Chevron/dsl/24hr, El Cheapo, Shell/Stuckey's/dsl, 🛏 Knights Inn, 7 Townsend Inn, 🔲 McIntosh Lake RV Park, Lake Harmony RV Park
55mm	**weigh sta both lanes, ☎**
49	GA 251, to Darien, **E** 🚗 Chevron, Mobil/dsl, 🍴 DQ, McDonald's, Waffle House, 🛏 King George Motel, 🔲 Ford, Inland Harbor RV Park, Tall Pines RV Park, **W** 🚗 BP, El Cheapo/Larry's Subs/dsl/scales, Shell/Stuckey's/dsl, 🍴 Burger King, KFC/Pizza Hut/Taco Bell, Ruby Tuesday, Smokey Joe's BBQ, Wendy's, 🛏 Clean Stay USA, Comfort Inn, Hampton Inn, Quality Inn, Super 8, 🔲 Preferred Outlets/famous brands
47mm	Darien River

D A R I E N

INTERSTATE 95 CONT'D

Exit	Services
46.5mm	Butler River
46mm	Champney River
45mm	Altamaha River
42	GA 99, **E** to Hofwyl Plantation HS
41mm	**rest area sb, full** ♿ **facilities, info,** 🕮, 🖾, **vending, litter barrels, petwalk**
38	US 17, GA 25, N Golden Isles Pkwy, Brunswick, **E** 🅿 RaceTrac/dsl, 🍴 Millhouse Steaks, Ole Tymes Country Buffet, 🛏 Comfort Suites, Country Inn&Suites, Embassy Suites (2mi), Fairfield Inn, Holiday Inn, Microtel, ⦿ 🏥, Nissan, **W** 🅿 BP, Chevron/dsl, Flash, Shell/dsl, 🍴 China Town, Denny's, Huddle House/24hr, Toucan's, Subway, Waffle House, 🛏 Baymont Inn, Courtyard, EconoLodge, Guest Cottage Motel, Hampton Inn, Quality Inn, Sleep Inn, ⦿ $General, Harley Davidson, Harvey's Foods, Toyota
36b a	US 25, US 341, to Jesup, Brunswick, **E** 🅿 Chevron/Subway/dsl, Exxon/dsl, RaceWay/dsl, 🍴 Burger King, Cracker Barrel, IHOP, KFC, Krystal/24hr, McDonald's, Pizza Hut, Starbucks, Taco Bell, Wendy's, 🛏 Days Inn, Hampton Inn, La Quinta, Red Roof Inn, Travelodge, Tropical Inn, ⦿ Newcastle RV Ctr, transmissions, **W** 🅿 BP, Mr Pete's, Parker's/dsl, Sunoco, 🍴 Capt Joe's Seafood, China Lee, Huddle House/24hr, Larry's Subs, Sonny's BBQ, Waffle House, 🛏 Best Western, Clarion, Comfort Inn, Motel 6, Ramada Inn, Rodeway Inn, Super 8, ⦿ Advance Parts, CVS Drug, $General, Fred's Drug, Winn-Dixie
33mm	Turtle River
30mm	S Brunswick River
29	US 17, US 82, GA 520, S GA Pkwy, Brunswick, **E** 🅿 Citgo/Church's/dsl, Exxon, **Love's**/Steak'n Shake/Subway/dsl/scales/24hr, Mobil/dsl, 🍴 GA BBQ, Huddle House, Krystal, McDonald's, Whataburger, 🛏 Comfort Suites, ⦿ Blue Beacon, SpeedCo Lube, **W** 🅿 Citgo, ⛽FLYING J/Dennys/dsl/LP/scales/24hr, Goasis/BP/Burger King/Subway/dsl/24hr, Mobil, 🍴 Domino's, Waffle House, Zachary's Steaks, 🛏 EconoLodge, Microtel, Super 8, ⦿ $General, Family$, Golden Isles Camping, Harvey's Foods, TA Truck Service
27.5mm	Little Satilla River
26	Dover Bluff Rd, **E** 🅿 Mobil/Stuckey's/dsl
21mm	White Oak Creek
19mm	Canoe Swamp
15mm	Satilla River
14	GA 25, to Woodbine, **W** 🍴 Chevron/Sunshine/dsl/rest./scales/24hr, 🛏 Stardust Motel (3mi)
7	Harrietts Bluff Rd, **E** 🅿 Exxon/dsl, Shell/Subway, **W** 🅿 BP/dsl
6.5mm	Crooked River
6	Laurel Island Pkwy, **E** 🅿 Green Cedar/Shell/dsl
3	GA 40, Kingsland, to St Marys, **E** 🅿 BP, Chevron, El Cheapo, Exxon/Krystal, Mobil, Murphy USA/dsl, Shell/Subway, 🍴 Applebee's, Burger King, Chick-fil-A, China King, China Wok, DQ, Hong Kong Buffet, KFC, McDonald's, Ruby Tuesday, Shoney's, Sonny's BBQ, St John's Seafood, Taco Bell, Waffle House, Wendy's, Zaxby's, 🛏 Comfort Inn, Country Inn&Suites, Fairfield Inn, 4Star Inn, Hawthorn Suites, Holiday Inn Express, Magnolia Inn, Microtel, Sleep Inn, Super 8, Red Roof Inn, Rodeway Inn,

3	Continued ⦿ 🏥, Urgent Care, Chevrolet/Buick, Chrysler/Dodge/Jeep, CVS Drug, $Tree, Ford/Mercury, K-Mart, Lowe's, Publix, Suzuki, Tire Kingdom, Verizon, Walgreens, Walmart, Winn-Dixie, to Submarine Base, **W** 🅿 Citgo/dsl, Flash/dsl, Petro/Church's/dsl/scales/24hr/@, RaceWay, 🍴 Cracker Barrel, Domino's, IHOP, Oasis Grill, Subway, Waffle House, 🛏 Clean Stay USA, Days Inn, EconoLodge, Hampton Inn, Jameson Inn, La Quinta, Western Motel, ⦿ Ace Hardware, Fred's Drug, Kiki RV Park
1	St Marys Rd, **E Welcome Ctr nb, full** ♿ **facilities,** 🕮, 🖾, **vending, litter barrels, petwalk,** 🅿 Shell/dsl, 🍴 to Cumberland Is Nat Seashore, **W** 🅿 BP/dsl, Chevron/dsl, Wilco/Hess/Dunkin Donuts/Wendy's/dsl/scales, 🍴 Jack's BBQ, ⦿ GS RV Park, KOA
0mm	Georgia/Florida state line, St Marys River

INTERSTATE 185 (COLUMBUS)

Exit	Services
48	I-85. I-185 begins/ends on I-85.
46	Big Springs Rd, **E** 🅿 Shell/dsl, **W** ⦿ tires
42	US 27, Pine Mountain, **E** 🅿 Shell/dsl, Summit, 🍴 Waffle House, ⦿ Pine Mtn Camping, to Callaway Gardens, Little White House HS
34	GA 18, to West Point, **E** to Callaway Gardens
30	Hopewell Church Rd, Whitesville, **W** 🅿 Shell/dsl
25	GA 116, to Hamilton, **W** RV camping
19	GA 315, Mulberry Grove, **W** 🅿 Chevron/dsl/24hr
14	Smith Rd
12	Williams Rd, **W Welcome Ctr/rest rooms,** 🅿 Summit/dsl, Shell, 🛏 Country Inn&Suites, Microtel
10	US 80, GA 22, to Phenix City, **W** Springer Opera House
8	Airport Thruway, **E** 🍴 China Moon, Great Wall, ⦿ $Tree, GNC, Home Depot, Walmart/Subway, **W** 🅿 BP/Circle K, Circle K, 🍴 Applebee's, Ben's Chophouse, Buffet City, Burger King, Capt D's, Hardee's, Houlihan's, IHOP, La Margarita Grill, McDonald's, Mikata Japanese, Pickle Barrel Cafe, River City Grill, Stevie B's Pizza, Taco Bell, 🛏 Comfort Suites, Doubletree, Extended Stay America, Hampton Inn, Sleep Inn, ⦿ BigLots, Hancock Fabrics, K-Mart, Office Depot
7	45th St, Manchester Expswy, **E** 🅿 Chevron, 🍴 Applebee's, Burger King, Carino's Italian, Krystal, Ruby Tuesday, 🛏 Courtyard, La Quinta, Super 8, ⦿ Best Buy, Cadillac/Chevrolet, Dillard's, JC Penney, Macy's, mall, **W** 🅿 BP, Chevron, Circle K, Marathon, 🍴 Arby's, China Express, Dunkin Donuts, Goldberg's Deli, Golden Corral, KFC, Logan's Roadhouse, Lucky China,

N ↑↓ S

GA

COLUMBUS

INTERSTATE 185 CONT'D (COLUMBUS)

Exit	Services
7	Continued
	McDonald's, Pizza Hut, Ryan's, Shogun Japanese, Sonic, Starbucks, Subway, Waffle House, 🛏 Fairfield Inn, Holiday Inn, TownePlace Suites, 🅞 🅗, Advance Parts, Big 10 Tire, $General, Mr. Transmissions, Civil War Naval Museum, vet
6	GA 22, Macon Rd, **E** 🅖 Chevron/dsl, Circle K/dsl, ⏹ Bruster's, Burger King, DQ, KFC, Little Caesars, Taco Bell, 🛏 Best Western, Comfort Inn, Days Inn, 🅞 $General, Kia, Rite Aid, U-Haul, Walgreens, vet, **W** 🅖 Chevron/dsl, Shell, ⏹ American Deli, Capt D's, ChuckeCheese, Cici's Pizza, Country BBQ, Denny's, Firehouse Subs, Jimmy John's, Longhorn Steaks, McDonald's, Subway, Zaxby's, 🛏 Efficiency Lodge, La Quinta, 🅞 AT&T, CVS Drug, Freds Store, GNC, Goodyear, K-Mart, Publix, Radio Shack, Tuesday Morning, Verizon
4	Buena Vista Rd, **E** 🅖 BP, Circle K, Solo, ⏹ Burger King, Capt D's, Chef Lee Chinese, Checker's, Church's, Krystal, McDonald's, Papa John's, Pizza Hut, Subway, Taco Bell, Waffle House, Zaxby's, 🅞 AutoZone, $Tree, Firestone/auto, Goodyear/auto, O'Reilly Parts, Rainbow Foods, Walgreens, Walmart, Winn-Dixie, repair, USPO, vet
3	St Marys Rd, **E** 🛏 Microtel, ⏹ Domino's, 🅞 Family$, **W** 🅖 FuelTech/dsl, Shell/dsl, ⏹ Hardee's, Zeb's Seafood Chicken, 🅞 Ace Hardware, $General, Piggly Wiggly
1b a	US 27, US 280, Victory Dr, **0-3 mi W** 🅖 Chevron/dsl, Circle K, Liberty, RaceWay/dsl, ⏹ Arby's, Burger King, Capt D's, Checker's, Krystal, McDonald's, Papa John's, Sonic, Subway, Taco Bell, Wendy's, 🛏 Candlewood Suites, Columbus Inn, EconoLodge, Holiday Inn Express, Motel 6, Suburban Lodge, 🅞 Advance Parts, AutoZone, $General, Family$, Mkt Place Foods, Piggly Wiggly, I-185 begins/ends.

INTERSTATE 285 (ATLANTA)

Exit	Services
62	GA 279, S Fulton Hwy, Old Nat Hwy, **N** 🅖 Chevron, Texaco, ⏹ City Cafe, 🛏 Econolodge, **S** 🅖 Chevron, Exxon, Shell, ⏹ Blimpie, Burger King, Checker's, China Cafeteria, Church's, El Nopal Mexican, KFC/Pizza Hut, Krystal, Longhorn Steaks, McDonald's, Mrs Winner's, Popeye's, Subway, Taco Bell, Waffle House, Wendy's, 🛏 Clarion, Comfort Inn, Day's Inn, Howard Johnson, Motel 6, Quality Inn, 🅞 AutoZone, Cottman Transmissions, Curves, Family$, NAPA, U-Haul
61	I-85, N to Atlanta, S to Montgomery, **Services 1 mi N GA I-85, exit 71 E** ⏹ Ruby Tuesday, 🛏 Comfort Suites, Courtyard, GA Conv Ctr, Microtel, Hampton Inn, Sheraton/grill, Sleep Inn, Sumner Suites, Super 8, Wingate Inn, **W** 🛏 Comfort Inn, Day's Inn, Embassy Suites, Marriott, Quality Inn, Ramada, Super 8, Travelodge, Westin Hotel
60	GA 139, Riverdale Rd, **N** 🛏 Fairfield Inn (2mi), Microtel (2mi), Wingate Inn (2mi), **S** 🅖 Exxon, QT, Shell/dsl, ⏹ Checker's, Church's, KFC/LJ Silver, McDonald's, 🛏 Best Western, Country Inn&Suites, Day's Inn, Quality Inn, Ramada Inn, 🅞 Advance Parts, Aldi Foods, $General, Family$, U-Haul
59	Clark Howell Hwy, **N** air cargo

ATLANTA AREA

ATLANTA AREA

Exit	Services
58	I-75, N to Atlanta, S to Macon (from eb), to US 19, US 41 , to Hapeville, **S** 🅖 BP, Chevron/24hr, ⏹ Bojangles, Philly Connection, Subway, Waffle House, Wendy's, 🛏 Home Lodge Motel
55	GA 54, Jonesboro Rd, **N** 🛏 Super 8, **S** 🅖 BP, Citgo/dsl, Phillips 66, Shell/dsl, ⏹ Alondra's Mexican/Chinese, Capt D's, Church's, DaiLai Vietnamese, Golden Gate Chinese, LJ Silver, McDonald's, Subway, Taco Bell, 🅞 Home Depot, repair
53	US 23, Moreland Ave, to Ft Gillem, **N** 🅖 BP, Citgo, Conoco/dsl, **S** 🅖 Citgo, Shell, TA/dsl/24hr/@, ⏹ Popeye's, Wendy's, 🛏 Economy Inn
52	I-675, S to Macon
51	Bouldercrest Rd, **N** 🅖 BP, 🍴/Wendy's/dsl/24hr, ⏹ A&W/LJ Silver, Hardee's, KFC/Pizza Hut, WK Wings, 🛏 DeKalb Inn, 🅞 Family$, Wayfield Foods, **S** 🅖 Chevron/dsl
48	GA 155, Flat Shoals Rd, Candler Rd, **N** 🅖 BP, Chevron, Marathon, Shell/dsl, Stop'n Go, ⏹ Arby's, Burger King, Checker's, DQ, KFC/Pizza Hut, McDonald's, Subway, Taco Bell, Waffle King, WK Wings, 🛏 Country Hearth Inn, Gulf American Inn, 🅞 BigLots, Macy's, Pep Boys, **S** 🅖 QT, Phillips 66, ⏹ Sonic
46b a	I-20, E to Augusta, W to Atlanta
44	GA 260, Glenwood Rd, **E** 🅖 Marathon, Super 8, 🛏 Old English Inn, **W** 🅖 Citgo, Shell, ⏹ Church's, Mrs Winner's, 🛏 Glenwood Inn
43	US 278, Covington Hwy, **E** 🅖 Chevron/Subway/24hr, Citgo/dsl, ⏹ Waffle House, 🅞 U-Haul, **W** 🅖 BP/24hr, QT, Shell/dsl, ⏹ Blimpie, Checker's, KFC/Taco Bell, Mrs Winner's, Wendy's, 🛏 Best Inn, 🅞 Advance Parts, Family$, Firestone/auto
42	(from nb), Marta Station
41	GA 10, Memorial Dr, Avondale Estates, **E** 🅖 Citgo, QT, Shell/dsl, ⏹ Applebee's, Arby's, Burger King, Church's, DQ, McDonald's, Pancake House, Pizza Hut, Super China, Waffle House, Wendy's, 🛏 Savannah Suites, Suburban Lodge, 🅞 Advance Parts, AutoZone, Big 10 Tire, $General, Firestone/auto, Office Depot, Radio Shack, U-Haul
40	Church St, to Clarkston, **E** 🅖 Chevron, Shell/dsl, Texaco, **W** 🅞 🅗
39b a	US 78, to Athens, Decatur
38	US 29, Lawrenceville Hwy, **E** 🅖 Phillips 66, Shell, ⏹ Waffle House, 🛏 Knight's Inn, Super 8, 🅞 🅗, **W** 🅖 BP, USA, ⏹ Waffle House, 🛏 Masters Inn, Motel 6
37	GA 236, to LaVista, Tucker, **E** 🅖 Chevron, Circle K, ⏹ Checker's, Chili's, Folks Rest., IHOP, O'Charley's, Olive Garden, Picadilly's, Schlotsky's, Steak&Ale, Waffle House, 🛏 Comfort Suites, Country Inn Suites, 🅞 Firestone, Target, **W** 🅖 BP/repair, Citgo/dsl, Shell, ⏹ Arby's, Blackeyed Pea, Blue Ribbon Grill, Capt D's, City Cafe, Domino's, DQ, Fuddrucker's, Jason's Deli, McDonald's, Panera Bread, Philly Connection, Pizza Hut, Red Lobster, Taco Bell, Wendy's, 🛏 Courtyard, Fairfield Inn, Holiday Inn, Magnolia Motel, Quality Inn, Radisson, 🅞 Best Buy, $Tree, Goodyear/auto, JC Penney, Kroger, Macy's, Michael's, Office Depot, Publix, TJ Maxx, mall
34	Chamblee-Tucker Rd, **E** 🅖 Chevron, Citgo, Phillips 66, Shell, ⏹ Arby's/Mrs Winner's, China Star, KFC/Taco Bell, Moe's SW Grill, S&S Cafeteria, Taco Bell, 🛏 Day's Inn, 🅞 Ace Hardware, Advance Parts,

INTERSTATE 285 CONT'D (ATLANTA)

Exit	Services
34	Continued
	Goodyear, Kroger, **W** © BP, Citgo, ⊓ Little Cuba, LoneStar Steaks, McDonald's, Subway, Waffle House, ⊙ BigLots, $Tree
33b a	I-85, N to Greenville, S to Atlanta
32	US 23, Buford Hwy, to Doraville, **E** © BP/24hr, ⊓ Baldino's Subs, Burger King/playland, Checker's, Chick-fil-A, El Pescador, Krystal, Wendy's, ⊙ Big 10 Tire, Firestone/auto, Goodyear/auto, K-Mart, 99c Store, **W** © Citgo, Shell, ⊓ First China, McDonald's, Monterrey Mexican, Waffle House, ⌂ Holiday Inn
31b a	GA 141, Peachtree Ind, to Chamblee, **W** © Citgo, Shell, Texaco, ⊓ Arby's, Chick-fil-A, Dunkin Donuts, McDonald's, Piccadilly, Pizza Hut, Waffle House, Wendy's, ⊙ Acura, Advance Parts, Audi/VW, Buick/GMC, Chevrolet, Chrysler/Jeep/Dodge, CVS Drug, Dodge, Firestone, Ford, Honda, Hyundai, Kia, Lexus, Mazda, Porsche, Saab, Toyota, VW
30	Chamblee-Dunwoody Rd, N Shallowford Rd, to, N Peachtree Rd, **N** © BP, Chevron, ⊓ Bagel&Co., Burger King, Garcia's Mexican, Guthrie's, Lucky China, Maggie's Creamery, McDonald's, Quizno's, Starbucks, Subway, Waffle House, ⊙ Kroger, **S** © Exxon/Blimpie/Arby's, Mobil, Phillips 66/dsl, Shell, ⊓ Bombay Grill, City Café, La Botana Mexican, Mad Italian Rest., Olde Mill Steaks, Papa John's, Taco Bell, Wendy's, Wild Ginger Thai, ⌂ Holiday Inn Select, Residence Inn
29	Ashford-Dunwoody Rd, **N** © BP, Exxon/Subway, ⊓ Applebee's, Brio Tuscan, Bloomingdale's, CA Pizza Kitchen, Denny's, Food Court, Garrison's Broiler, Goldfish, Houlihan's, Jason's Deli, J. Alexander's, Maggiano's Italian, McDonald's, McCormick & Shmick's, PF Chang's, Schlotsky's, ⌂ Crowne Plaza, Fairfield Inn, ⊙ Barnes&Noble, Best Buy, Border's, Dillard's, Firestone/auto, Goodyear/auto, Macey's, Marshall's, Old Navy, Walmart, USPO, mall, **S** © Chevron, ⊓ Arby's, ⌂ Hilton Garden
28	Peachtree-Dunwoody Rd (no EZ return wb), **N** ⊓ Arby's, Chequer's Grill, Fuddrucker's, Sweet Tomatos, ⌂ Comfort Suites, Courtyard, Extended Stay America, Extended Stay Deluxe, Fairfield Inn, Hampton Inn, Hilton Suites, Holiday Inn Express, Homestead Suites, La Quinta, Marriott, Microtel, Residence Inn, Westin, ⊙ Costco/gas, Home Depot, PetsMart, Publix, Rite Aid, Ross, Target, TJ Maxx, mall, **S** H
27	US 19 N, GA 400, **2 mi N** LDS Temple
26	Glenridge Dr (from eb), Johnson Ferry Rd
25	US 19 S, Roswell Rd, Sandy Springs, **N** © BP, Chevron, Exxon, Shell/dsl, ⊓ American Pie Rest., Applebee's, Arby's, Boston Mkt, Burger King, Caribbean Cafe, Chicago Pizza, Chick-fil-A, Chipotle Mexican, Domino's, Dunkin Donuts, El Azteca Mexican, El Toro Mexican, IHOP, KFC/Pizza Hut, Landmark Diner, La Rumba Cafe, Longhorn Steaks, Madarin House, McDonald's, Mellow Mushroom Cafe, Noodles Cafe, Panera Bread, Rumi's Kitchen, Ruth's Chris Steaks, Starbucks, Steak'n Shake, Subway, Taco Bell, Waffle House, Wendy's, ⌂ Comfort Inn, Hampton Inn, Homestead Suites, ⊙ H, CVS Drug, DeKalb Tire, $Tree, Hancock Fabrics, Marshall's, NAPA AutoCare, Office Depot, PepBoys, Publix, Target,

25	Continued
	Toyota, Whole Foods Mkt, **S** © Chevron/24hr, Shell, ⊓ El Taco Veloz, Frankie's Grill, Kobe Steaks, Mama's Café, ⌂ Day's Inn/rest., ⊙ Kroger/gas (1.5mi)
24	Riverside Dr
22	New Northside Dr, to Powers Ferry Rd, **N** © Shell, **S** © BP, Chevron/24hr, ⊓ McDonald's, Waffle House, Wendy's, ⌂ Candlewood Suites, Crowne Plaza, Hawthorn Suites, Homestead Suites, ⊙ CVS Drug
21	(from wb), **N** © Shell, ⊓ HillTop Café, Homestead Village, ⊙ BMW/Mini
20	I-75, N to Chattanooga, S to Atlanta (from wb), to US 41 N
19	US 41, Cobb Pkwy, to Dobbins AFB, **N** © BP, Chevron/24hr, Citgo, Shell, ⊓ Arby's, BBQ, Bruster's, Carrabba's, ChuckeCheese, Denny's, Dunkin Donuts, Hardee's, IHOP, Jade Palace, Joe's Crabshack, KFC, McDonald's, Olive Garden, Papa John's, Pizza Hut, Red Lobster, Steak'n Shake, Subway, Sunny's BBQ, The Border Mexican, Waffle House, Wendy's, Wingate Inn, ⌂ Hilton, Holiday Inn Express, ⊙ Best Buy, Cadillac, Buick/Subaru, Chevrolet/Saab, Honda, Hyundai, Lexus, Marshall's, Michael's, Office Depot, PetsMart, Ross, Target, Walgreen, **S** © Chevron/24hr, ⊓ Buffalo's Café, Cheese Factory, Chipotle Mexican, Chick-fil-A, El Toro Mexican, Hooters, Jason's Deli, Johnny Rocket's, Longhorn Steaks, Maggiano's Italian, Malone's Grill, Olde Mill Steaks, PF Chang, Pizza Hut, Ruby Tuesday, Schlotsky's, ⌂ Courtyard, Homewood Suites, Renaissance Motel, Sheraton Suites, Stouffer Waverly Hotel, Sumner Suites ⊙ A&P, Barnes&Noble, Costco/gas, JC Penney, Macy's, Sears/auto, USPO, mall
18	Paces Ferry Rd, to Vinings, **N** ⊓ Panera Bread, ⌂ Fairfield Inn, La Quinta, **S** © QT/24hr, ⊓ Chick-fil-A, Subway, Willy's Grill, ⌂ Extended Stay Deluxe, Hampton Inn, Wyndham, ⊙ , Goodyear/auto, Home Depot, Publix
16	S Atlanta Rd, to Smyrna, **N** ⊓ Five Guys Burgers, Waffle House, Zio's Italian, ⌂ Holiday Inn Express, ⊙ H, **S** © ⊙/Wendy's/dsl/scales/24hr, Shell/dsl, Texaco, ⊙ Kroger
15	GA 280, S Cobb Dr, **E** ⌂ Microtel, ⊙ U-Haul, **W** © BP/dsl, RaceTrac, Shell, ⊓ Arby's/Mrs Winners, Checker's, Chick-fil-A, China Buffet, IHOP, Krystal/24hr, McDonald's, Subway, Taco Bell, Wendy's, Zaxby's, ⌂ AmeriHost, Comfort Inn, Country Inn Suites, Knight's Inn, Sun Suites, ⊙ H
14mm	Chattahoochee River
13	Bolton Rd (from nb)
12	US 78, US 278, Bankhead Hwy, **E** © Citgo/dsl,

⛽ = gas 🍴 = food 🛏 = lodging 🅾 = other Copyright 2012 - The Next Exit®

INTERSTATE 285 CONT'D (ATLANTA)

Exit	Service
12	Continued
	Petro/Iron Skillet/dsl/rest./scales/24hr/@, Shell/dsl/24hr, 🍴 Mrs Winner's, 🅾 Blue Beacon, **W** 🅾 BP, Marathon
10b a	I-20, W to Birmingham, E to Atlanta (exits left from nb), **W** to Six Flags
9	GA 139, MLK Dr, to Adamsville, **E** 🅾 Phillips 66, Shell, 🍴 Mrs Winner's, 🅾 Family$, Wayfield Foods, **W** 🅾 Chevron, Shell, 🍴 Checker's, Church's, Golden House Chinese, KFC/Taco Bell, McDonald's
7	Cascade Rd, **E** 🅾 Marathon, 🍴 Papa John's, 🅾 Kroger, **W** 🅾 BP, Phillips 66, 🍴 Applebee's, China Express, KFC, McDonald's, Moe's SW Grill, Mrs Winner's, Pizza Hut, Quizno's, Starbucks, Subway, Up the Creek, Wendy's, 🅾 H, GNC, Home Depot, Publix, Radio Shack, Tires+
5b a	GA 166, Lakewood Fwy, **E** 🅾 Chevron, Shell, 🍴 Blimpie, Burger King, Capt D's, Checker's, IHOP, KFC, Taco Bell, Wendy's, 🅾 Goodyear, Firestone, Kroger, Macy's, mall, **W** 🅾 BP, Citgo/dsl, RaceWay, Shell/dsl/24hr, 🍴 Church's, KFC, Mrs Winner's, Wendy's, 🛏 Deluxe Inn, 🅾 VET, AutoZone, CVS Drug, Family$
2	Camp Creek Pkwy, to ✈, **E** 🅾 BP, Exxon, Texaco, 🍴 Checker's, McDonald's, Mrs Winner's, 🛏 Comfort Suites, **W** 🅾 🍴 American Deli, Brewster's, Carino's, Chick-fil-A, Jason's Deli, LongHorn Steaks, Panda Express, Red Lobster, Ruby Tuesday, Wendys, 🅾 Barnes&Noble, BJ's Whse/gas, Lowes Whse, Marshall's, Old Navy, PetsMart, Publix, Ross, Staples, Target, Walgreens
1	Washington Rd, **E** 🅾 Texaco/dsl, **W** 🅾 Chevron, 🛏 Regency Inn

INTERSTATE 475 (MACON)

Exit	Services
16mm	I-475 begins/ends on I-75, exit 177.
15	US 41, Bolingbroke, **1 mi E** 🅾 Exxon/dsl/LP, Marathon/dsl
9	Zebulon Rd, **E** 🅾 Citgo, Murphy USA/dsl, Shell/Circle K/24hr, 🍴 Buffalo's Café, Chen's Wok, Chick-fil-A, JL's BBQ, Krystal, Margarita's Mexican, McAlister's Deli, McDonald's, NU Way Wieners, Papa John's, Pizza Hut, Sonic, Subway, Taco Bell, Taki Japanese, Waffle House, Wendy's, 🛏 Baymont Inn, Comfort Suites, Fairfield Inn, Sleep Inn, 🅾 H, Goodyear/auto, GNC, Kohl's, Kroger/gas, Krystal, Lowe's, Walgreens, Walmart, USPO, **W** 🅾 Marathon, 🍴 Polly's Café, Zaxby's, 🅾 Advance Parts, CVS Drug
8mm	**rest area nb, full ♿ facilities, (⚡), 🚻, vending, litter barrels, petwalk**
5	GA 74, Macon, **E** 🅾 RaceWay, 🍴 Waffle House, 🅾 Harley-Davidson, to Mercer U, **W** 🅾 Flash/Subway/dsl, Texaco/Church's/dsl, 🍴 Capt D's, Wok&Roll Chinese, 🛏 Howard Johnson, 🅾 $General, Food Lion, Tires+, vet, to Lake Tobesofkee
3	US 80, Macon, **0-2 mi E** 🅾 Marathon/dsl, Murphy USA/dsl, RaceWay, Spectrum/Circle K/Subway, Sunoco/dsl, 🍴 Applebee's, Burger King, Chick-fil-A, China Buffet, Cracker Barrel, DQ, Golden Corral, JL's BBQ, KFC, Krystal, McDonald's, Ryan's, S&S Cafeteria, Sonny's BBQ, Taco Bell, Waffle House, Zaxby's, 🛏 Best Western, Country Hearth Inn, Days Inn, Discovery Inn,

---

3	Continued
	Economy Inn, Hampton Inn, Holiday Inn Express, La Quinta, Motel 6, Quality Inn, Ramada Inn, Red Roof Inn, Rodeway Inn, Super 8, Travelodge, ValuePlace, Villager Inn, 🅾 Best Buy, BigLots, Books-A-Million, CVS Drug, Dick's, Dillard's, Firestone/auto, Home Depot, Honda, JC Penney, Kroger, Lowe's, Macy's, Marshall's, Michael's, Nissan, Old Navy, Petsmart, Ross, Sam's Club/gas, Sears/auto, Staples, Target, VW, Walmart, mall, **W** 🅾 Marathon/dsl, Shell/Circle K, 🍴 Burger King, 🛏 EconoLodge, Knights Inn, Scottish Inn
1	Hartley Bridge Rd, same as I-75 exit 156
0mm	I-475 begins/ends on I-75, exit 156.

INTERSTATE 575

Exit	Services
30 mm	I-575 begins/ends on GA 5/515.
27	GA 5, Howell Br, to Ball Ground
24	Airport Dr
20	GA 5, to Canton, **E** 🅾 BP, 🍴 Casey's rest., Chick-fil-A, Hooters, Ryan's, Stevi B's Pizza, Waffle Wouse, Wendy's, 🛏 Comfort Inn, Homestead Inn, 🅾 Chevrolet, Toyota, Walmart, **W** 🅾 Citgo, RaceTrac, 🍴 Applebee's, Arby's, Cracker Barrel, Longhorn Steaks, McDonald's, O'Charley's, Outback Steaks, Panda Express, Red Lobster, Starbucks, Subway, Waffle House, Zaxby's, 🛏 Holiday Inn Express, 🅾 Belk, Home Depot, Michaels, Publix, Radio Shack, Ross
19	GA 20 E, Canton
17	GA 140, to Roswell (from sb), Canton
16	GA 20, GA 140, **E** 🅾 Pure, **W** 🅾 Citgo, Shell, 🍴 BBQ, Burger King, KFC, Mandarin House, LJ Silver, Papa John's, Taco Bell, Waffle House, 🅾 $General, K-Mart
14	Holly Springs, **E** 🅾 Citgo/dsl, 🍴 Domino's, Pizza Hut, 🛏 Pinecrest Motel, **W** 🅾 BP, Chevron, RaceTrac, Shell, 🍴 Subway, Viva Mexico, Wendy's, Zaxby's, 🅾 Kroger, Publix, Walgreens
11	Sixes Rd, **E** 🅾 Chevron, QT, **W** 🅾 Citgo
8	Towne Lake Pkwy, to Woodstock, **E** 🅾 Citgo, Shell, 🍴 McDonald's, Waffle House, Waffle King/24hr, 🅾 Ford, Hyundai, **W** 🅾 Phillips 66
7	GA 92, Woodstock, **E** 🅾 Chevron, QT, Shell, 🍴 Arby's, Burger King, Capt D's, Checker's, Chick-fil-A, DQ, Firehouse Subs, Folk's Kitchen, KFC, McDonald's, Moe's SW Grill, Mrs Winner's, O'Charley's, Resturante Mexico, Ruby Tuesday, Subway, Taco Bell, Waffle House, Wendy's, 🛏 Comfort Suites, Hampton Inn, Suburban Lodge, 🅾 Big 10 Tire, Camping World, CVS Drug, Firestone/auto, Goodyear/auto, Ingles, Just Brakes, **W** 🅾 BP, Caribou Coffee, IHOP, Mi Casa Mexican, Schlotzsky's, Steak'n Shake, Taco Mac, 🅾 Atlanta Bread, Big Lots, BJ's Whse/gas, Discout Tire, Honda, Home Depot, Kohl's, Lowe's Whse, Office Depot, Old Navy, Target
4	Bells Ferry Rd, **W** 🅾 QT/24hr, Shell/dsl, 🍴 Arby's, Burger King, Ralph's Grill, Subway, Waffle House. 🅾
3	Chastain Rd, to I-75 N, **W** 🅾 Chevron, Citgo, Shell, 🍴 Arby's, Cracker Barrel, Mrs. Winner's, Los Reyes, O'Charley's, Panda Express, Sidelines Grill, Subway, ToGo's/Baskin Robbins, Waffle House, Wendy's, 🛏 Best Western, Comfort Inn, Country Inn&Suites, Fairfield Inn, Residence Inn, Springhill Suites, Suburban Inn, 🅾 to Kennesaw St Coll

INTERSTATE 575 CONT'D

N ↕ S

Exit	Services
1	Barrett Pkwy, to I-75 N, US 41, **E** 📷 Chevron, Murphy USA/dsl, QT, 🍴 Barnacle's Cafe, Buffalo Wild Wings, Burger King, Fuddruckers, KFC, Moe's SW Grill, Quizno's, Starbucks, Texas Roadhouse, Waffle House, Wendy's, Zaxby's, ⊙ Atlanta Bread, Barnes&Noble, CVS Drug, $Tree, Firestone, Publix, Ross, SteinMart, Walmart/dsl, **W** 📷 Shell, Texaco, 🍴 Applebee's, Fuddrucker's, McDonald's, Olive Garden, Provino's Italian, Red Lobster, Smokey Bones, Starbucks, Waffle House, 🛏 Comfort Inn, Crestwood Suites, Day's Inn, Holiday Inn Express, La Quinta, Ramada Ltd, Red Roof Inn, ⊙ Big 10 Tire, Firestone/auto, Home Depot, Marshall's, Michael's, TJ Maxx, mall
0mm	I-575 begins/ends on I-75, exit 268.

INTERSTATE 675

N ↕ S STOCKBRIDGE

Exit	Services
10mm	I-285 W, to Atlanta ⊙, E to Augusta. I-675 begins/ends on I-285, exit 52.
7	Anvil Block Rd, Ft Gillem, **E** 📷 BP, 🍴 Subway, **W** 📷 Exxon
5	Forest Pkwy, **E** 📷 Texaco/dsl, **W** 📷 QT/dsl/scales, 🍴 McDonald's, Waffle House
2	US 23, GA 42, **E** 📷 BP, Texaco, 🍴 Horizon/Backyard Burger, Mo-Joe's Café, **W** 📷 Chevron/dsl, Citgo, 🍴 Teapot Chinese, Waffle House, ⊙ Family$, Food Depot, Goodyear/auto, USPO
1	GA 138, to I-75 N, Stockbridge, **E** 📷 BP, Chevron/24hr, Citgo/dsl, Exxon, Murphy USA/dsl, QT, Shell, 🍴 Arby's, Burger King, Capt D's, Checker's, Church's Chicken, DQ, Dunkin Donuts, Golden Corral, Hong Kong Buffet, KFC, McDonald's, Papa John's, Pizza Hut, Popeye's, Taco Bell, Waffle House, Wendy's, Zaxby's, 🛏 Best Value, Country Hearth Inn, Motel 6, Quality Inn, Sleep Inn, Stockbridge Inn, Suburban Lodge, ⊙ Ace Hardware, Advance Parts, Aldi Foods, BigLots, Big10 Tire, CVS Drug, $General, $Tree, Goodyear/auto, NAPA, Radio Shack, Walmart, USPO, **W** 📷 Exxon, Raceway/24hr, 🍴 Applebee's, Arby's, Broadway Diner, Burger King, Chick-fil-A, ChinChin Chinese, CiCi's, DQ, Folk's Rest., Frontera Mexican, Golden Corral, Honeybaked Ham, IHOP, KFC, Krystal, LJ Silver, McDonald's, Piccadilly's, Philly Connection, Shoney's, Subway, Taco Bell, Taco Mac, Tokyo Seafood, Waffle House, Wendy's, 🛏 Best Western,

1 Continued

Day's Inn, Comfort Inn, Holiday Inn, La Quinta, Hampton Inn, Motel 6, Red Roof Inn, ⊙ 🅷, GNC, Goodyear, K-Mart, Kroger, Lowes Whse, Office Depot, Tires+
I-675 begins/ends on I-75, exit 227.

INTERSTATE 985 (GAINESVILLE)

G A I N E S V I L L E   N ↕ S   B U F O R D

Exit	Services
	I-985 begins/ends on US 23, 25mm.
24	to US 129 N, GA 369 W, Gainesville, **N** ⊙ 🅷, GA Mtn Ctr, **S** 📷 BP/Subway/dsl, Chevron/dsl, Citgo, 🍴 Double B Burger, Rabbit Trail Cafe
22	GA 11, Gainesville, **N** 📷 BP/dsl, Citgo, QT/24hr, 🍴 Burger King, McDonald's, 🛏 Best Western/rest., **S** 📷 Chevron, Shell/dsl, 🍴 Waffle House, 🛏 Motel 6
20	GA 60, GA 53, Gainesville, **N** gas Citgo/dsl, 🍴 El Manarca, McDonald's, Mrs Winners, 🛏 Best Value Inn, Hampton Inn, **S** 📷 Kangaroo, 🍴 Subway, Waffle House
16	GA 53, Oakwood, **N** 📷 BP, Citgo, 🍴 Arby's, Baskin-Robbins/Dunkin Donuts, Burger King, DQ, El Sombrero Mexican, Hardee's, KFC, McDonald's, Pizza Hut, Subway, Taco Bell, Waffle House, Zaxby's, 🛏 Admiral Benbow Inn, Country Inn Suites, Jameson Inn, ⊙ Chrysler/Jeep, CVS Drug, Food Lion, RV Ctr, Sam's Club, **S** 📷 Citgo/dsl, QT/dsl, 🍴 Checker's, Krystal, Mrs Winners, Sonny's BBQ, Waffle House, Wendy's, 🛏 Comfort Inn, ⊙ AutoZone, Goodyear/auto, Publix, Walgreens
12	Spout Springs Rd, Flowery Branch, **N** 📷 Exxon/dsl, **S** 📷 BP/Subway, Chevron/dsl, 🍴 Burger&Shake, China Garden, CrossRoads Grill, Domino's, El Sombrero Mexican, TCBY, Thai Dish, ⊙ Publix
8	GA 347, Friendship Rd, Lake Lanier, **N** 📷 BP, Chevron, Shell, Texaco, 🍴 Backyard Burger, Blimpie, Burger King, China Garden, Huddle House, McDonald's, Sonia's Mexican, Subway, 3rd Coast, Waffle House, Wendy's, Vinny's NY Grill, Zaxby's, ⊙ Advance parts, Publix, **S** Harley Davidson, Camper City RV Ctr
4	US 23 S, GA 20, Buford, **N** 📷 QT, Shell, 🍴 Arby's, Burger King, Capt D's, Checker's, Golden Buddah, Golden Corral, Huddle House, IHOP, KFC, McDonald's, Saigon Bangkok, Taco Bell, Wendy's, Zaxby's, 🛏 Days Inn, Holiday Inn Express, ⊙ Ace Hardware, Buick/GMC, Dodge/Jeep, Home Depot, KIA, Tuesday Morning, **S** 📷 BP, Chevron, Citgo, Texaco, 🍴 Ryan's, Sonny's BBQ, Waffle House, ⊙ $Tree, Expert Tire, Honda, Lowes Whse, Walmart
0mm	I-985 begins/ends on I-85.

IDAHO

INTERSTATE 15

N ↕ S

Exit	Services
196mm	Idaho/Montana state line, Monida Pass, continental divide, elev 6870
190	Humphrey
184	Stoddard Creek Area, **E** Historical Site, RV camping, **W** Stoddard Creek Camping
180	Spencer, **E** 📷 Opal Mtn Mine/gas, 🍴 Opal Country Café, ⊙ High Country Opal Store, RV Park
172	no services
167	ID 22, Dubois, **E** 📷 Exxon/dsl/24hr, Phillips 66/dsl, 🍴 cafe, ⊙ USPO, city park, RV Dump, **rest area both**

D U B O I S

167 Continued

lanes, full ♿ **facilities,** 🚻**, picnic table, litter barrels, petwalk, W** to Craters NM, Nez Pearce Tr

Exit	Services
150	Hamer, **E** ⊙ Ron's Tire, USPO, Camus NWR, food, 🚻
143	ID 33, ID 28, to Mud Lake, Rexburg, **W** Sacajawea Hist Bywy, **weigh sta both lanes**
142mm	roadside parking, hist site
135	ID 48, Roberts, **E** 📷 Exxon/dsl/LP, 🍴 Amy's Cafe, ⊙ city park, **W** Western Wings RV Park
128	Osgood Area, **E** gas, camping (6mi)
119	US 20 E, to Rexburg, Idaho Falls, **E on Lindsay** 📷 Sinclair/dsl, 🍴 Denny's, Jaker's Steaks, Outback Steaks, Sandpiper Rest., 🛏 Best Western, Guesthouse Inn,

GA
ID

ID

INTERSTATE 15 CONT'D

Exit	Services
119	Continued
	Hilton Garden, LeRitz Hotel, Red Lion Hotel, Safari Inn, Shilo Inn/rest., Southfork Inn, Super 8, ⊙ KOA, LDS Temple, Snake River RV Park/camping, same as 118, **W** 🚘 ⊘FLYING J/dsl
118	US 20, Broadway St, Idaho Falls, **E** 🚘 Phillips 66/dsl, 🍴 Applebee's, Arctic Circle, Brownstone Rest., Cedric's Rest., Chili's, Domino's, Famous Dave's BBQ, Jalisco Mexican, Jimmy John's, Olive Garden, Quiznos, Shari's Rest., Smitty's Pancakes, Starbucks, Wendy's, 🛏 AmeriTel, Fairfield Inn, Hilton Garden, ⊙ H, Ford, Harley-Davidson, LDS Temple, Verizon, Walmart/Subway, tires, same as 119, **W** 🚘 Exxon, ⊘FLYING J/dsl, Phillips 66/dsl, Sinclair/McDonald's, 🍴 Arby's, Burger King, DQ, Hong Kong Rest., Jack-in-the-Box, Los Alberto's Mexican, O'Brady's, Papa Murphy's, Pizza Hut, Subway, 🛏 Comfort Inn, Motel 6, Motel West, ⊙ Albertsons, AutoZone, Checker Parts, Walgreens
116	US 26, Sunnyside Rd, Ammon, Jackson, **E** 🛏 Yellowstone Motel, ⊙ H, Sunnyside Acres RV Park, zoo, **W** 🚘 Exxon/diesel, 🍴 Ole Toro Mexican, 🛏 Sleep Inn
113	US 26, to Idaho Falls, Jackson, **E** 🚘 Chevron/A&W/dsl, Sinclair/Dad's/Subway/dsl/24hr/@, Exxon/dsl, ⊙ H, Jack's Tires, Peterbilt, Sunnyside RV Park, Targhee RV Park
108	Shelley, Firth Area, **1 mi E** ⊙ RV Park/dump
101mm	**rest area both lanes, full ♿ facilities, 🚻, 🛒, litter barrels, petwalk, geological site**
98	Rose-Firth Area
94.5mm	Snake River
93	US 26, ID 39, Blackfoot, **E** 🚘 Chevron/24hr, ⊘FLYING J /dsl/LP/24hr, Maverik, 🍴 Arby's, Golden China, Homestead Rest., Italiano's, Little Caesar's, McDonald's, Papa Murphy's, Pizza Hut, Rolberto's Mexican, Subway, Taco Bell, Taco Time, Wendy's, Wingers, 🛏 Super 8, ⊙ URGENT CARE, AutoZone, Checker Parts, Chrysler/Dodge/Ford/Jeep, Curves, Kesler's Foods, Radio Shack, Ridley's Mkt, Schwab Tire, Tire Factory, Walgreens, Walmart, city park, **W** Sinclair/A&W/dsl, ⊙ Riverside Boot/saddleshop (4mi)
90.5mm	Blackfoot River
89	US 91, S Blackfoot, **2 mi E** 🛏 Y Motel, **W** 🚘 Conoco/Sage Cafe/dsl
80	Ft Hall, **W** 🚘 Sinclair/rest./dsl/casino, ⊙ Shoshone Bannock Tribal Museum
72	I-86 W, to Twin Falls
71	Pocatello Creek Rd, Pocatello, **E** 🚘 Chevron/Burger King/dsl, Phillips 66/dsl, Shell/dsl/24hr, 🍴 Applebee's, Jack-in-the Box, Perkins, Sandpiper Rest., Subway, 🛏 AmeriTel, Best Western, Comfort Inn, Holiday Inn, Red Lion Inn, Super 8, ⊙ H, KOA (1mi), **0-2 mi W** 🚘 Exxon, Maverik/dsl, 🍴 Arby's, Bamboo Garden, Butterburr's, Changs Garden Chinese, DQ, Golden Corral, Jamba Juice, KFC, Mandarin House, McDonald's, Papa Kelsey's Pizza, Papa Murphy's, Pizza Hut, Puerto Vallarta, Ramires Mexican, Schlotzsky's, Senor Iguana's Mexican, SF Pizza, Sizzler, Sonic, Starbucks, Subway, Taco Bell, Taco Time, Wendy's, Winger's, ⊙ AT&T, AutoZone, Buick/GMC, Checker Parts, $Tree, Fred Meyer/gas, Grease Monkey, Harley-Davidson, Honda,

Exit	Services
71	Continued
	Radio Shack, Subaru, Toyota, Tuesday Morning, Walgreens, WinCo Foods
69	Clark St, Pocatello, **E** 🚘 Maverik/dsl, Shell/Blimpie/dsl, Sinclair/Arctic Circle/dsl, 🍴 Ruby Tuesday, 🛏 Hampton Inn, TownePlace Suites, **W** ⊙ H, to ID St U, museum
67	US 30/91, 5th St, Pocatello, **E** 🚘 Exxon/24hr, **1-2 mi W** 🚘 Phillips 66/dsl, Shell, Sinclair/dsl, 🍴 Elmer's Dining, 5th St Bagels Deli, Jimmy John's, McDonald's, Pizza Hut, Rosa's Mexican, Subway, Taco Bell, 🛏 Best Western, Rodeway Inn, Thunderbird Motel, ⊙ H, Cowboy RV Park, Old Fort Hall, info, museum, RV dump, zoo
63	Portneuf Area, **W** ⊙ to Mink Creek RA, RV camp/dump
59mm	**weigh sta both lanes**
58	Inkom (from sb), **1/2 mi W** 🚘 Sinclair/café/dsl, ⊙ Pebble Creek Ski Area, USPO, repair
57	Inkom (from nb), same as 58
47	US 30, to Lava Hot Springs, McCammon, **E** 🚘 Chevron/A&W/Taco Time/dsl, ⊘FLYING J/Denny's/dsl/LP/RV Dump/scales/24hr, 🍴 Subway, ⊙ to Lava Hot Springs RA, McCammon RV Park
44	Lp 15, Jenson Rd, McCammon, **E** access to food
40	Arimo, **E** 🚘 Sinclair/dsl/deli, ⊙ USPO
36	US 91, Virginia
31	ID 40, to Downey, Preston, **E** 🚘 Shell/Flags Westmotel/café/dsl/24hr/@, ⊙ Downata Hot Springs RV camping (6mi)
25mm	**rest area sb, full ♿ facilities, 🚻, 🛒, litter barrels, petwalk**
24.5mm	Malad Summit, elev 5574
22	to Devil Creek Reservoir, **E** RV camping
17	ID 36, to Weston, to Preston
13	ID 38, Malad City, **W** 🚘 Chevron/Burger King, Phillips 66/café/dsl, Texaco/dsl, 🍴 Me&Lou's Rest., Subway, 🛏 Village Inn Motel, ⊙ H, Family$, 3R's Tire, TrueValue, pioneer museum, repair, RV dump
7mm	**Welcome Ctr nb, full ♿ facilities, info, 🚻, 🛒, litter barrels, vending, petwalk**
3	to Samaria, Woodruff
0mm	Idaho/Utah state line

INTERSTATE 84

Exit		Services
275mm		Idaho/Utah state line
270mm		**rest area both lanes, full ♿ facilities, geological site, 🚻, 🛒, litter barrels, petwalk**
263		Juniper Rd
257mm		Sweetzer Summit, elev 5530
254		Sweetzer Rd
245	**E**	Sublett Rd, to Malta, **N** 🚘 Sinclair/dsl/café, ⊙ camping
237		Idahome Rd
234mm		Raft River
229mm		**rest area/weigh sta both lanes, full ♿ facilities, 🚻, 🛒, litter barrels, petwalk**
228		ID 81, Yale Rd, to Declo
222	**W**	I-86, US 30, E to Pocatello
216		ID 77, ID 25, to Declo, **N** 🚘 Phillips 66/FoodCourt/dsl, ⊙ H, Village of Trees RV Park, to Walcott SP, **S** 🚘 Shell/Jake's Café/dsl
215mm		Snake River

(left margin vertical text: IDAHO FALLS N↕S BLACKFOOT POCATELLO)

INTERSTATE 84 CONT'D

Exit	Services
211	ID 24, Heyburn, Burley, **N** 📭 Sinclair/ A&W/dsl/café, 🍴 Wayside Cafe, 🏠 Tops Motel, ⊙ 🏥, Country RV Village/park, **S** 📭 ❤️Loves/Carl's Jr./dsl/scales/24hr, ⊙ Riverside RV Park, truck repair
208	ID 27, Burley, **N** 📭 Phillips 66/dsl, 🍴 Conner's Cafe, 🏠 Super 8, **S** 📭 Chevron/Subway/dsl/24hr, Maverik/ dsl, Shell/Taco Bell, Sinclair, 🍴 Aguila's Mexican, Arby's, Burger King, Garibaldi Mexican, Jack-in-the-Box, JB's, Little Caesar's, McDonald's, Morey's Steaks, Perkins, Wendy's, 🏠 Best Western, Budget Motel, Fairfield Inn, ⊙ 🏥, Cal Store, $Tree, JC Penney, Radio Shack, Walmart/dsl, to Snake River RA, **1 mi** **S** 📭 Sinclair/dsl, 🍴 Guadalajara Mexican, KFC, ⊙ Buick/GMC, CarQuest, Checker Parts, Chrysler/Dodge/Jeep, Commercial Tire, NAPA, Stoke's Foods
201	ID 25, Kasota Rd, to Paul
194	ID 25, to Hazelton, **S** 📭 Sinclair/ dsl/café, ⊙ RV camping
188	Valley Rd, to Eden
182	ID 50, to Kimberly, Twin Falls, **N** 📭 Sinclair/dsl, ⊙ Gary's RV Ctr/park/ dump, **S** 📭 Shell/Blimpie/Taco Time/dsl/24hr/@, 🏠 Amber Inn, ⊙ 🏥, repair, to Shoshone Falls scenic attraction
173	US 93, Twin Falls, **N** 📭 ✈FLYING J /Thad's/dsl/24hr/@, 🍴 Subway, 🏠 Day's Inn, Wingate Inn, ⊙ KOA (1mi), Blue Beacon/24hr, Freightliner, to Sun Valley, **5 mi** **S** 📭 Chevron/ dsl, Exxon, Phillips 66, Shell, Sinclair, 🍴 Applebee's, Arby's, Arctic Circle, Aztlan Mexican, Baskin-Robbins, Blimpie, Burger King, Cafe Rio, Carino's Italian, Chili's, Coldstone Creamery, DQ, Elmer's, Golden Corral, Idaho Joe's, IHOP, Jack-in-the-Box, KFC, La Fiesta, Mandarin Chinese, McDonald's, Olive Garden, Outback Steaks, Papa Murphy's, Pizza Hut, Quizno's, Shari's, Sizzler, Sonic, Subway, Taco Bell, Tomato's Grill, Wendy's, Wok In Grill, 🏠 Ameritel, Best Western, Comfort Inn, Hampton Inn, Hilton Garden, Holiday Inn Express, Motel 6, Red Lion, Shilo Inn, Super 8, Weston Inn, ⊙ 🏥, AutoZone, Barnes&Noble, Best Buy, Buick/GMC, Cadillac/Chevrolet, Chrysler/Dodge/Jeep, Commercial Tire, Costco/gas, Curves, $Tree, Ford, Goodyear, Hancock Fabrics, Hastings, Home Depot, Honda, Hyundai, JC Penney, Jo-Ann Fabrics, Lowe's Whse, Macy's, Mazda/VW, Michael's, Nissan, Old Navy, Petsmart, Schwab Tire, ShopKO, Sportsman's Whse, Target, TJ Maxx, Tuesday Morning, WinCo Foods, Coll of, S ID, LDS Temple
171mm	rest area/weigh sta eb, full ♿ facilities, 📞, 🏕, vending, litter barrels, petwalk
168	ID 79, to Jerome, **N** 📭 Chevron/dsl, Mirastar/dsl, Shell/ Wendy's/dsl, Sinclair/dsl, 🍴 Burger King, Little

Exit	Services
168	Continued Caesar's, McDonald's, Sonic, 🏠 Best Western, Crest Motel, ⊙ AutoZone, Brockman RV Ctr, $Tree, Schwab Tire, Walmart, **2 mi** **N** 🍴 DQ, 🏠 Holiday Motel, ⊙ 🏥, **S** 🍴 Subway, ⊙ Chevrolet/GMC, ID RV Ctr/marine
165	ID 25, Jerome, **N** 📭 Sinclair/dsl, 🏠 Holiday Motel (1mi), ⊙ 🏥, RV camping/dump
157	ID 46, Wendell, **N** 🍴 Subway, **1 mi N** ⊙ 🏥, CarQuest, Family$, Intermountain RV Park, **S** 📭 Phillips 66/dsl, 🍴 Farmhouse Rest.
155	ID 46, to Wendell, **N** Intermountain RV Camp/ ctr
147	to Tuttle, **S** ⊙ to Malad Gorge SP, High Adventure RV Park/cafe
146mm	Malad River
141	US 26, to US 30, Gooding, **N** 🏥, **S** 📭 Phillips 66/dsl/café, Sinclair/ dsl/24hr, 🏠 Amber Inn, Hagerman Inn (9mi), ⊙ Hagerman RV Village (8mi)
137	Lp 84, to US 30, to

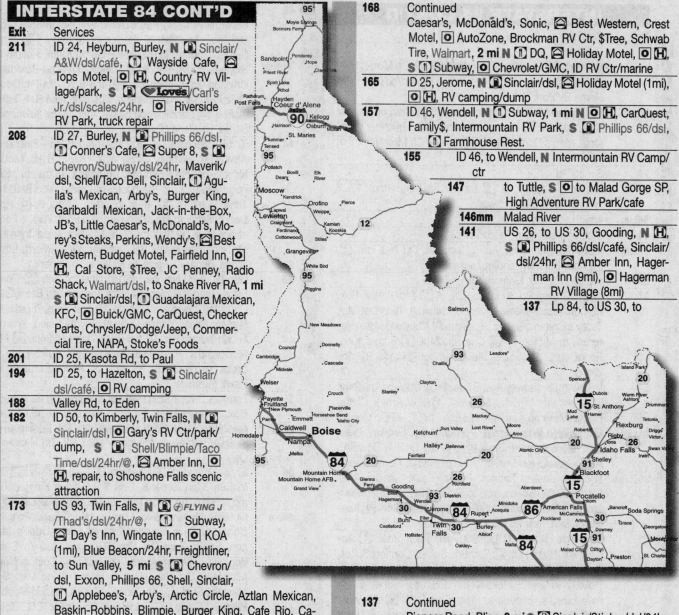

Exit	Services
137	Continued Pioneer Road, Bliss, **2 mi** **S** 📭 Sinclair/Stinker/dsl/24hr, ⊙ camping
133mm	rest area both lanes, full ♿ facilities, info, 🏕, litter barrels, petwalk, 📞
129	King Hill
128mm	Snake River
125	Paradise Valley
122mm	Snake River
121	Glenns Ferry, **1 mi** **S** 📭 Shell/dsl, Sinclair, 🏠 Redford Motel, ⊙ Carmela Winery/rest., NAPA, tires, to 3 Island SP, Trails Break RV camp/dump
120	Glenns Ferry (from eb), same as 121
114	ID 78 (from wb), to Hammett, **1 mi** **S** access to gas/dsl, to Bruneau Dunes SP
112	to ID 78, Hammett, **1 mi** **S** gas/dsl, food, to Bruneau Dunes SP
99	ID 51, ID 67, to Mountain Home, **2 mi** **S** 🏠 Maple Cove Motel, camping
95	US 20, Mountain Home, **N** 📭 Chevron/KFC/dsl/24hr, 🚛Arby's/dsl/scales/24hr, 🍴 AJ's Rest., Jack-in-the-Box, Subway, 🏠 Best Western, Hampton Inn, Sleep Inn, **S** 🍴 Golden Crown Chinese, McDonald's

Left margin:
E ← (arrow) → W
BURLEY
TWIN FALLS
(right edge tab) **ID**

MOUNTAIN HOME

E ↕ **W**

BOISE

Exit	Services
	INTERSTATE 84 CONT'D
95	Continued
	Wendy's, 🛏 Hilander Motel (1mi), Towne Ctr Motel (1mi), 🅞 🖸, Curves, $Tree, Family$, Walmart/gas, to Mtn Home RV Park
90	to ID 51, ID 67, W Mountain Home, **S** 🅟 Chevron/Burger King/dsl/24hr, 🍴 McDonald's (4mi), 🛏 to Hilander Motel (4mi), Maple Cove Motel (4mi), Towne Ctr Motel (4mi), 🅞 KOA
74	Simco Rd
71	Orchard, Mayfield, **S** 🅟 Sinclair/dsl/StageStop Motel/rest./24hr, 🅞 🖸, truckwash
66mm	**weigh sta both lanes**
64	Blacks Creek, Kuna historical site
62mm	**rest area both lanes, full ♿ facilities, OR Trail info, 🖸, 🚮, litter barrels, vending, petwalk**
59b a	S Eisenman Rd, Memory Rd
57	ID 21, Gowen Rd, to Idaho City, **N** 🍴 Jack-in-the-Box, McDonald's, Perkins, Quizno's, Subway, Taco Del Mar, Tulley's Coffee, 🛏 Best Western, 🅞 Albertsons/gas, Peterbilt, to Micron, **S** 🅟 Chevron/24hr, 🍴 Burger King, FoodCourt, 🅞 Boise Stores/famous brands, ID Ice World
54	US 20/26, Broadway Ave, Boise, **N** 🅟 Chevron/dsl/24hr, ⛽FLYING J/dsl/LP/24hr, Shell/dsl, 🍴 A&W, Arby's, Chili's, Fiesta Mexican, Jack-in-the-Box, IHOP, KFC, Mongol Grill, Nick'n Willy's Pizza, Port Of Subs, Subway, Wendy's, 🛏 Courtyard (3mi), 🅞 🖸, Big O Tire, Dowdie's Automotive, Fred Meyer, Goodyear/auto, Home Depot, Hyundai, Jo-Ann Fabrics, PetCo, Radio Shack, Ross, ShopKO, Walgreens, vet, to Boise St U, **S** 🅟 TA/Tesoro/Taco Bell/Subway/dsl/24hr/@, 🛏 Shilo Inn, 🅞 Kenworth, Mtn View RV Park
53	Vista Ave, Boise, **N** 🅟 Shell/dsl, Texaco/dsl, 🍴 Applebee's, Pizza Hut, 🛏 Cambria Suites, Comfort Suites, Extended Stay America, Fairfield Inn, Hampton Inn, Holiday Inn/rest., Holiday Inn Express, Super 8, 🅞 museums, st capitol, st police, zoo, **S** 🅟 Chevron/McDonald's/24hr, 🍴 Denny's, Kopper Kitchen, 🛏 Best Western, Comfort Inn, InnAmerica, Motel 6, Sleep Inn
52	Orchard St, Boise, **N** 🅟 Shell/dsl/24hr, 🅞 KIA, Mazda/Nissan, GMC, **1-2 mi N** 🍴 Burger King, Jack-in-the-Box, McDonald's, Raedean's Rest., Round Table Pizza, Wendy's, 🅞 Albertson's/gas, Walgreens
50b a	Cole Rd, Overland Rd, **N** 🅟 Chevron/24hr, Shell, Sinclair, 🍴 Cancun Mexican, Eddie's Rest., Golden Spoon Yogurt, McDonald's, Outback Steaks, Pizza Hut, Subway, Taco Bell, Taco Time, 🅞 LDS Temple, transmissions, **S** 🅟 ⛽FLYING J/Conoco/dsl/24hr, Phillips 66/dsl, 🍴 A&W/KFC, Bajio, Burger King, Carino's, Carl's Jr, Chappala Mexican, Chuck-a-Rama, Cracker Barrel, Fuddruckers, Goodwood BBQ, McGrath's FishHouse, Legend's Grill, Panda Express, Primo's, On the Border, Port Of Subs, Quizno's, Ruby River Steaks, Sonic, Starbucks, Tucano's, 🛏 AmeriTel, Budget Host, Hilton Garden, Homewood Suites, Oxford Suites, 🅞 Commercial Tire, Costco/gas, Dillon RV Ctr, Goodyear, Lowe's Whse, Schwab Tire, Walmart, vet
49	I-184 (exits left from eb), to, W Boise, **N** 🅞 🖸

EAGLE

NAMPA

46	ID 55, Eagle, **N** 🅟 Chevron/McDonald's/dsl/24hr, Shell/dsl/24hr, 🍴 Buffalo Wild Wings, Chronic Taco's, Del Taco, Los Beto's, Starbucks, Subway, 🛏 Comfort Suites, Country Inn&Suites, Hampton Inn, Holiday Inn Express, 🅞 🖸, vet, **S** 🅟 Shell/Jack-in-the-Box/dsl, 🍴 Chicago Connection, Jack-in-the-Box, Pita Pit, Qdoba, Quizno's, Sakana Japanese, Subway, Taco Bell, Tulley's Coffee, 🛏 Candlewood Suites, Courtyard, Towneplace Suites, 🅞 Harley Davidson,
44	ID 69, Meridian, **N** 🅟 Chevron/dsl/24hr, Sinclair, 🍴 A&W/KFC, Blimpie, China Wok, DQ, El Bajio, McDonald's, Mongolian Express, Mulligan's, Pizza Hut, Quizno's, Shari's/24hr, Starbucks, Subway, Taco Bell, Taco Time, Wendy's, 🛏 Best Western, Motel 6, 🅞 Home Depot, Schwab Tire, Sierra Trading Post, WinCo Foods, at police, **S** 🅟 Shell/dsl/24hr, 🍴 JB's, Papa John's, 🛏 Mr Sandman Motel, 🅞 Camping World, Ford, Lowe's Whse, Schuck's Parts, Walgreens, waterpark
38	Garrity Blvd, Nampa, **N** 🅟 Chevron/dsl, 🍴 Port of Subs, Taco Del Mar, 🛏 Hampton Inn, 🅞 Buick/GMC, Cadillac/Chevrolet, Chrysler/Dodge/Jeep, Ford, KIA, Nissan, Swiss Village Cheese, Toyota/Scion, Walmart, **S** 🅟 Phillips 66/dsl, Shell/Taco Time/dsl/24hr, 🍴 A&W, McDonald's, Pizza Hut, Subway, 🛏 Holiday Inn Express, 🅞 🖸, Garrity RV Park, JC Penney, Macy's, War Hawk Museum
36	Franklin Blvd, Nampa, **N** 🅟 Maverik, 🍴 Jack-in-the-Box, Noodles Rest., 🛏 Shilo Inn/rest., **S** 🅟 Chevron/dsl/24hr, Shell/dsl/RV dump/scales/4hr, 🛏 Sleep Inn, 🅞 🖸, Freightliner, Mason Cr RV Park, 7th Heaven RV Ctr
35	ID 55, Nampa, **S** 🅟 Shell/dsl, 🍴 Denny's/24hr, 🛏 Days Inn, Shilo Inn, Super 8, **1 mi S** 🍴 Burger King, McDonald's, Pizza Hut, Taco Time, El Tanampa Mexican, 🅞 🖸
33b a	ID 55 S, Midland Blvd, Marcine, **N** 🍴 Gandolfo's, McDonald's, Olive Garden, Port of Subs, Qdoba Mexican, Sonic, Taco Del Mar, TGIFriday, Tulley's Coffee, Winger's, 🛏 Fairfield Inn, 🅞 Best Buy, Costco, Kohl's, Michael's, Old Navy, PetCo, Target, World Mkt, **S** 🅟 Maverik, Shell, 🍴 Applebee's, Arby's, Baskin-Robbins, Blimpie, Carl's Jr, Coldstone Creamery, DQ, Golden Corral, IHOP, Jack-in-the-Box, Jade Garden, Outback Steaks, Primo's, Quizno's, Red Robin, Shari's Rest, Skipper's, Smokey Mtn Grill, Starbucks, Subway, Taco Bell, Wendy's, 🅞 BigLots, Big O Tire, $Tree, Home Depot, Jo-Ann Fabrics, K-Mart, Lowe's Whse, Macy's, Ross, Saver's, ShopKo, Staples, U-Haul, Walgreens, WinCo Foods
29	US 20/26, Franklin Rd, Caldwell, **N** 🅟 ⛽FLYING J/Denny's/dsl/LP/scales/24hr, 🅞 Ambassador RV camping, RV dump, **S** 🅟 Sage/Sinclair/cafe/dsl/24hr, 🍴 Perkins/24hr, 🛏 Best Western, La Quinta
28	10th Ave, Caldwell, **N** 🅟 Maverik/gas, 🛏 I-84 Motel, 🅞 city park, **S** 🅟 Chevron/24hr, Shell, 🍴 Carl's Jr, Domino's, Fiesta Mexican, Jack-in-the-Box, KFC, Mr V's Rest., Pizza Hut, Subway, Wendy's, 🛏 Sundowner Motel, 🅞 🖸, AutoZone, Paul's Food/Drug, Tire Factory, Walgreens
27	ID 19, to Wilder, **1 mi S** 🅟 Tesoro/dsl/24hr
26.5mm	Boise River
26	US 20/26, to Notus, **N** 🅞 Caldwell Campground, **S** 🅟 Sinclair/dsl

INTERSTATE 84 CONT'D

Exit	Services
25	ID 44, Middleton, **N** 📶 Shell/dsl, 🍴 44 Burgers/shakes, **S** Insp sta eb
17	Sand Hollow, **N** 🍴 Sand Hollow Café, ⊙ Country Corners RV Park
13	Black Canyon Jct, **S** 📶 Sinclair/dsl/motel/rest./scales/24hr, ⊙
9	US 30, to New Plymouth
3	US 95, Fruitland, **N** 📶 Shell/A&W/dsl, **5 mi N** ⊙ Neat Retreat RV Park, to Hell's Cyn RA
1mm	**Welcome Ctr eb, full** ♿ **facilities, info,** ⊙, 🛏, **litter barrels, petwalk**
0mm	Snake River, Idaho/Oregon state line

INTERSTATE 86

Exit	Services
63b a	I-15, N to Butte, S to SLC.
	I-86 begins/ends on I-15, exit 72.
61	US 91, Yellowstone Ave, Pocatello, **N** 📶 Exxon, Shell/dsl, 🍴 Arby's, Arctic Circle, Burger King, Chapala Mexican, Johnny B Goode's Diner, Lei's BBQ, Papa Murphy's, Pizza Hut, Subway, Wendy's, 🛏 Motel 6, Ramada Inn, ⊙ Budget RV Park, Checker Parts, $Tree, Family$, Smith's Foods/dsl, **S** 📶 Common Cents/dsl, Phillips 66/dsl, 🍴 Bajio, Chili's, Denny's, 5 Guys Burgers, IHOP, McDonald's, Pita Pit, Red Lobster, Taco John's, TX Roadhouse, ⊙ AT&T, Costco/gas, Ford, Home Depot, JC Penney, Jo-Ann Fabrics, K-Mart/Little Caesar's, Lowe's, PetCo, Radio Shack, Ross, Schwab Tire, Sears, ShopKo, Staples, TJ Maxx, Verizon, Walgreens, Walmart, dsl repair
58.5mm	Portneuf River
58	US 30, W Pocatello
56	**N** Pocatello Air Terminal, **S** 📶 Sinclair/dsl/24hr
52	Arbon Valley, **S** 📶 Sinclair/Bannock Peak/dsl, ⊙ casino
51mm	Bannock Creek
49	Rainbow Rd
44	Seagull Bay
40	ID 39, American Falls, **N** 📶 Phillips 66/dsl, Sinclair, 🍴 Pizza Hut, Subway, Tres Hermanos Mexican, 🛏 American Motel, ⊙ H, Alco, Jiffy Lube, King's, NAPA, Schwab Tire, to Am Falls RA, RV Park/dump, **S** 🛏 Hillview Motel
36	ID 37, to Rockland, American Falls, **2 mi N** 📶 Shell/dsl, 🛏 Falls Motel, ⊙ H, **2 mi S** Indian Springs RV Resort
33	Neeley Area
31mm	**rest area wb, full** ♿ **facilities,** ⊙, **picnic table, litter barrel, petwalk, vending, hist site**
28	**N** ⊙ to Massacre Rock SP, Register Rock Hist Site, RV camping/dump
21	Coldwater Area
19mm	**rest area eb, full** ♿ **facilities,** ⊙, **picnic table, litter barrel, petwalk, vending, hist site**
15	Raft River Area
1	I-84 E, to Ogden. I-86 begins/ends on I-84, exit 222.

INTERSTATE 90

Exit	Services
74mm	Idaho/Montana state line, Pacific/Central time zone Lookout Pass elev 4680
73mm	scenic area/hist site wb
72mm	scenic area/hist site eb
71mm	**runaway truck ramp wb**
70mm	**runaway truck ramp wb**
69	Lp 90, Mullan, **N** 📶 CFN/dsl, 🛏 Lookout Motel (1mi), ⊙ USPO, museum
68	Lp 90 (from eb), Mullan, same as 69
67	Morning District
66	Gold Creek (from eb)
65	Compressor District
64	Golconda District
62	ID 4, Wallace, **S** 📶 Conoco, 🍴 Pizza Factory, 🛏 Brooks Hotel, Stardust Motel, ⊙ H, Depot RV Park, Harvest Foods, TrueValue, museum, repair
61	Lp 90, Wallace, **S** 📶 Conoco/dsl, 🍴 Pizza Factory, Wallace Sta Rest./gifts, 🛏 Brooks Hotel/rest., Molly B-Damm Inn, Wallace Inn, ⊙ auto repair, info ctr, same as 62
60	Lp 90, Silverton, **S** 🛏 Molly B-Damm Inn, ⊙ RV camping
57	Lp 90, Osburn, **S** 📶 76/dsl, ⊙ Blue Anchor RV Park, auto repair, USPO
54	Big Creek, **N** ⊙ Elk Creek Store/repair, hist site, rv dump
51	Lp 90, Division St, Kellogg, **N** 📶 Conoco/dsl, 🛏 Trail Motel, ⊙ H, Buick/Cadillac/Chevrolet/GMC, Chrysler/Dodge/Jeep, Schwab Tire, Stein's Foods, Sunnyside Drug, **S** 🍴 In Cahoots Cafe, Moose Creek Grill, ⊙ USPO, auto repair, museum
50	Hill St (from eb), Kellogg, **N** 🍴 Humdinger Drive-In, Sunshine Rest., 🛏 Trail Motel, ⊙ Ace Hardware, NAPA, Stein's Foods, Sunnyside Drug, tires, **S** 📶 Conoco/dsl, 🍴 Greek Deli, ⊙ Silver Mtn Ski/summer resort/rec area, Yoke's Foods, museum
49	Bunker Ave, **N** 📶 Conoco/dsl, 🍴 McDonald's, Sam's Drive-In, Subway, 🛏 Silverhorn Motel/rest., ⊙ H, **S** 🍴 Noah's Canteen, Silver Mtn Rest., 🛏 GuestHouse Inn, Morning Star Lodge, ⊙ Silver Mtn RA, museum, RV dump
48	Smelterville, **S** 🍴 Sands Cafe, ⊙ Tire Factory, Walmart
45	Pinehurst, **S** 📶 Chevron/dsl/repair, Conoco/dsl, ⊙ By-the-way Camping, Harvest Foods, NAPA, TrueValue, USPO
43	Kingston, **N** 📶 Conoco/dsl, 🍴 Snakepit Café, 🛏 Enaville Resort, RV camping, **S** 📶 Exxon/dsl/rv dump, USPO
40	Cataldo, **N** 🍴 Mission Inn Rest., USPO, **S** RV Park
39.5mm	Coeur d' Alene River
39	Cataldo Mission, **S** ⊙ Old Mission SP, Nat Hist Landmark
34	ID 3, to St Maries, Rose Lake, **S** 📶 Conoco/dsl,

[gas] = gas [food] = food [lodging] = lodging [other] = other   Copyright 2012 - The Next Exit

INTERSTATE 90 CONT'D

Exit	Services
34	Continued
	Rose Lake/dsl, [food] Rose Lake Cafe, [other] White Pines Scenic Rte
33mm	**chain removal eb**
32mm	**chainup area/weigh sta wb**
31.5mm	Idaho Panhandle NF, eastern boundary, 4th of July Creek
28	4th of July Pass RA, elev 3069, Mullan Tree HS, ski area, snowmobile area, turnout both lanes
24mm	**chainup eb, removal wb**
22	ID 97, to St Maries, L Coeur d' Alene Scenic ByWay, Wolf Lodge District, Harrison, **1 mi** N Wolf Lodge Camping, S [other] Lake Coeur d'Alene RV Park, Squaw Bay Resort (7mi)
20.5mm	Lake Coeur d' Alene
17	Mullan Trail Rd
15	Lp 90, Sherman Ave, Coeur d' Alene, N [other] forest info, Lake Coeur D' Alene RA/HS, S [gas] Exxon/dsl, Tesoro/dsl/LP, Texaco, [food] Jimmy's Cafe, Michael D's Eatery, O'Shay's Rest., [lodging] Bates Motel, BudgetSaver Motel, Cedar Motel, El Rancho Motel, Holiday Motel, Japan House Suites, La Quinta, State Motel, [other] Peterson's Foods, NAPA Care, tourist info
14	15th St, Coeur d' Alene, S [gas] TAJ Mart, [other] Jordon's Grocery
13	4th St, Coeur d' Alene, N [gas] A&D/dsl, [food] Atilano's Mexican, Carl's Jr, DQ, Davis Donuts, Denny's, Fiesta Mexican, IHOP, Jimmy John's, Little Caesars, Original Mongolian BBQ, Panda Express, Subway, Taco Time, Wendy's, [lodging] Comfort Inn, [other] AutoZone, BigLots, Costco/gas, Hastings Books, NAPA, Radio Shack, Schwab Tire, same as 12, S [gas] Exxon/dsl, [food] Thai Bamboo
12	US 95, to Sandpoint, Moscow, N [gas] Exxon/dsl, Holiday/dsl, Mobil, [food] Applebee's, Arby's, Burger King, Cafe Chulo Mexican, Casa de Oro, Chili's, Del Taco, Dragon House Chinese, Elmer's, Garlic Jim's Pizza, MacKenzie River Pizza, McDonald's, Olive Garden, Panda Express, Perkins, Pizza Factory, Pizza Hut, Red Lobster, Skipper's, Taco Bell, Tomato St., TX Roadhouse, [lodging] Best Western, Guesthouse Inn, La Quinta, Motel 6, Shilo Suites, Super 8, [other] AT&T, Best Buy, Buick/GMC, Cadillac, Discount Tire, Dodge, $Tree, Ford/Lincoln/Mercury, Fred Meyer/dsl, GNC, Grocery Outlet, Harley-Davidson, Home Depot, JC Penney, Kia, K-Mart, Kohl's, Michael's, Office Depot, O'Reilly Parts, PetCo, Ross, Safeway/gas, Sears/auto, Super 1 Foods, Target, TireRama, TJ Maxx, Toyota/Scion, Tuesday Morning, U-Haul, Verizon, Walgreens, Walmart/Subway, S [gas] Conoco, [food] Greek St Pizza, Jack-in-the-Box, Jamba Juice, Papa Murphy's, Qdoba Mexican, Quiznos, Schlotzsky's, Shari's, Starbucks, [lodging] AmeriTel, [other] H, Albertson's/gas, AT&T, GNC, Rite Aid, ShopKO/drugs, Staples, same as 13
11	Northwest Blvd, N [gas] Conoco/dsl, [other] Lowe's, S [gas] Exxon/dsl, Texaco, [food] Azteca Mexican, Coldstone, Outback Steaks, Porky G's BBQ, Red Robin, SF Sourdough, Starbucks, Subway, Ugly Fish Rest., [lodging] Days Inn, Hampton Inn, Holiday Inn Express, [other] H, Honda, Riverwalk RV Park, Verizon
8.5mm	**Welcome Ctr/weigh sta eb, rest area both lanes, full [wheelchair] facilities, info, [C], [litter] litter barrels, petwalk**

7	ID 41, to Rathdrum, Spirit Lake, N [gas] Mirastar/dsl, 76/dsl, [food] Del Taco, La Cocina Mexican, Noodle Express, NY Pizza, Papa Murphy's, Pita Pit, Pizza Factory, Quiznos, Sonic, Starbucks, Subway, Wendy's, [other] Chevrolet, Chrysler/Dodge/Jeep, $Tree, Hyundai, Mazda, Nissan, Radio Shack, Subaru, Walmart/Subway, Couer d'Alene RV Park, S [gas] Chevron/dsl, [food] A&W/KFC, Capone's Grill, DQ, [lodging] Comfort Inn, [other] truck repair, vet
6	Seltice Way, N [gas] 7-11, [food] La Cabana Mexican, Pizza Hut, [other] Super 1 Foods, Walgreens, S [gas] Conoco/dsl, LP, [food] Denny's, Hot Rod Café, Little Caesars, McDonald's, Rancho Viejo Mexican, Taco Bell, Taco Time, [other] Ace Hardware, Curves, O'Reilly Parts, TireRama, Trading Co Foods, USPO, vet
5	Lp 90, Spokane St, Treaty Rock HS, N [gas] Exxon/dsl, 76, [food] Domino's, Golden Dragon Chinese, Hunter's Rest., Rob's Seafood/burgers, Subway, WhiteHouse Grill, [other] AutoZone, CarQuest, Perfection Tire/repair, Schwab Tire, Seltice RV Ctr, S [gas] 76/Pacific Pride/dsl, [food] Rosa's Italian, [lodging] Red Lion Inn, [other] visitors ctr
2	Pleasant View Rd, N [gas] Exxon/dsl, *FLYING J*/Conoco/Subway/dsl/LP/scales/24hr, *Loves*/rest/dsl/scales/24hr, [food] McDonald's, Toro Viejo Mexican, [lodging] Best Value Inn, [other] Suntree RV Park, RV/truckwash, S [gas] Exxon/Subway/dsl/24hr, [food] Zip's Drive-in, [lodging] Riverbend Inn, Sleep Inn, [other] dogtrack
0mm	Idaho/Washington state line

INTERSTATE 184 (BOISE)

Exit	Services
6mm	I-184 begins/ends on 13th St, downtown, [gas] Shell, [food] PF Chang's, [lodging] Hampton Inn, Safari Inn, [other] Harley-Davidson, Office Depot, USPO
5	River St (from eb), W [gas] Chevron, [food] McDonald's, [other] Ford/Mercury
4.5mm	Boise River
3	Fairview Ave, to US 20/26 E, W [food] McDonald's, [lodging] Budget Inn, DoubleTree Inn, Econolodge, [other] Commercial Tire
2	Curtis Rd, to Garden City, E [lodging] Rodeway Inn, [other] H
1b a	Cole Rd, Franklin Rd, E [gas] Chevron/Subway, [lodging] Harrison Hotel, [other] Acura/Honda, Buick, Dodge, Jaguar, Land Rover, Volvo, W [gas] Maverik, Sinclair, [food] Burger King, Carl's Jr, Cheesecake Factory, Chili's, Hooters, Jack-in-the-Box, LoneStar Steaks, Old Chicago Pizza, Perkins, Quizno's, Red Robin, Sizzler, Shari's, Starbucks, TGI Friday, Wendy's, Yang Sheng Chinese, [lodging] Ameritel, Residence Inn, [other] Best Buy, Cabela's, Dillard's, JC Penney, Macy's, Michael's, Office Depot, Old Navy, PetCo, Ross, Sears/auto, Target, TJ Maxx, mall, vet
0mm	I-184 begins/ends on I-84, exit 49.

ILLINOIS

INTERSTATE 24

Exit	Services
38mm	Illinois/Kentucky state line, Ohio River
37	US 45, Metropolis, N **rest area both lanes, full [wheelchair] facilities, info, vending, [litter] litter barrels, petwalk, 0-2 mi** S [gas] BP/Quiznos/dsl, [food] Huddle House, KFC, McDonald's, Pizza Hut, Sonic, [lodging] Best Value Inn, Holiday Inn Express, Metropolis Inn, Motel 6, Super 8, [other] H, Buick/Chrysler/Dodge/GMC/Jeep, Chevrolet, O'Reilly Parts, Plaza Tire,

gical

INTERSTATE 24 CONT'D

Exit	Services
37	Continued to Riverboat Casino, Ft Massac SP, camping
27	to New Columbia, Big Bay
16	IL 146, Vienna, **N** 🛏 Gambit Inn, **S** 📱 BP/dsl, FastStop, Roc/dsl, 🍴 Dolly's Rest., DQ, Jumbo Grill, McDonald's, Newt's Pizza, Subway, 🛏 Limited Inn
14	US 45, Vienna, **S** camping
7	to Goreville, Tunnel Hill, **N** 📱 Fast Stop/dsl, 🔵 winery, **S** 🔵 to Ferne Clyffe SP, camping
1	I-57, N to Chicago, S to Memphis. I-24 begins/ends on I-57, exit 44.

INTERSTATE 39

Exit	Srevices
	I-39 and I-90 run together into Wisconsin. See Illinois Interstate 90, exits 15mm through 1.
122b a	US 20 E, Harrison Ave, to Belvidere, **W** 📱 Mobil, Road Ranger/Subway/dsl, 🍴 Arby's, Bergner's, Burger King, DQ, Granite City Rest., Lung Fung, Sonic, Taco Bell, TGIFriday's, 🔵 AT&T, Barnes&Noble, BMW, Chevrolet, Collier RV Ctr, Goodyear/auto, Harley-Davidson, Hilander Foods/gas, JC Penney, Macy's, Menards, Sears/auto, Tires+, VW, Walgreens, mall, last nb exit before toll rd
119	US 20 W, Alpine Rd, to Rockford
116.5mm	Kishwaukee River
115	Baxter Rd, **E** 📱 Shell/dsl/scales/24hr/@
111	IL 72, to Monroe Center, **E** 📱 BP/Sunrise Family Rest./dsl/24hr, Marathon (1mi), 🍴 Roadhouse Rest. (1mi)
104	IL 64, to Oregon, Sycamore, **W** Grubsteakers Rest/truck parking (2mi)
99	IL 38, to De Kalb, Rochelle, **0-2 mi W** 📱 BP/dsl, Petro/Iron Skillet/dsl/scales/RV Dump/@, Road Ranger/Pilot/Subway/dsl/scales/24hr, Shell/dsl, 🍴 Arby's, Butterfly Rest, China Wok, Culver's, DQ, Little Ceasar's, McDonald's, New China, Taco Bell, Wendy's, 🛏 Baymont Inn, Comfort Inn, Holiday Inn Express, Super 8, 🔵 H, Blue Beacon, Curves, $General, Sullivan's Foods, Walgreens, Walmart
97b a	I-88 tollway, to Moline, Rock Island, Chicago
93	Steward
87	US 30, to Sterling, Rock Falls, **E** to Shabbona Lake SP, **W** Yogi Bear Camping (16mi)
84.5mm	**rest area both lanes, full ♿ facilities, 🔵, 🛏, litter barrels, vending, playground, petwalk**
82	Paw Paw, **3 mi E** Casey's, **W** many wind turbines
72	US 34, to Mendota, Earlville, **W** 📱 BP/Buster's Buffet/dsl/scales/24hr, Road Ranger/Pilot/dsl/scales/24hr, 🍴 KFC/Taco Bell, McDonald's, 🛏 Comfort Inn, Super 8/truck parking, 🔵 H
67.5mm	Little Vermilion River
66	US 52, Troy Grove, **E** KOA (1mi)
62.5mm	Tomahawk Creek
59b a	I-80, E to Chicago, W to Des Moines
57	US 6, to Peru, La Salle, **1-2 mi W** 📱 Casey's, Shell/24hr, 🛏 Daniel's Motel, 🔵 city park

Side labels (left margin): E ↕ W   R O C K F O R D   N ↕ S

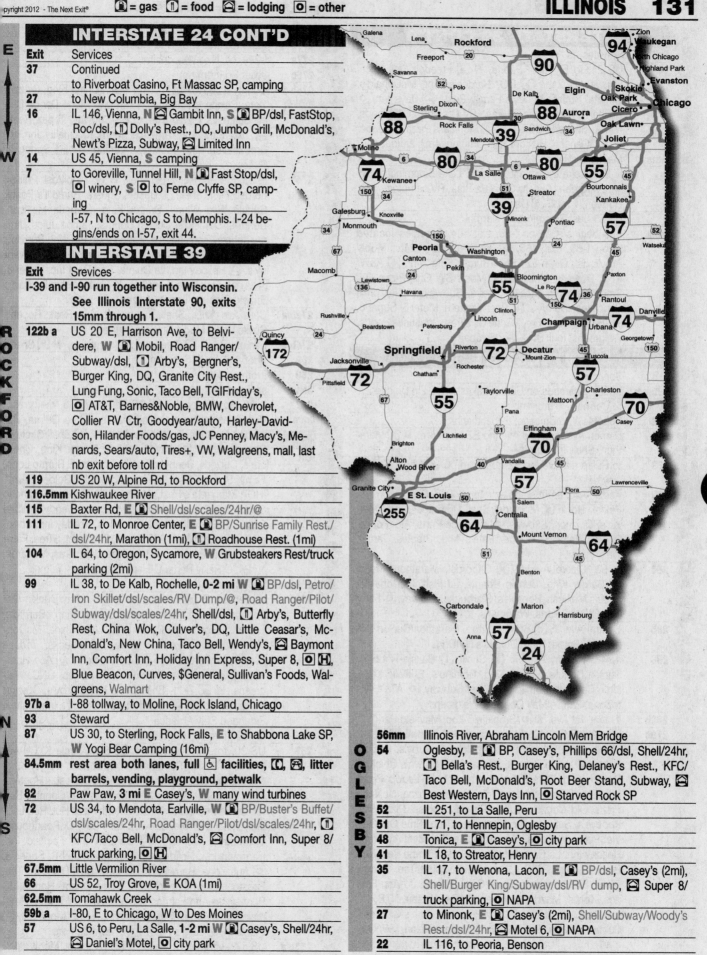

 IL

Exit	Services
56mm	Illinois River, Abraham Lincoln Mem Bridge
54	Oglesby, **E** 📱 BP, Casey's, Phillips 66/dsl, Shell/24hr, 🍴 Bella's Rest., Burger King, Delaney's Rest., KFC/Taco Bell, McDonald's, Root Beer Stand, Subway, 🛏 Best Western, Days Inn, 🔵 Starved Rock SP
52	IL 251, to La Salle, Peru
51	IL 71, to Hennepin, Oglesby
48	Tonica, **E** 📱 Casey's, 🔵 city park
41	IL 18, to Streator, Henry
35	IL 17, to Wenona, Lacon, **E** 📱 BP/dsl, Casey's (2mi), Shell/Burger King/Subway/dsl/RV dump, 🛏 Super 8/truck parking, 🔵 NAPA
27	to Minonk, **E** 📱 Casey's (2mi), Shell/Subway/Woody's Rest./dsl/24hr, 🛏 Motel 6, 🔵 NAPA
22	IL 116, to Peoria, Benson

Side label (left margin): O G L E S B Y

INTERSTATE 39 CONT'D

N ↕ S

Exit	Srevices
14	US 24, to El Paso, Peoria, **E** 🅐 Freedom/dsl, Shell/Subway/dsl/24hr, ⦿ DQ, Hardee's/24hr, McDonald's, Oriental Buffet, Woody's Family Rest., 🛏 Days Inn, ⊡ Bushert's Hardwaare, El Paso RV Ctr, Ford, IGA Foods, NAPA, city park, USPO, **W** ⦿ Monical's Pizza, 🛏 Super 8, ⊡ $General, Hickory Hill Camping (4mi), antiques
9mm	Mackinaw River
8	IL 251, Lake Bloomington Rd, **E** Lake Bloomington, **W** ⊡ Evergreen Lake, to Comlara Park, RV camping
5	Hudson, **1 mi E** 🅐 Casey's
2	US 51 bus, Bloomington, Normal
0mm	I-39 begins/ends on I-55, exit 164. **Services located N on I-55, exit 165, E** 🅐 BP/Circle K/24hr, Mobil/Arby's/dsl, Qik-n-EZ, Shell/Burger King/24hr, ⦿ A&W/KFC, Denny's, McDonald's, Moe's SW Grill, Pizza Hut, Smoothie King, Steak'n Shake, Subway, Uncle Tom's Pancakes, Wendy's, 🛏 Best Western, Motel 6, Super 8, ⊡ Ⓗ, Discount Tire, $General, $Tree, Schnucks Foods, Walgreens, to Ill St U, **W** dsl repair

INTERSTATE 55

N ↕ S CHICAGO AREA

Exit	Services
295mm	I-55 begins/ends on US 41, Lakeshore Dr, in Chicago.
293a	to Cermak Rd (from nb)
292	I-90/94, W to Chicago, E to Indiana
290	Damen Ave, Ashland Ave (no EZ nb return), **E** 🅐 Marathon, Shell, ⊡ Target
289	to California Ave (no EZ nb return), **E** 🅐 Citgo, Speedway/dsl
288	Kedzie Ave, (from sb no ez return), **E** 🅐 Citgo
287	Pulaski Rd, **E** 🅐 Mobil/dsl, Shell, ⦿ Burger King, Domino's, Quiznos, Subway, ⊡ Advance Parts, Aldi Foods, Dodge, Family$, Honda, Pete's Mkt, Staples, Target, Walgreens
286	IL 50, Cicero Ave, **E** 🅐 Citgo/dsl, Marathon, Mobil, ⦿ Burger King, Dunkin Donuts, JJ Fish, McDonald's, Pepe's Mexican, Popeye's, Starbucks, Subway, ⊡ Family$, O'Reilly Parts, Walgreens, to 🚻
285	Central Ave, **E** 🅐 BP/dsl, Citgo, Marathon/Dunkin Donuts, ⦿ Burger King, Donald's HotDogs
283	IL 43, Harlem Ave, **E** 🅐 Shell, ⦿ Baksin-Robbins/Dunkin Donuts, Burger King, Domino's, El Pollo Loco, Little Caesars, Portillo HotDogs, Subway, ⊡ AT&T, AutoZone, Fannie May Candies, Walgreens
282b a	IL 171, 1st Ave, **W** ⊡ Brookfield Zoo, Mayfield Park
279b	US 12, US 20, US 45, La Grange Rd, **0-2 mi W** 🅐 BP, Mobil, Shell, ⦿ Al's Beef, Applebee's, Arby's, Baskin-Robbins/Dunkin Donuts, Boston Mkt, Brown's Chicken, Burger King, Cafe Salsa, Jimmy John's, Ledo's Pizza, LoneStar Steaks, McDonald's, Nancy's Pizza, NoNno's Pizza, Old Country Buffet, Panda Express, Pizza Hut, Popeye's, Subway, Taco Bell, Taco Tico, Time Out Grill, Via Bella, Wendy's, White Castle, 🛏 Best Western, Holiday Inn, La Grange Motel, ⊡ Aldi Foods, Best Buy, Buick/Cadillac/GMC, Chevrolet, Discount Tire, Dodge, $Tree, Firestone/auto, Ford, GNC, Honda, Jo-Ann Fabrics, Kohl's, Mazda, Menards, NAPA, Nissan, NTB, Office Depot, PepBoys, PetCo, Petsmart, Sam's Club/gas, Subaru, Suzuki, Target, Toyota/Scion, Verizon, VW, Walmart

CHICAGO AREA / BOLINGBROOK / JOLIET

Exit	Services
279a	La Grange Rd, to I-294 toll, S to Indiana
277b	I-294 toll (from nb), S to Indiana
277a	I-294 toll, N to Wisconsin
276c	Joliet Rd (from nb)
276b a	County Line Rd, **E** ⦿ Capri Rest., China King, Ciazzi's Cafe, Cooper's Hawk, Max&Erma's, Moon Dance Diner, Salerno's Pizza, Starbucks, Subway, Topaz Rest., 🛏 Extended Stay America, Marriott, Quality Inn, ⊡ Brookhaven Mkt, Tuesday Morning, **W** 🛏 SpringHill Suites
274	IL 83, Kingery Rd, **E** 🅐 Shell, **W** 🅐 Mobil/dsl, Phillips 66/dsl, 7-11, Shell, ⦿ Bakers Square, Barnelli's Pasta, Buffalo Wild Wings, Burger King, Chipotle Mexican, Denny's, Domino's, Dunkin Donuts, Jamba Juice, Jimmy John's, Papa John's, Patio BBQ, Pei Wei, Portillo's HotDogs, Potbelly's Rest., Starbucks, Subway, Wendy's, 🛏 Holiday Inn, La Quinta, Red Roof Inn, Super 8, ⊡ AT&T, Firestone, Ford/KIA, K-Mart, Michael's, Radio Shack, Staples, Target, Verizon
273b a	Cass Ave, **W** 🅐 Shell, ⦿ La Notte Due Rest., Rosati's Pizza, Uncle Mao's Chinese, ⊡ vet
271b a	Lemont Rd, **E** 🛏 Extended Stay America, **W** 🅐 Shell
269	I-355 toll, to, W Suburbs
268	(from sb only)
Joliet	same as 267
267	IL 53, Bolingbrook, **E** 🅐 BP, Phillips 66/55 Trkstp/rest./dsl/scales/24hr/@, ⦿ McDonald's, 🛏 La Quinta, Ramada Ltd, Super 8, ⊡ Chevrolet, **W** 🅐 Shell/Circle K, Speedway/dsl, ⦿ A&W/LJ Silver, Burger King, Cheddar's, Culver's, Denny's, Dunkin Donuts, El Burrito Loco, Family Square Rest., Golden Chopsticks, Golden Corral, IHOP, Margarita's Rest., McDonald's, Popeye's, Rancho Santa Fe Mexican, Starbucks, Subway, Wendy's, White Castle, 🛏 AmericInn, Hampton Inn, Holiday Inn, SpringHill Suites, ⊡ AAA, Aldi Foods, CarQuest, $Tree, Family$, Fiesta Mkt, Food-4-Less/gas, Just Tires, Menards, NAPA, O'Reilly Parts, U-Haul, Walgreens, Walmart
266mm	**weigh sta both lanes**
263	Weber Rd, **E** 🅐 BP/dsl, 7-11, Speedway/Dunkin Donuts/dsl/e85, ⦿ Applebee's, Burger King, Burrito's, Culver's, Giovanny's Pizza, KFC, Little China, McDonald's, Michal's Pizza, Popeye's, Starbucks, Todake Steaks, White Castle, 🛏 Best Western, ⊡ Ace Hardware, Discount Tire, Dominick's Food/gas, GNC, Walgreens, **W** 🅐 7-11, Shell/Circle K, ⦿ Arby's, Cracker Barrel, Wendy's, 🛏 Comfort Inn, Country Inn&Suites, Extended Stay America
261	IL 126 (from sb), to Plainfield
257	US 30, to Joliet, Aurora, **E** 🅐 Shell/Circle K, ⦿ Applebee's, Baskin-Robbins/Dunkin Donuts, Burger King, ChuckeCheese, Denny's, Diamand's Rest., Hooters, KFC, LoneStar Steaks, McDonald's, Old Country Buffet, Outback Steaks, Panera Bread, Pizza Hut, Red Lobster, Steak'n Shake, Subway, Taco Bell, TX Roadhouse, TGIFriday's, Wendy's, 🛏 Comfort Inn, Fairfield Inn, Hampton Inn, Holiday Inn Express, Motel 6, Super 8, ⊡ AutoZone, Barnes&Noble, Best Buy, Discount Tire, Firestone/auto, Gander Mtn, Home Depot, Honda, JC Penney, Jo-Ann Fabrics, Macy's, NTB, Old Navy, Petsmart, Sears/auto, Target, Verizon, **W** 🅐 Mobil/dsl, ⦿ Blue's BBQ, Luigi's Pizza, ⊡ Chevrolet, Ford
253b a	US 52, Jefferson St, Joliet, **E** 🅐 Citgo/dsl, Mobil/dsl,

IL

INTERSTATE 55 CONT'D

Exit	Services
253b a	Continued Shell, □ Joe's Rest., KFC/Pizza Hut, McDonald's, □ Best Budget Inn, Best Western, Elk's Motel, Joliet Inn, Wingate Inn, □ □ Ford, Freightliner, Harley-Davidson, Rick's RV Ctr, □, W □ BP/dsl, □ Al's Beef, Burger King, Casa Maya, DQ, Louie's Chophouse, Nancy's Pizza, Rosati's Pizza, Subway, □ □ Chrysler/Dodge/Jeep, Jewel-Osco/gas, NAPA, 7-11
251	IL 59 (from nb), to Shorewood, access to same as 253 W
250b a	I-80, W to Iowa, E to Toledo
248	US 6, Joliet, E □ □ ▨▨▨/Dunkin Donuts/Subway/dsl/24hr, Speedway/dsl, □ Ivo's Rest., Quiznos, Taco Burrito King, □ Manor Motel, W □ BP/McDonald's, □ Lone Star Rest. (2mi), □ to Ill/Mich SP
247	Bluff Rd
245mm	Des Plaines River
245	Arsenal Rd, E □ Exxon/Mobil Refinery
241	to Wilmington
241mm	Kankakee River
240	Lorenzo Rd, E □ Valero/dsl, W □ Mobil/pizza/dsl/scales/24hr, □ River Rest., □ Knights Inn
238	IL 129 S, to Wilmington (exits left from sb), Braidwood
236	IL 113, Coal City, E □ Good Table Rest., □ Chrysler/Dodge/Jeep, Fossil Rock Camping, W □ Shell/DQ/dsl, □ Egizio's, □ EZ Living RV Ctr, 3 mi W □ BP, Mobil/dsl, □ McDonald's, Subway
233	Reed Rd, E □ Marathon/dsl, □ Sun Motel, W □ antiques
227	IL 53, Gardner, E □ Casey's, □ Gardner Rest., W □ Shell/dsl
220	IL 47, Dwight, E □ BP/Burger King/dsl, Casey's, ◆Loves /Hardee's/dsl/scales/24hr, Marathon/Circle K/dsl/24hr, □ Arby's, Dwight Chinese, Dwight Pizza, McDonald's, Pete's Rest., Subway, □ Classic Motel, Super 8
217	IL 17, Dwight, E □ Casey's, Shell/50's Rest./Circle K/dsl/24hr, □ DQ, Rte 66 Rest., □ Best Hardware, Doc's Drug, Family$, NAPA, Pamida
213mm	Mazon River
209	Odell, E □ BP, □ USPO
201	IL 23, Pontiac, 0-3 mi E □ Marathon, □ DQ, La Mex, □ 4H RV Camp (seasonal) RV Ctr, W truck repair
198mm	Vermilion River
197	IL 116, Pontiac, E □ BP/dsl, Freedom, Shell/dsl, Thornton's/dsl, □ Arby's, Baby Bull's Rest., Burger King, Cafe Fontana, KFC, LJ Silver, McDonald's, Monical's Pizza, Pizza Hut Buffet, Subway, Taco Bell, Wendy's, □ Comfort Inn, Fiesta Motel (1mi), Holiday Inn Express, Super 8, □ □ Aldi Foods, AT&T, AutoZone, Big R Store, Buick/Chevrolet, Cadillac/GMC, Dodge/Lincoln/Mercury, $Tree, Firestone/auto, Ford, K-Mart, Verizon, Walgreens, Walmart/Subway, st police, W □ FastStop
193mm	**rest area both lanes, full & facilities, □, □, litter barrels, vending, petwalk**
187	US 24, Chenoa, E □ Casey's, Phillips 66/McDonald's/dsl, Shell/Subway/dsl, □ Chenoa Family Rest., Super 8
179mm	Des Plaines River
178	Lexington, Lexington, E □ BP/McDonalds/dsl, Freedom/dsl, W Chevrolet
178mm	Mackinaw River

Exit	Services
171	Towanda, E □ FastStop
167	Lp 55, S Veterans Pkwy, to Normal, 0-3 mi E □ BP/Circle K, Marathon/Circle K/dsl, □ Applebee's, Blimpie, Biaggi's Ristorante, Bob Evans, Burger King, Carlos O'Kelly's, Chili's, Chipotle Mexican, ChuckeCheese, DQ, Fazoli's, Fiesta Ranchera Mexican, Fuji Grill, Hardee's, Jimmy John's, Krispy Kreme, Logan's Roadhouse, Lonestar Steaks, McDonald's, Noodles&Co, Olive Garden, Outback Steaks, Panera Bread, Papa John's, Papa Murphy's, Pizza Hut, Potbelly, Qdoba Mexican, Red Lobster, Schlotzsky's, Sonic, Starbucks, Steak'n Shake, Taco Bell, Wendy's, Wild Berries Rest., □ Baymont Inn, Candlewood Suites, Chateau, Clarion, Comfort Suites, Courtyard, Days Inn, Hampton Inn, Holiday Inn Express, Quality Inn, Signature Inn, Super8, □ □ Advance Parts, Aldi Foods, AT&T, AutoZone, Barnes&Noble, Best Buy, BigLots, Cub Foods, CVS Drug, Dick's, $Tree, Fresh Mkt, Goodyear/auto, Gordman's, Hobby Lobby, Home Depot, Honda, JC Penney, Jewel-Osco, Jo-Ann Fabrics, K-Mart, Kroger, Lowe's, Macy's, Meijer/dsl, Menards, Michael's, Mitsubishi, NAPA, Office Depot, Old Navy, PetCo, Sam's Club/gas, Schnuck's Foods, Sears/auto, Target, TJ Maxx, Tuesday Morning, Tuffy, Verizon, Von Maur, Walgreens, Walmart/Subway, mall, vet, to □
165b a	US 51 bus, to Bloomington, E □ BP/Circle K/24hr, Mobil/Arby's/dsl, Qik-n-EZ, Shell/Burger King/24hr, □ A&W/KFC, Denny's, McDonald's, Moe's SW Grill, Pizza Hut, Smoothie King, Steak'n Shake, Subway, Uncle Tom's Pancakes, Wendy's, □ Best Western, Motel 6, Super 8, □ □ Discount Tire, $General, $Tree, Schuncks Foods, Walgreens, to Ill St U, W dsl repair
164	I-39, US 51, N to Peru
163	I-74 W, to Peoria
160b a	US 150, IL 9, Market St, Bloomington, E □ BP/Circle K, Citgo/dsl, Freedom/dsl, ▨▨▨/Wendy's/dsl/scales/24hr, Shell/repair, TA/rest./dsl/scales/24hr/@, □ Arby's, Cracker Barrel, Culver's, JJ Fish&Chicken, KFC, La Bamba, McDonald's, Popeye's, Subway, Taco Bell, □ Best Inn, Days Inn, EconoLodge, Hawthorn Suites, La Quinta, Quality Suites, □ □ Advance Parts, Blue Beacon, Family$, W □ Marathon/Circle K/dsl, Murphy USA/dsl, □ Bob Evans, Fiesta Ranchera Mexican, Steak'n Shake/24hr, □ Comfort Suites, Country Inn&Suites, Fairfield Inn, Hampton Inn, Holiday Inn Express, Ramada Ltd, □ Aldi Foods, Farm&Fleet, Peterbilt, Radio Shack, Walmart
157b	Lp 55 N, Veterans Pkwy, Bloomington, E □ □ to □
157a	I-74 E, to Indianapolis, US 51 to Decatur
154	Shirley

INTERSTATE 55 CONT'D

N↕S LINCOLN

Exit	Services
149	**W** rest area both lanes, full ♿ facilities, 🅒, 🅐, litter barrels, vending, playground, petwalk
145	US 136, **E** RV Ctr, **W** 🅐 Dixie/BP/tuckey's/dsl/scales/24hr, Shell, 🍴 McDonald's, Subway, 🏠 Super 8
140	Atlanta, **E** RV camping, **W** 🅐 Casey's, Faststop/dsl, 🍴 Country-Aire Rest., 🏠 America's Value Inn, 🅞 $General, NAPA
133	Lp 55, Lincoln, **2 mi E** 🅞 H, Camp-A-While Camping
127	I-155 N, to Peoria
126	IL 10, IL 121 S, Lincoln, **0-2 mi E** 🅐 BP/Arby's, Thornton's/Pilot/dsl/scales/24hr, 🍴 Burger King, Cracker Barrel, Culver's, DQ, Daphne's Rest., Hardee's, KFC/Taco Bell, LJ Silver, McDonald's, Pizza Hut, Quiznos, Rio Grande Grill, Rusty's Clubhouse, Steak'n Shake, Wendy's, 🏠 Comfort Inn, Hampton Inn, Holiday Inn Express, Super 8, 🅞 H, Aldi Foods, AT&T, AutoZone, Chrysler/Dodge/Jeep, $General, $Tree, Family$, Ford/Lincoln/Mercury, Kroger, O'Reilly Parts, Russell Stover, Verizon, Walgreens, Walmart/Subway
123	Lp 55, to Lincoln, **E** 🅐 Phillips 66, 🏠 Best Western, 🅞 H
119	Broadwell
115	Elkhart
109	IL 123, Williamsville, **E** 🅐 Casey's, 🍴 Subway, **W** 🅐 Loves/McDonalds/dsl/scales/24hr, 🍴 Huddle House, 🅞 New Salem SHS
107mm	weigh sta sb
105	Lp 55, to Sherman, **W** 🅐 Casey's, 🍴 Cancun Mexican, DQ, Subway, 🅞 to Prairie Capitol Conv Ctr, Riverside Park Campground, Military Museum, hist sites, repair
103mm	rest area sb, full ♿ facilities, 🅒, 🅐, litter barrels, vending, petwalk
102mm	Sangamon River
102mm	rest area nb, full ♿ facilities, 🅒, 🅐, litter barrels, vending, petwalk

SPRINGFIELD

Exit	Services
100b	IL 54, Sangamon Ave, Springfield, **W** 🅐 BP/Circle K, Marathon/Circle K, Murphy USA/dsl, Shell/dsl, 🍴 Arby's, Buffalo Wild Wings, Burger King, Culver's, Hickory River BBQ, McDonald's, Parkway Cafe, Ryan's, Sonic, Steak'n Shake, Taco Bell, Thai Basil, Wendy's, Wings Etc, 🏠 Northfield Suites, Ramada, 🅞 AT&T, Harley-Davidson, Lowe's, Menards, Walmart/Subway, 🚑, to Vet Mem
100a	Il 54, **E** to Clinton, **E** 🅐 Road Ranger/Pilot/Subway/dsl/scales/24hr, 🅞 Kenworth/Ryder/Volvo, truckwash
98b	I-72, IL 97, Springfield, **W** 🅐 BP/Circle K/24hr, Casey's, Shell/dsl/24hr, 🍴 Arby's, Little Caesar's, McDonald's, Seafood House, Starbucks, Subway, 🏠 Best Rest Inn, Best Western, 🅞 H, Ford Trucks, Goodyear, K-Mart, Walgreens, city park, to Capitol Complex
98a	I-72 E, US 36 E, to Decatur
96b a	IL 29 N, S Grand Ave, Springfield, **W** 🅐 Marathon/dsl, Road Ranger/dsl/24hr, 🍴 Burger King, Godfather's, Popeye's, 🏠 Red Roof Inn, Super 8, 🅞 Advance Parts, AutoZone, Buick/GMC, Hyundai, Isuzu, JC Penney, O'Reilly Parts, Shop'n Save, Volvo, museum
94	Stevenson Dr, Springfield, **E** KOA (7mi), **W** 🅐 BP/Circle K/Quiznos, Mobil/Subway/dsl, 🍴 Antonio's Pizza, Applebee's, Arby's, Bob Evans, Cheddar's, Denny's, Di Piero's Italian, Gallina Pizza, Hardee's, Hooters, IHOP,

SPRINGFIELD

Exit	Services
94	Continued La Fiesta Mexican, LJ Silver, McDonald's, Outback Steaks, Panera Bread, Red Lobster, Smokey Bones BBQ, Steak'n Shake, Taste of Tai, 🏠 Candlewood Suites, Comfort Suites, Crowne Plaza, Days Inn/rest., Drury Inn, Hampton Inn, Hilton Garden, Holiday Inn Express, Microtel, Stevenson Inn, 🅞 BigLots, CVS Drug, $General, GNC, Jo-Ann Fabrics, NAPA, Radio Shack, Walgreens, USPO, zoo (4mi)
92b a	I-72 W, US 36 W, 6th St, Springfield, **W** 🅐 Road Ranger/dsl, Thornton's, 🍴 Arby's, Burger King, Chadito's Tacos, DQ, Golden Corral, Jimmy John's, KFC, McDonald's, New China, Pizza Hut, Sgt. Pepper's Cafe, Starbucks, Subway, Taco Bell, 🏠 Route 66, Super 8, Travelodge/rest., 🅞 H, AutoZone, CarX, County Mkt Foods, Family$, Lincoln/Mercury, Mazda, Verizon, Walgreens, Walmart
90	Toronto Rd, **E** 🅐 Qik-n-EZ/Wendy's/dsl, Shell/Circle K, 🍴 Antonio's Pizza, Centrum Cafe, Cracker Barrel, China Express, McDonald's, Subway, Taco Bell, 🏠 Baymont Inn, Motel 6, Ramada Ltd, 🅞 H
89mm	Lake Springfield
88	E Lake Dr, Chatham, **E** 🅞 to Lincoln Mem Garden/Nature Ctr, **W** 🅞 JJ RV Park/camping (2mi), KOA
83	Glenarm, **W** JJ RV Park/camping (4mi)
82	IL 104, to Pawnee, **E** to Sangchris Lake SP, **W** 🅐 Mobil/Auburn Trvl Ctr/Subway/scales/dsl/rest/24hr, 🍴 Myra's Rest., 🅞 antiques/crafts
80	Hist 66, Divernon, **W** 🅞 antiques
72	Farmersville, **W** 🅐 Jimmy's/Subway/dsl/24hr, Shell/24hr, 🏠 Art's Motel/rest.
65mm	rest area both lanes, full ♿ facilities, 🅒, 🅐, litter barrels, vending, playground, petwalk
63	IL 48, IL 127, to Raymond
60	IL 108, to Carlinville, **E** 🅞 Kamper Kampanion RV Park, truck parts, **W** 🅐 Shell/dsl/LP/café, 🏠 Magnuson Grand Hotel/cafe, 🅞 antiques, to Blackburn Coll
56mm	weigh sta nb

LITCHFIELD

Exit	Services
52	IL 16, Hist 66, Litchfield, **E** 🅐 BP, Casey's, Conoco/Jack-in-the-Box/dsl, Faststop/deli/dsl/scales, Murphy USA/dsl, Shell, 🍴 A&W/LJ Silver, Angus Chophouse, Arby's, Ariston Café, Burger King, China Town, DQ, Denny's, Domino's, E-52 Patio, N Grill, El Rancherito Mexican, Jubelt's Rest., KFC, Maverick Steaks, McDonald's, Pizza Hut, Ruby Tuesday, Taco Bell, Wendy's, 🏠 Best Value Inn, Hampton Inn, Holiday Inn Express, Quality Inn, Super 8, 🅞 H, Aldi Foods, AT&T, Buick/Cadillac/Chevrolet/GMC, $General, $Tree, Ford, Goodyear/auto, IGA Foods, NAPA, O'Reilly Parts, Radio Shack, Walgreens, Walmart/Subway, camping (8mi), **W** st police
44	IL 138, to Benld, Mt Olive, **E** 🅐 Jimmy's, 🍴 Crossroads Diner, 🅞 Mother Jones Mon
41	to Staunton, **E** Country Classic Cars, **W** 🅐 Casey's, 🍴 DQ, Las Cabanas Mexican, 🏠 Super 8, 🅞 H, $General
37	Livingston, New Douglas, **W** 🅐 BP/dsl/24hr, 🍴 Gasperoni's Café, 🏠 Country Inn/rest, 🅞 IGA Foods, NAPA
33	IL 4, to Staunton, Worden, **W** Gas & Tires
30	IL 140, Hamel, **E** Innkeeper Motel, **W** 🅐 Shell, 🍴 Weezy's Grill

Copyright 2012 - The Next Exit®

INTERSTATE 55 CONT'D

Exit	Services
28mm	rest area both lanes, full facilities, , , litter barrels, vending, petwalk
23	IL 143, Edwardsville, E Phillips 66/dsl, W Red Barn Camping (apr-oct)
20b	I-270 W, to Kansas City
20a	I-70 E, to Indianapolis
I-55 S and I-70 W run together 18 mi
18	IL 162, to Troy, E Phillips 66/dsl, /Arby's/dsl/scales/24hr, TA/BP/Country Pride/dsl/scales/24hr/@, ZX, Burger King, China King, DQ, Domino's, Jack-in-the-Box, Little Caesar's, McDonald's/playplace, Pizza Man, Pizza Hut, Subway, Troy Rest., , , Ace Hardware, $General, Speedco, SuperValu Foods, Walgreens, USPO, W Phillips 66/dsl/24hr, Callahan's Grill, Cracker Barrel, Imo's Pizza, Taco Bell, Congress Motel, Holiday Inn Express, Red Roof Inn, Super 8, Freightliner, Verizon
17	US 40 E, to Troy, to St Jacob
15b a	IL 159, Maryville, Collinsville, 0-2 mi E Phillips 66/dsl, Shell, Zx Gas, Carisillo's Mexican, Fazzi's Rest., KFC, McDonald's, Sonic, Steak-Out, Aldi Foods, AutoZone, CVS Drug, $General, Family$, Ford/Lincoln/Mercury, O'Reilly Parts, Walgreens, vet, W EconoLodge
14mm	weigh sta sb
11	IL 157, Collinsville, E Casey's, A&W/LJ Silver, Denny's, Golden Corral, Han's Buffet, Little Caesar's, McDonald's, Penn Sta Subs, Qdoba Mexican, St Louis Bread Co, Starbucks, Waffle House, Wendy's, Motel 6, AT&T, GNC, Home Depot, Midas, Radio Shack, Verizon, Walgreens, Walmart, W Motomart/dsl/24hr, Applebee's, Arby's, Bandana's BBQ, Bob Evans, Burger King, Culver's, DQ, Pizza Hut, Ponderosa, Ravanelli's Rest., Ruby Tuesday, Steak'n Shake, White Castle/24hr, Zapata's Mexican, Comfort Inn, Days Inn, Double-Tree Inn, Drury Inn, Extended Stay Suites, Fairfield Inn, Hampton Inn, Super 8, Buick/GMC, st police
10	I-255, S to Memphis, N to I-270
9	Black Lane (from nb, no return), E Fairmount RaceTrack
6	IL 111, Great River Rd, Fairmont City, E Phillips 66, Indian Mound Inn, Relax Inn, Royal Budget Inn, Cahokia Mounds SP, W Horseshoe SP
5mm	motorist callboxes begin at 1/2 mi intervals nb
4b a	IL 203, Granite City, E Phillips 66/dsl/24hr, Western Inn, W /Subway/Taco Bell/dsl/scales/24hr/@, Burger King, Gateway Int Raceway
3	Exchange Ave
2	I-64 E, IL 3 N, St Clair Ave
2b	3rd St
2a	M L King Bridge, to downtown, E St Louis
1	IL 3, to Sauget (from sb)
I-55 N and I-70 E run together 18 mi.
0mm	Illinois/Missouri state line, Mississippi River

INTERSTATE 57

Exit	Services
358mm	I-94, E to Indiana
I-57 begins/ends on I-94, exit 63 in Chicago.
357	IL 1, Halsted St, E BP, Mobil, auto repair, W Citgo/dsl, Shell/Dunkin Donuts, McDonald's, Shark's, Subway, Walgreens
355	111th St, Monterey Ave, W BP, Citgo
354	119th St, W Citgo/Dunkin Donuts, Chili's, Harold's Chicken, Panda Express, Subway, $Tree, Jewel-Osco, Marshall's, PetCo, Staples, Target
353	127th St, Burr Oak Ave, E Citgo, Marathon, Shell, Burger King, Dillinger's Drive-In, McDonald's, Wendy's, Motel 6, Plaza Inn, Red Roof Inn, , , Ace Hardware, Advance Parts, Aldi Foods, Family$, Walgreens, W BP, Citgo/dsl, JJ Fish&Chicken
352mm	Calumet Sag Channel
350	IL 83, 147th St, Sibley Blvd, E Marathon/dsl, Checker's, Dunkin Donuts, Harold's Chicken, McDonald's, Subway, Aldi Foods, Family$, O'Reilly Parts, W USPO
348	US 6, 159th St, E Citgo/dsl, Clark, Marathon/dsl, Baskin-Robbins/Dunkin Donuts, Burger King, Harold's Chicken, McDonald's, Popeye's, Subway, Taco Bell, White Castle, Comfort Inn, AutoZone, BigLots, $Tree, Family$, U-Haul, Walgreens, auto repair, W Citgo/dsl, Mobil/dsl
346	167th St, Cicero Ave, to IL 50, E BP, Citgo/dsl, Applebee's, Baskin-Robbins/Dunkin Donuts, Bee's Steaks, Harold's Chicken, McDonald's, Panda Express, Shark's Fish&Chicken, Sonic, Subway, Thom's BBQ, Wendy's, Best Western Oak Forest, Radio Shack, Verizon, Walmart/Subway, W Shell, 7-11
345b a	I-80, W to Iowa, E to Indiana, to I-294, N toll to Wisconsin
342	Vollmer Rd, E Shell/Circle K/dsl,
340b a	US 30, Lincoln Hwy, Matteson, E BP, Citgo/dsl, A&W/LJ Silver, Afusion Asian, Applebee's, Bocce's Grill, Burger King, ChuckeCheese, Cracker Barrel, Culver's, Dusties Buffet, Fuddrucker's, Hibachi Grill, IHOP, Jimmy John's, KFC, Knock-Outs Rest., McDonald's, Michael's Rest., Mr Benny's Rest., Olive Garden, Panda Express, Panera Bread, Pepe's, Perros Bros Gyros, Pizza Hut, Quiznos, Red Lobster, Shark's, Starbucks, Subway, Taco Bell, Wendy's, White Castle, Best Value Inn, Country Inn&Suites, Hampton Inn, La Quinta, Matteson Hotel, Aldi Foods, AT&T, Best Buy, Chrysler/Dodge/Jeep, Discount Tire, $Tree, Dominick's Foods, Firestone/auto, Home Depot, JC Penney, Marshall's, Menards, NTB, Old Navy, PepBoys, Prtsmart, Radio Shack, Sam's Club/gas, Sears/auto, Target, Verizon, Walgreens, Walmart, USPO, W Buick/Cadillac/GMC, Ford/Lincoln/Mercury, Honda, Hyundai, Kia, Nissan, Toyota/Scion, Walgreens
339	Sauk Trail, to Richton Park, E BP, Citgo/dsl, Domino's, McDonald's, Uncle John's BBQ/Ribs, Walgreens

INTERSTATE 57 CONT'D

Exit	Services
335	Monee, E ⛽ BP/Dunkin Donuts/Subway/dsl, Petro/Iron Skillet/dsl/e-85/scales/24hr/@, 🛢/McDonald's/dsl/scales/24hr, ⊞ Burger King, Lucky Burrito, Quiznos, Schoops Rest., ⌂ Best Western, Country Host Motel, Red Roof Inn, Super 8, ⊙ Blue Beacon
332mm	**Prairie View Rest Area both lanes, full ♿ facilities, info, 📞, 🚻, vending, litter barrels, petwalk**
330mm	**weigh sta both lanes**
327	to Peotone, E ⛽ Casey's, Shell/Circle K, ⊞ Bierstube German, McDonald's/RV parking
322	Manteno, E ⛽ Phillips 66/Subway, Shell/McDonald's, ⊞ Jimmy John's, KFC/Pizza Hut/Taco Bell, Monical's Pizza, Wendy's, ⌂ Country Inn&Suites, Howard Johnson, ⊙ Curves, Harley-Davidson, W ⛽ BP/dsl
315	IL 50, Bradley, E ⛽ F&F, Shell/Circle K/Burger King, ⊞ Buffalo Wild Wings, Cracker Barrel, LoneStar Steaks, McDonald's, Red Lobster, Ruby Tuesday, TGIFriday's, Tucci's Rest., White Castle, ⌂ Best Inn, Fairfield Inn, Hampton Inn, Holiday Inn Express, ⊙ Barnes&Noble, Best Buy, Chrysler/Dodge/Jeep, Dick's, JC Penney, Kohl's, Marshall's, Michael's, PetCo, Petsmart, Sears/auto, Staples, Target, Verizon, Walmart/Subway, mall, W ⛽ Phillips 66/dsl, Shell/Circle K/dsl, Speedway/dsl, ⊞ Applebee's, Arby's, Bakers Square, Coyote Canyon, Denny's, El Campesino Mexican, IHOP, LJ Silver, Mancino's Pizza, McDonald's, Oberweis Ice Cream, Old Country Buffet, Panda Express, Pizza Hut/Taco Bell, Starbucks, Steak'n Shake, Subway, VIP's Rest., Wendy's, ⌂ Motel 6, Quality Inn, Super 8, ⊙ Aldi Foods, AutoZone, Brown RV Ctr, Buick/GMC, Chevrolet, $Tree, Hobby Lobby, Honda, Hyundai, Jo-Ann Fabrics, Kia, K-Mart, Lowe's, Menards, Nissan, Verizon, vet, to Kankakee River SP
312	IL 17, Kankakee, E ⊙ Twin River's Camping, W ⛽ BP/dsl, Marathon/dsl, Shell/Circle K, ⊞ Cptn Hook's Fish&Chicken, McDonald's/RV parking, PoorBoy Rest., ⊙ H, Advance Parts, Family$, Walgreens, auto repair
310.5mm	**Kankakee River**
308	US 45, US 52, to Kankakee, E ⛽ Loves/Arby's/dsl/scales/24hr, ⊙ KOA (3mi), W ⛽ Speedway/Dunkin Donuts/Subway/dsl, Gas Depot, ⊞ El Mexicano, KFC/Taco Bell, ⌂ Fairview Motel, Hilton Garden, ⊙ Aldi Foods, $Tree, Walmart/Subway, 🛒
302	Chebanse, W truck repair
297	Clifton, W ⛽ Phillips 66/DQ/dsl, ⊞ CharGrilled Cheeseburgers
293	IL 116, Ashkum, E ⛽ Shell/Subway/dsl, W ⊞ Loft Rest., ⊙ st police, tires
283	US 24, IL 54, Gilman, E ⛽ Apollo/Marathon/dsl/scales/24hr, K&H Trkstp/BP/dsl/scales/24hr/@, Shell/dsl, ⊞ Burger King, DQ, McDonald's, Monical's Pizza, Red Door Rest., ⌂ Motel 6, Super 8, W ⛽ Shell/Subway/dsl
280	IL 54, Onarga, E ⛽ Casey's, Phillips 66, ⊙ USPO, W Lake Arrowhead RV camping
272	to Roberts, Buckley
268.5mm	**rest area both lanes, full ♿ facilities, vending, 📞, 🚻, litter barrels, petwalk**
261	IL 9, Paxton, 0-1 mi E ⛽ Casey's, Phillips 66/dsl, ⊞ Hardee's, Monical's Pizza, Pizza Hut, Subway,

Exit	Services
261	Continued ⊙ Buick/Cadillac/Chevrolet/GMC, Family$, IGA Foods, TrueValue, USPO, W ⛽ BP, Marathon, ⊞ Country Garden Rest., ⌂ Paxton Inn
250	US 136, Rantoul, 0-1 mi E ⛽ BP/Circle K, Casey's/dsl, ⊞ Arby's, Baskin-Robbins/Dunkin Donuts, Burger King, Hardee's, KFC/Taco Bell, LJ Silver, McDonald's, Monical's Pizza, Papa John's, Red Wheel Rest., Subway, ⌂ Best Western, Days Inn, Super 8, ⊙ Chrysler/Dodge/Jeep, $General, Ford, NAPA, Walgreens, Walmart/Subway, camping, vet, to Chanute AFB
240	Market St, E ⛽ Road Ranger/Pilot/McDonald's/dsl/scales, ⊙ D&W Lake Camping/RV Park, Kenworth/Volvo, truck/tire repair
238	Olympian Dr, to Champaign, W ⛽ Mobil/dsl, ⊞ DQ, ⌂ Microtel, ⊙ RV/dsl repair
237b a	I-74, W to Peoria, E to Urbana
235b	I-72 W, to Decatur
235a	University Ave, to Champaign, E H, U of Ill
232	Curtis Rd
229	to Savoy, Monticello, Tolono, E ⛽ Marathon/dsl/24hr
221.5mm	**rest area both lanes, full ♿ facilities, 📞s, 🚻, litter barrels, vending, petwalk**
220	US 45, Pesotum, W ⛽ Citgo, st police
212	US 36, Tuscola, E ⛽ FuelMart/dsl, W ⛽ BP/24hr, Marathon, 🛢/Road Ranger/dsl/scales/24hr, ⊞ Burger King, DQ, Denny's, McDonald's, Monical's Pizza, Pizza Hut, Subway, TJ's Grill, Woody's Rest., ⌂ Baymont Inn, Cooper Motel, Holiday Inn Express, Super 8, ⊙ Ford, IGA Foods, Pamida, Radio Shack, Tanger Outlets/Famous Brands, camping
203	IL 133, Arcola, E ⛽ Citgo/dsl/24hr, ⊙ CampALot, W ⛽ Marathon/Subway/dsl/24hr, Sunrise Gas, ⊞ DQ, Hen House, La Cazuela's, Mexican, Monical's Pizza, ⌂ Arcola Inn, Budget Inn, Comfort Inn, Flower Patch B&B, ⊙ Country Charm Amish, $General, NAPA, Rockome Gardens, Arcola Camping, vet
192	CR 1000n, Rd 18
190b a	IL 16, to Mattoon, E ⛽ BP/dsl, ⊙ H, to, E IL U, Fox Ridge SP, W ⛽ Huck's, Marathon/Subway, Murphy USA/dsl, Phillips 66, ⊞ Alamo Steaks, Arby's, Buffalo Wild Wings, Cody's Roadhouse, Cracker Barrel, Domino's, Don Sol Mexican, DQ, Jimmy John's, Jumbo Buffet, KFC, Lee's Chicken, McDonald's/playplace, Monical's Pizza, Pizza Hut, QQ Buffet, Quiznos, Stadium Grill, Steak'n Shake/24hr, Taco Bell, Wendy's, ⌂ Baymont Inn, Comfort Suites, Days Inn, Hampton Inn, Holiday Inn Express, Super 8, ⊙ Aldi Foods, BigLots, CVS Drug, $General, $Tree, Home Depot, Sears, Staples, Walgreens, Walmart
184	US 45, IL 121, to Mattoon, E ⛽ Marathon/pizza/dsl, W ⛽ Marathon/dsl, Subway, ⊞ McDonald's, ⌂ Budget Inn, US Grant Motel (2mi), ⊙ to Lake Shelbyville
177	US 45, Neoga, E ⛽ FuelMart/Subway/dsl/e-85, ⊙ NAPA, W ⛽ Casey's (1mi), Marathon/rest./dsl
166.5mm	**rest area both lanes, full ♿ facilities, vending, 📞, 🚻, litter barrels, petwalk**
163	I-70 E, to Indianapolis
	I-57 S and I-70 W run together 6 mi
162	US 45, Effingham, E ⛽ Motomart, ⊙ Harley-Davidson, W ⛽ 🛢/McDonald's/dsl/scales/24hr, ⊞ Foxx's Den Smokehouse, Subway, ⊙ Camp Lakewood (2mi), truck repair

INTERSTATE 57 CONT'D

Exit	Services

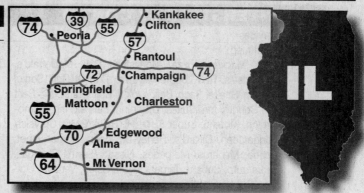

160   IL 33, IL 32, Effingham, **E** 🍴 Domino's, Jimmy John's, LoneStar Steaks, Papa John's, Pizza Hut, 🛏 Comfort Inn, Fairfield Inn, Hampton Inn, 🔲 🏨, Aldi Foods, AutoZone, $General, Family$, K-Mart, Midas, Save-a-Lot, Verizon, vet, **W** 🅿 BP/Quiznos/dsl, ⊛FLYING J/Denny's/dsl/LP/scales/24hr, Marathon, Murphy USA/dsl, TA/Country Pride/Popeye's/dsl/@, 🍴 Arby's, Bangkok Thai, Buffalo Wild Wings, Burger King, Cracker Barrel, Denny's, El Rancherito Mexican, KFC, LJ Silver, McDonald's, Ryan's, Ruby Tuesday, Starbucks, Steak'n Shake, Subway, Taco Bell, TGIFriday's, Wendy's, 🛏 Country Inn&Suites, Days Inn, Hilton Garden, Holiday Inn Express, Motel 6, Rodeway Inn, Super 8, 🔲 AT&T, Blue Beacon, Camp Lakewood RV Park, $Tree, Ford/Lincoln, Kohl's, Menards, Peterbilt, SpeedCo, Verizon, Walmart/Subway

159   US 40, Effingham, **E** 🅿 BP/dsl/24hr, Marathon/dsl, Phillips 66/dsl, 🍴 China Buffet, Culver's, Hardee's/24hr, Little Caesar's, Niemerg's Rest., Subway, 🛏 Abe Lincoln Motel, Best Value Inn, Comfort Suites, EconoLodge, 🔲 O'Reilly Parts, Walgreens, tires/repair, **W** 🅿 Petro/Iron Skillet/dsl/24hr/@, 🛏 Best Western, 🔲 Blue Beacon, Truck-O-Mat/IA-80/scales/wash

I-57 N and I-70 E run together 6 mi

157   I-70 W, to St Louis

151   Watson, **5 mi E** Percival Springs RV Park

150mm   Little Wabash River

145   Edgewood, **E** 🅿 Marathon

135   IL 185, Farina, **E** 🅿 BP/Subway/dsl, 🔲 $General, Ford

127   to Kinmundy, Patoka

116   US 50, Salem, **E** 🅿 Huck's/dsl, Shell/Circle K, Swifty, 🍴 Burger King, China Buffet, Domino's, Hardee's, LJ Silver, McDonald's, Pizza Hut, Pizza Man, Subway, Taco Bell, Village Garden, Wendy's, 🔲 AutoZone, Chrysler/Dodge/Jeep, $General, GMC, NAPA, O'Reilly Parts, to Forbes SP, **W** 🅿 Marathon/dsl, Murphy USA/dsl, 🍴 Applebee's, Arby's, Denny's, El Rancherito, KFC, 🛏 Comfort Inn, Salem Inn, Super 8, 🔲 Buick/Chevrolet, $Tree, Ford, Salem Tires, Walmart, Carlisle Lake (23mi)

114mm   rest area both lanes, full 🦽 facilities, 🚻s, 🖨, litter barrels, vending, petwalk, playground

109   IL 161, to Centralia, **W** 🅿 Biggie's General Store/cafe/dsl

103   Dix, **E** 🅿 Phillips 66/dsl, 🛏 Red Carpet Inn, 🔲 camping

96   I-64 W, to St Louis

95   IL 15, Mt Vernon, **E** 🅿 BP/dsl/24hr, Hucks, Jimmy's/dsl, Marathon/Circle K, Phillips 66, 🍴 El Rancherito Mexican, Fazoli's, Grand Buffet, Hardee's, KFC, Little Caesar's, LJ Silver, McDonald's, Papa John's, Pasta House, Pizza Hut, Steak'n Shake/24hr, Subway, Taco Bell, Wendy's, Waffle Co, 🛏 Best Inn, Best Value Inn, Comfort Suites, Drury Inn, Motel 6, Red Roof Inn, Super 8, Thrifty Inn, 🔲 🏨, Aldi Foods, AutoZone, Chevrolet, CVS Drug, $Tree, Ford, Harley-Davidson, JC Penney, K-Mart, Kroger/dsl, O'Reilly Parts, Prompt Care, Radio Shack, Sears, Verizon, Walgreens, vet, **W** 🅿 Hucks/rest/dsl/scales/24hr, Marathon/Circle K, ▥▥/Denny's/dsl/scales/24hr, Shell/Circle K/24hr, TA/Country Pride/Popeye's/dsl/24hr/@, 🍴 Applebee's, Arby's, Bob Evans,

---

95   Continued
Buffalo Wild Wings, Burger King, Chili's, Cracker Barrel, Jimmy John's, Kriger's Grill, LoneStar Steaks, McDonald's, Ryan's, Sonic, Subway, 🛏 Days Inn, Fairfield Inn, Hampton Inn, Holiday Inn, Quality Inn, 🔲 Buick/Cadillac/GMC, $Tree, Freightliner, Kohl's, Lowe's, NAPA, Outlet Mall, Quality Times RV Park, Staples, Toyota, Verizon, Walmart, truckwash

94   Veteran's Memorial Dr, **E** 🏨

92   I-64 E, to Louisville

83   Ina, **E** 🅿 ◆Loves/McDonald's/dsl/scales, Marathon/deli/dsl/scales/24hr, 🔲 Sherwood Camping (2mi), **W** to Rend Lake Coll

79mm   rest area sb, full 🦽 facilities, info, vending, 🚻s, 🖨, litter barrels, petwalk, playground

77   IL 154, to Whittington, **E** 🅿 Shell/24hr, 🔲 Whittington Woods RV Park, **W** 🍴 Gibby's Grill, 🛏 Seasons at Rend Lake Lodge/rest., 🔲 to Rend Lake, golf, Wayne Fitzgerrell SP

74mm   rest area nb, full 🦽 facilities, vending, 🚻s, 🖨, litter barrels, petwalk, playground

71   IL 14, Benton, **E** 🅿 Jumpin' Jimmy's/dsl, 🍴 Arby's, Hardee's, KFC/Taco Bell, Pizza Hut, 🛏 Days Inn/rest., Gray Plaza Motel, Super 8, 🔲 🏨, AutoZone, CVS Drug, KOA (1.5mi), O'Reilly Parts, Plaza Tire, **W** 🅿 BP/dsl, Murphy USA/dsl, Phillips 66/dsl/24hr, 🍴 Applebee's, Burger King, McDonald's, Subway, 🔲 Radio Shack, Verizon, Walmart, to Rend Lake

65   IL 149, W Frankfort, **E** 🅿 BP/dsl, Gas-4-Less, Marathon/dsl, Shell/dsl, 🍴 China Star, Dixie Cream Deli, Hardee's, La Fiesta Mexican, LJ Silver, Mike's Drive-In, Miranda's Rest., Sonic, Subway, 🛏 Gray Plaza Motel, 🔲 🏨, CarQuest, MadPricer Foods, repair, **W** 🅿 Casey's, 🍴 EEE BBQ, McDonald's, Pizza Hut, 🛏 Best Value Inn, 🔲 Buick/Chevrolet/GMC, $General, $Tree, K-Mart, Kroger, VF Factory Stores

59   to Herrin, Johnston City, **E** 🅿 ROC/dsl/e85, ZX/dsl, 🍴 DQ, McDonald's, Subway, 🔲 $General, NAPA, Sandy Drug, camping (2mi), **W** 🔲 🏨, camping (4mi)

54b a   IL 13, Marion, **E** 🅿 Phillips 66/dsl, 🍴 Arby's, Fazoli's, Hardee's, KFC, La Fiesta Mexican, LJ Silver, Papa John's, Pizza Hut, Quiznos, Subway, Tequila's Mexican, Wendy's, Western Sizzlin, 🛏 Days Inn, EconoLodge, 🔲 Aldi Foods, Advance Parts, AutoZone, Cadillac/Chevrolet, $General, Ford/Hyundai/Lincoln/Mercury, Kroger/gas, Plaza Tire, Menards, Radio Shack, Sav-A-Lot Foods, Walgreens, USPO, **W** 🅿 BP/Refuge Rest./dsl/scales/24hr/@, Marathon, 🍴 Applebee's, Asian Bistro, Backyard Burger, Bob Evans, Burger King, Hong Kong

N ↕ S

INTERSTATE 57 CONT'D

Exit	Services
54b a	Continued
	BBQ, Mackie's Pizza, McAlister's Deli, McDonald's, O'Charley's, Red Lobster, Ryan's, 17th St Grill, Sonic, Steak'n Shake, Taco Bell, Wok'n Roll Buffet, 🛏 Best Inn, Country Inn&Suites, Drury Inn, Fairfield Inn, Hampton Inn, Motel 6, Super 8, 🅾 H, Buick/GMC, Chrysler/Dodge/Jeep, Dillard's, Harley-Davidson, Home Depot, Honda, Menards, Mercedes, Nissan, Sam's Club/gas, Sears/auto, Subaru, Target, Toyota/Scion, Verizon, Walmart/Subway, mall
53	Main St, Marion, E 🍴 DQ, 🛏 Motel Marion, 🅾 H, Marion Camping/RV Park, NAPA, W ⛽ Motomart/24hr, 🍴 Cracker Barrel, HideOut Steaks, 🛏 Comfort Suites, Holiday Inn Express, Quality Inn
47mm	**weigh sta both lanes**
45	IL 148, **1 mi** E ⛽ King Tut's Food/dsl/24hr, 🛏 Lake Tree Inn, 🅾 camping, dsl repair
44	I-24, E to Nashville
40	Goreville Rd, E 🅾 Ferne Clyffe SP, camping, scenic overlook
36	Lick Creek Rd, W 🅾 vineyards
32mm	**Trail of Tears Rest Area both lanes, full 🦽 facilities, info, 📞s, 🚮, litter barrels, vending, petwalk, playground**
30	IL 146, Anna, Vienna, W ⛽ Shell/dsl/rest./24hr, 🅾 H, auto/tire repair
25	US 51, N (from nb, exits left), to Carbondale
24	Dongola Rd, W ⛽ BP/dsl
18	Ullin Rd, W ⛽ Citgo/dsl/24hr, 🍴 EEE BBQ, 🛏 Best Western, 🅾 st police
8	Mounds Rd, to Mound City, E 🅾 K&K AutoTruck/dsl/repair
1	IL 3, to US 51, Cairo, E 🛏 Belvedere Motel (2mi), Day's Inn, 🅾 $General, Mound City Nat Cem (4mi), camping, W camping
0mm	Illinois/Missouri state line, Mississippi River

INTERSTATE 64

E ↕ W

Exit	Services
131.5mm	Illinois/Indiana state line, Wabash River
131mm	**Skeeter Mtn Welcome Ctr wb, full 🦽 facilities, 📞, vending, 🚮, litter barrels, petwalk**
130	IL 1, to Grayville, N ⛽ Casey's (2mi), Shell/dsl/24hr, 🍴 Subway, 🛏 Super 8, Windsor Oaks Inn/rest., 🅾 museum, Beall Woods St Park
124mm	Little Wabash River
117	Burnt Prairie, S ⛽ Marathon/dsl, 🍴 ChuckWagon Charlie's Café, 🅾 antiques
110	US 45, Mill Shoals
100	IL 242, to Wayne City, N ⛽ Marathon/dsl
89	to Belle Rive, Bluford
86mm	**rest area wb, full 🦽 facilities, 📞, vending, 🚮, litter barrels, petwalk**
82.5mm	**rest area eb, full 🦽 facilities, 📞, vending, 🚮, litter barrels, petwalk**
80	IL 37, to Mt Vernon, **2 mi** N ⛽ BP/Burger King/dsl/24hr, Hucks/dsl/24hr, 🛏 Royal Inn, 🅾 $General, camping
78	I-57, S to Memphis, N to Chicago
95	Mt Vernon, **I-64 and I-57 run together 5 mi** N ⛽ BP/dsl/24hr, Hucks, Jimmy's/dsl, Marathon/Circle K,

M T V E R N O N

95	Continued
	Phillips 66, 🍴 El Rancherito Mexican, Fazoli's, Grand Buffet, Hardee's, KFC, Little Caesar's, LJ Silver, McDonald's, Papa John's, Pasta House, Pizza Hut, Steak'n Shake/24hr, Subway, Taco Bell, Wendy's, Waffle Co, 🛏 Best Inn, Best Value Inn, Comfort Suites, Drury Inn, Motel 6, Red Roof Inn, Super 8, Thrifty Inn, 🅾 🦽, Aldi Foods, AutoZone, Chevrolet, CVS Drug, $Tree, Ford, Harley-Davidson, JC Penney, K-Mart, Kroger/dsl, O'Reilly Parts, Prompt Care, Radio Shack, Sears, Verizon, Walgreens, vet, S ⛽ Hucks/rest/dsl/scales/24hr, Marathon/Circle K, 🍴/Denny's/dsl/scales/24hr, Shell/Circle K/24hr, TA/Country Pride/Popeye's/dsl/24hr/@, 🍴 Applebee's, Arby's, Bob Evans, Buffalo Wild Wings, Burger King, Chili's, Cracker Barrel, Jimmy John's, Kriger's Grill, LoneStar Steaks, McDonald's, Ryan's, Sonic, Subway, 🛏 Days Inn, Fairfield Inn, Hampton Inn, Holiday Inn, Quality Inn, 🅾 Buick/Cadillac/GMC, $Tree, Freightliner, Kohl's, Lowe's, NAPA, Outlet Mall, Quality Times RV Park, Staples, Toyota, Verizon, Walmart, truckwash
73	I-57, N to Chicago, S to Memphis
69	Woodlawn
61	US 51, to Centralia, Ashley no services
50	IL 127, to Nashville, N to Carlyle Lake, S ⛽ Citgo/rest/E-85/dsl, Little Nashville/Conoco/rest/dsl/scales/24hr, Shell/dsl/24hr, 🍴 McDonald's, 🛏 Best Western, 🅾 HOSPITAL
41	IL 177, Okawville, S ⛽ 🍴/Road Ranger/dsl/24hr, 🍴 Burger King, DQ, Hen House/24hr, Subway, 🛏 Original Springs Motel, Super 8, 🅾 $General, truck repair
37mm	Kaskaskia River
34	to Albers, **3 mi** N ⛽ Casey's
27	IL 161, New Baden, N ⛽ Shell/dsl/24hr, 🍴 Good Ol Days Rest., McDonald's, Subway, 🅾 Chevrolet, $General
25mm	**rest area both lanes, full 🦽 facilities, info, 📞, vending, 🚮, litter barrels, petwalk**
23	IL 4, to Mascoutah, N ⛽ Mobil, 🛏 La Quinta, **3mi** N 🍴 McDonald's, S 🛏
19b a	US 50, IL 158, N ⛽ Motomart/24hr, 🍴 Schiappa's Italian, Subway, 🛏 Settle Inn, S 🅾 H, to Scott AFB
18mm	**weigh sta eb**

O' F A L L O N

16	to O'Fallon, Shiloh, N 🍴 Sonic, 🛏 Hilton Garden, 🅾 URGENT CARE, CVS Drug, Harley-Davidson, S ⛽ Motomart/dsl, 🍴 Applebee's, Arby's, Buffalo Wild Wings, China Hing, Coldstone, Cracker Barrel, 54th St. Grille, Golden Corral, Jimmy John's, Little Caesar's, McAlister's Deli, McDonald's, Qdoba Mexican, Quiznos, St. Louis Bread Co., Starbucks, TX Roadhouse, White Castle, 🛏 Drury Inn, Holiday Inn Express, 🅾 AT&T, Dierbergs Foods, Dobb's Tire, Michael's, Radio Shack, Target, World Mkt
14	O'Fallon, N ⛽ Circle K, Motomart, Shell/24hr, 🍴 IHOP, Steak'n Shake/24hr, Subway, 🛏 Baymont Inn, Best Value Inn, Country Inn&Suites, Extended Stay America, Suburban Inn, 🅾 Cadillac, Chevrolet, Ford, O'Reilly Parts, S ⛽ Casey's, 🍴 Chevy's Mexican, Culver's, DQ, Hardee's, Jack-in-the-Box, KFC, LoneStar Steaks, McDonald's, O'Charley's, Papa Murphy's, Royal Bamboo, Sake Grill, Taco Bell, 🛏 Candlewood Suites, Days Inn, Quality Inn, 🅾 Aldi Foods, Home Depot, Honda, Hyundai, KIA, Mazda, Nissan, Petsmart, Sam's Club/gas, Toyota, VW, Walmart

INTERSTATE 64 CONT'D

C O L L I N S V I L L E

Exit	Services
12	IL 159, to Collinsville, N ☐ Shell/Circle K, ☐ Applebee's, Bob Evans, Ginger Buffet, Houlihan's, Joe's Crabshack, Lotawata Creek Grill, Olive Garden, Red Lobster, TGI-Friday's, ☐ Best Western, Comfort Suites, Drury Inn, Fairfield Inn, Hampton Inn, Holiday Inn, Ramada Inn, Sheraton, Super 8, ☐ Gordman's, S ☐ BP/24hr, Motomart/dsl/24hr, ☐ Arby's, Boston Mkt, Burger King, Capt D's, Casa Gallardo, Chili's, Chipotle Mexican, ChuckeCheese, Domino's, Fazoli's, 5 Guys Burgers, Haley's Grill, Hometown Buffet, Honeybaked Ham, Imo's Pizza, Krispy Kreme, Logan's Roadhouse, Longhorn Steaks, LJ Silver, McAlister's Deli, McDonald's, Pizza Hut, Popeye's, Qdoba Mexican, Quiznos, Red Robin, Ruby Tuesday, Smokey Bones BBQ, Steak'n Shake, St. Louis Bread, Subway, Taco Bell, White Castle, ☐ Aamco, AT&T, Barnes&Noble, Best Buy, BigLots, Dillard's, Dobb's Tire, $Tree, Firestone/auto, Hobby Lobby, JC Penney, Jo-Ann Fabrics, K-Mart, Kohl's, Lowe's, Macy's, Marshall's, NTB, Office Depot, Old Navy, O'Reilly Parts, PetCo, Russell Stover, Schnuck's Foods, Sears/auto, TJ Maxx, Verizon, Walgreens, USPO
9	IL 157, to Caseyville, N ☐ Huck's/dsl, Phillips 66/Subway/repair, ☐ Hardee's, ☐ Western Inn, S ☐ BP/dsl/repair, ☐ Cracker Barrel, DQ, Domino's, McDonald's, Pizza Hut/Taco Bell, ☐ Best Inn, Days Inn, Motel 6, Quality Inn
7	I-255, S to Memphis, N to Chicago
6	IL 111, Kingshighway, N☐ BP, Mobil/24hr, ☐ Popeye's, ☐ Econo Inn
5	25th St
4	15th St, Baugh
3	I-55 N, I-70 E, IL 3 N, to St Clair Ave, to stockyards
2b a	3rd St, S ☐
1	IL 3 S, 13th St, E St Louis, N Casino Queen
0mm	Illinois/Missouri state line,Mississippi River

INTERSTATE 70

E ↕ W

Exit	Services
156mm	Illinois/Indiana state line
154	US 40, W
151mm	weigh sta wb
149mm	rest area wb, full ☐ facilities, info, ☐, ☐, vending, litter barrels, petwalk
147	IL 1, Marshall, S ☐ Casey's (1mi), Jiffy/dsl/24hr, Marathon/Arby's/dsl, ☐ Burger King, Los Tres Caminos, McDonald's, Pizza Hut, Sam's Steaks, Subway, Wendy's, ☐ Lincoln Suites, Relax Inn, Super 8, ☐ Ford, Walmart, Lincoln Trail SP, antiques, camping
136	to Martinsville, S ☐ Fast Stop/dsl/24hr
134.5mm	N Fork Embarras River
129	IL 49, Casey, N ☐ RV service, KOA (seasonal), S ☐ BP/Subway/dsl, Casey's, Fast Stop/DQ, Marathon/Circle K/dsl, ☐ Hardee's, McDonald's, Pizza Hut, ☐ Comfort Inn, ☐ IGA Foods
119	IL 130, Greenup, S ☐ Casey's, Marathon/dsl, ☐ Backyard BBQ, Dandy Kitchen, DQ, Subway, ☐ Budget Host, Greenup Motel, ☐ $General, camping, hist sites
105	Montrose, N ☐ Spring Creek Camping (1mi), S ☐ BP/dsl, Marathon/dsl/24hr, ☐ Fairview Inn, Red Carpet Inn
98	I-57 N, to Chicago

Springfield • — 72
• Edinburg
Virden •
Carlinville •   • Raymond
55 70
70 Alton •
St Louis — 55
• Collinsville 57
• Oakville
44 55 64
IL

V A N D A L I A

	I-70 and I-57 run together 6 mi. See Interstate 57 exits 159-162.
92	I-57 S, to Mt Vernon
91mm	Little Wabash River
87mm	**rest area both lanes, full ☐ facilities, info, ☐, ☐, vending, litter barrels, playground, petwalk, RV dump**
82	IL 128, Altamont, N ☐ Casey's, Jumpin Jimmy's/Subway/dsl/24hr, Marathon/dsl, ☐ Dairy Bar, McDonald's, ☐ Altamont Motel, ☐ city park, S ☐ Super 8
76	US 40, St Elmo, N ☐ Casey's, ☐ Waldorf Motel, ☐ Timberline Camping (2mi)
71mm	weigh sta eb
68	US 40, Brownstown, N ☐ Okaw Valley Kamping, S truck repair
63.5mm	Kaskaskia River
63	US 51, Vandalia, N ☐ Chuck Wagon Cafe, LJ Silver, ☐ Days Inn, S ☐ BP/Burger King/24hr, Casey's, Phillips 66, ☐ Arby's, China Buffet, DQ, McDonald's, Pizza Hut, Rancho Nuevo Mexican, Sonic, Subway, Wendy's, ☐ Jay's Inn, Travelodge, ☐ ☐, Aldi Foods, County Mkt Foods, city park, hist site
61	US 40, Vandalia, N ☐ Fast Stop/Denny's/dsl/scales/24hr, S ☐ Murphy USA/dsl, ☐ KFC/Taco Bell, Ponderosa, ☐ Holiday Inn Express, Ramada Ltd, ☐ AutoZone, Verizon, Walmart
52	US 40, Mulberry Grove, N ☐ Jumpin Jimmy's/dsl, ☐ Timber Trail Camp-In (2mi), tires, S Cedar Brook Camping (1mi)
45	IL 127, Greenville, N ☐ Jumpin Jimmy's/Domino's/dsl, Loves/Subway/dsl/scales/24hr, Shell/dsl/24hr, ☐ Cunetto's Rest., Huddle House, KFC/Taco Bell, Lu-Bob's Rest., McDonald's, ☐ EconoLodge, M Hotel, Super 8, 2 Acre Motel, ☐ ☐, Ford, S ☐ La Hacienda Mexican, ☐ Sleep Inn, ☐ American Farm Heritage Museum, RV Service, to Carlyle Lake
41	US 40 E, to Greenville
36	US 40 E, Pocahontas, S ☐ Marathon/dsl/24hr, Phillips 66/dsl/24hr, ☐ Funderburks Grill, ☐ Lighthouse Lodge, Powhatan Motel/rest., Tahoe Motel, ☐ truck/tire repair
30	US 40, IL 143, to Highland, S ☐ Shell/dsl/wi-fi/24hr, ☐ Blue Springs Café, ☐ ☐, Tomahawk RV Park (7mi)
26.5mm	**Silver Lake rest area both lanes, full ☐ facilities, ☐, ☐, litter barrels, vending, petwalk**
24	IL 143, Marine, 4 mi S ☐ Ponderosa, ☐ Holiday Inn Express, ☐ ☐
21	IL 4, Lebanon
15b a	I-55, N to Chicago, S to St Louis, I-270, W to Kansas City
	I-70 and I-55 run together 18 mi. See Interstate 55, exits 1-18.
0mm	Illinois/Missouri state line, Mississippi River

⊞ = gas ⊞ = food ⊟ = lodging ⊡ = other Copyright 2012 - The Next Exit®

INTERSTATE 72

Exit	Services
183mm	**1 mi E on University** ⊞ Thornton's/dsl, ⊞ Arby's, Burger King, La Bamba Mexican, McDonald's, Monical's Pizza, Original Pancakes, Pizza Hut, Sonic, Taco Bell, Taffie's Rest., TX Roadhouse, Village Inn Pizza, ⊡ Advance Parts, Aldi Foods, AutoZone, CVS Drug, County Mkt Foods, Schnuck's Foods/gas, Walgreens
182b a	I-57, N to Chicago, S to Memphis, to I-74
176	IL 47, to Mahomet
172	IL 10, Clinton
169	White Heath Rd
166	IL 105 W, Market St, **N** Ford/Mercury, ⊡ ⊞, **S** ⊞ Mobil/Subway/dsl, ⊞ Red Wheel Rest., ⊟ Best Western, Foster Inn, ⊡ city park
165mm	Sangamon River
164	Bridge St, **1 mi S** ⊞ Mobil/dsl, ⊞ China Star, DQ, Hardee's, McDonald's, Monical's Pizza, Pizza Hut, Subway, ⊡ ⊞, Buick/Chevrolet, Chrysler/Dodge/Jeep, $General, USPO
156	IL 48, to Weldon, Cisco, **S** Friends Creek Camping (may-oct) (3mi)
153mm	**rest area both lanes, full** ♿ **facilities,** ⊞, ⊟, **litter barrels, vending, petwalk**
152mm	Friends Creek
150	Argenta
144	IL 48, Oreana, **S** ⊞ ⊞/McDonald's/Subway/dsl/scales/24hr, ⊟ Sleep Inn, ⊡ ⊞, Chrysler/Dodge, Honda, Hyundai, Tressley RV Ctr
141b a	US 51, Decatur, **N** ⊞ Shell/Circle K, ⊞ Applebee's, Buffalo Wild Wings, Cheddar's, Cracker Barrel, HomeTown Buffet, Junz Asian, McDonald's, Mi Jalapeno, O'Charley's, Pizza Hut, Red Lobster, Steak'n Shake, Subway, Taco Bell, TX Roadhouse, ⊟ Baymont Inn, Comfort Inn, Country Inn&Suites, Fairfield Inn, Hampton Inn, Holiday Inn Express, Homewood Suites, Ramada Ltd, ⊡ AT&T, Bergner's, Best Buy, Buick/Cadillac/GMC, $Tree, Harley-Davidson, JC Penney, Lowe's, Kohl's, Menards, Petsmart, Sears/auto, Staples, Von Maur, Verizon, mall, **S** ⊞ Arby's, Burger King, El Rodeo Mexican, Fuji Japanese, Monical's Pizza, Olive Garden, Panera Bread, Papa Murphy's, Starbucks, ⊡ ⊞, Jo-Ann Fabrics, Radio Shack, Sam's Club, Target, Verizon, Walgreens, Walmart/Subway
138	IL 121, Decatur, **S** ⊞
133b a	US 36 E, US 51, Decatur, **S** ⊞ Phillips 66/Subway/dsl, ⊟ Days Inn, Decatur Hotel/rest.
128	Niantic
122	to Mt Auburn, Illiopolis, **S** ⊞ Faststop
114	Buffalo, Mechanicsburg, **S** ⊞ Faststop
108	Riverton, Dawson
107mm	Sangamon River
104	Camp Butler, **2 mi N** ⊟ Best Rest Inn, Best Western, Park View Motel, ⊞ Chesapeake Seafood, Starbucks, ⊡ golf
103b a	I-55, N to Chicago, S to St Louis, Il 97, to Springfield
	I-72 and I-55 run together 6 mi. See Interstate 55, exits 92-98
93	IL 4, Springfield, **N** ⊞ Hucks, Thorntons/dsl, ⊞ Applebee's, Arby's, Bakers Square, Buffet King, Burger King, Cara BBQ, Chili's, Chipotle Mexican, Denny's, Ginger Asian, LoneStar Steaks, Longhorn Steaks, Los Rancheros Mexican, McDonald's, Olive Garden,

93	Continued
	Panera Bread, Pasta House, Popeye's, Qdoba Mexican, Sonic, Starbucks, Subway, Taco Bell, TGIFriday, TX Roadhouse, ⊟ Comfort Inn, Courtyard, Fairfield Inn, Sleep Inn, ⊡ Barnes&Noble, Best Buy, County Mkt Foods, Discount Tire, Gordman's, Hancock Fabrics, Jo-Ann Crafts, K-Mart, Kohl's, Lowe's Whse, Menards, Michael's, Office Depot, Old Navy, PetCo, PetsMart, Sam's Club/gas, Sears/auto, Staples, St Fair Camping, Target, TJ Maxx, Walgreens, Walmart, vet, **S** ⊞ Meijer/dsl/E85, ⊞ Bob Evans, Monical's Pizza, O'Charley's, Steak'n Shake, ⊟ Hampton Inn, Staybridge Suites, ⊡ Cadillac, Chevrolet, Chrysler/Jeep, Ford, Gander Mtn, Honda
91	Wabash Ave, to Springfield, **N** ⊞ Buffalo Wild Wings, Coz's Pizza, Culver's, ⊡ Dodge, Kia, Nissan, Toyota, **S** Colman RV SuperCtr
82	New Berlin, **S** ⊞ Phillips 66/Subway/dsl
76	IL 123, to Ashland, Alexander
68	to IL 104, to Jacksonville, **2 mi N** ⊞ BP, ⊡ ⊞
64	US 67, to Jacksonville, **N** ⊞ Clark/Quizno's/dsl, ⊞ Classic Diner, ⊟ Comfort Inn, Econolodge, Holiday Inn Express, ⊡ Hopper RV Ctr, **2 mi N** ⊞ BP/Circle K/dsl, Phillips 66, ⊞ DQ, KFC, McDonald's, ⊡ ⊞, CVS Drug, $General, Walgreens
60	to US 67 N, to Jacksonville, **6 mi N** ⊞ ⊞ ⊞ ⊟
52	to IL 106, Winchester, **N** golf, **2 mi S** ⊞ ⊞ ⊟
46	IL 100, to Bluffs
42mm	Illinois River
35	US 54, IL 107, to Pittsfield, Griggsville, **4 mi N** gas, food, lodging, **S** ⊡ ⊞, Pine Lakes Camping (6mi), st police
31	to Pittsfield, New Salem, **5 mi S** ⊞, gas, food, lodging, Pine Lake Camping
20	IL 106, Barry, **S** ⊞ Phillips 66/dsl/24hr, Shell/dsl/24hr, ⊞ Wendy's, ⊟ Ice House Inn, ⊡ antiques, winery
10	IL 96, to Payson, Hull
4a	I-172, N to Quincy
1	IL 106, to Hull
0mm	Illinois/Missouri state line, Mississippi River.
	Exits 157 & 156 are in Missouri.
157	to Hannibal, MO 179, **S** ⊞ Ayerco, BP, Phillips 66, Shell, ⊞ Mark Twain Dinette, ⊟ Hannibal Inn, Hotel Clemens, Super 7 Motel, Travelodge
156	US 61, New London, Palmyra. I-72 begins/ends in Hannibal, **MO on US 61 N** ⊞ BP, Conoco/dsl, Murphy USA/dsl, ⊞ Burger King, Country Kitchen, Golden Corral, Hardee's, Hunan Chinese, LJ Silver, McDonald's, Papa John's, Pizza Hut, Sonic, Taco Bell, ⊡ Aldi Foods, BigLots, $General, $Tree, Ford, Kroger, Radio Shack, TrueValue, Walmart, **0-2 mi S** ⊞ Ayerco, Shell/dsl, ⊞ Cassano's Subs, DQ, Domino's, Hardee's, KFC, Loge's Rest, Wendy's, ⊟ Comfort Inn, Days Inn, Econolodge, Hannibal Inn, Holiday Inn Express, Mark Twain Motel, Super 8, ⊡ AutoZone, Buick/Chevrolet, County Mkt Foods, Family$, Injun Joe's RV Camp, O'Reilly Parts, Walgreens

INTERSTATE 74

Exit	Services
221mm	Illinois/Indiana state line, Central/Eastern Time Zone
220	Lynch Rd, Danville, **N** ⊞ BP/dsl, Marathon/dsl (1mi), ⊞ Big Boy, ⊟ Best Western, Comfort Inn, Danville Inn, Fairfield Inn, Hampton Inn, Holiday Inn Express, Sleep Inn, Super 8

INTERSTATE 74 CONT'D

Exit	Services
216	Bowman Ave, Danville, N 📕 Mobil/dsl, Phillips 66/dsl, 🍴 Godfather's, KFC, ⊙ city park
215b a	US 150, IL 1, Gilbert St, Danville, N 📕 BP, Casey's/dsl, Circle K/dsl, 🍴 Arby's, El Toro, La Potosina, LJ Silver, McDonald's, Pizza Hut, Steak'n Shake, Subway, Taco Bell, 🛏 Best Western, Days Inn, ⊙ 🄷, Aldi Foods, BigLots, Ford/Lincoln/Mercury, S 📕 Casey's/dsl, Marathon/Circle K/dsl, 🍴 Burger King, Green Jade Chinese, Mike's Grill, Monical's Pizza, Rich's Rest., ⊙ AutoZone, Big R, Buick/Chevrolet/GMC, $General, Family$, Forest Glen Preserve Camping (11mi), Toyota/Scion
214	G St, Tilton
210	US 150, MLK Dr, **2 mi** N 📕 Marathon, 🍴 Little Nugget Steaks, ⊙ 🄷, to Kickapoo SP, S 🍴 PossumTrot Rest.
208mm	**Welcome Ctr wb, full ♿ facilities, info, 🅲s, 🚮, litter barrels, vending, petwalk**
206	Oakwood, S 📕 Phillips 66/Subway/dsl/scales, Casey's (1mi), Oakwood TP/Shell/rest/dsl/scales/24hr, 🍴 McDonald's, ⊙ $General
200	IL 49 N, to Rankin
197	IL 49 S, Ogden, S 📕 Phillips 66/Godfather's/dsl, 🍴 Rich's Rest., ⊙ city park
192	St Joseph, S 🍴 DQ, Monical's Pizza, ⊙ antiques
185	IL 130, University Ave
184	US 45, Cunningham Ave, Urbana, N 📕 F&F, ⊙ Hyundai, Kia, Mazda, Toyota/Scion, VW, S 📕 Marathon/Circle K/Subway/dsl, Shell, 🍴 Arby's, Cracker Barrel, Domino's, El Toro, Hickory River BBQ, McDonald's, MT Mike's Steaks, Steak'n Shake, 🛏 Eastland Suites, Motel 6, ⊙ $General, auto repair, vet
183	Lincoln Ave, Urbana, S 📕 Circle K/dsl, Marathon/Circle K/dsl, Mobil/dsl, 🍴 Urbana Garden Rest., 🛏 Comfort Suites, Holiday Inn/rest., Holiday Inn Express, Ramada Inn, Sleep Inn, Super 8, ⊙ 🄷, Harley-Davidson, to U of IL
182	Neil St, Champaign, N 🍴 Alexander's Steaks, Bob Evans, Chevy's Mexican, Food Court, McAlister's Deli, McDonald's, Old Chicago, Olive Garden, Panera Bread, Taco Bell, Zia's Italian, 🛏 Baymont Inn, La Quinta, Quality Inn, Red Roof Inn, Super 8, ⊙ Barnes&Noble, Bergner's, Cadillac/Chevrolet, Chrysler/Dodge/Jeep, Hobby Lobby, Gordman's, JC Penney, Kohl's, Macy's, Mercedes/Volvo, Office Depot, Old Navy, Sears/auto, TJ Maxx, mall, same as 181, S 📕 Mobil, ⊙ Jo-Ann Fabrics
181	Prospect Ave, Champaign, N 📕 Meijer/dsl, Murphy USA/dsl, 🍴 Applebee's, Best Wok, Buffalo Wild Wings, Burger King, Chili's, China Town, Culver's, Fazoli's, Hometown Buffet, LoneStar Steaks, Longhorn Steaks, O'Charley's, Oishi Asain, Outback Steaks, Panda Express, Penn Sta Subs, Red Lobster, Ruby Tuesday, Ryan's, Starbucks, Steak'n Shake, Subway, Wendy's, 🛏 Candlewood Suites, Country Inn&Suites, Courtyard, Drury Inn, Extended Stay America, Fairfield Inn, ValuePlace Hotel, Wingate Inn, ⊙ Advance Parts, AT&T, Best Buy, Dick's, $Tree, Lowe's, Menards, Michael's, Petsmart, Radio Shack, Sam's Club/gas, Staples, Target, Tires+, Walmart/Subway, same as 182, S 📕 Freedom/dsl, Marathon/Circle K, Mobil/Jimmy John's, 🍴 Arby's, Dos Reales Mexican, Dunkin Donuts, LJ Silver, 🛏 Days Inn, EconoLodge, ⊙ CarX, $General, Home Depot,

Exit	Services
181	Continued NAPA, Tire Barn, Walgreens
179b a	I-57, N to Chicago, S to Memphis
174	Lake of the Woods Rd, Prairieview Rd, N 📕 BP, Casey's, Mobil/dsl, ⊙ Tin Cup RV Park, Lake of the Woods SP, auto repair, S 📕 Marathon/Subway/dsl, 🍴 McDonald's
172	IL 47, Mahomet, N ⊙ R&S RV Sales, S 📕 BP/dsl, Mobil/dsl, Shell/Domino's/dsl, 🍴 Azteca, Arby's, DQ, HenHouse Rest., Jr's Burgers&Custard, Los Zarapes, Monical's Pizza, Peking House, Subway, The Wok, 🛏 Heritage Inn, ⊙ Ace Hardware, CVS Drug, IGA Foods, NAPA, Walgreens, vet
166	Mansfield, S 📕 BP/dsl, ⊙ Mansfield Gen. Store/Rest.
159	IL 54, Farmer City, S 📕 Casey's, Huck's/Quiznos/dsl, 🍴 Family Rest., 🛏 Budget Motel, Days Inn, ⊙ NAPA, USPO, to Clinton Lake RA
156mm	**rest area both lanes, full ♿ facilities, 🅲, 🚮, litter larrels, vending, playground, petwalk**
152	US 136, to Heyworth
149	Le Roy, N 📕 BP, Freedom/dsl, 🅻Loves/Arby's/dsl/scales/24hr, 🍴 Jack's Cafe, McDonald's, Roma Ralph's Pizza, Subway, 🛏 Holiday Inn Express, ⊙ Doc's Drug, $General, IGA Foods, NAPA, TrueValue, to Moraine View SP, S 📕 Shell/Woody's Rest./dsl/scales/24hr, 🛏 Red Roof Inn, ⊙ Clinton Lake, camping
142	Downs, N 📕 BP/Pizza/Subs/dsl/24hr, ⊙ USPO
135	US 51, Bloomington, N 📕 BP/Circle K/dsl, Huck's/dsl, Mobil/dsl, 🍴 McDonald's, ⊙ $General, S 📕 FastStop/dsl
134b[157]	Veterans Pkwy, Bloomington, N ⊙ 🄷, to ✈
134a	I-55, N to Chicago, S to St Louis, I-74, E
	I-74 and I-55 run together 6 mi
160b a	N 📕 BP/Circle K, Citgo/dsl, Freedom/dsl, 🅻/Wendy's/dsl/scales/24hr, Shell/repair, TA/rest./dsl/scales/24hr/@, 🍴 Arby's, Cracker Barrel, Culver's, JJ Fish&Chicken, KFC, La Bamba, McDonald's, Popeye's, Subway, Taco Bell, 🛏 Best Inn, Days Inn, EconoLodge, Hawthorn Suites, La Quinta, Quality Suites, ⊙ 🄷, Advance Parts, Blue Beacon, Family$, S 📕 Marathon/Circle K/dsl, Murphy USA/dsl, 🍴 Bob Evans, Fiesta Ranchera Mexican, Steak'n Shake/24hr, 🛏 Comfort Suites, Country Inn&Suites, Fairfield Inn, Hampton Inn, Holiday Inn Express, Ramada Ltd, ⊙ Aldi Foods, Farm&Fleet, Peterbilt, Radio Shack, Walmart
127[163]	I-55, N to Chicago, S to St Louis, I-74, W to Peoria
125	US 150, to Bloomington, Mitsubishi Motorway
123mm	**weigh sta wb**
122mm	**weigh sta eb**

Side markers: **DANVILLE** · E ↕ W · **CHAMPAIGN** · **BLOOMINGTON** · IL

INTERSTATE 74 CONT'D

Exit	Services
120	Carlock, **N** 🅿 BP/dsl/repair, 🍴 Carlock Rest., **S** Kamp Komfort Camping (Apr-Oct)
114.5mm	**rest area both lanes, full** 🛏 **facilities, vending,** 🅾, 🛏, **litter barrels, petwalk**
113.5mm	Mackinaw River
112	IL 117, Goodfield, **N** 🅿 Shell/Subway/dsl, 🍴 Busy Corner Rest., 🅾 to Timberline RA, Jellystone Camping (1mi), Eureka Coll, Reagan Home
102b a	Morton, **N** 🅿 BP/rest/dsl, Mobil/Arby's/dsl/scales/24hr, 🍴 Burger King, Pizza Ranch, Cracker Barrel, Culver's, Hardee's, Ruby Tuesday, Steak'n Shake, Subway, Taco Bell, 🛏 Baymont Inn, Best Western, Days Inn, Holiday Inn Express, Quality Inn, Travelodge, 🅾 Freightliner, Walmart, **S** 🅿 Marathon/Circle K, Shell/Subway/dsl/24hr, 🍴 China Dragon, KFC, La Fiesta, Lin's Buffet, McDonald's, Monical's Pizza, 🅾 Chrysler/Dodge/Jeep, Curves, CVS Drug, $Tree, Ford, GMC, K-Mart, Kroger, O'Reilly Parts
101	I-155 S, to Lincoln
99	I-474 W, 🅾
98	Pinecrest Dr
96	95c (from eb), US 150, IL 8, E Washington St, E Peoria, **N** 🅿 Fast Stop, 🍴 Monical's Pizza, 🛏 Super 8, 🅾 O'Reilly Parts
95b	IL 116, to Metamora, **N** 🅿 Shell/dsl, 🍴 Burger King, 🛏 Hampton Inn, Paradise Hotel, 🅾 casino
95a	N Main St, Peoria, **S** 🅿 BP/24hr, 🍴 A&W/LJ Silver, Bob Evans, China Buffet, Firehouse Pizza, Grand Village Buffet, Godfather's Pizza, Hardee's, IHOP, Jimmy John's, Subway, Taco Bell, 🛏 Holiday Inn Express, Motel 6, 🅾 Aldi Foods, Advance Parts, Curves, CVS Drug, Goodyear/auto, Kohl's, Kroger, Walgreens
94	IL 40, RiverFront Dr, **S** 🅿 Hucks/Godfather's/24hr, 🍴 Applebee's, Arby's, Buffalo Wild Wings, Chili's, Culver's, Grant City Grill, Logan's Roadhouse, Lorena's Mexican, Ming's Rest., Panera Bread, Papa John's, Quiznos, Schlotzky's, Steak'n Shake, TGIFriday's, TX Roadhouse, 🛏 Embassy Suites, 🅾 Lowe's, PetsMart, Radio Shack, Verizon, Walmart/Subway
93.5mm	Illinois River
93b	US 24, IL 29, Peoria, **N** 🅿 BP, **S** civic ctr
93a	Jefferson St, Peoria, **N** 🅿 BP, **S** 🍴 Chicago Grill, 🛏 Holiday Inn, Mark Twain Hotel, 🅾 to civic ctr
92b	Glendale Ave, Peoria, **S** 🅾 H, downtown
92a	IL 40 N, Knoxville Ave, Peoria, **S** 🛏 Holiday Inn, 🅾 H
91	University St, Peoria
90	Gale Ave, Peoria, **S** 🅿 Marathon, 🍴 Firehouse Pizza, 🅾 to Bradley U
89	US 150, War Memorial Dr, Peoria, **N on War Memorial** 🅿 BP/Circle K, Marathon/dsl, Shell, 🍴 Arby's, Avanti's Rest., Baskin-Robbins/Dunkin Donuts, Beef O'Brady's, Bob Evans, Brickhouse Grille, Burger King, Chucke-Cheese, Hometown Buffet, IHOP, McDonald's, Mickie's Pizza, Panera Bread, Perkins/24hr, Pizza Hut, Red Lobster, Ruby Tuesday, Schlotsky's, Sonic, Steak'n Shake, Subway, Wendy's, 🛏 Baymont Inn, Comfort Suites, Courtyard, Extended Stay America, Grand Hotel, Jamison Inn, Red Roof Inn, Residence Inn, Sleep Inn, SpringHill Suites, Super 8, 🅾 AutoZone, Barnes&Noble, Best Buy, Cadillac, Chevrolet, Cub Foods, Hobby Lobby,
89	Continued JC Penney, Lowe's, Macy's, Michael's, NAPA, PetsMart, Sears/auto, Target, Tires+, U-Haul, Verizon, Walgreens, Walmart, mall, vet
88	to US 150, War Memorial Dr, same as 89
87b a	I-474 E, IL 6, N to Chillicothe, **E** 🅾
82	Edwards Rd, Kickapoo, **N** 🅿 Mobil/dsl/service, Shell/Subway/dsl, 🍴 Jubilee Café, 🅾 to Jubilee Coll SP, **S** 🅾 USPO, Wildlife Prairie SP
75	Brimfield, Oak Hill, **N** 🅿 Casey's
71	to IL 78, to Canton, Elmwood
62mm	**rest area both lanes, full** 🛏 **facilities,** 🅾, 🛏, **litter barrels, vending, petwalk**
61.5mm	Spoon River
54	US 150, IL 97, Lewistown, **N** 🅾 TravL Park Camping (1mi), **S** 🅿 Mobil/dsl (2mi)
51	Knoxville, **S** 🅿 BP/dsl, Phillips 66/Charley's Subs/dsl/scales, 🍴 Hardee's/24hr, McDonald's, 🛏 Super 8
48b a	E Galesburg, Galesburg, **N** 🛏 Best Western, 🅾 Harley-Davidson, **S** 🅿 Beck's, BP/Circle K, HyVee/dsl, Mobil/dsl, 🍴 DQ, KFC, Hardee's, Jalisco Mexican, McDonald's, Pizza Hut, Subway, Taco Bell, 🛏 Holiday Inn Express, 🅾 Family$, Firestone, Goodyear, HyVee Foods, Sav-A-Lot Foods, Walgreens, to Sandburg Birthplace, Lincoln-Douglas Debates
46b a	US 34, to Monmouth, **N** 🅾 Nichol's dsl Service, **S** 🅾 H, 1 mi **S** 🍴 Buffalo Wild Wings, Chinese Buffet, Pepperonis Pizza, 🅾 Menards, Verizon, Walmart, vet
32	IL 17, Woodhull, **N** 🅿 BP/dsl, Shell/dsl/e-85/scales, 🍴 Homestead Rest., Subway, **S** 🅾 Shady Lakes Camping (8mi)
30mm	**rest area wb, full** 🛏 **facilities, vending,** 🛏, **litter barrels,** 🅾, **playground, petwalk, RV dump**
28mm	**rest area eb, full** 🛏 **facilities, vending,** 🛏, **litter barrels,** 🅾, **playground, petwalk, RV dump**
24	IL 81, Andover, **N** 🅿 Casey's (2mi), camping
14mm	I-80, E to Chicago, I-80/I-280, W to Des Moines
8mm	**weigh sta wb**
6mm	**weigh sta eb**
5b	US 6, Moline, **S** 🅿 Shell/dsl, 🍴 McDonald's, MT Jack's, 🛏 Best Inn, Country Inn&Suites, Days Inn, Hampton Inn, La Quinta, Motel 6, Ramada Inn, 🅾 🅾
5a	I-280 W, US 6 W, to Des Moines
4b a	IL 5, John Deere Rd, Moline, **N** 🅿 BP, Phillips 66, Shell/dsl, 🍴 Applebee's, Burger King, Carlos O'Kelly's, Culver's, Hungy Hobo, Panda Buffet, Panera Bread, Ryan's, Starbucks, Steak'n Shake, Subway, Wendy's, 🛏 Residence Inn, 🅾 Cadillac, Curves, $Tree, Lowe's, Radio Shack, Staples, Subaru, Tires+, Toyota/Scion, Volvo, Walmart, **S** 🅿 BP, 🍴 A&W/LJ Silver, Arby's, Buffalo Wild Wings, Denny's, IHOP, KFC, McDonald's, Miss Mamie's, New Mandarin Chinese, Qdoba Mexican, Taco Bell, Wendy's, 🛏 Best Western, Comfort Inn, Fairfield Inn, Super 8, 🅾 Best Buy, Buick/GMC, Chevrolet, Dillards, $General, Firestone/auto, Ford/Lincoln/Mercury, Goodyear/auto, Gordman's, Hancock Fabrics, JC Penney, Mazda, Nissan, Old Navy, PetCo, Sears/auto, Von Maur, Walgreens, Younkers, mall
3	23rd Ave, Moline, **N** 🛏 Economy Inn
2	7th Ave, Moline, **S** 🅿 Cenex, 🅾 USPO, to civic ctr, riverfront

E ↑ W

IL

P E O R I A

M O L I N E

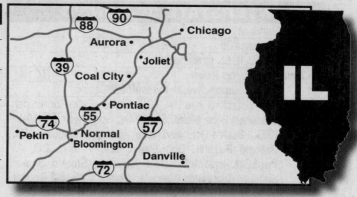

INTERSTATE 74 CONT'D

Exit	Services
1	3rd Ave (from eb), Moline, **S** ⓖ Cenex, 🛏 Stoney Creek Inn
0mm	**Illinois/Iowa state line, Mississippi River. Exits 4-1 are in Iowa.**
4	US 67, Grant St, State St, Bettendorf, **N** ⓖ BP, Phillips 66/dsl, Shell, 🍽 Ross' Rest./24hr, Subway, 🛏 Traveler Motel, Twin Bridges Motel, ⊙ CarQuest, **S** 🍽 Village Inn Rest., 🛏 City Ctr Motel, ⊙ $General
3	Middle Rd, Locust St, Bettendorf, **S** ⓖ BP, 🍽 China Taste, Grinders Rest., McDonald's, Starbucks, Subway, 🛏 Holiday Inn, ⊙ Ⓗ, Hobby Lobby, Home Depot, Marshall's, Schuck's Foods, Walgreens
2	US 6 W, Spruce Hills Dr, Bettendorf, **N** ⓖ BP/dsl, Phillips 66, 🍽 Domino's, Old Chicago Pizza, 🛏 Courtyard, EconoLodge, Ramada Inn, Super 8, The Lodge Hotel/rest., ⊙ U-Haul, **S** 🍽 Applebee's, Burger King, Godfather's, KFC, Panera Bread, Red Lobster, 🛏 Days Inn, Fairfield Inn, La Quinta, ⊙ Buick/Cadillac/GMC, Gander Mtn, Gordman's, Kohl's, Lowe's, PetCo, Sam's Club/gas, st patrol
1	53rd St, Hamilton, **N** ⓖ BP, 🍽 Biaggi's Italian, Buffalo Wild Wings, Chili's, Coldstone, Dickey's BBQ, Granite City Rest., Maggie Moo's, Osaka Steaks, Panchero's Mexican, Red Robin, Ruby Tuesday, Symposium Cafe, TX Roadhouse, 🛏 Hampton Inn, Staybridge Suites, ⊙ Ⓗ, Harley-Davidson, HyVee Foods, Michael's, Old Navy, TJ Maxx, Walgreens, **S** ⓖ Murphy USA, Phillips 66, 🍽 Arby's, Azteca Mexican, Chick-fil-A, China Cafe, DQ, Dynasty Buffet, Golden Corral, Hungry Hobo, IHOP, La Rancherita, Noodles&Co., Qdoba Mexican, Sonic, Starbucks, Steak'n Shake, Subway, TGIFriday's, Village Inn Rest., Taco Bell, Wendy's, 🛏 Sleep Inn, ⊙ Aldi Foods, AT&T, Best Buy, $Tree, PetsMart, Staples, Target, Verizon, Walmart
0mm	I-74 begins/ends on I-80, exit 298. **Exits 1-4 are in Iowa.**

INTERSTATE 80

Exit	Services
163mm	Illinois/Indiana state line
161	US 6, IL 83, Torrence Ave, **N** ⓖ BP, 🍽 Burger King, Chili's, Culver's, Dixie Kitchen, Hooters, IHOP, Kenny's Ribs, Liang's Garden, New China Buffet, Oberweiss, Olive Garden, Shark's, Taco-Burrito's, Wendy's, 🛏 Comfort Suites, Days Inn, Extended Stay America, Holiday Inn Express, Howard Johnson Express, Red Roof Inn, Sleep Inn, Super 8, ⊙ Aldi Foods, AT&T, Best Buy, CarEx, Chrysler/Jeep, Curves, $General, $Tree, Dunkin Donuts, Fannie May Candies, Firestone/auto, Home Depot, Honda, JustTires, K-Mart, PepBoys, Radio Shack, Ultra Foods, Walmart, **S** ⓖ Citgo, Marathon, Mobil, 🍽 China Chef, Burger King, DQ, Dunkin Donuts, Jonny's K's Cafe, McDonald's/playplace, Mr Gyros, Popolono's Italian, Subway, 🛏 Pioneer Motel, ⊙ Chevrolet, PetsMart, Saab, SunRise Foods, Tuesday Morning, Walgreens, vet
160b	I-94 W, to Chicago, tollway begins wb, ends eb
160a	IL 394 S, to Danville
159mm	Oasis, ⓖ Mobil/dsl, 🍽 McDonald's, Panda Express, Starbucks, Subway
157	IL 1, Halsted St, **N** ⓖ Citgo/dsl, Marathon/dsl, 🍽

157	**Continued** Burger King, 🛏 Chicago Southland Hotel, Clarion, Comfort Inn, Comfort Suites, EconoLodge, Regency Inn, **S** ⓖ Citgo, Delta Sonic, Shell, Speedway, 🍽 Applebee's, Athens Gyros, Arby's, Boston Mkt, Burger King, Chili's, Dunkin Donuts, Fannie May Candies, KFC, McDonald's, Panda Express, Pizza Hut, Popeye's, Starbucks, Subway, Taco Bell, Washington Square Rest., Wendy's, White Castle, 🛏 Homewood Hotel, Super 8, ⊙ Aldi Foods, AT&T, Best Buy, Chevrolet, Discount Tire, $Tree, Fanny May Candies, Firestone/auto, Goodyear/auto, Home Depot, Jewel-Osco, Jo-Ann Fabrics, K-Mart, Kohl's, Menards, PepBoys, PetCo, Radio Shack, Target, TJ Maxx, Walgreens
156	Dixie Hwy (from eb, no return), **S** ⓖ Mobil, 🍽 Leona's Rest., ⊙ golf
155	I-294 N, Tri-State Tollway, toll plaza
154	Kedzie Ave (from eb, no return), **N** ⓖ Speedway, **S** Ⓗ
151b a	I-57 (exits left from both directions), N to Chicago, S to Memphis
148b a	IL 43, Harlem Ave, **N** ⓖ Speedway/dsl, 🍽 Al's Beef, Buffalo Wild Wings, Burger King, Cracker Barrel, Culver's, Dunkin Donuts, Eggi Grill, Hamada of Japan, Pop's Italian Beef, Quizno's, Taco Fresco, Tin Fish Grill, Wendy's, 🛏 Comfort Suites, Fairfield Inn, Hampton Inn, Holiday Inn, La Quinta, Sleep Inn, Wingate Inn, **S** 🍽 Arby's, Boston's Grill, Subway, Taco Bell, TGIFriday's, ⊙ Best Buy, Carmax, Kohl's, Michael's, PetsMart, SuperTarget, ampitheater
147.5mm	**weigh sta wb**
145b a	US 45, 96th Ave, **N** 🍽 Arby's, Arrenello's Pizza, Baskin-Robbins/Dunkin Donuts, 4K Asian, Quizno's, Tokyo Steaks, TX Roadhouse, 🛏 Country Inn&Suites, Hilton Garden, ⊙ Harley-Davidson, 0-2 mi **S** ⓖ BP, Clark, Gas City, Shell/Circle K/dsl/24hr, 🍽 A&W, Applebee's, Beggar's Pizza, DQ, Denny's, KFC, Mindy's Ribs, Nick's Rest., Rising Sun Chinese, Stoney Pt Grill, Subway, White Castle, Wendy's, 🛏 Super 8, ⊙ Brookhaven Foods, CVS Drug, Tuesday Morning, repair
143mm	**weigh sta eb**
140	SW Hwy, I 355, N Tollway, US 6, S
137	US 30, New Lenox, **N** 🍽 Williamson's Rest., ⊙ K-Mart, **S** ⓖ Speedway/dsl, 🍽 Beggar's Pizza, Burger King, KFC, LJ Silver/Papa Joe's, McDonald's/playplace, Paisono's Pizza, Pizza Hut, Subway, Taco Bell, ⊙ Ace Hardware, Goodyear/auto, Jewel-Osco/dsl, Walgreens, city park, vet
134	Briggs St, **N** ⓖ Citgo, Speedway, ⊙ Ⓗ, **S** ⓖ Shell/dsl, Valero/dsl, ⊙ EZ Lube, Martin Camping, US RV Ctr

IL

Exit	Services
	INTERSTATE 80 CONT'D
133	Richards St
132b a	US 52, IL 53, Chicago St
131.5mm	Des Plaines River
131	US 6, Meadow Ave, N to Riverboat Casino
130b a	IL 7, Larkin Ave, N 🅖 Clark, Delta Sonic/dsl, Marathon/24hr, Mobil, Shell/24hr, Speedway, 🍴 A&W/KFC, Baskin-Robbins/Dunkin Donuts, Boston Mkt, Bellagio Pizzaria, Bob Evans, Burger King, DQ, JJ Fish&Chicken, McDonald's, Quizno's, Steak'n Shake, Subway, Taco Bell, Wendy's, White Castle, 🛏 Budget Inn, Comfort Inn, Holiday Inn, Motel 6, Red Roof Inn, Super 8, 🅞 H, Aldi Foods, Cadillac/Chevrolet, Discount Tire, Ford, Goodyear/auto, K-Mart, Pepboys, Radio Shack, Sam's Club/gas, 7-11, to Coll of St Francis, vet, S 🅖 Citgo, 🅞 auto repair
127	Houbolt Rd, to Joliet, N 🅖 BP/deli, 7-11, 🍴 Arby's, Burger King, China Kitchen, Cracker Barrel, Dunkin Donuts, Heros Sports Grill, Jimmy John's, McDonald's, Papa&Nana's Pizza, 🛏 Fairfield Inn, Hampton Inn, Ramada Inn, 🅞 Riverboat Casino
126b a	I-55, N to Chicago, S to St Louis
125.5mm	Du Page River
122	Minooka, N 🅖 Citgo/dsl/24hr, S 🅖 BP/24hr, Pilot/Arby's/scales/dsl/24hr, 🍴 Baskin-Robbins/Dunkin Donuts, Gino Angelo's Pizza, KFC/LJ Silver, McDonald's/playplace, Subway, Taco Bell, Wendy's, 🅞 $General, 7-11
119mm	**rest area wb, full ♿ facilities, vending, 🚻s, 🦶, litter barrels, playground, petwalk**
117mm	**rest area eb, full ♿ facilities, vending, 🚻, 🦶, litter barrels, playground, petwalk**
112	IL 47, Morris, N 🅖 Marathon/dsl, TA/BP/Quizno's/scales/dsl/24hr/@, 🍴 Bellacino's, Chili's, IHOP, 🛏 Comfort Inn, Days Inn, Holiday Inn Express, Quality Inn, 🅞 $General, Menards, S 🅖 BP, Mobil, Phillips 66, Shell/24hr, 🍴 Burger King, Culver's, DQ, Dunkin Donuts, Hong Kong Chinese, KFC/LJ Silver, Maria's Ristorante, McDonald's, Morris Diner, Pizza Hut, Rosati's Pizza, Taco Bell, Wendy's, 🛏 Park Motel, Sherwood Oaks Motel, Super 8, 🅞 Aldi Foods, AT&T, Big R Store, Buick/Cadillac/Chevrolet, Curves, Fisher Parts, Ford, GMC, Jewel-Osco, Morris Drug, Radio Shack, Verizon, Walgreens, Walmart/Subway/24hr, to Stratton SP, transmissions/repair
105	to Seneca
97	to Marseilles, S 🍴 Taco Time, 🅞 our Star Camping, Glenwood Camping (4mi), to Illini SP, RV camping
93	IL 71, Ottawa, N 🅖 Mobil/24hr, Shell/dsl/24hr, 🅞 Skydive Chicago RV Park (2mi), S 🍴 Hank's Farm Rest., 🅞 H
92.5mm	Fox River
90	IL 23, Ottawa, N 🅖 BP/Subway, 🍴 Arby's, Cracker Barrel, Taco Bell, 🛏 Hampton Inn, Holiday Inn Express, 🅞 AT&T, F&F, Ford/KIA/Lincoln/Mercury, Honda, Toyota/Scion, Verizon, Walmart/McDonald's, S 🅖 BP/dsl/LP, Thornton's/dsl 🍴 Culver's, Dunkin Donuts, KFC/LJ Silver, Papa Murphy's, 🛏 Comfort Inn, Fairfield Inn, Sands Motel (2mi), Super 8, Surrey Motel, 🅞 H, Aldi Foods, $Tree, Harley-Davidson, Kroger, Radio Shack
81	IL 178, Utica, N 🅖 Loves/McDonald's/Subway/dsl/scales/24hr, 🅞 Hickory Hollow Camping, KOA (2mi), S 🅖 Shell/Jimmy Johns/dsl, 🍴 Duffy's Tavern (2mi), 🛏 Starved Rock Inn, 🅞 to Starved Rock SP, repair

Exit	Services
79b a	I-39, US 51, N to Rockford, S to Bloomington
77.5mm	Little Vermilion River
77	IL 351, La Salle, S 🅖 *FLYING J*/Denny's/dsl/scales/24hr, 🍴 UpTown Grill (3mi), 🛏 Daniels Motel (1mi), 🅞 st police
75	IL 251, Peru, N 🅖 BP, Shell/dsl/rest./24hr, 🍴 Arby's, McDonald's, Quizno's, Starbucks, Taco Bell, 🛏 Baymont Inn, Holiday Inn Express, Kings Inn, Super 8, 🅞 Kohl's, Walmart/Dunkin Donuts/Subway, flea mkt, S 🅖 BP, Phillips 66, Shell, 🍴 Applebee's, Buffalo Wild Wings, Burger King, Culver's, DQ, IHOP, Los Jalepeno's Mexican, McDonald's, Mi Margarita, Papa John's, Pizza Hut, Red Lobster, Steak'n Shake, Subway, Wendy's, 🛏 Fairfield Inn, Hampton Inn, La Quinta, 🅞 H, Aldi Foods, AT&T, AutoZone, BigLots, Buick/Cadillac/GMC, Chevrolet/Mercedes/Nissan, Chrysler/Dodge/Jeep, CVS Drug, $Tree, Ford/Hyundai/Lincoln/Mercury, Goodyear/auto, Hobby Lobby, Home Depot, HyVee Food/gas, JC Penney, Jewel Foods, K-Mart, Marshall's, Menards, Mercedes, Nissan, Sears/auto, Staples, Target, Verizon, Walgreens
73	Plank Rd, N 🅖 Sapp Bros/Burger King/dsl/scales/@, 🍴 Big Apple Rest., 🅞 Kenworth, Volvo Trucks, camping
70	IL 89, to Ladd, N 🅖 Casey's, S 🅖 BP (3mi), Shell (3mi), 🛏 Spring Valley Motel, 🅞 H
61	I-180, to Hennepin
56	IL 26, Princeton, N 🅖 Road Ranger/Pilot/Stuckey's/scales/dsl/@, 🛏 Super 8, S 🅖 Beck's, Shell/dsl, 🍴 Big Apple Rest., Burger King, Coffee Cup Rest., Country Kitchen, Culver's, KFC, McDonald's, Wendy's, 🛏 Americinn, Days Inn, Econolodge, Princeton Motel, 🅞 H, AutoZone, Buick/Cadillac/Chevrolet, $General, O'Reilly Parts, Pennzoil, Sullivan's Food/gas, Walmart, antiques, vet
51mm	**rest area both lanes, full ♿ facilities, 🚻, 🦶, litter barrels, vending, playground, petwalk, RV dump**
45	IL 40, N 🅞 to Ronald Reagan Birthplace (21mi), antiques, S 🅞 Hennepin Canal SP, camping
44mm	Hennepin Canal
33	IL 78, to Kewanee, Annawan, N 🅖 Shabbona RV Ctr/Camp (3mi), S 🅖 Cenex, FS/dsl/e-85, Shell/dsl, 🍴 Burbons Rest., 🛏 Best Western, 🅞 to Johnson-Sauk Tr SP
27	to US 6, Atkinson, N 🅖 Casey's (1mi), Mobil/dsl/24hr
19	IL 82, Geneseo, N 🅖 BP, Phillips 66/dsl/scales/24hr, 🍴 Culvers, DQ, Hardee's, Happy Joe's Pizza, McDonald's, Pizza Hut, Quizno's, Sweet Pea's Grill, Subway, 🛏 Amerihost, Super 8 (1mi), 🅞 H, $General, Ford, Verizon, Walgreens, Walmart/drugs, vet
10	I-74, I-280, W to Moline, E to Peoria
9	US 6, to Geneseo, N 🍴 Lavender Crest Winery/Cafe, S 🅞 Niabi Zoo
7	Colona, N 🅖 Shell/dsl, 🍴 Country Fixins Rest.
5mm	Rock River
4a	IL 5, IL 92, W to Silvis, S 🅞 to Quad City Downs, Lundeen's Camping
4b	I-88, IL 92, E to Rock Falls
2mm	**weigh sta both lanes**
1.5mm	**Welcome Ctr eb, full ♿ facilities, info, 🚻, 🦶, litter barrels, petwalk, scenic overlook**
1	IL 84, 20th St, Great River Rd, E Moline, N 🅖 BP/diesel, Git-Go, 🍴 Brothers Rest., 🅞 auto repair, camping, The Great River Rd, **3 mi** S 🅖 BP, 🅞 camping
0mm	Illinois/Iowa state line, Mississippi River

Side markers: E / W, IL, MORRIS, PERU, E MOLINE

INTERSTATE 88

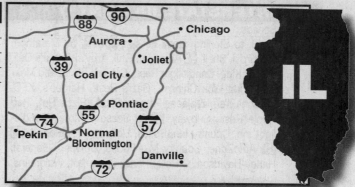

E ↕ W

CHICAGO AREA

Exit	Services
139.5mm	I-88 begins/ends on I-290.
139	I-294, S to Indiana, N to Milwaukee
138mm	toll plaza
137	IL 83 N, Cermak Rd, **N** [food] Clubhouse rest., Ditkas Rest., McDonald's, [lodging] Marriott, Renaissance Inn, [other] Barnes&Noble, Lord&Taylor, Macy's, Nieman-Marcus
136	IL 83 S, Midwest Rd (from eb), **N** [gas] Shell/Circle K, [food] All-Stars Rest., Burger King, Capri Ristorante, Chipotle Mexican, Denny's, Dunkin Donuts, Eggstacy, Giordano's Rest., Jamba Juice, McDonalds, Noodles&Co, Quizno's, Redstones, Starbucks, Subway, Subway, [lodging] Holiday Inn, La Quinta, [other] AT&T, Costco/gas, Home Depot, Nordstrom's, Old Navy, TJ Maxx, Walgreens, World Mkt
134	Highland Ave (no EZ wb return), **N** [food] Baker's Square, Bouna Beef, Brio Grille, Buca Italian, Burger King, Capital Grille, Champps Grill, Cheeseburger Paradise, Cici's, Claimjumper Rest., Fuddruckers, Harry Caray's, Hooters, Joe's Crabshack, Kona Grill, Kyoto, McCormick & Schmick's, Miller's Steakhouse, Olive Garden, Panera Bread, PF Chang's, Portilo's Hotdogs, Potbelly's, Qdoba, Red Lobster, Rockbottom Brewery, Ruby Tuesday, Starbucks, Subway, Taylor Brewing Co, TGIFriday's, Uncle Milio's, Weber Grill, [lodging] Comfort Inn, Embassy Suites, Holiday Inn Express, Homestead Studios, Hyatt Place, Marriott, Red Roof Inn, Westin Hotel, [other] [H], Best Buy, Firestone/auto, Home Depot, JC Penney, Kohl's, Marshall's, PetsMart, Vonmaur, mall, **S** [food] Parkers Ocean Grill
132	I-355, N (from wb)
131	I-355, S (from eb)
130	IL 53 (from wb), **1 mi N** [gas] BP, Mobil, [food] McDonald's, [other] Walmart
127	Naperville Rd, **N** [food] Mullen's Grill, [lodging] Hilton, Wyndam, **S** [gas] Mobil, [food] Buona Beef, Froots, HoneyBaked Ham, Jason's Deli, Maggiano's, McDonald's, Morton's Steaks, Pizza Hut, Subway, Taco Fresco, TGIFriday's, Wendy's, White Chocolate Grill, [lodging] Best Western, Courtyard, Days Inn, Fairfield Inn, Hampton Inn, Holiday Inn Select, [other] Dodge, Ford, Kia, Office Depot, Radio Shack, Subaru
125	Winfield Rd, **N** [gas] BP, Mobil, [lodging] Hamton Inn, [other] [H], Walgreens, **S** [food] Arby's, Atlanta Bread, Buffalo Wild Wings, CA Pizza Kitchen, Chipotle Mexican, Corner Bakery Cafe, GoRoma, Jamba Juice, Max&Erma's, McDonald's, Potbelly's, Red Robin, Rockbottom Brewery, Starbucks, StirCrazy Grill, [lodging] Hilton Garden, Springhill Suites, [other] SuperTarget
123	IL 59, **N** [gas] Gas City/dsl, [food] Omega Rest, [other] Carmax, **S** [gas] BP, Mobil/dsl, Speedway, [food] Baskin Robbins/Dunkin Donuts, Caribou Coffee, Cracker Barrel, Danny's Grill, Jimmy John's, Lee's Garden, Oberweis, Spicy Pickle, Starbucks, Steak'n Shake, Subway, TX Roadhouse, Wendy's, [lodging] Extended Stay America, Fairfield Inn, Red Roof Inn, Sleep Inn, SpringHill Suites, Towneplace Suites, [other] CVS Drug, 7-11, Walgreens
119	Farnsworth Ave, **N** [gas] BP, Shell, [food] McDonald's, Millet's Grill, Papa Bear Rest., Quizno's, Sonic, Starbucks, [lodging] Fox Valley Inn, Motel 6, [other] Firestone/auto, Premium Outlets/Famous Brands, Walmart, **S** [gas] Marathon, Phillips 66/dsl, Shell, Speedway, [food] Baskin-Robbins/Dunkin Donuts, Drive-Thru, Little Caesars, McDonald's, Mike&Denise's Pizza, Subway, Taco Bell, [other] AutoZone, Family$, Goodyear, 7-11, Walgreens

DEKALB

DIXON

Exit	Services
118mm	toll plaza
117	IL 31, IL 56, to Aurora, Batavia, **N** [gas] Citgo/dsl, [food] A&W, [other] 7-11, **S** [gas] Mobil, Thornton's, [food] Arby's, Baskin-Robbins/Dunkin Donuts, Burger King, Culver's, Denny's, KFC, LJ Silver, McDonald's, Nikary's, Rest., Popeye's, Quizno's, Subway, Taco Bell, White Castle, [lodging] Baymont Inn, [other] [H], Ace Hardware, AutoZone, Cermak Foods, $Store, Firestone, GNC, Jewel/Osco, Murray's Parts, Radio Shack, U-Haul, Walgreens
115	Orchard Rd, **N** [food] McDonald's, Subway, [other] Best Buy, Chrysler/Dodge/Jeep, Ford/Lincoln/Mercury, Hyundai, JC Penney, Michaels, Nissan, PetCo, Subaru, Target, Woodman's/dsl, **0-2 mi S** [gas] 7-11, [food] A&W/KFC, Arby's, Buffalo Wild Wings, Chili's, Cold Stone, IHOP, Jimmy John's, Panera Bread, Papa Saverio's, Pizza Hut, Quizno's, Starbucks, Wendy's, [lodging] Candlewood Suites, Hampton Inn, Holiday Inn, [other] AT&T, CVS Drug, Discount Tire, Home Depot, Lowe's Whse, Office Depot, T-Moble
114	IL 56W, to US 30 (from wb, no EZ return), to Sugar Grove
109	IL 47 (from eb), Elburn
94	Peace Rd, to IL 38, **N** [H]
93mm	**Dekalb Oasis/24hr both lanes, Dekalb Oasis/24hr both lanes,** [gas] Mobil/dsl, [food] McDonald's, Panda Express, Subway
92	IL 38, IL 23, Annie Glidden Rd, to DeKalb, **N** [lodging] Super 8, **2-3 mi N** [gas] BP, Road Ranger/dsl, Marathon, Shell, [food] Aldorado, Baskin-Robbins, Blackstone Rest, Burger King, Chipotle Mexican, El Burrito Loco, Gyro's, Happy Wok Chinese, Jct Rest., KFC, LJ Silver, Lukulo's Rest., McDonald's, Molly's Eatery, Pagliai's Pizza, Pancake Rest., Panda Express, Papa John's, Potbelly, Pizza Hut, Pizza Pros, Pizza Villa, Quizno's, Starbucks, Subway, Taco Bell, Tom&Jerry's, Topper's Pizza, Vinny's Pizza, Wendy's, [lodging] Best Western, Magneson Inn, Travelodge, [other] $General, Ford, Illini Tire, Schnuck's Food/Drug, Walgreens, to, N IL U
86mm	toll plaza
78	I-39, US 51, S to Bloomington, N to Rockford
76	IL 251, Rochelle, **N** [gas] BP, Casey's, Shell, [food] Olive Branch Rest., [other] [H], Ford/Mercury, GMC, tires/repair
56mm	toll plaza
54	IL 26, Dixon, **N** [gas] BP/Subway/scales/dsl, Murphy USA/dsl, [food] Panda Chinese, Pizza Hut, [lodging] Comfort Inn, Quality Inn, Super 8, [other] $Tree, Verizon, Walmart, **1-2 mi N** [food] Culver's, Hardee's, [other] [H], to Ronald Reagan Birthplace, to John Deere HS, to St Parks
44	US 30 (last free exit eb), **N** gas, food, lodging, [other] Leisure lake RV Ctr (2mi)

INTERSTATE 88 CONT'D

Exit	Services
41	IL 40, to Sterling, Rock Falls, **1-2 mi** N 🅟 Marathon, Mobil/dsl, Shell, 🍴 American Grill, Arby's, Arthur's Deli, Burger King, Candlelight Rest., Culver's, El Tapatio Mexican, First Wok Chinese, Gazi's Rest., Hardee's, KFC, McDonald's/playplace, Perna's Pizza, Pizza Hut, Red Apple Rest., Subway, 🛏 All Seasons Motel, Candlelight Inn, Country Inn&Suites, Holiday Inn, Super 8, ⊡ 🄷, AutoZone, Country Mkt Foods, Curves, $General, Harley-Davidson, O'Reilly Parts, Sav-a-Lot, Walgreens, Walmart
36	to US 30, Rock Falls, Sterling
26	IL 78, to Prophetstown, Morrison, N ⊡ to Morrison-Rockwood SP
18	to Albany, Erie
10	to Port Byron, Hillsdale, S 🅟 Phillips 66/dsl, Shell/Mama J's Rest./scales/dsl/24hr
6	IL 92 E, to Joslin, N 🍴 Jammerz Roadhouse (2mi), S ⊡ Sunset Lake Camping (1mi)
2	Former IL 2
1b a	I-80, W to Des Moines, E to Chicago
0mm	I-88 begins/ends on I-80, exit 4b. IL 5, IL 92, W to Silvis, to Quad City Downs, ⊡ Lundeen's Camping

INTERSTATE 90

Exit	Services
0mm	Illinois/Indiana state line, Chicago Skyway Toll Rd begins/ends
1mm	US 12, US 20, 106th St, Indianapolis Blvd, N 🅟 Citgo, Mobil, Shell/dsl, ⊡ casino, S 🍴 Burger King, KFC, McDonald's, ⊡ Aldi Foods, Jewel-Osco, auto repair
2.5mm	🅟 Skyway Oasis, 🍴 McDonald's, ⊡ toll plaza
3mm	87th St, (from wb)
4mm	79th St, services along 79th St and Stoney Island Ave
5.5mm	73rd St, (from wb)
6mm	State St, (from wb) S 🅟 Citgo
7mm	I-94 N, (mile markers decrease to IN state line)
I-90 E and I-94 E run together. See Interstate 94, exits 43b - 59a.	
84	I-94 W, Lawrence Ave N 🅟 BP
83b a	Foster Ave, (from wb), N 🅟 BP, 🍴 Checker's, Dunkin Donuts, ⊡ Firestone/auto, Goodyear/auto, Walgreen
82c	Austin Ave, to Foster Ave
82b	Byrn-Mawr, (from wb)
82a	Nagle Ave
81b	Sayre Ave, (from wb)
81a	IL 43, Harlem Ave, S 🅟 BP, Shell
80	Canfield Rd, (from wb), N ⊡ Walgreen
79b a	IL 171 S, Cumberland Ave, N 🅟 7-11, Marathon, 🍴 Hooters, McDonald's, Outback Steaks, Starbucks, 🛏 Holiday Inn, Marriott, SpringHill Suites, Westin Hotel, ⊡ Dominick's Foods, S 🍴🛏 Ramada, Renaissance
78.5mm	River Road Plaza, N 🍴 McDonald's, 🛏 Marriott, Westin Hotel, S Hyatt (mile markers increase to Rockford)
78mm	I-294, I-190 W, to O'Hare ⤵
76mm	IL 72, Lee St, (from wb), N 🛏 Extended Stay America, Quality Inn, Wyndham, S 🍴 McDonald's, 🛏 Best Western, Holiday Inn Express, Holiday Inn Select, Sheraton Gateway, Studio+
74.5mm	**Des Plaines Oasis both lanes** 🅟 Mobil/dsl/24hr, 🍴 McDonald's/24hr, Panda Express, Starbucks, Subway
73.5mm	Elmhurst Rd, (from wb), S 🅟 Shell, 🍴 McDonald's, 🛏

73.5mm	Continued Best Western, Comfort Inn, Days Inn, La Quinta, Microtel, Motel 6
70.5mm	Arlington Hts Rd, N **on Algonquin** 🅟 Shell, 🍴 Arby's, Baja Fresh, Birch River Grill, Buona Beef, Caribou Coffee, Chicago Pizza, Chili's, Chipotle Mexican, Denny's, Honey Baked Ham, Jimmy Johns, Magnum Steaks, McDonald's, Old Country Buffet, Panda Express, Pappadeaux Rest., Potbelly's, Steak'n Shake, Subway, Yanni's Greek Rest., 🛏 Courtyard, DoubleTree, Hyatt, Motel 6, Radisson, Red Roof Inn, Jameson Suites, ⊡ AT&T, GNC, Lowe's Whse, Meijer, NTB, Staples, Walmart, vet, S 🅟 Mobil, Shell, 🍴 Subway, 🛏 Sheraton
68mm	I-290, IL 53, N 🛏 Embassy Suites, Holiday Inn, Renaissance Inn, ⊡ mall, **1 mi** S 🍴 Houlihan's, Joe's Crabshack, Olive Garden, Ruby Tuesday, TGI Friday's, 🛏 Extended Stay America, Hyatt, Residence Inn, ⊡ Firestone, JC Penney, Macy's
65.5mm	Roselle Rd, (from wb), N ⊡ Medieval Times, S 🅟 Mobil, 🍴 Bahama Breeze, Boston Mkt, Caribou Coffee, Denny's, Fox&Hound, Fuddrucker's, KFC, Outback Steaks, Subway, Wendy's, 🛏 Country Inn&Suites, Extended Stay America, Homestead Suites, ⊡ BMW/Mini, Carmax, Firestone, Hancock Fabrics, Lexus, Michael's, Office Depot, PetCo, 7-11, TJ Maxx
62mm	Barrington Rd, (from wb), N 🍴 Apple Villa Pancake House, Hunan Beijing, Jimmy John's, La Strada Ristorante, Millrose Rest., Quizno's, Subway, 🛏 Hilton Garden, S 🅟 BP, Shell, 🍴 Chili's, IHOP, McDonald's, Starbucks, Steak'n Shake, TGI Friday's, 🛏 Comfort Inn, Hampton Inn, Hyatt Place, La Quinta, Red Roof Inn, ⊡ U-Haul
59.5mm	IL 59, N 🍴 Buffalo Wild Wings, Caribou Coffee, Chipotle Mexican, Claim Jumper Rest., Cooper's Hawk Rest., Hasta la Pasta, Jimmy John's, Moe's SW Grill, Noodles&Co, Panda Express, Potbelly's, Red Robin, Ruth's Chris Steaks, Subway, 🛏 Marriott, ⊡ AT&T, Cabela's, CVS Drug, Michael's, PetsMart, Target, TJ Maxx, to Poplar Creek Music Theatre
58mm	Beverly Rd (from wb)
56mm	IL 25, N 🛏 Days Inn, S 🅟 BP, Citgo, Shell, Speedway/dsl, 🍴 Arby's, Baker Hill Pancakes, Subway, Wendy's, ⊡ 🄷, Advance Parts, NAPA
54.5mm	IL 31 N, N 🅟 BP, Speedway, 🍴 Alexander's Rest., Baskin-Robbins/Dunkin Donuts, 🛏 Courtyard, Hampton Inn, Holiday Inn, Quality Inn, Super 8, TownePlace Suites
54mm	Elgin Toll Plaza, Ⓒ
52mm	Randall Rd, N 🍴 Big Sammy's Hot Dogs, Burnt Toast, Cafe Roma, Froots, Henessey Rest., Jimmy John's, Jimmy's Charhouse, Panera Bread, Rookies Grill, Starbucks, Village Pizza, 🛏 Comfort Inn, Country Inn&Suites, ⊡ Honda, S 🅟 7-11, 🛏 Candlewood Suites, ⊡ 🄷
46.5mm	IL 47 (from wb), to Woodstock N ⊡ Prime Outlets/famous brands, Chevrolet, Ford
42.5mm	US 20, Marengo, N 🅟 Citgo/Arrowhead Rest/dsl/scales/24hr, Subway/dsl/scales/24hr, TA/BP, Burger King/Popeye's/scales/dsl/24hr/@, 🍴 McDonald's, Wendy's, 🛏 Super 8, ⊡ Chevrolet, Ford, museums, to Prime Outlets at exit 46 (6mi)
38mm	Marengo Toll Plaza (from eb)
25mm	Genoa Rd, to Belvidere, N 🅟 Murphy USA, 🍴

INTERSTATE 90

Exit	Services
25mm	Continued
	Applebee's, Quizno's, Rosati's Pizza, Starbucks, Subway, Thai Basil, 🅞 Verizon, Walmart, camping
24mm	**Belvidere Oasis both lanes**, 🅖 Mobil/dsl/24hr, 🍴 Food Court, Kronos Cafe, McDonald's/24hr, Panda Express, Starbucks, Subway, Taco Bell, 🅒
23.5mm	Belvidere Toll Plaza
18mm	Kishwaukee River
17.5mm	I-39 S, US 20, US 51, to Rockford, 🅂 funpark
15mm	US 20, State St, N🅖 Mobil/dsl, Phillips 66/Subway/dsl, 🍴 Cracker Barrel, 🏨 Baymont Inn, Clocktower Best Western Resort, Days Inn, **0-2 mi** 🅂🅖 BP, Mobil/dsl, Road Ranger/dsl, 🍴 Applebee's, Buffalo Wild Wings, Burger King, Charley's Steaks, Chili's, China King, Chipotle Mexican, City Buffet, Culver's, Denny's, Dos Reales, Gerry's Pizza, Giovanni's Rest., Golden Corral, Hoffman House Rest., Hong Kong Buffet, Hooters, IHOP, Japanese Express, Jerry's Pizza, Jimmy John's, KFC/LJ Silver, Lino's Pizza, LoneStar Steaks, Machine Shed Rest., McDonald's, Noodles&Co, Old Chicago Grill, Old Country Buffet, Olive Garden, Outback Steaks, Panda Express, Panino's Drive-Thru, Perkins, Pizza Hut/Taco Bell, PotBelly, Quiznos, Red Lobster, Red Robin, Royal Dragon, Ruby Tuesday, Starbucks, Steak'n Shake, ThunderBay Grille, TX Roadhouse, Uncle Nick's, Wendy's, 🏨 Candlewood Suites, Comfort Inn, Courtyard, Extended Stay America, Fairfield Inn, Hampton Inn, Hilton Garden, Holiday Inn, Quality Suites, Radisson, Red Roof Inn, Residence Inn, Sleep Inn, Staybridge Suites, Studio+, Super 8, 🅞 🅷, Advance Parts, Aldi Foods, AT&T, Best Buy, Buick/GMC, Chrysler/Dodge/Jeep, Dick's, Discount Tire, Dodge, $Tree, Gordman's, Hancock Fabrics, Hobby Lobby, Home Depot, Hyundai, JoAnn Fabrics, K-Mart, Kohl's, Lexus, Lowe's, Marshall's, Michael's, Office Depot, Old Time Pottery, Old Navy, PetCo, Petsmart, Radio Shack, Sam's Club/gas, Target, Toyota/Scion, Tuesday Morning, Verizon, Walgreens, Walmart
12.5mm	E Riverside Blvd, Loves Park, **0-2 mi** 🅂🅖 BP, Mobil/dsl, Phillips 66/dsl, Road Ranger/Pilot/Subway/dsl, Shell, 🍴 Arby's, BeefARoo, Ciaobella, Culver's, DQ, Domino's, Happy Joe's Pizza, Japanese Express, KFC, McDonald's, 2nd Cousin's Grill, Taco Bell, Wendy's, 🏨 Holiday Inn Express, Quality Inn, 🅞 Audi/Honda/Jaguar/Mercedes, Autowerks, Farm&Fleet, Tuffy Auto, Walgreens, to Rock Cut SP, funpark
9mm	Il 173 🅂 to Rock Cut SP
3.5mm	S Beloit Toll Plaza, 🅒
2	Rockton Rd, 🅂🅖 ⬤Loves/Hardee's/dsl/scales/24hr
1.5mm	**Welcome Ctr/rest area eb, full ♿ facilities, info, 🚬, litter barrels, 🅒, petwalk, playground, RV dump**
1	US 51 N, IL 75 W, S Beloit N🅖 Road Ranger/McDonald's/dsl, 🅂 🅖 Road Ranger/⬤/Subway/dsl/E85/scales/24hr, ⬤FLYING J/Denny's/dsl/scales/24hr, Best Western, South Beloit Inn, 🅞 Finnegan's RV Ctr, Pearl Lake camping (2mi)
0mm	Illinois/Wisconsin state line

INTERSTATE 94

Exit	Services
77mm	Illinois/Indiana state line
161	US 6, IL 83, Torrence Ave, **I-94 and I-80 run**

161	Continued
	together 3 mi. N🅖 BP, 🍴 Arby's, Bob Evans, Chili's, Dixie Kitchen, Hooters, IHOP, Olive Garden, On-the-Border, Oriental Palace, Wendy's, 🏨 Comfort Suites, Days Inn, Extended Stay America, Fairfield Inn, Red Roof Inn, Sleep Inn, Super 8, 🅞 Best Buy, Chrysler/Jeep, Dominick's Foods, Firestone/auto, Home Depot, JustTires, K-Mart, PepBoys, Radio Shack, 🅂🅖 Gas City, Marathon, Mobil, 🍴 Al's Diner, Brown's Chicken/pasta, Burger King, Dunkin Donuts, Golden Crown Rest., McDonald's, Pappy's Gyro's, 🅞 Auto Clinic, Chevrolet, Saab, Sam's Club, SunRise Foods, Walgreen
I-94 and I-80 run together 3 mi.	
74b [160]	I-80/I-294, W
74a	IL 394 S, to Danville
73b a	US 6,159th St, N🅖 Mobil, 🍴 Applebee's, Buffalo Wild Wings, Fuddrucker's, Outback Steaks, Panda Express, Quiznos, Rib Ribs, Sonic, Starbucks, Taco Bell, White Castle, 🅞 BigLots, Hyundai, JC Penney, Kia, Lincoln/Mercury, Macy's, Marshall's, Michael's, Nissan, Office Depot, Old Navy, PetCo, Target, Toyota/Scion, USPO, vet, 🅂 🅖 BP, Marathon, 🍴 Harold's Chicken, McDonald's, Popeye's, Rally's, Shark's, Subway, 🏨 Cherry Lane Motel, 🅞 Aldi Foods, Jewel-Osco, Stanfa Tire/repair
71b a	Sibley Blvd, N 🅖 Citgo, Mobil/dsl, Valero/dsl, 🍴 McDonald's, Nicky's Gyros, Popeye's, Quiznos, Shark's, Subway, 🏨 Baymont Inn, 🅞 Family$, Pete's Mkt, 🅂🅖 Clark, Marathon/dsl, Shell, 🍴 Baskin-Robbins/Dunkin Donuts, Burger King, KFC, Snapper's Chicken, Family Wendy's, White Castle, 🏨 Best Motel, 🅞 Advance Parts, AutoZone, $General, Fairplay Foods, Food4Less/gas, Menards, Radio Shack, Walgreens
70b a	Dolton Ave
69	(from eb), Beaubien Woods Forest Preserve
68b a	130th St
66b	115th St, 🅂🍴 McDonald's
66a	111th Ave, 🅂🅖 Citgo/dsl, Shell, 🅞 🅷, Firestone/auto
65	103rd Ave, Stony Island Ave
63	I-57, S (exits left from wb)
62	Wentworth Ave (from eb), N🅖 Citgo, Mobil, 🍴 Subway
61b	87th St, N 🅖 BP, Shell, 🍴 Burger King, McDonald's, 🅂🍴 Stabucks, Subway, 🅞 AutoZone, Best Buy, Burlington Coats, $Tree, Food4Less, Home Depot, Jewel-Osco, Marshall's, O'Reilly Parts, Staples, Verizon
61a	83rd St (from eb), N🅖 Shell, 🍴 Subway, 🅞 st police
60c	79th St, N🅖 Mobil, Shell, 🍴 Brown's Chicken, 🅞 Walgreens, 🅂🅖 Citgo/dsl, 🍴 Church's
60b	76th St, N🅖 BP, Mobil, Shell, 🅞 Walgreens, 🅂🍴 KFC/Pizza Hut, Popeye's

📷 = gas 🍴 = food 🏨 = lodging 🄾 = other   Copyright 2012 - The Next Exit

Exit	Services

INTERSTATE 94 CONT'D

Exit	Services
60a	75th St (from eb), N 📷 BP, Mobil, Shell, 🄾 Aldi Foods, S 🍴 KFC, Pizza Hut, Popeye's, 🄾 Walgreens
59c	71st St, N 📷 BP, S 🍴 McDonald's
59a	I-90 E, to Indiana Toll Rd
58b	63rd St (from eb), N 📷 Citgo, S 📷 Mobil
58a	I-94 divides into local and express, 59th St, S 📷 BP
57b	Garfield Blvd, N 🍴 Al's Beef, Checker's, Grand Chinese Kitchen, Subway, 🄾 Family$, Walgreens, S 📷 Citgo, Mobil, Shell/24hr, 🍴 Wendy's, 🄾 🄷
57a	51st St
56b	47th St (from eb)
56a	43rd St, S 📷 BP/Subway/dsl, Citgo/dsl
55b	Pershing Rd
55a	35th St, S to New Comiskey Park
54	31st St
53c	I-55, Stevenson Pkwy, N to downtown, Lakeshore Dr
53b	I-55, Stevenson Pkwy, S to St Louis
52c	18th St (from eb), W 🄾 Dominick's Foods
52b	Roosevelt Rd, Taylor St (from wb), N 📷 Citgo, 🄾 Best Buy, Home Depot, Walgreens, Whole Foods Mkt
52a	Taylor St, Roosevelt Rd (from eb), N 📷 Citgo
51h-i	I-290 W, to, W Suburbs
51g	E Jackson Blvd, downtown
51f	W Adams St, downtown
51e	Monroe St (from eb), downtown, S 🏨 Crowne Plaza, 🄾 Dominick's Foods, Walgreens
51d	Madison St (from eb), downtown, S 🏨 Crowne Plaza, 🄾 Dominick's Foods, Walgreens
51c	E Washington Blvd, downtown
51b	W Randolph St, downtown
51a	Lake St (from wb)
50b	E Ohio St downtown, S 📷 Marathon
50a	Ogden Ave
49b a	Augusta Blvd, Division St, N 🄾 Lexus, S 📷 BP, Shell, 🍴 Pizza Hut
48b	IL 64, North Ave, N 📷 BP, S 📷 Valero, 🄾 Mercedes
48a	Armitage Ave, N 🄾 Best Buy, Kohl's, S 📷 Shell, 🄾 Jaguar, Land Rover, Volvo
47c b	Damen Ave, N 📷 Citgo, car/vanwash
47a	Western Ave, Fullerton Ave, N 📷 Citgo, 🍴 Burger King, Dunkin Donuts, Popeye's, Starbucks, Subway, 🄾 Costco/gas, Home Depot, Jo-Ann Fabrics, Pepboys, Petsmart, Staples, Target, S 📷 Marathon
46b a	Diversey Ave, California Ave, N 📷 Citgo, S 🍴 IHOP/24hr, Popeye's, 🄾 Walgreens
45c	Belmont Ave, N 🍴 Wendy's
45b	Kimball Ave, N 📷 Marathon/dsl, S 📷 Valero, 🍴 Dunkin Donuts, Pizza Hut, Subway, 🄾 Aldi Foods, Best Buy, Radio Shack, Walgreens
45a	Addison St
44b	Pulaski Ave, Irving Park Rd, N 📷 BP, Mobil
44a	IL 19, Keeler Ave, Irving Park Rd, N 📷 BP, Shell/24hr, 🄾 to Wrigley Field
43c	Montrose Ave
43b	I-90, W
43a	Wilson Ave
42	W Foster Ave (from wb), S 📷 Citgo, Marathon
41mm	Chicago River, N Branch
41c	IL 50 S, to Cicero, to I-90, W
41b a	US 14, Peterson Ave, N 🄾 Whole Foods Mkt
39b a	Touhy Ave, N 📷 BP/dsl, Shell/Circle K, 🄾 Cassidy Tire, Toyota/Scion, S 📷 BP, Citgo, Shell, 🍴 Baja Fresh, Baskin-Robbins/Dunkin Donuts, Buffalo Wild Wings, Burger King, Chili's, Chipotle Mexican, ChuckeCheese, Jack's Rest./24hr, McDonald's, Noodles&Co, Outback Steaks, Quiznos, Red Robin, Sander's Rest., Starbucks, Subway, 🏨 Holiday Inn, 🄾 Barnes&Noble, Best Buy, Dick's, GNC, Jewel-Osco, Lee's Parts, Nissan, Office Depot, PepBoys, PetCo, Petsmart, Radio Shack, Walgreens, Walmart, vet
37b a	IL 58, Dempster St
35	Old Orchard Rd, N 📷 BP, Shell, 🍴 Bloomingdale's, CA Pizza Kitchen, CheeseCake Factory, McCormick&Schmick's Rest., 🄾 🄷, Nissan, mall, S 🍴 Ruby Tuesday, 🏨 Extended Stay America, Hampton Inn
34c b	E Lake Ave, N 📷 BP, 🍴 Omaha Steaks, Panda Express, Starbucks, 🄾 Fresh Mkt Foods, GNC, S 📷 BP, Shell, 🍴 DQ
34a	US 41 S, Skokie Rd (from eb)
33b a	Willow Rd, S 📷 BP, Shell, 🍴 Starbucks, 🄾 Dominick's Foods, Walgreens
31	E Tower Rd, S 🄾 BMW, Carmax, Chrysler/Dodge/Jeep, Infiniti, Mercedes, Toyota/Scion, vet
30b a	Dundee Rd (from wb, no EZ return), S 📷 Citgo, Marathon, 🍴 Barnaby's Rest., Morton's Steaks, Potbelly's, Ruth's Chris Steaks, Starbucks, 🏨 Renaissance
29	US 41, to Waukegan, to Tri-state tollway
28mm	IL 43, Waukegan Rd, N 📷 BP, Shell, 🍴 Baja Fresh, Old Country Buffet, 🏨 Red Roof Inn, Embassy Suites, 🄾 Best Buy, Home Depot, Jewel-Osco, NTB, Steinmart, TJ Maxx
26mm	I-294 S, Lake-Cook Rd (from sb), E 🍴 J-Alexander's Rest., 🏨 Hyatt
25mm	Deerfield Rd toll plaza, 🄲
24mm	Deerfield Rd (from nb), W 📷 Mobil, 🏨 Marriott Suites
22mm	IL 22, Half Day Rd, E 🏨 La Quinta
19mm	IL 60, Town Line Rd, E 🄷, W 🏨 Hilton Garden, Residence Inn
18mm	**Lake Forest Oasis both lanes**, E 📷 Mobil/dsl, 🍴 KFC, McDonald's, Panda Express, Starbucks, Subway, Taco Bell, 🄾 info
16mm	IL 176, Rockland Rd (no nb re-entry), E 🄾 Harley-Davidson, to Lamb's Farm
14mm	IL 137, Buckley Rd, E 🄾 to VA 🄷, Chicago Med School
11mm	IL 120 E, Belvidere Rd (no nb re-entry), E 🄷
10mm	IL 21, Milwaukee Ave (from eb, no sb re-entry), E 🍴 Papa John's, 🄾 🄷, Six Flags
8mm	IL 132, Grand Ave, E 📷 Speedway/dsl, 🍴 Baskin-Robbins/Dunkin Donuts, Burger King, ChuckeCheese, Cracker Barrel, Culver's, Golden Corral, Ichibahn, IHOP, Joe's Crabshack, Jimmy John's, KFC/LJ Silver, McDonald's, Moe's SW Grill, Oberweiss, Old Chicago Red Hots, Olive Garden, Outback Steaks, Rosati's Pizza, Starbucks, Subway, 🏨 Best Western, Country Inn&Suites, Grand Hotel, Extended Stay America, Hampton Inn, Key Lime Cove Resort, La Quinta, 🄾 Six Flags Park, **0-2 mi W** 📷 Mobil, Shell/Circle K, 🍴 Applebee's, Bakers Square, Boston Mkt, Caribou Coffee, Chili's, Chipotle Mexican, Denny's, Giordano's Pizza, Jimano's Pizza,

Left margin (vertical): **E** ↑ **W** ↓ CHICAGO AREA · CHICAGO AREA · CHICAGO AREA

IL

Right margin (vertical): CHICAGO AREA · GURNEE

INTERSTATE 94 CONT'D

Exit	Services
8mm	Continued
	LoneStar Steaks, McDonald's, Noodles&Co, Panda Express, Panera Bread, Pizza Hut, Potbelly's, Red Lobster, Ruby Tuesday, Saluto's Italian, Starbucks, Steak'n Shake, Taco Bell, TGIFriday's, Uno, Wendy's, White Castle, 🛏 Comfort Inn, Fairfield Inn, Vista Inn, 🄾 URGENT CARE, AT&T, AutoZone, Bass Pro Shops, Best Buy, Buick/GMC, Chrysler/Dodge/Jeep, $Tree, Dominick's Foods, Firestone/auto, Ford, Goodyear, Gurnee Mills Outlet Mall/famous brands, Home Depot, Honda, Hyundai, Jewel-Osco, Kohl's, Lowe's, Menards, Michael's, Nissan, Old Navy, Petsmart, Radio Shack, Sam's Club, Sears Grand, Target, TJ Maxx, Verizon, VW, Walgreens, Walmart, World Mkt
5mm	Waukegan toll plaza, Waukegan toll plaza, 🄲
2mm	IL 173 (from nb, no return), Rosecrans Ave, **E** to IL Beach SP
1b	US 41 S, to Waukegan (from sb), **E** 🄾 Collier RV Ctr
1a	Russell Rd, **W** 🅿 Citgo/dsl/scales/24hr, TA/Country Pride/dsl/scales/24hr/@, 🄾 Peterbilt
0mm	Illinois/Wisconsin state line

INTERSTATE 255 (ST LOUIS)

Exit	Services
I-255 begins/ends on I-270, exit 7.	
30	I-270, W to Kansas City, E to Indianapolis
29	IL 162, to Glen Carbon, to Pontoon Beach, Granite City
26	Horseshoe Lake Rd, **E** st police
25b a	I-55/I-70, W to St Louis, E to Chicago, Indianapolis
24	Collinsville Rd, **E** 🅿 BP/24hr, 🍴 Jack-in-the-Box, 🄾 Shop'n Save, **W** Fairmount Racetrack
20	I-64, US 50, W to St Louis, E to Louisville, **services 1 mi E** off I-64, exit 9.
19	State St, E St Louis, **E** 🛏 Western Inn, 🄾 Holten SP
17b a	IL 15, E St Louis, to Belleville, Centreville, **E** 🅿 ⭐FLYING J /Denny's/dsl/scales/24hr, **W** 🅿 Phillips 66
15	Mousette Lane, **E** 🄷, **W** 🄾 Peterbilt
13	IL 157, to Cahokia, **E** 🅿 Phillips 66, **W** 🅿 BP/24hr, QT, 🍴 Capt D's, China Express, Classic K Burgers, DQ, Domino's, Hardee's, Jade Garden, KFC, McDonald's, Pizza Hut, Popeye's, Rally's, Subway, 🛏 Holiday Inn Express, 🄾 Advance Parts, Aldi Foods, AutoZone, Buick/GMC, Cahokia RV Park, CarQuest, Curves, Dobb's Tires, Family$, $General, Schnuck's, Shop'n Save Foods, Walgreens, Walmart/drugs, Cahokia RV Parque (2mi)
10	IL 3 N, to Cahokia, E St Louis, **W** 🅿 ZX/Subway/dsl
9	to Dupo, **W** 🅿 BP
6	IL 3 S, to Columbia (exits left from sb), **E** 🅿 Phillips 66, Shell/dsl/24hr, 🛏 Hampton Inn (2mi), 🄾 Chevrolet
4mm	Missouri/Illinois state line, Mississippi River
3	Koch Rd
2	MO 231, Telegraph Rd, **N** 🅿 Conoco, Shell/Circle K, 🍴 McDonald's, Pizza Hut/Taco Bell, Steak'n Shake, Waffle House, 🄾 Advance Parts, $Tree, Radio Shack, Walmart, Jefferson Barracks Nat Cem, **S** 🅿 CFM/dsl, Mobil, QT, Shell, 🍴 China Wok, DQ, Imo's Pizza, 🄾 Curves
1d c	US 50, US 61, US 67, Lindbergh Blvd, Lemay Ferry Rd, accesses same as I-55 exit 197 E, **N** 🅿 Phillips 66, 🍴 Arby's, Buffalo Wild Wings, ChuckeCheese, CiCi's Pizza, Dillard's, Hometown Buffet, HoneyBaked Ham,

Exit	Services
1d c	Continued
	Hooters, KFC, Krispy Kreme, Macaroni Grill, Noodles&Co, Qdoba Mexican, Quizno's, Station Subs, Steak'n Shake, St Louis Bread Co, Subway, Tucker's Place, 🄾 Advance Parts, Best Buy, Border's Book, Costco/gas, Dillard's, Discount Tire, Dodge, Ford, Home Depot, JC Penney, Kia, K-Mart, Macy's, Marshall's, NTB, Sears/auto, Tuesday Morning, mall, **S** 🅿 Phillips 66, 🍴 Jack-in-the-Box, McDonald's, Rich & Charlie's Italian, White Castle, 🄾 BigLots, $General, Firestone, Old Navy, Petsmart, Sam's Club/gas, Walgreens
1b a	I-55, S to Memphis, N to St Louis. I-255 begins/ends on I-55, exit 196.

INTERSTATE 270 (ST LOUIS)

See Missouri Interstate 270 (St Louis)

INTERSTATE 294 (CHICAGO)

Exit	Services
I-294 begins/ends on I-94, exit 74. Numbering descends from west to east.	
I-294 & I-80 run together 5 mi. See Interstate 80, exits 155-160.	
5mm	I-80 W, access to I-57
5.5mm	167th St, toll booth, 🄲
6mm	US 6, 159th St, **E** 🅿 BP, Citgo, Mobil, Shell, 🄾 Aldi Foods, AutoZone, Walgreen, **W** 🅿 Citgo/dsl, Marathon/ dsl, 🍴 Baskin-Robbins/Dunkin Donuts, Burger King, Harold's Chicken, McDonald's, Popeye's, Subway, Taco Bell, White Castle, 🛏 Comfort Inn, 🄾 AutoZone, Big-Lots, $Tree, Family$, U-Haul, Walgreens
11mm	Cal Sag Channel
12mm	IL 50, Cicero Ave, **E** 🅿 Citgo/7-11, Speedway, 🍴 Onion Field Rest., **W** 🅿 BP, Gas City/Subway/dsl/24hr, 🍴 Boston Mkt, IHOP, Pizza Hut, Pizzaria Uno, Popeye's, Portillo's Dogs, Quizno's, Starbucks, 🛏 Baymont Inn, Hampton Inn, 🄾 Best Buy, Dominick's Foods, NTB, PepBoys, Sears/auto
18mm	US 12/20, 95th St, **E** 🅿 Clark, 🍴 McDonald's, Papa John's, 🄾 🄷, Buick, Honda, Mazda, Sears/auto, mall, **W** 🅿 Citgo/7-11, Shell, Speedway/dsl, 🍴 Arby's, Burger King, Denny's, George's Rest., Quizno's, Schoop's Burgers, Wendy's, 🛏 Exel Inn, 🄾 🄷, Jewel-Osco, Walgreen
20mm	toll booth, 🄲
22mm	75th St, Willow Springs Rd
23mm	I-55, Wolf Rd, to Hawthorne Park
25mm	Hinsdale Oasis both lanes, 🅿 Mobil/dsl, 🍴 Baskin-Robbins, Wendy's/24hr
28mm	US 34, Ogden Ave, **E** zoo, **W** 🅿 BP, Shell/deli, 🍴 Dunkin Donuts, McDonald's, Starbucks, 🄾 🄷,

Left margin labels: **GURNEE** (E ↕ W, N ↕ S)　　**CHICAGO AREA** (E ↕ W)

Right margin: **IL**

INTERSTATE 294 CONT'D (CHICAGO)

Exit	Services
28mm	Continued Audi/Porsche, Firestone/auto, LandRover, Maserati, Rolls-Royce/Bentley/Ferrari/Lotus, Wild Oats Mkt
28.5mm	Cermak Rd (from sb, no return)
29mm	I-88 tollway
30mm	toll booth, 🅞
31mm	IL 38, Roosevelt Rd (no EZ nb return), E 🅖 Citgo/dsl, 🛏 Hillside Manor Motel
32mm	I-290 W, to Rockford (from nb)
34mm	I-290 (from sb), to Rockford
38mm	**O'Hare Oasis both lanes,** 🅖 Mobil/dsl, 🍴 Burger King, TCBY
39mm	IL 19, W (from sb), Irving Park Rd, E 🅖 Clark, Marathon/dsl, 🅞 7-11, Walgreen, **1 mi** E 🅖 BP/repair, Clark, 🍴 DQ, Dunkin Donuts, McDonald's, Subway, Wendy's, 🛏 Comfort Suites, 🅞 Aldi Foods, W 🛏 Candlewood Suites, Day's Inn, Hampton Inn, Howard Johnson, Sheraton
40mm	I-190 W, **E services from I-90, exit 79** 🅖 Mobil, 🍴 McDonald's, 🛏 Courtyard, Doubletree, Embassy Suites, Holiday Inn, Hotel Softel, Hyatt, Marriott, Radisson, Rosemont Suites, Westin
41mm	toll booth, 🅞
42mm	Touhy Ave, W 🅖 Mobil/service, 🍴 Tiffany's Rest., 🛏 Comfort Inn
43mm	Des Plaines River

44mm	Dempster St (from nb, no return), E 🏥, W 🍴 Dunkin Donuts, Subway
46mm	IL 58, Golf Rd, E 🅖 Citgo/dsl, Shell, 🍴 Omega Rest., Senoya Oriental, 🅞 Best Buy, CVS Drug, Golf Mill Mall, Target, auto repair
49mm	Willow Rd, W 🍴 TGIFriday, 🛏 Baymont Inn, Doubletree Suites, Courtyard, Fairfield Inn, Motel 6, **1 mi** W **on Mil-waukee** E 🅖 BP, 🍴 Burger King, Denny's, McDonald's, 🛏 Wingate Inn
53mm	Lake Cook Rd (no nb re-entry), E Hyatt, 🛏 Embassy Suites

I-294 begins/ends on I-94.

INTERSTATE 474 (PEORIA)

Exit	Services
15	I-74, E to Bloomington, W to Peoria
9	IL 29, E Peoria, to Pekin, N 🅖 Shell/Arby's, Thornton's, 🍴 Driftwood Pizza, DQ, Pizza Hut, Taco John's, 🛏 Ragon Motel, 🅞 Riverboat Casino (6mi), S 🅖 Casey's, Shell/Subway/dsl, 🍴 Denny's, KFC, McDonald's, Mickie's Pizza, 🅞 Chrysler/Dodge/Jeep, Toyota
8mm	Illinois River
6b a	US 24, Adams St, Bartonville, S 🅖 BP/dsl, Shell/24hr, 🍴 Hardee's, KFC, McDonald's, Tyroni's Café
5	Airport Rd, S 🅖 Phillips 66/e-85
3a	to IL 116, Farmington, S Wildlife Prairie Park
0b a	I-74, W to Moline, E to Peoria. I-474 begins/ends on I-74, exit 87.

INDIANA

INTERSTATE 64

Exit	Services
124mm	Indiana/Kentucky state line, Ohio River
123	IN 62 E, New Albany, N 🅖 Shell/Circle K, Sunoco, 🍴 DQ, 🅞 Firestone/auto, Save-a-Lot, U-Haul, S 🅖 BP, Marathon/dsl/24hr, Shell/Circle K, 🍴 Lancaster's Deli, Subway, Waffle House, 🛏 Hampton Inn, Holiday Inn Express, 🅞 🏥
121	I-265 E, to I-65 (exits left from eb), N access to 🏥
119	US 150 W, to Greenville, **1/2 mi** N 🅖 Marathon, 🍴 Bean St Cafe, Beef O'Brady's, China Cafe, Domino's, DQ, El Nopal, Los Indios, Papa John's, Sam's Family Rest., Subway, Taco Bell, Tumbleweed SW Grill, 🅞 Huber Winery, JayC Foods, Rite Aid, Walgreens, urgent care
118	IN 62, IN 64W, to Georgetown, N 🅖 Marathon/dsl/24hr, Shell/Circle K, 🍴 Korner Kitchen, McDonald's, 🛏 Motel 6, 🅞 Mr. Hardware, Thriftway Foods, vet, S 🅖 Marathon/dsl
115mm	**Welcome Ctr wb, full ♿ facilities, vending,** 🅞, 🚮, **litter barrels**
113	to Lanesville
105	IN 135, to Corydon, N 🅖 Marathon/dsl, Shell/24hr, 🍴 Big Boy, 🛏 Comfort Inn, S 🅖 BP/dsl, 5 Star, 🍴 Arby's, Beef O'Brady's, Burger King, Cracker Barrel, Culver's, Domino's, DQ, El Nopal Mexican, Hong Kong Buffet, KFC, Lee's Chicken, LJ Silver, McDonald's, O'Charley's, Papa John's, Papa Murphy's, Pizza Hut, Quiznos, Ryan's, Subway, Taco Bell, Waffle House, Wendy's, White Castle, 🛏 Baymont Inn, Hampton Inn, Holiday Inn Express, Super 8, 🅞 AutoZone, Big O Tire,

105	Continued Buick/Chevrolet, $Tree, Ford/Mercury, Radio Shack, Verizon, Walgreens, Walmart, RV camping
100mm	Blue River
97mm	parking area both lanes
92	IN 66, Carefree, N Marengo Caves, S 🅖 Marathon/dsl, rest./24hr, 🚛 Subway/dsl/scales/24hr, 🍴 Country Style Rest., 🛏 Days Inn, 🅞 to Wyandotte Caves, Harrison Crawford SF, Carefree Truckwash, repair
88mm	Hoosier Nat Forest eastern boundary
86	IN 37, to Sulphur, N to Patoka Lake, S 🅖 🍴 🅞 scenic route
79	IN 37, to Tell City, St Croix, S 🅖 Marathon/Subway/pizza/dsl, 🅞 to Hoosier NF, Rec. Facilities, 🅞, to OH River Br
76mm	Anderson River
72	IN 145, to Birdseye, N to Patoka Lake, S gas, winery (2mi), St Meinrad Coll
63	IN 162, to Ferdinand, N 🅖 Sunoco/dsl, 🍴 Subway, Wendy's, 🛏 Comfort Inn, 🅞 CVS Drug, Ferdinand SF, S (8mi)Lake Rudolph RV Camping
58mm	**rest areas both lanes, full ♿ facilities, info, vending,** 🚮, **litter barrels,** 🅞
57	US 231, to Dale, Huntingburg, N 🏥, S 🅖 Shell/dsl/24hr, 🍴 Denny's, Windell's Cafe, 🛏 Best Western, Motel 6, 🅞 Lincoln Boyhood Home, Lincoln SP
54	IN 161, to Holland, Tennyson
39	IN 61, Lynnville, N 🅖 Fast Fuel, 🍴 Thara Jean's Rest., 🅞 USPO
32mm	Wabash & Erie Canal

INTERSTATE 64 CONT'D

Exit	Services
29b a	I-164 S, IN 57 S, to Evansville
25b a	US 41, to Evansville **N** 🅿 *FLYING J*/ Denny's/dsl/scales/24hr, *Loves*/Wendy's/dsl/24hr, 🅿/Subway/dsl/24hr, 🏨 Quality Inn, 🄾 Blue Beacon, truck repair/ lube, **S** 🍴 Arby's, Denny's, McDonald's, Stoll's Amish Rest., 🏨 Best Western, Comfort Inn, Holiday Inn Express, Super 8, 🄾 st police, to U, S IN
18	IN 65, to Cynthiana, **S** 🅿 Motomart/ dsl/24hr
12	IN 165, Poseyville, **S** 🅿, dsl, 🍴, 🄾 Chevrolet, New Harmonie Hist Area/SP
7mm	**Black River Welcome Ctr eb, full ♿ facilities, 🅿, 🛉, litter barrels, petwalk**
5mm	Black River
4	IN 69 S, New Harmony, Griffin, **1 mi N** gas/dsl, food, motel, antiques, USPO, **S** Harmony St Park
2mm	Big Bayou River
0mm	Indiana/Illinois state line, Wabash River

INTERSTATE 65

Exit	Services
262	I-90, W to Chicago, E to Ohio, I-65 begins/ ends on US 12, US 20.
261	15th Ave, to Gary, **E** 🅿 Mack/Volvo Trucks, **W** 🅿 Clark
259b a	I-94/80, US 6W
258	US 6, Ridge Rd, **E** 🅿 Marathon/dsl, Speedway/dsl, 🍴 Country Lounge Diner, Diner's Choice Rest., **W** 🅿 Clark, Save Gas
255	61st Ave, Merrillville, **E** 🅿 Speedway/dsl, Thornton's, 🍴 Arby's, Cracker Barrel, McDonald's, Pizza Hut/Taco Bell, Wendy's, 🏨 Comfort Inn, $Inn, EconoLodge 🄾 Ⓗ, Chevrolet, I-65 Repair, Menards, Mr Tire, **1 mi W** 🅿 Shell, 🍴 Burger King, Subway
253b	US 30 W, Merrillville, **W** 🅿 Mobil/dsl, Shell, Speedway/dsl, 🍴 Abuelo's Mexican, Applebee's, Barnelli's Rest., Baskin-Robbins/ Dunkin Donuts, DQ, Denny's, Gino's Rest., Golden Corral, Hooters, House of Kobe, Ichiban Steaks, Johnnie's Rest., KFC, La Carreta's, Maloney's Grill, McDonald's, Old Chicago Pizza, Oriental Buffet, Outback Steaks, Panda Express, Panera Bread, Pepe's Mexican, Pizza Hut, Portillo's Hot Dogs, Starbucks, Steak'n Shake, Subway, TX Corral Steaks, Wendy's, White Castle, 🏨 Courtyard, Deluxe Inn, Fairfield Inn, Hampton Inn, Holiday Inn Express, Radisson, Red Roof Inn, Residence Inn, 🄾 Ⓗ, Aldi Foods, Buick/GMC, Cadillac, CarX, CarQuest, Chrysler/Dodge/Jeep, $Tree, Discount Tire, Fanny May Candies, Ford, Goodyear/auto, Hyundai, Jo-Ann Fabrics, K-Mart, Lincoln/Mercury, Mazda, Meijer/dsl, Midas, Mr Tire, NTB, Old Time Pottery, Staples, Subaru, U-Haul, Walgreens, Verizon

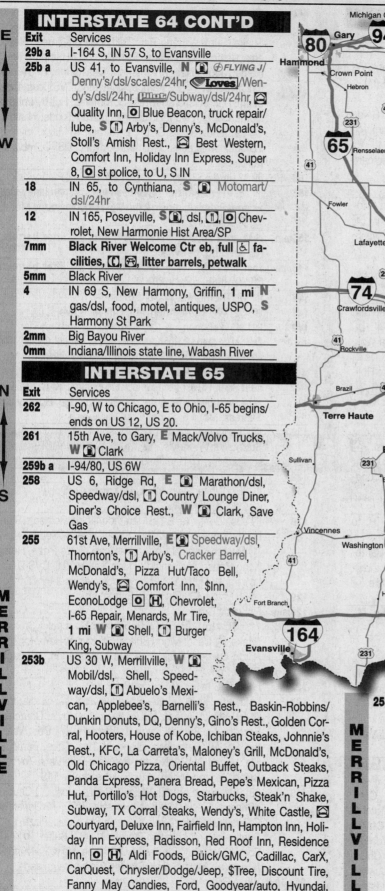

253a	US 30 E, **E** 🅿 BP/Noble Romans, Speedway/dsl, 🍴 Arby's, Bakers Square, Bob Evans, Buffalo Wild Wings, Chick-fil-A, Chili's, Chipotle Mexican, ChuckeCheese, Culver's, Don Pablo, IHOP, Jamba Juice, Jimmy John's, Joe's Crabshack, KFC/LJ Silver, Longhorn Steaks, McDonald's, Olive Garden, Peking Buffet, Popeye's, Potbelly, Red Lobster, Red Robin, Ruby Tuesday, Sheffield's Rest., Starbucks, Taco Bell, Taco Depot, TGIFriday's, Wendy's, 🏨 Best Value Inn, Best Western, Candlewood Suites, Comfort Suites, Country Inn&Suites, Economy Inn, Extended Stay America, Hilton Garden, La Quinta, Motel 6, Quality Inn, Super 8, 🄾 AT&T, Audi/VW, AutoZone, Best Buy, BigLots, Carmax, Costco/gas, Dick's, Firestone/auto, Gander Mtn, Hobby Lobby, Home Depot, Honda, JC Penney, Kia, Kohl's, Lowe's, Macy's, Michael's, Nissan, Office Depot, Old Navy, PetCo,

IN

INTERSTATE 65 CONT'D

Exit	Services
253a	Continued
	Petsmart, Sam's Club/gas, Sears/auto, Target, TJ Maxx, Tire Barn, Toyota/Scion, Tuesday Morning, Walmart/McDonald's, mall, vet
249	109th Ave, **W** 🍴 Beggars Pizza, China Garden, Golden Apple Rest., Jimmy John's, Oberweis Icecream, 🅾 GNC, Verizon, Walgreens
247	US 231, Crown Point, **W** 🅖 Mobil/dsl, 🅾 🅗, Vietnam Vet Mem
241mm	**weigh sta sb**
240	IN 2, Lowell, **E** 🅖 ⓕFLYING J/Denny's/dsl/24hr/@, Mobil/Burger King, 🅒/McDonalds/dsl/scales/24hr, 🍴 Arby's, Subway, 🛏 Comfort Inn, Super 8, 🅾 truck wash, **W** st police
234mm	Kankakee River
231mm	**rest area both lanes, full** 🦽 **facilities,** 🅒**, info,** 🅿**, litter barrels, vending, petwalk**
230	IN 10, Roselawn, **E** 🅖 Gas City/Kozy Kitchen/dsl/scales/24hr, ❤Loves/Arby's/dsl/scales/24hr, **W** 🅖 Family Express/e85, Marathon/Subway, 🍴 China Wok, J&J Pizza, Sycamore Drive-In, 🅾 CarQuest, CVS Drug, $General, Fagen Drug, IGA Foods, TrueValue, Lake Holiday Camping, Oak Lake Camping
220	IN 14, Winamac, **W** 🅖 BP/Subway/dsl, 🅾 Fair Oaks Farms Store
215	IN 114, Rensselaer, **E** 🅖 Family Express/dsl/e85/24hr, 🍴 Arby's, DQ, KFC, McDonald's, Rensselear Rest., 🛏 Holiday Inn Express, Knights Inn, 🅾 🅗, **W** 🅖 Marathon/Trail Tree Rest./dsl/24hr, 🍴 Burger King, 🛏 Economy Inn, 🅾 fireworks, tires/repair/towing/24hr
212mm	Iroquois River
205	US 231, Remington, **E** 🅖 BP/dsl, Crazy D/dsl, 🅾 🅗, to St Joseph's Coll
201	US 24/231, Remington, **E** 🅾 Caboose Lake RV Camping, **W** 🅖 Petro/Shell/Iron Skillet/dsl/scales/24hr/@, 🅒/Subway/dsl/scales/24hr, 🍴 KFC, McDonald's, 🛏 Sunset Inn, Super 8
196mm	**rest area both lanes, full** 🦽 **facilities, vending,** 🅒**, info,** 🅿**, litter barrels, petwalk**
193	US 231, to Chalmers, **E** 🅖 BP/DQ/Stuckey's
188	IN 18, to Brookston, Fowler, many windmills
178	IN 43, W Lafayette, **E** 🅖 GA/Taco Bell, Phillips 66/Subway/dsl, 🍴 McDonald's, Wendy's, 🛏 EconoLodge, 🅾 to Tippecanoe Bfd, museum, st police, **W** to Purdue U
176mm	Wabash River
175	IN 25, Lafayette, **E** 🅖 BP/dsl, Family Express/dsl/e85, **W** 🅾 🅗
172	IN 26, Lafayette, **E** 🍴 Cracker Barrel, DQ, El Rodeo, Starbucks, Steak'n Shake, Subway, Taj Mahal, White Castle, 🛏 Baymont Inn, Candlewood Suites, Comfort Inn, Comfort Suites, Days Inn, La Quinta, Motel 6, TownePlace Suites, 🅾 Meijer/dsl/e85, **Visitor's Ctr**, **W** 🅖 BP/Circle K/dsl/24hr, Citgo, Shell, Speedway/dsl, 🍴 Arby's, Bob Evans, Burger King, Camille's Cafe, Chick-fil-A, Chili's, ChuckeCheese, Country Cafe, Culvers, Denny's, Don Pablo, Fazoli's, Golden Corral, Grindstone Charlie's, Hour Time Rest., IHOP, Jimmy John's, KFC, Logan's Roadhouse, McAlister's Deli, McDonald's, Moe's SW Grill, Mt Jack's, Olive Garden, Outback Steaks,

N / S (Lafayette area markers on left margin)

Exit	Services
172	Continued
	Pizza Hut, Sonic, Spageddie's, Starbucks, Steak'n Shake, Subway, Taco Bell, TGIFriday's, 🛏 Best Western, Clarion, Courtyard, Fairfield Inn, Hampton Inn, Homewood Suites, Knights Inn, Quality Inn, Red Roof Inn, Super 8, 🅾 🅗, Aamco, Chevrolet, CVS Drug, Discount Tire, $General, $Tree, Gordman's, Hobby Lobby, Home Depot, Hyundai, Lowe's, Marsh Foods, Nissan, Office Depot, Sam's Club/gas, Target, TJ Maxx, Toyota, Verizon, Walgreens, Walmart/Subway, USPO, vet, to Purdue U
168	IN 38, IN 25 S, Dayton, **E** 🅖 BP/Subway, Pantry/dsl
158	IN 28, to Frankfort, **E** 🅖 BP/Subway/dsl, 🅾 Harley-Davidson, Peterbilt, repair, **2 mi W** 🛏 Lincoln Lodge Motel, 🅾 🅗, camping
150mm	**rest area sb, full** 🦽 **facilities, info,** 🅿**, litter barrels,** 🅒**, vending, petwalk**
148mm	**rest area nb, full** 🦽 **facilities, info,** 🅿**, litter barrels,** 🅒**, vending, petwalk**
146	IN 47, Thorntown, **W** 🅗, camping
141	US 52, W (exits left from sb), Lafayette Ave, **E** 🅗
140	IN 32, Lebanon, **E** 🅖 BP/repair, Marathon/dsl, 🍴 Denny's, Depot Rest., McDonald's, White Castle, 🛏 Comfort Inn, 🅾 🅗, AutoZone, Goodyear/auto, Menards, O'Reilly Parts, Pomp's Tires, **W** 🅖 McClure/dsl/e85, Shell, 🍴 Arby's, Flapjacks Pancakes, KFC, Steak'n Shake, Subway, Taco Bell, 🛏 EconoLodge, Holiday Inn Express, Motel 6, Super 8, 🅾 truckwash
139	IN 39, Lebanon, **E** 🅖 GA/dsl, 🍴 Penn Sta Subs, Starbucks, Wendy's, **W** 🅖 ⓕFLYING J/IHOP/dsl/LP/scales/24hr, 🅾 Donaldson's Chocolates
138	to US 52, Lebanon, **E** 🅖 BP/dsl
133	IN 267, Whitestown, **W** 🅖 ❤Loves/McDonald's/Subway/dsl/scales/24hr
130	IN 334, Zionsville, **E** 🅖 Marathon/Noble Roman's/Starbucks/Stuckey's/dsl/24hr, Shell/Circle K/Subway/dsl, 🍴 Burger King, El Rodeo Mexican, Fox's Pizza, Hong Kong House, McDonald's, Taco Bell, 🅾 🅗, CVS Drug, Lowe's, **W** 🅖 TA/BP/Popeye's/dsl/scales/24hr/@
129	I-865 E, to I-465 E, US 52, E (from sb)
126mm	Fishback Creek
124	71st St, **1 mi E** 🅖 BP, 🍴 Bob Evans, Starbucks, Steak'n Shake, 🛏 Candlewood Suites, Courtyard, Hampton Inn, Hilton Garden, Residence Inn, Wingate Inn, **W** Eagle Creek Park
123	I-465 S, S to 🖰
121	Lafayette Rd, **E** 🅖 GA, Speedway/dsl, 🛏 Quality Inn, **W** 🅖 Shell/Circle K, 🍴 Applebee's, Arby's, Church's, Fazoli's, La Bamba Burritos, Wendy's, 🛏 Best Value Inn, 🅾 🅗, Batteries+, Discount Tire, $Tree, Family$, Kia, Mazda, NAPA, Nissan, PepBoys, Tire Barn, Toyota/Scion, Verizon, Walmart/Subway, same as 119
119	38th St (no nb return), **W** 🅖 Speedway/dsl, 🍴 ChuckeCheese, Fiesta Mexican, Hooters, KFC, McDonald's, O'Charley's, Papa John's, Penn Sta Subs, Pizza Hut, Popeye's, Red Lobster, Taco Bell, WTT Buffet, 🅾 Aldi Foods, Best Buy, Chevrolet, CVS Drug, Honda, Hyundai, Meijer/dsl, Radio Shack, Staples, Tires+, same as 121
117.5mm	White River
117	MLK St (from sb), **W** 🅖 Marathon/dsl
116	29th St, 30th St (from nb), Marian Coll
115	21st St, **E** 🅖 Shell/Circle K, 🅾 🅗, **W** museums, zoo

(Side margin markers: LEBANON, INDIANAPOLIS AREA)

INTERSTATE 65 CONT'D

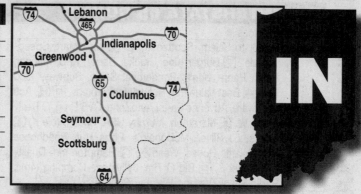

Exit	Services
114	MLK St, West St, downtown
113	US 31, IN 37, Meridian St, to downtown, 🅔🅞Ⓗ
112a	I-70 E, to Columbus
111	Market St, Michigan St, Ohio St, 🅔🍴 Hardee's, 🅦🅞 City Market, museum
110b	I-70 W, to St Louis
110a	Prospect St, Morris St, East St
109	Raymond St, 🅔Ⓗ, 🅦🅖 BP, Speedway/dsl, 🍴 Little Caesars, White Castle, 🅞 CVS Drug, Family$, Safeway
107	Keystone Ave, 🅔🅖 Mystik, 🛏 Best Value Inn, 🅞Ⓗ, 🅦🅖 Phillips 66/dsl, Speedway/dsl, Valero, 🍴 Big Kahuna Pizza, Burger King, Denny's, McDonald's, Subway, Wendy's, 🛏 Comfort Inn, 🅞 $General, Walmart Mkt, U of Indianapolis
106	I-465 and I-74
103	Southport Rd, 🅔🅖 BP/McDonald's, Shell/Circle K, 🍴 Arby's, Chick-fil-A, Chicago Grill, El Puerto, Hardee's, Hong Kong, Jimmy John's, Longhorn Steaks, Noble Roman's, O'Charley's, Panda Express, Panera Bread, Penn Sta Subs, Qdoba, Quiznos, Rally's, Starbucks, Taco Bell, 🅞 Aldi Foods, AT&T, Firestone/auto, Harley-Davidson, Home Depot, Kohl's, Menards, Meijer/dsl/e85, Radio Shack, Staples, Target, Verizon, 🅦🅖 Marathon/Circle K, Phillips 66, Speedway/dsl, 🍴 Bob Evans, Burger King, Carrabba's, Cheeseburger Paradise, Cracker Barrel, JT Johnson's Grill, KFC, McDonald's, Starbucks, Steak'n Shake, Subway, TX Roadhouse, Waffle House, Wendy's, 🛏 Best Western, Comfort Suites, Country Inn&Suites, Courtyard, Fairfield Inn, Hampton Inn, Jameson Inn, Quality Inn, Super 8, 🅞Ⓗ, 7-11
101	CountyLine Rd, 🅔🍴 Candlewood Suites, 🅦🅖 Murphy USA/dsl, 🍴 Buffalo Wild Wings, El Mason Mexican, Fireside Rest., Little Mexico, Pasquale's Pizza, Tokyo Buffet, 🛏 Hilton Garden, Holiday Inn Express, Value Place Hotel, 🅞Ⓗ, Gander Mtn, Kroger, Verizon, Walmart/Subway
99	Greenwood, 🅔🅖 Road Ranger/Pilot/Subway/dsl/scales/24hr, 🅦🅖 Marathon, Shell/Circle K, Sunoco, 🍴 Arby's, Bob Evans, Byrd's Cafeteria, China Wok, Denny's, McDonald's, Oaken Barrel Rest., Puerto Vallarta, Starbucks, Subway, Taco Bell, Waffle House, White Castle, 🛏 Baymont Inn, InTown Suites, Red Carpet Inn, Red Roof Inn, 🅞Ⓗ, Camping World RV Ctr, Sam's Club, vet
95	Whiteland, 🅔🅖 ⏚FLYING J/Denny's/scales/dsl/LP/RV dump/24hr, 🅞 Blue Beacon, SpeedCo, tires, 🅦🅖 ♥Loves/Arby's/dsl/scales/24hr, ⚏McDonald's/dsl/scales/24hr/@, 🅞 Family RV Ctr
90	IN 44, Franklin, 🅦🅖 Marathon/Chester's/Subway/dsl, Shell/Circle K, 🍴 Burger King, El Torito, McDonald's/RV Parking, Waffle House, 🛏 Comfort Inn, Howard Johnson, Quality Inn, Red Carpet Inn, Super 8, 🅞Ⓗ, golf
85mm	Sugar Creek
82mm	Big Blue River
80	IN 252, to Flat Rock, Edinburgh, 🅦🅖 Shell/dsl, Sunoco/dsl
76b a	US 31, Taylorsville, 🅔🅖 Shell/Circle K/dsl, Speedway/dsl, 🍴 A&W/KFC, Burger King, El Toreo Mexican, Waffle House, 🛏 Red Roof Inn, 🅞Ⓗ, Buick/Cadillac/Chevrolet/GMC, $ General, Toyota, 🅦🅖 Marathon,
76b a	Continued Thornton's/café/dsl, 🍴 Arby's, Cracker Barrel, Hardee's, Max&Erma's, McDonald's, MT Mikes, Ruby Tuesday, Snappy Tomato Pizza, Subway, Taco Bell, 🛏 Best Western, Comfort Inn, Hampton Inn, Hilton Garden, Holiday Inn Express, 🅞 Driftwood RV Camp, Goodyear, Harley-Davidson, Premium Outlets/famous brands, antiques, repair
73mm	**rest area both lanes, full ♿ facilities, 🅒, vending, info, ✉, litter barrels, petwalk**
68mm	Driftwood River
68	IN 46, Columbus, 🅔🅖 Shell/Circle K, Speedway/dsl, 🍴 Buffalo Wild Wings, Burger King, Coldstone, Culver's, Dimitri's Rest., IHOP, Jimmy John's, McDonald's, RuYi Asian, Snappy Tomato Pizza, Starbucks, Subway, Wendy's, 🛏 Comfort Inn&Suites, Holiday Inn/rest., Sleep Inn, Super 8, 🅞Ⓗ, AT&T, Menards, Sam's Club/gas, Verizon, Walgreens, Walmart/Subway, 🅦🅖 BP, Swifty, 🍴 Arby's, Bob Evans, Casa del Sol, Denny's, El Nopal Mexican, KFC, Noble Roman's, Papa's Grill, Taco Bell, 🛏 Courtyard, Days Inn, La Quinta, Motel 6, Residence Inn, 🅞 CVS Drug, $General, Jay-C Foods, to Brown Co SP
64	IN 58, Walesboro, 🅦🅖 Marathon/dsl, 🅞 to RV camping
55	IN 11, to Jonesville, Seymour
54mm	White River
51mm	**weigh sta both lanes**
50b a	US 50, Seymour, 🅔🅖 Marathon/Circle K/dsl, Swifty, TA/BP/Country Pride/dsl/24hr/@, 🍴 McDonald's, Waffle House, 🛏 Allstate Inn, Days Inn, EconoLodge, Motel 6, Super 8, 🅦🅖 Citgo/dsl, Shell/Circle K/dsl, Speedway/dsl, Sunoco/dsl, 🍴 Applebee's, Arby's, Buffalo Wild Wings, Buffet China, Burger King, Capt D's, Chili's, Cracker Barrel, Domino's, DQ, El Nopal Mexican, Hardee's, KFC, Little Caesars, LJ Silver, McDonalds, Papa John's, Pizza Hut, Rally's, Ryan's, Steak'n Shake, Subway, Taco Bell, Tumbleweed Grill, Wendy's, White Castle, 🛏 Fairfield Inn, Hampton Inn, Holiday Inn Express, Knights Inn, Quality Inn, 🅞Ⓗ, Advance Parts, Aldi Foods, AT&T, AutoZone, BigLots, Buick/Cadillac/Chevrolet/GMC, Chrysler/Dodge/Jeep, CVS Drug, $General, $Tree, Ford, GNC, Home Depot, Jay-C Foods, JC Penney, O'Reilly Parts, Radio Shack, Russell Stover Candies, Staples, Walgreens, Walmart/Subway, st police
41	IN 250, Uniontown, 🅔 tires, 🅦🅖 UnionTown/rest./dsl, 🅞 auto/truck repair
36	US 31, Crothersville, 🅔🅖 Shell, 🅦🅖 Marathon/dsl
34a b	IN 256, Austin, 🅔🅖 Shell/Circle K, 🅞 to Hardy Lake, Clifty Falls SP, 🅦🅖 Fuelmart/dsl/scales, Sunoco/Huddle House/dsl

Left margin vertical labels: INDIANAPOLIS AREA · GREENWOOD · COLUMBUS · SEYMOUR

INTERSTATE 65 CONT'D

Exit	Services
29b a	IN 56, to Salem, Scottsburg, **E** 🅖 MotoMart, Speedway/dsl, 🍴 Burger King, Cracker Barrel, KFC, Mariann Rest., Papa John's, Ponderosa, Sonic, Subway, Taco Bell, 🏨 Best Value Inn, Holiday Inn Express, 🅞 🅷, Ace Hardware, Advance Parts, AutoZone, CVS Drug, O'Reilly Parts, **W** 🅖 Marathon, Murphy USA, Shell/Circle K, 🍴 Arby's, LJ Silver, McDonald's, Pizza Hut, Roadhouse USA, Waffle House, Wendy's, 🏨 Hampton Inn, Quality Inn, Super 8, 🅞 Big O Tire, Jellystone Camping (4mi), Radio Shack, Verizon, Walmart/Subway
22mm	**rest area both lanes, full** ♿ **facilities, info,** 🚻, 🍴, **litter barrels, vending, petwalk**
19	IN 160, Henryville, **E** 🅖 Marathon/Subway/dsl, Shell/Circle K, 🍴 Schuler's Rest., 🅞 Family$
16	Memphis Rd, Memphis, **E** 🅖 ♥Loves/McDonald's/Subway/dsl/scales/24hr, 🍴 Fill'n Station Cafe, **W** 🅖 🚚/Arby's/dsl/scales/24hr/@, 🅞 Customers 1st RV Ctr
9	IN 311, to New Albany, Sellersburg, **E** 🅖 BP, 5 Star Gas, Shell/Circle K, Swifty, 🍴 Arby's, Cracker Barrel, DQ, Quiznos, Waffle House, 🏨 Ramada Inn, 🅞 Carmerica/repair, Ford, O'Reilly Parts, st police, **W** 🅖 Marathon/Circle K, 🍴 Burger King, El Nopal Mexican, McDonald's, Taco Bell, 🏨 Comfort Inn, 🅞 city park
7	IN 60, Hamburg, **E** 🅖 Clark/dsl, **W** 🍴 Cricket's Cafe, KFC/Pizza Hut, 🏨 Days Inn
6b a	I-265 W, to I-64 W, IN 265 E, New Albany
5	Veterans Parkway, **E** 🅖 Shell/Circle K, 🍴 Beef'O Brady's, 🅞 🅷, Tire Discounters, **W** 🍴 Buffalo Wild Wings, Cheddars, Chick-fil-A, Chuy's Mexican, DQ, Famous Dave's, IHOP, Krispy Kreme, Longhorn Steaks, McAlister's Deli, Moe's SW Grill, Olive Garden, Panera Bread, Papa Murphy's, Pizza Hut, Ruby Tuesday, Stevie B's Burgers, Studio Pizza, Subway, Taco Bell, 🅞 AT&T, Bass Pro Shops, Best Buy, Chevrolet, Lowe's, Michael's, Old Navy, Old Time Pottery, Petsmart, Rite Aid, Sam's Club/gas, Staples, Target, Verizon, Walmart/Subway
4	US 31 N, IN 131 S, Clarksville, New Albany, **E** 🅖 Thorntons/Dunkin Donuts/dsl, 🍴 White Castle, 🏨 Value Place Inn, 🅞 Raben Tire, **W** 🅖 Speedway/dsl, 🍴 Applebee's, Arby's, Bob Evans, Burger King, Capt D's, Chuck-eCheese, Denny's, Don Pablo, El Caporal, Fazoli's, Frisch's, Golden Corral, Hooters, Iguana Rest., Logan's Roadhouse, LJ Silver, McDonald's, O'Charley's, Outback Steaks, Papa John's, Rally's, Red Lobster, Steak'n Shake, Wendy's, 🏨 Best Western, Candlewood Suites, Hampton Inn, Suburban Lodge, 🅞 AT&T, AutoZone, BigLots, Books-A-Million, Buick/GMC, Dick's, Dillard's, $Tree, Firestone/auto, Ford, Hobby Lobby, Home Depot, Honda, JC Penney, Jo-Ann Fabrics, Kia, Kroger/gas, Office Depot, O'Reilly Parts, PepBoys, Sears/auto, Toyota/Scion, Tuesday Morning, USPO, VW, Walgreens
2	Eastern Blvd, Clarksville, **E** 🏨 Comfort Suites, Days Inn, Motel 6, Super 8, 🅞 🅷, U-Haul, **W** 🅖 Shell/Circle K, 🏨 Best Inn
1	US 31 S, IN 62, Stansifer Ave, **E** 🅖 Thorntons, 🍴 DQ, 🅞 🅷, Advance Parts, Walgreens, info ctr, **W** 🏨 Holiday Inn, 🅞 Stinnett RV Ctr
0	Jeffersonville, **E** 🅖 Thornton/Dunkin Donuts, 🍴

0	Continued Hardee's, McDonald's, Waffle House, 🅞 🅷, Chrysler/Jeep, Hyundai, Nissan, Walgreens, to Falls of OH SP, **W** 🍴 Subway, 🏨 Fairfield Inn, Sheraton, TownePlace Suites
0mm	Indiana/Kentucky state line, Ohio River

INTERSTATE 69

Exit	Service
158mm	Indiana/Michigan state line
157	Lake George Rd, to IN 120, Fremont, Lake James, **E** 🅖 Petro/Mobil/Baker St/dsl/LP/@, 🚚/Wendy's/dsl/scales/24hr, Shell/Subway/dsl, 🍴 McDonald's, Red Arrow Rest., 🏨 Redwood Inn, Lake George Inn, 🅞 Freightliner/Western Star/truck repair, **W** 🅖 Marathon/dsl/24hr, 🏨 Holiday Inn Express, 🅞 Freemont Outlet Shops/famous brands, GNC, **services on IN 120 E** 🏨 Comfort Inn, Hampton Inn, Travelers Inn, 🅞 golf/rest, **W** to Pokagon SP, Jellystone Camping (5mi)
156	I-80/90 Toll Rd, E to Toledo, W to Chicago
154	IN 127, to IN 120, IN 727, Fremont, Orland, **E** 🏨 Budgeteer Motel, Comfort Inn, Hampton Inn, Ramada, Travelers Inn, 🅞 Oak Hill RV camp, golf, **W** 🅖 Marathon/dsl, 🏨 Holiday Inn Express, 🅞 Freemont Outlets/Famous Brands, to Pokagon SP, Jellystone Camping (4mi)
150	rd 200 W, to Lake James, Crooked Lake, **E** 🅖 Sunoco/dsl, 🅞 fireworks, **W** 🅖 Marathon, Shell, 🍴 Caruso's Rest., Ritter's Custard, 🅞 Marine Ctr
148	US 20, to Angola, Lagrange, **E** 🅖 Citgo/Subway/dsl, GA/Taco Bell, Speedway/dsl, 🍴 McDonald's, 🏨 Happy Acres Camping (1mi), University Inn (2mi), 🅞 🅷, **W** 🅞 Circle B RV Prk (2mi)
145mm	Pigeon Creek
144mm	**rest area sb, full** ♿ **facilities, info,** 🚻, 🍴, **litter barrels, vending, petwalk**
140	IN 4, to Hamilton, Ashley, Hudson, **1 mi W** 🅖 Marathon/Ashley Deli/dsl
134	US 6, to Waterloo, Kendallville, **W** 🅖 BP/dsl, Marathon/dsl/24hr, 🍴 Maria's Pancakes
129	IN 8, to Garrett, Auburn, **E** 🅖 GA, Lassus, Speedway/dsl, Spirit, 🍴 Applebee's, Arby's, Bob Evans, Burger King, China Buffet, DQ, KFC, Lake Mtn Chinese, McDonald's, Papa John's, Papa Murphy's, Peking Buffet, Penguin Point Rest., Pizza Hut, Ponderosa, Richard's Rest., Starbucks, Steak'n Shake, Subway, Taco Bell, Wendy's, Zesto Drive-In, 🏨 Auburn Inn, Comfort Suites, Days Inn, Holiday Inn Express, La Quinta, Super 8, 🅞 🅷, Ace Hardware, Advance Parts, AT&T, AutoZone, Buick/Chevrolet/RV Ctr, Chrysler/Dodge/Jeep, CVS Drug, $General, $Tree, Ford, GNC, Kroger, Radio Shack, Staples, Walmart/Subway, museum, **W** 🅖 Marathon/dsl, 🍴 Buffalo Wild Wings, Cracker Barrel, Ryan's, Sonic, 🏨 Hampton Inn, 🅞 Home Depot, Verizon
126	IN 11-A, to Garrett, Auburn, **E** Kruse Auction Park, **W** camping
116	IN 1 N, Dupont Rd, **E** 🅖 Citgo/Burger King, 🍴 Arby's, Culver's, 🏨 Comfort Suites, 🅞 🅷, **W** 🅖 Lassus, Speedway/dsl, 🍴 Bandito's Mexican, Bob Evans, Cozy Nook Cafe, Mancino's Grinders, Pine Valley Grill, Roly-Poly, Starbucks, Trolley Grill, 🏨 La Quinta, Sleep Inn, 🅞 🅷, Tuesday Morning
115	I-469, US 30 E, **W** 🏨 Value Place Hotel

INTERSTATE 69 CONT'D

Exit	Service

N ↕ S

112b a   Coldwater Rd, **E** ⓡ BP/dsl/24hr, Marathon, Sunoco, 🍴 Agave's Mexican, Arby's, Chappell's, Chili's, Cork'N Cleaver, Hall's Factory Rest., Hunan Chinese, IHOP, Jimmy John's, LoneStar Steaks, McDonald's, Ozzy's Pancakes, Papa John's, Quiznos, Rally's, Red Lobster, Red River Steaks, Steak'n Shake, Taco Bell, Wendy's, 🛏 Hyatt Place, Marriott, ⦿ $Tree, Hobby Lobby, Hyundai, Jo-Ann Fabrics, NAPA, O'Reilly Parts, PetCo, Tuffy Auto, U-Haul, Walmart, **W** DQ (1mi)

111b a   US 27 S, IN 3 N, **E** ⓡ Shell, 🍴 Arby's, Cheddar's, ChuckeCheese, DQ, Fazoli's, Golden Corral, Hall's Rest., McDonald's, Olive Garden, TGIFriday's, 🛏 Candlewood Suites, Residence Inn, ⦿ Barnes&Noble, Chrysler/Dodge/Jeep, Discount Tire, Ford/Lincoln/Mercury, GMC, Honda, Infiniti, Macy's, Nissan, Sears, Suzuki, Toyota/Scion, **W** ⓡ Lassus/Elmo's Pizza/dsl, Marathon, 🍴 Applebee's, Burger King, Cosmos Rest., Cracker Barrel, IHOP, Logan's Roadhouse, McDonald's, O'Charley's, Starbucks, Subway, Taco Bell, 🛏 Baymont Inn, Best Value Inn, Courtyard, County Inn&Suites, Days Inn, Fairfield Inn, Guesthouse Motel, Hampton Inn, Quality Inn, Super 8, Studio+, ⦿ CVS Drug, Gander Mtn, Home Depot, Lowe's, Meijer/dsl/e-85, Sam's Club/gas, Walgreens, VW

109b a   US 33, Goshen Rd, Ft Wayne, **E** ⓡ BP, Citgo/Subway/dsl/scales, Marathon, 🍴 McDonald's, Point Rest., 🛏 Country Hearth Inn, Guest House Inn, Knights Inn, Motel 6, Red Roof Inn, Relax Inn, Travel Inn, ⦿ H, Blue Beacon, NAPA, auto/dsl repair

FT WAYNE

105b a   IN 14 W, Ft Wayne, **E** ⓡ Lassus, Murphy USA, Shell/Subway/dsl, Speedway/dsl/LP, 🍴 Arby's, Biaggi's, Bob Evans, Burger King, Chick-fil-A, Chipotle Mexican, Coldstone, Flat Top Grill, Great Wall Buffet, Logan's Roadhouse, McAlister's Deli, O'Charley's, Panera Bread, Papa Murphy's, Penn Sta Subs, Qdoba, Smokey Bones BBQ, Starbucks, Steak'n Shake, Wendy's, 🛏 Klopfenstein Suites, ⦿ H, Acura, AT&T, Audi/Porsche, Barnes&Noble, Best Buy, BigLots, BMW, Buick/GMC, Cadillac, Chevrolet, Chrysler/Jeep, Dick's, $General, $Tree, Ford/Lincoln/Mercury, Harley-Davidson, KIA, Kohl's, Lexus, Lowe's, Mazda, Meijer/dsl/24hr, Menards, Michael's, NAPA, Old Navy, Petsmart, Radio Shack, Staples, Subaru, Target, Toyota/Scion, Tuesday Morning, Volvo, Walmart, mall, vet, to St Francis U

102   US 24, to Jefferson Blvd, Ft Wayne, **E** 🍴 Subway (1mi), Taco Bell (1mi), 🛏 Extended Stay America, Hampton Inn, Residence Inn, ⦿ H, to In Wesleyan U, **W** ⓡ Lassus, Marathon, 🍴 Applebee's, Arby's, Bob Evans, Buffalo Wild Wings, Carlos O'Kelly's, Coventry Tavern Rest., McDonald's, Outback Steaks, Pizza Hut, Sara's Rest., Starbucks, Wendy's, Zesto Drive-In, 🛏 Best Western Luxury, Comfort Suites, Hilton Garden, Holiday Inn Express, Homewood Suites, Staybridge Suites, ⦿ Kroger, Scott's Foods, Walgreens, st police

99   Lower Huntington Rd, **E** to ♿

96b a   I-469, US 24 E, US 33 S, **E** to ♿

89mm   **rest area nb, full ♿ facilities, info, 🎮, 🛢, vending, litter barrels, pet walk**

86   US 224, to Huntington, Markle, **E** ⓡ Marathon/24hr

86   Continued (1mi), Sunoco/Subway, 🍴 DQ, Huddle House, Vinatelli's, 🛏 Guesthouse Inn, Super 8, ⦿ H, repair/tires, **W** to Huntington Reservoir, Roush Lake

80mm   **weigh sta sb/parking area nb**

78   IN 5, to Warren, Huntington, **E** ⓡ Sunoco/dsl, 🛏 Huggy Bear Motel, **W** ⓡ Gas City/rest/dsl/24hr, Marathon/Subway/dsl/24hr, 🍴 McDonald's, Ugalde's Rest., 🛏 Comfort Inn, Motel 6, ⦿ H, RV Camping, fireworks, to Salamonie Reservoir

76mm   **Salamonie River**

73   IN 218, to Warren

64   IN 18, to Marion, Montpelier, **E** ⓡ Loves/McDonalds/dsl/scales/24hr, **W** ⓡ BP/Subway/dsl, Marathon/dsl, 🍴 Arby's, 🛏 Days Inn, ⦿ H, Chrysler/Jeep, Harley-Davidson

60mm   **Walnut Creek**

59   US 35 N, IN 22, to Upland, **E** ⓡ Valero/Subway, 🍴 Burger King, Casa Grande Mexican, China 1, Cracker Barrel, E Chicago Pizza, Payne's Rest., 🛏 Best Western, Super 8, ⦿ Mar-Brook Camping, Taylor U, **W** ⓡ Marathon/dsl/24hr, McClure Trkstp/dsl/24hr, Shell/dsl, 🍴 KFC/Taco Bell, Starbucks, 🛏 Holiday Inn Express, ⦿ to IN Wesleyan

55   IN 26, to Fairmount

50mm   **rest area both lanes, full ♿ facilities, info, 🎮, 🛢, litter barrels, vending, pet walk**

45   US 35 S, IN 28, to Alexandria, Albany, **E** ⓡ Petro/Shell/Iron Skillet/Subway/dsl/scales/24hr/@, ⦿ RV Camping

41   IN 332, to Muncie, Frankton, **E** ⓡ BP/dsl, ⦿ H, to Ball St U

34   IN 67, to IN 32, Chesterfield, Daleville, **E** ⓡ Pilot/Subway/dsl/scales/24hr, Shell, 🍴 Arby's, Smokehouse BBQ, Taco Bell, Waffle House, White Castle, 🛏 Budget Inn, ⦿ H, **W** ⓡ GA/dsl, McClure/dsl/e-85, Pilot/Denny's/dsl/scales/24hr, 🍴 McDonald's, Subway, 3rd Generation Pizza, Wendy's, 🛏 Best Value Inn, ⦿ Timberline Valley Camping (3mi), flea mkt

26   IN 9, IN 109, to Anderson, **E** 🍴 A&W/KFC, Culver's, MT Mike's, Ryan's, 🛏 Deluxe Inn, Hampton Inn, Holiday Inn Express, Quality Inn, ⦿ Meijer/dsl, Menards, visitors ctr, **W** ⓡ BP, GA, Marathon/dsl, Speedway/dsl, 🍴 Applebee's, Arby's, Bob Evans, Buffalo Wild Wings, Burger King, China Buffet, Cracker Barrel, Fazoli's, Great Wall Chinese, IHOP, LoneStar Steaks, McDonald's, Olive Garden, Panera Bread, Papa Murphy's, Penn Sta. Subs, Perkins, Pizza Hut, Quiznos, Real Hacienda, Red Lobster, Ruby Tuesday, Starbucks, Steak'n Shake, Taco Bell, Waffle House, Wendy's, White Castle,

FT WAYNE

ANDERSON

= gas = food = lodging = other   Copyright 2012 - The Next Exit®

	INTERSTATE 69 CONT'D
Exit	**Service**
26	Continued
	Best Inn, Comfort Inn, Days Inn, Fairfield Inn, Garden Inn, Lee's Inn, Motel 6, Super 8, H, Aldi Foods, AT&T, Cadillac/Chevrolet, $General, Freightliner, GNC, Kohl's, Marshall's, Office Depot, Old Navy, O'Reilly Parts, Pay Less Foods, Petsmart, Radio Shack, Target, Tire Barn, Toyota/Scion, Verizon, Walgreens, Walmart/Subway, vet, to Anderson U, to Mounds SP
22	IN 9, IN 67, to Anderson, W GA, Skyline Chili, Anderson Country Inn (1mi), H, st police
19	IN 38, Pendleton, E Marathon, Burger King, Mc-Donald's, Subway, W Pine Lakes Camping
14	IN 13, to Lapel, E BP, Waffle House, W /Subway/dsl/scales/24hr, camping
10	IN 238, to Noblesville, Fortville, E Taco Bell, H, W Bella Pizzeria, Coldstone, 5 Guys Burgers, Houli-han's, McAlister's Deli, Mo's Cafe, Olive Garden, Paradise Cafe, Qdoba, Red Robin, Saku Japanese, loding Cam-bria Suites, CVS Drug, Dick's, $Tree, GNC, JC Penney, Radio Shack, Sleepy Bear Camping, Steinmart, Verizon
5	IN 37 N, 116th St, to Noblesville, Fishers, E BP, Mazatlan Rest., Penn Sta Subs, Sunrise Cafe, URGENT CARE, Curves, Kroger, W Shell/Circle K, Speedway, Coldstone, Greek Pizzaria, Handel's Ice Cream, KFC, McAlister's Deli, McDonald's, Nancy's Pizza, O'Charley's, Original Pancake House, Qdoba, Quiznos, Riviera Mayo Mexican, Starbucks, Steak'n Shake, Subway, Wendy's, Hampton Inn, CVS Drug, Super Target
3	96th St, E Marathon/dsl, Murphy USA/dsl, Shell, Applebee's, Blimpie, Cracker Barrel, Donato's Pizza, Golden Wok Chinese, Joe's Grille, King Chef, McDon-ald's, Noble Roman's, Panera Bread, Qdoba, Ruby Tues-day, Sahm's Grill, Starbucks, Steak'n Shake, Subway, Wendy's, Hilton Garden, Holiday Inn, Holiday Inn Ex-press, Indigo Hotel, Studio 6, AT&T, Fry's, GNC, Kohl's, Marsh Food, Meijer/dsl, PepBoys, PetCo, Radio Shack, Staples, Tuesday Morning, Walmart, W Marathon/dsl, Arby's, Bob Evans, Burger King, Cheeseburger Paradise, Culver's, Izakya Japanese, Panda Express, Peterson's Steaks/seafood, Quiznos, Shebella's Pizza, Starbucks, Taco Bell, Comfort Suites, Residence Inn, SpringHill Suites, Staybridge Suites, Aldi Foods, $Tree, Home Depot, Menards, NAPA, Sam's Club/gas
1	82nd St, Castleton, E Shell, Boston Mkt, Burger King, Golden Corral, O'Charley's, Castleton Inn, $Inn, Drury Inn, Extended Stay America, Hilton, Super 8, H, Lowe's, W Speedway/dsl, Applebee's, Arby's, Burger King, Cancun Mexican, Castleton Grill, Charles-ton's Rest., Denny's, Domino's, Fazoli's, Hooters, Houli-han's, Jimmy John's, Joe's Grille, KFC, LJ Silver, Loon-lake Lodge Rest., McDonald's, Olive Garden, Penn Sta Subs, Pizza Hut, Rally's, Red Lobster, Skyline Chili, Star-bucks, Taco Bell, Thai Orchid, Wendy's, Best West-ern, Candlewood Suites, Days Inn, Hampton Inn, Qual-ity Inn, Suburban Inn, Aamco, Advance Parts, Best Buy, Discount Tire, $Tree, Goodyear/auto, JC Penney, Macy's, Sears/auto, Tire Barn, Verizon, fireworks, mall
0mm	I-465 around Indianapolis. I-69 begins/ends on I-465, exit 37, at Indianapolis.

	INTERSTATE 70
Exit	**Services**
156.5mm	Indiana/Ohio state line, **weigh sta**
156b a	US 40 E, Richmond, N Petro/BP/Iron Skillet/dsl/24hr/@, Fairfield Inn, Blue Beacon, S BP/White Castle, Murphy USA/dsl, Shell, Speedway/dsl, A&W/LJ Silver, Applebee's, Arby's, Big Boy, Bob Evans, Buffalo Wild Wings, Burger King, Chili's, Chipotle Mexi-can, Cracker Barrel, Fazoli's, Golden Corral, Hacienda Mexican, IHOP, Jade House Chinese, KFC, McDonald's, MCL Cafeteria, O'Charley's, Pizza Hut, Rally's, Red Lobster, Starbucks, Steak'n Shake, Subway, Super China, Taco Bell, TX Roadhouse, Best Western, Days Inn, Hampton Inn, Lee's Inn, Motel 6, Quality Inn, Advance Parts, Aldi Foods, AT&T, Best Buy, BigLots, Buick/GMC, CarQuest, Chevrolet, Chrysler/Jeep, Dil-lard's, $General, $Tree, Expert Tire, Family$, Ford, Hast-ings Books, Hobby Lobby, Hyundai, JC Penney, Jo-Ann Fabrics, Kohl's, Kroger, Lowe's, Menards, Save-A-Lot Foods, Sears/auto, Tires+, Toyota/Scion, Tuffy, U-Haul, Verizon, Walgreens, Walmart
153	IN 227, to Whitewater, Richmond, **2 mi N** Grandpa's Farm RV Park (seasonal)
151b a	US 27, to Chester, Richmond, N Fricker's Rest., Honda, KOA, S Shell, Bob Evans, Burger King, Carver's Rest., China Buffet, McDonald's, Rally's, Sub-way, Taco Bell, Wendy's, Comfort Inn, Super 8, H, CVS Drug, Harley-Davidson, Meijer/dsl/E85
149b a	US 35, IN 38, to Muncie, N Loves/Hardee's/dsl/scales/24hr, S Shell/Quiznos/dsl, Raper RV Ctr
148mm	**weigh sta wb**
145	Centerville, N BP/DQ/Stuckey's, Super 8, Goodyear/truck repair, S Warm Glow Candles
145mm	Nolands Fork Creek
144mm	**rest area wb, full facilities, info, vending, , litter barrels, petwalk**
141mm	Greens Fork River
137	IN 1, to Hagerstown, Connersville, N Amish Cheese, S GA, Gas City/rest./dsl/24hr, Shell, Burger King, McDonald's
131	Wilbur Wright Rd, New Lisbon, S Shell/KFC/Taco Bell/dsl/scales/24hr/@, New Lisbon RV park
126mm	Flatrock River
123	IN 3, to New Castle, Spiceland, N All American Inn (3mi), Holiday Inn Express (3mi), H, S FLYING J/Denny's/Subway/dsl/LP/scales/24hr, tires/repair
117mm	Big Blue River
115	IN 109, to Knightstown, Wilkinson, N GA/rest/dsl/scales/24hr, Burger King, Jellystone Camping
107mm	**rest area both lanes, full facilities, vending, , litter barrels, petwalk**
104	IN 9, Greenfield, Maxwell, N GA/Miami Grill/dsl, S GA, Murphy USA/dsl, Shell/Circle K, Sunoco/dsl, Swifty, Applebee's, Arby's, Bamboo Garden, Bob Evans, Burger King, China Inn, Cracker Barrel, Culver's, El Rodeo Mexican, Hardee's, KFC, Little Caesars, Mc-Donald's, Mi Casa Mexican, MT Mike's Steaks, Mozzi's Pizza, O'Charley's, Papa John's, Papa Murphy's, Penn Sta Subs, Pizza Hut, Ponderosa, Qdoba, Quiznos, Star-bucks, Steak'n Shake, Subway, Taco Bell, Wendy's, White Castle, Comfort Inn, Country Inn&Suites, $Inn, Hampton Inn, Holiday Inn Express, Quality Inn, Super

Vertical side labels: **N / S**, **INDIANAPOLIS AREA**, **IN**, **RICHMOND**, **E / W**, **GREENFIELD**

INTERSTATE 70 CONT'D

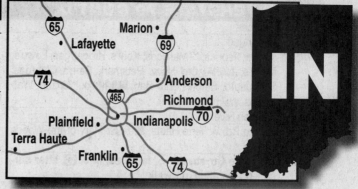

Exit	Services
104	Continued 8, 🅞 🄷, Advance Parts, Aldi Foods, BigLots, Big O Tire, CVS Drug, $General, $Tree, GNC, Home Depot, Kroger/dsl, Marsh Foods, Radio Shack, Walgreens, Walmart
96	Mt Comfort Rd, **N** 🅖 GA/Subway/dsl, 🍴/Pizza Hut/dsl/scales/24hr, 🍴 Burger King, El Nopal, Wendy's, **S** 🅖 Shell/Circle K, 🍴 McDonald's, 🅞 KOA (seasonal), Mt Comfort RV Ctr
91	Post Rd, to Ft Harrison, **N** 🅖 Citgo, 7-11, 🍴 Cracker Barrel, Denny's, Joe's Crabshack, McDonald's, Outback Steaks, Steak'n Shake, Wendy's, 🏠 InTown Suites, La Quinta, 🅞 Lowe's, st police, **S** 🅖 Admiral, BP/dsl, Shell/dsl, Speedway, 🍴 Hardee's, KFC/Taco Bell, Waffle House, 🏠 Country Hearth Inn, Days Inn, 🅞 CVS Drug, Family$, Home Depot, Marsh Foods
90	I-465 (from wb)
89	Shadeland Ave, I-465 (from eb), **N** 🅖 Marathon/dsl, 🍴 Bob Evans, 🏠 Comfort Inn, Hampton Inn, Holiday Inn Express, Motel 6, 🅞 Toyota/Scion, U-Haul, **S** 🅖 Admiral/dsl, Circle K, Marathon, Shell, Speedway/dsl, 🍴 Arby's, Burger King, Damon's, 4Seasons Diner, Lincoln's Rest., McDonald's, Noble Roman's, Papa John's, Penn Sta Subs, Rally's, Red Lobster, Ryan's, Starbucks, Subway, Taco Bell, TX Roadhouse, Wendy's, White Castle, Zelma's Rest., 🏠 Best Value Inn, Candlewood Suites, Fairfield Inn, Knights Inn, La Quinta, Marriott, Quality Inn, Ramada Inn, 🅞 Aamco, CarX, CVS Drug, Chevrolet, Chrysler/Dodge/Jeep, Honda, Kia, Kroger/gas, Mazda, Nissan
87	Emerson Ave, **N** 🅖 BP/McDonald's, Speedway/dsl, **S** 🅖 Shell, 🅞 🄷
85b a	Rural St, Keystone Ave, **N** fairgrounds
83b (112)	I-65 N, to Chicago
83a (111)	Michigan St, Market St, downtown, **S** 🍴 Hardee's
80 (110a)	I-65 S, to Louisville
79b	Illinois St, McCarty St, downtown
79a	West St, **N** 🅖 Speedway/dsl, 🏠 Comfort Inn, Holiday Inn Express, Hyatt, Staybridge Suites, 🅞 🄷, to Union Sta, Govt Ctr, Lucas Oil Stadium, zoo
78	Harding St, to downtown, **S** 🅖 Marathon, 🍴 Wendy's
77	Holt Rd, **N** 🍴 Steak'n Shake, **S** 🅖 Shell, 🍴 McDonald's, 🅞 Ford Trucks
75	Airport Expswy, to Raymond St (no EZ wb return), **N** 🅖 Marathon, Speedway/dsl, 🍴 Denny's, Indy's Rest., Library Rest., Waffle House, 🏠 Adam's Mark, Candlewood Suites, Courtyard, EconoLodge, Extended Stay Deluxe, Fairfield Inn, Hyatt Place, La Quinta, Quality Inn, Ramada, Residence Inn, 🅞 NAPA, to ✈
73b a	I-465 N/S, I-74 E/W
69	(only from eb) to I-74 E, to I-465, S
68	Six Points Rd, **N** 🍴 Subway, 🏠 Hampton Inn, Hilton Garden, 🅞 ✈
66	IN 267, to Plainfield, Mooresville, **N** 🅖 BP, Shell/Circle K, Speedway/dsl, Thornton's/dsl, 🍴 Arby's, Bob Evans, Burger King, Coachman Rest., Cracker Barrel, Denny's, Golden Corral, Hog Heaven BBQ, McDonald's, Quiznos, Steak'n Shake, Subway, White Castle, Wood Fire Grill, 🏠 Baymont Inn, Best Western, Budget Inn, Cambria Suites, Comfort Inn, Days Inn, Hampton Inn, Holiday Inn Express, Homewood Suites, Motel 6, Staybridge Suites, Super 8, ValuePlace Inn, Wingate Inn, 🅞 Buick/GMC, Chateau Thomas Winery, Harley-Davidson

Exit	Services
65mm	rest area both lanes, full ♿ facilities, info, vending, ⓒ, 🚻, litter barrels, petwalk
59	IN 39, to Belleville, **N** 🅖 Loves/Arby's/dsl/scales/24hr, 🅞 🄷, **S** 🅖 TA/Country Pride/dsl/scales/24hr/@, truckwash
51	rd 1100W, **S** 🅖 Koger's/Sunoco/dsl/rest/24hr, 🅞 repair/towing/24hr
41	US 231, to Greencastle, Cloverdale, **S** 🅖 BP/dsl, Casey's (2mi), Marathon/dsl/scales/24hr, 🍴 Arby's, Chicago's Pizza, El Cantarito, Icebox Rest., KFC, McDonald's, Subway, Taco Bell, Wendy's, 🏠 Days Inn, EconoLodge, Holiday Inn Express, Motel 6, Super 8, 🅞 🄷, Bill's Hardware, Discount Tire, $General, NAPA, Value Mkt Foods, to Lieber SRA
37	IN 243, to Putnamville, **S** 🅖 Marathon/dsl, 🍴 A-Frame Cafe, 🅞 Misty Morning Campground (4mi), to Lieber SRA
23	IN 59, to Brazil, **N** 🅖 🍴/McDonald's/Subway/dsl/scales/24hr, 🅞 🄷, **S** 🅖 AM Best/Brazil Grill/dsl/scales/24hr/@, BP/Rally's/dsl, Road Ranger/Pilot/Subway/dsl/scales, 🍴 Burger King, Family Table Rest., 🏠 Knights Inn
15mm	Honey Creek
11	IN 46, Terre Haute, **N** 🅖 🍴/Subway/dsl/scales/24hr, Thornton/dsl, 🍴 Burger King, McDonald's, lodging Holiday Inn Express, 🅞 ✈, **S** KOA
7	US 41, US 150, Terre Haute, **N** 🅖 Marathon/dsl, Thornton's/dsl, 🍴 Applebee's, Beef o'Brady's, Bob Evans, Cracker Barrel, China Buffet 8, Fazoli's, IHOP, LoneStar Steaks, Pasta House, Pizza Hut, Real Hacienda Mexican, Starbucks, Steak'n Shake, Sunrise Rest., TX Roadhouse, Tumbleweed SW Grill, 🏠 Best Value Inn, Comfort Suites, Days Inn, Drury Inn, EconoLodge, Fairfield Inn, PearTree Inn, Super 8, 🅞 AutoZone, Chrysler/Jeep, Kia, Mike's Mkt, O'Reilly Parts, **S** 🅖 Speedway/dsl, Thornton's/mart, 🍴 Arby's, Baskin-Robbins, Buffalo Wild Wings, Burger King, Cheeseburger Paradise, Crazy Buffet, DQ, Denny's, Garfield's Rest., Golden Corral, Hardee's, Ichiban Japanese, Jimmy John's, KFC, Little Caesar's, Los Tres Caminos, LJ Silver, McDonald's, Monical's Pizza, Olive Garden, Outback Steaks, Panda Garden, Panera Bread, Papa John's, Penn Sta. Subs, Rally's, Red Lobster, Ruby Tuesday, Ryan's, Starbucks, Subway, Taco Bell, TGIFriday's, Wendy's, White Castle, 🏠 Hampton Inn, Holiday Inn, Motel 6, SpringHill Suites, 🅞 🄷, Aldi Foods, AT&T, Best Buy, BigLots, BooksAMillion, Buick/Cadillac/GMC, Burlington Coats, Chevrolet, Dodge, $Tree, Ford, Gander Mtn., Goodyear/auto, Harley-Davidson, Hobby Lobby, Hyundai/Nissan,

Left margin (vertical): E ↕ W, INDIANAPOLIS AREA

Right margin (vertical): TERRE HAUTE

INTERSTATE 70 CONT'D

Exit	Services
7	Continued Jo-Ann Fabrics, K-Mart/gas, Kohl's, Kroger/gas, Lowe's, Macy's, NAPA, Old Navy, Petsmart, Sam's Club/gas, Sears/auto, Staples, Tire Barn, TJ Maxx, Verizon, Walgreens, Walmart
5.5mm	Wabash River
3	Darwin Rd, W Terre Haute, **N** to St Mary of-the-Woods Coll
1.5mm	**Welcome Ctr eb, full ♿ facilities, info, 🏨, litter barrels, 🅲, vending, petwalk**
1	US 40, E (from eb, exits left), to Terre Haute, W Terre Haute
.5mm	**weigh sta, eb only**
0mm	Indiana/Illinois state line

INTERSTATE 74

Exit	Services
171.5mm	Indiana/Ohio state line
171mm	**weigh sta wb**
169	US 52 W, to Brookville
168.5mm	Whitewater River
164	IN 1, St Leon, **N** 🅶 Exxon/Noble Romans, Shell/dsl, **S** 🅶 BP/Blimpie/dsl
156	IN 101, to Sunman, Milan, **S** 🅶 Exxon/dsl
152mm	**rest area both lanes, full ♿ facilities, 🅲, 🏨, litter barrels, vending, petwalk**
149	IN 229, to Oldenburg, Batesville, **N** 🅶 Marathon, Shell/dsl/24hr, Sunoco, 🍴 Acapulco Mexican, China Wok, McDonald's, Subway, Wendy's, 🛏 Hampton Inn, 🅾 Advance Parts, $General, Kroger/dsl, Pamida, Verizon, **S** 🅶 BP, 🍴 Arby's, DQ, KFC/Taco Bell, La Rosa's Pizza, Skyline Chili, 🛏 Comfort Inn, 🅾 🅷, CVS Drug
143	to IN 46, New Point, **N** 🅶 Petro/Marathon/Iron Skillet/Subway/dsl/scales/24hr/@, **S** 🅶 BP, 🛏 Hwy 46 Inn
134b a	IN 3, to Rushville, Greensburg, **S** 🅶 BP/dsl, Marathon/DQ/Subway, Speedway/dsl, Swifty, 🍴 A&W, Acapulco Mexican, Arby's, Big Boy, Burger King, Chili's, El Reparo Mexican, Great Wall Buffet, KFC/LJ Silver, McDonald's, Papa John's, Taco Bell, Waffle House, Wendy's, 🛏 Fairfield Inn, Lee's Inn, Holiday Inn Express, 🅾 AutoZone, Cadillac/Chevrolet, Chrysler/Dodge/Jeep, CVS Drug, $General, $Tree, Ford/Mercury, GNC, Marsh Foods, NTB, Radio Shack, Staples, TrueValue, Walgreens, Walmart, repair
132	US 421, to Greensburg, **S** 🅶 BP, 🛏 Hampton Inn, Holiday Inn Express (2mi)
130mm	Clifty Creek
123	Saint Paul, **S** 🅶 ♥Love's/McDonald's/Subway/dsl/scales/24hr, 🅾 repair, camping
119	IN 244 E, to Milroy
116	IN 44, to Shelbyville, Rushville, **N** 🅶 Marathon/Circle K/dsl, **S** 🅶 Marathon, Murphy USA/dsl, Shell/24hr, Swifty, 🍴 Applebee's, Arby's, Bellacino's, Bob Evans, Burger King, Cabells Ice Cream, China Buffet, China Inn, Denny's, Domino's, DQ, KFC, King Buffet, LJ Silver, McDonald's, Papa John's, Papa Murphy's, Pizza Hut, Rally's, Starbucks, Subway, Taco Bell, Wendy's, White Castle, 🛏 Quality Inn, 🅾 🅷, Ace Hardware, Advance Parts, Aldi Foods, AutoZone, BigLots, Chevrolet, $Tree, Ford/Lincoln/Mercury, Kroger/dsl, Radio Shack, Verizon, Walgreens, Walmart/McDonald's

Exit	Services
115mm	Little Blue River
113mm	Big Blue River
113	IN 9, to Shelbyville, **N** 🅶 GA/dsl, 🍴 Cracker Barrel, Wendy's, **S** 🅶 Shell, Shell/Circle K/Subway/dsl (1mi), 🍴 McDonald's, Waffle House, 🛏 Best Value Inn, Comfort Inn, Hampton Inn, Holiday Inn Express, Knights Inn, Super 8, 🅾 🅷
109	Fairland Rd, **N** 🅶 [blank]/McDonald's/dsl/scales/24hr, 🅾 Indiana Downs/casino, **S** 🅾 Brownie's Marine
103	London Rd, to Boggstown
102mm	Big Sugar Creek
101	Pleasant View Rd, **N** 🅶 Country Mark/dsl/repair
99	Acton Rd
96	Post Rd, **N** 🅶 Marathon/Subway/dsl/24hr, 🍴 McDonald's, **S** 🅶 Shell/Circle K/dsl, 🍴 Wendy's, 🅾 Chevrolet
94b a	I-465/I-74 W, I-465 N, US 421 N
	I-74 and I-465 run together 21 miles. See Interstate 465 exits 2-16, and 52-53.
73b	I-465 N, access to same services as 16a on I-465
73a	I-465 S, I-74, E
71mm	Eagle Creek
68	Ronald Reagan Pkwy
66	IN 267, Brownsburg, **N** 🅶 Citgo/dsl, Shell/Circle K, 🍴 Applebee's, Asia Wok, Buffalo Wild Wings, Dunkin Donuts, Hardee's, Steak'n Shake, Subway, Tequila Mexican, 🛏 Hampton Inn, Holiday Inn Express, 🅾 Big O Tire, **S** 🅶 BP/dsl, Speedway/dsl, 🍴 Arby's, Asian Fusion, Bob Evans, Burger King, China's Best, HoWah, Hurricane Grill, Jimmy John's, KFC, Little Caesars, Los Toros Mexican, McDonald's, Papa Murphy's, Penn Sta Subs, Starbucks, Taco Bell, Wendy's, White Castle, 🛏 Comfort Suites, Super 8, 🅾 AT&T, $Tree, Firestone/auto, Ford, Kohl's, Kroger/gas, K-Mart, Lowe's, Radio Shack, Walmart/Subway, USPO
61	to Pittsboro, **S** 🅶 ♥Love's/Godfather's/Subway/dsl/scales/24hr
58	IN 39, to Lebanon, Lizton, **S** 🅷
57mm	**rest area both lanes, full ♿ facilities, 🅲, 🏨, litter barrels, vending, petwalk**
52	IN 75, to Advance, Jamestown, **2 mi S** 🅶, food, camping
39	IN 32, to Crawfordsville, **S** 🅶 [blank]/Subway/dsl/scales/24hr
34	US 231, to Linden, **S** 🅶 BP/Circle K, GA, Marathon/dsl, 🍴 Burger King, McDonald's, Subway, 🛏 Candlewood Suites, Comfort Inn, Hampton Inn, Holiday Inn Express, Motel 6, Quality Inn, Ramada Ltd., Super 8, 🅾 🅷, Buick/GMC, KOA (1mi), Sugar Creek Campground (4mi)
25	IN 25, to Wingate, Waynetown
19mm	**weigh sta eb/parking area wb**
15	US 41, to Attica, Veedersburg, **1 mi S** 🅶 Marathon/dsl, 🍴 Apple Tree Diner, 🅾 to Turkey Run SP, camping
8	Covington, **N** 🅶 Marathon, Valero/dsl, 🍴 Benjamin's, Overpass Pizza, 🅾 Ford, fireworks
7mm	Wabash River
4	IN 63, to Newport, **N** 🅶 [blank]/Arby's/dsl/scales/24hr, 🍴 Beefhouse Rest., Wendy's
1mm	**Welcome Ctr eb, full ♿ facilities, info, 🅲, 🏨, litter barrels, vending, petwalk**
0mm	Indiana/Illinois state line, Eastern/Central Time Zone

INTERSTATE 80/90

E ↕ W

Exit	Services
157mm	Indiana/Ohio state line
153mm	toll plaza, litter barrels
146mm	TP both lanes, [gas] Mobil/dsl, [food] DQ, McDonald's
144	I-69, US 27, Angola, Ft Wayne, **N** [gas] Petro/Mobil/dsl/LP/@, Pilot/Wendy's/dsl/scales, Shell/Subway/dsl, [food] McDonald's, Red Arrow Rest., [lodging] Redwood Inn, Lake George Inn, [other] Freightliner/Western Star/truck repair, **S** [gas] Marathon/dsl/24hr, [lodging] Holiday Inn Express, [other] Freemont Outlet Shops/famous brands, GNC, **services on IN 120 E** [lodging] Comfort Inn, Hampton Inn, Travelers Inn, [other] golf/rest, **W** to Pokagon SP, Jellystone Camping (5mi)
131.5mm	Fawn River
126mm	TP both lanes, [gas] Mobil/dsl, [food] Fazoli's, Hardee's, [other] gifts, RV dump
121	IN 9, to Lagrange, Howe, **N** [food] Golden Buddha, [lodging] American Inn, Best Western, Hampton Inn, Travel Inn, [other] [H] (4mi), **2 mi N** [gas] Marathon, Murphy USA, Speedway/dsl, [food] Applebee's, Burger King, Fiesta Mexican, KFC, King Dragon, Little Caesar's, McDonald's, Pizza Hut, Subway, Taco Bell, Wendy's, [lodging] Regency Inn, Sturgess Inn, [other] AT&T, Cadillac/Chevrolet, CarQuest, $Tree, Family$, Ford, GNC, K-Mart, Kroger, Radio Shack, Rite Aid, Walgreens, Walmart, **S** [gas] Valero, [lodging] Holiday Inn Express, Super 8, [other] [H] (8mi)
120mm	Fawn River
108mm	**trucks only rest area both lanes**
107	US 131, IN 13, to Middlebury, Constantine, **0-3 mi N** [gas] Marathon/dsl, Speedway, [food] Country Table Rest., McDonald's, [lodging] Patchwork Quilt Inn, Plaza Motel, Tower Motel, [other] $General, Family$, **1 mi S** [gas] BP/Blimpie/dsl, [food] Yup's DairyLand, [lodging] McKenzie House B&B, [other] Eby's Pines RV Park, KOA (apr-nov)
101	IN 15, to Goshen, Bristol, **0-2 mi S** [gas] 7-11, Speedway/dsl, [food] River Inn Rest., Subway, [other] Eby's Pines Camping (3mi), USPO
96	Rd 1, E Elkhart, **2 mi S** [gas] BP/dsl, Marathon, 7-11, [food] Arby's, China Star, DQ, McDonald's, Subway, Taco Bell, [other] Ace Hardware
92	**ELKHART** IN 19, to Elkhart, **N** [gas] Marathon, Phillips 66/Subway/dsl, 7-11, [food] Applebee's, Cracker Barrel, Golden Egg Pancakes, Perkins, Steak'n Shake, [lodging] Best Western, Candlewood Suites, Comfort Suites, Country Inn&Suites, Diplomat Motel, EconoLodge, Fairway Inn, Hampton Inn, Hilton Garden, Holiday Inn Express, Microtel, Quality Inn, Sleep Inn, Staybridge Suties, Turnpike Motel, [other] Aldi Foods, CVS Drug, $General, Elkhart Campground (1mi), GNC, K-Mart, Martin's Foods, Walgreens, tires, transmissions, **0-2mi S** [gas] Marathon/dsl, Shell, Speedway, [food] Arby's, Bob Evans, Burger King, Callahan's, Chicago Grill, Chubby Trout, Culver's, Da Vinci's Pizza, DQ, El Camino Royal, Jimmy John's, KFC, King Wha Chinese, LJ Silver, Marco's Pizza, Matterhorn Rest., McDonald's, North Garden Buffet, Olive Garden, Papa John's, Pizza Hut, Red Lobster, Ryan's, Subway, Taco Bell, TX Roadhouse, Wendy's, Wings Etc., [lodging] Budget Inn, Days Inn, Jameson Inn, Ramada Inn, Red Roof Inn, Super 8, [other] [H], Ace Hardware, Advance Parts, AT&T, AutoZone, CarQuest, $Tree, Family$, Lowe's, Menards, O'Reilly Parts, Radio Shack, Verizon, Walmart, vet
91mm	Christiana Creek

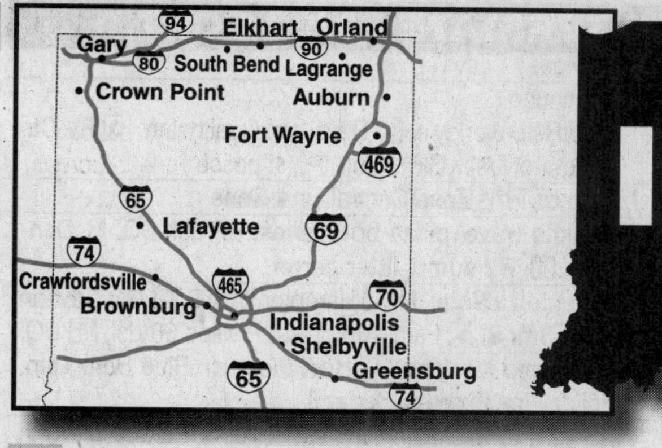

Exit	Services
90mm	TP both directions, [gas] BP/dsl, [food] Burger King, Pizza Hut, Starbucks, Z Mkt, [other] RV Dump, USPO
83	**MISHAWAKA** to Mishawaka, **N** [gas] BP/dsl, Phillips 66/Subway/dsl, [food] Applebee's, Moe's SW Grill, [lodging] Country Inn&Suites, Hampton Inn, Red Roof Inn, [other] CVS Drug, $Tree, Marshall's, Martin's Foods/gas, Menards, PetCo, Target, Walgreens, vet, **1-2 mi N on IN 23 W** [food] Barlouie, Famous Dave's BBQ, 5 Guys Burgers, Granite City Grill, King's Buffet, Olive Garden, Papa Murphy's, Pizza Hut, Subway, Wendy's, Wings Etc, [lodging] Fairfield Inn, Holiday Inn Express, Super 8, [other] Barnes&Noble, Best Buy, JC Penney, Macy's, Michael's, Sears/auto, KOA (mar-nov), mall, **2 mi S on Grape Rd & Main St (off IN 23W)** [gas] Meijer/dsl/24hr, [food] Arby's, Bob Evans, Buffalo Wild Wings, Burger King, Carraba's, Chick-fil-A, Chili's, Chipotle Mexican, CiCi's Pizza, Culver's, Del Taco, Hacienta Mexican, Houlihan's, Hooters, IHOP, Jimmy John's, Krispy Kreme, Logan's Roadhouse, Mancino's Pizza, Max&Erma's, McDonald's, Old Country Buffet, Outback Steaks, Panera Bread, Papa Vino's Italian, Quizno's, Red Lobster, Red Robin, Sonic, Starbucks, Steak'n Shake, Subway, Taste of Asia, TGIFriday's, [lodging] Comfort Inn, Courtyard, Extended Stay America, Hyatt Place Hotel, Residence Inn, SpringHill Suites, Studio+, [other] [H], Aldi Foods, Barnes&Noble, Buick/GMC/Hyundai, Christmas Tree Shop, Discount Tire, Hobby Lobby, Home Depot, Honda, Jo-Ann Fabrics, Kohl's, Lexus, Lowe's, Meijer/gas, Mercedes, Nissan, Office Depot, Old Navy, Petsmart, Sam's Club, TJ Maxx, VW, Walmart
77	**SOUTH BEND** US 33, US 31B, IN 933, South Bend, **N** [gas] Admiral, Mobil/dsl, [food] Arby's, DQ, Eleni's Rest., Fazoli's, Marco's Pizza, McDonald's, Papa John's, Ponderosa, Starbucks, Steak'nShake, Subway, [lodging] Comfort Suites, Hampton Inn, Motel 6, Suburban Lodge, Waterford Lodge, [other] AutoZone, BMW, Mazda, NAPA, O'Reilly Parts, TrueValue, Walgreens, **2 mi N on frtge rd** [gas] Meijer/dsl/24hr, Murphy USA, Phillips 66/Subway/dsl, [food] Applebee's, Burger King, Hacienda Mexican, Jimmy John's, KFC, McDonald's, Quizno's, Sonic, [other] Aldi Foods, $Tree, Meijer, Walmart, **S** [gas] Marathon, Phillips 66/Subway/dsl, [food] American Pancake House, Bob Evans, HoPing House, Mikados Japanese, Perkins, Taco Bell, Wendy's, [lodging] Best Value Inn, Hilton Garden, Holiday Inn Express, Howard Johnson, Jameson Inn, Knights Inn, Microtel, Quality Inn, St Marys Inn, [other] [H], vet, to Notre Dame
76mm	St Joseph River
72	US 31, to Niles, South Bend, **N** [gas] Pilot/Subway/dsl/scales/24hr, Speedway/Subway/dsl, [lodging] Super 8, **2 mi S on US 20** [food] 4 Seasons Rest., McDonald's, Ponderosa,

INTERSTATE 80/90 CONT'D

Exit	Services
72	Continued Taco Bell, Wendy's, 🛏 Days Inn, Quality Inn, 🅞 RV Ctr, to Potato Creek SP (20mi), 🛬, st police
62mm	Eastern Time Zone/Central Time Zone
56mm	**Rockne travel plaza both lanes**, BP/dsl, DQ, McDonald's, 🅒, **RV dump, litter barrel**
49	IN 39, to La Porte, **N** 🛏 Hampton Inn, **S** 🛏 Cassidy Inn & RV, **3mi S** 🅖 Family Express, Phillips 66/dsl, 🍴 DQ, El Bracero Mexican, 🛏 Best Western, Blue Heron Inn, Holiday Inn Express, Super 8
39	US 421, to Michigan City, Westville, **S** Purdue U North Cent
38mm	**trucks only rest area both lanes, litter barrels**
31	IN 49, to Chesterton, Valparaiso, **N** 🅖 Family Express, Phillips 66, Speedway/dsl, 🍴 Bob Evans, Clock Rest., 🛏 Hilton Garden, 🅞 CVS Drug, Goodyear, Sand Creek RV Park (3mi Apr-Oct), WiseWay Foods, to IN Dunes Nat Lakeshore, **S** 🛏 Hampton Inn (8mi), Super 89 (8mi)
24mm	toll plaza
23	Portage, Port of Indiana, **0-2 mi N** 🅖 Marathon, Shell, 🍴 Denny's, Mark's Grill, 🛏 Best Western, Days Inn, $Inn, Comfort Inn, Country Inn&Suites, Holiday Inn Express, Ramada Inn, Super 8, **S** 🅖 BP, Marathon, Speedway, 🍴 Burger King, CiCi's Pizza, Dunkin Donuts, DQ, El Contarito Mexican, First Wok Chinese, Jimmy John's, J&J's Pizza, KFC, Little Caesar's, McDonald's, Rosewood Rest., Starbucks, Subway, Wendy's, 🅞 Advance Parts, Ace Hardware, AutoZone, Family$, GNC, Town&Country Mkt, USPO, Walgreens
22mm	TP both lanes, info, 🅖 BP/dsl, 🍴 Fazoli's, Hardee's, 🅞 scales
21mm	**I-90 and I-80 run together eb, separate wb. I-80 runs with I-94 wb. For I-80 exits 1 through 15, see Indiana Interstate 94.**
21	I-94, E to Detroit, I-80/94 W, US 6, IN 51, Lake Station, **S** 🅖 ⚡FLYING J/Denny's/dsl/scales/24hr/@, Road Ranger/Subway/dsl/scales, TA/BP/Popeye's/dsl/scales/24hr/@, 🍴 McDonald's, 🅞 Blue Beacon
17	I-65 S, US 12, US 20, Dunes Hwy, to Indianapolis
14b	IN 53, to Gary, Broadway, **S** 🅖 Citgo
14a	Grant St, to Gary, **S** 🅗
10	IN 912, Cline Ave, to Gary, **N** 🛬, casino
5	US 41, Calumet Ave, to Hammond, **S** 🅖 Nice'n Easy, RaceCo, Speedway/dsl, 🍴 Arby's, Aurelio's Pizza, Dunkin Donuts, Johnel's Rest., KFC, McDonald's, Subway, Taco Bell, White Castle, 🛏 Quality Inn, Ramada Inn, Super 8, 🅞 Aldi Foods, AutoZone, Murray's Parts, Walgreens
3	IN 912, Cline Ave, to Hammond, to Gary Reg 🛬, **S** 🅖 BP
1.5mm	toll plaza
1mm	US 12, US 20, 106th St, Indianapolis Blvd, **N** 🅖 Citgo, Mobil, Shell/dsl, 🅞 casino, **S** 🍴 Burger King, KFC, McDonald's, 🅞 Aldi Foods, Jewel-Osco, auto repair
0mm	Indiana/Illinois state line

INTERSTATE 94

Exit	Services
46mm	Indiana/Michigan state line
43mm	Welcome Ctr wb, full ♿ **facilities, info,** 🅒, 🛬, **litter barrels, vending, petwalk**

Exit	Services
40b a	US 20, US 35, to Michigan City, **N** 🍴 McDonald's (3mi), 🅞 🅗, **S** 🅖 Speedway/dsl
34b a	US 421, to Michigan City, **N** 🅖 BP/dsl, Citgo/dsl, Family Express/e-85, Speedway/White Castle/dsl, 🍴 Applebee's, Arby's, Asian Buffet, Baskin-Robbins/Dunkin Donuts, Bob Evans, Buffalo Wild Wings, Burger King, Chili's, Culver's, Damon's, Denny's, Dynasty Buffet, El Bracero Mexican, IHOP, KFC, LJ Silver, McDonald's, Olive Garden, Papa John's, Pizza Hut/Taco Bell, Quizno's, Red Lobster, Ryan's, Schoop's Rest., Sophia's Pancakes, Starbucks, Steak'n Shake, Subway, TX Corral, Wendy's, 🛏 ABC Motel, Clarion, Comfort Inn, Country Inn&Suites, Knights Inn, Microtel, Milan Inn, Quality Inn, Red Roof Inn, Super 8, Travel Inn, 🅞 🅗, Advance Parts, Aldi Foods, AutoZone, BigLots, Big R, CVS Drug, $General, $Tree, Fannie May Candies, Ford/Lincoln/Mercury, Hobby Lobby, JC Penney, Jewel-Osco Drug/gas, Jo-Ann Fabrics, Lowe's, Meijer/dsl, Menards, NAPA, Office Depot, Radio Shack, Save-a-Lot, Sears/auto, Verizon, Walgreens, Walmart/Subway, **S** 🅖 Gas City/Subway/dsl/scales/e-85, 🅞 Buick/Chevrolet/GMC, Harley-Davidson
29mm	**weigh sta both lanes**
26b a	IN 49, Chesterton, **N** to IN Dunes SP, **S** 🅖 BP/White Castle, Speedway/dsl, 🍴 Applebee's, A&W/KFC, Arby's, Burger King, DQ, Dunkin Donuts, El Salto Mexican, Jimmy John's, Little Caesar's, LJ Silver, McDonald's, Pizza Hut, Quizno's, Subway, Sunrise Rest., Taco Bell, Tao Chins, Third Coast Cafe, Wendy's, 🛏 Best Western, EconoLodge, Hilton Garden (3mi), Super 8, 🅞 Advance Parts, AutoZone, Jewel-Osco, K-Mart, Sand Cr Camping (5mi), Walgreens, to Valparaiso
22b a	US 20, Burns Harbor, **N** 🅖 Steel City Express/dsl/e-85/scales/LP, TA/BP/Buckhorn Rest/Pizza Hut/Popeye's/Subway/Taco Bell/dsl/scales/24hr/@, 🛏 Comfort Inn, 🅞 Blue Beacon, fireworks, **S** 🍴 Luke/dsl, 🅿/McDonald's/Subway/dsl/scales/24hr, 🅞 Camp-Land RV Ctr, Chevrolet, Ford/Mercury, Nissan, Toyota/Scion, fireworks, repair
19	IN 249, to Port of IN, Portage, **N** 🅖 Family Express/dsl/e-85, 🍴 Deli Belly, Egg Face Grill, Longhorn Steaks, Quaker Steak&Lube, Starbucks, 🛏 Country Inn&Suites, 🅞 Bass Pro Shops, **S** 🅖 Marathon/dsl, Shell/Luke, 🍴 Denny's, Lure Burgers, Shenanigans Grill, 🛏 Best Western, Days Inn, Dollar Inn, Hampton Inn, Super 8, Travel Inn
16	access to I-80/90 toll road E, I-90 toll road W, IN 51N, Ripley St, same as 15b&a
	I-94/I-80 run together wb
15b	US 6W, IN 51, **N** 🅖 BP, ⚡FLYING J/Denny's/dsl/scales/24hr/@, Blue Ox/Subway/dsl/scales/24hr, TA/BP/Popeye's/Subway/dsl/scales/24hr/@, 🍴 McDonald's, 🅞 Blue Beacon, **N on US 20** 🅖 Dunes/Steel City/dsl/scales/dsl repair, 🍴 Paradise Rest., Ponderosa, Wing Wah
15a	US 6E, IN 51S, to US 20, **S** 🅖 GoLo, Road Ranger/Pilot/Subway/dsl/scales/24hr, Shell/Luke, 🍴 Burger King, DQ, Papa John's, LJ Silver, Ruben's Café, Wendy's, 🅞 Ace Hardware, Walgreens
13	Central Ave (from eb)
12b	I-65 N, to Gary and toll road
12a	I-65, S (from wb), to Indianapolis

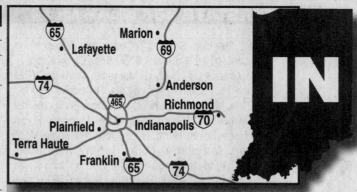

INTERSTATE 94 CONT'D

Exit	Services
11	I-65, S (from eb)
10b a	IN 53, Broadway, **N** 📩 Citgo, Gas for Less, 🍴 JJ Fish, **S** 📩 Mobil, 🍴 DQ, Rally's
9	Grant St, **N** 📩 Clark, 🍴 Chicago Hotdogs, 🔲 County Mkt Foods, Sav-a-Lot Foods, Walgreens, **S** 📩 Citgo, 🛢Love's/Denny's/dsl/scales/LP/24hr/@, Steel City/dsl/scales/rest./24hr, 🍴 A&W/KFC, Burger King, Church's, Dunkin Donuts, J&J Fish, McDonald's, Subway, 🔲 Aldi Foods, AutoZone, CarX, $Tree, Fagen Drug, Firestone/auto, Midas
6	Burr St, **N** 📩 🛢/Subway/dsl/scales/24hr/@, TA/Chester's/Pizza Hut/Taco Bell/dsl/scales/24hr/@, 🍴 J&J Fish & Chicken, Philly Steaks, Rico's Pizza, 🔲 SpeedCo, **S** 📩 Citgo/dsl/24hr
5	IN 912, Cline Ave, **S** 📩 BP, Clark, Marathon, Speedway, 🍴 Arby's, DQ, Jedi's Garden Rest., KFC, McDonald's, Pizza Hut, Popeye's, Taco Bell, Wendy's, White Castle, 🛏 Best Western, Hometowne Lodge, Motel 6, Super 8, 🔲 $Tree, Fannie May Candies, K-Mart, Radio Shack
3	Kennedy Ave, **N** 📩 Clark, Mobil/dsl, Speedway, 🍴 Burger King, Domino's, McDonald's, 🔲 Walgreens, repair, **S** 📩 Citgo, 🍴 Cholie's Pizza, Cracker Barrel, Squigi's Pizza, Subway, Wendy's, 🛏 Courtyard, Fairfield Inn, Residence Inn, 🔲 IN Welcome Ctr, USPO
2	US 41S, IN 152N, Indianapolis Blvd, **N** 📩 GoLo, Luke, SavAStop, 🍴 Arby's, Dunkin Donuts, House Of Pizza, La Rosa, Papa John's, Pizza Hut, Popeye's, Rally's, Schoop's Burgers, Taco Bell, Wheel Rest., Woodmar Rest., 🔲 CarEx, Goodyear, Midas, vet, **S** 📩 🛢/scales/dsl/24hr, 🛏 Hammond Inn, 🔲 Aldi Foods, Cabela's
1	US 41N, Calumet Ave, **N** 📩 BP/dsl, Gas City, 🍴 Barton's Pizza, Baskin-Robbins/Dunkin Donuts, Subway, 🔲 Walgreens, **S** 📩 BP, Mobil/dsl, Marathon, Shell, 🍴 Arby's, Baskin-Robbins/Dunkin Donuts, Boston Mkt, Burger King, Canton House Chinese, Edwardo's Pizza, Fortune House, Munster Gyros, Subway, Taco Bell, Wendy's, 🔲 $Jct, Jewel-Osco, Radio Shack, Staples, Target, vet
0mm	Indiana/Illinois state line

INTERSTATE 465 (INDIANAPOLIS)

Exit	Services
	I-465 loops around Indianapolis. Exit numbers begin/end on I-65, exit 108.
53b a	I-65, N to Indianapolis, S to Louisville
52	Emerson Ave, **I-74 W and I-465 S run together around S Indianapolis 21 miles.**, **N** 📩 Marathon, Shell/Circle K, Speedway, 🍴 Asian Spice, Burger King, Denny's, Domino's, KFC, LJ Silver, Subway, Taco Bell, Wendy's, 🛏 Motel 6, 🔲 H, $General, Family$, **S** 📩 Circle K, Shell/Circle K, Speedway/dsl, 🍴 Applebee's, Arby's, Bamboo House, Buffalo Wild Wings, China Buffet, DQ, Donato's Pizza, El Puerto Mexican, Fazoli's, Fujiyama, Hardee's, Hunan House, McDonald's, Papa John's, Pizza Hut, Ponderosa, Rally's, Starbucks, Steak'n Shake, Subway, Waffle House, Wendy's, White Castle/24hr, 🛏 Budget Inn, Holiday Inn, InnAmerica, La Quinta, Red Roof Inn, 🔲 Advance Parts, AutoZone, Curves, $Tree, GNC, Goodyear/auto, K-Mart, Kroger, Lowe's Whse, Marsh Foods, NAPA, Radio Shack, Walgreens, Walmart, vet

(I-74 W and I-465 S run together around S Indianapolis 21 miles)

Exit	Services
49	I-74 E, US 421, S
48	Shadeland Ave (from nb)
47	US 52 E, Brookville Rd, **E** 📩 GA, Marathon/Burger King, Speedway/dsl, 🍴 Bugsy's Grill, Huddle House, McDonald's, 🛏 Baymont Inn, 🔲 CVS Drug, vet
46	US 40, Washington St, **E** 📩 Crystal Flash, GA, Phillips 66, 🍴 Blueberry Hill Pancakes, China Buffet, Chuck-eCheese, Fajitas Mexican, LJ Silver, Olive Garden, Steak'n Shake, Yen Ching Chinese, 🔲 Advance Parts, AutoZone, Ford, O'Reilly Parts, Radio Shack, Target, **W** 📩 Thornton's, 🍴 Applebee's, Bob Evans, Fazoli's, McDonald's, Patio Burgers, 🛏 Best Western, 🔲 Buick/GMC, Hyundai, K-Mart, PepBoys
44b	I-70 E, to Columbus
44a	I-70 W, to Indianapolis
42	US 36, IN 67 N, Pendleton Pike, **E** 🍴 China Buffet, Hardee's, Rice King, Wendy's, 🛏 Ramada Inn, 🔲 $General, Family$, Sav-A-Lot Foods, U-Haul, **W** 📩 Speedway/dsl, Thornton's, 🍴 A&W/KFC, Arby's, Denny's, Domino's, Dunkin Donuts, Little Caesar's, LJ Silver, Los Ranchero's, McDonald's, Pizza Hut/Taco Bell, Rally's, Subway, Waffle House, White Castle, 🔲 H, Advance Parts, CVS Drug, Family$, K-Mart/gas, Menards, O'Reilly Parts, repair
40	56th St, Shadeland Ave, **E** 📩 Marathon, to Ft Harrison
37b a	I-69 N, to Ft Wayne, IN 37, **W** 🔲 H, services on frontage rds
35	Allisonville Rd, **N** 🍴 Bravo Italian, Buca Italian, Buffalo Wild Wings, Dave&Buster's, Hardee's, Max&Erma's, MCL Cafeteria, Melting Pot, On-the-Border, Outback Steaks, 🛏 Courtyard, 🔲 Costco/gas, Firestone/auto, Gander Mtn, JC Penney, Jo-Ann Fabrics, Macy's, Sear/auto, Target, Tires+, Van Maur, mall, **S** 📩 Shell, Speedway/dsl, 🍴 China Buffet, ChuckeCheese, 5 Guys Burgers, Panera Bread, Papa John's, Perkins/24hr, Qdoba, White Castle, 🛏 Jameson Inn, 🔲 Marsh Foods, Michael's, Petsmart, Radio Shack, TJ Maxx, Trader Joe's
33	IN 431, Keystone Ave, **N** 📩 BP/McDonald's, Marathon/dsl, 🍴 Arby's, Bob Evans, Burger King, Penn Sta Subs, Ruth Chris Steaks, Subway, 🔲 Acura, Audi, BMW/Mini, Chevrolet, Ford, Harley-Davidson, Honda, Hyundai, Infiniti, Nissan, Porsche, Scion/Toyota, Subaru, **S** 🍴 Blimpie, Champ's, Cheesecake Factory, El Torito Grill, Fleming's Steaks, LePeep's Rest, Lulu's Rest, Maggiano's, Maggie Moo's Icecream, McAlister's Deli, PF Changs, Pizza Hut, Shanghai Lil, Starbucks, Sullivan's Steaks, TGIFriday's, 🛏 Hyatt Place, Marriott, Sheraton, 🔲 Kohl's, Nordstrom's, mall

IN

INTERSTATE 465 (INDIANAPOLIS)

Exit	Services
31	US 31, Meridian St, **N** 🛏 Courtyard, Jameson Inn, Radisson, 🅾 H, Cadillac, **S** 📷 Shell/Circle K/dsl, 🍴 Arby's, Granite City Rest, La Margarita, McAlister's Deli, McDonald's, Paradise Bakery/Cafe, Starbucks
27	US 421 N, Michigan Rd, **N** 📷 Marathon, Phillips 66/dsl, Speedway/dsl, 🍴 Applebee's, Bajio Mexican, Burger King, HoneyBaked Ham, Jimmy John's, Maggie Moo's Icecream, McDonald's, Noble Roman's, Red Robin, Subway, Wendy's, Wings Etc, 🛏 Country Inn&Suites, Red Roof Inn, 🅾 AT&T, Best Buy, Buick/GMC, Chevrolet, Chrysler/Dodge/Jeep, Ford, Home Depot, Kohl's, Marshall's, PetCo, Target, Walgreens, **S** 📷 Citgo/dsl, Shell/Circle K, 🍴 Arby's, Burger King, Chic-fil-A, China Buffet, Chipotle Mexican, Cici's, Cracker Barrel, Denny's, El Meson Mexican, Famous Dave's, Hardee's, McAlister's Deli, McDonald's, Noodles&Co, O'Charley's, Outback Steaks, Panda Express, Papa Murphy's, Pizza Hut, Qdoba, Rally's, Ruby Tuesday, Steak'n Shake, Subway, Taco Bell, TX Roadhouse, Wendy's, White Castle, Yen Ching Chinese, 🛏 Best Western, Comfort Inn, Days Inn, Drury Inn, Embassy Suites, Extended Stay America, Extended Stay Deluxe, Holiday Inn, Homewood Suites, InTown Suites, La Quinta, Microtel, Residence Inn, Super 8, 🅾 Aamco, Aldi Foods, BigLots, Costco/gas, Discount Tire, $General, $Tree, Firestone, GNC, JC Penney, Lowe's Whse, Office Depot, Radio Shack, Sam's Club/gas, Staples, Walgreens, Walmart
25	I-865 W, I-465, N to Chicago
23	86th St, **E** 📷 BP, Speedway/dsl, 🍴 Abuelo's, Applebee's, Arby's, Chili's, Coldstone Creamery, Jimmy John's, Longhorn Steaks, Macaroni Grill, Monical's Pizza, Noodles&Co, Panera Bread, Quizno's, Starbucks, Steak'n Shake, Subway, Taco Bell, Ted's MT Grill, Traders Mill Grill, Wendy's, 🛏 Fairfield Inn, Homestead Suites, InTown Suites, 🅾 H, AT&T, Big-O Tires, BookAMillion, Marsh Foods, Michael's, Old Navy, Petsmart
21	71st St, **E** 📷 BP, 🍴 Bella Chino's Italian, Hardee's, McDonald's, Steak'n Shake, Subway, 🛏 Candlewood Suites, Clarion Inn, Courtyard, Hampton Inn, Holiday Inn Express, TownePlace Suites, 🅾 Curves, **W** 🍴 Bob Evans, LePeep's Rest, Los Agave's Mexican, Max&Erma's, Quizno's, Starbucks, 🛏 Hilton Garden, Residence Inn, Wingate Inn
20	I-65, N to Chicago, S to Indianapolis
19	56th St (from nb), **E** 📷 Marathon, Speedway/dsl
17	38th St,, **E** 📷 BP, Marathon/dsl, Shell/Circle K/24hr, Speedway, 🍴 ChuckeCheese, DQ, Domino's, El Maguey Mexican, Ginzo Japanese, Golden Corral, Hooters, Little Caesar's, LoneStar Steaks, LJ Silver, Machu Pichu Peruvian, O'Charley's, Penn Sta Subs, Popeye's, Red Lobster, Starbucks, Steak'n Shake, Subway, White Castle, World Buffet, 🛏 Best Value Inn, 🅾 AutoZone, Best Buy, Chevrolet, CVS Drug, $Tree, Family$, Ford, Home Depot, Kroger/gas, Meijer, O'Reilly Parts, Radio Shack, Staples, Walgreens, **W** 🍴 Arby's, Burger King, Chili's, Cracker Barrel, McDonald's, Mike's Subs, Pizza Hut/Taco Bell, Ruby Tuesday, TGIFriday's, 🛏 Ramada Ltd, Jameson Inn, 🅾 Marsh Foods, Target

I-74, W and I-465, S run together around, S Indianapolis 21 miles

Exit	Services
16b	I-74 W, to Peoria
16a	US 136, to Speedway, **E** 📷 Circle K, Shell/Circle K, Thornton's/dsl, 🍴 Applebee's, Arby's, Buffalo Wild Wings, Denny's, Hardee's, KFC, LJ Silver, McDonald's, Quizno's, Papa Murphy's, Pizza Hut, Subway, Taco Bell, Wendy's, 🛏 Budget Inn, $Inn, Motel 6, Red Roof Inn, 🅾 CVS Drug, $General, $Tree, Firestone/auto, Goodyear/auto, Kroger, Marsh Foods, PetCo, Radio Shack, **W** 🛏 Clarion
14b a	10th St, **E** 🍴 Peking Chinese, Penn Sta, Pizza Hut, Wendy's, 🅾 H, Lowe's Whse, **W** 📷 GA/Subway, Shell/Circle K, Speedway/24hr, 🍴 Arby's, Fazoli's, Hardee's, McDonald's, Rally's, Starbucks, Taco Bell, 🅾 CVS Drug
13b a	US 36, Rockville Rd, **E** 📷 Marathon, 🛏 Comfort Inn, Microtel, Sleep Inn, Wingate Inn, 🅾 Sam's Club, **W** 📷 Speedway/dsl/24hr, 🍴 Bob Evans, 🛏 Best Western
12b a	US 40 E, Washington St, **E** 🍴 Burger King, China Buffet, Church's, Fazoli's, McDonald's, Papa John's, Pizza Hut, Taco Bell, Wendy's, White Castle, 🅾 Ace Hardware, Advance Parts, AutoZone, CVS Drug, $Tree, Family$, Kroger/gas, Speedway Parts, U-Haul, Walgreens, repair, **W** 📷 Marathon/Circle K, Phillips 66/Noble Roman's/dsl, Thornton's/24hr, 🍴 Arby's, Hardee's, KFC, LJ Silver, McDonald's, Pizza Hut, Steak'n Shake, Subway, 🛏 $Inn, 🅾 Aamco, Goodyear, K-Mart, TireBarn
11b a	Sam Jones Expwy, **E** 📷 Marathon, 🍴 Denny's, Indy's Rest., Schlotzky's, Waffle House, 🛏 Adam's Mark Hotel, Candlewood Suites, Courtyard, Day's Hotel, Econolodge, Extended Stay America, Extended Stay Deluxe, Fairfield Inn, Hyatt Place, La Quinta, Quality Inn, Ramada Inn, Residence Inn, **W** 🛏 Crowne Plaza, Radisson
9b a	I-70, E to Indianapolis, W to Terre Haute
8	IN 67 S, Kentucky Ave, **E** H, **W** 📷 BP/McDonald's/dsl, Swifty, Speedway/dsl, Shell, Subway, 🍴 Burger King, Culver's, Damon's, Denny's, KFC, 🛏 Country Inn&Suites
7	Mann Rd (from wb), **E** H
4	IN 37 S, Harding St, **N** 📷 Mr Fuel/dsl/scales, 🚛 Subway/dsl/scales/24hr, 🍴 Omelette Shoppe, 🛏 Best Inn, Quality Inn, 🅾 H, Blue Beacon, **S** 📷 FLYING J/Denny's/dsl/LP/scales/24hr/@, Marathon, 🍴 Hardee's, McDonald's, Taco Bell, White Castle, 🛏 Knight's Inn, 🅾 Freightliner, SpeedCo, TruckoMat/scales
2b a	US 31, IN 37, **E** 📷 BP/24hr, 🍴 Arby's, China Garden, CiCi's, Domino's, DQ, El Azabache, KFC, King Gyros, LJ Silver, MCL Cafeteria, Old Country Buffet, Penn Sta, Pizza Hut, Steak'n Shake, White Castle, 🅾 Advance Parts, Aldi Foods, AutoZone, Chrysler/Jeep, $General, $Tree, Family$, Firestone, GNC, Goodyear, Jiffy Lube, Kroger/gas, Lincoln/Mercury, Office Depot, Radio Shack, Save-A-Lot, U-Haul, **W** 📷 Speedway, 🍴 Bob Evans, Denny's, 8Lucky Buffet, McDonald's, Red Lobster, Subway, Taco Bell, Wendy's, 🛏 Best Value Inn, Comfort Inn, Holiday Inn Express, Ramada, Super 8, Travelers Inn, Travelodge, 🅾 CVS Drug, Walgreens
53b a	I-65, N to Indianapolis, S to Louisville

I-465 loops around Indianapolis. Exit numbers begin/end on I-65, exit 108.

INTERSTATE 469 (FT WAYNE)

Exit	Services
31c b a	I-69, US 27 S., Auburn Road. I-469 begins/ends.
29.15mm	St Joseph River
29b a	Maplecrest Rd, **W** 📷 Lassus/DQ/Subway/dsl, Mara

Copyright 2012 - The Next Exit®

INTERSTATE 469 CONT'D (FT WAYNE)

Exit	Services
29b a	Continued
	thon/dsl, Mozzarelli's Pizza, Sonic
25	IN 37, to Ft Wayne, **W** Murphy USA/dsl, Antonio's Pizza, Applebee's, Bob Evans, Buffalo Wild Wings, Cracker Barrel, Golden Corral, HoneyBee Chinese, Steak'n Shake, Subway, Uno, Wendy's, Wings Etc, AT&T, Discount Tire, Kohl's, Marshall's, Meijer/dsl, Menards, Michael's, Office Depot, Petsmart, Walgreens, Walmart/McDonald's
21	US 24, E
19b a	US 30 E, to Ft Wayne, **E** Sunoco/Taco Bell/dsl, Freightliner, Mack, Peterbilt, truck/tire repair, **W**

FT WAYNE

Exit	Services
19b a	Continued
	Marathon, Garno's Italian, Golden Gate Chinese, Mancino's Grinders, Richard's Rest., Zesto Drive-In, Holiday Inn Express, $General
17	Minnich Rd
15	Tillman Rd
13	Marion Center Rd
11	US 27, US 33 S, to Decatur, Ft Wayne, **E** BP/Subway/dsl
10.5mm	St Marys River
9	Winchester Rd
6	IN 1, to Bluffton, Ft Wayne, **W** to
2	Indianapolis Rd, **W** to
1	Lafayette Ctr Rd

IOWA

INTERSTATE 29

SIOUX CITY

Exit	Services
152mm	Iowa/South Dakota state line, Big Sioux River
151	IA 12 N, Riverside Blvd, **E** Casey's, $General, Fareway Foods, Riverside Prk, to Stone SP, Pecaut Nature Ctr
149	Hamilton Blvd, **E** Conoco, Horizon Rest, Rodeway Inn, JiffyLube, tires, to Briar Cliff Coll, **W Iowa Welcome Ctr sb, full facilities,** Hilton Garden Inn, Riverboat Museum
148	US 77 S, to, S Sioux City, Nebraska, **W** Casey's, Conoco/dsl, Sam's, DQ, Kahill's Rest., La Fiesta Mexican, McDonald's, Pizza Hut, Taco Bell, Wendy's, Budget Host, Marina Inn, Regency Inn, Advance Parts, Curves, O'Reilly Parts
147b	US 20 bus, Sioux City, **E** Heritage Gas, Arby's, Burger King, Chili's, Famous Dave's, Hardee's, IHOP, Perkins/24hr, City Center Hotel, Holiday Inn, Ramada, , Chevrolet, Staples, USPO, Walgreens
147a	Floyd Blvd, **E** Home Depot, **W** to Riverboat Casino
146.5mm	Floyd River
144b	I-129 W, US 20 W, US 75, S
144a	US 20 E, US 75 N, to Ft Dodge, **1 mi E on Lakeport Rd** Casey's, Shell, Applebee's, Buffalo Wild Wings, Burger King, Carlos'o Kelly's, ChuckeCheese, Golden Corral, Hardee's, HuHot Chinese, Jimmy John's, LJ Silver/A&W, McDonald's, Olive Garden, Outback Steaks, Red Lobster, Red Robin, Starbucks, Taco Del Mar, TX Roadhouse, Comfort Inn, Fairfield Inn, Hampton Inn, Holiday Inn Express, URGENT CARE, Barnes&Noble, Best Buy, Buick/Honda/Isuzu, Gordman's, Hobby Lobby, Hy-Vee Foods/gas/24hr, JC Penney, Jiffy Lube, Kohls, Lowe's Whse, Michael's, Old Navy, PetsMart, Sears/auto, Target, Younkers, mall
143	US 75 N, Singing Hills Blvd, **E** Cenex/dsl, Murphy USA, Shell/Truck Haven/dsl/café/24hr/@, China Buffet, Culver's, KFC, McDonald's, Pizza Hut, Quizno's, Taco John's, AmericInn, Baymont Inn, Days Inn, Haven Motel, Urgent Care, Cadillac/GMC, $Tree, KIA, Nissan, Sam's Club/gas, Toyota/Scion, Walmart, Sgt Floyd Mon, **W** BP/Sioux Harbor/dsl/motel/café/24hr/@, Wendy's, Super 8, Kenworth/Peterbilt, truckwash/repair
141	D38, Sioux Gateway , **E** Phillips 66/dsl, Shell/dsl, Aggies Rest., China Wok, Godfather's, Pizza Ranch,

Exit	Services
141	Continued
	Subway, Econolodge, Curves, **W** Motel 6, , museum
139mm	**rest area both lanes, full facilities, info, litter barrels, RV dump, wireless internet**
135	Port Neal Landing
134	Salix, **W** camping
132mm	**weigh sta sb, rest area nb, , litter barrels, parking only**
127	IA 141, Sloan, **E** Casey's, Kum&Go/Subway/dsl, Shell/dsl, Rip Van Winkle Motel, WinnaVegas Inn, RV Park, **3 mi W** Heritage Express, to Winnebago Indian Res/casino
120	to Whiting, **W** camping
112	IA 175, Onawa, **E** Conoco/Subway/dsl, Phillips 66/dsl, Bamboo Village Chinese, DQ, McDonald's, Michael's Rest., Pizza Hut, Super 8, , NAPA, On-Ur-Wa RV Park, Pamida, **2 mi W** KOA, Lewis&Clark SP, Keel Boat Exhibit
110mm	**rest area both lanes, full facilities, info, litter barrels, petwalk, RV dump, wireless internet**
105	E60, Blencoe
96mm	Little Sioux River
95	F 20, Little Sioux, **E** gas, Loess Hills SF (9mi), **W** Woodland RV Park
92mm	Soldier River
91.5mm	**rest area both lanes, litter barrels, parking only**
89	IA 127, Mondamin, **1 mi E** Jiffy Mart/dsl
82	F50, Modale, **1 mi W** Cenex/dsl
79mm	**rest area both lanes, full facilities, info, , litter barrels, RV dump, wireless internet**
75	US 30, Missouri Valley, **E Iowa Welcome Ctr (5mi)**, Shell/dsl/24hr, Arby's, Bluegrass cafe, McDonald's, Subway, Oaktree Inn, (2mi), to Steamboat Exhibit, **W** BP/dsl, Phillips 66/rest/dsl, Burger King, Taco John's, Days Inn, Rath Inn, Super 8, Buick/Chevrolet
73.5mm	**weigh sta nb**
72.5mm	Boyer River
72	IA 362, Loveland, **E** Phillips 66/dsl, **W** to Wilson Island SP (6mi)
71	I-680 E, to Des Moines
	I-29 S & I-680 W run together 10 mi.
66	Honey Creek, **W** RV Camping
61b	I-680 W, to, N Omaha, **W** Mormon Trail Ctr

IN

IA

IA

INTERSTATE 29 CONT'D

COUNCIL BLUFFS

Exit	Services
61a	IA 988, to Crescent, **E** 🅐 Phillips 66/dsl, 🅾 to ski area
56	IA 192, S (sb only, exits left), Council Bluffs, **E** 🛏 Super 7 Inn, 🅾 🄷
55	N 25th, Council Bluffs, **E** 🅐 Pump'n Munch/dsl, Sinclair/24hr
54b	N 35th St (from nb), Council Bluffs
54a	G Ave (from sb), Council Bluffs
53b	I-480 W, US 6, to Omaha
53a	9th Ave, S 37th Ave, Council Bluffs, **E** 🅐 Shell, Valero, 🍴 Red Onion Cafe, 🛏 Days Inn, **W** 🅾 Harrah's Casino/hotel, RiverBoat Casino, camping
52	Nebraska Ave, **E** 🅐 Phillips 66/dsl, 🍴 Quaker Steak, Ruby Tuesday, 🛏 Comfort Suites, Microtel, SpringHill Suites, ValuePlace Inn, 🅾 Bass Pro Shops, **W** 🛏 Ameri-Star Hotel/casino, Hampton Inn, Holiday Inn, 🅾 River-Boat Casino
51	I-80 W, to Omaha
	I-29 and I-80 run together 3 miles. See Iowa Interstate 80 Exits 1b-3.
48	I-80, E (from nb), to Des Moines, **E** 🄷
47	US 275, IA 92, Lake Manawa, **E** 🅐 Phillips 66, 🅾 Iowa School for the Deaf, **W** 🍴 Buffalo Wild Wings, 🅾 $Tree, Hobby Lobby, Kohls, PetsMart, Radio Shack, Target
42	IA 370, to Bellevue, **W** 🅾 K&B Saddlery, to Offutt AFB, camping, truck parts
38mm	**rest area both lanes, full** 🚻 **facilities, 🅲, info, 🅿, litter barrels, RV dump, petwalk, wireless internet**
35	US 34 E, to Glenwood, **E** 🍴 McDonalds (4mi), 🛏 Western Inn (4mi), 🅾 RV Park, **W** 🅐 BP/dsl, 🛏 Bluff View Motel, 🅾 Harley-Davidson
32	US 34 W, Pacific Jct, to Plattsmouth
24	L31, to Tabor, Bartlett
20	IA 145, Thurman
15	J26, Percival, **1-2 mi E** gas/dsl
11.5mm	**weigh sta nb**
10	IA 2, to Nebraska City, Sidney, **E** to Waubonsie SP (5mi), **W** 🅐 BP/Sapp Bros/dsl/scales/24hr, Phillips 66/dsl, Shell/Subway/Crossroads Cafe/dsl/scales/24hr, 🍴 Antique Coffee Shop, Wendy's, 🛏 Best Value Inn, Super 8, 🅾 Victorian Acres RV Park (4mi), **IA Welcome Ctr**, to Arbor Lodge SP, antiques, tire repair
1	IA 333, Hamburg, **1 mi E** 🅐 Casey's/dsl, 🍴 Bootleggers Rest., 🛏 Hamburg Motel, 🅾 🄷, NAPA, Soda Fountain
0mm	Iowa/Missouri state line

INTERSTATE 35

Exit	Services
219mm	Iowa/Minnesota state line
214	rd 105, to Northwood, Lake Mills, **E** 🛏 Royal Motel (7mi), **W** Welcome Ctr both lanes, full 🚻 facilities, 🅿, litter barrels, vending, petwalk, RV dump, wireless internet, 🅐 BP/Burger King/dsl, 🛏 Country Inn&Suites, 🅾 casino
212mm	**weigh sta sb, rest area nb,** 🅿, **litter barrels, no services**
208	rd A38, to Joice, Kensett, windmills
203	IA 9, to Manly, Forest City, to Pilot Knob SP, no services
202mm	Winnebago River
197	rd B20, **8 mi E** Lime Creek Nature Ctr
196mm	**rest area both lanes, litter barrels, parking only**
194	US 18, to Mason City, Clear Lake, **E** 🅐 Ruby's/dsl,

CLEAR LAKE

Exit	Services
194	Continued 🅾 🄷 (8mi), Chevrolet, Freightliner, truck repair, **W** 🅐 Casey's, 🅐/Subway/dsl/scales, Kum&Go, Shell/Wendy's/dsl, 🍴 Arby's, Cancun mexican, Culver's, Denny's, DQ, KFC/Taco Bell, McDonald's, Perkins/24hr, Pizza Hut, Rice House Chinese, Subway, 🛏 AmericInn, Best Western/rest., Budget Inn, Microtel
193	rd B35, to Mason City, Emery, **E** 🅐 Kum&Go/Taco John's/dsl/e-85, 🛏 Super 8, 🅾 truckwash, **W** 🅾 Ford, to Clear Lake SP
190	US 18, rd 27 E, to Mason City
188	rd B43, to Burchinal
182	rd B60, to Rockwell, Swaledale
180	rd B65, to Thornton, **W** 🅐 Cenex (2mi), 🅾 camping
176	rd C13, to Sheffield, Belmond
170	rd C25, to Alexander
165	IA 3, **E** 🅐 Shell/dsl/rest., 🛏 AmericInn (9mi), Hampton Motel (9mi), 🅾 🄷 (7mi)
159	rd C47, Dows, **W rest area both lanes, full** 🚻 **facilities info, 🅲, 🅿, litter barrels, petwalk, vending, RV dump, wireless internet,** Shell/Arby's/Godfather's/dsl/24hr
155mm	Iowa River
151	rd R75, to Woolstock
147	rd D20, to US 20, E
144	rd D25, Williams, **E** 🅐 Boondocks Trkstp/cafe/dsl, Best Western, Boondocks Motel, 🅾 RV camping, **W** 🅐 🄵 FLYING J/Trump's Rest/dsl/scales/24hr
142b a	US 20, to Webster City, Ft Dodge
139	rd D41, to Kamrar
133	IA 175, to Jewell, Eldora, **W** 🅐 Kum&Go/Subway/dsl, Prarie Land
128	rd D65, to Stanhope, Randall, **5 mi W** Little Wall Lake Pk
124	rd 115, Story City, **W** 🅐 Casey's, Kum&Go/dsl/24hr, 🍴 DQ, Happy Chef/24hr, McDonald's, Old Hamburg Rest, Pizza Ranch, Subway, 🛏 Comfort Inn, Super 8, Viking Motel/rest, 🅾 Ford, Story City RV Ctr, VF Factory Stores/famous brands, Whispering Oaks Camping
123	rd E18, to Roland, McCallsburg
120mm	**rest area nb, full** 🚻 **facilities, info, 🅲, 🅿, litter barrels, vending, wireless internet, RV dump/scenic prairie area sb**
119mm	**rest area sb, full** 🚻 **facilities, 🅲, 🅿, litter barrels, vending, wireless internet, RV dump**
116	rd E29, to Story, **2 mi W** Story Co Conservation Ctr
113	13th St, Ames, **W** 🅐 Kum&Go/Burger King/dsl, Phillips 66/Arby's, 🍴 Pizza Ranch, 🛏 Holiday Inn Express, Quality Inn, 🅾 🄷, Harley-Davidson, to USDA Vet Labs, ISU
111b a	US 30, to Nevada, Ames, **E** Twin Acres Campground (11mi), **W** 🅐 Kum&Go/DQ/Subway/dsl, 🍴 Azteca Mexican, 🛏 AmericInn, Comfort Inn, Country Inn&Suites, Fairfield Inn, Hampton Inn, Heartland Inn, Microtel, Super 8, 🅾 to IA St U
109mm	S Skunk River
106mm	**weigh sta both lanes**
102	IA 210, to Slater, **3 mi W** 🍴 DQ, Subway
96	to Elkhart, **W** to Big Creek SP (11mi), Saylorville Lake
94mm	**rest area both lanes, full** 🚻 **facilities, info, 🅲, 🅿, litter barrels, vending, petwalk, wireless internet**
92	1st St, Ankeny, **W** 🅐 Kum&Go, QT, 🍴 Ankeny Diner, Applebee's, Arby's, Burger King, Cazador Mexican, Fazoli's, Guadalajara Mexican, KFC, Quizno's, Subway,

AMES

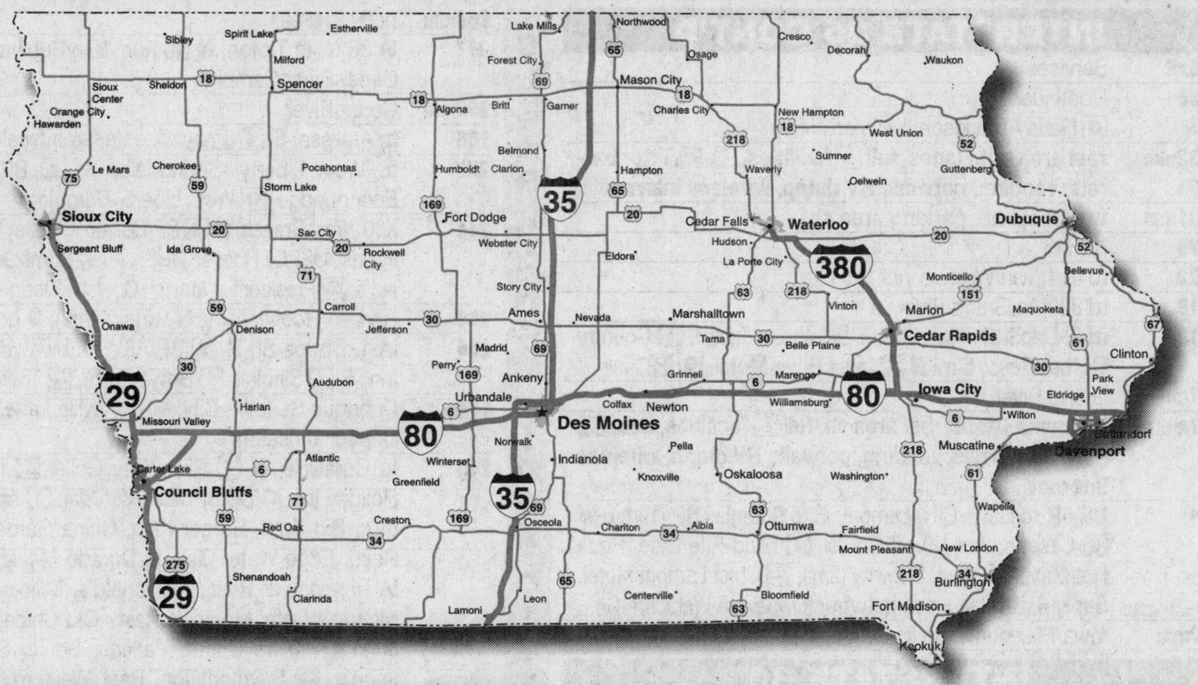

INTERSTATE 35 CONT'D

I-35 and I-80 run together 14 mi around NW Des Moines. See Iowa Interstate 80, exits 124-136.

Exit	Services
92	Continued
	Village Inn, 🛏 Best Western/rest., Days Inn, Fairfield Inn, Heartland Inn, Super 8, 🅾 🅷 Goodyear/auto, O'Reilly Parts, Staples, Tires+, auto repair
90	IA 160, Ankeny, E 🍴 Chip's Diner, Outback Steaks, 🛏 AmericInn, Comfort Inn, Country Inn&Suites, Holiday Inn Express, 🅾 Buick/GMC, W 🅰 Casey's/dsl, Phillips 66, 🍴 B-bops Rest., Buffalo Wild Wings, Burger King, Chili's, China Buffet, Culver's, El Charro, IHOP, Jimmy John's, Marble Slab, McDonald's, Old Chicago, Panchero's Mexican, Panera Bread, Starbucks, Wendy's, 🅾 Best Buy, Big O Tires, Chevrolet, Dodge/Jeep, Ford, GNC, Home Depot, Kohl's, Menards, Michael's, Petsmart, Radio Shack, Target, TJ Maxx, Tuesday Morning, Tuffy Auto, Walgreens, Walmart, vet, to Saylorville Lake (5mi)
89	Corporate Woods Dr, E 🛏 Hampton Inn, W 🛏 ValuePlace
87b a	I-235, I-35 and I-80
72c	University Ave, E 🅰 Kum&Go/Burger King, QT, 🍴 Biaggi's Rest, Boston's, Caribou Coffee, Cracker Barrel, El Rodeo Mexican, Red Rossa Pizza, Shane's Rib Shack, Wendy's, Z'Marik's Cafe, 🛏 Best Western, Country Inn&Suites, La Quinta, 🅾 🅷 Granite City Food, Walgreens, W 🅰 BP/MaidRite, 🍴 Applebee's, Bakers Square, Bandana's BBQ, Cheddar's, Chili's, Huhot Mongolian, Jason's Deli, KFC, Macaroni Grill, McDonald's, Mi Mexico, Outback Steaks, Qdoba Mexican, RockBottom Rest./brewery, TCBY, 🛏 Chase Suites, Courtyard, Heartland Inn, Ramada Inn, Sheraton, Wildwood Lodge, 🅾 AT&T, Barnes&Noble, Best Buy, Home Depot, K-Mart, Kohl's, Marshall's, Office Depot, Petsmart, Target, Verizon, World Mkt
72b	I-80, W
72a	I-235 E, to Des Moines
70	Civic Pkwy, Mills, E 🅰 Kum&Go/McDonald's, 🍴 Fire Creek Grill, Legend's Grill, Quizno's, 🅾 Hy-Vee Foods/gas, Walgreens, W 🅰 Casey's/MaidRite/dsl, 🍴 Applebee's, BoneFish Grill, Buffalo Wild Wings, Caribou Coffee, Champp's Grill, Cheesecake Factory, Cusina Italiana, Fleming's Rest., Fuddruckers, Iron Wok, Joe's Crabshack, Johnny's Italian Steaks, Joseph's Steaks, Mimi's Cafe, O'Charly's, On-the-Border, Panera Bread, PF Chang's, Quizno's, Red Robin, Starbucks, 🛏 Courtyard, Drury Inn, Hilton Garden, Holiday Inn, Residence Inn, 🅾 🅷 Barnes&Noble, Best Buy, Costco/gas, Dillards, Kohl's, Lowe's Whse, Old Navy, PetCo, Scheel's Sports, Target, TJ Maxx, Walmart
69b a	Grand Ave, W Des Moines
68.5mm	Racoon River
68	IA 5, 7 mi E to ⚓, to Walnut Woods SP
65	G14, to Norwalk, Cumming, 14 mi W John Wayne Birthplace, Madison Co Museum
61mm	North River
56	IA 92, to Indianola, Winterset, W 🅰 Kum&Go/cafe/dsl, Shamrock/dsl, 🍴 Hitchin Post Grill, 🅾 Diamond Trail RV Ctr
56mm	Middle River
53mm	rest area nb, litter barrels, no services
52	G50, St Charles, St Marys, W 🅰 Kum&Go, 🅾 14 mi John Wayne Birthplace, museum
51mm	rest area sb, litter barrels, parking only, no services
47	rd G64, to Truro, W 🅰 Kum&Go (1mi)
45.5mm	South River
43	rd 207, New Virginia, E 🅰 Kum&Go/Subway/dsl
36	rd 152, to US 69, 3 mi E 🛏 Blue Haven Motel, Evergreen Inn, W st patrol
34	Clay St, Osceola, W 🅰 Terrible, 🍴 Maid-Rite Cafe, 🅾 Lakeside Casino Resort/camping
33	US 34, Osceola, E 🅰 Casey's/dsl/scales, 🍴 McDonald's, Pizza Hut, Subway, 🛏 Best Value Inn, Days Inn, Super 8, 🅾 🅷 Ford/Mercury, Goodyear, Hy-Vee Foods, O'Reilly Parts, Pamida, Radio Shack, st patrol, tires, W 🅰 BP/Arby's/dsl, 🍴 KFC/Taco Bell, 🛏 AmericInn,

ANKENY

N
↑
↓
S

DES MOINES

IA

🖾 = gas 🍴 = food 🛏 = lodging 🅾 = other   Copyright 2012 - The Next Ex

	INTERSTATE 35 CONT'D
Exit	**Services**
33	Continued
	🅾 Harley-Davidson, Walmart
32mm	**rest area both lanes, full ♿ facilities, 🍴, 🖾, litter barrels, vending, petwalk, RV dump, wireless internet**
31mm	**weigh sta nb, parking area sb**
29	rd H45
22	rd J14, Van Wert
18	rd J20, to Grand River
12	rd 2, Decatur City, Leon, **E** 🖾 Shell/dsl/rest, 🍴 Country Corner Rest., **5 mi E** 🛏 Little River Motel, 🅾 🅷
7.5mm	Grand River
7mm	**Welcome Ctr nb/rest area sb, full ♿ facilities, info, 🍴, 🖾, litter barrels, vending, petwalk, RV dump, wireless internet**
4	US 69, to Davis City, Lamoni, **E** to 9 Eagles SP (10mi), **W** 🖾 Casey's (2mi), Kum&Go/dsl, 🍴 Maid-Rite Cafe, Pizza Hut (2mi), QC Rest, Subway (2mi), 🛏 Chief Lamoni Motel, Super 8, 🅾 CarQuest, auto/truck repair, IA Welcome Ctr
0mm	Iowa/Missouri state line

	INTERSTATE 80
Exit	**Services**
307mm	Iowa/Illinois state line, Mississippi River
306	US 67, to Le Claire, **N Welcome Ctr wb (no trucks), full ♿ facilities, 🖾, litter barrels, 🍴, petwalk,** 🖾 Phillips 66/dsl, 🍴 McDonald's, Subway, 🛏 Comfort Inn, Holiday Inn Express, Super 8, 🅾 Slagles Foods, **1 mi N** 🖾 BP, 🍴 A&W (2mi), 🅾 Buffalo Bill Museum, **S** 🖾 BP (2mi)
301	Middle Rd, to Bettendorf
300mm	**rest area both lanes, full ♿ facilities, 🍴, 🖾, litter barrels, vending, petwalk, RV dump, WiFi**
298	I-74 E, to Peoria, **S** 🅾 to 🅷, st patrol
295b a	US 61, Brady St, to Davenport, **N** 🖾 BP/dsl, 🅾 Hummer, to Scott CP, **0-2 mi S** 🖾 BP, Phillips 66, Shell, 🍴 Burger King, Cracker Barrel, Dickey's BBQ, Happy Joe's, Hardee's, Hooters, McDonald's, Royal Wok, ThunderBay Grille, Village Inn Rest., Yen Ching Chinese, 🛏 AmericInn, Best Western, Baymont Inn, Casa Loma Suites, Clarion, Country Inn&Suites, Davenport Inn, Days Inn, Motel 6, Residence Inn, Super 8, Travelodge, 🅾 AutoZone, Barnes&Noble, CarQuest, Chevrolet, $General, Firestone, Honda, Hyundai, JC Penney, KIA, Lexus, Menards, Nissan, Radio Shack, Sears/auto, Tires+, Toyota, US Adventures RV Ctr, Von Maur, mall, vet
292	IA 130 W, Northwest Blvd, **N** 🖾 ⓕFLYING J/Denny's/dsl/LP/scales/24hr, 🛏 Comfort Inn, 🅾 Interstate RV Park (1mi), Farm&Fleet, Peterbilt, truckwash, **S** 🖾 BP/McDonald's, Sinclair, 🍴 Machine Shed Rest., 🛏 EconoLodge
290	I-280 E, to Rock Island
284	Y40, to Walcott, **N** 🖾 🚛/Arby's/dsl/24hr/scales, TA/IA 80/BP/DQ/Wendy's/dsl/scales/24hr/@, 🍴 Gramma's Rest., 🛏 Comfort Inn, EconoLodge, 🅾 Blue Beacon, IA 80 Trucking Museum, IA 80 Truck-o-Mat, SpeedCo Lube, tires, **S** 🖾 🚛/Subway/dsl/24hr, 🍴 McDonald's, 🛏 Days Inn, 🅾 Cheyenne RV Ctr, Walcott CB
280	Y30, to Stockton, New Liberty
277	Durant, **2 mi S** 🖾 Sinclair/dsl/E85
271	US 6 W, IA 38 S, to Wilton
270mm	**rest area both lanes, full ♿ facilities, info, 🍴, 🖾, litter barrels, vending, petwalk, RV dump, WiFi**

268mm	parking areas
267	IA 38 N, to Tipton, **N** 🖾 Kum&Go/Subway/dsl/E85, 🅾 Cedar River Camping
266mm	Cedar River
265	to Atalissa, **S** 🖾 🚛/Chester's/dsl/scales/24hr
259	to West Liberty, Springdale, **S** 🖾 BP/dsl/24hr, 🛏 EconoLodge, 🅾 West Liberty Camping
254	X30, West Branch, **N** 🖾 BP/Quizno's, Casey's, 🅾 Jack&Jill Foods, USPO, Hoover NHS, **S** 🖾 Kum&Go, 🍴 McDonald's, 🛏 Presidential Inn, 🅾 Chrysler/Dodge/Jeep
249	Herbert Hoover Hwy, **N** winery (2mi), **S** golf
246	IA 1, Dodge St, **N** 🖾 BP/A&W/Subway/dsl, 🛏 Quality Inn, **S** 🖾 Sinclair, 🍴 Bob's Pizza, 🛏 Travelodge
244	Dubuque St, Iowa City, **N** Coralville Lake, **S** 🅷, to Old Capitol, museum
242	to Coralville, **N** 🍴 River City Grille, 🛏 Hampton Inn, Holiday Inn, **S** 🖾 BP, Kum&Go/dsl, 🍴 Applebee's, Arby's, Big Tenn, Burger King, China Garden, DQ, Edge Rest., Edge Water Grill, El Dorado Mexican, Hardee's, IA Riverpower Rest., McDonald's, Milio's Sandwiches, Mondo's Cafe, Monica's Rest., Old Chicago Grill, Papa John's, Peking Buffet, Perkins, Sonic, Subway, Taco John's, 🛏 Baymont Inn, Best Western, Comfort Inn, Days Inn, Fairfield Inn, Heartland Inn, IA Lodge, Marriott, Motel 6, Super 8, 🅾 🅷, Aamco, Walgreens, vet
240	IA 965, to US 6, Coralville, N Liberty, **N** 🖾 BP, Phillips 66/dsl, 🍴 Buffalo Wild Wings, Culver's, Jimmy John's, McDonald's, Steak'n Shake, TX Roadhouse, Village Inn, Wendy's, 🛏 AmericInn, Country Inn&Suites, Suburban Lodge, 🅾 Colony Country Camping (3mi), Gordman's, Harley-Davidson, Kohl's, Michael's, PetCo, Walgreens, Walmart/Subway, **S** 🖾 BP, Casey's/Blimpie, 🍴 Boston's Cafe, Caribou Coffee, Chili's, Coldstone, Food Court, Huhot Mongolian, IHOP, Old Country Buffet, Olive Garden, Outback Steaks, Panchero's Mexican, Papa Murphy's, Pizza Hut, Red Lobster, Starbucks, Taste of China, 🛏 Comfort Suites, Holiday Inn Express, 🅾 Ace Hardware, Barnes&Noble, Best Buy, Dillard's, Hobby Lobby, HyVee Foods/gas, JC Penney, Lowe's, Radio Shack, Scheel's Sports, Sears/auto, Target, Tires+, U-Haul, Verizon, Younkers, mall
239b	I-380 N, US 218 N, to Cedar Rapids
239a	US 218, S
237	Tiffin, **1 mi N** 🖾 Kum&Go/dsl, 🍴 Jon's Rest (seasonal)
236mm	**rest area both lanes, full ♿ facilities, 🍴, 🖾, litter barrels, vending, RV dump, petwalk, wireless internet**
230	W38, to Oxford, **N** 🅾 Sleepy Hollow Camping, Kalona Museum
225	US 151 N, W21 S, **N** to Amana Colonies, 🛏 Heritage Inn, **S Welcome Ctr**, 🖾 BP, Casey's, 🍴 Colony Village Rest., MaidRite Cafe, Little Amana Rest./Winery, 7 Villages Rest., Ox Yoke Rest., 🛏 Clarion, Super 8
220	IA 149 S, V77 N, to Williamsburg, **N** 🖾 BP, Casey's/rest/dsl, 🍴 Arby's, McDonald's, Subway, 🛏 Best Western, Crest Motel, Super 8, 🅾 GNC, Old Navy, factory outlets/famous brands, **S** 🛏 Days Inn
216	to Marengo, **N** 🖾 Kum&Go/Subway/dsl, 🛏 Sudbury Court Motel (7mi), 🅾 🅷 (8mi)
211	to Ladora, Millersburg, **S** Lake IA Park (5mi)
208mm	**rest area both lanes, full ♿ facilities, 🍴, 🖾, vending, litter barrels, petwalk, wireless internet, RV dump**
205	to Victor

INTERSTATE 80 CONT'D

E ↕ **W**

Exit	Services
201	IA 21, to Deep River, **N** 🛢 ▦/Subway/dsl/scales/24hr, 🍴 Nick's Rest., 🛏 Sleep Inn, **S** 🛢 KwikStar/Pinecone Rest./dsl/scales/24hr/@, truck repair
197	to Brooklyn, **N** RV camping
191	US 63, to Montezuma, **N** 🛢 Sinclair/dsl, **S** to Diamond Lake SP (9mi)
182	IA 146, to Grinnell, **0-2 mi N** 🛢 Casey's, Kum&Go/Subway/dsl, 🍴 Casa Margaritas, DQ, KFC, McDonald's, Taco Bell, 🛏 Best Western, Comfort Inn, Country Inn, Days Inn, Super 8, ⊙ Ⓗ (4mi), Buick/Chevrolet/GMC, Chrysler/Dodge/Jeep, $General, Hyvee Foods, O'Reilly Parts, Walmart, vet
180mm	**rest area both lanes, full** ♿ **facilities,** 🚻**, vending, weather info,** 📷**, litter barrels, petwalk, playground, RV dump (eb) wireless internet**
179	IA 124, to Oakland Acres, Lynnville
175mm	**N** Skunk River
173	IA 224, Kellogg, **N** 🛢 Phillips 66/Best Burger/dsl/24hr, ⊙ Kellogg RV Park, Rock Creek SP (9mi), **S** ⊙ Pella Museum
168	SE Beltline Dr, to Newton, **1 mi N** 🛢 Casey's/dsl, Murphy USA, 🍴 Arby's, 🛏 Mid-Iowa Motel, ⊙ $Tree, Radio Shack, Rolling Acres Camping (seasonal), Walmart, **S** 🛢 💙Loves/Chester's/McDonald's/dsl/scales, 🛏 AmericInn, ⊙ Iowa Speedway
164	US 6, IA 14, Newton, **N** 🛢 Casey's, Phillips 66/Subway/dsl, 🍴 Country Kitchen, Culver's, KFC/Taco Bell, Okoboji Grill, Perkins, Pizza Ranch, Senor Tequila Mexican, 🛏 Days Inn, EconoLodge, Quality Inn, Super 8, ⊙ Ⓗ, museum, **S** 🛏 Newton Inn/rest., ⊙ Chevrolet/Cadillac, Ford/Lincoln/Mercury, to Lake Red Rock
159	F48, to Jasper, Baxter
155	IA 117, Colfax, **N** 🛢 BP/McDonald's, 🛏 Comfort Inn, Microtel, ⊙ Pitstop RV Camping, truck repair, **S** 🛢 Casey's, Kum&Go/Subway/dsl/24hr
153mm	**S** Skunk River
151	weigh sta wb
149	Mitchellville
148mm	**rest area both lanes, full** ♿ **facilities,** 🚻**,** 📷**, litter barrels, petwalk, vending, RV dump, wireless internet**
143	Altoona, Bondurant, **0-2 mi S** 🛢 Casey's, Kum&Go, 🍴 Pizza Ranch, 🛏 Holiday Inn Express, ⊙ HyVee Foods
142b a	US 65, Hubble Ave, Des Moines, **S** 🛢 Bosselman/Pilot/Sinclair/dsl/rest./24hr/@, Git'n Go, 🍴 Big Steer Rest., Burger King, Culver's, KFC/Taco Bell, McDonald's/playpalce, Pizza Hut, Subway, Taco John's, 🛏 Adventureland Inn, Heartland Inn, Motel 6, Regency Inn, Settle Inn, ⊙ Adventureland Funpark, Blue Beacon, Freightliner, Peterbilt, camping, casino
141	US 6 W, US 65 S, Pleasant Hill, Des Moines, **S** 🍴 Uncle Buck's Grill, ⊙ Bass Pro Shops
137b a	I-35 N, I-235 S, to Des Moines
	I-80 W and I-35 S run together 14 mi.
136	US 69, E 14th St, Camp Sunnyside, **N** 🛢 BP/dsl, Casey's, 🍴 Bonanza Steaks, Country Kitchen, 🛏 Budget Inn, Motel 6, Red Roof Inn, Rodeway Inn, ⊙ Volvo/GMC, antiques, **0-1 mi S** 🛢 Casey's/dsl, Star Gas, QT/Burger King/scales/24hr, 🍴 Arby's, Fazoli's, KFC, McDonald's, Papa Murphy's, Pueblo Viejo Mexican,

D E S · M O I N E S

136	Continued
	Subway, Taco Bell, Taco John's, Village Inn, 🛏 Baymont Inn, Travelodge, ⊙ Advance Parts, Aldi Foods, CarQuest, $General, Family$, O'Reilly Parts, Tires+, TruckLube
135	IA 415, 2nd Ave, Polk City, **N** ⊙ Harley-Davidson, Rider Trucks, antiques, **S** 🛢 Git'n Go, QT, Shell, ⊙ Ⓗ, Earl's Tire, NAPA, USPO (2mi), st patrol
133mm	Des Moines River
131	IA 28 S, NW 58th St, **N** 🛢 Casey's, QT, 🍴 Bandit Burrito, Chopsticks, DQ, El Mariachi Mexican, Greenbriar Rest., Pagliai's Pizza, Panera Bread, Quizno's, Sonic, Subway, VanDee's Icecream/Sandwiches, 🛏 Best Inn, ⊙ Ace Hardware, Acura, Audi/VW, Goodyear/auto, Hy-Vee Food, USPO, vet, **S** 🛢 BP/dsl/24hr, Casey's, QT, 🍴 Applebee's, Arby's, Carlos O'Kelly's, Cici's Pizza, Daytona's Rest., Famous Dave's BBQ, Fazoli's, KFC, McDonald's, Old Chicago, Perkins, Popeye's, Quizno's, Shangrila Buffet, Starbucks, Wendy's, 🛏 Days Inn, Econolodge, Holiday Inn, Quality Inn, Ramada, Super 8, ⊙ Ⓗ, Advance Parts, Best Buy, BigLots, Chevrolet, Dahl's Food/Fuel, $Tree, Ford, Goodyear, Hobby Lobby, Kohl's, NAPA, Nissan, Office Depot, Old Navy, Scion/Toyota, Sears/auto, Staples, Target, mall, vet
129	NW 86th St, Camp Dodge, **N** 🛢 Kum&Go, 🍴 Burger King, Coldstone Creamery, Legends Grill, MaidRite Cafe, McDonald's, Okoboji Grill, Panchero's Mexican, Planet Sub, Starbucks, TX Roadhouse, Village Inn, 🛏 Hilton Garden, Stoney Creek Inn, TownePlace Suites, ⊙ Dahl's Foods, **S** 🛢 BP, Casey's, 🍴 Arby's, B-Bops Burgers, Culver's, Friedrich's Coffee, Happy Joe's Pizza, Overtime Grill, Ruby Tuesday, 🛏 Microtel, ⊙ Walgreens
127	IA 141 W, Grimes, **N** 🛢 BP/dsl, Phillips 66/dsl, 🍴 Maid-Rite Cafe, McCoy's Grill, Subway, 🛏 AmericInn (3mi), ⊙ Kia/Saab/Suzuki, to Saylorville Lake, **S** 🍴 Quizno's, ⊙ Home Depot, Target
126	Douglas Ave, Urbandale, **N** 🛢 ▦/Grandma Max's/Subway/dsl/24hr/scales/@, 🍴 Jimmy's Pizza, Maverick Grill, **S** 🍴 Dragon House, 🛏 Best Value Inn, Extended Stay America, Villa Lodge
125	US 6, Hickman Rd, **N** 🛢 💙Loves/Denny's/Food Court/dsl/LP/24hr, ⊙ Dodge/Jeep, Menards, to Living History Farms, **S** 🍴 IA Machine Shed Rest., 🛏 Clive Hotel, Comfort Suites, Sleep Inn, ⊙ Goodyear, Honda, Hyundai
124	(72c from I-35 nb), University Ave, **N** 🛢 Kum&Go/Burger King, QT, 🍴 Biaggi's Rest., Boston's, Caribou Coffee, Cracker Barrel, El Rodeo Mexican, Red Rossa Pizza, Shane's Rib Shack, Wendy's, Z'Marik's Cafe, 🛏 Best Western, Country Inn&Suites, La Quinta, ⊙ Ⓗ, Granite City Food, Walgreens, **S** 🛢 BP/MaidRite, 🍴

D E S · M O I N E S

IA

INTERSTATE 80 CONT'D

Exit	Services
124	Continued
	Applebee's, Bakers Square, Bandana's BBQ, Cheddar's, Chili's, Huhot Mongolian, Jason's Deli, KFC, Macaroni Grill, McDonald's, Mi Mexico, Outback Steaks, Qdoba Mexican, RockBottom Rest./brewery, TCBY, 🛏 Chase Suites, Courtyard, Heartland Inn, Ramada Inn, Sheraton, Wildwood Lodge, ⊡ AT&T, Barnes&Noble, Best Buy, Home Depot, K-Mart, Kohl's, Marshall's, Office Depot, Petsmart, Target, Verizon, World Mkt
	I-80 E and I-35 N run together 14 mi
123b a	I-80/I-35 N, I-35, S to Kansas City, I-235 to Des Moines
122	(from eb) 60th St, W Des Moines
121	74th St, W Des Moines, N 🍴 Biaggi's Rest., Panera Bread, Red Rossa Pizza, Shane's Rib Shack, 🛏 Hampton Inn, Staybridge Suites, ⊡ 🄷, Granite City Foods, HyVee Food/gas, Walgreens, S 🅖 Kum&Go/Subway, 🍴 Arby's, Burger King, CK's, Culver's, McDonald's, Perkins, Quizno's, Taco John's, 🛏 Candlewood Suites, Fairfield Inn, Marriott, Motel 6, SpringHill Suites, vet
119mm	**rest area both lanes, full ♿ facilities, info, vending, 🄲, 🄰, petwalk, RV dump, Wireless Internet**
117	R22, Booneville, Waukee, N 🍴 Organic Farm Rest., ⊡ Timberline Camping (2mi), S 🅖 Kum&Go/24hr, 🍴 Rube's Steaks, Waveland Rest. (2mi)
115mm	**weigh sta eb**
113	R16, Van Meter, **1 mi S** 🅖 Casey's, ⊡ Feller Museum, Veteran's Cemetary
112mm	N Racoon River
111mm	Middle Racoon River
110	US 169, to Adel, DeSoto, N John Wayne Birthplace, camping (6mi), S 🅖 Casey's, Kum&Go/dsl/e-85, 🛏 Countryside Inn, Edgetowner Motel
106	F90, P58, N KOA (apr-oct)
104	P57, Earlham, S 🅖 Casey's (2mi), 🍴 Master Griller (2mi)
100	US 6, to Redfield, Dexter, N 🅖 Casey's (2mi), 🍴 Drew's Chocolate
97	P48, to Dexter, N 🅖 Casey's (2mi), camping
93	P28, Stuart, N 🅖 BP/dsl/24hr, Casey's/dsl/scales, Kum&Go, 🍴 Burger King, McDonald's/playplace, Subway, 🛏 AmericInn, Super 8, ⊡ Chevrolet, $General, Hometown Foods, S 🅖 Phillips 66/dsl, 🍴 Country Kitchen, 🛏 Edgetowner Motel, ⊡ NAPA
88	P20, Menlo
86	IA 25, to Greenfield, Guthrie Ctr, S ⊡ 🄷 (13mi), to Preston/Spring Brook SP
85mm	Middle River
83	N77, Casey, **1 mi N** 🅖 Kum&Go, ⊡ camping
80.5mm	**rest area both lanes, full ♿ facilities, 🄲, 🄰, litter barrels, vending, petwalk, RV dump, wireless internet**
76	IA 925, N54, Adair, N 🅖 Casey's/dsl, Kum&Go/Subway/dsl, 🍴 Happy Chef, Smiley's Steaks, 🛏 Adair Budget Inn, Super 8, ⊡ camping
75	G30, to Adair
70	IA 148 S, Anita, S to Lake Anita SP (6mi)
64	N28, to Wiota
61mm	E Nishnabotna River
60	US 6, US 71, to Atlantic, Lorah, S 🅖 Phillips 66/Country Cafe/dsl/24hr, 🛏 Best Value Inn
57	N16, to Atlantic, S 🄷 (7mi)
54	IA 173, to Elk Horn, **6 mi N Welcome Ctr/Wireless Internet**, 🛏 AmericInn, ⊡ Windmill Museum, 🅖 🍴 (7mi)

Exit	Services
51	M56, to Marne
46	M47, Walnut, N 🅖 BP/McDonald's/24hr, 🍴 Villager Buffet, 🛏 Super 8, to Prairie Rose SP (8mi), S 🅖 Kum&Go/dsl/24hr, 🍴 Aunt B's Kitchen, 🛏 EconoLodge/RV Park, repair
44mm	**weigh sta, wb/parking area eb**
40	US 59, to Harlan, Avoca, N 🅖 Phillip 66/Taco John's/MaidRite Cafe/dsl/24hr/scales, 🍴 Subway, 🛏 Motel 6, ⊡ 🄷 (12mi), truckwash, S 🅖 Casey's/dsl, Shell/dsl, 🍴 Embers Rest., 🛏 Avoca Motel, Capri Motel, ⊡ Avoca Foods, Nishna Museum
39.5mm	W Nishnabotna River
34	M16, Shelby, N 🅖 BP/e-85, Shell/Cornstalk Cafe/dsl, 🍴 DQ, Godfather's, 🛏 Shelby Country Inn/RV Park, S ⊡ dsl/tire repair
32mm	**rest area both lanes, parking only**
29	L66, to Minden, S 🅖 Phillips 66/A&W/dsl, 🛏 Mid-Town Motel (2mi), ⊡ winery (4mi)
27	I-680 W, to, N Omaha
23	IA 244, L55, Neola, S 🅖 Kum&Go/dsl, ⊡ to Arrowhead Park, camping
20mm	**Welcome Ctr eb/rest area wb, full ♿ facilities, 🄲, 🄰, litter barrels, vending, petwalk, RV dump, Wireless Internet**
17	G30, Underwood, N 🅖 Phillips 66/Subway/dsl/24hr, 🛏 Underwood Motel, ⊡ truck/tire repair
8	US 6, Council Bluffs, N 🅖 Phillips 66/dsl (1mi), ⊡ 🄷
5	Madison Ave, Council Bluffs, N 🅖 BP, 🍴 Burger King, FoodCourt, Great Wall Chinese, KFC, McDonald's, Panera Bread, Pizza Hut, Subway, 🛏 Heartland Inn, ⊡ Barnes&Noble, HyVee Food/drug, Sears/auto, Verizon, Walgreens, S 🅖 Cenex/DQ/dsl, Phillips 66, 🍴 DQ, Sam&Louie's Pizza, Village Inn Rest., 🛏 Western Inn, ⊡ Curves, No Frills Mkt, TrueValue
4	I-29 S, to Kansas City
3	IA 192 N, Council Bluffs, N to Hist Dodge House, S 🅖 Phillips 66/dsl, Shell/dsl, TA/dsl/24hr/scales/@, 🍴 Applebee's, Burger King, Cracker Barrel, DQ, Fazoli's, Golden Corral, Hardee's, Huhot Mongolian, La Mesa Mexican, LJ Silver, McDonald's, Old River Pizza, Perkins, Red Lobster, Subway, Taco Bell, 🛏 Days Inn, Fairfield Inn, Motel 6, Settle Inn, ⊡ Advance Parts, Aldi Foods, Best Buy, Buick, Chrysler/Jeep/Suzuki, Ford, Freightliner, Gordman's, Home Depot, Hyundai/Subaru, Kia, Menards, Nissan, Outdoor Recreation RV, Sam's Club/gas, U-Haul, Walmart, truck/dsl repair
1b	S 24th St, Council Bluffs, N 🅖 BP, 🄻🄻🄻/Arby's/scales/dsl/24hr, Sapp Bros/Shell/Burger King/dsl/rest., 🍴 Famous Dave's BBQ, Hooters, Islamorada Fish Co, Quaker Steak, Ruby Tuesday, 🛏 American Inn, Best Western, Country Inn&Suites, Hilton Garden, Microtel, Sleep Inn, SpringHill Suites, Super 8, ⊡ Bass Pro Shop, Blue Beacon, Camping World RV Ctr, Horseshoe RV Park, Peterbilt, SpeedCo, casino, S **Welcome Ctr, full facilities**, 🍴 Culver's, ⊡ JC Penney, PetCo, ShopKO, Verizon
1a	I-29 N, to Sioux City
0mm	Iowa/Nebraska state line, Missouri River

INTERSTATE 235 (DES MOINES)

Exit	Services
15	I-80, E to Davenport
12	US 6, E Euclid Ave, E 🅖 Casey's, 🍴 Burger King, Dragon House Chinese, Papa John's, Perkins, Tastey Tacos, ⊡ $Tree, HyVee Foods/drug, Radio Shack, Walgreens

INTERSTATE 235 (DES MOINES)

N ↕ S — **D E S M O I N E S**

Exit	Services
12	Continued W 🅖 QT, 🅞 NAPA
11	Guthrie Ave, W 🅖 Kum&Go/dsl, 🅞 CarQuest
10a b	IA 163 W, E University Ave, Easton Dr
9	US 65/69, E 14th, E 15th, N 🅞 Walgreens, S 🅖 QT, 🍴 McDonald's, Quizno's, 🅞 🅷, st capitol, zoo
8b	E 6th St, Penn Ave (from wb), N 🅷
8a	3rd St, 5th Ave, N 🛏 Holiday Inn, 🅞 🅷, S 🛏 Embassy Suites, Marriott, Quality Inn, 🅞 Conv Ctr
7	Keo Way
6	MLK Blvd/31st St, Drake U, Governor's Mansion, S ✈
5b	42nd St, Science & Art Ctr, N 🅖 Git'n Go, 🍴 Papa John's, 🅞 Curves
5a	56th St (from wb), N golf
4	IA 28, 63rd St, to Windsor Heights, S Historic Valley Jct, zoo
3	8th St, W Des Moines, N 🅖 Kum&Go, 🍴 B-Bop's Café, Burger King, Starbucks, 🅞 HyVee Foods, PetCo, Sam's Club/gas, Sears AutoCtr, Walmart/Subway, S 🅖 BP, Kum&Go, 🍴 Jimmy's American Café, Q BBQ, 🛏 Days Inn
2	22nd St, 24th St, W Des Moines, N 🅖 BP, Phillips 66/dsl, 🍴 Arby's, Caffrey's Steaks, ChuckeCheese, Culver's, Famous Dave's BBQ, Hardee's, Hooters, LoneStar Steaks, Taco Bell, Village Inn, 🛏 Studio+, 🅞 $Tree, Firestone/auto, Goodyear/auto, Gordman's, Michael's, Walgreens
1b	Valley West Dr, W Des Moines, N 🅖 BP/dsl, 🍴 Carlos O'Kelly's, Chipotle Mexican, Jimmy John's, Olive Garden, Red Lobster, TGI Friday's, West Inn Diner, 🛏 Valley West Inn, 🅞 Best Buy, Home Depot, HyVee Foods, JC Penney, SteinMart, Target, Von Maur, Younker's, mall
0mm	I-235 begins/ends on I-80, exit 123.

INTERSTATE 280 (DAVENPORT)

N ↕ S — **E ↕ W**

Exit	Services
18b a	I-74, US 6, Moline, S 🅖 Shell/dsl, 🍴 McDonald's, MT Jack's, 🛏 Best Inn, Country Inn&Suites, Days Inn, Econolodge, Hampton Inn, La Quinta, Quality Inn, Ramada Inn, 🅞 ✈
15	Airport Rd, Milan, N 🍴 (1mi) MaidRite Café, Subway, 🅞 Buick/Chevrolet, Firestone
11b a	IL 92, to Andalusia, Rock Island, S KOA Camping
9.5mm	Iowa/Illinois state line, Mississippi River
8	rd 22, Rockingham Rd, to Buffalo
6	US 61, W River Dr, to Muscatine, W gas, camping
4	Locust St, rd F65, 160th St, E 🅷, to Palmer Coll, St Ambrose U, W 🅖 Shell/Dickey's BBQ/dsl
1	US 6 E, IA 927, Kimberly Rd, to Walcott, 3 mi E 🅖 Murphy USA, 🍴 Applebee's, Culver's, Sonic, Steak'n Shake, Subway, Wendy's, 🅞 K-Mart, Walmart
0mm	I-280 begins/ends on I-80, exit 290.

INTERSTATE 380 (CEDAR RAPIDS)

Exit	Services
73mm	I-380 begins/ends on US 218, 73mm in Waterloo, E 🅖 BP/dsl, W 🅖 Clark, 🍴 Pizza Hut
72	San Marnan Dr, W 🍴 A&W/LJ Silver, Applebee's, Bonanza, Burger King, Carlos O'Kelly's, Coldstone, Hardee's, Godfather's, Golden China, IHOP, Jimmy John's, Olive Garden, Panera Bread, Pizza Hut, Red Lobster, Starbucks, Subway, Taco John's, 🛏 Baymont Inn,

W (left margin)

W A T E R L O O / **C E D A R R A P I D S** (right column margin)

Exit	Services
72	Continued Candlewoods Suites, Comfort Inn, Country Inn&Suites, Days Inn, Fairfield Inn, Hampton Inn, Holiday Inn Express, Super 8, 🅞 Advance Parts, Aldi Foods, Barnes&Noble, Best Buy, Chevrolet, Chrysler/Dodge/Jeep, CVS Drug, Dillards, $General, Ford, Gordman's, Hobby Lobby, Hy-Vee Foods, JC Penney, Jo-Ann Fabrics, KIA, Menards, Old Navy, PetCo, PetsMart, Radio Shack, Sears/auto, Staples, Target, Tires+, TJ Maxx, Walmart
71	I-380, US 20, IA 27, Cedar Rapids, Cedar Falls, Dubuque US 18, S Isle Hotel/Casino
70	River Forest Rd
68	Elk Run Heights, Evansdale Dr, E 🅖 ⊕FLYING J/Denny's/dsl/scales/24hr, 🅿🚚/RR/Junie's/Subway/dsl/scales/24hr/@, 🍴 Arby's, McDonald's, 🛏 Days Inn, 🅞 Freightliner, Paine's RV Ctr, truckwash/repair
66	Gilbertville, Raymond
65	US 20 E, Dubuque
62	rd D 38, Gilbertville
55	rd V 65, Jesup, La Port, W 🅞 Hickory Hills Park, McFarlane Park
54mm	**weigh sta sb**
51mm	**weigh sta nb**
49	rd D 48, Brandon, **1 mi** W gas, food
43	IA 150, Independence, Vinton, E 🅖 Phillips 66/dsl/24hr, 🛏 Inn Suites, 🅞 truckwash
41	Urbana, E 🅞 Lazy Acres RV Park, W 🅖 Casey's/dsl
35	rd W 36, Center Point, E 🅖 BP, Casey's, Sinclair/McDonald's/Subway/dsl/scales/24hr, W 🅖 Pleasant Creek SRA (5mi)
28	rd E 34, Robins, Toddville, W 🅞 Wickiup Outdoor Learning Ctr (5mi)
25	Boyson Rd, Hiawatha, E 🅞 Ketelsen RV Ctr, W 🅖 BP, Casey's/Blimpie/Pizza, 🍴 Culver's, Pizza Wagon, 🅞 Toyota/Scion/VW
24	IA 100, Blairs Ferry Rd, E 🅖 KwikShop/dsl, 🍴 Happy Chef, Hardee's, KFC, La Glorias Mexican, McDonald's, 🛏 Days Inn, Hawthorn Suites, 🅞 CVS Drug, HyVee Foods, W 🅖 Road Ranger, 🍴 Arby's, Burger King, Metro Buffet, Pizza Hut, Subway, Taco Bell, 🅞 Aldi Foods, AutoZone, GNC, Lowe's, Sam's Club/gas, Walmart
22	Glass Rd, 32nd st, E 🅖 KwikShop/dsl, 🍴 Papa Johns
21	H St, Cedar Rapids, downtown
20b	7th St E, Cedar Rapids, downtown, E 🅷
20a	US 151 Bus., E 🛏 Crowne Plaza
19b	1st Ave W, W 🛏 Best Western, 🅞 NAPA
18	Wilson Ave, museums
17	33rd Ave SW, Hawkeye Downs, W 🅖 Casey's, 🍴 Burger King, McDonald's, Sonic, Taco Bell, Wendy's, 🛏 Clarion, Comfort Inn, Economy Inn, Hampton Inn, Heartland Inn, Holiday Inn Express, Motel 6, Red Roof Inn, Super 8
16	US 30 W, US 151 S, US 218 N, Tama
13	Ely, W 🅖 Casey's/A&W/dsl, Casey's/dsl/scales, 🍴 McDonald's, 🛏 AmericInn, Country Inn&Suites, 🅞 ✈
12mm	**rest area both lanes, 🅿, littler barrels, 🚻, petwalk, vending, RV Dump, wireless internet**
10	rd F 12, Shueyville, Swisher, E 🅖 BP/dsl, 🅞 Lake Mcbride SP, W 🅖 Amana Colonies
8mm	Iowa River
4	rd F 28, North Liberty, E 🅖 BP/dsl, Casey's/Blimpie, Kum&Go/dsl (2mi), 🛏 Sleep Inn, 🅞 Colony Country RV Park (5mi)
0b a	I-80, E to Iowa City, W to Des Moines, I-380 begins/ends on I-80

IA

INTERSTATE 35

N ↑ ↓ S

KANSAS CITY AREA

KS

Exit	Services
235mm	Kansas/Missouri state line
235	Cambridge Circle
234b a	US 169, Rainbow Blvd, E 🛢 QT, Shell, 🍴 Applebee's, Arby's, Burger King, McDonald's, Rosedale BBQ, Sonic, Wendy's, 🛏 Best Western, Sun Inn, 🅾 KU MED CTR, W 🍴 KFC, LJ Silver
233a	SW Blvd, Mission Rd
233b	37th Ave (from sb)
232b	US 69 N, E 🛢 QT, 🍴 Cici's, McDonald's, Taco Bell
232a	Lamar Ave, E 🛢 QT, 🛏 ValuePlace Inn
231b a	I-635 (exits left from sb)
230	Antioch Rd (from sb), E 🛢 QT
229	Johnson Dr, E 🛢 Phillips 66, 🍴 Arby's, Bob Evans, Chili's, Chipotle Mexican, McDonald's, Papa John's, Starbucks, 🅾 GNC, Hen House Mkt, Home Depot, Marshall's, Old Navy, Petsmart, Walgreens, W 🛢 Cenex/dsl
228b	US 56 E, US 69, Shawnee Mission Pkwy, E 🛢 Shell, 🍴 Caribou Coffee, Denny's, IHOP, Krispy Kreme, Pizza Hut, Taco Bell, 🛏 Drury Inn, Homestead Suites, Winsteads Suites, 🅾 BMW/Mini, Sears Grand, W 🛢 Valero, 🍴 A&W, LJ Silver, Panera Bread, Pizza Hut, Subway, Wendy's, 🅾 Cotman's Transmissions, Firestone, Ford, Goodyear/auto, Jo-Ann Fabrics, Office Depot, O'Reilly Parts, Russell Stover, Walgreens
228a	67th St, E 🛏 Quality Inn, 🅾 CarMax, W 🛢 Phillips 66/Circle K/dsl, 🅾 Jaguar, Land Rover, Maserati, Mercedes, Porsche, Saab, Smart
227	75th St, E 🍴 McDonald's, 🛏 Extended Stay America, 🅾 Ⓗ, Acura, Walmart, vet, W 🛢 QT/dsl, 🍴 Domino's, Sonic, Subway, Taco Bell, 2 Amigos Mexican, Wendy's, 🛏 Hampton Inn, 🅾 Hyundai
225b	US 69, S (from sb), Overland Pkwy
225a	87th St, E 🛢 Phillips 66, 🍴 Green Mill Rest, 🛏 Holiday Inn, W 🛢 Phillips 66/Circle K/dsl, 🍴 Taco Bell, Zarda BBQ, 🅾 auto repair
224	95th St, E 🛢 Phillips 66/Circle K, Shell, 🍴 Applebee's, BD Mongolian BBQ, Burger King, Chick-fil-A, Chipotle Mexican, Denny's, Houlihan's, KFC, McDonald's, Mimi's Café, On-the-Border, Outback Steaks, Panda Express, Subway, Taco Bell, TGIFriday, Winstead's Cafe, 🛏 Comfort Inn, Crowne Plaza, Days Inn, Extended Stay America, Knight's Inn, La Quinta, Motel 6, Super 8, 🅾 Ⓗ, Advance Parts, Barnes&Noble, Best Buy, Dillard's, Firestone/auto, Hy-Vee Foods, JC Penney, Kohl's, Macy's, Nordstrom's, Office Depot, PetCo, Sam's Club/gas, Target, mall, W 🛢 Phillips 66, 🍴 Mi Ranchito, 🅾 Costco/gas, O'Reilly Parts, U-Haul
222b a	I-435 W & E
220	119th St, E 🛢 Phillips 66/Circle K, Shell, 🍴 A&W, Burger King, Chick-fil-A, Chipotle Mexican, Coldstone Creamery, Cracker Barrel, 5 Guys Burgers, Granite City Cafe, Haru's Steak, Honey Baked Cafe, Hooters, IHOP, Jimmy John's, Joe's BBQ, Joe's Crabshack, LJ Silver, McDonald's, Noodles&Co, OK Joe's BBQ, Old Chicago, Olive Garden, On-the-Border, Panda Express, Panera Bread, Pei Wei, Planet Sub, Popeye's, Ruby Tuesday, Schlotsky's, Starbucks, Steak'n Shake, Subway, TX Roadhouse, Wendy's, Zio's Italian, 🛏 Best Western, Comfort Suites, Fairfield Inn, Hampton Inn, Residence

OLATHE

OTTAWA

Exit	Services
220	Continued Inn, SpringHill Suites, ValuePlace Inn, 🅾 Aamco, Best Buy, Chrysler/Dodge/Jeep, GNC, Goodyear/auto, Home Depot, Honda, Marshall's, Mazda, Michael's, NTB, Old Navy, Petsmart, Radio Shack, Target, U-Haul, transmissions, W Bass Pro Shop
218	135th, Santa Fe St, Olathe, E 🛢 Phillips 66, 🍴 Applebee's, Ari's Greek Rest, Buffalo Wild Wings, Burger King, Chapala Mexican, China Buffet, China Star, Church's, Corona Garden Mexican, Garozzo's Italian, Other Place Grill, Papa John's, Perkins, Pizza St, Quizno's, Sheridan's Custard, Taco World, 🅾 Ace Hardware, Aldi Foods, AutoZone, BigLots, CVS Drug, $General, $Tree, GNC, Hobby Lobby, Hy-Vee Foods, K-Mart, Kohl's, Office Depot, PriceChopper Foods, Tuesday Morning, vet, W 🛢 QT, 🍴 A&W, Domino's, KFC, La Hacienda Mexican, LJ Silver, McDonald's, New Fortune Chinese, Taco Bell, Waffle House, Wendy's, 🛏 Days Inn, 🅾 Advance Parts, Buick/GMC, Car-X, Chevrolet, Cottman Transmissions, Harley-Davidson, Hyundai, Kia, O'Reilly Parts, Radio Shack, Scion/Toyota
217	Old Hwy 56 (from sb), same as 215
215	US 169 S, KS 7, Olathe, E 🛢 Phillips 66/dsl, QT/dsl, 🍴 China Inn, Chipotle Mexican, IHOP, Outback Steaks, Panera Bread, Red Robin, Ryan's, 🛏 Candlewood Suites, Comfort Inn, 🅾 Aldi Foods, AT&T, Home Depot, NTB, Target, W 🛢 Presto, Shell/dsl/scales/24hr, 🍴 Applebee's, Burger King, Chili's, 54th St Grill, FoodCourt, Red Lobster, McDonald's, Taco Bell, Waffle House, Wendy's, 🛏 Best Western, Econolodge, Holiday Inn, La Quinta, Microtel, Sleep Inn, 🅾 Ⓗ, Mazda, mall
214	no services
213mm	weigh sta both lanes
210	US 56 W, Gardner, W 🛢 Phillips 66/Circle K/dsl, 🍴 Arby's, KFC, McDonald's, Mr Goodcents Subs, Pizza Hut, Subway, Taco Bell, Waffle House, 🛏 Super 8, 🅾 NAPA, Walmart
207	US 56 E, Gardner Rd, E Olathe RV Ctr, W 🛢 Gas City/dsl, Shell/dsl
202	Edgerton
198	KS 33, to Wellsville, W gas/dsl
193	Tennessee Rd, Baldwin
187	KS 68, Ottawa, W 🛢 Zarco/dsl/e-85, 🅾 Buick/Cadillac/Chevrolet, Crist RV Ctr
185	15th St, Ottawa
183	US 59, Ottawa, E 🛢 Loves/Hardee's/dsl/scales/24hr, W 🛢 BP, Conoco/dsl, Murphy USA, Ottawa Gas/dsl, 🍴 Applebee's, Burger King, KFC, McDonald's, Old 56 Rest, Pizza Hut, Sirloin Stockade, Subway, Taco Bell, Wendy's, 🛏 Best Western, Comfort Inn, Econolodge, Super 8, Travelodge, 🅾 Ⓗ, Advance Parts, CountryMart Foods, $General, $Tree, Walmart
182b a	US 50, Eisenhower Rd, Ottawa
176	Homewood, W RV camping
175mm	rest area both lanes, full ♿ facilities, 🅲, 🚮, litter barrels, vending, petwalk, RV dump, wireless internet
170	KS 273, Williamsburg, W 🛢 Sinclair/café/dsl
162	KS 31 S, Waverly
160	KS 31 N, Melvern
155	US 75, Burlington, Melvern Lake, E 🛢 BP/Subway/dsl, TA/Shell/Wendy's/dsl/scales/24hr/@, 🍴 Beto Jct Rest., 🛏 Wyatt Earp Inn, 🅾 dsl repair

Copyright 2012 - The Next Exit®   🅿 = gas   🍴 = food   🛏 = lodging   🄾 = other

INTERSTATE 35 CONT'D

N ↑↓ S

E M P O R I A

Exit	Services
148	KS 131, Lebo, **E** 🅿 Casey's, Cenex/dsl, 🍴 Lebo Diner, 🛏 Universal Inn, **W** to Melvern Lake
141	KS 130, Neosho Rapids, **E** NWR (8mi)
138	County Rd U
135	County Rd R1, **W** RV camping/🄲
133	US 50 W, 6th Ave, Emporia, **1-3 mi E** 🅿 Casey's, 🍴 McDonald's, Pizza Hut, 🛏 Budget Host
131	KS 57, KS 99, Burlingame Rd, **E** 🅿 Conoco/dsl, 🍴 Hardee's, Mr Goodcents Subs, 🄾 Dillon's Food, repair, tires
130	KS 99, Merchant St, **E** 🅿 Phillips 66/dsl, 🍴 Subway, 🄾 Emporia St U, Lyon Co Museum
128	Industrial Rd, **E** 🅿 Conoco, FL, 🍴 Arby's, Bruff's Steaks, Burger King, Centinela Mexican, China Buffet, Cobern's Drive Inn, Gambino's Pizza, Subway, 🛏 Econolodge, GuestHouse Inn, Motel 6, 🄾 🄷 Aldi Foods, CarQuest, $General, Family$, Goodyear/auto, Hastings Book, JC Penney, Walgreens, **W** 🅿 Phillips 66/Wendy's/dsl, 🍴 Applebee's, Golden Corral, KFC, McDonald's, MT Mike's Steaks, Papa Murphy's, Pizza Hut, Pizza Ranch, Planet Sub, Starbucks, Taco Bell, Village Inn, 🛏 Candlewood Suites, Comfort Inn, Fairfield Inn, Holiday Inn Express, 🄾 Medicine Shoppe, Radio Shack, Staples, Walmart
127c	KS Tpk, I-335 N, to Topeka
127 a b	US 50, KS 57, Newton, **E** 🅿 ⛽FLYING J/Denny's/dsl/scales/24hr, Shell, 🍴 Arby's, China Buffet, Papa John's, 🛏 Best Value Inn, Best Western/rest., Days Inn, Rodeway Inn, 🄾 Buick/Chevrolet, Chrysler/Dodge/Jeep/Toyota, Ford/Lincoln/Mercury/Nissan, Napa, PriceChopper Foods, Tires4Less, dsl repair, **W** Emporia RV Park
127mm	I-35 and I-335 KS Tpk, toll plaza,
I-35 S and KS Tpk S run together.	
125mm	Cottonwood River
111	Cattle Pens
97.5mm	Matfield Green Service Area (both lanes exit left), Phillips 66/dsl, McDonald's
92	KS 177, Cassoday, **E** 🅿 Fuel'n Service, 🄲
76	US 77, El Dorado N, **E** El Dorado SP, **3 mi E** 🅿 Casey's; 🍴 Pizza Hut, Taco Bell, 🄾 Ace Hardware, Dillon's

W I C H I T A

76	Continued Foods/gas, $General, Walgreens, city park
71	KS 254, KS 196, El Dorado, **E** 🅿 Conoco/dsl, Phillips 66/dsl, QT, 🍴 Arbys, Braum's, Burger King, China Star Buffet, DD Family Rest, Freddy's Frozen Custard, Gambino's Pizza, KFC, Kountry Kettle, LJ Silver, McDonald's, Papa Murphy's, Pizza Hut, Playa Azul Mexican, Sonic, Spangles, Subway, Taco Tico, 🛏 Best Western, Heritage Inn, Holiday Inn Express, Sunset Inn, Super 8, 🄾 🄷, Buick/Cadillac, Bumper Parts, Deer Grove RV Park, $General, KS Oil Museum, O'Reilly Parts, Radio Shack, Walmart
65mm	Towanda Service Area (both lanes exit left), Phillips 66/dsl, McDonald's
62mm	Whitewater River
57	21st St, Andover, **W** golf, 🄲
53	KS 96, Wichita, **1 mi W on Kellogg** Phillips 66
50	US 54, Kellogg Ave, **E** McConnell AFB, **W** 🛏 Comfort Inn, Fairfield Inn, GuestHouse Inn, Hampton Inn, Hawthorn Suites, Marriott, Motel 6, Studio+, Super 8, **E on Kellogg Ave** 🅿 Conoco/Wendy's/dsl, 🍴 Burger King, Golden Corral, IHOP, McDonald's, Pizza Hut, Sonic, Subway, Taco Bell, 🄾 Acura, AT&T, Buick/Infiniti, CarMax, Jaguar/Porsche, Lowe's Whse, Mazda, Michael's, PepBoys, VW, Walmart, **W on Kellogg Ave** 🍴 Arby's, Chipotle Mexican, Denny's, Green Mill Rest., Logan's Roadhouse, LJ Silver, McDonald's, Old Chicago Pizza, Pizza Hut, Red Lobster, Souper Salad, Steak&Ale, 🛏 Best Western, Econolodge, Garden Inn, Holiday Inn, La Quinta, Wichita Inn, 🄾 VA 🄷, Advance Parts, Barnes&Noble, BMW, Buick/GMC, Cadillac/Chevrolet, Carquest, Chrysler/Dodge/Jeep, Dillard's, Firestone/auto, Ford, Hancock Fabrics, Honda, Hyundai, JC Penney, Kia, Lincoln/Mercury, Nissan, Radio Shack, Scion/Toyota, Sears/auto, Target, TJ Maxx, mall
45	KS 15, Wichita, **E** Spirit Aero Systems
44.5mm	Arkansas River
42	47th St, I-135, to I-235, Wichita, **E** 🅿 Conoco, 🛏 Comfort Inn, Days Inn, Holiday Inn Express, **W** 🅿 Phillips 66, 🍴 Applebee's, Braum's, Burger King, Carlos O'Kelly's, Godfather's, KFC, LJ Silver, McDonald's, New China,

INTERSTATE 35 CONT'D

N ↑ S

Exit	Services
42	Continued
	Rest., Papa John's, Pizza Hut, Quizno's, Spangles Rest., Subway, Taco Bell, Taco Tico, 🏠 Best Western, Heritage Inn, Red Carpet Inn, Value Place, 🅞 Checker's Foods, Dillon's Foods/dsl, K-Mart, O'Reilly Parts, Radio Shack
39	US 81, Haysville, **W** 🏠 Haysville Inn
33	KS 53, Mulvane, **E** Mulvane Hist Museum, **W** Wyldewood Winery
26mm	**Belle Plaine Service Area (both lanes exit left),** 🅖 Phillips 66/dsl, 🍴 McDonald's
19	US 160, Wellington, **3 mi W** 🍴 KFC, Penny's Diner, 🏠 OakTree Inn, 🅞 RV camping
17mm	toll plaza
I-35 N and KS TPK N run together.	
4	US 166, to US 81, South Haven, **E** 🅖 G4TC/dsl/24hr, 🏠 Economy Inn/cafe, Motel 6, 🅞 repair/tires, **W** Oasis RV Park
1.5mm	**weigh sta nb**
0mm	Kansas/Oklahoma state line

INTERSTATE 70

E ↑ W KANSAS CITY

Exit	Services
423b	3rd St, James St
423a	5th St
422d c	Central Ave, service rd
422b a	US 69 N, US 169, S
421b	I-670
421a	**S** railroad yard
420b a	US 69 S, 18th St Expswy, **N** 🅖 Cenex, 🍴 China Town, Jack-in-the-Box, Tapatio Mexican, 🅞 SunFresh Foods
419	38th St, Park Dr, access to 10 motels
418b	I-635, N (eb only)
418a	I-635, S
417	57th St
415a	KS 32, E (from eb)
415b	to US 24 W, State Ave, Kansas City, **N on US 24** 🅖 Conoco Phillips 66/dsl, 🍴 Papa John's, Perkins, Taco Bell, 🏠 Gables Motel, 🅞 Chrysler/Jeep, Ford, Lowe's, Toyota/Scion
414mm	**vehicle insp sta wb, parking area both lanes,** 🍴
414	78th St, **N** 🅖 QT/dsl, 🍴 Wendy's, 🏠 Days Inn, **N on US 40** 🅖 Phillips 66, 🍴 Arby's, Burger King, Capt D's, DQ, Hardee's, Lucky Chinese, McDonald's, Sonic, Subway, 🅞 🏥, Advance Parts, BigLots, Buick/GMC, $Tree, Firestone, Goodyear/auto, K-Mart, O'Reilly Parts, PriceChopper Foods, Tires+, Walgreens, **S** 🅖 BP, 🏠 American Motel, Comfort Inn
411b	I-435 N, access to Woodlands Racetrack, to KCI ✈
411a	I-435 S
410	110th St, **N** 🏠 Great Wolf Lodge, 🅞 Cabela's, KS Speedway, Russell Stover Candies
225mm	**I-70, W and KS TPK, W run together**
224	KS 7, to US 73, Bonner Springs, Leavenworth, **N** 🅖 QT, Roadstar/dsl, 🍴 KFC/Taco Bell, Mazzio's, Subway, Waffle House, Wendy's, 🏠 Holiday Inn Express, Super 8, 🅞 museum, **S** 🅖 BP, 🍴 Arby's, Burger King, Evergreen Chinese, McDonald's, Mr Goodcents Subs, Quiznos, Subway, Taco John's, 🅞 Cottonwood RV Camp, $Tree, Ford, PriceChopper Foods, Radio Shack, Walgreens, Walmart, last free exit wb before KS TPK

LAWRENCE

217mm	toll booth
212	Eudora, Tonganoxie
209mm	**Lawrence Service Area (both lanes exit left), full facilities,** Phillips 66/dsl, McDonald's
204	US 24, US 59, to, E Lawrence, **S** 🅖 Presto/dsl, Woody's/dsl, 🍴 Burger King, Sonic, 🏠 Motel 6, SpringHill Suites (1mi), 🅞 Harley-Davidson, O'Reilly Parts
203mm	Kansas River
202	US 59 S to W Lawrence, **S on US 40** 🅖 BP, Conoco/dsl, Phillips 66/dsl, 🍴 Burger King, Domino's, McDonald's, Panda Garden, Sonic, Spangles, Subway, Taco Bell, Taco John's, Wendy's, 🏠 Baymont Inn, Days Inn, EconoLodge, Hampton Inn, Holiday Inn, Quality Inn, Rodeway Inn, Super 8, Virginia Inn, 🅞 🏥, Advance Parts, CarQuest, Dillon's Foods/gas, $General, to Clinton Lake SP, to U of KS
197	KS 10, Lecompton, Lawrence, **N** Perry Lake SP, **S** Clinton Lake SP
188mm	**Topeka Service Area, full** ♿ **facilities,** Conoco/dsl, Pizza Hut, Taco Bell, Hardee's
183	I-70, W (from wb), to Denver
367mm	toll plaza
366	I-470 W, to Wichita
I-70 E and KS TPK E run together	

TOPEKA

365	21st St, Rice Rd , access to Shawnee Lake RA
364b	US 40 E, Carnahan Ave, to Lake Shawnee
364a	California Ave, **0-1 mi S** 🅖 BP/dsl, Phillips 66/dsl, 🍴 Arby's, Baskin-Robbins, Burger King, Domino's, DQ, McDonald's, Pizza Hut, Subway, Tacos Mexicano, 🅞 Ace Hardware, Advance Parts, AutoZone, Dillon's Food/gas, $General, Family$, O'Reilly Parts, TrueValue, Walgreens, repair
363	Adams St, downtown
362c	10th Ave (from wb), **N** 🏠 Ramada Inn, Red Carpet Inn, **S** 🅞 st capitol
362b a	to 8th Ave downtown, **N** 🏠 Ramada, Red Carpet Inn, **S** 🅞 to St Capitol
361b	3rd St, Monroe St
361a	1st Ave, **S** Ryder
359	MacVicar Ave
358b a	Gage Blvd, **S** 🍴 McDonald's, Wendy's, 🅞 🏥
357b a	Fairlawn Rd, 6th Ave, **S** 🅖 Conoco/dsl, Phillips 66, 🍴 Casa Ramos, 🏠 Best Western, Holiday Inn/rest., Motel 6, 🅞 $General, NAPACare, zoo-rain forest, vet
356b a	Wanamaker Rd, **N** 🍴 Carino's, Red Robin, 🏠 Hyatt Place, 🅞 KS Museum of History, **S** 🅖 BP, Murphy Express/dsl, Phillips 66/dsl, 🍴 Applebee's, Arby's, Boston Mkt, Buffalo Wild Wings, Burger King, Chili's, Chipotle Mexican, ChuckeCheese, CiCi's Pizza, Coldstone, Coyote Canyon Café, Cracker Barrel, Denny's, Famous Dave's, Freddy's Custard, Golden Corral, Hardee's, Hooters, Huhot Chinese, IHOP, Jason's Deli, Jimmy John's, Jose Pepper's, Longhorn Steaks, McDonald's, Mike's Subs, Mr Goodcents, Old Chicago, Olive Garden, On-the-Border, Panda Buffet, Panera Bread, Papa John's, Perkins, Pizza Hut, Qdoba, Red Lobster, Rib Crib, Sonic, Spangles, Starbucks, Steak'n Shake, Taco Bell, Taco John's, TX Roadhouse, Wendy's, 🏠 Baymont Inn, Candlewood Suites, Clubhouse Inn, Comfort Inn, Comfort Suites, Country Inn&Suites, Courtyard, Days Inn, Fairfield Inn, Hampton Inn, Holiday Inn Express, Motel 6, Quality Inn, Residence Inn, Sleep Inn, Super 8,

KS

T O P E K A   E   ↕   W

INTERSTATE 70 CONT'D

Exit	Services
356b a	Continued ValuePlace, 🄾 Aldi Foods, AT&T, Barnes&Noble, Best Buy, Dick's, Dillard's, $Tree, Ford/Lincoln/Mercury, Goodyear/auto, Hobby Lobby, Home Depot, JC Penney, K-Mart, Kohl's, Lowe's, Macy's, Michael's, Office Depot, Old Navy, PetCo, Radio Shack, Sam's Club/gas, Sears/auto, Suzuki, Target, TJ Maxx, Tuesday Morning, Walmart, mall
355	I-470 E, US 75 S, to VA MED CTR
Topeka	air museum **1 mi S** same as 356
353	KS 4 W, to Auburn Rd
351	frontage rd (from eb), Mission Creek
350	Valencia Rd
347	West Union Rd
346	Carlson Rd, to Rossville, Willard
343	Ranch Rd
342	Keene-Eskridge Rd, access to Lake Wabaunsee
341	KS 30, Maple Hill, **S** 📷 24-7/Subway/café/dsl/RV dump
338	Vera Rd
336mm	**rest area (exits left from both lanes), full ♿ facilities, 🚻, 🪑, litter barrels, RV parking, wireless internet, petwalk**
335	Snokomo Rd
Paxico	Skyline Mill Creek Scenic Drive
333	KS 138, Paxico, **N** Mill Creek RV Park, winery
332	Spring Creek Rd
330	KS 185, to McFarland
329mm	**weigh sta both lanes**
328	KS 99, to Alma, **S** Wabaunsee Co Museum
324	Wabaunsee Rd, **N** Grandma Horners Store & Factory
322	Tallgrass Rd
318	frontage rd
316	Deep Creek Rd
313	KS 177, to Manhattan, **8 mi N** 📷 Phillips 66, 🍴 Applebee's, Chili's, McDonald's, Village Inn Rest., 🛏 Best Western, Comfort Inn, Fairfield Inn, Hampton Inn, Motel 6, Super 8, 🄾 Jeep, Nissan, Sears/auto, to KSU
311	Moritz Rd
310mm	**rest area both lanes, full ♿ facilities, 🚻, 🪑, litter barrels, petwalk, RV dump**
307	McDowell Creek Rd, scenic river rd to Manhattan
304	Humboldt Creek Rd
303	KS 18 E, to Ogden, Manhattan, **N** 🄾 to KSU
301	Marshall Field, **N** 🄾 Cavalry Museum, Custer's House, KS Terr Capitol, to Ft Riley
300	US 40, KS 57, Council Grove, **N** 🛏 Dreamland Motel, **S** hist church
299	Flinthills Blvd, to Jct City, Ft Riley, **N** 📷 Phillips 66/dsl, 🍴 Stacy's Rest., 🛏 EconoLodge, Great Western Inn, Red Carpet Inn, Super 8
298	Chestnut St, to Jct City, Ft Riley, **N** 📷 Shell/Burger King/dsl/24hr, 🍴 Arby's, Cracker Barrel, Family Buffet, Freddy's Steakburgers, Mr Goodcents Subs, Taco Bell, 🛏 Best Western, Candlewood Suites, Courtyard, Holiday Inn Express, Quality Inn, 🄾 Curves, $General, $Tree, Walmart/Subway
296	US 40, Washington St, Junction City, **N** 📷 Casey's, Cenex/dsl, Phillips 66, Shell/dsl/24hr, 🍴 IHOP, McDonald's, Napoli's Italian, Pizza Hut, Senor Tequila Mexican,

J C T   C I T Y

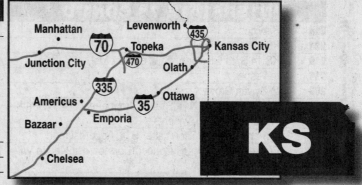

Exit	Services
296	Continued Sirloin Stockade, Sonic, Subway, 🛏 Budget Host, Days Inn, Hampton Inn, Howard Johnson, Ramada Ltd, ValuePlace Hotel, 🄾 Cadillac/Chevrolet, Haas Tire, Harley-Davidson, Jeep, city park
295	US 77, KS 18 W, Marysville, to Milford Lake, **N** 📷 Phillips 66/Sapp Bro's/A&W/dsl/24hr, 🛏 Motel 6, 🄾 Ⓗ, truckwash, **S** RV Ctr, truckwash
294mm	**rest area both lanes, full ♿ facilities, 🚻, 🪑, litter barrels, RV dump, petwalk**
290	Milford Lake Rd
286	KS 206, Chapman, **S** 📷 Cenex/dsl, 🄾 KS Auto Racing Museum, **1 mi S** 📷 Casey's
281	KS 43, to Enterprise, **N** 📷 Shell/dsl, 🄾 4 Seasons RV Ctr/Park
277	Jeep Rd
275	KS 15, to Clay Ctr, Abilene, **N** 🍴 DQ, 🛏 Brookville Hotel/rest., Holiday Inn Express, **S** 📷 KwikShop, 24-7/dsl, 🍴 Burger King, Joe Snuffy's Grill, Kuntz's Drive Inn, M&R Grill, McDonald's, Pizza Hut, Sonic, Subway, 🛏 Best Value Inn, Budget Inn, Super 8, 🄾 Ⓗ, Alco/gas, AutoZone, Buick/Cadillac/Chevrolet, Chrysler/Dodge/Jeep, CountryMart Foods, $General, Ford, O'Reilly Parts, Radio Shack, Ricco Drug, to Eisenhower Museum
272	Fair Rd, to Talmage, **S** Russell Stover Candies
266	KS 221, Solomon
265mm	**rest area both lanes, full ♿ facilities, 🚻, 🪑, litter barrels, vending, petwalk, RV dump**
264mm	Solomon River
260	Niles Rd, New Cambria
253mm	Saline River
253	Ohio St, **S** 📷 FLYING J/rest./dsl/LP/scales/24hr, 🄾 Ⓗ, Harley-Davidson, Kenworth
252	KS 143, 9th St, Salina, **N** 📷 Petro/Shell/Pizza Hut/Wendy's/dsl/24hr, 24-7/Subway/dsl/24hr, 🍴 Bayard's Café, IHOP, McDonald's, 🛏 Days Inn, Holiday Inn Express, Howard Johnson, La Quinta, Motel 6, Super 8, 🄾 Blue Beacon, Freightliner, KOA, dsl repair, **S** 📷 Bosselman/Pilot/Sinclair/rest./scales/dsl/24hr/@, 🛏 EconoLodge
250b a	I-135, US 81, N to Concordia, S to Wichita
249	Halstead Rd, to Trenton
244	Hedville, **N** Sundowner West RV Park, **S** gas&food/dsl, 🄾 Rolling Hills Park
238	to Brookville, Glendale, Tescott
233	290th Rd, Beverly
225	KS 156, to Ellsworth, **S** 📷 Elkhorn Corner/pizza/dsl, 🄾 Ft Harker Museum, Ft Larned HS
224mm	**rest area both lanes, full ♿ facilities, 🚻, 🪑, litter barrels, petwalk, RV dump**

A B I L E N E

S A L I N A

KS

INTERSTATE 70 CONT'D

E ↕ W

Exit	Services
221	KS 14 N, to Lincoln
219	KS 14 S, to Ellsworth, S ⛽ Conoco/dsl
216	to Vesper
209	to Sylvan Grove
206	KS 232, Wilson, N ⛽ Travel Shoppe/rest., ⊙ RV Park, Wilson Lake (6mi), winery
199	Dorrance, N to Wilson Lake, S ⛽ Agco/dsl/food
193	Bunker Hill Rd, N ⛽ Conoco/Quiznos/dsl/24hr, to Wilson Lake WA
189	US 40 bus, Pioneer Rd, Russell
187mm	**rest area both lanes, full ♿ facilities, 🅲, 🏕, litter barrels, RV dump, petwalk**
184	US 281, Russell, N ⛽ Phillips 66/Fossil Sta./dsl, 24-7/dsl, 🍴 A&W, McDonald's, Meridy's Rest., Pizza Hut, Sonic, Subway, 🛏 AmericInn, Days Inn, Russell's Inn, Super 8, ⊙ 🅷, Alco, CarQuest, $General, JJJ RV Park, Fossil Creek RV Park, st patrol, vet
180	Balta Rd, to Russell
175	Gorham, **1 mi** N ⛽ Co-Op, food, 🅲
172	Walker Ave
168	KS 255, to Victoria, S ⛽ Ampride/dsl, to Cathedral of the Plains
163	Toulon Ave
161	Commerce Parkway
159	US 183, Hays, N ⛽ Qwest/dsl, 🍴 Applebee's, Carlos O'Kelly's, Golden Corral, IHOP, Subway, 🛏 Best Western Butterfield, Comfort Inn, Fairfield Inn, Hampton Inn, Holiday Inn Express, Sleep Inn, ⊙ AT&T, Chrysler/Dodge/Jeep, Ford/Lincoln/Mercury, Harley-Davidson, Home Depot, Radio Shack, Toyota, Walmart, S ⛽ Conoco/dsl/24hr, Loves, Phillips 66/dsl, 24-7/dsl, 🍴 Arby's, Burger King, China Garden, Freddy's Steakburgers, KFC, LJ Silver, Lucky Buffet, McDonald's, MT Mike's Steaks, Pheasant Run Pancakes, Pizza Hut, Sonic, Subway, Taco Bell, Taco Grande, Vagabond Rest., Village Inn, Wendy's, Whiskey Creek Grill, 🛏 Baymont Inn, Best Value Inn, Days Inn, Knights Inn, Motel 6, Quality Inn, Ramada, Super 8, ⊙ 🅷, Ace Hardware, Advance Parts, Chevrolet, Dillon's Foods/gas, Firestone/auto, Hastings Books, JC Penney, NAPA, Tires 4 Less, Walgreens, st patrol
157	US 183, S byp, to Hays, S ⊙ museum, tourist info, to Ft Hays St U
153	Yocemento Ave
145	KS 247 S, Ellis, S ⛽ Casey's, Loves/DQ/Subway/dsl/24hr, 🛏 Days Inn, ⊙ to Chrysler Museum, Railroad Museum, RV camping, USPO
140	Riga Rd
135	KS 147, Ogallah, N ⛽ Frontier/dsl/24hr, S to Cedar Bluff SP (13mi)
132mm	**rest area both lanes, full ♿ facilities, 🏕, litter barrels, petwalk, RV dump**
128	US 283 N, WaKeeney, N ⛽ Travel Plaza/dsl/24hr, 🛏 Budget Host, Super 8, ⊙ 🅷
127	US 283 S, WaKeeney, N 🍴 Jade Garden Rest., McDonald's, Pizza Hut, 🛏 Best Western, KS Kountry Inn, ⊙ $General, city park, S ⛽ Conoco/Subway/dsl, 24-7/Real Country Cafe/dsl/24hr, 🛏 EconoLodge, ⊙ KOA, antiques, auto repair
120	Voda Rd

H A Y S

115	KS 198 N, Banner Rd, Collyer
107	KS 212, Castle Rock Rd, Quinter, N ⛽ Sinclair/dsl, 🛏 Budget Host, ⊙ 🅷, repair, S ⛽ Conoco/dsl/24hr, 🍴 DQ
99	KS 211, Park, **1 mi** N ⛽ Sinclair/dsl
97mm	**rest area both lanes, full ♿ facilities, 🏕, litter barrels, vending, petwalk, RV dump**
95	KS 23 N, to Hoxie
93	KS 23, Grainfield, N ⛽ Sinclair/dsl/24hr
85	KS 216, Grinnell, N gas (.5 mi)
79	Campus Rd
76	US 40, to Oakley, S ⛽ TA/Shell/Buckhorn Rest./Subway/dsl/e-85/scales/24hr/@, 🛏 EconoLodge (2mi), Relax Inn, Sleep Inn, ⊙ 🅷, Blue Beacon, Fick Museum
70	US 83, to Oakley, N 🛏 Free Breakfast Inn, S ⛽ Phillips 66/dsl, 🍴 Colonial Steaks, ⊙ 🅷, High-Plains RV Park, Prairie Dog Town, Fick Museum
62	rd K, Mingo, S ⛽ gas/dsl/🅲
54	Country Club Dr, Colby, N ⛽ 🚛/Sinclair/Bosselman's/Wendy's/dsl/scales/24hr, 🛏 Hampton Inn, ⊙ 🅷, truck/dsl repair
53	KS 25, Colby, N ⛽ Conoco, 24-7/dsl, 🍴 Arby's, Burger King, China Buffet, McDonald's, MT Mike's Steaks, Pizza Hut, Sonic, Subway, Taco John's, 🛏 Days Inn, Holiday Inn Express, Motel 6, Quality Inn, Sleep Inn, Super 8, ⊙ 🅷, AT&T, Dillon's Foods/gas, $General, Ford/Lincoln/Mercury, Haas Tire, Prairie Museum, Quilt Cabin, Radio Shack, Walmart, dsl repair, trucklube/wash, S ⛽ Petro/Phillips 66/scales/dsl/@, 🍴 Baskin-Robbins, Chester's, Quiznos, Starbucks, Village Inn, 🛏 Comfort Inn, Crown Inn, ⊙ Chrysler/Dodge/Jeep, truck wash
48.5mm	**rest area both lanes, full ♿ facilities, 🅲, 🏕, litter barrels, RV park/dump, vending, petwalk**
45	US 24 E, Levant
36	KS 184, Brewster, N ⛽ Fuel Depot/dsl/24hr
35.5mm	Mountain/Central time zone
27	KS 253, Edson
19	US 24, Goodland, N 🍴 Pizza Hut, 🛏 Motel 7, ⊙ $General, KOA, High Plains Museum
17	US 24, KS 27, Goodland, N ⛽ Cenex, Conoco, Phillips 66/dsl, 🍴 DQ, McDonald's, Mexico #3, Reynaldo's Mexican, Steakhouse, Subway, Taco John's, Wendy's, Wonderful House Chinese, 🛏 Best Value Inn, Comfort Inn, Days Inn, Motel 6, Super 8, ⊙ 🅷, Cadillac/GMC, Chevrolet, CarQuest/Firestone, Walmart, S ⛽ 24-7/dsl/scales, 🛏 Holiday Inn Express, ⊙ Mid-America Camping
12	rd 14, Caruso
9	rd 11, Ruleton
7.5mm	**Welcome Ctr eb/rest area wb, full ♿ facilities, info, 🅲, 🏕, litter barrels, petwalk, vending, wireless internet, RV dump**
1	KS 267, Kanorado, N gas, food
.5mm	**weigh sta eb**
0mm	Kansas/Colorado State Line

C O L B Y / G O O D L A N D

N ↕ S

INTERSTATE 135 (WICHITA)

Exit	Services
95b a	I-70, E to KS City, W to Denver.
	I-135 begins/ends on I-70, exit 250. US 81 continues nb.
93	KS 140, State St, Salina
92	Crawford St, E ⛽ Gas4Less/dsl, KwikShop, Phillips 66/dsl, Shell, Sinclair, 24-7/dsl, 🍴 Arby's, Braum's, Diamaru Steaks, Guitierre's Rest., Jim's Chicken, KFC,

INTERSTATE 135 CONT'D (WICHITA)

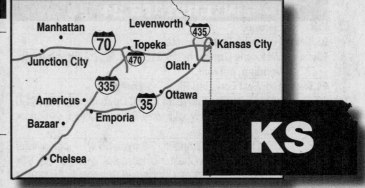

Exit	Services
92	Continued
	McDonald's, Russell's Rest., Spangles, Taco Bell, Subway, Western Sizzlin, 🛏 Best Western, Comfort Inn, Fairfield Inn, Ramada Inn, Rodeway Inn, 🅞 Advance Parts, Dillon's Foods, $General, K-Mart, O'Reilly Parts, Radio Shack, Royal Tire, Walgreens, **W** 🅖 Phillips 66/dsl, 🛏 Quality Inn
90	Magnolia Rd, **E** 🅖 Casey's, Phillips 66/dsl, 🍴 Burger King, Carlos O'Kelly's, Chili's, Cici's, Coyote Canyon Café, Domino's, Freddy's Custard, Hong Kong Buffet, IHOP, McDonald's, Mr Goodcents Subs, Papa Murphy's, Potrillo's Mexican, Quiznos, Schlotsky's, Sonic, Spangles, Taco Tico, Wild Hog BBQ, 🛏 Best Value Inn, Candlewood Suites, 🅞 AutoZone, BigLots, Buick/Subaru, Cadillac/Chevrolet, Dillard's, Dillon's Foods/dsl, $General, $Tree, Goodyear/auto, Hobby Lobby, Honda, JC Penney, Jo-Ann Fabrics, Kohl's, O'Reilly Parts, PetCo, Sears, Toyota, Tuesday Morning, Verizon, vet, **W** 🅖 Cenex/dsl
89	Schilling Rd, **E** 🅖 KwikShop/dsl, 🍴 Applebee's, Logan's Roadhouse, Pizza Hut, Red Lobster, Tucson's Steaks, Wendy's, 🛏 Country Inn&Suites, Courtyard, Hampton Inn, 🅞 Lowe's, Sam's Club/gas, Target, Walmart, **W** 🅖 Casey's, 🛏 Comfort Suites, Relax Inn, Super 8
88	Waterwell RD, **E** 🛏 Sleep Inn, 🅞 Ford/Mercury, Nissan
86	KS 104, Mentor, Smolan
82	KS 4, Falun Rd, Assaria, **E** 🅞 RV Camping
78	KS 4 W, Lindsborg, **E** 🅞 Sandz Gallery/Museum
72	US 81, Lindsborg, **4 mi E** 🅞 McPherson St Fishing Lake, Maxwell WR, **W** 🅞 🅗, 🅖🍴🛏 🅒, camping, museum
68mm	**rest areas (both lanes exit left), full 🅗 facilities, 🅒, 🚻, litter barrels petwalk, RV dump**
65	Pawnee Rd
60	US 56, McPherson, Marion, **W** 🅖 Midway Gas/dsl, Shell, 🍴 Applebee's, Arby's, Braum's, Golden Dragon Chinese, Hunan Chinese, KFC/LJ Silver, La Fiesta Mexican, McDonald's, MT Mike's, Perkins, Pizza Hut, Subway, Taco Bell, Taco Tico, Woodie's BBQ, 🛏 Best Value Inn, Best Western, Days Inn, EconoLodge, Holiday Inn Express, 🅞 🅗, AutoZone, Chrysler/Dodge/Jeep, $General, Ford, Walgreens, Walmart
58	US 81, KS 61, to Hutchinson, McPherson
54	Elyria
48	KS 260 E, Moundridge, **2 mi W** 🅖🍴🅒
46	KS 260 W, Moundridge, **2 mi W** truck repair, 🅖🍴🅒
40	Lincoln Blvd, Hesston, **E** 🍴 Ruffino's Italian, 🛏 AmericInn, **W** 🅖 Cenex/dsl, 🍴 El Cerrito Grill, Lincoln Perk Coffee, Pizza Hut, Sonic, Subway, 🛏 Best Value Inn
34	N Newton, Avalene, KS 15, **E** 🅞 RV camping, **W** 🍴 Subway (1mi), Taco Bell (1mi), 🅞 Kauffman Museum
33	US 50 E, to Peabody (from nb)
31	1st St, Broadway St, **E** 🅖 Conoco/dsl, Shamrock, 🍴 Applebee's, CJ's Rest., KFC, 🛏 Days Inn, EconoLodge, 1st Inn, 🅞 Cadillac/Chevrolet, Chrysler/Dodge/Jeep, Ford, **W** 🍴 Braum's, MT Mike's, 🛏 Best Western/rest., Comfort Inn
30	US 50 W, KS 15 (exits left from nb), to Hutchinson, Newton, **W** 🅖 KwikShop/dsl, 🍴 Arby's, Papa Murphy's, Pizza Hut, Sonic, Subway, 🅞 🅗, AutoZone, Buick/GMC, Dillon's Foods, $Tree, Radio Shack, Walmart
28	SE 36th St, **W** 🍴 Burger King, 🅞 Chisholm Trail Outlets/famous brands
25	KS 196, to Whitewater, El Dorado
23mm	**rest areas both lanes, full 🅗 facilities, 🅒, 🚻, litter barrels, vending, petwalk, RV dump**
22	125th St
19	101st St, **W** 🅞 RV camping
17	85th St, **E** Valley Ctr, KS Coliseum
16	77th St, **E** 🛏 Sleep Inn, 🅞 Wichita Greyhound Park
14	61st St, **E** 🅖 QT/dsl, Valero, 🍴 Applebee's, Chopstix, Cracker Barrel, Pizza Hut, Spangles Rest., Subway, Taco Bell, Wendy's, 🛏 Comfort Inn, 🅞 Chevrolet, TrueValue, vet, **W** 🅖 Phillips 66/dsl, 🍴 KFC, McDonald's, 🛏 Park City Inn, Super 8, 🅞 Goodyear/auto
13	53rd St, **E** Freightliner, Harley-Davidson, Mack Trucks, **W** 🅖 Phillips 66/dsl, 🍴 Country Kitchen, 🛏 Best Western, Days Inn
11b	I-235 W, KS 96, to Hutchinson
11a	KS 254, to El Dorado
10b	29th St, Hydraulic Ave
10a	KS 96 E
9	21st St, **E** 🍴 Sonic, 🅞 Wichita St U
8	13th St, **W** 🍴 Dad's BBQ
7a	downtown
7b	8th St, 9th St, Central Ave., **E** School of Medicine
6b	1st St, 2nd St, downtown
5b	US 54, US 400, Kellogg Ave, **E** 🅖 QT, US Gas, 🍴 Burger King, Chipotle Meixcan, Jimmy John's, Taco Bueno, 🛏 Wichata Suites
5a	Lincoln St, **E** 🍴 DQ, **W** 🅖 QT
4	Harry St, **1 mi E** 🅖 QT, 🍴 Brownstone Grill, Church's, Denny's, Dog'n Shake, McDonald's, NuWay Drive-Thru, Poblano Mexican, Spangles Rest., Subway, Taco Bell, Taco Tico, Wendy's, 🅞 🅗, BigLots, Firestone/auto, **W** gas/dsl
3	Pawnee Ave, **E** 🅖 QT, **W** 🅖 Phillips 66, Shell, 🍴 Burger King, Li'l Mexico, Pizza Hut, Spangles, 🛏 Pawnee Inn, 🅞 AutoZone, Checker's Foods, $General
2	Hydraulic Ave, **E** 🅖 QT, **W** 🍴 McDonald's, Subway
2mm	Arkansas River
1c	I-235 N, **2 mi W** Hilton
1b a	US 81 S, 47th St, **E** 🅖 Conoco, 🛏 AmericInn, Comfort Inn, Days Inn, **W** 🅖 Phillips 66, 🍴 Applebee's, Braum's, Burger King, Carlos O'Kelly's, Godfather's, KFC, LJ Silver, McDonald's, Mr Goodcents, New China, Papa John's, Pizza Hut, Spangles Rest., Subway, Taco Bell, Taco Tico, Wild Hog BBQ, 🛏 Best Western, Heritage Inn, Red Carpet Inn, ValuePlace, 🅞 Checker's Foods, Curves, Dillon's Foods/dsl, $General, $Tree, K-Mart, O'Reilly Parts, Radio Shack
0mm	I-135 begins/ends on I-35, exit 42.

Vertical margin labels (left): N ↕ S, MC PHERSON, NEWTON

Vertical margin label (right): WICHITA

KS

INTERSTATE 24

Exit	Services
93.5mm	Kentucky/Tennessee state line
93mm	**Welcome Ctr wb, full ♿ facilities, 🅒, 🏭, litter barrels, vending, petwalk**
91.5mm	Big West Fork Red River
89	KY 115, to Oak Grove, **N** to Jeff Davis Mon St HS, **S** ⛽ (💊)/McDonald's/dsl/scales/24hr, Shell/dsl, ⊡ truck repair
86	US 41A, to Ft Campbell, Pennyrile Pkwy, Hopkinsville, **N** ⛽ Marathon/Chester's/dsl/scales/24hr, **S** ⛽ BP/dsl/24hr, ⓕFLYING J/Denny's/dsl/LP/scales/24hr, (💊)/Subway/Wendy's/dsl/scales/24hr, 🍴 McDonald's, Waffle House, 🛏 Comfort Suites, Days Inn, Holiday Inn Express, Quality Inn, Sleep Inn, ⊡ Ⓗ, truck wash
81	Pennyrile Pky N, to Hopkinsville
79mm	Little River
73	KY 117, to Gracey, Newstead
65	US 68, KY 80, to Cadiz, **S** ⛽ BP/dsl, Marathon/dsl, Shell/dsl/24hr, 🍴 Cracker Barrel, KFC, McDonald's, Subway, Taco Bell, Wendy's, 🛏 Broadbent Inn, Knights Inn, Super 7 Inn, Super 8, ⊡ Ⓗ, Chevrolet, golf, to NRA
56	KY 139, to Cadiz, Princeton, **S** ⛽ Marathon/dsl, ⊡ KOA (9mi), NRA
47mm	Lake Barkley
45	KY 293, to Princeton, Saratoga, **S** ⛽ Marathon/dsl, ⊡ Mineral Mound SP, RV Camping, to KY St Penitentiary
42	to W KY Pkwy, Elizabethtown
40	US 62, US 641, Kuttawa, Eddyville, **N** 🛏 Regency Inn, Relax Inn, ⊡ Mineral Mound SP, camping, **S** ⛽ BP/Wendy's/dsl/24hr, Huck's/Quiznos/dsl/scales/24hr, Marathon, 🍴 Huddle House, SW Grill, 🛏 Days Inn, Hampton Inn, ⊡ to Lake Barkley, KY Lake Rec Areas, camping
36mm	**weigh sta both lanes, 🅒s**
34mm	Cumberland River
31	KY 453, to Grand Rivers, Smithland, **N** ⛽ BP/dsl, 🛏 Patti's Inn, **S** ⛽ Exxon/dsl, 🍴 Miss Scarlett's, 🛏 Best Value Inn, Grand Rivers Resort (3mi), Lighthouse Landing Resort, ⊡ Exit 31 RV Park, NRA
29mm	Tennessee River
27	US 62, to KY Dam, Calvert City, **N** ⛽ BP/dsl, 🍴 Cracker Barrel, DQ, Mama D's Italian, McDonald's, KFC, Waffle House, Willow Pond Rest., 🛏 Days Inn, KY Dam Motel, Super 8, ⊡ Cypress Lakes Camp, Freightliner, KOA, vet, **S** ⛽ ♥Loves♥/Arby's/dsl/scales/24hr, 🍴 Subway, ⊡ truck repair
25b a	to Calvert City, Carroll/Purchase Pkwy, **services 1 mi N**, **S** KY Lake RA
16	US 68, to Paducah, **S** ⛽ BP/Southern Pride/Subway/dsl/scales/24hr, ⊡ antiques, flea mkt
11	rd 1954, Husband Rd, to Paducah, **N** ⛽ Parkway/dsl, 🛏 Best Western, ⊡ Duck Creek RV Park, **S** ⊡ Harley-Davidson
7	US 45, US 62, to Paducah, **N** ⛽ BP/dsl, 🍴 Burger King, Taco Bell, ⊡ Ⓗ, **S** Welcome Ctr both lanes, full ♿ facilities, 🅒s, vending, 🏭, litter barrels, petwalk, ⛽ BP, Marathon/dsl, 🍴 Arby's, Backyard Burger, Chong's Chinese, Hardee's, KFC, Los Amigo's Mexican, McDonald's, Parker's Drive-In, Pizza Hut, Popeye's, Quiznos, Sonic, Waffle House, 🛏 Denton Motel, ⊡ K-Mart, O'Reilly Parts, Plaza Tires, SuperValu Foods/gas, Verizon
4	US 60, to Paducah, **N** ⛽ BP, 🍴 Applebee's, Bob

PADUCAH (side label)

E ↑ W (direction indicator)

PADUCAH (bottom side label)

KY (tab)

4	Continued
	Evans, Burger King, McDonald's, O'Charley's, Outback Steaks, Rafferty's, 🛏 Candlewood Suites, Courtyard, Days Inn, Drury Inn, Hampton Inn, Holiday Inn Express, Residence Inn, Westowne Inn, ⊡ Hancock Fabrics, Toyota/Scion, **S** ⛽ BP, Murphy USA/dsl, Superway, 🍴 Arby's, Backwoods BBQ, Backyard Burger, Buffalo Wild Wings, Capt D's,c Chick-fil-A, Chong's Chinese, Chuck-eCheese, Cracker Barrel, Domino's, El Chico's, Fazoli's, Hardee's, IHOP, Logan's Roadhouse, Los Amigos, McAlister's Deli, Olive Garden, Panera Bread, Pasta House, Penn Sta. Subs, Pizza Hut, Red Lobster, Ryan's, Sonic, Steak'n Shake, Taco Bell, TX Roadhouse, TGI-Friday's, Tokyo Hibachi, Wendy's, 🛏 Comfort Suites, Country Inn&Suites, Drury Suites, Motel 6, Paducah Inn, PearTree Inn, Thrifty Inn, ⊡ AAA, Advance Parts, Aldi Foods, AT&T, Best Buy, Books-A-Million, Dick's, Dillard's, Gander Mtn, Goodyear, Hobby Lobby, Home Depot, JC Penney, Kohl's, Lowe's, Michael's, Office Depot, Old Navy, Petsmart, Sam's Club/gas, Sears/auto, TJ Maxx, Tuesday Morning, Verizon, Walmart, mall
3	KY 305, to Paducah, **N** ⛽ Shell/dsl, 🛏 Best Value Inn, Comfort Inn/rest., EconoLodge, **S** ⛽ Cheers/Huddle House/pizza/subs/dsl/e85, (💊)/Subway/dsl/scales/24hr, 🍴 Yu's Kitchen, Waffle Hut, 🛏 Baymont Inn, ⊡ Fern Lake Camping
0mm	Kentucky/Illinois state line, Ohio River

PADUCAH (side label)

INTERSTATE 64

Exit	Services
192mm	Kentucky/West Virginia state line, Big Sandy River
191	US 23, to Ashland, **1-2 mi N** ⛽ Exxon, GoMart, Marathon/Subway/dsl, Speedway, 🍴 Arby's, Little Caesars, McDonald's, Waffle House, Wendy's, 🛏 Ramada Ltd, ⊡ Ⓗ, Rite Aid, Foodland Foods, USPO
185	KY 180, Cannonsburg, **0-3 mi N** ⛽ BP/dsl, Shell/McDonald's/USPO, Superquik, 🍴 Arby's, Bob Evans, Burger King, DQ, KFC, Subway, Taco Bell, Waffle House, Wendy's, 🛏 Days Inn, Fairfield Inn, Hampton Inn, Holiday Inn Express, ⊡ $Tree, st police, urgent care, **S** ⛽ ⓕFLYING J/Denny's/dsl/LP/scales/24hr, ⊡ Hidden Valley Camping
181	181 US 60, to Princess, **N** ⛽ BP/dsl, **S** ⛽ Marathon
179	rd 67, Industrial Parkway, **N** ⊡ KOA
174mm	**rest areas eb, full ♿ facilities, 🅒, 🏭, vending, litter barrels, petwalk**
173mm	**rest areas wb, full ♿ facilities, 🅒, 🏭, vending, litter barrels, petwalk**
172	rd 1, rd 7, Grayson, **N** ⛽ Superquik/dsl/24hr, 🍴 A&W/LJ Silver, Huddle House, KFC, Pizza Hut, Shoney's, Subway, 🛏 Days Inn, Guesthouse Inn, Quality Inn, ⊡ Chrysler/Dodge/Jeep, $General, $Tree, Ford, K-Mart, Save-a-Lot Foods, **S** ⛽ BP, Exxon/Hardees, ♥Loves♥/Wendy's/scales/dsl/24hr, Marathon, Shell, Speedway, 🍴 Arby's, Biscuit World, China House, DQ, Little Caesar's, McDonald's, Taco Bell, Toro Loco, 🛏 Super 8, ⊡ Advance Parts, AT&T, AutoZone, $General, Family$, FoodFair, Rite Aid, TrueValue, urgent care
161	US 60, to Olive Hill, **N** ⛽ BP, 🛏 Spanish Manor Motel, ⊡ to Carter Caves SP, camping
156	rd 2, to KY 59, to Olive Hill, **S** ⛽ BP, 🍴 DQ
148mm	**weigh sta both lanes**

E ↑ W (direction indicator)

GRAYSON (side label)

E ↕ W

INTERSTATE 64 CONT'D

Exit	Services
141mm	rest areas both lanes, full ♿ facilities, 🅲, 🚻, vending, litter barrels, petwalk
137	KY 32, to Morehead, N 🛢 BP/DQ/dsl, 🍴 CiCi's Pizza, Huddle House, Reno's Roadhouse, 🅾 AT&T, Big Lots, Curves, Kroger/dsl, Lowe's, Walmart/Subway, S 🛢 BP/McDonald's/dsl/24hr, Marathon/dsl, 🍴 China Star, Domino's, Hardee's, Lee's Chicken, McDonald's, Ponderosa, Shoney's, 🏠 Days Inn, Hampton Inn, Holiday Inn Express, Quality Inn, Super 8, 🅾 🏥, Ace Hardware, AutoZone, $General, Food Lion, GNC, Radio Shack, auto repair, st police
133	rd 801, to Sharkey, Farmers, N 🛢 Shell/dsl, S 🛢 BP/Subway/dsl, 🏠 Comfort Inn, 🅾 Outpost RV Park (4mi)
123	US 60, to Salt Lick, Owingsville, N 🛢 Chevron/dsl
121	KY 36, to Owingsville, N 🛢 BP/dsl, Exxon, Valero/dsl, 🍴 DQ, McDonald's, Subway, 🅾 $General, Family$
113	US 60, to Mt Sterling, S 🛢 Pilot/McDonald's/Subway/dsl/scales/24hr
110	US 460, KY 11, Mt Sterling, N 🛢 Shell/Krystal/dsl, Valero, 🍴 Cracker Barrel, 🏠 Fairfield Inn, Ramada Ltd, 🅾 golf, S 🛢 Exxon/Subway, Marathon/Huddle House, Speedway/dsl, 🍴 Applebee's, Arby's, Burger King, City King Buffet, El Camino Real, Jerry's Rest., KFC, Lee's Chicken, LJ Silver, McDonald's, Quiznos, Wendy's, 🏠 Budget Inn, Days Inn/rest., 🅾 🏥, AutoZone, Family$, O'Reilly Parts, USPO, S on KY 686...gas Marathon/Circle K, 🍴 El Cancun, Hardee's, Little Caesar's, Pizza Hut, Subway, Taco Bell, 🅾 Advance Parts, Chevrolet, Chrysler/Dodge/Jeep, $Tree, Ford/Mercury, JC Penney, Kroger, Lowe's, Verizon, Walmart/Subway
108mm	rest area wb, full ♿ facilities, 🅲, 🚻, vending, litter barrels, petwalk
101	US 60
98.5mm	rest area eb, full ♿ facilities, 🅲, 🚻, vending, litter barrels, petwalk
98	KY 402 (from eb), S Natural Bridge Resort SP
96b a	KY 627, to Winchester, Paris, N 🛢 BP/dsl, Marathon/96 Truck Plaza/dsl/rest./scales, S 🏠 Days Inn, Hampton Inn, Quality Inn, 🅾 Buick/Chevrolet/GMC

W I N C H E S T E R

94	KY 1958, Van Meter Rd, Winchester, N 🛢 Road Ranger/dsl/24hr, Shell/scales/dsl, 🏠 Best Value Inn, Holiday Inn Express, S 🛢 BP/dsl, Marathon, Murphy Express/dsl, Speedway/dsl, 🍴 Applebee's, Arby's, Big Boy, Burger King, Cantuckee Diner, Capt D's, Chester Hacienda, Domino's, Don Senor, DQ, El Camino Real, Fazoli's, Golden Corral, Great Wall Chinese, Hardee's, Jade Garden Chinese, KFC, Little Caesar's, McDonald's, Papa John's, Pizza Hut, Quiznos, Rally's, Sonic, Subway, Taco Bell, Taste Of China, Waffle House, Wendy's, 🏠 Best Western, 🅾 🏥, Advance Parts, AT&T, AutoZone, Chrysler/Dodge/Jeep, $General, $Tree, Ford/Mercury, K-Mart, Kroger, Lowe's, Office Depot, O'Reilly Parts, Radio Shack, Rite Aid, Walgreens, Walmart/Subway, to Ft Boonesborough Camping, auto repair
87	KY 859, Blue Grass Sta
81	I-75 S, to Knoxville
I-64 and I-75 run together 7 mi. See Kentucky Interstate 75, exits 113-115.	
75	I-75 N, to Cincinnati, access to KY Horse Park
69	US 62 E, to Georgetown, N antiques (6mi), to Georgetown Coll., S Equus Run Vineyards (2mi)
65	US 421, Midway, S 🛢 Wandy/dsl, antiques
60mm	rest area both lanes, full handicapped facilities, litter barrels, petwalk, vending
58	US 60, Frankfort, N 🛢 BP, Marathon/dsl, Speedway/dsl, 🍴 Arby's, Capt D's, Cattleman's Roadhouse, DQ, McDonald's, Miguel's Mexican, Starbucks, Taco Bell, Waffle House, Wendy's, White Castle, 🏠 Best Western, Bluegrass Inn, Fairfield Inn, 🅾 Chrysler/Dodge/Jeep, $General, $Tree, ElkHorn Camping (5mi), Ford/Lincoln/Mercury, Honda, Kohl's, Kroger/gas, Nissan, TireDiscounters, Toyota/Scion, Tuesday Morning, Walgreens, to KY St Capitol, KYSU, to Viet Vets Mem, transmissions
55mm	Kentucky River
53b a	US 127, Frankfort, N 🛢 Marathon, Speedway/dsl, 🍴 A&W/LJ Silver, Applebee's, Baskin-Robbins, Beef O'Brady's, Big Boy, Burger King, Capt D's, Carino's Italian, Chili's, China Buffet, DQ, Fazoli's, Ginza Japanese, Hardee's, KFC, Longhorn Steaks, McDonald's, O'Charley's, Panera Bread, Papa John's, Pizza Hut, Qdoba Mexican, Rio Grande Mexican, Shoney's,

KY

INTERSTATE 64 CONT'D

Exit	Services
53b a	Continued Sonic, Starbucks, Steak'n Shake, Subway, Taco Bell, Taco John's, Wendy's, 🏠 Best Value Inn, Days Inn, Hampton Inn, Holiday Inn Express, 🔲 🏥, Advance Parts, AT&T, BigLots, Big-O Tire, AutoZone, Family$, GNC, Goodyear/auto, JC Penney, K-Mart, Kroger/gas/24hr, Lowe's, Office Depot, Rite Aid, Verizon, Walgreens, Walmart/Subway, Ancient Age Tour, to KY St Capitol, st police, vet, **S** 🅰 BP/dsl
48	KY 151, to US 127 S, **S** 🅰 BP/dsl, ⏱ Subway
43	KY 395, Waddy, **N** 🅰 🟡FLYING J/Denny's/dsl/LP/scales/24hr, **S** 🅰 Loves/McDonald's/Subway/dsl/scales/24hr
38.5mm	weigh sta both lanes
35	KY 53, Shelbyville, **N** 🅰 BP/dsl, Chevron/dsl, Marathon/dsl, ⏱ Cracker Barrel, Kentex BBQ, KFC, Little Caesar's, McDonald's (1mi), Taco Bell, Waffle House, 🔲 Advance Parts, Family$, Ford/Mercury, Kroger/gas/deli, Lake Shelby Camping (3mi), vet, **S** 🅰 Chevron/White Castle/dsl, Shell/dsl, 🏠 Holiday Inn Express, 🔲 golf
32b a	KY 55, Shelbyville, **1-2 mi N** 🅰 Murphy USA/dsl, Shell, ⏱ Arby's, Asian Buffet, Firefresh BBQ, KFC, McDonald's, Pizza Hut, Quiznos, Subway, Waffle House, Wendy's, 🏠 Best Western, Country Hearth Inn, Days Inn, 🔲 🏥, AutoZone, Big O Tire, Buick/Chevrolet/GMC, $Tree, Lowe's, Rolling Hills Camping (16mi), Walgreens, Walmart, **S** ⏱ Cattleman's Roadhouse, 🏠 Ramada, 🔲 Taylorsville Lake SP
28mm	rest area eb, full ♿ facilities, info, 🚻, 🏞, litter barrels, vending, petwalk
28	KY 1848, Veechdale Rd, Simpsonville, **N** 🅰 ▦▦▦/Wendy's/dsl/scales/24hr, ⏱ DQ, Subway, 🔲 golf, **S** 🅰 BP/dsl
19b a	I-265, Gene Snyder Fwy, **N** to Tom Sawyer SP
17	S Blankenbaker, **N** 🅰 Circle K, Shell/dsl, 🏠 Staybridge Suites, 🔲 Harley-Davidson, **S** 🅰 BP/Subway, Marathon, Thornton's/dsl, ⏱ A&W, Arby's, BackYard Burger, Burger King, Cracker Barrel, HomeTown Buffet, KFC, King Buffet, Kingfish Rest., LJ Silver/Taco Bell, McDonald's, Penn Sta.; Ruby Tuesday, Waffle House, Wendy's, 🏠 Candlewood Suites, Comfort Suites, Country Inn&Suites, Fairfield Inn, Hampton Inn, Hilton Garden, Holiday Inn Express, Homestead Suites, Jameson Inn, La Quinta, Microtel, Sleep Inn, Wingate Inn, 🔲 Lexus, Sam's Club/gas
15	Hurstbourne Pkwy, Louisville, **0-2 mi N** 🅰 Shell/Circle K/dsl, Speedway, Thorton's/dsl, ⏱ Arby's, Bob Evans, Bonefish Grill, Carrabba's, Chili's, Fazoli's, Great Harvest, IHOP, Jimmy John's, Macaroni Grill, McDonald's, Mimi's Cafe, Olive Garden, Panera Bread, Papa John's, PF Changs, Qdoba, Sichuan Garden, Skyline Chili, Starbucks, Subway, Tony Roma's, Waffle House, 🏠 Baymont Inn, Courtyard, Days Inn, Drury Inn, Holiday Inn, Hyatt Place, Red Roof Inn, Residence Inn, 🔲 Barnes&Noble, Lowe's, Towery's Auto, Walgreens, **S** 🅰 Kroger, Marathon, Meijer/dsl/24hr, ⏱ Applebee's, BD BBQ, Buca Rest., Burger King, China Buffet, ChuckeCheese, Coldstone, DQ, El Toro, Famous Daves, Home Run Burgers, Jason's Deli, J Gumbo's Cajun, Jumbo Grill, Longhorn Steaks, Lonestar Steaks, McAlister's Deli, McDonald's,

Exit	Services
15	Continued Moe's SW Grill, O'Charley's, Old Chicago, Penn Sta. Subs, Piccadilly, Qdoba, Quiznos, Shogun Japanese, Smokey Bones BBQ, Starbucks, Steak'n Shake, Taco Bell, Taco Bueno, Tumbleweed SW Grill, Wendy's, White Castle, 🏠 Inn Place, Park Inn, Red Carpet Inn, 🔲 Autozone, Carmax, Chevrolet, $Tree, Hancock Fabrics, Home Depot, Honda, Infiniti, Kroger, Michael's, Office Depot, Radio Shack, Staples, Target, VW, Walgreens, Walmart/drugs
12b	I-264 E, Watterson Expswy **1 exit N on US 60** 🅰 Chevron, ⏱ Arby's, Big Boy, BJ's Rest., CA Pizza, Cheesecake Factory, Cosina Italian, Fox&Hound, J Alexander's, Logan's Roadhouse, McDonald's, Outback Steaks, Panera Bread, Taco Bell, Wendy's, 🔲 Acura, Best Buy, Dillard's, Ford/Lincoln/Mercury, Goodyear/auto, JC Penney, Kia, Kohl's, Macy's, Staples, SteinMart, Vonmaur, Whole Foods Mkt, mall
12a	I-264 W, access to 🏥
10	Cannons Lane
8	Grinstead Dr, Louisville, **S** ⏱ KT Cafe, Jim Porter's Rest., gas
7	US 42, US 62, Mellwood Ave, Story Ave
6	I-71, **N** (from eb), to Cincinnati
5a	I-65, **S** to Nashville, **N** to Indianapolis
5b	3rd St, Louisville, **N** ⏱ Joe's CrabShack, **S** 🏠 Galt House Hotel, Marriott, ⏱ Kingfish Rest., 🔲🏥
4	9th St, Roy Wilkins Ave, **S** KY Art Ctr, science museum, downtown
3	US 150 E, to 22nd St, **S** 🅰 Chevron/dsl, Shell/Circle K, ⏱ DQ, McDonald's, Subway
1	I-264 E, to Shively, **S** 🏞, zoo
0mm	Kentucky/Indiana state line, Ohio River

INTERSTATE 65

Exit	Services
138mm	Kentucky/Indiana state line, Ohio River
137	I-64 W, I-71 N, I-64 E, **W** to Galt House, downtown
136c	Jefferson St, Louisville, **E** 🔲🏥, Walgreens, **W** 🅰 Shell, ⏱ McDonald's, Papa John's, Subway, White Castle, 🏠 Courtyard, EconoLodge, Fairfield Inn, Hampton Inn, Hyatt, Marriott, SpringHill Suites, 🔲 Tires+
136b	Broadway St, Chestnut St (from nb), **E** 🔲🏥, NAPA, Walgreens, **W** 🅰 Shell, Thornton's, ⏱ McDonald's, Rally's, Subway, White Castle, 🏠 Courtyard, Fairfield Inn, Hampton Inn, Hyatt, Marriott, Springhill Suites, 🔲 Tires+, same as 136c
135	W St Catherine, **E** 🅰 Shell
134b a	KY 61, Jackson St, Woodbine St, **W** 🅰 Shell/Circle K, 🏠 Days Inn, Quality Inn, 🔲 Harley-Davidson
133b	US 60A, Eastern Pkwy, Taylor Blvd, **E** ⏱ Denny's, Pizza Mia, Snappy Tomato Pizza, Subway, **W** 🅰 Marathon, ⏱ Cracker Barrel, McDonald's, Papa John's, 🏠 Country Hearth Inn, 🔲 U of Louisville, Churchill Downs, museum
133b	Crittenden Dr (132from sb), **E** ⏱ Denny's, same as 133, **W** 🅰 BP, ⏱ Arby's, Burger King, Cracker Barrel, Hall of Fame Cafe, 🏠 Country Inn&Suites, Hilton Garden, Holiday Inn, Ramada Inn, Super 8
131b a	I-264, Watterson Expswy, **W** Cardinal Stadium, Expo Center, 🏞
130	KY 61, Preston Hwy, **E on Ky 61** 🅰 Shell/Circle K, Speedway/dsl, Thornton's, ⏱ Bob Evans, Burger

INTERSTATE 65 CONT'D

Exit	Services
130	Continued
	King, Domino's, Fazoli's, KFC, Little Caesars, McDonald's, Papa John's, Popeyes, Rally's, Royal Garden Buffet, Subway, Taco Bell, Waffle House, Wendy's, 🛏 EconoLodge, Red Roof Inn, Super 8, ⊡ Aamco, AutoZone, Big O Tire, BigLots, Chevrolet/Kia, Dodge, $General, Ford, O'Reilly Parts, PepBoys, Radio Shack, Sav-A-Lot Foods, Staples, Tires+, U-Haul
128	KY 1631, Fern Valley Rd, E 📹 BP, Marathon/Circle K, Thornton's/dsl, 🍴 Arby's, Big Boy, El Nopal Mexican, Hardee's, Indi's Rest., McDonald's, Outback Steaks, Shoney's, Subway, Taco Bell, Waffle House, Wendy's, White Castle, 🛏 Comfort Suites, Days Inn, Fern Valley Hotel, Holiday Inn, InTown Suites, Jameson Inn, ⊡ Sam's Club/gas, Walgreens, W UPS Depot
127	KY 1065, outer loop, E TX Roadhouse, W 🍴 McDonald's/RV Parking, to Motor Speedway,
125 b a	I-265 E, KY 841, Gene Snyder Fwy
121	KY 1526, Brooks Rd, E 📹 BP, Marathon, 🍴 Arby's, Burger King, Cracker Barrel, McDonald's, Tumbleweed Grill, 🛏 Comfort Inn, Fairfield Inn, Holiday Inn Express, ⊡ 🅷, Tinker's RV Ctr, W 📹 BP/dsl, 🔲Subway/Taco Bell/dsl/scales/24hr, 🍴 Waffle House, 🛏 Baymont Inn, EconoLodge, Hampton Inn, Quality Inn
117	KY 44, Shepherdsville, E 📹 Gulf, 🍴 Bearno's Pizza, Denny's, 🛏 Best Western/rest., Days Inn, ⊡ KOA (2mi), W 📹 Marathon, Speedway/dsl, 🍴 Arby's, Big Boy, Cattlelands Roadhouse, China Buffet, DQ, El Nopal, Fazoli's, LJ Silver, KFC, Little Caesars, McDonald's/playplace, Mr Gatti's, Quiznos, Sonic, Subway, Taco Bell, Triple Crown Steaks, Waffle House, Wendy's, White Castle, 🛏 Country Inn&Suites, Motel 6, Sleep Inn, Super 8, ⊡ Advance Parts, AutoZone, BigLots, $General, Family$, Kroger/gas, Lowe's, Radio Shack, Rite Aid, Sav-a-Lot, Walgreens, auto repair
116.5mm	Salt River
116	KY 480, to KY 61, E 📹 ❤Loves/Chester's/Subway/dsl/scales/24hr, Shell/dsl, ⊡ House of Quilts, W 📹 Marathon/dsl, ⊡ Grandma's RV Park/flea mkt
114mm	rest area sb, full 🦽 facilities, 🅲, 🛏, vending, litter barrels, petwalk
112	KY 245, Clermont, E 📹 Shell/dsl, ⊡ Jim Beam Outpost, Bernheim Forest, to My Old Kentucky Home SP
105	KY 61, Lebanon Jct, W 📹 🔲McDonald's/Subway/dsl/scales/24hr/@, 105 QuikStop/dsl, 🍴 Vegas Lou's BBQ
102	KY 313, to KY 434, Radcliff, W to Patton Museum
94	US 62, Elizabethtown, E 📹 BP/dsl, Marathon/dsl, 🍴 Denny's, Waffle House, White Castle, 🛏 Comfort Inn, Days Inn, Super 8, W 📹 BP/dsl, Speedway/dsl, 🍴 Arby's, Burger King, Cracker Barrel, Chalupa's Mexican, Gatti's Pizza, HoneyBaked Ham, KFC/Taco Bell, McDonald's, Papa John's, Ruby Tuesday, Ryan's, Shoney's, Snappy Tomato Pizza, Stone Hearth, Subway, TX Outlaw Steaks, TX Roadhouse, Wendy's, 🛏 Baymont Inn, Best Western, Comfort Suites, Fairfield Inn, Hampton Inn, Holiday Inn Express, Howard Johnson, La Quinta, Motel 6, Ramada Inn, ⊡ 🅷, Advance Parts, AutoZone, Crossroads Camping, $General, $Tree, Kroger/gas, Skagg's RV Ctr, Walgreens, USPO, st police, visitors ctr
93	to Bardstown, to BG Pky, E to My Old KY Home SP, Maker's Mark Distillery
91	US 31 W, KY 61, WK Pkwy, Elizabethtown, E 📹 Marathon/dsl, 🍴 LJ Silver, Subway, 🛏 Bluegrass Inn, Budget Motel, Commonwealth Lodge, ⊡ $General, to Lincoln B'Place, W 📹 Doug's/dsl, Marathon, 🍴 Jerry's Rest., 🛏 KY Cardinal Inn, Roadside Inn, ⊡ 🅷
90mm	weigh sta sb only
86	KY 222, Glendale, E 📹 🔲/McDonalds/dsl/scales/24hr, ⊡ Glendale Camping, trk repair, W 📹 Petro/Dunkin Donuts/dsl/scales/24hr/@, 🛏 Glendale Economy Inn, ⊡ Blue Beacon
83mm	Nolin River
81	KY 84, Sonora, E 📹 Marathon/dsl, 🔲/Subway/dsl/scales/24hr, ⊡ Blue Beacon, to Lincoln B'Place, W 📹 BP/dsl
76	KY 224, Upton, E 📹 Marathon/dsl, W to Nolin Lake
75mm	eastern/central time zone
71	KY 728, Bonnieville
65	US 31 W, Munfordville, E 📹 BP/Subway/dsl, FiveStar/dsl, 🍴 DQ, El Mazatlan, King Buffet, Pizza Hut, McDonald's, Sonic, 🛏 Super 11, ⊡ Advance Parts, $General, Family$, Fred's Store, IGA Foods, Pamida, Save-A-Lot, W 📹 Marathon/dsl, Shell, 🍴 Country Kitchen, to Nolin Lake
61mm	rest area both lanes, full 🦽 facilities, info, 🅲, 🛏, litter barrels, vending, petwalk, Green River
58	KY 218, Horse Cave, E 📹 ❤Loves/McDonald's/dsl/scales/24hr/@, ⊡ 🅷, W 📹 Gulf/dsl, Marathon/dsl/repair, 🛏 Country Hearth Inn, Hampton Inn, ⊡ KOA, to Mammoth Cave NP
53	KY 70, KY 90, Cave City, E 📹 BP/dsl, Gulf/dsl/repair, JR's, Marathon/dsl, Shell, 🍴 A&W/LJ Silver, Cracker Barrel, El Mazatlan, El Patron, KFC, McDonald's, Pizza Hut, Subway, Wendy's, 🛏 Best Value Inn, Best Western, Comfort Inn, Days Inn/rest., EconoLodge, Sleep Inn, Super 8, ⊡ 🅷, $General, Barren River Lake SP (24mi), W 🍴 Watermill Rest., ⊡ Onyx Cave, Mammoth Cave NP, Jellystone Camping
48	KY 255, Park City, E 📹 Shell/dsl, ⊡ $General, Park Mammoth Resort, W Diamond Caverns Resort, to Mammoth Cave NP
43	Nun/Cumberland Pky, to Barren River Lake SP
38	KY 101, Smiths Grove, W 📹 Exxon/dsl/scales, Marathon/Subway/dsl, Shell, 🍴 Bestway Pizza, McDonald's, Wendy's, 🛏 Bryce Motel, ⊡ $General, IGA Foods, Larry's Parts, auto repair, city park
36	US 68, KY 80, Oakland, (no nb return)
28	rd 446, to US 31 W, Bowling Green, W 📹 Shell/dsl, 🍴 Hardee's, Jerry's Rest., Wendy's, 🛏 Continental Inn,

INTERSTATE 65 CONT'D

Exit	Services
28	Continued
	Country Hearth Inn, Super 8, Value Lodge, 🅾 🅗, Corvette Museum/cafe, **3 mi** W to WKYU
26	KY 234, Bowling Green, W 🅖 Shell/dsl, 🍽 Subway, 🅾 🅗, IGA Foods
22	US 231, Bowling Green, E 🅖 Exxon/dsl Keystop Gas, Shell, 🍽 Catfish House, Cracker Barrel, Culver's, Denny's, Domino's, Godfather's, Hardee's, Mancino's Pizza, Motor City Grill, Ryan's, Sonic, Waffle House, Zaxby's, 🏨 Best Value Inn, Best Western, Comfort Inn, Days Inn, EconoLodge, Fairfield Inn, HomeTowne Suites, La Quinta, Microtel, Quality Inn, Ramada Inn, Sleep Inn, 🅾 Camping World/Gander Mtn, $General, Harley-Davidson, urgent care, USPO, W 🅖 Gulf/dsl, RaceWay, Shell/dsl, Speedway/dsl, 🍽 Applebee's, Arby's, Beijing Chinese, Bob Evans, Bruster's, Buffalo Wild Wings, Burger King, Capt D's, ChuckeCheese, Chick-fil-A, China Buffet, Double-Dog's Chowhouse, Fazoli's, Great Harvest Bread, Guadalajara Grill, KFC, Krystal, Kyoto Steaks, Linzie's Sandwiches, Logan's Roadhouse, Longhorn Steaks, McDonald's, Moe's SW Grill, MT Grille, O'Charley's, Olive Garden, Outback Steaks, Panera Bread, Pizza Hut, Rafferty's, Red Lobster, Ruby Tuesday, Shogun Japanese, Smokey Bones BBQ, Sonic, Starbucks, Steak'n Shake, Subway, Taco Bell, TGIFriday's, Toots Rest., Waffle House, Wendy's, White Castle, Zaxby's, 🏨 Baymont Inn, Candlewood Suites, Country Inn&Suites, Courtyard, Drury Inn, Hampton Inn, Hilton Garden, Holiday Inn, Motel 6, News Inn, Red Roof Inn, 🅾 🅗, Advance Parts, AT&T, Barnes&Noble, Best Buy, BMW/Mercedes, Buick/GMC, Chevrolet, Chrysler/Jeep, Curves, CVS Drug, Dillard's, $General, Fisher Parts, Ford/Lincoln, Goodyear/auto, Hancock Fabrics, Hobby Lobby, Home Depot, Honda, JC Penney, K-Mart, KOA, Kia, Kohl's, Kroger/gas, Lowe's, Nissan, Office Depot, Old Navy, PetCo, Sam's Club/gas, Sears, Staples, Target, TJ Maxx, Toyota, U-Haul, Walgreens, Walmart/McDonald's, mall, urgent care
20	WH Natcher Toll Rd, to Bowling Green, access to, W KY U, st police
6	KY 100, Franklin, E 🅖 BP/dsl, Shell/dsl/24hr, 🅾 truckwash, W 🅖 ⬛/Subway/dsl/scales/24hr, ⬛/Wendy's/dsl/scales/24hr, 🏨 Comfort Inn, Days Inn, Knights Inn, 🅾 🅗, Bluegrass RV Park, Petrolube, SpeedCo, truck&tires/repair, truckwash
4mm	**weigh sta nb**
2	US 31 W, to Franklin, E 🅖 ⊕FLYING J/Denny's/dsl/LP/scales/24hr, Keystop/Marathon/Burger King/dsl/24hr, W 🅖 BP/dsl, 🍽 Cracker Barrel, McDonald's, Oasis SW Grill, Waffle House, 🏨 Best Western, EconoLodge, Hampton Inn, Holiday Inn Express, Quality Inn, Super 8, 🅾 🅗, antiques
1mm	**Welcome Ctr nb, full** 🅦 **facilities,** ⬛, ⬛, **vending, litter barrels, petwalk**
0mm	Kentucky/Tennessee state line

INTERSTATE 71

Exit	Services
	Kentucky/Ohio state line, Ohio River. I-71 and I-75 run together 19 miles. See Kentucky I-75, exits 175-192.
77 [173]	I-75 S, to Lexington

Left side margin: **BOWLING GREEN** N↕S   **FRANKLIN**

75mm	weigh sta sb
72	KY 14, to Verona, E 🅖 BP/dsl, Marathon/dsl, 🅾 Oak Creek Camping (5mi)
62	US 127, to Glencoe, E 🅖 62 TrkPlaza/rest./dsl, W 🅖 BP/dsl/rest., 🏨 127 Motel
57	KY 35, to Sparta, E 🅖 Marathon/dsl, 🅾 Eagle Valley Camping (10mi), Sparta RV Park (3mi), W 🅖 BP/dsl, 🏨 Ramada, 🅾 KY Speedway
55	KY 1039, W 🅖 ⬤Loves/McDonald's/Subway/dsl/scales/24hr, 🅾 KY Speedway, casino
44	KY 227, to Indian Hills, W 🅖 BP/dsl, Marathon/dsl, Murphy USA/dsl, 🍽 Arby's, Burger King, El Nopal, Hometown Pizza, KFC, McDonald's, New China, Subway, Taco Bell, Waffle House, 🏨 Best Western, Hampton Inn, Holiday Inn Express, Super 8, 🅾 🅗, AutoZone, Chevrolet, $General, Ford, Kroger/dsl, Sav-a-Lot Foods, Verizon, Walmart, Gen. Butler SP
43.5mm	Kentucky River
43	KY 389, to KY 55, English
34	US 421, New Castle, Bedford, Campbellsburg, W 🅖 BP/Subway/dsl, Marathon/dsl, 🅾 st police
28	KY 153, KY 146, to US 42, Pendleton, E 🅖 BP/dsl, Marathon/dsl, ⬛/Subway/dsl/scales/24hr/@, W 🅖 ⬛/McDonald's/scales/dsl/24hr
22	KY 53, La Grange, E 🅖 BP/dsl, Speedway/Rally's/dsl, 🍽 Applebee's, Beef O'Brady's, Burger King, Jumbo Buffet, Papa John's, Papa Murphy's, Ponderosa, Sonic, Waffle House, Wendy's, 🏨 Best Western-Ashbury, Holiday Inn Express, 🅾 🅗, AT&T, Big-O Tire, GNC, Kroger/gas, Radio Shack, Walgreens, Walmart/Subway, urgent care, W 🅖 Marathon/dsl, Swifty, 🍽 Arby's, Cracker Barrel, Domino's, DQ, El Nopal, Hometown Pizza, KFC, LJ Silver, McDonald's, Taco Bell, 🏨 Comfort Suites, Super 8, 🅾 Advance Parts, Buick/Chevrolet, Curves, Lee Tires, NAPA, Rite Aid, Sav-a-Lot, flea mkt, USPO, vet
18	KY 393, Buckner, W 🅖 Marathon/dsl, 🍽 Subway
17	KY 146, Buckner, E 🅾 Ford, W 🅖 Thornton's/dsl/24hr, 🅾 USPO, st police
14	KY 329, Crestwood, Pewee Valley, Brownsboro, E 🅖 BP/dsl, 🍽 Starbucks, **2 mi** E 🍽 DQ, Hometown Pizza, McDonald's, Sonic, Subway
13mm	**rest area both lanes, full** 🅦 **facilities,** ⬛, ⬛, **vending, litter barrels, petwalk**
9b a	I-265, KY 841, Gene Snyder Fwy, E 🅾 Costco/gas, to Sawyer SP
5	I-264, Watterson Expswy (exits left from sb), E to Sawyer SP
2	Zorn Ave, E VA 🅗, W 🅖 BP, Shell/dsl, 🍽 El Nopal Mexican, KingFish Rest., 🏨 Ramada Inn, 🅾 WaterTower Art Museum
1b	I-65, S to Nashville, N to Indianapolis

INTERSTATE 75

Exit	Services
193mm	Kentucky/Ohio state line, Ohio River
192	5th St (from nb), Covington, E 🅖 BP, Shell, Speedway, 🍽 Big Boy, Burger King, GoldStar Chili, McDonald's, Riverfront Pizza, Skyline Chili, Subway, Taco Bell, Waffle House, White Castle, 🏨 Courtyard, Extended Stay America, Holiday Inn, Radisson, 🅾 Lexus, Toyota/Scion, Riverboat Casino, W 🏨 Hampton Inn
191	12th St, Covington, E 🅾 🅗, museum, same as 192

Right side margin: N↕S   **LOUISVILLE**   N↕S

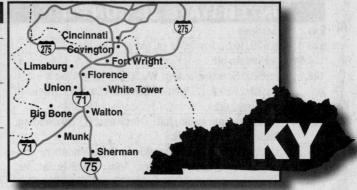

N

↑

↓

S

C O V I N G T O N

F L O R E N C E

INTERSTATE 75 CONT'D

Exit	Services
189	KY 1072, Kyles Lane, **W** ◎ BP/dsl, Marathon/dsl, Shell/dsl, ⑪ Big Boy, Skyline Chili, Substation II Subs, ⌂ Days Inn, Rodeway Inn, ◉ Walgreens, same as 188
188	US 25, US 42, Dixe Hwy, **E** ◎ Sunoco, ⑪ Subway, ◉ GNC, Kroger, Tuesday Morning, **W** ⌂ Days Inn, Rodeway Inn, USA Hotel, ◉ $Tree, same as 189
186	KY 371, Buttermilk Pike, Covington, **E** ◎ BP/dsl, Marathon/DQ, ⑪ Graeter's Ice Cream, Oriental Wok, Papa John's, ⌂ Drawbridge Inn/rest., Montgomery Inn, Super 8, **W** ◎ BP, Shell, Sunoco/dsl, ⑪ Arby's, Baskin-Robbins/Dunkin Donuts, Bonefish Grill, Burger King, Chipotle Mexican, Empire Buffet, GoldStar Chili, Jimmy John's, La Rosa's Pizza, McDonald's, Miyako Steaks, Outback Steaks, Papa Murphy's, Pizza Hut, Quiznos, Rima's Diner, Skyline Chili, Subway, ◉ AT&T, Home Depot, Remke Foods, Staples, Verizon, Walgreens
185	I-275, E and W, **W** to ✈
184	KY 236, Donaldson Rd, to Erlanger, **E** ◎ BP, Marathon, ⑪ Double Dragon Oriental, **W** ◎ Marathon, Speedway/dsl, Sunoco/Subway/dsl, ⑪ La Badeya Grill, Peecox Grill, Waffle House, ⌂ Comfort Inn, Country Hearth Inn, EconoLodge, Wingate Inn, ◉ Goodyear/auto
182	KY 1017, Turfway Rd, **E** ◎ BP/dsl, Shell, ⑪ Big Boy, China City, Lee's Chicken, McDonald's, Papa John's, Pizza Hut, Taco Bell, 3 Amigo's Mexican, Subway, ⌂ Clarion, Courtyard, Days Inn, ValuePlace, ◉ BigLots, CVS Drug, Family$, Office Depot, Remke Foods, Tuesday Morning, Verizon, USPO, **W** ◎ ⑪ Applebee's, Burger King, Chick-fil-A, Chili's, CiCi's Pizza, Cracker Barrel, Dynasty Buffet, Famous Dave's BBQ, Karlo's Italian, Longhorn Steaks, Noodles&Co., O'Charley's, Potbelly, Rafferty's, Skyline Chili, Steak'n Shake, Tumbleweed Grill, Wendy's, ⌂ Comfort Inn, Extended Stay America, Hampton Inn, Hilton, Hyatt Place, La Quinta, SpringHill Suites, Studio+, ◉ Ⓗ, Best Buy, Dick's, Home Depot, Kohl's, Lowe's, Meijer, Michael's, Petsmart, Radio Shack, Sam's Club, Target, Turfway Park Racing
181	KY 18, Florence, **E** ◎ Speedway/dsl, Swifty, TA/Sunoco/Pizza Hut/Popeye's/dsl/24hr/@, ⑪ Waffle House, ⌂ Best Value Inn, Best Western, Heritage Inn, ◉ Chevrolet, auto repair, vet, **W** ◎ BP/dsl, Shell, Speedway, ⑪ Buffalo Wild Wings, Cheddars, City BBQ, El Rio Grande, Fazoli's, Hooters, IHOP, La Rosa's, Logan's Roadhouse, Panera Bread, Quiznos, Red Robin, ⌂ Microtel, Stay Lodge, ◉ Buick/GMC, Chrysler/Jeep, $Tree, Dodge, Ford, Honda, Hyundai, K-Mart, Mazda, Nissan, Tire Discounters, Toyota/Scion, VW, Walmart
180a	Mall Rd (from sb), **W** ⑪ Asian Buffet, Chipotle Mexican, ChuckeCheese, Coldstone, GoldStar Chili, HoneyBaked Ham, Olive Garden, Pizza Hut, Qdoba, Quiznos, Skyline Chili, Smokey Bones BBQ, Starbucks, Subway, Taco Bell, ◉ AAA, AT&T, Barnes&Noble, $General, $Tree, Hobby Lobby, JC Penney, JoAnn Fabrics, Kroger, Macy's, Old Navy, Sears/auto, Staples, TJ Maxx, Verizon, mall, urgent care, same as 180
180	US 42, US 127, Florence, Union, **E** ◎ BP/dsl, Speedway/dsl, ⑪ Big Boy, Bob Evans, Burger King, Camino Real, Capt D's, Chipotle Mexican, Cielito Lino Mexican, Dunkin Donuts, Mai Thai, McDonald's, Rally's, Red Lobster, Subway, Wendy's, ⌂ Holiday Inn, Knights Inn,

Exit	Services
180	Continued Motel 6, Quality Inn, Super 8, ◉ Cadillac, Subaru, funpark, **W** ◎ Marathon/dsl, Shell/dsl Speedway, ⑪ Arby's, KFC, LJ Silver, Little Caesars, Perkins, Ponderosa, Waffle House, White Castle, ⌂ Ramada Inn, Travelodge, ◉ CarX, Midas, Old Time Pottery, PepBoys, Tire Discounters, Tires+, Walgreens
178	KY 536, Mt Zion Rd, **E** ◎ BP/Rally's/dsl, Mobil, Shell/dsl, Sunoco/Subway/dsl, ⑪ Buffalo Bob's, GoldStar Chili, Hot Head Burritos, Jersey Mike's Subs, La Rosa's Pizza, Sonic, Steak'n Shake, ◉ AT&T, AutoZone, Goodyear/auto, Kroger
177mm	Welcome Ctr sb/rest area nb, full ♿ facilities, Ⓒ, ⌂, vending, litter barrels, RV dump
175	KY 338, Richwood, **E** ◎ TA/BP/Country Pride/Taco Bell/dsl/24hr/@, ▭/Subway/dsl/24hr, ⑪ Arby's, Burger King, White Castle, ⌂ Comfort Inn, ◉ RV Park, **W** ◎ BP/dsl, ▭/Subway/dsl/scales/24hr, Shell/dsl, ⑪ GoldStar Chili, McDonald's, Penn Sta Subs, Skyline Chili, Waffle House, Wendy's, ⌂ EconoLodge, Holiday Inn Express, ◉ to Big Bone Lick SP
173	I-71 S, to Louisville
171	KY 14, KY 16, to Verona, Walton, **E** ◎ BP/dsl, Marathon/DQ/dsl, ⑪ China Moon, El Toro Mexican, McDonald's, Starbucks, Subway, Waffle House, ◉ AT&T, AutoZone, Kohl's, Kroger/dsl, Walton Drug, **W** ◎ ✈FLYING J/Denny's/dsl/scales/24hr ◉ Blue Beacon, Delightful Days RV Ctr, Oak Creek Camping (1mi), to Big Bone Lick SP
168mm	weigh sta/rest haven sb
166	KY 491, Crittenden, **E** ◎ Gulf/dsl, Marathon/dsl, ⑪ McDonald's, ◉ Chrysler/Dodge/Jeep, Cincinnati, S Camping (2mi), **W** ◎ Marathon/dsl, Shell/Gold Star Chili/dsl, ⑪ Subway, Wendy's, ◉ Curves, $General
159	KY 22, to Owenton, Dry Ridge, **E** ◎ BP, Marathon, Shell/dsl, ⑪ Arby's, Burger King, Happy Dragon Chinese, KFC/Taco Bell, LJ Silver, McDonald's, Pizza Hut, Skyline Chili, Subway, Waffle House, Wendy's, ⌂ Microtel, Super 8, ◉ Ⓗ, $General, O'Reilly Parts, Radio Shack, Walmart, **W** ◎ Roadranger/dsl, Speedway/dsl, ⑪ Cracker Barrel, ⌂ Comfort Inn, Hampton Inn, ◉ Camper Village, Dry Ridge Outlets/famous brands, Sav-A-Lot, Toyota/Scion, Tire Discounters
156	Barnes Rd, **E** ◉ Ⓗ
154	KY 36, Williamstown, **E** ◎ Marathon/dsl, Shell/dsl, ◉ Ⓗ, to Kincaid Lake SP, **W** ◎ Marathon/dsl, ⑪ El Jalisco Mexican, ⌂ Best Value Inn, Days Inn
144	KY 330, to Owenton, Corinth, **E** ◎ Marathon/dsl, Noble's Trk Plaza/rest./dsl, ◉ camping, **W** ◎ BP, ⑪ Danny's Diner, ⌂ 3 Springs Motel

KY

INTERSTATE 75 CONT'D

Exit	Services
136	KY 32, to Sadieville, **W** 🚗 Marathon
130.5mm	weigh sta nb
129	rd 620, Cherry Blossom Wy, **E** 🚗 ⛽/Wendy's/dsl/scales/24hr/@, 🍴 Waffle House, 🏨 Days Inn, Motel 6, **W** 🚗 ⛽/McDonald's/dsl/scales/24hr, Shell
127mm	rest area both lanes, full ♿ facilities, 🚻, 🐾, vending, litter barrels, petwalk
126	US 62, to US 460, Georgetown, **E** 🚗 Marathon, Murphy USA/dsl, 🍴 Applebee's, Asian Royal Buffet, Big Boy, Burger King, CiCi's, Golden Corral, Gold Star Chili, Jimmy John's, McDonald's, Mi Mexico, O'Charley's, Papa John's, Penn Sta Subs, Starbucks, Steak'n Shake, Subway, 🏨 Holiday Inn, 🅾 Kohl's, Lowe's, Tire Discounters, Verizon, Walmart/Subway, urgent care, vet, **W** 🚗 BP, Marathon, Shell/Subway, Speedway/dsl, 🍴 Chick-fil-A, Cracker Barrel, Fazoli's, KFC, Ruby Tuesday, Waffle House, 🏨 Best Western, Comfort Suites, Country Inn&Suites, Knights Inn, Fairfield Inn, Hampton Inn, Hilton Garden, Microtel, Quality Inn, Super 8, 🅾 �H, Buick/Chevrolet, to Georgetown Coll, same as 125
125	US 460 (from nb), Georgetown, **E** 🚗 Gulf, Shell, 🍴 Fat-Kats Pizza, 🏨 Knights Inn, **W** 🚗 Gulf/dsl, Swifty, 🍴 Arby's, DQ, Little Caesars, LJ Silver, Taco Bell, Wendy's, 🏨 Winner's Circle Motel, 🅾 Advance Parts, BigLots, K-Mart, Radio Shack, Outlets/Famous Brands, same as 126
120	rd 1973, to Ironworks Pike, KY Horse Park, **E** KY Horse Park Camping, **W** 🚗 Valero/dsl, 🅾 �H
118	I-64 W, to Frankfort, Louisville
115	rd 922, Lexington, **E** 🚗 Shell/Subway/dsl, 🍴 Cracker Barrel, McDonald's, Waffle House, 🏨 Fairfield Inn, Knights Inn, La Quinta, Sheraton, 🅾 SaddleHorse Museum (4mi), **W** 🚗 Marathon/dsl, 🍴 Cortland's Kitchen, Denny's, Happy Dragon Chinese, 🏨 Clarion, Embassy Suites, Marriott/rest., 🅾 museum
113	US 27, US 68, to Paris, Lexington, **E** 🚗 Marathon, Speedway, 🍴 Waffle House, 🏨 Ramada Inn, **W** 🚗 Marathon/dsl, Shell/dsl, Swifty, 🍴 Arby's, Burger King, Capt D's, DQ, Donato's Pizza, Fazoli's, Golden Corral, Hardee's, Horseshoes Grill, Little Caesars, McDonald's, Penn Sta Subs, Rally's, Taco Bell, 🏨 Catalina Motel, Days Inn, Red Roof Inn, 🅾 Advance Parts, AutoZone, Bluegrass RV Ctr, Chevrolet, CVS Drug, Northside RV Ctr, O'Reilly Parts, Walmart, to UK, Rupp Arena
111	I-64 E, to Huntington, WV
110	US 60, Lexington, **W** 🚗 Murphy USA/dsl, Shell/dsl, Speedway/dsl, Thorntons/dsl, 🍴 Arby's, Bajio, Bob Evans, Calistoga Cafe, Cane's Chicken, Cracker Barrel, McDonald's, Starbucks, Subway, Waffle House, Wendy's, 🏨 Baymont Inn, Best Western, Comfort Inn, Country Inn&Suites, Envoy Inn, Hampton Inn, Microtel, Motel 6, Ramada Ltd, Super 8, 🅾 �H, Lowe's, Rite Aid, Walmart/Subway
108	Man O War Blvd, **E** 🚗 Shell, 🅾 Rite Aid, **W** 🚗 Marathon/dsl, Meijer/dsl, Shell/KFC/Wendy's, 🍴 Applebee's, Arby's, Backyard Burger, BD Mongolian Grill, BoneFish Grill, Carino's, Carrabba's, Cheddar's, Chick-fil-A, Chipotle Mexican, Domino's, Fazoli's, GoldStar Chili, IChing Asian, Logan's Roadhouse, Malone's, McDonald's, Old Chicago, Outback Steaks, Pizza Hut, Qdoba, Quiznos, Rafferty's, Red Lobster, Saul Good Rest.,

Exit	Services
108	Continued Show-Me's Rest., Starbucks, Steak'n Shake, Taco Bell, TGIFriday's, Waffle House, 🏨 Courtyard, Hilton Garden, Homewood Suites, Hyatt Place, Sleep Inn, 🅾 �H, Audi, Barnes&Noble, Best Buy, BigLots, Dick's, GNC, Gordmans, Harley-Davidson, Kohl's, Marshall's, Michael's, Old Navy, Petsmart, Staples, Target, Tire Discounters, Walgreens
104	KY 418, Lexington, **E** 🚗 BP/Arby's/dsl, Shell/Hardee's, 🍴 Waffle House, 🏨 Best Western, Comfort Inn, Days Inn, EconoLodge, La Quinta, **W** 🚗 Marathon/dsl, Speedway/Subway, 🍴 Wendy's, 🅾 �H
99	US 25 N, US 421 N, Clays Ferry
98mm	Kentucky River
97	US 25 S, US 421 S, Clay's Ferry
95	rd 627, to Boonesborough, Winchester, **E** 🚗 BP/dsl, Loves/Arby's/dsl/scales/24hr, 🍴 McDonald's, 🅾 Ft Boonesborough SP, camping, **W** 🚗 Shell/dsl/24hr
90	US 25, US 421, Richmond, **E** 🚗 Shell, 🍴 Cracker Barrel, 🏨 Knights Inn, La Quinta, Red Roof Inn, Super 7, **W** 🚗 BP, Exxon/Arby's/dsl, Marathon, Shell, Thorobred, 🍴 Big Boy, DQ, Hanger's Rest., Hardee's, Pizza Hut, Subway, Waffle House, Wendy's, 🏨 Days Inn, Super 8, 🅾 $General, NTB, USPO
87	rd 876, Richmond, **E** 🚗 BP/dsl, Gulf, Marathon, Shell/dsl, Speedway/dsl, 🍴 A&W/LJ Silver, Arby's, Casa Fiesta Mexican, Domino's, Fazoli's, Fong's Chinese, Hardee's, Hooters, King Buffet, Lee's Chicken, Little Caesars, McDonald's, Papa John's, Penn Sta Subs, Pizza Hut, Qdoba, Rally's, Taco Bell, Waffle House, Wendy's, 🏨 Best Western, Country Hearth Inn, Quality Quarters Inn, 🅾 �H, Ace Hardware, AT&T, BigLots, $General, Goodyear/auto, Rite Aid, Suzuki, to EKU, **W** 🚗 BP/dsl, Marathon/Circle K, 🍴 Bob Evans, Buffalo Wild Wings, Burger King, Chick-fil-A, Culver's, Koto Japanese, Logan's Roadhouse, Olive Garden, Panera Bread, Ryan's, Starbucks, Steak'n Shake, Subway, 🏨 Comfort Suites, Hampton Inn, Holiday Inn Express, Jameson Inn, 🅾 Belk, Hastings Books, JC Penney, Meijer/dsl, Petsmart, Radio Shack, Tire Discounters, TJ Maxx, Verizon
83	to US 25, rd 2872, Duncannon Ln, Richmond, **E** 🅾 Bluegrass Army Depot
77	rd 595, Berea, **E** 🅾 �H, KY Artisan Ctr/Cafe/Travelers Ctr, to Berea Coll, **W** 🚗 BP/Subway/dsl, Shell/dsl, 🍴 Pizza+, Rio Grande Mexican, Smokehouse Grill, 🏨 Country Inn&Suites, Days Inn
76	KY 21, Berea, **E** 🚗 BP, Marathon/Circle K, Shell/Burger King, Speedway/dsl, 🍴 A&W/LJ Silver, Arby's, Cracker Barrel, Dinner Bell Rest., Hong Kong Buffet, KFC, Mariachi Mexican, Mario's Pizza, McDonald's, Old Town Amish Rest., Papa John's, Pizza Hut, Subway, Taco Bell, WanPen Chinese/Thai, Wendy's, 🏨 Best Value Inn, Holiday Motel, Knights Inn, 🅾 �H, $General, Radio Shack, Walmart, tires, urgent care, **W** 🚗 BP, Marathon/dsl, 76 Fuel/dsl, 🍴 Lee's Chicken, 🏨 Comfort Inn, EconoLodge, Fairfield Inn, 🅾 Oh! Kentucky Camping
62	US 25, to KY 461, Renfro Valley, **E** 🚗 Derby City/rest./dsl, Shell, 🍴 Hardee's, 🏨 Heritage Inn, 🅾 KOA (2mi), Renfro Valley RV Park/rest, **W** 🚗 BP, Marathon/Wendy's/dsl, Marathon/Chester's, Shell, 🍴 Arby's, Denny's, Godfather's/Subway, KFC, McDonald's, Rock Fire Steaks, 🏨 Days Inn, EconoLodge, 🅾 �H, Rite Aid, to Big South Fork NRA, Lake Cumberland

pyright 2012 - The Next Exit®   🛢 = gas   🍴 = food   🛏 = lodging   🅾 = other

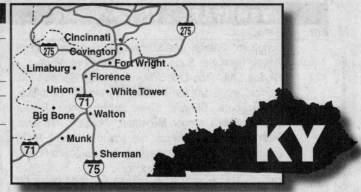

INTERSTATE 75 CONT'D

Exit	Services
59	US 25, to Livingston, Mt Vernon, **E** 🛢 BP, Shell/dsl, TravelCtr/dsl, 🍴 El Cazador Mexican, Pizza Hut, 🛏 Kastle Inn, **W** 🛢 BP, 🍴 Shakers Pizza, 🛏 Mtn View Inn
51mm	Rockcastle River
49	KY 909, to US 25, Livingston, **E** 🅾 Camp Wildcat BFD, **W** 🛢 49er/dsl/24hr, 🅾 RV Park, truck/tire repair
41	rd 80, to Somerset, London, **E** 🛢 Speedway, 🍴 Arby's, Azteca Mexican, Burger King, KFC, McDonald's, Sonic, White Castle, 🛏 Days Inn, EconoLodge, Quality Inn, Red Roof Inn, Super 8, 🅾 🅷 Advance Parts, AutoZone, CVS Drug, $General, Family$, Kroger/deli, Parsley's Tire/repair, st police, **W** 🛢 BP/rest/dsl/24hr, Clark/dsl, Marathon/McDonald's, Shell/pizza, 🍴 Cracker Barrel, LJ Silver, Shiloh Roadhouse, Subway, Taco Bell, Waffle House, Wendy's, 🛏 Budget Host, Hampton Inn, 🅾 Dog Patch Ctr, Westgate RV Camping
38	rd 192, to Rogers Pkwy, London, **E** 🛢 BP/dsl, Marathon, Shell/Quiznos/dsl, Speedway/dsl, 🍴 Big Boy, Burger King, Capt D's, DQ, Dino's Italian, Domino's, El Dorado Mexican, Fazoli's, Golden Corral, Great Wall Chinese, Hardee's, Huddle House, Krystal, McDonald's, Pizza Hut, Ruby Tuesday, Starbucks, Steak'n Shake, Taco Bell, 🛏 Baymont Inn, Comfort Suites, Country Inn&Suites, Holiday Inn Express, Microtel, 🅾 🅷 Advance Parts, $Tree, E Kentucky RV Ctr, K-Mart, Kroger/dsl, Lowe's, Nissan, Office Depot, Peterbilt, Radio Shack, USPO, Verizon, Walgreens, Walmart/Subway, 🖂, camping, Rogers Pkwy to Manchester/Hazard, to Levi Jackson SP, **W** to Laurel River Lake RA
34mm	**weigh sta both lanes, truck haven**
30.5mm	Laurel River
29	US 25, US 25E, Corbin, **E** 🛢 Marathon, Murphy USA, 🚚/McDonald's/Subway/dsl/scales/24hr, Stop-N-Go, 🍴 DQ, David's Steaks, Huddle House, Mi Jalisco Mexican, Shoney's, Taco Bell, 🛏 Super 8, 🅾 Aldi Foods, Blue Beacon, Lowe's, Radio Shack, Walmart/Subway, to Cumberland Gap NP, **W** 🛢 BP/Krystal/dsl, ♥Loves /Hardee's/dsl/scales/24hr/@, Marathon, Shell/dsl, 🍴 Cracker Barrel, Sonny's BBQ, 🛏 Baymont Inn, Comfort Suites, Fairfield Inn, Hampton Inn, Knights Inn, 🅾 KOA, tires/repair, to Laurel River Lake RA
25	US 25W, Corbin, **E** 🛢 Speedway/dsl, 🍴 Applebee's, Buckner's Grill, Burger King, McDonald's, O'Mally's, Wendy's, 🛏 Country Inn&Suites, Days Inn, Holiday Inn Express, Landmark Inn, 🅾 🅷 auto repair/tires, **W** 🛢 Shell/24hr, 🍴 Arby's, El Dorado Mexican, Jade China Buffet, Subway, Waffle House, 🛏 Best Western, Mtn View Lodge, 🅾 to Cumberland Falls SP
15	US 25W, to Williamsburg, Goldbug, **W** 🛢 Shell, Xpress/dsl, 🅾 Cumberland Falls SP
14.5mm	Cumberland River
11	KY 92, Williamsburg, **E** 🛢 BP/dsl, Shell, 🍴 Arby's, El Dorado Mexican, Hardee's, KFC, Little Caesars, McDonald's, Pizza Hut, Sonic, Subway, Taco Bell, 🛏 Cumberland Inn, Scottish Inn, Super 8, 🅾 Advance Parts, AutoZone, $General, Family$, Radio Shack, Sav-A-Lot, Windham Drug, museum, **W** 🛢 Shell/dsl, 🚚/Wendy's/dsl/scales/24hr, 🍴 Burger King, Huddle House, Krystal, LJ Silver, 🛏 Hampton Inn, 🅾 Walmart, to Big South Fork NRA
1.5mm	**Welcome Ctr nb, full ♿ facilities, 🚻, 🖼, vending, litter barrels, petwalk**
0mm	Kentucky/Tennesee state line

INTERSTATE 275 (CINCINNATI)

Exit	Services
84	I-75, I-71, N to Cincinnati, S to Lexington, Louisville
83	US 25, US 42, US 127, **S** 🛢 Shell/dsl, Speedway, Thorntons, 🍴 Abuelo's Mexican, Burger King, Carrabba's, Coldstone, Donato's Pizza, 5 Guys Burgers, John Phillip's Rest., KFC, Max&Erma's, McAlister's Deli, McDonald's, Moe's SW Grill, Panera Bread, Pizza Hut, Starbucks, Subway, Taco Bell, Wendy's, 🅾 Dillard's, $Tree, GNC, K-Mart, Walgreens
82	rd 1303, Turkeyfoot Rd, **S** 🅷
80	KY 17, Independence, **N** 🛢 Speedway/dsl, United/dsl, 🍴 Arby's, Big Boy, Bob Evans, Buffalo Wild Wings, Burger King, Golden Corral, Hot Wok, Penn Sta Subs, Snappy Tomato Pizza, Subway, TX Roadhouse, Wendy's, 🅾 TireDiscounters, Walmart, **S** 🛢 Thorntons/dsl, 🍴 McDonald's, 🅾 Chevrolet
79	KY 16, Taylor Mill Rd, **N** 🛢 BP, Marathon, Speedway, 🍴 Goldstar Chili, LJ Silver, McDonald's, Wendy's, 🅾 BigLots, CVS Drug, $Tree, Kroger/gas, Radio Shack, Walgreens, **S** 🛢 BP/dsl, 🍴 KFC/Taco Bell, McDonald's, Oriental Wok, Skyline Chili, Subway, 🅾 Remke's Foods
77	KY 9, Maysville, Wilder, **N** 🛏 Hampton Inn, **S** 🛢 Mobil/dsl, Thorntons/dsl, 🍴 DQ, Goldstar Chili, McDonald's, Waffle House
74a	Alexandria, to US 27, (exits left from sb)
74b	I-471 N, Newport, Cincinnati, **N** 🅷
73mm	OH/KY state line, OH River
72	US 52 W, Kellogg Ave, **S** 🛢 Marathor 🖂
71	US 52 E, New Richmond
69	5 Mile Rd **W** 🛢 BP/dsl, 🍴 Big Boy, IHOP, La Rosa's Mexican, McDonald's, TGIFriday's, Wendy's, 🅾 🅷, Kroger/gas
65	OH 125, Beechmont Ave, Amelia **E** 🛢 Mobil/dsl, Shell, Speedway, 🍴 Hibachi Grill, Hooters, Red Lobster, Wendy's, 🛏 Motel 6, 🅾 CarX, Ford, Lowe's, Tires+, Walgreens, **W** 🛢 BP, Speedway/dsl, Marathon, 🍴 Big Boy, Bob Evans, Burger King, Butterbee's Grille, Chick-fil-A, Chipotle Mexican, Dos Amigo's Mexican, McDonald's, Olive Garden, Smokey Bones BBQ, Starbucks, White Castle, 🛏 Best Western, Days Inn, Red Roof Inn, 🅾 Aldi Foods, AT&T, BigLots, $Tree, Goodyear/auto, Hancock Fabrics, Home Depot, Honda, Kroger, Staples, Sumerel Tire/repair, Target, TireDiscounters, TJ Maxx, Toyota/Scion, Verizon
63b a	OH 32, Batavia, Newtown, **W** 🛢 Marathon, Mobil, Thornton's, 🍴 Applebee's, Cheeseburger Paradise, Chick-fil-A, CiCi's Pizza, City BBQ, Bob Evans, Burger King, Fuji Steaks, Golden Corral, KFC, LJ Silver,

INTERSTATE 275 (CINCINNATI)

Exit	Services
	Longhorn, Steaks, Max&Erma's, McDonalds, Panera Bread, Penn Sta Subs, Perkins, Pizza Hut, Popeye's, Skyline Chili, Taco Bell, White Castle, 🛏 Comfort Inn, Fairfield Inn, Hampton Inn, Holiday Inn, 🅞 Best Buy, Bigg's Foods, Dillard's, $Tree, Hobby Lobby, Jo-Ann Fabrics, Kohl's, Kroger, Meijer/dsl, Michael's, PepBoys, Petsmart, Sam's Club/gas, Sears/auto, Walmart, **W** 🅖 Exxon, Marathon, Speedway/dsl, Sunoco, 🍴 La Rosa's Mexican, Roy Rogers, 🅞 Kroger
59	OH 452, US 50, Milford Pkwy, Hillsboro, **S** 🅖 Mobil, 🍴 Buffalo Wild Wings, Cracker Barrel, Goldstar Chili, Mio's Pizza, Quaker Steak&Lube, Red Robin, Ruby Tuesday, TX Roadhouse, Subway, Wendy's, 🛏 Homewood Suites, 🅞 Office Depot, Petsmart, Target, Walmart
57	OH 28, Blanchester, Milford, **0-1 mi N** 🍴 Applebee's, Arby's, Burger King, Chipotle Mexican, DQ, Dunkin Donuts, Goldstar Chili, IHOP, Panera Bread, Skyline Chili, Sonic, Subway, Steak'n Shake, Taco Bell, Wendy's, White Castle, 🅞 Home Depot, K-Mart, Kroger/gas, Lowe's, Meijer/dsl, **S** 🅖 Exxon, Shell, Speedway, Thorntons/dsl, 🍴 Big Boy, Bob Evans, Cazadore's Mexican, Hong Kong Wok, Little Caesar's, McDonald's, Putter's Grill, Quiznos, Roosters Grill, 🛏 Holiday Inn Express, 🅞 🏥, BigLots, CVS Drug, $Tree, Goodyear/auto, Kroger/gas, Tires+, USPO, vet
54	Wards Corner Rd, **N** 🅖 BP, **S** 🅖 Mobil/dsl, 🍴 Big Boy, Dominos, Goldstar Chili, Subway, 🛏 Hilton Garden
53mm	Little Miami River
52	Loveland, Indian Hill, **N** 🅖 Circle K/dsl, Marathon, Shell, Speedway/dsl, 🍴 Arby's, Burger King, Dragon Wok, Penn Sta Subs, Pizza Hut, Starbucks, Subway, Taco Bell, Wendy's, 🅞 CVS Drug, Verizon, VW, Walgreens
50	US 22, OH 3, Montgomery, **N** 🅖 Shell, 🍴 Buffalo Wild Wings, Chili's, DQ, Donato's Pizza, Melting Pot, Panera Bread, Starbucks, Subway, Taco Casa, 🅞 Acura, GNC, Hyundai, Kroger, **S** 🍴 BP/dsl, Shell, 🍴 Goldstar Chili, La Rosa's, McDonald's, Merlot's Rest., Quiznos, Skyline Chili, Wendy's, 🅞 🏥
49	I-71 N to Columbus, S to Cincinnati
47	Reed Hartman Hwy, Blue Ash, **S** 🍴 Goldstar Chili, McDonald's, Starbucks, 🛏 Amerisuites, Comfort Suites, Doubletree
46	US 42, Mason, **N** 🅖 BP, 🍴 Perkins, McDonald's, Taco Bell, Wendy's, White Castle, 🛏 Holiday Inn, Motel 6, 🅞 CVS Drug, **S** 🅖 Marathon, Shell, Speedway, 🍴 Arby's, Schezwan House, Waffle House, 🛏 Days Inn, 🅞 Goodyear, Tire Discounters
44	Mosteller Rd, **S** 🛏 Homewood Suites
43b a	I-75, N to Dayton, S to Cincinnati
42	OH 747, Springdale, Glendale
41	OH 4, Springfield Pk, **N** 🅖 Shell, Sunoco, 🍴 Bahama Breeze, Carlo's Bistro, Pappadeaux, 🛏 Baymont Inn, Ramada Inn, **S** 🅖 BP, Shell, 🍴 Applebee's, Big Boy, DQ, Penn Station Subs, Perkins, Ponderosa, Rosita's Mexican, White Castle, Wok'n Roll, 🛏 Extended Stay, Howard Johnson, Super 8, Holiday Inn Express, 🅞 Dillard's, Sears
39	Winton Rd, Winton Woods, **N** 🅖 BP, 🍴 Bob Evans, Chipotle Mexican, Golden Corral, IHOP, McDonald's,

Exit	Services
39	Continued Old Spagetti Factory, Panera Bread, Red Lobster, Roadhouse Grill, Ruby Tuesday, Ryan's, Steak'n Shake, 🛏 Hampton Inn, 🅞 Bass Pro Shops, Bigg's Foods, Home Depot, K-Mart, Kohl's, Meijer, Outdoor World, **S** 🅖 Marathon, Mobil, Shell, 🍴 Big Boy, Cracker Barrel, Fiesta Brava Mexican, Fuddrucker's, Popeye's, Skyline Chili, Subway, Wendy's, 🛏 Hyatt Place, Lee's Inn, 🅞 Goodyear, Jo-Ann Fabrics, Kroger/gas, Tires+, Walmart
36	US 127, Hamilton, Mt Healthy, **N** 🅖 Citgo, Speedway, 🍴 Skyline Chili, Wendy's, **S** 🅖 Sunoco, 🍴 Arby's, Big Boy, La Rosa's Pizza, McDonald's, Pizza Hut/Taco Bell, Subway, 🅞 Advance Parts, $General
33	US 27, US 126, Colerain Ave, **N** 🅖 BP, Speedway, 🍴 Burger King, Skyline Chili, Steak'n Shake, Wendy's, 🅞 Colerain RV Ctr, Walmart, **S** 🅖 Shell, 🍴 Arby's, Big Boy, Bob Evans, Cici's Pizza, KFC, LJ Silver, McDonald's, Olive Garden, Outback Steaks, Pizza Hut, Red Lobster, TGIFriday, White Castle, 🛏 Red Carpet Inn, 🅞 Isuzu, Kia, Macy's, Walgreens
31	Ronald Reagan Hwy, Blue Rock Rd
28	I-74, US 52, E to Cincinnati, W to Indianapolis
24	I-74, E to Cincinnati, W to Indianapolis
21	Kilby Rd, **W** 🅞 Indian Springs Camping (3mi)
18 mm	Ohio/Indiana State Line
16	US 50, Greendale, Lawrenceburg, **W** 🅖 Ameristop/dsl, Marathon/dsl, Shell/Circle K/Subway, 🍴 Buffalo's Cafe, Burger King, KFC, McDonald's, 🛏 Comfort Inn, Holiday Inn Express, Quality Inn, Riverside Inn, 🅞 Buick/Chevrolet/GMC, Chrysler/Dodge/Jeep, Ford, TireDiscounters, Walgreens, casino
14mm	Kentucky/Indiana state line, Ohio River
11	Petersburg
8b a	KY 237, Hebron, **N** 🅖 BP/DQ/dsl, Mobil/dsl, 🍴 Arby's, Beef'O'Brady's, China Wok, Edwardo's Pizza/Subs, El Mariachi, Jimmy John's, Penn Sta Subs, Vintage Deli, Wendy's, 🅞 Remke's Foods, **S** 🅖 Shell/Subway/dsl, 🍴 Bruster's, Burger King, Goldstar Chili, Waffle House
4a b	KY 212, KY 20, **N** 🅖 ValAir Gas, 🛏 Comfort Suites, Country Inn&Suites, Hampton Inn, Marriott, **S** 🛏 DoubleTree, 🅞 🏥, ✈
2	Mineola Pike, **N** 🅖 Mobil/Rally's/Subway/dsl, 🛏 Holiday Inn, Quality Inn, **S** 🛏 Courtyard Inn, Residence Inn

LOUISIANA

INTERSTATE 10

Exit	Services
274mm	Louisiana/Mississippi state line, Pearl River
272mm	West Pearl River
270mm	**Welcome Ctr wb, full ♿ facilities, info, 🚻, 🧺, litter barrels, petwalk, RV dump**
267b	I-12 W, to Baton Rouge
267a	I-59 N, to Meridian
266	US 190, Slidell, **N** 🅖 RaceTrac/dsl, Shell/dsl, TA/dsl/rest./scales/24hr/@, Valero, 🍴 Arby's, Baskin-Robbins, Cane's Rest., Chesterfield Grill, Chick-fil-A, Copeland's Rest., Golden Dragon Chinese, KFC, Los Tres Amigos, McDonald's, Panda Express, Quiznos, Retro Grill, Shoney's, Sonic, Subway, Taco Bell, Wendy's, 🛏 Best Value Inn, Best Western, Deluxe Motel, Motel 6, 🅞 🏥, Curves, CVS Drug, Firestone/auto, Harley-Davidson, Hobby Lobby,

KY

LA

245	Continued
	Home Depot, Nissan, PepBoys, Rite Aid, Tire Kingdom, Toyota/Scion, Walgreens
244	Read Blvd, N ⛽ Shell, 🍴 McDonald's, S ⛽ EZ Stop/dsl, 🍴 Popeye's, Subway, Wendy's, 🛏 Best Value, Best Western, Days Inn, 🅾 🎗, Lowe's, urgent care
242	Crowder Blvd, N ⛽ Chevron, S ⛽ Crowder Ctr, Exxon, 🍴 Subway, 🛏 Quality Inn, 🅾 Walgreens
241	Morrison Rd, N ⛽ Big E-Z/dsl
240b a	US 90 E, Chef Hwy, Downman Rd, N ⛽ Shell/dsl, 🛏 Super 8, 🅾 Chevrolet, U-Haul, USPO, S ⛽ Chevron/dsl, DZ, 🅾 Delta Tires
239b a	Louisa St, Almonaster Blvd, N ⛽ Chevron/dsl, FuelZone/dsl, 🍴 Burger King, Church's, McDonald's, Popeyes, Rally's, Subway, Taco Bell, Waffle House, Wendy's, 🛏 EconoLodge, Motel 6, 🅾 $General, Family$, Goodyear/auto, Home Depot, Walgreens, Winn-Dixie, S ⛽ Day&Night/dsl
238b	I-610, W (from wb)
237	Elysian Fields Ave, N 🅾 Lowe's
236c	St. Bernard Ave
236b	LA 39, N Claiborne Ave
236a	Esplanade Ave, downtown
235a	Orleans Ave, to Vieux Carre, French Qtr, S ⛽ Chevron, 🛏 Clarion, Marriott, Sheraton
235b	Poydras St, N 🎗, S to Superdome, downtown
234a	US 90A, Claiborne Ave, to Westbank Superdome
232	US 61, Airline Hwy, Tulane Ave, N 🍴 Burger King, S on Carolton ⛽ Exxon, Shell, 🍴 KFC, McDonald's, Popeye's, Rallys, 🅾 Family$, Pepboys, USPO, vet, to Xavier U
231b	Florida Blvd, WestEnd
231a	Metairie Rd
230	I-610, E (from eb), to Slidell
229	Bonnabel Blvd
228	Causeway Blvd, N ⛽ Exxon, Shell/dsl, 🍴 Burger King, Outback Steaks, PF Chang's, Red Lobster, TGIFriday's, 🛏 Best Western, Hampton Inn, Ramada, 🅾 Dillard's, Macy's, Old Navy, Whole Foods Mkt, S ⛽ DZ, Exxon, 🍴 IHOP, 🛏 Courtyard, Days Inn, Extended Stay America, Holiday Inn, La Quinta, Residence Inn, Sheraton
226	Clearview Pkwy, Huey Long Br, N ⛽ Chevron/dsl, Exxon, 🍴 Cafe Dumonde, Chili's, Copeland's Cheesecake Bistro, Corky's BBQ, Don's Seafood Hut, Hooters, Jimmy John's, Popeye's, Quiznos, Semolina's, Starbucks, Taco Bell, Taco Tico, Webster's Rest., 🛏 Sleep Inn, 🅾 Ford/Lincoln, Hancock Fabrics, Sears/auto, Target, Tire Kingdom, Walgreens, S ⛽ Chevron, Danny&Clyde, 🍴 Beijing Chinese, Burger King, Piccadilly, Shoney's, Smoothie King, Subway, TCBY, 🛏 Sun Suites, Super 8, 🅾 🎗, AT&T, Buick/GMC, Firestone/auto
225	Veterans Blvd, N ⛽ Chevron, DZ, Shell, 🍴 Burger King, Cuco's Mexican, Denny's, McDonald's, Subway, 🛏 La Quinta, 🅾 CVS Drug, Honda, Radio Shack, Rite Aid, Rouses Mkt, urgent care, S ⛽ DZ, Shell, 🍴 Casa Garcia, ChuckeCheese, Little Caesars, Louisiana

E ↑ W | S L I D E L L

INTERSTATE 10 CONT'D

Exit	Services
266	Continued
	Office Depot, O'Reilly Parts, PepBoys, Radio Shack, Rouses Mkt, U-Haul, Verizon, S ⛽ Chevron/Subway/dsl, Murphy USA, RaceTrac/dsl, 🍴 Applebee's, Big Easy Diner, Cracker Barrel, McAlister's Deli, Outback Steaks, Ruby Tuesday, Sonic, Starbucks, TX Roadhouse, Waffle House, 🛏 Days Inn, La Quinta, Relax Inn, Value Inn, 🅾 🎗, AT&T, Home Depot, Lowe's, Walmart/Subway, repair/transmissions, casino, vet
265	US 190, Fremaux Ave
263	LA 433, Slidell, N ⛽ Exxon, Shell/dsl, 🍴 China Buffet, Waffle House, 🛏 Hampton Inn, Super 8, 🅾 Hyundai, repair, S ⛽ Kangaroo/Subway/scales/dsl, Texaco/dsl, 🍴 McDonald's, Wendy's, 🛏 Holiday Inn, 🅾 Buick/GMC, Chevrolet, Chrysler/Dodge/Jeep, Ford/Lincoln, Honda, Kia, Nissan, Pinecrest RV Park, Toyota/Scion, Slidell Factory Outlet/famous brands, KOA (1mi)
261	Oak Harbor Blvd, Eden Isles, N ⛽ Exxon/dsl, 🍴 Waffle House, 🛏 Sleep Inn, S ⛽ Shell/Subway/dsl, 🅾 Bayou Country Store
255mm	Lake Pontchartrain
254	US 11, to Northshore, Irish Bayou, S ⛽ Texaco/dsl
251	Bayou Sauvage NWR, S swamp tours
248	Michoud Blvd
246b a	I-510 S, LA 47 N, S to Chalmette, N to Little Woods
245	Bullard Ave, N ⛽ Chevron, Shell, 🛏 Comfort Suites, Holiday Inn Express, 🅾 Honda, S ⛽ Chevron, Shell, 🍴 Burger King, IHOP, KFC/Taco Bell, McDonald's, Papa John's, Subway, Super Cajun Seafood, 🛏 La Quinta, Motel 6, 🅾 BigLots, Chrysler/Dodge/Jeep, Ford,

N E W   O R L E A N S   A R E A

LA

INTERSTATE 10 CONT'D

E → W — NEW ORLEANS AREA

Exit	Services
225	Continued Purchase Kitchen, New Orleans Burgers, O'Henry's, Popeye's, Subway, Tiffin Pancakes, Wendy's, 🛏 Evergreen Inn, Sheraton, Ⓞ Acura, Best Buy, BigLots, BMW, Chevrolet, $General, GNC, Home Depot, Jo-Ann Fabrics, Kia, K-Mart, Lexus, Nissan, Office Depot, PepBoys, Petsmart, TJ Maxx, Verizon, VW, Walgreens, Walmart, vet
224	Power Blvd (from wb)
223b a	LA 49, Williams Blvd, N 🛢 DZ/dsl, Exxon, Shell, 🍴 Cafe Dumonde, Cane's Chicken, Casa Tequila, Fisherman's Cove, IHOP, Papa's Pizza, Popeye's, Rally's, Sakura Asian, Subway, Taquiera Jalisco, Taco Bell, Wendy's, 🛏 Fairfield Inn, Ⓞ AutoZone, Dillards, $Tree, Family$, Ford, Macy's, Office Depot, PetCo, Rite Aid, Save-a-Lot Foods, Target, TrueValue, Walmart Mkt, S 🛢 Exxon/dsl, Shell, 🍴 American Pie Diner, Brick Oven, Dot's Diner, KFC/LJ Silver, McDonald's, Prime Time Steaks/Seafood, Sonic, Taco Tico, Subway, 🛏 🔄 Inn, Comfort Suites, Contempra Inn, Country Inn&Suites, Crowne Plaza, DoubleTree, EconoLodge, La Quinta, Ⓞ CVS Drug, $General, Family$, Firestone/auto, Goodyear/auto, NAPA, Toyota/Scion, U-Haul, Winn-Dixie, USPO
221	Loyola Dr, N 🛢 Chevron, Circle K, Exxon/dsl, Shell/dsl, 🍴 Church's, McDonald's, Piccadilly, Popeye's, Rally's, Taco Bell, Ⓞ Advance Parts, Sam's Club/gas, S 🛢 Citgo/dsl, DZ, 🍴 Wendy's, 🛏 Sleep Inn, Ⓞ Family$, Super Foods, 🔄, info
220	I-310 S, to Houma
214mm	Lake Pontchartrain
210	I-55N (from wb)
209	I-55 N, US 51, to Jackson, LaPlace, Hammond, N 🛢 Shell/Huddle House/casino/dsl, 🛏 Suburban Lodge, S 🛢 Chevron, Circle K/dsl, 🛢/Subway/dsl/24hr/scales, Shell/dsl, 🍴 Bully's Seafood, Burger King, McDonald's, Shoney's, Waffle House, Wendy's, 🛏 Best Western, Days Inn, Hampton Inn, Holiday Inn Express, Quality Inn
207mm	**weigh sta both lanes**
206	LA 3188 S, La Place, S 🛢 Shell/dsl, Ⓞ Ⓗ, Chrysler/Dodge/Jeep, Ford, Goodyear/auto
194	LA 641 S, to Gramercy, **4-6 mi** S 🛢 Chevron, Shell, Taylors/dsl, 🍴 Golden Grove Rest, McDonald's, Popeye's, Ⓞ Ⓗ, **11-15 mi** S plantations
187	US 61, N to Sorrento, S to Gramercy
182	LA 22, Sorrento, N 🛢 Shell/Popeye's/dsl, Texaco/dsl, S 🛢 Chevron/Subway/dsl/scales/24hr, SJ/dsl, 🍴 McDonald's, Subway, Waffle House, Ⓞ tourist info
179	LA 44, Gonzales, N 🛢 Exxon/Popingo's Cafe/dsl, **1 mi** N Ⓞ Buick/GMC, $General, Fred's Store, Walgreens
177	LA 30, Gonzales, N 🛢 Cracker Barrel/dsl, Shell, 🍴 Burger King, Jack-in-the-Box, McDonald's, Outback Steaks, Shoney's, Taco Bell, Waffle House, 🛏 Best Western, Budget Inn, Clarion, Highland Inn, Western Inn, Ⓞ Ⓗ, Home Depot, S 🛢 Chevron, RaceTrac/dsl, Shell/dsl, 🍴 Chili's, Cracker Barrel, Don's Seafood Hut, KFC, Popeye's, Sonic, Starbucks, Subway, Wendy's, 🛏 Hampton Inn, Holiday Inn Express, Supreme Inn, TownePlace Suites, Ⓞ Cabela's, Tanger/famous brands, Vesta RV Park
173	LA 73, to Geismar, Prairieville, N 🛢 Shell/dsl, S 🛢 Chevron/dsl, Conoco/dsl, Exxon/TCBY/dsl, Mobil/McDonald's/dsl, RaceTrac/dsl, 🍴 Burger King, Griffin Grill, Godfather's Pizza, Good Eats Cafe, Hot Wok, Las Palmas Mexican,

BATON ROUGE

Exit	Services
173	Continued Papa Murphy's, Pizza Hut, Popeye's, Smoothie King, Sonic, Subway, Ⓞ Curves, Family$, Harvest Foods, Twin Lakes RV Park (1mi), Walgreens
166	LA 42, LA 427, Highland Rd, Perkins Rd, N 🛢 Chevron/Church's/dsl, Exxon/dsl, 🍴 Church's, Las Palmas Mexican, Popeye's, Sonic, Starbucks, Waffle House, Ⓞ Goodyear/auto, Home Depot, funpark, S 🛢 Shell/BBQ, Texaco/dsl, 🍴 Subway
163	Siegen Lane, N 🛢 Chevron/dsl, RaceTrac/dsl, Shell, Circle K, 🍴 Arby's, Burger King, Cane's, Chee Burger, Chick-fil-A, China 1, CiCi's Pizza, Hooter's, IHOP, Jason's Deli, McAlister's, McDonald's, Olive Garden, Pancho's Mexican, Pizza Hut/Taco Bell, Quiznos, Ribs Chophouse, Smoothie King, Subway, Twin Peaks Rest., Waffle House, Whataburger, 🛏 Best Western, Days Inn, Hampton Inn, Holiday Inn Express, La Quinta, Microtel, Motel 6, Super 8, Ⓞ Advance Parts, AT&T, BigLots, Cadillac, CarMax, $Tree, Firestone/auto, Harley-Davidson, Honda, Kia, Office Depot, PetCo, Radio Shack, Saab, Target, Verizon, S 🍴 Backyard Burger, Chili's, ChuckeCheese, Joe's Crabshack, TX Roadhouse, Zapata's Mexican, 🛏 Courtyard, Residence Inn, Ⓞ BooksAMillion, Kohl's, Lowe's/Subway, Old Navy, Petsmart, Sam's Club/gas, Old Navy, TJ Maxx, Walmart/Subway
162	Bluebonnet Rd, N 🛢 Chevron/dsl, 🍴 Cadillac Cafe, Kabuki Japanese, 🛏 Quality Suites, Ⓞ vet, S 🛢 Raceway, 🍴 BJ's Brewhouse, Bravo Italiano, Copeland's Cheesecake Bistro, J Alexander's, King Buffet, Logan's Roadhouse, Pluckers Wing Bar, Ralph&Kacoo's, Red Lobster, Sake Cafe, 🛏 Hyatt Place, Ⓞ Best Buy, Dick's, Dillard's, JC Penney, Macy's, Sears/auto, Mall of LA, mall, World Mkt, Ⓗ
160	LA 3064, Essen Lane, S 🛢 Exxon, RaceTrac/dsl, Valero, 🍴 Burger King, Copeland's Bistro, Domino's, McDonald's, Piccadilly, Popeye's, Quiznos, Sakura Hibachi, Smoothie King, Subway, Taco Bell, Times Grill, Wasabi Grill, Wendy's, 🛏 Drury Inn, Fairfield Inn, Springhill Suites, Ⓞ Albertson's, $General, Firestone, O'Reilly Parts, Rite Aid, Tire Kingdom, Walgreens, Ⓗ
159	I-12 E, to Hammond
158	College Dr, Baton Rouge, N 🛢 Valero, 🍴 Alabasha Café, Cane's, CiCi's, Coto Rest., Fox&Hound Grill, Hooters, Izzo's Grill, Jason's Deli, Mansurs Rest., Marble Slab Creamery, Melting Pot, On-the-Border, Ruby Tuesday, Subway, Sullivan's Rest., Waffle House, Wendy's, 🛏 Best Western, Chase Suites, Extended Stay America, Homewood Suites, Marriott, Ⓞ Ⓗ, Barnes&Noble, S 🛢 Chevron/24hr, Exxon, Shell/Circle K, 🍴 Casa Maria Mexican, Chick-fil-A, Chili's, Gino's Rest., Great Wall Chinese, IHOP, McDonald's, Ninfa's Mexican, Ruth's Chris Steaks, Sporting News Grill, Starbucks, Taco Bell, 🛏 Aspen Suites, Comfort Inn, Comfort Suites, Crowne Plaza, Embassy Suites, Hampton Inn, Holiday Inn, Holiday Inn Express, Ⓞ Albertson's/Sav-On, AutoZone, $Tree, Hobby Lobby, Office Depot, Radio Shack, Walgreens, Walmart/Subway
157b	Acadian Thwy, N 🛢 Chevron, Shell/Circle K, 🍴 Mestizo's Grill, Rib's Rest., 🛏 La Quinta, Radisson, Ⓞ Ⓗ, S 🛢 Shell/Circle K, 🍴 Acme Oyster House, Coyote Blues Mexican, Outback Steaks, 🛏 Courtyard, Ⓞ AT&T, CVS Drug, Tuesday Morning
157a	Perkins Rd (from eb), same as 157b
156b	Dalrymple Dr, S to LSU

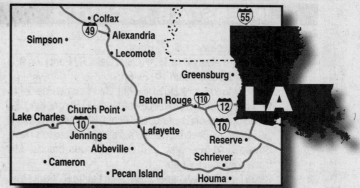

INTERSTATE 10 CONT'D

E ↕ W

Exit	Services
156a	Washington St
155c	Louise St (from wb)
155b	I-110 N, to Baton Rouge bus dist 🖐
155a	LA 30, Nicholson Dr, Baton Rouge, N Belle Hotel, S to LSU
154mm	Mississippi River
153	LA 1, Port Allen, N 📱 Chevron, Shell/Circle K/dsl, 🍴 Church's, ⊙ AutoZone, Family$, Kenworth, repair, S 📱 Chevron, LA 1S Truck Plaza/Exxon/Casino/dsl/24hr, RaceTrac/dsl, 🍴 Quiznos, Smoothie King, Waffle House, 🛏 EconoLodge, ⊙ AT&T, $Tree, Walmart/Subway
151	LA 415, to US 190, N 📱 Cash's Trk Plaza/dsl/scales/casino, Chevron, Exxon/dsl, Gold Mine/Domino's/dsl/casino, Nino's Trkstp/casino, Shell/Blimpie/dsl, 🍴 Burger King, KFC/Taco Bell, McDonald's, Popeye's, Waffle House, 🛏 Best Western, Comfort Suites, Hampton Inn, Holiday Inn Express, Quality Inn, West Inn, S 📱 Loves/Arby's/dsl/scales/24hr, Shell/dsl/24hr, 🛏 Audubon Inn, Motel 6, Super 8, ⊙ truck repair
139	LA 77, Grosse Tete, N 📱 Shell/Subway/dsl, ⊙ Chevrolet, casino, S 📱 Tiger/Conoco/dsl/rest./@
135	LA 3000, to Ramah
127	LA 975, to Whiskey Bay
126.5mm	Pilot Channel of Whiskey Bay
122mm	Atchafalaya River
121	Butte La Rose, **visitors ctr/rest area, both lanes, full facilities**, 🖐, **litter barrels, vending, petwalk, tourist info,** S 🍴 Lazy Cajun Grill (2mi), ⊙ Frenchman's Wilderness Camground (.5mi)
115	LA 347, to Cecilia, Henderson, N 📱 Exxon/dsl/24hr, Shamrock, Texaco/dsl, 🍴 Chicken on the Bayou, Landry's Seafood, 🛏 Holiday Inn Express, ⊙ casinos, S 📱 Chevron/dsl, Exxon/Subway/dsl, Shell/McDonald's, Texaco/dsl, Valero, 🍴 Popeye's, Waffle House
109	LA 328, to Breaux Bridge, N 📱 Shell/dsl, Texaco/grill/dsl/casino, 🛏 Microtel, ⊙ Poaches RV Park, S 📱 Chevron/Popeye's/dsl, Exxon/Domino's/dsl, 🚚/Arby's/dsl/scales/24hr, 🍴 Burger King, City Buffet, Crazy Bout Cajun, McDonald's, Mulate's, Pizza Hut, Sonic, Taco Bell, Waffle House, Wendy's, Zapote Mexican, 🛏 Bayou Cabins B&B, Sona Inn, Super 8, ⊙ Chevrolet, $General, $Tree, Family$, Ford/Lincoln, O'Reilly Parts, Pioneer Camping, Walgreens, Walmart/Subway, Winn-Dixie, city park
108mm	**weigh sta both lanes**
104	Louisiana Ave, S 🍴 Chick-fil-A, Subway, Taco Bell, ⊙ AT&T, GNC, JC Penney, Office Depot, PetCo, Ross, Target
103b	I-49 N, to Opelousas
103a	US 167 S, to Lafayette, US 167 S 📱 Chevron/dsl/24hr, Murphy USA/dsl, RaceTrac/dsl, Shell/dsl, Valero, 🍴 Checker's, KFC, McDonald's, Pizza Hut, Popeye's, Shoney's, Subway, Taco Bell, Waffle House, 🛏 Best Western, Comfort Inn, EconoLodge, Fairfield Inn, Holiday Inn, Howard Johnson, Jameson Inn, La Quinta, Quality Inn, Royal Inn, Super 8, TravelHost Inn, ⊙ H, Albertson's, CVS Drug, Home Depot, Super 1 Foods/gas, Walmart/Subway, transmissions
101	LA 182, to Lafayette, N 📱 Chevron/McDonald's, TA/Country Pride/dsl/scales/24hr/@, Shell, Valero/Subway/dsl, 🍴 Burger King, Waffle House, Whataburger, 🛏 Red Roof Inn, S 📱 Exxon, RaceTrac/dsl, Shell/dsl, Texaco, 🍴 Cracker Barrel, 🛏 Best Value Inn, Days Inn, Drury Inn,

LAFAYETTE

101	Continued
	Hilton Garden (2mi), Peartree Inn, ⊙ H, $General, Family$, Kia/Suzuki, O'Reilly Parts
100	Ambassador Caffery Pkwy, N 📱 Exxon/Subway/dsl/24hr, ⊙ Curves, Gauthier's RV Ctr, Peterbilt, S 📱 Chevron/dsl, RaceTrac/dsl, Shell, 🍴 Burger King, McDonald's, Pizza Hut/Taco Bell, Sonic, Waffle House, Wendy's, 🛏 Ambassador Inn, Hampton Inn, Sleep Inn, Microtel, ⊙ H, tires
97	LA 93, to Scott, S 📱 Chevron/McDonald's, Shell/Church's/dsl/24hr, 🍴 Fezzo's Seafood, Rochetto's Pizza, 🛏 Comfort Inn, Holiday Inn Express, Howard Johnson, ⊙ Harley-Davidson, KOA
92	LA 95, to Duson, N 📱 Exxon/dsl/casino/RV dump/scales/24hr, S 📱 Chevron/dsl, Roadies/cafe/dsl/casino, Shell/Subway/dsl/casino, 🛏 Super 8, ⊙ Frog City RV Park
87	LA 35, to Rayne, N 📱 Chevron/dsl, Shell/Subway/casino/dsl, 🍴 Burger King, Chef Roy's Rest., McDonald's, 🛏 Days Inn, ⊙ $General, RV camping, S 📱 Frog City/Exxon/dsl, Mobil/dsl, Shop Rite, Valero/dsl, 🍴 Candyland Ice Cream, DQ, Frog City Grill, Gabe's Café, Pizza Hut, Popeye's, Sonic, 🛏 Best Western, ⊙ H, Advance Parts, CVS Drug, Family$, O'Reilly Parts, Walgreens, Winn-Dixie
82	LA 1111, to, E Crowley, S 📱 Chevron/dsl, Murphy USA, 🍴 Chili's, Wendy's, ⊙ H, AT&T, $Tree, GNC, Lowe's, Radio Shack, Walgreens, Walmart/Subway
80	LA 13, to Crowley, N 📱 Conoco/Exit 80/dsl/rest./24hr, 🍴 Fezzo's Seafood/steaks, Waffle House, 🛏 Crowley Inn, Days Inn, La Quinta, S 📱 Chevron, Exxon, Raceway/dsl, Valero/dsl, 🍴 Burger King, Cajun Way, El Dorado Mexican, Gatti's Pizza, KFC, McDonald's, Mr Wok, Pizza Hut, PJ's Grill, Popeye's, Sonic, Subway, Taco Bell, ⊙ AutoZone, Chrysler/Dodge/Jeep, $General, Family$, Ford, O'Reilly Parts, Radio Shack, Rite Aid, Verizon, Winn-Dixie
76	LA 91, to Iota, S 📱 Petro/Shell/Subway/dsl/scales/24hr
72	Egan, N 🍴 Cajun Haven RV Park
65	LA 97, to Jennings, S 📱 Shell/dsl/casino, 🛏 Best Value
64	LA 26, to Jennings, N 🍴 Los Tres Potrillos, 🛏 Boudreaux Inn, ⊙ RV Park, S 📱 Exxon/dsl, EZ Mart, Murphy USA, Jennings Trvl Ctr/dsl/casino, Valero/dsl, 🍴 Burger King, Gatti's Pizza, General Wok Chinese, McDonald's, Pizza Hut, Popeye's, Shoney's, Sonic, Subway, Waffle House, Walker's Cajun Rest., Wendy's, 🛏 Days Inn, Hampton Inn, Red Carpet Inn, ⊙ H, AutoZone, Chrysler/Dodge/Jeep, $General, $Tree, Fred's Store, O'Reilly Parts, Radio Shack, Verizon, Walmart/Subway
59	LA 395, to Roanoke, N 📱 Petos TrvlCtr/Chevron/dsl/scales/24hr
54	LA 99, Welsh, S 📱 Circle R/Perky's Pizza, Cajun Lunch/dsl, Exxon/dsl/24hr, 🍴 Cajun Tales Seafood, DQ

CROWLEY
JENNINGS

LA

	INTERSTATE 10 CONT'D
Exit	**Services**
48	LA 101, Lacassine, **S** 🅖 Exxon
44	US 165, to Alexandria, **N** 🄾 Quiet Oaks RV Park (10mi), **S** 🍴 Rabideaux's Cajun, 🄾 RV Park
43	LA 383, to Iowa, **N** 🅖 Exxon/Pit Grill/Quiznos/dsl/24hr, ✦Loves✦/Hardee's/dsl/scales/24hr, 🍴 Burger King, 🛏 Howard Johnson Express, La Quinta, 🄾 United RV Ctr, **S** 🅖 Citgo/dsl, Shell/McDonald's, Valero, 🍴 Fausto's Rest., Subway, 🄾 $General, I-10 Outlet/famous brands, Mkt Basket Foods, RV park
36	LA 397, to Creole, Cameron, **N** Jean Lafitte RV Park (2mi), I-10 RV Camping, Jellystone Camping, **S** 🅖 Cash Magic/grill/dsl/RV Dump, Chevron/dsl, 🛏 Red Roof Inn, 🄾 casino, RV Camping
34	I-210 W, to Lake Charles
33	US 171 N, **N** 🅖 Citgo, Conoco/dsl, Exxon/dsl, Murphy USA/dsl, Shell, Tobacco Place, Valero, 🍴 Burger King, Church's, Subway, Taco Bell, 🛏 Baymont Inn, Best Value, Comfort Suites, La Quinta, Richmond Suites, 🄾 AutoZone, $General, Family$, O'Reilly Parts, Walgreens, Walmart/McDonalds, to Sam Houston Jones SP, **S** 🛏 Holiday Inn Express, Motel 6, Treasure Inn
32	Opelousas St, **N** 🅖 Exxon, **S** 🛏 Holiday Inn Express, Motel 6, Treasure Inn
31b	US 90 E, Shattuck St, to LA 14, **N** 🅖 Shell/cafe/dsl/casino
31a	US 90 bus, Enterprise Blvd, **S** 🍴 Popeye's
30b	downtown
30a	LA 385, N Lakeshore Dr, Ryan St, **N** 🅖 Exxon, 🍴 Steamboat Bill's Rest., Waffle House, 🛏 Days Inn, Oasis Inn, **S** 🅖 Citgo, 🍴 Wendy's, 🛏 Best Suites
29	LA 385 (from eb), same as 30a
28mm	Calcasieu Bayou, Lake Charles
27	LA 378, to Westlake, **N** 🅖 Chevron/dsl, Conoco/dsl, Shell/dsl, 🍴 Burger King, McDonald's, Popeye's, Sonic, Subway, 🄾 Bumper Parts, $General, O'Reilly Parts, to Sam Houston Jones SP, **S** 🛏 Inn at the Isle, 🄾 Riverboat Casinos
26	US 90 W, Southern Rd, Columbia, **N** 🅖 Circle K/gas
25	I-210 E, to Lake Charles
23	LA 108, to Sulphur, **N** 🅖 Circle K, Citgo, Exxon, Murphy USA, 🍴 Burger King, Cane's, Chili's, China Wok, McDonald's, Popeye's, Subway, Taco Bell, Wendy's, 🛏 Quality Inn, 🄾 $General, $Tree, Lowe's, Radio Shack, Walgreens, Walmart, **S** 🅖 Cash Magic/dsl, Chevron/Jack-in-the-Box/dsl, Sulfur Trkstp/Citgo/dsl, 🍴 Cracker Barrel, Waffle House, 🛏 Best Western, Days Inn, Comfort Suites, Crossland Suites, Holiday Inn Express, Super 8, 🄾 casino, tires
21	LA 3077, Arizona St, **N** 🅖 Conoco, Shell, 🍴 Boiling Point Cajun, China Taste, Papa John's, 🄾 AT&T, CVS Drug, $General, Ford, GNC, Kroger/gas, NAPA, Walgreens, vet, **S** 🅖 Chevron/dsl, Valero/dsl/casino, 🄾 Ⓗ, Hidden Ponds RV Park
20	LA 27, to Sulphur, **N** 🅖 Bayou, Chevron, Circle K, Conoco, Valero, 🍴 Burger King, Casa Ole Mexican, Cajun Charlie's, Checker's, Gatti's Pizza, Hollier's Cajun, Johnny T's Grill, McDonald's, Mr Bills Steaks, Pitt Grill Cajun, Popeye's, Subway, Taco Bell, Wendy's, 🛏 EconoLodge, Hampton Inn, Sulphur Inn, 🄾 Brookshire Bros/gas, Family$, Firestone/auto, Goodyear/auto, Jiffy Lube, **S** 🅖 Conoco/dsl, Shell/dsl, 🍴 Navroskey's Burgers, Pizza Hut, Sonic, Waffle House, 🛏 Baymont Inn, Candlewood Suites, Fairfield Inn, Holiday Inn, La Quinta, Microtel, Wingate Inn, 🄾 Ⓗ, Stine, casino, to Creole Nature Trail

8	LA 108, Vinton, **N** 🅖 Chevron/dsl, Exxon/dsl, 🍴 Cajun Cowboy's Rest., 🄾 V RV Park
7	LA 3063, Vinton, **N** 🅖 Exxon/dsl, 🍴 Burger King, Sonic, Subway, 🄾 $General, casino, **S** 🅖 ✦Loves✦/Arby's/dsl/scales/24hr
4	US 90, LA 109, Toomey, **N** 🅖 Cash Magic/dsl/grill/casino, Chevron/dsl/casino, 🄾 truck repair, **S** 🅖 Cash Magic, Exxon/dsl, Shell/dsl/rest, 🍴 Subway, 🄾 RV Park, casinos
2.5mm	weigh sta both lanes
1.5mm	Welcome Ctr eb, full ♿ facilities, 🄲, 🛋, litter barrels, petwalk
1	(from wb), Sabine River Turnaround
0mm	Louisiana/Texas state line, Sabine River

	INTERSTATE 12
Exit	**Services**
85c	I-10 E, to Biloxi. I-12 begins/ends on I-10, exit 267.
85b	I-59 N, to Hattiesburg
85a	I-10 W, to New Orleans
83	US 11, to Slidell, **N** 🅖 Chevron/dsl/24hr, Exxon/dsl, Freedom, 🍴 Burger King, McDonald's, Sonic, Waffle House, 🄾 $General, **S** 🅖 Ride USA/dsl, Shell, 🄾 Ⓗ
80	Airport Dr, North Shore Blvd, **N** 🅖 Kangaroo, 🍴 IHOP, PJ's Coffee, Quiznos, Sonic, 🄾 Petsmart, Ross, Target, 🅖 Chevron/24hr, Shell/dsl, 🍴 Burger King, Chili's, Chuck-eCheese, McDonald's, Olive Garden, Pizza Hut/Taco Bell, Starbucks, Subway, Wendy's, Vera's Seafood, 🛏 Candlewood Suites, La Quinta, 🄾 Best Buy, Dillard's, $Tree, Goodyear/auto, Home Depot, JC Penney, Marshall's, Office Depot, Sam's Club/gas, Sears/auto, Walmart, mall
74	LA 434, to Lacombe, **N** 🅖 Chevron/Subway/dsl, 🄾 Ⓗ, **S** Big Branch Marsh NWR
68	LA 1088, to Mandeville,
65	LA 59, to Mandeville, **N** 🅖 Chevron/dsl, Danny&Clyde's/cafe, Shell, 🍴 Sonic, Waffle House, **S** 🅖 Kangaroo/Arby's/dsl, Texaco/Domino's/dsl, 🍴 McDonald's, PJ's Coffee, Quiznos, 🄾 Winn-Dixie, to Fontainebleau SP, camping, vet
63b a	US 190, Covington, Mandeville, **N** 🅖 Chevron, Exxon, RaceTrac, Shell/Circle K, 🍴 Acme Oyster House, Applebee's, Bonefish Grill, Burger King, Cane's, Chick-fil-A, Copeland's Grill, 4 Seasons Chinese, Ground Pati, IHOP, Lee's Hamburgers, McAlister's Deli, Mellow Mushroom Cafe, Osaka Japanese, Outback Steaks, Picadilly, Pueblo Viejo, Sonic, Subway, Thai Chili, Waffle House, Wendy's, 🛏 Best Western, Comfort Inn, Country Inn&Suites, Courtyard, Hampton Inn, Holiday Inn, Homewood Suites, Residence Inn, 🄾 Ace Hardware, AT&T, AutoZone, Books-A-Million, Chevrolet, Chrysler/Dodge/Jeep, CVS Drug, Firestone/auto, GNC, Home Depot, Honda, Hyundai, Lowe's, Nissan, Office Depot, Petsmart, Rouses Mkt, Subaru, Suzuki, Toyota, Verizon, Walmart, **S** 🄾 Ⓗ, Chrysler, st police, to New Orleans via toll causeway
60	Pinnacle Pkwy, to Covington, **N** 🅖 TX Roadhouse, 🄾 $Tree, Hobby Lobby, Kohl's
59	LA 21, to Covington, Madisonville, **N** 🅖 Chevron/dsl, Kangaroo, Shell, 🍴 Carreta's Grill, Coldstone, Golden Wok, Isabella's Pizza, Italian Pie, Izzo's Burrito, Jerk's Island Grill, Lee's Hamburgers, McDonald's, Osaka Steaks, Smoothie King, Subway, TX Roadhouse, Wow Cafe, 🛏 La Quinta, 🄾 Ⓗ, URGENT CARE, CVS Drug, Hobby Lobby, Kohl's, Walgreens, Winn-Dixie, **S** 🅖 Texaco, 🍴 Chick-fil-A, Domino's, Longhorn Steaks, Moe's SW Grill

LAKE CHARLES

SULPHUR

LA

COVINGTON

INTERSTATE 12 CONT'D

Exit	Services
59	Continued
	Taco Bell, Wendy's, ⊙ AT&T, Belk, Best Buy, GNC, JC Penney, Marshall's, Ross, Target, World Mkt, Fairview Riverside SP
57	LA 1077, to Goodbee, Madisonville, S 🍴 Best Wok, PJ's Coffee, Subway, other:Family RV Park, to Fairview Riverside SP
47	LA 445, to Robert, **1-3 mi N** ⊙ Jellystone Camping, to Global Wildlife Ctr
42	LA 3158, to ✈, N ⛽ Chevron/dsl/24hr, 🍴 McDonald's, 🛏 Friendly Inn, ⊙ truck/trailer repair, truckwash, S ⛽ Shell/dsl, ⊙ H, Berryland RV Ctr
40	US 51, to Hammond, N ⛽ RaceTrac, Shell/Circle K/24hr, 🍴 Burger King, Cane's, China Garden, Church's, Coldstone, IHOP, McDonald's, Pizza Hut, Quiznos, Ryan's, Santa Fe Steaks, Smoothie King, Sonic, Subway, Taco Bell, Wendy's, 🛏 Best Western, Holiday Inn, Supreme Inn, ⊙ AT&T, Best Buy, Books-A-Million, Dillard's, Harley Davidson, JC Penney, Rite Aid, Sears/auto, Target, U-Haul, Walgreens, Verizon, mall, S ⛽ Petro/Mobil/Subway/dsl/scales/24hr/@, 🍴 Arby's/dsl/scales/24hr, Shell, 🍴 Waffle House, 🛏 Colonial Inn, Days Inn, ⊙ H, Blue Beacon, $General, KOA, SpeedCo
38b a	I-55, N to Jackson, S to New Orleans
37mm	**weigh sta both lanes**
35	Pumpkin Ctr, Baptist, N ⛽ Exxon/dsl, Texaco, ⊙ Dixie Camping World RV Service/Supplies, $General, Punkin RV Park (2mi), S ⛽ Chevron/Bayou Boyz/dsl/24hr
32	LA 43, to Albany, N ⛽ Chevron/Subway, Exxon/dsl, S ⛽ Potluck/dsl, ⊙ to Tickfaw SP, tourist info
29	LA 441, to Holden, N gas/dsl, ⊙ Berryland Campers, RV RestStop (1mi), st police
22	LA 63, to Frost, Livingston, N ⛽ Chevron/dsl, 🍴 Subway, Wayne's BBQ, ⊙ Carters Foods, Curves, Family$, S ⊙ Lakeside RV Park (1mi)
19	to Satsuma
15	LA 447, to Walker, N ⛽ Murphy Express/dsl, Shell/Subway/24hr, Texaco, 🍴 Burger King, Domino's, Jack-in-the-Box, McDonald's, Papa Johns, Popeye's, Sherwood PoBoy's, Sonic, Taco Bell, Waffle House, Wendy's, 🛏 La Quinta, ⊙ AutoZone, $Tree, NAPA, O'Reilly Parts, Walgreens, Walmart, Winn-Dixie, vet, S ⛽ Chevron/dsl
12	LA 1036, Juban Rd, **2 mi N** ⛽ Valero/dsl
10	LA 3002, to Denham Springs, N ⛽ Chevron, Circle K, RaceTrac, Shell/Circle K/dsl, 🍴 Arby's, Baskin-Robbins, Burger King, Cactus Café, Cane's, Chili's, Don's Seafood, Gatti's Pizza, IHOP, Papi's Fajita, Popeye's, Ryan's, Sonic, Starbucks, Subway, Waffle House, Wendy's, 🛏 Best Western, Hampton Inn, Quality Inn, Travel Inn, ⊙ Advance Parts, AT&T, CVS Drug, $General, $Tree, Firestone/auto, Home Depot, PetCo, Radio Shack, Rite Aid, Tire Kingdom, Verizon, Walmart, S ⛽ Pilot/Subway/dsl/scales/24hr, Shell, 🍴 Backyard Burger, Fish Co Rest., Hooters, Islamorada Fish Co, Longhorn Steaks, Piccadilly, Shoney's, Subway, 🛏 Days Inn, Highland Inn, ⊙ Bass Pro Shops, Dodge, Ford, KOA, Walgreens
8.5mm	Amite River
7	O'Neal Lane, N ⛽ Mobil, 🛏 Comfort Suites, La Quinta, ⊙ Hobby Lobby, Office Depot, Toyota/Scion, S ⛽ RaceTrac, Shell, 🍴 LA Boilers Seafood, Las Palmas Mexican,

7	Continued
	Little Caesars, LoneStar Steaks, McDonald's, Pizza Hut/Taco Bell, Popeye's, Sonic, Subway, Waffle House, Wendy's, ⊙ H, AutoZone, $Tree, Radio Shack, Walgreens, Walmart
6	Millerville Rd, N ⛽ Chevron/dsl/24hr, 🍴 Chick-fil-A, Chili's, ⊙ Best Buy, Lowe's, Office Depot, Petsmart, Super Target, S ⛽ Texaco/dsl, 🍴 Tiger Bait Grill, ⊙ Ace Hardware
4	Sherwood Forest Blvd, N ⛽ Exxon, Shell/Circl K/dsl, 🍴 Burger King, ChuckeCheese, Jack-in-the-Box, McDonald's, Popeye's, Sonic, Subway, Taco Bell, Waffle House, 🛏 Crossland Suites, Red Roof Inn, Super 8, Value Place, ⊙ Fred's, Goodyear/auto, Rite Aid, S ⛽ RaceTrac/dsl, Shell/24hr, 🍴 Baskin-Robbins, Cane's, Dos Hermanos Mexican, Nagoya, Picadilly, Pie Works, Pizza Hut, Podnuh's BBQ, Sherwood PoBoys, 🛏 Calloway Inn, ⊙ AT&T
2b	US 61 N, N ⛽ B-Quik, Chevron, Shell/Circle K, Rendes/dsl, 🍴 Applebee's, Chinese Inn, Cracker Barrel, McDonald's, Pizza Hut/Taco Bell, Subway, 🛏 Days Inn, Holiday Inn, Knights Inn, Microtel, Motel 6, Ramada Inn, Sleep Inn, ⊙ Albertsons/gas, Dodge, $Tree, Ford/Lincoln/Mercury, Hyundai, Marshall's, Michael's, Nissan, PepBoys, SteinMart, Suzuki, Toyota/Scion, Walgreens, Wal-Mart Mkt, repair/transmissions
2a	US 61 S, S ⛽ Chevron, Circle K/gas, Exxon/dsl, Ride USA, 🍴 Burger King, China 1, Isabella's Pizza, McDonald's, Subway, Waffle House, 🛏 Deluxe Inn, ⊙ Cadillac/Volvo, Home Depot
1b	LA 1068, to LA 73, Essen Lane, N ⛽ Shell/Circle K/dsl, 🍴 Cane's, McDonald's, VooDoo BBQ, ⊙ H, Family$, Hancock Fabrics, Hi-Nabor Foods, Radio Shack
1a	I-10 (from wb). I-12 begins/ends on I-10, exit 159 in Baton Rouge

INTERSTATE 20

Exit	Services
189mm	Louisiana/Mississippi state line, Mississippi River
187mm	**weigh sta both lanes**
186	US 80, Delta, S ⛽ Chevron/Subway/dsl/24hr
184mm	**rest area wb, full ♿ facilities, 📞, 🏪, litter barrels, petwalk, RV dump**
182	LA 602, Mound
173	LA 602, Richmond
171	US 65, Tallulah, N ⛽ Chevron/Subway/dsl, Kangaroo/dsl, 🍴 McDonald's, Wendy's, 🛏 Days Inn, Super 8, ⊙ H, S ⛽ Conoco/dsl/scales, Loves/Arby's/dsl/scales/24hr, TA/dsl/rest./scales/24hr/@, Texaco
164mm	Tensas River
157	LA 577, Waverly, N ⛽ Tiger Trkstp/dsl/rest./24hr, to Tensas River NWR, S ⛽ Chevron/Subway/24hr, Shell/dsl, ⊙ Casino

🅿 = gas 🍴 = food 🛏 = lodging 🅾 = other   Copyright 2012 - The Next Exit®

Exit	Services
	INTERSTATE 20 CONT'D
155mm	Bayou Macon
153	LA 17, Delhi, **N** 🅿 Chevron/Subway/dsl, Texaco/Chester's/dsl, 🍴 Burger King, Boomer's rest., China Garden, Pizza Hut, Sonic, 🅾 🅷, Brookshire's Foods, $General, Fred's Drugs, USPO, **S** 🅿 Valero/dsl, 🛏 Best Western, Executive Inn
148	LA 609, Dunn
145	LA 183, rd 202, Holly Ridge
141	LA 583, Bee Bayou Rd
138	LA 137, Rayville, **N** 🅿 Bud's, Wendy's/dsl/scales/24hr, 🍴 Johnny's Pizza, McDonald's, Sonic, 🛏 Days Inn, 🅾 🅷, AutoZone, Buick/Chevrolet, $General, Family$, Kaye's Foods, Walmart, **S** 🅿 Chevron/Subway/dsl/24hr, Exxon/Circle K/Quizno's/dsl, RaceWay, 🍴 Big John's Rest., Popeye's, Waffle House, 🛏 Super 8
135mm	Boeuf River
132	LA 133, Start, **N** 🅿 Exxon/dsl
128mm	Lafourche Bayou
124	LA 594, Millhaven, **N** 🅿 EZ Mart/dsl, 🅾 st police, to Arsage Wildlife Area
120	Garrett Rd, Pecanland Mall Dr, **N** 🅿 Chevron/dsl, 🍴 Applebee's, Copeland's Rest., Eastern Empire Chinese, IHOP, Longhorn Steaks, McAlister's, O'Charleys, Olive Garden, Red Lobster, Ronin Habachi, Sonic, Subway, 🛏 Courtyard, Residence Inn, 🅾 Belk, Best Buy, Dillard's, Firestone/auto, Home Depot, JC Penney, Kohl's, Michael's, Old Navy, Ross, Sears/auto, Target, TJ Maxx, mall, **S** 🅿 Kangaroo/dsl, 🛏 Best Western, Days Inn, 🅾 Freightliner, Harley-Davidson, Hope's RV Ctr, Lowe's, Pecanland RV Park, Sam's Club/gas, Shilo RV Camp
118b a	US 165, **N** 🅿 Valero, 🛏 Holiday Inn, La Quinta, Stratford House Inn, 🅾 Goodyear, KIA, Nissan, to NE LA U, **S** 🅿 Chevron, Conoco/dsl, Exxon, Shell/Circle K, 🍴 Burger King, Capt D's, Church's, KFC, McDonald's, Popeye's, Sonic, Subway, Taco Bell, Wendy's, 🛏 Comfort Suites, Hampton Inn, Motel 6, Super 8
117b	LA 594, Texas Ave, **N** 🅿 Now Save/dsl
117a	Hall St, Monroe, **N** 🅷, Civic Ctr
116b	US 165 bus, LA 15, Jackson St, **N** 🅷
116a	5th St, Monroe
115	LA 34, Mill St, **N** 🅿 Chevron, **S** 🅾 Clay's RV Service
114	LA 617, Thomas Rd, **N** 🅿 Murphy USA, Raceway, Shell, 🍴 Burger King, Cane's, Capt D's, Chick-fil-A, El Chico, El Chile Verde, Grandy's, IHOP, KFC, McAlister's Deli, McDonald's, Popeye's, Shoney's, Taco Bell, TCBY, Waffle House, Wendy's, 🛏 Shoney's Inn, Super 8, Wingate Inn, 🅾 🅷, AutoZone Big Lots, Hobby Lobby, Office Depot, O'Reilly Parts, Rite Aid, Walgreens, Walmart, **S** 🅿 Chevron, Exxon/Circle K/Subway/dsl, 🍴 Chili's, China Garden, Cracker Barrel, Hooters, Logan's Roadhouse, LoneStar Steaks, Los Parrilleros, Mohawk Seafood, Outback Steaks, Peking Chinese, Pizza Hut, Sonic, Waffle House, 🛏 Best Western, Jameson Inn, Motel 6, Quality Inn, Red Roof Inn, 🅾 Firestone, Radio Shack
113	Downing Pines Rd, **S** 🛏 Hilton Garden, Holiday Inn Express, 🅾 Chrysler/Dodge/Jeep
112	Well Rd, **N** 🅿 Conoco, Shell/Circle K/dsl/24hr, Texaco/dsl, 🍴 Domino's, McDonald's, Sonic, Subway, Taco Bell, Waffle House, 🅾 Advance Parts, Walgreens, **S** 🅿 /Subway/Wendy's/dsl/scales/24hr, 🅾 Pavilion RV Park
108	LA 546, to US 80, Cheniere, **N** 🅿 Shell/dsl
107	Camp Rd, rd 25, Cheniere, **N** RV Park
103	US 80, Calhoun, **N** 🅿 Shell/rest/dsl/24hr, 🍴 Johnny's Pizza (1mi), 🛏 Avant Motel
101	LA 151, to Calhoun, **S** 🅿 Chevron/Huddle House/dsl, Exxon, 🍴 Sonic
97mm	rest area wb, full ♿ facilities, 🚻, 📵, litter barrels, petwalk, RV dump
95mm	rest area eb, full ♿ facilities, 🚻, 📵, litter barrels, petwalk, RV dump
93	LA 145, Choudrant, **S** 🅿 Chevron, 🅾 Jimmy Davis St Park, camping
86	LA 33, Ruston, **N** 🅿 Citgo, Murphy USA, RaceWay/dsl, Shell/Circle K/Quizno's/dsl, 🍴 Cajun Cafe, Cane's Chicken, Chili's, Hot Rod BBQ, Log Cabin Grill, Portico Grill, Ryan's, Sonic, Z Buffet, 🛏 Comfort Inn, Days Inn, 🅾 Buick/GMC, Cadillac/Chevrolet, Chrysler/Dodge/Jeep, $Tree, Ford/Lincoln/Mercury, Fred's Drug, Lowe's, Toyota, Walmart, **S** 🅿 Spirit/dsl, 🛏 Fairfield Inn, Holiday Inn Express
85	US 167, Ruston, **N** 🅿 Chevron/Subway, Exxon, Shell/Circle K, 🍴 Applebee's, Burger King, Capt D's, McDonald's, Peking Chinese, Wendy's, 🛏 Budget Lodge, Hampton Inn, Howard Johnson, Relax Inn, 🅾 AT&T, $General, Office Depot, Radio Shack, Super 1 Foods, TrueValue, Walgreens, **S** 🅿 Texaco, Valero/dsl, 🍴 Pizza Hut, 🛏 Best Value Inn, Sleep Inn, 🅾 🅷, Advance Parts
84	LA 544, Ruston, **N** 🅿 Mobil/dsl, **S** 🅿 Chevron, Exxon, 🍴 Domino's, Johnny's Pizza, Pizza Inn, Quizno's, Starbucks, Subway, Waffle House, 🛏 Super 8
81	LA 141, Grambling, **S** 🅿 Chevron/Church's/dsl/24hr, Exxon, 🅾 to Grambling St U
78	LA 563, Industry, **S** 🅿 Texaco/dsl
77	LA 507, Simsboro
69	LA 151, Arcadia, **N** 🅿 Mobil/Burger King/dsl, **S** 🅿 Clark/dsl, Exxon/dsl, Shell, 🍴 Country Cottage Rest., McDonald's, Sonic, Subway, 🛏 Express Inn, 🅾 🅷, Bonnie&Clyde RV Park, Brookshire Foods, $General, Factory Stores/famous brands, Fred's Drugs, tires/repair
67	LA 9, Arcadia, **N** to Lake Claiborne SP, **S** 🅿 Shell/dsl
61	LA 154, Gibsland, **N** to Lake Claibourne SP, Bonnie&Clyde Museum
55	US 80, Ada, Taylor
52	LA 532, to US 80, Dubberly, **N** 🅿 Texaco/CJ's Diner/dsl
49	LA 531, Minden, **N** 🅿 Loves/Arby's/dsl/scales/24hr, Minden TrkStp/Shell/dsl/rest./24hr, Murphy USA, QuickDraw/Subway/dsl, 🍴 KFC (3mi), Pizza Hut (3mi), Taco Bell (3mi), 🅾 Walmart (3mi), **S** truck/tire repair
47	US 371 S, LA 159 N, Minden, **N** 🅿 Chevron/dsl, Exxon/dsl, Mobil/dsl, 🍴 Golden Biscuit, 🛏 Best Western, Exacta Inn/rest., Holiday Inn Express, Southern Inn, 🅾 🅷, **S** to Lake Bistineau SP, camping
44	US 371 N, Cotton Valley, **N** 🅿 Chevron, Exxon/Huddle House/dsl, 🍴 Crawfish Hole #2, Nicky's Cantina, Sonic, 🛏 Minden Motel (2mi), 🅾 Cinnamon Creek RV/camping, Family$
38	Goodwill Rd, Ammo Plant, **S** 🅿 Clark/Rainbow Diner/dsl/24hr, 🅾 Interstate RV Park, truck/trailer repair
33	LA 157, Fillmore, **N** 🅿 Texaco, **S** 🅿 Exxon, Arby's/dsl/scales/24hr, 🍴 Waffle House, 🅾 $General, Family$, USPO, Lake Bistineau SP
26	I-220, Shreveport, **1 mi N** 🅿 Raceway, 🅾 Casino
23	Industrial Dr, **N** 🅿 Exxon, Shell/Circle K, 🍴 Barnhill's Buffet, Burger King, McDonald's, Sue's Country Kitchen, Popeye's, Taco Bell, Wendy's 🛏 Ramada Inn, 🅾

Left margin: E ← W RAYVILLE MONROE

Right margin: RUSTON MINDEN

LA

INTERSTATE 20 CONT'D

Exit	Services
23	Continued
	O'Reilly Parts, st police, S 📳 Mobil/dsl, 🛏 EconoLodge, 🔲 Southern RV Ctr
22	Airline Dr, N 📳 Chevron/McDonald's/dsl, Citgo/dsl, Shell/Circle K, Valero/dsl, 🍴 Applebee's, Arby's, Backyard Burger, Burger King, Chili's, China Inn, ChuckeCheese, CiCi's Pizza, DQ, Gatti's Pizza, IHOP, Notini's Italian, Pizza Hut, Popeye's, Red Lobster, Sonic, Starbucks, Taco Bell, Waffle House, 🛏 Best Western, Crossland Suites, Rodeway Inn, Super 8, 🔲 Albertsons/gas, BigLots, Books-A-Million, CVS Drug, Dillard's, Firestone/auto, Goodyear/auto, Home Depot, JC Penney, K-Mart, Michael's, Office Depot, Old Navy, Sears/auto, Walgreens, mall, S 📳 Exxon/dsl, Texaco/dsl/24hr, 🍴 Capt John's, Church's, Darrell's Grill, Outback Steaks, Quizno's, 🛏 Microtel, Quality Inn, Red Carpet Inn, 🔲 Ⓗ, AutoZone, Fred's Store, Super1 Foods, to Barksdale AFB
21	LA 72, to US 71 S, Old Minden Rd, N 📳 Circle K, Valero, 🍴 Burger King, El Chico, McDonald's, Podnah's BBQ, Poncho's Mexican, Posado's Mexican, Ralph&Kacoo's, Shoney's, Subway, TX Roadhouse, Whataburger, 🛏 Best Value Inn, Hampton Inn, Holiday Inn, La Quinta, Residence Inn, TownePlace Suites, 🔲 Audi/Mazda/Porsche, O'Reilly Parts, VW, S 📳 RaceWay, 🍴 Waffle House, Wendy's, 🛏 Days Inn, Motel 6, ValuePlace Inn, 🔲 visitor info
20c	to US 71 S, to Barksdale Blvd
20b	LA 3, Benton Rd, same as 21
20a	Hamilton Rd, Isle of Capri Blvd, N 📳 Circle K, 🛏 Comfort Inn, S 📳 Exxon, 🛏 Bossier Inn, 🔲 casino
19b	Traffic St, Shreveport downtown, N 🛏 Courtyard, 🔲 Bass Pro Shop, Chevrolet, casino, S 🔲 casino
19a	US 71 N, LA 1 N, Spring St, Shreveport, N 🍴 Don's Seafood, 🛏 Best Western, Hilton, Holiday Inn
18b-d	Fairfield Ave (from wb), downtown Shreveport, S Ⓗ
18a	Line Ave, Common St (from eb), downtown, S 📳 1st Stop, 🔲 Ⓗ
17b	I-49 S, to Alexandria
17a	Lakeshore Dr, Linwood Ave
16b	US 79/80, Greenwood Rd, N Ⓗ, S 📳 Citgo/dsl, 🍴 El Chico, 🛏 Travelodge
16a	US 171, Hearne Ave, N 📳 Clark/dsl, 🍴 Subway, 🔲 Ⓗ, S 📳 Raceway, Texaco/dsl, 🍴 KFC, 🛏 Cajun Inn
14	Jewella Ave, Shreveport, N 📳 Citgo/dsl, Texaco/dsl/24hr, Valero, 🍴 Burger King, China Hat, Church's, McDonald's, Popeye's, Subway, Sonic, Whataburger, 🔲 Advance Parts, AutoZone, County Mkt Foods, Family$, O'Reilly Parts, Rite Aid, Super 1 Foods, Walgreens
13	Monkhouse Dr, Shreveport, N 🍴 Bro's Cafe, 🛏 Best Value Inn, Days Inn, Ramada, Residence Inn, Super 8, Value Inn, S 📳 Chevron/dsl, Citgo/dsl, Exxon/Subway/dsl, 🍴 Waffle House, 🛏 Best Western, Candlewood Suites, Hampton Inn, Holiday Inn Express, Merryton Inn, Quality Inn, Regency Inn, 🔲 to ✈
11	I-220 E, LA 3132 E, to I-49 S
10	Pines Rd, N 📳 Clark/dsl, 🍴 DQ, Pizza Hut, Popeye's, Subway, S 📳 Exxon/dsl, Murphy USA/dsl, Shell/Circle K, 🍴 Burger King, CiCi's Pizza, Cracker Barrel, Domino's, Dragon Chinese, Grandy's, IHOP, KFC, Nicky's Cantina, Quizno's, Sonic, Subway, Taco Bell, Waffle House, Wendy's, Whataburger, 🛏 Comfort Suites, Courtyard, Fairfield Inn, La Quinta, Hilton Garden, Holiday Inn, Homewood

10	Continued
	Suites, Jameson Inn, Sleep Inn, ValuePlace Inn, 🔲 CVS, $Tree, $General, Family$, GNC, Home Depot, O'Reilly Parts, Radio Shack, Rite Aid, Walgreens, Walmart, USPO
8	US 80, LA 526 E, N 🛏 Motel 6, 🔲 Freightliner, S 📳 Chevron/dsl, Citgo/dsl, Petro/Mobil/dsl/rest./scales/@, 🍴 Wendy's, 🔲 Blue Beacon, Camper's RV Ctr/park, Tall Pines RV Park (1mi)
5	US 79 N, US 80, to Greenwood, N 📳 TA/Country Fried/Subway/dsl/scales/24hr/@, Shell, 🛏 Country Inn, Mid Continent Motel, S 🔲 $General, Southern Living RV Park
3	US 79 S, LA 169, Mooringsport, S 📳 ⊕FLYING J/Denny's/dsl/LP/scales/24hr, ♥Loves/Arby's/dsl/scales/24hr, 🍴 Sonic, 🔲 Alligator RV Park (4mi), SpeedCo
2mm	**Welcome Ctr eb, full ♿ facilities, 🔲, 🛏, litter barrels, petwalk, RV dump**
1mm	**weigh sta both lanes**
0mm	Louisiana/Texas state line

INTERSTATE 49

Exit	Services
	I-49 begins/ends in Shreveport on I-20, exit 17.
206	I-20, E to Monroe, W to Dallas
205	King's Hwy, E 🍴 Cane's, McDonald's, Piccadilly's, Taco Bell, 🔲 Dillard's, Sears/auto, mall, W 📳 Valero/dsl, 🍴 Burger King, LJ Silver, Subway, Taco Bell, 🔲 SHRINERS Ⓗ
203	Hollywood Ave, Pierremont Rd, W 📳 Chevron/dsl
202	LA 511, E 70th St, E 📳 RaceWay/dsl, W 📳 Circle K, 🍴 SC Chicken
201	LA 3132, to Dallas, Texarkana
199	LA 526, Bert Kouns Loop, E 📳 Chevron/Arby's/dsl/24hr, Exxon/Circle K, 🍴 Burger King, KFC, Taco Bell, Wendy's, 🛏 Comfort Inn, 🔲 Home Depot, W 📳 RaceWay, Shell/dsl, 🍴 McDonald's, Sonic, Starbucks, 🔲 Brookshire Foods
196	Southern Loop
196mm	Bayou Pierre
191	LA 16, LA 3276, to Stonewall
186	LA 175, to Frierson, Kingston, W 📳 Relay Sta./rest./casino/dsl/scales
177	LA 509, to Carmel, E 📳 Texaco/Eagles Trkstp/casino/dsl/rest.
172	US 84, to Grand Bayou, Mansfield, W New Rockdale RV Prk, Civil War Site
169	Asseff Rd
162	US 371, LA 177, to Evelyn, Coushatta, Pleasant Hill
155	LA 174, to Ajax, Lake End, W 🔲 Country Livin' RV Pk, gas/dsl
148	LA 485, Powhatan, Allen
142	LA 547, Posey Rd

INTERSTATE 49 CONT'D

Exit	Services
138	LA 6, to Natchitoches, **E** 🅖 French Mkt/cafe, RaceWay, 🍴 Popeye's, Shoney's, Wendy's, 🛏 Best Western, Days Inn, Holiday Inn Express, Super 8 (5mi), 🅞 🎗 Walmart (5mi), **W** 🅖 Chevron/dsl, Exxon, Texaco/dsl, 🍴 Burger King, Huddle House, McDonald's, 🛏 EconoLodge, Hampton Inn, Quality Inn, 🅞 Nakatosh RV Park, to Kisatchie NF
132	LA 478, rd 620
127	LA 120, to Cypress, Flora, **E** 🅖 Texaco, 🅞 to Cane River Plantations
119	LA 119, to Derry, Cloutierville, **E** to Cane River Plantations
113	LA 490, to Chopin, **E** 🅖 Express Mart TrkStp/dsl
107	to Lena, **E** USPO
103	LA 8 W, to Flatwoods, **W** 🅖 Shell/dsl, 🅞 to Cotile Lake, RV camping
99	LA 8, LA 1200, to Boyce, Colfax, **6 mi W** Cotile Lake, RV camping
98	LA 1 (from nb), to Boyce
94	rd 23, to Rapides Sta Rd, **E** 🅖 Rapides/dsl, **W** **LA Welcome Ctr, full** 🦽 **facilities, litter barrels, petwalk,** 🚻, **vending,** 🅞 I-49 RV Ctr
90	LA 498, Air Base Rd, **W** 🅖 Chevron/dsl/24hr, Exxon/dsl, Shell, Texaco/BBQ/dsl, 🍴 Burger King, Cracker Barrel, McDonald's, 🛏 Comfort Suites, Hampton Inn, La Quinta, Super 8, Travel Express Inn
86	US 71, US 165, MacArthur Dr, **0-2 mi W** 🅖 Chevron, Conoco/dsl, Exxon/dsl, Shell/Circle K/dsl, Texaco/dsl, 🍴 Applebee's, Arby's, Burger King, Cane's, Cajun Landing Rest., Checkers, Chick-fil-A, Church's, Dominos, DQ, Eddie's BBQ, El Reparo Mexican, Little Caesar's, McDonald's, Outlaw's BBQ, Picadilly, Popeye's, Ryan's, Schlotzky's, Sonic, Subway, Taco Bell, Taco Bueno, 🛏 Alexandria Inn, Baymont Inn, Best Western, Comfort Inn, Days Inn, EconoLodge, Guesthouse Inn, Holiday Inn Express, Motel 6, Ramada Ltd, Super 8, Value Place Inn, 🅞 Advance Parts, AutoZone, BigLots, $General, $Tree, Family$, Hastings Books, Kroger, NAPA, O'Reilly Parts, Rite Aid, Staples, Super 1 Foods
85b	Monroe St, Medical Ctr Dr (from nb), **E** 🎗
85a	LA 1, 10th St, MLK Dr, downtown
84	US 167 N, LA 28, LA 1, Pineville Expswy (no ez return nb)
83	Broadway Ave, **E** 🅖 **1 mi W** 🍴 Wendy's, 🅞 Books-A-Million, Harley-Davidson, Hobby Lobby, Lowe's, Sam's Club/gas, Target, Walmart
81	US 71 N, LA 3250, Sugarhouse Rd, MacArthur Dr (from sb), **W** same as 80 and 83
80	US 71 S, US 167, MacArthur Dr, Alexandria, **0-3 mi W** 🅖 Chevron/dsl, Exxon/dsl, Shell, 🍴 Burger King, Capt D's, Carino's Italian, Chili's, Hana Steaks, KFC, Logan's Roadhouse, McDonald's, Outback Steaks, Pizza Hut, Popeye's, Sonic, Subway, Taco Bell, 🛏 Courtyard, 🅞 Albertsons, Dillard's, Dodge, $General, Family$, Ford, Hyundai, JC Penney, Marshalls, Mazda, Michael's, Petsmart, Sam's Club/gas, Sears/auto, U-Haul, mall
73	LA 3265, rd 22, to Woodworth, **E** dsl repair, **W** 🅖 Exxon/Coops/dsl, 🅞 LA Conf Ctr, to Indian Creek RA, RV camping
66	LA 112, to Lecompte, **E** 🅖 Chevron/Burger King/dsl, 🍴 Lea's Lunch, **W** 🅖 Exxon/dsl, 🅞 museum
61	US 167, to Meeker, Turkey Creek, **E** to Loyd Hall Plantation (3mi)
56	LA 181, Cheneyville
53	LA 115, to Bunkie, **E** 🅖 Sammy's/Chevron/dsl/casino/24hr

Exit	Services
46	LA 106, to St Landry, **W** to Chicot SP
40	LA 29, to Ville Platte, **E** 🅖 Exxon/Cafe Mangeur/casino/dsl, 35mm, **E** rest area/rec area both lanes, full 🦽 facilities, 🚻, litter barrels, vending, petwalk, RV dump
27	LA 10, to Lebeau
25	LA 103, to Washington, Port Barre, **W** 🅖 Citgo, Mobil, 🅞 Family$
23	US 167 N, LA 744, to Ville Platte, **E** 🅖 Chevron/Subway/Stuckey's/dsl/scales/casino, Texaco/dsl/casino, **W** 🅖 Exxon/dsl/casino
19b a	US 190, to Opelousas, **E** Evangeline Downs Racetrack, **W** 🅖 Exxon/dsl, Mobil, RaceTrac/dsl, 🅞 🎗, Lowe's, tourist info, USPO
18	LA 31, to Cresswell Lane, **E** 🅖 Murphy USA/dsl, 🍴 Casa Ole's, 🛏 Comfort Inn, Holiday Inn, 🅞 URGENT CARE, Chrysler/Dodge/Jeep, Radio Shack, Walmart, **W** 🅖 Chevron/dsl/24hr, Shell, Valero/dsl, 🍴 Burger King, Cane's, Cresswell Lane, Domino's, Hacienda Mexican, McDonald's, Mr Gatti's, Peking Buffet, Pizza Hut, Subway, Taco Bell, Wendy's, 🛏 Days Inn, Super 8, 🅞 AT&T, Buick/Cadillac/GMC, CVS Drug, Family$, Nissan, Piggly Wiggly, Save-a-Lot, Walgreens, repair
17	Judson Walsh Dr, **E** 🅖 Texaco/dsl
15	LA 3233, Harry Guilbeau Rd, **W** 🛏 Best Value Inn, 🅞 🎗, Toyota/Scion, RV Ctr
11	LA 93, to Grand Coteau, Sunset, **E** 🅖 Citgo/rest./dsl/24hr, Exxon/Popeye's/dsl, 🍴 Beau Chere Rest., **W** 🍴 Subway, 🅞 $General, Family$, Janise's Foods
7	LA 182, **W** Primeaux RV Ctr
4	LA 726, Carencro, **W** 🅖 Chevron/Popeye's/dsl, Texaco/Subway/dsl, 🍴 Burger King, McDonald's, 🛏 Economy Inn, 🅞 Mack, Kenworth
2	LA 98, Gloria Switch Rd, **E** 🅖 Chevron/dsl/deli, 🍴 Chili's, IHOP, Prejean's Rest., Wendy's, 🅞 Southern RV Ctr, Lowe's, **W** 🅖 Shell/Church's/dsl, 🍴 Domino's, Picante Mexican, Subway
1b	Pont Des Mouton Rd, **E** 🅖 Exxon/dsl, Texaco/dsl, 🍴 Burger King, 🛏 Motel 6, Plantation Inn, 🅞 st police, **W** Ford
1a	I-10, **W** to Lake Charles, **E** to Baton Rouge, **US 167 S** 🅖 Chevron/dsl/24hr, Murphy USA/dsl, RaceTrac, Shell/dsl, Valero, 🍴 Checker's, KFC, McDonald's, Pizza Hut, Popeye's, Shoney's, Subway, Taco Bell, Waffle House, Wendy's, 🛏 Baymont Inn, Comfort Inn, EconoLodge, Fairfield Inn, Holiday Inn, Howard Johnson, Jameson Inn, La Quinta, Quality Inn, Royal Inn, Super 8, TravelHost Inn, 🅞 🎗, Albertson's, CVS Drug, Home Depot, Super 1 Foods/gas, Walmart, transmissions

I-49 begins/ends on I-10, exit 103.

INTERSTATE 55

Exit	Services
66mm	Louisiana/Mississippi state line
65mm	**Welcome Ctr sb, full** 🦽 **facilities, tourist info,** 🍴, 🚻, **litter barrels, petwalk**
64mm	**weigh sta nb**
61	LA 38, Kentwood, **E** 🅖 Chevron/dsl, Texaco, 🍴 Jam Chicken, Popeye's, Sonic, 🅞 🎗, AutoZone, Brown Drug, $General, Family$, IGA Foods, Super$, **W** 🅖 Exxon/Subway/dsl, Kangaroo/dsl
58.5mm	**weigh sta sb**
57	LA 440, Tangipahoa, **E** to Camp Moore Confederate Site
53	LA 10, to Greensburg, Fluker, **W** 🎗

LA

INTERSTATE 55 CONT'D

Exit	Services
50	LA 1048, Roseland, **E** 🅿 Chevron/dsl/24hr, 🍴 Subway (1mi)
46	LA 16, Amite, **E** 🅿 Exxon/dsl, Murphy USA/dsl, RaceTrac/dsl, 🍴 Burger King, Hot Wok, KFC, McDonald's, Mike's Catfish, Popeye's, Sonic, Subway, Waffle House, Wendy's, 🛏 Comfort Inn, 🅾 H, AutoZone, $Tree, Fred's, O'Reilly Parts, Walgreens, Walmart, Winn-Dixie, **W** 🅿 Amite Trk-stp/grill/dsl (2mi), 🍴 Ardillo's, Dub's BBQ, 🛏 Colonial Inn, Holiday Inn Express, 🅾 Buick/Chevrolet/GMC
40	LA 40, Independence, **E** 🅿 Best Stop, 🅾 H, Sweetwater Camping (7mi), **W** Indian Cr Camping (2mi)
36	LA 442, Tickfaw, **E** 🅿 Chevron/dsl/24hr, 🅾 camping, to Global Wildlife Ctr (15mi), **W** 🅿 Exxon/dsl
32	LA 3234, Wardline Rd, **E** 🅿 Chevron, Kangaroo/dsl, Texaco, 🍴 Burger King, Chilly Willy's Grill, McDonald's, Popeye's, Sonic, Subway, Taco Bell, Wendy's, 🛏 Best Western, 🅾 Tony's Tire
31	US 190, Hammond, **E** 🅿 Exxon/Subway/dsl, Murphy USA/dsl, RaceTrac/dsl, Shell/dsl/scales/24hr, 🍴 Applebee's, Baskin-Robbins, Buffalo Wild Wings, Burger King, Cane's, Chili's, CiCi's Pizza, Cracker Barrel, Hi-Ho BBQ, KFC, McDonald's, Pizza Hut, Quiznos, Sonic, Subway, Taco Bell, Waffle House, Wendy's, 🛏 Comfort Inn, Hampton Inn, Super 8, ValuePlace, Western Inn, 🅾 H, Aamco, Advance Parts, AT&T, AutoZone, BigLots, Books-A-Million, Chrysler/Dodge/Jeep, CVS Drug, $General, $Tree, Family$, Hobby Lobby, LeBlanc's Foods Lowe's, Office Depot, Radio Shack, Ross, Sav-A-Lot Foods, Tuesday Morning, Walgreens, Walmart, Winn-Dixie, transmissions/repair
29b a	I-12, W to Baton Rouge, E to Slidell
28	US 51 N, Hammond, **E** 🅿 Exxon, RaceTrac/dsl, 🍴 Don's Seafood/Steaks, 🛏 Motel 6, Quality Inn, 🅾 H, Mitchell RV Ctr, Toyota/Scion, dsl repair
26	LA 22, to Springfield, Ponchatoula, **E** 🅿 Chevron/dsl, Exxon/dsl, Shell, 🍴 Burger King, China King, Hi-Ho BBQ, KFC, McDonald's/playplace, Papa John's, Popeye's, Smoothie King, Sonic, Subway, Waffle House, Wendy's, 🛏 Microtel, 🅾 AutoZone, Bohning's Foods, Curves, CVS Drug, $General, Family$, Ford, O'Reilly Parts, Walgreens, Winn-Dixie, **W** 🅿 Exxon/Domino's/dsl, 🅾 Tickfaw SP (13mi)
23	US 51, Ponchatoula
22	frontage rd (from sb)
15	Manchac, **E** 🍴 Middendorf Café, 🅾 🅲, swamp tours
7	Ruddock
1	US 51, to I-10, Baton Rouge, La Place, **S** 🅿 Circle K/dsl, 🅿🍴/Subway/dsl/24hr/scales, Shell/Huddle House/casino/dsl, 🍴 Bully's Seafood, Burger King, McDonald's, Shoney's, Waffle House, Wendy's, 🛏 Best Western, Days Inn, Hampton Inn, Holiday Inn Express, Quality Inn, Suburban Lodge
	I-55 begins/ends on I-10, exit 209.

INTERSTATE 59

Exits	Services
11	Pearl River Turnaround. Callboxes begin sb.
5b	Honey Island Swamp
5a	LA 41, Pearl River, **E** 🅿 Riverside TrvlCtr/dsl
3	US 11 S, LA 1090, Pearl River, **0-1 mi W** 🅿 Chevron/dsl, Shell/Subway/dsl, Texaco, 🍴 McDonald's, Sonic, Waffle House, 🛏 Microtel, 🅾 AutoZone, Family$, Jubilee Foods/drug, NAPA

[Louisiana state map showing: Minden, Monroe, Shreveport, Bawcomville, I-20, Stonewall, Mansfield, Coushatta, Pleasant Hill, Natchitoches, Provencal, Coifax, Flatwoods, I-49, Alexandria, Woodworth, Lecompte, Pine Prairie, Opelousas, Baton Rouge, I-12, Lake Charles, I-10, Lafayette, LA]

1.5mm	Welcome Ctr sb, full ♿ facilities, info, 🅲, ⛽, litter barrels, petwalk, RV dump
1c b	I-10, E to Bay St Louis, W to New Orleans
1a	I-12 W, to Hammond. I-59 begins/ends on I-10/I-12.

INTERSTATE 220 (SHREVEPORT)

Exit	Services
	I-220 begins/ends on I-20, exit 26.
17b	I-20, W to Shreveport, E to Monroe
17a	US 79, US 80, **N** 🅿 RaceWay, Shell/Circle K, 🍴 McDonald's, Taco Bell, Waffle House, 🛏 SpringHill Suites, 🅾 LA Downs Racetrack/casino, **S** 🅿 Chevron/Huddle House/dsl
15	Shed Rd
13	Swan Lake Rd
12	LA 3105, Airline Dr, **N** 🅿 🍴 Baskin-Robbins, Chick-fil-A, Firehouse Subs, McAlister's Deli, Olive Garden, Papa Murphy's, Quiznos, Starbucks, Subway, TaMolly's, 🅾 H, AT&T, Belk, Best Buy, Petsmart, Ross, Target, Verizon, Walgreens, **S** 🅿 Exxon/dsl, Murphy USA/dsl, Shell/Circle K/Subway, Valero/dsl, 🍴 Applebee's, Burger King, Cane's, Capt D's, China Flag, CiCi's Pizza, Gatti's Pizza, McDonald's, Moe's SW Grill, Nicky's Rest., Ruby Tuesday, Ryan's, Sonic, Taco Bell, Trejo's Mexican, Wendy's, 🅾 $Tree, Home Depot, Lowe's, Radio Shack, Walmart, USPO, vet
11	LA 3, Bossier City, **N** 🅾 H, Buick/GMC, Ford, Harley-Davidson, Lexus, Suzuki, Toyota, RV Park, **S** 🅿 Chevron/dsl/24hr, 🅾 Chrysler/Dodge/Jeep, Nissan
7b a	US 71, LA 1, Shreveport, **N** 🅿 Citgo, Exxon/dsl, 🍴 Domino's, Rally's, Sonic, Subway, Waffle House, Whataburger/24hr, 🅾 Brookshire Foods/gas, Curves, $General, Walgreens, **S** 🅿 Chevron/24hr, RaceWay/dsl, Shell, 🍴 Burger King, Church's, KFC, Gumbo Daddy's, McDonald's, Podnah's BBQ, Popeye's, Taco Bell, Wendy's, 🛏 Royal Inn, 🅾 Advance Parts, AutoZone, County Mkt Foods, CVS Drug, Family$, O'Reilly Parts, Radio Shack, Rite Aid, U-Haul, repair/transmissions
5	LA 173, Blanchard Rd, **S** 🅿 Citgo
2	Lakeshore Dr, **N** 🅿 Citgo
1a	Jefferson Paige Rd, **S** 🛏 Best Western, Days Inn, Hampton Inn, Ramada Inn, Residence Inn, Super 8, Value Inn
1b c	I-20, E to Shreveport, W to Dallas. I-220 begins/ends on I-20, exit 11.

INTERSTATE 610 (NEW ORLEANS)

Exit	Services
	I-610 begins/ends on I-10
4	Franklin Ave (from eb)
3	Elysian fields, **N** H, **S** 🅿 B Express, Shell, 🍴 Burger King, McDonald's, 🅾 Lowe's
2b	US 90, N Broad St, New Orleans St (from wb)

⛽ = gas 🍴 = food 🛏 = lodging ⊡ = other Copyright 2012 - The Next Exit®

INTERSTATE 610 CONT'D (NEW ORLEANS)

Exit	Services
2c	Paris Ave (from wb, no return), S ⛽ Shell/24hr, Spur, 🍴 Popeye's
2a	St Bernard Ave (from eb), to LSU School of Dentistry, auto racetrack
1a	Canal Blvd
1b	I-10, to New Orleans
	I-610 begins/ends on I-10

MAINE

INTERSTATE 95

Exit	Services
305mm	US/Canada border, Maine state line, US Customs. I-95 begins/ends. US Customs
305	US 2, to Houlton, E ⊡ Houlton 🛏, DFA Duty Free Shop
303mm	Meduxnekeag River
302	US 1, Houlton, E ⛽ Irving/Circle K/dsl/24hr, 🍴 Burger King, KFC, McDonald's, Pizza Hut, Tang's Chinese, ⊡ 🛏, IGA Foods, Mardens, Rite Aid, VIP Parts/service, W **rest area both lanes, full ♿ facilities, ⦿, 🚻, litter barrels, petwalk,** ⛽ Citgo/Subway/dsl, Irving/Circle K/dsl/scales/@, Shell/Dunkin Donuts/dsl, 🍴 Elmtree North, Tim Hortons, 🛏 Ivey's Motel, Shiretown Motel, ⊡ Family$, Ford/Lincoln/Mercury, Shop'n Save, Toyota, Walmart, Arrowstook SP
301mm	B Stream
291	US 2, to Smyrna, E 🛏 Brookside Motel/rest.
286	Oakfield Rd, to ME 11, Eagle Lake, Ashland, W ⛽ Irving/Circle K/dsl, Valero/dsl, 🍴 A Place To Eat, ⊡ USPO
277mm	Mattawamkeag River, W Branch
276	ME 159, Island Falls, E ⛽ Porter's/rest., Dysarts Fuel, ⊡ Bishop's Mkt, USPO, W to Baxter SP (N entrance), RV camping
264	to ME 11, Sherman, E ⛽ Shell/dsl/LP/rest., W ⛽ Irving/Circle K/dsl, 🛏 Katahdin Valley Motel, ⊡ to Baxter SP (N entrance)
259	Benedicta (from nb, no re-entry)
252mm	scenic view Mt Katahdin, nb
247mm	Salmon Stream
244	ME 157, to Medway, E Millinocket, W ⛽ Irving/Circle K/dsl, 🛏 Gateway Inn, ⊡ 🛏, Pine Grove Camping (4mi), USPO, vet, to Baxter SP (S entrance), city park
244mm	Penobscot River
243mm	**rest area both lanes, full ♿ facilities, ⦿, 🚻, litter barrels, petwalk**
227	to US 2, ME 6, Lincoln, **4 mi** E 🛏, ⛽, 🍴, 🛏, RV camping
219mm	Piscataquis River
217	ME 6, Howland, E ⛽ Irving/95 Diner/dsl, 🍴 Jim & Jill's Grill, ⊡ 95er Towing/repair, LP, camping
201mm	Birch Stream
199	ME 16 (no nb re-entry), to LaGrange
197	ME 43, to Old Town, E gas/dsl
196mm	Pushaw Stream
193	Stillwater Ave, to Old Town, E ⛽ Citgo/dsl, Irving/Circle K/dsl, Mobil/Subway/dsl, 🍴 Burger King, Dunkin Donuts, Governor's Rest., KFC/Taco Bell, McDonald's/playplace, Wendy's, 🛏 Black Bear Inn, ⊡ $Tree, IGA Foods, VIP Parts, mall
191	Kelly Rd, to Orono, **2-3 mi** E gas, 🍴, 🛏, camping
187	Hogan Rd, Bangor Mall Blvd, to Bangor, E ⛽ Citgo, 🍴 Denny's, 🛏 Courtyard, Hilton Garden, ⊡ 🛏, Audi/VW,

Exit	Services
187	**Continued** Cadillac/Chevrolet, Chrysler/Dodge, Firestone/auto, Ford, GMC, Honda, Hyundai, Jeep, Mazda, Mercedes, Nissan, Sam's Club/gas, Subaru, Volvo, W ⛽ Citgo/dsl, Irving/Circle K/dsl, 🍴 Applebee's, Arby's, Bugaboo Creek Café, Burger King, Chicago Grill, Chili's, Dunkin Donuts, Green Tea Japanese, Happy China, KFC, Longhorn Steaks, McDonald's, Miguel's Mexican, 99 Rest., Olive Garden, Papa Johns, Pizza Hut, Quiznos, Starbucks, Subway, TX Roadhouse, Wendy's, 🛏 Bangor Motel, Comfort Inn, Country Inn, Hampton Inn, ⊡ Advance Parts, Best Buy, BigLots, Dick's, $Tree, Goodyear/auto, Harley-Davidson, Hannaford Foods, Home Depot, JC Penney, Jo-Ann Fabrics, K-Mart/Little Caesars, Kia, Kohl's, LL Bean, Lowe's, Macy's, Old Navy, PetCo, Sears/auto, Staples, Suzuki, Target, Verizon, VIP Parts, Walmart, mall, urgent care
186	Stillwater Ave, same as 187
185	ME 15, to Broadway, Bangor, E ⛽ Irving/Circle K/dsl, 🍴 Tri-City Pizza, ⊡ 🛏, W ⛽ Citgo, Mobil, 🍴 Amato's, Coldstone/Tim Hortons, China Light, DQ, Governor's Rest., Jimmy V's Cafe, KFC, McDonald's, Pizza Hut, Subway, Taco Bell, ⊡ CarQuest, Hannaford Foods, Rite Aid, TJ Maxx, Walgreens
184	ME 222, Union St, to Ohio St, Bangor, E ⛽ Citgo, Irving, ⊡ Rite Aid, W ⛽ Citgo, Exxon, Gulf, Mobil/dsl, 🍴 Burger King, Capt Nick's Rest., Dunkin Donuts, McDonald's, Nicky's Rest., Wendy's, 🛏 Sheraton, ⊡ $Tree, Hannaford Foods, Marshall's, Staples, RV Camping, to 🛏
183	US 2, ME 2, Hammond St, Bangor, E ⛽ Citgo, 🍴 Papa Gambino's Pizza, Pipino's Mexican, ⊡ Corner Store, Fairmont Mkt, NAPA, TrueValue, W 🛏
182b	US 2, ME 100 W, W ⛽ Irving/Subway/dsl, 🍴 Dunkin Donuts, Ground Round, Tim Hortons, 🛏 Days Inn, EconoLodge, Fairfield Inn, Holiday Inn, Howard Johnson, Motel 6, Ramada Inn, Super 8, Travelodge, ⊡ RV camping, VIP Parts/service
182a	I-395, to US 2, US 1A
Bangor	downtown
180	Cold Brook Rd, to Hampden, E Citgo, 🍴 Angler's Rest. (1mi), W ⛽ Citgo/dsl/24hr/@, Dysarts Fleet Fuel/dsl, 🛏 Best Western, ⊡ Mack, Volvo, dsl repair
178mm	**rest area sb, full ♿ facilities, info, ⦿, 🚻, vending, litter barrels, petwalk, wireless internet**
177mm	Soudabscook Stream
176mm	**rest area nb, full ♿ facilities, info, ⦿, 🚻, vending, litter barrels, petwalk, wireless internet**
174	ME 69, to Carmel, E ⛽ Citgo/dsl, W RV camping
167	ME 69, ME 143, to Etna
161	ME 7, to, E Newport, Plymouth, E LP, W RV camping
159	Ridge Rd (from sb), to Plymouth, Newport
157	to US 2, ME 7, ME 11, Newport, W ⛽ Citgo, Irving/Circle K/dsl/24hr, Mobil/dsl, 🍴 Burger King, China Way, Dunkin Donuts, McDonald's, Pizza House, Pizza Hut, Sawyers Dairy Bar, Subway, Tim Hortons, 🛏 Lovley's Motel, ⊡ Aubuchon Hardware, Auto Value Parts, CarQuest, Chrysler/Dodge/Jeep, Rite Aid, Shop'n Save, Verizon, Walmart
151mm	Sebasticook River
150	Somerset Ave, Pittsfield, E ⛽ Irving, 🍴 Subway, 🛏 Pittsfield Motel, ⊡ 🛏, CarQuest, Chevrolet, Family$, Rite Aid, Shop'n Save Foods
138	Hinckley Rd, Clinton, W ⛽ ME Country Store/dsl
134mm	Kennebec River
133	US 201, Fairfield, E 🍴 Purple Cow Pancakes

E ↕ W

N ↑ S HOULTON · BANGOR

BANGOR · NEWPORT

LA
ME

🅖 = gas 🍴 = food 🛏 = lodging 🅾 = other

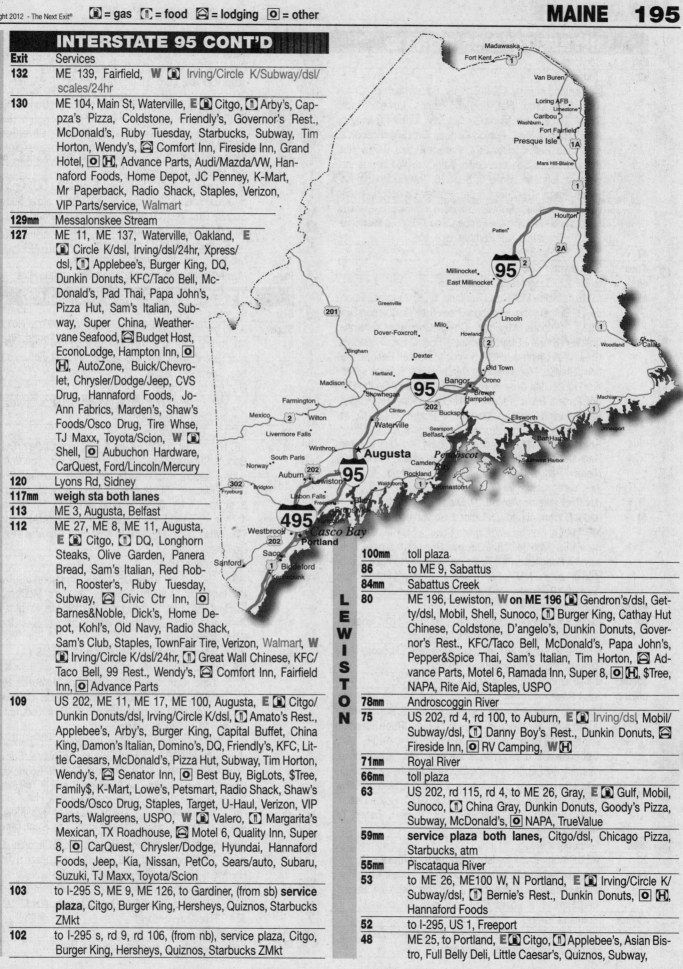

INTERSTATE 95 CONT'D

WATERVILLE N ↕ S

AUGUSTA

Exit	Services
132	ME 139, Fairfield, **W** 🅖 Irving/Circle K/Subway/dsl/scales/24hr
130	ME 104, Main St, Waterville, **E** 🅖 Citgo, 🍴 Arby's, Cap-pza's Pizza, Coldstone, Friendly's, Governor's Rest., McDonald's, Ruby Tuesday, Starbucks, Subway, Tim Horton, Wendy's, 🛏 Comfort Inn, Fireside Inn, Grand Hotel, 🅾 🄷, Advance Parts, Audi/Mazda/VW, Hannaford Foods, Home Depot, JC Penney, K-Mart, Mr Paperback, Radio Shack, Staples, Verizon, VIP Parts/service, Walmart
129mm	Messalonskee Stream
127	ME 11, ME 137, Waterville, Oakland, **E** 🅖 Circle K/dsl, Irving/dsl/24hr, Xpress/dsl, 🍴 Applebee's, Burger King, DQ, Dunkin Donuts, KFC/Taco Bell, Mc-Donald's, Pad Thai, Papa John's, Pizza Hut, Sam's Italian, Sub-way, Super China, Weather-vane Seafood, 🛏 Budget Host, EconoLodge, Hampton Inn, 🅾 🄷, AutoZone, Buick/Chevro-let, Chrysler/Dodge/Jeep, CVS Drug, Hannaford Foods, Jo-Ann Fabrics, Marden's, Shaw's Foods/Osco Drug, Tire Whse, TJ Maxx, Toyota/Scion, **W** 🅖 Shell, 🅾 Aubuchon Hardware, CarQuest, Ford/Lincoln/Mercury
120	Lyons Rd, Sidney
117mm	weigh sta both lanes
113	ME 3, Augusta, Belfast
112	ME 27, ME 8, ME 11, Augusta, **E** 🅖 Citgo, 🍴 DQ, Longhorn Steaks, Olive Garden, Panera Bread, Sam's Italian, Red Rob-in, Rooster's, Ruby Tuesday, Subway, 🛏 Civic Ctr Inn, 🅾 Barnes&Noble, Dick's, Home De-pot, Kohl's, Old Navy, Radio Shack, Sam's Club, Staples, TownFair Tire, Verizon, Walmart, **W** 🅖 Irving/Circle K/dsl/24hr, 🍴 Great Wall Chinese, KFC/Taco Bell, 99 Rest., Wendy's, 🛏 Comfort Inn, Fairfield Inn, 🅾 Advance Parts
109	US 202, ME 11, ME 17, ME 100, Augusta, **E** 🅖 Citgo/Dunkin Donuts/dsl, Irving/Circle K/dsl, 🍴 Amato's Rest., Applebee's, Arby's, Burger King, Capital Buffet, China King, Damon's Italian, Domino's, DQ, Friendly's, KFC, Lit-tle Caesars, McDonald's, Pizza Hut, Subway, Tim Horton, Wendy's, 🛏 Senator Inn, 🅾 Best Buy, BigLots, $Tree, Family$, K-Mart, Lowe's, Petsmart, Radio Shack, Shaw's Foods/Osco Drug, Staples, Target, U-Haul, Verizon, VIP Parts, Walgreens, USPO, **W** 🅖 Valero, 🍴 Margarita's Mexican, TX Roadhouse, 🛏 Motel 6, Quality Inn, Super 8, 🅾 CarQuest, Chrysler/Dodge, Hyundai, Hannaford Foods, Jeep, Kia, Nissan, PetCo, Sears/auto, Subaru, Suzuki, TJ Maxx, Toyota/Scion
103	to I-295 S, ME 9, ME 126, to Gardiner, (from sb) **service plaza**, Citgo, Burger King, Hersheys, Quiznos, Starbucks ZMkt
102	to I-295 s, rd 9, rd 106, (from nb), service plaza, Citgo, Burger King, Hersheys, Quiznos, Starbucks ZMkt

LEWISTON

Exit	Services
100mm	toll plaza
86	to ME 9, Sabattus
84mm	Sabattus Creek
80	ME 196, Lewiston, **W on ME 196** 🅖 Gendron's/dsl, Get-ty/dsl, Mobil, Shell, Sunoco, 🍴 Burger King, Cathay Hut Chinese, Coldstone, D'angelo's, Dunkin Donuts, Gover-nor's Rest., KFC/Taco Bell, McDonald's, Papa John's, Pepper&Spice Thai, Sam's Italian, Tim Horton, 🛏 Ad-vance Parts, Motel 6, Ramada Inn, Super 8, 🅾 🄷, $Tree, NAPA, Rite Aid, Staples, USPO
78mm	Androscoggin River
75	US 202, rd 4, rd 100, to Auburn, **E** 🅖 Irving/dsl, Mobil/Subway/dsl, 🍴 Danny Boy's Rest., Dunkin Donuts, 🛏 Fireside Inn, 🅾 RV Camping, **W** 🄷
71mm	Royal River
66mm	toll plaza
63	US 202, rd 115, rd 4, to ME 26, Gray, **E** 🅖 Gulf, Mobil, Sunoco, 🍴 China Gray, Dunkin Donuts, Goody's Pizza, Subway, McDonald's, 🅾 NAPA, TrueValue
59mm	**service plaza both lanes,** Citgo/dsl, Chicago Pizza, Starbucks, atm
55mm	Piscataqua River
53	to ME 26, ME100 W, N Portland, **E** 🅖 Irving/Circle K/Subway/dsl, 🍴 Bernie's Rest., Dunkin Donuts, 🅾 🄷, Hannaford Foods
52	to I-295, US 1, Freeport
48	ME 25, to Portland, **E** 🅖 Citgo, 🍴 Applebee's, Asian Bis-tro, Full Belly Deli, Little Caesar's, Quiznos, Subway,

ME

🅖 = gas 🍴 = food 🛏 = lodging 🅞 = other   Copyright 2012 - The Next Exit®

INTERSTATE 95 CONT'D

Exit	Services
48	Continued
	🛏 Portland Inn, 🅞 AT&T, BigLots, BJ's Whse/gas, Chevrolet, CVS Drug, Fiat, Jo-Ann Fabrics, Lowe's, Radio Shack, **W** 🅖 Citgo, Irving/Circle K/dsl, Mobil, 🍴 Amato's Rest., Burger King, Dunkin Donuts, Denny's, Friendly's, KFC/Taco Bell, McDonald's, Panera Bread, Pizza Hut, Ruby Tuesday, Seasons Grille, Wendy's, 🛏 Fireside Inn, Howard Johnson, Motel 6, Super 8, Travelodge, 🅞 Advance Parts, CarQuest, Ford, Harley-Davidson, Home Depot, Hyundai, Kohl's, Lexus/Toyota/Scion, Lincoln/Mercury, NAPA, Shaw's Foods/Osco Drug, Sullivan Tire, Suzuki, Tire Whse, VIP Parts/service, vet
47	to ME 25, Rand Rd
47mm	Stroudwater River
46	to ME 22, Congress St, same as 45
45	to US 1, Maine Mall Rd, S Portland, **E** 🅖 Citgo/dsl, Sunoco, 🍴 Burger King, Bugaboo Creek Steaks, Chicago Grill, Chili's, Chipotle Mexican, ChuckeCheese, Coldstone, Cracker Barrel, Dunkin Donuts, FoodCourt, Friendly's, Great Wall Chinese, IHOP, Jimmy the Greek Rest., Longhorn Steaks, Macaroni Grill, McDonald's, Newick's Lobster House, Old Country Buffet, Olive Garden, On the Border, Panera Bread, Pizza Hut, Ruby Tuesday, Tim Horton, Weathervane Seafood, Wendy's, 🛏 Comfort Inn, Courtyard, Days Inn, EconoLodge, Fairfield Inn, Hampton Inn, Homewood Suites, Wyndham, 🅞 Best Buy, Dick's, $Tree, Hannaford Foods, Honda, JC Penney, Macy's, Michael's, Nissan, PetCo, Sears/auto, Staples, TJ Maxx, TownFair Tire, Verizon, mall, **W** 🍴 Applebee's, Starbucks, 🛏 Holiday Inn Express, Marriott, 🅞 Old Navy, Target
44	I-295, N (from nb), to, S Portland, Scarborough, **1 mi E on ME 114** 🅖 Cumberland/Dunkin Donuts, 🍴 Chia Sen Chinese, KFC/Taco Bell, Little Caesars, Shogun Japanese, Subway, TX Roadhouse, 🛏 Residence Inn, TownePlace Suites, 🅞 🏥, Lowe's, NAPA, Sam's Club/gas, Shaw's Foods/Osco Drug, VIP Parts/service, Walmart/Dunkin Donuts
42mm	Nonesuch River
42	to US 1, **E** 🛏 Courtyard, Homewood Suites, 🅞 Cabela's, Scarborough Downs Racetrack (seasonal)
36	I-195 E, to Saco, Old Orchard Beach, **E** 🛏 Hampton Inn, 🅞 KOA, Paradise Park Resort RV
35mm	**E** 🛏 Ramada Inn/Saco Hotel Conference Ctr
33mm	Saco River
32	ME 111, to Biddeford, **E** 🅖 Irving/Circle K/Subway/dsl, 🍴 Amato's Sandwiches, Dunkin Donuts, Ruby Tuesday, Wendy's, 🛏 Best Value Inn, Comfort Suites, 🅞 🏥, AAA, AutoZone, Osco Drug, Shaw's Foods, VIP Parts/Service, Walmart, **W** 🅖 Cumberland/dsl, 🍴 Applebees, Casa Fiesta Mexican, Kobe Japanese, Longhorn Steaks, Olive Garden, Panera Bread, 🅞 Best Buy, GNC, Home Depot, Kohl's, Lowe's, Old Navy, Petsmart, Staples, Target, TJ Maxx, TownFair Tire, Verizon
25mm	Kennebunk River
25	ME 35, Kennebunk Beach, **E** 🛏 Turnpike Motel
24mm	**service plaza both lanes sb** Citgo/dsl, Burger King, Hersheys, Popeye's, Starbucks, Z Mkt, **nb** Citgo/dsl, Burger King, Hershey's, Sbarro's, Starbucks, Z Mkt, atm,
19.5mm	Merriland River
19	ME 9, ME 109, to Wells, Sanford, **W** to Sanford RA
7mm	Maine Tpk begins/ends, toll booth

Exit	Services
7	ME 91, to US 1, The Yorks, **E** 🅖 Gulf, Irving/Circle K/dsl, Mobil/dsl, Shell, 🍴 China Bistro, Norma's Rest., Wildcat Pizza, 🛏 Best Western, Microtel, 🅞 🏥, Chrysler/Dodge/Jeep, Curves, Ford, Hannaford Foods, NAPA, Rite Aid, TrueValue, vet, last exit before toll rd nb
5.5mm	**weigh sta nb**
5mm	York River
4mm	**weigh sta sb**
3mm	**Welcome Ctr nb, full** ♿ **facilities, info,** 🅒, 🅵, **vending, litter barrels, petwalk**
2	(2 & 3 from nb), US 1, to Kittery, **E on US 1** 🅖 Irving/Circle K/dsl/scales, 7-11/dsl, 🍴 DQ, McDonald's, Subway, Sunrise Grill, Tasty Thai, Weathervane Seafood Rest., 🛏 Blue Roof Motel, Days Inn, Kittery Motel, Northeaster Hotel, Ramada Inn, 🅞 Outlets/Famous Brands, vet
1	ME 103 (from nb, no re-entry), to Kittery
0mm	Maine/New Hampshire state line, Piscataqua River

INTERSTATE 295 (PORTLAND)

Exit	Services
52mm	I-295 begins/ends on I-95 exit 103
51	ME 9, ME 126, to Gardiner, Litchfield Toll Plaza, **W** toll plaza, service plaza, Citgo, Burger King, Hersheys, Quiznos, Starbucks, ZMkt
49	US 201, to Gardiner
43	ME 197, to Richmond, **E** 🅖 Irving/Quincey's Deli/dsl, 🍴 Dunkin Donuts, Subway
37	ME 125, Bowdoinham
31b a	ME 196, to Lisbon, Topsham, **E** 🅖 Irving/Circle K/Dunkin Donuts/Subway, Gibbs/dsl, 🍴 Arby's, Fairground Cafe, Little Caesars, McDonald's, 99 Rest., Romeo's Pizza, Ruby Tuesday, Starbucks, Tim Horton's, Wendy's, 🅞 Best Buy, Dick's, $Tree, Hannaford Foods, Home Depot, Jo-Ann Fabrics, PetCo, Radio Shack, Rite Aid, Target, Tire Whse, Toyota/Scion, Verizon, VIP Parts/service, **W** 🅖 Xpress Stop
30mm	Androscoggin River
28	US 1, Bath, **1 mi E on US 1** 🅖 Cumberland/Subway/dsl, Irving/dsl, Mobil/dsl, Shell, 🍴 Amato's, McDonald's, 🛏 Best Value Inn, Comfort Inn, Fairfield Inn, Knights Inn, Travelers Inn, 🅞 🏥, Chevrolet/Mazda, Chrysler/Dodge/Ford, Jeep, repair
24	to Freeport (from nb), **services 1 mi E on US 1**
22	ME 125, to Pownal, **E on US 1** 🅖 Irving/Circle K, 🍴 Azure Cafe, Corsican Rest., Friendly's, Jameson Rest., McDonald's, Sam's Italian, Siano's Pizza, Starbucks, Subway, 🅞 CVS Drug, LL Bean, USPO, outlets/famous brands, **W** to Bradbury Mtn SP
20	Desert Rd, Freeport, **E** 🅖 Irving/Circle K, 🍴 Antonia's Pizza, Buck's BBQ, Dunkin Donuts, Friendly's, Subway, Thai Garden Rest., 🛏 Comfort Suites, Econolodge, Hampton Inn, Holiday Inn Express, Super 8, 🅞 Shaw's Foods, outlets/famous brands, RV camping
17	US 1, Yarmouth, **E rest area both lanes, full** ♿ **facilities, info,** 🍴 Day's Takeout, Muddy Rudder Rest., 🛏 Best Western, 🅞 Ford, Delorme Mapping, **W** 🅖 Citgo/dsl, Gulf/dsl, 🍴 Dominos Pizza, McDonald's, Pat's Pizza, 🅞 Ace Hardware, Hannaford Foods, NAPA, VIP Parts/service, vet
15	US 1, to Cumberland, Yarmouth, **W** 🅖 Irving/dsl, Mobil, 🍴 Romeo's Pizza, 233 Grill, 🛏 Brookside Motel, 🅞 AT&T, Rite Aid, Verizon
11	to I-95, ME Tpk (from sb)
	I-295 begins/ends on I-95, exit 103.

Left margin (top to bottom): N, S, PORTLAND, BIDDEFORD, **ME**

Center margin (top to bottom): KITTERY, N, S, BATH, YARMOUTH

INTERSTATE 295 (PORTLAND)

N ↑ ↓ S

Exit	Services
10	US 1, to Falmouth, **E** ⛽ Citgo/dsl, Irving/dsl, 🍴 Dunkin Donuts, Foreside Rest., House of Pizza, Hugs Italian, Lotus Japanese, McDonald's, Ricetta's Pizza, Starbucks, Stony Field Cafe, Subway, Wendy's, ⊙ Ace Hardware, Audi/VW, Mazda, Radio Shack, Rite Aid, Shaw's Foods, Walmart
9mm	Presumpscot River
9	US 1 S, ME 26, to Baxter Blvd
8	ME 26 S, Washington Ave, **E** ⊙ U-Haul
7	US 1A, Franklin St, **E** ⊙ AAA, CarQuest, Freightliner, NAPA, Walgreens
6b a	US 1, Forest Ave, **E** ⛽ Citgo, ⊙ 🅷, Firestone/auto, USPO, **W** ⛽ Mobil/dsl, 🍴 Arby's, Burger King, Leonardo's Pizza, Stavro's Pizza, Whaddipita, ⊙ CVS Drug, Hannaford Foods, U of SME

P O R T L A N D

5b a	ME 22, Congress St, **E** 🍴 Amato's Rest., Denny's, D'Angelos, Dunkin Donuts, Lang's Chinese, McDonald's, 🏨 La Quinta, ⊙ 🅷, Sullivan Tire, **W** ⛽ Citgo/Dunkin Donuts, Mobil/dsl, 🍴 Anania's Italian, 🏨 Clarion
3mm	Fore River
4	US 1 S, to Main St, to, S Portland, **US 1 S E** services on US 1
3	ME 9, to Westbrook St, no sb return, **W** ⛽ Citgo/dsl, Irving/Circle K/dsl, 🍴 Buffalo Wild Wings, Olive Garden, Outback Steaks, Seadog Brew Co., Subway, Wild Willy's Burger, ⊙ Chevrolet, Home Depot, Marshalls
2	to US 1 S, S Portland, **services E** on US 1 ⛽ Irving/Circle K/dsl, Mobil, 7-11, 🍴 Dunkin Donuts, Governor's Rest., 🏨 Best Western, Howard Johnson, Knights Inn, Super 8, ⊙ Discount Tire
1	to I-95, to US 1, **multiple services E on US 1**, same as 2 I-295 begins/ends on I-95, exit 44.

MARYLAND

INTERSTATE 68

H A N C O C K

E ↑ ↓ W

C U M B E R L A N D

Exit	Services
82c	I-70 W, to Breezewood. I-68 begins/ends on I-70, exit 1.
82b	I-70 E, US 40 E, to Hagerstown
82a	US 522, Hancock, **N** Chevrolet, Chrysler/Dodge/Jeep, **S** ⛽ Sheetz/24hr, 🍴 Hardee's, Pizza Hut, Park'n Dine, Weaver's Rest., 🏨 Best Value Inn, Super 8, ⊙ $General, Happy Hills Camping, Sav-a-Lot Foods
77	US 40, MD 144, Woodmont Rd, **S** RV camping
75mm	runaway truck ramp eb
74mm	**Sideling Hill rest area/exhibit both lanes, full ♿ facilities, vending,** 1269 ft (seasonal)
74	US 40, Mountain Rd (no return from eb)
73mm	Sideling Hill Creek
72mm	truck ramp wb
72	US 40, High Germany Rd, Swain Rd, **S** ⛽ BP/dsl
68	Orleans Rd, **N** ⛽ Exxon/dsl
67mm	Town Hill, elevation 940 ft
64	MV Smith Rd, **S** to Green Ridge SF HQ, scenic overlook, 🅲, 1040 ft
62	US 40, 15 Mile Creek Rd, **N** Billmeyer Wildlife Mgt Area
58.7mm	Polish Mtn, elevation 1246 ft
57mm	Town Creek
56mm	Flintstone Creek
56	MD 144, National Pike, Flintstone, **S** ⛽ Flintstone Petroleum
52	MD 144, Pleasant Valley Rd (from eb), National Pike
50	Pleasant Valley Rd, **N** 🍴 Lakeside Grill, Signature's Grill, 🏨 Rocky Gap Lodge/golf/rest., ⊙ to Rocky Gap SP
47	US 220 N, MD 144, Dehaven Rd (from wb), Old National Pike, Bedford, same as 46
46	US 220 N, Dehaven Rd, Baltimore Pike, Naves Crossroads, **N** 🏨 Cumberland Motel, ⊙ Advance Parts, Foodland, vet, **S** 🍴 Puccini's Rest.
45	Hillcrest Dr, **S** ⛽ BP/dsl
44	US 40A, Baltimore Ave, Willow Brook Rd, to Allegany Comm Coll, **S** 🅷, to Allegany Comm Coll
43d	Maryland Ave, **N** 🏨 Holiday Inn, ⊙ 🅷, USPO, **S** 🍴 Chick-fil-A, Papa John's, Quizno's, ⊙ AutoZone, Martin's Foods/gas
43c	(from wb), same as 43b

F R O S T B U R G

43b	Maryland Ave, **N** 🍴 McDonald's, 🏨 Holiday Inn, ⊙ Family$, **S** ⛽ Citgo/dsl, 🍴 Papa John's, Pizza Hut/Taco Bell, Roy Rogers, Wendy's
43a	to WV 28A, Beall St, Industrial Blvd, to Cumberland, **N** ⛽ Sheetz
42	US 220 S, Greene St, Ridgedale
41	Seton Dr (from wb, no directory turn)
41mm	Haystack Mtn, elev 1240 ft
40	US 220 S, to US 40A, Vocke Rd, La Vale, **N** ⛽ BP/dsl, Exxon/repair, Sunoco, 🍴 Arby's, Asian Garden, Bob Evans, Burger King, D'Atri Rest., DQ, Denny's, Grand China, KFC, LJ Silver, McDonald's, Pizza Hut, Ruby Tuesday, Subway, TX Grill, Wendy's, 🏨 Best Western/rest, Comfort Inn, Slumberland Motel, Super 8, ⊙ 🅷, Advance Parts, CVS Drug, $General, Harley-Davidson, Jo-Ann Fabrics, Lowe's, Mr Tire, Staples, st police, **S** 🍴 Applebee's, Dragon China Buffet, CiCi's Pizza, Ponderosa, 🏨 Red Roof Inn, ⊙ BonTon, $Tree, JC Penney, Kohl's, Martin's Foods/gas, Sears/auto, Walmart, mall
39	US 40A (from wb), same as 40
34	MD 36, to Westernport, Frostburg, **N** ⛽ BP, Sheetz, 🍴 Burger King, Fox's Pizza, McDonald's, Peking House, Pizza Hut, Subway, Taco Del Mar, 🏨 Days Inn, Hampton Inn, ⊙ 🅷, CarQuest, $General, Family$, Food Lion, Rite Aid, **S** to Dans Mtn SP
33	Midlothian Rd, to Frostburg, **N** 🅷, **S** to Dans Mt SP
31mm	weigh sta eb
30mm	Big Savage Mtn, elevation 2800 ft
29	MD 546, Finzel, **N** 🍴 Hen House Rest., ⊙ Mason-Dixon Camping (4mi/seasonal), **S** Savage River Lodge Rest.
25.8mm	eastern continental divide, elevation 2610 ft
24	Lower New Germany Rd, to US 40A, **S** to New Germany SP, to Savage River SF
23mm	Meadow Mtn, elevation 2780 ft
22	US 219 N, to Meyersdale, **N** ⛽ BP/dsl/24hr, 🍴 /Arby's/dsl/scales/24hr, 🍴 Burger King, Penn Alps Rest., Subway, 🏨 Elliott House Inn, ⊙ $Discount, $General, Foodland, TrueValue Hardware, Hilltop Fruit Mkt, NAPA, Rite Aid, **S** ⛽ BP/dsl, 🏨 Comfort Inn, ⊙ New Germany SP, Savage River SF
20mm	Casselman River
19	MD 495, to US 40A, Grantsville, **N** ⛽ Exxon/dsl,

INTERSTATE 68 CONT'D

Exit	Services
19	Continued Sunoco/dsl, ⓕ Parkside Grill, ⓛ Casselman Motel/rest., ⓞ Beachy's Drug, CarQuest, Chevrolet, USPO
15mm	Mt Negro, elevation 2740 ft
14mm	Keyser's Ridge, elevation 2880 ft
14b a	US 219, US 40 W, Oakland, **N** ⓖ Citgo/7-11/dsl, BP/Ridge/dsl/rest., ⓕ McDonald's, repair
6mm	Welcome Ctr eb, full ♿ facilities, info, Ⓒ, 🚻, litter barrels, vending, petwalk
4.5mm	Bear Creek
4mm	Youghiogheny River
4	MD 42, Friendsville, **N** ⓖ BP/dsl, Marathon/dsl, ⓕ Jubilee Junction Rest., Old Mill Rest., ⓛ Yough Valley Motel, ⓞ S&S Mkt, USPO, **S** ⓛ Sunset Inn, ⓞ to Deep Creek Lake SP, camping
0mm	Maryland/West Virginia state line

INTERSTATE 70

Exit	Services
	I-70 begins/ends in Baltimore at Cooks Lane.
94	Security Blvd N, **S** ⓖ Shell
91b a	I-695, **N** off exit 17 ⓖ Exxon, Sunoco, ⓕ Burger King, 5 Guys Burgers, McDonald's, Panera Bread, Popeye's, Quizno's, ⓛ Best Western, ⓞ Best Buy, Ford, Macy's, Old Navy, Sears/auto, SuperFresh Foods, mall, **S** ⓖ BP/repair, Shell, ⓕ Dunkin Donuts, Subway, Wendy's, ⓛ Day's Inn, Motel 6, Quality Inn, ⓞ Chevrolet, Nissan
87b a	US 29 (exits left from wb) to MD 99, Columbia, **2 mi S** on **US 40** ⓖ BP/dsl, Shell, Sunoco, ⓕ Boston Mkt, Burger King, Checker's, Crab Shanty, Domino's, Dunkin Donuts, Jerry's Subs, McDonald's, Oriental Rest., Papa John's, Qdoba Mexican, Quizno's, Subway, ⓞ Acura/Infiniti, Advance Parts, Cadillac/Chevrolet, Carmax, Curves, Ford, Giant Foods, Home Depot, Honda, Mars Foods, Mr Tire, NAPA, Nissan, Rite Aid, Safeway Foods, 7-11, SuperFresh Food, Walmart
83	US 40, Marriottsville (no EZ wb return), **2 mi S** ⓛ Turf Valley Hotel/Country Club/rest.
82	US 40, E (from eb), same as 83
80	MD 32, Sykesville, **N** golf, **S** ⓖ Citgo, ⓕ Subway
79mm	weigh/insp sta wb, Ⓒ
76	MD 97, Olney, **S** ⓖ Citgo
73	MD 94, Woodbine, **N** ⓖ Shell, ⓕ Baskin Robbins, China Yee, Dunkin Donuts, Harvest Chicken, McDonald's, Pizza Hut, Subway, ⓞ $Tree, Food Lion, Ramblin Pines RV Park (6mi), **S** ⓖ BP/dsl, Citgo
68	MD 27, Mt Airy, **N** ⓖ BP/Blimpie/dsl, 7-11, Shell, ⓕ Arby's, Burger King, China Taste, Domino's, KFC/Taco Bell, Ledo's Pizza, McDonald's, Papa John's, Pizza Hut, Subway, TCBY, ⓞ Ace Hardware, Food Lion, Goodyear, Mr Tire, Radio Shack, Rite Aid, Safeway, SuperFresh Foods, Walmart/auto, vet, **S** ⓖ Exxon/dsl, Shell, ⓕ 4 Seasons Rest., ⓛ Budget Inn
66mm	truckers parking area eb
64mm	weigh/insp sta eb
62	MD 75, Libertytown, **N** ⓖ Shell, ⓕ Baskin Robbins, Domino's, Dunkin Donuts, McDonald's, Morgan's Grill, ⓞ Food Lion, vet, New Market Hist Dist
59	MD 144
57mm	Monocacy River

Exit	Services
56	MD 144, **N** ⓖ Citgo, Sheetz, ⓕ Beijing, Burger King, JR's Pizza, McDonald's, Roy Rogers, Taco Bell, Waffle House, Wendy's, ⓞ $General, to Hist Dist **S** ⓞ Triangle RV Ctr
55	South St, **1 mi N** ⓖ Citgo, Pacific Pride, Sheetz
54	Market St, to I-270, **N** ⓖ Costco/gas, ⓛ Travelodge, **S** ⓖ Exxon/dsl, Lowest Price, 7-11, Sheetz, Shell, SouStates/dsl, ⓕ Arby's, Bob Evans, Burger King, Checker's, Cracker Barrel, El Paso Cantina, Jerry's Rest., KFC, Longhorn Steaks, McDonald's, Papa John's, Peking Gourmet, Popeye's, Roy Rogers, Ruby Tuesday, Subway, Waffle House, Wendy's, ⓛ Days Inn, Econolodge, Fairfield Inn, Hampton Inn, Holiday Inn Express, Sleep Inn, ⓞ Aamco, Audi, Best Buy, Buick, Chrysler, CVS Drug, Ford/Lincoln/Mercury/Isuzu, Home Depot, Honda, Hyundai, JC Penney, Kohl's, Lowes Whse, Michael's, Nissan, Ross, Sam's Club, Sears/auto, Staples, Tires+, Volvo, Walmart, mall
53b a	I-270 S, US 15 N, US 40 W, to Frederick
52b a	US 15 S, US 340 W, Leesburg
49	US 40A, Braddock Heights, **N** on US 40 ⓖ Chevron, Citgo/dsl, Exxon/dsl, Freestate/dsl, GetGo, Shell, Sunoco, ⓕ Arby's, Bob Evans, Boston Mkt, Burger King, Casarico Mexican, Denny's, Fritchie's Rest., Ground Round, Hunter's Rest., McDonald's, Miyako Japanese, Mtn View Diner, Outback Steaks, Pizza Hut, Popeye's, Red Horse Rest., Red Lobster, Roy Rogers, Starbucks, Subway, Taco Bell, Wendy's, ⓛ Comfort Inn, Holiday Inn, ⓞ Ⓗ, Advance Parts, CVS Drug, Ford/Subaru, Giant Eagle Foods, Home Depot, JC Penney, Jo-Ann Fabrics, K-Mart, Merchant Tire, Mr. Tire, PepBoys, 7-11, Toyota, Weis Foods, st police, **S** to Washington Mon SP, camping
48	US 40 E, US 340 (from eb, no return), **1 mi N** same as 49
42	MD 17, Myersville, **N** ⓖ Exxon, Sunoco/dsl/24hr, ⓕ Burger King, McDonald's, Myersville Rest., ⓞ to Gambrill SP (6mi), Greenbrier SP (4mi), **S** ⓖ BP/dsl
39mm	rest area both lanes, full ♿ facilities, Ⓒ, 🚻, vending, litter barrels, petwalk
35	MD 66, to Boonsboro, **S** ⓖ Sheetz (1mi), ⓞ to Greenbrier SP, camping
32b a	US 40, Hagerstown, **0-3 mi N** ⓖ BP, Exxon/24hr, 7-11, Sunoco, ⓕ Baskin-Robbins/Dunkin Donuts, Bob Evans, Burger King, Cancun Cantina, Denny's, DQ, 5 Guys Burgers, Hong Kong Chinese, KFC, Ledo's Pizza, McDonald's, Pacific Ocean Buffet, Pizza Hut, Popeye's, Quizno's, Subway, Super Buffet, Taco Bell, TX Roadhouse, ⓛ Best Western, Clarion, Comfort Suites, Days Inn, EconoLodge, Hagerstown Hotel, Hampton Inn, Sheraton, Super 8, ⓞ Ⓗ, Advance Parts, Aldi Foods, AT&T, Cadillac/Chevrolet, Chrysler/Dodge/Jeep, CVS Drug, $General, $Tree, Goodyear/auto, Martin's Foods, Mercedes, Nissan, Scion/Toyota, Suzuki, Weis Foods, **S** ⓞ Buick/GMC, Honda, Kia, Subaru, VW
29b a	MD 65, to Sharpsburg, **N** ⓖ Exxon/dsl, Sheetz, ⓕ FoodCourt, Longhorn Steaks, Starbucks, ⓞ Ⓗ, Prime Outlets/famous brands, st police, **S** ⓖ Shell/dsl, ⓕ Burger King, Cracker Barrel, McDonald's, Waffle House, Wendy's, ⓛ Sleep Inn, ⓞ Safari Camping, to Antietam Bfd
28	MD 632, Hagerstown
26	I-81, N to Harrisburg, S to Martinsburg
24	MD 63, Huyett, **N** ⓖ 🌭/Subway/dsl/24hr, Sheetz (2mi), **S** ⓞ KOA (2mi), C&O Canal
18	MD 68 E, Clear Spring, **N** ⓖ BP, Chevron, ⓕ McDonald's, ⓛ Sleep Inn, **S** ⓖ Exxon/dsl, ⓕ Wendy Hill Café
12	MD 56, Indian Springs, **S** ⓖ Exxon/dsl, ⓞ Ft Frederick SP
9	US 40, E (from eb, exits left), Indian Springs

MD

Left margin I-68: E / W

Left margin I-70: BALTIMORE, E / W

Right margin: FREDERICK, HAGERSTOWN

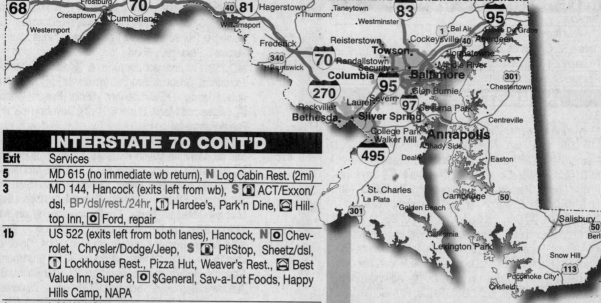

INTERSTATE 70 CONT'D

Exit	Services
5	MD 615 (no immediate wb return), **N** Log Cabin Rest. (2mi)
3	MD 144, Hancock (exits left from wb), **S** 🅿 ACT/Exxon/dsl, BP/dsl/rest./24hr, 🍴 Hardee's, Park'n Dine, 🛏 Hilltop Inn, 🅾 Ford, repair
1b	US 522 (exits left from both lanes), Hancock, **N** 🅾 Chevrolet, Chrysler/Dodge/Jeep, **S** 🅿 PitStop, Sheetz/dsl, 🍴 Lockhouse Rest., Pizza Hut, Weaver's Rest., 🛏 Best Value Inn, Super 8, 🅾 $General, Sav-a-Lot Foods, Happy Hills Camp, NAPA
1a	I-68 W, US 40, W to Cumberland
0mm	Maryland/Pennsylvania state line, Mason-Dixon Line

INTERSTATE 81

Exit	Services
12mm	Maryland/Pennsylvania state line
10b a	Showalter Rd, 🛏 to e
9	Maugans Ave, **E** 🅿 BP, Sheetz, Shell/Domino's/dsl, 🍴 McDonald's, Pizza Hut, Quizno's, Taco Bell, Waffle House, 🛏 Hampton Inn, 🅾 AutoZone, Curves, CVS Drug, $General, Martin's Foods/gas, vet, **W** 🍴 Burger King, 🛏 Microtel, 🅾 Kenworth, Volvo
7b a	MD 58, Hagerstown, same as 6
6b a	US 40, Hagerstown, **E** 🅿 Liberty, Shell, 🛏 Clarion, Days Inn, EconoLodge, 🅾 🖽, **W** 🍴 Arby's, Chipotle Mexican, 5 Guys Burgers, IHOP, KFC, McDonald's, Panera Bread, Uno Pizza, Ryan's, Starbucks, Subway, TGIFriday's, Wendy's, 🅾 AT&T, Best Buy, Dick's, $Tree, Home Depot, Marshall's, Petsmart, Walmart
5	Halfway Blvd, **E** 🅿 AC&T/dsl, 🍴 Bob Evans, Boston Mkt, Buffalo Wild Wings, Burger King, Chick-fil-A, China Garden, ChuckeCheese, CiCi's Pizza, Coldstone, Crazy Horse Steaks, El Ranchero Mexican, Garfield's Rest., Golden Corral, McDonald's, Olive Garden, Orchid Garden, Outback Steaks, Pizza Hut, Popeye's, Quizno's, Red Lobster, Roy Rogers, Ruby Tuesday, Sakura Steaks, Shoney's, Taco Bell, Wendy's, 🛏 Aloft Hotel, Country Inn&Suites, Holiday Inn Express, Homewood Suites, Motel 6, Plaza Hotel, SpringHill Suites, 🅾 AT&T, BonTon, CVS Drug, $Tree, Firestone/auto, Ford/Lincoln/Mercury, Hyundai, JC Penney, K-Mart, Kohl's, Lowe's, Macy's, Martin's Foods/gas, Michael's, PetCo, Ross, Sam's Club/gas, Sears/auto, Staples, Target, mall, **W** 🍴 Exxon/dsl/scales/24hr, 🍴/McDonald's/Subway/dsl/scales/24hr, 🛏 Super 8, 🅾 Freightliner
4	I-70, E to Frederick, W to Hancock, to I-68
2	US 11, Williamsport, **E** 🅿 AC&T/dsl, **W** 🅿 Exxon/dsl, Sunoco/dsl/24hr, 🍴 China 88, McDonald's, Waffle House, 🛏 Red Roof Inn, 🅾 KOA (4mi)
1	MD 63, MD 68, Williamsport, **E** 🅿 Bowman/dsl, 🅾 Jellystone, KOA, to Antietam Bfd, **W** 🅿 Citgo, 🅾 NAPA
0mm	Maryland/West Virginia state line, Potomac River

INTERSTATE 83

Exit	Services
38mm	Maryland/Pennsylvania state line, Mason-Dixon Line
37	to Freeland
36	MD 439, Bel Air, **W** 🅿 Sub-Shop, 🍴 Maryland Line Inn Grill, 🅾 Holiday Travel Park (5mi), Morris Meadows Camping (5mi)
35mm	**weigh/insp sta sb**
33	MD 45, Parkton, **E** USPO
31	Middletown Rd, to Parkton, golf
27	MD 137, Mt Carmel, Hereford, **E** 🅿 Exxon/dsl, 🍴 Subway, 🅾 Graul's Foods, Hereford Drug, Mt Carmel Drug, NAPA, USPO, vet
24	Belfast Rd, to Butler, Sparks
20	Shawan Rd, Hunt Valley, **E** 🅿 BP, Exxon/dsl, 🍴 Burger King, Caribou Coffee, Carmine's Pizza, Carrabba's, Chipotle Mexican, McDonald's, Noodles&Co, Outback Steaks, Quizno's, Panera Bread, Subway, Wendy's, Wong's Kitchen, 🛏 Chase Suites, Courtyard, Embassy Suites, Hampton Inn, Hunt Valley Marriott, Ramada Ltd, 🅾 Giant Foods, Goodyear/auto, Sears/auto, 7-11, Wegman's Foods, mall, vet
18	Warren Rd (from nb, no return), Cockeysville, **E** 🅿 Exxon, 🛏 Residence Inn, services, E on York Rd
17	Padonia Rd, Deereco Rd, **E** 🅿 BP/dsl, Hess, Shell, 🍴 Applebee's, Bob Evans, Chili's, Macaroni Grill, Wendy's, 🛏 Day's Hotel, Extended Stay America, 🅾 Audi/VW, Chevrolet, Goodyear/auto, Mars Foods, Mr Tire, Porsche, Shopper's Foods, Subaru, Target, USPO, services **E** on York Rd
16b a	Timonium Rd, **E** 🅿 BP, Petro/Subway, Sunoco/dsl, 🍴 Baja Fresh, McDonald's, 🛏 Crowne Plaza, Red Roof Inn, 🅾 Infiniti/Nissan, Rite Aid
14	I-695, N
13	I-695 S, Falls Rd, 🖽, st police
12	Ruxton Rd (from nb, no return)
10b a	Northern Parkway, **E** 🅿 Exxon, Shell, 🅾 🖽
9b a	Cold Spring Lane
8	MD 25, N (from nb), Falls Rd
7b a	28th St, **E** 🖽, **W** Baltimore Zoo
6	US 1, US 40T, North Ave, downtown

E ↕ **W** / **N** ↕ **S**   **HAGERSTOWN**

N ↕ **S**   **BALTIMORE**

MD

INTERSTATE 83 CONT'D

Exit	Services
5	MD Ave (from sb), downtown
3	Chase St, Gilford St, downtown
2	Pleasant St (from sb), downtown
1	Fayette St, I-83 begins/ends, downtown Baltimore

INTERSTATE 95

Exit	Services
110mm	Maryland/Delaware state line
109b a	MD 279, to Elkton, Newark, E FLYING J/Patriot Farms/dsl/scales/24hr/@, Shell/dsl, Cracker Barrel, KFC/Taco Bell, McDonald's, Waffle House, Days Inn, Elkton Lodge, Hampton Inn, Knights Inn, La Quinta, Motel 6, H, Blue Beacon, W TA/Subway/dsl/24hr/@, 7-11, WaWa, Comfort Suites, to U of DE
100	MD 272, to North East, Rising Sun, E FLYING J/Denny's/dsl/LP/24hr, Sunoco/dsl, Burger King, Dunkin Donuts, Empire Rest., Frank's Pizza, McDonald's, Waffle House, Wendy's, Comfort Inn, Holiday Inn Express, Advance Parts, AT&T, $General, $Tree, Food Lion, PetCo, Rite Aid, Verizon, Walgreens, Walmart/Subway, auto repair, st police, to Elk Neck SP, W Citgo, Best Western, zoo
96mm	Chesapeake House service area (exits left from both lanes), Exxon/dsl, Sunoco/dsl, Burger King, Popeye's, Quiznos, Starbucks, gifts
93	MD 275, to Rising Sun, US 222, to Perryville, E Exxon/dsl, /Subway/dsl/scales/24hr, Denny's, KFC/Taco Bell, Ramada Inn, H, Perryville Outlets/famous brands, Riverview Camping
92mm	weigh sta/toll booth
91.5mm	Susquehanna River
89	MD 155, to Havre de Grace (last nb exit before toll), 1-3 mi E Burger King, Chesapeake Grill, Dunkin Donuts, MacGregor's Rest., McDonald's, Waffle House, Best Budget Inn, Super 8, Van Divers B&B, H, W to Susquehanna SP
85	MD 22, to Aberdeen, E BP/dsl, 7-11, Shell/dsl, Royal Farms/dsl, Applebee's, Arby's, Baskin-Robbins/Dunkin Donuts, Bob Evans, Burger King, Durango's, Family Buffet, KFC, Korea House, Little Caesars, Mamie's Cafe, McDonald's, Olive Tree Italian, Panera Bread, Papa John's, Pizza Hut, Rita's Custard, Subway, Taco Bell, Wendy's, Clarion, Days Inn, Hilton Garden, Holiday Inn, La Quinta, Red Roof Inn, Super 8, Travelodge, $General, $Tree, Home Depot, Mars Foods, Radio Shack, Rite Aid, ShopRite Foods, Target, Verizon, Walgreens, auto repair, museum, E Courtyard, Residence Inn
81mm	MD House service area (exits left from both lanes), Exxon/dsl, Sunoco/dsl, Phillips Seafood, Roy Rogers, Sbarro's, Starbucks, TCBY, gifts
80	MD 543, to Riverside, Churchville, E BP/Burger King, 7-11, Shell/Quiznos/dsl, Sunoco, Arby's, China Moon, Cracker Barrel, McDonald's, Pizza Hut, Riverside Crabs, Riverside Grille, Riverside Pizzeria, Ruby Tuesday, Subway, Waffle House, Candlewood Suites, Country Inn&Suites, Extended Stay America, Homewood Suites, SpringHill Suites, Wingate Inn, Bar Harbor RV Park (4mi), Rite Aid, ShopRite Foods, Verizon
77b a	MD 24, to Edgewood, Bel Air, E BP/dsl, Citgo/dsl, Exxon/dsl, Royal Farms/dsl, Denny's, Dimitri's Pizza, El Rodeo, My 3 Sons Rest., Waffle House, Best Western, Days Inn, Hampton Inn, Holiday Inn Express, Ramada

Exit	Services
77b a	Continued Inn, Sleep Inn, urgent care, W Exxon/dsl, WaWa/dsl, Chick-fil-A, KFC/Taco Bell, McDonald's, Starbucks, H, BJ's Whse, $Tree, Lowe's, Target, Walmart/Subway, Wegman's Foods
74	MD 152, Fallston, Joppatowne, E BP/dsl, Citgo/dsl, Exxon/dsl, Sheetz, Shell/dsl, WaWa/dsl, Dunkin Donuts, Friendly's, KFC, Subway, Venitian Palace, Wendy's, Edgewood Motel, Super 8, H, Toyota (1mi), W Royal Farms/dsl
70mm	Big Gunpowder Falls
67b a	MD 43, to White Marsh Blvd, US 1, US 40, E on MD 7 BP/dsl, Chick-fil-A, 5 Guys Burgers, McDonald's, Noodles&Co, Panera Bread, Qdoba Mexian, Starbucks, Subway, Best Buy, Carmax, Chevrolet, Dick's, Lowe's, Michael's, Nissan, Target, Tire Discounters, W on White Marsh Blvd gas Exxon/dsl, 7-11, Bertucci's, Buffalo Wild Wings, Burger King, Chili's, China Wok, Coldstone, Don Pablo, Lin's Chinese, McDonald's, Olive Garden, PF Chang's, Red Brick Sta., Red Lobster, Red Robin, Ruby Tuesday, Starbucks, Taco Bell, TGIFriday's, Wendy's, Z-Burger, Zack's Hotdogs, Fairfield Inn, Hampton Inn, Hilton Garden, Residence Inn, AT&T, Barnes&Noble, Giant Foods, JC Penney, Macy's, Old Navy, Sears/auto, Staples, USPO, Verizon, mall, to Gunpowder SP
64b a	I-695 (exits left), E to Essex, W to Towson
62	to I-895 (from sb)
61	US 40, Pulaski Hwy, E BP, Shell/dsl, McDonald's
60	Moravia Rd
59	Eastern Ave, W BP/dsl, Exxon, Royal Farms/dsl, WaWa, Broadway Diner, McDonald's, Subway, Wendy's, H, AT&T, Shoppers Foods
58	Dundalk Ave, (from nb), E Citgo, Sunoco
57	O'Donnell St, Boston St, E TA/Buckhorn/Subway/dsl/scales/motel/@, McDonald's, Best Western
56	Keith Ave
56mm	McHenry Tunnel, toll plaza (north side of tunnel)
55	Key Hwy, to Ft McHenry NM, last nb exit before toll
54	MD 2 S, to Hanover St, W downtown, H, Harris Teeter
53	I-395 N, to MLK, W downtown, Oriole Park
52	Russell St N, W H
51	Washington Blvd
50.5mm	inspection sta nb
50	Caton Ave, E Citgo, Hess/dsl, Quest, Shell/dsl, Caton House, McDonald's, Polock Johnny Sausages, Motel 6, Aldi Foods, Toyota/Scion, auto repair, W H
49b a	I-695, E to Key Bridge, Glen Burnie, W to Towson, to I-70, to I-83
47b a	I-195, to MD 166, to BWI , to Baltimore
46	I-895, to Harbor Tunnel Thruway
43b a	MD 100, to Glen Burnie, 1 mi E on US 1 Exxon/Wendy's, Xtra, Best Western
41b a	MD 175, to Columbia, E Citgo, Exxon/dsl, Shell/dsl, TA/Country Pride/Subway/dsl/scales/24hr/@, Arby's, Burger King, Fortune Star Chinese, Julia's, McDonald's, Panda Express, Starbucks, Comfort Suites, Holiday Inn, La Quinta, Red Roof Inn, Sleep Inn, Super 8, Mom's Organic Mkt, W Exxon, Applebee's, Bob Evans, Fat Burger, Houlihan's, Mamma Lucia, McDonald's, Mimi's Cafe, Olive Garden, On the Border, TGIFriday's, Homewood Suites, Studio+, H, Best Buy, Costco/gas, Lowe's, Office Depot, Royal Farms, 7-11, Trader Joe's, to Johns Hopkins U, Loyola U

N ← S

ABERDEEN

BALTIMORE

MD

INTERSTATE 95

Exit	Services
38b a	MD 32, to Ft Meade, **2 mi E on US 1** 🅖 BP, Royal Farms, Shell/dsl, 🍴 Burger King, Dunkin Donuts, McDonald's, Subway, Taco Bell, 🛏 Comfort Inn, Extended Stay America, 🅞 to BWI 🛬
37mm	**Welcome Ctr both lanes, full ♿ facilities, info, 🍴, 🚻, vending, litter barrels, petwalk, RV Dump**
35b a	MD 216, to Laurel, **E** 🅖 Exxon, Shell/dsl, 🍴 McDonald's, Subway, 🅞 Weis Food/drug
34mm	Patuxent River
33b a	MD 198, to Laurel, **E** 🅖 Exxon, 🅞 🏥, **W** 🅖 Exxon/Blimpie, Shell, 🍴 Outback Steaks, Starbucks, 🛏 Holiday Inn
31	MD 200 (toll)
29	MD 212, to Beltsville, **W** 🅖 Exxon/Blimpie/dsl, 🍴 Baskin-Robbins, Danny's Subs, KFC, McDonald's, Taco Bell, The Villa Rest., Wendy's, 🛏 Comfort Inn, Sheraton, 🅞 Cherry Hill Park, CVS Drug, Giant Foods
27	I-495, S around Washington
25b a	US 1, Baltimore Ave, to Laurel, College Park, **E** 🅖 BP/dsl, Chevron, Exxon/dsl, 7-11, Shell/24hr, 🍴 Arby's, Buffalo Wild Wings, Burger King, Dickey's BBQ, Domino's, El Mexicano, Jerry's Subs, KFC, McDonald's, Moose Creek Steaks, Papa John's, Pizza Hut/Taco Bell, Potbelly's, Quizno's, Subway, 3 Bro's Rest., Wendy's, 🛏 Holiday Inn, 🅞 URGENT CARE, Advance Parts, Costco, CVS Drug, PetCo, Radio Shack, Rite Aid, US Agri Library, Verizon, **W** 🅖 BP/24hr, Shell, Xtra, 🍴 Burger King, Dunkin Donuts, China Buffet, College Park Diner, Hard Times Cafe, IHOP, Pizza Hut, Starbucks, Taco Bell, 🛏 Clarion, Comfort Inn, Days Inn, EconoLodge, Hampton Inn, Howard Johnson, Ramada Ltd, Super 8, 🅞 GNC, Home Depot, Honda, Hyundai, Nissan, Shoppers Foods, VW, vet, to U of MD
24	(from sb), to metro
23	MD 201, Kenilworth Ave, **E** 🛏 Marriott/rest., **1 mi W on Greenbelt** 🅖 Shell, 🍴 Atlanta Bread, Boston Mkt, Checker's, Chipotle Mexican, KFC, McDonald's, Popeye's, Quizno's, Silver Diner, TGIFriday's, Wendy's, William's Bistro, 🛏 Courtyard, Hilton Garden, Residence Inn, 🅞 Cadillac, CVS Drug, Giant Food/drug, Jo-Ann Fabrics, Marshall's, Staples, Target
22	Baltimore-Washington Pkwy, **E** to NASA
20b a	MD 450, Annapolis Rd, Lanham, **E** 🍴 Burger King, Jerry's Subs, McDonald's, Red Lobster, 🛏 Best Western, Days Inn/rest., Red Roof Inn, 🅞 Ford/KIA, **W** 🅖 BP, Chevron/dsl, Liberty, 7-11, Shell, Sunoco/24hr, Texaco, 🍴 Bojangles, Domino's, Dunkin Donuts, El Gran Chaparral, 5 Guys Burgers, IHOP, KFC, Manny&Olga's Pizza, Popeye's, Quizno's, Subway, Wendy's, 🛏 Sheraton, 🅞 🏥, Aamco, Advance Parts, Chevrolet, Chrysler/Dodge/Jeep, Curves, CVS Drug, $Value, Foodway Foods, Giant Foods, JustTires, Lincoln/Mercury, Lowe's, Office Depot, Radio Shack, Shoppers Foods, Staples
19b a	US 50, to Annapolis, Washington
17	MD 202, Landover Rd, to Upper Marlboro, **E** 🍴 Jasper's Rest., Outback Steaks, Ruby Tuesday, 🛏 Holiday Inn Express, Radisson, **W** 🅞 FedEx Center, Sears/auto
16	Arena Dr, **E** 🍴 Bugaboo Creek Steaks, Carolina Kitchen, Chick-fil-A, ChuckeCheese, 5 Guys Burgers, Golden Corral, Kobe Japanese, Momma Rosa, Panda Express, Qdoba, Quizno's, Stonefish Grill, 🅞 **W** to Arena
15	MD 214, Central Ave, **E** 🛏 Extended Stay America, Hampton Inn, 🅞 to Six Flags, **W** 🅖 Exxon/dsl, Liberty,

WASHINGTON DC AREA

15	Continued Shell, Texaco/dsl, 🍴 A&W/LJ Silver, Checker's, Dunkin Donuts, KFC, IHOP, Jerry's Subs, McDonald's, Panda Express, Pizza Hut, Subway, Taco Bell, Wendy's, 🛏 Comfort Inn, Country Inn&Suites, 🅞 URGENT CARE, Family$, Goodyear/auto, Home Depot, NTB, Staples, U-Haul
13	Ritchie-Marlboro Rd, Capitol Hgts, **W** 🅖 WaWa, 🍴 Chick-fil-A, 🅞 BJ Whse/gas
11	MD 4, Pennsylvania Ave, to Upper Marlboro, **W** 🅖 Exxon, Shell, Sunoco, 🍴 Applebee's, Arby's, Domino's, 5 Guys Burgers, IHOP, LJ Silver, Old Country Buffet, Pizza Hut, Starbucks, Subway, Taco Bell, Wendy's, 🅞 CVS Drug, $Tree, Hancock Fabrics, JC Penney, Marshall's, PetCo, Shoppers Foods, Staples, Target, st police
9	MD 337, to Allentown Rd, **E** 🅖 Shell/repair, Texaco, 🍴 Arby's, Checker's, Dunkin Donuts, McDonald's, Popeye's, 🛏 Days Inn, Quality Inn, Super 8, 🅞 🏥, U-Haul, to Andrews AFB, **W** 🅖 Sunoco
7	MD 5, Branch Ave, to Silver Hill, **E** 🅖 Exxon, Getty, Sunoco, 🍴 Dunkin Donuts, Wendy's, **W** 🅖 Shell/Subway/dsl, 🍴 Red Lobster, 🛏 Holiday Inn Express, 🅞 🏥, BMW, Chrysler/Dodge/Jeep, Ford, KIA, Lincoln/Mercury, Nissan, Scion/Toyota, VW
4b a	MD 414, St Barnabas Rd, Marlow Hgts, **E** 🅖 Citgo/dsl, Zip-in, 🍴 Burger King, Checker's, IHOP, KFC, McDonald's, Outback Steaks, Wendy's, loding Red Roof Inn, 🅞 CVS Drug, $Tree, GNC, Home Depot, K-Mart, Old Navy, Petsmart, Safeway Foods, Staples, **W** 🅖 Exxon/dsl, Shell/autocare, 🍴 China Best, McDonald's, Subway, 🅞 Family$
3b a	MD 210, Indian Head Hwy, to Forest Hgts, **E** 🅖 Chevron, Shell, Sunoco, 🍴 Dunkin Donuts, Popeye's, Ranch House Rest., Subway, Taco Bell, 🛏 Clarion, Comfort Inn, Red Roof Inn, 🅞 Advance Parts, Aldi Foods, Radio Shack, Sav-A-Lot Foods, Shoppers Foods, USPO, **W** 🅖 BP/dsl/24hr, Pure, Shell, Texaco, 🍴 Burger King, McDonald's, Papa John's, Popeye's, Subway, 🍴 CVS Drug, Family$, Giant Foods, Goodyear/auto, Radio Shack, Rite Aid, 7-11
2b a	I-295, N to Washington
0mm	Maryland/Virginia state line, Potomac River, Woodrow Wilson Bridge

INTERSTATE 97

Exit	Services
17	I-695. I-97 begins/ends on I-695.
16	MD 648, Ferndale, Glen Burnie, **E** 🅖 BP, Shell, 🍴 Hong Kong Cafe, KFC, McDonald's, Rita's Custard, Wendy's, 🅞 $General, Giant Foods, **W** 🅖 Citgo
15b a	MD 176 W, Dorsey Rd, Aviation Blvd, **E** 🅖 BP, Shell, 🍴 KFC, McDonald's, Wendy's, **W** 🅞 to BWI, st police
14b a	MD 100, Ellicott City, Gibson Island

MD

INTERSTATE 97 CONT'D

Exit	Services
13b a	MD 174, Quarterfield Rd, E 🅖 AP/dsl, Gulf, 7-11, 🍴 Subway, The Grill, 🅞 WaWa, W 🅖 Shell/dsl, 🍴 Chick-fil-A, Pizza Hut, Quiznos, 🅞 AT&T, Kohl's, Lowe's, Rite Aid, Sam's Club/dsl, Shoppers Foods, Walmart
12	MD 3, New Cut Rd, Glen Burnie E on Veterans Hwy 🅖 BP, Gulf, Royal Farms, WaWa, 🍴 Domino's, KFC, McDonald's, Taco Bell, 🅞 CVS Drug, vet, E 🅖 Exxon, Sunoco, 🍴 Burger King, Fortune Cooky, Friendly's, Hardee's, Squisto NY Pizza, Subway, Wendy's, 🅞 🅷, Ace Hardware, Giant Foods, Goodyear/auto, Target, Walgreens
10b a	Benfield Blvd, Severna Park, E 🅖 BP/dsl, Exxon/Quiznos/dsl, Transit/dsl/scales, 🍴 Baskin-Robbins/Dunkin Donuts, Hella's Rest., Ledo's Pizza, 🅞 KOA, 7-11, access to same as 12
7	MD 3, MD 32, Bowie, Odenton, E motel
5	MD 178 (from sb, no EZ return), Crownsville
0mm	I-97 begins/ends on US 50/301.

INTERSTATE 270 (ROCKVILLE)

Exit	Services
32	I-270 begins/ends on I-70, exit 53.
31b a	MD 85, N 🅖 Lowest Price/dsl, 7-11, Sheetz/24hr, Shell/24hr, SouStates/dsl, 🍴 Applebee's, Arby's, Bob Evans, Burger King, Checker's, Chick-fil-A, El Ranchero Mexican, Golden Corral, Houlihan's, Jerry's Pizza, KFC, Longhorn Steaks, McDonald's, Olive Garden, Panera Bread, Papa John's, Peking Gourmet, Perkin's, Pizza Hut, Popeye's, Roy Rogers, Ruby Tuesday, Silver Diner, Subway, Taco Bell, UNO Grill, Waffle House, Wendy's, 🛏 Days Inn, EconoLodge, Holiday Inn Express, Sleep Inn, Travelodge, 🅞 Aamco, Audi, Barnes&Noble, Best Buy, Buick/GMC, Chrysler/Dodge/Jeep, Costco/gas, Harley-Davidson, Home Depot, Hyundai, JC Penney, Kohl's, Lincoln/Mercury, Lowe's, Macy's, Michael's, Mr Tire, Nissan, Office Depot, Ross, Sam's Club, Sears/auto, Staples, Tires+, Volvo, vet, Walmart, mall, S 🅖 BP, 🍴 Chipotle Mexican, Cracker Barrel, Firehouse Subs, IHOP, Macaroni Grill, Maggie Moo's, McDonald's, Mediterranean Grill, Mimi's Cafe, Panda Express, Quizno's, Starbucks, TGIFriday's, 🛏 Comfort Inn, Courtyard, Extended Stay America, Fairfield Inn, Hampton Inn, Hilton Garden, MainStay Suites, Residence Inn, 🅞 Honda, Toyota
30mm	Monocacy River
28mm	scenic view, no restrooms (wb only)
26	MD 80, Urbana, N 🅖 Exxon, 7-11, 🍴 Buffalo Wild Wings, China Taste, Dunkin Donuts, Foster's Grill, Ledo's Pizza, McDonald's, Waffle House
22	MD 109, to Barnesville, Hyattstown, N 🅖 BP/dsl, 🍴 Hyattstown Deli, 🅞 Food+
21mm	weigh/insp sta both lanes
18	MD 121, to Clarksburg, Boyds, N Little Bennett Pk, camping, gas, S Blackhill Pk
16	MD 27, Father Hurley Blvd, to Damascus, N 🅖 Chevron, Exxon, Free State/dsl, Sunoco, 🍴 Applebee's, Bob Evans, Burger King, Jersey Mike's Subs, McDonald's, Starbucks, Subway, 🛏 Extended Stay America, Hampton Inn, 🅞 AT&T, Best Buy, Giant Foods, GNC, Home Depot, Kohl's, Michael's, PepBoys, Petsmart, TJ Maxx, Target, Verizon, Walmart, S 🅖 BP, Exxon, 7-11, Shell, Sunoco, 🍴 Bailey's Grill, Baja Fresh, Burger King, Carrabba's, Chick-fil-A, Domino's, Dunkin Donuts, 5 Guys Burgers,

Exit	Services
16	Continued Hardtimes Cafe, IHOP, Jerry's Subs, Longhorn Steaks, McDonald's, Mi Rancho, Panera Bread, Pizza Hut, Quizno's, Red Robin, Ruby Tuesday, Starbucks, Subway, Taco Bell, Wendy's, 🛏 Fairfield Inn, Homestead Suites, 🅞 Giant Foods, Mercedes, NAPA, NTB, Office Depot, PetCo, Rite Aid, Safeway Foods, SmartCar, USPO, same as 15
15b a	MD 118, to MD 355, S 🅞 Honda, Nissan, same as 16
13b a	Middlebrook Rd (from wb)
11	MD 124, Quince Orchard Rd, N 🅖 Exxon, Shell, 🍴 Boston Mkt, ChuckeCheese, Honeybaked Ham, Ichiban Rest., KFC, McDonald's, Panera Bread, Popeye's, Subway, 🛏 Hilton, Holiday Inn, TownePlace Suites, Wyndham Garden, 🅞 Aamco, Acura, AT&T, Costco, CVS Drugs, Ford, Hyundai, JC Penney, JustTires, Lincoln/Mercury, Lord&Taylor, Macy's, Mazda, NAPA, Nissan, Ross, Sam's Club, Sears/auto, Toyota, VW, mall, S 🅖 Shell/dsl, 🍴 Chevy's Mexican, CiCi's Pizza, Jerry's Subs, Rita's Ice Cream, Starbucks, 🛏 Motel 6, 🅞 Advance Parts, Chevrolet, Chrysler/Dodge/Jeep, Giant Foods, JoAnn Fabrics, McGruder's Foods, Rite Aid, Staples, Seneca Creek SP
10	MD 117, Clopper Rd (from wb), same as 11
9b a	I-370, to Gaithersburg, Sam Eig Hwy, S on Washington Blvd 🅖 Chevron, 🍴 Joe's Crabshack, Macaroni Grill, Pizza Hut, Red Rock Grill, Subway, Uncle Julio's, 🛏 Courtyard, 🅞 Barnes&Noble, Kohl's, Target, Weis Mkt
8	Shady Grove Rd, N 🅖 Chevron, Shell/dsl, 🍴 Bugaboo Creek Steaks, Burger King, Red Lobster, 🛏 Sheraton, 🅞 AT&T, Best Buy, Home Depot, Office Depot, 7-11, vet, S 🍴 Thatsamore, 🛏 Courtyard, Crowne Plaza, Marriott, Residence Inn, Sleep Inn, SpringHill Suites, 🅞 🅷
6b a	MD 28, W Montgomery Ave, N 🅞 🅷, S 🅖 Shell, 🛏 Best Western
5b a	MD 189, Falls Rd
4b a	Montrose Rd, N 🅖 S 🍴 Starbucks, 🅞 Harris Teeter, Walgreens st police
2	I-270/I-270 spur diverges eb, converges wb
1	MD 187, Old Georgetown Rd, S 🅖 Exxon, 🍴 Hamburger Hamlet, 🅞 🅷, Balducci's Foods, Giant Foods, GNC
1b a	(I-270 spur)Democracy Blvd, E 🛏 Marriott, W 🅖 Exxon/dsl, Shell/dsl, 🅞 Macy's, Nordstrom's, Sears, mall
0mm	I-270 begins/ends on I-495, exit 35.

INTERSTATE 495 (DC)

See Virginia Interstate 495 (DC)

INTERSTATE 695 (BALTIMORE)

Exit	Services
48mm	Patapsco River, Francis Scott Key Br
44	MD 695 (from nb)
43mm	toll plaza
42	MD 151 S, Sparrows Point (last exit before toll sb), E 🅖 Citgo/dsl, 🅞 North Point SP
41	MD 20, Cove Rd, W 🅖 Royal Farms, WaWa, 🍴 Burger King, McDonald's, Subway
40	MD 150, MD 151, North Point Blvd, (nb only)
39	Merritt Blvd, W 🅖 BP, 🍴 Burger King, McDonald's, 🅞 Aldi Foods, $Tree, Ford, Giant Foods, Honda, Hyundai, JC Penney, Mazda, Mr Tire, Walmart
38b a	MD 150, Eastern Blvd, to Baltimore, E 🅖 Royal Farms, W 🍴 Applebee's, Arby's, Burger King, Cactus Willy's Steaks, Checker's, Chick-fil-A, Dunkin Donuts, 🅞 AT&T, Kia/Nissan, Sears/auto, Staples, Walgreens, mall
36	MD 702, S (exits left from sb), Essex

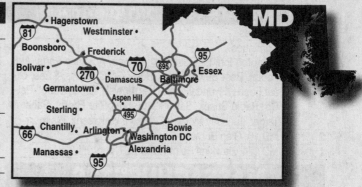

INTERSTATE 695 CONT'D (BALTIMORE)

Exit	Services
35	US 40, **N** 🅖 WaWa/gas, Sunoco, 🍴 Arby's, Bateman's Bistro, Chipotle Mexican, DQ, Dunkin Donuts, Grand Buffet, Longhorn Steaks, Panda Express, Panera Bread, 🅞 Aldi Foods, Best Buy, Harley-Davidson, Home Depot, NTB, Office Depot, PetCo, Sam's Club/gas, U-Haul, Walmart, same as 34
34	MD 7, Philadelphia Rd, **N** 🍴 McDonald's, Wendy's, 🛏 La Quinta, 🅞 🅷 $General, $Tree, Giant Foods, Goodyear/auto, Marshall's, **S** 🅖 Exxon, 🅞 Walgreens, same as 35
33b a	I-95, N to Philadelphia, S to Baltimore
32b a	US 1, Bel Air, **N** 🅖 Exxon, 🍴 Arby's, Bob Evans, Burger King, Denny's, Dunkin Donuts, Golden Corral, IHOP, McDonald's, Taco Bell, 🅞 BJ's Whse, $Tree, Giant Foods, K-Mart, Merchants Tire/auto, Mr Tire/auto, 7-11, Toyota/Scion, Verizon, vet, **S** 🅖 Shell, 🍴 Baskin-Robbins/Dunkin Donuts, Carrabba's, McDonald's, Rita's Custard, Subway, Szechuan Taste, 🅞 Goodyear/auto, 7-11
31c	MD 43, E (from eb, exits left)
31b a	MD 147, Harford Rd, **N** 🅖 BP, CF/dsl, 7-11, Shell/dsl, 🍴 Dunkin Donuts, Wendy's, 🅞 CVS Drug, Chrysler/Jeep, Goodyear/auto, Honda, Mars Foods, VW, Walgreens
30b a	MD 41, Perring Pkwy, **N** 🅖 Shell, 🍴 Burger King, Checker's, Chick-fil-A, Denny's, Dunkin Donuts, 5 Guys Burgers, KFC, McDonald's, Popeye's, Rita's Custard, Subway, Taco Bell, 🅞 Advance Parts, Chevrolet, Ford, Home Depot, Jo-Ann Fabrics, K-Mart, NTB, Office Depot, Ross, Safeway Foods, Shoppers Foods, Tuesday Morning, Verizon
29b	MD 542, Loch Raven Blvd, **S** 🅖 BP, Gulf, Hess, 🍴 Bel-Loch Diner, Hooters, McDonald's, Pizza Hut, Subway, 🛏 Comfort Inn, Ramada Inn, 🅞 Mr Tire, PepBoys
29a	Cromwell Bridge Rd, **S** 🛏 Best Western
28	Providence Rd, **S** 🅖 Citgo, 🅞 Royal Farms
27b a	MD 146, Dulaney Valley Rd, **N** Hampton NHS, **S** 🅖 Exxon, 🍴 Bahama Breeze, Cheesecake Factory, PF Chang's, Starbucks, Stoney River Steaks, 🛏 Sheraton, 🅞 Barnes&Noble, Fresh Mkt, Macy's, mall
26b a	MD 45, York Rd, Towson, **N** 🅖 BP, Exxon/dsl, Oceanic, Sunoco/dsl, 🍴 Dunkin Donuts, Friendly's, Ocean Pride Rest., Pizza Hut, Subway, 🅞 Best Buy, Kia, Mr Tire, NTB, Rite Aid, **S** 🅖 Exxon, Shell, 🍴 Burger King, 5 Guys Burgers, McDonald's, 🅞 CVS Drug, Goodyear/auto, Honda, Hyundai, Lexus, Safeway Foods, Walgreens, vet
25	MD 139, Charles St, **S** 🅷
24	I-83 N, to York
23b	MD 25, Falls Rd, **N** 🅖 Exxon/dsl
23a	I-83 S, MD 25 N, Baltimore
22	Greenspring Ave
21	MD 129, to Stevenson Rd, Park Hghts Rd
20	MD 140, Reisterstown Rd, Pikesville, **N** 🅖 Exxon/7-11/dsl, 🍴 Chipotle Mexican, 🅞 AT&T, Barnes&Noble, Trader Joe's, **S** 🅖 BP/dsl, Shell/dsl, Sunoco/Subway, 🍴 McDonald's, Olive Branch Italian, 🛏 Hilton, Ramada Inn, 🅞 Target, vet
19	I-795, NW Expswy
18b a	MD 26, Randallstown, Lochearn, **E** 🅖 Shell/dsl, Sunoco/dsl, 🍴 Baskin-Robbins/Dunkin Donuts, KFC, Subway, 🅞 $General, Family$, **W** 🅖 BP, Exxon/dsl Shell, 🍴 Burger King, Dunkin Donuts, McDonald's, Sonic, Subway, Taco Bell, 🅞 🅷 Firestone/auto, Giant Foods, 7-11, Shoppers Foods, Walgreens, auto repair
17	MD 122, Security Blvd, **E** 🅖 BP/repair, Shell, 🍴 City View Grill, Dunkin Donuts, McDonald's, Subway, Wendy's,

17	Continued 🛏 Days Inn, Motel 6, Quality Inn, 🅞 Chevrolet, Family$, Nissan, PriceRite Foods, Rite Aid, **W** 🅖 Exxon/dsl, Sunoco, 🍴 Burger King, 5 Guys Burgers, McDonald's, Panera Bread, Popeye's, Quiznos, Rita's Custard, 🛏 Best Western, 🅞 Best Buy, Ford, Macy's, Old Navy, Rite Aid, Sears/auto, mall
16b a	I-70, E to Baltimore, W to Frederick
15b a	US 40, Ellicott City, Baltimore, **E** 🅖 BP, 🍴 Burger King, Checker's, Chick-fil-A, ChuckECheese's, KFC, McDonald's, Panda Express, Quiznos, Shirley's Diner, Subway, 🛏 Comfort Inn, 🅞 BigLots, CVS Drug, Dodge, $Tree, Firestone/auto, Lowe's, Marshall's, Rite Aid, Ross, Safeway Foods/gas, Sam's Club/gas, Shoppers Foods, U-Haul, Walgreens, **W** 🅖 BP/dsl, Exxon, Gulf, Shell, 🍴 Applebee's, Bob Evans, CiCi's Pizza, McDonald's, Old Country Buffet, Popeye's, Starbucks, Subway, Taco Bell, TT Diner, 🛏 Ramada Ltd, 🅞 Aamco, Chrysler/Jeep, $Tree, Firestone/auto, Giant Foods, Goodyear/auto, Home Depot, Hyundai, Mr Tire, NTB, Office Depot, PepBoys, Petsmart, Staples, Toyota/Scion, Verizon, Walgreens, Walmart/McDonald's
14	Edmondson Ave, **E** 🅖 Sunoco, 🍴 Grilled Cheese&Co, 🅞 Royal Farms, **W** 🅖 CF, 🍴 Papa John's
13	MD 144, Frederick Rd, Catonsville, **W** 🅖 BP, CF, Gulf, 🍴 Baskin-Robbins/Dunkin Donuts, McDonald's, Subway, 🅞 7-11
12c b	MD 372 E, Wilkens, **E** 🅷
11b a	I-95, N to Baltimore, S to Washington
10	US 1, Washington Blvd, (from wb only), **E** 🅖 Royal Farms/dsl, 🍴 Chick-fil-A, Dunkin Donuts, 3 Bros Pizza, Quiznos, Wendy's, 🛏 Beltway Motel/rest., 🅞 Goodyear/auto, Home Depot, Office Depot, PetCo, Radio Shack, Walmart, **W** 🍴 Burger King
9	Hollins Ferry Rd, Lansdowne, **E** 🅖 BP, Sunoco/7-11/dsl, 🍴 Victor's Deli, 🅞 Royal Farms
8	MD 168, Nursery Rd, **N** 🅖 Exxon, Shell, 🍴 Hardee's, KFC, McDonald's, Taco Bell, Wendy's, 🛏 Motel 6, **S** 🅖 BP, Citgo/dsl, 🍴 G&M Rest., Happy Garden Chinese, Rita's Custard, Seasons Pizza
7b a	MD 295, **N** to Baltimore, **S** BWI 🛫
6b a	Camp Mead Rd (from eb)
5	MD 648, Ferndale, **N** 🅖 Shell, Xtra/7-11/dsl, 🍴 Checker's, Dunkin Donuts, Hot Wok, 🛏 Comfort Inn, 🅞 NAPA, police
4b a	I-97 S, to Annapolis
3b a	MD 2, Brooklyn Park, **S** 🅖 Exxon, Hess, Royal Farms/dsl, Shell, Sunoco, 🍴 Best Buffet, Bob Evans, BoneFish Grill, Checker's, Chick-fil-A, ChuckECheese's, Coldstone, Denny's, 5 Guys Burgers, Golden Corral, HipHop Fish&Chicken, KFC, McDonald's, Panera Bread, Pappas Rest., Pizza Hut, Qdoba, Quiznos, Starbucks, Subway, Taco Bell, 🛏 Days Inn, Extended Stay America,

MD

INTERSTATE 695 CONT'D (BALTIMORE)

E ↕ W

Exit	Services
3b a	Continued
	Hampton Inn, La Quinta, 🅞 Aamco, Advance Parts, Aldi Foods, Best Buy, BigLots, Buick/GMC, Dick's, $Tree, Giant Foods, Hyundai, Just Tires, Lowe's, Office Depot, PetCo, Radio Shack, Salvo Parts, ShopRite Foods, Subaru, Target, Tuesday Morning, Verizon, Walgreens, Walmart
2	MD 10, Glen Burnie
1	MD 174, Hawkins Point Rd, **S** 🅖 Citgo/deli/dsl

MASSACHUSETTS

INTERSTATE 84

STURBRIDGE   **E ↕ W**

Exit	Services
4 (11)	I-84 begins/ends on I-90, Exit 9.
3b a (9)	US 20, Sturbridge, **0-2 mi N** 🅖 Citgo, Cumberland Farms, Mobil/dsl, 🍴 Burger King, Friendly's, McDonald's, Piccadilly, Smokehouse BBQ, Thai Place, Village Pizza, Whistling Swan, 🏨 Hampton Inn, Motel 6, Quality Inn, Sturbridge Host Motel, Super 8, 🅞 🄷, USPO, **0-2 mi S** 🅖 BeeZee, Citgo/Xtra/Dunkin Donuts/Subway, NE TrkStp/dsl, 🍴 Applebee's, Cracker Barrel, Uno Pizzaria, Wendy's, 🏨 Comfort Inn, 🅞 Marshall's, Old Navy, Staples, Stop&Shop, Walmart
2 (5)	MA 131, to Old Sturbridge Village, Sturbridge, **S** 🏨 Days Inn, RV camping
4mm	🅟 **wb, litter barrels**
1 (2.5)	Mashapaug Rd, to Southbridge, **S** 🅖 Mobil/dsl/24hr, ⛽/dsl/rest./scales/24hr/@, 🍴 Roy Rogers, Sbarro's, 🏨 Travelodge
2mm	**weigh sta both lanes**
.5mm	🅟 area eb
0mm	Massachusetts/Connecticut state line

INTERSTATE 90

E ↕ W

Exit	Services
137mm	I-90 begins/ends on I-93, exit 20 in Boston.
25	to I-93, to downtown Boston
24	to I-93, to downtown Boston
22 (134)	Presidential Ctr, downtown
20 (132)	MA 28, Alston, Brighton, Cambridge, **N** 🏨 Courtyard, Doubletree Inn, 🅞 🄷, **S** 🅖 Sunoco
131mm	toll plaza
19 (130)	MA Ave (from eb), **N** 🍴 IHOP, McDonald's, 🏨 Day's Inn
17 (128)	Centre St, Newton, **N** 🏨 Sheraton, 🅞 Cadillac, Chevrolet, Honda, Nissan
16 (125)	MA 16, W Newton, **S** 🅖 Mobil/repair
15 (124)	I-95, **N** 🏨 Marriott
123mm	toll plaza
14 (122)	MA 30, Weston
117mm	**Natick Travel Plaza eb,** Gulf/dsl, McDonald's, Dunkin Donuts, info
13 (116)	MA 30, Natick, **S** 🅖 Getty, Gulf, Shell, 🍴 Bickford's, Boston Mkt, Bugaboo Creek Steaks, Burger King, Harvard's Steaks, Lotus Flower Chinese, McDonald's, Papagino's, Panera Bread, Quizno's, 🏨 Best Western, Red Roof Inn, 🅞 🄷, BJ's Whse, Home Depot, Isuzu, Kohl's, Lowe's, Macy's, Marshalls, Target, Walmart, mall, USPO
114mm	**Framingham Travel Plaza wb,** Gulf/dsl, Boston Mkt, McDonald's, info
12 (111)	MA 9, Framington, **N** 🅖 Getty, Hess, 🍴 Acapulco

MD MA

BOSTON AREA

Exit	Services
12 (111)	Continued
	Mexican, Dunkin Donuts, Molly Malone's Grill, Tin Alley Grill, 🏨 Motel 6, Sheraton, 🅞 🄷, **S** 🍴 Chef Orient, 🅞 Chrysler/Isuzu/Jeep, Target, Toyota/Scion, mall
11a (106)	I-495, N to NH, S to Cape Cod
105mm	**Westborough Travel Plaza wb,** Gulf/dsl, Boston Mkt, D'angelo, Dunkin Donuts, Papagino's, gifts
11 (96)	MA 122, to Millbury, **N** UMA Med Ctr
10a (95)	MA 146
94mm	Blackstone River
10 (90)	I-395 S, to Auburn, I-290 N, Worcester, **N** 🅖 Shell, 🍴 Piccadilly's, 🏨 Comfort Inn, Holiday Inn Express, **S** 🅖 Shell/repair/24hr, 🍴 Applebee's, D'angelo's, Dunkin Donuts, Friendly's, Wendy's, 🏨 Fairfield Inn, 🅞 🄷, CVS Drug, Hyundai, Park'n Shop, TJ Maxx
84mm	**Charlton Travel Plaza wb,** Exxon/dsl, McDonald's, info
80mm	**Charlton Travel Plaza eb,** Exxon/dsl, McDonald's, info, st police
79mm	toll plaza
9 (78)	I-84, to Hartford, NYC, Sturbridge, access to 🄷
67mm	Quaboag River
8 (62)	MA 32, to US 20, Palmer, **S on MA 32** 🅖 Hess/Godfather's, Pride, Shell/dsl, 🍴 Jimmy Chan's Chinese, McDonald's, Subway, Wendy's, 🅞 🄷, Big Y Foods, Buick/Chevrolet, CVS Drug, Rite Aid, repair/transmissions
58mm	Chicopee River
56mm	**Ludlow Travel Plaza wb,** Gulf/dsl, Boston Mkt, D'angelo's
55mm	**Ludlow Travel Plaza eb,** Gulf/dsl, McDonald's
7 (54)	MA 21, to Ludlow, **N** 🅖 Gulf, Pride, Sunoco, 🍴 Burger King, Dunkin Donuts, Friendly's, Joy's Rest., McDonald's, Subway, 🅞 🄷, Ace Hardware, Big Y Foods, CVS Drug, Jo-Ann Fabrics, NAPA, repair, **S** 🅖 Shell/dsl, 🍴 Taco Bell, 🏨 Comfort Inn
6 (51)	I-291, to Springfield, Hartford CT, **N** 🅖 Gulf, Pride/50's Diner/Subway/dsl, 🍴 Dr Deegan's Steaks, Dunkin Donuts, McDonald's, Po's Chinese, 🏨 Econolodge, Motel 6, 🅞 🄷, to Bradley Int ✈, Basketball Hall of Fame
5 (49)	MA 33, to Chicopee, Westover AFB, **N** 🅖 Gulf, 🍴 Applebee's, Arby's, Denny's, Dunkin Donuts, Friendly's, 99 Rest., Popeye's, Royal Buffet, Starbucks, Subway, Wendy's, 🏨 Days Inn, Hampton Inn, Quality Inn, 🅞 BJ's Whse/gas, Big Y Foods, Cadillac, Dodge, $Tree, Home Depot, Honda, Marshall's, Staples, Stop&Shop/gas, TownFair Tire, U-Haul, Walmart, mall, **S** 🅖 Pride/Dunkin Donuts/Subway/dsl, 🅞 Buick/GMC
46mm	Connecticut River
4 (46)	I-91, US 5, to Holyoke, W Springfield, **N on US 5** 🅖 Shell, 🍴 Dunkin Donuts, 🏨 Welcome Inn, **S on US 5** 🅖 Pride/dsl, 🍴 Dougnut Dip, Hooters, On the Border, Outback Steaks, Piccadilly's, Subway, 🏨 Knights Inn, Red Roof Inn, Springfield Inn, Super 8, 🅞 AAA, BMW, Honda/Lexus/Toyota/Scion, repair
41mm	st police wb
3 (40)	US 202, to Westfield, **N** 🅖 Mobil, 🍴 Amalfi Pizza, Dunkin Donuts, 🏨 Country Court Motel, **S** 🅖 Citgo/Subway/dsl, Shell, 🍴 Friendly's, Whip City Brewery/rest., Wendy's, 🏨 EconoLodge, Holiday Inn Express, 🅞 🄷, repair
36mm	Westfield River
35.5mm	**runaway truck ramp eb**
29mm	**Blandford Travel Plaza both lanes, S** Gulf/dsl, Honeydew Donuts, McDonalds, gifts, info, vending
20mm	1724 ft, highest point on MA Tpk

SPRINGFIELD

INTERSTATE 90 CONT'D

Exit	Services
14.5mm	Appalachian Trail
12mm	**parking area both lanes, litter barrels**
2 (11)	US 20, to Lee, Pittsfield, **N** 🅖 Citgo, Shell/dsl/24hr, Sunoco, 🍴 Arizona Pizza, Athena's Rest., Dunkin Donuts, Food Ct, Friendly's, Jonathan's Bistro, McDonald's, Orientaste, Red Apple Chinese, Simply Grillicious, Subway, Villa Pizza, 🛏 Pilgrim Inn, Sunset Motel, Super 8, 🅞 PriceChopper Foods, Rite Aid, True Value, **S** 🅖 JFJ's/repair, Lee/dsl, 🍴 Orient Taste, Subway, Villa Pizza, 🅞 Prime Outlets/famous brands
10.5mm	Hoosatonic River
8mm	**Lee Travel Plaza both lanes**, Gulf/dsl, McDonald's, TCBY, atm, bank, info, vending
4mm	**toll booth**, 🅒
1 (2)	MA 41 (from wb, no return), to MA 102, W Stockbridge, the Berkshires, **N** 🛏 Pleasant Valley Motel, 🅞 to Bousquet Ski Area
0mm	Massachusetts/New York state line

INTERSTATE 91

Exit	Services
55mm	Massachusetts/Vermont state line, call boxes
54mm	**parking area both lanes,** 🅿
28 (51)	US 5, MA 10, Bernardston, **E** 🍴 Bella Notte Ristorante, 🛏 Fox Inn, **W** 🅖 Sunoco, 🍴 Antonío's II Ristorante, Four-leaf Clover Rest., 🅞 Country Corner Store, RV camping, USPO
27 (45)	MA 2, **E** (exits left from sb), Greenfield, US 5 **E** 🅖 Gulf, Magic, Sunoco, 🍴 Burger King, Denny's Pantry, Dunkin Donuts, Friendly's, McDonald's, Subway, 🅞 🅷, Auburchon Hardware, AutoZone, Bond Parts, Buick/GMC, Chrysler/Dodge/Jeep, Honda, Walgreens
26 (43)	MA 2 W, MA 2A E, Greenfield, **E** 🅖 Mobil, Planet/dsl, 🍴 Applebee's, China Gourmet, D'Angelo, Dunkin Donuts, 🛏 Quality Inn, 🅞 🅷, Chevrolet, Ford/Lincoln/Mercury, Toyota, **W** 🅖 Irving/Circle K, Valero, 🍴 Asian Buffet, Friendly's, KFC/Pizza Hut/Taco Bell, McDonald's, 99 Rest., 🛏 CandleLight Motel, Days Inn, Hampton Inn, 🅞 Big Y Foods, BJ's Whse, $Tree, Family$, Home Depot, Hyundai, Staples, to Mohawk Tr
39mm	Deerfield River
37mm	**weigh sta both lanes**
25 (36)	MA 116 (from sb), S Deerfield, hist dist, camping, same as 24
24 (35)	US 5, MA 10, MA 116, Deerfield (no EZ return), **E** 🅖 Irving/Circle K/Dunkin Donuts/Subway/dsl, 🍴 Chandler's Rest., 🛏 Red Roof Inn, 🅞 Yankee Candle Co, vet, **W** 🅖 Roady's Trkstp/diner/dsl/24hr, 🍴 24hr Diner, 🛏 Whatley Inn
34.5mm	**parking area both lanes, no services**

Exit	Services
23 (34)	US 5 (from sb), **E** 🅞 Orchard Trailers, Rainbow Motel/camping
22 (30)	US 5, MA 10 (from nb), N Hatfield, **W** Diamond RV Ctr
21 (28)	US 5, MA 10, Hatfield, **W** 🅖 Sunoco, 🛏 Scottish Inn, 🅞 st police
20 (26)	US 5, MA 9, MA 10 (from sb), Northampton, **W** 🅖 Hess/dsl, Pride/Dunkin Donuts/dsl, 🍴 Burger King, D'angelo's, Domino's, KFC, McDonald's, PapaGino's Italian, Sakura, Taco Bell, 🅞 🅷, BigLots, Big Y Food/Drug, CVS Drug, Firestone/auto, Ford, GMC, Honda, NAPA, Radio Shack, Staples, Stop&Shop, Subaru, Toyota/Scion, TownFair Tire, U-Haul, Verizon, VW, Walgreens, Walmart/Subway, transmissions
19 (25)	MA 9, to Amherst, Northampton, **0-2 mi E** 🅖 Getty, Gulf, Phillips 66/Dunkin Donuts, Shell, 🍴 Butterfly Asian, 🛏 Hampton Inn, 🅞 🅷, Nissan, vet, to Elwell SP
18 (22)	US 5, Northampton, **E** 🍴 Page's Loft Rest., 🛏 Clarion, Country Inn&Suites (5mi), **W** 🅖 Shell/Dunkin Donuts, 🛏 Quality Inn, Northampton Hotel, 🅞 to Smith Coll
18mm	scenic area both lanes
17b a (16)	MA 141, S Hadley, **E** 🅖 Mobil/dsl, Shell/dsl, 🍴 Dunkin Donuts, Nick's Nest, Real China, Subway, 🛏 Days Inn, 🅞 Rite Aid, Walgreens, **W** to Mt Tom Ski Area
16 (14)	US 202, Holyoke, **W** Soldier's Home
15 (12)	to US 5, Ingleside, **E** 🅖 Shell, 🍴 Chicago Grill, Cracker Barrel, Friendly's, 99 Rest., Red Robin, Ruby Tuesday, 🛏 Holyoke Hotel, 🅞 🅷, AT&T, Barnes&Noble, Best Buy, JC Penney, Macy's, Old Navy, PetCo, Sears/auto, Target, mall, **W** 🛏 Homewood Suites
14 (11)	to US 5, to I-90 (Mass Tpk), E to Boston, W to Albany, **E** 🅷
13b a (9)	US 5 N, W Springfield, **E** 🅖 Pride/dsl, 🍴 Dougnut Dip, Hooters, On-the-Border, Outback Steaks, Piccadilly's, Shallot Thai, Subway, 🛏 Knights Inn, Red Roof Inn, Residence Inn, Springfield Inn, Super 8, 🅞 BMW, Lexus/Toyota/Scion, **W** 🅖 Mobil/dsl, Pride/dsl, 🍴 Arby's, Bertucci's, Burger King, Cal's Grill, Carrabba's, Chili's, D'angelo's, Friendly's, Geraldine's Rest., HomeTown Buffet, IHOP, KFC, Longhorn Steaks, McDonald's, 99 Rest.,

MA

INTERSTATE 91 CONT'D

SPRINGFIELD N ← → S

Exit	Services
13b a (9)	Continued
	Olive Garden, Panera Bread, Pizza Hut, Tokyo Cuisine, 🛏 Bel Air Inn, Candlewood Suites, Clarion, Days Inn, EconoLodge, Hampton Inn, Quality Inn, Red Carpet Inn, Travelodge, 🅾 AT&T, Chrysler/Dodge/Jeep, Costco, CVS Drug, Dick's, GNC, Home Depot, Honda, Kohl's, Mazda, Michael's, Nissan, PepBoys, Stop&Shop, Subaru, Town-Fair Tire, Verizon
12 (8.5)	I-391 N, to Chicopee
11 (8)	Birnie Ave (from sb), E 🅰 Mobil, 🅾 🅷
10 (7.5) *	Main St (from nb), Springfield, E 🅰 Mobil
9 (7)	US 20 W, MA 20A, E (from nb), E 🍴 McDonald's
8 (6.5)	I-291, US 20 E, to I-90, E downtown
7 (6)	Columbus Ave (from sb), E 🛏 Marriott, Sheraton, W 🅰 Pride/Subway/dsl, 🅾 to Basketball Hall of Fame
6 (5.5)	Springfield Ctr, W 🅰 Pride/Dunkin Donuts/Subway/dsl, 🍴 Starbucks
5 (5)	Broad St, E 🅰 Mobil/dsl, Shell/dsl, 🅾 Hyundai, W 🅰 Sunoco/dsl, 🍴 Chicago Grill, Subway, 🛏 Hilton Garden, 🅾 Buick/GMC, same as 4
4 (4.5)	MA 83, Broad St, Main St, E 🅰 Mobil/dsl, 🍴 Antonio's Grinders, 🅾 Hyundai, W 🅰 Sunoco, 🍴 Chicago Grill, Subway, 🛏 Hilton Garden 🅾 Buick/GMC, Chevrolet, same as 5
3 (4)	US 5 N, to MA 57, Columbus Ave, W Springfield, E 🅰 Sunoco, 🅾 Cadillac, W Chevrolet
2 (3.5)	MA 83, S (from nb), to, E Longmeadow, E 🍴 Friendly's
1 (3)	US 5, S (from sb)
0mm	Massachusetts/Connecticut state line, callboxes begin/end

INTERSTATE 93

N ← → S

Exit	Services
47mm	Massachusetts/New Hampshire state line, callboxes begin/end
48 (46)	MA 213 E, to Methuen, E 🅷
47 (45)	Pelham St, Methuen, E 🅰 Sunoco/24hr, 🍴 Dunkin Donuts, McDonald's, Outback Steaks, W 🅰 BP, Irving/Circle K/Subway/dsl, 🍴 Fireside Rest., NE Seafood, 🛏 Day's Hotel/rest., Guesthouse Inn, 🅾 Chrysler/Jeep
46 (44)	MA 110, MA 113, to Lawrence, E 🅰 BP/repair, Mobil, Shell, 🍴 Burger King, Dunkin Donuts, KFC/Taco Bell, McDonald's/24hr, PapaGino's, Pizza Hut, Taco Bell, 🅾 $Tree, 🅷, MktBasket Foods, Rite Aid, W 🅰 Citgo, Super, 🍴 Dunkin Donuts, Irish Cottage Rest., Jackson's Rest., Jay Gee's Ice Cream, Riverside Pizza, 🛏 Passport Inn
45 (43)	Andover St, River Rd, to Lawrence, E 🛏 Courtyard, Homewood Suites, Wyndham, W 🅰 Mobil/Dunkin Donuts, 🍴 Chateu Italian, Chili's, 🛏 La Quinta, Residence Inn, SpringHill Suites, 🅾 vet
44b a (40)	I-495, to Lowell, Lawrence, E 🅷
43 (39)	MA 133, N Tewksbury, E 🅰 Mobil/Dunkin Donuts, W 🍴 99 Rest
42 (38)	Dascomb Rd, East St, Tewksbury, W 🅰 Citgo/dsl, 🍴 Dunkin Donuts
41 (35)	MA 125, Andover, st police
40 (34)	MA 62, Wilmington
39 (33)	Concord St, E Shriners Auditorium
38 (31)	MA 129, Reading, W 🅰 Mobil/Dunkin Donuts/dsl, 🍴 Burger King, 99 Rest.
37c (30)	Commerce Way, Atlantic Ave, W 🍴 Chipotle Mexican, Starbucks, 🛏 Red Roof Inn, Residence Inn, 🅾 PetCo, Petsmart, Target, Verizon

BOSTON AREA

Exit	Services
37b a (29)	I-95, S to Waltham, N to Peabody
36 (28)	Montvale Ave, E 🅰 Mobil, 🍴 Deli Works, Dunkin Donuts, Kiotoya Japanese, 🛏 Courtyard, W 🅰 BP, Gulf, 🍴 Bickford's Grille, Dunkin Donuts, McDonald's, Polcari's Italian, Wendy's, 🛏 Best Western, Comfort Inn, 🅾 🅷
35 (27)	Winchester Highlands, Melrose, E 🅷 (no EZ return to sb)
34 (26)	MA 28, N (from nb, no EZ return), Stoneham, E 🅰 Mobil, 🍴 Friendly's, 🅾 🅷
33 (25)	MA 28, Fellsway West, Winchester, E 🅷
32 (23)	MA 60, Salem Ave, Medford Square, W 🛏 Hyatt Place, 🅾 🅷, to Tufts U
31 (22)	MA 16 E, to Revere (no EZ return sb), W 🅰 Fred's Gas, Mr. C's/dsl, 🍴 Avellino's Italian, Burger King, Dunkin Donuts, Pizza Hut, 🅾 AutoZone, Chrysler/Dodge/Jeep, Kia, Nissan, Staples
30 (21)	MA 28, MA 38, Mystic Ave, Somerville, W 🅰 Mr. C's/dsl, 🍴 Burger King, 🅾 AutoZone, Lincoln/Mercury
29 (20)	MA 28 (from nb), Somerville, E 🍴 Dunkin Donuts, 99 Rest., 🛏 La Quinta, 🅾 Home Depot, K-Mart, Staples, TJ Maxx, mall, W 🅰 Gulf, Hess, 🅾 Radio Shack, Stop&Shop, same as 30
28 (19)	Sullivans Square, Charles Town, downtown
27	US 1, N (from nb)
26 (18.5)	MA 28 N, Storrow Dr, North Sta, downtown
25	Haymarket Sq. Gov't Center
24 (18)	Callahan Tunnel, E 🚇
23 (17.5)	High St, Congress St, W 🛏 Marriott
22 (17)	Atlantic Ave, Northern Ave, South Sta, Boston World Trade Ctr
21 (16.5)	Kneeland St, ChinaTown
20 (16)	I-90 W, to Mass Tpk
19 (15.5)	Albany St (from sb), W 🅰 Mobil/dsl, 🅾 🅷
18 (15)	Mass Ave, to Roxbury, W 🅷
17 (14.5)	E Berkeley (from nb), E New Boston Food Mkt
16 (14)	S Hampton St, Andrew Square, W 🍴 Applebee's, Olive Garden, 🛏 Holiday Inn Express, 🅾 Best Buy, Home Depot, Marshall's, Old Navy, Stop&Shop/gas, Target, TJ Maxx
15 (13)	Columbia Rd, Everett Square, E 🛏 DoubleTree, 🅾 JFK Library, to UMA, W 🅰 Shell
14 (12.5)	Morissey Blvd (from nb no return), E JFK Library, W 🅰 Shell
13 (12)	Freeport St, to Dorchester, (from nb), W 🅰 BP, 7-11, 🍴 Boston Mkt, D'Angelo's, Deadwood Cafe, Freeport Tavern, 🛏 Comfort Inn, Ramada, 🅾 CVS Drug, Lambert's Mkt, NAPACare, Stop&Shop, Toyota/Scion
12 (11.5)	MA 3A, S (from sb, no EZ return), Quincy, E 🅰 Shell, repair, W 🅰 Gulf/Dunkin Donuts, Hess, 🍴 PapaGino's, 🅾 AutoZone, CVS Drug, Lincoln/Mercury, Staples, Verizon, Walgreens
11b a (11)	to MA 203, Granite Ave, Ashmont
10 (10)	Squantum Ave (from sb), Milton, W 🅷
9 (9)	Adams St, Bryant Ave, to, N Quincy, E 🅰 Milton Fuel, 🍴 Dunkin Donuts, W 🅰 Shell/repair
8 (8)	Brook Pkwy, to Quincy, Furnace, E 🅰 Gulf/dsl, Mobil/dsl
7 (7)	MA 3 S, to Cape Cod (exits left from sb), Braintree, E 🛏 Marriott
6 (6)	MA 37, to Holbrook, Braintree, E 🅰 Mobil/24hr, 🍴 Boardwalk Café, CA Pizza Kitchen, Cheesecake Factory, Chicago Grill, D'angelo's, 99 Rest., Legal Seafood, TGIFriday's, Tokyo Japanese, 🅾 Lord&Taylor, Macy's, Nordstrom's, Sears/auto, Target, mall, W 🅰 Citgo, 🍴 Ascari Café, Wood Road Deli, 🛏 Candlewood Suites, Extended Stay America, Hampton Inn, Holiday Inn Express, 🅾 Ford, VW

MA

INTERSTATE 93 CONT'D

Exit	Services
5b a (4)	MA 28 S, to Randolph, Milton, **E** 🗗 Citgo, Mobil/dsl, Mutual, Shell/dsl/24hr, 🍴 Domino's, Dunkin Donuts, La Scala, Lombardo's, Picadilly's Pub, Randolph Cafe, Sal's Calzone Rest., Stash's Pizza, Wong's Chinese, 🛏 Comfort Inn, 🅾 AT&T
4 (3)	MA 24, S (exits left from sb); to Brockton
3 (2)	MA 138 N, to Ponkapoag Trail, Houghtons Pond
2b a (1)	MA 138 S, to Stoughton, Milton, **E** golf, **W** 🗗 Mobil, BlueHill/dsl, Shell/dsl, 🍴 Dunkin Donuts, 🛏 Homewood Suites
1 (0)	I-95 N, S to Providence. I-93 begins/ends on I-95, exit 12.

INTERSTATE 95

Exit	Services
89.5mm	Massachusetts/New Hampshire state line, **Welcome Ctr/ rest area sb, full** ♿ **facilities,** 🚻, **litter barrels**
60 (89)	MA 286, to Salisbury, beaches, **E** 🗗 Mobil/dsl, 🍴 Cosmos Rest., Dunkin Donuts, Lena's Seafood Rest., 🅾 camping (seasonal)
59 (88)	I-495, S (from sb)
58b a (78)	rd 110, to I-495 S, to Amesbury, Salisbury, **E** 🗗 Sunoco/ Dunkin Donuts/Subway/dsl, 🍴 China Buffet, Niko's Place, Sylvan St Grille, Winner's Circle Rest., 🅾 A-1 Radiators, U-Haul, **W** 🗗 Irving Gas/Circle K, Mobil, Sunoco, 🍴 Acapulco's Mexican, Burger King, Dunkin Donuts, Friendly's, McDonald's, PapaGino's, 🛏 Fairfield Inn, 🅾 AT&T, Chevrolet, Stop&Shop, Verizon
57 (85)	MA 113, to W Newbury, **E** 🗗 Mobil, Shell/dsl/repair/24hr, Sunoco, 🍴 China One, d'Angelo's, Dunkin Donuts, Giuseppe's Italian, Hana Japan, McDonald's, Panera Bread, PapaGino's, Wendy's, 🅾 Ⓗ, GNC, K-Mart, Marshall's, MktBasket Foods, Radio Shack, Rite Aid, 7-11, Shaw's Foods, Verizon, Walgreens
56 (83)	Scotland Rd, to Newbury, **E** st police
55 (82)	Central St, to Byfield, **E** 🍴 Gen Store Eatery, Village Diner, **W** 🗗 Prime/dsl/repair
54b a (78)	MA 133, E to Rowley, W to Groveland
77mm	**weigh sta both lanes**
53b a (76)	MA 97, S to Topsfield, N to Georgetown
52 (74)	Topsfield Rd, to Topsfield, Boxford
51 (72)	Endicott Rd, to Topsfield, Middleton
50 (71)	US 1, to MA 62, Topsfield, **E** 🗗 Gulf/dsl, Mobil/dsl, 🅾 Honda, **W** 🍴 TX Roadhouse, 🛏 Knights Inn, 🅾 CVS Drug, Hyundai, Staples, Stop&Shop, st police
49 (70)	MA 62 (from nb), Danvers, Middleton, **W** same as 50
48 (69)	Hobart St (from sb), **W** 🍴 Italian Rest., 🛏 Comfort Inn, Extended Stay America, Motel 6, 🅾 Home Depot, Kia
47b a (68)	MA 114, to Middleton, Peabody, **E** 🗗 Gulf/Dunkin Donuts, Sunoco, 🍴 Grassfields Grill, Honey Dew Donuts, McDonald's, Olive Garden, Outback Steaks, PapaGino's, 🅾 Audi, BMW, Cadillac/Chevrolet, Chrysler/Dodge/Jeep, Fiat, Infiniti, Lexus, Lowe's, Mazda, NTB, Petsmart, Subaru, TJ Maxx, Toyota/Scion, Trader Joe's, Walmart, **W on US 1** 🗗 Hess, 🍴 Chili's, Hardcover Rest., TGIFriday's, 🛏 Motel 6, Residence Inn, TownePlace Suites, 🅾 Costco/ gas, Home Depot, LandRover, NAPA
46 (67)	to US 1, **W** 🗗 Best, Global, Gulf/dsl, Sunoco, 🍴 Dunkin Donuts, 🅾 auto repair
45 (66)	MA 128 N, to Peabody
44b a (65)	US 1 N, MA 129, **E** 🗗 Shell, **W** 🗗 7-11, Sunoco, 🍴 Bertucci's, Carrabba's, Dunkin Donuts, Santarpio's Pizza,

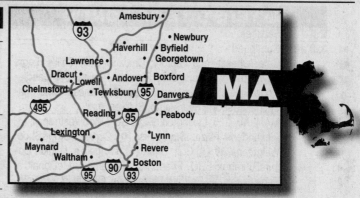

Exit	Services
44b a (65)	Continued
	Sonic, Wendy's, 🛏 Carriage House Hotel, Hampton Inn, Holiday Inn, Homewood Suites, SpringHill Suites, 🅾 Ⓗ
43 (61)	Walnut St, Lynnfield, **E** to Saugus Iron Works NHS (3mi), **W** 🛏 Sheraton, 🅾 golf
42 (62)	Salem St, Montrose, **E** 🗗 Irving/Circle K/Subway, Sunoco, 🍴 Dunkin Donuts, **W** 🛏 Sheraton
41 (60)	Main St, Lynnfield Ctr, **E** 🗗 Shell
40 (59)	MA 129, Wakefield Ctr, N Reading, **E** 🗗 Gulf, 🍴 Bellino's Italian, Honey Dew Donuts, 🅾 city park, vet, **W** 🗗 Gulf, 🍴 Dunkin Donuts, Mandarin Chinese, 🅾 Chevrolet, Mazda, REI
39 (58)	North Ave, Reading, **E** 🗗 Citgo/repair, 🅾 Saab/Volvo, city park, **W** 🗗 Shell/dsl, 🍴 Bertucci's, Chili's, Fuddrucker's, Longhorn Steaks, Oye's Rest., Starbucks, 🅾 Ⓗ, Home Depot, Honda, Mkt Basket Foods, Staples, Stop&Shop Foods, Verizon
38b a (57)	MA 28, to Reading, **E** 🗗 Gulf/repair, Hess/dsl, 🍴 Boston Mkt, Burger King, D'Angelo's/PapaGino's, Dunkin Donuts, 5 Guys Burgers, 99 Rest., Subway, 🅾 Advance Parts, AutoZone, CVS Drug, Ford, GNC, Marshall's, Radio Shack, Stop&Shop, **W** 🗗 Gulf, Mobil/dsl, Shell, Sunoco, 🍴 Anthony's Roastbeef, Burger King, Calariso's Farm Stand, Domino's, Dunkin Donuts, Harrow's Chicken Pies, McDonald's, Sam's Bistro, Starbucks
37b a (56)	I-93, N to Manchester, S to Boston
36 (55)	Washington St, to Winchester, **E** 🗗 BP/Dunkin Donuts, 🍴 FarEast Chinese, Fresh City, Munchies, Sal's Pizza, Starbucks, Subway, 🛏 Hilton, 🅾 Hogan's Tires, Jaguar, Nissan, Staples, Toyota, **W** 🗗 Sunoco, 🍴 Chicago Grill, d'Angelo's, Joe's Grill, McDonald's, 99 Rest., Panera Bread, Papa Gino's, Qdoba, Sarku Japan, 🛏 Courtyard, Fairfield Inn, Hampton Inn, Red Roof Inn, 🅾 AT&T, CVS Drug, Kohl's, Lowe's, Mkt Basket Foods, NTB, Office Depot, Radio Shack, Sullivan's Tire, TJ Maxx, mall
35 (54)	MA 38, to Woburn, **E** 🛏 Holiday Inn Select, 🍴 Scoreboard Grill, 🅾 Ⓗ, **W** 🗗 Mobil/dsl, 🍴 Applebee's, Beacon Grille, Dunkin Donuts, 🛏 Extended Stay Delux, 🅾 Stop&Shop Foods, city park
34 (53)	Winn St, Woburn
33b a (52)	US 3 S, MA 3A N, to Winchester, **E** 🍴 Bickford's Grille, Café Escadrille, Capital Grille, ChuckeCheese, Dunkin Donuts, Outback Steaks, Panera Bread, Paparazzi's, Subway, 🅾 Ⓗ, AAA, CVS Drug, Honda, Marshall's, Michael's, Roche Bro's Foods, **W** 🗗 Hess, Prime, 🛏 Marriott, 🅾 Ⓗ, Audi/Porsche, Kia, repair
32b a (51)	US 3 N, MA 2A S, to Lowell, **E** 🗗 Mobil, Shell, 🍴 Burger King, d'Angelo's, Dunkin Donuts, McDonald's, Subway, 🛏 Hilton Garden, 🅾 Best Buy, Mkt Basket Foods, Old Navy, PetCo, Trader Joe's, Verizon, other:, **W** 🍴 Border

MA

INTERSTATE 95 CONT'D

Exit	Services
32b a (51)	Continued Cafe, Cheesecake Factory, Chicago Grill, Chili's, Legal Seafoods, Macaroni Grill, Pizzaria Regina, 🛏 Candlewood Suites, Homestead Suites, ⊙ Barnes&Noble, Macy's, Nordstrom, Sears/auto, Staples, mall
31b a (48)	MA 4, MA 225, Lexington, **E** 🅿 Gulf, Mobil/dsl/repair, 🍴 Alexander's Pizza, Starbucks, ⊙ Curves, Stop&Shop, Walgreens, **W** 🅿 Gulf, Shell, 🍴 d'Angelo's, Dunkin Donuts, Firebox BBQ, Friendly's, Margarita's, McDonald's, Papa Gino's, 🛏 Bedford Plaza Hotel, Quality Inn, Travelodge, ⊙ Staples, TJ Maxx, vet
30b a (47)	MA 2A, Lexington, **E** 🅿 Sunoco/Dunkin Donuts/dsl, ⊙ H, **W** 🛏 ALoft, Element Hotel, ⊙ to MinuteMan NP, Hanscom AFB
46.5mm	travel plaza nb, Gulf/dsl, Honey Dew Donuts, McDonald's, gifts
29b a (46)	MA 2 W, Cambridge
28b a (45)	Trapelo Rd, Belmont, **E** 🅿 Gulf/dsl, Mobil/dsl, 🍴 Boston Mkt, Burger King, Dunkin Donuts, Friendly's, McDonald's, Panera Bread, Papa Gino's, ⊙ AT&T, Radio Shack, Shaw's Foods/Osco Drugs, city park
27b a (44)	Totten Pond Rd, Waltham, **E** 🅿 Shell, 🍴 Naked Fish Rest., 🛏 Best Western, Courtyard, Hilton Garden, Holiday Inn Express, Home Suites, Westin Hotel, **W** 🍴 Bertucci's Rest., Green Papaya Thai, 🛏 Embassy Suites/The Grill, ⊙ AT&T, Costco, Home Depot
26 (43)	US 20, to MA 117, to Waltham, **E** 🅿 Sunoco/dsl, **W** 🅿 Mobil/dsl, 🍴 Chicago Grill, ⊙ NTB, vet
25 (42)	I-90, MA Tpk
24 (41)	MA 30, Newton, Wayland, **E** 🅿 Hess, 🛏 Marriott/rest.
23 (40)	Recreation Rd (from nb), to MA Tpk
22b a (39)	Grove St, **E** 🛏 Holiday Inn Express, ⊙ golf
38.5mm	**travel plaza sb**, Gulf/dsl, HoneyDew Donuts, McDonald's, gifts
21b a (38)	MA 16, Newton, Wellesley, **E** H, **W** 🅿 Sunoco, 🍴 Dunkin Donuts, House of Pizza, Paparazzi, Starbucks
20b a (36)	MA 9, Brookline, Framingham
19 (35)	Highland Ave, Newton, Needham, **E** 🅿 Hess, 🍴 Acupulcos, Chipotle Mexican, D'Angelo's, Mandarin Cuisine, Mighty Subs, Panera Bread, Pronto Bistro, Starbucks, 🛏 Sheraton/rest., ⊙ AAA, CVS Drug, Marshall's, PetCo, Radio Shack, Staples, TJ Maxx, **W** 🍴 Bickford's, ⊙ Chevrolet, Ford
18 (34)	Great Plain Ave, W Roxbury
33.5mm	**parking area sb**, 🚻, litter barrels
17 (33)	MA 135, Needham, Wellesley
32mm	truck turnout sb
16b a (31)	MA 109, High St, Dedham, **W** 🅿 Mobil/dsl
15b a (29)	US 1, MA 128, **0-2 mi E** 🅿 Gulf, Monro/service, 🍴 Bugaboo Creek Steaks, Chili's, Domino's, Joe's Grill, Panera Bread, PapaGino's, PF Chang's, TGIFriday's, 🛏 Fairfield Inn, Holiday Inn, Residence Inn, ⊙ AT&T, Best Buy, BJ's Whse, Costco, CVS Drug, Lincoln, LL Bean, NTB, PepBoys, PetCo, Staples, Star Foods, Tuesday Morning, Verizon, Volvo, Walgreens, Whole Foods Mkt, vet, **0-2 mi W** 🅿 Irving/dsl, Shell/dsl/24hr, 🍴 Burger King, Dunkin Donuts, Jade Chinese, McDonald's, 🛏 Budget Inn, ⊙ AAA, AT&T, Audi/Porsche, Buick/GMC, Chevrolet, Chrysler/Dodge/Jeep, Fiat, Honda, Kia, Mercedes, Toyota/Scion
14 (28)	East St, Canton St, **E** 🛏 Hilton

27mm	**rest area sb, full 🚻 facilities, 🚻, 📵, litter barrels**
13 (26.5)	University Ave
12 (26)	I-93 N, to Braintree, Boston, motorist callboxes end nb
11b a (23)	Neponset St, to Canton, **E** 🅿 Citgo/repair, Sunoco, 🍴 Dunkin Donuts, Rosario's Grill, **2 mi W on US 1** 🅿 Gulf, Sunoco, 🍴 Jake&Joe's, 🛏 The Chateau, Hampton Inn, ⊙ H, Chevrolet, Ferrari, Hyundai, Maserati, Nissan
22.5mm	Neponset River
10 (20)	Coney St (from sb, no EZ return), to US 1, Sharon, Walpole **1 mi W on US 1** 🅿 Mobil, 🍴 Bertucci's, Chili's, Chipotle Mexican, Dunkin Donuts, 5 Guys Burgers, Friendly's, HoneyDew Donuts, IHOP, McDonald's, 99 Rest., Old Country Buffet, Outback Steaks, Panda Express, Panera Bread, PapaGino's, Pizza Hut, Starbucks, Subway, Taco Bell, TGIFriday's, TX Roadhouse, 🛏 Courtyard, Residence Inn, Sheraton, ⊙ Acura, Advance Parts, Barnes&Noble, CVS Drug, Home Depot, Kohl's, Lexus, Old Navy, PetCo, Radio Shack, Staples, Stop&Shop, TownFair Tire, VW, Walgreens, mall
9 (19)	US 1, to MA 27, Walpole, **W** 🅿 Gulf, Mobil/dsl, 🍴 Applebee's, Asia Treasures, Dunkin Donuts, Starbucks, 🛏 Boston View, EconoLodge, Holiday Inn Express, ⊙ BigY Foods/drug, Stop&Shop, Walmart, same as 10
8 (16)	S Main St, Sharon, **E** 🍴 Dunkin Donuts, ⊙ Rite Aid, Shaw's Foods, whaling museum
7b a (13)	MA 140, to Mansfield, **E** 🍴 Domino's, 99 Rest., Piccadilly's, 🛏 Comfort Inn, Courtyard, Holiday Inn, Red Roof Inn, Residence Inn., **W** 🅿 Shell/HoneyDew Donuts/dsl, 🍴 Dunkin Donuts, PapaGino's, ⊙ AT&T
6b a (12)	I-495, S to Cape Cod, N to NH
10mm	**Welcome Ctr/rest area nb, full 🚻 facilities, info, 🚻, 📵, litter barrels, petwalk**
9mm	**truck parking area sb**
5 (7)	MA 152, Attleboro, **E** H, **W** 🅿 Gulf/dsl, 🍴 Bill's Pizza, Piccadilly Rest., Wendy's, ⊙ Shaw's Foods/Osco Drug
4 (6)	I-295 S, to Woonsocket
3 (4)	MA 123, to Attleboro, **E** 🅿 Shell/dsl, 🍴 Dunkin Donuts, ⊙ H, zoo
2.5mm	**parking area/weigh sta both lanes, no restrooms, litter barrels**
2b a (1)	US 1A, Newport Ave, Attleboro, **E** 🅿 Mobil/dsl, Shell, 🍴 Archie's Pizza, HoneyDew Donuts, McDonald's, Olive Garden, Spumoni's Italian, ⊙ Home Depot, K-Mart, Monroe's Service, **W** 🅿 BP
1 (.5)	US 1 (from sb), **E** 🛏 Days Inn, ⊙ Kia, Rite Aid, Volvo, **W** 🅿 Hess
0mm	Massachusetts/Rhode Island state line

INTERSTATE 195

Exit	Services
22 (41)	I-495 N, MA 25 S, to Cape Cod. I-195 begins/ends on I-495, exit 1.
21 (39)	MA 28, to Wareham, **N** 🅿 Maxi/dsl/24hr, 🍴 Longhorn Steaks, Pomodore's Italian, Qdoba Mexican, Red Robin, ⊙ Best Buy, JC Penney, LL Bean, Lowe's, Michaels, Old Navy, PetCo, Staples, Target, TJ Maxx, **S** 🅿 Irving/dsl, Mobil/Dunkin Donuts/dsl, ⊙ H, repair
37mm	parking area eb, info, boatramp
36mm	Sippican River
20 (35)	MA 105, to Marion, **S** RV camping (seasonal)
19b a (31)	to Mattapoisett, **S** 🅿 Mobil, 🍴 Nick's Pizza, Panino's Rest., Ying Dynasty, ⊙ USPO
18 (26)	MA 240 S, to Fairhaven, **1 mi S** 🅿 7-11, Valero/dsl,

Side markers: LEXINGTON / N ↕ S / NEWTON / DEDHAM (left column); ATTLEBORO / E ↕ W (right column); **MA**

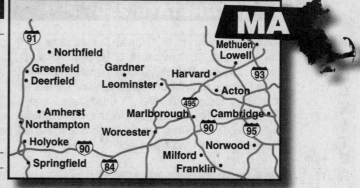

INTERSTATE 195 CONT'D

E ↕ W

Exit	Services
18 (26)	Continued [food] Burger King, Dunkin Donuts, Jake's Diner, McDonald's, 99 Rest., PapaGino's, Pasta House, Pizza Hut, Subway, Sweet Ginger Asian, Taco Bell, Wendy's, [lodging] Hampton Inn, [other] AutoZone, Brahman Handbags, Buick/GMC, $Tree, GNC, K-Mart, Marshalls, Mazda, Radio Shack, Shaw's Foods, Staples, Stop&Shop/gas, Sullivan Tire, TownFair Tire, Verizon, Walgreens, Walmart
25.5mm	Acushnet River
17 (24)	Coggeshall St, (from wb only), New Bedford, N [gas] Petro, 7-11/gas, Sunoco, [food] Dunkin Donuts, HoneyDew Donuts, McDonald's, Papa Johns, Subway, [other] Market Basket Foods, same as 16
16 (23)	Washburn St (from eb), N [gas] Sunoco, [food] McDonald's, Papa John's
15 (22)	MA 18 S, New Bedford, S [gas] Lukoil, [lodging] Fairfield Inn, [other] Whaling Museum, hist dist, to downtown,
14 (21)	Penniman St (from eb), New Bedford, downtown
13b a (20)	MA 140, N [airport], S [gas] 1 Stop, Sunoco, [food] Dunkin Donuts, [other] [H], Buttonwood Park/zoo, CVS Drug, Honda, Shaw's Foods, Walgreens
12b a (19)	N Dartmouth, S [gas] Hess, Mobil/dsl, [food] Applebee's, Azuma Asian, Burger King, ChuckeCheese, Coldstone, Dunkin Donuts, 5 Guys Burgers, Friendly's, IHOP, Jimmy's Pizza, McDonald's, 99 Rest., Old Country Buffet, Olive Garden, Panera Bread, PapaGino's, Peking Garden, Quiznos, Rose&Vicki's Bistro, Ruby Tuesday, Subway, Taco Bell, TGIFriday's, Tropical Smoothie, TX Roadhouse, Wendy's, [lodging] Residence Inn, [other] AT&T, Barnes&Noble, Best Buy, BJ's Whse/gas, Chevrolet, Curves, Dick's, $Tree, Firestone/auto, JC Penney, Kohl's, Lowe's, Macy's, Michael's, Nissan, Old Navy, PetCo, Sears/auto, Stop&Shop/gas, Target, TJ Maxx, TownFair Tire, Toyota/Scion, Verizon, Walgreens, Walmart, USPO, mall, st police
11b a (17)	Reed Rd, to Dartmouth, 2 mi S [gas] Shell
10 (16)	MA 88 S, to US 6, Westport, S [gas] Gulf, [other] CVS Drug, same as 9
9 (15.5)	MA 24, N (from nb), Stanford Rd, Westport, S [gas] Supreme, Rte 6 Gas, Valero, [food] Dunkin Donuts, Galley Grill, [lodging] Hampton Inn, [other] White's Hospitality
8b	MA 24 N, (exits left from eb)
8a (15)	MA 24 S, Fall River, Westport
7 (14)	MA 81 S, Plymouth Ave, Fall River, N [gas] BP, Hess, [food] Boston Mkt, Burger King, D'angelo's Rest., Dunkin Donuts, HoneyDew Donuts, KFC, 99 Rest., Subway, Wendy's, [other] [H], CVS Drug, S [gas] Gulf, Shell, [food] Applebee's, McDonald's, [other] Sullivan Tire, Stop&Shop, Walgreens
6 (13.5)	Pleasant St, Fall River, downtown
5 (13)	MA 79, MA 138, to Taunton, S [gas] Hess, 7-11, [food] Dunkin Donuts
12mm	Assonet Bay
4b a (10)	MA 103, to Swansea, Somerset, N [gas] BP, [food] Rogers Rest., [other] repair, vet, S [gas] Shell/24hr, [food] Jillian's Grill, [lodging] Quality Inn, Super 8
3 (8)	US 6, to MA 118, Swansea, Rehoboth, N [gas] Citgo/dsl, Hess, Mobil/Dunkin Donuts, [food] Friendly's, McDonald's, Subway, Thai Taste, Wendy's, [other] BigLots, CarQuest, $Tree, Firestone/auto, Jo-Ann Fabrics, Macy's, Marshall's, Old Navy, Price Rite Foods, Radio Shack, Sears/auto, Target, mall, S [gas] Gulf, [food] Anthony's Seafood, [lodging] Swansea

FALL RIVER

Exit	Services
3 (8)	Continued Motel, [other] Kia, NAPA
6mm	**rest area eb, full [handicapped] facilities, [phone], [picnic], litter barrels, petwalk**
5.5mm	**parking area wb**
2 (5)	MA 136, to Newport, S [gas] Mobil/24hr, Shell/24hr, [food] Cathay Pearl Chinese, Dunkin Donuts, McDonald's, Michael's Rest., Subway, [other] CVS Drug
3mm	**weigh sta both lanes**
1 (1)	MA 114A, to Seekonk, N [gas] Citgo, Gulf, Shell/24hr, [food] Dunkin Donuts, HoneyDew Donuts, Lums Sandwiches, Newport Creamery, 99 Rest., [lodging] Motel 6, [other] vet, S [gas] Hess/dsl, Mobil/24hr, Stop&Shop Gas/repair, [food] Applebee's, BigLots, Buca Italian, Burger King, Chili's, D'Angelo's, Dicky's BBQ, Diparma Italian, Dunkin Donuts, 1149, E Rest., 5 Guys Burgers, Friendly's, McDonald's, Old Country Buffet, Outback Steaks, Panera Bread, PapaGino's, Starbucks, Subway, Taco Bell, TGIFriday's, Wendy's, [lodging] Best Western, Comfort Inn, Extended Stay America, Hampton Inn, Knights Inn, Mary's Motel, Ramada Inn, Town&Country Motel, [other] Acura, Advance Parts, AT&T, Best Buy, BigLots, Bob's Stores, Dick's, $Tree, Firestone/auto, Home Depot, Kohl's, Lowe's, Michael's, PepBoys, PetCo, Sam's Club, Staples, Stop&Shop Foods, Target, TJMaxx, TownFair Tire, Tuesday Morning, Verizon, Walmart
0mm	Massachusetts/Rhode Island state line, Exits 8-1 are in RI.
8 (5)	US 1A N, Pawtucket, S [gas] Mobil/dsl, [food] Subway, [other] CVS Drug
7 (4)	US 6 E, CT 114 S, to Barrington, Seekonk
6 (3)	Broadway Ave, N [gas] Speedy AutoService, S [gas] Shell, Sunoco/dsl
5 (2.5)	RI 103 E, Warren Ave
4 (2)	US 44 E, RI 103 E, Taunton Ave, Warren Ave, N [gas] Sunoco
3 (1.5)	Gano St, N [other] Wyndham Garden
2 (1)	US 44 W, Wickenden St, India Pt, downtown, N [gas] Shell/dsl, [other] Wyndham Garden
1 (.5)	Providence, downtown
0mm	I-195 begins/ends on I-95, exit 20 in Providence, RI Exits 1-8 are in RI.

INTERSTATE 290

N ↕ S

Exit	Services
26b a (20)	I-495. I-290 begins/ends on I-495, exit 25.
25b a (17)	Solomon Pond Mall Rd, to Berlin, N [food] Bertucci's, TGIFriday's, [food] Olive Garden, [lodging] Comfort Inn, Residence Inn, [other] Best Buy, JC Penney, Macy's, Old Navy, Sears/auto, Target, mall/foodcourt, S [food] Guiseppe's Grill
24 (15)	Church St, Northborough
23b a (13)	MA 140, Boylston, N [gas] Citgo/Dunkin Donuts/dsl
22 (11)	Main St, Worchester, N [food] Dunkin Donuts

INTERSTATE 290

WORCESTER E W N

Exit	Services
21 (10)	Plantation St (from eb), N 🍴 Dunkin Donuts, same as 20
20 (8)	MA 70, Lincoln St, Burncoat St, N 🅖 Gulf/Subway, 🍴 Crown Chicken, Denny's, Dunkin Donuts, 5&Diner, 5 Guys Burgers, KFC, McDonald's, PapaGino's, Plaza Azteca, Ruby Tuesday, Taco Bell, TX Roadhouse, Wendy's, 🛏 Quality Inn, 🅞 Aldi Foods, AutoZone, Barnes&Noble, CVS Drug, Dick's, $Tree, Lowe's, Radio Shack, Staples, Stop&Shop, Target, Walgreens, USPO
19 (7)	I-190 N, MA 12
18	MA 9, Framington, Ware, Worcester ⌂, N 🏥
16	Central St, Worcester, N 🍴 99 Rest., Starbucks, 🛏 Crowne Plaza, Hilton Garden, mall
14	MA 122, Barre, Worcester, downtown
13	MA 122A, Vernon St, Worcester, downtown
12	MA 146 S, to Millbury
11	Southbridge St, College Square, N 🅖 Shell/dsl, 🍴 Golden House Chinese, Wendy's, 🅞 Family$
10	MA 12, N (from wb), Hope Ave
9	Auburn St, to Auburn, E 🅖 BP, Shell, 🍴 Arby's, Auburn Town Pizza, Dunkin Donuts, McDonald's, PapaGino's, Starbucks, Yong Shing, 🛏 Comfort Inn, Holiday Inn Express (1mi), La Quinta, 🅞 Acura, Macy's, Sears/auto, Shaw's Foods, TownFair Tire, mall
8	MA 12, S (from sb), Webster, W 🅖 Shell, 🛏 Holiday Inn Express
7	I-90 E to Boston, W to Springfield. I-290 begins/ends on I-90.

INTERSTATE 395

N S

Exit	Services
	I-395 begins/ends on I-90, exit 10.
7 (12)	to I-90 (MA Tpk), MA 12, E 🅖 Shell, 🍴 Piccadilly's, 🛏 Holiday Inn Express
6b a (11)	US 20, E 🅖 BP, Gulf, 🍴 Frank&Nancy's Cafe, 🅞 NAPA, Honda, Saab/VW, truck tires/repair, W 🅖 Shell, 🍴 Chuck's Steakhouse, Dunkin Donuts, Friendly's, 🛏 Fairfield Inn, Hampton Inn, 🅞 BJ's Whse, Buick/Cadillac/GMC, Chevrolet, Ford, Home Depot, Nissan, TJ Maxx, transmissions
5 (8)	Depot Rd, N Oxford
4b a (6)	Sutton Ave, to Oxford, E 🅞 MktBasket Foods, W 🅖 Cumberland Farms, Mobil/24hr, 🍴 Dunkin Donuts, McDonald's, NE Pizza, Subway, Veranda Cafe, 🅞 Cahill's Tire/repair, CVS Drug, Home Depot, MktBasket Foods, Verizon
3 (4)	Cudworth Rd, to N Webster, S Oxford
2 (3)	MA 16, to Webster, E 🅞 Subaru, RV Camping, W 🅖 BP/repair, Gulf, Hi-Lo Gas, Sunoco, 🍴 Burger King, D'angelo's, Dunkin Donuts, Empire Wok, Friendly's, HoneyDew Donuts, KFC/Taco Bell, McDonald's, PapaGino's, 🅞 🏥 Advance Parts, AT&T, Consumer Parts, CVS Drug, Ford, PriceChopper Foods, Rite Aid, Verizon, Walgreens, vet.
1 (1)	MA 193, to Webster, E 🏥, W 🅖 Citgo/dsl, 🍴 Golden Greek Rest., Wind Tiki Chinese, 🅞 Goodyear/auto
0mm	Massachusetts/Connecticut state line

INTERSTATE 495

Exit	Services
	I-495 begins/ends on I-95, exit 59.
55 (119)	MA 110 (from nb, no return), to I-95 S, E 🅖 Irving/Circle K, Mobil, Sunoco, 🍴 Acupulco Mexican, Burger King, Dunkin Donuts, Friendly's, McDonald's, PapaGino's,

N S HAVERHILL LOWELL

Exit	Services
55 (119)	Continued 🛏 Fairfield Inn, 🅞 AT&T, Chevrolet, Stop&Shop, Verizon, W 🅖 BP, Gulf, 🍴 Amesbury Pizza, Irene's Pizza, Weiloon Cafe, Whistling Kettle, 🅞 Curves, NAPA
54 (118)	MA 150, to Amesbury, W RV camping
53 (115)	Broad St, Merrimac, W 🅖 Citgo, 🍴 Dunkin Donuts
114mm	parking area sb, restrooms, 🚻, litter barrels (6AM-8PM)
52 (111)	MA 110, to Haverhill, E 🍴 Seafood Etc., 🅞 🏥, W 🅖 BP, Mobil/dsl, 🍴 Dunkin Donuts
110mm	parking area nb, 🚻, litter barrels
51 (109)	MA 125, to Haverhill, E 🅖 Gulf, Mobil, 🍴 Bros Pizza, China King, Dunkin Donuts, Super Buffet, 🅞 🏥, Family$, W 🅖 Mobil/dsl, 🍴 Dunkin Donuts, Friendly's, Li's Asian, Longhorn Steaks, Lucky Corner Chinese, McDonald's, Mr. Mikes Grill, Starbucks, Wendy's, 🅞 Monro Service
50 (107)	MA 97, to Haverhill, W 🅞 Ford, Lowe's, Target
49 (106)	MA 110, to Haverhill, E 🅖 Gulf, Sunoco/24hr, 🍴 Athens Pizza, Dunkin Donuts, McDonald's, Oriental Garden, 99 Rest., PapaGino's, 🛏 Best Western, Comfort Inn, 🅞 Buick/Chevrolet/GMC, Chrysler/Dodge/Jeep, CVS Drug, MktBasket Foods, Walgreens
105.8mm	Merrimac River
48 (105.5)	MA 125, to Bradford, E 🅖 BJ's Whse/gas
47 (105)	MA 213, to Methuen, 1-2 mi W 🍴 Bugaboo Steaks, Burger King, ChuckeCheese, McDonald's, Olive Garden, Starbucks, TGIFriday's, Wendy's, 🅞 🏥, Home Depot, The Mann Orchards/Bakery, Marshalls, MktBasket Foods, Old Navy, Radio Shack, Stop&Shop, Target, Walmart/Subway
46 (104)	MA 110, E 🅖 Pleasant Valley Gas, Sunoco/24hr, 🍴 Giovanni's Deli, 🅞 Lincoln/Mercury, W 🏥
45 (103)	Marston St, to Lawrence, W 🅞 Chevrolet, Honda, Kia, VW
44 (102)	Merrimac St, to Lawrence
43 (101)	Mass Ave
42 (100)	MA 114, E 🅖 Gulf, Mobil, Wave, 🍴 Bertucci's, Boston Mkt, Burger King, Burtons Grill, Chipotle Mexican, Dunkin Donuts, Friendly's, Lee Chin Chinese, Panera Bread, 🛏 Holiday Inn Express, 🅞 Ace Hardware, CVS Drug, MktBasket Foods, PetCo, Staples, TJ Maxx, Walgreens, W 🅖 Gas-N-Go, 🍴 Denny's, KFC, Pizza Hut/Taco Bell, Subway, Wendy's, 🅞 🏥, Monroe Service, Rite Aid, Save-a-Lot Foods, VIP Parts/service, vet
41 (99)	MA 28, to Andover, E 🍴 Dunkin Donuts, 🅞 Cadillac/Chevrolet
40b a (98)	I-93, N to Methuen, S to Boston
39 (94)	MA 133, to Dracut, E 🅖 Hess, 🍴 Longhorn Steaks, McDonald's, 🛏 Extended Stay America, W 🅖 Mobil/dsl, 🍴 Cracker Barrel, Wendy's, 🛏 Fairfield Inn, Holiday Inn/rest., Residence Inn
38 (93)	MA 38, to Lowell, E 🅖 Petroil/dsl, Shell/dsl, 🍴 Applebee's, Burger King, Dunkin Donuts, IHOP, Jade East, 99 Rest., Waffle House, 🛏 Motel Caswell, Motel 6, 🅞 Home Depot, Honda/VW, TownFair Tire, Walmart, W 🅖 Citgo, Mobil, Sunoco, USA/dsl, 🍴 Dunkin Donuts, Jillie's Rest., Milan Pizza, McDonald's, Wendy's, 🅞 Buick/GMC, Chevrolet, Chrysler/Dodge/Jeep, CVS Drug, Hannaford Foods, Mazda, MktBasket Foods, Marshalls, Sears Essentials, Staples
37 (91)	Woburn St, to, S Lowell, W 🅖 Gulf/Dunkin Donuts/Subway
35c (90)	to Lowell SP, Lowell ConX, 0-2 mi W services on US 3 🍴 Burger King, Chili's, McDonald's, Outback Steaks, Wendy's, 🛏 Courtyard, 🅞 Kia, Lowe's, Shop&Save, Walgreens
35b a (89)	US 3, S to Burlington, N to Nashua, NH

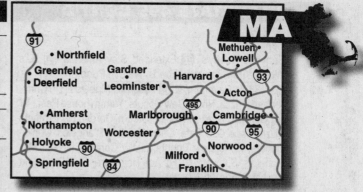

INTERSTATE 495 CONT'D

Exit	Services
34 (88)	MA 4, Chelmsford, **E** 🅖 Ampet, Mobil, Sunoco, 🍽 Cafe Madrid, Domino's, Dunkin Donuts, Jimmy's Pizza, PapaGino's, 🛏 Radisson, 🅞 CVS Drug, Walgreens, **W** 🅖 Shell, 🍽 Moonstone's Rest., 🛏 Best Western
33	MA 4, N Chelmsford (from nb)
87mm	**rest area both lanes, full** ♿ **facilities,** 🚻, 🚻, **litter barrels, vending, (8AM-8PM)**
32 (83)	Boston Rd, to MA 225, **E** 🅖 Cumberland Farms, Gulf, Mobil, 🍽 Applebee's, British Beer Co Rest., Burger King, Chili's, D'angelo's, Dunkin Donuts, McDonald's, PapaGino's, Starbucks, Subway, Westford Grill, 🛏 Hampton Inn, Residence Inn, 🅞 H, CVS Drug, Jo-Ann Fabrics, MktBasket Foods, Radio Shack, Rite Aid, Walgreens, to Nashoba Valley Ski Area
31 (80)	MA 119, to Groton, **E** 🅖 Gulf, Mobil/dsl/24hr, Shell, 🍽 Dunkin Donuts, Littleton's Subs, Subway, Tre Amici Ristorante, 🅞 Aubuchon Hardware, CVS Drug, Donelan's Foods, Toyota/Scion, Verizon, vet
30 (78)	MA 110, to Littleton, **1 mi E** 🅖 Shell/Dunkin Donuts, 🍽 CVS Drug, RV Camping, USPO, vet, **W** 🅖 Shell/Dunkin Donuts, 🅞 H, vet
29b a (77)	MA 2, to Leominster, **E** to Walden Pond St Reserve
28 (75)	MA 111, to Boxborough, Harvard, **E** 🅖 Gulf/Dunkin Donuts, 🛏 Holiday Inn
27 (70)	MA 117, to Bolton, **E** 🅖 Mobil/dsl, 🍽 Subway, **W** 🍽 Bolton Pizza, 🅞 vet
26 (68)	MA 62, to Berlin, **E** 🅖 Gulf/Dunkin Donuts, 🛏 Holiday Inn Express, 🅞 H, BJ's Whse/gas, Lowe's, **W** 🅖 Shell/dsl, 🍽 Berlin Farms Cafe
66mm	Assabet River
25b (64)	I-290, to Worcester
25a	to MA 85, Marlboro, **1 mi E** 🅖 Gulf, Mobil/dsl, 🍽 Applebee's, Burger King, Checkerboards Rest., Domino's, HoneyDew Donuts, KFC/Taco Bell, 99 Rest., PapaGino's, 🅞 AutoZone, Chevrolet, CVS Drug, $Tree, Family$, Hannaford Foods, PetCo, Stop&Shop/gas, TJ Maxx, Verizon, Walgreens
24b a (63)	US 20, to Northboro, Marlboro, **E** 🅖 Mobil, 🍽 Allora Rest., D'angelo's, Dunkin Donuts, Lake Williams Pizza, 🛏 Holiday Inn, **W** 🅖 Gulf, Shell, 🍽 Boston Mkt, China Taste, Chipotle Mexican, 5 Guys Burgers, Japan 1, Longhorn Steaks, McDonald's/playplace, 99 Rest., Panera Bread, PapaGino's, Quiznos, Starbucks, Tandoori Grill, Wendy's, 🛏 Best Western, Courtyard, Embassy Suites, Hampton Inn, Homestead Suites, 🅞 $Tree, GNC, Hannaford Foods
23c (60)	Simrano Dr, Marlboro
23b a (59)	MA 9, to Shrewsbury, Framingham, **E** 🅖 Cumberland/Dunkin Donuts, Gulf, 🍽 Wendy's, 🛏 Red Roof Inn, **0-2 mi W** 🅖 Mobil/dsl/24hr, Shell, 🍽 Bertucci's, Burger King, Chateau Rest., Chengdu, Chipotle Mexican, D'angelo's, Dunkin Donuts, Friendly's, Harry's Rest., McDonald's, Piccadilly Cafe, Ruby Tuesday, Starbucks, 🛏 Doubletree Inn, Extended Stay America, Extended Stay Deluxe, Residence Inn, 🅞 H, Buick/GMC, Chrysler/Dodge/Jeep, Marshall's, Staples, Stop&Shop, VW
22 (58)	I-90, MA TPK, E to Boston, W to Albany
21b a (54)	MA 135, to Hopkinton, Upton, **E** 🅖 Cumberland, Mobil, 🍽 Dino's Pizza, Dynasty Chinese, Golden Spoon Rest.
20 (50)	MA 85, to Milford, **W** 🅖 Gulf/dsl/LP, Mobil/dsl, 🍽 99 Rest., Pizza 85/deli, TGIFriday's, Wendy's, 🛏 Comfort
20 (50)	Continued Inn, Courtyard, Fairfield Inn, Holiday Inn Express, 🅞 H, Best Buy, Lowe's, PetCo, Staples, Stop&Shop, Target, TJ Maxx, Toyota/Scion
19 (48)	MA 109, to Milford, **W** 🅖 Mobil/Dunkin Donuts/dsl, Shell, 🍽 Alamo Mexican, Applebee's, Bugaboo Cr Steaks, Burger King, D'angelo's, 5 Guys Burgers, Friendly's, KFC/Pizza Hut, Maria's Italian, McDonald's/playplace, Panera Bread, PapaGino's, Subway, 🛏 Doubletree, La Quinta, 🅞 AutoZone, CVS Drug, $Tree, Hannaford Foods, Jo-Ann Fabrics, K-Mart, Kohl's, Radio Shack, Rite Aid, TownFair Tire
18 (46)	MA 126, to Bellingham, **E** 🍽 Chili's, Coldstone, McDonald's, 🅞 Barnes&Noble, Michael's, MktBasket Foods, Old Navy, Staples, Verizon, Walmart/Subway, Whole Foods Mkt, **W** 🅖 Hess/dsl, Mobil/24hr, Sunoco/dsl, 🍽 Chicago Grill, DQ, Dunkin Donuts, Outback Steaks, 🅞 Home Depot, Petsmart
17 (44)	MA 140, to Franklin, Bellingham, **E** 🅖 Mobil/dsl, Shell, Sunoco, 🍽 Burger King, D'angelo's, Dunkin Donuts, Franklin Cafe, HoneyDew Donuts, Longhorn Steaks, Panera Bread, PapaGino's, Pepper Terrace Thai, Subway, Taco Bell, Tepanyaki Asian, 🅞 AT&T, AutoZone, Buick/GMC, CVS Drug, GNC, Marshalls, Radio Shack, Stop&Shop, **W** 🍽 Encontro Rest., 99 Rest., 🛏 Residence Inn, 🅞 H, BJ's Whse/Subway/gas
16 (42)	King St, to Franklin, **E** 🅖 Sunoco, 🍽 Dunkin Donuts, Joe's Grill, King St Cafe, Spruce Pond Creamery, 🛏 Hampton Inn, **W** 🛏 Hawthorn Inn
15 (39)	MA 1A, to Plainville, Wrentham, **E** 🅖 Shell, 🍽 Assisi Pizza, 🅞 H, **W** 🅖 Mobil/dsl, 🍽 Chicago Grill, Cracker Barrel, Dunkin Donuts, Friendly's, Ruby Tuesday, 🅞 Premium Outlets/famous brands
14b a (37)	US 1, to N Attleboro, **E** 🅖 Interstate/D'angelo's/PapaGino's/dsl, 🍽 Luciano's Rest., 🛏 Arbor Motel, 🅞 Bass Pro Shops (4mi), **W** 🅖 Citgo/dsl, Mobil, 🍽 Chili's, Dunkin Donuts, Panera Bread, The Tavern, 🛏 Holiday Inn Express, 🅞 Macdonald's RV Ctr, Stop&Shop, Lowe's, NTB, Stop&Shop, Target, TJ Maxx, vet
13 (32)	I-95, N to Boston, S to Providence, access to H
12 (30)	MA 140, to Mansfield, **E** 🍽 Asian Grill, Bertucci's Italian, Chipotle Mexican, Friendly's Express, Longhorn Steaks, Qdoba Mexican, Sake Japanese, TGIFriday's, Wendy's, 🅞 AT&T, Best Buy, Home Depot, LL Bean, Michael's, PetCo, Kohl's, Radio Shack, Shaw's Foods, Staples, Verizon
11 (29)	MA 140, S (from sb), **1 mi W** 🅖 Gulf, 🍽 Dunkin Donuts, Mandarin Chinese, McDonald's, Subway, 🅞 $Tree
10 (26)	MA 123, to Norton, **E** 🍽 Dunkin Donuts, 🅞 QuickStop, **W** H
9 (24)	Bay St, to Taunton, **E** 🍽 Chateau Rest., **W** 🍽 Dunkin Donuts, Jaybo Cafe, NE Hotdog, Ruby Tuesday,

N ↕ S (left margin)

MARLBORO (left margin)

MIFFORD (center margin)

MA (right margin)

INTERSTATE 495 CONT'D

Exit	Services
9 (24)	Continued Subway, Wendy's, 🏠 Extended Stay America, ◻ BJ's Whse, $Tree, Tadeschi Foods, Watson Pond SP
8 (22)	MA 138, to Raynham, **E** 🅖 Hess/dsl, Mobil/dsl, 🍴 Christopher's Pizza, HoneyDew Donuts, Yummyhouse Rest., **W** 🅖 Gulf/dsl, Shell/dsl/repair, Stop'n Go/dsl, 🍴 Brothers Pizza, Cape Cod Cafe, China Garden, D'angelos, Dunkin Donuts, HoneyDew Donuts, Lucky Corner Chinese, McDonald's, Subway, ◻ Ⓗ, Ace Hardware, CVS Drug, Mkt Basket Foods, USPO, vet
7b a (19)	MA 24, to Fall River, Boston, **1/2 mi E** 🅖 Mobil/dsl, 🍴 Burger King
18mm	**weigh sta both lanes**
17mm	Taunton River
6 (15)	US 44, to Middleboro, **E** 🅖 Super/dsl, 🍴 Burger King, Dunkin Donuts, Fireside Grille, Friendly's, Hong Kong Taste, PapaGino's, Subway, **W** 🅖 Mobil/Dunkin Donuts/

MIDDLEBORO	
6 (15)	Continued dsl, 🏠 Fairfield Inn, Holiday Inn Express
5 (14)	MA 18, to Lakeville, **E** 🅖 Shell, Super/dsl, 🍴 D'Angelo's, Dave's Diner, Fireside Grille, Harry's Grille, Lorenzo's Rest., PapaGino's, Persy's Place Cafe, ◻ CVS Drug, Kelly's Tire, Stop&Shop, **W** ◻ Massasoit SP, RV camping (seasonal)
4 (12)	MA 105, to Middleboro, **E** 🅖 Gulf/dsl, Shell/24hr, Sunoco/24hr, 🍴 China Sails, DQ, Dunkin Donuts, McDonald's, Tuttabella Pizza, 🏠 Days Inn, ◻ AutoZone, Rite Aid
11mm	**parking area eb**
10mm	**parking area both lanes**
3 (8)	MA 28, to Rock Village, S Middleboro, **E** 🅖 Irving/dsl, ◻ Fred's Repair, **W** 🅖 Mobil/Dunkin Donuts/Subway/dsl
2 (3)	MA 58, W Wareham, **E** ◻ RV camping, to Myles Standish SF, **W** 🅖 7-11
2mm	Weweantic River
1 (0)	I-495 begins/ends on I-195, MA 25 S.

MICHIGAN

INTERSTATE 69

Exit	Services
275mm	I-69/I-94 begin/end on MI 25, **Pinegrove Ave in Port Huron N** 🅖 BP/24hr, Clark, Marathon, Shell/24hr, Speedway, 🍴 Little Caesar's, McDonald's, Tim Horton, Wendy's, White Castle, 🏠 Best Western, Day's Inn, Holiday Inn Express, ◻ Can-Am DutyFree, Family$, Honda, Rite Aid, tollbridge to Canada
275mm	Black River
274	Water St, Port Huron, **N Welcome Ctr/rest area wb full facilities,** 🍴 Cracker Barrel, 🏠 Ramada Inn, **S** 🅖 Bylo/dsl, Speedway/Taco Bell/dsl, 🍴 Bob Evans, 🏠 Comfort Inn, Fairfield Inn, Hampton Inn, Knight's Inn, ◻ Lake Port SP, RV camping
199	Lp 69 (from eb, no return), to Port Huron, **0-2 mi S on Lp 69 S** 🅖 Mobil/dsl, Speedway, 🍴 Arby's, Baskin-Robbins, Burger King, Dunkin Donuts, McDonalds, KFC, Quay St Grill, Taco Bell, Wendy's, ◻ Advance Parts, AutoZone, Kroger/gas, K-Mart, Sam's Club/gas, repair, to Port Huron
	I-69 E and I-94 E run together into Port Huron.
198	I-94, to Detroit and Canada
196	Wadhams Rd, **N** 🅖 Marathon, Speedy Q/dsl, Shell/Wendy's, 🍴 Hungry Howie's, McDonald's, Peking Kitchen, Subway, ◻ Vinckier Foods, Wadham's Drugs, KOA (1mi), **S** golf
194	Taylor Rd, **N** Goodells CP, RV camping
189	Wales Center Rd, to Goodells, **S** golf
184	MI 19, to Emmett, **N** 🅖 Citgo/Steverino's/dsl/scales/24hr, ◻ repair, **S** 🅖 Marathon/dsl/24hr
180	Riley Center Rd, **N** KOA
176	Capac Rd, **N** 🅖 BP/McDonald's/dsl/scales, 🍴 Subway (2mi)
174mm	**rest area wb, full** ♿ **facilities,** ⦅⦆, 🚻, **litter barrels, vending, petwalk**
168	MI 53, Imlay City, **N** 🅖 BP/dsl/24hr, Speedway/dsl, 🍴 Big Boy, Big Joe's Pizza, Burger King, DQ, Hungry Howie's, John's Country Kitchen, Little Caesar's, Lucky's

LAPEER	
168	Continued Steaks, McDonald's, New China, Taco Bell, Wah Wong Chinese, Wendy's/Tim Horton, 🏠 Days Inn, M53 Motel, Super 8, ◻ AutoZone, Chevrolet, Chrysler/Dodge/Jeep, $Discount, Ford, GNC, Grocery Outlet, Kroger/gas, NAPA, Pamida, Radio Shack, Sav-On Drug, **S** camping
163	Lake Pleasant Rd, to Attica
160mm	**rest area eb, full** ♿ **facilities,** ⦅⦆, 🚻, **litter barrels, vending, petwalk**
159	Wilder Rd
158mm	Flint River
155	MI 24, Lapeer, **1 mi N** 🅖 BP, Clark/dsl, FS, Speedy Q, 🍴 Applebee's, Apple Tree Rest., Arby's, Blind Fish Rest., Brian's Rest., Burger King, Checker's, DQ, Farmhouse Rest., Jet's Pizza, Jimmy John's, KFC, Little Caesar's, Mancino's, McDonald's, Mr Pita, Nick's Rest., Sonic, Starbucks, Subway, Taco Bell, Tim Horton, Wah Wong Chinese, Wendy's, 🏠 Best Western, Lapeer Hotel, ◻ Ⓗ, AutoZone, $Tree, Home Depot, K-Mart, Kohl's, Kroger, Meijer/dsl, Office Depot, O'Reilly Parts, Radio Shack, Save-a-Lot, Walgreens, st police, vet, **S** 🅖 Mobil/dsl, ◻ Chrylser/Dodge/Jeep
153	Lake Nepessing Rd, **S** to Thumb Correctional, camping, golf
149	Elba Rd, **N** ◻ Torzwski CP, **S** ◻ Country Mkt, RV/truck repair
145	MI 15, Davison, **N** 🅖 Marathon, Shell/dsl, Speedway, 🍴 Apollo Rest., Applebee's, Arby's, Big Boy, Big John's Rest., Burger King, Chee Kong Chinese, Flag City Diner, Hungry Howie's, Italia Gardens, KFC, Little Caesar's, McDonald's, Pizza Hut, Senor Lucky, Subway, Taco Bell, Tim Horton, 🏠 Comfort Inn, ◻ AutoValue Parts, Buick/GMC, GNC, Radio Shack, Rite Aid, Valley Tire, Walgreens, repair, **S** 🅖 Mobil/dsl
143	Irish Rd, **N** 🅖 Speedway/dsl, **S** 🅖 Shell/McDonald's/24hr, ◻ Meijer/dsl/e-85, 7-11
141	Belsay Rd, Flint, **N** 🅖 1 stop, Shell/Wendy's/dsl/24hr, 🍴 Country Kitchen, McDonald's, Taco Bell, ◻ Curves, K-Mart, Kroger, Walmart/Subway, **S** 🅖 Sunoco/A&W/LJ Silver/dsl
139	Center Rd, Flint, **N** 🅖 Speedway/dsl, 🍴 Applebee's,

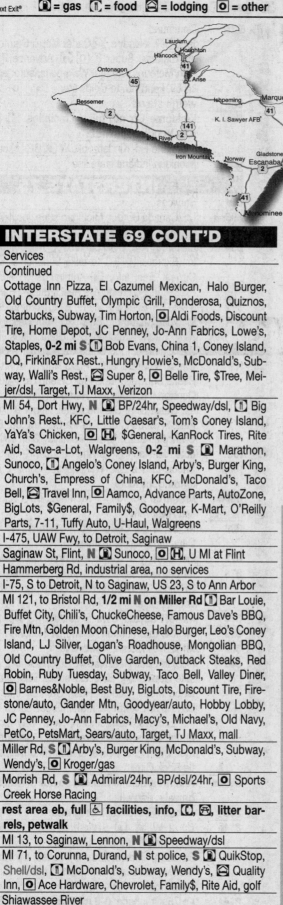

FLINT N ↕ S

INTERSTATE 69 CONT'D

Exit	Services
139	Continued Cottage Inn Pizza, El Cazumel Mexican, Halo Burger, Old Country Buffet, Olympic Grill, Ponderosa, Quiznos, Starbucks, Subway, Tim Horton, ⊙ Aldi Foods, Discount Tire, Home Depot, JC Penney, Jo-Ann Fabrics, Lowe's, Staples, **0-2 mi S** 🍴 Bob Evans, China 1, Coney Island, DQ, Firkin&Fox Rest., Hungry Howie's, McDonald's, Subway, Walli's Rest., 🏠 Super 8, ⊙ Belle Tire, $Tree, Meijer/dsl, Target, TJ Maxx, Verizon
138	MI 54, Dort Hwy, **N** 🚗 BP/24hr, Speedway/dsl, 🍴 Big John's Rest., KFC, Little Caesar's, Tom's Coney Island, YaYa's Chicken, ⊙ Ⓗ, $General, KanRock Tires, Rite Aid, Save-a-Lot, Walgreens, **0-2 mi S** 🚗 Marathon, Sunoco, 🍴 Angelo's Coney Island, Arby's, Burger King, Church's, Empress of China, KFC, McDonald's, Taco Bell, 🏠 Travel Inn, ⊙ Aamco, Advance Parts, AutoZone, BigLots, $General, Family$, Goodyear, K-Mart, O'Reilly Parts, 7-11, Tuffy Auto, U-Haul, Walgreens
137	I-475, UAW Fwy, to Detroit, Saginaw
136	Saginaw St, Flint, **N** 🚗 Sunoco, ⊙ Ⓗ, U MI at Flint
135	Hammerberg Rd, industrial area, no services
133b a	I-75, S to Detroit, N to Saginaw, US 23, S to Ann Arbor
131	MI 121, to Bristol Rd, **1/2 mi N** on Miller Rd 🍴 Bar Louie, Buffet City, Chili's, ChuckeCheese, Famous Dave's BBQ, Fire Mtn, Golden Moon Chinese, Halo Burger, Leo's Coney Island, LJ Silver, Logan's Roadhouse, Mongolian BBQ, Old Country Buffet, Olive Garden, Outback Steaks, Red Robin, Ruby Tuesday, Subway, Taco Bell, Valley Diner, ⊙ Barnes&Noble, Best Buy, BigLots, Discount Tire, Firestone/auto, Gander Mtn, Goodyear/auto, Hobby Lobby, JC Penney, Jo-Ann Fabrics, Macy's, Michael's, Old Navy, PetCo, PetsMart, Sears/auto, Target, TJ Maxx, mall
129	Miller Rd, **S** 🍴 Arby's, Burger King, McDonald's, Subway, Wendy's, ⊙ Kroger/gas
128	Morrish Rd, **S** 🚗 Admiral/24hr, BP/dsl/24hr, ⊙ Sports Creek Horse Racing
126mm	**rest area eb, full ♿ facilities, info, 🍴, 🏕, litter barrels, petwalk**
123	MI 13, to Saginaw, Lennon, **N** 🚗 Speedway/dsl
118	MI 71, to Corunna, Durand, **N** st police, **S** 🚗 QuikStop, Shell/dsl, 🍴 McDonald's, Subway, Wendy's, 🏠 Quality Inn, ⊙ Ace Hardware, Chevrolet, Family$, Rite Aid, golf
115mm	Shiawassee River
113	Bancroft, **S** 🚗 BP/dsl, ⊙ RV camping
105	MI 52, to Owosso, Perry, **S** 🚗 Mobil, PS/Subway/dsl, 7-11, Sunoco/dsl/scales, 🍴 Burger King, Café Sports,

LANSING

Exit	Services
105	Continued McDonald's, Taco Bell, 🏠 Heb's Inn, ⊙ Family$, Ford, IGA Foods, Rite Aid, RV camping, truck repair (1mi)
101mm	**rest area wb, full ♿ facilities, 🍴, 🏕, litter barrels, petwalk**
98.5mm	Looking Glass River
98	Woodbury Rd, to Laingsburg, Shaftsburg, **S** RV camping
94	Lp 69, Marsh Rd, to, E Lansing, Okemos, **S** 🚗 Admiral/dsl, Speedway/dsl, 🍴 McDonald's, ⊙ Gillett RV Ctr, Save-a-Lot
92	Webster Rd, Bath
89	US 127 S, to, E Lansing
87	Old US 27, to Clare, Lansing, **N** 🚗 Marathon, Speedway/dsl, 🍴 Arby's, Bob Evans, Burger King, China Gourmet, FlapJack Rest., Little Ceasars, McDonald's, Subway, Tim Horton, 🏠 Sleep Inn, ⊙ Annie Rae RV Ctr, Chevrolet, Meijer/dsl, TrueValue, vet, **S** 🚗 Speedway/dsl, 🏠 Baymont, ⊙ GNC
85	DeWitt Rd, to DeWitt
84	Airport Rd
91	I-96 (from sb), W to Grand Rapids, Grand River Ave, Frances Rd, **W** 🚗 ⊙FLYING J/Denny's/dsl/24hr, 🍴 Pepperoni's Rest.
93b a	MI 43, Lp 69, Saginaw Hwy, to Grand Ledge, **0-2 mi N** 🚗 Shell, Speedway/dsl, 🍴 Burger King, Carrabba's, Cheddar's, Denny's, Fazoli's, Frank's Grill, Hibachi Grill, Honeybaked Ham, Houlihan's, Logan's Roadhouse, McDonald's, Outback Steaks, Panera Bread, Qdoba, Red Robin, Subway, Younkers, 🏠 Days Inn, Fairfield Inn, Hampton Inn, Motel 6, Quality Inn, Ramada Inn,

🚗 = gas 🍴 = food 🏠 = lodging 🔲 = other   Copyright 2012 - The Next Exit

INTERSTATE 69 CONT'D

LANSING

Exit	Services
93b a	Continued Red Roof Inn, Residence Inn, 🔲 🅷, Barnes&Noble, Big-Lots, Chrysler/Dodge/Jeep, Hobby Lobby, JC Penney, Kohl's, Kroger, Macy's, Meijer/dsl/24hr, NAPA, Radio Shack, Target, Walgreens, S 🚗 BP/24hr, QD, Sunoco/McDonald's, 🍴 Arby's, Bob Evans, Cracker Barrel, Ingcredible Chinese, Rudino's Pizza, Steak'n Shake, Subway, 🏠 SpringHill Suites, 🔲 urgent care, AT&T, Belle Tire, Buick/GMC, Dick's, Discount Tire, Gander Mtn, Mazda, Lowe's, Menards, Michael's, PetsMart, Staples, Walmart
95	I-496, to Lansing
72	I-96, E to Detroit, W to Grand Rapids
70	Lansing Rd
68mm	**rest area nb, full** ♿ **facilities,** 🚻, 🐾, **litter barrels, vending, petwalk**
66	MI 100, to Grand Ledge, Potterville, W 🚗 BP, Shell/Subway, 🍴 McDonald's, to Fox Co Park
61	Lansing Rd, E 🍴 Applebee's, 🏠 Comfort Inn, 🔲 Auto-Zone, Buick/Chevrolet/GMC, $Tree, Walmart/Subway, W 🚗 Speedway/dsl, QD, 🍴 Arby's, Biggby Coffee, Big Boy, Burger King, KFC, Little Caesar's, Mancino's Pizza, McDonald's, Pizza Hut, Rally's, Taco Bell, Tasty Twist, Top Chinese, Wendy's, 🔲 🅷, Advance Parts, CarQuest, Family$, Ford/Mercury, Geldhof Tire/auto, TrueValue, vet
60	MI 50, Charlotte, E 🏠 Holiday Inn Express, 🔲 Meijer/dsl/24hr, W 🚗 Admiral, 🏠 Super 8, 🔲 🅷, RV camping
57	Lp 69, Cochran Rd, to Charlotte, E RV camping
51	Ainger Rd, **1 mi** E 🚗 🍴, RV camping
48	MI 78, to Bellevue, Olivet, **1 mi** E 🚗 BP/Subway/dsl, 🔲 to Olivet Coll
42	N Drive N, Turkeyville Rd, W 🍴 Cornwell's Rest. (1mi)
41mm	**rest area sb, full** ♿ **facilities,** 🚻, 🐾, **litter barrels, petwalk**
38	I-94, E to Detroit, W to Chicago
36	Michigan Ave, to Marshall, E 🚗 Admiral, Citgo/dsl/e-85, Shell/Subway, 🍴 Applebee's, Arby's, Biggby Coffee, Burger King, Little Caesar's, McDonald's, Pizza Hut, Taco Bell, Wendy's, Yin Hai Chinese, 🏠 Comfort Inn, 🔲 🅷, Ace Hardware, Auto Value Parts, AutoZone, Chevrolet, $General, $Tree, Family Fare Foods, K-Mart, NAPA, Radio Shack, Rite Aid, Save-a-Lot, Tuffy Auto, W 🏠 Arbor Inn, 🔲 Chrysler/Dodge/Jeep
32	F Drive S, E 🚗 Shell (3/4 mi), 🍴 Moonraker Rest. (3mi), W 🔲 RV Camping
25	MI 60, to Three Rivers, Jackson, E 🚗 BP/dsl, Citgo/Te-Kon/Norma's/Subway/dsl/scales/24hr, Sunoco/dsl, 🍴 McDonald's, 🔲 Auto Value Parts, auto/truck repair, RV camping
23	Tekonsha, E 🚗 Citgo, W access to RV camping
16	Jonesville Rd, W Waffle Farm Camping (2mi)
13	US 12, to Quincy, Coldwater, E 🚗 Speedway/dsl, 🍴 Applebee's, Biggby Coffee, Bob Evans, Buffalo Wild Wings, China 1, Grand Buffet, Papa Murphy's, Subway, 🏠 Hampton Inn, Red Roof Inn, 🔲 Aldi Foods, AT&T, AutoZone, BigLots, Cadillac/Chevrolet, $Tree, Elder-Beerman, Gander Mtn, GNC, Home Depot, Meijer/dsl, N Country RV Ctr, Radio Shack, Walmart, W 🚗 Citgo, Speedway/dsl, 🍴 Arby's, Benedict's Steaks, Big Boy, Burger King, Coldwater Garden Rest., Cottage Inn Pizza, KFC, Little Caesar's, McDonald's, Pizza Hut, Ponderosa, Subway,

MARSHALL

Exit	Services
13	Continued Taco Bell, Wendy's, 🏠 Cadet Motel, Comfort Inn, Holiday Inn Express, Super 8, 🔲 🅷, Advance Parts, Ford/Lincoln/Mercury, Rite Aid, Walgreens, auto repair, st police
10	Lp 69, Fenn Rd, to Coldwater
8mm	**weigh sta nb**
6mm	**Welcome Ctr nb, full** ♿ **facilities,** 🚻, 🐾, **litter barrels, vending, petwalk**
3	Copeland Rd, Kinderhook, W 🚗 BP, 🍴 camping
0mm	Michigan/Indiana state line

INTERSTATE 75

SAULT STE MARIE

Exit	Services
395mm	US/Canada Border, Michigan state line, I-75 begins/ends at toll bridge to Canada
394	Easterday Ave, E 🚗 Citgo/dsl, 🍴 McDonald's, 🏠 Holiday Inn Express, 🔲 🅷, to Lake Superior St U, W Welcome Ctr/rest area, info, 🚗 Admiral/dsl, Holiday/dsl/currency exchange, 🍴 Freighter's Rest (2mi), 🏠 Ramada Inn (2mi)
392	3 Mile Rd, Sault Ste Marie, E 🚗 Admiral/dsl, BP/dsl, Holiday/dsl, Marathon, Shell, 🍴 Applebee's, Arby's, Burger King, Country Kitchen, DQ, Great Lakes Fishouse, Great Wall Chinese, Indo China Garden, Jeff's Café, KFC, Little Caesar's, McDonald's, Pizza Hut, Quizno's, Studebaker's Rest., Subway, Taco Bell, Wendy's, 🏠 Best Western, Comfort Inn, Days Inn, Hampton Inn, Park Inn, Plaza Motel, Quality Inn, Skyline Motel, Super 8, 🔲 🅷, Advance Parts, AT&T, Auto Value Parts, BigLots, Buick/Cadillac/Chevrolet/GMC, $Tree, Family$, Glen's Mkt, Goodyear/auto, JC Penney, Jo-Ann Fabrics, K-Mart, NAPA, Radio Shack, Sav-a-Lot, Walgreens, Walmart, st police, Soo Locks Boat Tours
389mm	**rest area nb, full** ♿ **facilities, info,** 🚻, 🐾, **litter barrels, petwalk**
386	MI 28, E 🏠 Cedar Log Motel/rest., W 🔲 Clear Lake Camping (5mi), to Brimley SP
379	Gaines Hwy, E to Barbeau Area, Clear Lake Camping
378	MI 80, Kinross, E 🚗 BP/dsl, 🍴 Frank&Jim's Diner, 🔲 URGENT CARE, RV West Camping, to Kinross Correctional, 🚑, golf
373	MI 48, Rudyard, **2 mi** W gas/dsl, 🍴, 🏠
359	MI 134, to Drummond Island, W National Forest Camping
352	MI 123, to Moran, Newberry
348	H63, to Sault Reservation, St Ignace, **0-2 mi** E 🍴 Dockside Steaks, 🏠 Bear Cove Inn, Best Value Inn, Birchwood Motel, Budget Host, Comfort Inn, Cedars Motel, Days Inn, Evergreen Motel, Great Lakes Motel, Holiday Inn Express, Kewadin Inn, North Bay Inn, NorthernAire Motel, Pines Motel, Quality Inn, Royale Inn, Tradewinds Motel, 🔲 🚑, st police, to Mackinac Trail, casino, W Castle Rock Gifts
346mm	**rest area/scenic turnout sb, full** ♿ **facilities,** 🐾, **litter barrels, petwalk**
345	Portage St (from sb), St Ignace
344b	US 2 W, W 🚗 BP/dsl/rest./24hr, Holiday/dsl, Shell/dsl/24hr, 🍴 Big Boy, Burger King, Clyde's Drive-In McDonald's, Subway, Suzy's Pasties, Up North Rest, 🏠 4 Star Motel, Quality Inn, Sunset Motel, Super 8, 🔲 Ford, Lakeshore RV Park
344a	Lp 75, St Ignace, **0-2 mi** E 🚗 Shell, 🍴 BC Pizza, Driftwood Rest, Flame Rest., Galley Rest., Mackinac Grille, Marina Rest., Northern Lights Rest., Subway, 🏠 Aurora Borealis Motel, Best Value Inn, Best Western, Boardwalk

MI

INTERSTATE 75 CONT'D

MACKINAW CITY

Exit	Services
344a	Continued
	Inn, Budget Host, Colonial House, Comfort Inn, Days Inn, Econolodge, Getaway Inn, Holiday Inn Express, Huron Motel, K Royale Motel, Moran Bay Motel, Normandy Motel, Quality Inn, Sunbar Motel, Thunderbird Motel, Village Inn/rest., Vitek's Motel, Voyager Motel, ᵒ ᴴ, Ace Hardware, Bay Drug, Family$, Glen's Mkt, Radio Shack, TrueValue, USPO, to Island Ferrys, Straits SP, KOA, public marina, st police, E KOA
343mm	toll booth to toll bridge, E Welcome Ctr nb, **full** ♿ **facilities, ᵖ, ᵖ, litter barrels, W museum**
341mm	toll bridge, Lake Huron, Lake Michigan
339	US 23, Jamet St, E ᵖ Audie's Rest., ᵖ Budget Host, Days Inn, Econolodge, LightHouse View Motel, Parkside Motel, Riviera Motel, Super 8, W ᵖ Shell, ᵖ Darrow's Rest., Mackinaw Cookie Co, ᵖ Holiday Inn Express, Trails Inn, Vindel Motel,
338	US 23 (from sb), E **Welcome Ctr/rest area**, ᵖ Marathon/dsl, ᵖ BC Pizza, Burger King, Cunningham's Rest., DQ, KFC, Mama Mia's Pizza, Pancake Chef, Subway, Up North Cafe, ᵖ Baymont Inn, Courtyard Inn, ᵖ IGA Foods/supplies, Mackinaw Outfitters, same as 337, W ᵖ Ft Mackinaw Motel, Holiday Inn Express
337	MI 108 (from nb, no EZ return), Nicolet St, Mackinaw City, E ᵖ Citgo/dsl/LP, ᵖ Admiral's Table Rest, Anna's Country Buffet, Blue Water Grill, Embers Rest., Lighthouse Rest., Mancino's Pizza, ᵖ Anchor Inn, BeachComber Motel, Best Value Inn, Best Western, Budget Inn, Capri Motel, Clearwater Motel, Comfort Inn, Comfort Suites, Dale's Motel, Days Inn, Econolodge, Grand Mackinaw Resort, Great Lakes Inn, Hamilton Inn, Hampton Inn, Nicolet Inn, NorthPointe Inn, North Winds Motel, Quality Inn, Rainbow Motel, Ramada Ltd, Sundown Motel, Sunrise Beach Motel, Super 8, Waterfront Inn, ᵖ Mackinaw Camping (2mi), Old Mill Creek SP, TeePee Campground, to Island Ferrys, W Wilderness SP
336	US 31, S (from sb), to Petoskey
328mm	**rest area sb, full** ♿ **facilities, info, ᵖ, ᵖ, litter barrels, petwalk**
326	C66, to Cheboygan, E ᵖ Marathon, ᵖ ᴴ, Sea Shell City/gifts, ᵖ st police
322	C64, to Cheboygan, E ᴴ, LP, ᵖ, st police
317mm	**rest area/scenic turnout nb, full** ♿ **facilities, info, ᵖ, ᵖ, litter barrels, petwalk**
313	MI 27 N, Topinabee, E ᵖ Johnson Motel, Indian River RV Resort/Camping
311mm	Indian River
310	MI 33, MI 68, E ᵖ Hometown Inn, ᵖ Jellystone Park (3mi), W ᵖ BP/dsl, Ken's Gas, Shell/McDonald's/24hr, ᵖ Burger King, DQ, Paula's Cafe, Subway, ᵖ Coach House Motel, ᵖ Family$, Ken's Mkt, Village Mkt/Drug, to Indian River Trading Post/RV Resort, to Burt Lake SP
301	C58, Wolverine, E ᵖ Marathon/dsl, ᵖ Whistle Stop Rest., ᵖ Elkwood Campground (5mi), W ᵖ Sturgin River Campground (3mi)
297mm	Sturgeon River
290	Vanderbilt, E ᵖ BP/dsl/LP/RV dump, Spirit, ᵖ Village Mkt Foods, USPO, W ᵖ Mobil/dsl
287mm	**rest area sb, full** ♿ **facilities, info, ᵖ, ᵖ, litter barrels**
282	MI 32, Gaylord, E ᵖ BP, Clark, Holiday/24hr, Marathon/dsl, Speedway/dsl, ᵖ Alpine Oven, Arby's, Big Buck

GAYLORD

GRAYLING

Exit	Services
282	Continued
	Steaks, Burger King, DQ, KFC, La Senorita Mexican, McDonald's, Quizno's, Subway, Wendy's, ᵖ Alpine Lodge, Baymont Inn, Quality Inn/Gino's Italian, Royal Crest Motel, ᵖ ᴴ, Advance Parts, AutoZone, Ben Franklin, Glen's Foods, Harley-Davidson, Johnson Tires, K-Mart, NAPA, Rite Aid, st police, W ᵖ BP/dsl, Citgo/dsl, Marathon/dsl, Mobil/dsl, Shell/dsl, ᵖ Applebee's, BC Pizza, Big Boy, Bob Evans, China 1, Culver's, Little Caesar's, Mancino's Pizza, Ponderosa, Ruby Tuesday, Spicy Bob's, Taco Bell, ᵖ Hampton Inn, Holiday Inn Express, Timberly Motel, ᵖ URGENT CARE, AT&T, BigLots, Chrysler/Dodge/Jeep, Dayton Tire, $General, $Tree, GNC, Home Depot, Lowe's Whse, Radio Shack, Save-A-Lot Foods, Walgreens, Walmart/Subway, RV camping, transmissions, tires
279mm	45th Parallel - halfway between the equator & north pole
279	Old US 27, Gaylord, E ᵖ Marathon/Subway/dsl, Mobil/dsl, Shell, ᵖ Burger King, Mama Leone's, ᵖ Best Value Inn, ᵖ Ace Hardware, Buick/GMC, Chevrolet, Ford/Lincoln/Mercury, st police, W ᵖ Bennethums Rest, Stampede Saloon, ᵖ Marsh Ridge Motel (2mi), KOA (3mi)
277mm	**rest area nb, full** ♿ **facilities, info, ᵖ, ᵖ, litter barrels, petwalk**
270	Waters, E ᵖ BP/dsl, ᵖ Hilltop Rest., W ᵖ, Waters Inn, ᵖ IGA Food/gas, RV repair, Waters RV Ctr, USPO, to Otsego Lake SP
264	Lewiston, Frederic, W access to ᵖ, camping
262mm	**rest area sb, full** ♿ **facilities, ᵖ, ᵖ, litter barrels, petwalk**
259	MI 93, E Hartwick Pines SP, **2-4 mi** W ᵖ Fay's Motel, North Country Lodge, Pointe North Motel, River Country Motel, Woodland Motel, ᵖ Buick/Cadillac/Chevrolet, Chrysler/Dodge/Jeep, Curves, auto/rv repair, rv camping
256	(from sb), to MI 72, Grayling, access to same as 254
254	MI 72 (exits left from nb, no return), Grayling, **1 mi** W ᵖ Admiral/dsl, Citgo, 7-11, Clark, Speedway, Valero, ᵖ Big Boy, Burger King, Canadian Steaks, DQ, McDonald's, Pizza Hut, Subway, Taco Bell, Wendy's, ᵖ Days Inn, Ramada, ᵖ ᴴ, Ace Hardware, $General, Family$, Ford/Mercury, Glen's Foods/24hr, K-Mart, NAPA, Rite Aid, Save-A-Lot Foods, Walgreens
251mm	**rest area nb, full** ♿ **facilities, info, ᵖ, ᵖ, litter barrels, petwalk, vending**
251	4 Mile Rd, E Jellystone RV Park (5mi), skiing, W ᵖ Marathon/Arby's/dsl/scales/RV Dump/24hr, ᵖ Super 8
249	US 127, S (from sb), to Clare
244	MI 18, Roscommon, **3 mi** E ᵖ McDonald's, W ᵖ Valero/dsl, ᵖ KOA (1mi), Higgins Lake SP, museum
239	MI 18, Roscommon, S Higgins Lake SP, **3 mi** E ᵖ Marathon/McDonald's/dsl, ᵖ camping, W Higgins Lake SP, campling

gas = gas   food = food   lodging = lodging   other = other   Copyright 2012 - The Next Exit®

N ↑ ↓ S	

INTERSTATE 75 CONT'D

Exit	Services
235mm	rest area sb, full ♿ facilities, 🍴, info, 🛦, litter barrels, petwalk, vending
227	MI 55 W, rd F97, to Houghton Lake; 5 mi W food
222	Old 76, to St Helen, 5 mi E🍴, 🛌, camping
215	MI 55 E, West Branch, E 🅖 Citgo/dsl, 🍴 Carver's Rest., Willow Tree Rest. (2mi), 🔵🅗
212	MI 55, West Branch, E 🅖 Murphy USA/dsl, 7-11, Shell/Subway, 🍴 Applebee's, Arby's, Big Boy, Burger King, KFC, Lumberjack Rest., McDonald's, Ponderosa, Taco Bell, Wendy's, 🛌 Quality Inn, Super 8, 🔵🅗, Home Depot, Tanger Outlet/famous brands, Walmart/Subway, st police, W 🅖 BP/dsl
210mm	rest area nb, full ♿ facilities, info, 🍴, 🛦, litter barrels, petwalk, vending
202	MI 33, to Rose City, Alger, E 🅖 BP/Narski's Mkt/jerky (1/2mi), Mobil/jerky outlet/dsl, Shell/Subway, 🔵 camping
201mm	rest area sb, full ♿ facilities, 🍴, 🛦, litter barrels, petwalk, vending
195	Sterling Rd, to Sterling, 6 mi E gas, Riverview Camping (seasonal)
190	MI 61, to Standish, E 🔵🅗, Standish Correctional, W 🅖 Marathon, Mobil/jerky
188	US 23, to Standish, 2-3 mi E gas,🍴, camping
181	Pinconning Rd, E 🅖 Mobil, Shell/McDonald's, 🍴 Cheesehouse Diner, 🛌 Pinconning Inn (2mi), 🔵 Pinconning Camping, W 🅖 Sunoco/pizza/dsl/24hr
175mm	rest area nb, full ♿ facilities, 🍴, 🛦, litter barrels, petwalk, vending
173	Linwood Rd, to Linwood, E 🅖 Mobil/dsl/jerky
171mm	Kawkawlin River
168	Beaver Rd, to Willard, E 🔵 to Bay City SP, W 🅖 Mobil/jerky
166mm	Kawkawlin River
164	to MI 13, Wilder Rd, to Kawkawlin, E🍴Applebee's, Cracker Barrel, Lucky Steaks, McDonald's, Ponderosa, Tim Horton, Uno, 🛌 AmericInn, Fairfield Inn (3mi), Holiday Inn Express, 🔵 KanRock Tire, Meijer/dsl, Menards
162b a	US 10, MI 25, to Midland, E🅗
160	MI 84, Delta, E 🅖 Mobil/Subway, Shell, W 🅖 7-11, Speedway, 🍴 Berger's Rest., Burger King, KFC/Taco Bell, McDonald's, 🛌 Econolodge, 🔵 RV World Super Ctr, to Saginaw Valley Coll
158mm	rest area sb, full ♿ facilities, 🍴, 🛦, litter barrels, vending, petwalk
155	I-675 S, to downtown Saginaw, 4 mi W 🍴 Outback Steaks, 🛌 Hampton Inn, Super 8
154	to Zilwaukee
153mm	Saginaw River
153	MI 13, E Bay City Rd, Saginaw, 2-3 mi W 🛌
151	MI 81, to Reese, Caro, E 🅖 Sunoco/McDonald's/dsl, 🔵 GMC/Volvo Trucks, W 🅖 ✈FLYING J/Wendy's/dsl/LP/24hr
150	I-675 N, to downtown Saginaw, 6 mi W 🍴 Outback Steaks, 🛌 Hampton Inn, Super 8
149b a	MI 46, Holland Ave, to Saginaw, W 🅖 Admiral, Marathon, Speedway/dsl, Sunoco, 🍴 Arby's, Big John's Steaks, Burger King, McDonald's, Subway, Taco Bell, Texan Rest., 🛌 Best Value Inn, Motel 6, Super 7 Inn, 🔵🅗, Advance Parts, Sav-a-Lot Foods, USPO
144b a	Bridgeport, E 🅖 Marathon/dsl, Speedway/dsl/24hr,

Left margin vertical: S A G I N A W

Bottom left: MI

Exit	Services
144b a	Continued 🔵 Jellystone Camping (9mi), W 🅖 Mobil/dsl/e-85, TA/Country Pride/dsl/scales/24hr/@, 🍴Arby's, Big Boy, Cracker Barrel, Hungry Howie's, Little Caesar's, McDonald's, Peking City, Subway, Taco Bell, Wendy's, 🛌 Baymont Inn, Knight's Inn, 🔵 Kroger/gas, Rite Aid, st police
143mm	Cass River
138mm	pull off both lanes
136	MI 54, MI 83, Birch Run, E 🅖 Mobil/dsl/24hr, 🍴 Exit Rest., Halo Burger, KFC, Subway, 🛌 Best Western, Comfort Inn, Hampton Inn, Holiday Inn Express, Super 8, 🔵 CarQuest, General RV Ctr, Meijer/dsl, Totten Tires, W 🅖 Marathon, 7-11, Sunoco/dsl, 🍴 A&W, Arby's, Applebee's, Big Boy, Bob Evans, Culver's, DQ, Little Caesar's, McDonald's, Quizno's, Sonic, Starbucks, Taco Bell, Tony's Rest., Uno, Victor&Merek's Pizza, Wendy's, 🛌 Country Inn&Suites, 🔵 Buick/Chevrolet, GNC, Harley-Davidson, Old Navy, Prime Outlet/famous brands
131	MI 57, to Montrose, E 🅖 Shell, Sunoco, 🍴 Arby's, Big John's Steaks, Burger King, DQ, KFC, McDonald's, Oriental Express, Subway, Taco Bell, Twins Pizza, Tim Horton, Wendy's, 🔵 AutoZone, Chevrolet, Chrysler/Dodge/Jeep, Ford, KanRock Tire, K-Mart, W 🅖 Mobil/Rally's/dsl, Murphy USA/dsl, 🍴 Big Boy, Lucky Steaks, Quizno's, 🔵 Menards, Walmart/Subway
129mm	rest area both lanes, full ♿ facilities, 🍴, 🛦, litter barrels, vending, petwalk
126	to Mt Morris, E 🅖 B&B/Burger King/dsl/24hr, W 🅖 BP/dsl, carwash
125	I-475 S, UAW Fwy, to Flint
122	Pierson Rd, to Flint, E 🅖 BP, Marathon/dsl, 🍴 McDonald's, Papa's Coney's, Subway, 🛌 Econolodge, 🔵 Kroger/gas, Murray's Parts, NW Tire, Tuffy Auto, W 🅖 Citgo, Shell/dsl, 🍴 A&W/KFC, Applebee's, Arby's, Big John's Steaks, Bob Evans, Burger King, Cottage Inn Pizza, Cracker Barrel, Denny's, Halo Burger, LJ Silver, Red Lobster, Taco Bell, Tim Horton, Wendy's, YaYa Chicken, 🛌 Baymont Inn, Great Western Inn, 🔵 Aldi Foods, AT&T, Discount Tire, $Tree, Home Depot, Meijer/dsl
118	MI 21, Corunna Rd, E 🅖 Sunoco, 🍴 Atlas Coney Island, Badawest Lebanese, Big John's Steaks, Burger King, Halo Burger, Hollywood Diner, Hungry Howie's, Little Caesar's, Taco Bell, Wing Fong Chinese, YaYa Chicken, 🔵🅗, CarQuest, $Zone, Family$, Kroger/gas, Rite Aid, W 🅖 BP/dsl, Mobil, Shell/Wendy's, Speedway, Valero, 🍴 A&W/KFC, Blue Collar Grill, Burger King, Fazoli's, Happy Valley Rest., McDonald's, Mega Diner, Tim Horton, White Castle, 🛌 Economy Motel, 🔵 Aldi Foods, AutoZone, Buick, Chevrolet, $General, GMC, Home Depot, KanRock Tire, Kroger/gas, Lowe's Whse, Rite Aid, Sam's Club/gas, VG's Foods, Walgreens, Walmart/auto, st police
117b	Miller Rd, to Flint, E 🅖 Speedway/dsl, Sunoco/dsl, 🍴 Applebee's, Arby's, Cottage Inn, Pizza, Don Pablo, Fuddrucker's, KFC, LoneStar Steaks, McDonald's, Qdoba, Sonic, Subway, West Side Diner, 🛌 Comfort Inn, Motel 6, Sleep Inn, 🔵 URGENT CARE, Belle Tire, K-Mart, Tuffy Auto, W 🅖 BP, Marathon, 🍴 BD's BBQ, Big Boy, Bob Evans, Chili's, ChuckeCheese, Famous Dave's BBQ, Fire Mtn Grill, Happy's Pizza, HoneyBaked Ham, Hooters, Italia Garden, Logan's Roadhouse, Old Country Buffet, Olive Garden, Outback Steaks, Pizza Hut, Rib City, Quizno's, Red Robin, Salvatori's Ristorante, Starbucks, Subway, Taco Bell, Telly's Coney Island, Valley Rest., 🛌

Right margin vertical: F L I N T

INTERSTATE 75 CONT'D

FLINT   N ↑ S

DETROIT AREA

Exit	Services
117b	Continued
	Hometown Inn, Red Roof Inn, Super 8, 🅞 AT&T, Barnes&Noble, Best Buy, Dale's Foods, Discount Tire, Dodge, Gander Mtn, Goodyear, Hobby Lobby, JC Penney, Jo-Ann Fabrics, Macy's, Michael's, Office Depot, Old Navy, PetCo, Radio Shack, Sears/auto, Target, U-Haul, Valley Tire, mall, vet
117a	I-69, E to Lansing, W to Port Huron
116	MI 121, Bristol Rd, **E** 🅖 Citgo, Speedway/dsl, 🍴 Capitol Coney Island, KFC, McDonald's, 🛏 Days Inn, Rodeway Inn, 🅞 AutoZone, **W** 🅖 Mobil/dsl, 🅞 ⊕
115	US 23 (from sb), **W on Hill Rd** 🅖 Citgo, Meijer/dsl/24hr, Mobil, 🍴 Hill St Grill, Maxie's Rest., McDonald's, Redwood Lodge, Turkey Farm Deli, 🛏 AmericInn, Courtyard, Holiday Inn, Residence Inn
111	I-475, N (from nb), UAW Fwy, to Flint
109	MI 54, Dort Hwy (no EZ return to sb)
108	Holly Rd, to Grand Blanc, **E** 🅖 Sunoco/dsl, 🍴 Big Apple Bagels, Buffalo Wild Wings, Da Edoardo Ristorante, Quizno's, Taco Bell, 🛏 Comfort Inn, Holiday Inn Express, 🅞 URGENT CARE, BMW/Mercedes/Toyota, **W** 🅖 BP/McDonald's/dsl, 🍴 Arby's, 🅞 🅗
106	Dixie Hwy (exits left from sb, no nb return), Saginaw Rd, to Grand Blanc
101	Grange Hall Rd, Ortonville, **E** 🅞 Holly RA, KOA, st police, **W** 🅖 Mobil/dsl, 🅞 to Seven Lakes/Groveland Oaks SP, RV camping
98	E Holly Rd, **E** 🅖 Mobil/Subway/dsl/24hr, 🅞 Ford, golf
96mm	**rest area nb, full** ♿ **facilities,** 📷 **, litter barrels, info,** 🅒, **vending, petwalk**
95mm	**rest area sb, full** ♿ **facilities,** 📷 **, litter barrels, info,** 🅒, **vending, petwalk**
93	US 24, Dixie Hwy, Waterford, **E** 🅖 BP/dsl, 🅞 Dodge, Kroger/gas (2mi), **1-3 mi W** 🅖 Speedway, 🍴 Big Boy, McDonald's, Subway, Taco Bell, Wendy's, 🅞 Chrysler/Jeep, Walgreens, to Pontiac Lake RA
91	MI 15, Davison, Clarkston, **E** 🅖 Sunoco/dsl, 🍴 Bullfrog's (5mi), Subway (5mi), 🅞 camping, **W** 🅖 Shell/dsl, 🍴 Brioni Grill, Mesquite Creek Café, 🅞 🅗
89	Sashabaw Rd, **E** 🅖 Shell/dsl, 🍴 Culvers, Ruby Tuesday, Tropical Smoothie Cafe, 🅞 county park, **W** 🅖 BP/24hr, Citgo, 🍴 Caribou Coffee, Chicken Shack, Dunkin Donuts, E Ocean Chinese, Guido's Pizza, Hong Kong Chinese, Hungry Howie's, Leo's Coney Island, Little Caesars, McDonald's, Quizno's, Rio Wraps, Subway, Tim Horton, Wendy's, 🅞 CVS Drug, $Tree, Kroger, vet
86mm	**weigh sta sb, parking area nb**
84b a	Baldwin Ave, **E** 🅖 Shell/24hr, 🍴 Arby's, Big Boy, Joe's Crabshack, Longhorn Steaks, Wendy's, 🅞 Best Buy, Costco/gas, Discount Tire, $Castle, Kohl's, Michael's, Old Navy, PetCo, Staples, **W** 🅖 Mobil/24hr, 🍴 Chili's, Jimmy John's, Kerry's Coney Island, Max&Erma's, McDonald's, On-the-Border, Oriental Forest, Quizno's, Rainforest Cafe, Starbucks, Steak'n Shake/24hr, Subway, 🛏 Holiday Inn Express, 🅞 AT&T, Bass Pro Shops, Great Lakes Crossing Outlet/famous brands, Marshall's, TJ Maxx, Vitamin Shoppe, USPO
83b a	Joslyn Rd, **E** 🅖 🍴 Applebee's, Olive Garden, 🅞 Belle Tire, Home Depot, Jo-Ann Fabrics, Meijer/dsl, Sam's Club/gas, Target, **W** 🅖 Sunoco

Exit	Services
81	MI 24, Pontiac (no EZ return), **E** The Palace Arena
79	University Dr, **E** 🅖 BP, 🍴 Jimmy John's, Rio Wraps, Spargo Coney Island, Subway, Taste of Thailand, **W** 🅖 Mobil, Speedway/dsl, 🍴 A&W/KFC, Burger King, Lelli's Steaks, McDonald's, Taco Bell, Wendy's/Tim Horton, 🛏 Candlewood Suites, Comfort Suites, Courtyard, Crowne Plaza, Extended Stay America, Extended Stay Deluxe, Fairfield Inn, Hampton Inn, Hilton, Holiday Inn, Hyatt, Motel 6, Staybridge Suites, Wingate Inn, 🅞 🅗, GM, Jakes Auto
78	Chrysler Dr, **E** 🅞 Chrysler, Chrysler Museum, Oakland Tech Ctr
77b a	MI 59, to Pontiac, **2 mi E on Adams** 🍴 5 Guys Burgers, Panera Bread, 🅞 Meijer/dsl, PetsMart, Walmart/auto, **1 mi W on Opdyke** 🅖 Fastrack/Tubby's/dsl
75	Square Lake Rd (exits left from nb), to Pontiac, **W** 🅗, St Mary's Coll
74	Adams Rd
72	Crooks Rd, to Troy, **W** 🍴 Charlie's Crabs, Kerby's Coney Island, Loccino Italian, Quizno's, Red Robin, Starbucks, 🛏 Embassy Suites, Ramada Inn
69	Big Beaver Rd, **E** 🍴 Champp's Grill, Kona Grill, Shula's Steaks, TGIFriday's, 🛏 Drury Inn, Marriott, other:, **W** 🅖 BP, 🍴 Benihana, Chipotle Mexican, Maggiano's Italian, Melting Pot Rest., Morton's Steaks, Noodles&Co, Potbelly's, Ruth's Chris Steaks, Starbucks, 🅞 mall
67	Rochester Rd, to Stevenson Hwy, **E** 🅖 BP, Marathon, Shell, 🍴 Arby's, Bahama Breeze, Burger King, Caribou Coffee, Hooter's, Hungry Howies, Jimmy John's, Mr Pita, Ntl Coney Island, Orchid Rest., Panera Bread, Papa John's, Peiwei, Qdoba, Ram's Horn Rest., Rio Wraps, Subway, Taco Bell, Troy Deli, 🅞 Discount Tire, Nordstrom's, Office Depot, PetsMart, Radio Shack, transmissions, **W** 🛏 Holiday Inn, Red Roof Inn, 🅞 tires/repair
65b a	14 Mile Rd, Madison Heights, **E** 🅖 Marathon/dsl, Mobil, 🍴 Azteca Mexican, Bob Evans, Burger King, Chili's, Krispy Kreme, Logan's Roadhouse, McCool's Grill, McDonald's, Panera Bread, Pizza Papalis, Starbucks, Steak'n Shake, Taco Bell, Wendy's, 🛏 Motel 6, Red Roof Inn, 🅞 AT&T, Barnes&Noble, Belle Tire, Best Buy, Dodge, Firestone, Ford, Home Depot, JC Penney, Kohl's, Lowe's Whse, Macy's, NAPA, Office Depot, Radio Shack, Sam's Club, Sears/auto, Target, TJ Maxx, mall, **W** 🅖 Mobil, Valero, 🍴 Applebee's, Big Fish Seafood, Caribou Coffee, Dolly's Pizza, McDonald's, NY Coney Island, Outback Steaks, Quizno's, 🛏 Best Western, Courtyard, Econolodge, Extended Stay America, Fairfield Inn, Hampton Inn, Residence Inn, 🅞 Chevrolet, Costco/gas, Value Ctr Foods
63	12 Mile Rd, **E** 🅖 Marathon, 🍴 Blimpie, Green Lantern Rest., Marinelli's Pizza, McDonald's, Red Lobster, Sero's Rest., Starbucks, TX Roadhouse, Tim Horton, 🅞

MI

N ↕ S

DETROIT AREA

INTERSTATE 75 CONT'D

Exit	Services
63	Continued Curves, Home Depot, K-Mart/foods, Lowe's Whse, Radio Shack, Uncle Ed's Oil, auto repair, vet, **W** 🅖 Marathon/Dunkin Donuts, Speedway, 🍴 Col's Rest., 🅞 Chevrolet, Costco/gas
62	11 Mile Rd, **E** 🅖 Mobil, 🍴 Boodles Rest., Cottage Pizza, Jets Pizza, 🅞 Advance Parts, CVS Drug, Sav-a-Lot, 7-11, Tuffy Auto, Walgreens, repair/tires, vet, **W** 🅖 BP, Marathon/dsl, Mobil, 🍴 KFC, Taco Bell, Tim Horton, Tubby's Subs, 🅞 Belle Tire
61	I-696 E, to Port Huron, W to Lansing, to Hazel Park Raceway
60	9 Mile Rd, John R St, **E** 🍴 Checkers, China 1 Buffet, DQ, Hardee's, McDonald's, Subway, Wendy's, 🅞 $Store, Kroger, USPO, **W** 🅖 Exxon, Mobil, 🍴 Tubby's Subs, Wendy's, 🅞 Hasting's Parts, repair
59	MI 102, 8 Mile Rd, **3 mi** **W** st fairgrounds
58	7 Mile Rd, **W** 🅖 BP/dsl
57	McNichols Rd, **E** 🅖 Shell/dsl, 🍴 KFC, LA Coney Island, Taco Bell, 🅞 Auto Parts/Repair
56b a	Davison Fwy
55	Holbrook Ave, Caniff St, **E** 🅖 Mobil/dsl, **W** 🍴 Grandy's Coney Island
54	E Grand Blvd, Clay Ave, **W** 🅖 BP/dsl, 🍴 Super Coney Island
53b	I-94, Ford Fwy, to Port Huron, Chicago
53a	Warren Ave, **E** 🅖 Mobil, **W** 🅖 BP
52	Mack Ave, **E** 🅖 Shell, 🍴 McDonald's
51c	I-375 to civic center, tunnel to Canada, downtown
51b	MI 3 (exits left from nb), Gratiot Ave, downtown
50	Grand River Ave, downtown
49b	MI 10, Lodge Fwy, downtown
49a	Rosa Parks Blvd, **E** Tiger Stadium, **W** 🅖 Mobil, 🅞 Firestone
48	I-96 begins/ends
47b	Porter St, **E** bridge to Canada, DutyFree/24hr
47a	MI 3, Clark Ave, **E** 🅖 Mobil, Sunoco, **W** 🅖 Marathon
46	Livernois Ave, to Hist Ft Wayne, **E** 🅖 Marathon, 🍴 Coney Island, KFC/Taco Bell
45	Fort St, Springwells Ave, **E** 🅖 BP/dsl, Pure Petro/dsl, **W** 🅖 Mobil, 🍴 McDonald's
44	Deerborn St (from nb)
43b a	MI 85, Fort St, to Schaefer Hwy, **E** 🅖 BP, **W** 🅖 Marathon Refinery, 🅞 to River Rouge Ford Plant
42	Outer Dr, **E** 🅖 Marathon, 🍴 Happy's Pizza, 🅞 URGENT CARE, **W** 🅖 BP/Subway/dsl, 🅞 Family$, truck tires
41	MI 39, Southfield Rd, to Lincoln Park, **E** 🍴 A&W, Bill's Place Rest., Tim Horton, White Castle, 🅞 Aldi Foods, Family$, Murray Parts, Walgreens, **W** 🅖 Shell/Tim Horton, 🍴 Big Boy, Starbucks, Wendy's, 🛏 Sleep Inn, 🅞 AT&T, Kroger/gas, Rite Aid, Walgreens
40	Dix Hwy, **E** 🅖 Marathon/A&W/dsl, Welcome, 🍴 Baskin-Robbins/Dunkin Donuts, Coney Island Diner, 🅞 URGENT CARE, CVS Drug, Meijer, 7-11, repair, **W** 🅖 Marathon, Mobil, 🍴 Big Boy, Burger King, Checker's, DQ, LJ Silver, McDonald's, Pizza Hut, Quizno's, Taco Bell, 🅞 AT&T, Belle Tire, Family$, Kroger, Rite Aid, Sav-a-Lot, Sears/auto, Walgreens
37	Allen Rd, North Line Rd, to Wyandotte, **E** 🅖 BP, Shell/Tim Horton, 🛏 Holiday Inn, 🅞 H, Sam's Club/gas, **W** 🅖 Mobil, Sunoco, 🍴 Arby's, Burger King, Mallie's Grill, McDonald's, Wendy's, 🛏 Comfort Suites, La Quinta, Motel 6

MONROE

Exit	Services
36	Eureka Rd, **E** 🅖 BP, 🍴 Bob Evans, Denny's, Fire Mtn Grill, Orleans Steaks, 🛏 Ramada Inn, Super 8, 🅞 vet, **W** 🍴 American Thai Grill, Big Boy, Coldstone Creamery, Culver's, HoneyBaked Ham, Hooters, Jimmy John's, Little Daddy's Rest., McDonald's, Ruby Tuesday, Starbucks, Subway, TX Roadhouse, Wendy's, 🛏 Red Roof Inn, 🅞 AT&T, Belle Tire, Best Buy, Discount Tire, Home Depot, JC Penney, Kohl's, Macy's, Meijer/dsl, PetsMart, mall
35	US 24, Telegraph Rd, (from nb, exits left)
34b	Sibley Rd, Riverview, **W** 🅖 Sunoco/Baskin-Robbins/Dunkin Donuts/Subway, 🅞 RV Ctr
34a	to US 24 (from sb), Telegraph Rd
32	West Rd, to Trenton, Woodhaven, **E** 🅖 Detroiter/Sunoco/dsl/rest./scales/24hr/@, Speedway/dsl, 🍴 Applebee's, Baskin-Robbins/Dunkin Donuts, Bellacino's Italian, Blue Margarita Mexican, Bob Evans, Burger King, Christoff's Rest., Grand Buffet, Ground Round, IHOP, Jersey Subs, Panera Bread, Pizza Hut, Quizno's, Steak'n Shake, Subway, Taco Bell, Tim Horton, Wendy's, White Castle, 🅞 Chevrolet, Discount Tire, Firestone/auto, Ford, GNC, Home Depot, K-Mart, Kohl's, Kroger, Lowe's Whse, Meijer/dsl, Michael's, Murray Parts, Office Depot, PetsMart, Radio Shack, Target, Walmart/auto, **W** 🅖 BP/Tim Horton/24hr, Shell, 🍴 Amigo's Mexican, Andy's Pizza, Domino's, McDonald's, Ram's Horn Rest., Sunday's Ice Cream, 🛏 Best Western/rest., Holiday Inn Express, Westwood Inn, 🅞 SavOn Drug
29	Gilbralter Rd, to Flat Rock, Lake Erie Metropark, **E** 🅖 FasTrack/dsl, 🍴 Chinese Food, Cottage Inn Pizza, McDonald's, Subway, Wendy's, 🅞 H, Curves, GNC, Kroger, **W** 🅖 Marathon/dsl, 🛏 Sleep Inn, 🅞 Ford, st police
28	rd 85 (from nb), Fort St, **E** H
27	N Huron River Dr, to Rockwood, **E** 🅖 Marathon/Subway/dsl, 🍴 Benito's Pizza, Famous Coney Island, Huron River Rest., Ocean Duck Chinese, 🅞 Curves, FoodTown Foods, Rite Aid, **W** 🅖 Speedway/dsl, 🍴 Riverfront Rest.
26	S Huron River Dr, to, S Rockwood, **E** 🅖 Sunoco/dsl, 🍴 Dixie Cafe, Drift Inn, 🅞 USPO
21	Newport Rd, to Newport, **E** 🅖 BP/Subway/dsl, 🅞 repair, **W** 🅖 Marathon/Burger King/dsl/24hr
20	I-275 N, to Flint
18	Nadeau Rd, **W** 🅖 🍴/Arby's/dsl/scales/24hr, 🅞 H, RV camping
15	MI 50, Dixie Hwy, to Monroe, **E** 🅖 Shell, 🍴 Bob Evans, Burger King, Red Lobster, 🛏 Best Value Inn, Best Western, Hampton Inn, Motel 6, 🅞 to Sterling SP, **W** 🅖 🍴/Subway/dsl/scales/24hr, TA/BP/Country Pride/Pizza Hut/Popeye's/Tim Horton/dsl/scales/24hr/@, 🍴 Big Boy, Cracker Barrel, Denny's, El Maguey, McDonald's, Wendy's, 🛏 Holiday Inn Express, Knight's Inn, 🅞 H, to Viet Vet Mem
14	Elm Ave, to Monroe
13	Front St, Monroe
11	La Plaisance Rd, to Bolles Harbor, **W** 🅖 Marathon/Taco Bell/dsl, Speedway, 🍴 Burger King, McDonald's, Wendy's, 🛏 Baymont Inn, Comfort Inn, Harbor Town RV Resort, 🅞 Outlet Mall/famous brands, st police
10mm	**Welcome Ctr nb, full ♿ services, 🅒, info, 🛏, litter barrels, vending, petwalk**
9	S Otter Creek Rd, to La Salle, **W** antiques
7mm	**weigh sta both lanes**
6	Luna Pier, **E** 🅖 Sunoco/dsl, 🍴 Beef Jerky Ultd. Ganders Rest., Roma's Pizza, 🛏 Super 8, **W** st police
5	to Erie, Temperance
2	Summit St
0mm	Michigan/Ohio state line

MI

INTERSTATE 94

Exit	Services

PORT HURON   E   W

275mm   I-69/I-94 begin/end on MI 25, **Pinegrove Ave in Port Huron** 🅖 BP/24hr, Shell, Speedway, 🍴 Jet's Pizza, McDonald's, Tim Horton, Wendy's, 🛏 Days Inn, Quality Inn, 🅞 Buick, Family$, Honda, Rite Aid, tollbridge to Canada

274.5mm   Black River

274   Water St, Port Huron, **N Welcome Ctr/rest area, full facilities,** (from wb only), 🍴 Cracker Barrel, 🛏 Best Western, **S** 🅖 SpeedyQ/dsl, Speedway/dsl, 🍴 Bob Evans, 🛏 Comfort Inn, Fairfield Inn, Hampton Inn, 🅞 Lake Port SP, RV camping

271   **I-69 E and I-94 E run together eb, Lp I-69, 0-2 mi S on Lp 69 S** 🅖 Mobil/dsl, Speedway, 🍴 Arby's, Baskin-Robbins, Burger King, Dunkin Donuts, McDonalds, KFC, Quay St Grill, Taco Bell, Wendy's, 🅞 Advance Parts, AutoZone, Kroger/gas, K-Mart, Sam's Club/gas, repair, to Port Huron

269   Dove St, Range Rd, **N** 🅖 Speedway/dsl/24hr, 🍴 Billy Boy's Diner, 🛏 Baymont Inn

266   Gratiot Rd, Marysville, **0-2 mi, S** 🅖 Admiral, BP/dsl/scales/24hr, Marathon/scales/dsl, Speedway, 🍴 Arby's, Big Boy, Burger King, Dairy Boy, Daliono's, KFC, 4 Star Rest., Hungry Howie's, Jimmy John's, Little Caesars, McDonald's, Mr Pita, Pelican Café, Pizza Hut, Seros, Subway, Taco Bell, Tim Horton, 🛏 Super 8, 🅞 H, AutoZone, CarQuest, CVS Drug, $General, $Plus, Meijer/dsl, Rite Aid, Wally's Foods, vet

262   Wadhams Rd, **N** camping, **S** 🅖 Mobil/dsl

257   St Clair, Richmond, **S** 🅖 BP/dsl, 🅞 st police

255mm   **rest area eb, full ♿ facilities, 🚰, info, 🛢, litter barrels, petwalk**

251mm   **rest area wb, full ♿ facilities, 🚰, info, 🛢, litter barrels, petwalk**

248   26 Mile Rd, to Marine City, **N** 🍴 McDonald's (2mi), **S** 🅖 7-11/gas, Speedy Q (1mi), 🍴 Asian Garden, My Place Cafe, Tim Horton, 🅞 Meijer/dsl

247mm   Salt River

247   MI 19 (no eb return), New Haven

243   MI 29, MI 3, Utica, New Baltimore, **N** 🅖 BP, Marathon/dsl, Sunoco/dsl, 🍴 Applebee's, Arby's, Buffalo Wings, Burger King, Chophouse, Coney Island, Dimitri's Rest., Empire Buffet, Little Caesars, McDonald's, Outback Steaks, Panera Bread, Ruby Tuesday, Starbucks, Subway, Stevie B's Pizza, Tim Horton, Waffle House, Wendy's, White Castle, 🛏 Chesterfield Motel, 🅞 AutoZone, Best Buy, Dick's, Discount Tire, $Tree, GNC, Home Depot, JC Penney, Jo-Ann Fabrics, K-Mart, Kohl's, Lowe's, Meijer/dsl/24hr, Michael's, NAPA, O'Reilly Parts, PetCo, PetsMart, Radio Shack, Rite Aid, Staples, Target, TJ Maxx, Walgreens, **S** 🅖 Marathon/dsl/24hr, 7-11/gas, Speedway/dsl/24hr, 🍴 Big Boy, Buscemi's Pizza, Hot'n Now Burgers, Taco Bell, 🛏 LodgeKeeper

241   21 Mile Rd, Selfridge, **N** 🅖 Exxon/dsl, Speedway, 🍴 China King, Hungry Howie's, 🅞 Advance Parts, AT&T, CVS Drug, Verizon, vet, same as 240

240   to MI 59, **N** 🅖 7-11/gas, Marathon, Mobil, 🍴 Arby's, Bob Evans, Burger King, Coney Island, KFC, McDonald's, O'Charley's, Taco Bell, Tim Horton, 🛏 Hampton Inn, Holiday Inn Express, 🅞 Ford, Harley-Davidson, Tuffy Auto, Walmart

237   N River Rd, Mt Clemens, **N** 🅖 BP/dsl, Mobil/Subway/dsl, 🍴 McDonald's, 🛏 Victory Inn, 🅞 H, General RV Ctr, Gibraltar Trade Ctr

236.5mm   Clinton River

DETROIT AREA

236   Metro Parkway, **S** 🍴 Big Apple Bagels, Empire Chinese, Little Caesars, McDonald's, Subway, 🅞 H, Curves, CVS Drug, GNC, Kroger

235   Shook Rd (from wb)

234b a   Harper Rd, 15 Mile Rd, **N** 🅖 BP/McDonald's, Marathon/dsl, SpeedyQ, Sunoco/dsl/24hr, 🍴 Dan Good Pizza, Gina's Cafe, 🅞 vet, **S** 🅖 FL Gas, 🍴 China Moon, Subway, Travis Rest., Winners Grill, 🅞 Urgent Care

232   Little Mack Ave (from wb only), **N** 🅖 Marathon, 7-11, Shell, Speedway, Sunoco, 🍴 Coldstone, Denny's, Hooters, Longhorn Steaks, McDonald's, Pizza Hut, Red Robin, Sea Breeze Diner, Woody's Grill, 🛏 Holiday Inn Express, Red Roof Inn, Relax Inn, Super 8, Victory Inn, 🅞 Advance Parts, Aldi Foods, Belle Tire, Discount Tire, Firestone, JC Penney, O'Reilly Parts, Sam's Club, Sears/Auto, Staples, Target, **S** 🅖 Marathon, Speedway/dsl, 🍴 Cracker Barrel, Culvers, IHOP, Izzy's Cafe, 🛏 Baymont Inn, 🅞 Family$, Home Depot, Jo-Ann Fabrics, Meijer/dsl/24hr, PetsMart, same as 231

231   (from eb), MI 3, Gratiot Ave, **N** 🅖 Marathon, Sunoco, 🍴 Applebee's, Arby's, Big Boy, Bob Evans, Burger King, Chili's, ChuckeCheese, Cici's, Del Taco, Denny's, Famous Dave's BBQ, Logan's Roadhouse, Longhorn Steaks, Marco's Italian, McDonald's, Panera Bread, PetCo, Pizza Hut, Ruby Tuesday, Sajo's Rest., Starbucks, Subway, Tim Horton, TX Roadhouse, 🛏 Best Western, Days Inn, EconoLodge, Extended Stay America, Microtel, 🅞 Best Buy, Discount Tire, Firestone/auto, Honda/Acura, Kia, Kohl's, Kroger, Michael's, Nissan, Radio Shack, Sam's Club/gas, Staples, Toyota, U-Haul, mall

230   12 Mile Rd, **N** 🅖 Mobil/dsl, Sunoco/dsl, 🍴 BD's Mongolian, Jimmy John's, Noni's Grill, Outback Steaks, Starbucks, Taco Bell, 🅞 AT&T, CVS Drug, $Tree, Marshall's, NAPA, Walmart/Subway

229   I-696 W, Reuther Fwy, to 11 Mile Rd, **S** 🅖 BP/dsl, Speedway, 🅞 7-11

228   10 Mile Rd, **N** 🅖 BP/24hr, Mobil, Shell, 🍴 Baskin-Robbins, Coney Island, Eastwind Chinese, Friendly Rest., Jet's Pizza, 🅞 CVS Drug, Save More Drugs

227   9 Mile Rd, **N** 🅖 Mobil/dsl, Speedway/dsl, Sunoco, 🍴 McDonald's, Papa John's, Pizza Hut/Taco Bell, Subway, Wendy's, 🅞 Aldi Foods, CVS Drug, $Tree, Family$, Fresh Choice Foods, Office Depot, TrueValue, vet, **S** 🅖 Mobil/dsl, 🛏 Shore Pointe Motel, 🅞 Cadillac, Mercedes

225   MI 102, Vernier Rd, 8 Mile Rd, **S** 🅖 BP/Subway, Mobil, Sunoco/dsl, 🍴 Coney Island, KFC, Taco Bell, Wendy's, 🅞 Kroger, Walgreens

224b   Allard Ave, Eastwood Ave

224a   Moross Rd, **S** 🅖 Shell, 🅞 Family Foods H

223   Cadieux Rd, **S** 🅖 BP/Subway, Mobil, Shell, Sunoco, 🍴 McDonald's, Papa's Pizza, Popeye's, Taco Bell, Tubby's

Exit	Services
	INTERSTATE 94 CONT'D
223	Continued Subs, Wendy's, White Castle, Rite Aid
222b	Harper Ave (from eb), S Hastings Auto
222a	Chalmers Ave, Outer Dr, N BP/Subway/dsl, Zoom, Coney Island, KFC, Little Caesars, White Castle, Family$
220b	Conner Ave, N BP, Zoom
220a	French Rd, S Marathon
219	MI 3, Gratiot Ave, N Marathon/Subway, Speedy, Coney Island, KFC, McDonald's, Family$, Farmer John's Foods, S GasMart, Burger King
218	MI 53, Van Dyke Ave, N BP, Mobil/dsl
217b	Mt Elliott Ave, S Marathon, Sunoco/dsl, Royal BBQ
217a	E Grand Blvd, Chene St, S Marathon
216b	Russell St (from eb), to downtown
216a	I-75, Chrysler Fwy, to tunnel to Canada
215c	MI 1, Woodward Ave, John R St
215b	MI 10 N, Lodge Fwy
215a	MI 10 S, tunnel to Canada, downtown
214b	Trumbull Ave, to Ford
214a	(from wb)Grand River Ave
213b	I-96, W to Lansing, E to Canada, bridge to Canada, to Tiger Stadium
213a	W Grand (exits left from eb)
212b	Warren Ave (from eb)
212a	Livernois Ave, S Marathon/Subway/dsl, Sunoco
211b	Cecil Ave (from wb), Central Ave
211a	Lonyo Rd
210	US 12, Michigan Ave, Wyoming Ave, N Mobil/dsl, S BP/dsl, Sunoco/dsl, Valero
209	Rotunda Dr (from wb)
208	Greenfield Rd, Schaefer Rd, N Mobil/dsl, 7-11, S River Rouge Ford Plant
207mm	Rouge River
206	Oakwood Blvd, Melvindale, N Marathon, Shell, Applebee's, Carino's, Coney Island, Chili's, Coldstone, Famous Hamburger, Little Caesar's, Longhorn Steaks, Moe's SW Grill, On-the-Border, Panera Bread, Pottbelly, Quizno's, Starbucks, Taco Bell, AAA, Barnes&Noble, Best Buy, GNC, Home Depot, Jo-Ann Fabrics, Lowe's, Meijer, Michael's, Old Navy, PetCo, Staples, Target, TJ Maxx, Verizon, Greenfield Village Museum, S BP/dsl, Burger King, McDonald's, Melvindale Coney Island, O'Henry's, Sabina's, Subway, Best Western, Holiday Inn Express, Curves, CVS Drug, $General, Rite Aid, 7-11
205mm	Largest Uniroyal Tire in the World
204b a	MI 39, Southfield Fwy, Pelham Rd, N Marathon/dsl, Mobil, Valero/dsl, 7-11, to Greenfield Village, S Marathon/dsl, Papa's Pizza, Walgreens
202b a	US 24, Telegraph Rd, N Citgo, Shell, Sunoco, Burger King, Checkers, Dunkin Donuts, KFC, McDonald's, Pizza Hut, Ram's Horn Rest., Subway, Taco Bell, Wendy's, Advance Parts, Aldi Foods, Rite Aid, True Value, Walgreen, 0-2 mi S BP, Marathon/dsl, Valero/dsl, Arby's, Big Boy, Burger King, Hungry Howie's, KFC, Leo's Coney Island, Leon's, Rest., Little Caesar's, LJ Silver, Marina's Pizza, McDonald's, New Hong Kong, Old Country Buffet, Pizza Hut, Popeye's, Taco Bell, Subway, Super China, Wendy's, Yum Yum Donuts, Comfort Inn, AT&T, AutoZone, Curves, $Tree, Family$, Firestone/auto, Radio Shack, Rite Aid, U-Haul, Walgreens, Walmart, st police, USPO

Exit	Services
200	Ecorse Rd, (no ez eb return), to Taylor, N Marathon/Subway/dsl/scales, S Rich, Speedy/dsl, Danny's Pizza, Norm's Subs, Webster's BBQ, USPO
199	Middle Belt Rd, S BP/dsl/24hr, Checkers, McDonald's, Wendy's, Days Inn, Quality Inn, Super 8
198	Merriman Rd, N Marathon, Speedway, Big Boy, Bob Evans, Leonardo's Italian, McDonald's, Merriman St Grill, Subway, Toramino's Pizza, Baymont Inn, Best Western, Clarion, Comfort Inn, Courtyard, Crowne Plaza Hotel, Embassy Suites, Extended Stay America, Fairfield Inn, Hampton Inn, Holiday Inn, Howard Johnson, La Quinta, Lee's Inn, Lexington Motel, Marriott, Metro Inn, Metropolitan Hotel, Ramada Inn, Red Roof Inn, Rodeway Inn, Sheraton, SpringHill Suites, USPO, S Wayne Co
197	Vining Rd
196	Wayne Rd, Romulus, N Shell/dsl, McDonald's, S Mobil/dsl, Burger King, Subway
194b a	I-275, N to Flint, S to Toledo
192	Haggerty Rd, N BP/dsl, Mobil/24hr, Sub Station, S Lower Huron Metro Park
190	Belleville Rd, to Belleville, N BP/24hr, Applebee's, Arby's, Big Boy, Coney Island, Cracker Barrel, Culver's, Happy's Pizza, Hungry Howie's, McDonald's, O'Charley's, Quizno's, Taco Bell, Tim Horton, Wendy's, Holiday Inn Express, Red Roof Inn, Camping World RV Service/supplies, CVS Drug, $Tree, Ford, Meijer/dsl, Verizon, Walgreens, Walmart, vet, S Shell, Burger King, China City, China King, Dimitri's Kitchen, Dos Pesos Mexican, Subway, Comfort Inn, Super 8, URGENT CARE, USPO
189mm	**rest area wb, full facilities, info, , , litter barrels, vending, petwalk**
187	Rawsonville Rd, N Freightliner, S Mobil/dsl, Speedway/dsl, Burger King, Denny's, KFC, Little Caesar's, McDonald's, Pizza Hut, Tim Horton, Wendy's, Detroit Greenfield RV Park, $General, $Tree, GNC, K-Mart
185	US 12, Michigan Ave (from eb, exits left, no return), to frontage rds,
184mm	Ford Lake
183	US 12, Huron St, Ypsilanti, N BP/dsl, Marathon/pizza/dsl, to, E MI U, S Buffalo Wild Wings, Coney Island, Jet's Pizza, McDonald's, Rio Wraps, Marriott , st police
181b a	US 12 W, Michigan Ave, Ypsilanti, N Meijer/dsl/24hr, Speedway/dsl, Burger King, Coney Island, Dunkin Donuts, Hong Kong Chinese, Pizza Hut/Taco Bell, Roundtree Grill, Tim Horton/Wendy's, , Aamco, BigLots, $Tree, Firestone/auto, GNC, Meijer/dsl, Radio Shack, Rose Mkt, Walmart, 0-2 mi S BP/Circle K, Shell/dsl, Sunoco, Harvest Moon Rest., McDonald's, Subway, Sam's Club/gas
180b a	US 23, to Toledo, Flint
177	State St, N BP/24hr, Mobil, Shell, Burger King, CA Pizza Kitchen, Chipotle Mexican, Damon's, El Camino Royal, Graham's Steaks, Macaroni Grill, Max&Erma's, Mediterrano Rest., Olive Garden, Red Robin, Seoul Garden, Wendy's, Comfort Inn, Courtyard, Fairfield Inn, Hampton Inn, Holiday Inn, Holiday Inn Express, Red Roof Inn, Sheraton, Firestone/auto, Honda, JC Penney, Macy's, Porsche, Sears/auto, VW, World Mkt, mall, to UMI, S Citgo/Subway, Speedway, Coney Island, McDonald's, Taco Bell, Motel 6, U-Haul

E
W

D E T R O I T   A R E A

MI

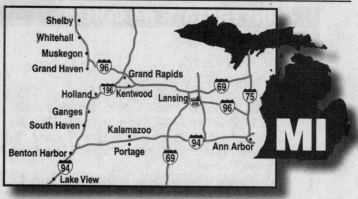

INTERSTATE 94 CONT'D

Exit	Services

ANN ARBOR · E ← → W

175 Ann Arbor-Saline Rd, N 🅶 Shell, 🍴 Applebee's, Coney Island, Dibella Subs, Moe's SW Grill, Old Country Buffet, Panera Bread, Papa Romano's Pizza, Paradise Asian, Pottbelly, Subway, 🛏 Candlewood Suites, ⊙ Office Depot, Whole Foods Mkt, mall, vet, to UMI Stadium, S 🍴 ChuckeCheese, Jet's Pizza, Joe's Crabshack, McDonald's, Nick's Pancakes, Outback Steaks, TGIFriday's, ⊙ Best Buy, Jo-Ann Fabrics, Kohl's, Meijer/dsl/e-85, Petsmart, Target, Tuesday Morning

172 Jackson Ave, to Ann Arbor, N 🅶 BP, Marathon, Shell, Sunoco/dsl, 🍴 Burger King, Gourmet Garden, Holiday's Rest., KFC, Marathon, McDonald's, Quarter Rest., Quizno's, Starbucks, Subway, Taco Bell, Zingerman's Roadhouse, ⊙ H, CVS Drug, $Tree, Discount Tire, Goodyear/auto, K-Mart, Kroger, O'Reilly Parts, Rite Aid, Staples, TJ Maxx, Verizon, Walgreens, S 🛏 Best Western, Super 8, ⊙ Chevrolet/Cadillac, Ford

171 MI 14 (from eb, exits left), to Ann Arbor, to Flint by US 23

169 Zeeb Rd, N 🅶 BP/dsl/24hr, 🍴 Big Boy, Grand Pies Co, Metzger's Rest., McDonald's, S 🅶 Citgo/dsl, 🍴 Arby's, Burger King, Creekside Grill, Domino's, Panera Bread, Pizza Hut, Subway, Taco Bell, Wendy's, Westside Grill, ⊙ CVS Drug, Harley-Davidson, Lowe's, Meijer/dsl

167 Baker Rd, Dexter, N 🅶 ⬛/Subway/scales/dsl/24hr, S 🅶 ⬛/Arby's/dsl/scales/24hr, TA/BP/Popeye's/dsl/scales/24hr/@, 🍴 McDonald's, ⊙ Blue Beacon

162 Jackson Rd, Fletcher Rd, S 🅶 BP/Subway/dsl/24hr, 🍴 Stiver's Rest.

161mm rest area eb, full ♿ facilities, 🚻, 🍽, litter barrels, vending, petwalk

159 MI 52, Chelsea, N 🅶 Mobil/dsl, Rich Gas, Sunoco/dsl, 🍴 Big Boy, Chelsea Grill, China Garden, Chinese Tonite, KFC/Taco Bell, McDonald's, Subway, Uptown Coney Island, Wendy's, 🛏 Comfort Inn, Holiday Inn Express, ⊙ H, Buick/Chevrolet, Chelsea Drug, Chrysler/Dodge/Jeep, Country Mkt Foods/drug, CVS Drug, Pamida, Travel Land RV Ctr, USPO, vet

157 Jackson Rd, Pierce Rd, N Gerald Eddy Geology Ctr

156 Kalmbach Rd, N to Waterloo RA

153 Clear Lake Rd, N 🅶 Marathon/dsl

151.5mm weigh sta both lanes

150 to Grass Lake, S 🅶 Mobil/Subway

150mm rest area wb, full ♿ facilities, 🚻, 🍽, litter barrels, vending, petwalk

147 Race Rd, N Holiday RV Camp, to Waterloo RA, camping, S 🛏

145 Sargent Rd, S 🅶 BP/dsl, Mobil/145 Rest/dsl/scales/rest./24hr, 🍴 McDonald's, Wendy's, 🛏 Colonial Inn

144 Lp 94 (from wb), to Jackson

142 US 127 S, to Hudson, 3 mi S 🅶 Meijer/dsl/24hr, Speedway, 🍴 Domino's, McDonald's, Wendy's, ⊙ Advance Parts, Kroger, Parts+, Rite Aid, to MI Speedway

141 Elm Rd, N 🛏 Travelodge, ⊙ Chevrolet, Chrysler/Dodge/Jeep, Ford/Lincoln/Mercury, Honda, Nissan, S H

139 MI 106, Cooper St, to Jackson, N st police/prison, S 🅶 Citgo/Subway, ⊙ H

138 US 127 N, MI 50, to Lansing, Jackson, N 🍴 Red Lobster, 🛏 Avalon Hotel, Baymont Inn, Best Value Inn, Comfort Inn, Country Inn&Suites, Fairfield Inn, Hampton Inn, ⊙ vet, S 🅶 Admiral, BP, Shell/24hr, 🍴 Arby's, Big Boy,

JACKSON

138 Continued
Bob Evans, Burger King, Dunkin Donuts, Fazoli's, Ground Round, Jumbo Buffet, KFC, LJ Silver, Los Tres Amigos, McDonald's, Old Country Buffet, Outback Steaks, Panera Bread, Papa John's, Pizza Hut, Quizno's, Starbucks, Subway, Tim Horton, 🛏 Country Hearth Inn, Motel 6, ⊙ Advance Parts, Aldi Foods, AT&T, AutoZone, Belle Tire, Best Buy, $Tree, Family$, Home Depot, Jo-Ann Fabrics, Kohl's, Kroger/gas, Lowe's, Michael's, Office Depot, Sears/auto, Target, TJ Maxx, Walgreens

137 Airport Rd, N 🅶 Mobil, Shell/Taco Bell/24hr, 🍴 Burger King, Denny's, Hudson's Rest., McDonald's, Steak'n Shake, Subway, Wendy's, 🛏 Holiday Inn, ⊙ Bumper Parts, Meijer/dsl, 7-11, S 🅶 BP/24hr, 🍴 Cracker Barrel, Culvers, Olive Garden, LoneStar Steaks, 🛏 Country Inn&Suites, ⊙ K-Mart, Sam's Club/gas, Sav-A-Lot Foods

136 Lp 94, MI 60, to Jackson

135mm rest area eb, full ♿ facilities, 🚻, 🍽, litter barrels, vending, petwalk

133 Dearing Rd, Spring Arbor, S to Spring Arbor U

130 Parma, S 🅶 Citgo/rest/dsl/24hr

128 Michigan Ave, N 🅶 BP/Burger King/scales/dsl/24hr, Marathon/dsl/24hr, ⊙ RV camping

127 Concord Rd, N wineries

124 MI 99, to Eaton Rapids, S 🛏

121 28 Mile Rd, to Albion, N 🅶 Mobil/dsl, 🍴 Arby's, 🛏 Albion Inn, S 🅶 BP, Speedway/dsl/24hr, 🍴 Albion Garden, Burger King, Frosty Dan's, Full Moon, KFC, La Casa Mexican, McDonald's, Pizza Hut, 🛏 Super 9, ⊙ H, AutoZone, Buick/Chevrolet, $General, Family$, Family Fare Foods, Ford/Mercury, Radio Shack, RV camping, Tire City

119 MI 199, 26 Mile Rd

115 22.5 Mile Rd, N 🅶 Citgo/115 Rest./dsl/24hr

113mm rest area wb, full ♿ facilities, 🚻, 🍽, litter barrels, vending, petwalk

112 Partello Rd, S 🅶 Loves/Hardee's/scales/dsl/24hr, 🍴 Schuler's Rest.

MARSHALL

110 Old US 27, Marshall, N 🅶 Shell/Country Kitchen/Subway/dsl/24hr, S 🅶 Citgo/dsl, 🍴 Denny's, Pizza Hut (2mi), Schuler's Rest. (2mi), 🛏 Hampton Inn, Holiday Inn Express, ⊙ H, sheriff

108 I-69, US 27, N to Lansing, S to Ft Wayne

104 11 Mile Rd, Michigan Ave, N 🅶 ⬛/McDonald's/dsl/scales/24hr, Sunoco/Te-Khi Trkstp/rest./dsl/scales/24hr/@, S 🅶 Citgo/Subway/dsl/e-85/24hr, Quality Inn/rest., ⊙ casino

103 Lp 94 (from wb, no return), to Battle Creek, N H

102mm Kalamazoo River

100 Beadle Lake Rd, N 🍴 Moonraker Rest., S 🅶 Citgo/dsl,

MI

INTERSTATE 94 CONT'D

Exit	Services
100	Continued 🅞 Binder Park Zoo
98b	I-194 N, to Battle Creek
98a	MI 66, to Sturgis, S 🅖 Citgo/dsl, 🍴 Caribou Coffee, Chili's, McDonald's, Ruby Tuesday, Schlotzsky's, Starbucks, Steak'n Shake, 🛏 Holiday Inn, 🅞 AT&T, Best Buy, Discount Tire, Kohl's, Lowe's, Meijer/dsl, Menards, Michael's, PetCo, Sam's Club/gas, Staples, TJ Maxx, Walgreens, Walmart/Subway, same as 97
97	Capital Ave, to Battle Creek, N 🅖 BP/24hr, Marathon, 🍴 Arby's, Great Harvest Bread, LoneStar Steaks, Lux Cafe, McDonald's, Old China, Red Lobster, 🛏 Comfort Inn, Knights Inn, 🅞 AT&T, S 🅖 Shell/24hr, Sunoco/Subway/24hr, 🍴 Applebee's, Bob Evans, China House, Coney Island, Cracker Barrel, Culver's, Denny's, Don Pablo, Fazoli's, Old Country Buffet, Panera Bread, Pizza Hut, Taco Bell, Wendy's, 🛏 Baymont Inn, Best Western, Days Inn, Fairfield Inn, Hampton Inn, Howard Johnson, Motel 6, Super 8, 🅞 URGENT CARE, AAA, Barnes&Noble, Belle Tire, $Tree, Firestone/auto, Goodyear/auto, Harley-Davidson, Hobby Lobby, JC Penney, Macy's, Sears/auto, Target, Verizon, mall, vet
96mm	**rest area eb, full ♿ facilities, 🚽, 🛇, litter barrels, vending, petwalk**
95	Helmer Rd, N 🅖 Citgo/dsl, 🅞 st police, **2 mi** N 🍴 Big Boy, 🅞 Meijer/dsl/e-85/24hr,
92	Lp 94, to Battle Creek, Springfield, N 🅖 Citgo/Arlene's Trkstp/dsl/rest./24hr, Shell/24hr, 🅞 RV camping, to Ft Custer RA
88	Climax, N Galesburg Speedway
85	35th St, Galesburg, N 🅖 Shell/dsl/24hr, 🍴 McDonald's, Subway, 🅞 Galesburg Speedway, to Ft Custer RA, River Oaks CP, S 🅞 Colebrook CP, Scottsville CP, Winery Tours, RV camping
85mm	**rest area wb, full ♿ facilities, 🚽, 🛇, litter barrels, vending, petwalk**
81	Lp 94 (from wb), to Kalamazoo
80	Cork St, Sprinkle Rd, to Kalamazoo, N 🅖 Citgo/dsl, Marathon/dsl, Speedway/dsl, 🍴 Arby's, Burger King, Chicken Coop, Denny's, Godfather's, Perkins, Taco Bell, 🛏 Best Western, Clarion, Fairfield Inn, Holiday Inn Express, Red Roof Inn, 🅞 vet, S 🅖 BP/dsl/24hr, Speedway/dsl, 🍴 Derk's Rest., McDonald's, Nob Hill Grill, Subway/24hr, Wendy's, 🛏 Candlewood Suites, EconoLodge, Motel 6, Quality Inn
78	Portage Rd, Kilgore Rd, N 🅖 BP/Circle K, 🍴 China Hut, Cottage Pizza, Uncle Earnie Pancakes, 🛏 Hampton Inn, 🅞 Ⓗ, repair, S 🅖 Marathon/dsl, Shell/24hr, Speedway, 🍴 Angelo's Italian, Bravo Rest., Brewster's, Callahan's Rest., Fat Tony's, McDonald's, Pizza King, Quizno's, Taco Bell, Theo&Stacy's Rest., Subway, 🛏 Country Inn&Suites, Lee's Inn, 🅞 AutoValue Parts, Fields Fabrics, museum
76b a	Westnedge Ave, N 🅖 Admiral, Meijer/dsl/24hr, Speedway/dsl, 🍴 Arby's, Beaners, BD BBQ, Hooters, IHOP, Kazoopie's, Lee's Chicken, Mancino's Eatery, Outback Steaks, Papa John's, Pappy's Mexican, Pizza Hut, Root Beer Stand, Steak'n Shake, Stirmax Asian, Subway, Taco Bell, Theo & Stacy's Rest., 🅞 BigLots, Discount Tire, Gander Mtn, Goodyear/auto, Lowe's Whse, Meijer, Midas, Office Depot, Rite Aid, S 🅖 Shell/24hr, 🍴 Antique Kitchen, Applebee's, Bilbo's Pizza, Bob Evans, Burger King, Carrabba's, Chili's, ChuckeCheese, Cold Stone, Culvers,

Exit	Services
76b a	Continued Empire Chinese, Fazoli's, Heavenly Ham, Jimmy Johns, KFC, Krispy Kreme, Little Caesar's, LJ Silver, Logan's Roadhouse, MacKenzie's Bakery, McDonald's, Noodles & Co, Old Country Buffet, Olive Garden, Panchero's Mexican, Panera Bread, Pizza Hut, Qdoba Mexican, Red Lobster, Red Robin, Schlotsky's, Subway, Taco Bell, TX Roadhouse, Wendy's, 🛏 Holiday Motel, 🅞 AutoZone, Barnes&Noble, Belle Tire, Best Buy, Cadillac/Nissan, $Tree, Fannie Mae Candies, Firestone/auto, Harding's Foods, Home Depot, JC Penney, Jo-Ann Fabrics, K-Mart, Kohl's, MktPlace Foods, Michael's, Old Navy, PepBoys, Cadillac, Radio Shack, Sam's Club, Sears/auto, Target, Walgreens, WorldMkt, mall
75	Oakland Dr
74b a	US 131, to Kalamazoo, N to W MI U, Kalamazoo Coll
72	Oshtemo, N 🅖 BP, Speedway/dsl, 🍴 Arby's, Culver's, McDonald's, Taco Bell, Wendy's, 🛏 Hampton Inn, S 🍴 Cracker Barrel, 🛏 Fairfield Inn, Microtel, Towne Place Suites
66	Mattawan, N 🅖 Speedway/Subway/dsl/scales/24hr, 🍴 Main St Grill, Mancino's Italian, 🅞 Family$, Freightliner, Rossman Auto/repair, R&S RV Service, S 🅖 Shell/dsl
60	MI 40, Paw Paw, N 🅖 BP/24hr, Speedway/dsl/24hr, 🍴 Arby's, Burger King, Chicken Coop, Copper Grille, Gallagher's Eatery, McDonald's, Pizza Hut, Root Beer Stand, Subway, Taco Bell, Wendy's, 🛏 Comfort Inn, EconoLodge, Super 8, 🅞 Ⓗ, Advance Parts, AT&T, Buick/Chevrolet/GMC, Chrysler/Dodge/Jeep, Curves, Family Fare Foods, St Julian Winery, Walgreens
56	MI 51, to Decatur, N st police, S 🅖 Citgo/dsl, Marathon/dsl/24hr
52	Lawrence, N 🍴 Waffle House of America
46	Hartford, N 🅖 Shell/dsl/24hr, 🍴 McDonald's, Panel Room Rest., S fruit stand
42mm	**rest area wb, full ♿ facilities, 🚽, 🛇, litter barrels, vending, petwalk**
41	MI 140, to Niles, Watervliet, N 🅖 BP/24hr, Citgo, Marathon/dsl, 🍴 Burger King, Chicken Coop, Subway, Taco Bell, Waffle House, 🛏 Ramada, 🅞 Ⓗ, KOA (Apr-Oct)
39	Millburg, Coloma, Deer Forest, **0-1 mi** N 🅖 BP/dsl, Marathon, Speedway, Westco/dsl, 🍴 Diggins Rest., Friendly Grill, J&P Cafe, McDonald's, Subway, 🅞 Family$, Krenek RV Ctr, S 🅞 Chocolate Garden
36mm	**rest area eb, full ♿ facilities, 🚽, 🛇, litter barrels, vending, petwalk**
34	I-196 N, US 31 N, to Holland, Grand Rapids
33	Lp I-94, to Benton Harbor, **2-4 mi** N ⛴, sheriff's dept
30	Napier Ave, Benton Harbor, N 🅖 FLYING J/Wendy's/dsl/LP/24hr/@, Shell/dsl/24hr, 🛏 Knights Inn, 🅞 Ⓗ, Blue Beacon, S Honda
29	Pipestone Rd, Benton Harbor, N 🍴 Applebee's, Asian Grill, Burger King, IHOP, Isabella's Rest., Mancino's Pizza, McDonald's, Pizza Hut, Sophia's Pancake House, Steak'n Shake, Super Buffet, TX Corral, 🛏 Courtyard, Motel 6, Red Roof Inn, Twin City Inn, 🅞 Aldi Foods, Best Buy, Home Depot, JC Penney, Jo-Ann Fabrics, Lowe's, Meijer/dsl, Radio Shack, Staples, Walmart/Subway, S 🅖 Mobil/dsl/24hr, 🍴 Bob Evans, 🛏 Comfort Suites, Holiday Inn Express
28	US 31 S, MI 139 N, Scottdale Rd, to Niles, N 🅖 Citgo/dsl, Marathon/dsl, 🍴 Bejing House, Burger King, Chicken Coop, Country Kitchen, DQ, Henry's Burgers, KFC,

Sidebar labels: **E / W**, **KALAMAZOO**, **BENTON HARBOR**

INTERSTATE 94 CONT'D

Exit	Services
28	**Continued**
	Little Caesar's, Pizza Hut, Taco Bell, Wendy's, 🛏 Economy Inn, Howard Johnson, ◉ 🅷, AutoZone, BigLots, Chevrolet, $Tree, Family$, Kohl's, M&W Tire, Michael's, Midas, NAPA, Office Depot, Old Navy, Petsmart, Rite Aid, Save-a-Lot, Target, TJ Maxx, U-Haul, Walgreens, radiators/repair/transmissions, st police
27mm	St Joseph River
27	MI 63, Niles Ave, to St Joseph, **N** 🔛 BP/24hr, 🍴 Nye's Apple Barn, **S** 🍴 Panera Bread, Tulips Asian, ◉ Goodyear
23	Red Arrow Hwy, Stevensville, **N** 🔛 Admiral, BP, Marathon/dsl, Mobil, Shell/dsl/24hr, 🍴 Big Boy, Burger King, Cracker Barrel, Culver's, DQ, LJ Silver, McDonald's, Nacho Papa's Cantina, Nick's Rest., Papa John's, Popeye's, Quizno's, Subway, 🛏 Baymont Inn, Candlewood Suites, Comfort Suites, ◉ Walgreens, **S** 🍴 Five O'Clock Grill, 🛏 Hampton Inn, ◉ Meijer/dsl
22	John Beers Rd, Stevensville, **N** 🛏 Chalet on the Lake, ◉ to Grand Mere SP, **S** 🔛 Marathon/dsl, 🍴 Pizza Hut
16	Bridgman, **N** 🔛 BP/A&W/dsl/24hr, ◉ camping, to Warren Dunes SP, **S** 🍴 McDonald's, Olympus Rest., Pizza Hut, Roma Pizza, Sammies Rest., Subway, 🛏 Bridgman Inn, ◉ Chevrolet, auto repair, st police, vet
12	Sawyer, **N** 🔛 Citgo/deli/scales/dsl/24hr, ◉ truck wash, **S** 🔛 TA/Burger King/Pizza Hut/Popeye's/Taco Bell/scales/dsl/24hr/@, 🛏 Super 8, ◉ Schlipp's Drug, USPO
6	Lakeside, Union Pier, **N** ◉ St Julian's Winery, antiques, **S** RV camping
4b a	US 12, to Three Oaks, New Buffalo, **N** 🍴 Pizza Hut, ◉ st police
2.5mm	**weigh sta both lanes**
1	MI 239, to Grand Beach, New Buffalo, **0-2 mi N** 🔛 Shell/Quizno's, 🍴 Bruster's Italian, Casey's Grille, Hannah's Rest., Jimmy's Grill, McDonald's, Nancy's, Rosie's Rest., Stray Dog Grill, Subway, Wheel Inn Rest., 🛏 Best Western, Comfort Inn, Fairfield Inn, Holiday Inn Express, Super Inn, ◉ $General, **S** 🔛 New Buffalo/rest/dsl/scales/24hr, 🍴 Jimmy Dawgs, Wendy's, 🛏 Obrien's Inn, ◉ casino
.5mm	**Welcome Ctr eb, full ♿ facilities, info, 🅲, 🚻, litter barrels, vending, petwalk**
0mm	Michigan/Indiana state line

INTERSTATE 96 CONT'D

Exit	Services
	I-96 begins/ends on I-75, exit 48 in Detroit.
191	I-75, N to Flint, S to Toledo, US 12, to MLK Blvd, to Michigan Ave
190b	Warren Ave, **N** 🔛 BP/dsl, **S** 🔛 Marathon
190a	I-94, E to Port Huron
189	W Grand Blvd, Tireman Rd, **N** 🔛 BP/Subway, Mobil
188b	Joy Rd, **N** 🍴 Church's
188a	Livernois, **N** 🔛 Mobil, Shell/Subway, 🍴 Burger King, KFC, McDonald's, Wendy's
187	Grand River Ave (from eb)
186b	Davison Ave, I-96 local and I-96 express divide no exits from express
186a	Wyoming Ave
185	Schaefer Hwy, to Grand River Ave, **N** 🔛 BP/24hr, Mobil, 🍴 Coney Island, McDonald's, ◉ CVS Drug, **S** 🔛 Sunoco
184	Greenfield Rd

Exit	Services
183	MI 39, Southfield Fwy, exit from expswy and local
182	Evergreen Rd
180	Outer Dr, **N** 🔛 BP/dsl/lube
180mm	I-96 local/express unite/divide
179	US 24, Telegraph Rd, **N** 🔛 BP, Marathon/dsl, 🍴 Arby's, Baskin-Robbins/Dunkin Donuts, China King, McDonald's, White Castle, Wendy's, ◉ Chevrolet, Family$, NAPA, **S** 🔛 BP, Marathon/dsl
178	Beech Daly Rd, **N** gas
177	Inkster Rd, **N** 🔛 BP/Tim Horton, 🍴 Subway, 🛏 Best Value Inn, ◉ URGENT CARE, $General, 7-11
176	Middlebelt Rd, **N** 🍴 Bob Evans, IHOP, Olive Garden, 🛏 Comfort Inn, **0-1 mi S** 🍴 Biggby Coffee, Chili's, Logan's Roadhouse, Noodles&Co, Pottbelly, Qdoba, Red Lobster, 🛏 Crossland Suites, ◉ BigLots, Costco/gas, $Tree, Firestone/auto, Home Depot, Marshall's, Meijer, Michael's, Office Depot, Petsmart, Target, Verizon, Walgreens, Walmart, auto repair/transmissions
175	Merriman Rd, **N** 🔛 Mobil/dsl, Speedway/dsl, **S** 🔛 Exxon/dsl, 🍴 Blimpie, Royal Coney Island
174	Farmington Rd, **N** 🔛 Mobil/dsl, Sunoco, 🍴 Looney Baker, **S** 🔛 BP, 🍴 KFC
173b	Levan Rd, **N** 🅷, to Madonna U
173a	Newburgh Rd
171mm	**I-275 and I-96 run together 9 miles**
170	6 Mile Rd, **N** 🍴 Bar Louie's, Big Boy, Buffalo Wild Wings, CA Pizza Kitchen, Carry's Coney Island, Jimmy John's, La Feast, Max&Erma's, Qdoba, Red Robin, Spanga's, Taco Del Mar, Thai Basil, Traveling Fork, 🛏 Best Western, Courtyard, Marriott, Radisson, ◉ 🅷, ACO Hardware, AT&T, Busch's Foods, GNC, O'Reilly Parts, Rite Aid, Walgreens, mall, **S** 🔛 BP, Mobil, 🍴 Applebee's, Brann's Steaks, Bravo Italian, Buca Italian, Caribou Coffee, Charlie's Grill, Cheeburger Cheeburger, Claddagh Rest., Flemings, McDonald's, Mitchell's Fishmarket, Noodles&Co, Panchero's, PF Chang, Pottbelly, Tim Horton, Wendy's, 🛏 Fairfield Inn, Residence Inn, TownePlace Suites, ◉ Barnes&Noble, CVS Drug, Kroger, Office Depot, Petsmart
169b a	7 Mile Rd, **N** 🍴 Doc's Grill, 🛏 Embassy Suites, **S** 🍴 Alexander's Rest., Andiamo Cafe, Bahama Breeze Rest., Champp's Rest., Gaucho Steaks, Macaroni Grill, 🛏 Hyatt Place, ◉ Home Depot
167	8 Mile Rd, to Northville, **S** 🔛 BP, Speedway/dsl, 🍴 Aubree's Pizza, Benihana, Big Boy, Biggby Coffee, Chili's, McDonald's, Kerry's Koney Island, On-the-Border, Panera Bread, Quizno's, Starbucks, Taco Bell, TGIFriday's, 🛏 Country Inn&Suites, Extended Stay America, Hampton Inn, Holiday Inn Express, Sheraton, ◉ Best Buy, Costco, Dick's, Firestone/auto, Kohl's, Meijer/dsl, Target, Trader Joe's, Verizon, to Maybury SP

E ↕ **W** (Interstate 94 direction indicator, left margin)

D E T R O I T A R E A (left margin, lower section)

E ↕ **W** (Interstate 96 direction indicator, right column)

MI

INTERSTATE 96 CONT'D

Exit	Services
165	I-696, I-275, MI 5, Grand River Ave.
I-275 and I-96 run together 9 miles	
163	I-696 (from eb)
162	Novi Rd, to Walled Lake, Novi, **N** 🅶 BP, 🍴 CA Pizza Kitchen, Carrabba's, ChuckeCheese, Denny's, McDonald's, Red Lobster, Starbucks, Tin Fish, 🛏 Crowne Plaza, Hilton Garden, Renaissance, Residence Inn, Ⓞ 🅷, Best Buy, Dick's, Gander Mtn, JC Penney, Jo-Ann Fabrics, Lord&Taylor, Macy's, Michael's, Nordstrom's, Sears/auto, mall, **S** 🅶 Mobil/dsl, 🍴 Athenian Coney Island, Big Boy, Biggby Coffee, Bonefish Grill, Boston Mkt, Famous Dave's, Kim's Chinese, Melting Pot, Mongolian BBQ, Olive Garden, Panera Bread, Pei Wei, Pottbelly, Red Robin, Steve&Rocky's, TGIFriday's, Wendy's, 🛏 DoubleTree, Courtyard, Towne Place Suites, Ⓞ URGENT CARE, AT&T, Better Health Foods, Firestone/auto, NAPA, TJ Maxx, Tuesday Morning, vet
161mm	**rest area eb, full** 🦽 **facilities,** 🍴, 🛏, **vending, litter barrels, petwalk**
160	Beck Rd, 12 Mile Rd, **S** 🍴 Applebee's, Caribou Coffee, Olga's Kitchen, loding Staybridge Suites, Ⓞ 🅷, Home Depot, Kroger, Staples, to Maybury SP
159	Wixom Rd, Walled Lake, **N** 🅶 Marathon/dsl, Sunoco/dsl, 🍴 Wendy's, 🛏 Holiday Inn Express, Ⓞ to Proud Lake RA, **S** 🅶 Mobil, Shell, Valero/dsl, 🍴 A&W/KFC, Arby's, Baskin-Robbins/Dunkin Donuts, Burger King, Don's Diner, McDonald's, Stinger's Grill, Taco Bell, 🛏 Comfort Suites, Ⓞ General RV Ctr, Lincoln/Mercury, Meijer/dsl, Sam's Club/gas, Target
155b a	to Milford, New Hudson, **N** Ford, to RV camping, to Lion Oaks CP, **S** 🅶 Sunoco, 🍴 Applebee's, Arby's, Jet's Pizza, Leo's Coney Island, McDonald's, Starbucks, Subway, Ⓞ URGENT CARE, AT&T, Chevrolet, Discount Tire, Hyundai, Lowe's, Walmart
153	Kent Lake Rd, **N** Kensington Metropark, **S** 🅶 Mobil/dsl, loding Country Meadows Inn (3mi)
151	Kensington Rd, **N** Kensington Metropark, **S** Island Lake RA, 🍴, 🛏
150	Pleasant Valley Rd (no return wb)
148b a	US 23, N to Flint, S to Ann Arbor
147	Spencer Rd, **N** 🅶 Mobil, Ⓞ st police, **S** to Brighton St RA
145	Grand River Ave, to Brighton, **N** 🅶 BP, Shell/dsl, 🍴 Arby's, Cracker Barrel, Outback Steaks, Pizza Hut, 🛏 Courtyard, Ⓞ Buick, Cadillac/GMC, Curves, $General, Ford/Mercury, Honda, camping, **S** 🅶 BP, Marathon/Subway, Sunoco, 🍴 Big Boy, Biggby Coffee, Border Cantina, Burger King, Chili's, DQ, IHOP, Hungry Howie's, Jimmy John's, Leo's Coney Island, Lil Chef, McDonald's, Olga's Kitchen, Panera Bread, Pi's Asian, Red Robin, Starbucks, Stillwater Grill, Taco Bell, Tim Horton, Wendy's, 🛏 Holiday Inn Express, Homewood Suites, Ⓞ AAA, Belle Tire, Best Buy, Bob's Tire, CVS Drug, $Tree, Home Depot, Jo-Ann Fabrics, Marshall's, Mazda, Meijer/dsl, Michael's, O'Reilly Parts, Radio Shack, Rite Aid, Petsmart, Staples, Target, Verizon, Walgreens, USPO, to Brighton Ski Area
141	Lp 96 (from wb, no EZ return), to Howell, **0-2 mi N** 🅶 Shell, Speedway, Sunoco/dsl, 🍴 Applebee's, Arby's, Biggby Coffee, Bluefin Steaks, Bob Evans, Buffalo Wild Wings, KFC, Little Caesar's, McDonald's, New Century Buffet, Subway, Taco Bell, Wendy's, White Castle, 🛏 Grandview Inn, Ⓞ AT&T, Chevrolet, Discount Tire, $Tree, Home Depot, Kohl's, Lowe's, Meijer, O'Reilly Parts, Staples, TJ Maxx, Walmart

Exit	Services
141mm	**rest area wb, full** 🦽 **facilities,** 🍴, 🛏, **vending, litter barrels, petwalk**
137	D19, to Pinckney, Howell, **N** 🅶 Mobil, Shell/dsl, Speedway/dsl, Sunoco/Baskin-Robbins/Dunkin Donuts/dsl, 🍴 All-Star Coney Island, Jonna's Pizza, Mario Bro's Pizza, Wendy's, 🛏 Kensington Inn, Ⓞ 🅷, Parts+, Spartan Tire, True Value, **S** 🍴 Country Kitchen, 🛏 Best Western
135mm	**rest area eb, full** 🦽 **facilities, vending,** 🍴, 🛏, **litter barrels, petwalk**
133	MI 59, Highland Rd, **N** 🅶 Marathon/McDonald's/dsl, 🍴 Arby's, Leo's Coney Island, 🛏 Baymont, Holiday Inn Express, Ⓞ Tanger Outlets/famous brands
129	Fowlerville Rd, Fowlerville, **N** 🅶 BP, Shell/dsl, Sunoco/dsl, 🍴 A&W/KFC, Fowlerville Rest., McDonald's, Pizza Hut/Taco Bell, Wendy's, 🛏 Magnuson Hotel, Ⓞ Chevrolet, Walmart, **S** 🅶 Mobil/dsl, 🍴 Subway, Ⓞ Chysler/Dodge/Jeep, Ford
126mm	**weigh sta both lanes**
122	MI 43, MI 52, Webberville, **N** 🅶 Mobil/dsl/24hr, 🍴 McDonald's, Ⓞ MI Brewing Co
117	to Dansville, Williamston, **N** 🅶 Marathon/Jersey's Giant Subs/dsl, 🍴 Spag's Grill (3mi), **S** 🅶 Sunoco/dsl
111mm	**rest area wb, full** 🦽 **facilities,** 🍴, 🛏, **litter barrels, vending, petwalk**
110	Okemos, Mason, **N** 🅶 BP/Dunkin Donuts/24hr, Marathon, Sunoco, 🍴 Applebee's, Arby's, Backyard BBQ, Biggby Coffee, Big John's Steaks, Cracker Barrel, Gilbert&Blake's Seafood, Grand Traverse, Little Caesar's, McDonald's, Panchero's Mexican, Sheshiang Garden, Starbucks, Stillwater Grill, Subway, Taco Bell, 🛏 Comfort Inn, Fairfield Inn, Hampton Inn, Holiday Inn Express, Staybridge Suites, Ⓞ 7-11, to stadium
106b a	I-496, US 127, to Jackson, Lansing, **N** St Police
104	Lp 96, Cedar St, to Holt, Lansing, **N** 🅶 Speedway, 🍴 Aldaco's Mexican, Applebee's, Arby's, Asia's Finest, Barley's Grill, Biggby Coffee, Blimpie, Bob Evans, Boston Mkt, Burger King, China King, Cici's, Finley's Rest., Happy's Pizza, Hooters, Jet's Pizza, KFC, Los Tres Amigos, Pizza Hut, Steak'n Shake, TX Roadhouse, Wendy's, White Castle/Church's, Zeus Coney Island, 🛏 Best Value Inn, Dad's Inn, Super 8, Ⓞ 🅷, Aldi Foods, Belle Tire, Cadillac, Chevrolet, Discount Tire, Dodge, $Tree, Family$, KIA, Lexus, Meijer/dsl, Menards, Nissan, Radio Shack, Sam's Club/gas, Scion/Toyota, Target, Walgreens, auto repair, **S** 🅶 Marathon, Speedway/24hr, 🍴 Burger King, Champion's Grill, China East Buffet, Dairy Dan, Flapjack Rest., McDonald's, Ponderosa, Subway, Tim Horton, 🛏 Causeway Bay Hotel, Ⓞ AutoZone, Budget Tire, CarQuest, CVS Drug, Family$, Kroger/gas, L&L Foods, Lowe's, Rite Aid
101	MI 99, MLK Blvd, to Eaton Rapids, **0-3 mi N** 🅶 QD, 🍴 Arby's, Tim Horton, Ⓞ Kroger/gas, Meijer/dsl, **S** 🅶 Speedway/Subway/dsl/24hr, Sunoco/dsl, 🍴 Coach's Grill, McDonald's, Wendy's
98b a	Lansing Rd, to Lansing, **N** 🍴 Arby's, Wendy's, 🛏 Comfort Inn, Ⓞ Harley-Davidson
97	I-69, US 27 S, S to Ft Wayne, N to Lansing
95	I-496, to Lansing
93b a	MI 43, Lp 69, Saginaw Hwy, to Grand Ledge, **0-2 mi N** 🅶 Shell, Speedway/dsl, 🍴 Burger King, Carrabba's, Cheddar's, Denny's, Fazoli's, Frank's Grill, Hibachi Grill, Honeybaked Ham, Houlihan's, Logan's Roadhouse, McDonald's, Outback Steaks, Panera Bread, Qdoba, Red Robin, Subway, Younkers, 🛏 Days Inn, Fairfield Inn,

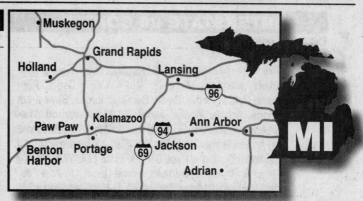

INTERSTATE 96 CONT'D

Exit	Services
93b a	Continued
	Hampton Inn, Motel 6, Quality Inn, Ramada Inn, Red Roof Inn, Residence Inn, ⊙ H, Barnes&Noble, BigLots, Chrysler/Dodge/Jeep, Hobby Lobby, JC Penney, Kohl's, Kroger, Macy's, Meijer/dsl/24hr, NAPA, Radio Shack, Target, Walgreens, S 📖 BP/24hr, QD, Sunoco/McDonald's, 🍴 Arby's, Bob Evans, Cracker Barrel, Ing-credible Chinese, Rudino's Pizza, Steak'n Shake, Subway, 🏨 SpringHill Suites, ⊙ URGENT CARE, AT&T, Belle Tire, Buick/GMC, Dick's, Discount Tire, Gander Mtn, Mazda, Lowe's, Menards, Michael's, Petsmart, Staples, Walmart
92mm	Grand River
91	I-69 N (from wb), US 27 N, to Flint, S 📖 ⟋FLYING J/Denny's/dsl/24hr, 🍴 Pepperoni's Rest.
90	Grand River Ave, to ✈ (from wb)
89	I-69 N, US 27 N (from eb), to Flint
87mm	**rest area eb, full ♿ facilities, 🍴, 🚻, litter barrels, vending, petwalk**
86	MI 100, Wright Rd, to Grand Ledge, S 📖 Mobil/McDonald's/dsl, Speedway/Subway/24hr
84	to Eagle, Westphalia
79mm	**rest area wb, full ♿ facilities, info, 🍴, 🚻, litter barrels, vending, petwalk**
77	Lp 96, Grand River Ave, Portland, N 📖 BP/24hr, Shell/Burger King, Speedway/dsl, 🍴 Arby's, Biggby Coffee, KFC/Taco Bell, Little Caesar's, Hungry Howie's, McDonald's, 🏨 Best Western, ⊙ Curves, Family$, Rite Aid, Tom's Foods, S 🍴 Wendy's, ⊙ Ford
76	Kent St, Portland
76mm	Grand River
73	to Lyons-Muir, Grand River Ave
69mm	**weigh sta both lanes**
67	MI 66, to Ionia, Battle Creek, N 📖 ▦▦▦/Subway/dsl/scales/24hr, 🍴 Corner Landing Grill, 🏨 Midway Motel, Super 8, ⊙ H, Meijer/dsl (4mi), Walmart (4mi), RV camping, st police, truck wash
64	to Lake Odessa, Saranac, N Ionia St RA, S I-96 Speedway
63mm	**rest area eb, full ♿ facilities, 🍴, 🚻, litter barrels, petwalk, vending**
59	Clarksville
52	MI 50, to Lowell, N 📖 Mobil/Subway/dsl, ⊙ fairgrounds, S 📖 Marathon/Noble Roman's/dsl (2mi), ⊙ RV camping
46	rd 6, to rd 37
46mm	Thornapple River
44	36 St, S ✈
43b a	MI 11, 28th St, Cascade, N 📖 Marathon/dsl, 🍴 Biggby Coffee, Brann's Steaks, Burger King, Culver's, Jet's Pizza, Jimmy John's, Macaroni Grill, Panera Bread, Papa John's, Pizza Hut, Quizno's, Stabucks, Sundance Grill, Subway, Taco Boy, Wendy's, 🏨 Baymont Inn, Best Western, Country Inn&Suites, Crowne Plaza, EconoLodge, Holiday Inn Express, ⊙ Audi/Porsche/Subaru, Fresh Mkt, GNC, Meijer/dsl, Mercedes/Volvo/VW, True Value, Walmart, 0-3 mi S 📖 BP, Citgo, Shell, Speedway/dsl, 🍴 Applebee's, Arby's, Arnie's Rest., Baskin-Robbins/Dunkin Donuts, Burger King, Carabba's, Carlos O'Kelley's, Cantina Mexican, Chili's, Chipotle Mexican, ChuckeCheese, Coldstone, Denny's, Don Julio's, Grand Rapids Brewery, Honey Baked Ham, Hooters, Jimmy John's, Krispy Kreme, Longhorn Steaks,

Exit	Services
43b a	Continued
	McDonald's, Moe's SW Grill, Noodles&Co, Old Chicago, Olive Garden, Outback Steaks, Panera Bread, Papa Vino's, Perkins, Pizza Hut, Quaker Steak&Lube, Red Lobster, Red Robin, Red Sun Buffet, Ruby Tuesday, Smokey Bones, Starbucks, Steak'n Shake, Subway, Taco Bell, TX Roadhouse, Wendy's, Yin Ching Chinese, 🏨 Clarion, Comfort Inn, Courtyard, Hampton Inn, Hilton, Motel 6, Quality Inn, Ramada, Red Roof Inn, SpringHill Suites, Super 8, ⊙ Belle Tire, Best Buy, CarQuest, Costco/gas, Dick's, $Tree, Ford, Gander Mtn, Hobby Lobby, Home Depot, Honda, Hyundai/KIA, JoAnn Fabrics, Lentz Automotive, Lowe's, Michael's, Nissan, Office Depot, Old Navy, Petsmart, Radio Shack, Sam's Club/gas, Sears/auto, Staples, Target, TJ Maxx, U-Haul
40b a	Cascade Rd, N 📖 Forrest Hills Fuel, Marathon/dsl, 🍴 Biggby Coffee, China Garden, Forrest Hills Rest, Great Harvest, Little Bangkok, Little Caesar's, Subway, ⊙ 7-11, vet, S 📖 Shell/Quizno's/dsl, Speedway/dsl, 🍴 Bonefish Grill, Jimmy John's, Zoup, ⊙ H, Keystone Drug
39	MI 21 (from eb), to Flint
38	E Beltline Ave, to MI 21, MI 37, MI 44, N 📖 BP, 🍴 O'Charley's, ⊙ Meijer/dsl, RV camping, S 🍴 Uno Pizzaria, 🏨 Country Inn&Suites, ⊙ H
37	I-196 (from wb, exits left), Gerald Ford Fwy, to Grand Rapids
36	Leonard St, **2 mi**, S 🍴 Arby's, Jimmy John's, McDonald's, ⊙ sheriff's dept
33	Plainfield Ave, MI 44 Connector, N 📖 BP, Speedway/dsl, 🍴 Arby's, Baskin-Robbins, Blimpie, Charley's Grille, Cheers Grill, Fred's Italian, Golden Dragon, KFC, Little Caesar's, LJ Silver, McDonald's, Pizza Hut, Russ' Rest., Subway, Taco Bell, Tokyo Roadhouse, Wendy's, 🏨 Grand Inn, Lazy T Motel, ⊙ AutoZone, Belle Tire, BigLots, Chevrolet, Chrysler/Jeep, Curves, Discount Tire, Dodge, $Tree, Firestone/auto, Ford, Goodyear/auto, K-Mart, Lowe's, Meijer/dsl, NAPA, Nissan/VW, Radio Shack, Save-A-Lot Foods, Toyota, U-Haul, Walgreens, S 📖 BP, 🍴 Denny's
31mm	Grand River
31b a	US 131, N to Cadillac, S to Kalamazoo, **1 mi** N 📖 BP, 🍴 McDonald's
30b a	Alpine Ave, Grand Rapids, N 📖 BP, Marathon/dsl, 7-11, 🍴 Applebee's, Buffalo Wild Wings, Checkers, Chucke-Cheese, Coldstone, Culvers, El Burrito Mexican, Empire Buffet, Fire Mtn Grill, First Wok, Golden Corral, Hibachi Grill, IHOP, Jimmy John's, Little Caesar's, Logan's Roadhouse, Mafia Mike's Pizza, McDonald's, Olive Garden, Outback Steaks, Panera Bread, Perkins, Qdoba, Quizno's, Russ' Rest., Sonic, Starbucks, Steak'n Shake, Subway, Taco Bell, TGIFriday's, Thai Basil, 🏨 Hampton Inn, Holiday Inn Express, SpringHill Suites, ⊙ Aldi Foods, AT&T, AutoZone, Belle Tire, Best Buy, CarQuest, Discount

E ↕ W

GRAND RAPIDS

GRAND RAPIDS

MI

INTERSTATE 96 CONT'D

E ↕ W

MUSKEGON

Exit	Services
30b a	Continued
	Tire, $Tree, Ford/KIA, GNC, Hobby Lobby, Kohl's, Marshall's, Menards, Michael's, NAPA, Office Depot, PepBoys, PetCo, Radio Shack, Sam's Club/gas, Save-a-Lot Foods, Schuler Books, Target, TJ Maxx, Verizon, Walgreens, Walmart/auto, **S** 🗶 Admiral/dsl, Speedway/dsl, 🗶 Arby's, Burger King, Fazoli's, First 1 Chinese, KFC, LJ Silver, McDonald's, Papa John's, Pizza Hut, Wendy's, 🗶 Motel 6, 🗶 Goodyear/auto, Home Depot, Jo-Ann Fabrics, Meijer/dsl, Midas, Tuffy Auto, U-Haul, auto repair
28	Walker Ave, **S** 🗶 Meijer/dsl/24hr, 🗶 Bob Evans, McDonald's, 🗶 Baymont Inn, Quality Inn
26	Fruit Ridge Ave, **N** 🗶 Citgo/dsl, **S** 🗶 Citgo/deli/dsl
25mm	**rest area eb, full** 🗶 **facilities,** 🗶, 🗶, **litter barrels, petwalk**
25	8th Ave, 4 Mile Rd (from wb), **S** 🗶 Marathon/dsl, 🗶 Wayside Motel
24	8th Ave, 4 Mile Rd (from eb), **S** 🗶 Marathon/dsl, 🗶 Wayside Motel
23	Marne, **N** 🗶 tires, **S** 🗶 Depot Café, Rinaldi's Café, 🗶 Ernie's Mkt, USPO, fairgrounds/raceway
19	Lamont, Coopersville, **N** 🗶 **S** 🗶 Sam's Joint Rest., 🗶 LP
16	B-35, Eastmanville, **N** 🗶 BP/Subway/dsl, Speedway/dsl/24hr, Shell/Burger King/dsl, 🗶 Arby's, Hungry Howie's, Little Caesar's, McDonald's, #1 Chinese, Taco Bell, 🗶 Rodeway Inn, 🗶 Buick/Chevrolet/Pontiac, Curves, Family$, Family Fare Foods, Fun 'N Sun RV Ctr, Rite Aid, vet, **S** 🗶 Pacific Pride/dsl, 🗶 RV camping
10	B-31 (exits left from eb), Nunica, **N** 🗶 Turk's Rest., **S** 🗶 Conestoga RV camping, golf course/rest.
9	MI 104 (from wb, exits left), to Grand Haven, Spring Lake, **S** 🗶 Marathon, 🗶 to Grand Haven SP
8mm	**rest area wb, full** 🗶 **facilities,** 🗶, 🗶, **litter barrels, vending, petwalk**
5	Fruitport (from wb, no return)
4	Airline Rd, **N** 🗶 NAPA, **S** 🗶 Speedway/dsl, Wesco/dsl, 🗶 Burger Crest Diner, Dairy Bar, McDonald's, Subway, Village Inn, 🗶 Grover Drug, Orchard Mkt Foods, Water Park (5mi), USPO, auto/tire repair, to PJ Hoffmaster SP
1c	Hile Rd (from eb), **S** 🗶 Arby's, Brann's Grille, Buffalo Wild Wings, ChuckeCheese, Dynasty Buffet, Golden Corral, KFC, Logan's Roadhouse, Perkins, Quizno's, Red Robin, TX Roadhouse, 🗶 Baymont Inn, Fairfield Inn, Hampton Inn, 🗶 AT&T, Barnes&Noble, Best Buy, Hobby Lobby, JC Penney, Jo-Ann Fabrics, Kohl's, Meijer/dsl, Menards, Old Navy, PetCo, Target, TJ Maxx, VW, Younkers, mall
1b a	US 31, to Ludington, Grand Haven, **N** 🗶 Airline Motel, Alpine Motel, Bel-aire Motel, 🗶 All Seasons RV Ctr, **2 mi N on Sherman Blvd** 🗶 Citgo/dsl, 🗶 Applebee's, Arby's, Fazoli's, McDonald's, Pizza Ranch, Red Wok, Subway, Wendy's, 🗶 Comfort Inn/rest., 🗶 🗶, $Tree, GNC, Lowe's, Petsmart, Radio Shack, Sam's Club/gas, Staples, Walmart, **S** same as 1c
	I-96 begins/ends on US 31 at Muskegon.

INTERSTATE 196 (GRAND RAPIDS)

Exit	Services
81mm	I-196 begins/ends on I-96, 37mm in, E Grand Rapids.
79	Fuller Ave, **N** sheriff, **S** 🗶 Shell/dsl, Speedway/dsl, 🗶 Biggby Coffee, Bill's Rest., Checkers, Elbow Room, KFC, Subway, Taco Bell, Wendy's, 🗶 🗶, Ace Hardware, Walgreens

MI

E ↕ W

Exit	Services
78	College Ave, **S** 🗶 Marathon/Circle K, 🗶 McDonald's, Omelette Shop, 🗶 🗶, Ford Museum
77c	Ottawa Ave, downtown, **S** Gerald R Ford Museum
77b a	US 131, S to Kalamazoo, N to Cadillac
76	MI 45 E, Lane Ave, **S** 🗶 El Granjero Mexican, 🗶 Gerald R Ford Museum, John Ball Park&Zoo, auto repair
75	MI 45 W, Lake Michigan Dr, **N** to Grand Valley St U
74mm	Grand River
73	Market Ave, **N** to Vanandel Arena
72	Lp 196, Chicago Dr, E (from eb)
70	MI 11 (exits left from wb), Grandville, Walker, **S** 🗶 BP/dsl, Shell, 🗶 Days Inn, 🗶 Auto Value Parts, USPO
69c	Baldwin St (from wb)
69b a	Chicago Dr, **N** 🗶 Speedway, 🗶 Culver's, Hungry Howie's, KFC, McDonald's, Papa John's, Peppino's Pizza, Perkins, Subway, Taco Bell, Youming Chinese, 🗶 Aldi Foods, AutoZone, Curves, $Tree, Meijer/dsl, Radio Shack, Target, Walgreens, USPO, **S** 🗶 Admiral, Speedway/dsl, 🗶 Adobe Mexican, Arby's, Baskin-Robbins/Dunkin Donuts, Biggby Coffee, Burger King, Little Caesar's, Pizza Hut, Rainbow Grill, Russ' Rest., Subway, Wendy's, 🗶 Best Western, Holiday Inn Express, 🗶 USPO
67	44th St, **N** 🗶 Mobil/dsl, 🗶 Burger King, Cracker Barrel, Panera Bread, Steak'n Shake, 🗶 Comfort Suites, 🗶 Honda, Walmart/auto, **0-2 mi S** 🗶 Famous Dave's, Jimmy John's, IHOP, Logan's Roadhouse, Max&Erma's, Qdoba, Quizno's, Starbucks, Subway, TX Roadhouse, Wendy's, 🗶 Residence Inn, 🗶 Best Buy, Chrysler/Dodge/Jeep, Costco/gas, Dick's, Discount Tire, $Tree, Fresh Mkt Foods, Gander Mtn., Hobby Lobby, Home Depot, JC Penney, Kohl's, Lowe's, Macy's, Marshall's, Michael's, Old Navy, Petsmart, Sear/auto, World Mkt
64	MI 6 E, to Lansing (exits left from wb)
62	32nd Ave, to Hudsonville, **N** 🗶 BP/dsl/24hr, Citgo/dsl, 🗶 Arby's, Burger King, Hudsonville Grill, Little Caesar's, McDonald's, 🗶 Quality Inn, 🗶 Chevrolet, camping, **S** 🗶 Mobil/Subway/dsl/24hr, 🗶 Rainbow Grill, 🗶 Super 8, 🗶 Harley-Davidson, Harvest Foods
58mm	**rest area eb, full** 🗶 **facilities,** 🗶, 🗶, **litter barrels, vending, petwalk**
55	Byron Rd, Zeeland, **N** 🗶 7-11, 🗶 Blimpie, McDonald's, **3-5 mi N** 🗶, to Holland SP
52	16th St, Adams St, **2 mi N** 🗶 Wendy's, 🗶 EconoLodge, 🗶 🗶, Meijer/dsl/e-85, **S** 🗶 Mobil/Subway/dsl, 🗶 Burger King
49	MI 40, to Allegan, **N** 🗶 BP/McDonald's/dsl, 🗶 Residence Inn, **S** 🗶 Tulip City/Marathon/Subway/dsl/scales/24hr, 🗶 Rock Island Rest., 🗶 truck repair, truck wash
44	US 31 N (from eb), to Holland, **3-5 mi N** 🗶 Country Inn, 🗶 🗶, gas, food
43mm	**rest area wb, full** 🗶 **facilities, info,** 🗶, 🗶, **litter barrels, vending, petwalk**
41	rd A-2, Douglas, Saugatuck, **N** 🗶 Marathon/dsl, Shell/Subway/dsl, 🗶 Burger King, Spectators Grill, 🗶 Best Western (1mi), Timberline Motel (3mi), 🗶 $General, NAPA, to Saugatuck SP, **S** 🗶 Belvedere Inn, 🗶 Red Barn Gifts
38mm	Kalamazoo River
36	rd A-2, Ganges, **N** 🗶 Shell, 🗶 Christo's Rest., Kalico Kitchen, 🗶 AmericInn
34	MI 89, to Fennville, **N** to West Side CP, **S** 🗶 Shell/24hr, 🗶 Cranes Pie Pantry (4mi, seasonal), Lyons Fruits, Winery Tours

Copyright 2012 - The Next Exit®

INTERSTATE 196 CONT'D (GRAND RAPIDS)

Exit	Services
30	rd A-2, Glenn, Ganges, N to Westside CP (4mi)
28mm	**rest area eb, full facilities, , , litter barrels, vending, petwalk**
26	109th Ave, to Pullman, N Dutch Farm Mkt
22	N Shore Dr, N to Kal Haven Trail SP, Cousin's RV Camping/rest.
20	rd A-2, Phoenix Rd, N BP/dsl, Marathon/dsl, Arby's, China Buffet, Taco Bell, , AutoZone, $Tree, Walgreens, st police, S Murphy USA/dsl, Shell/dsl, Big Boy, McDonald's, Sherman's Dairybar, Wendy's, Comfort Suites, Hampton Inn, Holiday Inn Express, Ramada, $General, Menards, Walmart
18	MI 140, MI 43, to Watervliet, 0-2 mi N BP/dsl, Shell/dsl/24hr, Xpress/dsl, Burger King, 50's Drive Inn, Hungry Howie's, Little Caesar's, McDonald's, Pizza Hut, Willy O's Pizza, Great Lakes Inn, LakeBluff Motel, AutoValue Parts, Buick/Cadillac/GMC, Chevrolet, Chrysler/Dodge/Jeep, Ford/Lincoln/Mercury, Village Mkt Foods, auto repair, st police, 7 mi S KOA (Apr-Oct),
13	to Covert, N to Van Buren SP, RV camping
7	MI 63, to Benton Harbor, N DiMaggio's Pizza, Vitale's Mkt/subs, RV camping
4	to Coloma, Riverside, S Marathon/dsl, KOA (Apr-Oct)
2mm	Paw Paw River
1	Red Arrow Hwy, N SW Michigan
0mm	I-94, E to Detroit, W to Chicago
	I-196 begins/ends on I-94, exit 34 at Benton Harbor.

INTERSTATE 275 (LIVONIA)

Exit	Services
	I-275 and I-96 run together 9 miles. See Michigan Interstate 96, exits 165-170.
29	I-96 E, to Detroit, MI 14 W, to Ann Arbor
28	Ann Arbor Rd, Plymouth, E BP/Dunkin Donuts/24hr, Shell, Atlantis Rest., Denny's, Little Caesars, Days Inn, Red Roof Inn, W Burger King, McDonald's, Steak&Ale, Comfort Inn, Cadillac, CVS Drug, Dodge, K-Mart, Lincoln/Mercury, vet
25	MI 153, Ford Rd, Garden City, W BP, Shell, Speedway, Valero, Applebee's, Arby's, BD Mongolian BBQ, Bob Evans, Boston Mkt., Bowery Grille, Buffalo Wild Wings, Carrabba's, Chili's, ChuckeCheese, Coney Island, Dunkin Donuts/Baskin-Robbins, Hunan Empire Chinese, KFC, Little Caesar's, Outback Steaks, Panera Bread, Quizno's, Roman Forum Rest., Subway, TGIFriday, Tim Horton, TX Corral, Wendy's, White Castle/Church's, Extended Stay America, Fairfield Inn, La Quinta, Motel 6, Discount Tire, Firestone, Lowe's, PetCo, Richardson Drug, Target, Walgreens, vet
23	**rest area nb, full facilities, , info, , litter barrels**
22	US 12, Michigan Ave, to Wayne, E BP/24hr, Marathon, Shell, Valero/dsl, Arby's, Jonathan's Rest., McDonald's, Subway, Wendy's, Day's Inn, Fellows Cr Motel, Holiday Inn Express, Super 8, Willo Acres Motel, W Marathon/dsl, 7-11, Dunkin Donuts, McDonald's
20	Ecorse Rd, to Romulus, E 7-11, W Mobil/Burger King/scales/dsl/24hr
17	I-94, E to Detroit, W to Ann Arbor, E
15	Eureka Rd, E Shell,
13	Sibley Rd, New Boston, W Fusion/Subway/dsl, LC's Chicken, to Lower Huron Metro Park

11	S Huron Rd, **1 mi** W Sunoco/Burger King/dsl, Jacob's Rest, RV LP (1mi)
8	Will Carleton Rd, to Flat Rock
5	Carleton, South Rockwood, W food
4mm	**rest area sb, full facilities, , , litter barrels**
2	US 24, to Telegraph Rd, W Marathon/dsl,
0mm	I-275 begins/ends on I-75, exit 20.

INTERSTATE 475 (FLINT)

Exit	Services
17.5mm	I-475 begins/ends on I-75, exit 125.
15	Clio Rd, W BP, Chevrolet
13	Saginaw St, E BP, McDonald's, Papa John's, Taco Bell, Advanced Parts, Family$, Kroger/gas, W Marathon, Sunoco, Burger King, KFC, Little Caesar's
11	Carpenter Rd
10	Pierson Rd
9	rd 54, Dort Hwy, Stewart Ave, E Citgo, McDonald's
8mm	Flint River
8b	Davison Rd, Hamilton Ave
8a	Longway Blvd, W China 1 Buffet, Holiday Inn Express, , USPO
7	rd 21, Court St, downtown Flint
6	I-69, W to Lansing, E to Port Huron
5	Atherton Rd (from sb), E Citgo, Marathon, Curves
4	Hemphill Rd, Bristol Rd, E Sunoco, Benitos Pizza, McDonald's, New China, Rite Aid, W Speedway, Little Caesars, Ole Time Burgers, Tim Horton, Wendy's, Family$, Kroger/gas
2	Hill Rd, E Speedway, Applebee's, Bob Evans, Wingate Inn, Ford, vet, W Sunoco/Tim Horton, Arby's, Bangkok Peppers, Blimpie, Burger St Grill, Little Caesars, Pizza Hut, Wendy's, Courtyard, Holiday Inn, Residence Inn, Rite Aid
0mm	I-475 begins/ends on I-75, exit 111.

INTERSTATE 696 (DETROIT)

Exit	Services
	I-696 begins/ends on I-94.
28	I-94, E to Port Huron, W to Detroit, 11 Mile Rd, E BP/dsl, Speedway, 7-11
27	MI 3, Gratiot Ave, N BP, Valero, Checkers, McDonald's, National Coney Island, Tubby's Subs, Costco/gas, 7-11, S Marathon, Mobil/McDonald's, Shell, Biggby Coffee, DQ, 8 China Buffet, Subway, White Castle, GNC, Goodyear/auto, K-Mart, Kroger/gas, Radio Shack, Rite Aid, Sav-A-Lot Foods
26	MI 97, Groesbeck Ave, Roseville, N Shell/dsl, S Omega Grill
24	Hoover Rd, Schoenherr Rd, N BP, Burger King,

MI

DETROIT ↕ E W

INTERSTATE 696 (DETROIT)

Exit	Services
24	Continued
	KFC, **S** 🅖 BP, Mobil, 🍴 Boston Mkt, Carlito's Pizza, Del Taco, Doc's Rest., Pizza Hut, Quizno's, Red Lobster, Subway, Taco Bell, Tim Horton, 🛏 Holiday Inn Express, 🅞 Curves, CVS Drug, $Tree, GNC, Home Depot, Kroger, Marshall's
23	MI 53, Van Dyke Ave, **N** 🅖 BP, Mobil/dsl, 🍴 Angelo's Rest., Arby's, Baskin-Robbins/Dunkin Donuts, Juliano's Rest., McDonald's, 🅞 Cadillac, Dodge, $General, Scion/Toyota, **S** 🅖 Citgo, 🍴 Luca's Coney Island, 🅞 Chevrolet, Discount Tire, Ford, Rite Aid, USPO, vet
22	Mound Rd, **N** 🅖 BP/Burger King
20	Ryan Rd, Dequindre Rd, **N** 🅖 BP, Citgo, Marathon, 7-11, Shell, 🍴 Azteca Mexican, Ponderosa, 🛏 Knights Inn, Red Roof Inn, 🅞 BigLots, vet, **S** 🍴 Bob Evans, Chicken Shack, Church's, LA Coney Island, McDonald's, 🛏 Best Value Inn, Comfort Suites, 🅞 Rite Aid, Sears, transmissions
19	Couzens St, 10 Mile Rd, **S** Hazel Park Racetrack
18	I-75, N to Flint, S to Detroit
17	Campbell Ave, Hilton Ave, Bermuda, Mohawk, **S** 🅖 Marathon/dsl
16	MI 1, Woodward Ave, Main St, **N** zoo, **S** 🅖 Sunoco
14	Coolidge Rd, 10 Mile Rd, **S** 🅖 Speedway, 🍴 Hungry Howie's, Jade Palace Chinese, Little Caesar's, Subway, 🅞 CVS Drug, Farm Fresh Foods
13	Greenfield Rd, **N** 🅖 Mobil, Marathon, 🍴 Church's,

Exit	Services
13	Continued
	L George Coney Island, McDonald's, Ponderosa, Popeye's, White Castle, 🅞 Aldi Foods, Family$, K-Mart, Sav-A-Lot Foods, **S** 🅖 Mobil, Sunoco, 🍴 Baskin-Robbins/Dunkin Donuts, Front Page Deli, Pita Cafe, Starbucks, 🅞 Rite Aid
12	MI 39, Southfield Rd, 11 Mile Rd, **N** 🅞 Discount Tire, **S** 🅖 Shell, 🍴 Happy's Pizza, 🅞 AT&T
11	Evergreen Rd, **S** 🛏 Hawthorn Suites
10	US 24, Telegraph Rd, **N** 🅖 Marathon, Mobil, Sunoco, 🍴 Baja Fresh, Copper Canyon Rest., Denny's, Fat Burger, 5 Guys Burgers, Pottbelly, Quizno's, Starbucks, Wendy's, 🛏 Embassy Suites, Hampton Inn, Red Roof Inn, 🅞 AT&T, Belle Tire, Best Buy, Buick/GMC, Chrysler/Dodge/Jeep, Ford, Honda, Hyundai, Lexus, Lincoln/Mercury, Lowe's, Meijer/dsl, Michael's, Nissan, Office Depot, Petsmart, Subaru, Verizon, mall, **S** 🅖 Mobil, Sunoco, 🍴 Big Boy, Kerry's Koney Island, 🛏 Best Western, Candlewood Suites, Courtyard, Holiday Resort Hotel, Marriott
8	MI 10, Lodge Fwy
7	American Dr (from eb), **S** 🛏 Extended Stay America, Hilton Garden
5	Orchard Lake Rd, Farmington Hills, **N** 🅖 Marathon, Mobil/dsl, Shell, 🍴 Arby's, Camelia's Mexican, Coney Island, Hong Hua Chinese, Jet's Pizza, Jimmy John's, Roberto's Rest., Ruby Tuesday, Starbucks, Steak&Tavern, Subway, Wendy's, 🛏 Comfort Inn, Courtyard, Extended Stay America, Fairfield Inn, 🅞 Discount Tire, to St Mary's Coll
1	(from wb), I-96 W, I-275 S, to MI 5, Grand River Ave

MINNESOTA

N ↕ **S DULUTH**

INTERSTATE 35

Exit	Services
260mm	I-35 begins/ends on MN 61 in Duluth.
259	MN 61, London Rd, to Two Harbors, North Shore, **W** 🅖 BP, Holiday/dsl, ICO/dsl, 🍴 Blackwoods Grill, Burger King, KFC, McDonald's, Perkins, Pizza Hut, Subway, Taco John's, Wendy's, 🛏 Edgewater Inn, 🅞 vet
258	21st Ave, E (from nb), to U of MN at Duluth, same as 259
256b	Mesaba Ave, Superior St, **E** 🅖 ICO/DQ, 🍴 Bellicio's, Caribou Coffee, Grandma's Grill, Famous Dave's BBQ, Greenmill Rest., Little Angie's Cantina, Old Chicago, Red Lobster, Subway, Timberlodge Steaks, Tradewinds Rest., 🛏 Canal Park Lodge, Comfort Suites, Hampton Inn, Hawthorn Suites, Inn at Lake Superior, Suites Motel, The Inn, **W** 🛏 Holiday Inn, Radisson, Sheraton
256a	Michigan St, **E** waterfront, **W** 🅗, downtown
255a	US 53, N (exits left from nb), downtown, mall, **W** 🅞 Auto Value Parts, Kia
255b	I-535 spur, to Wisconsin
254	27th Ave W, **W** 🅖 Holiday/Burger King/dsl, Spur/dsl, 🍴 Duluth Grill, Quizno's, Subway, 🛏 Motel 6, 🅞 USPO
253b	40th Ave W, **W** 🅖 BP/dsl/24hr, 🍴 Perkins/24hr, 🛏 Comfort Inn, Super 8
253a	US 2 E, US 53, to Wisconsin
252	Central Ave, W Duluth, **W** 🅖 Holiday/dsl/24hr, Little Store/dsl, 🍴 Beaner's Cafe, Giant Panda, Herbert&Gerbert Subs, Jade Fountain Rest., FC, McDonald's, Pizza Hut, Sammy's Café, 🅞 Advance Parts, $Tree, Falk's Drug, K-Mart, Menards, O'Reilly Parts, Sav-a-Lot Foods, Super 1 Foods, Walgreens, vet
251b	MN 23 S, Grand Ave, **E** 🛏 Holiday Inn Express
251a	Cody St, **E** 🛏 Allyndale Motel, 🅞 zoo
250	US 2, W (from sb), to Grand Rapids, **1/2 mi W** 🅖 Holiday/dsl, Mobil/dsl/LP, 🍴 Blackwoods Grill, 🛏 AmericInn
249	Boundary Ave, Skyline Pkwy, **E** 🅖 Holiday/McDonald's/dsl, 🛏 Country Inn&Suites, 🅞 to ski area, **W** rest area both lanes, full 🚻 facilities, info, 🅲, 🛏, litter barrels, vending, 🅖 Little Store/dsl/e-85/24hr, 🍴 Blackwoods Grill, 🛏 AmericInn, Red Roof Inn
246	rd 13, Midway Rd, Nopeming, **W** 🅖 Armor/dsl, 🍴 Dry Dock Rest.
245	rd 61, **E** 🍴 Buffalo House Rest./camping
242	rd 1, Esko, Thomson, **E** 🅖 BP/dsl
239.5mm	St Louis River
239	MN 45, to Cloquet, Scanlon, **E** 🅞 Jay Cooke SP, KOA (May-Oct), **W** 🅖 Holiday, 🍴 Pantry Rest., Trapper Pete's Steaks, 🛏 Golden Gate Motel, 🅞 🅗, Buick/Chevrolet, camping, dsl repair
237	MN 33, Cloquet, **1 mi W** 🅖 BP/24hr, Cenex, Lemon Tree/dsl, Murphy USA/dsl, 🍴 Applebee's, Arby's, DQ, Herbert&Gerberts, McDonald's, Papa Murphy's, Perkins/24hr, Pizza Hut, South Gate Pizza, Subway, Taco John's, Wendy's, 🛏 AmericInn, Super 8, 🅞 🅗, ATT Store, Chrysler/Dodge/Jeep, $Tree, Family$, Ford, NAPA, Super 1 Foods, Verizon, Walmart, White Drug
236mm	weigh sta both lanes
235	MN 210, to Cromwell, Carlton, **E** 🅖 Armor Fuel, BP/dsl/rest., Spur/dsl/24hr, 🍴 Spirits Rest., 🛏 AmericInn, Royal Pines Motel, 🅞 to Jay Cooke SP, **W** 🅞 Black Bear Casino/Hotel/rest.
235mm	Big Otter Creek
233mm	Little Otter Creek

MI MN

INTERSTATE 35 CONT'D

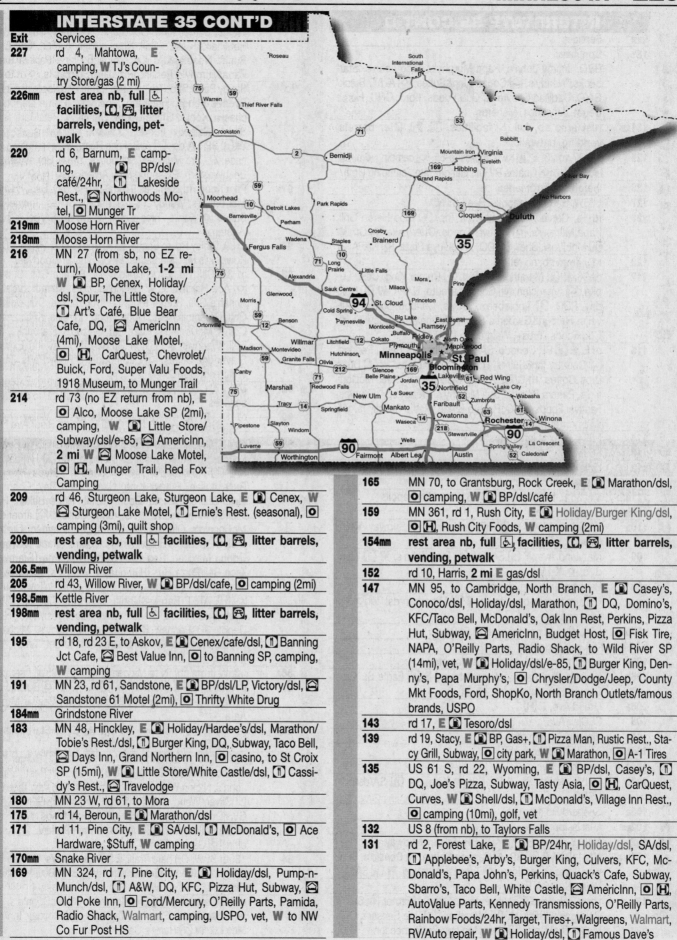

Exit	Services
227	rd 4, Mahtowa, **E** camping, **W** TJ's Country Store/gas (2 mi)
226mm	**rest area nb, full ♿ facilities, 🅒, 🛏, litter barrels, vending, pet-walk**
220	rd 6, Barnum, **E** camping, **W** 🅖 BP/dsl/café/24hr, 🍴 Lakeside Rest., 🛏 Northwoods Motel, 🅞 Munger Tr
219mm	Moose Horn River
218mm	Moose Horn River
216	MN 27 (from sb, no EZ return), Moose Lake, **1-2 mi W** 🅖 BP, Cenex, Holiday/dsl, Spur, The Little Store, 🍴 Art's Café, Blue Bear Cafe, DQ, 🛏 AmericInn (4mi), Moose Lake Motel, 🅞 🏥, CarQuest, Chevrolet/Buick, Ford, Super Valu Foods, 1918 Museum, to Munger Trail
214	rd 73 (no EZ return from nb), **E** 🅞 Alco, Moose Lake SP (2mi), camping, **W** 🅖 Little Store/Subway/dsl/e-85, 🛏 AmericInn, **2 mi W** 🛏 Moose Lake Motel, 🅞 🏥, Munger Trail, Red Fox Camping
209	rd 46, Sturgeon Lake, Sturgeon Lake, **E** 🅖 Cenex, **W** 🛏 Sturgeon Lake Motel, 🍴 Ernie's Rest. (seasonal), 🅞 camping (3mi), quilt shop
209mm	**rest area sb, full ♿ facilities, 🅒, 🛏, litter barrels, vending, petwalk**
206.5mm	Willow River
205	rd 43, Willow River, **W** 🅖 BP/dsl/cafe, 🅞 camping (2mi)
198.5mm	Kettle River
198mm	**rest area nb, full ♿ facilities, 🅒, 🛏, litter barrels, vending, petwalk**
195	rd 18, rd 23 E, to Askov, **E** 🅖 Cenex/cafe/dsl, 🍴 Banning Jct Cafe, 🛏 Best Value Inn, 🅞 to Banning SP, camping, **W** camping
191	MN 23, rd 61, Sandstone, **E** 🅖 BP/dsl/LP, Victory/dsl, 🛏 Sandstone 61 Motel (2mi), 🅞 Thrifty White Drug
184mm	Grindstone River
183	MN 48, Hinckley, **E** 🅖 Holiday/Hardee's/dsl, Marathon/Tobie's Rest./dsl, 🍴 Burger King, DQ, Subway, Taco Bell, 🛏 Days Inn, Grand Northern Inn, 🅞 casino, to St Croix SP (15mi), **W** 🅖 Little Store/White Castle/dsl, 🍴 Cassidy's Rest., 🛏 Travelodge
180	MN 23 W, rd 61, to Mora
175	rd 14, Beroun, **E** 🅖 Marathon/dsl
171	rd 11, Pine City, **E** 🅖 SA/dsl, 🍴 McDonald's, 🅞 Ace Hardware, $Stuff, **W** camping
170mm	Snake River
169	MN 324, rd 7, Pine City, **E** 🅖 Holiday/dsl, Pump-n-Munch/dsl, 🍴 A&W, DQ, KFC, Pizza Hut, Subway, 🛏 Old Poke Inn, 🅞 Ford/Mercury, O'Reilly Parts, Pamida, Radio Shack, Walmart, camping, USPO, vet, **W** to NW Co Fur Post HS
165	MN 70, to Grantsburg, Rock Creek, **E** 🅖 Marathon/dsl, 🅞 camping, **W** 🅖 BP/dsl/café
159	MN 361, rd 1, Rush City, **E** 🅖 Holiday/Burger King/dsl, 🅞 🏥, Rush City Foods, **W** camping (2mi)
154mm	**rest area nb, full ♿ facilities, 🅒, 🛏, litter barrels, vending, petwalk**
152	rd 10, Harris, **2 mi E** gas/dsl
147	MN 95, to Cambridge, North Branch, **E** 🅖 Casey's, Conoco/dsl, Holiday/dsl, Marathon, 🍴 DQ, Domino's, KFC/Taco Bell, McDonald's, Oak Inn Rest, Perkins, Pizza Hut, Subway, 🛏 AmericInn, Budget Host, 🅞 Fisk Tire, NAPA, O'Reilly Parts, Radio Shack, to Wild River SP (14mi), vet, **W** 🅖 Holiday/dsl/e-85, 🍴 Burger King, Denny's, Papa Murphy's, 🅞 Chrysler/Dodge/Jeep, County Mkt Foods, Ford, ShopKo, North Branch Outlets/famous brands, USPO
143	rd 17, **E** 🅖 Tesoro/dsl
139	rd 19, Stacy, **E** 🅖 BP, Gas+, 🍴 Pizza Man, Rustic Rest., Stacy Grill, Subway, 🅞 city park, **W** 🅖 Marathon, 🅞 A-1 Tires
135	US 61 S, rd 22, Wyoming, **E** 🅖 BP/dsl, Casey's, 🍴 DQ, Joe's Pizza, Subway, Tasty Asia, 🅞 🏥, CarQuest, Curves, **W** 🅖 Shell/dsl, 🍴 McDonald's, Village Inn Rest., 🅞 camping (10mi), golf, vet
132	US 8 (from nb), to Taylors Falls
131	rd 2, Forest Lake, **E** 🅖 BP/24hr, Holiday/dsl, SA/dsl, 🍴 Applebee's, Arby's, Burger King, Culvers, KFC, McDonald's, Papa John's, Perkins, Quack's Cafe, Subway, Sbarro's, Taco Bell, White Castle, 🛏 AmericInn, 🅞 🏥, AutoValue Parts, Kennedy Transmissions, O'Reilly Parts, Rainbow Foods/24hr, Target, Tires+, Walgreens, Walmart, RV/Auto repair, **W** 🅖 Holiday/dsl, 🍴 Famous Dave's

N ↕ S

H I N C K L E Y

MN

INTERSTATE 35 CONT'D

Exit	Services
131	Continued BBQ, Jimmy John's, Papa Murphy's, Taco John's, Starbucks, Wendy's, 🛏 Country Inn&Suites, 🅞 AT&T, Buick/GMC, Cadillac/Chevrolet, Cub Foods, Ford, GNC, Home Depot, Jiffy Lube, Menards
131mm	**rest area sb, full 🚻 facilities, 🅒, 🚬, litter barrels, vending, petwalk**
129	MN 97, rd 23, **E** 🅖 Kwik Trip/dsl/e-85, 🅞 camping (6mi), **W** 🅖 BP/dsl, 🅞 Coates RV Ctr, Gander Mtn., camping (1mi)
128mm	**weigh sta both lanes**
127	I-35W, S to Minneapolis. See I-35W.
123	rd 14, Centerville, **E** 🅖 Kwik Trip, 🍴 Blue Heron Grill, Papa Murphy's, 🅞 Festival Foods, Otter Lake RV Ctr, **W** 🅖 Mobil/dsl, Shell, 🍴 DQ, WiseGuys Pizza, 🅞 NAPA
120	rd J (from nb, no return)
117	rd 96, **E** 🅖 Marathon, SA/dsl, 🍴 Burger King, Casa Lupita, 🛏 AmericInn, 🅞 Goodyear/auto, NAPA, **W** 🅖 Holiday, PDQ, 🍴 Applebee's, Arby's, Caribou Coffee, Culver's, Herbert&Gerbert's Subs, McDonald's, Subway, 🅞 Cub Foods, Tires+, Walgreens, USPO
115	rd E, **E** 🅖 BP, Conoco, SA/dsl, 🍴 Jimmy's Rest., Perkins, 🛏 Country Inn&Suites, Holiday Inn Express, **W** 🍴 Dunn Bros Coffee, KFC/Pizza Hut, Mad Jack's Cafe, McDonald's, Panera Bread, Papa Murphy's, Wendy's, 🅞 Curves, Festival Foods, GNC, Panera Bread, Radio Shack, Target, Walmart/auto
114	I-694, E (exits left from sb)
113	I-694, W
112	Little Canada Rd, **E** 🅖 BP, **W** 🅖 Sinclair/dsl, 🍴 Porterhouse Rest
111a/b	MN 36 E, to Stillwater/MN 36 W, to Minneapolis
110b	Roselawn Ave
110a	Wheelock Pkwy, **E** 🅖 BP, Oasis Mkt, 🍴 Subway, **W** 🍴 Champps Grill
109	Maryland Ave, **E** 🅖 SA/dsl, 🍴 Taco John's, **W** 🍴 Wendy's, 🅞 K-Mart
108	Pennsylvania Ave, downtown
107c	University Ave, downtown, **E** 🅖 Marathon/dsl, **W** 🅞 🏥, to st capitol
107b a	I-94, W to Minneapolis, E to St Paul.
	I-35 and I-94 run together.
106c	11th St (from nb), Marion St, downtown
106b	Kellogg Blvd (from nb), downtown, **E** 🍴 Eagle St. Grill, Subway, 🛏 Holiday Inn, 🅞 🏥
106a	Grand Ave, **E** 🏥
105	St Clair Ave
104c	Victoria St, Jefferson Ave
104b	Ayd Mill Rd (from nb)
104a	Randolph Ave
103b	MN 5, W 7th St, **E** 🍴 Burger King, **W** 🅖 SA/dsl, 🅞 USPO
103a	Shepard Rd (from nb)
102mm	Mississippi River
102	MN 13, Sibley Hwy, **W** 🅖 BP, Holiday/Subway
101b a	MN 110 W, **E** 🅖 BP, 🍴 Caribou Coffee, McDonald's, Subway, Teresa's Mexican, 🅞 Tuesday Morning, **W** 🅖 SA
99b a	I-494 W/I-494, E
98	Lone Oak Rd, **E** 🛏 Homestead Suites, Microtel, 🅞 Sam's Club/gas, USPO, **W** 🅖 Marathon, 🍴 Joe Senser's Grill, Magic Thai Café, 🛏 Hampton Inn, Residence Inn

Exit	Services
97b	Yankee Doodle Rd, **E** 🍴 Applebee's, Arby's, Buffalo Wild Wings, Burger King, Coldstone Creamery, Culver's, DQ, Houlihan's, Jake's Grill, Jimmy John's, KFC, New China Buffet, Noodles&Co, Old Chicago Pizza, Panera Bread, Papa Murphy's, Perkins, Pizza Hut, Pizza Man, Pot Bellys, Savoy Pizza, Taco Bell, 🅞 At&T, Barnes&Noble, Best Buy, Byerly's Foods, Firestone, Goodyear, Home Depot, Michael's, Kohl's, Office Depot, Old Navy, PetsMart, Radio Shack, Rainbow Foods, TJ Maxx, Walgreens, Walmart, **W** 🅖 BP, SA/dsl, 🍴 Al Baker's Rest., Dragon Palace Chinese, El Loro Mexican, Starbucks, Steak Bones Grill, 🛏 Best Western, Extended Stay America, 🅞 NAPA
97a	Pilot Knob Rd, same as 97b, **E** 🅖 Holiday, SA, 🍴 Chili's, McDonald's, Wendy's, 🛏 SpringHill Suites, TownePlace Suites, 🅞 Kohl's, Tires+, mall, **W** 🅖 BP, SA/dsl, 🛏 Best Western
94	rd 30, Diffley Rd, to Eagan, **E** 🅖 Holiday/dsl, 🅞 CVS Drug, Kowalski's Mkt/Starbucks, **W** 🅖 Sinclair/Goodyear
93	rd 32, Cliff Rd, **E** 🅖 Holiday, 🍴 Bonfire Grill, Subway, 🅞 Ace Hardware, **W** 🅖 Holiday/dsl, Marathon/dsl, 🍴 Ansari's Grill, Burger King, Caribou Coffee, DQ, Dolittle's Grill, Greenmill Rest., Hong Wong Chinese, KFC, Leeann Chin's, McDonald's, Pizza Hut, Quizno's, Starbucks, Taco Bell, Wendy's, 🛏 Hilton Garden, Holiday Inn Express, Staybridge Suites, 🅞 Cub Foods, O'Reilly Parts, Target, Walgreen, USPO
92	MN 77, Cedar Ave, **E** Zoo, **1 mi W** access to Cliff Rd services
90	rd 11, **E** 🅖 KwikTrip, 🍴 Subway, 🅞 Valley Natural Foods, **W** 🅖 SA/dsl
88b	rd 42, Crystal Lake Rd, **E** 🍴 Chianti Grill, 🅞 Byerly's Foods, PetsMart, Tuesday Morning, **W** 🅖 Holiday/dsl, SA, 🍴 Applebee's, Arby's/Sbarro's, Azteca Mexican, Buca Italian, Burger King, Cam Aranh Bay, Champp's Grill, Chili's, Dakota County Grill, HoneyBaked Ham, IHOP, Jimmy John's, KFC, Kings Buffet, Macaroni Grill, McDonald's, Old Country Buffet, Olive Garden, Outback Steaks, Panera Bread, Papa John's, Papa Murphy's, Qdoba Mexican, Red Lobster, Roasted Pear, Starbucks, Taco Bell/Pizza Hut, TGIFriday's, Wendy's, 🛏 Days Inn, Fairfield Inn, Hampton Inn, Holiday Inn, InTown Suites, 🅞 🏥, AT&T, Barnes&Noble, Best Buy, Cadillac, Chevrolet, Cub Foods, Discount Tire, Goodyear/auto, Home Depot, JC Penney, K-Mart, Kohl's, Macy's, Michael's, PetCo, Rainbow Foods, Sears/auto, Target, Tires+, Walgreens, mall, USPO
88a	I-35W (from nb), N to Minneapolis. See I-35W.
87	Crystal Lake Rd (from nb), **W** 🅖 KwikTrip, 🅞 Buick, Ford/Lincoln/Mercury, Honda/Nissan, Toyota, Beaver Mtn Ski Area
86	rd 46, **E** 🅖 KwikTrip, SA/dsl, 🍴 KFC, Starbucks, 🅞 Harley-Davidson, **W** 🅞 O'Reilly Parts
85	MN 50, **E** 🅖 BP/24hr, F&F/dsl, SA/dsl, 🍴 Burger King, Caribou Coffee, Culver's, DQ, Greenmill Rest., Jimmy John's, Nick'n Willy's Pizza, Pizza Hut, Subway, Taco Bell, LJ Silver, Wendy's, 🛏 Comfort Inn, 🅞 URGENT CARE, CVS Drug, Goodyear, Tires+, Rainbow foods, Walgreens, **W** 🅖 Holiday/dsl, 🍴 Cracker Barrel, Perkins, 🛏 AmericInn, 🅞 Gander Mtn.
84	185th St W, Orchard Trail, **E** 🍴 Applebee's, Buffalo Wild Wings, Caribou Coffee, Quizno's, 🅞 Best Buy, Marshall's, Target
81	rd 70, Lakeville, **E** 🅖 Holiday/dsl, 🍴 McDonald's, Porterhouse Rest., Subway, Tacoville, 🛏 Holiday Inn/rest, Motel 6, **W** 🍴 Harry's Cafe

INTERSTATE 35 CONT'D

Exit	Services
76	rd 2, Elko, **E** gas/dsl, **W** 🍴 Endzone Grill, 🅾 Elko Speedway
76mm	**rest area sb, full ♿ facilities, 🚻, 🛗, litter barrels, vending, petwalk**
69	MN 19, to Northfield, New Prague, **6-8 mi E** 🅿 KwikTrip, 🍴 Applebee's, McDonald's, Subway, Taco Bell, 🛏 AmericInn, College City Motel, Country Inn&Suites, Super 8, 🅾 🅷, Carleton Coll, St Olaf Coll, **W** 🅿 Shell/dsl/rest./scales
68mm	**rest area nb, full ♿ facilities, 🚻, 🛗, litter barrels, vending, petwalk**
66	rd 1, to Dundas, **1 mi W** 🍴 Boonie's Grill
59	MN 21, Faribault, **0-2 mi E** 🅿 BP/dsl/rest./scales/24hr, KwikTrip, SA, 🍴 A&W, Arbys, Burger King, DQ, Hardee's, KFC, Pizza Hut, Taco John's, 🛏 AmericInn, Best Value Inn, Days Inn, Galaxy Inn, Grandstay, Lyndale Motel, 🅾 Aldi Foods, Chevrolet/GMC, Ford, O'Reilly Parts, Satakah St Trail, vet, **W** 🅾 Harley-Davidson, camping
56	MN 60, Faribault, same as 59, **E** 🅿 KwikTrip, 🍴 Arby's, Burger King, Great China Buffet, Hardee's, Jimmy John's, KFC, Perkins, Pizza Hut, Subway, Taco John's, 🅾 🅷, Aldi Foods, Auto Value Parts, Buick, Chevrolet, Chrysler/Jeep, Dodge, $Tree, Family$, Goodyear/auto, Hy-Vee Foods/gas, JC Penney, O'Reilly Parts, Radio Shack, Tires+, True Value, Walmart, mall, **W** 🅿 Petro/dsl, 🍴 Country Kitchen, DQ, 🛏 Regency Inn, 🅾 Sakatah Lake SP, camping
55	rd 48, (from nb, no return), **1 mi E** 🅿 SA/dsl, KwikTrip, Mobil/dsl, 🍴 A&W, Broaster Rest., Burger King, DQ, KFC, Pizza Hut, Southern China Cafe, Subway, Taco John's, 🛏 AmericInn, Galaxy Inn, 🅾 Ford
48	rd 12, rd 23, Medford, **W** 🍴 McDonald's, 🅾 Outlet Mall/famous brands
45	rd 9, Clinton Falls, **W** 🅿 KwikTrip/dsl, 🍴 Caribou Coffee, Famous Dave's BBQ, Sportsman's Grille, Subway, TimberLodge Steaks, Wendy's, 🛏 Comfort Inn, Holiday Inn, 🅾 Cabela's Sporting Goods, Russell-Stover Candies, museum
43	rd 34, 26th St, 🅿 Rd, Owatonna, **W** 🅾 Noble RV Ctr
42b a	US 14 W, rd 45, to Waseca, Owatonna, **E** 🍴 Kernel Rest., 🛏 Budget Host, 🅾 AutoZone, CashWise Foods, Chrysler/Dodge/Jeep, Ford/Lincoln/Mercury, O'Reilly Parts, **W** 🅿 KwikTrip/dsl, 🍴 Big 10 Rest., Culver's, Dunn Bros Coffee, Eastwind Buffet, McDonald's, Perkins, 🛏 Best Budget Inn, Super 8, 🅾 $Tree, GNC, Kohls, Lowe's Whse, Radio Shack, Walmart/Subway
41	Bridge St, Owatonna, **E** 🅿 BP, Holiday/dsl, 🍴 Applebee's, Arby's, Burger King, DQ, KFC, Papa Murphy's, Quizno's, Starbucks, Subway, Taco Bell, 🛏 AmericInn, Country Inn&Suites, 🅾 🅷, **W** 🅿 F&F/dsl, 🛏 Microtel, 🅾 Target
40	US 14 E, US 218, Owatonna, **1 mi E on rd 6** 🍴 El Tequila Mexican, Godfather's, Taco John's, 🛏 Oakdale Motel, 🅾 🅷, Buick/Cadillac/Chevrolet, Curves, Hy-Vee Foods/24hr, TrueValue, Walgreens, WholesaleTire
38mm	Turtle Creek
35mm	**rest area both lanes, full ♿ facilities, 🚻, 🛗, litter barrels, vending, petwalk**
34.5mm	Straight River
32	rd 4, Hope, **1/2 mi E** camping, **1 mi W** gas, food
26	MN 30, to Blooming Prairie, Ellendale, **E** 🅿 Cenex/dsl/rest., **W** 🅿 BP/pizza/dsl
22	rd 35, to Hartland, Geneva, **1 mi E** gas, food

Exit	Services
18	MN 251, to Hollandale, Clarks Grove, **W** 🅿 BP/dsl/LP, 🅾 camping
17mm	**weigh sta, both lanes**
13b a	I-90, W to Sioux Falls, E to Austin, **W** 🅷
12	US 65, S (from sb), Lp 35, Albert Lea, same as 11
11	rd 46, Albert Lea, **E** 🅿 Loves/Wendy's/dsl/scales/24hr, TA/Shell/Coldstone/Pizza Hut/dsl/scales/24hr/@, 🍴 McDonald's, 🛏 Comfort Inn, 🅾 KOA (may-oct/6mi), dsl repair, **W** 🅿 KwikTrip, Shell/dsl, 🍴 Burger King, Casa Zamora Mexican, China Buffet, Domino's, Godfather's, Green Mill Rest., McDonald's, Perkins, Pizza Hut, Quizno's, Subway, Taco Bell, Taco John's, Trumble's Rest., Wok'n Roll, 🛏 Albert Lee Inn, Best Value Inn, Country Inn&Suites, Countryside Inn, Super 8, 🅾 🅷, Advance Parts, Auto Value Parts, AutoZone, Buick/Cadillac/GMC, CarQuest, Chrysler/Dodge/Jeep, $Tree, Ford, Goodyear/auto, Home Depot, Honda, NAPA, Nissan/VW, O'Reilly Parts, Radio Shack, Walgreens, Walmart, to Myre-Big Island SP
9mm	Albert Lea Lake
8	US 65, Lp 35US 65, Lp 35, Albert Lea, **2 mi W** 🅿 Freeborn City Co-op/dsl, 🍴 DQ, Hardee's
5	rd 13, to Glenville, Twin Lakes, **3 mi W** camping
2	rd 5
1mm	**Welcome Ctr nb, full ♿ facilities, 🚻, 🛗, litter barrels, vending, petwalk**
0mm	Minnesota/Iowa state line

INTERSTATE 35 W

Exit	Services
41mm	I-35W begins/ends on I-35, exit 127.
36	rd 23, **E** 🅿 Holiday/dsl, 🛏 Country Inn&Suites, **W** 🅿 US/dsl, 🍴 Caribou Coffee, DQ, McDonald's, Subway, 🛏 Hampton Inn, 🅾 Discount Tire, Kohl's, Super Target
33	rd 17, Lexington Ave, **E** 🅿 F&F/dsl, Holiday, **1 mi E** 🍴 Burger King, McDonald's, **W** 🍴 Applebee's, Arby's, Bonfire Rest., Caribou Coffee, Green Mill Rest., Quizno's, Taco Bell/LJ Silver, Wendy's, Zantigo's Mexican, 🅾 Cub Foods, GNC, Home Depot, Michael's, Radio Shack, Walgreens, Walmart
32	95th Ave NE, to Lexington, Circle Pines, **W** Nat Sports Ctr
31b a	Lake Dr, **E** 🅿 Shell/dsl, 🍴 Quizno's, Red Ginger Asian, Steamin Bean Coffee, 🛏 Country Inn&Suites
30	US 10 W, MN 118, to MN 65
29	rd I
28c b	rd 10, rd H, **W** 🅿 BP, 🍴 KFC, LJ Silver/Taco Bell, McDonald's, Mermaid Café, RJ Riches Rest., 🛏 AmericInn, Days Inn, 🅾 NAPA, carwash
28a	MN 96
27b a	I-694 E and W

INTERSTATE 35 CONT'D WEST

Exit	Services
N	
26	rd E2, W 🅖 Exxon/dsl, 🍴 Jimmy John's, Limu Coffee
25b	MN 88, to Roseville (no EZ return to sb), same as 25a
25a	rd D (from nb), E 🅖 BP/dsl, 🍴 Blimpie, 🏨 Courtyard, Fairfield Inn, Residence Inn, W 🅖 PDQ, SA, 🍴 Barley John's, Caribou Coffee, Jake's Café, McDonald's, New Hong Kong, Perkins/24hr, Sarpino's Italian, Subway
S	
24	rd C, E 🍴 Burger King, India Palace Rest., Joe Senser's Rest., 🏨 Days Inn, Motel 6, Radisson, 🅞 USPO, W 🏨 Holiday Inn Express, 🅞 Chevrolet/GMC, Chrysler/Dodge/Jeep, Volvo
23b	Cleveland Ave, MN 36
23a	MN 280, Industrial Blvd (from sb)
22	MN 280, Industrial Blvd (from nb), E 🏨 Ramada Plaza
21b a	Broadway St, Stinson Blvd, E Ford/Isuzu Trucks, W 🍴 Baja Sol, Burger King, Caribou Coffee, Cousins Subs, Leeann Chin, McDonald's, Pizza Hut/Taco Bell, 🅞 GNC, Home Depot, Old Navy, Rainbow Foods/24hr, Target
19	E Hennepin (from nb)
18	US 52, 4th St SE, University Ave, to U of MN, E 🅖 BP/repair
17c	11th St, Washington Ave, E 🏨 Holiday Inn, W 🅖 Mobil, 🅞 H, Goodyear, to Metrodome
17b	I-94 W, (from sb)
17a	MN 55, Hiawatha
16b a	I-94 (from nb), E to St Paul, W to St Cloud, to MN 65
15	31st St (from nb), Lake St, E 🍴 McDonald's, Taco Bell, 🅞 Auto Zone, W H
14	35th St, 36th St
13	46th St
13mm	Minnehaha Creek
12b	Diamond Lake Rd
12a	60th St (from sb), W 🅖 Mobil, 🅞 Cub Foods
11b	MN 62 E, to ✈
11a	Lyndale Ave (from sb)
10b	MN 62 W, 58th St
10a	rd 53, 66th St, E 🅖 SA
9c	76th St (from sb)
9b a	I-494, MN 5, to ✈
8	82nd St, E 🅞 BMW, W 🍴 Caribou Coffee, Jimmy Johns, Red Lobster, Sonic, Timberlodge Steaks, Wendy's, 🏨 Embassy Suites, 🅞 Chevrolet, Chrysler/Dodge/Jeep, Hyundai, Infiniti, Kia, Kohl's, TJ Maxx, Walgreens
7b	90th St
7a	94th St, E 🅞 Goodyear/auto, W 🏨 Holiday Inn
6	rd 1, 98th St, E 🅖 Holiday, 🍴 Applebee's, Bakers Square, Burger King, Coldstone, Domino's, Golden Wok, Jimmy John's, Leeann Chen, McDonald's, Starbucks, Wendy's, White Castle, URGENT CARE, Bloomington Drug, Festival Foods, Ford, Radio Shack, Walgreens, W 🅖 SA/dsl, 🍴 Denny's
5	106th St
5mm	Minnesota River
4b	113th St, Black Dog Rd
4a	Cliff Rd, E Dodge, Subaru, W VW
3b a	MN 13, Shakopee, Canterbury Downs, E 🏨 Select Inn
2	Burnsville Pkwy, E 🅖 BP, Marathon, 🍴 Bumpers Grill, W 🅖 Holiday, 🍴 Gourmet Chinese, Hooters, Perkins, Timberlodge Steaks, 🏨 Best Value Inn, LivInn, Prime Rate Motel, Travelodge, 🅞 Best Buy, Goodyear/auto, vet
1	rd 42, Crystal Lake Rd, E 🍴 Chianti Grill, 🅞 Byerly's Foods, PetsMart, Tuesday Morning, W 🅖 Holiday/dsl,

Side label: MINNEAPOLIS

(I-35 continued, right column)

Exit	Services
1	Continued
	SA, 🍴 Applebee's, Arby's/Sbarro's, Azteca Mexican, Buca Italian, Burger King, Cam Aranh Bay, Champp's Grill, Chili's, Dakota County Grill, HoneyBaked Ham, IHOP, Jimmy John's, KFC, Kings Buffet, Macaroni Grill, McDonald's, Old Country Buffet, Olive Garden, Outback Steaks, Panera Bread, Papa John's, Papa Murphy's, Qdoba Mexican, Red Lobster, Roasted Pear, Starbucks, Taco Bell, Pizza Hut, TGIFriday's, Wendy's, 🏨 Days Inn, Fairfield Inn, Hampton Inn, Holiday Inn, InTown Suites, 🅞 H, AT&T, Barnes&Noble, Best Buy, Cadillac, Chevrolet, Cub Foods, Discount Tire, Goodyear/auto, Home Depot, JC Penney, K-Mart, Kohl's, Macy's, Michael's, PetCo, Rainbow Foods, Sears/auto, Target, Tires+, Walgreens, mall, USPO
Qmm	I-35W begins/ends on I-35, exit 88a.

INTERSTATE 90

Exit	Services
E	
278mm	Minnesota/Wisconsin state line, Mississippi River
276	US 14, US 61, to MN 16, La Crescent, N **Welcome Ctr wb, full** ♿ **facilities, info,** 🎧, 🚻, **litter barrels, vending, petwalk,** S 🅖 Kwik Trip (1mi)
273b a	Dresbach
271	Dakota
W	
270	US 14, US 61, to Winona (from wb), N to OL Kipp SP/camping
267	rd 12, Nodine, N 🅞 Great River Bluffs SP, camping, S 🅖 Kwik Trip/dsl/Hearty Platter/scales/24hr/@
261mm	**weigh sta both lanes**
258	MN 76, to Houston, Ridgeway, Witoka, N gas, S camping
252	MN 43 N, to Winona, **7 mi** N 🍴 Taco Bell, 🏨 Express Inn, Holiday Inn, Holiday Inn Express, Quality Inn, 🅞 H
249	MN 43 S, to Rushford, N 🅞 Peterbilt Trucks/repair
244mm	**rest area eb, full** ♿ **facilities,** 🎧, 🚻, **litter barrels, vending, petwalk**
242	rd 29, Lewiston
233	MN 74, to Chatfield, St Charles, N 🅖 Kwik Trip/LP/24hr (2mi), 🍴 A&W (2mi), Subway (2mi), 🅞 Whitewater SP, S 🅖 BP/Amish Ovens Rest./dsl/RV dump/LP, 🅞 auto/truck repair
229	rd 10, Dover
224	MN 42, rd 7, Eyota, N 🅖 KwikTrip/dsl/E-85 (3mi), 🍴 Country Cafe
222mm	**rest area wb, full** ♿ **facilities,** 🎧, 🚻, **litter barrels, vending, petwalk**
218	US 52, to Rochester, S 🅖 BP/dsl, 🅞 KOA (Mar-Oct) (1mi)
209b a	US 63, MN 30, to Rochester, Stewartville, **8-10 mi** N 🏨 Clarion, Comfort Inn, EconoLodge, Hampton Inn, Holiday Inn, Relax Inn, **1 mi** S 🅖 KwikTrip/dsl, 🍴 DQ, Subway, 🏨 AmericInn
205	rd 6
202mm	**rest area eb, full** ♿ **facilities,** 🎧, 🚻, **litter barrels, vending, petwalk**
193	MN 16, Dexter, N 🅖 BP/Oasis Rest./dsl
189	rd 13, to Elkton
187	rd 20, S Jelly Stone Camping
183	MN 56, to Rose Creek, Brownsdale, S 🅖 Freeborn County Co-op/dsl/LP
181	28th St NE
180b a	US 218, 21st St NE, to Austin, Oakland Place, S 🅖 Shell, 🏨 Rodeway Inn
179	11th Dr NE, to Austin, N 🅖 BP/rest./dsl/24hr

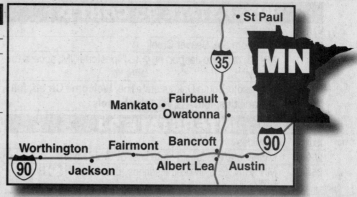

AUSTIN E→W

INTERSTATE 90 CONT'D

Exit	Services
178b	6th St NE, to Austin, **S** Spam Museum
178a	4th St NW, **N** 🍴 Culver's, Perkins, Torge's Grille, 🛏 AmericInn, Days Inn, Holiday Inn ⊙ AutoValue Parts, Buick/Chevrolet/GMC, vet, **S** 🚗 KwikTrip/dsl, 🍴 A&W, Burger King, Subway, ⊙ Ⓗ
177	US 218 N, to Owatonna, Austin, Mapleview, **N** 🍴 Applebee's, Arby's, China Star, El Patron Mexican, KFC/LJ Silver, King Buffet, Quiznos, Wendy's, ⊙ Aldi Foods, $Tree, Family$, Hy-Vee Foods/gas, JoAnn Fabrics, O'Reilly Parts, Radio Shack, ShopKO, Staples, Target, Verizon, Walmart/Subway, Younkers, mall, **S** 🚗 Sinclair/McDonald's/dsl, 🛏 Super 8
175	MN 105, rd 46, to Oakland Rd, **N** 🛏 Countryside Inn, **S** 🚗 BP, Shell/dsl, ⊙ Chrysler/Dodge/Jeep, Ford/Lincoln/Mercury, camping, vet
171mm	**rest area wb, full** ♿ **facilities,** 🚻, 🖼, **litter barrels, petwalk**
166	rd 46, Oakland Rd, **N** ⊙ KOA/LP, golf (par3)
163	rd 26, Hayward, **S** 🚗 Freeborn County Co-op/dsl, 🍴 Pizza Hut (4mi), Trails Rest. (4mi), ⊙ Myre-Big Island SP, camping
161.5mm	**rest area eb, full** ♿ **facilities,** 🚻, 🖼 **litter barrels, petwalk**

ALBERT LEA

159b a	I-35, N to Twin Cities, S to Des Moines
157	rd 22, Albert Lea, **N** ⊙ Kenworth, **S** 🍴 Applebee's, Arby's, DQ, Herberger's, McDonald's, Pizza Ranch, Plaza Morina Mexican, 🛏 AmericInn, Best Western, ⊙ Ⓗ, Ace Hardware, Chevrolet, GNC, Harley-Davidson, Hy-Vee Foods/gas/24hr, ShopKO, Verizon, mall
154	MN 13, to US 69, to Manchester, Albert Lea, **N** 🚗 SA/dsl, **3 mi S** 🛏 BelAire Motel
146	MN 109, to Wells, Alden, **S** 🚗 BP/dsl/rest., Freeborn Co-Op Gas/dsl/E-85, ⊙ truck/dsl repair
138	MN 22, to Wells, Kiester, **S** camping
134	MN 253, rd 21, to Bricelyn, MN Lake
128	MN 254, rd 17, Frost, Easton
119	US 169, to Winnebago, Blue Earth, **S** 🚗 Shell/dsl, Sinclair/dsl, 🍴 Country Kitchen, DQ, McDonald's, Pizza Hut, Subway, 🛏 AmericInn, Super 8, ⊙ Ⓗ, $General, Walmart, Jolly Green Giant, camping
119mm	**rest area both lanes, full** ♿ **facilities,** 🚻, 🖼, **litter barrels, petwalk, playground**
113	rd 1, Guckeen

FAIRMONT

107	MN 262, rd 53, to East Chain, Granada, **S** ⊙ camping (May-Oct) (1mi), gas/dsl
102	MN 15, to Madelia, Fairmont, **N** 🚗 Verizon, Walmart/Subway, **0-2 mi S** 🚗 BP, Cenex/dsl, ProFuel/dsl, SA/dsl/24hr, 🍴 Arby's, Burger King, China Buffet, DQ, Green Mill Rest., McDonald's, Perkins, Pizza Ranch, Ranch Family Rest., Subway, Taco John's, 🛏 Budget Inn, Comfort Inn, Hampton Inn, Holiday Inn, Super 8, ⊙ Ⓗ, Ace Hardware, CarQuest, Chevrolet, Chrysler/Dodge/Jeep, $Tree, Fareway Foods, Ford, Freightliner, Goodyear/auto, Hy-Vee Foods, JC Penney, NAPA, Radio Shack, Sears, ShopKO, Walgreens, USPO, camping, auto repair
99	rd 39, Fairmont, **services 2 mi S**
93	MN 263, rd 27, Welcome, **1/2 mi S** 🚗 Cenex, camping
87	MN 4, Sherburn, **N** ⊙ Everett Park Camping, **S** 🚗 Cenex, Kum&Go/Subway/dsl/E-85
80	rd 29, Alpha

WORTHINGTON

73	US 71, Jackson, **N** 🚗 SA/dsl, 🍴 Burger King, 🛏 EconoLodge, Super 8, ⊙ KOA, to Kilen Woods SP, **S** 🍴 BP/DQ, Casey's, 🍴 Embers Rest., Pizza Ranch, Subway, 🛏 AmericInn, Budget Host, Earth Inn, Prairie Winds Motel, ⊙ Ⓗ, Ace Hardware, Family$, Buick/Chevrolet, Chrysler/Dodge/Jeep, Sunshine Foods, city park, to Spirit Lake
72.5mm	W Fork Des Moines River
72mm	**rest area wb, full** ♿ **facilities,** 🚻, 🖼, **litter barrels, vending, petwalk**
69mm	**rest area eb, full** ♿ **facilities,** 🚻, 🖼, **litter barrels, vending, petwalk**
64	MN 86, Lakefield, **N** Ⓗ, gas/dsl, food, camping, to Kilen SP (12mi)
57	rd 9, to Heron Lake, Spafford
50	MN 264, rd 1, to Brewster, Round Lake, **S** camping
47	rd 3 (from eb), no return, no services
46mm	**weigh sta eb**
45	MN 60, Worthington, **N** 🚗 BP/Blueline Cafe/dsl/scales, **S** 🚗 Casey's, Shell/dsl/scales/24hr, ⊙ camping, truckwash
43	US 59, Worthington, **N** 🚗 Mobil/dsl, 🛏 Travelodge, **S** 🚗 Casey's, Cenex/dsl, Shell, 🍴 Arby's, Burger King, DQ, Ground Round, Hardee's, KFC, McDonald's, Perkins, Pizza Hut, Pizza Ranch, Subway, Taco John's, 🛏 AmericInn, Holiday Inn Express, ⊙ Ⓗ, Ace Hardware, CarQuest, Fareway Foods, F&F, Ford, Hy-Vee Foods/dsl, Buick/Cadillac/Chevrolet, $General, $Tree, JC Penney, NAPA, O'Reilly Parts, Radio Shack, ShopKO, Walgreens, Walmart/Subway
42	MN 266, rd 25, to Reading, **S** 🛏 Days Inn, Super 8
33	rd 13, to Wilmont, Rushmore
26	MN 91, Adrian, **S** 🚗 Cenex/dsl, Kum&Go/Subway/dsl/E-85/24hr, 🍴 Countryside Steaks, Crystal Steaks, ⊙ Adrian Camping, city park
25mm	**rest area wb, full** ♿ **facilities,** 🚻, 🖼, **litter barrels, petwalk**
24mm	**rest area eb, full** ♿ **facilities,** 🚻, 🖼, **litter barrels, petwalk**
18	rd 3, Kanaranzi, Magnolia, **N** camping
12	US 75, Luverne, **N** 🚗 BP/dsl/E-85, Casey's, Cenex/dsl, Shell/Subway/dsl, 🍴 ChitChat's Grill, McDonald's, Taco John's, Tasty Drive-In, 🛏 Comfort Inn, Cozy Rest Motel (1mi), Sunrise Motel, ⊙ Ⓗ, Ace Hardware, Buick/Cadillac/Chevrolet/GMC, Chrysler/Dodge/Jeep, $General, Family$, Lewis Drugs, True Value, to Blue Mounds SP, Pipestone NM, **S** 🍴 Magnolia Steaks, 🛏 Super 8, ⊙ Pamida
5	rd 6, Beaver Creek, **N** 🚗 Shell/dsl

MN

INTERSTATE 90 CONT'D

Exit	Services
3	rd 4 (from eb), Beaver Creek
1	MN 23, rd 17, to Jasper, **N** 🅞 to Pipestone NM, access to gas/dsl
0mm	Minnesota/South Dakota state line, **Welcome Ctr eb, full** ♿ **facilities, info,** 🅒, 🚻, **litter barrels**

INTERSTATE 94

Exit	Services
259mm	Minnesota/Wisconsin state line, St Croix River
258	MN 95 N, to Stillwater, Hastings, Lakeland, **N** 🍴 Bungalow Grill
257mm	**weigh sta wb, Welcome Ctr wb, full** ♿ **facilities,** 🅒, 🚻, **litter barrels, vending, petwalk**
253	MN 95 S, rd 15, Manning Ave, **N** 🅞 StoneRidge Golf, **S** to Afton Alps SP, ski area
251	Rd 19, Keats Ave, Woodbury Dr, **S** 🅖 KwikTrip, SA/dsl, 🍴 Applebee's, Arby's, Boston's Rest., Burger King, Caribou Coffee, Chili's, Chipotle Mexican, Dino's Rest, Las Margaritas, LeeAnn Chin, Outback Steaks, Ray J's Grill, SmashBurger, 🛏 Extended Stay America, Holiday Inn Express, 🅞 $Tree, Gander Mtn, Hancock Fabrics, Michael's, Sam's Club/gas, Staples, Target, Tuesday Morning, Walmart/Subway, Woodbury Lakes Outlets/famous brands
250	rd 13, Radio Dr, Inwood Ave, **N** 🍴 Baja Sol, Buffalo Wild Wings, Caribou Coffee, Machine Shed Rest., Milio's Rest., Red Lobster, Olive Garden, 🛏 Hilton Garden, Wild Wood Lodge, 🅞 Best Buy, **S** 🅖 Holiday, 🍴 Champp's, Jamba Juice, Little Caesar's, Pei Wei, Starbucks, Sunsets Grill, Taco Bell, TGIFriday's, Vietnam Rest., Wendy's, 🅞 Cub Foods, CVS Drug, Dick's, GNC, Hepner's Auto Ctr, Home Depot, JC Penney, Jo-Ann, LandsEnd Inlet, Old Navy, Petsmart, Tires+, vet
249	I-694, N & I-494, S
247	MN 120, Century Ave, **N** 🍴 Denny's, Olympus Grill, 🛏 LivInn, 🅞 Harley-Davidson, **S** 🅖 SA, 🍴 GreenMill Rest., 🛏 Country Inn/rest., 🅞 Chevrolet
246c b	McKnight Ave, **N** 3M
246a	Ruth St (from eb, no return), **N** 🍴 Culver's, Domino's, Jimmy John's, LeeAnn Chin, Perkins, 🅞 Cub Foods, $Tree, Firestone/auto, Michael's, Radio Shack, TJ Maxx
245	White Bear Ave, **N** 🅖 BP, SA/dsl, 🍴 Subway, 🛏 La Quinta, Super 8, 🅞 Walgreens, **S** 🅖 BP, 🍴 Arby's, Davanni's Pizza/subs, KFC, McDonald's, Papa John's, Sonic, Taco Bell, Wendy's, 🅞 Aldi Foods, Byerly's Foods, Family$, NAPA, O'Reilly Parts, Target
244	US 10 E, US 61 S, Mounds/Kellogg
243	US 61, Mounds Blvd, **S** River Centre
242d	US 52 S, MN 3, 6th St, (exits left from wb), **N** 🅖 Holiday, 🍴 Subway
242c	7th St, **S** 🅖 SA
242b a	I-35E N, US 10 W, I-35E, S (from eb)
241c	I-35E, S (from wb)
241b	10th St, 5th St, to downtown
241a	12th St, Marion St, Kellogg Blvd, **N** 🛏 Best Western Kelly Inn, **S** St. Paul's Cathedral
240	Dale Ave
239b a	Lexington Pkwy, Hamline Ave, **N** 🅖 BP, SA, 🍴 Hardee's, 🅞 🅗, Cub Foods, K-Mart, Target, **S** 🅖 Holiday
238	Snelling Ave, **N** 🍴 Applebee's, McDonald's, Perkins, 🛏 Sheraton, 🅞 CVS Drug, Jo-Ann Fabrics, Rainbow Foods, Walgreens, same as 239

Exit	Services
237	Cretin Ave, Vandalia Ave, to downtown
236	MN 280, University Ave, to downtown
235b	Huron Blvd
235mm	Mississippi River
235a	Riverside Ave, 25th Ave, **N** 🅖 Winner, 🍴 Starbucks, **S** 🍴 Perkins, Taco Bell
234c	Cedar Ave, downtown
234b a	MN 55, Hiawatha Ave, 5th St, **N** 🛏 Holiday Inn, 🅞 to downtown
233b	I-35W N, I-35W, S (exits left from wb)
233a	11th St (from wb), **N** downtown
231b	Hennepin Ave, Lyndale Ave, to downtown
231a	I-394, US 12 W, to downtown
230	US 52, MN 55, 4th St, 7th St, Olson Hwy, **N** Metrodome, **S** 🅗, Int Mkt Square
229	W Broadway, Washington Ave, **N** 🅖 Old Colony/dsl, **S** 🅖 Winner, 🍴 Buger King, Little Caesar's, KFC, McDonald's, Subway, Taco Bell, Wendy's, 🅞 Cub Foods, Walgreens
228	Dowling Ave, N
226	53rd Ave N, 49th Ave, N
225	I-694 E, MN 252 N, to Minneapolis
34	to MN 100, Shingle Creek Pkwy, **N** 🍴 Denny's, Oak City Rest., Tango Mango, 🛏 AmericInn, Comfort Inn, Country Inn&Suites, Crowne Plaza, Days Inn, Extended Stay America, Motel 6, Super 8, **S** 🍴 C1 Buffet, Great India, Panera Bread, Perkins, 🛏 Embassy Suites, 🅞 AT&T, Best Buy, Curves, Kohl's, PepBoys, Target, Tires+
33	rd 152, Brooklyn Blvd, **N** 🅖 SA, Shell, 🍴 Culver's, Subway, 🅞 Buick/GMC, Chevrolet, Honda, **S** 🅖 BP, 🍴 Burger King, 🅞 Cub Foods, CVS Drug, Family$, Sun Foods, Walgreens
31	rd 81, Lakeland Ave, **N** 🅖 SA, Shell, 🍴 Beach House Grille, Chipotle Mexican, Wagner's Drive-In, Wendy's, 🛏 Ramada Inn, **S** 🛏 Best Value Inn, Budget Host
30	Boone Ave, **N** 🛏 La Quinta, Northland Inn/rest., **S** 🅞 Discount Tire, Home Depot
29b a	US 169, to Hopkins, Osseo
28	rd 61, Hemlock Lane, **N on Elm Creek** 🍴 Arby's/Sbarro's, Bella Sera, Benihana, Biaggi's Italian, Boston's Grill, Broadway Pizza, Buca Italian, CA Pizza Kitchen, Caribou Coffee, Champp's, Chipotle Mexican, ChuckeCheese, Coldstone, Dave&Buster's, Dickey's BBQ, Don Pablo's, El Rodeo Mexican, Famous Dave's BBQ, Granite City Rest., Herbert&Gerbert's Subs, Houlihan's, Jimmy John's, Leeann Chin, Noodles&Co, Old Country Buffet, Olive Garden, Panera Bread, Papa John's, PF Chang's, Pittsburgh Blue, Potbelly's, Qdoba, Red Lobster, Starbucks, TimberLodge Steaks, TGIFriday's, 🛏 Courtyard, Hampton Inn, Holiday Inn, Staybridge Suites, 🅞 URGENT CARE, Best Buy, Border's, Byerly's Foods, Costco/gas, Cub Foods, $Tree, Jo-Ann Fabrics, Kohl's, Lowe's, Marshall's, Michael's, Old Navy, PetCo, **S** 🅖 BP, 🍴 Perkins/24hr, 🛏 Select Inn
216	I-94 W and I-494
215	rd 109, Weaver Lake Rd, **N** 🅖 SA/dsl, 🍴 Bakers Square, Bella Sera, Broadway Pizza, Bucadibeppo, Burger King, Cattle Co Steaks, ChuckeCheese, DQ, Don Pablo, El Rodeo Mexican, Famous Dave's BBQ, Houlihan's, J Cousineau's Rest., KFC, Krispy Kreme, McDonald's, Old Country Buffet, Papa John's, Pizza Hut, Ricky Shawl's, Starbucks, Subway, Taco Bell, Timberlodge Steaks, Wendy's, 🅞 Barnes&Noble, Byerly's Foods, Cub Foods, Gander Mtn, GNC, Goodyear/auto, JC Penney, K-Mart,

MINNEAPOLIS

ST PAUL

INTERSTATE 94 CONT'D

Exit	Services
215	Continued
	Michael's, PetCo, Tires+, USPO, Walgreens, mall, same as 28, **S**🍴 Applebee's, Fuddrucker's
214mm	**rest area eb, full** 🦽 **facilities,** 🅲, 🏕, **litter barrels**
213	rd 30, 95th Ave, N Maple Grove, **N**🅶 SA/dsl, 🍴 Chipotle Mexican, Subway, 🛏 Cambria Suites, 🅾 H, Home Depot, Target, **S**🅶 Holiday/dsl, 🍴 Culver's, McDonald's, Orient Buffet, Quiznos, Subway, 🅾 Firestone, Goodyear/auto, Menards, Rainbow Foods, Sam's Club/gas, Walgreens, Walmart, KOA (2mi)
207	MN 101, to Elk River, Rogers, **N**🅶 Holiday, SA/dsl, TA/rest/dsl/scales/24hr/@, 🍴 Applebee's, Arby's, Burger King, Culver's, Davanni's Pizza, Denny's, Domino's, DQ, Jimmy John's, Maynard's, McDonald's, Noodles&Co, Subway, Taco Bell, Wendy's, 🛏 Hampton Inn, Sleep Inn, Super 8, 🅾 AT&T, Best Buy, Cabela's, Camping World, Cub Foods, Discount Tire, $Tree, Goodyear/auto, Kohl's, Lowe's, NAPA, O'Reilly Parts, Target, Tires+, Verizon, Walgreens, vet, **S**🅶 BP/dsl, Holiday, 🍴 Black Bear Rest., BoBo Asian, Cottage Grill, Guadalajara Mexican, 🛏 AmericInn, 🅾 URGENT CARE, Chevrolet, Curves, CVS Drug
205.5mm	Crow River
205	MN 241, rd 36, St Michael, **S**🅶 SA/dsl
202	rd 37, Albertville, **N**🅶 Hacks/dsl, Shell/dsl, **S**🅶 BP/dsl, Sunoco/dsl, same as 201
201	rd 19 (from eb), Albertville, St Michael, **N**🅶 Hack's/dsl, Shell/dsl, 🍴 Burger King, Jimmy's Pizza, Michael B's Grill, Perkins, 🛏 Country Inn&Suites, 🅾 Albertville Outlets/famous brands, Old Navy, **S**🅶 BP/dsl, Casey's, Mobil/Subway, Sunoco/dsl, 🍴 Caribou Coffee, China Dragon, Culver's, Major's Cafe, Papa Murphy's, Rancho Grande Mexican, Space Aliens Grill, Subway, 🅾 Ace Hardware, Coburn's Foods, Goodyear/auto, auto repair
194	rd 18, rd 39, Monticello, **N**🅶 Cruiser's/dsl, Marathon/dsl/E85, 🍴 Caribou Coffee, Little Caesar's, McDonald's, Taco Bell, 🅾 H, GNC, Home Depot, Petsmart, Target, Verizon
193	MN 25, to Buffalo, Monticello, Big Lake, **N**🅶 Holiday/dsl, 🍴 Burger King, Caribou Coffee, Guadalajara Mexican, KFC, Papa Murphy's, Perkins, Quiznos, Rancho Grande Mexican, Taco Bell, 🛏 AmericInn, 🅾 AutoValue Parts, Cub Foods, K-Mart, Monticello RV Ctr, Walgreens, USPO, **S**🅶 KwikTrip/dsl, Holiday/dsl, SA/dsl, Shell, 🍴 Applebee's, Arby's, Blue Stone Grill, Buffalo Wild Wings, Chatter's Grill, China Buffet, Culver's, DQ, McDonald's, Subway, Taco John's, 🛏 Best Western, Days Inn, Regency Inn, 🅾 Buick/GMC, Chevrolet, Goodyear/auto, O'Reilly Parts, Verizon, Walmart, vet, Lake Maria SP
187mm	**rest area eb, full** 🦽 **facilities,** 🅲, 🏕, **litter barrels, vending, petwalk**
183	rd 8, to Silver Creek, Hasty, Maple Lake, **S**🅶 BP/dsl/rest./scales/24hr/@, 🅾 to Lake Maria SP, camping
178	MN 24, to Annandale, Clearwater, **N**🅶 Holiday/Petro/dsl/scales/24hr/@, 🍴 Burger King, DQ, Jimmy's Pizza, Keith's Rest., Subway, Taco Gringo, 🛏 Best Value Inn, 🅾 GS Camping (1mi), Coburn's Foods, Parts City, TrueValue, repair, USPO, **S**🅾 RV Camping (1mi)
178mm	**rest area wb, full** 🦽 **facilities,** 🅲, 🏕, **litter barrels, petwalk, vending**
173	Opportunity Dr.
171	rd 7, rd 75, St Augusta, **N**🅶 ▨▨▨/McDonald's/dsl/scales/24hr, 🍴 MadeRite Grill, RJ's Grill, Subway,

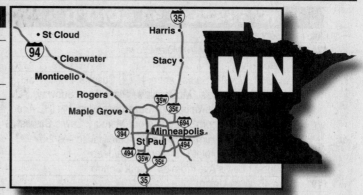

Exit	Services
171	Continued
	🛏 AmericInn, Holiday Inn Express, Travelodge, 🅾 H, Goodyear/auto, **S**🅾 Pleasureland RV Ctr
167b a	MN 15, to St Cloud, Kimball, **4 mi N**🅶 Holiday, SA/dsl, 🍴 Applebee's, Arby's, Bonanza, Buffalo Wild Wings, Burger King, Caribou Coffee, Domino's, Famous Dave's BBQ, 5 Guys Burgers, Granite City Grill, Grizzly's Grill, IHOP, La Casita Mexican, McDonald's, Noodles&Co, Old Chicago Pizza, Old Country Buffet, Olive Garden, Perkins, Pizza Hut, Pizza Ranch, Qdoba, Red Lobster, Sammy's Pizza, Starbucks, Subway, Taco John's, TGIFriday's, TimberLodge Steaks, Wendy's, 🛏 Country Inn&Suites, Days Inn, Fairfield Inn, Hampton Inn, Holiday Inn, Homewood Suites, Quality Inn, Super 8, 🅾 H, Barnes&Noble, Best Buy, CashWise Foods, Gander Mtn, Home Depot, JC Penney, Kohl's, K-Mart, Macy's, Michael's, Office Depot, Old Navy, Petsmart, Sam's Club, Scheel's Sports, Sears/auto, ShopKo, Subaru, Target, Walgreens, Walmart, USPO, **S**🅶 Shell/dsl (2mi)
164	MN 23, to St Cloud, Rockville, **N** Grande Depot Gourmet Foods, **4-6 mi N**🅶 Holiday, 🍴 Culver's, IHOP, KFC, Subway, Taco Bell, Wendy's, 🛏 Motel 6, 🅾 Discount Tire, Gander Mtn, Hyundai, Kia, Menards, Petsmart, Toyota/Scion
162.5mm	Sauk River
160	rd 2, to Cold Spring, St Joseph, **N**🅶 BP, 🛏 Super 8 (3mi), 🅾 Coll of St Benedict
158	rd 75 (from eb exits left), to St Cloud, **3 mi N** same as 160
156	rd 159, St Joseph, **N** St Johns U, no services
153	rd 9, Avon, **N**🅶 Shell/dsl, Tesoro/McDonald's/dsl, 🍴 Joseph's Rest., Subway, 🛏 Budget Host, 🅾 TrueValue, city park, 🏕, USPO, **S**🅾 El Rancho Manana Camping (10mi)
152mm	**rest area both lanes, full** 🦽 **facilities,** 🅲, 🏕, **litter barrels, vending, petwalk**
147	MN 238, rd 10, Albany, **N**🅶 Holiday/dsl/24hr, Shell/A&W/Subway/dsl, 🍴 Chesters, DQ, Godfather's Pizza, Hillcrest Rest., 🛏 Country Inn&Suites, 🅾 H, Amby's Foods, **S**🅾 Chrysler/Dodge/Jeep, NAPA
140	rd 11, Freeport, **N**🅶 Cenex/dsl, Freeport/dsl, 🍴 Ackie's Pioneer Rest., Charlie's Café, 🅾 Corner Store Foods, auto repair, USPO, vet
137	MN 237, rd 65, New Munich
137mm	Sauk River
135	rd 13, Melrose, **N**🅶 Clark/dsl/repair, Tesoro/Subway/dsl/24hr, 🍴 Burger King, 🅾 H, Ernie's Foods, NAPA, **S**🅶 Casey's/dsl, 🍴 DQ, El Portal Mexican, 🛏 Super 8, 🅾 Save Foods, vet
132.5mm	Sauk River

ST CLOUD (vertical side tab)

INTERSTATE 94 CONT'D

Exit	Services
131	MN 4, to Paynesville, Meire Grove
128mm	Sauk River
127	US 71, MN 28, Sauk Centre, **N** Casey's, Holiday/dsl, DQ, Hardee's, McDonald's, Pizza Hut, Subway, AmericInn, Best Value Inn, Guesthouse Inn, H, Ace Hardware, Coborn's Foods, Ford/Mercury, Lewis Ctr/rest area, NAPA, Walmart, **S** BP/café/dsl/scales/24hr/@, Buick/Chevrolet/Chrysler/Dodge/Jeep
124	Sinclair Lewis Ave (from eb), Sauk Centre
119	rd 46, West Union
114	MN 127, rd 3, to Westport, Osakis, **3 mi N** A&W, Subway, gas,
105mm	**rest area wb, full facilities, , , litter barrels, vending, petwalk**
103	MN 29, to Glenwood, Alexandria, **N** F&F/dsl, Holiday, Tesoro, Arby's, Burger King, Caribou Coffee, China Buffet, Culver's, Dolittle's Café, Dunn Bros Coffee, Godfather's Pizza, Great Hunan, Hardee's, Jimmy John's, KFC, McDonald's, Perkins, Subway, Taco Bell, TN Roadhouse, Wendy's, AmericInn, Days Inn, Motel USA, Super 8, H, Cadillac/Chevrolet/Mazda, County Mkt Foods, Goodyear/auto, Harley-Davidson, Jeep, K-Mart, Menards, Radio Shack, Target, Tires+, Walmart, **S** Holiday/dsl, Country Inn&Suites, Holiday Inn, Alexandria RV Ctr, Buick/GMC
100	MN 27, **N** Shell/Subway/dsl/scales, L Motel/RV Park, Skyline Motel, H, **S** camping
100mm	Lake Latoka
99mm	**rest area eb, full facilities, , , litter barrels, vending, petwalk**
97	MN 114, rd 40, to Lowry, Garfield
90	rd 7, Brandon, **S** camping, ski area
82	MN 79, rd 41, to Erdahl, Evansville, **2 mi N** BP/dsl, **S** H, camping
77	MN 78, rd 10, to Barrett, Ashby, **N** gas/dsl, Ruby's City Rest. (4mi), Prarie Cove Camping, **S** camping
69mm	**rest area wb, full facilities, , , litter barrels, petwalk, vending**
67	rd 35, Dalton, **N** camping, **S** camping
61	US 59 S, rd 82, to Elbow Lake, **N** Tesoro/café/dsl/LP/24hr, H, Pine Plaza RV Ctr, camping (4mi), **S** camping
60mm	**rest area eb, full facilities, , , litter barrels, petwalk, vending**
57	MN 210 E, rd 25, Fergus Falls, **N** H
55	rd 1, to Wendell, Fergus Falls
54	MN 210 W, Lincoln Ave, Fergus Falls, **N** Cenex/dsl, F&F/dsl, Holiday, Tesoro/dsl, Applebee's, Arby's, Burger King, Debbie's Kitchen, El Tequilas Mexican, KFC, McDonald's, Papa Murphy's, Perkins, Pizza Hut, Pizza Ranch, Subway, AmericInn, Best Western, Comfort Inn, Fergus Inn, Motel 7, Super 8, H, AT&T, CarQuest, Checker Parts, Chrysler/Dodge/Jeep, $Tree, Ford/Lincoln/Mercury, GMC, Herbergers, Home Depot, K-Mart, NAPA, O'Reilly Parts, SunMart Foods, Target, Tires+, Toyota, **S** Mabel Murphy's Rest., Walmart
50	rd 88, rd 52, to US 59, to Fergus Falls, Elizabeth, **N** NorthTown/dsl
38	rd 88, Rothsay, **S** Tesoro/cafe/dsl/24hr, Comfort Zone Inn, Tires

Exit	Services
32	MN 108, rd 30,to Pelican Rapids, Lawndale, **19 mi N** Maplewood SP
24	MN 34, Barnesville, **N** Renee's Drive-in, **1 mi S** Cenex/dsl, Tesoro/dsl, DQ, Subway, motel, Wagner Park Camping, city park
22	MN 9, Barnesville, **1 mi S** Cenex/dsl, Tesoro/dsl, DQ, Subway, motel
15	rd 10, Downer
8mm	Buffalo River
6	MN 336, rd 11, to US 10, Dilworth
5mm	**Red River weigh sta eb**
3	34th St, to Moorhead, **2 mi N** Tesoro, Arby's, McDonald's, Perkins, Pizza Ranch, Subway, Taco Bell, Travelodge, H, CVS Drug, K-Mart, KOA, Radio Shack, Target, Walmart
2	rd 52, Moorhead, **N** Menards, **S** antiques
2mm	**Welcome Ctr eb, full facilities, info, , , litter barrels, vending**
1b	20th St, Moorhead (from eb, no return)
1a	US 75, Moorhead, **N** Clark/dsl, Burger King, Papa Murphy's, Qdoba, Quiznos, Starbucks, Village Inn, Courtyard, Curves, SunMart Foods, **S** Casey's, Orton's Gas, DQ, Panchero's Mexican, Snapdragon Rest., Subway, AmericInn, Grand Inn, Super 8, CVS Drug, Kia, Loopy's $Store, TrueValue, Walgreens, vet
0mm	Minnesota/North Dakota state line, Red River

INTERSTATE 494/694

Exit	Services
	I-494/I-694 loops around Minneapolis/St Paul.
71	rd 31, Pilot Knob Rd, **N** Courtyard, Fairfield Inn, **S** Best Western, Crowne Plaza, LoneOak Café
70	I-35E, N to St Paul, S to Albert Lea
69	MN 149, MN 55, Dodd Rd, **N** Ziggy's Deli, **S** Caribou Coffee, McDonald's, Subway, Budget Host, Country Inn&Suites,
67	MN 3, Roberts St, **1 mi N** BP, Mobil, Holiday, Acre's Rest., Arby's/Sbarro's, Baker's Square, Buffalo Wings, Burger King, Chipotle Mexican, ChuckeCheese, Culver's, Grand Buffet, KFC, Old Country Buffet, Pizza Hut, Taco Bell, Timber Lodge Steaks, White Castle, Aamco, Best Buy, Buick, Checker Parts, Chevrolet, Cub Foods, Dodge, Ford, Jo-Ann Fabrics, Kia, K-Mart, Lincoln/Mercury, Mazda, NAPA, Nissan, Rainbow Foods/24hr, Target, Tires+, Toyota, VW, Walmart, **S** PDQ
66	US 52, **S** SA, Old World Pizza, Outback Steaks, Country Inn&Suites, Microtel
65	7th Ave, 5th Ave
64b a	MN 56, Concord St, **N** Conoco/dsl, Best Western Drovers, Ford Trucks, Goodyear, Peterbilt, **S** EZ Stop, Chrysler/Jeep/Dodge, Parts+
63mm	Mississippi River
63c	Maxwell Ave
63b a	US 10, US 61, to St Paul, Hastings, **S** BP, SA, Burger King, Subway, Boyd's Motel, NAPA
60	Lake Rd, **E** SA/dsl, **W** Country Inn&Suites
59	Valley Creek Rd, **E** BP/repair, SA/dsl/LP, America's Burger, Applebees, Broadway Pizza, Chipotle Mexican, DQ, Old Country Buffet, Papa Murphy's, Perkins, Potbelly's Rest., Yang's Chinese, Red Roof Inn, Barnes&Noble, Kohl's, Marshall's, Office Depot, PetCo, Rainbow Foods, Target, Walgreens, USPO, **W** PBQ, Bonfire Rest., Burger King, McDonald's, Pizza Hut, Subway, Hampton Inn, H, Ace Hardware, Goodyear

⛽ = gas   🍴 = food   🛏 = lodging   🅾 = other   **MINNESOTA 237**

INTERSTATE 494/694

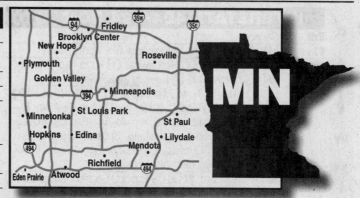

ST PAUL

E ↕ W

Exit	Services
58c	Tamarack Rd, **E** 🍴 Paisano's Cafe, Woodbury's Cafe, 🛏 Sheraton
58b a	I-94, E to Madison, W to St Paul.
	I-494 S begins/ends, I-694 N begins/ends
57	rd 10, 10th St N, **E** ⛽ SA 🍴 IHOP, Quizno's, 🛏 Wingate Inn, **W** ⛽ Holiday, 🍴 Burger King, Hunan Buffet, KFC, 🅾 $Tree, K-Mart, Rainbow Foods/24hr, mall, vet
55	MN 5, **E** 🅾 Target, **W** ⛽ Holiday/dsl, 🍴 Subway, 🅾 Menards, st patrol
52b a	MN 36, N St Paul, to Stillwater, **W** ⛽ F&F/dsl
51	MN 120, **E** ⛽ BP, SA/dsl, 🍴 Jethro's, Starbucks, **W** ⛽ Kellie's Corner/gas
50	White Bear Ave, **E** ⛽ SA, 🅾 K-Mart, Sam's Club/gas, **W** ⛽ BP, Shell, 🍴 Acupulco Chicken, Arby's, Bakers Square, Buffalo Wild Wings, Caribou Coffee, Chili's, Denny's, Great Moon Buffet, IHOP, Jake's Grill, Jimmy John's, KFC, McDonald's, Noodles&Co, North China, Old Country Buffet, Outback Steaks, Peiwei Asian, Perkins/24hr, Red Lobster, Taco Bell, TGI Friday, Wendy's, 🛏 Emerald Inn, 🅾 Aamco, Best Buy, Goodyear/auto, JC Penney, Jo-Ann Fabrics, Kohl's, Macy's, Marshall's, Michael's, PetCo, Sears/auto, Tires+, Tuesday Morning, Walgreens, mall
48	US 61 (from wb), **E** 🅾 Acura, Chrysler/Dodge/Jeep, Ford, Honda, Hyundai, Isuzu/Subaru, Lincoln/Mercury, **W** 🍴 Chili's, Gulden's Rest., McDonald's, Olive Garden, 🛏 Best Western, 🅾 🅷 Audi/Porsche, Lexus, Mercedes, Toyota, Venburg Tire, Volvo
47	I-35E, N to Duluth
46	I-35E, US 10, S to St Paul
45	rd 49, Rice St, **N** ⛽ Gas+, Marathon/dsl, 🍴 Papa John's, Subway, Taco Bell, 🅾 Checker Parts, **S** ⛽ Marathon/dsl, 🍴 A&W, Burger King, Caribou Coffee, Taco John's, 🅾 Kath Parts
43b	Victoria St, **S** Bill's Foods
43a	Lexington Ave, **N** 🍴 Greenmill Rest., Red Robin, 🛏 Hampton Inn, Hilton Garden, **S** ⛽ Exxon, Sinclair, 🍴 Blue Fox Grill, Burger King, Davanni's Pizza, Papa Murphy's, Perkins, Subway, Wendy's, 🛏 Holiday Inn, Super 8, 🅾 Cub Foods, Goodyear/auto, Target, transmissions
42b	US 10, W (from wb), to Anoka
42a	MN 51, Snelling Ave, **1 mi S** ⛽ Shell, 🍴 Flaherty's Grill, Lindey's Steaks, McDonald's, 🛏 Country Inn&Suites, Holiday Inn
41b a	I-35W, S to Minneapolis, N to Duluth
40	Long Lake Rd, 10th St NW
39	Silver Lake Rd, **N** ⛽ BP, 🍴 Acupulco Mexican, Champps, McDonald's, Subway, 🅾 Fairview Drug, Ford, U-Haul
38b a	MN 65, Central Ave, **N** ⛽ Holiday/dsl, 🍴 Subway, **S** ⛽ SA, SuperStop, 🍴 A&W/KFC, Applebee's, Asia Rest., Big Marina Deli, Buffalo Wild Wings, Flameburger Rest., La Casita Mexican, McDonald's, Mr BBQ, Papa John's, Ricky's, Sonic, Subway, Taco Bell, Wendy's, White Castle, 🛏 LivInn Hotel, 🅾 Advance Parts, AutoZone, $General, Discount Tire, Menards, O'Reilly Parts, PetCo, Rainbow Foods, Target, Tires+, Walgreens, vet
37	rd 47, University Ave, **N** ⛽ Holiday, SA/dsl, 🍴 Burger King, McDonald's, Papa Murphy's Pizza, Zantigo's Rest., 🅾 Cub Foods, CVS Drug, Goodyear, Home Depot, **S** ⛽ Bona Bros/repair, Shell
36	E River Rd
35mm	**I-494 W begins/ends. I-694 E begins/ends.**

MINNEAPOLIS

MINNEAPOLIS

Exit	Services
35c	MN 252, **N** ⛽ Holiday, SA
35b a	I-94, E to Minneapolis
34	to MN 100, Shingle Creek Pkwy, **N** 🍴 Denny's, Oak City Rest., Tango Mango, 🛏 AmericInn, Comfort Inn, Country Inn&Suites, Crowne Plaza, Days Inn, Extended Stay America, Motel 6, Super 8, **S** 🍴 C1 Buffet, Great India, Panera Bread, Perkins, 🛏 Embassy Suites, 🅾 AT&T, Best Buy, Curves, Kohl's, PepBoys, Target, Tires+
33	rd 152, Brooklyn Blvd, **N** ⛽ SA, Shell, 🍴 Culver's, Subway, 🅾 Buick/GMC, Chevrolet, Honda, **S** ⛽ BP, 🍴 Burger King, 🅾 Cub Foods, CVS Drug, Family$, Sun Foods, Walgreens
31	rd 81, Lakeland Ave, **N** ⛽ SA, Shell, 🍴 Beach House Grille, Chipotle Mexican, Wagner's Drive-In, Wendy's, 🛏 Ramada Inn, **S** 🛏 Best Value Inn, Budget Host
30	Boone Ave, **N** 🛏 La Quinta, Northland Inn/rest., **S** 🅾 Discount Tire, Home Depot
29b a	US 169, to Hopkins, Osseo
28	rd 61, Hemlock Lane, **N on Elm Creek** 🍴 Arby's/Sbarro's, Bella Sera, Benihana, Biaggi's Italian, Boston's Grill, Broadway Pizza, Buca Italian, CA Pizza Kitchen, Caribou Coffee, Champp's, Chipotle Mexican, ChuckeCheese, Coldstone, Dave&Buster's, Dickey's BBQ, Don Pablo's, El Rodeo Mexican, Famous Dave's BBQ, Granite City Rest., Herbert&Gerbert's Subs, Houlihan's, Jimmy John's, Leeann Chin, Noodles&Co, Old Country Buffet, Olive Garden, Panera Bread, Papa John's, PF Chang's, Pittsburgh Blue, Potbelly's, Qdoba, Red Lobster, Starbucks, TimberLodge Steaks, TGIFriday's, 🛏 Courtyard, Hampton Inn, Holiday Inn, Staybridge Suites, 🅾 URGENT CARE, Best Buy, Border's, Byerly's Foods, Costco/gas, Cub Foods, $Tree, Jo-Ann Fabrics, Kohl's, Lowe's, Marshall's, Michael's, Old Navy, PetCo, **S** ⛽ BP, 🍴 Perkins/24hr, 🛏 Select Inn
27	I-94, W to St Cloud, I-94/694, E to Minneapolis
26	rd 10, Bass Lake Rd, **E** ⛽ Freedom, 🍴 Caribou Coffee, Culver's, McDonald's, Subway, 🛏 Extended Stay America, 🅾 mall, vet, **W** ⛽ BP, Marathon/dsl, 🍴 Dunn Bro's Cofee, Milio's Sandwiches, Pancake House, Pizza Hut, 🛏 Hilton Garden, 🅾 CVS Drug
23	rd 9, Rockford Rd, **E** ⛽ Holiday, 🍴 Chili's, Peony's Chinese, 🅾 GNC, O'Reilly Parts, PetsMart, Rainbow Foods, Target, TJ Maxx, Walgreens, vet, **W** ⛽ PDQ, 🍴 Cousins Subs, DQ, LeAnn Chin, Panchero's, Subway
22	MN 55, **E** ⛽ Holiday/dsl, 🍴 Broadway Pizza, Caribou Coffee, Green Mill Rest., Jimmy John's, McDonald's, Red Robin, Solos Pizza, Starbucks, 🛏 Best Western Kelly, Radisson, Red Roof Inn, Residence Inn, **W** ⛽ Holiday/dsl, 🍴 Arby's, Burger King, Davanni's Rest., Jake's Rest., Perkins, Wendy's, 🛏 Comfort Inn, Days Inn, 🅾 Goodyear/auto, Tires+

MN

🅖 = gas 🍴 = food 🛏 = lodging 🅞 = other   Copyright 2012 - The Next Exit®

INTERSTATE 494/694 CONT'D

Exit	Services
21	rd 6, **E** 🅖 KwikTrip, 🅞 Discount Tire, Home Depot
20	Carlson Pkwy, **E** 🅖 Holiday/dsl, 🍴 Pizza Hut, Subway, **W** 🍴 Woody's Grill, 🛏 Country Inn&Suites
19b a	I-394 E, US 12 W, to Minneapolis, **1 mi E** off of I-394 🍴 Applebee's, Wendy's, 🅞 Barnes&Noble, Best Buy, By- erly's Foods, Ford, JC Penney, Jo-Ann Fabrics, Mazda, Mazerati, Mercedes, Sears/auto, Subaru, Target, Tires+, 1/2 mi, **W** 🅖 BP, Holiday, 🍴 KFC, McDonald's, 🅞 BMW, Chevrolet, Lexus, Mitsubishi, Nissan
17b a	Minnetonka Blvd, **W** 🅖 US Gas, 🍴 Cousin's Subs, Dunn Bros Coffee
16b a	MN 7, **1 mi W** 🅖 Marathon, 🍴 Christo's Rest., Davanni's Rest., Famous Dave's BBQ, Taco Bell, 🅞 Goodyear
13	MN 62, rd 62
12	Valleyview Rd, rd 39 (from sb)
11c	MN 5 W, same as 11 a b
11b a	US 169 S, US 212 W, **N** 🍴 Don Pablo, Subway, 🛏 Court- yard, Fairfield Inn, Hampton Inn, Hyatt Place, Residence Inn, **S** 🅖 BP, Marathon, Holiday, 🍴 Caribou Coffee, Da- vanni's Rest., Fuddruckers, Jake's Grill, Jason's Deli, KFC, Leeann Chin, Old Chicago, Panera Bread, Papa John's, Qdoba, Starbucks, 🛏 Best Western, Discount Tire, Homestead Suites, SpringHill Suites, JC Penney, Office Depot, Sears/auto, Target, Walgreens, Walmart
10	US 169 N, to rd 18
8	rd 28 (from wb, no return), E Bush Lake Rd, same as 7 a b
7b a	MN 100, rd 34, Normandale Blvd, **N** 🅖 Shell/dsl, 🍴 Burger King, Caribou Coffee, Chili's, DQ, Subway, TGIFri- day, 🛏 Days Inn, Sheraton, Sofatel, **S** 🍴 Oak City Rest., 🛏 Country Inn&Suites, Crowne Plaza, Hilton Garden, La Quinta, Staybridge Inn
6b	rd 17, France Ave, **N** 🅖 Mobil, 🍴 Cattle Co Rest., Chuck- eCheese, Fuddrucker's, Hot Wok, Macaroni Grill, McDon- ald's, Perkins, Quizno's, 🛏 Best Western, Le Bourget, Park Plaza Hotel, 🅞 H, Michael's, Office Depot, **S**

Exit	Services
6b	Continued 🍴 Denny's, Joe Senser's Grill, Olive Garden, 🛏 Hamp- ton Inn, Hilton, 🅞 Buick/GMC, Ford, Mercedes, Nissan, Toyota/Scion
6a	Penn Ave (no EZ eb return), **N** 🛏 Residence Inn, 🅞 Best Buy, Buick, Hyundai, Isuzu, **S** 🍴 Applebee's, Atlantic Buffet, McDonald's, Starbucks, Steak&Ale, Subway, 🛏 Embassy Suites, 🅞 Chevrolet, Chrysler/Jeep/Plymouth, Dodge, Hancock Fabrics, Herberger's, Kohl's, Rainbow Foods, Target, TJ Maxx
5b a	I-35W, S to Albert Lea, N to Minneapolis
4b	Lyndale Ave, **N** 🍴 Boston Mkt, Chipotle Mexican, Don Pablo's, DQ, Eddie Cheng's, Papa John's, Subway, 🛏 Candlewood Suites, Hampton Inn, Ramada Inn, 🅞 Best Buy, Honda, Lands End, PetsMart, Tires+, **S** 🛏 Extended Stay America, 🅞 Lincoln/Mercury, Mazda, Subaru
4a	MN 52, Nicollet Ave, **N** 🅖 SA/dsl, 🍴 Burger King, Em- ber's, Rest, Jumbo Chinese, 🛏 Candlewood Suites, 🅞 Honda, Menards, **S** 🅖 Mobil, Shell, 🍴 Culver's, Kwik Mart, Big Boy, McDonald's, 🛏 La Quinta, Super 8, 🅞 Home Depot, Sam's Club
3	Portland Ave, 12th Ave, **N** 🅖 Phillips 66, Sinclair, PDQ Mart, 🍴 Arby's, 🛏 AmericInn, **S** 🅖 BP, 🍴 Denny's, Out- back Steaks, Subway, 🛏 Comfort Inn/rest., Holiday Inn Express, Microtel, Quality Inn, Residence Inn, Travelodge, 🅞 Walgreens, Walmart
2c b	MN 77, **N** 🛏 Motel 6, **S** 🅖 BP, SA, 🛏 AmeriSuites, Best Western, Courtyard, Embassy Suites, Exel Inn, Fairfield Inn, Grand Motel, Marriott, Sheraton, 🅞 Nordstrom's, Sears, Mall of America
2a	24th Ave, same as 2c b
1b	34th Ave, Nat Cemetary, **S** 🛏 Embassy Suites, Hilton, Holiday Inn
1a	MN 5 E, **N** 🅞
0mm	Minnesota River. I-494/I-694 loops around Minneapolis/ St Paul.

MISSISSIPPI

INTERSTATE 10

Exit	Services
77mm	Mississippi/Alabama state line, **weigh sta wb**
75	Franklin Creek Rd
75mm	**Welcome Ctr wb, full** ♿ **facilities,** ⓒ, 🚻, **litter bar- rels, petwalk, RV dump, weigh sta eb**
74mm	Escatawpa River
69	MS 63, to, E Moss Point, **N** 🅖 Raceway, Texaco/Dom- ino's/dsl/24hr, 🍴 Waffle House, 🛏 Best Value, Deluxe Inn, La Quinta, **S** 🅖 Chevron/dsl, Cone/dsl, Exxon/ Subway/24hr, Shell, 🍴 Barnhill's Buffet, Burger King, Cracker Barrel, Hardee's, KFC, McDonald's, Pizza Hut, Ruby Tuesday, San Miguel Mexican, Waffle House, Wen- dy's, 🛏 Best Western, Comfort Inn, Days Inn, Hampton Inn, Holiday Inn Express, Quality Inn, Shular Inn, 🅞 H
68	MS 613, to Moss Point, Pascagoula, **N** 🅖 BP, Chevron/ dsl, 🍴 Coco Loco, 🛏 Super 8, **S** 🅖 BP/dsl, 🅞 H
64mm	Pascagoula River
63.5mm	**rest area both lanes, full** ♿ **facilities,** ⓒ, 🚻, **litter barrels, petwalk, RV dump, 24hr security**
61	to Gautier, **N** 🅞 MS Nat Golf Course, **1-3 mi S** 🅖 BP/ dsl, 🍴 Hardee's, KFC, McDonald's, Pizza Hut, Wendy's, 🛏 Best Western, Suburban Lodge, 🅞 Shephard

Exit	Services
61	Continued Camping, Sandhill Crane WR
57	MS 57, to Vancleave, **N** 🅖 Chevron/dsl, 🍴 Shed BBQ, 🅞 Journey's End Camping, tires, **S** 🅖 Exxon, 🅞 H
50	MS 609 S, Ocean Springs, **N** 🅖 Texaco/Domino's/dsl, 🍴 Waffle House, 🛏 Best Western, Comfort Inn, Country Inn&Suites, Motel 6, Ramada Ltd, Scottish Inn, Super 8, 🅞 Martin Lake Camping (1mi), **S** 🅖 BP/dsl, Chevron/ McDonald's, Kangaroo/Subway/dsl, 🍴 Denny's, Lil Italy, Waffle House, Wendy's, 🛏 Comfort Inn, Days Inn, Hamp- ton Inn, Holiday Inn Express, Howard Johnson, Quality Inn, 🅞 $General, Family$, Nat Seashore, vet
46b a	I-110, MS 15 N, to Biloxi, **N** 🍴 Beef O'Brady's, Beijing Chinese, Buffalo Wild Wings, Chick-fil-A, Chili's, China Town, 5 Guys Burgers, Fox's Pizza, Logan's Road- house, Moe's SW Grill, Olive Garden, Outback Steaks, Papa John's, Red Lobster, Ruby Tuesday, Samurai, Sonic, Strami's Italian, Subway, Waffle House, Wendy's, Whataburger, 🛏 Courtyard, Regency Inn, Wingate Inn, 🅞 AT&T, Best Buy, Dick's, Kohl's, Lowe's, Marshalls, Of- fice Depot, PetsMart, Radio Shack, Target, Tire Kingdom, Verizon, Walgreens, Walmart, **S** 🅞 H, to beaches
44	Cedar Lake Rd, to Biloxi, **N** 🅖 Loves/Subway/dsl/ scales/24hr, 🅞 Chevrolet, **S** 🅖 Chevron/dsl, Shell/dsl,

INTERSTATE 10 CONT'D

Exit	Services
44	Continued 🍴 Applebee's, El Saltillo, KFC/LJ Silver, McDonald's, Red Eye Grill, Sonic, Subway, Waffle House, Wow Cafe, 🛏 La Quinta, 🅾 🏥 $General, Harley-Davidson, Home Depot, O'Reilly Parts, to Jeff Davis Shrine (Beauvoir), Biloxi Nat Cem
41	MS 67 N, to Woolmarket, N 🅿 Chevron/dsl, Texaco/dsl, 🅾 golf (6mi), S Mazalea RV Prk, Parkers Landing RV Prk
39.5mm	Biloxi River
38	Lorraine-Cowan Rd, N 🅿 Exxon/Subway, Kangaroo/dsl, 🍴 Capt Al's Cafe, Domino's, McDonald's, Sonic, 🅾 Toyota/Scion, S 🅿 Pure/dsl, 🅾 🏥 Baywood RV Park (3mi), Foxes RV Park (8mi), to beaches
34b a	US 49, to Gulfport, N 🅿 Exxon, Kangaroo/dsl, Texaco/dsl, 🍴 Backyard Burger, Barnhill's Buffet, Beef O'Brady's, Burger King, Cane's Chicken, Chick-fil-A, Chili's, ChuckeCheese, CiCi's Pizza, Cracker Barrel, Domino's, Golden Corral, Hardee's, KFC, Krystal, Little Caesars, Logan's Roadhouse, Longhorn Steaks, McDonald's, Newk's Cafe, O'Charley's, Panda Palace, Papa John's, Pizza Hut, Pepper's Deli, Popeye's, Sonic, Starbucks, Subway, Taco Bell, Taco Sombrero, TGIFriday's, Waffle House, Wendy's, Whataburger, 🅾 Advance Parts, Barnes&Noble, Belk, Best Buy, Buick/Cadillac/Chevrolet, CVS Drug, $General, Foley's RV Ctr, Food Giant/gas, Fred's Store, Goodyear/auto, Honda, K-Mart, Michael's, Office Depot, Old Navy, Petsmart, Radio Shack, Rite Aid, Ross, Sam's Club/gas, Tire Kingdom, TJ Maxx, USPO, Walgreens, Winn-Dixie, urgent care, S 🅿 Chevron, Kangaroo/dsl, Murphy USA, RaceTrac, RaceWay/dsl, Shell/dsl, 🍴 Applebee's, Arby's/24hr, Burger King, Choung's Garden, Hooters, IHOP, KFC/LJ Silver, Krispy Kreme, Los Tres Amigos, McAlister's Deli, McDonald's, Morelia's Mexican, Sonic, Subway, Waffle House, Wendy's, 🛏 Best Value, Best Western, Comfort Suites, Days Inn, EconoLodge, Fairfield Inn, Hampton Inn, Holiday Inn, Motel 6, Quality Inn, Ramada, Sun Suites, Value Place, 🅾 🏥 Ford/Lincoln/Mercury, Freightliner, Home Depot, Kia, Mazda, Michael's, Nissan, Premium Outlets/famous brands, Verizon, Walmart/McDonald's, transmissions
31	Canal Rd, to Gulfport, N 🅿 Clarks/Subway/dsl, 🅾 Bayberry RV Park, S 🅿 ✈FLYING J/Denny's/dsl/LP/scales/24hr, Shell/McDonald's/dsl/24hr, 🍴 Waffle House, Wendy's, 🛏 Legacy Inn, Magnolia Bay Inn, 🅾 Plantation Pines RV Prk
28	to Long Beach, S 🅿 Chevron/dsl, Shell/dsl, 🍴 Subway, 🅾 RV camping, tires
27mm	Wolf River
24	Menge Ave, N🅿 Chevron/Subway/dsl/scales, 🅾 $General, S 🅿 Texaco, 🅾 flea mkt/RV Park, golf, to beaches
20	to De Lisle, to Pass Christian, N 🅿 Kin-Mart
16	Diamondhead, N 🅿 Chevron/dsl, Shell/Domino's, 🍴 Burger King, DQ, Lenny's Subs, Red Zone Grill, Subway, Waffle House, 🛏 Diamondhead Resort, 🅾 Ace

Exit	Services
16	Continued Hardware, Diamondhead Drug, Rouse's Mkt, repair, urgent care, USPO, S🍴 Hula's Grill, 🛏 EconoLodge
15mm	Jourdan River
13	MS 43, MS 603, to Kiln, Bay St Louis, N McLeod SP, S 🅿 Bay Fuel/dsl, Exxon/Subway/dsl, Pure, 🛏 Knights Inn (6mi), 🅾 🏥 RV Camping (8-13mi)
10mm	weigh sta, eb
2	MS 607, to Waveland, NASA Test Site, S Welcome Ctr both lanes, full ♿ facilities, 🔌, 🛒, litter barrels, RV dump, petwalk, 24hr security, Buccaneer SP, camping, to beaches
1mm	weigh sta, wb
0mm	Mississippi/Louisiana state line, Pearl River

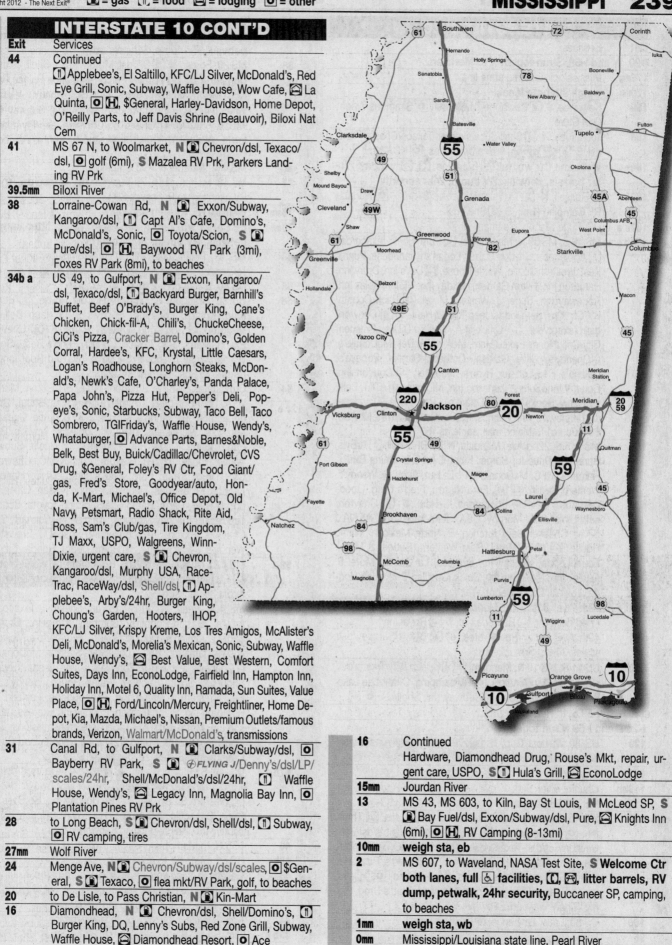

🅖 = gas 🍴 = food 🏨 = lodging 🅞 = other Copyright 2011 - The Next Ex

MS

INTERSTATE 20

Exit	Services
	I-20, W and I-59, S run together to Meridian.
172mm	Mississippi/Alabama state line
170mm	**weigh sta both lanes**
169	Kewanee, S 🅖Kewanee Trkstp/dsl, 🅞 Simmons Wright Gen Store
165	Toomsuba, N 🅖 Shell/Subway/24hr, Texaco/ChesterFried/dsl, S 🅖 ⬤Loves/Arby's/dsl/scales, 🅞 KOA (2mi)
164mm	**Welcome Ctr wb, full ♿ facilities, 🅒, 🏨, vending, litter barrels, petwalk, RV dump, 24hr security**
160	to Russell, N 🅖TA/dsl/rest./scales/24hr/@, 🅞 Nanabe RV Camping (1mi), S 🅖Shell/dsl
157b a	US 45, to Macon, Quitman
154b a	MS 19 S, MS 39 N, Meridian, N 🅖 Pure, Shell, Texaco/dsl, 🍴 Applebee's, Cracker Barrel, Logan's Roadhouse, Penn's Rest, Western Sizzlin, Waffle House, 🏨 Days Inn, Drury Inn, Hampton Inn, Hilton Garden, Holiday Inn, NE Inn, Relax Inn, Rodeway Inn, Super 8, Western Motel, 🅞 Back Country RV Ctr, Chrysler/Dodge/Jeep/Kia, U-Haul, S 🅖 Chevron/dsl, Texaco/dsl, 🍴 Chick-fil-A, Chili's, CiCi's, Crescent City Grill, Honey Baked Ham, McAlister's Deli, McDonald's, O'Charley's, Olive Garden, Outback Steaks, Popeye's, Quizno's, Red Lobster, Ryan's, Taco Bell, 🏨 Comfort Inn, Country Inn&Suites, Jameson Inn, Microtel, 🅞 AT&T, Belk, Best Buy, BooksAMillion, Dillard's, $Tree, Harley-Davidson, JC Penney, Jo-Ann Fabrics, PetCo, Ross, Sam's Club/gas, Sears/auto, TJ Maxx, mall, same as 153
153	MS 145 S, 22nd Ave, Meridian, N 🅖 BP, Shell, 🍴 Arby's, Bumper's Drive-In, Burger King, Capt D's, China Buffet, Hardee's, KFC, McDonald's, Pizza Hut, Subway, Wendy's, Western Sizzlin, 🅞 🄷, Ford/Nissan, Fred's Drug, Goodyear/auto, SavRite Foods/gas, U-Haul, S 🅖 Chevron/dsl, Exxon/dsl, Murphy USA, Texaco/dsl, 🍴 A&W/LJ Silver, Checkerboard Kitchen, El Norte Mexican, Waffle House, 🏨 Astro Motel, Best Western, Budget 8 Motel, EconoLodge, Holiday Inn Express, La Quinta, Motel 6, Quality Inn, Sleep Inn, 🅞 Buick, Cadillac/Chevrolet, Honda, Lowe's, Office Depot, Walmart
152	29th Ave, 31st Ave, Meridian, N 🅖 Chevron/ChesterFried/dsl/24hr, 🏨 Ramada Ltd, S 🏨 Royal Inn
151	49th Ave, Valley Rd, N 🅖 tires, S 🅖 ⬤Loves/Subway/dsl/scales/24hr, 🅞 stockyards
150	US 11 S, MS 19 N, Meridian, N 🅖Queen City Trkstp/dsl/rest./@, 🍴 McDonald's, 🅞RV camping, Okatibbee Lake, S 🅖Chevron/Stuckey's/Subway/dsl, Shell/dsl 🅞🄴
130 [149]	I-59 S, to Hattiesburg.
	I-20 E and I-59 N run together.
129	US 80 W, Lost Gap, S 🅖 Spaceway/Grill King/dsl/RV Dump/24hr
121	Chunky
119mm	Chunky River
115	MS 503, Hickory
109	MS 15, Newton, N 🅖 Shell/Wendy's/dsl/24hr, 🏨 Thrifty Inn, 🅞 lube/repair, S 🅖 BP, Chevron/Quizno's/dsl/24hr, Newton Jct/dsl, Texaco/dsl, 🍴 Cooks BBQ, El Parrillero Mexican, Hardee's, KFC/Taco Bell, McDonald's, Pizza Hut, Sonic, Subway, Zack's Steaks, 🏨 Days Inn, 🅞 🄷, Advance Parts, AT&T, AutoZone, $General, Fred's Drug, Piggly Wiggly, Walmart/Subway
100	US 80, Lake, Lawrence, N 🅖BP/rest/dsl
96	Lake

95mm	Bienville Nat Forest, eastern boundary
90mm	**rest area eb, full ♿ facilities, 🅒, 🏨, litter barrels, petwalk, RV dump, 24hr security**
88	MS 35, Forest, N 🅖 BP/dsl, Murphy USA, Shell, Texaco/Domino's/dsl, 🍴 Garden Patch Rest, Jade Palace Rest, KFC, McDonald's, Popeye's, Taco Bell, Wendy's, 🏨 Best Value Inn, Days Inn, EconoLodge, Holiday Inn Express, 🅞 🄷, AutoZone, Buick/Chevrolet/GMC, $Tree, O'Reilly Parts, Walgreens, Walmart, S 🅖 Chevron/dsl/24hr, 🍴 Penn's Rest.
80	MS 481, Morton, S RV Camping
77	MS 13, Morton, N 🅖 77 Truck Ctr/dsl, Texaco/dsl, 🅞🄷, RV camping, to Roosevelt SP
76mm	Bienville NF, western boundary
75mm	**rest area wb, full ♿ facilities, 🅒, 🏨, litter barrels, petwalk, RV dump, 24hr security**
68	MS 43, Pelahatchie, N 🅖 Chevron/Subway/dsl/24hr, Texaco/dsl/rest./24hr, 🅞 RV camping, S 🅖BP/dsl
59	US 80, E Brandon, 2 mi S 🅖 Texaco
56	US 80, Brandon, N 🅖 Shell/Huddle House, 🍴 Burger King, Krystal, Popeye's, Sonny's BBQ, Taco Bell, 🏨 Microtel, 🅞 AutoZone, O'Reilly Parts, S 🅖 Chevron, Exxon, Mac's Gas, Texaco, 🍴 DQ, Penn's Rest., Sonic, Waffle House, Wendy's, 🏨 Days Inn, Red Roof Inn, 🅞 Parts+, to Ross Barnett Reservoir
54	Crossgates Blvd, W Brandon, N 🅖 BP, Exxon, Murphy USA, 🍴 Applebee's, Burger King, China Buffet, Dragon Palace, Fernando's Mexican, KFC, Little Caesar's, Mazzio's, McAlister's Deli, McDonald's, Nuwk's Rest, Papa John's, Pizza Hut, Popeye's, Quizno's, Subway, Waffle House, 🅞 🄷, BigLots, Buick/GMC, Chevrolet, CVS Drug, $Tree, Ford, Fred's Drug, GNC, Hancock Fabrics, Kroger/gas, Lincoln/Mercury, Nissan, Office Depot, O'Reilly Parts, Radio Shack, Scion/Toyota, Scotty's Tire/repair, Tuesday Morning, Walgreens, Walmart, S 🅖 Chevron, Exxon, Texaco/Domino's/dsl, 🍴 Brewsters, Wendy's, 🏨 La Quinta, 🅞 Home Depot, Honda
52	MS 475, N 🅖 Chevron/dsl, Texaco/dsl, 🍴 Waffle House, 🏨 Quality Inn, Ramada Ltd, Sleep Inn, Super 8, 🅞 Peterbilt, to Jackson 🄴
48	MS 468, Pearl, N 🅖 BP, Exxon, Shell/dsl, Texaco, 🍴 Arby's, Baskin-Robbins, Bumpers Drive-In, Cracker Barrel, Domino's, Dunkin Donuts, El Charro's Mexican, Jose's Tamales, KFC, LoneStar Steaks, McDonald's, O'Charley's, Pizza Hut, Popeye's, Ruby Tuesday, Ryan's, Shoney's, Sonic, Subway, Waffle House, Wendy's, 🏨 Best Western, Comfort Inn, EconoLodge, Fairfield Inn, Hampton Inn, Hilton Garden, Holiday Inn Express, Jameson Inn, Motel 6, 🅞 AT&T, CarCare, transmissions, S 🅖 Chevron/dsl/24hr, Huff/dsl/24hr, 🏨 Candlewood Suites, Country Inn&Suites, La Quinta, 🅞 $General
47b a	US 49 S, Flowood, N 🅖 ⊕FLYING J/Denny's/dsl/LP/RV dump/24hr, ⬤Loves/Chester's/Subway/dsl/24hr, 🍴 Western Sizzlin, 🏨🄴 Inn, Holiday Inn, 🅞 Bass Pro Shop, SpeedCo, 2-3 mi S 🍴 DQ, Waffle House, 🏨 Executive Inn, 🅞 Freightliner, Kenworth, tires
46	I-55 N, to Memphis
45b	US 51, State St, to downtown
45a	Gallatin St, to downtown, N 🅖BP, Petro/dsl/rest./24hr/@, Shell, 🅞 Blue Beacon, tires/truck repair, vet, S 🅖⬤Loves/McDonald's/dsl, 🏨 Hilltop Inn, 🅞 Nissan
44	I-55, S (exits left from wb), to New Orleans
43b a	Terry Rd, N 🅖 Exxon/dsl, Jasco, 🍴 Krystal, 🅞 S&S RV Ctr

INTERSTATE 20 CONT'D

Exit	Services
42b a	Ellis Ave, Belvidere, **N** 🚗 BP, Shell, 🍴 Capt D's, Church's, McDonald's, Pizza Hut, Popeye's, Rally's, Sonny's BBQ, Wendy's, 🛏 Best Inn, Days Inn, Deluxe Inn, Metro Inn, Super 8, 🅾 Advance Parts, AutoZone, Family$, Firestone, Kia, O'Reilly Parts, Sav-a-Lot Foods, U-Haul, transmissions, zoo, **S** 🚗 Exxon/dsl, QuickPay, 🍴 DQ
41	I-220 N, US 49 N, to Jackson
40b a	MS 18 W, Robinson Rd, **N** 🚗 BP, Exxon/dsl, Shell/dsl, 🍴 Arby's, China Buffet, Krystal, Mazzio's, Piccadilly's, Popeye's, 🅾 Office Depot, Sears/auto, auto repair, **S** 🚗 Chevron/Chester's, Murphy USA, Shell/dsl, 🍴 Chan's Garden, Church's, IHOP, McDonald's, Waffle House, Wendy's, 🛏 Comfort Inn, 🅾 H, $Tree, GNC, Lowes, Radio Shack, Walmart
36	Springridge Rd, Clinton, **N** 🚗 Chevron/Burger King, Murphy USA, Orbit Gas, Shell, 🍴 Capt D's, Chick-fil-A, DQ, El Sombrero, KFC, Little Ceasar's, Mazzio's, McAlister's, McDonald's, Newk's Cafe, Sonic, Starbucks, Subway, Taco Bell, Waffle House, Wendy's, Zaxby's, 🛏 Clinton Inn, Comfort Inn, Days Inn, 🅾 Advance Parts, $Tree, Home Depot, Kroger/gas, O'Reilly Parts, Radio Shack, Walgreens, Walmart (2mi), **S** 🚗 Exxon/Baskin-Robbins/Quizno's, Texaco/dsl, 🍴 Applebee's, Corky's BBQ, Egg Head Grill, Pizza Hut, Popeye's, Salsa's Mexican, Shoney's, 🛏 Best Western, Econolodge, Hampton Inn, Holiday Inn Express, Quality Inn, 🅾 Curves, Davis Tire, Springridge RV Park, vet
35	US 80 E, Clinton, **N** 🚗 Chevron/dsl, Texaco/dsl, Shell/dsl
34	Natchez Trace Pkwy
31	Norrell Rd
27	Bolton, **S** 🚗 Chevron/dsl/24hr
19	MS 22, Edwards, Flora, **N** 🅾 RV Camping (2mi), **S** gas/dsl
17mm	Big Black River
15	Flowers
11	Bovina, **N** 🚗 Texaco/Subway/dsl/24hr, 🅾 RV camping
10mm	weigh sta wb
8mm	weigh sta eb
6.5mm	parking area eb
5b a	US 61, MS 27 S, **N** 🚗 Exxon, Kangaroo/dsl, 🍴 Sonic, **S** same as 4a
4b a	Clay St, **N** 🚗 Kangaroo, Texaco, 🍴 KFC, Pizza Hut, 🛏 Battlefield Inn, Hampton Inn, Motel 6, Quality Inn, 🅾 H, RV Park, to Vicksburg NP, **S** 🚗 Texaco/Domino's/dsl, 🍴 Bumper's Drive-In, China Buffet, Cracker Barrel, Pizza Inn, McAlister's deli, Rowdy's Rest., Waffle House, 🛏 Beechwood Inn/rest., Comfort Suites, Courtyard, Econolodge, Holiday Inn Express, Jameson Inn, La Quinta, Scottish Inn, 🅾 Chrysler/Jeep, $General, Outlet Mall/famous brands/deli, Toyota, same as 5
3	Indiana Ave, **N** 🚗 Texaco/Subway/dsl, 🍴 China King, McDonald's, Waffle House, 🛏 Best Western, Deluxe Inn, 🅾 Chevrolet, Chrysler/Dodge/Jeep, Corner Mkt Foods, Ford/Lincoln/Mercury, Honda, Mazda, Nissan, Rite Aid, **S** 🚗 BP, 🍴 KFC, Goldie's BBQ, 🛏 Best Inn, 🅾 Buick/Cadillac/GMC, Family$,
1c	Halls Ferry Rd, **N** 🚗 Exxon, 🍴 Burger King, Sonic, 🛏 Travel Inn, 🅾 H, Durst Drugs, **S** 🚗 Kangaroo/dsl, 🍴 Capt D's, DQ, El Sombrero Mexican, Goldie's BBQ, Pizza Hut, Popeye's, Shoney's, Subway, Taco Bell, Taco Casa, Wendy's, Whataburger, 🛏 Candlewood Suites,

1c	**Continued** Fairfield Inn, Rodeway Inn, Super 8, Wingate Inn, 🅾 Advance Parts, AT&T, Belk, Big Lots, Dillard's, Home Depot, Fred's Drug, JC Penney, Kroger/dsl, Walgreens, USPO, mall
1b	US 61 S, **S** 🚗 Kangaroo/Domino's, Murphy Express/dsl, 🍴 McDonald's, Panda Buffet, 🅾 Verizon, Walmart/Subway, same as 1c
1a	Washington St, Vicksburg, **N Welcome Ctr both lanes, full ♿ facilities**, 🚗, 🚗 Kangaroo/dsl, Shell/Subway/dsl, 🛏 AmeriStar Hotel/Casio/RV Park, **S** 🍴 Waffle House, 🛏 Best Value Inn, Days Inn
0mm	Mississippi/Louisiana state line, Mississippi River

INTERSTATE 22 (FUTURE)

Exit	Services
118mm	I-22 (future), Alabama/Mississippi State Line
115mm	**Welcome Ctr/Rest Area wb, ♿, litter barrels, petwalk, vending, RV dump**
113	rd 23, Tremont, Smithville
108	rd 25 N, Belmont, Iuka
106mm	**weigh sta, both lanes**
104	rd 25 S, Fulton, Amory, **N** 🚗 Shell/cafe/dsl/scales, Texaco/dsl, 🍴 Baskin-Robbins/Huddle House, Burger King, Hardee's, McDonald's, Sonic, Subway, 🛏 Days Inn, Holiday Inn Express, 🅾 AutoZone, $General, Food Giant/gas, Fred's, O'Reilly Parts, RV camping, Whitten HS, **S** 🚗 Murphy USA/dsl, 🍴 KFC, Los Compadres Mexican, Pizza Hut, Wendy's, 🅾 Walmart
104mm	Tombigbee River/Tenn-Tom Waterway
101	rd 178, rd 363, Peppertown, Mantachie, **N** 🚗 Exxon, **S** 🚗 Dorsey Fuel/dsl (2mi)
97	Fawn Grove Rd
94	rd 371, Mantachie, Mooreville, **N** 🚗 Woco/Pizza Inn/dsl
90	Auburn Rd, **N** 🚗 Dee's Oil/dsl
87	Veterans Blvd, **N** 🚗 Shell/Chix Rest/dsl, 🍴 Huddle House, 🛏 Wingate Inn, 🅾 E. Presley Campground/Park, **S** Tombigbee SP
86	US 45 N, Tupelo, to Corinth, **1 exit N** 🚗 BP, Shell, Texaco, 🍴 Abner's Rest., Applebees, Burger King, Capt D's, Chick-fil-A, Chili's, ChuckeCheese, Cici's Pizza, Cracker Barrel, IHOP, Kyoto Japanese, Lenny's Subs, Logan's Roadhouse, McDonald's, New China, O'Charley's, Olive Garden, Pizza Hut, Red Lobster, Ryan's, Sonic, Subway, Taco Bell, Wendy's, 🛏 Baymont Inn, Best Inn, Comfort Inn, Days Inn, Jameson Inn, La Quinta, 🅾 AutoZone, Barnes&Noble, Belk, Best Buy, Books-A-Million, Dick's, $General, Ford/Lincoln/Mercury, Hobby Lobby, Home Depot, Hyundai, JC Penney, Kohl's, Kroger/gas, Lowe's, Mazda, NAPA, Old Navy, Petsmart, Ross,

MS

E ↕ W

INTERSTATE 22 (FUTURE)

Exit	Services
86	Continued Sam's Club/gas, Sears, Staples, Toyota, Tuesday Morning, Walgreens, Walmart
85	Natchez Trace Pkwy
81	rd 178, McCullough Blvd, N 🅖 Love's/McDonald's/dsl/scales/24hr, S 🅖 Exxon/dsl, Shell/dsl, Texaco/dsl, 🍴 Old Venice Pizza, Sonic, 🛏 Super 8, 🅞 $General, USPO
76	rd 9 S, Sherman, Pontotoc, N 🅖 Wild Bill's/dsl, 🅞 Sherman RV Ctr
73	rd 9 N, Blue Springs
64	rd 15, rd 30 E, Pontotoc, Ripley, N 🅖 Eagle/dsl, S 🅖 ⛽/Arby's/scales/dsl/24hr, Shell/dsl
63	New Albany, N 🅖 Dee's Oil/dsl, 🅞 Buick/Chevrolet/GMC, Ford, HP
62mm	Tallahatchie River
61	rd 30 W, W New Albany, N 🅖 Express, 🍴 China Buffet, McAlister's Deli, McDonald's, Pizza Hut, Subway, Wendy's, 🛏 Hampton Inn, 🅞 🅗, Rite Aid, Walgreens, S 🅖 Murphy USA/dsl, Shell/Baskin-Robbins, 🍴 Burger King, Capt D's, Huddle House, KFC, Mi Pueblo Mexican, Taco Bell, Wendy's, Western Sizzlin, 🛏 Comfort Inn, Economy Inn, Hallmarc Inn, Holiday Inn Express, 🅞 🅗, $Tree, Lowe's, Radio Shack, Walmart, to U of MS
60	Glenfield, to Oxford, N 🛏 Budget Inn, S to U of MS
55	Myrtle
48	rd 178, Hickory Flat, S 🅖 BP/rest/dsl/24hr
41	rd 346, Potts Camp, S 🅖 BP/dsl, 🅞 CarQuest, $General
41mm	Tippah River
37	Lake Center, N 🅞 Chewalla Lake/RV camping
30	rd 7, rd 4, Holly Springs, Oxford, N 🅖 Exxon, Shell/Chester's/BBQ, 🍴 Capt D's, El Nopalito, Huddle House, KFC, McDonalds, Panda Buffet, Pizza Hut, Popeye's, Sonic, Subway, Taco Bell, Wendy's, 🛏 Magnolia Inn, 🅞 🅗, AutoZone, $General, Libby's Drug, Save-a-Lot, Wall Doxey SP/RV camping, S 🅖 Exxon, 🛏 Days Inn, Le Brooks Inn, 🅞 Walmart
26	W Holly Springs
21	Red Banks, N 🅖 Dee's Oil/dsl, Texaco/dsl
18	Victoria, E Byhalia, N 🅖 BP
14	rd 309, Byhalia, N 🅖 Exxon, Shell/Chester's/dsl, 🛏 Best Value Inn
10	W Byhalia
6	Bethel Rd, Hacks Crossroad, N 🅖 BP, Flying J/Denny's/dsl/scales/LP/RV dump/24hr, Shell/Chesters/dsl, 🍴 JR's Grill, Tops BBQ, 🛏 Best Western, Super 8, 🅞 truck repair
6mm	parking area both lanes
4	rd 305, Olive Branch, Independence, N 🅖 BP/dsl, Mobil/Huddle House, Shell/Circle K, 🍴 Old Style BBQ, Pizza Hut, 🛏 Holiday Inn Express, S 🅖 BP/Quiznos, 🅞 CVS Drug
3.5mm	weigh sta, both lanes
2	rd 302, Olive Branch, N 🍴 Abbay's Rest., Baskin-Robbins, Buffalo Wild Wings, Chick-fil-A, Chili's, Colton's Steaks, IHOP, Krystal, Lenny's Subs, McAlisters Deli, O'Charley's, Starbucks, Subway, Wendy's, 🛏 Candlewood Suites, Comfort Suites, 🅞 $Tree, Ford, Home Depot, Lowe's, Radio Shack, Walmart, S 🅖 Chevron/dsl, Shell/Circle

OLIVE BRANCH (vertical)

S O U T H A V E N (vertical)

N ↕ S

2	Continued K, 🍴 Applebees, Backyard Burger, Burger King, Casa Mexicana, McDonald's, Steak Escape, Subway, Taco Bell, Waffle House, Zaxby's, 🛏 Comfort Inn, Hampton Inn, 🅞 AutoZone, CVS Drug, GNC, Goodyear/auto, Kroger/gas
1	Craft Rd, N 🅞 American RV Ctr, Chevrolet, Hyundai, Suzuki
0mm	Mississippi/Tennessee state line, I-22 (future) begins/ends. US 78 continues wb.

INTERSTATE 55

Exit	Services
291.5mm	Mississippi/Tennessee state line
291	State Line Rd, Southaven, E 🅖 Exxon, Shell/dsl, 🍴 Exline Pizza, Little Caesars, Subway, Tops BBQ, Waffle House, 🛏 Comfort Inn, Holiday Inn Express, Quality Inn, Southern Inn, Super 8, 🅞 Family$, Firestone/auto, Goodyear/auto, Kroger, Southaven RV Park, Walgreens, W 🅖 Exxon, 🍴 Capt D's, Checker's, Dales Rest, El Patron Mexican, Lucky China, Mrs Winner's, Sonic, Taco Bell, Wendy's, 🅞 Big-Lots, Fred's, Mainstreet Auto, Rite Aid, USPO, tires
289	MS 302, to US 51, Horn Lake, E 🅖 BP/Circle K, Shell, 🍴 Backyard Burger, Buffalo Wild Wings, Burger King, Chick-fil-A, Chili's, Fazoli's, Firehouse Subs, Fox&Hound, Gordman's, IHOP, Krystal, Huey's Rest., La Hacienda, Logan's Roadhouse, Longhorn Steaks, McDonald's, Nagoya Japanese, O'Charley's, Olive Garden, On-the-Border, Outback Steaks, Qdoba Mexican, Red Lobster, Sonic, Steak'n Shake, Subway, TGIFriday's, Wendy's, 🛏 Comfort Suites, Courtyard, Fairfield Inn, Hampton Inn, Hilton Garden, Holiday Inn, Residence Inn, 🅞 🅗, Aldi Foods, AT&T, Best Buy, BooksAMillion, Chevrolet, Chrysler/Jeep/Dodge, CVS Drug, Dillards, $Tree, Ford, GNC, Gordman's, Hancock Fabrics, JC Penney, Jo-Ann Fabrics, Lowe's, Marshall's, Nissan, Office Depot, Old Navy, PetCo, Radio Shack, Sam's Club/gas, Tuesday Morning, Verizon, Walmart, W 🅖 BP/Circle K, Phillips 66/dsl, Shell/Circle K/dsl, 🍴 Applebee's, Arby's, Country Home Buffet, ChuckeCheese, Cracker Barrel, Grand Buffet, Hooters, KFC, McDonald's, Mrs Winner's, Papa John's, Pizza Hut, Popeye's, Ryan's, Sekisui Japan, Taco Bell, TX Roadhouse, Waffle House, Wendy's, Zaxby's, 🛏 Best Western, Days Inn, Drury Inn, EconoLodge, La Quinta, Motel 6, Ramada Ltd, Sleep Inn, 🅞 CVS Drug, Family$, Gateway Tires/repair, Home Depot, Kroger, Save-a-Lot Foods, Target, Walgreens
287	Church Rd, E 🅖 Citgo/dsl, 🅞 AutoZone, W 🅖 Citgo, Shell/Circle K/DQ/dsl, 🍴 Boiling Point Seafood, Casa Mexicana, McDonald's, Quiznos, Sonic, Subway, Taco Bell, Waffle House, 🛏 Keywest Inn, Magnolia Inn, 🅞 El Daze RV Camping (1mi), Harley-Davidson, Jellystone Camping, Southaven RV Ctr, Walgreens
285mm	weigh sta both lanes
284	to US 51, Nesbit Rd, W 🅖 BP, 🍴 Happy Daze Dairybar, 🅞 USPO
283	I-69, Tunica
280	MS 304, US 51, Hernando, E 🅖 Exxon, Murphy USA/dsl, 🍴 Arby's, Capt D's, Dominos, Guadalahara Mexican, KFC, King Buffet, Kyoto, Sonic, Steak Escape, Taco Bell, Zaxby's, 🛏 Days Inn, Hernando Inn, 🅞 URGENT CARE, $Tree, Ultimate Tires/repair, Walmart, Walgreens, W 🅖 BP, GasMart, Shell/Circle K/dsl, 🍴 Brick Oven Rest., Coleman's BBQ, McDonald's, Mi Pueblo, Mr Chen's, Papa John's, Pizza Hut, Subway, Taco Felix, Waffle House, Wendy's, 🛏 Super 8, 🅞 AutoZone, Desoto Museum, Family$

INTERSTATE 55

Exit	Services
280	Continued Fred's, Kroger/gas, Memphis, S Camping (2mi), NAPA, USPO, to Arkabutla Lake
279mm	**Welcome Ctr sb, full 🅗 facilities, 🍴, 🛏, litter barrels, petwalk, RV dump, 24hr security**
276mm	**rest area nb, full 🅗 facilities, 🍴, 🛏, litter barrels, petwalk, RV dump, 24hr security**
273mm	Coldwater River
271	MS 306, Coldwater, **W** 🅟 BP, 🍴 Subway, 🅞 Memphis, S RV Park, Lake Arkabutla
265	MS 4, Senatobia, **W** 🅟 BP/dsl, Exxon, Kangaroo/Stuckey's/Huddle House/dsl/scales/24hr, Shell/dsl, 🍴 Backyard Burger, Coleman's BBQ, Domino's, KFC, McDonald's/playplace, New China Buffet, Pizza Hut, Popeye's, Rio Lindo Mexican, Sonic, Subway, Taco Bell, Waffle House, Wendy's, 🛏 Motel 6, Senatobia Inn, 🅞 🅗, CarQuest, City Drug, Curves, Fred's, Kaye Mkt, transmissions, USPO
263	rd 740, S Senatobia
257	MS 310, Como, **E** other:, N Sardis Lake, **W** 🅟 Citgo/dsl, 🍴 Windy City Grille (1mi)
252	MS 315, Sardis, **E** 🅟 Chevron/dsl, Pure/dsl, 🍴 McDonald's, 🛏 Lake Inn, Super 8, 🅞 NAPA, to Kyle SP, Sardis Dam, RV camping, **W** 🅟 BP/Chester's/dsl, Shell/dsl, 🍴 Sonic, 🅞 🅗, $General, Family$, Fred's
246	MS 35, N Batesville, **E** to Sardis Lake, **W** 🅟 ᴸᵒᵛᵉˢ/McDonald's/Subway/dsl/scales/24hr, Shell/dsl
243b a	MS 6, to Batesville, **E** 🅟 BP/dsl, Murphy USA/dsl, Shell/dsl, 🍴 Backyard Burger, Chili's, Mi Pueblo Mexican, Zaxby's, 🅞 Lowe's, Walmart/Subway, to Sardis Lake, U of MS, **W** 🅟 BP, Chevron/dsl, Exxon/dsl, Phillips 66/dsl, Shell/dsl, 🍴 Arby's, Burger King, Burn's BBQ, Cafe Ole, Capt D's, Cracker Barrel, Domino's, Hardee's, Huddle House, KFC, McDonald's, Pizza Hut, Popeye's, Sonic, Subway, Taco Bell, Waffle House, Wendy's, Western Sizzlin, 🛏 Days Inn, Hampton Inn, Holiday Inn, Quality Inn, Ramada Ltd, 🅞 🅗, AutoZone, Curves, $General, Factory Stores/famous brands, Fred's, Kroger, O'Reilly Parts, Radio Shack, Save-a-Lot, Walgreens, USPO
240mm	**rest area both lanes, full 🅗 facilities, 🍴, 🛏, litter barrels, petwalk, RV dump, 24hr security**
237	to US 51, Courtland, **E** 🅟 Pure/dsl, **W** 🅞 $General
233	to Enid Dam, **E** to Enid Lake, RV camping
227	MS 32, Oakland, **E** to Cossar SP, Sunrise RV Park, **W** 🅟 Exxon/Chester's/dsl, Shell/dsl, 🅞 $General, antiques
220	MS 330, Tillatoba, **E** 🅟 Conoco/rest./dsl/@
211	MS 7 N, to Coffeeville, **E** Frog Hollow RV Park, **W** 🅟 Shell/Chester's/dsl
208	Papermill Rd, **E** Grenada 🍴
206	MS 8, MS 7 S, to Grenada, **E** 🅟 Exxon/dsl, RaceWay/dsl, Shell/dsl, 🍴 Burger King, China Buffet, Clubhouse Rest., Domino's, Great Wall Chinese, Jake&Rip's Café, La Cabana Mexican, McAlister's Deli, McDonald's, Pizza Hut, Pizza Inn, Shoney's, Subway, Taco Bell, Wendy's, Western Sizzlin, 🛏 Best Value Inn, Budget Inn, Comfort Inn, Hampton Inn, Jameson Inn, Knights Inn, Quality Inn, Super 8, 🅞 🅗, Advance Parts, AT&T, AutoZone, Chrysler/Dodge, Curves, CVS Drug, $General, $Tree, Ford/Lincoln/Mercury, GNC, O'Reilly Parts, Radio Shack, USPO, Walmart, to Grenada Lake/RV camping, **W** 🅟 Exxon/Huddle House, 🍴 Waffle House, 🛏 Country Inn&Suites, EconoLodge, 🅞 NAPA, Nissan

Exit	Services
204mm	parking area sb, 🍴, litter barrels
202mm	parking area nb, 🍴, litter barrels
199	Trout Rd, S Grenada, **E** to camp McCain
195	MS 404, Duck Hill, **E** to Camp McCain, **W** 🅟 Conoco/dsl
185	US 82, Winona, **E** 🅟 Exxon, Shell/dsl, 🍴 Huddle House, KFC, McDonald's, Sonic, Subway, 🛏 Holiday Inn Express, Magnolia Lodge, Relax Inn, Western Inn, 🅞 🅗, **W** 🅟 ᴴᴴᴳ/Taco Bell/dsl/24hr/scales/repair
174	MS 35, MS 430, Vaiden, **E** 🅟 Chevron/dsl, 35-55 Trkstp/rest/dsl/scales/24hr, Shell, 🅞 NAPA, Vaiden Camping
173mm	**rest area sb, full 🅗 facilities, 🍴, 🛏, litter barrels, petwalk, RV dump, 24hr security**
164	to West, **W** 🅟 West Trkstp/dsl
163mm	**rest area nb, full 🅗 facilities, 🍴, 🛏, litter barrels, petwalk, RV dump, 24hr security**
156	MS 12, Durant, **E** 🅟 Shell/dsl, 🛏 Durant Motel/rest. (3mi), Super 8, **W** 🅗 (7mi)
150	**E** Holmes Co SP, RV camping
146	MS 14, Goodman, **W** to Little Red Schoolhouse
144	MS 17, to Pickens, **E** 🅟 Texaco/J's Deli/dsl/24hr, **W** 🅟 BP/Baskin-Robbins/dsl/24hr, 🅞 to Little Red Schoolhouse
139	MS 432, to Pickens
133	Vaughan, **E** to Casey Jones Museum
128mm	Big Black River
124	MS 16, to, N Canton
119	MS 22, to MS 16 E, Canton, **E** 🅟 BP/Subway/dsl, Canton Jct/dsl, Cappy's/dsl, Exxon, Shell/Domino's, 🍴 El Sombrero Mexican, McDonald's, Pizza Hut, Popeye's, Sonic, Subway, Waffle House, Wendy's, Western Sizzlin, 🛏 Best Value Inn, Best Western, Comfort Inn, Days Inn, Hampton Inn, Holiday Inn Express, La Quinta, Quality Inn, 🅞 🅗, $General, Hyundai, O'Reilly Parts, to Ross Barnett Reservoir, **W** 🅟 Chevron/KFC/dsl, ᴸᵒᵛᵉˢ/Arby's/dsl/scales/24hr/@, Texaco/Penn's/dsl, 🍴 Bumpers Drive-In, 2 Rivers Steaks
118a b	Nissan Parkway, **E** to Nissan
114a b	Sowell Rd
112	US 51, Gluckstadt, **E** 🅟 Exxon/Krystal/dsl, Kangaroo/Subway/dsl, 🛏 Super 8, **W** Camper Corral RV Ctr
108	MS 463, Madison, **E** 🅟 Shell/dsl, Texaco/dsl, 🍴 Applebee's, Backyard Burger, Burger King, Chick-Fil-A, Chili's, Coldstone, El Potrillo, Haute Pig Café, Little Caesars, Roma's Cafe, 🅞 AT&T, Best Buy, Dick's, $Tree, Lowe's, SteinMart, Walmart, **W** 🅟 Exxon/KFC/dsl, 🍴 BoneFish Grill, Nagoya Japanese, Papito's Grill, PieWorks, Pinecone, Subway, Wendy's, 🛏 Hilton Garden, 🅞 🅗, CVS Drug, Home Depot, Kroger

(Left margin, top to bottom: N ↑ S)

(Left margin vertical labels: BATESVILLE, GRENADA)

(Center margin vertical labels: CANTON, MADISON)

Map of Mississippi showing cities: Batesville, Courtland, Canton, Ridgeland, Jackson, Meridian, Vicksburg, Raymond, Pearl, Crystal Springs, Paulding, Stonewall, Hazlehurst, Wesson, Soso, Laurel, Magnolia, McComb, Purvis, Hattiesburg, Lumberton, Osyka. Interstates 20, 55, 59.

= gas = food = lodging = other Copyright 2011 - The Next Exit

INTERSTATE 55

Exit	Services
105b	Old Agency Rd, **E** Chevron/dsl, Honda, **W** Biaggi's Ristorante, 5 Guys Burgers, Maggie Moo's, Peppers Cafe, PF Changs, Ruth's Chris Steaks, Hyatt Place, Barnes&Noble, Fresh Mkt Foods
105a	Natchez Trace Pkwy
104	I-220, to, W Jackson
103	County Line Rd, **E** Chevron, Exxon/dsl, Murphy Express/dsl, Applebee's, Bop's Custard, Bulldog Grill, Cane's, Chick-fil-A, ChuckeCheese, 'Cozumel Mexican, Grand China, HoneyBaked Ham, Huntington's Grille, Jason's Deli, KFC, King Buffet, Krispy Kreme, Marble Slab, Mazzio's, O'Charley's, Pizza Hut, Popeye's, Shoney's, Wendy's, Whataburger, Zaxby's, Best Western, Cabot Lodge, Courtyard, Days Inn, EconoLodge, Hilton, Quality Inn, Red Roof Inn, Acura, Barnes&Noble, Belk, Best Buy, Cadillac, Dillard's, $Tree, JC Penney, Lowe's, Marshall's, Michael's, Office Depot, Old Navy, Radio Shack, Sam's Club/gas, TJ Maxx, Tuesday Morning, Verizon, Walgreens, Walmart, to Barnett Reservoir, **W** Chili's, Nagoya Japanese, Olive Garden, Red Lobster, Logan's Roadhouse, Subway, Comfort Suites, Drury Inn, Holiday Inn Express, Motel 6, Studio 6, Fred's, Home Depot, Office Depot, Petsmart, Target, Upton Tire
102b	Beasley Rd, Adkins Blvd, **E** Cracker Barrel, LoneStar Steaks, Outback Steaks, Super 8, Chevrolet, Ford, Nissan, Toyota/Scion, **W** Exxon/dsl, Shell/dsl, Burger King, Chili's, IHOP, McDonald's, Baymont Inn, Best Western, Extended Stay Deluxe, Fairfield Inn, Jameson Inn, Hampton Inn, InTown Suites, BigLots, CarMax, Mercedes, frontage rds access 102a
102a	Briarwood, **E** La Quinta, **W** Capt D's, ChuckeCheese, Popeye's, Best Value Inn, Clarion, Hampton Inn, Porsche/Smart
100	North Side Dr W, **E** BP/dsl, Chevron, Burger King, Char Rest., Charokee Drive-In, Jule's Rest., McAlister's Deli, New China, Papa John's, Piccadilly's, Pinecone Rest., Pizza Hut, SteakOut, Subway, Wendy's, Extended Stay America, AT&T, Audi, Books-A-Million, CVS Drug, Jaguar/LandRover, Kroger/gas, Office Depot, SteinMart, Tuesday Morning, VW, Walgreens, **W** BP, Exxon/dsl, Shell, Domino's, Hooters, Waffle House, Select Motel, USA Inn
99	Meadowbrook Rd, Northside Dr, E (from nb)
98c b	MS 25 N, Lakeland Dr, **E** Shell, Parkside Inn, LaFleur's Bluff SP, museum, **W** H,
98a	Woodrow Wilson Dr, downtown
96c	Fortification St, **E** Inn Place Suites, **W** H, Bellhaven College
96b	High St, Jackson, **E** BMW, Chevrolet, Infiniti, Lexus, **W** Shell/Subway/dsl, Texaco/dsl, Arby's, Chimneyville Cafe, Domino's, Popeye's, Shoney's, Taco Bell, Waffle House, Wendy's, Whataburger, Best Western, Colosseum Inn, Jackson Hotel, Hampton Inn, Quality Inn, Red Roof Inn, Regency Hotel, H, Honda, Subaru/Volvo, museum, st capitol
96a	Pearl St (from nb), Jackson, **W** downtown, access to same as 96b
94	(46 from nb), I-20 E, to Meridian, US 49, S
45b [I-20]	US 51, State St, to downtown, **N** BP, Petro, Shell, **S** Pilot
45a	Gallatin St (from sb), **N** Petro/dsl, Shell, **S** /McDonald's/dsl, Nissan
92c	(I-44 from sb), I-20 W, to Vicksburg, US 49, N
92b	US 51 N, State St, Gallatin St
92a	McDowell Rd, **E** Petro/dsl, /McDonald's/dsl, **W** BP/dsl, BJ's/dsl, Citgo, Dixie, Exxon, Shell, McDonald's, Waffle House, Best Value Inn, Fred's, Rite Aid, Roses
90b	Daniel Lake Blvd (from sb), **W** Shell, Harley-Davidson
90a	Savanna St, **E** transmissions, **W** BP, Bodan's Seafood, Turning Wheel RV Center
88	Elton Rd, **W** Exxon/Chester's/dsl, Shell/Subway/dsl
85	Byram, **E** Blue Sky/dsl, BP/Penn's/dsl, Krystal, Mexican Grill, Tin Shed BBQ, Comfort Inn, ValuePlace, Swinging Bridge RV Park, **W** Byrem/dsl, Chevron, Exxon/dsl, Texaco/dsl, Backyard Burger, Capt D's, KFC, Mazzio's, McAlister's Deli, McDonald's, New China, Pizza Hut, Popeye's, Quiznos, Sonic, Subway, Taco Bell, Waffle House, Wendy's, Holiday Inn Express, AutoZone, $General, Mkt Place Foods, NAPA, O'Reilly Parts, Super D Drugs, Tire Depot, Walgreens
81	Wynndale Rd, **W** Chevron/dsl
78	Terry, **E** Texaco/Subway/dsl/24hr, USPO, **W** Mac's, $General
72	MS 27, Crystal Springs, **E** Exxon/Subway/dsl, Phillips 66/dsl, McDonald's, Pit BBQ, Popeye's, Ford/Lincoln/Mercury, vet
68	to US 51, S Crystal Springs, gas/dsl, Red Barn Produce, vet
65	to US 51, Gallman, **E** Stuckey's/dsl
61	MS 28, Hazlehurst, **E** BP, Exxon, Murphy Express/dsl, Phillips 66/dsl, Pump&Save, Bumpers Drive Inn, Burger King, KFC/Taco Bell, McDonald's, Pizza Hut, Sonic, Stark's Rest., Subway, Waffle House, Wendy's, Best Value Inn, Claridge Inn, Western Inn, H, Advance Parts, $General, $Tree, Family$, Fred's, Piggly Wiggly, Walgreens, Walmart
59	to, S Hazlehurst
56	to Martinsville
54mm	**rest area both lanes, full facilities, , , litter barrels, petwalk, RV dump, vending, 24hr security**
51	to Wesson, **E** Lake Lincoln SP, **W** Country Jct Trkstp/rest/dsl
48	Mt Zion Rd, to Wesson
42	to US 51, N Brookhaven, **E** Exxon/Subway, Shell/Kasko/dsl/scales/24hr, H, **W** Super 8
40	to MS 550, Brookhaven, **E** BP/Domino's/dsl, Blue Sky, Exxon/Subway, Murphy USA/dsl, Shell/dsl, Bowie BBQ, Burger King, China Buffet, Cracker Barrel, DQ, Hudgey's Rest., KFC, Krystal, El Sombrero Little Caesars, McDonald's, Mitchell's Steaks, Pizza Hut, Popeye's, Sonic, Taco Bell, Waffle House, Wendy's, Western Sizzlin, Best Inn, Comfort Inn, Days Inn, Lincoln Inn, Hampton Inn, Spanish Inn, H, AutoZone, Buick/Cadillac/Chevrolet/GMC, CarQuest, $Tree, Family$, Ford/Lincoln/Mercury, Fred's, Gene's Tires, Honda, Nissan, O'Reilly Parts, Rite Aid, Save-A-Lot Foods, Super D Drugs, Toyota, Walgreens, Walmart, **W** Home Depot
38	US 84, S Brookhaven, **W** Chevron/dsl/24hr
30	Bogue Chitto, Norfield, **E** Shell/BogueChitto/dsl, Bogue Chitto RV Park
24	Johnston Station, **E** to Lake Dixie Springs
20b a	US 98 W, to Natchez, Summit, **E** BP/dsl, Shell/dsl, Stop'n Shop/dsl, **W** Exxon/Subway/dsl, Phillips 66/dsl

MS

INTERSTATE 55 CONT'D

Exit	Services
18	MS 570, Smithdale Rd, N McComb, **E** @ BP, 🍴 Burger King, China Buffet, McDonald's, Piccadilly's, Ruby Tuesday, 🛏 Holiday Inn Express, ▣ H, Belk, JC Penney, Kia, Lowe's, Radio Shack, Sears/auto, Walgreens, Walmart/ Subway, mall, **W** @ Chevron/Quiznos/dsl, 🍴 Arby's, El Dorado Mexican, Santa Fe Grille, 🛏 Deerfield Inn, Hampton Inn, Ramada, ▣ Ford/Lincoln/Mercury
17	Delaware Ave, McComb, **E** @ BP/Subway, Blue Sky, Chevron/dsl, Exxon/Penn's, Pump&Savor, Pure, RaceWay/dsl, Shell/dsl, 🍴 Backyard BBQ, Burger King, China Palace, Domino's, Golden Corral, New China, Papa's Pizza, Pizza Hut, Pizza Inn, Popeye's, Smoothie King, Sonic, Taco Bell, Tortillo Soup, Waffle House, Wendy's, 🛏 Best Western, Comfort Inn, Executive Inn, ▣ H, AutoZone, CVS Drug, $General, Family$, Fred's, Kroger, O'Reilly Parts, Rite Aid, **W** 🛏 Days Inn, ▣ Chrysler/Dodge/Jeep
15b a	US 98 E, MS 48 W, McComb, **1 mi** **E** @ Exxon/Subway, Pure, Shell, 🍴 Church's, KFC, 🛏 Camellian Motel, ▣ Advance Parts, $General, Family$, tires, vet, **W** @ BP/dsl
13	Fernwood Rd, **E** truck repair, **W** @ Loves/Chester's/ McDonald's/dsl/scales/24hr/@, ▣ golf, to Percy Quin SP
10	MS 48, Magnolia, **1 mi** **E** @ Exxon, MTS, 🍴 Subway, ▣ RV camping
8	MS 568, Magnolia, **E** Pike Co Speedway
4	Chatawa
3mm	**Welcome Ctr nb, full** ♿ **facilities,** 🔌, 🚻, **litter barrels, petwalk, RV dump, 24hr security**
2mm	**weigh station, nb only**
1	MS 584, Osyka, Gillsburg
0mm	Mississippi/Louisiana state line

INTERSTATE 59

Exit	Services
	I-59 S and I-20 W run together to Meridian.
172mm	Mississippi/Alabama state line
170mm	**weigh sta both lanes**
169	Kewanee, **S** @ Kewanee Trkstp/dsl
165	Toomsuba, **N** @ Shell/Subway/24hr, Texaco/ChesterFried/dsl, **S** @ Loves/Arby's/dsl/scales, ▣ KOA (2mi)
164mm	**Welcome Ctr wb, full** ♿ **facilities,** 🔌, 🚻, **vending, litter barrels, petwalk, RV dump, 24hr security**
160	to Russell, **N** @ TA/BP/dsl/rest./scales/24hr/@, ▣ Nanabe RV Camping (1mi), **S** @ Shell/dsl
157b a	US 45, to Macon, Quitman
154b a	MS 19 S, MS 39 N, Meridian, **N** @ BP/dsl, Pure, Shell, Texaco/Domino's, 🍴 Applebee's, Cracker Barrel, Penn's Rest., Western Sizzlin, Waffle House, 🛏 Day's Inn, Drury Inn, Hampton Inn, Hilton Garden, Holiday Inn, Relax Inn, Rodeway Inn, Super 8, ▣ Benchmark RV Park, Cadillac, Chrysler/Jeep/Kia, Hyundai, Lincoln/Mercury, Mitsubishi, U-Haul, **S** @ Chevron, Texaco, 🍴 Chick-fil-A, CiCi's, Crescent City Grill, Garfield's Rest., McAlister's, McDonald's, O'Charley's, Outback Steaks, Popeye's, Red Lobster, Ryan's, Taco Bell, 🛏 Comfort Inn, Jameson Inn, Microtel, ▣ Belk, Best Buy, BooksAMillion, Dillard's, $Tree, Ethridge RV Ctr, Harley-Davidson, JC Penney, Old Navy, PetCo, Ross, Sam's Club/gas, Sears/auto, TJ Maxx, mall, same as 153
153	MS 145 S, 22nd Ave, Meridian, **N** @ BP, Shell, 🍴 Arby's, Barnhill's Buffet, Burger King, Capt D's, China Buffet,

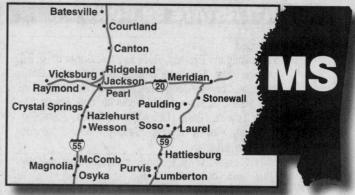

Exit	Services
153	Continued
	Hardee's, KFC, McDonald's, Pizza Hut, Subway, Wendy's, Western Sizzlin, 🛏 Relax Inn, Super Inn, ▣ H, Firestone, Ford/Nissan, Fred's Drug, $General, Ford, Saverite Foods, **S** @ Chevron/dsl, Exxon/dsl, Texaco/dsl, 🍴 A&W/ LJ Silver, Waffle House, 🛏 Best Western, Budget 8 Motel, Econolodge, Holiday Inn Express, La Quinta, Motel 6, Quality Inn, Sleep Inn, ▣ Buick, Cadillac/Chevrolet, Chrysler/Jeep, Honda, Suzuki, Lowes Whse, Walmart/gas
152	29th Ave, 31st Ave, Meridian, **N** @ Chevron/ChesterFried/ dsl/24hr, 🛏 Ramada Ltd, **S** 🛏 Royal Inn
151	49th Ave, Valley Rd, **N** tires, **S** @ Pilot/Subway/dsl/24hr, ▣ stockyards
150	US 11 S, MS 19 N, Meridian, **N** @ Queen City Trkstp/dsl/ rest./@, 🍴 McDonald's, ▣ RV camping, Okatibbee Lake, **S** @ Chevron/Stuckey's/Subway/dsl, Shell/dsl ▣ ✈
149mm	**I-59 N and I-20 E run together 22 mi**
142	to US 11, Savoy, **W** to Dunns Falls
137	to, N Enterprise, to Stonewall
134	MS 513, S Enterprise
126	MS 18, to Rose Hill, Pachuta, **E** @ BB/dsl/24hr
118	to Vossburg, Paulding
113	MS 528, to Heidelberg, **E** @ Chevron/dsl, Exxon/Subway/dsl, JR's/dsl/24hr, Shell, 🍴 Heidelberg Rest., Ward's Burgers
109mm	**parking area sb, litter barrels, no restrooms**
106mm	**parking area nb, litter barrels, no restrooms**
104	Sandersville
99	US 11, **E** ▣ Sleepy Hollow RV Park (1mi)
97	US 84 E, **E** @ Exxon/Huddle House/dsl/scales, Kangaroo/Subway/dsl/24hr, 🍴 Hardee's, Ward's Burgers, **W** @ Shell/24hr, 🍴 KFC, Vic's Rest.
96b	MS 15 S, Cook Ave
96a	Masonite Rd, 4th Ave
95d	(from nb)
95c	Beacon St, Laurel, **W** @ Pump&Save Gas, 🍴 Burger King, Church's, McDonald's, Popeye's, 🛏 TownHouse Motel, ▣ Expert Tire, Family$, Goodyear/auto, JC Penney, NAPA, Save Rite Foods, museum of art
95b a	US 84 W, MS 15 N, 16th Ave, Laurel, **0-2 mi** **W** @ Chevron, Exxon/dsl, Murphy Express/dsl, Pure, Shell, Spaceway, Texaco, 🍴 Applebee's, Arby's, Buffalo Wild Wings, Buffet City, Burger King, Capt D's, Checkers, China Town, China Wok, Dickey's BBQ, Domino's, Eatza Pizza, Hardee's, KFC, Laredo Grill, McDonald's, Mi Casita, Papa John's, Pizza Hut, Popeye's, Quiznos, Ryan's, Shipley's Doughnuts, Shoney's, Sonic, Subway, Sweet Peppers Deli, Taco Bell, Waffle House, Ward's Burgers, Wendy's, Western Sizzlin, 🛏 Best Western, Comfort Suites, EconoLodge, Hampton

■ = gas ⑪ = food ☒ = lodging ◙ = other Copyright 2011 - The Next Exit

MS
N
↕
S

INTERSTATE 59 CONT'D

Exit	Services
95b a	Continued Inn, Holiday Inn Express, Rodeway Inn, Super 8, ◙ Ⓗ, Advance Parts, AutoZone, BigLots, Buick/Cadillac/GMC, Chevrolet, Chrysler/Dodge/Jeep, Corner Mkt Foods, CVS Drug, $General, $Tree, Ford/Lincoln/Mercury, Fred's, Kia, Kroger, Lowe's, Nissan, Office Depot, O'Reilly Parts, Piggly Wiggly, Roses, Toyota, Tuesday Morning, Verizon, Walgreens, Walmart
93	US 11, S Laurel, W ■ Exxon/Subway/dsl, Shell/dsl/24hr, ⑪ Hardee's, ◙ Southern Tires
90	US 11, Ellisville Blvd, E ■ Texaco/dsl, ⑪ Huddle House, W ■ Dixie/dsl
88	MS 588, MS 29, Ellisville, E ■ Chevron/dsl, ⑪ Domino's, KFC, McDonald's, Pizza Hut, Sonic, Subway, Ward's Burgers, ◙ AutoZone, $General, Ellisville Drug, Food Tiger, Family$, NAPA, O'Reilly Parts, W ■ Exxon/dsl, ☒ Best Western
85	MS 590, to Ellisville, W auto repair
80	to US 11, Moselle, E ■ Chevron/dsl
78	Sanford Rd, 76 W to Hattiesburg-Laurel Reg ✈
73	Monroe Rd, to Monroe
69	to Glendale, Eatonville Rd
67b a	US 49, Hattiesburg, E ■ Exxon, Shell, Texaco/dsl, ⑪ Arby's, Burger King, Cracker Barrel, DQ, Krystal, McDonald's, Pizza Hut, Waffle House, ☒ Budget Inn, Comfort Inn, EconoLodge, La Quinta, Motel 6, Quality Inn, Ramada, Red Carpet Inn, Regency Inn, Scottish Inn, Sleep Inn, Super 8, ◙ $General, Hattiesburg Cycles, W ■ Chevron, MapleLeaf/dsl, Pure/dsl, Shell/Subway, Stuckey's Express/dsl, Texaco, ⑪ Sonic, Waffle House, Ward's Burgers, Wendy's, ☒ Candlewood Suites, Holiday Inn, North Gate Inn
65b a	US 98 W, Hardy St, Hattiesburg, E ■ Shell/dsl, Texaco/dsl, ⑪ Applebee's, Bop's Custard, Buffalo Wild Wings, Caliente Grille, Cane's, Checkers, CiCi's Pizza, Domino's, IHOP, KFC, Lenny's Subs, Little Caesars, McDonald's, Pizza Hut, Purple Parrot Cafe, Qdoba, Smoothie King, Starbucks, Subway, Taco Bell, Ward's Burgers, ☒ Days Inn, Fairfield Inn, Residence Inn, Super 8, Western Motel, ◙ CarQuest, Corner Mkt Foods, CVS Drug, Goodyear/auto, Home Depot, Roses, Walgreens, to USM, W ■ Exxon/Domino's, Kangaroo, Pump&Save, Shell, Texaco, ⑪ Arby's, Backyard Burger, Burger King, Chick-fil-A, Chili's, China Buffet, ChuckeCheese, Coldstone, Dickey's BBQ, FireHouse Subs, Gatty Town Pizza, Hardee's, Krispy Kreme, Logan's Roadhouse, Longhorn Steaks, Marble Slab, Mazzio's, McDonald's, Mellow Mushroom, Newk's Grill, O'Charley's, Olive Garden, Outback Steaks, Peking Garden, Pepper's Deli, Pizza Hut, Pizza Inn, Popeye's, Red Lobster, Ryan's, Subway, Taco Bell, TGIFriday's, Waffle House, Ward's Burgers, Wendy's, Zaxby's, ☒ Baymont Inn, Comfort Suites, Hampton Inn, Hilton Garden, Microtel, Sun Suites, ◙ Ⓗ, Advance Parts, AT&T, AutoZone, Belk, Best Buy, BigLots, Books-A-Million, Dillard's, $Tree, Firestone/auto, Gander Mtn, Goodyear/auto, Hancock Fabrics, Hobby Lobby, JC Penney, Kohl's, Lowe's, Michael's, Mr Transmission, Nissan, Office Depot, Old Navy, Petsmart, Radio Shack, Rite Aid, Ross, SaveRite Foods, Sam's Club/gas, Sears/auto, Target, TJ Maxx, Verizon, Walgreens, Walmart, mall
60	US 11, S Hattiesburg, E ■ Shell/dsl, W ■ Kangaroo/

H
A
T
T
I
E
S
B
U
R
G

P
I
C
A
Y
U
N
E

Exit	Services
60	Continued Subway/dsl/24hr, Texaco, ⑪ Huddle House, ◙ Freight-liner, Peterbilt
59	US 98 E, to US 49, Lucedale, MS Gulf Coast
56mm	**parking area both lanes, litter barrels, no restrooms**
51	RD 589, to Purvis, W ■ Chevron/dsl, Pinebelt Oil/dsl, Shell/dsl (2mi), ⑪ McDonald's (2mi), Pizza Hut (2mi), to Little Black Cr Water Park
48mm	Little Black Creek
41	MS 13, to Lumberton, W ■ Pure, ◙ Bass Pecan Store, $General, to Little Black Cr Water Park
35	Hillsdale Rd, E ■ Pitstop/dsl, ☒ to Kings Arrow Ranch, to Lake Hillside Resort
32mm	Wolf River
29	RD 26, to Poplarville, W ■ Pure/dsl, ⑪ Burger King (2mi)
27	MS 53, to Poplarville, Necaise, W ■ Shell/dsl, ◙ RV Camping (2mi)
19	to US 11, Millard
15	to McNeill, W ■ McNeill Trkstop/rest./dsl
13mm	**parking area sb, litter barrels, no restrooms**
10	to US 11, Carriere, E ■ Texaco/Huddle House/dsl, ◙ Clearwater RV Camp (5mi), repair/tires
8mm	**parking area nb, litter barrels, no restrooms**
6	MS 43 N, N Picayune, E ⑪ Marble Slab, Paul's Pastries, W ■ Chevron/dsl, ⑪ Dockside Rest. (1mi), ☒ Best Value Inn, Picayune Motel (1mi), ◙ Ⓗ, CVS Drug, Winn-Dixie
4	MS 43 S, to Picayune, E ■ Murphy USA/dsl, RaceTrac/dsl, ⑪ Kobe Grill, McDonald's, Ryan's, Subway, Wow Wingery, ◙ Buick/Cadillac/Chevrolet/GMC, $Tree, GNC, Home Depot, Nissan, Sun Roamers RV Park (1mi), Verizon, Walgreens, Walmart, W ■ Chevron/dsl, Exxon/dsl, K&T/dsl, Shell/dsl, ⑪ Burger King, Domino's, Hardee's, KFC, New Buffet City, Papa John's, Pizza Hut, Popeye's, Subway, Taco Bell, Waffle House, Wendy's, ☒ Comfort Inn, Days Inn, Heritage Inn, Holiday Inn Express, ◙ Ⓗ, URGENT CARE, Advance Parts, AutoZone, $General, Firestone, Ford/Lincoln/Mercury, Fred's, O'Reilly Parts, Paw Paw's RV Ctr, Radio Shack, Rite Aid, Winn-Dixie
3mm	**Welcome Ctr nb, full ♿ facilities, ⒞, 🚻, vending, litter barrels, petwalk, RV dump**
1.5mm	**weigh sta both lanes**
1	US 11, MS 607, E NASA, W ■ Chevron/dsl, Shell/Subway/dsl
0mm	Mississippi/Louisiana state line, Pearl River. **Exits 11-1 are in Louisiana**
11	Pearl River Turnaround. Callboxes begin sb.
5b	Honey Island Swamp
5a	LA 41, Pearl River, E ■ Riverside TrvlCtr/dsl
3	US 11 S, LA 1090, Pearl River, 0-1 mi W ■ Chevron/dsl, Shell/Subway/dsl, Texaco, ⑪ McDonald's, Sonic, Waffle House, ☒ Microtel, ◙ AutoZone, Family$, Jubilee Foods/drug, NAPA
1.5mm	**Welcome Ctr sb, full ♿ facilities, info, ⒞, 🚻, litter barrels, petwalk, RV dump**
1c b	I-10, E to Bay St Louis, W to New Orleans
1a	I-12 W, to Hammond.
I-59 begins/ends on I-10/I-12. Exits 1-11 are in Louisiana.	

INTERSTATE 220 (JACKSON)

Exit	Services
11mm	I-220 begins/ends on I-55, exit 104.
9	Hanging Moss Rd, County Line Rd, E ■ BP
8	Watkins Dr, E ■ Exxon, Shell/Chester's/dsl

INTERSTATE 220 CONT'D (JACKSON)

Exit	Services
5b a	US 49 N, Evers Blvd, to Yazoo City, **E** 🅰 BP, 🍴 KFC, Sonic, 🏨 Star Motel, 🅾 Family$, Food Depot/gas, **W** 🅰 BP, Exxon/Burger King, Gas+, Shell/Subway/dsl
3	Industrial Dr
2b a	Clinton Blvd, Capitol St, **E** to Jackson Zoo, **W** 🅰 Race

2b a	Continued
	Way, Shell, 🍴 McDonald's, Popeye's, Sonic, 🅾 Family$
1b a	US 80, **E** 🍴 Bumper's Drive-In, Capt D's, Hunan Garden, KFC, McDonald's, Pizza Hut, Popeye's, Sonny's BBQ, Taco Bell, Wendy's, 🏨 Best Inn, Days Inn, Scottish Inn, Super 8, **W** 🅰 BP, Exxon/dsl, 🍴 Arby's, Krystal, 🅾 $General, Sears/auto
0mm	I-220 begins/ends on I-20, exit 41.

MISSOURI

INTERSTATE 29

Exit	Services
124mm	Missouri/Iowa state line
123mm	Nishnabotna River
121.5mm	**weigh sta both lanes**
116	rd A, rd B, to Watson, **W** fireworks
110	US 136, Rock Port, Phelps City, **E** 🅰 Shell/dsl, 🏨 Rockport Inn, fireworks, to NW MO St U, **W** 🅰 BP/dsl/24hr, Phillips 66/Stuckey's/Subway/dsl/24hr, 🍴 Black Iron Grill, McDonald's, Trails End Rest., 🏨 Super 8, 🅾 KOA, fireworks, truck repair
109.5mm	**Welcome Ctr sb, full ♿ facilities, info, 🚻, 🛢, litter barrels, petwalk**
107	MO 111, to Rock Port
106.5mm	Rock Creek
102mm	Mill Creek
99	rd W, Corning
97mm	Tarkio River
92	US 59, to Fairfax, Craig, **W** 🅰 Sinclair/dsl
90.5mm	Little Tarkio Creek
86.5mm	Squaw Creek
84	MO 118, Mound City, **E** 🅰 FL/Subway/dsl, Shamrock/dsl, 🍴 Breadeaux Pizza, McDonald's, Quacker's Steaks, Shakers Icecream, 🏨 Audrey's Motel, Super 8, 🅾 Bumper Parts, Chrysler/Dodge/Jeep, $General, **W** 🅰 Shell/Baskin-Robbins/dsl/24hr, 🅾 Big Lake SP (12mi)
82mm	**rest area both lanes, full ♿ facilities, 🚻, 🛢, litter barrels, vending, petwalk**
79	US 159, Rulo, **E** 🅰 Squaw Creek Trkstp/dsl/rest/RV dump/@, **W** to Big Lake SP (12mi), to Squaw Creek NWR (3mi)
78mm	Kimsey Creek
75	US 59, to Oregon
67	US 59 N, to Oregon
66.5mm	Nodaway River
65	US 59, rd RA, to Fillmore, Savannah, **E** 🅰 Conoco/dsl, 🅾 antiques, fireworks
60	rd K, rd CC, Amazonia, **W** 🅾 Hunt's Fruit Barn, antiques
58.5mm	Hopkins Creek
56b a	I-229 S, US 71 N, US 59 N, to St Joseph, Maryville
55mm	Dillon Creek
53	US 59, US 71 bus, to St Joseph, Savannah, **E** AOK Camping, fireworks, **W** 🅰 Phillips 66/dsl, 🅾 antiques
50	US 169, St Joseph, King City, **1-3 mi W on Belt Hwy** 🅰 BP, Conoco, Phillips 66, Shell, Sinclair, 🍴 Bob Evans, Buffalo Wild Wings, Cheddar's, Chick-fil-A, Chili's, Chipotle Mexican, Coldstone, Culver's, Famous Dave's, 54th St Grill, Hardee's, IHOP, KFC, McDonald's, Olive Garden, Panda Express, Ryan's, Sonic, Subway, Taco Bell, 🅾 Advance Parts, Best Buy, Home Depot, Kohl's, Lowe's,

50	Continued
	Michael's, Old Navy, Sam's Club/gas, Target, Tires+, TJ Maxx, Walgreens, Walmart
47	MO 6, Frederick Blvd, to Clarksdale, St Joseph, **E** 🅰 Conoco, 🍴 Bandanas BBQ, Basil's Italian, 🏨 Days Inn, Drury Inn, **W** 🅰 Phillips 66/dsl, Sinclair, 🍴 Applebee's, Burger King, Carlos O'Kelly's, Cracker Barrel, Denny's, Dunkin Donuts, Ground Round, Hazel's Coffee, Panera Bread, Perkins, Pizza Hut, Red Lobster, Taco Bell, Whiskey Creek Steaks, 🏨 Comfort Suites, Hampton Inn, Motel 6, Ramada, Stoney Creek Inn, Super 8, 🅾 �H, Apple Mkt Foods, Chevrolet, CVS Drug, Dillard's, Firestone/auto, Honda, JC Penney, Nissan, Sears, Walgreens, **1 mi W on US 169** 🍴 Arby's, Church's, Fazoli's, El Maguey Mexican, KFC, LJ Silver, McDonald's, Mr Goodcents, New China Super Buffet, Papa Murphy's, Quiznos, Rib Crib BBQ, Sonic, Starbucks, Subway, Taco Bell, Taco John's, Wendy's, 🅾 Advance Parts, Aldi Foods, AutoZone, BigLots, Buick/GMC, $General, Ford/Lincoln/Mercury, Hastings Books, Hobby Lobby, HyVee Foods, Jo-Ann Fabrics, Office Depot, Radio Shack, Toyota/Scion, U-Haul, vet
46b a	US 36, to Cameron, St Joseph, **1 mi W on US 169** 🅰 BP/dsl, FL, Murphy USA/dsl, Roadstar/dsl, Shell, Sinclair/dsl, 🍴 Burger King, Godfather's, Jimmy John's, Pizza Hut, Taco John's, 🅾 URGENT CARE, Ace Hardware, AT&T, $General, KIA, Klein RV Ctr, O'Reilly Parts, Suzuki, Walgreens, Walmart, to MO, W St Coll
44	US 169, to Gower, St Joseph, **E** 🅰 Phillips 66, 🟥Loves /Arby's/dsl/scales/24hr, 🍴 Nelly's Mexican, Subway, 🏨 Best Western, 🅾 dsl repair, **W** 🅰 Murphy USA/dsl, Shell/dsl/24hr, 🍴 DQ, McDonald's, Mr Goodcents, San Jose Steaks, Sonic, Taco Bell, Waffle House, 🅾 Apple Mkt Foods, Chrysler/Dodge/Jeep, $Tree, Goodyear, Harley-Davidson, Hyundai, K-Mart, Menards, Walmart
43	I-229 N, to St Joseph
39.5mm	Pigeon Creek
35	rd DD, Faucett, **W** 🅰 Farris Trkstp/dsl/motel/rest/24hr/@
33.5mm	Bee Creek
30	rd Z, rd H, Dearborn, New Market, **E** 🅰 Conoco/Subway/dsl/24hr
29.5mm	Bee Creek
27mm	**rest area both lanes, full ♿ facilities, 🚻, 🛢, litter barrels, vending, petwalk**
25	rd E, rd U, to Camden Point, **E** 🅰 Phillips 66/dsl
24mm	**weigh sta nb/truck parking sb**
20	MO 92, MO 273, to Atchison, Leavenworth, **W** antiques, to Weston Bend SP
19.5mm	Platte River
19	rd HH, Platte City, **E** antiques, **W** 🅰 Casey's, Platte-Clay Fuel/dsl, 🍴 DQ, Maria's Mexican, Pizza Hut, Red Dragon Chinese, 🏨 Comfort Inn, Travelodge, 🅾 ▷ RV Park, ALPS Foods, CarQuest, $General, O'Reilly Parts, USPO, vet, same as 18

[■] = gas [🍴] = food [🛏] = lodging [◉] = other Copyright 2011 - The Next Exit

INTERSTATE 29 CONT'D

Exit	Services
18	MO 92, Platte City, **E** Basswood RV Park (5mi), **W** [■] Conoco/KFC, QT/dsl, [🍴] Arby's, Burger King, China Wok, DQ, McDonald's, Mr GoodCents Subs, Pizza Hut/Taco Bell, Pizza Shoppe, Sonic, Subway, Waffle House, [🛏] Best Western, Super 8, [◉] Buick/Chevrolet, CVS Drug, Ford, Goodyear/auto, PriceChopper Foods, TrueValue, Walgreens, same as 19
17	I-435 S, to Topeka
15	Mexico City Ave, **W** [🛏] Marriott, [◉] [✈]
14	I-435, E (from sb), to St Louis
13	to I-435 E, **E** [🛏] Extended Stay America, Fairfield Inn, Hawthorn Suites, Holiday Inn, Microtel, Radisson, Sheraton, Super 8, **W** [🛏] Marriott, [◉] KCI [✈]
12	NW 112th St, **E** [■] BP, Conoco/dsl, [🛏] Candlewood Suites, Comfort Inn, Days Inn, Extended Stay America, Hampton Inn, Hilton, Holiday Inn Express, **W** [🛏] EconoLodge
10	Tiffany Springs Pkwy, **E** [■] Phillips 66, [🍴] Cirque d'Alex, SmokeBox BBQ, [🛏] Embassy Suites, Homewood Suites, Residence Inn, **W** [🍴] Cracker Barrel, Marco's Pizza, Ruby Tuesday, Waffle House, Wendy's, [🛏] Chase Suites, Courtyard, Drury Inn, Homestead Suites, Hyatt Place, Sleep Inn, [◉] Buick/GMC, Harley-Davidson, Honda, Lexus, Nissan, Toyota
9b a	MO 152, to Liberty, Topeka
8	MO 9, rd T, NW Barry Rd, **E** [■] Valero/dsl, [🍴] Applebee's, Boston Mkt, Chili's, China Wok, Chipotle Mexican, Honeybaked Cafe, Hong's Buffet, Hooters, Houlihan's, Kato Japanese, LoneStar Steaks, On the Border, Panda Express, Panera Bread, Pizza Hut/Taco Bell, Sheradon's Custard, Starbucks, Subway, Wendy's, Winstead's Rest., [◉] [H], Best Buy, $Tree, Ford, Hobby Lobby, Home Depot, HyVee Foods, JC Penney, Lowe's, SteinMart, Target, Walmart, **W** [■] Phillips 66, QT/dsl, [🍴] A&W/LJSilver, Arby's, BoLings Chinese, 54th St Grill, Jimmy John's, McDonald's, Mimi's Cafe, Minsky's Pizza, Outback Steaks, Quiznos, Rainbow Oriental, Smokehouse BBQ, Sonic, Stone Canyon Pizza, Taco Bueno, [🛏] La Quinta, Motel 6, Super 8, [◉] AT&T, Barnes&Noble, CVS Drug, Dick's, Dillard's, Marshall's, Old Navy, Staples
6	NW 72nd St, Platte Woods, **E** [■] Sinclair/dsl, [◉] vet, **W** [■] Phillips 66, [🍴] Iron Wok, KFC, Papa John's, Tasty Thai, [◉] Sears Grand
5	MO 45 N, NW 64th St, **W** [■] Shell/dsl, [🍴] All-star Pizza&Subs, Bonefish Grill, Caribou Coffee, Chamas Brazilian Grill, Goodcents Subs, IHOP, McDonald's, O'Quigley's Grill, Papa Murphy's, Quiznos, Starbucks, Subway, Taco Bell, [◉] CVS Drug, $General, GNC, Radio Shack
4	NW 56th St (from nb), **W** [■] Phillips 66
3c	rd A (from sb), Riverside, **W** [■] QT, [🍴] Argosy Café, Corner Café, Sonic, [🛏] Skyline Inn, Super 8, [◉] USPO
3b	I-635, S
3a	Waukomis Dr, rd AA (from nb)
2b	US 169, S (from sb), to KC
2a	US 169, N (from nb), to Smithville
1e	US 69, Vivion Rd, **E** [■] Phillips66/dsl, [🍴] Steak'n Shake, [◉] Cadillac/Chevrolet, Chrysler/Jeep, Home Depot, Lincoln/Mercury, Suzuki, **W** [■] Shell, [🍴] McDonald's, Subway
1d	MO 283 S, Oak Tfwy (from sb), **W** [■] Phillips 66, [🍴] McDonald's
1c	Gladstone (from nb), **E** [■] Phillips 66, [🍴] CiCi's Pizza,

1c	Continued
	Panda Express, Quiznos, Taco Bueno, [◉] [H], BigLots, Lowe's, Office Depot, PriceChopper Foods
1b	I-35, N (from sb), to Des Moines
1a	Davidson Rd
8mm	**I-35 N, I-29 and I-35 run together 6 mi.**

See Missouri Interstate 35, exits 3-8a.

INTERSTATE 35

Exit	Services
114mm	Missouri/Iowa state line
114	US 69, to Lamoni, **W** [■] Conoco/dsl/24hr, [◉] RV camping
113.5mm	Zadie Creek
112mm	**MO welcome ctr sb, full [♿] facilities, [🚻], [🌲], litter barrels, petwalk, wireless internet**
110	**weigh sta both lanes**
106	rd N, Blythedale, **E** [■] Conoco/fireworks, Phillips 66/dsl/café/motel/24hr/@, [🍴] DinnerBell Rest., [🛏] Eagle's Landing Motel, [◉] dsl repair, **W** [■] Phillips 66/dsl/24hr, [◉] Eagle Ridge RV Park (2mi)
99	rd A, to Ridgeway, **5 mi W** Eagle RV Camping
94mm	E Fork Big Creek
93	US 69, Bethany, **W** [🍴] Big Boys BBQ (1mi), Dos Chiquitas Mexican
92	US 136, Bethany, **E** [■] Phillips 66/dsl/24hr, [🍴] KFC/Taco Bell, McDonald's, [🛏] Budget Inn, **W** [■] BP/dsl, Kum&Go, Wendy's/dsl, MFA, [🍴] Breadeaux Pizza, Country Kitchen, DQ, Nopal Mexican, Sonic, Subway, Taco Bell, TootToot Rest., [🛏] Comfort Inn, Super 8, [◉] [H], Russell Stover, Walmart
90mm	Pole Cat Creek
88	MO 13, to Bethany, Gallatin
84	rds AA, H, to Gilman City, **E** Crowder SP (24mi)
81mm	**rest area both lanes, full [♿] facilities**
80	rds B, N, to Coffey
78	rd C, Pattonsburg, **W** [■] Phillips 66/dsl
74.5mm	Grand River
72	rd DD
68	US 69, to Pattonsburg
64	MO 6, to Maysville, Gallatin
61	US 69, Winston, Gallatin, **E** [■] Shell/dsl/rest./24hr
54	US 36, Cameron, **E** [■] Shell/Wendy's/dsl/24hr, Sinclair/dsl/scales, [🍴] McDonald's, Subway, [🛏] Best Western, Budget Inn, Comfort Inn, [◉] Crossroads RV Park, **W** [■] Valero, [🍴] Burger King, Domino's, DQ, El Maguey Mexican, Ma&Pa's Kettle Rest., KFC/Taco Bell, Pizza Hut, Sonic, [🛏] Days Inn, Econolodge, Relax Inn, Super 8, [◉] [H], Advance Parts, Ford, Buick/Chevrolet, CountryMart Foods, $General, Ford/Mercury, O'Reilly Parts, Radio Shack, UPSO Walmart, W MO Corr Ctr, tires
52	rd BB, Lp 35, to Cameron, **E** [◉] [H], **W** [■] Casey's, Kum&Go, same as 54
49mm	Brushy Creek
48.5mm	Shoal Creek
48	US 69, Cameron, **E** to Wallace SP (2mi), **W** [■] Shamrock, [◉] fireworks
40	MO 116, Lathrop, **E** [■] Phillips 66/Country Café/dsl, [◉] antiques
34.5mm	**rest area both lanes, full [♿] facilities, [🚻], [🌲], litter barrels, vending, petwalk**
33	rd PP, Holt, **E** [🍴] Hilltop Grill, [◉] RV Dump, **W** [■] Conoco/dsl, [🛏] American Eagle Inn
30mm	Holt Creek

Side markers (vertical): MO · PLATTE CITY · N↕S · KANSAS CITY (left column); N↕S · BETHANY · CAMERON (right column)

Copyright 2011 - The Next Exit® 🅿 = **gas** 🍴 = **food** 🛏 = **lodging** 🅾 = **other**

MO

INTERSTATE 35 CONT'D

Exit	Services
26	MO 92, Kearney, E 🅿🍴 China Wok, McDonald's, Pizza Hut, Sonic, 🛏 Comfort Inn, Super 8, 🅾 CountryMart Foods, CVS Drug, Kramer Hardware, Red Cross Drug, to Watkins Mill SP, W 🅿🍴/ Taco Bell/dsl/scales/24hr, Platte Clay Fuel/dsl, 🍴 Arby's, Burger King, Hunan Garden Chinese, Pizza Shoppe, Stables Grill, Subway, 🛏 Econolodge, 🅾 Curves, Goodyear/auto, John's Foods, O'Reilly Parts, to Smithville Lake
22mm	weigh sta nb, parking area sb
20	US 69, MO 33, to Excelsior Springs, E 🅷
17	MO 291, rd A, **1 mi** E 🅿 BP, QT, 🍴 A&W, Arby's, CiCi's, LJ Silver, McDonald's, Minsky's Pizza, Papa John's, Papa Murphy's, Perkins, Sonic, Subway, Taco Bell, 🛏 Days Inn, 🅾 Chevrolet, $General, Firestone, Lifestyle RV Ctr, O'Reilly Parts, Walgreens, same as 16, W 🅿 Phillips 66/dsl, QT, 🍴 McDonald's, Sonic, Subway, 🛏 ValuePlace Inn, 🅾 KCI ✈, Price Chopper Foods
16	MO 152, Liberty, E 🅿 Phillips 66/Circle K, 🍴 Baskin-Robbins, Chick-fil-A, Culver's, 5 Guys Burgers, Godfather's, Olive Garden, Pizza Hut, Planet Sub, Red Robin, Texas Roadhouse, Wendy's, 🛏 Days Inn, Super 8, 🅾 🅷, Advance Parts, Chevrolet, CVS Drug, Firestone/auto, Ford, Hy-Vee Foods, Lowe's Whse, Sears Grand, Walgreens, W 🅿 Phillips 66/Circle K/dsl, 🍴 Applebee's, Backyard Burger, Bob Evans, Buffalo Wild Wings, Burger King, Chili's, Cracker Barrel, 54th St Grill, Golden Corral,

KEARNEY N ↕ S

LIBERTY

Exit	Services
16	Continued KFC, LongHorn Steaks, McDonald's, O'Charley's, Panera Bread, Panda Express, Quizno's, Schlotsky's, SmokeBox BBQ, Steak'n Shake, Subway, Taco Bell, Uno, Waffle House, 🛏 Comfort Suites, Fairfield Inn, Hampton Inn, Holiday Inn Express, 🅾 Aldi Foods, AT&T, Best Buy, Ford, Home Depot, JC Penney, Jiffy Lube, Kohl's, Michael's, NAPA, NTB, Office Depot, Radio Shack, Target, TJ Maxx, Walmart
14	US 69 (exits left from sb), Liberty Dr, to Glenaire, Pleasant Valley, E 🅿 Phillips 66, Sinclair, Shell, 🅾 I-35 RV Ctr, W 🅿 QT/dsl
13	US 69 (from nb), to Pleasant Valley, E 🅿 Phillips 66/dsl, Shell, Sinclair/24hr, 🍴 KFC, McDonald's, 🅾 auto repair, W 🅿 QT/dsl
12b a	I-435, to St Louis
11	US 69 N, Vivion Rd, E 🅿 BP/dsl, Shell/dsl, 🍴 Church's, McDonald's, W 🅿 QT, 🍴 Sonic, Stroud's Rest.
10	N Brighton Ave (from nb), E 🍴 Church's, McDonald's
9	MO 269 S, Chouteau Trfwy, E 🅿 Phillips 66, 🍴 IHOP, McDonald's, Ming Garden, Outback Steaks, Papa Murphy's, Popeye's, Subway, Wing Stop, 🅾 AT&T, Food Festival, GNC, Harrah's Casino/rest., Radio Shack, Target, W 🍴 Wendy's (1mi)
8c	MO 1, Antioch Rd, E 🅿 7-11, 🍴 Domino's, 🛏 Best Western, 🅾 auto repair, W 🅿 Phillips 66, 🍴 Catfish Rest.,

INTERSTATE 35 CONT'D

Exit	Services
8c	Continued
	Waffle House, 🅾 Walgreens
8b	I-29 N, US 71 N, KCI ✈
	I-35 S and I-29 S run together 6 mi.
8a	Parvin Rd, **E** ⛽ BP, Shell, 🅾 O'Reilly Parts, **W** 🛏 Super Inn
6b a	Armour Rd, **E** ⛽ Phillips 66/dsl, 🍴 Arby's, Burger King, Denny's, McDonald's, Quizno's, 🛏 Best Value Inn, La Quinta, 🅾 H, repair, to Riverboat Casino, **W** ⛽ Conoco/dsl, QT, Phillips 66, 🍴 DQ, Lucky Dragon Chinese, Pizza Hut, Subway, Taco Bell, Wendy's, 🛏 American Inn, Quality Inn, 🅾 USPO
5b	16th Ave, industrial district
5a	Levee Rd, Bedford St, industrial district
4.5mm	Missouri River
4b	Front St, **E** Isle of Capri Riverboat Casino/rest.
4a	US 24 E, Independence Ave
3	I-70 E, US 71 S, to St Louis
2g	**I-35 N and I-29 N run together 6 mi**
2e	Oak St, Grand-Walnut St, **E** ⛽ Phillips 66, 🛏 Marriott
2d	Main-Delaware, Wyandotte St, downtown
2a	I-70 W, to Topeka
2y	US 169, Broadway, to downtown
2w	12th St, Kemper Arena, to downtown
2v	14th St, to downtown
2u	I-70 E, to Broadway, **E** 🍴 Denny's
1e	US 69, Vivion Rd, **E** ⛽ Phillips66/dsl, 🍴 Steak'n Shake, 🅾 Cadillac/Chevrolet, Chrysler/Jeep, Home Depot, Lincoln/Mercury, Suzuki, **W** ⛽ Shell, 🍴 McDonald's, Subway
1d	20th St (from sb), **W** ⛽ Phillips 66, 🍴 McDonald's
1c	27th St, SW Blvd, W Pennway (from nb), **E** ⛽ Phillips 66, 🍴 CiCi's Pizza, Panda Express, Quiznos, Taco Bueno, 🅾 H, BigLots, Lowe's, Office Depot, PriceChopper Foods
1b	I-29 (from nb), to Des Moines
1a	SW Trafficway (from sb)
0mm	Missouri/Kansas state line

INTERSTATE 44

Exit	Services
290mm	I-44 begins/ends on I-55, exit 207 in St Louis.
290a	I-55 S, to Memphis
290c	Gravois Ave (from wb), 12th St, **S** 🍴 McDonald's
290b	18th St (from eb), downtown
289	Jefferson Ave, St Louis, **N** ⛽ Phillips 66, 🛏 Holiday Inn Express, Residence Inn, **S** ⛽ Conoco, 🍴 Lee's Chicken, McDonald's
288	Grand Blvd, St Louis, **N** ⛽ BP, 🛏 Water Tower Inn, 🅾 H, **S** 🍴 Jack-in-the-Box, Qdoba, St Louis Bread
287b a	Kingshighway, Vandeventer Ave, St Louis, **N** ⛽ BP, 🅾 H, Jiffy Lube, U-Haul, **S** ⛽ BP, 🅾 Chevrolet, Walgreens, to MO Botanical Garden
286	Hampton Ave, St Louis, **N** ⛽ BP, Mobil, Phillips 66, Shell/Circle K, 🍴 Denny's, Jack-in-the-Box, McDonald's, Steak'n Shake, Subway, Taco Bell, **S** ⛽ Shell/Circle K, 🍴 Hardee's, 🛏 Drury Inn, Holiday Inn, Red Roof Inn, 🅾 museums, zoo
285	SW Ave (from wb, no EZ return)
284b a	Arsenal St, Jamieson St
283	Shrewsbury (from wb), some services same as 282

Exit	Services
282	Laclede Sta Rd, Murdock Ave (from eb), St Louis, **N** ⛽ Phillips 66, 🍴 DQ, Front Row Grill, Imo's Pizza, McDonald's, Racanelli's Pizza, Starbucks, Subway, Webster Wok Chinese, 🅾 Ben Franklin Crafts, Subaru, vet
280	Elm Ave, St Louis, **N** ⛽ BP/repair, 🍴 Lenny's Subs, 🅾 Schnuck's Food/24hr, **S** ⛽ BP (1mi), Circle K, 🅾 Walgreens
279	(from wb), Berry Rd
278	Big Bend Rd, St Louis, **N** 🍴 Hardee's, Sonic, 🅾 H, Sam's Club/gas, **S** ⛽ Mobil/dsl, QT
277b	US 67, US 61, US 50, Lindbergh Blvd, **N** ⛽ Shell, 🍴 Arby's, Chili's, Chipotle Mexican, O'Charley's, Steak&Rice Chinese, TX Roadhouse, Uno, White Castle, 🛏 Best Western, 🅾 H, AT&T, $Tree, Hancock Fabrics, Harley-Davidson, Hobby Lobby, Lowe's Whse, Office Depot, PetCo, Target, TJ Maxx, Verizon, Walmart, **S** ⛽ Phillips 66, Shell, Circle K, 🍴 Burger King, Denny's, Fuddrucker's, Helen Fitzgerald's Grill, IHOP, Lion's Choice, Longhorn Steaks, Ruby Tuesday, Steak'n Shake, St Louis Bread, Viking Rest, 🛏 Days Inn/rest., Hampton Inn, Holiday Inn, Quality Inn, 🅾 Dobb's Auto/Tire, Home Depot, Marshall's, Old Navy, Petsmart, WorldMkt
277a	MO 366 E, Watson Rd, access to same as 277b S
276b a	I-270, N to Chicago, S Memphis
275	N Highway Dr (from wb), Soccer Pk Rd, **N** ⛽ Road Ranger/dsl/rest.
274a b	Bowles Ave, **N** ⛽ Road Ranger/🍴/Subway/dsl, **S** ⛽ Phillips 66, QT, ZX/dsl, 🍴 Bandana's BBQ, Cracker Barrel, Denny's, Jack-in-the-Box, Krispy Kreme, Mandarin Cuisine, McDonald's, Quizno's, Sonic, White Castle, 🛏 Drury Inn, Fairfield Inn, Holiday Inn Express, Motel 6, PearTree Inn, Stratford Inn, Super 8, TownePlace Inn, 🅾 Goodyear
272	MO 141, Fenton, Valley Park, **N** ⛽ Motomart, **S** ⛽ Phillips 66, QT, 🍴 Bob Evans, Burger King, Dickey's BBQ, Domino's, Hardee's, Imo's Pizza, Jimmy John's, McDonald's, Ruby Tuesday, Starbucks, Steak'n Shake, Subway, Taco Bell, 🛏 Drury Inn, Hampton Inn, 🅾 AT&T, Curves, Sav-A-Lot Foods
269	Antire Rd, Beaumont
266	Lewis Rd, **N** 🅾 Rte 66 SP, golf
266mm	Meramec River
265	Williams Rd (from eb)
264	MO 109, rd W, Eureka, **N** ⛽ Phillips 66, 🍴 Arby's, Burger King, Domino's, DQ, El Lopel Mexican, McDonald's, Pizza Hut, Ponderosa, Rich&Charlie's Italian, Smokers BBQ, St Louis Bread, Subway, Taco Bell, White Castle, 🛏 Days Inn, 🅾 AT&T, AutoTire, O'Reilly Parts, Schnuck's Foods, to Babler SP, **S** ⛽ QT, 🅾 Walgreens
261	Lp 44, to Allenton, **N** ⛽ Motomart/McDonald's/dsl, 🍴 Applebee's, China King, Denny's, Imo's Pizza, KFC, Lion's Choice, Pizza Hut, Steak'n Shake, Taco Bell, White Castle, 🛏 Econolodge, Holiday Inn, Super 8, 🅾 AutoZone, $Tree, GNC, O'Reilly Parts, Radio Shack, Verizon, Walmart, to Six Flags, same as 264, **S** ⛽ Shell/Circle K/dsl, 🅾 Ford, KOA
257	Lp 44, Pacific, **N** ⛽ Phillips 66, 🍴/Subway/dsl/scales/24hr, 🍴 Huddle House, 🛏 Comfort Inn, 🅾 fireworks, **S** ⛽ BP/dsl, Mobil/dsl/24hr, Motomart/24hr, 🍴 Hardee's, KFC, McDonald's, New China, Pizza Hut, Taco Bell, 🛏 Quality Inn, 🅾 Chevrolet, Chrysler/Dodge/Jeep, $General, NAPA, O'Reilly Parts, Queen's Foods
253	MO 100 E, to Gray Summit, **S** ⛽ Phillips 66/dsl, 🛏 Travelodge, 🅾 fireworks

INTERSTATE 44 CONT'D

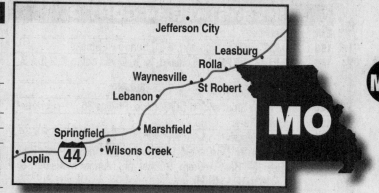

Exit	Services
251	MO 100 W, to Washington, **N** BP/dsl/24hr, Mr Fuel/dsl/scales, Phillips 66/Burger King/dsl, Domino's, Subway
247	US 50 W, rd AT, rd O, to Union, **N** Harley-Davidson, **S** to Robertsville SP
247mm	Bourbeuse River
242	rd AH, to Hist Rte 66
240	MO 47, St Clair, **N** Phillips 66/Taco Bell/dsl, Burger King, Reed RV Ctr, **S** Mobil/dsl, McDonald's, Subway, Budget Lodge, Super 8, $General, USPO
239	MO 30, rds AB, WW, St Clair, **N** repair, **S** Phillips 66/dsl
238mm	**weigh sta both lanes**
235mm	**rest area both lanes (both lanes exit left), full facilities, , , litter barrels, vending, petwalk**
230	rds W, Stanton, **S** Shell/fireworks, KOA, Meramec Caverns Camping (3mi)
226	MO 185 S, Sullivan, **N** FLYING J/Denny's/dsl/LP/scales/24hr, **S** Phillips 66/Burger King, Applebee's, Arby's, Bison Grill, DQ, Hardee's, KFC, McDonald's, Steak'n Shake, Subway, Taco Bell, AutoZone, $General, Lowe's Whse, O'Reilly Parts, Walmart, RV Camping, to Meramec SP, same as 225
225	MO 185 N, rd D, Sullivan, **N** Mobil, Phillips 66/dsl, Domino's, Dukumn Rest, Baymont Inn, Econolodge, Family Inn, Super 8, Chrysler/Dodge/Jeep, Ford/Mercury, **S** Fas-Trip/dsl/café, ZX, China Buffet, Cracker Barrel, Jack-in-the-Box, Lion's Choice, Pizza Hut, Sonic, Comfort Inn, , Aldi Foods, AT&T, Goodyear, city park, same as 226
218	rds N, C, J, Bourbon, **N** BP, Budget Inn, **S** Mobil/24hr, HenHouse Rest., Bourban RV Ctr, Blue Sprgs Camping (6mi), Riverview Ranch Camping (8mi)
214	rd H, Leasburg, **N** Mobil/dsl, **S** Skippy's Rest, to Onandaga Cave SP (7mi)
210	rd UU, **N** Meremac Valley Resort, **S** MO Hick BBQ (2mi), Rte 66 Roadhouse, winery
208	MO 19, Cuba, **N** Phillips 66, Voss/dsl/rest./scales/24hr/@, Country Kitchen, Huddle House, Pizza Hut, Best Western, Super 8, Blue Beacon, **S** Casey's, Delano/dsl, Mobil/24hr, Domino's, East Sun Chinese, Hardee's, Jack-in-the-Box, McDonald's, Sonic, Subway, Holiday Inn Express, $General, Mace Foods, O'Reilly Parts, Walmart, to Ozark Nat Scenic Riverways, vet
203	rds F, ZZ, **N** Ladybug RV Park, **S** Rosatti Winery (2mi)
195	MO 8, MO 68, St James, Maramec Sprg Park, **N** Mobil/dsl, Shell, McDonald's, Pizza Hut, Sonic, Subway, Days Inn, Economy Inn, Ford, NAPA, O'Reilly Parts, Ray's Tires, to Maremac Winery, **S** Delano/dsl, Phillips 66/dsl, Burger King, CountryMart Foods
189	rd V, **S** Loves/McDonald's/Subway/dsl/scales/24hr, Matt's Steaks
186	US 63, MO 72, Rolla, **N** Sinclair, Steak'n Shake, Drury Inn, Hampton Inn, Sooter Inn, Big O Tire, Kia, Nissan, Lowe's Whse, Plaza Tire, **S** BP, Mobil/dsl, Phillips 66, Denny's, Donut King, Lee's Chicken, Budget Motel, Fortune Inn,
185	rd E, to Rolla, **S** Delano, Phillips 66, Applebee's, Arby's, DQ, Hardee's, Huddle House, Kyoto Japanese,

Exit	Services
185	Continued Papa John's, Subway, Taco Bell, , Ford/Lincoln/Mercury, Walgreens, UMO at Rolla, st patrol
184	US 63 S, to Rolla, **N** Comfort Suites, Holiday Inn Express, **S** Delano, Gas+, MotoMart, Arby's, Burger King, Little Caesar's, LJ Silver, Lucky House Chinese, Maid-Rite, McDonald's, Pizza Hut, Pizza Inn, Shoney's, Sirloin Stockade, Waffle House, Wendy's, Zeno's Steaks, Ziggy's, Baymont Inn, Best Inn, Best Way Inn, Best Western, Days Inn, Econolodge, Quality Inn, Rolla Inn, Super 8, Wayfarer Inn, , Buick/Cadillac/Chevrolet/GMC, Goodyear/auto, Kroger, city park
179	rds T, C, to Doolittle, Newburg, **S** BP/24hr, Cookin' From Scratch Rest.
178mm	**rest area both lanes, full facilities, , , litter barrels, vending, petwalk**
176	Sugar Tree Rd, **N** Vernelle's Motel, **S** Arlington River Resort Camping (2mi)
172	rd D, Jerome, **N** camping
169	rd J
166	to Big Piney
164mm	Big Piney River
163	MO 28, to Dixon, **N** /Road Ranger/Chesters/Subway/dsl/scales/24hr, **S** Phillips 66/dsl, Country Café, Sweetwater BBQ, Best Western, Country Hearth Inn, Days Inn, RV Park
161b a	rd Y, to Ft Leonard Wood, **N** Mobil/dsl, Aussie Jack's, Cracker Barrel, Domino's, Home Cookin' Diner, Kyoto Japanese, Miller's Grill, Pizza Hut, Ruby Tuesday, Ryan's, Subway, Wendy's, Baymont Inn, Best Value Inn, Candlewood Suites, Comfort Inn, Fairfield Inn, Hampton Inn, Mainstay Suites, Red Roof Inn, $Tree, Lowe's Whse, Scion/Toyota, Walmart, **S** Cenex/dsl, Conoco, Arby's, China Buffet, El Sombrero, KFC, McDonald's, Mediterranean Grill, Papa John's, Subway, Taco Bell, Waffle House, Budget Inn, Econolodge, Holiday Inn Express, Motel 6, Ramada Inn, AutoZone, Chrysler/Dodge, $General, Family$, Ford/Lincoln/Mercury/Mazda, Goodyear/auto, NAPA, O'Reilly Parts, Radio Shack
159	Lp 44, to Waynesville, St Robert, **N** Gas City/dsl, DQ, Sonic, Star Motel, Super 8, O'Reilly Parts, True Value, auto repair, **S** BP/dsl, Pepper's Grill, Microtel, Big O Tire, Cadillac/GMC
158mm	Roubidoux Creek
156	rd H, Waynesville, **N** BP, Casey's, Kum&Go/dsl, McDonald's, Subway, Buick/Chevrolet, $General, Price Cutter+, vet
153	MO 17, to Buckhorn, **N** Whitmor Farms/dsl, Ft Wood Inn, **S** Shell/dsl, Glen Oaks RV Park

MO

E W LEBANON MARSHFIELD

INTERSTATE 44 CONT'D

Exit	Services
150	MO 7, rd P to Richland, S Sundown Steaks
145	MO 133, rd AB, to Richland, N Oasis/dsl/rest./24hr, S camping
143mm	Gasconade River
140	rd N, to Stoutland, S Conoco, Phillips 66
139mm	Bear Creek
135	rd F, Sleeper
130	rd MM, N Cenex, Phillips 66, Andy's Rest, Bell Rest, Best Western, Budget Inn, Munger Moss Inn, S Kum&Go, H
129	MO 5, MO 32, MO 64, to Hartville, Lebanon, N Break-Time, Kum&Go, A&W, Applebee's, Arby's, Bamboo Garden, Burger King, Country Kitchen, DQ, KFC, LJ Silver, McDonald's, Papa John's, Shoney's, Sonic, Steak'n Shake, Subway, Taco Bell, Wendy's, Western Sizzlin, Aldi Foods, AT&T, AutoZone, Chevrolet, Ford, O'Reilly Parts, Radio Shack, Smitty's Foods, Walgreens, Walnut Bowl Factory, to Bennett Sprgs SP, S Conoco/dsl, Phillips 66, Capt D's, Domino's, Hardee's, Pizza Hut, T's Steaks, H, $General, $Tree, FSA/Famous Brands, Goodyear, Lowe's Whse, Walmart, tires, vet, to Lake of the Ozarks
127	Lp 44, Lebanon, N B&D/rest/dsl/scales, Sinclair/dsl, Dowd's BBQ, El Sombrero Mexican, Great Wall Chinese, Maid-Rite, Waffle House, Days Inn, Hampton Inn, Holiday Inn Express, Midwest Inn, Super 8, Travelers Inn, Cutlery/Walnut Bowl Outlet, Chrysler/Dodge/Jeep, tires, S Phillips 66/dsl, Buick/Cadillac/GMC, Harley-Davidson, MO Cheese Outlet, Russell Stover
123	County Rd, S Happy Trails RV Ctr, KOA
118	rds C, A, Phillipsburg, N Conoco/dsl, S Phillips 66, antiques, tourist info
113	rds J, Y, Conway, N Conoco/dsl, Phillips 66, Rockin Chair Café, Budget Inn, to Den of Metal Arts, S Sinclair/dsl, SummerFresh Foods, USPO
111mm	**rest area both lanes, full facilities, vending, litter barrels, petwalk**
108mm	Bowen Creek
107	Sparkle Brooke Rd, Sampson Rd
106mm	Niangua River
100	MO 38, rd W, Marshfield, N Murphy USA, Phillips 66, Subway, Tiny's Smokehouse, Big O Tires, Chevrolet, Ford, Radio Shack, Walmart, S Conoco/dsl, Kum&Go/dsl, Phillips 66/dsl/24hr, DQ, El Charro, KFC/Rib Crib, La Hacienda Mexican, McDonald's, Pizza Hut, Pizza Inn, Quizno's, Sonic, Subway, Taco Bell, Ziggy's, Holiday Inn Express, AutoZone, $General, O'Reilly Parts, PriceCutter Foods, RV Express RV Park, Walgreens
96	rd B, Northview
89mm	**weigh sta both lanes**
88	MO 125, to Fair Grove, Strafford, N Loves/Hardee's/dsl/scales/24hr, Shell/scales, TA/Country Pride/Subway/Taco Bell/dsl/scales/24hr/@, McDonald's, Camping World RV Ctr, truckwash, S Conoco/dsl, Kum&Go, Fox's Pizza, Super 8, $Station, Strafford RV Park
84	MO 744, S Peterbilt
82b a	US 65, to Branson, Fedalia, S Kum&Go, Phillips 66/dsl, Waffle House, American Inn, st patrol, to Table Rock Lake, Bull Shoals Lake

SPRINGFIELD

Exit	Services
80b a	rd H to Pleasant Hope, Springfield, N Conoco/dsl/rest./24hr, Waffle House, Budget Lodge, Days Inn, Super 8, to SWSU, S Conoco/dsl, Kum&Go, Phillips 66/dsl, QT, Shell, Sinclair, Andy's Custard, Applebee's, Backyard Burger, Bob Evans, Braum's, Brueadeaux Pizza, Buckingham Smokehouse, Burger King, Chicago Gyros, Costa Mesa Mexican, Cracker Barrel, El Maguey Mexican, Fazoli's, Hardee's, Hong Kong Garden, Houlihan's, Jade East Chinese, Kyoto Japanese, Krispy Kreme, Little Tokyo, LJ Silver, McDonald's, Papa Murphy's, Pizza Hut, Rib Crib, Ruby Tuesday, Ryan's, Schlotzsky's, Shoney's, Sonic, Steak'n Shake, Subway, Taco Bell, Western Sizzlin, Ziggy's Cafe, Best Value Inn, Best Western, Budget Inn, Candlewood Suites, Comfort Inn, Dogwood Park Inn, Doubletree Hotel, Drury Inn, Eagles Lodge, Econolodge, Economy Inn, Flagship Motel, Hampton Inn, Holiday Inn, Lamplighter Hotel, La Quinta, Motel 6, Ozark Inn, Plaza Inn, Quality Inn, Ramada, Rancho Motel, H, Aldi Foods, AutoZone, $General, Goodyear, K-Mart, O'Reilly Parts, PriceCutter Foods, U-Haul, Walmart/auto, vet
77	MO 13, KS Expswy, N Kum&Go/dsl/e-85, Lowe's Whse, S Gas+, Phillips 66/dsl, QT, Buffalo Wild Wings, Braum's, CiCi's, Golden Corral, IHOP, Jimmy John's, McAlister's Deli, McDonald's, Mr Goodcents, Panera Bread, Papa John's, Papa Murphys, Pizza Inn, Subway, Taco Bell, Waffle House, Econolodge, AT&T, BigLots, Dillon's Foods, $Tree, Drug Mart, GNC, Goodyear/auto, Hobby Lobby, Radio Shack, ShopKO, Staples, Walgreens, Walmart
75	US 160, W byp, to Willard, Stockton Lake, S Kum&Go, Quizno's, Wendy's, Baymont Inn, Courtyard
72	MO 266, to Chesnut Expwy, 1-2 mi S Casey's, Cenex, Kum&Go, Alli's Rest, Arby's, Hardee's, KFC, La Hacienda Mexican, LJ Silver, McDonald's, Sonic, Subway, Taco Bell, Taco Bueno, Waffle House, Best Budget Inn, Ramada Ltd, Redwood Motel, AutoZone, Curves, $General, city park
70	rds MM, B, N antiques, fireworks, S Wilson's Creek Nat Bfd (5mi), KOA (1mi)
69	to US 60, Springfield
67	rds N, T, Bois D' Arc, to Republic, S Shell/dsl, AmericInn (5mi), art glass
66mm	Pond Creek
64.6mm	Dry Branch
64.5mm	Pickerel Creek
61	rds K, PP, N Cenex/Hoods/dsl/rest./motel/scales/24hr, Phillips 66
58	MO 96, rds O, Z, to Carthage, Halltown, S Shell/dsl, antiques, RV/truck parts
57	to rd PP (from wb)
56.5mm	Turnback Creek
56mm	Goose Creek
52.5mm	**rest area both lanes, full facilities, , litter barrels, vending, petwalk**
49	MO 174E, rd CCW, Chesapeake
46	MO 39, MO 265, Mt Vernon, Aurora, N Casey's/dsl, Phillips 66/dsl, TA/Conoco/Country Pride/dsl/24hr/@, Bamboo Garden Chinese, KFC/LJ Silver, Mazzio's, McDonald's, Sonic, Subway, Taco Bell, Super 8, USA Inn, $General, Family$, Hometown Drug, O'Reilly Parts, Radio Shack, Summer Fresh Foods, True Value, S Conoco/dsl, Relax Inn, to Table Rock Lake, Stockton Lake

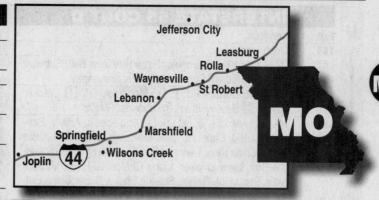

INTERSTATE 44 CONT'D

Exit	Services
44	rd H, to Monett, Mt Vernon, **N** 🍴 Subway (1mi), 🅞 Mid-America Dental/Hearing
43.5mm	Spring River
38	MO 97, to Stotts City, Pierce City, **N** gas/repair, **S** U of MO SW Ctr
33	MO 97 S, to Pierce City, **S** 🅖 Sinclair/dsl, 🍴 Hungry House Cafe, truck/tire repair
29	rd U, to La Russell, Sarcoxie, **N** Ozark Village Gifts, WAC RV Park, antiques, **S** 🅖 Casey's (1mi), Conoco/rest/dsl, Kum&Go/Subway/dsl
29mm	Center Creek
26	MO 37, to Reeds, Sarcoxie, **N** Bill's Truck/trailer repair
22	rd 100 N, **N** Colaw RV Ctr
21mm	Jones Creek
18b a	US 71 N, MO 59 S, to Carthage, Neosho, **N** 🅞 Big Barn Camping, Coachlight RV Ctr/Camping
15	MO 66 W, Lp 44 (from wb), Joplin, **N** 🛏 Tara Motel
15mm	Grove Creek
14mm	Turkey Creek
11b a	US 71 S, MO 249 N, to Neosho, Ft Smith, **S** 🅖 FLYING J /Denny's/dsl/LP/scales/24hr, Phillips 66, Speedco, 🅞 Blue Beacon, Kenworth
8b a	US 71, to Neosho, Joplin, **N** 🅖 Conoco, Kum&Go/dsl, Phillips 66, 🍴 Applebee's, Arby's, Backyard Burger, Bella Pepper's, Bob Evans, Braum's, Burger King, Carino's Italian, Casa Montez Mexican, Cheddar's, Chick-fil-A, CiCi's, ChuckeCheese, Denny's, Domino's, Freddy's Custard, Golden Corral, Great Wall Chinese, Hardee's, IHOP, Jim Bob's Steaks, Jimmy John's, KFC, King Palace, Logan's Roadhouse, LJ Silver, Mazzio's, McAlister's, McDonald's, Noodle&Grill, Olive Garden, Outback Steaks, Pizza Hut, Pizza Inn, Quizno's, Red Hot&Blue Grill, Red Lobster, Rib Crib, Ruby Tuesday, Ryan's, Schlotzsky's, Sonic, Starbucks, Steak'n Shake, Subway, Taco Bell, Taco Hut, Waffle House, Wendy's, Whiskey Creek Steaks, 🛏 Baymont Inn, Best Western, Candlewood Suites, Comfort Inn, Days Inn, Drury Inn, Fairfield Inn, Halmark Inn, Hampton Inn, Hilton Garden, Holiday Inn, La Quinta, Motel 6, Quality Inn, Residence Inn, Rodesite Inn, Super 8, 🅞 Aldi Foods, AT&T, AutoZone, Best Buy, Books-A-Million, Chrysler/Dodge/Jeep, $Tree, Firestone, Food4Less/24hr, Ford/Lincoln/Mercury, Freightliner, Goodyear/auto, Hasting's, Hobby Lobby, Home Depot, Honda, Hyundai, JC Penney, Jo-Ann Fabrics, Kia, Kohl's, Lowe's Whse, Macy's, Michael's, Nissan, Office Depot, Old Navy, O'Reilly Parts, Petsmart, Sam's Club/gas, Scion/Toyota, Sears, Target, TJ Maxx, Verizon, Walgreens, Walmart, **S** 🅖 Casey's, 🍴 Cracker Barrel, Fazoli's, 🛏 Microtel, TownePlace Suites, 🅞 Wheelen RV Ctr
6	MO 86, MO 43 N, to Racine, Joplin, **N** 🅖 Phillips 66, 🍴 KFC (1mi), Schlotzsky's (1mi), 🅞 Walgreens (2mi), **S** Harley-Davidson
5.5mm	Shoal Creek
4	MO 43 to Seneca, **N** 🅖 Loves/Hardee's/dsl/24hr, 🅞 Peterbilt, antiques, **S** 🅖 Conoco/Subway/dsl, Petro/Iron Skillet/dsl/scales/@, 🅖 /Wendy's/dsl/scales/24hr, 🍴 McDonald's, 🛏 Sleep Inn, 🅞 IA 80 Truckomat, KOA, fireworks
3mm	weigh sta both lanes
2mm	Welcome Ctr eb, rest area wb, full ♿ facilities, 🅿, litter barrels, 🅒, vending

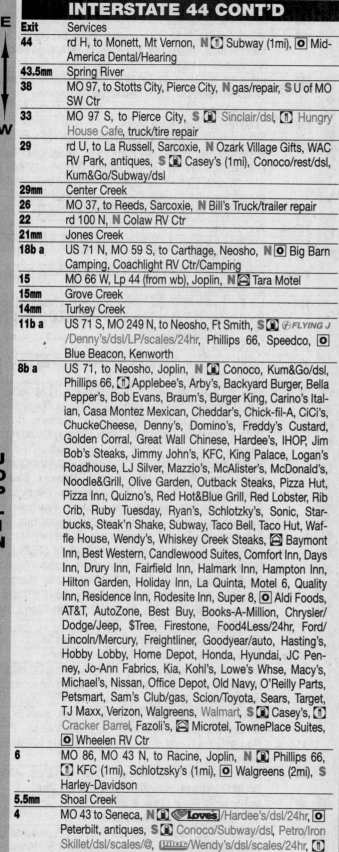

Exit	Services
1	US 400, US 166W, to Baxter Springs, KS, **S** 🅞 Sandstone Gardens
0mm	Missouri/Oklahoma state line

INTERSTATE 55

Exit	Services
209mm	Missouri/Illinois state line at St. Louis, Mississippi River
209b	I-70, W to Kansas City
209a	to Arch, Busch Stadium
208	Park Ave, 7th St, **W** 🅖 BP, 🍴 Rally's, Taco Bell, White Castle, 🛏 Hilton
207c b	Truman Pkwy, **W** I-44 W, to Tulsa
207a	Gravois St (from nb), **E** 🅖 Midwest Petroleum, **W** 🍴 A-1 Chinese Wok, Jack-in-the-Box
206c	Arsenal St, **E** Anheuser-Busch Tour Ctr, **W** 🅖 Shell
206b	Broadway (from nb)
206a	Potomac St (from nb)
205	Gasconade, **W** 🅗
204	Broadway, **E** 🅖 Phillips 66/repair, **W** 🅖 Sinclair/dsl, 🍴 Hardee's, McDonald's, Subway, 🅞 Radio Shack, Walgreen/24hr
203	Bates St, Virginia Ave, **W** 🅖 BP, 7-11
202c	Loughborough Ave, **W** 🍴 St Louis Bread Co, Starbucks, 🅞 Lowe's Whse, Schnuck's Foods
202b	Germania (from sb)
202a	Carondelet (from nb)
201b	Weber Rd
201a	Bayless Ave, **E** 🅖 BP, 🍴 McDonald's, **W** 🅖 Mobil, 7-11/gas, 🍴 China Wok, DQ, Jack-in-the-Box, Pizza Hut/Taco Bell, Subway, Taco Bell, 🅞 Walgreens, auto repair
200	Union Rd (from sb)
199	Reavis Barracks Rd, **E** 🅖 Shell, 🍴 Pennie's BBQ, 🅞 Hancock Fabrics
197	US 50, US 61, US 67, Lindbergh Blvd, **E** 🅖 Phillips 66, 🍴 Arby's, Buffalo Wild Wings, ChuckeCheese, Dillard's, HoneyBaked Ham, Hooters, KFC, Krispy Kreme, Macaroni Grill, Noodles&Co, Qdoba, Quiznos, Station Subs, Steak'n Shake, St Louis Bread Co, Subway, Tucker's Place, 🛏 Holiday Inn, 🅞 Advance Parts, Best Buy, Border's Book, Costco/gas, Dillard's, Discount Tire, Dodge, Ford, Home Depot, JC Penney, Kia, K-Mart, Macy's, Marshall's, NTB, Sears/auto, Tuesday Morning, mall, **W** 🅖 QT, 🍴 Bob Evans, Casa Gallardo, Culvers, Denny's, Lenny's Subs, O'Charley's, Ponderosa, 🛏 Best Value Inn, Motel 6, 🅞 Aldi Foods, AT&T, Costco/gas, Ford/Lincoln/Mercury, Honda, Hyundai, Mazda, Office Depot, Target
196b	I-270 W, to Kansas City
196a	I-255 E, to Chicago
195	Butler Hill Rd, **E** 🅖 Phillips 66, 🛏 Hampton Inn, Holiday Inn/rest., 🅞 Advance Parts, Walgreens, **W** 🅖 Phillips 66,

INTERSTATE 55 CONT'D	
Exit	**Services**
195	Continued 🍴 Burger King, Hardee's, Pizza Hut/Taco Bell, Subway, Waffle House, ⊙ Schnuck's Foods, tires/repair
193	Meramec Bottom Rd, **E** ⛽ Mobil/dsl, QT, 🍴 Cracker Barrel, 🛏 Best Western, ⊙ Midwest RV Ctr
191	MO 141, Arnold, **E** ⛽ QT, 🍴 Applebee's, Arby's, Bandana's BBQ, Capt D's, Casa Mexicana, Chick-fil-A, Cici's Pizza, China King, Denny's, Fazoli's, 54th St Grill, Jack-in-the-Box, Lee's Chicken, Lion's Choice, LJ Silver, McDonald's, Pizza Hut, Rally's, Steak'n Shake, Super China Buffet, Taco Bell, Terrazza Grill, 🛏 Drury Inn, Ramada Ltd, ⊙ AT&T, Dobbs Tire, Hobby Lobby, Kohl's, NAPA, O'Reilly Parts, PetCo, Shop'n Save Foods, Walgreens, Walmart, vet, **W** ⛽ Phillips 66/dsl, 🍴 Chili's, Pasta House, Qdoba, St Louis Bread, TX Roadhouse, 🛏 ValuePlace Hotel, ⊙ Dierberg's Foods, $Tree, Lowe's, Office Depot, Petsmart
190	Richardson Rd, **E** ⛽ Phillips 66/dsl, QT, Shell/Circle K/dsl, 🍴 Culver's, DQ, Domino's, Pizza Hut, Ponderosa, Quiznos, Roly-Poly Sandwiches, Sonic, Taco Bell, White Castle, ⊙ URGENT CARE, Advance Parts, Auto Tire, $Tree, Firestone, Ford, Sav-A-Lot Foods, **W** ⛽ Phillips 66/dsl, 7-11, Shell/Circle K/dsl, 🍴 Burger King, Happy Wok, Imo's Pizza, McDonald's/playplace, Mr. Goodcents Subs, Pizza Den, Ruby Tuesday, Waffle House, 🛏 Comfort Inn, ⊙ Aamco, AutoZone, GNC, Home Depot, Plaza Tire, Radio Shack, Schnuck's Foods/24hr, Target, Walgreens
186	Imperial, Kimmswick, **E** ⛽ Mobil, Shell/Circle K, 🍴 Blue Owl (1mi), Main St BBQ, ⊙ auto repair, **W** ⛽ Phillips 66/Jack-in-the-Box/dsl, 🍴 China Wok, Domino's, Gianno's Grill, O'aces Grill, Papa John's, Subway, ⊙ USPO, to Mastodon SP
185	rd M, Barnhart, Antonia, **E** ⛽ BP/dsl, 🍴 Ginny's Kitchen, **W** ⛽ BP, Phillips 66/dsl, 7-11, ⊙ Walgreens
184.5mm	**weigh sta both lanes**
180	rd Z, to Hillsboro, Pevely, **E** ⛽ Mobil/dsl, 🍴 Bobby Tom's BBQ, Burger King, China House, Domino's, Subway, The Kitchen, ⊙ $General, Queens Foods, **W** ⛽ Mr. Fuel, Phillips 66/McDonald's/scales/dsl, 🛏 Super 8, ⊙ auto repair, rv camping
178	Herculaneum, **E** ⛽ QT/Wendy's/scales/dsl, Shell/Circle K, 🍴 Cracker Barrel, DQ, Dog House Diner, Jack-in-the-Box, La Pachanga Mexican, ⊙ Toyota/Scion, **W** Buick/GMC, Cadillac/Chevrolet, Ford, vet
175	rd A, Festus, **E** ⛽ Mobil, Murphy USA/dsl, Phillips 66/dsl, 🍴 Arby's, Bob Evans, Burger King, Capt D's, China 1, Cici's Pizza, Fazoli's, Imo's Pizza, Jack-in-the-Box, McDonald's/playplace, Papa John's, Ryan's, Sonic, St. Louis Bread Co, Steak'n Shake, Subway, Taco Bell, Tanglefoot Steaks, White Castle, 🛏 Best Western, Drury Inn, ⊙ Advance Parts, Aldi Foods, AutoZone, $Tree, GNC, Home Depot, Plaza Tire, Radio Shack, Schnuck's Foods, Walgreens, Walmart, **W** ⛽ Phillips 66/Domino's/dsl, 7-11/dsl, 🍴 Hardee's, Jimmy John's, Ruby Tuesday, Waffle House, Whittaker's Pizza, 🛏 Comfort Inn, Holiday Inn Express, ⊙ Dodge, Lowe's
174b a	US 67, Lp 55, Festus, Crystal City, **E** ⛽ Phillips 66/dsl
170	US 61, **W** ⛽ BP/dsl/LP, 🍴 Laddie Boy Rest
165	rd TT (from sb)
162	rds DD, OO
160mm	**rest areas both lanes, full** ♿ **facilities,** 🚮 **litter barrels,** 🚻 **vending, petwalk**

157	rd Y, Bloomsdale, **E** ⛽ Phillips 66, **W** ⛽ Shell/dsl
154	rd O, to St Genevieve
150	MO 32, rds B, A, to St Genevieve, **E** ⛽ BP, 🍴 DQ, 🛏 Microtel (4mi), ⊙ Ⓗ, Hist Site (6mi), **W** ⛽ Phillips 66/dsl, ⊙ Hawn SP (11mi)
143	rds J, M, N, Ozora, **W** ⛽ BP/buffet/dsl, Ozora Country Store/dsl, Shell/dsl/, 🍴 Zone Grill, 🛏 Regency Inn
141	rd Z, St Mary
135	rd M, Brewer, **E** propane depot
129	MO 51, to Perryville, **E** ⛽ MotoMart/McDonald's/dsl, Phillips 66/dsl, 🍴 Burger King, KFC, Ponderosa, Taco Bell, ⊙ Ⓗ, Ford, **W** ⛽ Rhodes/dsl, 🍴 China Buffet, 5 Star Chinese, 🛏 Best Value Inn, Comfort Inn, Super 8, ⊙ Buick/Chevrolet, Chrysler/Dodge/Jeep, $Tree, Walmart
123	rd B, Biehle, **W** ⛽ Rhodes/dsl, 🍴 Missy's Country Kettle
119mm	Apple Creek
117	rd KK, to Appleton, **E** 🍴 Terri's Cafe, ⊙ Ron's Grocery
111	rd E, Oak Ridge
110mm	**rest area both lanes, full** ♿ **facilities,** 🚮 **litter barrels,** 🚻 **vending, petwalk**
105	US 61, Fruitland, **E** ⛽ BP/dsl, Casey's, Phillips 66/dsl, Rhodes/dsl, ⊙ Trail of Tears SP (11mi), **W** ⛽ D-Mart, 🍴 DQ, Pizza Inn, 🛏 Drury Inn
102	LaSalle Ave, E Main St
99	US 61, MO 34, to Jackson, **E** RV camping, **W** 🛏 Comfort Suites, ⊙ McDowell South RV Ctr
96	rd K, to Cape Girardeau, **E** ⛽ Phillips 66, 🍴 Applebee's (1mi), Blimpie, Bob Evans, Buffalo Wild Wings, Burger King, Cici's Pizza, Cracker Barrel, DQ (1mi), Denny's, Dexter BBQ, El Acapulco, Great Wall Chinese, Honey Baked Ham, Logan's Roadhouse, O'Charley's, Olive Garden, Panera Bread, Pizza Hut, Pizza Inn, Ponderosa, Popeye's, Qdoba, Red Lobster, Ruby Tuesday, Ryan's, Starbucks, Steak'n Shake, Subway, Taco Bell, TX Roadhouse, Wendy's, 🛏 Drury Lodge/rest., Holiday Inn Express, PearTree Inn, Victorian Inn, ⊙ Ⓗ, AT&T, Barnes&Noble, Best Buy, BigLots, Hancock Fabrics, Hobby Lobby, JC Penney, Macy's, NAPA, Old Navy, Schnuck's Foods, mall, to SEMSU, **W** ⛽ Shell/24hr, 🍴 McDonald's/playplace, Outback Steaks, Sonic, Subway, White Castle, 🛏 Drury Suites, Hampton Inn, ⊙ $Tree, Honda, Hyundai, Kohl's, Lowe's, Mazda, Nissan, PetCo, Plaza Tire, Sam's Club, Sears Grand, Staples, Target, Toyota, Walmart, USPO
95	MO 74 E, **E** 🛏 Candlewood Suites, same as 96
93a b	MO 74 W, Cape Girardeau, **E** ⊙ diesel repair
91	rd AB, to Cape Girardeau, **E** ⛽ Rhodes/dsl, 🍴 Huddle House, ⊙ Harley-Davidson, RV America, tire repair, vet, **W** ⊙ Capetown RV Ctr, ↩
89	US 61, rds K, M, Scott City, **E** ⛽ Rhodes, Store 24, 🍴 Burger King, Ice Cream Corner, Las Brisas Mexican, Pizza Pro, ⊙ Bob's Foods, $General, Medicap Drug, NAPA, Plaza Tires
80	MO 77, Benton, **E** ⛽ Express/dsl, **W** ⛽ Phillips 66/McDonald's/dsl/fireworks, ⊙ antiques, winery (8mi)
69	rd HH, to Sikeston, Miner, **E** ⊙ Peterbilt, **W** ⛽ Keller Trkstp/dsl (1mi), ⊙ Ⓗ, RV America, golf
67	US 60, US 62, Miner, **E** ⛽ Breaktime/dsl, Express/dsl, 🛏 Best Western, Holiday Inn Express, Motel 6, ⊙ Hinton RV Park, **0-2 mi W** ⛽ Cenex, Hucks, Jasper's Gas, 🍴 Bo's BBQ, Buffalo Wild Wings, Burger King, El Tapatio Mexican, Hunan Chinese, Lambert's Rest., Pizza Hut, Pizza Inn, Ruby Tuesday, Sonic, Subway, Taco John's, Uncle Frank's Chicken, Wendy's, 🛏 Comfort Inn, Country Hearth Inn,

Sidebar (vertical): **MO** · **PERRYVILLE** · **CAPE GIRARDEAU** · **MINER**

INTERSTATE 55 CONT'D

Exit	Services
67	Continued
	Drury Inn, PearTree Inn, Super 8, Thrifty Inn, 🅾 🅗, AutoZone, Buick/Chevrolet, Cadillac/GMC, $General, Family$, Food Giant, Raben Tires, Sikeston Outlets/famous brands, Walgreens, vet
66b	US 60 W, to Poplar Bluff, **3 mi W on US 61/62** 🅰 Breaktime, Sinclair, 🍴 A&W/LJ Silver, Applebee's, Arby's, China Buffet, DQ, El Bracero Mexican, Hardee's, KFC, McDonald's, Sonic, Subway, Taco Bell, 🏠 Days Inn, 🅾 Aldi Foods, Chrysler/Dodge/Jeep, $Tree, Ford/Lincoln/Mercury, GNC, JC Penney, Lowe's, Mkt Place Foods, O'Reilly Parts, Radio Shack, Walmart
66a	I-57 E, to Chicago, US 60, W
59mm	St Johns Bayou
58	MO 80, Matthews, **E** 🅰 TA/Taco Bell/dsl/scales/24hr/@, 🅾 to Big Oak Tree SP (24mi), truck repair, **W** 🅰 FLYING J /Denny's/dsl/LP/RV dump/scales/24hr, Loves/ Chester's/Subway/dsl/scales/24hr, 🅾 truckwash/repair
52	rd P, Kewanee, **E** 🅰 gas/dsl
49	US 61, US 62, New Madrid, **E** 🅾 Hunter-Dawson HS (3mi)
44	US 61, US 62, Lp 55, New Madrid, **E** 🅰 Cenex/dsl (1mi), 🅾 hist site
42mm	**Welcome Ctr nb/rest area both lanes, full ♿ facilities, 🚻, litter barrels, 📞, vending, petwalk**
40	rd EE, St Jude Rd, Marston, **E** 🅰 ▦Arby's/dsl/scales/24hr, 🏠 Super 8, **W** 🍴 MFA, 🏠 Moore's Landing Suites
32	US 61, MO 162, Portageville, **W** 🅰 Phillips 66/dsl, Casey's, 🍴 China King, McDonald's, Sonic, 🏠 New Orleans Inn, 🅾 $General, dsl repair
27	rds K, A, BB, to Wardell, **E** 🅾 KOA (2mi)
19	MO 84, Hayti, **E** 🅰 BreakTime/dsl, ▦Arby's/dsl/scales/24hr, 🍴 McDonald's, KFC/Taco Bell, Pizza Hut, 🏠 Comfort Inn/rest., M Motel, 🅾 🅗, KOA (6mi), Lady Luck Casino/camping, **W** 🅰 BP/dsl, Hayti Trvl Ctr/Subway/dsl, R&P/dsl, 🍴 Apple Barrel, Chubby's BBQ, Los Portales, Patty Ann's BBQ, 🏠 Drury Inn, 🅾 🅗, $General, Fred's Store, Goodyear/auto, Hay's Foods, repair
17b a	I-155 E, US 412, to TN
14	rds J, H, U, to Caruthersville, Braggadocio
10mm	**weigh sta nb**
8	US 61, MO 164, Steele, **W** 🅰 BP/Chester's/Subway/scales/dsl, 🏠 Deerfield Inn, 🅾 truck repair
4	rd E, to Holland, Cooter
3mm	**rest area both lanes, full ♿ facilities, 🚻, litter barrels, 📞, vending, petwalk**
1	US 61, rd O, Holland, **W** 🅰 Shell/dsl/24hr
0mm	Missouri/Arkansas state line

INTERSTATE 57

Exit	Services
22mm	Missouri/Illinois state line, Mississippi River
18.5mm	**weigh sta both lanes**
12	US 62, MO 77, Charleston, **E** 🅰 Exxon/Cheers/Quiznos/dsl/scales/24hr, 🏠 Eagle Inn, **W** 🅰 Casey's (1mi), Phillips 66/dsl, 🍴 Las Brisas Mexican, 🏠 EconoLodge
10	MO 105, Charleston, **E** 🅰 Conoco/Boomland/dsl, ▦/Subway/dsl/scales/24hr, 🍴 Wally's Rest., 🅾 Boomland RV Park, **W** 🅰 Casey's, 🍴 China Buffet, McDonald's,

Exit	Services
10	Continued
	Pizza Hut, 🏠 Quality Inn, 🅾 Alco, CountryMart Foods, Plaza Tire, city park
4	rd B, Bertrand
1b a	I-55, N to St Louis, S to Memphis.
	I-57 begins/ends on I-55, exit 66.

INTERSTATE 64

Exit	Services
41mm	Missouri/Illinois state line, Mississippi River
40b a	Broadway St, to Stadium, to the Arch, **N** 🏠 Hilton, Sheraton, stadium, **S** 🅾 Dobb's Tire
40c	(from wb), I-44 W, I-55 S
39c	11th St (exits left), downtown
39b	14th St, downtown, **N** 🏠 Sheraton, **S** 🅰 BP
39a	21st St, Market St (from wb), **N** 🏠 Drury Inn, Hampton Inn
38d	Chestnut at 20th St, **N** 🏠 Drury Inn, Hampton Inn
38c	Jefferson Ave, St Louis Union Sta, **N** 🅾 Joplin House, **S** 🏠 Residence Inn
38a	Forest Park Blvd (from wb), **N** 🅰 Shell
37b a	Market St, Bernard St, Grand Blvd, **N** 🅰 Shell, 🍴 Del Taco, 🏠 Courtyard, Hampton Inn, Hyatt, Drury Inn, Adam's Mark Hotel, Marriott
36d	Vandeventer Ave, Chouteau Ave
36b a	Kingshighway, **N** 🅾 🅗, **S** 🅰 BP
34d c	Hampton Ave, Forest Park, **N** museums, zoo, **S** 🅰 BP, Mobil, Phillips 66, 🍴 Courtesy Diner, Hardee's, Imo's Pizza, Jack-in-the-Box, Smokin' Al's BBQ, Steak'n Shake, Subway, Taco Bell, 🏠 Hampton Inn
34a	Oakland Ave, **N** 🅰 BP, 🍴 Del Taco, Subway, 🅾 🅗
33d	McCausland Ave, **N** 🅰 BP, 🍴 Del Taco
33c	Bellevue Ave, **N** 🅗
33b	Big Bend Blvd
32b a	Eager Rd, Hanley Rd, **S** 🅰 Shell, 🍴 Lion's Choice, Macaroni Grill, McDonald's, St Louis Bread Co, Subway, 🅾 Best Buy, Dierberg's Foods, Home Depot, Target, Whole Foods Mkt
31b a	I-170 N, **N** 🅰 Shell, 🍴 Burger King, DQ, IHOP, KFC, Steak'n Shake, TGIFriday, Dillard's, 🅾 mall, **S** 🅰 BP, 🍴 Macaroni Grill, Subway, 🅾 Dierberg's Foods, Goodyear, Target
30	McKnight Rd
28c	Clayton Rd (from wb)
28b a	US 67, US 61, Lindbergh Blvd, **S** 🅰 BP, 🍴 Brio Grill, Fleming's Rest., Schneithouse Rest., Starbucks, 🏠 Hilton, 🅾 Honda, Shnuck's Foods, mall
27	Spoede Rd
26	rd JJ, Ballas Rd, **N** 🅗, **S** 🅗
25	I-270, N to Chicago, S to Memphis
24	Mason Rd, **N** 🏠 Courtyard, Marriott, 🅾 LDS Temple, hwy patrol

INTERSTATE 64 CONT'D

Exit	Services
23	Maryville Centre Dr (from wb), N 🛏 Courtyard, Marriott
22	MO 141, N 🍴 Regatta Grille, 🅾 H, S 🍴 5 Guys Burgers, Pizza Hut
21	Timberlake Manor Pkwy
20	Chesterfield Pkwy (from wb), same as 19b a
19b a	MO 340, Chesterfield Pkwy, Olive Blvd, N 🅖 BP, Shell, 🍴 Applebee's, Pizzaria Uno, Sheridan's Custard, Taco Bell, Yaya's Cafe, 🛏 DoubleTree Hotel, Hampton Inn, Homewood Suites, Residence Inn, 🅾 USPO, Dobb's Tire, Schnucks Foods, Walgreens, S 🅖 Mobil, 🍴 Bahama Breeze Rest., Bacana Cafe, Casa Gallardo's, California Pizza Kitchen, Chili's, Houlihans, Macaroni Grill, PF Chang's, 🛏 Drury Plaza Hotel, 🅾 Dillard's, mall
17	Boones Crossing, Long Rd, Chesterfield 🍴 Rd, **1 mi** S 🅖 Mobil, 🍴 Bob Evans, Chick-fil-A, Coldstone, Cousins Subs, Culver's, East Coast Pizza, Emperor's Buffet, Fox&Hound, Golden China, Hardee's, Hometown Buffet, IHOP, IMO's Pizza, Joe's Crabshack, Kaldi's Coffee, Lion's Choice, Longhorn Steaks, Matador Cafe., McDonald's, Mimi's Cafe, O'Charley's, Old Country Buffet, Old Spaghetti Factory, Olive Garden, Original Pancakes, Qdoba Mexican, Quiznos, Red Lobster, Red Robin, SmokeHouse Rest., Sonic, Starbucks, Steak'n Shake, Subway, Taco Bell, 🛏 Hampton Inn, Hilton Garden, 🅾 Best Buy, Dick's, Dobb's Tire, $Tree, Firestone, Ford, Home Depot, KIA, Lowe's, Michael's, Petsmart, Radio Shack, Sam's Club, Target, Walmart, WorldMkt, vet
14	Chesterfield 🍴 Rd (from eb), S 🅖 Phillips 66, 🛏 Comfort Inn
13mm	Missouri River
11	Research Park Ctr Dr
10	MO 94, St. Charles, N 🅖 Mobil, QT, Shell, 🍴 Jack-in-the-Box, McDonald's, 🅾 Mercedes, Busch Wildlife Area
9	rd k, O'Fallon, N 🅖 Mobil, QT, 🍴 Cracker Barrel, Ruby Tuesday, Starbucks, 🛏 Holiday Inn Express, Residence Inn, Staybridge Suites, 🅾 Chevrolet, Honda, Volvo
6	rd DD, Wing Haven Blvd, N 🅖 Phillips 66, 🍴 Bristol Seafood, Hunan King, Massa's Italian, Outback Steaks, Subway, VA BBQ, 🛏 Hilton Garden
4	rd N, N 🅖 PetroMart, Phillips 66, 🍴 McDonald's, Qdoba Mexican, Red Robin, Steak'n Shake, St. Louis Bread Co., 🅾 JC Penney, Shop'n Save, Target, S 🅖 Murphy USA/dsl, Phillips 66, 🍴 Dragon Buffet, El Maguay, Jack-in-the-Box, McDonald's, Sonic, Starbucks, Subway, Taco Bell, Wendy's, White Castle, 🅾 Aldi Foods, AutoZone, Dobb's Tire, $Tree, Firestone, GNC, Lowe's, Radio Shack, Walmart
2	Lake St. Louis Blvd, N 🍴 BC's Rest., Max&Erma's, 🅾 Old Navy, Schnuck's Foods, Von Maur, Walgreens
1	Prospect Rd, N 🅖 Shell
0mm	I-70, E to St Louis, W to Kansas City

INTERSTATE 70

Exit	Services
252mm	Missouri/Illinois state line, Mississippi River
251a	I-55 S, to Memphis, to I-44, to downtown/no return
250b	Memorial Dr, downtown, Stadium, S 🅖 Shell, 🍴 McDonald's, 🛏 Day's Inn
250a	Arch, Riverfront, N 🅾 The Arch, S 🛏 Drury Inn, Econolodge, Hampton Inn, Millineal Hotel, Renaissance, Edward Jones Dome

Exit	Services
249c	6th St (from eb)
249a	Madison St, 10th St, N 🅖 ZX/dsl
248b	St Louis Ave, Branch St
248a	Salisbury St, McKinley Br, N truck repair/24hr, S 🅖 BP, Phillips 66
247	Grand Ave, N 🅖 Phillips 66/dsl, 🛏 Western Inn
246b	Adelaide Ave
246a	N Broadway, O'Fallon Park, N 🅖 Mobil/dsl, 🅾 Freightliner
245b	W Florissant
245a	Shreve Ave, S 🅖 BP
244b	Kingshighway, 3/4 mi S 🍴 Burger King, McDonald's, Subway
244a	Bircher Blvd, Union Blvd
243b	(243c from eb) Bircher Blvd
243a	Riverview Blvd
243	Goodfellow Blvd, N 🅖 Shell
242b a	Jennings Sta Rd, N 🅖 Shell, S 🛏 Western Inn
241b	Lucas-Hunt Rd, N 🅖 Shell, 3/4 mi S 🍴 Lee's Chicken, McDonald's
241a	Bermuda Rd, S 🅖 Sinclair, 🅾 H
240b a	Florissant Rd, N 🅖 BP/McDonald's, 🍴 DQ, Sonic, Taco Bell, 🅾 Schnuck's Foods, Walgreens
239	N Hanley Rd, N 🍴 Jack-in-the-Box, 🛏 Hilton Garden, S 🅖 Mobil, 🍴 McDonald's
238c b	I-170 N, I-170 S, no return
238a	N Lambert-St Louis ✈, S 🛏 Renaissance Hotel
237	Natural Bridge Rd (from eb), S 🅖 BP, Phillips 66, Shell, 🍴 ✈ Diner, Arby's, Burger King, Denny's, Jack-in-the-Box, KFC, Pizza Hut, Steak'n Shake, Waffle House, Wendy's, DoubleTree, 🛏 Best Western, Days Inn, Double Tree, Holiday Inn, Renaissance, Travelodge
236	Lambert-St Louis ✈, S 🅖 BP, 🍴 BBQ, Big Boy, Coco's, Grone Cafeteria, Hardee's, Lombardo's Café Rafferty's Rest., Tiffany's Rest., 🛏 Best Western, Day's Inn, Drury Inn/rest., Hampton Inn, Hilton Garden, Holiday Inn, Marriott, Motel 6
235c	Cypress Rd, rd B W, N to ✈
235b a	US 67, Lindbergh Blvd, N 🅖 Shell, 🛏 Executive Intn'l Inn, Holiday Inn/café, Howard Johnson, S 🅖 Shell, 🍴 Lion's Choice Rest., Steak'n Shake, TGIFriday, 🛏 Congress Inn, Embassy Suites, Homestead Studios, Radisson, 🅾 Chevrolet, Dillard's, Firestone, JC Penney, Sears/auto, mall
234	MO 180, St Charles Rock Rd, N 🅖 Phillips 66, Shell, 🍴 Applebee's, Casa Gallardo's, Fazoli's, Hardee's, Hatfield's/McCoy's Rest., Jack-in-the-Box, LoneStar Steaks, LJ Silver, McDonald's, Old Country Buffet, Ponderosa, Quizno's, Red Lobster, Shoney's, Steak'n Shake, Taco Bell, Tony Bono's Rest., 🛏 Economy Inn, 🅾 H, Best Buy, $Tree, GrandPa's Food/drug, Honda, K-Mart, NTB, Office Depot, Sam's Club, Target, Walgreens/24hr, S Isuzu
232	I-270, N to Chicago, S to Memphis
231b a	Earth City Expwy, N 🅖 Motomart, Phillips 66/Jack-in-the-Box/dsl, 🍴 McDonald's, Quizno's, 🛏 Candlewood Suites, Courtyard, Holiday Inn, Residence Inn, Studio+, S 🅖 Mobil, 🍴 Burger King, Dave&Buster's, 🛏 Holiday Inn Express, Homewood Suites, Wingate Inn, 🅾 Harrah's Casino/Hotel, Riverport Amphitheatre
230mm	Missouri River
229b a	5th St, St Charles, N 🅖 BP, Mobil/dsl, 🍴 Bellacino's Italian, Buffalo Wild Wings, Denny's, El Tio Pepe, Gordman's, Jack-in-the-Box, KFC, Lee's Chicken, McDonald's, Waffle House, 🛏 Best Western, Comfort Suites, Quality Inn, 🅾 Aldi Foods, Ameristar Casino, Bass Pro Shops,

MO

E↕W

ST LOUIS

E↕W

INTERSTATE 70 CONT'D

Exit	Services
229b a	Continued Walgreens/24hr, **S** 🅶 QT/dsl, 🍴 Cracker Barrel, 🛏 Embassy Suites, Fairfield Inn, 🅾 malls
228	MO 94, to Weldon Springs, St Charles, **N** 🅶 Phillips 66, ZX/dsl, 🍴 Arby's, Chinatown Express, DQ, Imo's Pizza, Papa John's, Steak'n Shake, 🅾 Advance Parts, Chevrolet, NAPA, Walgreen, Valvoline, **S** 🅶 QT, 🍴 Chinese Express, ChuckeCheese, Fazoli's, Gingham's Rest., Grappa Grill, McAlister's Deli, Outback Steaks, Pizza Hut, 🛏 Days Inn, Intown Suites, 🅾 Dobb's Tire, vet, access to 227
227	Zumbehl Rd, **N** 🅶 Phillips 66/dsl, ZX, 🍴 Culpepper's Grill, 🛏 Super 8, 🅾 Lowe's, Sav-A-Lot Foods, **S** 🅶 BP, Hucks/dsl, 🍴 Applebee's, Bob Evans, Boston Mkt, Capt D's, Chevy's Mexican, Chirco's Grill, CiCi's Pizza, El Mariachi Mexican, Fazoli's, Gingham's Rest., Golden Corral, Great Wall Chinese, Hardee's, Hoho Chinese, Jack-in-the-Box, McCalister's, McDonald's, Quiznos, Subway, Taco Bell/Pizza Hut, Wiliker's Cafe, 🛏 Days Inn, Red Roof Inn, TownePlace Suites, Travelodge, 🅾 BigLots, Dierberg's Foods, $Tree, GNC, Jiffy Lube, Michael's, NTB, Petsmart, Radio Shack, Sam's Club/gas, Schnuck's Foods, Walmart/Blimpie, Walgreens, vet, access to 228
225	Truman Rd, to Cave Springs, **N** 🅶 BP, Casey's, Shell, ZX Gas, 🛏 Hampton Inn, Motel 6, 🅾 Buick/GMC, Cadillac, Kenworth, Mazda, Subaru, U-Haul, VW, **S** 🅶 Conoco, Mobil, QT, 🍴 Bandanas BBQ, Big Boy, Burger King, China Wok, Culver's, DQ, Denny's, El Tio Pepe, Hooters, IHOP, Jack-in-the-Box, Longhorn Steaks, Lion's Choice Rest., LJ Silver, McDonald's, O'Charley's, Pasta House, Pizza Hut, Pizza St, Red Lobster, Steak'n Shake, Subway, Taco Bell, Thai Kitchen, White Castle, 🛏 Country Inn&Suites, 🅾 H, Batteries+, Chrysler/Dodge/Jeep, Firestone, Home Depot, Kia, Office Depot, Shop'n Save, Target, TJ Maxx
224	MO 370, E
222	Mid-Rivers Mall Dr, rd C, St Peters, **N** 🅶 QT/dsl/24hr, 🍴 Burger King, 🅾 Chevrolet, Honda, Lincoln/Mercury, Toyota/Scion, **S** 🅶 Mobil, ZX Gas/dsl, 🍴 Arby's, Bob Evans, Buffalo Wild Wings, Chili's, China Wok, Domino's, Honey-Baked Ham, Jack-in-the-Box, Joe's Crabshack, Macaroni Grill, Max & Erma's, McDonald's/playplace, Olive Garden, Pizza Hut/Taco Bell, Qdoba, Red Robin, Ruby Tuesday, Steak'n Shake, Subway, Wendy's, 🛏 Drury Inn, Extended Stay America, 🅾 Aldi Foods, AutoZone, Barnes&Noble, Best Buy, BigLots, Costco/gas, Dick's, Dillard's, Discount Tire, Hancock Fabrics, Hyundai/Nissan/VW, JC Penney, Jo-Ann Fabrics, Marshall's, NTB, Sears/auto, Tuesday Morning, Walgreens
220	MO 79, to Elsberry, **N** Cherokee Lakes Camping (7mi), **S** 🅶 BP, Phillips 66/dsl, 7-11/gas, 🍴 Caleco's Rest., El Mezon, Jack-in-the-Box, McDonald's/playplace, Pirrone's Pizzaria, Quiznos, Roly Poly Sandwiches, Sonic, Subway, 🛏 Days Inn, 🅾 Curves, Dierberg's Foods, O'Reilly Parts, Walgreens
219	T R Hughes Blvd, **S** 🅶 QT, 🍴 Ethyl's Smokehouse, 🛏 Comfort Inn
217	rds K, M, O'Fallon, **N** 🅶 Hucks/dsl, 🍴 Baskin-Robbins, Burger King, Jack-in-the-Box, Rally's, Piggy's BBQ, Pizza Hut/Taco Bell, Sonic, Waffle House, 🅾 Firestone, Jiffy Lube, O'Reilly Parts, Radio Shack, **S** 🅶 Phillips 66/dsl, QT, ZX, 🍴 Applebee's, Arby's, Bob Evans, Chick-fil-A, Domino's, Fazoli's, IHOP, KFC, Krieger's Grill, Lion's
217	Continued Choice Rest., McDonald's/playplace, Pantera's Pizza, Papa John's, Pizza Hut, Red Robin, Stefanina's Pizza, Subway, 🅾 Advance Parts, Aldi Foods, Auto Tire, AutoZone, GNC, Home Depot, K-Mart/drugs, Lowe's, Schnuck's Foods, Shop'n Save Foods, TrueValue, Walgreens, Walmart, camping
216	Bryan Rd, **N** 🛏 Super 8, 🅾 CarQuest, Ford, Peterbilt, **S** 🅶 Conoco, Phillips 66/Jack-in-the-Box/dsl, QT, 🍴 DQ, Cappuccino's, Mr. Goodcents, Wendy's
214	Lake St Louis, **N** 🅶 Phillips 66/McDonald's/dsl, Q-Stop, 🍴 McDonald's, **S** 🅶 Phillips 66/dsl, Shell/Circle K, 🍴 Denny's, El Maguey Mexican, Hardee's, Subway, 🛏 Days Inn, 🅾 H, Wharf Drug
212	rd A, **N** 🛏 Economy Inn, **S** 🅶 Mobil, 🍴 Imo's Pizza, 🛏 Motel 6, 🅾 Chrysler/Dodge/Jeep
210b a	to I-64, US 40 E, US 61 S, **S** 🅶 Shell, 🅾 H
209	rd Z, Church St, New Melle, **N** 🍴 DQ, **S** 🅶 Phillips 66/dsl
208	Pearce Blvd, Wentzville Pkwy, Wentzville, **N** 🅶 Mobil, Phillips 66, QT/dsl, 🍴 Applebee's, Arby's, Bob Evans, Buffalo Wild Wings, China Buffet, Culver's, Domino's, 54th St Grill, Fritz's Custard, Hardee's, Imo's Pizza, Jack-in-the-Box, Jimmy John's, KFC, Lion's Choice, McDonald's, Mr Goodcents, Olive Garden, Papa John's, Penn Sta., Pizza Hut, Pizza Pro, Qdoba, Ruby Tuesday, Starbucks, Steak'n Shake, St Louis Bread, Subway, Taco Bell, Waffle House, Wendy's, White Castle, 🅾 H, AT&T, AutoZone, Best Buy, Chevrolet, Dierberg's Foods, Dobb's Tire, $General, Family$, Home Depot, Hyundai, Kohl's, Lowe's, Michael's, O'Reilly Parts, Petsmart, Radio Shack, Save-A-Lot, Schnuck's Food, Target, Walgreens, Walmart, urgent care, **S** 🅶 BP, 🍴 Bandana's BBQ, IHOP, 🛏 Super 8, 🅾 Thomas RV Ctr
204mm	**weigh sta both lanes**
203	rds W, T, Foristell, **N** 🅶 TA/BP/Pizza Hut/Popeye's/Taco Bell/dsl/scales/24hr/@, Mr Fuel/dsl/scales, 🛏 Best Western, 🅾 Freightliner, **S** 🅶 Phillips 66/McDonald's/dsl, 🅾 dsl repair
200	rds J, H, F (from wb), Wright City, **N** 🅶 Midwest/dsl, 🍴 Ruiz Castillo's Mexican (1mi), **S** 🅶 Phillips 66, 🍴 New China, 🛏 Super 7 Inn
199	rd J, H, F, Wright City, **N** 🅶 Shell/McDonald's/dsl, 🅾 $General, **S** 🛏 Super 7 Inn, 🅾 Volvo Trucks
198mm	**rest area both lanes, full ♿ facilities, 🅲, 🏕, litter barrels, petwalk**
193	MO 47, Warrenton, **N** 🅶 Phillips 66/dsl, ZX Gas/dsl, 🍴 Applebee's, Burger King, China House, Dominos, Jack-in-the-Box, KFC, McDonald's, Pizza Hut, Subway, Waffle House, 🛏 Best Value Inn, Holiday Inn Express, Super 8, 🅾 Mosers Foods, Radio Shack, Walmart, USPO, **S** 🅶

INTERSTATE 70 CONT'D

Exit	Services

WARRENTON

193 Continued
BP, Conoco/dsl, Phillips 66/dsl, 🍴 Denny's, Taco Bell, 🛏 Comfort Inn, 🅞 Aamco, AutoZone, CarQuest, Chevrolet/GMC, Walgreens, Warrenton Outlets/famous brands

188 rds A, B, to Truxton, **S** 🅖 ⊕FLYING J/Denny's/dsl/LP/RV Dump/scales/24hr, 🛏 Budget Inn

183 rds E, NN, Y, Jonesburg, **1 mi N** Jonesburg Gardens Camping, **S** 🅖 Phillips 66/dsl, 🅞 USPO

179 rd F, High Hill, **S** 🛏 Budget Motel, Colonial Inn

175 MO 19, New Florence, **N** 🅖 BP/Hardee's/dsl, Shell/dsl/24hr, 🍴 JJ's BBQ, McDonald's, 🛏 Best Inn, Best Value Inn, Days Inn, 🅞 Stone Hill Winery/gifts (15mi), auto repair

170 MO 161, rd J, Danville, **N** 🅖 Sinclair/dsl, 🅞 to Graham Cave SP, Kan-Do RV Park, **S** Lazy Day RV Park

169.5mm truck parking

168mm Loutre River

167mm truck parking eb

161 rds D, YY, Williamsburg, **N** 🅖 Cranes/mkt, 🍴 Marlene's Rest, 🅞 USPO, **S** 🅖 Conoco/dsl/24hr

155 rds A, Z, to Calwood, **N** antiques

148 US 54, Kingdom City, **N** 🅖 BP/dsl, Phillips 66/dsl, 🍴 Taco Bell, 🅞 MO Tourism Ctr, to Mark Twain Lake, **S** 🅖 Conoco/Subway/dsl/scales/24hr, Petro/Mobil/Iron Skillet/dsl/scales/24hr/@, Phillips 66/dsl, Shell/Gasper's/Arby's/dsl/scales/@, 🍴 Denny's, McDonald's, 🛏 Comfort Inn, Days Inn, Motel 6, Super 8, 🅞 Wheeler's Truckwash

144 rds M, HH, to Hatton, **S** 🅞 fireworks

137 rds DD, J, to Millersburg, Stephens, **S** Freightliner, antiques, to Little Dixie WA (4mi)

133 rd Z, to Centralia, **N** 🅞 Loveall's RV

131 Lake of the Woods Rd, **N** 🅖 BP, Phillips 66/Subway/dsl, 🍴 George's Rest,, Sonic, 🛏 Super 8, 🅞 Harley-Davidson, **S** 🅖 Conoco/dsl/24hr, 🛏 Holiday Inn

COLUMBIA

128a US 63, to Jefferson City, Columbia, **N** 🅖 BP, QT, 🍴 Bob Evans, Burger King, China Garden, Cracker Barrel, Golden Corral, Hooters, KFC, Lee's Chicken, Lonestar Steaks, McDonald's, Pizza Hut, Ruby Tuesday, Steak'n Shake, Taco Bell, Waffle House, Wendy's, 🛏 Comfort Inn, Fairfield Inn, Hampton Inn, Hilton Garden, Residence Inn, Super 8, 🅞 Bass Pro Shop, Cottonwood RV Park, Home Depot, Menards, **S** 🅖 BreakTime/dsl, 🍴 Applebee's, Baskin-Robbins, Chili's, Chipotle Mexican, CiCi's, Culver's, El Magueay, Houlihan's, IHOP, Kobe Japanese, Longhorn Steaks, Sonic, Starbucks, Subway, TGIFriday's, 🛏 Baymont Inn, Best Western, Candlewood Suites, Country Inn&Suites, Motel 6, Ramada, Staybridge Suites, Wingate Inn, 🅞 H, AT&T, $Tree, HyVee Foods, Lowe's, Patricia's Foods, Sam's Club, Staples, Walmart

128 Lp 70 (from wb), Columbia, **N** 🍴 Hardee's, **S** 🍴 Capt D's, 🛏 Eastwood Motel, 🅞 H, Big O Tire, same as 128a

127 MO 763, to Moberly, Columbia, **N** 🅖 BreakTime/dsl, 🍴 Waffle House, 🛏 Travelodge, 🅞 Cadillac, Dodge, Hyundai, Mazda, transmissions, **S** 🅖 Midwest, Phillips 66/dsl, 🛏 Super 7 Motel

126 MO 163, Providence Rd, Columbia, **N** 🅖 Phillips 66, 🍴 Bandanas BBQ, Country Kitchen, 🛏 Best Value Inn, Quality Inn, Red Roof Inn, 🅞 CarQuest, Honda, McKnight Tire, same as 127, **S** 🅖 BreakTime/dsl, 🍴 Burger King, Church's, DQ, LJ Silver, McDonald's, Pizza Hut,

COLUMBIA

126 Continued
Sonic, Subway, Taco Bell, 🅞 H, Aldi Foods, AutoZone, Buick/Chevrolet/GMC, $General, Nissan, O'Reilly Parts, Transmissions+

125 Lp 70, West Blvd, Columbia, **N** 🛏 Comfort Suites, **S** 🅖 Phillips 66/dsl, Shell/dsl, 🍴 Chevy's Mexican, Domino's, Fazoli's, JJ's Cafe, Olive Garden, Outback Steaks, Teppanyaki Grill, 🛏 EconoLodge, 🅞 BMW, Firestone/auto, Kia, Mosers Foods, Subaru, U-Haul, same as 124

124 MO 740, rd E, Stadium Blvd, Columbia, **N** 🛏 Extended Stay America, **S** 🅖 BreakTime, Phillips 66, 🍴 Applebee's, ChuckeCheese, Denny's, Hardee's, KFC, Macaroni Grill, McDonald's, Panera Bread, Pizza Hut, Red Lobster, Ruby Tuesday, Steak'n Shake, Subway, Taco Bell, Wendy's, 🛏 Days Inn, Drury Inn, Holiday Inn, La Quinta, Motel 6, 🅞 Barnes&Noble, Best Buy, Dick's, Dillard's, Ford, Hobby Lobby, Macy's, Michael's, Old Navy, PetCo, PetsMart, Radio Shack, Sears/auto, Target, mall, to U of MO, same as 125

122mm Perche Creek

121 US 40, rd UU, Midway, **N** 🅖 Conoco/dsl/rest., Phillips 66, 🛏 Budget Inn, 🅞 tires/repair, **S** golf

117 rds J, O, to Huntsdale, Harrisburg

115 rd BB N, Rocheport, **N** to Katy Tr SP, winery

114.5mm Missouri River

111 MO 98, MO 179, to Wooldridge, Overton, **S** 🅖 Phillips 66/dsl/repair, 🅞 RV Park

106 MO 87, Bingham Rd, to Boonville, **S** 🅖 Phillips 66/dsl

104mm **rest area both lanes, full ♿ facilities, 🚻, 🅿, litter barrels, vending, petwalk**

BOONVILLE

103 rd B, Main St, Boonville, **N** 🅖 Breaktime, Murphy USA/dsl, Phillips 66/Circle K/dsl, 🍴 Breadeaux Pisa, Happy China, KFC/LJ Silver, La Hacienda Mexican, McDonald's, Pizza Hut, Sonic, Subway, Taco Bell, 🛏 Days Inn, Super 8, 🅞 H, Dave's Mkt, $General, Radio Shack, RV Express Camping, Walmart, to Katy Tr SP, **S** 🅖 Cenex/dsl, Shell/Bobber Cafe/dsl/24hr, 🛏 QT Inn

101 US 40, MO 5, to Boonville, **N** 🅖 ⊞/Wendy's/dsl/24hr, 🍴 Arby's, 🛏 Comfort Inn, Holiday Inn Express, 🅞 Buick/Cadillac/Chevrolet/GMC, Ford/Mercury, Russell Stover Candies, **S** 🅖 ⬥Loves/Hardee's/scales/dsl/24hr, to Lake of the Ozarks

98 MO 41, MO 135, Arrow Rock, **N** to Arrow Rock HS (13mi), tires, **S** 🅖 Conoco/Dogwood Rest./dsl, Phillips 66/dsl, 🅞 repair

93mm Lamine River

89 rd K, to Arrow Rock, **N** to Arrow Rock HS

84 rd J, **N** 🅖 Valero/DQ/Stuckey's, truck repair

78b a US 65, to Marshall, **N** 🅖 Conoco/dsl, 🅞 RV Park, fireworks

77mm Blackwater River

74 rd YY, **N** 🅖 Shell/Betty's/cafe/dsl/repair/24hr, motel

71 rds EE, K, to Houstonia

CONCORDIA

66 MO 127, Sweet Springs, **N** H, **S** 🅖 BreakTime/dsl, Casey's/dsl, 🛏 Rodeway Inn, 🅞 $General, NAPA

65.5mm Davis Creek

62 rds VV, Y, Emma

58 MO 23, Concordia, **N** 🅖 TA/Country Pride/Subway/dsl/scales/24hr/@, 🍴 KFC/Taco Bell, McDonald's, 🅞 $General, Patricia's Foods, truck/RV wash, **S** 🅖 Breaktime/dsl, Casey's, Conoco/dsl, Phillips 66 🍴 Biffle's BBQ, Hardee's, Pizza Hut, 🛏 Budget Inn, Days Inn, Travelodge, 🅞 NAPA

57.5mm **rest area both lanes, full ♿ facilities, 🚻, 🅿, litter barrels, vending, petwalk**

MO

INTERSTATE 70 CONT'D

Exit	Services
52	rd T, Aullville
49	MO 13, to Higginsville, N 🅖 Casey's, ▭▭▭/McDonald's/Subway/dsl/scales/24hr, 🛏 Camelot Inn/rest, 🅾 to Confederate Mem, S 🛏 Super 8, 🅾 Great Escape RV Resort, Interstate RV Park
45	rd H, to Mayview
43mm	**weigh sta both lanes**
41	rds O, M, to Lexington, Mayview
38	MO 131 (from wb), Odessa, S 🅖 BP/dsl, Shell, Sinclair, 🍴 McDonald's, Pizza Hut, Sonic, Subway, Taco John's, 🅾 $General, Radio Shack, camping, same as 37
37	MO 131, Odessa, N 🅾 Country Gardens RV Park/dump, S 🅖 BP/dsl, Shell, Sinclair, 🍴 El Camino Real, McDonald's, Morgan's Rest., Pizza Hut, Sonic, Subway, Taco John's, 🛏 Parkside Inn, 🅾 $General, O'Reilly Parts, Patricia's Foods, fireworks, same as 38
35mm	**truck parking both lanes**
31	rds D, Z, to Bates City, Napoleon, N 🅾 Bates City RV Camping, S 🅖 Valero/dsl, 🍴 Bates City BBQ, 🅾 fireworks
29.5mm	Horse Shoe Creek
28	rd H, rd F, Oak Grove, N 🅖 TA/Pizza Hut/Popeye's/dsl/scales/24hr/@, 🛏 Days Inn, 🅾 Blue Beacon, Freightliner, KOA, S 🅖 Petro/BP/DQ/Wendy's/scales/dsl/@, QT/dsl/24hr, 🍴 Hardee's, KFC/Taco Bell, McDonald's, Pizza Hut, PJ's Rest., Subway, Waffle House, 🛏 EconoLodge, 🅾 O'Reilly Parts, Patricia's Foods, SpeedCo Lube, Walgreens, Walmart
24	US 40, rds AA, BB, to Buckner, N 🅖 McShop/dsl, Phillips 66/dsl, 🛏 Best Value Inn, Comfort Inn, 🅾 Show Me RV Ctr, auto/dsl repair, S 🅖 Conoco/Subway/dsl/scales/24hr, 🍴 Sonic, 🅾 Trailside RV Park/Ctr
21	Adams Dairy Pkwy, N 🛏 Days Inn, 🅾 Nationwide RV Ctr (1mi), S 🅖 Murphy USA, Phillips 66/Burger King/dsl, 🍴 Chipotle Mexican, Olive Garden, Panda Express, Panera Bread, Sonic, Taco Bell, TX Roadhouse, 🛏 Courtyard, 🅾 AT&T, Gordman's, Home Depot, Kohl's, Michael's, NTB, PetCo, Staples, Target, Verizon, Walmart
20	MO 7, Blue Springs, N 🅖 Phillips 66/Circle K/dsl, QT, Valero/dsl, 🍴 Backyard Burger, Bob Evans, China 1, Dos Amigo's Mexican, Harley Grill, Minsky's Pizza, Papa Murphy's, Pizza Shoppe, Pizza St, Rancho Grande, Sonic, Steamin Bean, 🛏 Best Value Inn, Comfort Inn, Days Inn, Motel 6, 🅾 Ace Hardware, Curves, CVS Drug, $General, O'Reilly Parts, PriceChopper Foods, Walgreens, S 🅖 BP/dsl/24hr, QT, Shell, Valero, 🍴 Applebee's, Arby's, Big Biscuit, Bua Thai, Clancy's Cafe, Denny's, Jimmy John's, Jin's Buffet, KFC, McDonald's, Original Pizza, Starbucks, Subway, Taco Bueno, Winsteads Cafe, Zarda's BBQ, 🛏 Hampton Inn, Quality Inn, 🅾 🅷, Advance Parts, AutoZone, Chevrolet, Firestone/auto, Goodyear/auto, Hobby Lobby, NAPA, Office Depot, Russell Stover
18	Woods Chapel Rd, N 🅖 BP, 🛏 American Inn, La Quinta, Night's Inn, Super 8, 🅾 Harley-Davidson, S 🅖 Conoco/dsl, Phillips 66/dsl, QT, 🍴 China Kitchen, KFC/Taco Bell, Las Playas Mexican, McDonald's, Pizza Hut, Sonic, Subway, Taco John's, Waffle House, 🅾 Ford/Lincoln/Mercury, Hyundai, Nissan, same as 20
17	Little Blue Pkwy, 39th St, N 🍴 Buffalo Wild Wings, Coldstone, Hereford House, Joe's Crabshack, O'Charley's, On the Border, Sonic, 🛏 Hilton Garden, 🅾 🅷, World Mkt,

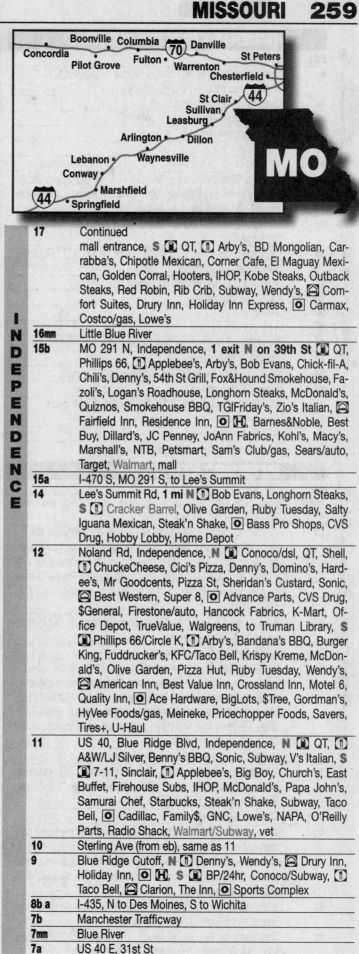

17	**Continued** mall entrance, S 🅖 QT, 🍴 Arby's, BD Mongolian, Carrabba's, Chipotle Mexican, Corner Cafe, El Maguay Mexican, Golden Corral, Hooters, IHOP, Kobe Steaks, Outback Steaks, Red Robin, Rib Crib, Subway, Wendy's, 🛏 Comfort Suites, Drury Inn, Holiday Inn Express, 🅾 Carmax, Costco/gas, Lowe's
16mm	Little Blue River
15b	MO 291 N, Independence, **1 exit** N on 39th St 🅖 QT, Phillips 66, 🍴 Applebee's, Arby's, Bob Evans, Chick-fil-A, Chili's, Denny's, 54th St Grill, Fox&Hound Smokehouse, Fazoli's, Logan's Roadhouse, Longhorn Steaks, McDonald's, Quiznos, Smokehouse BBQ, TGIFriday's, Zio's Italian, 🛏 Fairfield Inn, Residence Inn, 🅾 🅷, Barnes&Noble, Best Buy, Dillard's, JC Penney, JoAnn Fabrics, Kohl's, Macy's, Marshall's, NTB, Petsmart, Sam's Club/gas, Sears/auto, Target, Walmart, mall
15a	I-470 S, MO 291 S, to Lee's Summit
14	Lee's Summit Rd, **1 mi** N 🍴 Bob Evans, Longhorn Steaks, S 🍴 Cracker Barrel, Olive Garden, Ruby Tuesday, Salty Iguana Mexican, Steak'n Shake, 🅾 Bass Pro Shops, CVS Drug, Hobby Lobby, Home Depot
12	Noland Rd, Independence, N 🅖 Conoco/dsl, QT, Shell, 🍴 ChuckeCheese, Cici's Pizza, Denny's, Domino's, Hardee's, Mr Goodcents, Pizza St, Sheridan's Custard, Sonic, 🛏 Best Western, Super 8, 🅾 Advance Parts, CVS Drug, $General, Firestone/auto, Hancock Fabrics, K-Mart, Office Depot, TrueValue, Walgreens, to Truman Library, S 🅖 Phillips 66/Circle K, 🍴 Arby's, Bandana's BBQ, Burger King, Fuddrucker's, KFC/Taco Bell, Krispy Kreme, McDonald's, Olive Garden, Pizza Hut, Ruby Tuesday, Wendy's, 🛏 American Inn, Best Value Inn, Crossland Inn, Motel 6, Quality Inn, 🅾 Ace Hardware, BigLots, $Tree, Gordman's, HyVee Foods/gas, Meineke, Pricechopper Foods, Savers, Tires+, U-Haul
11	US 40, Blue Ridge Blvd, Independence, N 🅖 QT, 🍴 A&W/LJ Silver, Benny's BBQ, Sonic, Subway, V's Italian, S 🅖 7-11, Sinclair, 🍴 Applebee's, Big Boy, Church's, East Buffet, Firehouse Subs, IHOP, McDonald's, Papa John's, Samurai Chef, Starbucks, Steak'n Shake, Subway, Taco Bell, 🅾 Cadillac, Family$, GNC, Lowe's, NAPA, O'Reilly Parts, Radio Shack, Walmart/Subway, vet
10	Sterling Ave (from eb), same as 11
9	Blue Ridge Cutoff, N 🍴 Denny's, Wendy's, 🛏 Drury Inn, Holiday Inn, 🅾 🅷, S 🅖 BP/24hr, Conoco/Subway, 🍴 Taco Bell, 🛏 Clarion, The Inn, 🅾 Sports Complex
8b a	I-435, N to Des Moines, S to Wichita
7b	Manchester Trafficway
7mm	Blue River
7a	US 40 E, 31st St

INTERSTATE 70 CONT'D

Exit	Services
6	Van Brunt Blvd, N 🅿 Phillips 66/dsl, S 🅿 BP, 🍴 McDonald's, Pizza Hut, 🄾 VA 🏥, NAPA
5c	Jackson Ave (from wb)
5b	31st St (from eb)
5a	27th St (from eb)
4c	23rd Ave
4b	18th St
4a	Benton Blvd (from eb), Truman Rd, N 🅿 Super Stop/Wendy's/dsl, 🍴 Subway, 🄾 Advance Parts, Save-A-Lot Foods
3c	Prospect Ave, N 🅿 BP, 🍴 Church's, Gates BBQ, S 🍴 McDonald's
3b	Brooklyn Ave (from eb), N 🍴 Gates BBQ, S 🍴 Bryant's, Church's, McDonald's
3a	Paseo St, S 🅿 BP/dsl, 🄾 tires
2m	US 71 S, downtown
2l	I-670, to I-35 S
2j	11th St, downtown
2g	I-29/35 N, US 71 N, to Des Moines
2h	US 24 E, downtown
2e	MO 9 N, Oak St, S 🅿 Shell, Valero, 🏨 Marriott
2d	Main St, downtown
2c	US 169 N, Broadway, S 🅿 Phillips 66, 🏨 Marriott
2b	Beardsley Rd
2a	I-35 S, to Wichita
0mm	Missouri/Kansas state line, Kansas River

INTERSTATE 270 (ST LOUIS)

Exit	Services
15b a	I-55, N to Chicago, S to St Louis. I-270 begins/ends in Illinois on I-55/I-70, exit 20.
12	IL 159, to Collinsville, **1 mi** N 🅿 Conoco, Phillips 66, 🍴 Applebee's, China Rest., DQ, Denny's, Hardee's, Jack-in-the-Box, KFC, Papa John's, Ponderosa, Quizno's 🄾 Aldi Foods, Buick/GMC, Chrysler/Dodge/Jeep, Home Depot, Lowes Whse, PetsMart, Radio Shack, Walgreens, Walmart, S 🏥
9	IL 157, to Collinsville, N 🍴 Comfort Inn, S 🅿 Phillips 66/24hr, 🏨 Hampton Inn
7	I-255, to I-55, S to Memphis
6b a	IL 111, N 🅿 BP, ⊕FLYING J/Denny's/dsl/scales/24hr, 🍴 Hen House Rest., 🏨 Magnuson Hotel, 🄾 Blue Beacon/scales, Speedco, truck/trailer repair, S 🅿 Mobil/dsl, 🍴 Denny's, McDonald's/playplace, La Mexicana Rest., Taco Bell, 🏨 Days Inn, Holiday Inn Express, Sleep Inn, Super 8, 🄾 🏥, to Pontoon Beach
4	IL 203, Old Alton Rd, to Granite City
3b a	IL 3, N Riverboat Casino, S 🅿 Phillips 66, 🍴 Hardee's, Waffle House, 🏨 Budget Motel, EconoLodge, Sun Motel, 🄾 KOA, MGM Camping
2mm	Chain of Rocks Canal
0mm	Illinois/Missouri state line, Mississippi River, motorist callboxes begin eb
34	Riverview Dr, to St Louis, N 🅿 Moto Mart/Subway, **Welcome Ctr/rest area both lanes, full ♿ facilities, info, 🚮 litter barrels, 🅲**
33	Lilac Ave, N USPO, S 🅿 Phillips 66/Jack-in-the-Box/dsl, QT/dsl/scales/24hr, 🍴 Hardee's
32	Bellefontaine Rd, N 🅿 Mobil, QT, Shell, 🍴 China King, KFC, McDonald's, Pizza Hut, Steak'n Shake,

Exit	Services
32	Continued 🏨 Economy Inn, Motel 6, 🄾 Advance Parts, Firestone, Schnuck's Foods, S 🅿 BP, 🍴 White Castle, 🄾 Aldi Foods
31b a	MO 367, N 🅿 BP, QT/dsl, 🍴 Jack-in-the-Box, McDonalds, Subway, 🄾 🏥, Chevrolet, $General, Shop'n Save Foods, U-Haul, Walgreens
30b a	Hall's Ferry Rd, rd AC, N 🅿 Mobil/dsl, Phillips 66/dsl, QT, ZX, 🍴 Applebee's, Capt. D's, Popeye's, Waffle House, White Castle, 🏨 Knights Inn, 🄾 Ford/Lincoln/Mercury, 🅿 BP/dsl, Conoco, Phillips 66, 🍴 China Wok, Church's, CiCi's Pizza, Cracker Barrel, IHOP, Steak'n Shake, Subway, 🄾 AutoZone, $Buster, Family$, Home Depot, JoAnn Fabrics, O'Reilly Parts, Shop'n Save Foods
29	W Florissant Rd, N 🍴 Jack-in-the-Box, Lion's Choice, Pasta House, 🄾 Dobb's Tire/auto, $General, K-Mart, Firestone, Office Depot, S 🅿 Phillips 66, 🍴 Arby's, Burger King, Krispy Kreme, Malone's Grill, McDonald's, Pantera's Pizza, Sonic, 🄾 BigLots, $Tree, Mazda, NTB, Radio Shack, Sam's Club/gas, Walmart, Walgreens
28	Elizabeth Ave, Washington St, N 🅿 Phillips 66/dsl, 🍴 Jack-in-the-Box, Jerome's Pizza, Pizza Hut/Taco Bell, Subway, 🄾 Chevrolet, Schnuck's Foods, Walgreens, S 🅿 BP
27	New Florissant Rd, rd N, N 🅿 BP, Shell/Circle K
26b	Graham Rd, N Hanley, N 🅿 7-11/dsl 🍴 Arby's, LJ Silver, Starbucks, 🏨 Hampton Inn, Motel 6, 🄾 🏥, S 🅿 QT, 🍴 McDonald's, 🏨 Days Inn, 🄾 $General, Hancock Fabrics
26a	I-170, S
25b a	US 67, Lindbergh Blvd, N 🅿 BP, Phillips 66, QT, 🍴 Bandana's BBQ, Burger King, China Wok, Church's, Del Taco, IHOP, Imo's Pizza, Jack-in-the-Box, McDonald's, Outback Steaks, Papa John's, Pizza Hut/Taco Bell, Pueblo Nuevo Mexican, Quiznos, Rally's, Sonic, Starbucks, Waffle House, Wendy's, 🏨 Comfort Inn, InTown Suites, La Quinta, Ramada Inn, 🄾 AutoZone, Cadillac, Dierberg's Deli, Family$, Firestone/auto, Ford, GNC, Goodyear, NAPA, Nissan, Radio Shack, Sav-a-Lot Foods, Schnuck's Foods, Toyota, Scion, Walgreens, S 🅿 7-11, 🍴 Subway, 🏨 Budget Inn, EconoLodge, Extended Stay America, Studio+, 🄾 Honda, VW, transmissions, USPO
23	McDonnell Blvd, E 🍴 Denny's, Quiznos, 🏨 La Quinta, W 🅿 BP, QT, ZX, 🍴 Arby's, Jack-in-the-Box, Lion's Choice, McDonald's, Starbucks, Steak'n Shake, 🄾 Buick/GMC
22b a	MO 370 W, to MO Bottom Rd
20c	MO 180, St Charles Rock Rd, E 🅿 Phillips 66/dsl, 🍴 A&W, LJ Silver, Arby's, Casa Gallardo's, Hometown Buffet, Fazoli's, Jack-in-the-Box, Lonestar Steaks, McDonald's, Ponderosa, Red Lobster, St. Louis Bread, Subway, Taco Bell, Wendy's, White Castle, 🏨 Economy Inn, 🄾 🏥, Aldi Foods, AutoZone, Best Buy, $Tree, K-Mart, Kohl's, Lowe's, NTB, Office Depot, Petsmart, Target, Tuesday Morning, Verizon, Walgreens, vet, W 🅿 QT, ZX, 🍴 Bob Evans, Olive Garden, Waffle House, 🏨 Best Value Inn, Motel 6, Super 8
20b a	I-70, E to St Louis, W to Kansas City
17	Dorsett Rd, E 🅿 BP, QT, 🍴 BBQ, Syberg's Grill, 🏨 Best Western, Drury Inn, Hampton Inn, W 🅿 Mobil, Phillips 66, Shell, 🍴 Arby's, Denny's, Fuddrucker's, McDonald's, Steak'n Shake, Subway, 🏨 Baymont Inn
16b a	Page Ave, rd D, MO 364 W, E 🅿 BP, CFM, Citgo/7-11, QT, Sinclair, 🍴 Blimpie, Copperfield's Rest., Hardee's, Hooters, Malone's Grill, McDonald's, Stazio's Café, 🏨 Comfort Inn, Courtyard, DoubleTree, Holiday Inn, Homestead Suites, Red Roof Inn, Residence Inn, Sheraton

INTERSTATE 270 (ST LOUIS)

Exit	Services
14	MO 340, Olive Blvd, **E** [gas] BP, Mobil, [food] Applebee's, Bristol Cafe, Denny's, Domino's, KFC, McDonald's, Lion's Choice Rest., Pasta House, Steakout, [lodging] Courtyard, Drury Inn, [other] [H], BMW/Land Rover/Cadillac, Chevrolet, Crysler/Jeep, Lexus, **W** [gas] Schnucks, [food] Coldstone Creamery, Culpepper's Café, House of Wong, Subway, TGIFriday, [other] Dierberg's Foods, Kohl's, Walgreens
13	rd AB, Ladue Rd
12b a	I-64, US 40, US 61, E to St Louis, W to Wentzville, **E** [H]
9	MO 100, Manchester Rd, **E** [gas] BP, [food] Café America, Houlihan's Rest, IHOP, Lion's Choice Rest., McDonald's, [other] Famous Barr, Galyan's, Lord&Taylor, Nordstrom's, mall, **W** [gas] Phillips 66, Shell, [food] Applebee's, Casa Gallardo's Mexican, Olive Garden, Red Robin
8	Dougherty Ferry Rd, **S** [gas] Citgo/7-11, Mobil, [food] McDonald's, [other] [H]
7	Big Ben Rd, **N** [H]
5b a	I-44, US 50, MO 366, E to St Louis, W to Tulsa
3	MO 30, Gravois Rd, **N** [gas] BP, Phillips 66, [food] Bandana BBQ, Olive Garden, Outback Steaks, [lodging] Days Inn, Quality Inn, [other] Ford
2	MO 21, Tesson Ferry Rd, **N** [gas] BP, [food] El Muguey Mexican, Jimmy John's, Panda Chinese, Pizza Hut, [other] Acura, AutoZone, Buick, Dobb's Auto, O'Reilly Parts, Scion/Toyota, vet, **N on Lindbergh** [gas] Mobil, [food] Burger King, Church's, 54th St Grill, Jack-in-the-Box, Olive Garden, Outback Steaks, Quizno's, Red Lobster, Subway, Taco Bell, TGIFriday's, Waffle House, White Castle, [other] Buick/GMC, Honda, Schnuck's Foods, Shop'n Save, Walgreens, **S** [gas] Shell/Circle K/dsl, [food] Little Caesar's, other Dierberg's Foods
1b a	I-55, N to St Louis, S to Memphis

INTERSTATE 435 (KANSAS CITY)

Exit	Services
83	I-35, N to KS City, S to Wichita
82	Quivira Rd, Overland Park, **N** [food] Burger King, Old Chicago Pizza, Pizza Hut, Ponderosa, Taco Bell, [other] [H], CVS Drug, **S** [food] McDonald's, Subway, Wendy's, [lodging] Extended Stay America
81	US 69 S, to Ft Scott
79	US 169, Metcalf Ave., **N** [gas] BP, Shell, [food] Denny's, Dick Clark's Grill, Hooters, Tippin's Café, [lodging] Clubhouse Inn, Embassy Suites, Hampton Inn, Red Roof Inn, Super 8, Wyndham Garden, [other] [H], Chrysler/Dodge, **S** [food] KC BBQ, McDonald's, [lodging] Courtyard, Drury Inn, Marriott, PearTree Inn
77b a	Nall Ave, Roe Ave, **N** [gas] BP, Shell, [food] DQ, On-the-Border, Panera Bread, Winstead's Grill, [lodging] Fairfield Inn, **S** [gas] BP, [food] Cactus Grill, McDonald's, Wendy's, [lodging] AmeriSuites, Courtyard, Hilton Garden, Holiday Inn, Homestead Suites, Sheraton
75b	State Line Rd, **N** [gas] BP, Conoco, [food] Applebee's, McDonald's, Taco Bell, Waid's Rest., Wendy's, [other] Buick/Cadillac, Ford, Goodyear, Infiniti, Lexus, Volvo, **S** [H], city park
75a	Wornall Rd, **N** [gas] QT, [food] Applebees, Coach's Rest, Wendy's, [other] Chevrolet, Honda, Toyota, VW, **S** [gas] BP
74	Holmes Rd, **S** [gas] Phillips 66, [food] Burger King, Guacamole Grill, Patrikio's Mexican, Subway, [lodging] Courtyard, Extended Stay America
73	103rd St (from sb)
71b a	I-470, US 71 S, US 50 E

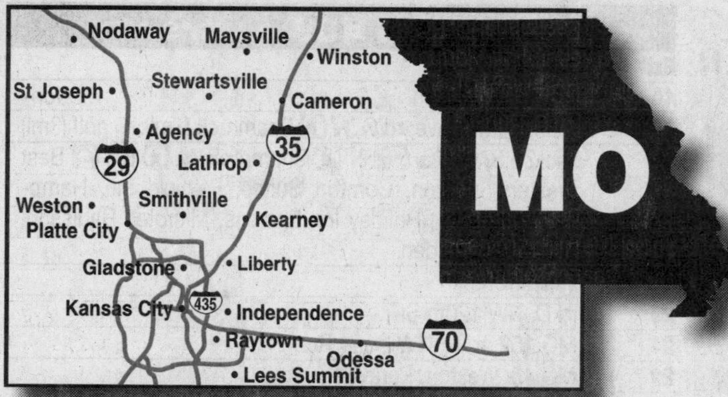

KANSAS CITY

Exit	Services
70	Bannister Rd, **E** [gas] Shell, [food] China Buffet, McDonalds, Wendy's, [other] K-Mart, **W** [food] HomeTown Buffet, KFC/Taco Bell, LJ Silver/A&W, Pizza Hut, [other] Firestone/auto, Home Depot
69	87th St., **E** [food] Subway, [lodging] Day's Inn, Motel 6, Super 8, [other] Suzuki, **W** [gas] BP/dsl, [lodging] Baymont Inn
67	Gregory Blvd (same as 66a b), **E** [gas] Shell, [food] Applebee's, Niece's Rest., Wendy's, [other] Big Lots, $General, PriceChopper Foods, **W** Nature Ctr, IMAX Theatre, zoo
66a b	MO 350 E, 63rd st, **E** [gas] Shell, [food] Applebee's, Wendy's, [other] Big Lots, $General, PriceChopper Foods, **W** [food] LC's BBQ, [lodging] Relax Inn
65	Eastwood Tfwy, **W** [gas] Conoco, [food] KFC, LC's BBQ, McDonald's, Peachtree Buffet, Pizza Hut, [lodging] Relax Inn
63c	Raytown Rd, Stadium Dr (nb only), **E** [lodging] Day's Inn, Sports Stadium Motel, Villager Lodge, [other] Sports Complex
63b a	I-70, W to KC, E to St Louis
61	MO 78, **1 mi E** Church's Chicken
60	MO 12 E, Truman Rd, 12th St, **E** [gas] BP/dsl, Shamrock, **W** [gas] QT
59	US 24, Independence Ave, **E** [gas] QT, [food] Hardee's, [other] to Truman Library, **W** [other] CarQuest, Waffle House
57	Front St, **E** [gas] FLYING J/Conoco/dsl/rest./scales/24hr, [other] Blue Beacon, Freightliner, Kenworth, **W** [gas] Phillips 66, QT, [food] Denny's, McDonald's, Pizza Hut, Smugglers Rest, Subway, Taco Bell, Waffle House, Wendy's, [lodging] La Quinta, Park Place Hotel
56mm	Missouri River
55b a	MO 210, **E** [lodging] Ameristar Hotel/Casino, Red Roof Inn, [other] Riverboat Casino, Ford/Volvo/GMC/Mercedes Trucks, **W** [food] Arby's, Burger King, Denny's
54	48th St, Parvin Rd, **E** RV Park, **W** [gas] QT, [food] Alamo Mexican, Golden Buffet, KFC, Mama Jo's BBQ, Ponderosa, Waffle House, Wendy's, [lodging] Comfort Inn, Crossland Suites, Day's Inn, Fairfield Inn, Hampton Inn, Holiday Inn, Super 8
52a	US 69, **E** [gas] Phillips 66, Shell, Sinclair, **W** [gas] Fuel Outlet, [food] McDonald's, Pizza Hut, Subway, Taco Bell, [other] CVS Drug, $General, Osco Drug, Sav-A-Lot Foods
52b	I-35, S to KC
51	Shoal Creek Dr
49b a	MO 152 E, to I-35 N, Liberty, **E** [food] Applebee's, Bob Evans, Buffalo Wild Wings, Cracker Barrel, 54th St Grill, Longhorn Steaks, Steak'n Shake, [lodging] Best Western, Comfort Inn, Fairfield Inn, Hampton Inn, Holiday Inn Express, Super 8
47	NE 96th St
46	NE 108th St
45	MO 291, NE Cookingham Ave, **E** to I-35 N
42	N Woodland Ave
41b a	US 169, Smithville, **N** [food] Burger King, McDonald's, Sonic, [lodging] Super 8

[R] = gas [food icon] = food [lodging icon] = lodging [O] = other Copyright 2011 - The Next Ex

INTERSTATE 435 (KANSAS CITY)

Exit	Services
40	NW Cookingham
37	NW Skyview Ave, rd C, **N** [R] Shamrock (1mi), **S** golf (3mi)
36	to I-29 S, to KCI [air], **N** [R] Shamrock, **S** [R] BP, [lodging] Best Western, Clarion, Comfort Suites, Fairfield Inn, Hampton Inn, Hilton, Holiday Inn Express, Microtel, Radisson, Wyndham Garden
31mm	Prairie Creek
29	rd D, NW 120th St
24	MO 152, rd N, NW Berry Rd
22	MO 45, Weston, Parkville
20mm	Missouri/Kansas state line, Missouri River
18	KS 5 N, Wolcott Dr, **E** to Wyandotte Co Lake Park
15b a	Leavenworth Rd, **E** Woodlands Racetrack
14b a	Parallel Pkwy, **E** [R] QT, [O] [H]
13b a	US 24, US 40, State Ave, **E** [food] Frontier Steaks, **W** [O] Cabela's Sporting Goods, KS Race Track
12b a	I-70, KS Tpk, to Topeka, St Louis

Exit	Services
11	Kansas Ave
9	KS 32, KS City, Bonner Springs, **W** [R] Phillips 66/dsl
8b	Woodend Rd, **E** Peterbilt
8.8mm	Kansas River
8a	Holliday Dr, to Lake Quivira
6c	Johnson Dr
6b a	Shawnee Mission Pkwy, **E** [R] BP/dsl, [food] Sonic, [O] museum
5	Midland Dr, Shawnee Mission Park, **E** [R] Conoco, Shell, Blimpie, [food] Arizona's Grille, Barley's Brewhaus, Jose Pepper's Grill, Paula&Bill's Ristorante, Wendy's, [lodging] Hampton Inn
3	87th Ave, **E** [R] BP, Phillips 66, Shell, [food] McDonald's, [O] NY Burrito, Panera Bread, Sonic, Zarda BBQ, K-Mart, museum
2	95th St
1b	KS 10, to Lawrence
1a	Lackman Rd, **N** [R] QT, Shell
0mm	I-435 begins/ends on I-35.

MONTANA

INTERSTATE 15

Exit	Services
398mm	Montana/US/Canada Border
397	Sweetgrass, **W** rest area both lanes, full [access] facilities, [picnic], litter barrels, petwalk, [C], [R] Gastrak, [lodging] Glocca Morra Motel/cafe, [O] Duty Free
394	ranch access
389	MT 552, Sunburst, **W** gas/dsl, [O] Prairie Mkt foods, Sunburst RV Park, USPO
385	Swayze Rd
379	MT 215, MT 343, to Kevin, Oilmont, **W** [food] Four Corners Café
373	Potter Rd
369	Bronken Rd
366.5mm	weigh sta sb
364	Shelby, **E** Lewis&Clark RV Park, **W** [air]
363	US 2, Shelby, to Cut Bank, **0-1 mi E** [R] Cenex, [food] /Exxon/Subway/dsl/scales/24hr, Sinclair/dsl, [food] Dash Drive-In, Dixie Inn Steaks, Pizza Hut, South of the Border, The Griddle, [lodging] Comfort Inn, Crossroads Inn, Glacier Motel/RV Park, O'Haire Motel, [O] [H], Albertsons, CarQuest, Mark's Tire, Parts+, Radio Shack, TrueValue, city park, **W** [O] Pamida/drugs, to Glacier NP
361mm	parking area nb
358	Marias Valley Rd, to Golf Course Rd, **E** camping
357mm	Marias River
352	Bullhead Rd
348	rd 44, to Valier, **W** Lake Frances RA (15mi)
345	MT 366, Ledger Rd, **E** to Tiber Dam (42mi)
339	Conrad, **W** [R] Cenex/dsl, Dan's Gas/Tires, Exxon/Subway/dsl, MRC/dsl, [food] A&W/KFC, Home Cafe, Keg Rest., Main Drive-In, [lodging] Northgate Motel, Super 8, [O] [H], Buick/Chevrolet/GMC, G&D Hardware, IGA Foods, Olson's Drug, Radio Shack, Ford, Pondera RV Park, TrueValue, Westco RV Ctr, auto/tire repair, museum, vet, USPO
335	Midway Rd, Conrad, **4 mi W** [H], gas, food, [C], [lodging], RV camping
328	MT 365, Brady, **W** [R] Mtn View Co-op/dsl, [O] city park, tires, USPO

Exit	Services
321	Collins Rd
319mm	Teton River, **rest area both lanes, full** [access] **facilities,** [C], [picnic], **litter barrels, petwalk**
313	MT 221, MT 379, Dutton, **W** [R] Cenex/dsl, [food] Café Dutton [O] city park, USPO
302	MT 431, Power
297	Gordon
290	US 89 N, rd 200 W, to Choteau, **W** [R] Exxon/dsl, Sinclair dsl/LP/RV dump, [O] USPO
288mm	parking area both lanes
286	Manchester, **W** livestock auction, same as 290 (2mi)
282	US 87, N (from sb), NW bypass, **2-3 mi E** [R] Conoco dsl, Holiday/dsl, [food] Arby's, Burger King, McDonald's, New Peking, Subway, Taco Bell, Taco John's, [lodging] Days Inn, [O] Albertsons/Osco/gas, $Tree, K-Mart, O'Reilly Parts, Sam's Club/gas, ShopKo, Staples, Tire-Rama, Walgreens, Walmart
280	US 87 N, Central Ave W, Great Falls, **E** [R] Loaf 'N Jug [food] A&W/KFC, Arby's, Double Barrel Diner, Ford's Drive-In Hardee's, Papa John's, [lodging] Alberta Inn, Central Motel, Days Inn, Quality Inn (2mi), [O] Central RV Ctr, NAPA, U-Haul/LP Whalen Tire, to Giant Sprgs SP, city park, vet
280mm	Sun River
278	US 89 S, rd 200 E, 10th Ave, Great Falls, **E** [food] Chili's, Classic 50s Diner/casino, Coldstone, Golden Corral, Macaroni Grill, McDonald's, On-the-Border Mexican, Pizza Hut, Taco Del Mar, [lodging] Comfort Inn, Hampton Inn, Hilton Garden, Holiday Inn Express, [O] Barnes&Noble, Home Depot, Michael's, Old Navy, PetCo, Smith's Foods, **1-3 mi E** [R] Cenex/dsl Conoco, Exxon, Holiday/Subway/dsl, MRC/dsl, Sinclair dsl, [food] A&W/KFC, Applebee's, Arby's, Boston's Pizza, Burger King, China Buffet, DQ, 4B's Rest., Fuddrucker's, Godfather's Pizza, Hardee's, JB's Rest., Jimmy John's, MacKenzie River Pizza, Ming's Chinese, Monty's Rest., Noodle Express, Papa John's, Papa Murphy's, Pizza Hut PrimeCut Rest., Quiznos, Sonic, Starbucks, Subway, Taco Bell, Taco John's, Taco Treat, Wendy's, [lodging] Best Western, Comfort Inn, Extended Stay America, Fairfield Inn, Holiday Inn, La Quinta, Motel 6, Plaza Inn, Super 8, Townhouse Inn, Western Motel, [O] [H], Ace Hardware,

MO MT (side tab)

N / S (directional, I-435)

KANSAS CITY (side tab)

N / S (directional, I-15)

SHELBY (side tab)

GREAT FALLS (side tab)

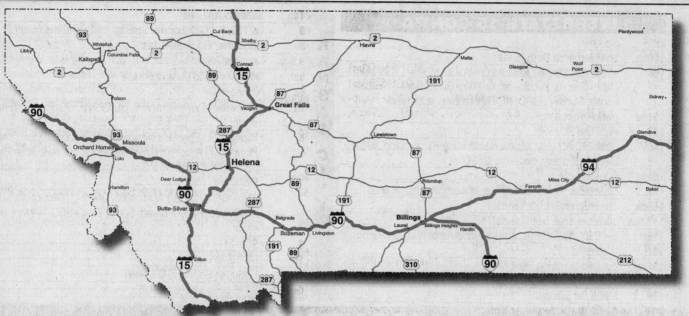

INTERSTATE 15 CONT'D

Exit	Services
278	Continued Albertsons/gas, Big-O Tires, Cadillac/Chevrolet/Toyota, CarQuest, Chrysler/Dodge/Jeep, CVS Drug, Dick's RV Park, Discount Drug, Discount Parts, $Tree, Firestone/auto, Ford, Harley-Davidson, Hastings Books, Honda, Hyundai, JC Penney, Jo-Ann Fabrics, KOA, McCollum RV Ctr, NAPA, Nissan, O'Reilly Parts, Parts+, Ross, Scheels Sports, Sears/auto, Target, Tire-Rama, Van's Foods, Verizon, VW, Walgreens, USPO, transmissions, vet, to Malmstrom AFB
277	Airport Rd, **E** 🅰 Flying J/Denny's/dsl/scales/24hr, 🖩/Conoco/Subway/casino/dsl/scales/24hr, 🏠 Crystal Inn, **W** ✈
275mm	**weigh sta nb**
270	MT 330, Ulm, **E** 🅰 Conoco/dsl/LP, 🅾 USPO, **W** to Ulm SP
256	rd 68, Cascade, **1/2 mi E** 🅰 Sinclair, 🏠 Badger Motel, 🅾 NAPA, Tom's Foods, USPO
254	rd 68, Cascade, **1/2 mi E** same as 256
250	local access
247	Hardy Creek, **W** to Tower Rock SP, food, 🍽, RV camping
246.5mm	Missouri River
245mm	scenic overlook sb
244	Canyon Access, **2 mi W** Prewett Creek Camping, food, RV camping, rec area
240	Dearborn, **E** RV park
239mm	**rest area both lanes, full** ♿ **facilities,** 🍽, 🚻, **litter barrels, petwalk**
238mm	Stickney Creek
236mm	Missouri River
234	Craig, **E** 🍽 Izaak's Cafe, Trout Shop Café/lodge, 🅾 rec area, boating, camping
228	US 287 N, to Augusta, Choteau
226	MT 434, Wolf Creek, **E** 🅰 Exxon/dsl, 🍽 Oasis Café, 🅾 MT River Outfitters/lodge/flyshop, camping, **W** 🍽 Frenchman&Me Café, 🅾 USPO
222mm	**parking area both lanes**
219	Spring Creek, Recreation Rd (from nb), boating, camping

Exit	Services
218mm	Little Prickly Pear Creek
216	Sieben, 209 E to Gates of the Mtns RA
205mm	turnout both directions
202mm	**weigh sta sb**
200	MT 279, MT 453, Lincoln Rd, **W** 🅰 Sinclair/Bob's Mkt/dsl, 🍽 GrubStake Rest., 🅾 Lincoln Rd RV Park, to ski area
193	Cedar St, Helena, **E** 🅰 Conoco, 🍽 Buffalo Wild Wings, Chili's, Hardee's, IHOP, Macaroni Grill, 🅾 Costco/gas, Helena RV Park (5mi), Home Depot, Whalen Tire, **W** 🅰 Conoco/dsl, Exxon/dsl, 🍽 Perkins, Subway, Wheat MT/deli, 🏠 Quality Inn, Wingate Inn, 🅾 Chevrolet, K-Mart, Tire Rama, USPO, vet, **W on Montana Ave** 🅰 Cenex/dsl, Exxon/dsl, 🍽 Applebee's, Arby's, DQ, Godfather's Pizza, McDonald's, McKenzie River Pizza, Papa Murphy's, Pizza Hut, Quiznos, Taco Bell, Taco Del Mar, Taco John's, 🅾 Albertsons, AutoZone, CarQuest, $Tree, Hastings Books, Jo-Ann Fabrics, Lowe's, Macy's, Office Depot, O'Reilly Parts, PetCo, Ross, ShopKo, Target, Verizon
192b a	US 12, US 287, Helena, Townsend, **E** 🅰 Cenex, 🍽 Burger King, Pizza Hut, Subway, 🏠 Hampton Inn, 🅾 Buick/GMC, Chrysler/Dodge/Jeep, D&D RV Ctr, Ford/Lincoln/Mercury, Honda, MT RV Ctr, Nissan, Schwab Tire, Staples, Toyota, Walmart, st patrol, **W** 🅰 Exxon/dsl, Sinclair/dsl/24hr, 🍽 A&W/KFC, China Wok, DQ, JB's Rest, L&D Chinese, McDonald's, Overland Express Rest., Papa John's, Papa Murphy's, Quiznos, Starbucks, Taco John's, Taco Treat, Village Inn Pizza, Wendy's, 🏠 Comfort Inn, Days Inn, Fairfield Inn, Holiday Inn Express, Howard Johnson, Jorgenson's Inn, Motel 6, Red Lion Inn, Shilo Inn, Super 8, 🅾 🅷, AAA, Albertsons/gas, CVS Drug, JC Penney, Safeway/gas, Tire Factory, Walgreens
190	S Helena, **W** 🅷
187	MT 518, Montana City, Clancy, **E** 🍽 Hugo's Pizza/casino, **W** 🅰 Cenex/dsl, 🍽 Jackson Creek Cafe, MT City Grill, 🏠 Elkhorn Inn
182	Clancy, **E** RV camping, **W** 🍽 Chubby's Grill, 🅾 USPO, to NF
178mm	**rest area both lanes, full** ♿ **facilities,** 🍽, 🚻, **litter barrels, petwalk**
176	Jefferson City, NF access
174.5mm	**chain up area both lanes**

MT

INTERSTATE 15 CONT'D

N ↕ S

Exit	Services
168mm	**chainup area both lanes**
164	rd 69, Boulder, **E** 🅖 Exxon/dsl/casino/24hr, 🍴 Elkhorn Cafe, Gator's Pizza Parlour, Mtn Good Rest., 🅾 L&P Foods, Parts+, USPO, RC RV camping, auto repair
161mm	**parking area nb**
160	High Ore Rd
156	Basin, **E** 🅾 Merry Widow Health Mine/RV camping, **W** 🅾 Basin Cr Pottery, camping, USPO
154mm	Boulder River
151	to Boulder River Rd, Bernice, **W** camping, picnic area
148mm	**chainup area both lanes**
143.5mm	**chainup area both lanes**
138	Elk Park, **W** 🅾 Sheepshead Picnic Area, wildlife viewing
134	Woodville
133mm	continental divide, elev 6368
130.5mm	scenic overlook sb
129	I-90 E, to Billings

I-15 S and I-90 W run together 8 mi

127	Harrison Ave, Butte, **E** 🅖 Conoco/dsl, Exxon/dsl/24hr, Sinclair, 🍴 A&W/KFC, Arby's, Burger King, 4B's Rest., McDonald's, MacKenzie River Pizza, MT Club Rest., Perkins, Pizza Hut, Silver Bow Pizza, Starbucks, Subway, Taco Bell, Wendy's, 🛏 Best Western, Comfort Inn, Copper King Hotel, Hampton Inn, Super 8, 🅾 American Car Care, Buick/GMC, Cadillac/Chevrolet, Chrysler/Dodge/Jeep, $Tree, Ford, Hart's RV Ctr, Herberger's, Honda, JC Penney, Jo-Ann Fabrics, K-Mart, NAPA, Rocky Mtn RV Ctr, Staples, Subaru, Toyota/Scion, Verizon, Walmart, casinos, **W** 🅖 Cenex/dsl, Conoco, 🍴 Denny's, Derby Steaks, Domino's, El Taco Mexican, Hanging 5 Rest., John's Rest., L&D Chinese, Papa John's, Papa Murphy's, Quiznos, Royse's Burgers, Taco John's, 🛏 Days Inn, Holiday Inn Express, War Bonnet Inn, 🅾 Ace Hardware, Hastings Books, O'Reilly Parts, Safeway
126	Montana St, Butte, **E** 🅖 Conoco, Exxon/dsl, **W** 🍴 Chef's Garden Italian, 🛏 Eddy's Motel, 🅾 🅷, KOA, Safeway, Schwab Tire
124	I-115 (from eb), to Butte City Ctr
123mm	**weigh sta nb**
122	Rocker, **E** 🅖 ▒▒▒/Conoco/Arby's/McDonald's/Subway/dsl/scales/24hr, 🛏 Motel 6, 🅾 repair, **W** 🅖 ⓕFLYING J/rest./dsl/LP/24hr, 🛏 Rocker Inn Motel, 🅾 weigh sta eb, RV camping

I-15 N and I-90 E run together 8 mi

121	I-90 W, to Missoula, **W** 2 Bar Lazy-H RV Camping
119	Silver Bow, Port of MT Transportation Hub
116	Buxton
112mm	Continental Divide, elevation 5879
111	Feely
109mm	**rest area both lanes, full** ♿ **facilities,** 🅲, 🚮, **litter barrels, petwalk**
102	rd 43, to Wisdom, Divide, **W** 🍴 Blue Moon Cafe, 🅾 to Big Hole Nat Bfd (62mi)
99	Moose Creek Rd
93	Melrose, **W** 🍴 Melrose Café/grill/dsl, Hitchin Post Rest., 🛏 Pioneer Mtn Cabins, 🅾 Sportsman Motel/RV Park, Sunrise Flyshop, USPO
85.5mm	Big Hole River
85	Glen, **E** 🅾 Willis Sta RV camping
74	Apex, Birch Creek

DILLON

64mm	Beaverhead River
63	Lp 15, rd 41, Dillon, Twin Bridges, **E** 🅖 Cenex/dsl/LP/RV Dump, Exxon/KFC/dsl/24hr, Phillips 66/dsl, 🍴 Lions Den, McDonald's, Pizza Hut, Subway, 🛏 Best Western/rest., Comfort Inn, GuestHouse Inn, Motel 6, Sundowner Motel, Super 8, 🅾 🅷, Buick/Cadillac/Chevrolet, CarQuest, KOA, O'Reilly Parts, Safeway/drug/gas, Schwab Tire, auto repair/tires, city park, museum, W MT Coll
62	Lp 15, Dillon, **E** 🍴 DQ, El Toro Mexican, Sparky's Rest., Taco John's, 🛏 Creston Motel, Flyshop Inn, 🅾 🅷, KOA, Southside RV Park, to WMT
60mm	Beaverhead River
59	MT 278, to Jackson, **W** 🅾 Bannack SP, Countryside RV Park
56	Barretts, **E** RV camping, **W** Big Sky TrkStp/rest/dsl/casino
52	Grasshopper Creek
51	Dalys (from sb, no return)
50mm	Beaverhead River
46mm	Beaverhead River
45mm	Beaverhead River
44	MT 324, **E** 🍴 Buffalo Lodge, 🅾 Armstead RV Park, Beaverhead Flyshop, **W** 🅾 Clark Cyn Reservoir/RA, RV camping
38.5mm	Red Rock River
37	Red Rock
34mm	**parking area both lanes, litter barrels, restrooms**
29	Kidd
23	Dell, **E** 🅖 Cenex/dsl, 🍴 Yesterdays Cafe, 🅾 USPO
16.5mm	**weigh sta both lanes**
15	Lima, **E** 🅖 Exxon/dsl, 🍴 Jan's Café, 🛏 Mtn View Motel/RV Park, 🅾 Big Sky Tire/auto, USPO, ambulance, **rest area, both lanes,** ♿ **facilities, litter barrels, petwalk**
9	Snowline
0	Monida, **E** 🅲, to Red Rock Lakes
0mm	Montana/Idaho state line, Monida Pass, elevation 6870

INTERSTATE 90

E ↕ W

Exit	Services
559.5mm	**weigh sta both lanes**
554.5mm	Montana/Wyoming state line
549	Aberdeen
544	Wyola
530	MT 463, Lodge Grass, **1 mi S** 🅖 gas, dsl, food, 🛏, 🅲
517.5mm	Little Bighorn River
514	Garryowen, **N** 🅖 Conoco/Subway, 🅾 Custer Bfd Museum, **S** 🅾 7th Ranch RV camp
511.5mm	Little Bighorn River
510	US 212 E, **N** 🅖 Exxon/KFC/dsl/café/gifts, 🍴 Crows Nest Café, 🅾🅷, to Little Bighorn Bfd, casino, **S** 🅾 Little Bighorn RV Camp/dump
509.5mm	**weigh sta, both lanes exit left**
509.3mm	Little Bighorn River
509	Crow Agency, **N** 🅖 Conoco/24hr, **S** to Bighorn Canyon NRA
503	Dunmore
498mm	Bighorn River
497	MT 384, 3rd St, Hardin, **S** 🅷, Bighorn Cty Museum, **2 mi S** 🛏 Western Motel, 🅾 Casino Rest./lounge
495	MT 47, City Ctr, Hardin, **N** 🅖 Shell/dsl, 🍴 Purple Cow Rest., 🅾 KOA, **S** 🅖 Cenex/dsl, Conoco/Subway/dsl/LP/24hr, Exxon/dsl, Sinclair/dsl, 🍴 DQ, McDonald's, Pizza Hut, Shawna's Steaks, Taco John's, 🛏 American

BUTTE

E / W

HARDIN

INTERSTATE 90 CONT'D

Exit	Services
495	Continued
	Inn, Super 8, Western Motel, ⊙ 🏥, Grand View Camping/ RV Park, Sunset Village RV Park, casinos
484	Toluca
478	Fly Creek Rd
477mm	**rest area both lanes, full ♿ facilities, 🚻, ⛲, litter barrels, petwalk**
469	Arrow Creek Rd, **N** 🍴 Rock Shop/Cafe
462	Pryor Creek Rd
456	I-94 E, to Bismarck, ND
455	Johnson Lane, **N** 🛢 ⛽/Conoco/McDonald's/dsl/ scales/24hr, **S** 🛢 Exxon/A&W/dsl/24hr, ⚜FLYING J/Denny's/dsl/LP/scales/24hr, 🍴 Burger King, DQ, Subway, 🏨 Holiday Inn Express, ⊙ Tour America RV Ctr (1mi)
452	US 87 N, City Ctr, Billings, **N** 🛢 Conoco/Arby's/dsl/LP, Exxon, 🏨 Best Western, ⊙ American Spirit RV Ctr, Metra Rv Ctr, transmissions, **2-4 mi N on US 87** 🛢 Cenex/dsl, Conoco/dsl, Holiday/dsl, 🍴 Applebee's, Arby's, Badabing Italian, Bugz Rest./casino, Burger King, DQ, Fuddrucker's, Godfather's Pizza, Golden Phoenix, KFC, Little Caesar's, MacKenzie River Pizza, Main St Grill, McDonald's, MT Jack's, Papa John's, Papa Murphy's, Pizza Hut, Shanghai Buffet, Subway, Taco Bell, Taco John's, Wendy's, 🏨 Country Inn&Suites, Foothills Inn, Heights Motel, ⊙ Ace Hardware, Albertsons/Osco, BigLots, CarQuest, Curves, CVS Drug, $Tree, O'Reilly Parts, Office Depot, Target, Tire Rama, U-Haul, Verizon, Walgreens, Walmart, vet, **S** 🛢 Cenex/dsl, ⊙ RV Camping
451.5mm	Yellowstone River
450	MT 3, 27th St, Billings, **N** 🛢 Conoco/dsl/24hr, Sinclair, 🍴 Blondy's Cafe, Pizza Hut, 🏨 Crowne Plaza, War Bonnet Inn/rest., 🛢 🏥, CarQuest, city park, USPO, **S** KOA, Yellowstone River Camping
447	S Billings Blvd, **N** 🛢 Conoco/Subway/dsl/24hr, Holiday/dsl, 🍴 Burger King, DQ, El Corral Mexican, McDonald's, 🏨 Best Western/Kelly, Days Inn, Extended Stay America, Hampton Inn, Sleep Inn, Super 8, Cabela's Sporting Goods, NAPA, Sam's Club/gas, **S** 🛢 Billings RV Park (2mi), Freightliner, Kenworth, KOA (2mi), Yellowstone River Campground
446	King Ave, Billings, **N on King Ave** 🛢 Exxon, Conoco/dsl, Holiday/dsl/LP/RV dump, 🍴 Applebee's, Arbys, Bruno's Italian, Burger King, Cactus Creek Steaks, Carino's Italian, City Brew Coffee, DQ, Del Taco, Denny's, Dos Machos, Emporium Rest., Famous Dave's, Fuddrucker's, Gusicks Rest., HuHot Mongolian, IHOP, Jade Palace, Jake's Grill, Olive Garden, Old Chicago, Outback Steaks, Perkins, Pizza Hut, Quiznos, Red Lobster, Ruby Red Grill, Subway, Taco John's, TX Roadhouse, Wheat MT, 🏨 C'Mon Inn, Comfort Inn, Fairfield Inn, Hilton Garden, La Quinta, Quality Inn, Residence Inn, SpringHill Suites, Western Executive Inn, ⊙ Best Buy, Chevrolet, Chrysler/Dodge/ Jeep, Costco/gas, Ford, Home Depot, Lowe's, Mercedes, Michael's, Nissan, Office Depot, Old Navy, O'Reilly Parts, Petsmart, Ross, ShopKo, Suzuki, Toyota, Verizon, Walmart, World Mkt, USPO, **N on 24th** 🛢 Conoco/dsl, Exxon/Subway, 🍴 Buffalo Wild Wings, Golden Corral, Guadalajara Mexican, Hardee's, KFC, Little Caesar's, McDonald's, Papa John's, Starbucks, Taco Bell, Wendy's, ⊙ Albertsons/Osco, Barnes&Noble, Cadillac/GMC, Dillards, Hobby Lobby, Kia, K-Mart, Subaru, mall, **S** 🛢 Conoco/

Exit	Services
446	Continued
	dsl/24hr, 🍴 Cracker Barrel, Emporium Rest., 🏨 Billings Hotel, ClubHouse Inn, Holiday Inn, Howard Johnson, Kelly Inn, Motel 6, ⊙ Volvo/Mack Trucks, water funpark
443	Zoo Dr, to Shiloh Rd, **N** 🛢 Holiday/dsl, 🍴 MT Rib/Chophouse, 🏨 Hampton Inn, Wingate Inn, ⊙ Honda, Pierce RV Ctr, zoo, **S** ⊙ Harley-Davidson, vet
439mm	**weigh sta both lanes**
437	E Laurel, **S** 🛢 Sinclair/dsl/rest./casino/motel/RV Park/24hr
434	US 212, US 310, to Red Lodge, Laurel, **N** 🛢 Cenex/dsl, Conoco/dsl, Exxon/dsl/24hr, 🍴 Burger King, City Brew Coffee, Hardee's, McDonald's, Pizza Hut, Subway, Taco John's, 🏨 Best Western, Locomotive Inn, ⊙ Ace Hardware, Chevrolet, CVS Drug, Ford, IGA Foods, Rapid Tire, Verizon, Walmart, **S** ⊙ Riverside Park/RV Camping, vet, to Yellowstone NP
433	Lp 90 (from eb), same as 434
426	Park City, **S** 🛢 Cenex/dsl/café/24hr, KwikStop, 🍴 The Other Cafe, 🏨 CJ's Motel, ⊙ auto/tire repair
419mm	**rest area both lanes, full ♿ facilities, 🚻, ⛲, litter barrels, petwalk**
408	rd 78, Columbus, **N** Mtn Range RV Park, **S** 🛢 Conoco, ⛽/Exxon/dsl/24hr, 🍴 Apple Village Café/gifts, McDonald's, Subway, 🏨 Big Sky Motel, Super 8, ⊙ 🏥, Chevrolet, casino, city park, museum, tires/repair, to Yellowstone
400	Springtime Rd
398mm	Yellowstone River
396	ranch access
392	Reed Point, **N** 🛢 Sinclair/dsl, ⊙ Old West RV Park, USPO
384	Bridger Creek Rd
381mm	**rest area both lanes, full ♿ facilities, 🚻, ⛲, litter barrels, petwalk**
377	Greycliff, **S** ⊙ Prairie Dog Town SP, KOA
370	US 191, Big Timber, **1 mi N** 🛢 Cenex/dsl, Sinclair/dsl, 🏨 Grand Hotel, Lazy J Motel, ⊙ 🏥, Spring Creek RV Ranch (4mi), USPO, vet
369mm	Boulder River
367	US 191 N, Big Timber, **N** 🛢 Exxon/dsl, Conoco/dsl, 🍴 Country Skillet, 🏨 River Valley Inn, Super 8, ⊙ CarQuest, Chevrolet, Ford, Spring Creek Camping (3mi), historic site/ visitor info
362	De Hart
354	MT 563, Springdale
352	ranch access
350	East End access
343	Mission Creek Rd, **N** Ft Parker HS
340	US 89 N, to White Sulphur Sprgs, **S** ✈

MT

INTERSTATE 90 CONT'D

Exit	Services
337	Lp 90, to Livingston, **2 mi N** services
333mm	Yellowstone River
333	US 89 S, Livingston, **N** 🍴 Clark's Rest., DQ, Pizza Hut, Taco John's, 🛏 Best Western, Budget Host, Livingston Inn, Quality Inn, Rodeway Inn, 🅞 🏥, Ace Hardware, Chrysler/Dodge/Jeep, Pamida, Radio Shack, RV Park, Town&Country Foods, **S** 🅖 Cenex/dsl, Conoco/dsl, Exxon/dsl, 🍴 Arby's, Buffalo Jump Steaks, McDonald's, Rosa's Pizza, Subway, 🛏 Comfort Inn, Super 8, 🅞 Albertsons/Osco, Osen's RV Park, Windmill RV Park, LP, vet, to Yellowstone
330	Lp 90, Livingston, **1 mi N** 🅖 Yellowstone Trkstp/dsl/rest./24hr
326.5mm	**chainup/chain removal area both lanes**
324	ranch access
323mm	**chainup/chain removal area wb**
322mm	Bridger Mountain Range
321mm	turnouts/hist marker both lanes
319	Jackson Creek Rd
319mm	**chainup area both lanes**
316	Trail Creek Rd
313	Bear Canyon Rd, **S** 🅞 Bear Canyon Camping
309	US 191 S, Main St, Bozeman, **N** 🅞 Subaru, Sunrise RV Park, VW, **S** 🅖 Cenex/dsl, Exxon/dsl, 🍴 MT AleWorks, 🛏 Blue Sky Motel, Continental Motel, Ranch House Motel, Western Heritage Inn, 🅞 🏥, Heeb's Foods, to Yellowstone, repair, vet
306	MT 205, N 7th, to US 191, Bozeman, **N** 🅖 Sinclair, 🍴 McDonald's, Panda Buffet, 🛏 Fairfield Inn, La Quinta, Microtel, Ramada Ltd, Rodeway Inn, Super 8, The Inn, TLC Inn, 🅞 Whalen Tire, RV supplies, ski area, **S** 🅖 Conoco/Arby's/dsl, Exxon, 🍴 Applebee's, Bar-3 BBQ, Dominos, DQ, Famous Dave's BBQ, McDonald's, Papa John's, Santa Fe Red's Cafe, Taco John's, The Wok Chinese, 🛏 Best Western, Bozeman, Comfort Inn, Days Inn, Hampton Inn, Holiday Inn, Homewood Suites, Royal 7 Inn, 🅞 Big O Tire, CarQuest, Firestone/auto, K-Mart, U-Haul, Van's Foods, Walmart, Museum of the Rockies
305	MT412, N 19th Ave, **N** 🅖 Exxon, 🛏 AmericInn, **0-3 mi S** 🍴 A&W/KFC, Baja Fresh, Buffalo Wild Wings, Canyons Grill, Carino's Italian, City Brew Coffee, IHOP, Mackenzie River Pizza, Old Chicago Pizza, Outback Steaks, Papa Murphy's, Subway, Wendy's, Wheat MT Bakery, 🛏 C'mon Inn, Hilton Garden, Residence Inn, Wingate Inn, 🅞 Costco/gas, Ford/Lincoln/Mercury/RV Ctr, Home Depot, Lowe's, Michaels, Old Navy, Office Depot, Petsmart, Target, Radio Shack, Ross, Smith's Foods, Staples, UPS, World MKT, USPO, vet, **rest area, full ♿ facilities, 🚮/litter barrels, petwalk**
298	MT 291, rd 85, Belgrade, **N** 🅖 Cenex/dsl, Conoco, Exxon/Subway/dsl, 🍴 Burger King, DQ, McDonald's, Pizza Hut, 🅞 Albertson's/Osco, IGA Foods, NAPA, Radio Shack, Whalen Tire, **S** 🅖 ✈FLYING J/Conoco/dsl/scales/LP, 🛏 Holiday Inn Express, La Quinta, Super 8, 🅞 Freightliner, Harley-Davidson, KOA (9mi), Tire Factory, TrueValue, repair, truckwash, to Yellowstone NP
292.5mm	Gallatin River
288	MT 288, MT 346, Manhattan, **N** 🅖 Conoco/Subway/dsl, 🅞 RV camping
283	Logan, **S** 🅞 Madison Buffalo Jump SP (7mi)

Exit	Services
279mm	Madison River
278	MT 205, rd 2, Three Forks, Trident, **N** Missouri Headwaters SP, **1 mi S** 🅖 Conoco/dsl, Sinclair/dsl, 🛏 Broken Spur Motel, Sacajawea Hotel, 🅞 camping, 🍴
277.5mm	Jefferson River
274	US 287, to Helena, Ennis, **N** 🅖 Sinclair/dsl, 🍴 Wheat MT Bakery/deli, 🛏 Ft 3 Forks Motel, 🅞 KOA (2mi), to Canyon Ferry SP, dsl repair, **S** 🅖 🚚Exxon/Subway/dsl/scales/24hr, 🅞 Camp 3 Forks, Lewis&Clark Caverns SP, to Yellowstone NP
267	Milligan Canyon Rd
261.5mm	**chain-up area**
257mm	Boulder River
256	MT 359, Cardwell, **S** 🅖 Cenex/dsl/RV Park, 🅞 to Yellowstone NP, Lewis&Clark Caverns SP, RV camping
249	rd 55, to rd 69, Whitehall, **S** 🅖 Exxon/Subway/dsl/24hr, 🍴 A&W/KFC, 🛏 Super 8, 🅞 Virginia City NHS, camping, casino
241	Pipestone
240.5mm	**chainup/chain removal area both lanes**
238.5mm	**runaway ramp eb**
237.5mm	pulloff eb
235mm	**truck parking both lanes, litter barrels, rest rooms**
233	Homestake, Continental Divide, elev 6393
230mm	**chain-up area both lanes**
228	MT 375, Continental Dr, **S** 🅖 Conoco/dsl, 🅞 Harley-Davidson, 3 Bears Foods
227	I-15 N, to Helena, Great Falls
	I-90 and I-15 run together 8 mi. See Montana I-15, exits 122-127.
219	I-15 S, to Dillon, Idaho Falls
216	Ramsay
211	MT 441, Gregson, **3-5 mi S** food, 🛏 Fairmont RV Park (Apr-Oct)
210.5mm	parking area wb, Pintlar Scenic route info
208	rd 1, Pintler Scenic Loop, Georgetown Lake RA, Opportunity, Anaconda, **S** 🅞 🏥, gas, food, 🛏, RV camp/dump, ski area, **rest area both lanes, full ♿ facilities, 🚮 litter barrels, petwalk**
201	Warm Springs, to Anaconda, **S** MT ST 🏥
197	MT 273, Galen, **S** to MT ST 🏥
195	Racetrack, **S** 🅞 dsl repair
187	Lp 90, Deer Lodge (no wb return), **2 mi S** 🍴 Monty's Subs, 🛏 Budget Inn, Downtowner Motel, Scharf's Motel/rest., 🅞 🏥, KOA (seasonal), Radio Shack, Valley Foods, Old MT Prison, Tow Ford Museum, same as 184
184	Deer Lodge, **0-1 mi S** 🅖 Exxon/dsl/casino, Conoco/dsl/casino, Sinclair/dsl, 🍴 A&W, 4B's Rest., McDonald's, Pizza Hut, Yak Yak Cafe, 🛏 Downtowner Motel, Rodeway Inn, Western Big Sky Inn, 🅞 🏥, Indian Creek Camping, Keystone Drug, KOA, Safeway/deli, Schwab Tire, city park, Grant-Kohrs Ranch NHS, USPO
179	Beck Hill Rd
175	US 12 E, Garrison, **N** 🅞 RiverFront RV Park, 🍴, hist site
175mm	Little Blackfoot River
174	US 12, E (from eb), **S** 🍴 Ranch House Cafe/RV Park, same as 175
170	Phosphate
168mm	**rest area both lanes, full ♿ facilities, 🍴, 🚮, litter barrels, petwalk, hist site**
166	Gold Creek, **S** 🅞 Camp Mak-A-Dream
162	Jens

Side labels: **LIVINGSTON E ↕ W BOZEMAN BELGRADE** / **BUTTE DEER LODGE**

INTERSTATE 90 CONT'D

Exit	Services
154	to MT 1 (from wb), Drummond, **S** ▣ Conoco/dsl, Mtn West/dsl, Sinclair/dsl, ▣ Parker's Rest., Wagon Wheel Café, ▣ Drummond Motel, Sky Motel, Wagon Wheel Motel, ▣ Front St Mkt, Pintler Scenic Lp, Georgetown Lake RA, Goodtime RV Park (3mi)
153	MT 1 (from eb), **N** ▣ Garnet GhostTown, Goodtime RV Park (3mi) **S** same as 154
150.5mm	weigh sta both lanes
143mm	rest area both lanes, full ▣ facilities, ▣, ▣, litter barrels, petwalk
138	Bearmouth Area, **N** ▣ Chalet Bearmouth Camp/rest., to gas, food, ▣
130	Beavertail Rd, **S** ▣ to Beavertail Hill SP, rec area, camping (seasonal)
128mm	parking area both lanes, litter barrels/restrooms
126	Rock Creek Rd, **S** ▣ Rock Creek Lodge/gas/casino, ▣ rec area
120	Clinton, **N** ▣ Sinclair/dsl, ▣ Poor Henry's Café (1mi, W in on frtg rd), ▣ Clinton Market, **S** ▣ USPO
113	Turah, **S** ▣ Turah RV Park/gas
109.5mm	Clark Fork
109mm	Blackfoot River
109	MT 200 E, Bonner, **N** ▣ ▣ Exxon/Arby's/Subway/dsl/scales/casino/LP/24hr, Sinclair/dsl, ▣ River City Grill, ▣ USPO, hist site
108.5mm	Clark Fork
107	E Missoula, **N** ▣ Ole's Mkt/Conoco/diner/dsl, Sinclair/Chester's, ▣ Reno Cafe ▣ Aspen Motel, ▣ dsl repair, **2 mi S** ▣ Holiday Inn Express
105	US 12 W, Missoula, **S** ▣ Cenex/dsl, Conoco/dsl, Sinclair/dsl, ▣ Burger King, 5 Guys Burgers, McDonald's, Pizza Hut, Quiznos, Subway, Taco Bell, ▣ Campus Inn, Days Inn, DoubleTree, Family Inn, Holiday Inn, Holiday Inn Express, Motel 6, Ponderosa Motel, Thunderbird Motel, ▣ Ace Hardware, Albertson's, Kingfisher Flyshop, O'Reilly Parts, Verizon, U of MT, Vietnam Vet's Mem
104	Orange St, Missoula, **S** ▣ Conoco/dsl, ▣ Pagoda Chinese, Subway, Taco John's, ▣ Mountain Valley Inn, Red Lion Inn, ▣ ▣, Curves, TireRama, to City Ctr
101	US 93 S, Reserve St, **N** ▣ Conoco/dsl, ▣ Cracker Barrel, MacKenzie River Pizza, Starbucks, ▣ Best Western, C'Mon Inn, Motel 6, ▣ ski area, **0-2 mi S** ▣ Cenex/dsl/LP, Conoco, Exxon/dsl, Sinclair, ▣ Arby's, Blue Canyon Rest., Burger King, Carino's, China Bowl, Coldstone, DQ, Famous Dave's BBQ, Fuddrucker's, HoagiVille, Hooters, IHOP, Little Caesars, McDonald's, MT Club rest./casino, Outback Steaks, Perkins, Quiznos, Rowdy's Mexican, Stone Of Accord, Taco Bell, Taco Time/TCBY, Wendy's, ▣ AmericInn, Courtyard, EconoLodge, Hampton Inn, Hilton Garden, Holiday Inn Express, La Quinta, Ruby's Inn/rest., Staybridge Suites, Super 8, Travelers Inn, ▣ Albertson's, AT&T, Barnes&Noble, Best Buy, Bretz RV/Marine, Chevrolet, Costco/gas, Firestone/auto, Home Depot, Lowe's, Michael's, Old Navy, Petsmart, Radio Shack, Ross, Staples, Target, TJ Maxx, Walgreens, Walmart, casinos, dsl repair
99	Airway Blvd, **S** ▣ Mobil/dsl/24hr, Sinclair/dsl, ▣ Hawthorn Suites, Wingate Inn, ▣ Chrysler/Dodge, Harley-Davidson, ▣
96	US 93 N, MT 200W, Kalispell, **N** ▣ Conoco/rest./dsl/

96	Continued scales/24hr/@, ▣ Days Inn/rest., ▣ Freightliner, Peterbilt, Jellystone RV Park (1mi), Jim&Mary's RV Park (1mi), to Flathead Lake&Glacier NP, **S** ▣ CrossroadsTC/Sinclair/rest/dsl/24hr, ▣ Redwood Lodge, ▣ Kenworth, RV repair
92.5mm	inspection sta both lanes
89	Frenchtown, **S** ▣ Conoco/dsl/café, ▣ Alcan Grill, French Connectino Grill, Quiznos, ▣ Frenchtown Drug, USPO, to Frenchtown Pond SP
85	Huson, **S** gas, cafe, ▣
82	Nine Mile Rd, **N** ▣ Mile House Rest., ▣ Hist Ranger Sta/info, food, ▣
81.5mm	Clark Fork
80mm	Clark Fork
77	MT 507, Petty Creek Rd, Alberton, **S** access to gas, food, ▣, ▣
75	Alberton, **N** ▣ Ghost Rails Inn, **S** ▣ River Edge Rest., ▣ casino, motel, RV camp
73mm	parking area wb, litter barrels
72mm	parking area eb, litter barrels
70	Cyr
70mm	Clark Fork
66	Fish Creek Rd
66mm	Clark Fork
61	Tarkio
59mm	Clark Fork
58mm	rest area both lanes, full ▣ facilities, ▣, ▣, litter barrels, petwalk, NF camping (seasonal)
55	Lozeau, Quartz
53.5mm	Clark Fork
49mm	Clark Fork
47	MT 257, Superior, **N** ▣ Conoco/dsl, Mtn West/LP, Sinclair/Durango's Rest., ▣ Jackie's Rest., ▣ Budget Host, Hilltop Motel, ▣ ▣, Family Foods, Mineral Drug, NAPA, USPO, **S** ▣ ▣ Exxon/dsl/casino/24hr, ▣ repair
45mm	Clark Fork
43	Dry Creek Rd, **N** NP camping (seasonal)
37	Sloway Area
34mm	Clark Fork
33	MT 135, St Regis, **N** ▣ Conoco/rest/dsl/gifts, Exxon, Sinclair, ▣ Frosty Drive-In, Huck's Grill, Jasper's Rest., OK Café/casino, Subway, ▣ Little River Motel, Super 8, ▣ Nugget Camground, St Regis Campground, USPO, antiques, to Glacier NP
30	Two Mile Rd, **S** fishing access
29mm	fishing access, wb
26	Ward Creek Rd (from eb)
25	Drexel

INTERSTATE 90 CONT'D

Exit	Services
22	Camels Hump Rd, Henderson, **N** 🅞 camping (seasonal), antiques (1mi)
18	DeBorgia, **N** 🍴 Billy Big Riggers, O'aces Rest., 🅞 Black Diamond Guest Ranch
16	Haugan, **N** Exxon/dsl/24hr, 🛏 50,000 Silver $/motel/ rest./casino/RV park
15mm	**weigh sta both lanes, exits left from both lanes**
10	Saltese, **N** 🍴 MT Grill, 🛏 Mangold's Motel, 🅞 antiques
10mm	St Regis River
5	Taft Area, access to Hiawatha Trail
4.5mm	**rest area both lanes, full (handicapped)♿, litter barrels, petwalk, chainup/removal**
0	Lookout Pass, 🅞 access to Lookout Pass ski area/lodge, info
0mm	Montana/Idaho state line, Central/Pacific time zone, Lookout Pass elev 4680

INTERSTATE 94

Exit	Services
250mm	Montana/North Dakota state line
248	Carlyle Rd
242	MT 7 (from wb), Wibaux, **S rest area both lanes, full ♿ facilities, 🌫, 🐾, litter barrels,** 🅑 Amsler's/dsl, Cenex/ dsl/service, 🍴 Tastee Hut, 🛏 Beaver Creek Inn, 🅞 RV camping
241	MT 261 (from eb), to MT 7, Wibaux, **S same as 242**
240mm	**weigh sta both lanes**
236	ranch access
231	Hodges Rd
224	Griffith Creek, frontage road
222.5mm	Griffith Creek
215	MT 335, Glendive, City Ctr, **N** 🅑 Cenex, 🍴 C's Family Café, 🛏 Comfort Inn, Days Inn, Super 8, Yellowstone River Inn, 🅞 Glendive Camping (apr-oct), Running's Hardware, museum, **S** 🅑 Exxon/dsl, Holiday/dsl, Sinclair/dsl/ repair, 🍴 DQ, Subway, Taco John's, 🛏 Best Western, Budget Motel, El Centro Motel, 🅞 🅗, to Makoshika SP
215mm	Yellowstone River
213	MT 16, to Sidney, Glendive, **N** 🅑 Exxon/dsl, 🅞 Green Valley Camping, st patrol, truck tire/repair, **S** 🅑 Cenex/ dsl, Conoco/dsl, Sinclair/dsl, 🍴 Pizza Hut, 🛏 Riverside Inn, 🅞 Ace Hardware, Albertson's/Osco, Ford, K-Mart, NAPA
211	MT 200S (from wb, no EZ return), to Circle
210	Lp 94, to rd 200S, W Glendive, **S** 🅑 Cenex/dsl, 🅞 Buick/ Chevrolet, Chrysler/Dodge/Jeep, Makoshika SP
206	Pleasant View Rd
204	Whoopup Creek Rd
198	Cracker Box Rd
192	Bad Route Rd, **S rest area/weigh sta both lanes, full ♿ facilities, weather info, 🌫, 🐾, litter barrels, camping, petwalk**
187mm	Yellowstone River
185	MT 340, Fallon, **S café,** 🌫
184mm	Fallon Creek
176	MT 253, Terry, **N** 🅑 Conoco/dsl, 🍴 Dizzy Diner, 🛏 Kempton Hotel, 🅞 🅗, Terry RV Oasis
170mm	Powder River
169	Powder River Rd
159	Diamond Ring

Exit	Services
148	Valley Access
141	US 12 E, Miles City, **N** 🅞 RV Camping
138	MT 59, Miles City, **N** 🅑 Cenex/dsl/24hr, Conoco/dsl, 🍴/Exxon/dsl/24hr, 🍴 Arby's, Brewster's Coffee, DQ, 4B's Rest., Gallagher's Rest., Little Caesar's, McDonald's, Pizza Hut, R&B Chophouse, Subway, Taco John's, Wendy's, 🛏 Best Western, EconoLodge, Motel 6, 🅞 🅗, Ace Hardware, Albertsons/Osco Drug, O'Reilly Parts, Radio Shack, Verizon, Walmart, casinos, RV Park, **S** 🍴 Hunan Chinese, 🛏 Comfort Inn, Guesthouse Inn, Holiday Inn Express, Super 8
137mm	Tongue River
135	Lp 94, Miles City, **N** 🅞 KOA (April-October)
128	local access
126	Moon Creek Rd
117	Hathaway
114mm	**rest area eb, full ♿ facilities, 🌫, 🐾, litter barrels, petwalk**
113mm	**rest area wb, full ♿ facilities, 🌫, 🐾, litter barrels, petwalk, overlook**
106	Butte Creek Rd, to Rosebud, **N** food, 🌫
103	MT 446, MT 447, Rosebud Creek Rd, **N** food, 🌫
98.5mm	**weigh sta both lanes**
95	Forsyth, **N** 🅑 Exxon/dsl/24hr, Kum&Go, 🍴 DQ, 🛏 Sundowner Motel, 🅞 🅗, Ford, NAPA, Van's Foods, Yellowstone Drug, to Rosebud RA, **S** camping
93	US 12 W, Forsyth, **N** 🅑 Exxon/dsl/24hr, Kum&Go, 🍴 Top That Eatery, 🛏 Rails Inn, Restwel Inn, WestWind Motel, 🅞 🅗, repair/tires, RV camping
87	MT 39, to Colstrip
82	Reservation Creek Rd
72	MT 384, Sarpy Creek Rd
67	Hysham, **1-2 mi N** gas, 🌫, food, 🛏
65mm	**rest area both lanes, full ♿ facilities, 🌫, 🐾, litter barrels, petwalk**
63	ranch access
53	Bighorn, access to 🌫
52mm	Bighorn River
49	MT 47, to Hardin, Custer, **S** 🍴 Ft Custer Café, 🅞 to Little Bighorn Bfd, camping
47	Custer, **S** 🅑 Custer Sta./dsl, 🍴 Jct City Saloon/café, 🅞 USPO
41.5mm	**rest area wb, full ♿ facilities, 🌫, 🐾, litter barrels, petwalk**
38mm	**rest area eb, full ♿ facilities, 🌫, 🐾, litter barrels, petwalk**
36	frontage rd, Waco
23	Pompeys Pillar, **N** 🅞 Pompeys Pillar Nat Landmark
14	Ballentine, Worden, **S** 🍴 Long Branch Café/casino
6	MT 522, Huntley, **N** gas 🌫, 🍴 Pryor Creek Café, **S** golf
0mm	I-90, E to Sheridan, W to Billings, I-94 begins/ends on I-90 exit 456.

NEBRASKA

INTERSTATE 80

Exit	Services
455mm	Nebraska/Iowa state line, Missouri River
454	13th St, **N** 🅑 BP/dsl, Midtown, Valero, 🍴 Big Horn BBQ, Burger King, McDonald's/playplace, 🛏 Comfort Inn, 🅞 Family$, tires/repair, **S** 🍴 King Kong Burgers, 🅞 Doorl Zoo, Imax, stadium

Side tab: MT NE

Side labels (I-90): E / W

Side labels (I-94): E / W / GLENDIVE

Side labels (right column): MILES CITY / FORSYTH / E / W

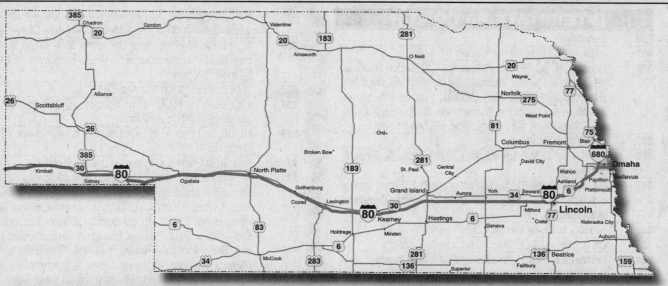

NE

INTERSTATE 80 CONT'D

Exit	Services
453	24th St (from eb)
452b	I-480 N, US 75 N, to Henry Ford's Birthplace, Eppley Airfield
452a	US 75 S
451	42nd St, **N** BP/dsl **S** Phillips 66, Burger King, McDonald's, Taco Bell, H, Pitstop Lube
450	60th St, **N** Phillips 66, NAPA, to U of NE Omaha, **S** Omaha 66/dsl, transmissions
449	72nd St, to Ralston, **N** BP, QT, Arby's, Burger King, Margarita's Mexican, Perkins, Spezia Italian, Comfort Inn, DoubleTree, Holiday Inn/rest., Omaha Executive Inn, Quality Inn, Super 8, Travelodge, H, **S** Cenex/dsl, Anthony's Steaks
448	84th St, **N** Arby's, Denny's, Farmhouse Café, Husker Hounds, McDonald's, Subway, Taco Bell, Top of the World, Motel 6, Ace Hardware, Advance Parts, Curves, Hancock Fabrics, Jensen's Tire/auto, Jo-Ann Fabrics, Mangelson's Crafts, ShopKO, USPO, **S** QT, Shell/dsl, Wendy's, Chevrolet, Kia
446	I-680 N, to Boystown
445	US 275, NE 92, I thru L St, **N** Cenex, Famous Dave's BBQ, Hardee's, Jason's Deli, Smash Burger, Wendy's, Carol Hotel, Best Buy, Book-A-Million, Buick/GMC, Home Depot, Michael's, Nelsen's RV Ctr, PetCo, Sam's Club/gas, Super Target, Verizon, Walmart, **S** Brew Burgers, Perkins, Village Inn, Baymont Inn, Best Western, Carlisle Hotel, Comfort Inn, Days Inn, EconoLodge, Hawthorn Suites, Holiday Inn Express, Howard Johnson, La Quinta, Motel 6, Super 8, Goodyear, NE Beef Co, **S on 108th** BP, QT/dsl, Arby's, Burger King, Godfather's Pizza, Hong Kong Café, Jimmy John's, LJ Silver, McDonald's, Pizza Hut/Taco Bell, Quizno's, Runza, Sonic, Subway, Valentino's, Wongs Hunan Garden, Bag'n Save Foods, O'Reilly Parts
444	Q St, **N** Cenex/dsl
442	126th St, Harrison St, **N** Chrysler/Dodge/Jeep, Toyota, VW, **S** Phillips 66, Burger King, Jimmy John's, Pizza Gourmet, Runza, Courtyard, Embassy Suites, Hampton Inn, ValuePlace Hotel, Cabela's
440	NE 50, to Springfield, **N** Phillips 66, Shell/Sapp Bros/Subway/dsl/24hr/@, Azteca Mexican, Cracker Barrel,

440	Continued Hardee's, McDonald's, Comfort Inn, Countryside Suites, Hometowne Lodge, Motel 6, Quality Inn, Red Carpet Inn, H, Ford, truckwash, **S** BP/dsl, to Platte River SP
439	439 NE 370, to Gretna, **N** Kum&Go/Quizno's/dsl, Phillips 66/dsl, **S** H, Volvo Trucks, museum
432	US 6, NE 31, to Gretna, **N** Sinclair/rest/dsl/24hr, McDonald's, Super 8, Curves, Nebraska X-ing/famous brands, **S** FLYING J/Denny's/dsl/LP/24hr, KOA, to Schramm SP
431mm	**rest area wb, full facilities, info, litter barrels, petwalk**
427mm	Platte River
426	NE 66, to Southbend, **N** to Mahoney SP, museum, rv camping
425.5	**rest area eb, full facilities, litter barrels, petwalk, vending**
420	NE 63, Greenwood, **N** Cenex/cafe/dsl/scales/24hr, Pine Grove RV Park, **S** Shell/dsl, Big Inn, antiques, to Platte River SP, WWII Museum
416mm	**weigh sta both lanes**
409	US 6, to, E Lincoln, Waverly, **N** McDonald's, **S** H
405	US 77 N, 56th St, Lincoln, **S** Phillips 66, Freightliner, antiques, truck parking, **1 mi S** Misty's Rest., GuestHouse Inn, Star City Inn
403	27th St, Lincoln, **0-3 mi S** Conoco/Wendy's/dsl, Mobil, Phillips 66/Subway/dsl, Shell, Arby's, Applebee's, Beacon Hills Rest., Burger King, Carlos O'Kelly's, China Inn, CiCi's Pizza, Cracker Barrel, Culver's, DQ, daVinci's Italian, Godfather's Pizza, Golden Corral, IHOP, Jimmy John's, King Kong Burger, Mazatlan Mexican, McDonald's, Mr Goodcents, Papa John's, Popeye's/Taco Inn, Quizno's, Ruby Tuesday, Runza, Schlotzsky's, Sonic, Taco Bell, Taco John's, Village Inn, AmericInn, Best Western, Comfort Suites, Country Inn&Suites, Countryside Suites, Fairfield Inn, Hampton Inn, Holiday Inn Express, La Quinta, Microtel, Settle Inn, Staybridge Suites, Super 8, ValuePlace Inn, URGENT CARE, AutoZone, BMW, Cadillac/Chevrolet/GMC, Chrysler, Curves, Dodge/Jeep, $Tree, Ford/Lincoln/Mercury, GNC, Haas Tire, Home Depot, HyVee Foods, Lexus, Mazda, Menards, Mercedes, Petsmart, Sam's Club/gas, ShopKO, Super Saver Foods, Toyota, Verizon, Walmart, to U NE, st fairpark
401b	US 34 W, **S** RV camping

NE

E → W

INTERSTATE 80 CONT'D

Exit	Services
401a	I-180, US 34 E, to 9th St, Lincoln
399	Lincoln, **N** 🚰 BP/dsl, Phillips 66, 🍴 Baskin-Robbins, McDonald's, Perkins, Quizno's, 🏨 Comfort Inn, Days Inn, Hampton Inn, Holiday Inn Express, Horizon Inn, Luxury Inn, Motel 6, Quality Inn, Ramada Inn, Sleep Inn, 🄾 to 🚇, **S** 🚰 Sinclair/dsl, 🏨 EconoLodge, Economy Lodge
397	US 77 S, to Beatrice
396	US 6, West O St (from eb), **S** 🚰 Sinclair/dsl, 🏨 Super 8, Travelodge
395	US 6, NW 48th St, **S** 🚰 Phillips 66/dsl, Shoemaker's/ Shell/dsl/scales/@, 🏨 Cobbler Inn, 🄾 Harley-Davidson, truck repair
388	NE 103, to Crete, Pleasant Dale
382	US 6, Milford, **S** 🚰 Mobil/Godfather's Pizza/dsl
381mm	**rest area eb, full** ♿ **facilities,** 🚻, 🏕, **litter barrels, pet-walk, vending**
379	NE 15, to Seward, **N** 🄾 Buick/Chevrolet/GMC, Ford, **2-3 mi N** 🍴 McDonald's, 🏨 Super 8, 🄾 H, antiques, **S** 🚰 Shell/dsl,
375mm	truck parking
373	80G, Goehner, **N** 🚰 Sinclair
369	80E, Beaver Crossing, Friend, **3 mi S** H, food, RV camping
366	80F, to Utica
360	93B, to Waco, **N** 🚰 BP/Waco Rest/dsl/24hr, **S** 🏨 Double Nickel Camping
355mm	**rest area wb, full** ♿ **facilities, info,** 🚻, 🏕, **litter barrels, vending, petwalk**
353	US 81, to York, **N** 🚰 BP/dsl, Byco Fuel, SappBros/Sinclair/Subway/scales/dsl, Shell/dsl, 🍴 Arby's, Burger King, Chinese Buffet, Country Kitchen, Golden Gate Chinese, KFC/Taco Bell, McDonald's, Runza, Starbucks, Taco John's, Wendy's, 🏨 Comfort Inn, Days Inn, Hampton Inn, New Victorian Inn, Super 8, Yorkshire Motel, 🄾 H, Buick/GMC, Chevrolet, rv park, Walmart/Subway, **S** 🚰 Petro/Phillips 66/Iron Skillet/Pizza Hut/dsl/24hr/@, Shell/rest/dsl/24hr, 🍴 Applebee's, 🏨 Camelot Inn, Holiday Inn, 🄾 Blue Beacon, tires/wash/lube
351mm	**rest area eb, full** ♿ **facilities, info,** 🚻, 🏕, **litter barrels, petwalk, vending**
348	93E, to Bradshaw
342	93A, Henderson, **N** 🄾 Prarie Oasis Camping, **S** 🚰 Fuel/dsl, 🍴 Subway, 🄾 H
338	41D, to Hampton
332	NE 14, Aurora, **2-3 mi N** 🚰 Casey's, 🍴 McDonald's, Pizza Hut, Subway, 🏨 Budget Host, 🄾 H, to Plainsman Museum, **S** 🚰 Loves/Arby's/dsl/scales/24hr
324	41B, to Giltner
318	NE 2, to Grand Island, **S** 🄾 KOA (seasonal)
317mm	**rest area wb, full** ♿ **facilities, info,** 🚻, 🏕, **litter barrels, vending, petwalk**
315mm	**rest area eb, full** ♿ **facilities, info,** 🚻, 🏕, **litter barrels, vending, petwalk**
314mm	Platte River
314	Locust Street, to Grand Island, **4-6 mi N** gas, food, 🏨
312	US 34/281, to Grand Island, **N** 🚰 Bosselman/🅿🅻🅾🆅🅴/Sinclair/Little Caesar's/Max's/Subway/scales/dsl/24hr, Phillips 66, 🏨 Motel 6, USA Inn, 🄾 H, Mormon Island RA, to Stuhr Pioneer Museum, **S** 🚰 Sinclair/Arby's/dsl, 🏨 Holiday Inn Express/rest, 🄾 Peterbilt, Hastings Museum (15mi)

YORK
AURORA

KEARNEY
LEXINGTON

Exit	Services
305	40C, to Alda, **N** 🚰 Sinclair/dsl, TA/Country Pride/dsl/scales/24hr/@, **S** 🄾 Crane Meadows Nature Ctr/rest area
300	NE 11, Wood River, **N** to Cheyenne SRA, **S** 🚰 Bosselman/🅿🅻🅾🆅🅴/Sinclair/Grandma Max's/Subway/dsl/24hr/@, 🏨 motel/RV park
291	10D, Shelton, **N** 🄾 War Axe SRA
285	10C, Gibbon, **N** 🚰 Petro Oasis/dsl, 🄾 Windmill SP, RV camping, **S** 🏨 Country Inn
279	NE 10, to Minden, **N** 🚰 Shell/dsl, **S** 🄾 Pioneer Village Camping
275mm	The Great Platte River Road Archway Monument
272	NE 44, Kearney, **N** 🚰 Casey's, Cenex/Subway/dsl, Gas Stop, Shell/dsl, Sinclair, Valero, 🍴 Amigo's, Arby's, Burger King, Carlos O'Kelly's, DQ, Egg&I, Gourmet House Japanese, Hunan's Rest., King's Buffet, LJ Silver, McDonald's, Old Chicago Rest., Perkins, Pizza Hut, Quizno's, Red Lobster, Ruby Tuesday, Runza, Taco Bell, Taco John's, USA Steaks, Wendy's, Whiskey Creek, 🏨 AmericInn, Best Western, Comfort Inn, Country Inn&Suites, Days Inn, EconoLodge, Hampton Inn, Holiday Inn, Microtel, Midtown Western Inn, Motel 6, Quality Inn, Ramada Inn, Rodeway Inn, Super 8, Western Inn South, Wingate Inn, 🄾 H, Big Apple Foods, Boogaart's Foods, Buick/Cadillac, Chevrolet, Chrysler/Dodge/Jeep, $General, NAPA, Verizon, Walmart (3mi), to Archway Mon, U NE Kearney, Museum of NE Art, **S** 🚰 Qwest/dsl, 🍴 Grandpa's Steaks, Runza, Skeeter's BBQ, 🏨 Best Western, Holiday Inn Express
271mm	**rest area wb, full** ♿ **facilities, info,** 🚻, 🏕, **litter barrels petwalk**
269mm	**rest area eb, full** ♿ **facilities, info,** 🚻, 🏕, **litter barrels petwalk**
263	Rd 10 b, Odessa, **N** 🚰 Sapp Bros./Shell/rest/dsl, 🄾 motel, UP Wayside
257	US 183, Elm Creek, **N** 🚰 Bosselman/🅿🅻🅾🆅🅴/Sinclair/Little Caesar's/Subway/dsl/scales/24hr, 🏨 1st Interstate Inn, 🄾 Antique Car Museum, Nebraska Prarie Museum, Sunny Meadows Camping
248	Overton
237	US 283, Lexington, **N** 🚰 Casey's, Cenex/dsl, Conoco/dsl Shell, 🍴 Arby's, Baskin-Robbins, Burger King, DQ, Delight Donuts, Hong Kong Buffet, KFC/Taco Bell, Little Caesar's McDonald's, Pizza Hut, San Pedro Mexican, Sonic, Wendy's, 🏨 Comfort Inn, Days Inn, 1st Interstate Inn, Gable View Inn, Holiday Inn Express, Minute Man Motel, 🄾 H Advance Parts, Buick/Cadillac/Chevrolet, $General, Plum Creek Foods, Walmart/Subway, Military Vehicle Museum **S** 🚰 Sinclair/dsl/@, 🍴 Kirk's Café, 🏨 Super 8, 🄾 to Johnson Lake RA
231	Darr Rd, **S** truckwash/24hr
227mm	**rest area both lanes, full** ♿ **facilities, info,** 🚻, 🏕, **litter barrels, vending, petwalk**
222	NE 21, Cozad, **N** 🚰 Cenex/dsl, Casey's/dsl, 🍴 Burger King, DQ, El Paraiso Mexican, Pizza Hut, Runza, Subway 🏨 Circle, S Motel, Rodeway Inn, 🄾 H, Alco, museum
211	NE 47, Gothenburg, **N** 🚰 Shell/dsl/24hr, Sinclair/dsl, 🍴 China Cafe, Lasso Espresso, McDonald's, Mi Ranchito Mexican, Pizza Hut, Randazzle Cafe, Runza, 🏨 Comfort Suites, Pony Express Inn, Super 8, Travel Inn, 🄾 H, Buick, Chevrolet, Pony Express Sta Museum (1mi), NAPA, Pamida truck permit sta, **S** KOA/Sinclair
199	Brady, **N** 🚰 Brady 1 Stop/DQ/dsl
194mm	**rest area both lanes, full** ♿ **facilities,** 🚻, 🏕, **litter barrels, vending, petwalk**

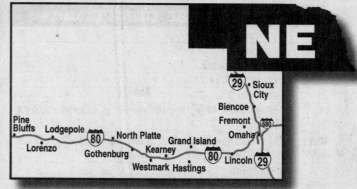

INTERSTATE 80 CONT'D

Exit	Services
190	Maxwell, **N** Sinclair/dsl, **S** to Ft McPherson Nat Cemetary, RV camping
181mm	**weigh sta both lanes, **
179	to US 30, N Platte, **N** Sinclair, La Quinta, RV camping, **S** FLYING J/Denny's/dsl/scales/LP/24hr, Loves/McDonald's/Subway/dsl/scales/24hr, tire/lube/repair, truckwash
177	US 83, N Platte, **N** Cenex/dsl, Shell/dsl, Sinclair, Quizno's/dsl, A&W, Amigo's Rest., Applebee's, Arby's, Burger King, Coldstone, DQ, Hong Kong Chinese, Jimmy John's, KFC, King Buffet, Little Caesar's, LJ Silver/Taco Bell, McDonald's, Penny's Diner, Perkins, Pizza Hut, Roger's Diner, Ruby Tuesday, Runza, San Pedro Mexican, Sonic, Starbucks, Subway, Valentino's, Village Inn, Wendy's, Whiskey Creek Steaks, Blue Spruce Motel, Fairfield Inn, Hampton Inn, Hospitality Inn, Howard Johnson, Motel 6, Oak Tree Inn, Quality Inn, Royal Colonial Inn, , Advance Parts, $General, $Tree, Goodyear/auto, Harley-Davidson, Holiday RV Park, JC Penney, ShopKO, Staples, SunMart Foods, Walgreens, Walmart, mall, museum, to Buffalo Bill's Ranch, vet, **S** Cenex, Conoco/Taco Bell/dsl/24hr, Shell/dsl/rest./RV Dump/24hr, Hunan Chinese, Taco John's, Comfort Inn, Days Inn, Holiday Inn Express, Ramada Ltd, Super 8, Cadillac, Chevrolet, Chrysler/Dodge/Jeep, Ford/Lincoln/Mercury, Honda, Menards, Nissan, Toyota, truck permit sta, to Lake Maloney RA, vet
164	56C, Hershey, **N** Western/Western Cafe/dsl/24hr/@, Rivers Edge Ranch Store
160mm	**rest area both lanes, full facilities, info, , , litter barrels, petwalk**
158	NE 25, Sutherland, **N** Park Motel (1mi), **S** Sinclair/Godfather's Pizza/dsl/24hr, RV camping
149mm	Central/Mountain time zone
145	51C, Paxton, **N** Shell/dsl/24hr, Days Inn, RV camping
133	51B, Roscoe
132mm	**rest area wb, full facilities, info, , , litter barrels, petwalk**
126	US 26, NE 61, Ogallala, **N** Cenex/dsl, Petro, Sapp Bros/Shell/dsl/24hr, Sinclair, Arby's, Country Kitchen, Front Street Cafe, McDonald's, Mi Ranchito, Peking Chinese, Pizza Hut, Runza, Taco John's, Valentino's, Best Western, Days Inn, Gray Goose Lodge, Holiday Inn Express, , Alco, Cadillac/GMC, Chrysler/Dodge/Jeep, Firestone/auto, Ford/Lincoln/Mercury, NAPA, SunMart Foods, TrueValue, U-Save Drug, to Lake McConaughy, **S** Conoco/Subway/dsl, TA/Country Pride/dsl/scales/24hr/@, DQ, KFC/Taco Bell, Wendy's, Comfort Inn, Rodeway Inn, Super 8, $General, Corral RV Park, Countryview Camping, Pamida
124mm	**rest area eb, full facilities, info, , , litter barrels, petwalk**
117	51A, Brule, **N** Sinclair/dsl, Riverside RV camping
107	25B, Big Springs, **N** Big Springs/dsl, Bosselman/Sinclair/Grandma Max's/Little Caesar's/Subway/dsl/scales/@, Sam Bass' Steaks, Motel 6, truckwash, **S** McGreer's Camping
102	I-76 S, to Denver
102mm	S Platte River

Exit	Services
101	US 138, to Julesburg, **S** truck parking
99mm	scenic turnout eb
95	NE 27, to Julesburg
85	25A, Chappell, **N** Cenex/dsl, Shell, Sinclair/dsl, Creekside RV Park/Camping, USPO, wayside park
76	17F, Lodgepole, **1 mi N** gas/dsl,
69	17E, to Sunol
61mm	**rest area wb, full facilities, , , litter barrels, vending, petwalk**
59	US 385, 17J, Sidney, **N** Conoco/KFC/Taco Bell/dsl, Sapp Bros/Shell/dsl/24hr, Arby's, Buffalo Paint Rest., China 1 Buffet, DQ, McDonald's, Mi Ranchito Mexican, Perkins, Pizza Hut, Runza, AmericInn, Comfort Inn, Days Inn, Motel 6, Cabela's RV Park/Outfitter, Chrysler/Dodge/Jeep, Ford, Maddox RV Ctr, Radio Shack, Walmart, RV camping (2mi), golf, truck permit sta, **S** Shamrock, Holiday Inn/rest., truckwash, auto tire/truck repair
55	NE 19, to Sterling, Sidney
51.5mm	**rest area/hist marker eb, full facilities, , , litter barrels, vending, petwalk**
48	to Brownson
38	rd 17 b, Potter, **N** Cenex/dsl/LP, repair
29	53A, Dix, **1/2 mi N** gas, food
25mm	**rest area wb, full facilities, , , litter barrels, vending, petwalk**
22	53E, Kimball, **1-2 mi N** Sinclair, Vince's/dsl, DQ, Pizza Hut, Subway, Days Inn, Motel Kimball, Sleep4Less Motel, Co-op Foods, Family$, Kimball RV Park (seasonal), city park, golf
20	NE 71, Kimball, **0-2 mi N** Cenex/dsl, Sinclair, Vince's/dsl, DQ, O'Henry's Diner, Pizza Hut, Subway, Days Inn, 1st Interstate Inn, Motel Kimball, Sleep4Less Motel, Super 8, Co-op Foods, Family$, Kimball RV Park (seasonal), Pamida, city park, golf
18mm	**parking area eb, litter barrel**
10mm	**rest area eb, full facilities, info, , , litter barrels, petwalk**
8	53C, to Bushnell
1	53B, Pine Bluffs, **1 mi N** RV camping
0mm	Nebraska/Wyoming state line

INTERSTATE 680 (OMAHA)

Exit	Services
29b a	I-80, W to Omaha, E to Des Moines. I-680 begins/ends on I-80, exit 27.
28	IA 191, to Neola, Persia
21	L34, Beebeetown
19mm	**rest area wb, full facilities, info, , , litter barrels, petwalk**
16mm	**rest area eb, full facilities, info, , , litter**

INTERSTATE 680 CONT'D (OMAHA)

Exit	Services
15mm	Continued
	barrels, petwalk
15mm	scenic overlook
71	I-29 N, to Sioux City
66	Honey Creek, W 🛢 Sinclair/dsl/rest., 🍴 Iowa Feed&Grain Co Rest.
3b a	**(61 b a from wb)** I-29, S to Council Bluffs, IA 988, to Crescent, E 🛢 Phillips 66, ⊙ to ski area
1	County Rd
14mm	Nebraska/Iowa state line, Missouri River, Mormon Bridge
13	US 75 S, 30th St, Florence, E 🛢 Shell/dsl, 🍴 Jimmy C's Cafe, Zesto Diner, 🛏 Mormon Trail Motel, ⊙ HyVee Drug, LDS Temple, Mormon Trail Ctr, vet, W 🛢 Florence
12	US 75 N, 48th St, E 🛢 Cenex/dsl, 🍴 Burger King (2mi), Taco Bell (2mi)
9	72nd St, **1-2 mi** E 🛢 QuikShop, 🍴 Applebee's, Burger King, Famous Dave's BBQ, IHOP, Jimmy John's, Sonic, Taco Bueno, Village Inn, ⊙ H, W Cunningham Lake RA
6	NE 133, Irvington, E 🛢 Phillips 66, 🍴 Burger King, Jimmy John's, Wings'n Things, ⊙ Walmart/Subway/drugs, W 🍴 Legend's Grill, Zesto Cafe, 🛏 Holiday Inn Express
5	Fort St, W 🛢 KwikShop, ⊙ URGENT CARE, CVS Drug,

5	Continued
	Goodyear/auto, HyVee Foods, Walgreens, USPO
4	NE 64, Maple St, E 🛢 BP, W 🛢 Kum&Go/dsl, Shell, 🍴 Burger King, China 1, Godfather's Pizza, Jimmy John's, KFC, La Mesa Mexican, McDonald's, Pizza Hut, Runza, Subway, Taco Bell, Taco John's, 🛏 Comfort Suites, La Quinta, ⊙ Bag'n Save, $General, O'Reilly Parts, vet
3	US 6, Dodge St, E 🍴 Cheesecake Factory, Granite City Rest., JC Manderin Chinese, Panera Bread, PF Chang's, TGIFriday's, 🛏 Hampton Inn, Marriott, ⊙ AAA, Audi/VW, BMW, Hynundai, Jaguar/Land Rover, JC Penney, Mazda, Mini, Subaru, Whole Foods Mkt, Von Maur, Younkers, mall, W 🛢 BP, Phillips 66, 🍴 Boston Mkt, Burger King, DQ, Grand China Buffet, Grisanti's, McDonald's, Starbucks, 🛏 Best Western, Crowne Plaza Motel, Holiday Inn, Super 8, TownPlace Suites, ⊙ Bag'n Save Foods, Cadillac, Chevrolet, Costco/gas, Ford, Hummer, Menards, Nissan, Toyota
2	Pacific St, E 🛢 BP, 🛏 Regency Lodge
1	NE 38, W Center Rd, E 🛢 Cenex/dsl, 🍴 Don Carmelo's, Don&Millie's Rest., W 🛢 Phillips 66, 🍴 Arby's, Burger King, Godfather's Pizza, Krispy Kreme, Ozark BBQ, Taco Bell, Wendy's, ⊙ Baker's Foods, $Tree, Haas Tire, TJ Maxx
0mm	I-680 begins/ends on I-80, exit 446

NEVADA

INTERSTATE 15

Exit	Services
123mm	Nevada/Arizona state line, Pacific/Mountain time zone
122	Lp 15, Mesquite, E **NV Welcome Ctr both lanes, full ♿ facilities, petwalk,** 🛢 Maverik, Shell/DQ/dsl, Sinclair/Arby's, 🍴 Canton Chinese, Dominos, Golden West Rest./casino, Home Plate Diner, Jack-in-the-Box, KFC, Los Cazadores, Los Lupes, Panda Garden, Smith's/Subway/dsl, 🛏 Best Western, ⊙ Ace Hardware, AutoZone, Big O Tire, CarQuest, Radio Shack, Smith's Foods, The Ranch Mkt, Walgreens, USPO, W 🛢 Rebel/dsl/LP/RV park, 🍴 McDonald's, Starbucks, 🛏 Eureka Motel/casino, Virgin River Hotel/casino
120	Lp 15, Mesquite, Bunkerville, E 🛢 Chevron/dsl, Shell/dsl, Terrible's, 🍴 McDonald's, 🛏 Casablanca Resort/casino/RV Park, Oasis Resort/casino/RV Park, ⊙ USPO, W 🛢 Chevron/dsl, 🍴 Del Taco, Little Caesar's, Mia's Mexican, Papa Murphy's, Popeye's, 🛏 Falcon Ridge, ⊙ H, Beall's, $Tree, Ford, Verizon, Walmart/Subway
112	NV 170, Riverside, Bunkerville
110mm	**truck parking both lanes, litter barrels**
100	to Carp, Elgin
96mm	**truck parking nb, litter barrels**
93	NV 169, to Logandale, Overton, E 🛢 Chevron (3mi), ⊙ Lake Mead NRA, Lost City Museum
91	NV 168, Glendale, W 🛢 Sinclair/dsl/rest, 🍴 Muddy River Rest., ⊙ USPO
90.5mm	Muddy River
90	NV 168 (from nb), Glendale, Moapa, W 🛢 ⊙ Moapa Indian Reservation, USPO
88	Hidden Valley
88mm	**parking area both lanes, litter barrels**
84	Byron

80	Ute
75	Valley of Fire SP, Lake Mead NRA, E 🛢 Sinclair/dsl, ⊙ casino, fireworks
64	US 93 N, Great Basin Hwy, to Ely, Great Basin NP, W 🛢 Loves/Subway/Godfather's/dsl/scales/24hr
60mm	**livestock check sta sb**
58	NV 604, Las Vegas Blvd, to Apex, Nellis AFB
54	Speedway Blvd, Hollywood Blvd, E 🛢 Valero/dsl/24hr/@, 🍴 Shelby Cafe/museum, ⊙ Las Vegas Speedway
52	rd 215, W
50	Lamb Ave, **1-2 mi** E 🛢 Shell/dsl, 🛏 Comfort Inn, ⊙ Hitchin Post RV Park
48	Craig Rd, E 🛢 Arco, 🍴 KFC/Pizza Hut/dsl/scales/24hr, 7-11, Shell, Sinclair/Subway/dsl, 🍴 Burger King, Jack-in-the-Box, Zapata's Cantina, ⊙ Firestone, to Nellis AFB, W 🛢 7-11, 🍴 Cannery Grill, Carl's Jr, Chipotle Mexican, Del Taco, Jamba Juice, Famous Dave's BBQ, Marble Slab, Mulligan's, Panda Express, Poppa's Grill, Quizno's, Sonic, Starbucks, Subway, 🛏 Hampton Inn, Holiday Inn Express, ⊙ Freightliner, Just Brakes, Lowe's, Sam's Club/gas, dsl repair
46	Cheyenne Ave, E 🛢 Arco/24hr, 🍴 CiCi's Pizza, Lucy's Grill, Marianna's Mkt, Panda Express, Starbucks, Subway, ⊙ $Tree, NAPA, 7-11, vet, W 🛢 /Mortons/dsl/LP/rest./24hr, 7-11, Sinclair/Jack-in-the-Box, 🍴 Denny's, McDonald's, 🛏 Comfort Inn, ⊙ Blue Beacon, Kenworth, Mack, SpeedCo, Volvo, dsl repair, tires
45	Lake Mead Blvd, E 🛢 Chevron, Rebel/dsl, 🍴 Burger King, Carl's Jr., Jack-in-the-Box, McDonald's, ⊙ PepBoys, 7-11, W 🛢 Arco/dsl, 🍴 Jack-in-the-Box, McDonald's, ⊙ CVS Drug
44	Washington Ave (from sb), E casinos
43	D St (from nb), same as 44
42b a	I-515 to LV, US 95, N to Reno, US 93, S to Phoenix

Copyright 2011 - The Next Exit®

INTERSTATE 15 CONT'D

Exit	Services
41b a	NV 159, Charleston Blvd, **E** ⓐ Arco/dsl, 7-11, ⓞ Walgreens, antiques, **W** ⓐ Rebel, Terrible's/E-85/dsl/casino, ⓕ Bentley's Coffee, Carl's Jr, Del Taco, McDonald's, Wendy's, ⓞ Ⓗ, CVS Drug, Smith's Foods
40	Sahara Ave, **E** The Strip, ⓐ Artisan Hotel, Vagabond Inn, ⓞ KOA, NV Tire/Repair, multiple casinos/hotels, **W** ⓐ Chevron, Rebel/dsl, 7-11, Shell, ⓕ Carl's Jr, Chipotle Mexican, El Pollo Loco, In-N-Out, Jack-in-the-Box, Jimmy Johns, KFC, Landry's Seafood, Los Tacos, Macaroni Grill, McDonald's, Panda Express, Pizza Hut, Shilla BBQ, Starbucks, TGIFriday's, Wendy's, ⓐ Palace Sta. Hotel/Casino, ⓞ CVS Drug, Food4Less, Office Depot, Ross, TJ Maxx, Von's Foods, Walgreens, casinos
39	Spring Mtn Rd (from sb), **E** ⓞ multiple hotels/casinos, **W** ⓕ Multiple Asian Cuisine, Quiznos, Starbucks, ⓞ Firestone/auto
38b a	Flamingo Rd, **E** The Strip, to UNLV, multiple casinos/hotels, **W** ⓐ Chevron, ⓕ Burger King, McDonald's, Sonic, Starbucks, Subway, Taco Bell, TGIFriday's, Wendy's, ⓐ Gold Coast Hotel, Palms Hotel, Rio Hotel, ⓞ Discount Tire
37	Tropicana Ave, **E** ⓐ Rebel, ⓕ Coco's Rest., McDonald's, ⓐ Bellagio, Excaliber Hotel, Hooters Hotel/casino, Mandalay Bay, MGM Grand, Monte Carlo, Motel 6, Tropicana Hotel, ⓞ ⓧ, multiple hotels/casinos, **W** ⓐ Rebel/dsl, Shell/Subway, Standard, Texaco, ⓕ Burger King, Dennys, In-N-Out, Jack-in-the-Box, McDonald's, Taco's Mexico, Wendy's, ⓐ Budget Suites, Days Inn, Hampton Inn, La Quinta, Motel 6, Orleans Hotel, Siegel Suites
36	Russell Rd, **E** ⓞ multiple hotels/casinos, to ⓧ, **W** ⓐ Chevron/Herbst/dsl, ⓐ Courtyard, Fairfield Inn, Holiday Inn Express, Residence Inn, Staybridge Suites
34	to I-215 E, Las Vegas Blvd, to The Strip, McCarran ⓧ
33	NV 160, to Blue Diamond, Death Valley, **E** ⓐ Chevron, Rebel/dsl, 7-11/dsl, ⓕ Bootlegger Bistro, Burger King, Buffalo Wild Wings, Chili's, Cane's Rest, Chipotle Mexican, Dickey's BBQ, Dunkin Donuts, IHOP, McDonald's, Outback Steaks, Panda Express, Popeyes, Quizno's, Starbucks, Subway, Wienerschnitzel, ⓐ Budget Suites, Carib Resort, Crestwood Suites, Hilton Garden, Microtel, ⓞ CVS Drug, Food4Less, Oasis RV Resort, Verizon, factory outlet/famous brands, **W** ⓐ Chevron/dsl, Fills/dsl, Shell, TA/Burger King/Subway/TacoTime/dsl/LP/scales/24hr/@, ⓕ Bilbo's Grill, Cafe Rio, Carl's Jr, Del Taco, Famous Dave's BBQ, In-N-Out, Jack-in-the-Box, Panda Express, Quiznos, Taco Bell, ⓐ Silverton Lodge/Casino, ⓞ Albertson's, Bass ProShops, BigLots, Discount Tire, $Tree, GNC, Kohl's, Office Depot, PetCo, Radio Shack, Ross, Target, Verizon, Walgreens, WorldMkt
31	Silverado Ranch Blvd, **E** ⓕ Steak'n Shake, ⓐ South Point Hotel/Casino
27	NV 146, to Henderson, Lake Mead, Hoover Dam, **0-2 mi** **E** ⓐ Arco, Chevron, Shell, ⓕ Jack-in-the-Box, Starbucks, Subway, ⓐ Hampton Inn, Wingate Inn, ⓞ Camping World, casino, USPO, **W** vet

Exit	Services
25	NV 161, Sloan, **1 mi E** Camping World
24mm	bus/truck check sta nb
12	NV 161, to Goodsprings, Jean, **E** ⓐ Shell/dsl, ⓞ Gold Strike Casino/hotel, NV Correctional, NV HP, USPO, skydiving, **W** ⓐ Shell
1	Primm, **E** ⓐ Chevron/dsl, Texaco/dsl, ⓕ Carl's Jr, Dennys, KFC, Mad Greek Cafe, McDonald's, Panda Express, Starbucks, Taco Bell, Tony Roma, ⓞ Buffalo Bill's Resort/casino, Primm Valley Resort/casino, factory outlets, **W** ⓐ Chevron/dsl/scales, ⓐ Whiskey Pete's Hotel/casino
0mm	Nevada/California state line

INTERSTATE 80

Exit	Services
411mm	Nevada/Utah state line
410	US 93A, to Ely, W Wendover, **S NV Welcome Ctr/info, full** ⓹ **facilities**, ⓒ, ⓐ Chevron/dsl, ⓧ/Arby's/dsl/scales/24hr, Shell/Taco Time/dsl, ⓕ Burger King, McDonald's, Pizza Hut, Subway, ⓐ Best Value Inn, Days Inn, Knights Inn, Motel 6, Nugget Hotel/casino, Peppermill Hotel/casino/RV parking, Rainbow Hotel/casino, Red Garter Hotel/casino, ⓞ Best Hardware, Smith's Foods/dsl, KOA, city park
407	Ola, W Wendover
405mm	Pacific/Mountain time zone
398	to Pilot Peak
390mm	Silverzone Pass, Silverzone Pass, elev 5940

NV

INTERSTATE 80 CONT'D

Exit	Services
387	to Shafter
378	NV 233, to Montello, Oasis
376	to Pequop
373mm	Pequop Summit, elev 6967, **rest area both lanes, 🛉, litter barrels, rest rooms**
365	to Independence Valley, **N** prison camp
360	to Moor
354mm	**parking area eb**
352b a	US 93, Great Basin Hwy, E Wells, **N** 🅖 Sinclair/dsl/café/casino, Shell/Quiznos/dsl/LP, 🍴 Bella's Diner, Burger King/Subway, 🛏 LoneStar Motel, Motel 6, Rest Inn Motel, Sharon Motel, Super 8, 🅞 Crossroads RV Park, 4-Way Casino/Rest., Schwab Tire, repair, truckwash, **S** 🅖 *FLYING J*/dsl/scales/LP/casino/RV Dump/24hr, ♥Loves/McDonalds/dsl/scales/24hr, 🅞 Great Basin NP
351	W Wells, **N** 🅖 Wells/dsl/LP, 🅞 Mtn Shadows RV Park, NAPA, Roy's Foods, Well's Hardware, USPO, **S** 🅞 Angel Lake RV Park, to Angel Lake RA
348	to Beverly Hills, **N** RV camping
343	to Welcome, Starr Valley, **N** Welcome RV Park, 🅒, food
333	Deeth, Starr Valley
328	to River Ranch
321	NV 229, Halleck, Ruby Valley
318mm	N Fork Humboldt River
317	to Elburz
314	to Ryndon, Devils Gate, **N** 🅖 Sinclair/cafe/dsl, **S** RV camping
312mm	**check sta both lanes**
310	to Osino, **4 mi S** Valley View RV Park
303	E Elko, **N** 🅖 CFN/dsl, Sinclair/Arctic Circle/dsl/24hr, 🍴 Wingers, 🛏 TownePlace Suites, **S** 🅖 Chevron/dsl, Conoco/dsl, Maverik/dsl, Sinclair/dsl, Tesoro/dsl, 🍴 Burger King, Chef Cheng's Chinese, DQ, Grilled Pepper Mexican, J Ossies Rest., King Buffet, McDonald's/playplace, Monkey Sun Chinese, Pizza Barn, Pizza Hut, Subway, Taco Time, Toki Ona Diner, Wendy's, 🛏 Best Value Inn, Best Western, Budget Inn, Comfort Inn, Days Inn, EconoLodge, High Desert Inn, Hilton Garden, Holiday Inn Express, Holiday Motel, Motel 6, Red Lion Inn/casino, Super 8, Travelodge, 🅞 H, Albertson's, AT&T, Big O Tires, Buick/Cadillac/Chevrolet/GMC, Cal Store, Curves, Double Dice RV Park, Ford, Gold Country RV Park, Goodyear/auto, Iron Horse RV Park, JC Penney, Valley View RV Park, auto repair, city park, USPO
301	NV 225, Elko, **N** 🅖 Maverik/dsl, 🍴 Arby's, Burger King, Coffee Mug Rest., Greatwall Chinese, Mattie's Grill, McDonald's/playplace, 9 Beans/Burrito, Papa Murphy's, Port of Subs, 🛏 OakTree Inn, Shilo Inn Suites, 🅞 AT&T, GNC, Home Depot, JoAnn Fabrics, K-Mart, Raley's Foods, Ross, Verizon, Walmart/Subway, **S** 🅖 Shell, 🍴 Cimarron West Rest., Dominos, Dos Amigos, KFC, Little Caesar's, Sergio's Mexican, Starbucks, Taco Bell, 🛏 American Inn, Centre Motel, Economy Inn, Elko Inn, Esquire Inn, Key Motel, Manor Inn, Midtown Motel, Rodeway Inn, Stampede Motel, Stockmen's Hotel/casino, Thunderbird Motel, 🅞 H, CarQuest, CVS Drug, Family$, O'Reilly Parts, Smith's Foods/dsl, Verizon, casino/rest., 🖃
298	W Elko
292	to Hunter

285mm	Humboldt River, tunnel
282	NV 221, E Carlin, **N** prison area
280	NV 766, Carlin, **N** 🅞 Desert Gold RV Park, dsl repair, **S** 🅖 ▦/Subway/dsl/scales/24hr, Texaco/Burger King/dsl, 🍴 Chin's Cafe, Rigobertos Mexican, State Café/casino, 🛏 Cavalier Motel, Comfort Inn, 🅞 Ace Hardware, USPO, tires
279	NV 278 (from eb), to, W Carlin, **1 mi S** gas/dsl
271	to Palisade
270mm	Emigrant Summit, elev 6114, **truck parking both lanes, litter barrels**
268	to Emigrant
261	NV 306, to Beowawe, Crescent Valley
258mm	**rest area both lanes, full 🛉 facilities, 🛉, litter barrels, petwalk**
257mm	Humboldt River
254	to Dunphy
244	to Argenta
233	NV 304, to Battle Mountain, **N** 🅖 Conoco/dsl, 🍴 Mama's Pizza/deli, 🛏 Best Value Inn, 🅞 H, FoodTown, Royal Hardware
231	NV 305, Battle Mountain, **N** 🅖 Chevron/dsl, Quickmart/pizza, 🍴 Hide-a-way Steaks, McDonald's, 🛏 Super 8, 🅞 Family$, Mills Drug, NAPA, USPO, **1 mi N** 🅖 *FLYING J*/76/Blimpie/dsl/casino/24hr, 🍴 El Aguila Real, Ming Dynasty, Owl Rest., 🛏 Big Chief Motel, Nevada Hotel, Owl Motel, 🅞 H, NAPA Care, Tire Factory
229	NV 304, W Battle Mountain, **N** 🅖 *FLYING J*/76/Blimpie/dsl/casino/scales/24hr, Shell/dsl, 🛏 Battle Mtn. Inn, Big Chief Motel, 🅞 Colt RV camping, NAPA Care
222	to Mote
216	Valmy, **N** 🅖 Shell/USPO/dsl, **S** rest area both lanes, **full 🛉 facilities, 🅒, 🛉, litter barrels, petwalk, RV dump**
212	to Stonehouse
205	to Pumpernickel Valley
203	to Iron Point
200	Golconda Summit, elev 5145, **truck parking area both lanes, litter barrels**
194	Golconda, **N** 🍴 Waterhole #1 Cafe, 🅞 USPO
187	to Button Point, **N** rest area both lanes, **full 🛉 facilities, 🅒, 🛉, litter barrels, petwalk, RV dump**
180	NV 794, E Winnemucca Blvd
178	NV 289, Winnemucca Blvd, Winnemucca, **S** 🅖 Maverik/dsl, Sinclair/dsl, 🍴 Las Margaritas, Rte 66 Grill, 🛏 Budget Inn, Cozy Motel, Frontier Motel, Valu Motel, 🅞 H, CarQuest, carwash
176	US 95 N, Winnemucca, **N** 🅖 Pacific Pride/dsl, **S** 🅖 Chevron/dsl/24hr, *FLYING J*/dsl/LP/RV dump/24hr, KwikServ, Shell/dsl, Texaco, 🍴 Arby's, Burger King, Dos Amigos Mexican, Griddle Rest., Jack-in-the-Box, KFC/LJ Silver, McDonald's/playplace, Pig BBQ, Pizza Hut, RoundTable Pizza, Sid's Rest., Subway, Taco Time, Wonderful House Chinese, 🛏 Best Western, Days Inn, Economy Inn, Holiday Inn Express, Holiday Motel, Motel 6, Park Hotel, Pyrenees Motel, Quality Inn, Regency Inn, Santa Fe Inn, Scott Motel, Scottish Inn, Winnemucca Inn/casino, Winner Hotel/casino, Super 8, 🅞 H, AutoZone, Ford, Freightliner, O'Reilly Parts, Raley's Foods, Schwab Tire, Verizon, Walmart/Subway, RV camping, auto/truck repair, casino
173	W Winnemucca, **N** 🅖 ▦/Subway/dsl/scales/24hr, **S** 🖃

CARLIN — **BATTLE MTN** — **WINNEMUCCA**

E ↕ **W** — **WELLS** — **ELKO**

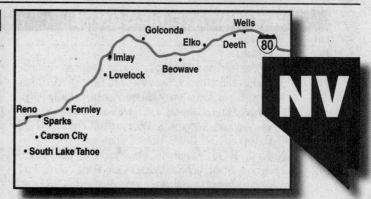

INTERSTATE 80 CONT'D

Exit	Services
168	to Rose Creek, **S** prison area
158	to Cosgrave, **S** rest area both lanes, full 🅰 facilities, 🅒, 🅰, litter barrels, petwalk
151	Mill City, **N** 🅖 TA/Subway/Taco Bell/Fork/dsl/casino/24hr/@
149	NV 400, Mill City, **1 mi N** 🅖 TA/Subway/Taco Bell/Fork/dsl/24hr/@, **S** Star Point Gen. Store/RV camping
145	Imlay
138	Humboldt
129	Rye Patch Dam, **N** 🍴 Oasis Pizza, 🅞 to Rye Patch SRA, **S** 🅖 Rye Patch Trkstp/dsl
119	to Rochester, Oreana
112	to Coal Canyon, **S** to correctional ctr
107	E Lovelock (from wb), same as 106
106	Main St, Lovelock, **N** 🅖 Chevron/dsl/LP, PJ's Gas/subs/dsl, 2 Stiffs, 🍴 Cowpoke Cafe, Las Palomas Mexican, McDonald's, Pizza Factory, Ricardo's BBQ, 🏨 Cadillac Inn, Covered Wagon Motel, Royal Inn, Sturgeons Motel/rest., Super 10 Motel, 🅞 🅗, Ace Hardware, Lazy K Camping, Safeway Foods, city park/playground/restrooms, dsl repair
105	W Lovelock (from eb), **N** 🅖 Shell/dsl, Shop'n Go/dsl, 🍴 La Casita Mexican, 🅞 🅗, Brookwood RV Park, NAPA, museum, same as 106
93	to Toulon, **S** 🔁
83	US 95 S, to Fallon, **S** rest area both lanes, full 🅰 facilities, 🅒, 🅰, litter barrels
78	to Jessup
65	to Hot Springs, Nightingale
50	NV Pacific Pkwy, Fernley
48	US 50A, US 95A, to Fallon, E Fernley, **S** 🅖 Shell/dsl, Silverado/dsl, 🍴 Burger King, Domino's, Jack-in-the-Box, KFC, Louie's China, McDonald's, Papa Murphy's, Pizza Factory, Pizza Hut, Port Of Subs, Silverado Rest./casino, Starbucks, Taco Bell, 🏨 Best Western, Super 8, 🅞 urgent care, AutoZone, Curves, $Tree, Lowe's, O'Reilly Parts, Radio Shack, Scolari's Foods, Walgreens, Walmart/Subway, USPO, casinos, tires, to Great Basin NP
46	US 95A, W Fernley, **N** 🅖 ♥Loves/Arby's/dsl/scales/24hr, **S** 🅖 🍺/DQ/Wendy's/dsl/scales/24hr, 🍴 Chukars Grill/Casino, 🏨 Comfort Suties, 🅞 Blue Beacon, SpeedCo
45mm	Truckee River
43	to Pyramid Lake, Wadsworth, **N** 🅖 Pyramid Lake gas/dsl/RV camping
42mm	rest area wb, full 🅰 facilities, 🅒, 🅰, litter barrels, petwalk, wireless internet, check sta eb
40	Painted Rock
38	Orchard
36	Derby Dam
32	USA Pkwy, Tracy, Clark Station
28	NV 655, Waltham Way, Patrick
27mm	scenic view, eb
25mm	check sta wb
23	Mustang, **S** 🅖 Chevron/dsl, truck repair
22	Lockwood
21	Vista Blvd, Greg St, Sparks, **N** 🅖 Chevron/McDonald's, QwikStop, 🍴 Del Taco, 🏨 Fairfield Inn, 🅞 🅗, **S** 🅖 Petro/Iron Skillet/dsl/24hr/@, 🏨 Super 8, 🅞 Peterbilt, truckwash

	Exit	Services
S P A R K S	20	Sparks Blvd, Sparks, **N** 🅖 7-11, Shell/dsl, 🍴 BJ's Rest., Carl's Jr, Fuddruckers, Grimaldi's Pizza, Jamba Juice, Olive Garden, Outback Steaks, Panda Express, Popeye's, starbucks, Subway, Taco del Mar, 🅞 AT&T, Best Buy, GNC, Scheel's Sports, Schwab Tire, Target, water funpark, **S** 🅖 Petro/Iron Skillet/dsl/scales/24hr/@, 🏨 Super 8, 🅞 Freightliner
	19	E McCarran Blvd, Sparks, **N** 🅖 Arco, TA/rest/dsl/scales/@, Sinclair, Texaco/dsl, 🍴 Applebee's, Baskin-Robbins, Black Bear Diner, Burger King, El Pollo Loco, Hogwild Cafe, Hong Kong Kitchen, Jack-in-the-Box, KFC, McDonald's, Port Of Subs, Sizzler, Subway, Taco Bell, Wendy's, Wienerschnitzel, 🏨 Aloha Inn, Sunrise Motel, Windsor Inn, 🅞 BigLots, CVS Drug, $Tree, Goodyear/auto, O'Reilly Parts, Pep Boys, Radio Shack, Ross, Savemart Foods, Victorian RV Park, **S** 🍴 Denny's, Super Burrito, 🏨 Holiday Inn, 🅞 NAPA
	18	NV 445, Pyramid Way, Sparks, **N** 🅖 7-11, 🍴 In-N-Out, Starbucks, 🏨 Nugget Courtyard, Silver Club Hotel/casino, **S** 🏨 Nugget Hotel/casino
	17	Rock Blvd, Nugget Ave, Sparks, **N** 🅖 Arco, Chevron, V/dsl, 🏨 Safari Motel, Victorian Inn, Wagon Train Motel, 🅞 O'Reilly Parts, casinos, **S** 🏨 Nugget Hotel/casino
	16	B St, E 4th St, Victorian Ave, **N** 🅖 Arco, KwikServ, 🍴 Jack's Cafe, 🏨 Motel 6, 🅞 Rail City Casino, **S** 🅖 Chevron/repair
	15	US 395, to Carson City, Susanville, **1 mi N on McCarran Blvd** 🅖 Shell/dsl, 🍴 Arby's, Burger King, Del Taco, Fat Burger, Littel Caesar's, Port Of Subs, Sonic, Wendy's, 🅞 CVS Drug, Home Depot, Office Depot, O'Reilly Parts, PetCo, Ross, Tires+, WinCo Foods, **0-1 mi S** 🏨 Holiday Inn Express, Hyatt Place, La Quinta, 🅞 Costco/gas, Grand Sierra Resort
	14	Wells Ave, Reno, **N** 🏨 Motel 6, **S** 🅖 Chevron/dsl, 🍴 Carrow's Rest., Denny's, 🏨 America's Best Inn, Days Inn, Ramada Inn, 🅞 Goodyear, auto repair
	13	US 395, Virginia St, Reno, **N** 🅖 Shell/dsl, 🍴 Giant Burger, **S** 🅖 Shell/dsl, 🅞 🅗, Circus Circus, NAPA, Walgreens, to downtown hotels/casinos, to UNVReno
R E N O	12	Keystone Ave, Reno, **N** 🅖 Arco, 🍴 Pizza Hut, Rose Garden Asian, Starbucks, 🏨 Gateway Inn, Motel 6, 🅞 CVS Drug, Raley's Foods, 7-11, **S** 🅖 Chevron/dsl, Texaco/dsl, 🍴 Burger King, Jack-in-the-Box, KFC, Little Caesar's, McDonald's, Port of Subs, Round Table Pizza, Taco Bell, Wendy's, 🅞 Keystone RV Park, Meineke, NAPA, O'Reilly Parts, Radio Shack, SaveMart/drug, casinos
	10	McCarran Blvd, Reno, **N** 🅖 Arco, 7-11/dsl, 🍴 Arby's, Asian Wok, Baskin-Robbins, Burger King, Bully's Grill, Carl's Jr, Chili's, Del Taco, DQ, El Pollo Loco, Hacienda Mexican, IHOP, Jack-in-the-Box, KFC, Keva Juice,

NV NH

INTERSTATE 80 CONT'D

Exit	Services
10	Continued McDonald's, Papa Murphy's, Qdoba Mexican, Round-Table Pizza, Starbucks, Subway, Taco Bell, 🄾 AT&T, AutoZone, Big O Tire, Curves, $Tree, Kohl's, O'Reilly Parts, Petsmart, Ross, Safeway/dsl, SaveMart Foods, Staples, Tires+, Verizon, Walgreens, Walmart/McDonald's, **S** 🅖 7-11, 🄾 URGENT CARE, Home Depot, vet
9	Robb Dr, **N** 🅖 Chevron/dsl, Maverik/dsl, 🍴 Bully's Grill, Domino's, Jimmy John's, Moxie's Cafe, Papa John's, Port Of Subs, Starbucks, Subway, Tahoe Burger, 🄾 CVS Drug, Raley's Foods, Scolari's Foods
8	W 4th St (from eb), Robb Dr, Reno, **S** RV camping

7	Mogul
6.5mm	truck parking/hist marker/scenic view both lanes
5	to, E Verdi (from wb no return), **N** Backstop Grill
4.5mm	scenic view eb
4	Garson Rd, Boomtown, **N** 🅖 Chevron/Boomtown Hotel/dsl/casino, 🍴 Cassidy's Rest., Denny's, Peet's Rest., 🄾 Cabela's, KOA/RV dump
3.5mm	**check sta eb**
3	Verdi (from wb)
2.5mm	Truckee River
2	Lp 80, to Verdi, **N** 🅖 Terribles/Chevron/dsl/24hr, 🍴 Jack-in-the-Box, Taco Bell, 🛏 Gold Ranch RV Resort/casino
0mm	Nevada/California state line

NEW HAMPSHIRE

INTERSTATE 89

Exit	Services
61mm	New Hampshire/Vermont state line, Connecticut River
20 (60)	NH 12A, W Lebanon, **E** 🅖 Sunoco/24hr, 🍴 Benning St Grill, Brick Oven Pizza, Chili's, Domino's, Dunkin Donuts, KFC/Taco Bell, 99 Rest., Oriental Wok, Parthenon Pizza, Subway, 🄾 GNC, Hannaford Foods, Jo-Ann Fabrics, K-Mart, LL Bean, Rite Aid, Shaw's Foods, TJ Maxx, **W** 🍴 Applebee's, Burger King, D'angelo's, Denny's, Friendly's, Koto Japanese, McDonald's, Panera Bread, Pizza Hut, 7 Barrel Rest., Weathervane Seafood, Wendy's, 🛏 Baymont Inn, Fireside Inn, 🄾 AT&T, Best Buy, BJ's Whse, CVS Drug, $Tree, Home Depot, JC Penney, Kohl's, PriceChopper Foods, Radio Shack, Sears, Shaw's Foods, Staples, Verizon, Walgreens, Walmart
19 (58)	US 4, NH 10, W Lebanon, **E** 🅖 Gulf/dsl, Shell, 🍴 China Station, 🄾 AutoZone, Family$, Ford, Harley-Davidson, Honda, Pricechopper Foods, **W** 🅖 Irving, Sunoco
57mm	**Welcome Ctr/rest area/weigh sta sb, full ♿ facilities, ⓒ, 🚮, litter barrels, vending, petwalk, weigh sta nb**
18 (56)	NH 120, Lebanon, **E** 🛏 Courtyard (3mi), Days Inn, Residence Inn (2mi), 🄾 Ⓗ, Cadillac/Chevrolet, Chrysler/Dodge/Jeep, Freightliner, Nissan, Volvo/VW, Wilson Tire/repair, to Dartmouth Coll, **W** 🅖 Mobil/Subway/dsl, Shell, 🄾 U-Haul
17 (54)	US 4, to NH 4A, Enfield, **E** 🍴 Riverside Grill, Shaker Museum, 🄾 Northern States Tire, RV Camping, vet
16 (52)	Eastman Hill Rd, **E** 🅖 Gulf/Subway/dsl, **W** 🅖 Mobil/Dunkin Donuts/dsl, 🄾 Whaleback Ski Area
15 (50)	Montcalm
14 (47)	NH 10 (from sb), N Grantham
13 (43)	NH 10, Grantham, **E** 🅖 Irving/Gen Store/dsl, **W** 🅖 Irving/Circle K, 🍴 Dunkin Donuts, Pizza Chef, 🄾 repair
40mm	**rest area nb, full ♿ facilities, info, ⓒ, 🚮, litter barrels, vending, petwalk**
12A (37)	Georges Mills, **W** 🄾 to Sunapee SP, food, ⓒ, 🛏, RV camping
12 (34)	NH 11 W, New London, **2 mi E** 🅖 Irving/dsl, 🍴 McKenna Rest., 🛏 Maple Hill Country Inn, New London Inn, 🄾 Ⓗ
11 (31)	NH 11 E, King Hill Rd, New London, **2-3 mi E** 🍴 Hole in the Fence Cafe, 🛏 Fairway Motel, New London Inn, ski area
10 (27)	to NH 114, Sutton, **E** to Winslow SP, **1 mi W** 🛏, to Wadleigh SB

WARNER

26mm	**rest area sb, full ♿ facilities, info, ⓒ, 🚮, litter barrels vending, petwalk**
9 (19)	NH 103, Warner, **E** 🅖 Irving/Circle K/Dunkin Donuts/ds Shell/Subway/pizza, 🍴 McDonald's, 🄾 Aubuchon Hardware, MktBasket Foods, Rollins SP, **W** to Sunapee SP, sk area
8 (17)	NH 103 (from nb, no EZ return), Warner, **1 mi W** gas, food museum, to Rollins SP
15mm	Warner River
7 (14)	NH 103, Davisville, **E** camping, **W** Pleasant Lake Camping
12mm	Contoocook River
6 (10)	NH 127, Contoocook, **1 mi E** 🅖 Sunoco, **W** 🄾 Elm Broo Park, Sandy Beach Camping (3mi)
5 (8)	US 202 W, NH 9 (exits left from nb), Hopkinton, **W** food, R camping (seasonal)
4 (7)	NH 103, Hopkinton (from nb, no EZ return), **E** HorseSho Tavern, gas
3 (4)	Stickney Hill Rd (from nb)
2 (2)	NH 13, Clinton St, Concord, **E** Ⓗ, **W** NH Audubon Ctr
1 (1)	Logging Hill Rd, Bow, **E** 🅖 Mobil/24hr, 🍴 Chen Yang I Chinese, 🛏 Hampton Inn
0mm	I-93, N to Concord, S to Manchester, I-89 begins/ends o I-93, 36mm.

INTERSTATE 93

N ← → S LITTLETON

Exit	Services
2 (11)	I-91, N to St Johnsbury, S to White River Jct. I-93 begins ends on I-91, exit 19.
1 (8)	VT 18, to US 2, to St Johnsbury, **2 mi E** gas, food, 🛏 camping
1mm	**Welcome Ctr nb, full ♿ facilities, info, ⓒ, 🚮, litter bar rels, vending, petwalk, WiFi**
131mm	Vermont/New Hampshire state line, Connecticut River. E its 1-2 are in VT.
44 (130)	NH 18, NH 135, **W Welcome Ctr (8am-8pm)/sceni vista both lanes, full ♿ facilities, info, ⓒ, 🚮, litter bar rels, petwalk**
43 (125)	NH 135 (from sb), to NH 18, Littleton, **1-2 mi W** Ⓗ, sam as 42
42 (124)	US 302 E, NH 10 N, Littleton, **E** 🅖 Citgo/Quiznos, Gu Irving, Sunoco/24hr, 🍴 Burger King, Deluxe Pizza, Dunki Donuts, Littleton Diner, Pizza Hut, Subway, 🛏 Beal House Littleton Motel, 🄾 Bond Parts, Rite Aid, Verizon, Wa greens, USPO, **W** 🅖 Mobil, 🍴 Applebee's, Asian Garde Chinese, Dunkin Donuts, McDonald's, 99 Rest., Oriental

NH

INTERSTATE 93 CONT'D

Exit	Services
42 (124)	Continued Cafe, 🏠 Hampton Inn, 🔲 Aubuchan Hardware, Buick/ Chevrolet, Chrysler/Dodge/Jeep, $Tree, Home Depot, KOA (5mi), Lowe's, Shaw's Foods/Osco Drug, Staples, Tire Whse, TJ Maxx, VIP Parts/service, Walmart/drug, camping
41 (122)	US 302, NH 18, NH 116, Littleton, **E** 🍴 Irving/Circle K/ dsl/24hr, 🏠 Eastgate Motel/rest., Travel Inn, 🔲 food co- op, **W** 🔲 NE Tire
40 (121)	US 302, NH 10 E, Bethlehem, **E** 🏠 Adair Country Inn/ Rest., 🔲 to Mt Washington
39 (119)	NH 116, NH 18 (from sb), N Franconia, Sugar Hill, **W** 🏠
38 (117)	NH 116, NH 117, NH 142, NH 18, Sugar Hill, **E** 🍴 Shaw's Rest., 🏠 Best Western, **W** 🍴 Citgo, 🍴 DutchTreat Rest., Wendell's Deli, 🔲 Franconia Hardware, Franconia Village Store, Frost Museum, Mac's Mkt, USPO, camping, gifts, info
37 (115)	NH 142, NH 18 (from nb), Franconia, Bethlehem, **W** 🏠 Cannon Mtn View Motel, Hillwinds Lodge, Stonybrook Motel, 🔲 Franstead Camping
36 (114)	NH 141, to US 3, S Franconia, **W** golf, food, 🏠
35 (113)	US 3 N (from nb), to Twin Mtn Lake
112mm	S Franconia, Franconia Notch SP begins sb
34c (111)	NH 18, S Franconia, Echo Beach Ski Area, view area, info
34b	Cannon Mtn Tramway, **W** 🔲 Boise Rock, Old Man View- ing, Lafayette Place Camping
109mm	trailhead parking
108mm	Lafayette Place Camping, trailhead parking
107mm	The Basin
34a	US 3, The Flume Gorge, info; camping (sea- sonal)
104mm	Franconia Notch SP begins nb
33 (103)	US 3, N Woodstock, **E** 🍴 Irving/dsl, 🍴 Dad's Rest., Fresolones Pizza, Longhorn Pal- ace Rest., Notchview Country Kitchen, 🏠 EconoLodge, Green Village Cottages, Lin- coln Inn, Mt Coolidge Motel, Pemi Motel, Profile Motel, Rodeway Inn, Woodward's Resort/Rest., 🔲 Indian Head viewing, to Franconia Notch SP, waterpark, **W** 🍴 Sunny Day Diner, 🏠 Country Bumpkin Cottages/Camping, Cozy Cabins, Mt Liberty Cabins, White Mtn Motel/Cot- tages, 🔲 Arnold's NAPACare, Clark's Trading Post, Cold Springs Camping, Tim's Repair
32 (101)	NH 112, Loon Mtn Rd, N Woodstock, **E** 🍴 Irving, Mobil, Munce's/dsl, Shell/dsl, 🍴 Bill&Bob's Roast Beef, Cheng Garden Chinese, Common Man Rest., Dunkin Donuts, Elvio's Pizza, Flapjack's Pancakes, George's Rest., GH Pizza, Gordi's Fish&Steaks, Hamburger Heaven, Mc- Donald's, Mr. W's Pancakes, Mtn View Pizza, Nacho's Mexican Grill, Subway, 3 Cultures Deli, White Mtn Bagel Deli, 🏠 Comfort Inn, Inn Season Resorts, Kancamagu's Lodge, Lincoln Sta. Lodge, Nordic Inn, 🔲 Aubuchan Hardware, CarQuest, Family$, PriceChopper Foods, Rite Aid, Village Shops, USPO, to North Country Art Ctr, **W** 🍴 Sunoco, 🍴 Imperial Palace Japanese, Landmark II Rest., Lafayette Dinner Train, Peg's Café, Truant's Rest., Woodstock Inn Rest., 🏠 Alpine Lodge, Autumn Breeze Motel, Cascade Lodge, Carriage Motel, 🔲 NAPA, USPO, candy/fudge/gifts
31 (97)	to NH 175, Tripoli Rd, **E** RV camping (seasonal), **W** KOA (2mi)
30 (95)	US 3, Woodstock, **E** 🍴 Lanterns End Grill, Tony's Rest., 🏠 Jack-O-Lantern Inn/rest., 🔲 golf, **W** flea mkt, camping (seasonal)
29 (89)	US 3, Thornton, **E** Pemi River RV Park/LP, **W** 🏠 Gilcrest Motel
28 (87)	NH 49, Campton, **E** 🍴 Gulf, Mobil, 🍴 Dunkin Donuts, Exit 28 Pizza, 🔲 Handy Man Hardware, USPO, to ski area, RV camping, **W** 🍴 Irving/dsl, 🍴 Sunset Grill, 🔲 Branch Brook Camping, Chesley's Glory Sta., Mtn Vista RV Park
27 (84)	Blair Rd, Beebe River, **E** 🍴 Country Cow Rest., 🏠 Days Inn, Red Sleigh Condos
26 (83)	US 3, NH 25, NH 3A, Tenney Mtn Hwy, **W** on US 3 🍴 Mc- Donald's, 🏠 Common Man Inn, Pilgrim Inn, Red Roof Inn, 🔲 Ⓗ

INTERSTATE 93 CONT'D

Exit	Services
25 (81)	NH 175 (from nb), Plymouth, **W** 🅖 Citgo/dsl, Irving/Circle K/dsl, 🍴 Annie's Rest., College Town Pizza, Downtown Pizza, HongKong Garden, Lucky Dog Grill, Mark's Cafe, Subway, Thai Smile, 🅞 🛏, Chase St Mkt, USPO, Plymouth State U
24 (76)	US 3, NH 25, Ashland, **E** 🅖 Gulf, Irving/Circle K/dsl, Mobil/dsl, 🍴 Ashland Pizza, Bullwinkle's Grill, Burger King, Common Man Diner, Dunkin Dounts, John's Cafe, Lucky Dragon Chinese, Village Grill, 🏨 Comfort Inn, 🅞 AutoValue Parts, Bob's Mkt, Jellystone RV Camp (4mi), TrueValue, USPO, repair
23 (71)	NH 104, NH 132, to Mt Washington Valley, New Hampton, **E** 🅖 Citgo/dsl, Irving/Circle K/dsl, 🍴 Dunkin Donuts, Rossi Italian, Subway, 🅞 Clearwater Campground, Jellystone, New Hampton Parts, info, USPO, **W** 🍴 Homestead Rest. (2mi), 🅞 RV Park (2mi), ski area
22 (62)	NH 127, Sanbornton, **1-5 mi W** 🅞 🛏, gas/dsl, food, 🅒
61mm	**rest area sb, full** ♿ **facilities, info,** 🅒, 🍽, **litter barrels, vending, petwalk**
20 (57)	US 3, NH 11, NH 132, NH 140, Tilton, **E** 🅖 Irving/Circle K/dsl/24hr, Shell/Subway/dsl, 🍴 Applebees, Burger King, Chicago Grill, Dunkin Donuts, Green Ginger Chinese, KFC, McDonald's, 99 Rest., Starbucks, Thai Cuisine, Tilt'n Diner, UpperCrust Pizza, Wendy's, 🏨 Hampton Inn, Holiday Inn Express, Super 8, 🅞 BJ's Whse/gas, Home Depot, Old Navy, Shaw's Foods/Osco Drug, Staples, Tanger Outlet/famous brands, VIP Auto, Walgreens, **W** 🍴 Chili's, Pizza Hut, 🅞 Chrysler/Dodge/Jeep, Ford, Kohl's, Lowe's, MktBasket Foods, Nissan, VW, Walmart/auto, USPO
56mm	Winnipesaukee River
19 (55)	NH 132 (from nb no ez return), Franklin, **W** 🅖 Gulf, 🅞 🛏, NH Vet Home, antiques
51mm	**rest area nb, full** ♿ **facilities,** 🅒, **info,** 🍽, **litter barrels, vending, petwalk**
18 (49)	to NH 132, Canterbury, **E** 🅖 Sunoco, 🅞 to Shaker Village HS
17 (46)	US 4 W, to US 3, NH 132, Boscawen, **4 mi W** gas
16 (41)	NH 132, E Concord, **E** 🅖 Mobil/dsl, 🅞 Quality Cash Mkt
15W (40)	US 202 W, to US 3, N Main St, Concord, **W** 🅖 Citgo, Cumberland/Dunkin Donuts, Hess, 🍴 Domino's, Friendly's, 🏨 Courtyard/café
15E	I-393 E, US 4 E, to Portsmouth
14 (39)	NH 9, Loudon Rd, Concord, **E** 🅖 Shell/dsl, 🍴 Boloco Burritos, Chicago Grill, Moritomo Japanese, Outback Steaks, Panera Bread, Wok Inn, 🅞 AAA, Ace Hardware, AutoZone, $Tree, GNC, Hannaford Foods, LLBean, Lowe's, Mkt Basket Foods, PetCo, Radio Shack, Rite Aid, Shaws Foods/24hr, Staples, TJ Maxx, Verizon, USPO, **1-2 mi E on Loudon Rd** 🅖 Irving/Circle K/Subway/dsl, Mobil, 7-11, Shell/dsl, Sunoco, 🍴 Applebee's, Arnie's Place, Burger King, D'angelo's, Dunkin Donuts, Friendly's, KFC, LJ Silver/Taco Bell, Longhorn Steaks, McDonald's, Newick's Lobster House, 99 Rest., Olive Garden, PapaGino's, Pizza Hut, Red Apple Buffet, Ruby Tuesday, Starbucks, Sunshine Oriental, TGIFriday's, Wendy's, Windmill Rest., 🅞 Advance Parts, Best Buy, Bon-Ton, Dick's, Home Depot, JC Penney, Michael's, Petsmart, Sam's Club/gas, Sears/auto, Shaw's Foods/Osco Drug, Target, TownFair Tire, Verizon, Walgreens, city park, Walmart, **W** 🅖 Citgo, Gulf/dsl, Hess, 🍴 Domino's, Gas Lighter Rest., Nonni's Rest., Siam Orchid, Tea Garden Rest., 🏨 Holiday Inn, 🅞 Pill MktPlace, to state offices, hist sites, museum

13 (38)	to US 3, Manchester St, Concord, **E** 🅖 Gulf, Sunoco/dsl/deli, 🍴 Beefside Rest., Cityside Grille, Dunkin Donuts, Ichiban Japanese, Kaylen's Pizza, Red Blazer Rest., 🅞 Buick/GMC, Cadillac/Chevrolet, Chrysler/Dodge/Jeep, Harley-Davidson, Kia, Lincoln/Mercury, Nissan, Outdoor RV Ctr, Saab, Subaru, Tire Whse, VIP Auto, Volvo, **W** 🅖 Hess, Mobil/dsl, 🍴 Burger King, Common Man Diner, D'angelo's, KFC, McDonald's, 🏨 Best Western, Comfort Inn, Fairfield Inn, Residence Inn, 🅞 🛏, Aubuchon Hardware, CVS Drug, Firestone, Goodyear/auto, NAPA
12N (37)	NH 3A N, S Main, **E** 🅖 Gulf, Irving/Subway/dsl/24hr, 🍴 Dunkin Donuts, 🏨 Days Inn, 🅞 Ford, Honda, Hyundai, Mazda, Toyota/Scion, **W** 🅞 🛏
12S	NH 3A S, Bow Junction
36mm	I-89, N to Lebanon, toll road begins/ends
31mm	**rest area both lanes, full** ♿ **facilities, info,** 🅒, **vending**
11 (28)	NH 3A, to Hooksett, toll plaza, 🅒, **4 mi E** 🍴 Trkstp/dsl/rest.
28mm	I-293, Everett Tpk
10 (27)	NH 3A, Hooksett, **E** 🅖 Irving/Circle K/dsl, 🍴 Dunkin Donuts, Subway, Wendy's, 🅞 BJ's Whse, Home Depot, Kohl's, Staples, Target, **W** 🅖 Irving/Circle K/Dunkin Donuts/dsl, 🅞 Lowe's, Walmart
26mm	Merrimac River
9N S (24)	US 3, NH 28, Manchester, **E** 🏨 Fairfield Inn, **W** 🅖 Manchester/dsl, Sunoco/dsl, 🍴 Burger King, Cheng Du Chinese, D'Angelo's, Happy Garden Chinese, KFC, La Carreta Mexican, Lusia's Italian, PapaGino's, Puritan Rest., Shogun Japanese, Shorty's Mexican, Subway, 🅞 🛏, Chrysler/Dodge/Jeep, Ford, Hannaford Foods, Kia, Lincoln/Mercury, U-Haul, VIP Auto, city park
8 (23)	to NH 28a, Wellington Rd, **W** VA 🛏, Currier Gallery
7 (22)	NH 101 E, to Portsmouth, Seacoast
6 (21)	Hanover St, Candia Rd, Manchester, **E** 🍴 Dunkin Donuts, Wendy's, 🅞 vet, **W** 🅖 Citgo/dsl, Mobil/dsl, Shell, 🍴 McDonald's, Subway, 🅞 Hannaford Foods, repair
19mm	I-293 W, to Manchester, (from nb), to 🍴
5 (15)	NH 28, to, N Londonderry, **E** 🅖 Sunoco/Dunkin Donuts/dsl, 🍴 Poor Boy's Diner, **W** 🅖 Shell/dsl, 🍴 Subway, 🏨 Sleep Inn
4 (12)	NH 102, Derry, **E** 🅖 Citgo/dsl, Mobil, Rte 102 Gas, Shell/24hr, Sunoco/dsl, 🍴 Burger King, Cracker Barrel, Derry Rest., Poorboys Drive-In, Subway, 🅞 🛏, R. Frost Farm, **W** 🅖 Global, Gulf/dsl/repair, Hess, 7-11, 🍴 Avandi's Rest., Dunkin Donuts, KFC, McDonald's, 99 Rest., PapaGino's, Taco Bell, Wendy's, 🅞 AT&T, Curves, Ford, Hannaford Foods, Home Depot, Mkt Basket Foods, Radio Shack, Shaw's Foods, Staples, TJ Maxx, USPO, Verizon, VIP Auto
7mm	**weigh sta both lanes**
3 (6)	NH 111, Windham, **E** 🅖 Mobil/McDonald's, 🍴 House of Pizza, Windham Rest., 🅞 vet, **W** 🅖 B&H, 🍴 Capri Pizza, Clemm's Bakery, Gourmet Grille, 🅞 Castleton Conference Ctr, CVS Drug, Osco Drug, Shaw's Foods, USPO
2 (3)	to NH 38, NH 97, Salem, **E** 🍴 Tuscan Kitchen, 🏨 Red Roof Inn, **W** 🍴 A&A Rest., Dunkin Donuts, Margarita's Cafe, 🏨 Holiday Inn, La Quinta
1 (2)	NH 28, Salem, **E** 🅖 BP/dsl, Citgo/dsl, Gulf, 🍴 Bickfords, Burger King, Chili's, Denny's, Grand China, LJ Silver, McDonald's, 99 Rest., Taco Bell, T-Bones, 🏨 Park View Inn, 🅞 AT&T, Barnes&Noble, Best Buy, Home Depot, JC Penney, Kohl's, K-Mart, Lord&Taylor, Macy's, Marshall's,

INTERSTATE 93 CONT'D

Exit	Services
1 (2)	Continued MktBasket Foods, Michael's, NTB, PetCo, Radio Shack, Sears/auto, Shaw's Foods, Staples, Target, TJ Maxx, TownFair Tire, mall, racetrack
1mm	**Welcome Ctr nb, full ♿ facilities, info, 🚻, ☕, litter barrels, vending, petwalk**
0mm	New Hampshire/Massachusetts state line

INTERSTATE 95

Exit	Services
17mm	New Hampshire/Maine state line, Piscataqua River
7 (16)	Market St, Portsmouth, Port Authority, waterfront hist sites, **E** 🛏 Sheraton, **0-2 mi W** 📱 BP, Gulf, Mobil, 🍴 Applebee's, D'Angelo's, Dunkin Donuts, Panera Bread, Ruby Tuesday, Wendy's, 🛏 Courtyard, Hampton Inn, Homewood Suites, 🅾 BJ's Whse/gas, Chevrolet, $Tree, K-Mart, Marshall's, MktBasket Foods, PepBoys, PetCo, Rite Aid, Shaw's Foods, TJ Maxx, Verizon
6 (15)	Woodbury Ave (from nb), Portsmouth, **E** 🛏 Best Inn, **W** same as 7
5 (14)	US 1, US 4, NH 16, The Circle, Portsmouth, **E** 📱 Citgo/dsl, Gulf, Shell/dsl, 🍴 Roudabout Diner, 🛏 Anchorage Inn, Best Inn, Best Western, Fairfield Inn, Holiday Inn, Port Inn, 🅾 🏥, Buick/Cadillac/GMC, U-Haul, **W** 📱 Gulf, 🍴 D'Angelo's, Longhorn Steaks, McDonald's, 🛏 Hampton Inn, Motel 6, Residence Inn, 🅾 Barnes&Noble, Best Buy, Dick's, Ford, Home Depot, Kohl's, Mazda, Michael's, Nissan, Old Navy, Staples
4 (13.5)	US 4 (exits left from nb), to White Mtns, Spaulding TPK, **E** 🏥, **W** to Pease Int Trade Port
3a (13)	NH 33, Greenland
3b (12)	NH 33, to Portsmouth, **E** 🏥, **0-2 mi W** 📱 Sunoco/dsl, TA/dsl/rest./scales/24hr/@, 🍴 Dunkin Donuts, McDonald's, 🅾 Lowe's, Mercedes, Target, VW
6.5mm	toll plaza
2 (6)	NH 101, to Hampton, **E** 🏥
4mm	Taylor River
1 (1)	NH 107, to Seabrook, toll rd begins/ends, **E** 📱 BP, Irving/Circle K/dsl, 1 Stop, Prime, Richdale, Sunoco/Subway/dsl, Xtra, 🍴 Applebees, Chili's, Dunkin Donuts, Honey-Dew Donuts, KFC/Taco Bell, McDonald's, 99 rest., PapaGino's, Pizza Hut, Sal's Pizza, Starbucks, Wendy's, 🛏 Hampshire Inn, Holiday Inn Express, 🅾 Advance Parts, AutoZone, CVS Drug, $Tree, GNC, Home Depot, Jo-Ann Fabrics, Kohl's, Lowe's, MktBasket Foods, NTB, Radio Shack, Shaw's Foods, Staples, Sullivan Tire, TJ Maxx, TownFair Tire, Walmart, to Seacoast RA, **W** 📱 Citgo, 🍴 McGrath's Dining, 🛏 Best Western, 🅾 NAPA, Sam's Club

.5mm	Welcome Ctr nb, full ♿ facilities, 🚻, ☕, vending, litter barrels, petwalk
0mm	New Hampshire/Massachusetts state line

INTERSTATE 293 (MANCHESTER)

Exit	Services
8 (9)	I-93, N to Concord, S to Derry. I-293 begins/ends on I-93, 28mm.
7 (6.5)	NH 3A N, Dunbarton Rd (from nb)
6 (6)	Amoskeag Rd, Goffstown, **E** 📱 Sunoco/dsl, **W** 📱 Mobil, Shell/dsl, 🍴 Dunkin Donuts, Hot Stone Pizza, 🅾 🏥
5 (5)	Granite St, Manchester, **E** 🛏 Radisson, **W** 📱 Gulf, 7-11, 🍴 Dunkin Donuts, 🅾 🏥, Walgreens, tires
4 (4)	US 3, NH 3A, NH 114A, Queen City Br, **E** 📱 7-11, Mobil/dsl, Sunoco, 🍴 Emperial Kitchen, 🛏 Elliott Hotel, **W on US 3** 📱 Hess/dsl, Mobil, Z1 Gas/dsl, 🍴 Applebee's, Burger King, Chen's Garden, CJ's Grill, Clam King, D'angelo's, DQ, Dunkin Donuts, KC's Rib Shack, KFC, Little Caesars, McDonald's, Outback Steaks, Panera Bread, Taco Bell, T-Bones, Wendy's, 🛏 Comfort Inn, EconoLodge, 🅾 CVS Drug, Hannaford Foods, Subaru
3 (3)	NH 101, **0-2 mi W on US 3** 📱 Bugaboo Creek Steaks, Carrabba's, Dunkin Donuts, IHOP, Panera Bread, PapaGino's, 🛏 Country Inn& Suites, Hampton Inn, 🅾 CVS Drug, House of Cloth, Lowe's, Macy's, Marshalls, Mini, Radio Shack, Rite Aid, Stop'n Shop/gas, Staples, Target, VIP Auto, urgent care, vet
2.5mm	Merrimac River
2 (2)	NH 3A, Brown Ave, **S** 📱 Mobil/dsl, 7-11, Shell/Subway/dsl, 🍴 ☕ Diner, Dunkin Donuts, McDonald's, 🛏 Holiday Inn, Super 8, 🅾 Manchester ☕
1 (1)	NH 28, S Willow Rd, **N** 📱 Irving, Mobil/dsl, Sunoco/dsl, 🍴 Boston Mkt, Burger King, Cactus Jack's, Chili's, Chipotle Mexican, Coldstone, D'angelo's, Dunkin Donuts, 5 Guys Burgers, Friendly's, McDonald's, Panera Bread, PapaGino's, Papa John's, Pizza Hut, Quiznos, Sal's Pizza, Starbucks, Taco Bell, Wendy's, Yee Dynasty Chinese, 🛏 Fairfield Inn, Holiday Inn Express, Sheraton, 🅾 🏥, AT&T, AutoZone, Batteries+, Buick/GMC, Chevrolet, CVS Drug, $Tree, GMC, Harley-Davidson, Hannaford Foods, Home Depot, Michael's, PepBoys, PetCo, Petsmart, Mazda, Radio Shack, Sam's Club, Shaw's Foods/Osco Drug, Stop'n Shop, Sullivan Tire/repair, Tire Whse, TJ Maxx, TownFair Tire, U-Haul, Verizon, Volvo, VW, vet, **S** 📱 Shell, 🍴 Bertucci's, ChuckeCheese, D'angelo's, Dunkin Donuts, Famous Dave's, FoodCourt, Great Buffet, La Carreta, Longhorn Steaks, 99 Rest., Olive Garden, Ruby Tuesday, TGIFriday's, 🛏 Courtyard, TownePlace Suites, 🅾 🏥, Barnes&Noble, Best Buy, Ford, Hobby Lobby, Honda, Hyundai, JC Penney, Lexus, LL Bean, Lowe's, Nissan, Macy's, NTB, Old Navy, Sears/auto, Staples, Toyota/Scion, Walmart, mall
0mm	I-93, N to Concord, S to Derry. I-293 begins/ends on I-93.

NEW JERSEY

INTERSTATE 78

Exit	Services
58b a	US 1N, US 9N, NJ Tpk
57	US 1S, US 9S, **N** 🛏 Holiday Inn, Ramada Inn, Sheraton, **S** 🛏 Courtyard, Fairfield Inn, SpringHill Suites, 🅾 to Newark ☕
56	Clinton Ave (exits left from eb)
55	Irvington (from wb), **N** 📱 Delta, 🍴 Wendy's, 🅾 🏥, Goodyear
54	Hillside, Irvington (from eb), **N** 📱 Delta, 🍴 Wendy's, 🅾 🏥, Goodyear
52	Garden State Pkwy
50b a	Millburn (from wb), **N** 📱 BP, Exxon, Lukoil, 🍴 Manny's Wieners, 🅾 Best Buy, Firestone/auto, Ford/Lincoln/Mer

🅖 = gas 🍴 = food 🏠 = lodging 🅞 = other Copyright 2011 - The Next Ex

NJ

INTERSTATE 78 CONT'D

NEWARK

E

W

CLINTON

Exit	Services
50b a	Continued
	cury, Home Depot Superstore, Target, USPO, Whole Foods Mkt
49b a	NJ 124 (from eb), to Maplewood, same as 50b a
48	to NJ 24, to I-287 N, (exits left from eb), Springfield
48mm	I-78 eb divides into express & local
45	NJ 527 (from eb), Glenside Ave, Summit
44	(from eb), to Berkeley Heights, New Providence
43	to New Providence, Berkley Heights
41	to Berkeley Heights, Scotch Plains
40	NJ 531, The Plainfields, S 🅖 Valero, 🅞 🅷
36	NJ 651, to Warrenville, Basking Ridge, N 🅖 Exxon/repair, 🍴 Dunkin Donuts, 🅞 A&P, S 🅖 Exxon
33	NJ 525, to Martinsville, Bernardsville, USGA Golf Museum, N 🍴 Ciao Italian, LingLing Chinese, Starbucks, 🏠 Courtyard, Hotel Indigo, Somerset Hills Inn, S 🅖 Exxon/7-11, 🍴 Panera Bread
32mm	scenic overlook wb
29	I-287, to US 202, US 206, I-80, to Morristown, Somerville, S 🅷
26	NJ 523 spur, to North Branch, Lamington
24	NJ 523, to NJ 517, to Oldwick, Whitehouse, **2-3 mi** S 🅖 Exxon/dsl, 🍴 McDonald's, Readington Diner, Starbucks
20b a	NJ 639 (from wb), to Cokesbury, Lebanon, S 🅖 Exxon, Shell, Sunoco, 🍴 Bagelsmith Deli, Dunkin Donuts, Kirsten's Italian Grill, 🏠 Courtyard, 🅞 to Round Valley RA
18	US 22 E, Annandale, Lebanon, N 🅷, same as 17, S Honda
17	NJ 31 S, Clinton, N 🅖 Exxon, Hess, Valero/dsl, 🍴 Baskin-Robbins/Dunkin Donuts, Blimpie, Country Griddle, Finnigan's, McDonald's, 🅞 to Voorhee's SP
16	NJ 31, N (from eb), Clinton, N same as 17
15	NJ 173 E, to Pittstown, Clinton, N 🅖 Express/repair, Shell/dsl, 🍴 Subway, 🏠 Holiday Inn Select, 🅞 museum, S 🍴 Cracker Barrel, Frank's Italian, Hunan Wok, Quiznos, 🏠 Hampton Inn, 🅞 🅷, GNC, ShopRite Foods, TJMaxx, Verizon, Walmart/McDonald's
13	NJ 173, W (from wb), N 🍴 Clinton Sta Diner, same as 12
12	NJ 173, to Jutland, Norton, N 🅖 Clinton/dsl, Exxon/Dunkin Donuts/dsl, ▐▐▐/Subway/dsl/scales/24hr, 🍴 Grand Colonial Rest., 🅞 vet, to Spruce Run RA, S 🅖 Shell/dsl, 🍴 Bagelsmith Deli, Perryville Inn Rest.
11	NJ 173, West Portal, Pattenburg, N 🅖 Mobil, Shell/pizza/dsl, 🍴 Chalet Rest., Landslide Rest., 🅞 Jugtown Camping, st police
8mm	**rest area both lanes, 🚻, litter barrels, no restrooms**
7	NJ 173, to Bloomsbury, West Portal, N RV camping, S 🅖 Citgo/deli, ▐▐▐/Subway/dsl/scales/24hr, TA/Burger King/Country Pride/dsl/scales/24hr/@
6mm	**weigh sta both lanes**
6	Warren Glen, Asbury (from eb)
4	Warren Glen, Stewartsville (from wb)
3	US 22, NJ 173, to Phillipsburg, **0-2 mi** N 🅖 Getty/dsl, Hess/dsl, Penn Jersey Trkstp/dsl/scales/24hr, US/dsl, 🍴 Applebee's, Burger King, Friendly's, Key City Diner, McDonald's, Panera Bread, Perkins, Pizza Hut, Ruby Tuesday, Sammy's Drive-in, Sonic, Taco Bell, 🏠 Phillipsburg Inn, 🅞 🅷, Advance Parts, Best Buy, BonTon, $Tree, Home Depot, Honda, JC Penney, Kohl's, Lowe's, Michael's, Old Navy, PetCo, ShopRite Foods, Staples, Stop&Shop, Target, Walmart, S 🅞 Chevrolet
0mm	New Jersey/Pennsylvania state line, Delaware River

INTERSTATE 80

E

W

PATERSON

Exit	Services
I-80 begins/ends at G Washington Bridge in Ft Lee, NJ.	
73mm	toll plaza eb
72b	US 1 S, US 9, N 🍴 Red Oak Rest., 🅞 Staples
72a	US 46, NJ 4, N 🅖 BP, Exxon/Subway, Gulf, Hess/Blimpie/dsl, Lukoil, Sunoco, 🏠 Best Western, Holiday Inn, S 🅖 Lukoil, 🏠 Courtesy Inn, DoubleTree Inn
71	Broad Ave, Leonia, Englewood
70b a	NJ 93, Leonia, Teaneck, N 🏠 Marriott, 🅞 🅷
68b a	I-95, N to New York, S to Philadelphia, to US 46
67	to Bogota (from eb)
66	Hudson St, to Hackensack
65	Green St, S Hackensack
64b a	NJ 17 S, to US 46 E, Newark, Paramus, S 🅖 BP, Exxon, 🍴 Baskin-Robbins, Dunkin Donuts, Sea Shack Rest., 🏠 Crowne Plaza, Hilton, 🅞 PathMark Foods
63	NJ 17 N, N 🅖 BP, Hess/dsl, Valero, 🍴 Boston Mkt, Subway, 🅞 🅷, CVS Drug, Harley-Davidson, Home Depot, 7-11
62b a	GS Pkwy, to Saddle Brook, N 🅖 Shell, 🏠 Marriott, S 🏠 Wyndham
61	NJ 507, to Garfield, Elmwood Park, N Marcal Paper Co, S 🅖 Sunoco
60	NJ 20, N to Hawthorne, N 🅞 🅷, Lowe's, Michelin/Cooper Tires
59	Market St (from wb), to Paterson
58b a	Madison Ave, to Paterson, Clifton, S 🅷
57c	Main St (from wb), to Paterson
57b a	NJ 19 S, to Clifton, downtown Paterson
56b a	Squirrelwood Rd, to Paterson, S 🅖 Lukoil
55b a	Union Blvd (from wb, no EZ return), Totowa, N 🅖 Sunoco/dsl, S 🏠 Holiday Inn
54	Minnisink Rd, to Paterson, S 🅖 BP, 🅞 Home Depot, JC Penney, Marshall's, Staples, mall
53	US 46 E, to NJ 3 (no eb return), to Wayne, Cliffton, **0-2 mi** S 🅖 Exxon, Gulf, Sunoco, 🍴 Applebee's, Burger King, Cheeseburger Paradise, Dunkin Donuts, IHOP, Pizza Hut, Red Lobster, Sonic, TX Wieners, Wendy's, 🏠 Holiday Inn, Ramada Inn, 🅞 A&P Mkt, Barnes&Noble, Best Buy, Buick/GMC, Cadillac, Ford, Kohl's, Nissan, Office Depot, PetCo, Toyota, Verizon
52	US 46, the Caldwells
48	to Montville (from wb), Pine Brook
47b	US 46 W, to Montclair, N 🅖 BP, 🏠 Holiday Inn, S 🅖 Gulf, Shell, 🍴 Dunkin Donuts, Montville Diner, Subway, Wendy's, 🅞 Porsche
47a	I-280 E, to The Oranges, Newark
45	to US 46, Lake Hiawatha, Whippany, **0-2 mi** N on US 46 🅖 BP, Gulf, Sunoco, 🍴 Applebee's, Black Thorn Rest., Burger King, Chili's, Eccola Rest., Empire Diner, 5 Guys Burgers, Franco's Pizza, IHOP, Jasper Chinese, KFC, Longhorn Steaks, McDonald's, Moe's SW Grill, Outback Steaks, Quin Dynasty, Subway, Taco Bell, Wendy's, 🏠 Budget Inn, Holiday Inn/rest., Howard Johnson, Ramada Ltd, Red Roof Inn, 🅞 $Tree, Firestone, Home Depot, K-Mart, Michael's, PathMark Foods, PepBoys, PetCo, Radio Shack, ShopRite Foods, Staples, Verizon, Walgreens
43b a	I-287, to US 46, Boonton, Morristown
42b a	US 202, US 46, to Morris Plains, Parsippany, **0-1 mi** N on US 46 🅖 Delta/Dunkin Donuts/dsl, Exxon, Shell, Sunoco, 🍴 Fuddrucker's, McDonald's, TGIFriday's, Wendy's,

INTERSTATE 80 CONT'D

Exit	Services
42b a	Continued 🛏 Courtyard, Days Inn, Fairfield Inn, Hampton Inn, 🅾 Chrysler/Dodge, Ford, Marshall's, Subaru, same as 39
39	(38 from eb), US 46 E, to NJ 53, Denville, **0-2 mi N on US 46** 🅿 Citgo/dsl, Enrite Gas, Exxon, Hess/Dunkin Donuts, Sunoco, 🍴 Burger King, Casa Bella Italian, Charlie Brown's Steaks, Paul's Diner, Wendy's, 🅾 H, BMW, Chevrolet, Discount Tire, Firestone, Walgreens, vet, **S** 🅿 Shell
37	NJ 513, to Hibernia, Rockaway, **N** 🅿 Exxon/dsl, Shell, 🍴 Hibernia Diner, 🛏 Best Western, Hampton Inn, **S** 🅿 BP, 🅾 H
35b a	to Dover, Mount Hope, **S** 🅿 Exxon, 🍴 Coldstone, Dunkin Donuts, Fat Burger, La Salsa Mexican, Olive Garden, Quiznos, Red Robin, 🛏 Hilton Garden, Homewood Suites, 🅾 H, Acme Foods, Best Buy, FoodWorks, JC Penney, Lord&Taylor, Macy's, Michael's, Sears/auto, Verizon, mall
34b a	NJ 15, to Sparta, Wharton, **N** 🅿 Exxon/dsl, 🍴 Ming Buffet, Subway, 🅾 Rite Aid, **S** 🍴 Dunkin Donuts, Good 5 Chinese, Townsquare Diner, 🅾 H, Costco, Dick's, $Tree, Home Depot, Petsmart, ShopRite Foods, Target, Walmart
32mm	**truck rest area wb, no services**
30	Howard Blvd, to Mt Arlington, **N** 🅿 Exxon/dsl, 🍴 Cracker Barrel, Davy's Hotdogs, Dunkin Donuts, IHOP, Wingman, 🛏 Courtyard, Holiday Inn Express, 🅾 QuickChek Foods
28	US 46, to NJ 10, to Ledgewood, Lake Hopatcong, **1-2 mi S on US 46, NJ 10** 🅿 Delta Gas, Gas&Go, Hess/dsl, Sunoco, 🍴 Boston Mkt, Burger King, Dunkin Donuts, Fuddruckers, KFC/LJ Silver, McDonald's, Muldoons Diner, Outback Steaks, Panera Bread, Pizza Hut, Red Lobster, Roxbury Diner, Ruby Tuesday, Subway, Taco Bell, TGIFriday's, Wendy's, White Castle, 🅾 AutoZone, Barnes&Noble, BJ's Whse, CVS Drug, Home Depot, Kohl's, Radio Shack, ShopRite Foods, Toyota, Walgreens, Walmart
27	US 206 S, NJ 182, to Netcong, Somerville, **N** 🅿 Valero/dsl, 🍴 Dunkin Donuts, Perkins, 🛏 Comfort Suites, Quality Inn, 🅾 Ford, **S** 🅿 Shell/dsl, 🍴 Applebee's, Chili's, Longhorn Steaks, Macaroni Grill, McDonald's, Panera Bread, Subway, Wendy's, 🛏 Extended Stay America, 🅾 AT&T, Lowe's, Michael's, Old Navy, Petsmart, Sam's Club, Staples, TJMaxx, Walmart
26	US 46, W (from wb, no EZ return), to Budd Lake, **S** 🅿 Shell/dsl, same as 27
25	US 206 N, to Newton, Stanhope, **1-2 mi N on US 206** 🅿 Exxon, Shell/dsl, 🍴 Blackforest Rest., Byram Diner, Byram Pizza, Dunkin Donuts, Frank's Pizza, Lockwood Tavern, McDonald's, Subway, 🛏 Extended Stay America, Holiday Inn, Residence Inn, 🅾 CVS Drug, GNC, Nissan, Radio Shack, ShopRite Foods, STS tires/repair, to Waterloo Village, Int Trade Ctr, vet
23.5mm	Musconetcong River
21mm	**rest area both lanes, NO TRUCKS, scenic overlook (eb)**, 🗑 litter barrels, petwalk, no facilities
19	NJ 517, to Hackettstown, Andover, **N** 🅿 Shell, 🅾 RV camping, **1-2 mi S** 🅿 Shell, 🍴 Foxy's Grill, Terranova Pizza, 🛏 Panther Valley Inn/rest., 🅾 H, 7-11, Stephen's SP, USPO

Exit	Services
12	NJ 521, to Blairstown, Hope, **N** 🍴 Mediterranean Diner, 🅾 Harley-Davidson, st police, **S** 🅿 US Gas, 🍴 Gio's Pizza, 🅾 RV camping (5mi), Land of Make Believe, Jenny Jump SF, USPO
7mm	**rest area eb, full** ♿ **facilities, info,** 🅿 🛏 **litter barrels, vending, petwalk**
6mm	scenic overlook wb, no trailers
4c	to NJ 94, N (from eb), to Blairstown
4b	to US 46 E, to Buttzville
4a	NJ 94, to US 46 E, to Portland, Columbia, **N** 🅿 TA/Pizza Hut/Taco Bell/dsl/scales/24hr/@, 🍴 McDonald's, 🅾 RV camping, **S** USPO
3.5mm	Hainesburg Rd (from wb), accesses services at 4
1mm	Worthington SF, **S rest area both lanes, restrooms, info,** 🛏 **litter barrels, petwalk**
1	to Millbrook (from wb), **N** Worthington SF
0mm	New Jersey/Pennsylvania state line, Delaware River

INTERSTATE 95

Exit	Services
124mm	New Jersey/New York state line, Geo Washington Br, Hudson River
123mm	Palisades Pkwy (from sb)
72 (122)	US 1, US 9, US 46, Ft Lee, **E** Mobil, Shell, Courtesy Motel, Hilton
71 (121)	Broad Ave, Leonia, Englewood, **E** Shell, **W** Gulf, Day's Inn, Executive Inn
70 (120)	to NJ 93,, Leonia, Teaneck, **W** Marriott
69 (119)	I-80, W (from sb), to Paterson
68 (118)	US 46, Challenger Blvd, Ridgefield Park, **E** Exxon, Hampton Inn
I-95 and NJ Turnpike run together sb. See NJ TPK exits 7a-18	
I-95 nb becomes I-295 sb at US 1	
67b a	US 1, to Trenton, New Brunswick, **E** Shell, Michael's Diner, Howard Johnson, Sleepy Hollow Motel, Acura, **0-3 mi W** Gulf, LukOil/dsl, Applebee's, Big Fish Bistro, Cheeburger Cheeburger, Chevy's Mexican, Chili's, ChuckECheese's, Dunkin Donuts, Hooters, Houlihan's, Joe's Crabshack, Macaroni Grill, NY Deli, Olive Garden, On-the-Border, Panera Bread, PF Chang's, Princetonian Diner, Pure Rest., Red Lobster, Rita's Custard, Starbucks, Subway, TGIFriday's, Wendy's, Clarion, Comfort Inn, Extended Stay America, Hyatt Place, Hyatt Regency, Red Roof Inn, Residence Inn, AT&T, Barnes&Noble, Best Buy, Buick/Cadillac, Chevrolet, Dick's, Firestone/auto, Home Depot, JC Penney, Jo-Ann Fabrics, Kohl's, Lord&Taylor, Lowe's, Macy's, Marshall's, Michael's, Mini, NTB, Office Depot, Old Navy, PepBoys, PetCo, Petsmart, Ross, Sam's Club, Sears/auto, ShopRite Foods, Staples, Target, TJ Maxx, Trader Joe's, Verizon, Walmart, Wegman's Foods, Whole Foods Mkt, malls
8b a	NJ 583, NJ 546, to Princeton Pike
7b a	US 206, **W** Tastee Subs, **W** LukOil/dsl, Fox's Pizza
5b a	Federal City Rd (sb only)
4b a	NJ 31, to Ewing, Pennington, **E** Citgo/repair, Exxon/repair, LukOil/Dunkin Donuts/dsl, Robbins Drug, 7-11, USPO, SpringHill Suites, **W** Exxon, LukOil/Blimpie/dsl, Mizuki Asian, Starbucks, AT&T, ShopRite Foods, Stop&Shop Foods
3b a	Scotch Rd, **E** Courtyard, **W** H
2	NJ 579, to Harbourton, **E** LukOil (1mi), Dunkin Donuts, Red Star Pizza, 7-11, **W** BP
1	1 NJ 29, to Trenton, **2 mi W** museum, st police
0mm	New Jersey/Pennsylvania state line, Delaware River

NEW JERSEY TURNPIKE

Exit	Services
18 (117)	US 46 E, Ft Lee, Hackensack, last exit before toll sb
17 (116)	Lincoln Tunnel
115mm	**Vince Lombardi Service Plaza nb** Sunoco/dsl, Big Boy, Nathan's, Roy Rogers, TCBY, gifts
114mm	toll plaza, C
16W (113)	NJ 3, Secaucus, Rutherford, **E** Hess, Shell, Hilton, M Plaza Hotel, **W** Sheraton, Meadowlands
112mm	**Alexander Hamilton Service Area sb** Sunoco, Roy Rogers, gifts
16E (112)	NJ 3, Secaucus, **E** Lincoln Tunnel
15W (109)	I-280, Newark, The Oranges
15E (107)	US 1, US 9, Newark, Jersey City, **E** Lincoln Tunnel
14c	Holland Tunnel
14b	Jersey City
14a	Bayonne
14 (105)	I-78 W, US 1, US 9, **2 mi W** Fairfield Inn, Holiday Inn, SpringHill Suites,
102mm	**Halsey Service Area**, Sunoco, Roy Rogers, other services in Elizabeth
13a (102)	Elizabeth, **E** Courtyard, Extended Stay America, Residence Inn, **W** McDonald's, DoubleTree, Econolodge, Hilton, Sheraton, Wyndham Garden, services on US1/US9
13 (100)	I-278, to Verrazano Narrows Bridge
12 (96)	Carteret, Rahway, **E** McDonald's, Holiday Inn, **W** Radisson
93mm	**Cleveland Service Area nb** Nathans, Roy Roger's, Starbucks, **T Edison Service Area sb** Sunoco/dsl, Burger King, Dunkin Donuts, Popeye's, Sbarro's, Starbucks
11 (91)	US 9, Garden State Pkwy, to Woodbridge, **E** Hampton Inn, Homestead Suites, Home Depot
10 (88)	I-287, NJ 514, to Perth Amboy, **E** Courtyard, **W** Hess/dsl, Holiday Inn
9 (83)	US 1, NJ 18, to New Brunswick, E Brunswick, **E** Gulf, Hess/dsl, Bone Fish Grill, Boston Mkt, Burger King, Carrabba's, Dunkin Donuts, Grand Buffet, KFC, Perkins, Starbucks, Days Inn, Motel 6, Best Buy, Goodyear auto, Lowe's, Office Depot, Petsmart, Rite Aid, Sam's Club, Shopper's World Foods, ShopRite Foods, Staples, TJ Maxx, **W** Exxon, Fuddruckers, Hilton, Holiday Inn Express, Howard Johnson
79mm	**Kilmer Service Area nb** Sunoco/dsl, Burger King, Cookies and Creamery, Sbarro, Starbucks
8a (74)	to Jamesburg, Cranbury, **W** Courtyard, Crowne Plaza
72mm	**Pitcher Service Area sb** Sunoco/dsl, Arthur Treacher's, Cinnabon, Dick Clark's AB Grill, Nathan's, Roy Rogers, Starbucks
8 (67)	NJ 33, NJ 571, Hightstown, **E** Hess/dsl, Petro/dsl, RaceWay, Shell/Dunkin Donuts, Prestige Diner, Days Inn, Hampton Inn, Holiday Inn, CVS Drug, vet, **W** Quality Inn
7a (60)	I-195, W to Trenton, E to Neptune
59mm	**Richard Stockton Service Area sb** Sunoco/dsl, Burger King, Pizza Hut, Quiznos, Starbucks, TCBY, **Woodrow Wilson Service Area nb** Sunoco, Nathan's, Roy Rogers
7 (54)	US 206, to Bordentown, to Ft Dix, McGuire AFB, to I-295, **Trenton Services, W on US 206** Citgo, Delta/dsl, Exxon, Gulf, Loves/Wendy's/dsl/scales/24hr, Petro/Iron Skillet/dsl/scales/24hr/, Sunoco, Valero/dsl, Denny's, Dunkin Donuts, McDonald's, Wendy's, Best Western, Comfort Inn, Days Inn, Hampton Inn, Ramada Inn, WaWa
6 (51)	I-276, to PA Tpk
5 (44)	to Mount Holly, Willingboro, **E** US Gas/dsl, Applebee's, Charlie Brown's Steaks, Cracker Barrel, McDonald's, Recovery Grill, Best Western, Hampton Inn, Hilton Garden, Quality Inn, **W** BP, Exxon/dsl, Valero/dsl, Burger King, China House, ChuckECheese's, Dunkin Donuts, IHOP, Subway, TGIFriday's, Quiznos, Courtyard, Holiday Inn Express, $Tree, Home Depot, JC Penney, Kohl's, Sears/auto, Target, vet

NEW JERSEY TURNPIKE CONT'D

Exit	Services
39mm	**James Fenimore Cooper Service Area nb** 🅖 Sunoco/dsl, 🍴 Burger King, Cinnabon, Popeye's, Roy Rogers, TCBY, 🅞 gifts
4 (34)	NJ 73, to Philadelphia, Camden, **E** 🅖 Exxon, WaWa/dsl, 🍴 Chick-fil-A, Cracker Barrel, Chili's, Denny's, Dunkin Donuts, Macaroni Grill, McDonald's, On-the-Border, Sage Rest., TGIFriday's, Wendy's, 🛏 Candlewood Suites, Comfort Inn, Extended Stay America, Hampton Inn, Hilton Garden, Hyatt Place, Knights Inn, Rodeway Inn, Staybridge Suites, Wingate Inn, Wyndham Hotel, 🅞 BMW, Cadillac, Lexus, Rite Aid, 7-11, Toyota/Scion, Verizon, Whole Foods Mkt, **W** 🅖 Gulf/dsl, Hess, Lukoil, Shell, 🍴 Bob Evans, Burger King, Dunkin Donuts, KFC, Pizza Hut, 🛏 aLoft, Courtyard, DoubleTree Motel, Fairfield Inn, Marriott, Motel 6, Ramada Inn, Red Roof Inn, Super 8, 🅞 Lincoln/Mercury, Mazda, transmissions, to st aquarium
30mm	**Walt Whitman Service Area sb** 🅖 Sunoco, 🍴 Cinnabon, Roy Rogers, Nathan's, TCBY, 🅞 gifts
3 (26)	NJ 168, Atlantic City Expwy, Walt Whitman Br, Camden, Woodbury, **E** 🅖 Pioneer, 7-11, WaWa, 🍴 Antonietta's, Bella Rizzo's Pizza, Luigi's Pizza, Pat's Pizza, Phily Diner, Rita's Custard, 🛏 Comfort Inn, Runnymead Suites, 🅞 CVS Drug, Toyota/Scion, Walgreens, **W** 🅖 Citgo, Gulf/repair, Shell/dsl, Shamrock/dsl, 🍴 Burger King, Club Diner, Dunkin Donuts, Italia Pizza, Wendy's, 🛏 Bellmawr Motel, Comfort Inn, EconoLodge, Holiday Inn, Howard Johnson, Motel 6, Red Roof Inn, Super 8, 🅞 CVS Drug, Walgreens, transmissions
2 (13)	US 322, to Swedesboro, **W** 🅖 Shell/Dunkin Donuts/dsl
5mm	**Barton Service Area sb** 🅖 Sunoco, Burger King, Nathan's, Pizza Hut, Starbucks, TCBY, **Fenwick Service Area nb** 🅖 Sunoco, 🍴 TCBY
1 (1.2)	Deepwater, **W** 🅖 Gulf, 🚚/Subway/dsl/scales/24hr, 🛏 Comfort Inn, Friendship Motor Inn, Holiday Inn Express, Wellesley Inn
1mm	toll road begins/ends
2 (I-295)	I-295, N divides from toll road, I-295, S converges with toll road, **W** 🅖 Shell/Dunkin Donuts/dsl
1 (I-295)	NJ 49, to Pennsville, **E** 🅖 Exxon/dsl/repair, 🍴 Applebees, Burger King, Cracker Barrel, Dunkin Donuts, KFC/Taco Bell, McDonald's, Subway, 🛏 Hampton Inn, Super 8, 🅞 Peterbilt, **W** 🅖 Gulf, 🚚/Subway/dsl/scales/24hr, 🛏 Best Value, Comfort Inn, Friendship Motor Inn, Quality Inn, Seaview Motel
0mm	New Jersey/Delaware state line, Delaware River, Delaware Memorial Bridge

INTERSTATE 195

Exit	Services
36	Garden State Parkway N. I-195 begins/ends on GS Pkwy, exit 98.
35b a	NJ 34, to Brielle, GS Pkwy S., Pt Pleasant, **0-2 mi S** 🅖 Exxon/dsl, Getty, Lukoil/dsl, 🍴 Legends Japanese
31b a	NJ 547, NJ 524, to Farmingdale, **N** to Allaire SP
28b a	US 9, to Freehold, Lakewood, **N** 🅖 LukOil/7-11/dsl, 🍴 Ivy League Grill, Stewart's Drive-In, 🛏 At 9 Motel, **S** 🅖 Exxon, Getty, Gulf, LukOil, WaWa, 🍴 Applebee's, Arby's, Baskin-Robbins/Dunkin Donuts, Boston Mkt, Burger King, Carino's, Chick-fil-A, China Moon,

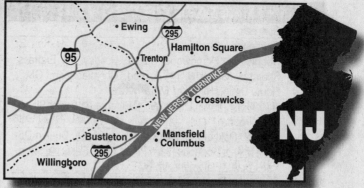

Exit	Services
28b a	Continued Coldstone, Domino's, 5 Guys Burgers, Jersey Mike's Subs, Longhorn Steaks, Luigi's Pizza, McDonald's, Panera Bread, Pizza Hut, Rojo Loco, Ruby Tuesday, Sonic, Starbucks, Taco Bell, 🛏 Capri Inn, 🅞 Barnes&Noble, Best Buy, GNC, K-Mart, Kohl's, Lowe's, Michael's, PathMark Foods, PepBoys, PetCo, Petsmart, Radio Shack, Staples, Stop&Shop, Target, TJ Maxx, Verizon, Walgreens, Walmart/McDonald's, repair, USPO
22	to Jackson Mills, Georgia, **N** to Turkey Swamp Park, **2 mi S** 🍴 McDonald's, 🅞 ShopRite Foods
21	NJ 526, NJ 527, to Jackson, Siloam
16	NJ 537, to Freehold, **N** 🅖 Remington/dsl/LP, Sunoco, 🍴 DQ, FoodCourt, GianMarco's Pizza, Java Moon Café, 🅞 🅗, Jackson Outlets/famous brands, **S** 🅖 WaWa/dsl, 🍴 BellaV Pizzaria, Burger King, Chicken Holiday, Dunkin Donuts, KFC/LJ Silver, McDonald's, McGinns Pizzaria, Rio Grande Mexican, Tommy's Rest., 🅞 6Flags Themepark
11	NJ 524, Imlaystown, **S** to Horse Park of NJ
8	NJ 539, Hightstown, Allentown, **S** 🅖 Shell (1mi), Valero/repair, 🍴 American Hero Deli, 🅞 Crosswicks HP, vet
7	NJ 526 (no eb return), Robbinsville, Allentown, **1 mi S** 🍴 La Piazza Ristorante
6	NJ Tpk, N to NY, S to DE Memorial Br
5b a	US 130, **N** 🅖 Delta/dsl/repair, Valero/dsl, 🍴 Domino's, Dunkin Donuts, Rusert's Deli, ShrimpKing Rest., 🅞 AAA, Harley-Davidson, vet, **S** 🅖 GS Fuel/dsl, 🍴 Chick-fil-A, Chili's, China Grill, Cracker Barrel, DQ, Jersey Mike's Subs, Longhorn Steaks, McDonald's, Outback Steaks, Panera Bread, Red Robin, Ruby Tuesday, Subway, TGIFriday's, Wendy's, 🛏 Hilton Garden, 🅞 AT&T, Barnes&Noble, BJ's Whse, $Tree, GNC, Hamilton Shops/famous brands, Harry's Army Navy, Home Depot, Kohl's, Lowe's, Michael's, Old Navy, Petsmart, Ross, ShopRite Foods, Staples, USPO, Verizon, Walmart, mall, to state aquarium
3b a	Hamilton Square, Yardville, **N** 🅗
2	US 206 S, S Broad St, Yardville, **N** 🍴 Rosa's Ristorante, **S** 🅖 Shell, Valero, 🍴 Subway, 🅞 CVS Drug, Rite Aid, 7-11
1b a	US 206 (eb only), **N** 🍴 Circle Deli, Taco Bell, 🅞 Advance Parts, **S** 🍴 Papa John's, 🅞 ShopRite Foods
0mm	I-295, I-195 begins/ends.

INTERSTATE 287

Exit	Services
68mm	New Jersey/New York state line
66	NJ 17 S, Mahwah, **1-3 mi E** 🅖 Getty, Gulf, 🚚/dsl, Royal, Sunoco, Valero/Subway/dsl, 🍴 Boston Mkt, Burger King, Dunkin Donuts, McDonald's, State Line Diner, Wendy's, 🛏 Best Western, Comfort Suites, Courtyard,

INTERSTATE 287 CONT'D

Exit	Services
66	Continued Doubletree, Homewood Suites, Holiday Inn Express, Sheraton, Super 8, 🅞 Aamco, Chrysler/Jeep, GMC, Home Depot, Hyundai, Mini
59	NJ 208 S, Franklin Lakes, **W** 🍴 Blimpie, 🅞 Super Stop'n Shop Foods
58	US 202, Oakland, **E** 🅖 Gulf/dsl, Lukoil, 🍴 Dunkin Donuts, Mike's Doghouse, Jr's Pizza, Ruga Rest., 🅞 ShopRite Foods, Walgreens, **W** 🅖 Exxon/24hr
57	Skyline Dr, Ringwood
55	NJ 511, Pompton Lakes, **E** 🍴 Frank's Pizza, Quizno's, Wendy's 🅞 A&P, **W** 🅖 Getty/dsl, 🍴 Baskin-Robbins, Burger King, Dunkin Donuts, 🛏 Holiday Inn Express, 🅞 Stop'n Shop
53	NJ 511A, rd 694, Bloomingdale, Pompton Lakes, **E** 🅖 Sunoco, Valero, 🍴 Blimpie, 🅞 USPO
52b a	NJ 23, Riverdale, Wayne, Butler, **0-3 mi** **E** 🅖 BP, Lukoil, United/dsl, 🍴 Baskin-Robbins, Dunkin Donuts, Friendly's, Fuddrucker's, McDonald's, Pompton Queen Diner, 23 Buffet, 🛏 Best Western, La Quinta, 🅞 🅷, A&P, Buick/GMC, Goodyear/auto, Honda, TJ Maxx, Toyota/Scion, **W** 🅖 Getty, Lukoil, 🍴 Applebees, Chili's, Ruppert's Rest., Subway, Wendy's, 🅞 BJ's Whse, Harley-Davidson, Home Depot, Lowes Whse, Staples, Target, Walmart
47	US 202, Montville, Lincoln Park, **E** 🅖 Exxon/24hr, 🍴 Harrigan's Rest.
45	Myrtle Ave, Boonton, **W** 🅖 Hess, Shell, 🍴 Dunkin Donuts, IHOP, McDonald's, Subway, 🅞 A&P/24hr, Buick/Chevrolet, Drug Fair
43	Intervale Rd, to Mountain Lakes, **E** 🅖 Valero, **W** Dodge
42	US 46, US 202 (from sb only), **W** 🅖 Exxon, Shell, Sunoco, 🍴 Applebees, Dunkin Donuts, Fuddrucker's, Longhorn Steaks, McDonald's, Subway, Wendy's, 🛏 Courtyard, Day's Inn, Embassy Suites, Fairfield Inn, Hampton Inn, 🅞 Ford, GNC, Marshall's, Michael's, Subaru, USPO
41b a	I-80, E to New York, W to Delaware Water Gap
40	NJ 511, Parsippany Rd, to Whippany, **W** 🅖 BP, Shell/dsl, Woroco Gas, 🍴 Fuddrucker's (2mi), Marco's Pizza, Wok's Chinese, Subway, 🛏 Embassy Suites (1mi)
39b a	NJ 10, Dover, Whippany, **E** 🅖 Exxon, Shell, 🍴 Bensi Italian, Brookside Diner, Capriccio's Italian, Dunkin Donuts, Melting Pot, Nikko's Japanese, Pancake House, 🅞 CVS Drug, PathMark Foods, Tuesday Morning, **W** 🅖 Lukoil, Raceway, 🍴 Atlanta Bread, Chevy's Mexican, Ruth Criss Steak, Subway, Wendy's, 🛏 Candlewoods Suites, Hilton, Marriott, Red Carpet Inn, Residence Inn, Welsley Motel, 🅞 Barnes&Noble, Buick/GMC, GNC, Kohl's, Shoprite, Stop'n Shop
37	NJ 24 E, Springfield
36b a	rd 510, Morris Ave, Lafayette
35	NJ 124, South St, Madison Ave, Morristown, **E** 🍴 Friendly's, **W** 🍴 Brick Oven, Calaloo Cafe, 🛏 Best Western, 🅞 🅷, Rite Aid, Walgreens
33	Harter Rd
33mm	**rest area nb, full ♿ facilities, 🚻, ♻, litter barrels, vending, petwalk**
30b a	to US 202, N Maple Ave, Basking Ridge, **E** 🍴 Bamboo Grill, 🛏 Dolce Resort, **W** 🅖 Gulf, 🍴 Burger King,

30b a	Continued Friendly's, GrainHouse Rest., 🛏 Olde Mill Inn/rest.
26b a	rd 525 S, Mt Airy Rd, Liberty Corner, **3 mi** **E** 🅖 Exxon/24hr, 🛏 Courtyard, Somerset Hotel, 🅞 Kwik-Pik Foods
22b a	US 202, US 206, Pluckemin, Bedminster, **E** 🅖 Exxon, 🍴 Burger King, Golden Chinese, 🅞 King's Foods, **W** 🅖 Shell, 🍴 Dunkin Donuts
21b a	I-78, E to NY, W to PA
17	US 206 (from sb), Bridgewater, **E** 🅞 Buick, 🅖 Exxon, Hess, 🍴 Chipotle Mexican, Dunkin Donuts, Friendly's, KFC, Lonestar Steaks, Magginos Italian, McDonald's, Red Town Diner, Starbucks, TGIFriday, Wendy's, 🛏 Marriott, 🅞 Best Buy, Bloomingdale's, Lord&Taylor, Macy's, TJ Maxx, mall
14b a	US 22, to US 202/206, **E** 🅖 Hess/dsl, 🅞 Chevrolet/Lexus, **W** 🍴 Fuddrucker's, Houlihan's, Red Lobster, 🛏 Day's Inn, 🅞 Acura, Buick/Cadillac, Infiniti, Mercedes
13b a	NJ 28, Bound Brook, **E** 🅖 BP/24hr, Sunoco, 🍴 Amazing Hot Dog, Burger King, Dunkin Donuts, Frank's Pizza, Girasole Rest., Joey's Grill, Rosinas Rest., Subway, 🅞 Radio Shack, Rite Aid, 7-11, ShopRite Foods, Walgreens, **W** 🍴 Applebees, ChuckeCheese, McDonald's, 🛏 Hilton Garden, 🅞 🅷, Costco, Home Depot, Marshall's, Michael's, Old Navy, PepBoys, PetsMart, Target
12	Weston Canal Rd, Manville, **E** 🅞 ShopRite (3mi), USPO, **W** 🍴 SportsTime Rest., 🛏 Ramada Inn
10	NJ 527, Easton Ave, New Brunswick, **E** 🛏 Crowne Plaza, **W** 🅖 Exxon, 🍴 Burger King (2mi), Dunkin Donuts, McDonald's (2mi), Ruby Tuesday, 🛏 Courtyard, Holiday Inn, Doubletree, Hampton Inn, Madison Suites, Quality Inn, Staybridge Suites, 🅞 🅷, Drug Fair, Garden State Exhibit Ctr
9	NJ 514, River Rd, **W** 🅖 Delta, 🛏 Embassy Suites, Radisson
8.5mm	**weigh sta nb**
8	Possumtown Rd, Highland Park
7	S Randolphville Rd, Piscataway, **E** 🅖 Lukoil/dsl
6	Washington Ave, Piscataway, **E** 🅖 Shell, **W** 🍴 Applebees, Burger King, Friendly's, KFC, McDonald's, TGIFriday, Johnny Carino's, Longhorn Steaks, Panera Bread, Ray's Pizza, Red Lobster, White Castle, 🅞 GNC, Lowes Whse, PetCo, ShopRite Foods, same as 5
5	NJ 529, Stelton Rd, Dunellen, **E** 🅖 Gulf/dsl, Lukoil, Shell, 🍴 Banzai Japanese, KFC, 🛏 Ramada Ltd., 🅞 Home Depot, Stop'n Shop, **W** 🅖 Exxon, 🍴 Baja Fresh, Burger King, Chicago Grill, Dunkin Donuts, Friendly's, Gianni Pizza, IHOP, Fontainbleu Diner, Gabrieles Grill, Grand Buffet, McDonald's, New York Deli, Red Lobster, Red Robin, Quiznos, Starbucks, Taco Bell, Wendy's, 🛏 Best Western, Motel 6, Hampton Inn, Holiday Inn, 🅞 Burlington Coats, $Tree, Kohl's, Lowes Whse, Macy's, Marshall's, PathMark Foods, Pep Boys, Radio Shack, Sears Essentials/auto, Staples, Target, Walmart/auto
4	Durham Ave (no EZ nb return), S Plainfield, **E** 🅖 Lukoil, 🅞 🅷
3	New Durham Rd (from sb), **E** 🅖 Shell, **W** 🍴 Dunkin Donuts, 🛏 Fairfield Inn, Red Roof Inn, 🅞 Walgreens
2b a	NJ 27, Metuchen, New Brunswick, **W** 🅖 BP, Lukoil, 🍴 Dunkin Donuts, 🅞 Costco, USPO, Walmart
1b a	US 1, **1-2 mi** **N** on US 1 🅖 Exxon/dsl, Getty, Gulf, Race Way/dsl, 🍴 Bone Fish Grill, Cheese Burger Paradise, China Cafe, Dunkin Donuts, Famous Dave's BBQ, KFC,

B R I D G E W A T E R

N ↕ **S**

NJ

INTERSTATE 287 CONT'D

N ↕ S

Exit	Services
1b a	Continued Macaroni Grill, McDonald's, Menlo Park Diner, Panera Bread, Polo Tropical, Red Lobster, Ruby Tuesday, TGI Friday, Uno, White Castle, [lodging] Woodbridge Hotel, [other] A&P Foods, Best Buy, Goodyear/auto, Macy's, Marshall's, Nordstrom's, Rite Aid, Sears/auto, 7-11, mall, **S** [gas] Shell, [food] Applebees, Boston Mkt, ChuckeCheese, Grand Buffet, McDonald's, Quizno's, [lodging] Holiday Inn Express, [other] Astin Martin/Jaguar/Porche, BJ's Whse, BMW, Home Depot, Infiniti, Mercedes, Office Depot, PepBoys, PetCo, Staples, Stop'n Shop Foods
0mm	I-287 begins/ends on NJ 440, I-95, NJ Tpk.

INTERSTATE 295

N ↕ S — TRENTON

Exit	Services
67b a	US 1. I-295 nb becomes I-95 sb at US 1. See NJ I-95, exit 67b a.
65b a	Sloan Ave, **E** [gas] Exxon, [food] Burger King, Dunkin Donuts, New China Buffet, Subway, Taco Bell, Uno Grill, [other] Goodyear/auto, Rizoldi's Mkt
64	NJ 535, N (from sb), to NJ 33 E, same as 63
63b a	NJ 33 W, rd 535, Mercerville, Trenton, **E on rd 33** [gas] Hess/dsl, Lukoil, Valero, [food] Applebee's, Asia Buffet, McDonald's, Pizza Hut, Popeye's, Stewart's Rootbeer, Subway, Vincent's Pizza, [other] Ace Hardware, CVS Drug, Ford/Subaru, Rite Aid, Staples, auto repair, USPO, **W** [gas] Exxon, [food] Dunkin Donuts, Hamilton Diner, Szechuan House, [other] Advance Parts, Family$, Walgreens, WaWa, transmissions
62	Olden Ave, N (from sb, no return), **W** [gas] Delta
61b a	Arena Dr, White Horse Ave, **W** [gas] 7-11
60b a	I-195, to I-95, W to Trenton, E to Neptune
58mm	scenic overlook both lanes
57b a	US 130, to US 206, **E** [gas] Shell, Valero, [food] Denny's, McDonald's, [lodging] Best Western, Comfort Inn, Days Inn, EconoLodge, Hampton Inn, [other] Blue Beacon, **W** [lodging] Candlewood Suites, [other] st police
56	to US 206, S (from nb, no return), to NJ Tpk, Ft Dix, McGuire AFB, **E** [gas] Loves/Wendy's/dsl/scales/24hr, Petro/Iron Skillet/dsl/scales/24hr/@, [lodging] Days Inn, Hampton Inn, same as 57, **W** [lodging] Candlewood Suites, [other] st police
52b a	rd 656, to Columbus, Florence, **3 mi E** [gas] Petro/Iron Skillet/dsl/scales/24hr/@, Loves/Wendy's/dsl/scales/24hr
47b a	NJ 541, to Mount Holly, NJ Tpk, Burlington, **E** [gas] BP, Exxon/dsl, Valero/dsl, [food] Applebee's, Burger King, China House, ChuckECheese's, Coldstone, Cracker Barrel, Dunkin Donuts, IHOP, Quiznos, Recovery Grill, TGIFriday's, [lodging] Best Western, Budget Inn, Courtyard, Hampton Inn, Hilton Garden, Holiday Inn Express, Quality Inn, [other] AT&T, Dick's, $Tree, Home Depot, JC Penney, Kohl's, Sears/auto, Target, mall, vet, **W** [gas] Citgo/dsl, US Gas, WaWa/dsl, [food] Checker's, Friendly's, Subway, Villa Pizza, Wedgewood Farms Rest., Wendy's, [other] [H], Acme Foods, AutoZone, Marshall's, Walmart
45b a	to Mt Holly, Willingboro, **W** [gas] LukOil, [other] [H], auto repair
43b a	rd 636, to Rancocas Woods, Delran, **W** [gas] Exxon, [food] Carlucci's Rest.

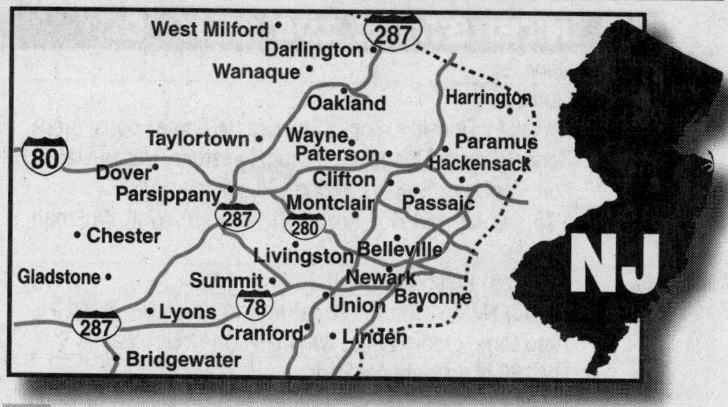

CHERRY HILL

Exit	Services
40b a	NJ 38, to Mount Holly, Moorestown, **W** [gas] Shell/dsl, [food] Arby's, Baja Fresh, Chick-fil-A, Dunkin Donuts, Panera Bread, Ruby Tuesday, Starbucks, Subway, TGIFriday's, [lodging] Residence Inn (4mi), [other] [H], Costco, GNC, Jo-Ann Fabrics, Petsmart, Radio Shack, Target, TJ Maxx, U-Haul, Wegman's Foods
36b a	NJ 73, to NJ Tpk, Tacony Br, Berlin, **E** [gas] Exxon, LukOil/dsl, [food] Bob Evans, [lodging] aLoft, Courtyard, EconoLodge, Fairfield Inn, Red Roof Inn, Super 8, **W** [gas] Citgo, Shell, [food] Bertucci's, Boscov's, Boston Mkt, Chick-fil-A, Chipotle Mexican, Don Pablo, Dunkin Donuts, 5 Guys Burgers, Friendly's, Mikado Japanese, Old Town Buffet, Panera Bread, PeiWei, Perkins, PJ Whelahin's, Popeye's, Uno Grill, Wendy's, [lodging] Bel-Air Motel, Crossland Suites, Homewood Suites, Motel 6, Quality Inn, [other] Acura, AT&T, AutoZone, Barnes&Noble, Best Buy, Chevrolet, Dick's, $Tree, Fiat, Firestone/auto, Ford/Lincoln, Home Depot, Infiniti, K-Mart, Lord&Taylor, Lowe's, Macy's, Marshall's, Michael's, Old Navy, PepBoys, Petsmart, Ross, Sears/auto, ShopRite Foods, Staples, mall
34b a	NJ 70, to Camden, Cherry Hill, **E** [gas] BP, Exxon, WaWa, [food] Big John's Steaks, Burger King, Dunkin Donuts, PJ Whelihans, [lodging] Extended Stay America, [other] Curves, Tires+, **W** [gas] Exxon, Gulf/dsl, LukOil, US Gas, [food] Dunkin Donuts, Famous Dave's BBQ, McDonald's, Mirabella Cafe, Norma's Cafe, Ponzio's Rest, Qdoba, Salad Works, Seasons Pizza, Steak&Ale, Starbucks, Subway, [lodging] Crowne Plaza (3mi), [other] [H], AT&T, CVS Drug, $Tree, Goodyear/auto, Rite Aid, WaWa, vet
32	NJ 561, to Haddonfield, Voorhees, **3 mi E** [gas] LukOil/dsl, [food] Applebee's, 5 Guys Burgers, Olive Garden, Panera Bread, Vito's Pizza, [lodging] Hampton Inn, Wingate Inn, [other] [H], USPO, **W** [gas] Pioneer/dsl, Sunoco, [food] Burger King, Dunkin Donuts, Subway, [other] Ford, 7-11, vet
31	Woodcrest Station
30	Warwick Rd (from sb)
29b a	US 30, to Berlin, Collingswood, **E** [gas] Astro/dsl, Citgo/dsl, Exxon, LukOil/dsl, [food] Arby's, Church's, Dunkin Donuts, McDonald's, Popeye's, Subway, Wendy's, [other] AutoZone, Home Depot, Lowe's, PathMark Foods, Petsmart, Sears Essentials
28	NJ 168, to NJ Tpk, Belmawr, Mt Ephraim, **E** [gas] Citgo, Gulf/repair, Shell/dsl, Shamrock/dsl, [food] Burger King, Club Diner, Dunkin Donuts, Italia Pizza, Wendy's, [lodging] Bellmawr Motel, Comfort Inn, EconoLodge, Holiday Inn, Howard Johnson, Motel 6, Red Roof Inn, Super 8, [other] CVS Drug, Walgreens, transmissions, **W** [gas] BP, Exxon/LP, Hess/dsl, WaWa, [food] Applebee's, Arby's, Black Horse Diner, Chick-fil-A, Domino's, Dunkin Donuts, 5 Guys Burgers, Golden

INTERSTATE 295 CONT'D

Exit	Services
28	Continued
	Corral, McDonald's, Sonic, Subway, ⊙ Acme Foods, Auto-Zone, Chrysler/Dodge, CVS Drug, Firestone, Harley-David-son, PepBoys, Staples, Walgreens, Walmart, USPO
26	I-76, NJ 42, to I-676 (exits left from sb), Walt Whitman Bridge
25b a	NJ 47, to Westville, Deptford
24b a	NJ 45, NJ 551 (no EZ sb return), to Westville, E ⊙ Ⓗ, AutoZone, repair, W 🅖 WaWa ⊙ Chevrolet, Family$
23	US 130 N, to National Park
22	NJ 644, to Red Bank, Woodbury, E 🅖 LukOil, 1 mi W 🅖 Crown Point Trkstp/dsl/@, WaWa, 🍴 Wendy's
21	NJ 44 S, Paulsboro, Woodbury, W 🍴 WaWa, Wendy's, 🛏 Westwood Motor Lodge
20	NJ 44, rd 643, to National Park, Thorofare, E 🛏 Best Western, W 🛏 Red Bank Inn
19	to NJ 44, rd 656, Mantua
18b a	rd 667, to rd 678, Clarksboro, Mt Royal, E 🅖 BP/dsl, TA/Exxon/Buckhorn Rest./dsl/scales/@, 🍴 Dunkin Donuts, KFC/Taco Bell, McDonald's, Wendy's, ⊙ RV camping, W 🅖 Valero, WaWa/dsl
17	rd 680, to Mickleton, Gibbstown, W 🍴 Burger King, Domino's, 🛏 Motel 6, ⊙ Advance Parts, Family$, GNC, Rite Aid, ShopRite Foods, WaWa
16b	rd 551, to Gibbstown, Mickleton
16a	rd 653, to Paulsboro, Swedesboro
15	rd 607, to Gibbstown

Exit	Services
14	rd 684, to Repaupo
13	US 130 S, US 322 W, to Bridgeport (from sb, no return)
11	US 322 E, to Mullica Hill
10	Ctr Square Rd, to Swedesboro, E 🅖 BP/dsl, WaWa/dsl, 🍴 Applebee's, Dunkin Donuts, McDonald's, Subway, Wendy's, 🛏 Hampton Inn, Holiday Inn, ⊙ Acme Foods/Sav-On, Firestone/auto, Rite Aid, W ⊙ Camping World RV Supplies/service
7	to Auburn, Pedricktown
4	NJ 48, Woodstown, Penns Grove
3mm	**weigh sta nb**
2mm	**rest area nb, full 🅿 facilities, info, Ⓒ, picnic table, litter barrels, rv dump, vending**
2c	to US 130 (from sb), Deepwater, E same as 2b, W 🅖 ⊕FLYING J/Denny's/dsl/scales/LP/24hr, Sunoco/Dunkin Donuts/dsl/scales/24hr, ⊙ Ⓗ
2b	US 40 E, to NJ Tpk, E 🅖 Gulf, 🍴Subway/dsl/scales/24hr, 🛏 Best Value, Comfort Inn, Friendship Motor Inn, Knights Inn, Quality Inn, W same as 2c
2a	US 40, W (from nb), to Delaware Bridge
1c	NJ 551 S, Hook Rd, to Salem, E 🛏 White Oaks Motel, W Ⓗ
1b	US 130, N (from nb), Penns Grove
1a	NJ 49 E, to Pennsville, Salem, E 🅖 Exxon/dsl/repair, 🍴 Applebees, Burger King, Cracker Barrel, Dunkin Donuts, KFC/Taco Bell, McDonald's, Subway, 🛏 Hampton Inn, Super 8, ⊙ Peterbilt, W 🅖 Coastal/dsl, 🛏 Seaview Motel
0mm	New Jersey/Delaware state line, Delaware River, Delaware Memorial Bridge

NEW MEXICO

INTERSTATE 10

Exit	Services
164.5mm	New Mexico/Texas state line
164mm	**Welcome Ctr wb, full 🅿 facilities, Ⓒ, 🛉, litter barrels, petwalk**
162	NM 404, Anthony, S 🅖 Fina/dsl, other:RV camping
160mm	**weigh sta wb**
155	155 NM 227 W, to Vado, N Western Sky's RV Park, S 🅖 NTS/dsl/rest./scales/@, Texaco/rest./dsl/scales/24hr, ⊙ El Camino Real HS
151	Mesquite
144	I-25 N, to Las Cruces
142	Rd 188, Rd 101, Valley Dr, Las Cruces, N 🅖 Chevron/dsl, 🍴 Chilito's Mexican, Dick's Cafe, Whataburger/24hr, 🛏 Best Western, Comfort Inn, Holiday Inn Express, Motel 6, Quality Inn, Ramada Inn, Super 8, Teakwood Inn, ⊙ Ⓗ, Chevrolet/Cadillac, Dalmont's RV Camping, Ford/Lincoln/Mercury, Honda, Hyundai, Mazda, Nissan, auto/RV repair/tires, NMSU, vet, S 🅖 Fina, ⊙ USPO
140	NM 28, to Mesilla, Las Cruces, N 🅖 Fina/dsl, 🍴 Applebee's, Blake's Lotaburger, BurgerTime, Cracker Barrel, Eddie's Grill, McDonald's, Murry Express, Quiznos, Starbucks, Subway, 🛏 Days Inn, Drury Inn, Hampton Inn, La Quinta, SpringHill Suites, ⊙ Buick/GMC, Radio Shack, Walmart, **N on Valley Dr** 🍴 American BBQ, Domino's, Old Town Rest., ⊙ Dodge, Toyota, VW, S 🍴 Gadsden Purchase Grill, 🛏 Comfort Inn, ⊙ Hacienda RV Resort, Harley-Davidson, Siesta RV Park, Sunland RV Ctr, United RV Ctr

Exit	Services
139	NM 292, Amador Ave, Motel Blvd, Las Cruces, N 🅖 🍴/Subway/dsl/scales/24hr, TA/Burger King/Pizza Hut/Taco Bell/dsl/rest./24hr/scales/@, S 🍴 PitStop Café, 🛏 Coachlight Inn/RV Park, ⊙ NAPACare
138mm	Rio Grande River
135.5mm	**rest area eb, full 🅿 facilities, 🛉, litter barrels, petwalk, scenic view, RV dump**
135	US 70 E, to, W Las Cruces, Alamogordo, 1 mi N ⊙ KOA
132	N to ✈, fairgrounds, S 🅖 Loves/Subway/dsl/scales/24hr
127	Corralitos Rd, N 🅖 Exxon, ⊙ Bowlin's Trading Post, to fairgrounds
120.5mm	**insp sta wb**
116	NM 549
111mm	**parking area wb, litter barrels**
102	Akela, N 🅖 Exxon/dsl/gifts
85	East Motel Dr, Deming, S 🅖 Chevron/dsl, Fina, Save Gas/dsl, 🛏 Hampton Inn, Holiday Inn, La Quinta, Motel 6, ⊙ Chrysler/Dodge/Jeep
82b	Railroad Blvd, Deming, N 🅖 Chevron/dsl, S 🅖 Fina, 🍴 Burger King, China Wok, DQ, KFC, La Fonda Mexican, Wendy's, 🛏 Day's Inn, Grand Motel, Mirador Motel, ⊙ AutoZone, Big O Tire, Checker Parts, Chevrolet/GMC, $General, $Tree, Ford/Lincoln/Mercury, Firestone, Goodyear, K-Mart, Little Vinyard RV Park, NAPA, Roadrunner RV Park, Sunrise RV Park, Wagon Wheel RV Park, Walmart, Subway, to Rock Hound SP, st police
82a	US 180, NM 26, NM 11, Deming, N 🅖 Chevron, 🍴 Blake's Lotaburger, S 🅖 Exxon, Phillips 66, Save Gas, Shell/dsl,

NJ / NM

🅿 = gas   🍴 = food   🛏 = lodging   ⊙ = other

INTERSTATE 10 CONT'D

Exit	Services
82a	Continued
	🍴 Burger King, China Star, Denny's, KFC, Palma's Italian, Pizza Hut, Rancher's Grill, Si Senor, 🛏 Butterfield Stage Motel, ⊙ Budget Tire, CarQuest, Goodyear, Radio Shack, museum, tires, to Pancho Villa SP, Rockhound SP
81	NM 11, W Motel Dr, Deming, **S** 🅿 Shamrock/dsl, 🍴 Burger Time, McDonald's, Sonic, Subway, Taco Bell, 🛏 Best Western, Comfort Inn, Deming Motel, Deluxe Inn, Executive Motel, Super 8, Western Motel, ⊙ 81 Palms RV Park, Hitchin Post RV Park, to Pancho Villa SP, Rock Hound SP
68	NM 418, **S** 🅿 Savoy/dsl/rest./24hr, tires/repair
62	Gage, **S** 🅿 Butterfield Station/Exxon/DQ/dsl/RV Park
61mm	**rest area wb, full** ♿ **facilities,** 🍼 **litter barrels, vending, petwalk**
55	Quincy
53mm	**rest area eb, full** ♿ **facilities,** 🍼 **litter barrels, vending, petwalk**
51.5mm	Continental Divide, elev 4585
49	NM 146 S, to Hachita, Antelope Wells
42	Separ, **S** Bowlin's Continental Divide Trading Post/Gifts, truck/auto repair
34	NM 113 S, Muir, Playas
29	no services
24	US 70, E Motel Dr, Lordsburg, **N** 🅿 ⊕FLYING J/Denny's/dsl/LP/scales/RV Dump/24hr, 🍴Arby's/dsl/scales/24hr, 🛏 American Motel, ⊙ Horseman RV Park
23.5mm	**weigh sta both lanes**
22	NM 494, Main St, Lordsburg, **N** 🍴 Don Juan Mexican, McDonald's, 🛏 Comfort Inn, Hampton Inn, Holiday Motel, ⊙ CarQuest, Chevrolet, Family$, Ford, Saucedo's Foods, USPO, **S** 🅿 Shamrock/dsl, Texaco, 🍴 KFC/Taco Bell, Kranberry's Rest., 🛏 Best Western, Econolodge, Motel 10, Super 8, ⊙ KOA
20b a	W Motel Dr, Lordsburg, **Visitors Ctr/full** ♿ **facilities, info, N** 🅿 🍴Loves/Godfather's Pizza/Subway/scales/dsl, 🛏 Day's Inn, **S** 🅿 Chevron/dsl
15	to Gary
11	NM 338 S, to Animas
5	NM 80 S, to Road Forks, **S** 🛏 Desert West Motel/rest., ⊙ USPO, fireworks
3	Steins
0mm	New Mexico/Arizona state line

INTERSTATE 25

Exit	Services
460.5mm	New Mexico/Colorado state line

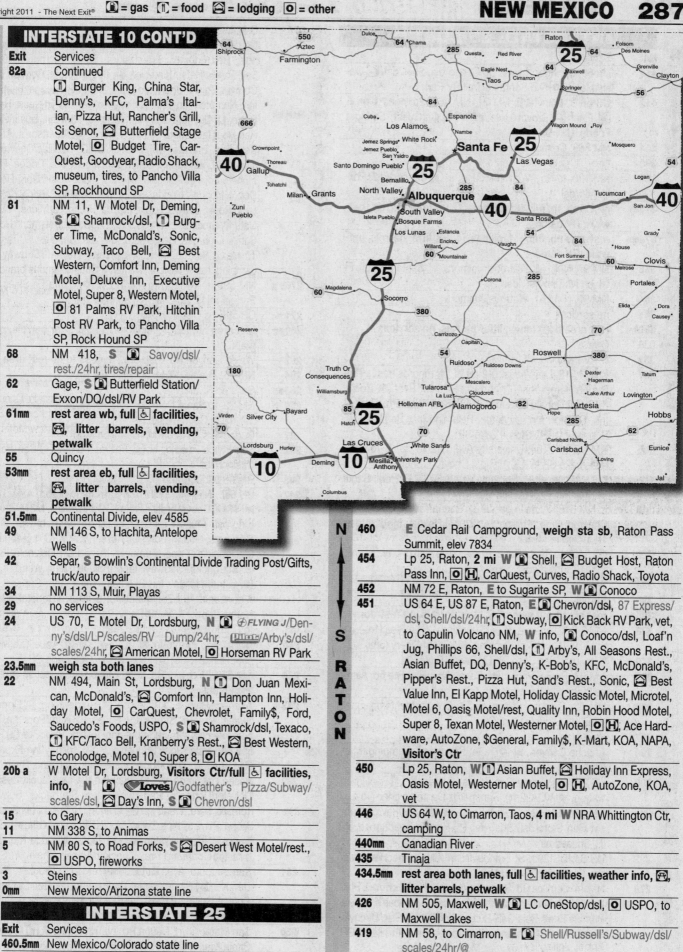

N ↕ S

R A T O N

Exit	Services
460	**E** Cedar Rail Campground, **weigh sta sb**, Raton Pass Summit, elev 7834
454	Lp 25, Raton, **2 mi W** 🍴 Shell, 🛏 Budget Host, Raton Pass Inn, ⊙ Ⓗ, CarQuest, Curves, Radio Shack, Toyota
452	NM 72 E, Raton, **E** to Sugarite SP, **W** 🅿 Conoco
451	US 64 E, US 87 E, Raton, **E** 🅿 Chevron/dsl, 87 Express/dsl, Shell/dsl/24hr, 🍴 Subway, ⊙ Kick Back RV Park, vet, to Capulin Volcano NM, **W** info, 🅿 Conoco/dsl, Loaf'n Jug, Phillips 66, Shell/dsl, 🍴 Arby's, All Seasons Rest., Asian Buffet, DQ, Denny's, K-Bob's, KFC, McDonald's, Pipper's Rest., Pizza Hut, Sand's Rest., Sonic, 🛏 Best Value Inn, El Kapp Motel, Holiday Classic Motel, Microtel, Motel 6, Oasis Motel/rest, Quality Inn, Robin Hood Motel, Super 8, Texan Motel, Westerner Motel, ⊙ Ⓗ, Ace Hardware, AutoZone, $General, Family$, K-Mart, KOA, NAPA, **Visitor's Ctr**
450	Lp 25, Raton, **W** 🍴 Asian Buffet, 🛏 Holiday Inn Express, Oasis Motel, Westerner Motel, ⊙ Ⓗ, AutoZone, KOA, vet
446	US 64 W, to Cimarron, Taos, **4 mi W** NRA Whittington Ctr, camping
440mm	Canadian River
435	Tinaja
434.5mm	**rest area both lanes, full** ♿ **facilities, weather info,** 🍼 **litter barrels, petwalk**
426	NM 505, Maxwell, **W** 🅿 LC OneStop/dsl, ⊙ USPO, to Maxwell Lakes
419	NM 58, to Cimarron, **E** 🅿 Shell/Russell's/Subway/dsl/scales/24hr/@

🅖 = gas 🍴 = food 🛏 = lodging 🅞 = other   Copyright 2011 - The Next Exit

NM

INTERSTATE 25 CONT'D

Exit	Services
414	US 56, Springer, **1 mi** **E** 🅖 Conco/dsl, Shell/dsl, 🛏 Oasis Motel, 🅞 Old Santa Fe Trail RV Park
412	US 56 E, US 412 E, NM 21, NM 468, Springer, **1 mi** **E** 🅖 Fina, 🛏 Brown Hotel/cafe, 🅞 CarQuest, Springer Foods, USPO
404	NM 569, Colmor, Charette Lakes
393	Levy
387	NM 120, to Roy, Wagon Mound, **E** 🅖 Conoco/dsl, Phillips 66/dsl
376mm	**rest area sb, full** ♿ **facilities,** 🍴, 🚻, **litter barrels, petwalk, RV camp**
374mm	**rest area nb, full** ♿ **facilities,** 🍴, 🚻, **litter barrels, petwalk, RV camp**
366	NM 97, NM 161, Watrous, Valmora, **W** Santa Fe Trail, Ft Union NM, no services
364	NM 97, NM 161, Watrous, Valmora
361	no services
360mm	**rest area both lanes, litter barrels, no services**
356	Onava
352	**E** RV camping, **W** 🚮
347	to NM 518, Las Vegas, **0-2 mi W** 🅖 Pino/dsl/rest., Phillips 66/Burger King, 🍴 Arby's, Hillcrest Rest., K-Bob's, KFC, McDonald's, Subway, 🛏 Best Western, Budget Inn, Comfort Inn, Days Inn, Palamino Inn, Regal Motel, Super 8, 🅞 ♿, Storrie Lake SP
345	NM 65, NM 104, University Ave, Las Vegas, **E** to Conchas Lake SP, **W** 🅖 Allsups, Chevron, Shell/dsl, 🍴 DQ, KFC, McDonald's, Subway, Wendy's, 🛏 El Fidel, Sante Fe Trail Inn, 🅞 ♿, Hist. Old Town Plaza
343	to NM 518 N, Las Vegas, **E** 🅞 Garcia Tires, **0-2 mi W** 🅖 Chevron, Fina, Phillips 66/dsl, 🛏 Holiday Inn Express, Thunderbird Motel
339	US 84 S, to Santa Rosa, Romeroville, **E** KOA, **W** 🅖 Phillips 66/Subway/dsl
335	Tecolote
330	Bernal
325mm	**rest area both lanes,** 🚻, **litter barrels, no restrooms**
323	NM 3 S, Villanueva, **E** 🅖 Sunshine, 🍴 La Risa (1mi), 🅞 to Villanueva SP/rv camping, Madison Winery (6mi)
319	San Juan, San Jose, **W** 🅖 Pecos River Sta.
307	NM 63, Rowe, Pecos, **W** Pecos NM, Hist Rte 66, same as 299
299	NM 50, Glorieta, Pecos, **W** 🅖 Conoco/dsl (4mi), Shell (6mi), 🅞 Glorieta Conf Ctr
297	Valencia
294	Apache Canyon, **W** 🅞 KOA, Rancheros Camping (Mar-Nov) (3mi)
290	US 285 S, to Lamy, S to Clines Corners, **W** 🍴 Real Food Nation, 🅞 KOA (2mi), Rancheros Camping (Mar-Nov)
284	NM 466, Old Pecos Trail, Santa Fe, **W** 🅖 Chevron/Sunset Gen Store/dsl, Shell/dsl, 🍴 Harry's Roadhouse, 🅞 ♿, museums
282	US 84, US 285, St Francis Dr, **W** 🅖 Conoco/Wendy's/dsl, Giant/dsl, 🍴 Church's
278	NM 14, Cerrillos Rd, Santa Fe, **0-4 mi W** 🅖 Giant/dsl, Phillips 66/dsl, Shell, 🍴 Adelita's Mexican, Applebee's, Arby's, Bumble Bee's Baja Grill, Burger King, China Star, Denny's, Domino's, El Campanaro Mexican, Flying Tortilla, IHOP, KFC, LJ Silver, Lotaburger, McDonald's, Olive

LAS VEGAS · **SANTA FE**

Exit	Services
278	Continued
	Garden, Outback Steaks, Panda Express, Pizza Hut, Quizno's, Red Lobster, Schlotzsky's, Sonic, Starbucks, Taco Bell, Tortilla Flats, Village Inn, 🛏 Best Western, Comfort Inn, Comfort Suites, Courtyard, Days Inn, EconoLodge, Fairfield Inn, Hampton Inn, Holiday Inn, Holiday Inn Express, Hyatt Place, La Quinta, Luxury Inn, Motel 6, Park Inn, Quality Inn, Red Roof Inn, Santa Fe Inn, Super 8, 🅞 Albertson's, AT&T, Best Buy, BigLots, BMW, Buick/GMC, Cadillac/Chevrolet, Chrysler/Dodge/Jeep, Dillard's, Discount Tire, Dodge, Firestone/auto, Ford/Lincoln/Mercury, Harley-Davidson, Home Depot, Honda, Hyundai, JC Penney, Jo-Ann Fabrics, Kohl's, Land Rover, Lowe's, Lexus, Mazda, Michael's, Midas, NAPA, Natural Grocers, Peerless Tire, PepBoys, Petsmart, Ross, Sam's Club/gas, Sears/auto, Staples, Subaru/VW, Target, TJ Maxx, Verizon, Volvo, Walgreens, Walmart/Subway, rv camping, transmissions, Santa Fe Outlets/famous brands
276b a	NM 599, to NM 14, to Madrid, **E** 🅞 Santa Fe Skies RV Park, **4 mi W** 🅖 Shell, 🅞 Sunrise Springs
271	CR 50F, La Cienega
269mm	**rest area nb, full** ♿ **facilities,** 🍴, 🚻, **litter barrels, petwalk**
267	Waldo Canyon Rd, **insp sta., access to nb rest area**
264	NM 16, Pueblo, **W** to Cochiti Lake RA
263mm	Galisteo River
259	NM 22, to Santo Domingo Pueblo, **W** 🅖 Phillips 66/cafe/dsl, 🅞 to Cochiti Lake RA
257	Budaghers, **W** Mormon Battalion Mon
252	San Felipe Pueblo, **E** 🅖 Phillips 66/dsl, 🍴 San Felipe Casino/rest.
248	Rte 66, Algodones
242	US 550, NM 44 W, NM 165 E, to Farmington, Aztec, **0-2 mi W** 🅖 Chevron/dsl, Circle K, Conoco/dsl, M&M/Burger King/dsl, Phillips 66/dsl, 🍴 Coronado Rest., Denny's, Domino's, Guang Dong Chinese, IHOP, KFC, Lotaburger, McDonald's, Papa Murphy's, Pizza Hut, Quizno's, Sonic, Starbucks, Subway, Taco Bell, Twisters, Wendy's, 🛏 Days Inn, Holiday Inn Express, Quality Inn, Super 8, 🅞 Albertsons, AutoZone, Casino, Curves, $General, $Tree, Home Depot, KOA, O'Reilly Parts, Walgreens, Walmart, to Coronado SP
240	NM 473, to Bernalillo, **W** 🅖 Tri-H/dsl, 🍴 Abuelita's Mexican, Range Café, 🅞 KOA, vet, to Coronado SP
234	NM 556, Tramway Rd, **E** 🅖 Valero, 🅞 casino, **W** 🅖 Phillips 66/dsl
233	Alameda Blvd, **E** 🅖 Chevron, 🍴 Burger King, 🛏 Comfort Suites, Motel 6, Staybridge Suites, 🅞 Audi/Porsche, Lincoln/Mercury, Mercedes, Scion/Toyota, Volvo, **W** 🅖 Phillips 66/Circle K/dsl, 🍴 Carl's Jr, 🛏 Holiday Inn Express, Ramada Ltd, 🅞 Balloon Fiesta Park, CarMax
232	Paseo del Norte, **E** 🍴 Chick-fil-A, China Luck, Jason's Deli, McDonald's, Red Brick Pizza, Starbucks, Subway, Tomato Cafe, Wendy's, 🛏 Clarion, Howard Johnson, 🅞 Aloha RV Ctr, AutoZone, Kohl's, Lowe's, Office Depot, Target, Verizon, Walgreens, **W** 🅖 Shell/Circle K, 🍴 Arby's, 🛏 Courtyard
231	San Antonio Ave, **E** 🅖 Fina/7-11, 🍴 Cracker Barrel, Denny's, 🛏 Hilton Garden, Homewood Suites, La Quinta, Quality Suites, 🅞 ♿, USPO, **W** 🛏 Crossland Suites, Hampton Inn, La Quinta, 🅞 Mazda, VW
230	San Mateo Blvd, Osuna Rd, Albuquerque, **E** 🅖 Chevron, Circle K, Giant/dsl, Phillips 66/Circle K, Shell,

SANTA FE

INTERSTATE 25 CONT'D

Exit	Services

N ↑ **S**

230 Continued
🍴 Applebee's, Arby's, Azuma Grill, Bob's Burgers, Burger King, Chili's, Cici's Pizza, Furrs Buffet, Hooters, KFC, McDonald's, Olive Garden, Pizza Hut/Taco Bell, Schloztsky's, Sonic, Souper Salad, Starbucks, Subway, SweetTomatoes, Taco Bueno, Taco Cabana, Teriyaki Chicken, TX Roadhouse, Village Inn, Wendy's, Wiener-schnitzel, 🛏 Nativo Lodge, 🅾 🅷, AT&T, AutoZone, Brake Masters, Cadillac, Curves, CVS Drug, $Tree, Fire-stone/auto, GNC, Hummer, Just Brakes, Midas, NAPA, PepBoys, PetCo, Ross, Subaru/Isuzu, Sunflower Mkt, Suzuki, Tires-4-less, Tuesday Morning, U-Haul Verizon, Walgreens, **W** 🅿 Chevron, Valero/dsl, 🍴 Cajun Kitch-en, McDonald's, Oasis Cafe, Quizno's, Whataburger, 🛏 Studio 6, 🅾 BMW/Mini

229 Jefferson St, **E** 🍴 Carrabba's, Landry's Seafood, Out-back Steaks, 🛏 Holiday Inn, 🅾 🅷, same as 230, **W** 🍴 Boston's Pizza, Chama River Rest., Coldstone Creamery, Food Ct, Fox&Hound, Fuddrucker's, Genghis Grill, Jersey Jack's, Mimi's Café, Nick&Jimmy's Grill, Pappadeaux, PF Chang's, Red Robin, Subway, TX Land&Cattle Steaks, Twin Peaks Rest., 🛏 Drury Inn, Residence Inn, 🅾 Lexus

228 Montgomery Blvd, **E** 🅿 Chevron/dsl, Conoco/dsl, Fina/7-11, 🍴 Fiestas Cantina, Lotaburger, 🛏 Best West-ern, 🅾 🅷, Discount Tire, **W** 🅿 Shell/Circle K, 🍴 Arby's, Carl's Jr, IHOP, McDonald's, Panda Express, Starbucks, Wendy's, 🛏 InTowne Suites, 🅾 Acura, Ford, Costco/gas, Home Depot, Infiniti, Office Depot, Petsmart, Sam's Club/gas, Sportsman's Whse

227b Comanche Rd, Griegos Rd, **E** UPS Depot

227a Candelaria Rd, Albuquerque, **E** 🅿 Circle K/dsl, Pump'n'Save/dsl, Shell, TA/dsl/scales/24hr/@, 🍴 Ap-plebee's, Little Anita's, Mesa Grill, Range Cafe, Subway, Village Inn, 🛏 Candlewood Suites, Clubhouse Inn, Days Inn, Elegante Hotel, Fairfield Inn, Hilton, Holiday Inn Ex-press, La Quinta, Ramada, Rodeway Inn, Motel 1, Motel 76, Super 8, Travelodge, 🅾 Kenworth, **W** 🅿 Chevron, 🛏 Ambassador Inn, Red Roof Inn, 🅾 Volvo

226b a I-40, E to Amarillo, W to Flagstaff

225 Lomas Blvd, **E** 🅿 Chevron, 7-11, 🍴 JB's, 🛏 Plaza Inn/rest., 🅾 Chevrolet, **W** 🅿 Chevron, Shell/Circle K/McDonald's, 🍴 Burger King, Starbucks, 🛏 Embassy Suites 🅾 🅷

224 Lead Ave, Coal Ave, Grand Ave, Central Ave, **E** 🅿 7-11, 🍴 66 Diner, Souper Salad, 🛏 Crossroads Motel, 🅾 🅷, **W** 🅿 M&M, 🍴 Milton's Rest., 🛏 Best Value Inn, EconoLodge, Stardust Inn

223 Chavez Ave, **E** 🛏 Motel 6, 🅾 sports arena

222b a Gibson Blvd, **E** 🅿 Phillips 66/dsl, 🍴 Applebee's, Burger King, Fuddrucker's, IHOP, Subway, Waffle House, Village Inn, 🛏 Best Western, Comfort Inn, Country Inn&Suites, Courtyard, Days Inn, EconoLodge, Extended Stay De-luxe, Fairfield Inn, Hampton Inn, Hawthorn Suites, Hilton Garden, Holiday Inn Express, La Quinta, Quality Suites, Residence Inn, Sleep Inn, TownePlace Suites, Vagabond Inn, 🅾 🅷, Kirtland AFB, museum, vet, **W** 🅿 Fina/7-11, 🍴 Church's, Lotaburger

221 Sunport, **E** 🛏 Holiday Inn, Homewood Suites, Hyatt

221 Continued
Place, Staybridge Suites, 🅾 USPO, 🍴

220 Rio Bravo Blvd, Mountain View, **E** 🅾 golf, 1-2 mi **W** 🅿 Shell/dsl, Valero, 🍴 A&W, Bob's Burgers, Burger King, Church's, KFC, McDonald's, Pizza Hut, Subway, Super China, Taco Bell, 🅾 Albertsons/Sav-On, Family$, Wal-greens, vet

215 NM 47, **E** 🅿 Conoco/dsl, Phillips 66/dsl, 🅾 to Isleta Lakes RA/RV Camping, casino, golf, st police

214mm Rio Grande

213 NM 314, Isleta Blvd, **W** 🅿 Chevron/Subway/dsl/24hr

209 NM 45, to Isleta Pueblo

203 NM 6, to Los Lunas, **E** 🅿 Chevron/dsl, Shell/Circle K/Wendy's/dsl/24hr, Valero/dsl, 🍴 Benny's, Del Taco, Den-ny's, Papa John's, Quiznos, Sonic, Starbucks, 🛏 Days Inn, Los Lumas Inn, 🅾 AutoZone, Big O Tire, Chevrolet, Ford, Home Depot, Walgreens, **W** 🅿 Phillips 66/Subway/dsl, 🍴 Carl's Jr, Coldstone, Chili's, KFC, Panda Express, 🛏 Western Skies Inn, 🅾 Buick/GMC, Discount Tire, Ve-rizon, Walmart

195 Lp 25, Los Chavez, 1 mi **E** 🅿 Mirastar, Roadrunner/grill/dsl, 🍴 Pizza Hut/Taco Bell, 🅾 Walmart/Subway

191 NM 548, Belen, 1 mi **E** 🅿 Conoco/dsl, 🍴 McDonald's, 🛏 Super 8, 🅾 $General, **W** 🍴 Rio Grande Diner, 🛏 Holi-day Inn Express, La Mirada Hotel/RV park

190 Lp 25, Belen, 1-2 mi **E** 🅿 Conoco/dsl, Phillips 66, 🍴 A&W, Arby's, Casa de Pizza, McDonald's, 🛏 Super 8, 🅾 AutoZone, Big O Tire

175 US 60, Bernardo, **E** Salinas NM, **W** 🅾 Kiva RV Park

174mm Rio Puerco, 169, **E** La Joya St Game Refuge, Sevilleta NWR

167mm rest area both lanes, full ♿ facilities, 🚰 litter barrels, vending, petwalk

166mm Rio Salado

165mm weigh sta/parking area both lanes

163 San Acacia

156 Lemitar, **W** Phillis 66/dsl/24hr

152 Escondida, **W** to st police

150 US 60 W, Socorro, **W** 🅿 Chevron, Exxon/dsl, Phillips 66/dsl, Valero/dsl, 🍴 Burger King, China Best, Denny's, K-Bob's, Lotaburger, McDonald's, Pizza Hut, RoadRun-ner Steaks, Socorro Springs Rest., Sonic, Subway, Taco Bell, 🛏 Best Western, Comfort Inn, Days Inn, Economy Inn, EconoLodge, Holiday Inn Express, Howard John-son, Sands Motel, Super 8, 🅾 Ace Hardware, Auto-Zone, Brooks Foods, CarQuest, $General, Family$, Ford, NAPA, Radio Shack, Smith's Foods, TrueValue, Verizon, Walmart, vet, to NM Tech

147 US 60 W, Socorro, **W** 🅿 Conoco/dsl/LP, Pump, N Save/

Side labels: ALBUQUERQUE, BELEN, SOCORRO

NM

N ↑ S

INTERSTATE 25 CONT'D

Exit	Services
147	Continued dsl, Shell/Circle K/dsl, 🍴 Arby's, 🛏 Motel 6, 🅾 🄷, Socorro RV Park, repair/transmissions, to ✈
139	US 380 E, to San Antonio, **E** gas/food, to Bosque Del Apache NWR
124	to San Marcial, **E** 🅾 to Bosque del Apache NWR, Ft Craig
115	NM 107, **E** Truck Plaza/dsl/rest./24hr, to Camino Real Heritage Ctr
114mm	**rest areas both lanes, full ♿ facilities, 🗑 litter barrels, petwalk, RV parking, vending**
107mm	Nogal Canyon
100	Red Rock
92	Mitchell Point
90mm	La Canada Alamosa, La Canada Alamosa
89	NM 181, to Cuchillo, to Monticello, **4 mi E** 🅾 Monticello RV Park
83	NM 52, NM 181, to Cuchillo, **3 mi E** 🍴 Ivory Tusk Inn& Tavern, 🛏 Elephant Butte Inn/rest., 🅾 RV Park, Elephant Lake Butte SP
82mm	**insp sta nb**
79	Lp 25, to Truth or Consequences, **E** 🚗 Chevron/dsl, Circle K, Phillips 66/dsl, 🍴 Denny's, Hilltop Café, K-Bob's, KFC/Taco Bell, La Cocina Mexican, Los Arcos Steaks, McDonald's, Pizza Hut, Sonic, Subway, 🛏 Ace Lodge, Comfort Inn, Desert View Motel, Hot Springs Inn, Motel 6, Oasis Motel, 🅾 🄷, AutoZone, $General, IGA Foods, O'Reilly Parts, Radio Shack, Walmart, USPO, to Elephant Butte SP
76	(75 from nb)Lp 25, to Williamsburg, **E** 🚗 Chevron/24hr, Conoco/dsl, Phillips 66/dsl, Shell/dsl, 🍴 Big-A-Burger, 🛏 Rio Grande Motel, 🅾 Alco, Buick/Chevrolet/GMC, Cielo Vista RV Park, NAPA, RJ RV Park, Shady Corner RV Park, USPO, auto/tire repair, city park
71	Las Palomas
63	NM 152, to Hillsboro, Caballo, **E** 🅾 Lakeview RV Park/dsl/LP
59	rd 187, Arrey, Derry, **E** to Caballo-Percha SPs
58mm	Rio Grande
51	rd 546, to Arrey, Garfield, Derry
41	NM 26 W, Hatch, **1 mi W** 🚗 Fina/Subway/dsl, 🍴 Burgers&More, 🛏 Village Plaza Motel, 🅾 Chile Pepper Outlets, Franciscan RV Ctr, USPO
35	NM 140 W, Rincon
32	Upham
27mm	**scenic view nb, 🗑 litter barrels**
26mm	**insp sta nb**
23mm	**rest area both lanes, full ♿ facilities, 🗑 litter barrels, vending, petwalk**
19	Radium Springs, **W** Leasburg SP, Fort Selden St Mon, RV camping
9	Dona Ana, **W** 🚗 Circle K/dsl, Chucky's/dsl, Texaco, 🍴 Alejandro's Mexican, Jake's Cafe, 🅾 Family$, RV camping, USPO
6	US 70, to Alamogordo, Las Cruces, **E** 🚗 Fina/dsl, Shell, 🍴 Chicago Grill, Coldstone Creamery, IHOP, Outback Steaks, Papa Johns, Peter Piper Pizza, Pizzaria Uno, Red Brick Pizza, Ruby Tuesday, Starbucks, 🛏 Fairfield Inn, Motel 6, Staybridge Suites, Towneplace Suites, 🅾 🄷, AT&T, Curves, K-Mart, Sam's Club/gas, USPO,

LAS CRUCES

E ↕ **W**

Exit	Services
6	Continued **W** 🚗 Chevron, Chucky's/dsl, Fina, Shell, Valero, 🍴 Burger King, BurgerTime, DQ, Domino's, KFC, Little Caesar's, Lotaburger, McDonald's, Quizno's, Sonic, Spanish Kitchen, Subway, Taco Bell, Whataburger/24hr, 🅾 Albertson's, AutoZone, $General, Family$, Kohl's, Jiffy Lube, Lowe's, O'Reilly Parts, Radio Shack, Verizon, Walgreens, golf, vet
3	Lohman Ave, Las Cruces, **E** 🚗 Fina, Shell, 🍴 Applebee's, Buffalo Wild Wings, Burger King, Cattle Baron Steaks, Chili's, ChuckeCheese, Farley's Grill, Fidencio's Mexican, Golden Corral, Hooters, Jack-in-the-Box, KFC, McAlister's Deli, Olive Garden, Pecan Grill, Red Lobster, Sonic, Starbucks, Village Inn, Whataburger, 🛏 Hotel Encanto, 🅾 Albertsons, AutoZone, Barnes&Noble, Dillard's, Discount Tire, Home Depot, JC Penney, Marshalls, PetCo, Ross, Sears/auto, Target, mall, **W** 🍴 Arby's, Carl's Jr, Furr's Buffet, McDonald's, Mesilla Valley Kitchen, Papa Murphy's, Si Senor, Subway, Taco Bell, TX Roadhouse, Wendy's, Wienerschnitzel, 🛏 Hampton Inn, 🅾 Best Buy, Big Lots, Brake Masters, Hastings Books, Hobby Lobby, Martin Tires, NAPA, Old Navy, PepBoys, Petsmart, Staples, Verizon, Walgreens, Walmart, urgent care, vet
1	University Ave, Las Cruces, **E** 🚗 Fina/Subway/dsl, 🛏 Hilton Garden, 🅾 🄷, golf, museum, st police, **W** 🚗 Western/dsl, 🍴 DQ, Dublin's Cafe, Lorenzo's Italian, McDonald's, 🛏 Comfort Suites, Sleep Inn, ValuePlace, 🅾 $Tree, Jo-Ann Fabrics, NMSU
0mm	I-25 begins/ends on I-10, exit 144 at Las Cruces.

INTERSTATE 40

Exit	Services
373.5mm	New Mexico/Texas state line, Mountain/Central time zone
373mm	**Welcome Ctr wb, full ♿ facilities, ☎, 🗑 litter barrels, petwalk**
369	NM 93 S, NM 392 N, Endee, **N** 🚗 Chevron/Russell's Truck&Travel/Subway/dsl/scales/24hr
361	Bard
358mm	**weigh sta both lanes**
356	NM 469, San Jon, **N** 🚗 Dhillon/cafe/dsl/24hr, 🅾 repair, to Ute Lake SP, **S** 🚗 Phillips 66/dsl, 🛏 San Jon Motel, 🅾 USPO, city park
343	no services
339	NM 278, **N** ✈
335	Lp 40, E Tucumcari Blvd, Tucumcari, **N** 🚗 Conoco/dsl, Phillips 66, 🛏 EconoLodge, Gateway Inn, Hampton Inn, Motel 6, Quality Inn, Rodeway Inn, Super 8, 🅾 Empty Saddle RV Park, to Conchas Lake SP, **S** 🚗 KOA
333	US 54 E, Tucumcari, **0-1 mi N** 🚗 ⊕FLYING J/Denny's/dsl/LP/scales/RV Dump/24hr, ●Loves/Arbys/Chester's/Godfather's/dsl/scales, 🍴 Rockin Y's Roadhouse, 🛏 Tucumcari Inn, 🅾 K-Mart, Mtn Rd RV Park, city park, truckwash, truck repair
332	NM 209, NM 104, 1st St, Tucumcari, **0-2 mi N** 🚗 Phillips 66/Allsups, Shell/Circle K/Subway/dsl, 🍴 Blake's Lotaburger, KFC, K-Bob's, McDonald's, Pizza Hut, Sonic, 🛏 Best Western, Days Inn, Holiday Inn Express, La Quinta, Microtel, 🅾 🄷, Ace Hardware, $General, Family$, Lowe's Foods, st police, to Conchas Lake SP
331	Camino del Coronado, Tucumcari
329	US 54, US 66 E, W Tucumcari Ave
321	Palomas, **S** 🚗 Shell/DQ/Stuckey's/dsl
311	Montoya

TUCUMCARI

🛢 = gas 🍴 = food 🛏 = lodging ◻ = other

INTERSTATE 40 CONT'D

Exit	Services
302mm	rest area both lanes, full ♿ facilities, 🍴, 🚻, litter barrels, petwalk, RV dump
300	NM 129, Newkirk, N 🛢 Rte 66/dsl, ◻ USPO, to Conchas Lake SP
291	to Rte 66, Cuervo, N Cuervo Gas/repair
284	no services
277	US 84 S, to Ft Sumner, N 🛢 Phillips 66/dsl, 🍴 DQ, Denny's, Silver Moon Café, 🛏 Best Western, Budget Inn, Comfort Inn, Hampton Inn, Holiday Inn Express, Motel 6, Quality Inn, ◻ NAPACare, RV/auto repair, S 🛢 Loves/Carl's Jr/dsl/24hr, TA/Shell/Subway/dsl/24hr/@, ◻ truck/tire repair
275	US 54 W, Santa Rosa, N 🛢 Phillips 66, 🍴 McDonald's, Rte 66 Rest., Santa Fe Grill, 🛏 Best Western, Days Inn, La Quinta, Travelodge, ◻ Donnie's RV Park, Santa Rosa Camping, st police, S 🛢 Shell/Circle K/dsl/24hr, 🍴 Joseph's Grill, Papo's Pizza, 🛏 American Inn; Laloma Motel/RV Park, Sun'n Sand Motel/rest., Super 8, Tower Motel, ◻ H, CarQuest, Family$, NAPA, Rte 66 Drug, USPO
273.5mm	Pecos River
273	US 54 S, Santa Rosa, N ◻ Santa Rosa Lake SP, S 🛢 Phillips 66, 🛏 Budget 10 Inn, ◻ NAPACare, to Carlsbad Caverns NP
267	Colonias, N 🛢 Shell/Stuckey's/dsl/rest.
263	San Ignacio
256	US 84 N, NM 219, to Las Vegas
252	no services
251.5mm	rest area both lanes, full ♿ facilities, 🍴, 🚻, litter barrels, petwalk, RV dump
243	Milagro, N 🛢 Phillips 66/dsl
239	no services
234	N 🛢 Exxon/Flying C/DQ/dsl/gifts
230	NM 3, to Encino, N ◻ to Villanueva SP
226	no services
220mm	parking area both lanes, litter barrels
218b a	US 285, Clines Corners, N 🛢 Conoco/Subway/dsl/24hr, Shell/dsl, 🍴 Clines Corners Rest., S ◻ to Carlsbad Caverns NP
208	Wagon Wheel
207mm	rest area both lanes, full ♿ facilities, 🚻, litter barrels, petwalk
203	N RV Park
197	to Rte 66, Moriarty, S 🛢 Lisa's TC/dsl/rest./@, ◻ auto/RV repair, 1-2 mi S same as 194, 196
196	NM 41, Howard Cavasos Blvd, S 🛢 Phillips 66/dsl, 🍴 Blakes Lotaburger, SuperChina Buffet, 🛏 Comfort Inn, Sunset Motel, ◻ Family$, NAPA, USPO, to Salinas NM (35mi), auto repair
194	NM 41, Moriarty, S 🛢 Conoco, Pump'n Save, Route 66, TA/Shell/Pizza Hut/CF/Burger King/dsl/24hr/scales/@, 🍴 Arby's, KFC/Taco Bell, McDonald's, Subway, 🛏 Best Western, Luxury Inn, Motel 6, Ponderosa Motel, Super 8, ◻ Alco, Chevrolet/GMC, $General, IGA Foods, RV Ctr
187	NM 344, Edgewood, N 🛢 Conoco/DQ/dsl, ◻ Walmart/McDonald's, S 🛢 Phillips 66/dsl, 🍴 Chili Hills Mexican, China Chef, McDonald's, Pizza Barn, Subway, ◻ AutoZone, Family$, Ford, NAPA, Smith's Foods/gas, Walgreens, USPO, RV Camping, vet

Exit	Services
181	NM 217, Sedillo, S 🛢 Route 66/dsl
178	Zuzax, S 🛢 Shelby's/dsl, ◻ Hidden Valley RV Park, Leisure Mtn RV Park
175	NM 337, NM 14, Tijeras, N ◻ to Cibola NF, Turquoise Trail RV Park, S 🍴 Subway
170	Carnuel
167	Central Ave, to Tramway Blvd, S 🛢 Fina/7-11, Phillips 66, Valvoline, 🍴 Blakes Lotaburger, Carl's Jr., KFC, McDonald's, Pizza Hut/Taco Bell, Starbucks, Subway, Waffle House, 🛏 Best Value, Budget Host, Comfort Inn, Deluxe Inn, EconoLodge, Travelodge, Value Place, ◻ Albertsons, $Tree, Rocky Mtn RV/marine, Smith's/gas, to Kirtland AFB
166	Juan Tabo Blvd, N 🛢 Phillips 66/Circle K, Texaco, 🍴 AA Buffet, China King, Dominos, Fedrico's Mexican, Lin's Chinese, McDonald's, Olive Garden, Paul's Rest., Pizza Hut/Taco Bell, Twisters Diner, Village Inn Rest., Wendy's, 🛏 Best Value, Super 8, ◻ Albertson's, Big O Tire, Discount Tire, $General, Hastings Books, Hobby Lobby, Family$, Sav-On Drug, Tuesday Morning, transmissions, vet, S 🍴 Little Caesars, Sonic, Wienerschnitzel, ◻ $General, Holiday RV Ctr, KOA/LP, Meyer's RV Ctr, repair
165	Eubank Blvd, N 🛢 Chevron, Phillips 66/Circle K, 🍴 Applebee's, Owl Cafe, Panda Express, Sadie's Rest., Sonic, 🛏 Days Inn, EconoLodge, Guesthouse Inn, Holiday Inn Express, Quality Inn, Rodeway Inn, ◻ Best Buy, CarQuest, PetCo, Radio Shack, Target, S 🛢 Conoco/dsl, Valero, 🍴 Bob's Burgers, Boston Mkt, Chili's, Church's, Del Taco, Golden Corral, IHOP, Jack-in-the-Box, Pizza Hut, Starbucks, Subway, Taco Bell, Taco Cabana, Twister's Burritos, Wendy's, ◻ AutoZone, Costco/gas, Home Depot, Office Depot, O'Reilly Parts, Peerless Tires, PetsMart, Sam's Club/gas, Toyota, Walgreens, Walmart, repair
164	Lomas Blvd, Wyoming Blvd, N 🛢 Circle K/dsl, Phillips 66/dsl, 🍴 Dominos, Eloy's Mexican, South China, Wandy's, ◻ H, NAPA, Walgreens, vet, S ◻ Dodge, Ford, Honda, Hyundai, Kia, transmissions, Kirtland AFB
162b a	Louisiana Blvd, N 🍴 Bravo Italian, Buca Italian, CA Pizza Kitchen, Chili's, Elephant Bar Rest., Fuddrucker's, Garduno's, Jasons Deli, LePeep, Macaroni Grill, Marcello's, McAlister's Diner, Peiwei Asian, Shoney's, Starbucks, 🛏 Homewood Suites, Hilton Garden, Hyatt Place, Marriott, Sheraton, ◻ Barnes&Noble, Big O Tire, Dillard's, Firestone, JC Penney, Kohl's, Macy's, Sears/auto, Trader Joe's, Verizon, S 🛢 Shell, 🍴 Burger King, ◻ atomic museum
161b a	San Mateo Blvd, Albuquerque, N 🛢 Giant/dsl, Shell, 🍴 Bob's Burgers, Boston Mkt, Carl's Jr., Denny's, KFC, Pizza Hut, Starbucks, Subway, Taco Bell, Wendy's,

E ↑ ↓ **W**

S A N T A R O S A

M O R I A R T Y

A L B U Q U E R Q U E

NM

NM

⛽ = gas 🍴 = food 🏨 = lodging ⊙ = other   Copyright 2011 - The Next Exit

INTERSTATE 40 CONT'D

Exit	Services

E ↕ W

A L B U Q U E R Q U E

NM

161b a Continued
🏨 La Quinta, ⊙ $Tree, Office Depot, Old Navy, **S** ⛽ Chevron/dsl

160 Carlisle Blvd, Albuquerque, **N** ⛽ Circle K/gas, Premier, Pump'n Save, Shell, 🍴 Applebee's, Blakes Lotaburger, Cheesecake Factory, China Wok, Little Anita's, McDonald's, Pizza Hut, Range Cafe, Rudy's BBQ, Sonic, Subway, Twisters Grill, Village Inn Rest., Whataburger, 🏨 Candlewood Suites, Days Inn, EconoLodge, Elegante Hotel, Hampton Inn, Hilton, Holiday Inn Express, La Quinta, Motel 6, Radisson, Residence Inn, Rodeway Inn, Suburban Motel, Super 8, ⊙ Firestone/auto, JC Penney, Smith's Foods, Walgreens, **S** ⛽ Phillips 66/Subway/dsl, 🍴 Burger King, ⊙ 🏥 K-Mart, Whole Foods Mkt

159b c I-25, S to Las Cruces, N to Santa Fe

158 6th St, 8th St, 12th St, Albuquerque, **N** ⛽ ❤Love's/Subway/dsl, ⊙ U-Haul, **S** ⛽ Chevron, 🏨 Quality Inn

157b 12th St (from eb), **N** ⛽ Fina/dsl, 🏨 Holiday Inn Express, ⊙ Lowe's, Walgreens

157a Rio Grande Blvd, Albuquerque, **N** ⛽ Valero, **S** ⛽ Shell, 🍴 Ben Michaels, Blakes Lotaburger, Little Anita's, Starbucks, 🏨 Best Western/grill, Hotel Albuquerque, ⊙ repair

156mm Rio Grande River

155 Coors Rd, Albuquerque, **N** ⛽ Circle K, Duke City/dsl, Giant Gas/dsl, Valero/dsl, 🍴 Applebee's, Arby's, Baskin-Robbins, Carl's Jr, Chili's, Cracker Barrel, Golden Corral, IHOP, McDonald's, Mimmo's Pizza, Noodles, Panda Express, Papa Murphy's, Quiznos, Red Brick Pizza, Sonic, Starbucks, Subway, Taco Cabana, Twisters Burritos, Wendy's, Wing Stop, ⊙ URGENT CARE, AutoZone, Brake Masters, Brook's Foods, Curves, $Tree, Family$, Goodyear/auto, Home Depot, Jiffy Lube, Radio Shack, Staples, Verizon, Walgreens, Walmart, vet, **S** ⛽ Fina, Shell, Valero, 🍴 Altamar Mexican, Blakes Lotaburger, Del Taco, Denny's, Furr's Rest., McDonald's, New China, Pizza Hut/Taco Bell, Subway, Twisters Burritos, Village Inn Rest., 🏨 Days Inn, EconoLodge, Hampton Inn, La Quinta, Motel 6, Motel 76, Quality Inn, Super 8, ⊙ Big-Lots, Discount Tire, O'Reilly Parts, dsl repair

154 Unser Blvd, **N** ⛽ Valero, ⊙ to Petroglyph NM

153 98th St, **S** ⛽ ✈FLYING J/Denny's/dsl/LP/24hr, Valero, 🍴 Burger King, Little Caesars, McDonald's, Subway, 🏨 Microtel, ⊙ AutoZone, $Tree, truckwash/tire/lube

149 Central Ave, Paseo del Volcan, **N** ⊙ Camping World, Enchanted Trails RV Camping, Freightliner, to Shooting Range SP, **S** ⊙ American RV Park, High Desert RV Park

140.5mm Rio Puerco River, **N** ⛽ 66 Pit Stop

140 Rio Puerco, **N** ⛽ 66 Pit Stop/dsl, **S** ⛽ Rte 66 TC/DQ/Road Runner Cafe/hotel/casino/dsl/@

131 To'Hajiilee

126 NM 6, to Los Lunas

120mm Rio San Jose

117 Mesita

114 NM 124, Laguna, **1/2 mi N** ⛽ 66 Pit Stop/dsl

113.5mm scenic view both lanes, litter barrels

108 Casa Blanca, Paraje, **S** ⛽ Dancing Eagle TC/DQ/dsl/24hr, ⊙ Ace Hardware, casino, RV park

104 Cubero, Budville

102 Sky City Rd, Acomita, **N** ⛽ Sky City/McDonald's/hotel/casino/dsl, 🍴 Huwak'a Rest., ⊙ RV Park/laundry,

102 Continued
casino, **S** rest area both lanes, **full** ♿ **facilities**, ⊙, 🚻, litter barrels, petwalk, 🏥

100 San Fidel

96 McCartys

89 NM 117, to Quemado, **N** ⛽ Skyway/Shell/Subway/dsl/gifts, **S** El Malpais NM

G R A N T S

85 NM 122, NM 547, Grants, **N** ⛽ Fina/dsl, Phillips 66, Shell/dsl, 🍴 Asian Buffet, Blakes Lotaburger, Canton Cafe, Denny's, Pizza Hut, Subway, Taco Bell, 🏨 Best Western, Comfort Inn, Days Inn, Holiday Inn Express, Motel 6, Quality Inn, Sands Motel, South West Motel, Super 8, Travelodge, ⊙ 🏥, AutoZone, Delta Tire, O'Reilly Parts, $Tree, Walmart, repair/transmissions/towing, **S** Lavaland RV Park

81b a NM 53 S, Grants, **N** ⛽ Phillips 66, 🍴 Domino's, KFC, McDonald's, ⊙ 🏥, Ford/Lincoln/Mercury, NAPA, USPO, **S** ⊙ Blue Spruce RV Park, KOA/Cibola Sands RV Park, El Malpais NM

79 NM 122, NM 605, Milan, **N** ⛽ Chevron/dsl, ❤Love's/Chester's/Subway/dsl/scales/24hr, 🍴 DQ, 🏨 Crossroads Motel, ⊙ Bar-S RV Park, **S** ⛽ Petro/Iron Skillet/dsl/scales/24hr/@, ⊙ Speedco Lube, st police

72 Bluewater Village, **N** ⛽ Exxon/DQ/dsl

63 NM 412, Prewitt, **S** to Bluewater Lake SP (7mi)

53 NM 371, NM 612, Thoreau, **N** ⛽ Giant/Blimpie/dsl, ⊙ Family$, NAPA, USPO

47 Continental Divide, 7275 ft, **N** ⛽ Phillips 66, ⊙ Continental Divide Trdg Post, towing/repair, **S** USPO

44 Coolidge

39 Refinery, **N** ⛽ ▓▓▓/Subway/Dennys/dsl/scales/24hr/@

36 Iyanbito

33 NM 400, McGaffey, Ft Wingate, **N** ⊙ to Red Rock SP, RV camping, museum

G A L L U P

26 E 66th Ave, E Gallup, **N** ⛽ Shell/Subway/dsl, 🍴 Denny's/24hr, 🏨 Comfort Suites, La Quinta, Sleep Inn, ⊙ KOA, to Red Rock SP, museum, st police, **S on Rte 66** ⛽ Conoco/dsl, Fina/dsl, Mustang, Shell/Ortega Gifts, 🍴 Aurelie's Diner, Blakes Lotaburger, Burger King, KFC, McDonald's, Sonic, Wendy's, 🏨 Best Western, Hacienda Motel, Roadrunner Motel, ⊙ 🏥

22 Montoya Blvd, Gallup, **N** rest area both lanes, full facilities, info, **S on Rte 66** 🍴 Duke City, Gas Up, Phillips 66, 🍴 Big Cheese Pizza, Church's, DQ, Earl's Rest., LJ Silver, Panz Alegra, Papa John's, Pizza Hut, Subway, Taco Bell, Wendy's, 🏨 Blue Spruce Motel, El Capitan Motel, El Rancho Motel/rest., ⊙ Albertson's, Radio Shack, Shop'n Save, Walgreens

20 US 491, to Shiprock, Gallup, **N** ⛽ Fina, Giant/dsl, 🍴 Applebee's, Arby's, Big Cheese Pizza, Blakes Lotaburger, Burger King, CA Chinese, Carl's Jr., Church's, Cracker Barrel, DQ, Denny's, Furr's Café, Golden Corral, KFC, King Dragon Chinese, Little Caesars, McDonald's, Pizza Hut, Sizzler, Sonic, Super Buffet, Taco Bell, Wendy's, 🏨 Hampton Inn, Quality Inn, Ramada Ltd, ⊙ AutoZone, Beall's, Big Lots, CarQuest, Chrysler/Dodge/Jeep, $Tree, Family$, Home Depot, JC Penney, NAPA, Nissan, O'Reilly Parts, PepBoys, Radio Shack, Safeway, Walmart, mall, **S on Rte 66** ⛽ Tarro's/dsl, 🍴 Badlands Grill, Blakes Lotaburger, Don Diego's, El Charrito Mexican, El Dorado Rest., Garcia's Rest., Royal Holiday, Rte 66 Diner, Sonic, McDonald's, 🏨 Ambassador Motel, Best Value Inn,

INTERSTATE 40 CONT'D

Exit	Services
20	Continued
	Days Inn, Desert Skies, Rodeway Inn, Royal Holiday Hotel, Super 8, 🅞 🅗, Big O Tire, Ford/Lincoln/Mercury, RV camping
16	NM 118, W Gallup, Mentmore, **N** 🅖 ▪Love's▪/Chester's/Subway/dsl/24hr, Navajo/dsl/24hr, TA/Country Pride/dsl/scales/24hr/@, 🅞 Blue Beacon, dsl repair, **S** 🅖 Best Value/dsl, Conoco, Fina, Phillips 66/Allsup's,

16	Continued
	🍴 Ranch Kitchen, Taco Bell, 🛏 Best Western, Budget Inn, Comfort Inn, EconoLodge, Hampton Inn, Howard Johnson, Microtel, Motel 6, Red Roof Inn, Travelodge, 🅞 USA RV Park
12mm	**inspection/weigh sta eb**
8	to Manuelito
3mm	**Welcome Ctr eb, full ♿ facilities, 🅒, 🚻, litter barrels, petwalk**
0mm	New Mexico/Arizona state line

NEW YORK

INTERSTATE 81

Exit	Services
184mm	US/Canada border, New York state line. I-81 begins/ends.
183.5mm	US Customs (sb)
52 (183)	Island Rd, to De Wolf Point, last US exit nb, **E** food
51 (180)	Island Rd, to Fineview, Islands Parks, **2-3 mi E** 🍴 Thousand Islands Club, 🛏 Seaway Island Resort, Torchlite Motel, 🅞 Nature Ctr, camping, golf, USPO, **W** 🅖 Sunoco/dsl
179mm	St Lawrence River
178.5mm	**Thousand Islands Toll Bridge Booth, rest area sb, full ♿ facilities, 🅒, 🚻, litter barrels, petwalk**
50NS (178)	NY 12, **N** to Alexandria Bay, 🅖 Mobil/dsl, 🍴 Kountry Kottage Rest., Subway, 🛏 Bonnie Castle/rest., Green Acres River Motel, PineHurst Motel, River Edge Hotel, 🅞 🅗, funpark (seasonal), to Thousand Island Region, **S** to Clayton, 🅖 Mobil, 🛏 Bridgeview Motel, PJ's Motel, 🅞 **NY Welcome Ctr**, to RV camping
174mm	**rest area nb, full ♿ facilities, 🅒, vending, 🚻, litter barrels, petwalk, st police**
49 (171)	NY 411, to Theresa, Indian River Lakes, **E** 🅖 Mobil/dsl (4mi)
168mm	parking area sb, 🚻
161mm	parking area nb
48 (158)	US 11, NY 37, **1-4 mi E** 🅖 Mobil/dsl, Nice'n Easy/dsl, Sunoco/dsl, 🍴 Arby's, McDonald's, Longway's Diner, 🛏 Allen's Budget Motel, Hotis Motel, Microtel, Royal Inn, 🅞 st police
156.5mm	parking area both lanes
47 (155)	NY 12, Bradley St, Watertown, **E** 🅖 Nice'n Easy/Subway/dsl, 🅞 🅗**W** 🛏 Rainbow Motel
154.5mm	Black River
46 (154)	NY 12F, Coffeen St, Watertown, **E** 🅖 Mobil, 🍴 Cracker Barrel, Shorty's Diner, 🅞 Home Depot, urgent care
45 (152)	NY 3, to Arsenal St, Watertown, **E** 🅖 Mobil, Sunoco, 🍴 Applebee's, Arby's, Buffalo Wild Wings, Burger King, China Buffet, Dunkin Donuts, Friendly's, Jreck Subs, KFC, LJ Silver, McDonald's, Panda Buffet, Ponderosa, Quiznos, Ruby Tuesday, Starbucks, Taco Bell, 🛏 Days Inn, EconoLodge, Hampton Inn, Holiday Inn Express, The Inn, 🅞 Advance Parts, Aldi Foods, AutoZone, BigLots, Chrysler/Dodge/Jeep, $General, $Tree, Jo-Ann Fabrics, Kost Tire, Michael's, PriceChopper Foods/24hr, Radio Shack, Rite Aid, Staples, TJ Maxx, USPO, Walgreens, **W** 🅖 Fastrac, 🍴 Bob Evans, Panera Bread, Pizza Hut, Red Lobster, Subway, TX Roadhouse, TGIFriday's, 🛏 Ramada Inn, 🅞 Best Buy, Ford, Gander Mtn,

45 (152)	Continued
	Hannaford Foods, JC Penney, K-Mart, Kohl's, Lowe's, Old Navy, PetCo, Sam's Club, Sears/auto, Target, Walmart, mall, to Sackets Harbor
149mm	parking area nb, 🅒
44 (148)	NY 232, to Watertown Ctr, **3 mi E** 🅖 Mobil, 🛏 Best Western
147mm	**rest area sb, full ♿ facilities, 🅒, 🚻, litter barrels, vending, petwalk**
43 (146)	US 11, to Kellogg Hill
42 (144)	NY 177, Adams Center, **E** 🅖 Nice'n Easy/dsl, 🍴 Depot Cafe, 🅞 Harley-Davidson, Tucker's Camping
41 (140)	NY 178, Adams, **E** 🅖 Citgo/dsl, 🍴 2 Bros Pizza, McDonald's, 🅞 st police
138mm	South Sandy Creek
40 (135)	NY 193, to Ellisburg, Pierrepont Manor
134mm	parking area, 🚻, both lanes
39 (133)	Mannsville
38 (131)	US 11, **E** 🛏 81-11 Motel
37 (128)	Lacona, Sandy Creek, **E** 🍴 J&R Diner, 🛏 Harris Lodge, Lake Effect Inn, **W** 🅖 Citgo, Sunoco/dsl, 🍴 Sandy Creek Diner, 🛏 Pink House Inn, Salmon River Motel, 🅞 Sandy Island Beach SP, USPO
36 (121)	NY 13, Pulaski, **E** 🅖 Citgo, 🍴 Ponderosa, 🛏 Red Carpet Inn, Scottish Inn, **W** 🅖 KwikFill, Mobil/dsl, Nice'n Easy/Subway, Sunoco/dsl, 🍴 Arby's, Burger King, Dunkin Donuts, Eddy's Place, McDonald's, River House Rest., Stefano's Rest., 🛏 Super 8, 🅞 Aldi Foods, Buick/Chevrolet, Family$, Kinney Drug, NAPA, P&C Foods, Radio Shack, Rite Aid, to Selkirk Shores SP, camping, fish hatchery
35 (118)	to US 11, Tinker Tavern Rd, **W** Grandpa Bob's Animal Park
34 (115)	NY 104, to Mexico, **E** 🅖 Sunoco/dsl/scales/24hr, 🍴 Maple View Rest., **2-12 mi W** 🅖 Citgo, 🛏 Cedar Creek, 🅞 J&J/Salmon Country/Dowiedale/Jellystone Camping
33 (111)	NY 69, Parish, **E** 🅖 Sunoco/dsl/24hr, 🍴 Grist Mill Rest., 🛏 E Coast Resort (4mi), 🅞 Up Country RV Park (8mi), **W** 🅖 Citgo, Mobil/dsl, 🛏 Parish Motel, 🅞 USPO
32 (103)	NY 49, to Central Square, **E** 🅖 Mobil/dsl, Sunoco/Subway/dsl, 🍴 Golly's Rest., 🅞 NAPA, **W** 🅖 Fastrac/gas, Quick Mart, 🍴 Burger King, Dunkin Donuts, McDonald's, Quinto's NY Pizza, 🛏 Town&Country, 🅞 Advance Parts, $Tree, Ford, Rite Aid, Skips Pit Stop/dsl/RV repair, Walmart, st police
101mm	**rest area sb, full ♿ facilities, 🅒, 🚻, litter barrels, vending, petwalk**
31 (99)	to US 11, Brewerton, **E** Oneida Shores Camping, **W** 🅖 Mobil/dsl, Nice'n Easy, 🍴 Brickhouse Cafe, Burger

(side margins: E, W, N, S; PULASKI; WATERTOWN)

NM / NY

INTERSTATE 81 CONT'D

N ↑ S

Exit	Services
31 (99)	**Continued** King, Castaway's Cafe, Dunkin Donuts, LinLi's Chinese, Little Caesar's, McDonald's, Subway, 🛏 BelAir Motel, Brewerton Motel, Holiday Inn Express, 🅞 $General, Kinney Drugs, vet
30 (96)	NY 31, to Cicero, **0-1 mi E** 🅟 Fastrac/dsl, Hess/dsl, KwikFill, 🍽 Arby's, Cracker Barrel, Dunkin Donuts, Gino's&Joe's Pizza, McDonald's, 🅞 Gander Mtn, Rite Aid, Walgreens, **W** 🅟 Citgo/dsl, Kwikfill, 🍽 Cicero Pizza, Denny's, Frank's Café, Plainville Farms Rest., 🅞 Bellair Motel, Brewerton Motel, 🅞 RV Ctrs
29 (93)	I-481 S, NY 481, to Oswego, Syracuse, **1 mi W on US 11** 🅟 Hess, Mobil/dsl, 🍽 Buffalo Wild Wings, Burger King, Denny's, KFC, McDonald's, Moe's SW Grill, Panera Bread, Pizza Hut, Quizno's, Starbucks, Taco Bell, Tully's Rest., Wendy's, 🛏 Budget Inn, 🅞 Advance Parts, Audi/Porsche/VW, Buick/GMC, Burlington Coats, Curves, $Tree, Dunn Tire, Firestone/auto, Goodyear/auto, Home Depot, Hyundai, KIA, Lincoln/Mercury, Lowes Whse, Marshall's, Nissan, PepBoys, PriceChopper Foods, Rite Aid, Target, Toyota, Wegman's Foods, Walmart, mall
28 (91)	N Syracuse, Taft Rd, **E** 🅟 KwikFill, Sunoco/dsl, 🅞 U-Haul, **W** 🅟 Mobil, 🅞 Auto Value Parts, USPO
27 (90)	N Syracuse, **E** 🍽
26 (89)	US 11, Mattydale, **E** 🅟 Mobil, 🍽 Asian 98 Buffet, Hofmann Rest., Pizza Hut, 🛏 Red Carpet Inn, 🅞 Big Lots, $Tree, Goodyear/auto, K-Mart, Michael's, PetCo, Rite Aid, Staples, TJ Maxx, vet, **W** 🅟 Delta Sonic, 🍽 Arby's, Burger King, Denny's, Dunkin Donuts, Jreck Subs, KFC, McDonald's, Ponderosa, Subway, Taco Bell, Wendy's, 🛏 Candlewood Suites, Econolodge, Holiday Inn Express, 🅞 Advance Parts, Aldi Foods, Kost Tire, P&C Foods
25a (88)	I-90, NY Thruway
25 (87.5)	7th North St, **E** 🅟 ▦/McDonald's/dsl/scales/24hr, 🅞 NAPA, repair, **W** 🅟 Mobil, 🍽 Arthur Treacher's, Burger King, Colorado Steaks, Denny's, Dunkin Donuts, Jreck Subs, North Buffet, Ruddy's Pizza, Tully's Rest., 🛏 Comfort Inn, Hampton Inn, Maplewood Inn/cafe, Quality Inn, Ramada Inn, Super 8, United Inn
24 (86)	NY 370 W, to Liverpool, same as 23
23 (86)	NY 370 E, Hiawatha Blvd, **W** 🅟 Hess, 🅞 Best Buy, Border's, JC Penney, Macy's, mall
22 (85)	NY 298, Court St
21 (84.5)	Spencer St, Catawba St (from sb), industrial area
20 (84)	I-690 W (from sb), Franklin St, West St
19 (84)	I-690 E, Clinton St, Salina St, to E Syracuse
18 (84)	Harrison St, Adams St, **E** 🛏 ParkView Hotel, Renaissance Hotel, 🅞 H, to Syracuse U, Civic Ctr
17 (82)	Brighton Ave, S Salina St, **W** 🅟 KwikFill, Valero/Subway
16a (81)	I-481 N, to DeWitt
16 (78)	US 11, to Nedrow, Onondaga Nation, **1-2 mi W** 🅟 Hess, Valero, 🍽 McDonald's, Pizza Hut
15 (73)	US 20, La Fayette, **E** 🅟 Sunoco/dsl/deli, 🍽 Old Tymes Rest., 🅞 La Fayette Inn, 🅞 $General, NAPA, USPO, st police, vet, **W** 🍽 McDonald's
71mm	**truck insp sta both lanes,** 🍽
14 (67)	NY 80, Tully, **E** 🅟 Nice'n Easy/deli/dsl, 🛏 Best Western, 🅞 Chevrolet, Kinney Drug, **W** 🍽 Burger King

CORTLAND · **SYRACUSE** · **BINGHAMTON**

Exit	Services
13 (63)	NY 281, Preble, **E** to Song Mtn Ski Resort
60mm	**rest area/truck insp nb, full** ♿ **facilities,** 🍽, ▦, **litter barrels, vending, petwalk**
12 (53)	US 11, NY 281, to Homer, **W** 🅟 Mobil/dsl/24hr, KwikFill, Valero, 🍽 Applebees, Burger King, Doug's Fishfry, Fabio's Italian, Little Italy, Ponderosa, 🛏 Budget Inn, Country Inn&Suites, 🅞 H, to Fillmore Glen SP
11 (52)	NY 13, Cortland, **E** 🍽 Apple Annie's, 🛏 Comfort Inn, Quality Inn, **W** 🅟 Mobil/dsl, 🍽 Arby's, China Moon, Crown City Rest., Friendly's, Golden Skillet, McDonald's, Subway, Taco Bell, Wendy's, 🛏 Hampton Inn, Ramada Inn, 🅞 Advance Parts, Family$, Jo-Ann Fabrics, Kost Tire, P&C Foods/24hr, camping, museum
10 (50)	US 11, NY 41, to Cortland, McGraw, **W** 🅟 Citgo/Dunkin Donuts/dsl/cafe, Mobil/Subway/dsl/24hr, Sunoco/dsl, 🛏 Cortland Motel, Day's Inn, 🅞 NAPa
9 (38)	US 11, NY 221, **W** 🅟 Citgo, Sunoco/XtraMart/dsl/24hr, 🍽 NY Pizzaria, 🛏 3 Bear Inn/rest., Greek Peak Lodge, 🅞 NAPA, Country Hills Camping
33mm	**rest area sb, full** ♿ **facilities,** 🍽, ▦, **litter barrels, vending, petwalk**
8 (30)	NY 79, to US 11, NY 26, NY 206 (no EZ return), Whitney Pt, **E** 🅟 Hess, Kwikfill, Mobil/dsl/24hr, Sunoco, 🍽 Aiello's Ristorante, Arby's, McDonald's, Subway, 🛏 Point Motel, 🅞 Chevrolet, $General, Gregg's Mkt, NAPA, Parts+, Radio Shack, Strawberry Valley Farms (3mi), USPO, to Dorchester Park
7 (21)	US 11, Castle Creek
6 (16)	US 11, to NY 12, I-88E, Chenango Bridge, **E on US 11** 🅟 Citgo/dsl, Exxon, Hess/dsl, 🍽 Arby's, Burger King, Denny's, Dunkin Donuts, King Buffet, Pizza Hut, Ponderosa, Subway, Wendy's, 🅞 Advance Parts, Curves, CVS Drug, Giant Foods, Kost Tire, Lowes Whse, Radio Shack, Rite Aid, Staples, vet, **W** 🅟 Diamond Fuel, KwikFill, 🍽 Friendly's, McDonald's, Nirchi's Pizza, Spot Diner, Subway, 🛏 Comfort Inn, Howard Johnson, Motel 6, 🅞 $Bazaar, Harley-Davidson, Walgreens
15mm	I-88 begins eb
5 (14)	US 11, Front St, **1 mi W** 🅟 Sunoco, Valero, 🍽 Applebees, Coldstone Creamery, Cracker Barrel, KFC/Taco Bell, McDonald's, Quizno's, Starbucks, 🛏 Comfort Inn, Econolodge, Fairfield Inn, 🅞 Cutler Botanical Garden
4 (13)	NY 17, Binghamton
3 (12)	Broad Ave, Binghamton, **W** 🅟 Valero, 🍽 KFC, 🅞 CVS Drug, Giant Foods
3 (10)	Industrial Park, same as 2
2 (8)	US 11, NY 17, **1-2 mi W** 🅟 Exxon/dsl, ♥Loves, Wendy's/dsl/scales/24hr, TA/dsl/rest./24hr@/, 🍽 Arby's, Burger King, McDonald's, Subway, 🛏 Del Motel
1 (4)	US 11, NY 7, Kirkwood, **1-2 mi W** 🅟 Mobil/dsl/24hr, Xtra, 🛏 Kirkwood Motel, Wright Motel
2mm	**Welcome ctr nb, full** ♿ **facilities,** 🍽, ▦, **litter barrels, vending, petwalk**
1mm	**weigh sta nb**
0mm	New York/Pennsylvania state line

INTERSTATE 84

Exit	Services
71.5mm	New York/Connecticut state line
21 (68)	US 6, US 202, NY 121 (from wb), N Salem, same as 20
20N (67.5)	US 6, US 202, NY 22, **N** 🅟 Mobil/24hr, Shell, Valero, 🍽 Dunkin Donuts, 🅞 Cadillac/Chevrolet, Ford, Honda,

INTERSTATE 84 CONT'D

E ↑ ↓ W

Exit	Services
20N (67.5)	Continued Subaru, vet
20S	I-684, to NYC
20S	I-684, to NYC
19 (65)	NY 312, Carmel, **S** ⊙ st police, **S** 🍴 Applebee's, Dunkin Donuts, Eveready Diner, Gaetano's Deli, Wendy's, ⊙ Ⓗ, Home Depot, Kohl's, Marshall's, Michael's
18 (62)	NY 311, Lake Carmel, **S** 🍴 Lakeview Pizza
17 (59)	Ludingtonville Rd, **S** 📱 Hess/Blimpie/dsl/24hr, Sunoco/dsl, 🍴 Cacciatore's Pizzaria, Cutiloo's Rest., Dunkin Donuts, Gappy's Pizza, Lou's Deli
56mm	elevation 970 ft
55mm	**rest area both lanes, full ♿ facilities, Ⓒ, vending, ⛽, litter barrels, petwalk**
16 (53)	Taconic Parkway, N to Albany, S to New York
15 (51)	Lime Kiln NY, **3 mi N** 📱 Mobil/24hr, 🍴 Dunkin Donuts, 🛏 Arbor Ridge Inn
13 (46)	US 9, to Poughkeepsie, **N** 📱 Citgo, Gulf, Mobil/dsl, 🍴 A&W/KFC, Boston Mkt, Antonella Italian, Burger King, Charlie Brown Steaks, Coldstone, Cracker Barrel, Dunkin Donuts, Fishkill Grill, Hudson Buffet, Izumi Japanese, Panera Bread, Pizza Hut, Ruby Tuesday, Starbucks, Subway, Taco Bell, Wendy's, 🛏 Comfort Inn, Courtyard, Extended Stay America, Hampton Inn, Hilton Garden, Holiday Inn, Holiday Inn Express, Homestead Suites, Hotel Sierra, Residence Inn, ⊙ $Tree, Mavis Tire, Radio Shack, Rite Aid, Sam's Club, ShopRite Foods, Verizon, Walmart, **S** 📱 Hess/Blimpie/dsl/24hr, 🍴 Maya Cafe, McDonald's, ⊙ Home Depot
12 (45)	NY 52 E, Fishkill, **N** 📱 Valero, 🍴 Chan's Buffet, Golden Buddha, Sal's Pizza, ⊙ CVS Drug, $King, **S** 📱 Mobil, Sunoco/dsl, 🍴 84 Diner, Hometown Deli, 🛏 Quality Inn, ⊙ Lincoln/Mercury
11 (42)	NY 9D, to Wappingers Falls, **1 mi N** 📱 Mobil/dsl, Sunoco
41mm	toll booth
40mm	Hudson River
10 (39)	US 9W, NY 32, to Newburgh, **N** 📱 Citgo, Extra, Mobil, Sunoco, 🍴 Alexis Diner, Andiamo Pizza, Burger King, Dunkin Donuts, Great Wall, Green Garden Chinese, McDonald's, New China, Pizza Hut, ⊙ Advance Parts,

N E W B U R G H

10 (39)	Continued BigLots, $Tree, Family$, Firestone/auto, PriceChopper Foods, Rite Aid, Shop Rite Foods, Walgreens, **S** 📱 Gulf, Shell/dsl, Sunoco/dsl, 🛏 Travel Inn, ⊙ Ⓗ
8 (37)	NY 52, to Walden, **N** 📱 Shell, Sunoco/24hr
7b (36)	NY 300, to I-87, (NY Thruway), Newburgh, **N** 📱 Mobil, 🍴 DQ, Dunkin Donuts, Green Onion Grill, Jak Steaks, King Buffet, Leo's Pizzaria, Marshall's, McDonald's, Newburgh Buffet, Old Town Buffet, Perkins, Taco Bell, Wendy's, ⊙ AT&T, AutoZone, BonTon, Discount Tire, $Tree, Marshall's, Mavis Tire, Office Depot, Old Navy, Sears, Stop&Shop Foods, **S** 📱 Getty, Hess/dsl, Sunoco, 🍴 Applebee's, Burger King, Chili's, China City, Cosimos Ristorante, Denny's, 5 Guys Burgers, Gateway Diner, Johnny D's, Longhorn Steaks, Neptune Diner, Panera Bread, Sonic, Steak'n Stein, Subway, TGIFriday's, Union Sq Rest., 🛏 Hampton Inn, Hilton Garden, Howard Johnson, Knights Inn, Ramada Inn, Super 8, ⊙ Adam's Food Mkt, Associated Foods, Barnes&Noble, Buick/GMC, Cadillac/Chevrolet, Chrysler/Dodge/Jeep, Ford/Lincoln/Mercury, Home Depot, Honda, Lowe's, Michael's, Midas, Nissan, Kohl's, PetsMart, Radio Shack, Target, Verizon, Walmart
7a (35)	no services
6 (34)	NY 17K, to Newburgh, **N** 📱 Mobil/24, 🚛/Arby's/dsl/scales/24hr, 🍴🍽 Diner, 🛏 Comfort Inn, **S** 🛏 Courtyard, **3 mi S** 🛏 Days Inn, Hilton Garden, Howard Johnson, Quality Inn
5a	NY 747, International Blvd, to Stewart 🍽
5 (29)	NY 208, Maybrook, **N** 📱 Mobil/dsl, Sunoco/dsl, 🍴 Burger King, Dunkin Donuts, McDonald's, ⊙ NAPA, Rite Aid, ShopRite Foods, **S** 📱 Hess, Stewart's, TA/Pizza Hut/dsl/rest./@, 🍴 Prima's Deli, Renee's Deli, Subway, 🛏 Super 8, ⊙ Blue Beacon, auto/truck repair, st police

INTERSTATE 84 CONT'D

Exit	Services
24mm	**rest area wb, full ♿ facilities, 🅲, vending, ⛽, litter barrels, petwalk**
4 (19)	NY 17, Middletown, **N** 🅿 Mobil/24hr, ⏹ Americana Diner, Applebee's, Arby's, Baskin-Robbins/Dunkin Donuts, Boston Mkt, Burger King, Cheeseburger Paradise, ChuckeCheese, Denny's, Friendly's, KFC, McDonald's, Olive Garden, Panera Bread, Papa John's, Perkins, Pizza Hut, Red Lobster, Ruby Tuesday, Starbucks, Subway, Taco Bell, Wendy's, Youyou Japanese, 🛏 Howard Johnson, Middletown Motel, Super 8, 🅾 Ⓗ, Aldi Foods, AutoZone, Best Buy, Big Lots, $Tree, Firestone/auto, Gander Mtn, Hannaford Foods, Home Depot, Honda, JC Penney, Jo-Ann Fabrics, Kohl's, Lowe's, Marshall's, Michael's, Old Navy, PetCo, PetsMart, PriceChopper Foods, Rite Aid, Sam's Club, Sears/auto, ShopRite Foods, Staples, Tire Discount, TJ Maxx, U-Haul, Verizon, Walmart, mall, urgent care, vet, **S** 🅿 Citgo/dsl, ⏹ Chili's, El Bandido Mexican, Outback Steaks, TGIFriday, 🛏 Courtyard, Hampton Inn, Holiday Inn, Microtel, 🅾 st police
17mm	**rest area eb, full ♿ facilities, 🅲, vending, ⛽, litter barrels, petwalk**
3 (15)	US 6, to Middletown, **N** 🅿 Citgo/dsl, Mobil, QuickChek/dsl, Shell, Sunoco, Valero, ⏹ Bro Bruno's Pizza, Dunkin Donuts, IHOP, McDonald's, NY Buffet, Peking Chinese, Quizno's, Subway, Taco Bell, Wendy's, 🅾 Ⓗ, Acura, AutoZone, Goodyear, Mazda, Radio Shack, Rite Aid, ShopRite Foods, Subaru, VW, **S** 🅿 Citgo, Geo/Dunkin Donuts, Sunoco/dsl, 🛏 Days Inn, Global Budget Inn, 🅾 KIA, Nissan, Scion/Toyota
2 (5)	Mountain Rd, **S** Greenville's Deli
4mm	elevation 1254 ft wb, 1272 ft eb
3mm	parking area both lanes
1 (1)	US 6, NY 23, Port Jervis, **N** 🅿 JC, ⏹ Arlene&Tom's Diner, Baskin-Robbins/Dunkin Donuts, Deerpark Cafe, 🅾 Ⓗ, 84 RV Ctr, Ford/Lincoln/Mercury, **S** 🅿 BP, Citgo/dsl, Gulf/dsl, Lukoil/dsl, Valero/dsl, ⏹ DQ, McDonald's, 🛏 Days Inn, 🅾 Ⓗ, $Tree, GNC, ShopRite Foods, TJ Maxx, mall
0mm	New York/Pennsylvania state line, Delaware River

INTERSTATE 86 (New York)

Exit	Services
	I-86 begins/ends on I-87, exit 16, toll booth
131 (379)	NY 17, **N** 🅾 Outlets/famous brands, **S** 🅿 Exxon/dsl, ⏹ Chicago Grill, Chili's, McDonald's, TGIFriday's, 🛏 American Budget Inn, Hampton Inn, 🅾 Home Depot, Kohls, Staples, TJMaxx
130a (378)	US 6, Bear Mtn, to West Point (from eb), **S** ⏹ Sonny's Pizza, Outback Steaks, 🅾 Best Buy, BJ's Whse, BMW, Home Depot, PetsMart, Target, TJ Maxx, Walmart
130 (377)	NY 208, Monroe, Washingtonville, **N** 🛏 James Motel, Lake Anne Motel, 🅾 Chrysler/Dodge/Jeep, Isuzu, st police, **S** 🅿 Mobil/dsl, Sunoco, Valero, ⏹ Burger King, Dunkin Donuts, Monroe Diner, 🛏 American Budget Inn, 🅾 Kohl's, Michael's, ShopRite Foods, Staples
129 (375)	Museum Village Rd
128 (374)	rd 51 (only from wb), Oxford Depot
127 (373)	Greycourt Rd (from wb only), Sugar Loaf, Warwick
126 (372)	NY 94 (no EZ wb return), Chester, Florida, **N** 🅿 Mobil,

126 (372)	Continued Shell, Sunoco/dsl, ⏹ Chester Diner, McDonald's, Wendy's, 🛏 Holiday Inn Express, 🅾 CVS Drug, Radio Shack, Rite Aid, ShopRite Foods, USPO, **S** 🅾 Lowes Whse
125 (369)	NY 17M E, South St, **S** ⏹ Hacienda Mexican, Pizza Deli, 🅾 Ⓗ
124 (368)	NY 17A, NY 207, **N** 🅿 Exxon/Subway/dsl, Mobil/dsl, ⏹ Burger King, Friendly's, Dunkin Donuts, Pizza Hut, 🅾 Ⓗ, CVS Drug, **S** 🛏 Comfort Inn, 🅾 Chrysler/Dodge/Jeep, Hyundai
123	US 6, NY 17M (wb only), Port Jervis
122a (367)	Fletcher St, Goshen
122 (364)	rd 67, E Main St, Crystal Run Rd, **N** 🅿 Mobil, ⏹ Chili's, El Bandido Rest., Outback Steaks, TGIFriday's, 🛏 Courtyard, Hampton Inn, Holiday Inn, Microtel, **S** 🅿 Citgo/dsl
121 (363)	I-84, E to Newburgh, W to Port Jervis
120 (363)	NY 211, **N** 🅿 Lukoil, Mobil, Sunoco, ⏹ Cosimo's Ristorante, Olive Garden, 🛏 Howard Johnson, Middletown Motel, Super 8, 🅾 Best Buy, Gander Mtn, Macy's, Hannaford's Foods, JC Penney, Rite Aid, Sam's Club, Target, **S** 🅿 Valero, ⏹ Americana Diner, Arby's, Boston Mkt, Burger King, Cheeseburger Paradise, Denny's, Dunkin Donuts, Friendly's, KFC, Panera Bread, Pizza Hut, Red Lobster, Subway, Taco Bell, Wendy's, Youyou Chinese, 🅾 Aldi Foods, AutoZone, $Tree, Home Depot, Kohl's, Lowes Whse, PriceChopper, Rite Aid, ShopRite Foods, Staples, TJMaxx, U-Haul, Walmart
119 (360)	NY 309, Pine Bush, **S** 🅿 Best Gas/dsl
118a (358)	NY 17M, Fair Oaks
118 (358)	Circleville, **S** 🅿 Exxon/dsl, Mobil, ⏹ Subway
116 (355)	NY 17K, Bloomingburg, **S** 🅿 Citgo/dsl, ⏹ Quickway Diner
114	Wurtsboro, Highview (from wb)
113 (350)	US 209, Wurtsboro, Ellenville, **N** 🅿 Mobil/dsl, Stewarts/gas, ⏹ Giovanni's Café, Subway, 🛏 Gold Mtn Chalet, Day's Inn, Valley Brook Motel, 🅾 Spring Glen Camping, **S** 🅾 American Family Campground
112 (347)	Masten Lake, Yankee Lake, **N** ⏹ Potager Diner, 🛏 Days Inn, ValleyBrook Motel, 🅾 Catskill Mtn Ranch Camping, WonderWood Camping, Yankee Lake
111 (344)	(eb only), Wolf Lake
110 (343)	Lake Louise Marie, **N** ⏹ Dodge Inn Rest, 🛏 Rock Hill Lodge
109 (342)	Rock Hill, Woodridge, **N** 🅿 Exxon/dsl, ⏹ Dutch's Cafe, RockHill Diner, Rock Pizza, 🛏 Rock Hill Lodge, Rosemond Motel, 🅾 Ace Harware, Hilltop Farms Camping, auto repair, **S** 🅿 Mobil/dsl
108 (341)	Bridgeville, same as 109
107 (340)	Thompsonville, **S** ⏹ Hana Rest., Old Homestead Diner, 🛏 Pines Motel, Raleigh Motel, 🅾 Chevrolet, Chrysler/Dodge/Jeep, Toyota
106 (339)	(wb only), E Broadway, **N** Ford/Lincoln/Mercury, **S** 🅿 Mobil/dsl, ⏹ Monitcello Cafe, 🛏 Super 8 (2 mi), Travel Inn (2mi), 🅾 GMC Trucks, Hyundai, tires
105 (337)	NY 42, Monticello, **N** 🅿 Exxon/dsl, Mobil, Valero, ⏹ Bro Bruno's, Blue Horizon Diner, Burger King, Dunkin Donuts, KFC, McDonald's, Subway, 🅾 AutoZone, Home Depot, ShopRite Foods, Staples, Walmart, **S** 🅿 Citgo, Sunoco/dsl, ⏹ Pizza Hut, Wendy's, 🛏 Ramada Ltd, Super 8, 🅾 Advance Parts, Family$, NAPA, Rite Aid
104 (336)	NY 17B, Raceway, Monticello, **S** 🅿 Citgo, Exxon/dsl, ⏹ Colosseo Rest., Taco Maker, 🛏 Best Western, Raceway

INTERSTATE 86 CONT'D (New York)

Exit	Services
104 (336)	Continued
	Motel, Super 8 (2mi), Travel Inn, ⊡ Monticello Raceway, Swinging Bridge Camp, Woodstock Camping, ⊡
103	Rapp Rd (wb only)
102 (332)	Harris, S ⊡ H, Swan Lake Camping
101 (327)	Ferndale, Swan Lake, S ⊡ Exxon/dsl
100 (327)	NY 52 E, Liberty, N ⊡ Citgo, Mobil, Sunoco, ⫿ Albert's Rest., Burger King, Dunkin Donuts, Grapevine Grill, Last Licks Cafe, McDonald's, Piccolo Italian, Pizza Hut, Subway, Taco Bell, Wendy's, ⊟ Day's Inn, Howard Johnson, ⊡ Ace Hardware, Advance Parts, Curves, ShopRite Foods, USPO, S ⊡ Exxon/dsl, Xtra, ⊟ Lincoln Motel, ⊡ Ford/Lincoln/Mercury, Buick, Southend Parts, Neversink River Camping, Swan Lake Camping, Yogi Bear Camping
100a	NY 52 W (no wb return), Liberty, S ⫿ McCabe's Rest., ⊡ st police
99 (325)	NY 52 W, to NY 55, Liberty, S ⊡ Exxon, Sunoco, ⊟ Catskill Motel
98 (321)	Cooley, Parksville, N ⊡ Mobil, ⫿ Charlie's Rest., DariKing, I-86 Diner, ⊟ Best Western, ⊡ USPO
97 (319)	Morsston
96 (316)	Livingston Manor, N ⫿ Tony's Pizza, ⊟ Econo Motel, ⊡ Covered Bridge Camping, Mongaup Pond Camping, S ⫿ Tony's Pizza, Puleez Lueez, ⊟ DeBruce Inn, OZ B&B, Willowemoc Motel
313mm	**rest area eb, full** ⛭ **facilities,** ⊟ **litter barrels,** ⊡ **vending, petwalk, truck insp. sta (eb)**
94 (311)	NY 206, Roscoe, Lew Beach, N ⊡ Exxon/dsl, Sunoco/dsl, ⫿ 1910 Coffeshop, Raimondo's Diner, Roscoe Diner, ⊟ Reynolds House Motel, Rockland House Motel, Roscoe Motel, Tennanah Lake Motel, ⊡ Roscoe Camping, S ⊡ Mobil/dsl, ⊡ Beaverkill St Camping (8mi)
93 (305)	to Cooks Falls (from wb)
92 (303)	Horton, Cooks Falls, Colchester, S ⊡ Sunoco/dsl, ⫿ Riverside Café/lodge, ⊡ Russell Brook Camping
90 (297)	NY 30, East Branch, Downsville, N ⊡ Sunoco, ⊡ Beaver-Del Camping, Catskill Mtn Camping, Oxbow Camping, Peaceful Valley Camping, S ⊟ E Branch Motel
295mm	**rest area wb, full** ⛭ **facilities,** ⊟ **litter barrels,** ⊡ **vending, petwalk**
89 (293)	Fishs Eddy
87a (288)	NY 268 (from wb), same as 87
87 (284)	NY 97, to NY 268, to NY 191, Hancock, Cadosia, S ⊡ Getty, Mobil/Subway, Sunoco, ⫿ Bluestone Grill, Family Rest., McDonald's, ⊟ Capra Inn, Colonial Motel, Starlight Lake Inn, ⊡ Buick/Chevrolet, Grand Union Foods, NAPA, Parts+, Rite Aid
276mm	parking area wb, litter barrels
84 (274)	Deposit, N ⊡ Citgo/dsl/24hr, ⫿ Grand Stand Rest., Pines Rest., Wendy's, ⊟ Deposit Motel, Laurel Bank Motel, Scott's Motel, ⊡ Family$, QuickWay, st police
83 (272)	Deposit, Oquaga Lake
82 (270)	NY 41, McClure, Sanford, N ⊡ Kellystone Park, S ⊟ Chestnut Inn/rest., Mountain Hollow B&B/diner, ⊡ Guestward Camping (3mi)
265mm	parking area eb, ⊟, litter barrels
81 (263)	E Bosket Rd
80 (261)	Damascus, N ⊡ Exxon/dsl, ⊡ Forest Hill Lake Park

Exit	Services
80 (261)	Continued
	Camping, auto repair
79 (259)	NY 79, Windsor, N ⊡ Citgo, Sunoco/dsl, ⫿ Chip's Pizza, Subway, ⊡ Big M Foods, S ⫿ Golden Oak Rest., Marian's Pizza, ⊡ Lakeside Camping
78 (256)	Dunbar Rd, Occanum
77 (254)	W Windsor, N ⊡ Mobil/dsl, ⫿ McDonald's
76 (251)	Haskins Rd, to Foley Rd
75 (250)	I-81 S, to PA (exits left from wb), N ⊡ Exxon/dsl, ⫿ Subway, ⊟ Dell Motel
72 (244)	I-81 N, US 11, Front St, Clinton St, (no wb re-entry), S ⫿ McDonald's, ⊡ Advance Parts, K-Mart, antiques
71 (242)	Airport Rd, Johnson City, S ⊡ Valero
70 (241)	NY 201, Johnson City, N ⊡ Hess/Blimpie, Valero, ⫿ China Buffet, Christy's Grill, Dunkin Donuts, Friendly's, Ground Round, McDonald's, Papa John's, Pizza Hut, Ponderosa, Quizno's, Ruby Tuesday, Taco Bell, ⊟ Best Western, Hampton Inn, La Quinta, Red Roof Inn, ⊡ $Tree, Gander Mtn, Giant Foods, JC Penney, Kost Tire, Macy's, PetCo, Sears/auto, Wegman's Foods, mall, vet, S Home Depot
69 (239)	NY 17C
238mm	Susquehanna River
68 (237)	NY 17C, Old Vestal Rd, (from eb)
67 (236)	NY 26, NY 434, Vestal, Endicott, S on NY 434 ⊡ Hess, Stop'N Gas, Valero/dsl, ⫿ A&W/LJ Silver, Arby's, Burger King, California Grill, Chicago Grill, China Wok, Dunkin Donuts, La Vita Bella, McDonald's, Old Country Buffet, Olive Garden, Outback Steaks, Quizno's, Red Lobster, Starbucks, Subway, Taco Bell, TGIFriday, ⊟ Parkway Motel, Skylark Mote/Diner, Vestal Motel, ⊡ Advance Parts, Barnes&Noble, Chevrolet, Chrysler/Jeep/Subaru, CVS Drug, $Tree, Firestone/auto, Ford/Lincoln/Mercury, Giant Foods, Jo-Ann Fabrics, Kohl's, Kost Tire, Lowe's Whse, Michael's, Nissan, Sam's Club, Subaru, Target, TJ Maxx, Volvo, Walmart, USPO, vet
66 (231)	NY 434, Apalachin, S ⊡ KwikFill, Mobil/dsl, ⫿ Blue Dolphin Diner, Dunkin Donuts, McDonald's, Subway, ⊟ Econolodge, Quality Inn, ⊡ Evelyn's Mkt, Red Apple
65 (225)	NY 17C, NY 434, Owego, N ⊡ Citgo, Mobil/dsl, ⫿ A&W/KFC, Arbys, McDonald's, Panda Wok, Papa John's, Pizza Hut, Subway, Wendy's, ⊟ Hampton Inn, Holiday Inn Express, Treadway Motel/rest., ⊡ $General, Hickories Park Camping, Kost Tire, Medicine Shop Drug, P&C Foods, S st police
64 (223)	NY 96, Owego, N ⊡ CVS Drug, USPO, S ⊡ Citgo, ⊡ auto repair, vet
222mm	**rest area wb, full** ⛭ **facilities,** ⊡ **vending,** ⊟ **litter barrels, petwalk**

INTERSTATE 86 CONT'D (New York)

Exit	Services
63 (218)	Lounsberry, S Ⓖ Valero/rest./24hr/dsl
62 (214)	NY 282, Nichols, S Ⓖ Citgo/Pizza Hut/dsl, Ⓞ Jim's RV Ctr, Tioga Downs Race Track (2mi)
212mm	rest area eb, full Ⓗ facilities, 🅿, litter barrels, Ⓒ, vending, petwalk
208mm	Susquehanna River
61 (206)	NY 34, PA 199, Waverly, Sayre, N Ⓞ $General, Goodyear/gas, S Ⓖ Gulf/24hr, Sunoco, Ⓕ McDonald's, Ⓛ Best Western/rest., Ⓞ Chevrolet/Buick, Chrysler/Jeep/Dodge, Joe's RV Ctr, Nissan
60 (204)	US 220, to Sayre, Waverly, N Ⓛ O'brien's Inn, Ⓞ Clark's Foods, S Ⓖ Citgo/dsl, Xtra/dsl, Ⓕ Wendy's (3mi), Ⓛ Hampton Inn, Ⓞ Advance Parts, Aldi Foods, K-Mart, Rite Aid, Top's Foods
59a (202)	Wilawana, S Ⓖ Sunoco/Subway/dsl
59 (200)	NY 427, Chemung, N Ⓖ Dandy/dsl
58 (195)	rd 2, Lowman, Wellsburg, N Ⓕ W Diner, Ⓛ Red Jacket Motel, S Ⓞ Gardiner Hill Campsites (4mi)
56 (190)	Jerusalem Hill, S Ⓖ Citgo/dsl, KwikFill, Sunoco/Subway, Ⓕ Hilltop Rest., McDonalds, Pizza Hut, Ⓛ Coachman Motel, Holiday Inn, Mark Twain Motel
54 (186)	NY 13, to Ithaca
54	I-86 begins ends., S Ⓖ Mobil, Sunoco, Ⓕ Burger King, Dunkin Donuts, Guiseppe's Pizza, LJ Silver, McDonald's, Subway, Wendy's, Ⓛ Motel 6, Red Carpet Inn, Ⓞ Advance Parts, Family$, K-Mart, Rite Aid, Sav-A-Lot Foods
53	Horseheads, same as 54
52b (184)	NY 14, to Watkins Glen, N Ⓕ Friendly's, Ⓛ Holiday Inn, Knight's Inn, Landmark Inn, S Ⓕ Denny's
52a (183)	Commerce Ctr, same as 52b
51 (182)	Chambers Rd, N Ⓖ Mobil/Subway/dsl, Sunoco/dsl, Ⓕ Bon Ton, Chili's, Dunkin Donuts, Friendly's, McDonald's, Olive Garden, Outback Steaks, Red Lobster, Ruby Tuesday, Ⓛ Country Inn&Suites, Hilton Garden, Holiday Inn Express, Knights Inn, Ⓞ Firestone/auto, JC Penney, Jo-Anne Fabrics, Sears/auto, mall, S Ⓕ Applebee's, Charlie's Subs, Old Country Buffet, Panera Bread, Taco Bell, TGIFriday, Wendy's, Ⓛ Econolodge, Ⓞ Barnes&Noble, Best Buy, Buick/GMC, $Tree, Kohl's, Kost Tire, Lowe's Whse, Macy's, Michael's, Nissan, Old Navy, PetCo, PetsMart, Sam's Club, Staples, Subaru, Target, TJ Maxx, Toyota/Scion, Walmart, museum
50 (180)	Kahler Rd, N to 🛈
49 (178)	Olcott Rd, Canal St, Big Flats, N 🛈, antiques, S Ⓖ Sunoco, Ⓕ Picnic Pizza, Ⓞ $General
48 (171)	NY 352, E Corning, N Ⓖ Citgo, Ⓕ Tag's Rest., Ⓛ Budget Inn, Gatehouse Motel
47 (174)	NY 352, Gibson, Corning, N Ⓛ Radisson Inn, to Ⓗ, Museum of Glass
46 (171)	NY 414, to Watkins Glen, Corning, 5mi N Ⓞ Ferenbaugh Camping, KOA, Watkins Glen Camping, S Ⓖ Citgo/dsl, Ⓛ Comfort Inn, Day's Inn, Staybridge Suites, Ⓞ Ⓗ, museums
45 (170)	NY 352, Corning, N Ⓖ Sunoco, Ⓕ McDonald's, S Ⓖ Fastrac, Ⓕ Bob Evans, Burger King, EnEn Chinese, Friendly's, Subway, Wendy's, Ⓛ Fairfield Inn, Ⓞ AutoZone, CarQuest, Rite Aid
44 (168)	US 15 S, NY 417 W, Gang Mills

Exit	Services
43 (167)	NY 415, Painted Post, N Ⓖ Citgo, Ⓕ Burger King, Ⓞ AutoValue Parts, $General, Firestone/auto, Jo-Ann Fabrics, S Ⓖ Sunoco, Ⓕ Denny's, Ⓛ Hampton Inn
167mm	parking area wb, litter barrels
42 (165)	Coopers Plains, N st police
41 (161)	rd 333, Campbell, N Ⓞ Camp Bell Camping (1mi), S Ⓖ Sunoco, Ⓞ Cardinal Campsites (6mi), antiques
160mm	rest area eb, full Ⓗ facilities, 🅿, litter barrels, Ⓒ, vending, petwalk
40 (156)	NY 226, Savona, N Ⓖ Mobil/dsl, Ⓕ Savona Diner, Subway, Ⓞ Green Acres Camping
39 (153)	NY 415, Bath, N Ⓕ Chat-a-Whyle Rest. (3mi), Ⓛ Holland American Country Inn, National Hotel, S Ⓞ Babcock Hollow Camping (2mi)
38 (150)	NY 54, to Hammondsport, Bath, N Ⓖ Citgo, KwikFill, Mobil, Sunoco, Ⓕ Arby's, Burger King, Dunkin Donuts, Ling Chinese, McDonald's/playplace, Pizza Hut, Ponderosa, Subway, Ⓛ Budget Inn, Day's Inn, Microtel, Super 8, VineHurst Inn, Ⓞ Ⓗ, Advance Parts, AutoValue Parts, Camping World RV Ctr, $General, Family$, Hickory Hill Camping (3mi), K-Mart, Rite Aid, Top's Foods/gas, Walgreens, museum, st police, winery, to Keuka Lake
147mm	rest area wb, full Ⓗ facilities, Ⓒ, 🅿, litter barrels, vending, petwalk
37 (146)	NY 53, to Prattsburg, Kanona, S Ⓖ ⓘ/Subway/dsl/scales/@, Sunoco/Smokey's/dsl/scales, Ⓕ Tally-Ho Rest., Ⓞ Wagon Wheel Camping, Wilkin's RV Ctr (1mi), USPO
36 (145)	I-390 N, NY 15, to Rochester
35 (138)	Howard, S to Lake Demmon RA, Ⓒ
34 (130)	NY 36, Hornell, Arkport, 0-3 mi S Ⓖ KwikFill, Sunoco, Ⓕ Burger King (3mi), China King, Country Kitchen, Dunkin Donuts, Friendly's (3mi), McDonald's, Subway, Ⓛ Comfort Inn (3mi), Day's Inn, Econolodge, Sunshine Motel, Ⓞ Aldi, Chevrolet, Chrysler/Dodge/Jeep, $Tree, Ford, GNC, NAPA, Walmart/auto, Wegman's Foods
125mm	scenic overlook eb, litter barrels, 33 (124) N Y 21, to Alfred, Almond, Andover, S Ⓖ Mobil, Ⓛ Economy Inn, Saxon Inn Hotel, Ⓞ Lake Lodge Camping (8mi), Kanakadea Camping
117mm	highest elevation on I-86, elev 2110 ft eb, 2080 ft wb
32 (116)	W Almond
31 (108)	Angelica, N Ⓖ Citgo, Ⓛ Angelica Inn B&B
30 (104)	NY 19, Belmont, Wellsville, N 6-S Camping (3mi), S Ⓕ Iron Kettle Rest., Ⓞ Mothers Piknchikn Camping (6mi)
101mm	rest area eb, full Ⓗ facilities, Ⓒ, 🅿, litter barrels, vending, petwalk
29 (99)	NY 275, to Bolivar, Friendship, S Ⓖ Mobil, Sunoco, Miller&Brandes Gas, Ⓕ Subway
28 (92)	NY 305, Cuba, N Ⓕ Moonwink's Rest., Ⓛ Econolodge, Ⓞ $General, Maple Lane RV Park, S Ⓖ Sunoco/dsl, Valero/dsl, Ⓕ McDonald's, Ⓞ Ⓗ, Cuba Drug, Giant Foods
27 (84)	NY 16, NY 446, Hinsdale, N Ⓕ S Ⓖ, lodging
26 (79)	NY 16, Olean, S Ⓖ Sunoco, Ⓕ Burger King, Wendy's, Ⓞ Ⓗ
25 (77)	Buffalo St, Olean, S Ⓖ Citgo/dsl, Ⓞ Ⓗ, 2 mi S on Constitution N Ⓖ KwikFill, Ⓕ Applebee's, Burger King, Dunkin Donuts, Friendly's, McDonald's, Perkins, Pizza Hut, Ponderosa, Quizno's, Tim Horton, Ⓛ Best Western Comfort Inn, Country Inn, Knight's Inn, Microtel, Ⓞ Advance Parts, BJ's Whse/gas, $Tree, GNC, Home Depot Jo-Ann Fabrics, K-Mart, NAPA, Old Navy, Radio Shack,

Vertical left margin labels: **NY** **E** ↕ **W** **ELMIRA** **CORNING**

Vertical right margin labels: **BATH** **HORNELL** **OLEAN**

INTERSTATE 86 CONT'D (New York)

Exit	Services
25 (77)	Continued
	Tops Foods/gas, Walmart, St Bonaventure U
24 (74)	NY 417, Allegany, **1mi S** 🅰 Mobil/dsl, 🅾 to St Bonaventure U
73mm	**rest area wb, full** ♿ **facilities,** 🪑 **, litter barrels, petwalk**
23 (68)	US 219 S, **N** 🅰 Allegany Jct./Subway/dsl
66mm	Allegheny River
21 (61)	US 219 N, Salamanca, **S** 🍴 Red Garter Rest
20 (58)	NY 417, NY 353, Salamanca, **N** 🅰 Antone's Gas, Nafco Quickstop/Burger King/24hr, Seneca OneStop/dsl/24hr, VIP Gas, 🍴 McDonald's/24hr, 🏨 Holiday Inn Express, Westgate Motel, 🅾 AutoZone, Rail Museum, Seneca-Iroquis Museum, **S** casino
19 (54)	**S** 🅾 Allegany SP, Red House Area
18 (51)	NY 280, **S** 🅾 Allegany SP, Quaker Run Area
17 (48)	NY 394, Steamburg, **N** 🅰, 🅾 RV camping, **S** 🍴 M&M/dsl/rest., 🅾 camping
16 (42)	W Main St, Randolph, **N** 🅰 Mobil/dsl, 🍴 R&M Rest., 🅾 RV camping
41mm	**rest area eb,** 🚻 🪑 **, litter barrel**
15 (40)	School House Rd
39mm	**rest area wb,** 🚻 🪑 **, litter barrel**
14 (36)	US 62, Kennedy, **N** 🅰 Keystone Gas, 🍴 Office Pizza/Subs, **S** RV camping
32mm	Cassadaga Creek
13 (31)	NY 394, Falconer, **S** 🅰 Mobil/dsl, Sunoco, 🍴 Burger King, McDonald's, Tim Horton, Wendy's, 🏨 Budget Inn, Red Roof Inn, 🅾 CVS Drug, Sugar Creek Stores, Harley-Davidson
12 (28)	NY 60, Jamestown, **N** 🅰 KwikFill/deli/dsl, **S** 🅰 Mobil/McDonald's/dsl, 🍴 Bob Evans, 🏨 Comfort Inn, Hampton Inn, 🅾 Ⓗ, st police
11 (25)	to NY 430, Jamestown, **S** 🅰, dsl, 🍴 lodging
22mm	**welcome ctr/rest area eb, full** ♿ **facilities,** 🪑 **, litter barrels, petwalk, vending**
10 (21)	NY 430 W, Bemus Point
9 (20)	NY 430 E, **N** 🅰 Mobil, **S** 🅰, 🍴 lodging
19mm	Chautauqua Lake
8 (18)	NY 394, Mayville, **N** 🅰 Mobil/dsl, lodging, 🅾 RV camping
7 (15)	Panama
6 (9)	NY 76, Sherman, **N** 🅰 Keystone Gas, 🍴 Village Pizzeria, 🅾 NAPA, Sherman Drug, USPO
4 (1)	NY 430, Findley Lake, **N** 🏨 Holiday Inn Express, Peek'n Peak Motel, **S** 🅰, 🍴 lodging, 🅾 RV camping, to Peek'n Peak Ski Area
0mm	New York/Pennsylvania state line. **Exits 3-1 are in PA.**
3	PA 89, North East, Wattsburg, **N** 🅰, food
1 b a	I-90, W to Erie, E to Buffalo. I-86 begins/ends on I-90, exit 37.

INTERSTATE 87

Exit	Services
176mm	US/Canada Border, NY state line, I-87 begins/ends.
43 (175)	US 9, Champlain, **E** World Duty Free, **W** 🅰 Peterbilt Trkstp/deli/dsl/scales/24hr/@, 🅾 repair
42 (174)	US 11 S, to Rouse's Point, Champlain, **E** 🅰 Irving/dsl, 🍴 J-reck Subs, Pizza+, Subway, 🅾 Ace Hardware, Chevrolet (3mi), Kinney Drug, PriceChopper, Rite Aid,

Exit	Services
42 (174)	Continued
	USPO, **W** 🅰 Mobil/dsl, Valero, 🍴 Dunkin Donuts, McDonald's, Papa John's
41 (167)	NY 191, Chazy, **E** st police, **W** Miner Institute
162mm	**rest area both lanes, full** ♿ **facilities, info,** 🚻 🪑 **, litter barrels, petwalk**
40 (160)	NY 456, Beekmantown, **E** 🅰 Mobil/dsl, 🍴 Conroy's Organics, 🏨 Pt Auroche Lodge, Stonehelm Motel/café, **W** Twin Ells Camping
39 (158)	NY 314, Moffitt Rd, Plattsburgh Bay, **E** 🅰 Mobil/dsl, Stewarts, 🍴 A&W, Bill's Cafe, Dunkin Donuts, Gus' Rest, McDonald's, 🏨 Rip van Winkle Motel, Sundance Inn, Super 8, 🅾 Plattsburgh RV Park, to VT Ferry, **W** 🅾 Shady Oaks Camping, to Adirondacks
38 (154)	NY 22, NY 374, to Plattsburgh, **E** 🅰 Mobil/dsl, 🍴 Checker Hill Farm Cafe, 🅾 Kinney Drug
37 (153)	NY 3, Plattsburgh, **E** 🅰 Mobil/dsl, Stewarts, Sunoco, 🍴 Burger King, China Buffet, Domino's, Dunkin Donuts, Guiseppe's Pizza, Jade Buffet, KFC, Koto Japanese, Legends Cafe, Mangia Pizza, McDonald's, #1 Chinese, Panera Bread, Papa John's, Perkins, Pizza Hut, Quiznos, Starbucks, Subway, Taco Bell, Wendy's, 🏨 Comfort Inn, Holiday Inn, 🅾 Ⓗ, BigLots, Buick/Cadillac/GMC, Family$, Ford, Kinny Drug, Michael's, Petsmart, PriceChopper Foods, Radio Shack, Rite Aid, Sam's Club, Staples, TJ Maxx, TrueValue, Verizon, Walgreens, Walmart, vet, **W** 🅰 Mobil, Shell, Sunoco/Jreck Subs, 🍴 Anthony's Rest., Applebee's, Butcher Block Rest., Dunkin Donuts, Friendly's, Ground Round, Moe's SW Grill, 99 Rest., Uno, 🏨 Best Value Inn, Best Western, Days Inn, EconoLodge, Hampton Inn, La Quinta, Microtel, 🅾 Advance Parts, AT&T, AutoZone, Best Buy, Dick's, $Tree, Gander Mtn, Hannaford Foods, Harley-Davidson, Honda, JC Penney, Kinny Drug, K-Mart, Lowe's, Prays Mkt, Sears/auto, Suzuki, Target, vet
151mm	Saranac River
36 (150)	NY 22, Plattsburgh 🛬, **E** 🅰 Mobil/dsl/24hr, 🅾 U-Haul, st police, **E** 🅰 Shell/dsl, 🍴 Bluff Point Rest.
146mm	**truck insp sta both lanes, rest area nb full** ♿ **facilities,** 🪑 **, litter barrels,** 🚻 **petwalk**
35 (144)	NY 442, to Port Kent, Peru, **2-8 mi E** 🅾 Iroquois/Ausable Pines Camping, to VT Ferry, **W** 🅰 Mobil/Dunkin Donuts/Subway/dsl, Wilson Farms, 🍴 Cricket's Rest., McDonald's, Pasquale's Rest., 🅾 Auchuban Hardware, USPO, vet
143mm	emergency 🚻 at **2 mi** intervals begin sb/end nb
34 (137)	NY 9 N, Ausable Forks, **E** 🅰 Sunoco/dsl, 🍴 Pleasant Corner Rest., Mac's Drive-in, 🅾 vet, **W** 🅾 Prays Mkt, Ausable River RV Camping, auto repair
136mm	Ausable River

Side tab (left): S A L A M A N C A — E ↕ W — J A M E S T O W N — N ↕ S

Side tab (right): P L A T T S B U R G H

Map labels: Rock Stream, Reading Center, Burdett, Bath, Montour Falls, Beaver Dams, Savona, Thurston, Campbell, Rush Run, Painted Post, Gang Mills, Horseheads, Elmira, Lindley, Pine City, 86, NY

Tab: NY

INTERSTATE 87 CONT'D

Exit	Services
33 (135)	US 9, NY 22, to Willsboro, **E** ⛽/dsl, 🍴 lodging, RV camping, to Essex Ferry
125mm	N Boquet River
32 (124)	Lewis, **E** 🄾 RV Camping, **W** ⛽ Lukoil/dsl, 🍴 Trkstp Diner, 🄾 RV Camping, st police
123mm	**rest area sb, full 🄳 facilities, info, 🄲, 🄰, petwalk, rest area nb, no restrooms**
120mm	Boquet River
31 (117)	NY 9 N, to Elizabethtown, Westport, **E** ⛽ Mobil, 🏨 Hill-Top Motel, 🄾 RV camp/dump, **W** 🄾 🄷, st police, vet
111mm	**trk insp sta both lanes, rest area nb only, full 🄳 facilities, 🄲, 🄰, litter barrels, vending, petwalk**
30 (104)	US 9, NY 73, Keene Valley
99mm	**trk insp sta, rest area both lanes, full 🄳 facilities, 🄲, 🄰, litter barrels, petwalk**
29 (94)	N Hudson, **E** 🄾 Jellystone Camping, USPO, **W** Blue Ridge Falls Camping
28 (88)	NY 74 E, to Ticonderoga, Schroon Lake, **E** ⛽ Mt Severance Country Store, Sunoco/dsl, 🏨 Maple Leaf Motel, Schroon Lake B&B, 🄾 RV camp/dump, st police, services on US 9
83mm	**rest area both lanes, full 🄳 facilities, 🄲, 🄰, litter barrels, petwalk, vending**
27 (81)	US 9 (from nb, no EZ return), Schroon Lake, to ⛽/dsl, 🍴 lodging
26 (78)	US 9 (no EZ return), Pottersville, Schroon Lake, (from sb) **E** 🍴 Cafe Adirondack, 🏨 Lee's Corner Motel, 🄾 RV Camping, (from nb) **W** ⛽ Valero, 🍴 Black Bear Diner
25 (73)	NY 8, Chestertown, **E** ⛽ Crossroads Country Store, 🄾 Riverside Pines Camping **W** ⛽ Mobil/dsl
24 (67)	Bolton Landing, **E** RV camping
67mm	Schroon River
66mm	parking area sb, 🄰
64mm	parking area nb, 🄰
23 (58)	to US 9, Diamond Point, Warrensburg, **W** ⛽ Citgo/dsl, Cumberland, Mobil/Dunkin Donuts/e85, Stewarts, 🍴 Geroge Henry's Rest., Gino's Pizza, McDonald's, Subway, 🏨 Season's B&B, Super 8, 🄾 Family$, Family Mkt Foods, Ford, Central Adirondack Tr, Riverview Camping, Schroon River Camping (3mi), ski area
22 (54)	US 9, NY 9 N, to Diamond Pt, Lake George, **E on US 9** 🍴 Gino&Tony's, Guiseppe's Pizza, John Barleycorn, KFC, Mario's Italian, Monte Cristo's, Moose Tooth Grill, Paolini's, 🏨 Admiral Motel, Balsam Motel, Barberry Ct, Best Value Inn, Blue Moon Motel, Brookside Motel, EconoLodge, Georgian Lakeside Resort, Heritage Motel, Lake Crest Inn, Lake Motel, Lake George Inn, Lake Haven Motel, Marine Village Resort, Motel Montreal, Nordick's Motel, Oasis Motel, O'Sullivan's Motel, Park Lane Motel, 7 Dwarfs Motel, Sundowner Motel, Surfside Motel, multiple services, 🄾 PriceChopper Foods, same as 21, **W** parking area both lanes
21 (53)	NY 9 N, Lake Geo, Ft Wm Henry, **E on US 9** ⛽ Stewarts, Sunoco, Valero, 🍴 Adirondack Brewery, A&W, Barnsider BBQ, Dining Room, DJ's Cafe, Gourmet Subs, Howard Johnson's Rest., Jasper's Steaks, Lobster Pot, Mama Riso's Italian, McDonald's, Mezzaluna's, Pizza Hut, Smokey Joe's Grill, Sub City, 🏨 Best Western, Country Hearth Inn, Ft William Henry Inn, Hampton Inn,

Exit	Services
21 (53)	Continued Holiday Inn Resort, HollyTree Hotel, Lake Crest Hotel, Lakeview Hotel, Lincoln Log Motel, Marine Village Resort, Quality Inn, Travelodge, Tiki Hotel, Super 8, Villager Motel, Windsor Hotel, Wingate Inn, 🄾 Harley-Davidson, King Phillip/Lake George Camping (2mi), Rite Aid, USPO, city park, waterpark, multiple services, same as 22, **W** ⛽ Mobil/dsl/LP, 🏨 Kathy's Cottages
51mm	Adirondack Park
20 (49)	NY 149, to Ft Ann, **E N on US 9** ⛽ Mobil/Dunkin Donuts/dsl, Sunoco/dsl, 🍴 Frank's Pizza, Logjam Rest., Montcalm Rest., Olde Post Grille, 🏨 Clarion, Comfort Suites, Mohican Motel, Rodeway Inn, 🄾 Ledgeview RV Park (3mi), Factory Outlets/famous brands, st police, **E S on US 9** 🍴 Blue Moose Rest., Johnny Rocket's, 🏨 Country Inn&Suites, 🄾 6 Flags Funpark, waterpark
19 (47)	NY 254, Glens Falls, **E** ⛽ Getty, Hess, Mobil, Sunoco, 🍴 A&W/KFC, Burger King, Chicago Grill, Dunkin Donuts, 5 Guys Burgers, Friendly's, Gavano's, Golden Corral, LJ Silver, McDonald's, Moe's SW Grill, Mr B's Rest., Old China Buffet, Olive Garden, Outback Steaks, Panera Bread, Papa John's, Pizza Hut, Red Lobster, Silo Rest., Starbucks, Subway, Taco Bell, Wendy's, 🏨 Alpen Haus, Budget Inn, EconoLodge, Quality Inn, Red Roof Inn, Sleep Inn, 🄾 Ace Hardware, AT&T, AutoZone, Bon Ton, Firestone/auto, Goodyear, Home Depot, JC Penney, Jo-Ann Fabrics, PriceChopper Foods, Radio Shack, Rite Aid, Sears, Staples, Target, TJ Maxx, Verizon, Walmart, mall, **W** ⛽ Mobil/Dunkin Donuts/Subway/dsl, Stewarts, 🏨 Ramada/rest., st police
18 (45)	Glens Falls, **E** ⛽ Gulf/Subway/e-85, Hess/dsl/24hr, Sunoco, 🍴 Carl R's Café, Dunkin Donuts, Pizza Hut, Steve's Place Rest., 🏨 Best Inn, Queensbury Hotel, 🄾 🄷, CVS Drug, Hannaford Foods, Toyota/Scion, U-Haul, Walgreens, **W** ⛽ Stewarts, 🍴 McDonald's, 🄾 Super 8
43mm	**rest area both lanes, full 🄳 facilities, 🄰, litter barrels, 🄲, vending, petwalk**
42mm	Hudson River
17 (40)	US 9, S Glen Falls, **E** ⛽ Citgo/dsl, Gulf, Hess/Blimpie/Dunkin Donuts, Sunoco/dsl, Valero/Subway/dsl/24hr, 🍴 Fitzgerald's Steaks, 🏨 Budget Inn, Landmark Motel (1mi), Sara-Glen Motel, Town&Country Motel, 🄾 Adirondack RV Camp, Suzuki, auto/truck repair/transmissions, vet, **W** Moreau Lake SP
16 (36)	Ballard Rd, Wilton, **E** 🄾 Coldbrook Campsites, golf, **W** ⛽ Mobil, Stewart's, Sunoco/Scotty's Rest./dsl/scales/24hr, 🏨 Mt View Acres Motel, 🄾 Alpin Haus RV Ctr
15 (30)	NY 50, NY 29, Saratoga Springs, **E** ⛽ Hess/dsl, Sunoco, 🍴 Applebee's, Burger King, Chicago Grill, Chipotle Mexican, Denny's, Dunkin Donuts, 5 Guys Burgers, Friendly's, Giavanno's Pizza, Golden Corral, KFC/Taco Bell, McDonald's, Moe's SW Grill, 99 Rest., Osaka, Panera Bread, Ruby Tuesday, Subway, Sunny Wok, TGIFriday's, 🏨 Comfort Inn, 🄾 AT&T, Barnes&Noble, Best Buy, BJ's Whse, BonTon, Dick's, Ford, Hannaford Foods, Home Depot, JC Penney, Kohl's, Lowe's, Mazda, Old Navy, Petsmart, PriceChopper Foods, Rite Aid, Sears/auto, Staples, Subaru, Target, TJ Maxx, Toyota/Scion, Walgreens, Walmart, **W** 🏨 Residence Inn, 🄾 🄷
14 (38)	NY 9P, Schuylerville, **2 mi W** 🏨 Hampton Inn, Holiday Inn, 🄾 🄷, museum, racetrack
13 (25)	US 9, Saratoga Springs, **E** 🍴 Bentley's Rest., DeLucia's

Vertical side text: **N** ↕ **S** — **NY** — **LAKE GEORGE** — **GLENS FALLS** — **SARATOGA SPRINGS**

= gas = food = lodging = other

INTERSTATE 87 CONT'D

Exit	Services
13 (25)	**Continued**

Deli, Saratoga Pizza Place, Budget Inn, Locust Grove Motel, Maggiore's Motel, Nissan, Ballston Spa SP, **W** Mobil/Dunkin Donuts/dsl, Stewarts, Finish Line Rest., Hibachi Grill,, PJ's BBQ, Best Western, Hilton Garden (4mi), Roosevelt Inn/rest., Top Hill Hotel, Saratoga SP, vet

12 (21) NY 67, Malta, **E** Getty/dsl, Sunoco/dsl, Bentley's Rest., Dunkin Donuts, KFC, Malta Diner, McDonald's, Subway, Taco Bell, Cocca's Motel, Fairfield Inn, CVS Drug, GNC, PriceChopper Foods, Stewart's, Verizon, Saratoga NHP, st police, **W** Hyatt Place

11 (18) Round Lake Rd, Round Lake, **W** Gulf/dsl, Sunoco/dsl, Lake Ridge Rest., Mulligan's Rest., Rite Aid, Stewarts

10 (16) Ushers Rd, **E** Hess/Dunkin Donuts/dsl, Xtra/dsl, Ferretti's Rest., auto repair, **W** Stewarts

14mm **rest area nb, full facilities, info, , , litter barrels, vending, petwalk**

9 (13) NY 146, Clifton Park, **E** Hess/Dunkin Donuts/dsl, USA, Burger King, Caputo's Pizza, Chili's, Cracker Barrel, Giffy's BBQ, Harborhouse Fish Fry, Peddler's Grill, Red Robin, Snyder's Rest., Subway, Comfort Suites, Holiday Inn Express, Advance Parts, Aldi Foods, BigLots, Goodyear/auto, Home Depot, Kohl's, Lowe's, Michael's, NAPA, Rite Aid, Target, vet, **W** Mobil, Sunoco/dsl, Arizona Pizza, Bellini's Italian, Buffalo Wild Wings, Chipotle Mexican, Domino's, Dunkin Donuts, East Palace, East Wok, 5 Guys Burgers, Friendly's, IHOP, La Fiesta, LJ Silver/Taco Bell, McDonald's, Moe's SW Grill, 99 Rest., Outback Steaks, Panera Bread, Pasta Pane, Ruby Tuesday, Salad Creations, Shane's Rib Shack, Starbucks, Subway, TGIFriday's, Wendy's, Best Western, Hampton Inn, AT&T, Chevrolet, CVS Drug, $Tree, GNC, Hannaford Foods, JC Penney, Jo-Ann Fabrics, K-Mart, Marshall's, Petsmart, PriceChopper Foods, Staples, Toys-R-Us, Verizon, Walgreens, st police

8a (12) Grooms Rd, to Waterford

8 (10) Crescent, Vischer Ferry, **E** Hess/Blimpie/Godfather's/dsl/24hr, McDonald's, **W** Gulf/dsl, Sunoco, Pancho's Mexican, Tufan Pizza, CVS Drug, Stewarts

8mm Mohawk River

7 (7) NY 7, Troy, **E on US 9 N** Hess/dsl, Century House, Clarion, Holiday Inn Express, Ramada Inn, Sycamore Motel, Stay Inn, Acura, $General, Ford, Infiniti, Lexus, Lincoln/Mercury, Nissan, Rite Aid, Volvo, **E on US 9 S** Mobil, Dunkin Donuts, McDonald's, Red Robin, Subway, Hobby Lobby, Marshall's

6 (6) NY 2, to US 9, Schenectady, **E on US 9** Hess, Boston Mkt, Circle Diner, Dakota Steaks, Friendly's, KFC, Red Robin, Wendy's, Cocca's Inn, La Quinta, Travelodge, CVS Drug, JC Penney, Mavis Discount Tire, Lowe's, PriceChopper Foods, Toyota/Scion, same as 7, **E** Mobil, Applebee's, Chicago Grill, ChuckeCheese, Panera Bread, Starbucks, GNC, Hannaford Foods, Home Depot, Michael's, Petsmart, Sam's Club, Staples, VW, Walmart, **W** Mobil/dsl, Carrabba's, Chipotle Mexican, DiBella's Subs, Dunkin Donuts, Fillet 7, Friendly's, Kings Buffet, Ruby Tuesday, Subway,

6 (6) **Continued**

 Fairfield Inn, Microtel, Quality Inn, Super 8, Goodyear/auto, Target, TJ Maxx, Verizon

5 (5) NY 155 E, Latham, **E** DeeDee's Rest., Philly's Grill, Vintage Pizza, EconoLodge, USPO

4 (4) NY 155 W, Wolf Rd, **E on Wolf Rd** Hess/dsl, Mobil/Subway, Sunoco, Arby's, Buffalo Wagon, Burger King, Capital Buffet, Chipotle Mexican, CiCi's Pizza, Denny's, Dunkin Donuts, Macaroni Grill, Maurice's Subs, Maxie's Grill, McDonald's, Moe's SW Grill, 99 Rest., Olive Garden, Outback Steaks, Pizza Hut, Red Lobster, Reel Seafood Co, Starbucks, Ted's Fishfry, Wolfs 1-11, Wolf Rd Diner, Best Western, Courtyard, Hampton Inn, Holiday Inn, Homewood Suites, Marriott, Red Roof Inn, Chevrolet, CVS Drug, Hannfords Foods, Kia, Lincoln, **W** Bluestone Bistro, Koto Japanese, Desmond Hotel, Hotel Indigo, to Heritage Park

2 (2) NY 5, Central Ave, **E** Mobil/dsl, Sunoco, Wendy's, Cocca's Inn, Scottish Inn, SpringHill Suites, BJ's Whse, Jo-Ann Fabrics, Kost Tire, Marshall's, Lowe's, PetCo, Staples, Target, **E on Wolf Rd...** Mobil/Subway/dsl, Bucca Italian, Cheesecake Factory, Chili's, Dunkin Donuts, Emperor Chinese, Friendly's, Honeybaked Ham, Hooters, IHOP, LJ Silver/Taco Bell, Panera Bread, PF Chang's, Starbucks, Days Inn, Travelodge, Barnes&Noble, Firestone/auto, Goodyear/auto, LL Bean, Macy's, Sears/auto, mall, **W** Gulf/dsl, Mobil, Blue Spice Thai, Central Steak, Delmonico's Steaks, Domino's, Dunkin Donuts, La Fiesta, McDonald's, Moe's SW Grill, Mr Subb, Smokey Bones BBQ, Subway, Truman's Grill, Wendy's, Baymont Inn, EconoLodge, Green Park Inn, Howard Johnson, Motel 6, Quality Inn, Super 8, Advance Parts, AT&T, Buick/GMC, Cadillac, Krause's Candy, PepBoys, Subaru, Verizon

1W (1) NY State Thruway (from sb), I-87 S to NYC, I-90 W to Buffalo

1E (1) I-90 E (from sb), to Albany, Boston

1S (1) to US 20, Western Ave, **E on US 20** Getty, Burger King, Chipotle Mexican, Coldstone, Creo, Dunkin Donuts, 5 Guys Burgers, 99 Rest., Starbucks, TGIFriday's, Best Western, Days Inn, Holiday Inn Express, other AT&T, CVS Drug, Verizon, **W on US 20** Mobil/Subway, USA, Capital City Diner, Chicago Grill, Friendly's, Hana Grill, Ichyban Japanese, McDonald's, Starbucks, Adirondack Tires, Best Buy, Dick's, Home Depot, JC Penney, Macy's, Michael's, Old Navy, Petsmart, PriceChopper Foods, Walmart, mall, USPO, vet

1N (1) I-87 N (from nb), to Plattsburgh

NY State Thruway goes west to Buffalo (I-90), S to NYC (I-87), I-87 N to Montreal

ALBANY

NY

■ = gas ⑪ = food ⌂ = lodging ⊙ = other   Copyright 2011 - The Next Exit®

INTERSTATE 87 CONT'D

Exit	Services
24 (148)	I-90 and I-87 N
23 (142)	I-787, to Albany, US 9 W, **E on US 9 W** ■ Cumberland Farms/Dunkin Donuts/dsl, Sunoco/dsl, ⌂ Comfort Inn, Regency Inn, ⊙ transmissions, to Knickerbocker Arena, **W** ■ Stewarts, ⌂ EconoLodge
139mm	**parking area sb, ⓒ, ㋐, litter barrel**
22 (135)	NY 396, to Selkirk
21a (134)	I-90 E, to MA Tpk, Boston
127mm	**New Balimtore Travel Plaza both lanes,** Mobil/dsl, Famous Famiglia, Quiznos, Roy Rogers, Starbucks, TCBY, atm, info, wi-fi
21b (124)	US 9 W, NY 81, to Coxsackie, **W** ■ Trvl Plaza/Citgo/rest./dsl/scales/24hr, Sunoco/dsl, ⑪ McDonald's (5mi), ⌂ Best Western, Budget Inn, Holiday Inn Express, Red Carpet Inn, ⊙ Boat'n RV Whse, repair, vet
21 (114)	NY 23, Catskill, **E** ■ Mobil, Sunoco/dsl, ⌂ Catskill Motel/rest. (2mi), Pelokes Motel (2mi), Quality Inn, ⊙ Home Depot, transmissions, visitors ctr, to Rip van Winkle Br, **W** ⑪ Anthony's Rest, Koch's Rest., Southside Rest., ⌂ Astoria Motel, Budget Inn (3mi), Rip Van Winkle Motel, ⊙ to Hunter Mtn/Windham Ski Areas
103mm	**Malden Service Area nb,** Mobil/dsl, Carvel Ice Cream, Hotdogs, McDonald's, atm, ⓒ, parking area sb
20 (102)	NY 32, to Saugerties, **E** ■ Citgo, Mobil/dsl, Stewarts, Sunoco, ⑪ Dunkin Donuts, Emiliani Italian, Giordano's Pizza, McDonald's, Pizza Star, Starway Café, Subway, ⊙ CarQuest, Chrysler/Dodge/Jeep, Curves, CVS Drug, Family$, NAPA, PriceChopper Foods, vet, **W** ■ Hess/Blimpie/Dunkin Donuts/dsl, Sunoco/dsl, ⑪ Johnny G's Diner, Land&Sea Grill, ⌂ Comfort Inn, Howard Johnson/rest., ⊙ Blue Mtn Campground (5mi), Brookside Campground (10mi), KOA (2mi), Rip Van Winkle Campground (3mi), to Catskills
99mm	**parking area nb, ⓒ, ㋐, litter barrels**
96mm	**Ulster Travel Plaza sb,** Sunoco/dsl, Arthur Treacher's Fish&Chips, Nathan's, Pizza Hut, Roy Rogers, Starbucks, TCBY, atm, ⓒ, wi-fi
19 (91)	NY 28, Rhinecliff Br, Kingston, **E** ■ Mobil, QuickChek/dsl, ⑪ Blimpie, Friendly's, Olympic Diner, Picnic Pizza, ⌂ Holiday Inn, Super 8, ⊙ Advance Parts, CVS Drug, Hannaford Foods, Radio Shack, Walgreens, access to I-587 E, **W** ⑪ Family Diner, Lorenzo's Pizza, Roudigan's Steaks, Skytop Steaks, ⌂ Motel 19, Quality Inn, Rodeway Inn, SuperLodge, ⊙ Camper's Barn RV Ctr, Ford, Nissan, access to US 209
18 (76)	NY 299, to Poughkeepsie, New Paltz, **E** ■ Cumberland Farms, Mobil, Shell/dsl, ⑪ College Diner, Genesis Rest., Village Grill, ⌂ EconoLodge, 87 Motel, ⊙ repair, to Mid-Hudson Br, **W** ■ Sunoco, ⑪ Burger King, Dunkin Donuts, Gabaletos Sea ⑪ McDonald's, Pasquale's Pizza, Plaza Diner, Rino's Pizza, Rococo's Pizza, Subway, TCBY, ⌂ Super 8, ⊙ Advance Parts, AT&T, Midas, Radio Shack, Rite Aid, ShopRite Foods, Stop'n Shop, Jellystone (9mi), KOA (10mi), vet
66mm	**Modena service area sb,** ■ Sunoco/dsl, ⑪ Carvel's Ice Cream, Chicago Grill, McDonald's, Moe's SW Grill, ⊙ atm, UPS, wi-fi
65mm	**Plattekill Travel Plaza nb,** ■ Sunoco/dsl, ⑪ Nathan's, Roy Rogers, Starbucks, ⊙ atm, info, wi-fi

NY

N ↑↓ S

NEWBURGH

17 (60)	I-84, NY 17K, to Newburgh, **E on NY 300 N** ■ Mobil, ⑪ DQ, Dunkin Donuts, Green Olive Grill, Joe's Deli, King Buffet, McDonald's, Newburgh Buffet, Old Town Buffet, Perkins, Subway, Taco Bell, Wendy's, ⊙ AT&T, AutoZone, BonTon, $Tree, Marshall's, Mavis Tire, Midas, Office Depot, Old Navy, Radio Shack, Sears/auto, Stop&Shop, mall, **E on NY 300 S** ■ Getty, Hess/dsl, Sunoco/dsl, ⑪ Applebee's, Burger King, Chili's, Cosimos Ristorante, Denny's, Gateway Diner, Johnny D's Diner, Longhorn Steaks, Neptune Diner, Panera Bread, Sonic, Steak&Stein, Subway, TGIFriday's, Union Sq Rest., ⌂ Days Inn, Hampton Inn, Howard Johnson, Knights Inn, Ramada Inn, Super 8, ⊙ Adam's Food Mkt, Aldi Foods, Barnes&Noble, Buick/GMC, Cadillac/Chevrolet, Chrysler/Dodge/Jeep, Ford/Lincoln/Mercury, Home Depot, Honda, Kohl's, Lowe's, Michael's, Nissan, Petsmart, Target, Verizon, Walmart/McDonald's, **W on NY 17K** ⌂ Hilton Garden
16 (45)	US 6, NY 17, to West Point, Harriman, **W** ■ Gulf/dsl, ⑪ Applebee's, Chicago Grill, Chili's, Dunkin Donuts, KFC, Outback Steaks, Taco Bell, TGIFriday's, Wendy's, ⌂ American Budget Inn, Hampton Inn, ⊙ Best Buy, BJ's Whse, BMW, $Tree, GNC, Home Depot, Kohl's, Petsmart, Radio Shack, Staples, Target, TJ Maxx, Walmart/Subway (1mi), Woodbury Outlet/famous brands, st police
34mm	**Ramapo Service Area sb,** ■ Sunoco/dsl, ⑪ Carvel, McDonald's, Uno Pizza, ⊙ atm, wi-fi
33mm	**Sloatsburg Travel Plaza nb,** ■ Sunoco/dsl, ⑪ Burger King, Dunkin Donuts, Quiznos, Sbarro's, ⊙ atm, gifts, info
15a (31)	NY 17 N, NY 59, Sloatsburg
15 (30)	**I-287 S, NY 17 S, to NJ. I-87 S & I-287 E run together.**
14b (27)	Airmont Rd, Montebello, **E** ⌂ Crowne Plaza, **W on NY9** ■ Gulf/Dunkin Donuts/dsl, ⑪ Airmont Diner, Applebee's, Bagel Boys Cafe, Friendly's, Pasta Cucina, Starbucks, Subway, Sutter's Mill Rest., Water Wheel Cafe, ⌂ Howard Johnson, ⊙ Ⓗ, DrugMart, ShopRite Foods, Tall Man Tires, Walgreens, Walmart, vet
14a (23)	Garden State Pkwy, to NJ, Chestnut Ridge
14 (22)	NY 59, Spring Valley, Nanuet, **E** ■ Citgo/dsl, Shell/dsl, Valero/dsl, ⑪ Burger King, Deliziosa Pizza, IHOP, McDonald's, Planet Wings, ⌂ Fairfield Inn, ⊙ BMW/Ferrari, CarQuest, Maserati, Michael's, Target, TJ Maxx, Verizon, **W** ■ Citgo, Gulf, ⑪ Baskin-Robbins/Dunkin Donuts, ChuckeCheese, Franko's Pizza, KFC, Nanuet Diner, Panera Bread, Red Lobster, Starbucks, Taco Bell, White Castle, ⌂ Days Inn, Hampton Inn, Hilton Garden, ⊙ AT&T, Barnes&Noble, $Tree, Home Depot, Hyundai, Macy's, Marshall's, PetCo, Sears/auto, Staples, Stop&Shop Foods, Verizon, transmissions

NYACK

13 (20)	Palisades Pkwy, N to Bear Mtn, S to NJ
12 (19)	NY 303, Palisades Ctr Dr, W Nyack, **W** ■ Mobil, ⑪ Cheesecake Factory, Dunkin Donuts, Tony Roma's, ⌂ Nyack Motel, ⊙ Barnes&Noble, Best Buy, BJ's Whse, Dave&Buster's, Macy's, Home Depot, JC Penney, Lord&Taylor, Old Navy, Staples, ShopRite Foods, STS Tires, Target, mall
11 (18)	US 9W, to Nyack, **E** ■ Gulf, Mobil, Shell, ⌂ Best Western, **W** ■ Shell/dsl, ⑪ Dunkin Donuts, McDonald's, ⌂ Super 8, ⊙ Ⓗ, J&L Repair/tire, Old World Food Mkt
10 (17)	Nyack (from nb), same as 11
14mm	Tappan Zee Br, Hudson River
13mm	toll plaza

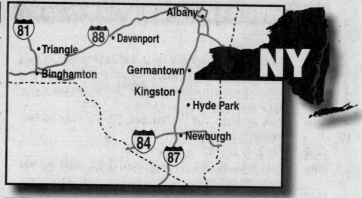

INTERSTATE 87 CONT'D

Exit	Services
9 (12)	to US 9, to Tarrytown, **E** 📷 Hess/dsl, ⊙ Stop&Shop, **W** 📷 Mobil, 🍴 El Dorado West Diner, 🛏 DoubleTree Hotel, ⊙ Honda, Mavis Tire
8 (11)	I-287 E, to Saw Mill Pkwy, White Plains, **E** 🛏 Hampton Inn, Marriott
7a (10)	Saw Mill River Pkwy S, to Saw Mill River SP, Taconic SP
7 (8)	NY 9A (from nb), Ardsley, **W** 🛏 Ardsley Acres Motel, ⊙ Ⓗ
6mm	**Ardsley Travel Plaza nb**, Sunoco/dsl, Burger King, Popeye's, vending
5.5mm	toll plaza, (📞)
6ba (5)	Stew Leonard Dr, to Ridge Hill, **W** ⊙ Costco, Home Depot, Stew Leonard's Farmfresh Foods
6 (4.5)	Tuckahoe Dr, Yonkers, **E** 📷 Getty/repair, 🍴 Marcellino's Pizza, McDonald's, Subway, 🛏 Tuckahoe Motel, ⊙ ShopRite Foods/drug, **W** 📷 Gulf, Mobil/dsl, 🍴 Domino's, Dunkin Donuts, Kim Wei Chinese, 🛏 Ramada Inn, Royal Regency Hotel
5 (4.3)	NY 100 N (from nb), Central Park Ave, White Plains
4 (4)	Cross Country Pkwy, Mile Sq Rd, **E** 📷 Lukoil, ⊙ Ford/Lincoln/Subaru, Macy's, Marshll's, Sears/auto, TJ Maxx, **W** 📷 Getty, Shell/Dunkin Donuts/dsl, 🍴 Burger King, ⊙ Chevrolet, Mavis Tire
3 (3)	Mile Square Rd, **E** ⊙ GNC, Stop&Shop, Thriftway Drug, mall, **W** 📷 Getty, Shell
2 (2)	Yonkers Ave (from nb), Westchester Fair, **E** 📷 Mobil, ⊙ Yonkers Speedway
1 (1)	Hall Place, McLean Ave, **E** ⊙ A&P Foods/Subway, 🍴 Dunkin Donuts
0mm	New York St Thruway and I-87 N run together to Albany
14 (11)	McLean Ave, **E** 📷 A&P/dsl, 🍴 Dunkin Donuts, Subway
13 (10)	E 233rd, NE Tollway **service plaza both lanes**/Mobil
12 (9.5)	Hudson Pkwy (from nb), Sawmill Pkwy
11 (9)	Van Cortlandt Pk S
10 (8.5)	W 230th St (from sb), W 240th (from nb), **E** 📷 Lukoil, **W** 📷 Getty, 🍴 Dunkin Donuts, ⊙ Ⓗ, Marshall's, Target
9 (8)	W Fordham Rd, **E** 📷 BP/dsl, 🍴 Dallas BBQ, ⊙ Ⓗ
8 (7)	W 179th (from nb), **W** Roberto Clemente SP
7 (6)	I-95, US 1, S to Trenton, NJ, N to New Haven, CT
6 (5)	E 153rd t, River Ave, Stadium Rd, **E** ⊙ Yankee Stadium
5 (5)	E 161st, Macombs Dam Br, (exit 4 from nb), **E** ⊙ AT&T, Best Buy, Michael's, Target, Yankee Stadium
3 (3)	E 138th St, Madison Ave Br, **E** 📷 BP/dsl
2 (2)	Willis Ave, 3rd Ave Br, **E** 📷 Mobil/dsl, **W** 🍴 McDonald's
1 (1)	Brook Ave, Hunts Point, **E** 📷 BP, Hess
0mm	I-87 begins/ends on I-278.

INTERSTATE 88 (New York)

Exit	Services
25a	I-90/NY Thruway. I-88 begins/ends on I-90, exit 25a.
117mm	toll booth (to enter or exit NY Thruway)
25 (116)	NY 7, to Rotterdam, Schenectady, **S** 📷 Citgo/Friendly's/Dunkin Donuts/dsl/24hr, **3 mi S** 📷 Gulf, 🍴 Burger King, McDonald's, Top's Diner, 🛏 L&M Motel, Rotterdam Motel, ⊙ Frosty Acres Camping
24 (112)	US 20, NY 7, to Duanesburg, **N** 📷 Mobil, Stewarts, 🍴 Dunkin Donuts, ⊙ st police, **S** 🍴 Duanesburg Diner, ⊙ USPO
23 (101)	NY 30, to Schoharie, Central Bridge, **N** 🛏 Holiday

Exit	Services
23 (101)	Continued Motel, ⊙ Hideaway Camping, Locust Park Camping, **S** 📷 Mobil/Subway/dsl, 🍴 Dunkin Donuts, 🛏 Holiday Inn Express, Hyland House B&B (2mi), Parrott House 1870 Inn (4mi), Wedgewood B&B (2mi)
22 (95)	NY 7, NY 145, to Cobleskill, Middleburgh, **2-5 mi N** 📷 Hess/dsl, Mobil, 🍴 Dunkin Donuts, Pizza Hut, Subway, 🛏 Colonial CT Motel, Holiday Inn Express, Holiday Motel, Super 8, ⊙ Ⓗ, Advance Parts, Buick/Chevrolet/GMC, Chrysler/Dodge/Jeep, $General, $Tree, Ford, Howe Caverns Camping, PriceChopper Foods, Walmart, to Howe Caverns, **S** ⊙ Twin Oaks Camping, st police
21 (90)	NY 7, NY 10, to Cobleskill, Warnerville, **2-3 mi N** 📷 Hess, Mobil/dsl, 🍴 Arby's, Burger King, Dairy Deli, KFC/Taco Bell, McDonald's, Pizza Hut, Red Apple Rest., 🛏 Bast Western, Gables B&B, ⊙ Ⓗ, Ace Hardware, CarQuest, PriceChopper Foods, Walmart/24hr
20 (87)	NY 7, NY 10, to Richmondville, **S** 📷 Mobil/dsl/24hr, Sunoco, 🍴 Reinhardt's Deli, Sub Express, 🛏 Rodeway Inn, ⊙ USPO
79mm	**rest area wb, full ♿ facilities**, (📞), **vending**, 🚮, **litter barrels, petwalk**
19 (76)	to NY 7, Worcester, **N** 📷 Stewarts, Sunoco/dsl
73mm	**rest area eb, full ♿ facilities**, (📞), **vending**, 🚮, **litter barrels, petwalk**
18 (71)	to Schenevus, **N** 📷 Citgo, 🍴 Schenevus Rest.
17 (61)	NY 7, to NY 28 N, Colliersville, Cooperstown, **2 mi N** 📷 Mobil/dsl, 🍴 La Teranella, 🛏 Amber Life Motel, Best Western (14mi), Knott's Motel, Redwood Motel, ⊙ to Baseball Hall of Fame
16 (59)	NY 7, to Emmons, **N** 🍴 Arby's, Brooks BBQ, Farmhouse Rest., Morey's Rest., Perrucci's Pizza, Pizza Hut, Sonny's Pizza, 🛏 Rainbow Inn, ⊙ PriceChopper Foods, Rite Aid
15 (56)	NY 28, NY 23, Oneonta, **N** 📷 Citgo, Hess, KwikFill, 🍴 Friendly's, KFC, 🛏 Clarion, Townhouse Inn, ⊙ Ⓗ, Advance Parts, to Soccer Hall of Fame, **S** 📷 Citgo, Hess, 🍴 Applebees, Burger King, Denny's, LJ Silver/Taco Bell, McDonald's, Neptune Diner/24hr, Quizno's, Sabatini's Italian, Subway, Wendy's, 🛏 Budget Inn, Christopher's Lodge/rest., Holiday Inn, Sun Lodge, Super 8, ⊙ Aldi Foods, Beaver Spring Camping, BJ's Whse/gas, $Tree, Hannaford Foods, Home Depot, JC Penney, Kost Tire, NAPA, Steve&Barry's, Walmart/24hr
14 (55)	Main St (from eb), Oneonta, **N** 📷 Citgo, Kwikfill, Stewarts, Sunoco, 🍴 Alfresco's Italian, ⊙ CVS Drug, **S** 🍴 Denny's, McDonald's
13 (53)	NY 205, **1-2 mi N** 📷 Citgo, Hess, Mobil, 🍴 Burger King, China Buffet King, DQ, Dunkin Donuts, McDonald's, Ponderosa, 🛏 Celtic Motel, Hampton Inn, Maple Terrace

NYC AREA

N ↕ S

COBLESKILL

ONEONTA

NY

🅖 = gas 🍽 = food 🛏 = lodging 🄾 = other Copyright 2011 - The Next Exit®

INTERSTATE 88 CONT'D (New York)

Exit	Services
13 (53)	Continued Motel, Oasis Motor Inn, 🄾 Buick/Cadillac/GMC, Chevrolet, Chrysler/Jeep, Honda, Nissan, Parts+, Rite Aid, to Susquehanna Tr, Gilbert Lake SP (11mi), camping
12 (47)	NY 7, to Otego, S 🅖 Citgo/dsl/cafe, Lukoil
43mm	**rest area wb, full** 🚻 **facilities,** 🅲, 🎪, **litter barrels, vending, petwalk**
11 (40)	NY 357, to Unadilla, Delhi, N KOA
39mm	**rest area eb, full** 🚻 **facilities,** 🅲, 🎪, **litter barrels, vending, petwalk**
10 (38)	NY 7, to Unadilla, **2 mi** N 🅖 Apple Gas, 🛏 Country Motel (4mi), 🄾 Great American Foods, USPO, st police
9 (33)	NY 8, to Sidney, N 🅖 Citgo/QuickWay/dsl, Hess/dsl, Mobil/dsl, 🍽 China Buffet, McDonald's, Pizza Hut, Subway, 🛏 Algonkin Motel, Country Motel, Super 8, 🄾 🄷, Advance Parts, $General, K-Mart/Little Caesar's, PriceChopper Foods, Tall Pines Camping, USPO
8 (29)	NY 206, to Bainbridge, N 🅖 Citgo, Sunoco/Taco Xtra/dsl/24hr, 🍽 Bob's Family Diner, 🛏 Algonkin Motel, 🄾 Chevrolet/GMC, Riverside RV Park, Parts+, USPO, to Oquage Creek Park
7 (22)	NY 41, to Afton, **1-2 mi** N 🅖 Mobil/24hr, Sunoco/dsl, Xtra, 🍽 RiverClub Rest., Vincent's Rest., 🄾 Afton Golf/rest., Echo Lake Park, Kellystone Park, Smith-Hale HS
6 (16)	NY 79, to NY 7, Harpursville, Ninevah, N 🍽 Gramma's Country Cafe, S 🅖 Citgo/Quickway/dsl, 🄾 USPO, to Nathanial Cole Park
5 (12)	Martin Hill Rd, to Belden, N 🄾 Belden Manor Camping
4 (8)	NY 7, to Sanitaria Springs, S 🅖 Hess/dsl
3 (4)	NY 369, Port Crane, N to Chenango Valley SP, S 🅖 Fastrac/dsl, KwikFill
2 (2)	NY 12a W, to Chenango Bridge, N 🅖 Mirabito, 🄾 Red&White Foods, USPO
1 (1)	NY 7 W (no wb return), to Binghamton
0mm	I-81, N to Syracuse, S to Binghamton. I-88 begins/ends on I-81.

INTERSTATE 90

Exit	Services
B24.5mm	New York/Massachusetts state line
B3 (B23)	NY 22, to Austerlitz, New Lebanon, W Stockbridge, N 🅖 Citgo/dsl/scales/24hr, S 🅖 Sunoco/dsl, 🛏 Berkshire Travel Lodge, 🄾 Woodland Hills Camp
B18mm	toll plaza, 🅲
B2 (B15)	NY 295, Taconic Pkwy, **1-2 mi** S 🅖
B1 (B7)	US 9, NY Thruway W, to I-87, toll booth, 🅲
12 (20)	US 9, to Hudson, N 🅖 🏪/dsl/scales/24hr, **0-3 mi** S 🄾 to Van Buren NHS
18.5mm	**rest area/weigh sta wb, full** 🚻 **facilities,** 🅲, 🎪, **litter barrels, vending, petwalk**
11 (15)	US 9, US 20, E Greenbush, Nassau, N 🅖 Citgo/Subway/dsl, Hess/dsl, 🍽 Dunkin Donuts, 🄾 st police, S 🅖 Mobil (2mi), Stewarts, 🍽 Burger King, Goomba's Pizza, Lighthouse Rest., Mercato's, My Place Rest., 🛏 Host Field Inn, Knights Inn, 🄾 Rite Aid, USPO, repair, vet
10 (10)	Miller Rd, to E Greenbush, S 🅖 Mobil/dsl, 🛏 Comfort Inn, **1-3 mi** S 🅖 Stewarts, 🍽 Dunkin Donuts, My Place Rest., Pizza Hut
9 (9)	US 4, to Rensselaer, Troy, N 🅖 Mobil, 🍽 Applebee's, Domino's, Dunkin Donuts, 5 Guys Burgers, McDonald's,

9 (9)	Continued OffShore Pier Rest., Panera Bread, Starbucks, Subway, The Sports Grill, 🛏 Holiday Inn Express, Residence Inn, 🄾 $Tree, Home Depot, PetsMart, Radio Shack, Staples, Target, Walmart, S 🅖 Mobil/dsl, Stewart's, 🍽 Cracker Barrel, Denny's, Dunkin Donuts, 🄾 Fairfield Inn
8 (8)	NY 43, Defreestville
7 (7)	Washington Ave (from eb), Rensselaer
6.5mm	Hudson River
6a	I-787, to Albany
6 (4.5)	US 9, Northern Blvd, to Loudonville, N 🅖 Stewarts, 🍽 Mr Subb, NY Pizza, Ta-Ke Japanese, 🛏 Red Carpet Inn, 🄾 🄷
5a (4)	Corporate Woods Blvd
5 (3.5)	Everett Rd, to NY 5, **S on NY 5, Central Ave** 🅖 Hess/dsl, Mobil, 🍽 Bob&Ron's Fishfry, Chinese Buffet, Friendly's, Gateway Diner, McDonald's, Popeye's, Quiznos, Subway, 🄾 🄷, Advance Parts, Chevrolet, Chrysler/Jeep, CVS Drug, Dodge, $Shop, Ford, Hannaford's Foods/24hr, Home Depot, Honda, Hyundai, Mavis Tire, Mazda, Nissan, PepBoys, PriceChopper Foods, Radio Shack, Rite Aid, Suzuki
4 (3)	NY 85 S, to Slingerlands
3 (2.5)	State Offices
2 (2)	Fuller Rd, Washington Ave, S 🅖 Sunoco, 🍽 Dunkin Donuts, 🛏 Courtyard, CrestHill Suites, Extended Stay America, Fairfield Inn, Hilton Garden, Red Carpet Inn, TownePlace Inn, same as 1S
1N (1)	I-87 N, to Montreal, to Albany 🛏
1S (1)	US 20, Western Ave, S 🅖 Mobil, 🍽 Burger King, Dunkin Donuts, 5 Guys Burgers, Friendly's, Hana Grill, Ichyban Japanese, McDonald's, Metro 20 Diner, Moe's SW Grill, 99 Rest., Panera Bread, Side Door Cafe, Starbucks, TGI-Friday's, Uno Grill, Wendy's, 🛏 Holiday Inn Express, 🄾 Best Buy, Dick's, Home Depot, JC Penney, Macy's, Michael's, Old Navy, PetsMart, PriceChopper Foods, Walmart, mall, USPO, vet
24 (149)	I-87 N, to Albany, Montreal, S to NYC
153mm	**Guilderland Service Area eb,** Mobil/dsl, McDonald's
25 (154)	I-890, NY 7, NY 146, to Schenectady
25a (159)	I-88 S, NY 7, to Binghamton
26 (162)	I-890, NY 5 S, Schenectady
168mm	**Pattersonville Service Area wb,** Mobil/dsl, Big Boy, Famous Famiglia, Quiznos, Roy Rogers, Starbucks, TCBY, atm, fax, gifts, info, UPS
172mm	**Mohawk Service Area eb,** Mobil/dsl, McDonald's
27 (174)	NY 30, Amsterdam, N 🅖 Mobil/dsl, Valero, 🛏 Super 8/diner/24hr, Valleyview Motel, **1 mi** N 🛏 Best Value Inn, 🄾 Camping World RV Ctr (3mi)
28 (182)	NY 30A, Fonda, N 🅖 Citgo/dsl/rest./motel/24hr, Lukoil, Mobil (1mi), TA/dsl/rest/motel/scales/24hr/@, 🍽 Dunkin Donuts, McDonald's, 🛏 EconoLodge, Riverside Motel, 🄾 🄷, st police, truck repair
184mm	**parking area both lanes,** 🅲, **litter barrels**
29 (194)	NY 10, Canajoharie, N 🅖 Gulf, Stewarts, 🍽 McDonald's, Subway, 🄾 Ace Hardware, $General, Rite Aid, USPO, S 🅖 Lukoil/dsl, Petro USA/dsl, Sunoco, 🍽 Joey D's Sea 🍽 🛏 Rodeway Inn, 🄾 NAPACare, USPO
210mm	**Indian Castle Service area eb** 🅖 Mobil/dsl, 🍽 Hershey's Ice Cream, Roy Rogers, Starbucks, 🄾 atm, gifts UPS. **Iroquois Service Area wb** 🅖 Mobil/dsl, Burger King, Dunkin Donuts, Freshen's Treats, gifts, UPS

NY

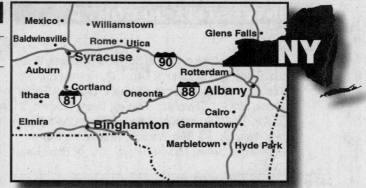

INTERSTATE 90 CONT'D

Exit	Services
29a (211)	NY 169, to Little Falls, N 🛏 Knights Inn (3mi), ⊙ H, to Herkimer Home
30 (220)	NY 28, to Mohawk, Herkimer, N ⛽ FasTrac/dsl, Mobil/Subway/dsl, Stewarts, 🍴 Applebee's, Burger King, Denny's, Dunkin Donuts, KFC/Taco Bell, McDonald's, Pizza Hut, Tony's Pizzaria, Vinny's Pizza, 🛏 Best Inn, Budget Motel, Herkimer Motel, ⊙ Advance Parts, Aubuchon Hardware, AutoZone, $General, $Tree, Goodyear, Rite Aid, Verizon, Walmart, S ⛽ FasTrac, 🍴 Little Caesars, Red Apple Chinese, 🛏 Red Carpet Inn (2mi), ⊙ Factory Depot, Family$, to Cooperstown (Baseball Hall of Fame)
227mm	**Schuyler Service Area wb**, Mobil/dsl, Breyer's, Fresh Fudge, McDonald's, atm, st police
31 (233)	I-790, NY 8, NY 12, to Utica, N ⛽ Citgo/dsl, Fastrac, Sunoco, 🍴 Burger King, Franco's Pizza, Good Friend Chinese, ⊙ BigLots, Curves, $Tree, PriceChopper Foods, Rite Aid, **1 mi N on frontage rd** 🍴 Applebees, ⊙ BJ's Whse/gas, Lowe's, Walmart/McDonald's, S ⛽ Hess/dsl, 🍴 Babe's Grill, Delmonico's Steaks, Denny's, Dunkin Donuts, Friendly's, Knock-Out Pizza, McDonald's, Pizza Hut, Romeo's Italian, Subway, Taco Bell, Wendy's, 🛏 Best Western, Days Inn, Hampton Inn, Happy Journey Motel, Red Roof Inn, Scottish Inn, Super 8, ⊙ AT&T
236mm	I-790 (from eb), to Utica
237.5mm	Erie Canal
238mm	Mohawk River
32 (243)	NY 232, Westmoreland, N 🛏 Quality Inn, Ramada Inn, Red Carpet Inn, **1 mi S** ⛽/dsl, **4-8 mi S** 🛏 Carriage House Motel, EconoLodge, Pinecrest Motel, Quality Inn, Ramada Inn, Red Carpet Inn
244mm	**Oneida Service Area eb**, Sunoco/dsl, Burger King, Sbarro's, Starbucks, atm, gifts
250mm	**parking area eb**, ♿, ⛽, litter barrel
33 (253)	NY 365, to Vernon Downs, Verona, N ⛽ SavOn Gas/dsl, 🍴 Joel's Frontyard Steaks, 🛏 EconoLodge (8mi), Inn at Turning Stone, Quality Inn (9mi), S ⛽ SavOn Gas/LP/repair, 🍴 Dunkin Donuts, Recovery Grill, 🛏 Fairfield Inn, ⊙ H, Turning Stone Casino
256mm	**parking area wb**, ♿, ⛽, litter barrel
34 (262)	NY 13, to Canastota, S ⛽ KwikFill, SavOn/dsl/24hr, Sunoco, 🍴 Dunkin Donuts, McDonald's, 🛏 Days Inn, Graziano Motel/rest., ⊙ Boxing Hall of Fame, Verona Beach SP Camping
266mm	**Chittenango Service Area wb**, Sunoco/dsl, Dunkin Donuts, Sbarro's, Starbucks atm, gifts
34a (277)	I-481, to Syracuse, Chittenango
35 (279)	NY 298, The Circle, Syracuse, S ⛽ Mobil, Valero/dsl, 🍴 Burger King, Denny's, Dunkin Donuts, East Wok, Green Onion Rest., Grimaldi's, Joey's Italian, Jreck Subs, Justin's Grill, McDonald's, Ruby Tuesday, Weigh Lock Cafe, 🛏 Candlewood Suites, Comfort Inn, Courtyard, Cresthill Suites, Days Inn, Doubletree Inn, Embassy Suites, Extended Stay America, Hampton Inn, Hilton Garden, Holiday Inn, John Milton Inn, Microtel, Motel 6, Quality Inn, Ramada Ltd, Red Roof Inn, Residence Inn, Super 8, ⊙ Goodyear/auto
280mm	**Dewitt Service Area eb**, Sunoco/dsl, McDonald's, ice cream
36 (283)	I-81, N to Watertown, S to Binghamton
37 (284)	7th St, Electronics Pkwy, to Liverpool, N 🛏 Best Western, S ⛽ Hess/Blimpie/Godfather's/24hr, 🍴 KFC/Taco Bell, 🛏 Hilton Garden, Holiday Inn, Homewood Suites, Knights Inn, ⊙ Kinny Drug
38 (286)	NY 57, to Liverpool, Syracuse, N ⛽ Fastrac/dsl, Hess, KwikFill, 🍴 Bangkok Thai, Hooligan's, Kirby's Rest., Pier 57 Diner, Pizza Hut, Quiznos, Salsarita's Grill, 🛏 Hampton Inn (7mi), Super 8, ⊙ Aldi Foods, $Tree, NAPA, Rite Aid
39 (290)	I-690, NY 690, Syracuse, N 🛏 Comfort Inn/rest., ⊙ Camping World RV Ctr
292mm	**Warners Service Area wb**, Mobil/dsl/rest., Boston Pizza, Edy's Ice Cream, McDonald's
40 (304)	NY 34, to Owasco Lake, Weedsport, N Riverforest RV Park, S ⛽ Fastrac, KwikFill, Sunoco/dsl, 🍴 Arby's, Arnold's Rest., Cj's Rest., DB's Drive-In, Jreck Subs, Lin Bo Chinese, Old Erie Diner, 🛏 Best Western, Days Inn, Holiday Inn (12mi), ⊙ Ace Hardware, Bass Pro Shops (12mi), Big M Foods, $General, Kinney Drug, NAPA
310mm	**Port Byron Service Area eb**, Mobil/dsl/rest., Edy's Ice Cream, McDonald's, Original Pizza
318mm	parking area wb, litter barrels, ♿
41 (320)	NY 414, to Cayuga Lake, Waterloo, S ⛽ Nice'n Easy/dsl, Petro/dsl/rest./scales/24hr/@, 🍴 MaGee Country Diner, 🛏 Holiday Inn (4mi), Microtel (4mi), ⊙ Cayuga Lake SP, Waterloo Outlets/famous brands (3mi)
324mm	**Junius Ponds Service Area wb**, Sunoco/dsl, Dunkin Donuts, Roy Rogers
42 (327)	NY 14, to Geneva, Lyons, N RV camping, S ⛽ Mobil/dsl/scales, 🛏 Red Carpet Inn, ⊙ Waterloo Outlets/famous brands (3mi), Junius Ponds RV Camping, **6 mi S** 🛏 Belherst, Best Value Inn, Hampton Inn, Motel 6, Ramada Inn
337mm	**Clifton Springs Service Area eb**, Sunoco/dsl, Roy Rogers, Sbarro's, Starbucks, atm, gifts
43 (340)	NY 21, to Palmyra, Manchester, N Hill Cumorah LDS HS (6mi), S ⛽ Sunoco/dsl/24hr, 🍴 Lehigh Valley Rest., McDonald's, 🛏 Scottish Inn
44 (347)	NY 332, Victor, S ⛽ Getty/Subway/dsl, Sunoco/dsl, 🍴 Dairy-Ann, Dunkin Donuts, KFC, King's Wok, McDonald's, NY Pizza, 🛏 Best Value Inn, Budget Inn, Comfort Inn, ⊙ Aldi Foods, CVS Drug, KOA (4mi), Wade's Foods, casino, st police
350mm	**Seneca Service Area wb**, ⛽ Mobil/dsl, 🍴 Checker's, Tim Horton's, Villa Pizza, ⊙ atm, info, ♿
45 (351)	I-490, NY 96, to Rochester, N ⛽ Citgo, 🍴 Biaggi's Rest., BoneFish Grill, Champp's Grill, Moe's SW Grill, Olive Garden, PF Chang's, Starbucks, TGIFriday's, Uno Chicago

E ↕ W

R O C H E S T E R

NY

INTERSTATE 90 CONT'D

Exit	Services
45 (351)	**Continued** Grill, 🅰 Hampton Inn, 🅾 Best Buy, BJ's Whse/gas, Bonton, Border's, Dick's, Home Depot, JC Penney, K-Mart, Kohl's, Lord&Taylor, Macy's, Michael's, Old Navy, Radio Shack, Rite Aid, Sears/auto, Staples, Target, Walmart, **S** 🅰 KwikFill, 🍴 Burger King, Charlie's Rest., Chili's, Denny's, Wendy's, 🅰 Best Western, Holiday Inn Express, Homewood Suites, Microtel, Royal Inn, 🅾 Ballantyne RV Ctr
353mm	parking area eb, 🅲, litter barrels
46 (362)	I-390, to Rochester, **N on NY 253 W** 🅰 Gulf/dsl, Hess, Sunoco/dsl, 🍴 Lehigh Rest., McDonald's, Peppermint's Rest., Tim Horton, Wendy's, 🅰 Country Inn&Suites, Days Inn, Fairfield Inn, Microtel, Red Carpet Inn, Red Roof Inn, Super 8 🅾 Buick/GMC
366mm	**Scottsville Service Area eb**, 🅰 Mobil/dsl, 🍴 Arby's, Tim Horton, 🅾 atm, info
376mm	**Ontario Service Area wb**, 🅰 Sunoco/dsl, 🍴 Boston Pizza, McDonald's
47 (379)	I-490, NY 19, to Rochester, **N** Timberline Camping
48 (390)	NY 98, to Batavia, **N** 🅰 Comfort Inn, Hampton Inn, **S** 🅰 Citgo, 🍴 Applebee's, Bob Evans, Peking Buffet, 🅰 Best Western, Budget Inn, Days Inn, Holiday Inn, Quality Inn, Super 8, Travelodge, 🅾 AT&T, AutoZone, BJ's Whse, Home Depot, K-Mart, Lowe's, Michael's, PetCo, Radio Shack, Target, Walmart
397mm	**Pembroke Service Area eb**, 🅰 Sunoco/dsl, 🍴 Fuddrucker's, Tim Horton, 🅾 atm, gifts, 🅲, UPS
48a (402)	NY 77, Pembroke, **S** 🅰 *FLYING J*/Denny's/dsl/LP/scales/24hr, TA/dsl/rest./scales/24hr/@, 🍴 Subway, 🅰 EconoLodge, 6 Flags Motel/RV Park (5mi), 🅾 Sleepy Hollow Camping (8mi)
412mm	**Clarence Service Area wb, full ♿ facilities,** 🅰 Sunoco/dsl, 🍴 Arby's, Fuddrucker's, Tim Horton, 🅾 info, 🅲
49 (417)	NY 78, Depew, **0-3 mi N** 🅰 Delta Sonic, Mobil/dsl, Sunoco, 🍴 Applebee's, Arby's, Burger King, Carmen's Rest., Chili's, Coldstone, Cracker Barrel, Denny's, Dibella's Subs, DQ, Dunkin Donuts, Friendly's, Frog Hair Grille, Just Pizza, KFC, La Tolteca, McDonald's, Mighty Taco, Moe's SW Grill, Mr Pita, Old Country Buffet, Panera Bread, Perkins, Picasso's Pizza, Pizza Hut, Pizza Plant, Pomegranate, Protocol Rest., Quaker Steak&Lube, Quiznos, Red Lobster, Russel's Steaks, Salsarita's, Spilio's Rest., Starbucks, Subway, Taco Bell, Ted's HotDogs, TGIFriday's, Tim Horton, Tully's Rest., Wendy's, 🅰 Clarion, Microtel, Motel 6, Rodeway Inn, Salvatore's Hotel, Staybridge Suites, Super 8, 🅾 Acura, Aldi Foods, AT&T, Barnes&Noble, Best Buy, BigLots, BJ's Whse/gas, BonTon, Buick/GMC, Chrysler/Dodge/Jeep, Dick's, $Tree, Dunn Tire, Firestone/auto, Ford, Goodyear, Home Depot, Honda, JC Penney, Jo-Ann Fabrics, Kohl's, Lowe's, Michael's, PetCo, PetsMart, Rite Aid, Sears/auto, Stein-Mart, Suzuki, Target, TJ Maxx, Top's Food/deli, Tuesday Morning, Walgreens, Walmart, Wegman's Foods, mall, vet, **S** 🅰 Kwikfill, Mobil, 🍴 Bob Evans, China 1, Dunkin Donuts, John&Mary's Cafe, McDonald's, Salvatore's Italian, Subway, Tim Horton, 🅰 Garden Place Hotel, 🅷 ity Inn, La Quinta, Red Roof Inn, 🅾 Aamco, CarQuest, $Tree, Top's Foods

B U F F A L O

Exit	Services
419mm	toll booth
50 (420)	I-290 to Niagara Falls
50a (421)	Cleveland Dr (from eb)
51 (422)	NY 33 E, Buffalo, **S** 🅰, st police
52 (423)	Walden Ave, to Buffalo, **N** 🍴 Applebees, Burger King, Famous Dave's BBQ, IHOP, McDonald's, Ruby Tuesday, Starbucks, Subway, TGIFriday's, Tim Horton, 🅰 Hampton Inn, Residence Inn, 🅾 Aldi Foods, AT&T, $Tree, Firestone, Ford, Goodyear/auto, Home Depot, Michael's, Office Depot, PetsMart, PriceRight, Target, Top's Foods, Walmart, **S** 🅰 Delta Sonic, Jim's Trk Plaza/Sunoco/dsl/rest./scales/24hr, KwikFill, 🍴 Alton's Rest., Bar Louie's, Bravo Italiano, Cheesecake Factory, Dunkin Donuts, Fuddrucker's, Hyde Park Steaks, Jack Astor's Grill, McDonald's, Melting Pot, Mighty Taco, Milton's Rest., Olive Garden, PF Chang's, Pizza Hut, Smokey Bones BBQ, Zahng's Buffet, 🅰 Millenium Hotel, Oak Tree Inn, 🅾 Best Buy, Burlington Coats, Dick's, Dunn Tire, Lord&Taylor, Macy's, JC Penney, K-Mart, NAPA, Niagara Hobby, Old Navy, Sears, mall
52a (424)	William St
53 (425)	I-190, to Buffalo, Niagara Falls, **N** 🅰 Holiday Inn Express
54 (428)	NY 400, NY 16, to W Seneca, E Aurora
55 (430)	US 219, Ridge Rd, Orchard Park, to Rich Stadium, **S** 🅰 Delta Sonic, Valero, 🍴 Denny's, Mighty Taco, Subway, Tim Horton, Wendy's, 🅰 Hampton Inn, Staybridge Suites, 🅾 Aldi Foods, BigLots, $General, Goodyear/auto, Home Depot, K-Mart, Mr Tire, Tops Foods, Wegman's Foods
431mm	toll booth
56 (432)	NY 179, Mile Strip Rd, **N** 🅰 Sunoco, Valero, 🍴 Blasdale Pizza, China King, DiPallo's Rest., Odyssey Rest., Whse Rest., 🅰 EconoLodge, 🅾 CarQuest, CVS Drug, $General, Family$, Jubilee Foods, Rite Aid, repair, USPO, **S** 🍴 Applebee's, Boston Mkt, Buffalo Wild Wings, Chuck-eCheese, Friendly's, McDonald's, Mongolian Buffet, Olive Garden, Outback Steaks, Panera Bread, Pizza Hut, Red Lobster, Ruby Tuesday, Starbucks, Subway, TGIFriday's, Wasabi Japanese, Wendy's, 🅰 McKinley's Hotel, Red Carpet Inn (2mi), 🅾 Aldi Foods, Barnes&Noble, Best Buy, BJ's Whse, BonTon, Dick's, $Tree, Firestone/auto, Home Depot, JC Penney, Jo-Ann Etc, Macy's, Old Navy, PepBoys, Sears, TJ Maxx, Wegman's Foods, mall
57 (436)	NY 75, to Hamburg, **N** 🅰 Mobil/Dunkin Donuts/dsl, 🍴 Anthony's Diner, Bozanna's Pizza, Denny's, McDonald's, Tim Horton, Uncle Joe's Diner, Wendy's, 🅰 Comfort Inn, Red Roof Inn, Tallyho Motel, 🅾 Chevrolet, Chrysler/Dodge/Jeep, Ford, Lowe's, Wal-Mart (3mi), repair, transmissions, **S** 🅰 Go Gas, Kwikfill/dsl, Stop&Gas, 🍴 Arby's, Burger King, Hideaways Rest., Pizza Hut, Subway, Tim Horton, 🅰 Quality Inn, Super 8, 🅾 AutoZone, $General, Goodyear/auto, USPO, vet
442mm	parking area both lanes, 🅲, litter barrels
57a (445)	to Eden, Angola, **2 mi N** 🅰 Sunoco/dsl
447mm	**Angola Service Area both lanes**, Sunoco/dsl, Denny's, Ella's Pizza, McDonald's, 🅲/fax, gifts
58 (456)	US 20, NY 5, to Silver Creek, Irving, **N** 🅰 Citgo, Kwikfill, 🍴 Burger King, Colony Rest., Millie's Rest., Primo's Rest., Subway, Sunset Bay, Tim Horton, Tom's Rest., 🅰 Lighthouse Inn, 🅾 🅷, to Evangola SP
59 (468)	NY 60, Fredonia, Dunkirk, **N** 🅰 Clarion (2mi), Dunkirk Motel (4mi), 🅾 Lake Erie SP (7mi), **S** 🅰 Country Fair, Fuel Ctr/dsl, Kwikfill/dsl, Mobil/dsl, 🍴 Applebee's, Arby's, Azteca Mexican, Best Buffet, Bob Evans, Burger King,

H A M B U R G

INTERSTATE 90 CONT'D

Exit	Services
59 (468)	Continued
	Denny's, Dunkin Donuts, KFC/Taco Bell, McDonald's, Pizza Hut, Subway, Tim Horton, Wendy's, Wing City Grille, 🛏 Best Western, Comfort Inn, Days Inn, 🅞 Advance Parts, Aldi Foods, AutoZone, $Tree, Ford/Lincoln/Mercury, GMC, GNC, Home Depot, Radio Shack, Rite Aid, Tops Foods/gas, TJ Maxx, Walmart
60 (485)	NY 394, Westfield, N 🅞 KOA, to Lake Erie SP, S 🛏 Holiday Motel, 🅞 Ⓗ
494mm	toll booth
61 (495)	Shortman Rd, to Ripley, N 🅞 Lakeshore RV Park
496mm	New York/Pennsylvania state line

INTERSTATE 95

Exit	Services
32mm	New York/Connecticut state line
22 (30)	Midland Ave (from nb), Port Chester, Rye, W 🍴 Subway, 🅞 Ⓗ, Home Depot, Staples
21 (29)	I-287 W, US 1 N, to White Plains, Port Chester, Tappan Zee
20 (28)	US 1 S (from nb), Port Chester, E 🅖 Shell, 🅞 CVS Drug, Ford, Subaru, USPO
19 (27)	Playland Pkwy, Rye, Harrison
18b (25)	Mamaroneck Ave, to White Plains, E 🅖 Hess, Shell, 🍴 Domino's, 🅞 A&P Foods, Mavis Tire
18a (24)	Fenimore Rd (from nb), Mamaroneck, E 🅖 Sunoco/dsl
17 (20)	Chatsworth Ave (from nb, no return), Larchmont
19.5mm	toll plaza
16 (19)	North Ave, Cedar St, New Rochelle, E 🍴 Applebee's, Buffalo Wild Wings, 🛏 Residence Inn, 🅞 ShopRite, Toyota, USPO, W Ⓗ
15 (16)	US 1, New Rochelle, The Pelhams, E 🅖 Getty/dsl, SuperGas, 🅞 AutoZone, Costco, CVS Drug, Harley-Davidson, Home Depot, NAPA, Walgreens, W auto repair
14 (15)	Hutchinson Pkwy (from sb), to Whitestone Br
13 (16)	Conner St, to Mt Vernon, E 🅖 Gulf/dsl, 🛏 Ramada Inn, W 🅖 BP, 🍴 McDonald's, 🛏 Exit 13 Motel, Holiday Motel, 🅞 Ⓗ
12 (15.5)	Baychester Ave (exits left from nb)
11 (15)	Bartow Ave, Co-op City Blvd, E 🅖 Mobil, 🍴 Applebee's, Baskin-Robbins, Barto Pizza, Burger King, Checker's, Genarro's Pizza, Little Caesars, McDonald's, Panera Bread, Popeye's, Red Lobster, Zinhi Chinese, 🅞 Barnes&Noble, JC Penney, K-Mart, Marshall's, Old Navy, PathMark Foods, Pay Half, Staples, Verizon, W 🅖 Gulf, Shell/mart, Sunoco/dsl, 🍴 ChuckeCheese, Dunkin Donuts, Eastern Wok, Pizza Hut, Subway, TGIFriday's, 🅞 Home Depot
10 (14.5)	Gun Hill Rd (exits left from nb), W 🛏 Pelham Bay Hotel/diner
9 (14)	Hutchinson Pkwy
8c (13.5)	Pelham Pkwy W
8b (13)	Orchard Beach, City Island
8a (12.5)	Westchester Ave (from sb)
7c (12)	Pelham Bay Park (from nb), Country Club Rd
7b (11.5)	E Tremont (from sb), W 🅞 Super FoodTown
7a (11)	I-695 (from sb), to I-295 S, Throgs Neck Br
6b (10.5)	I-278 W (from sb), I-295 S (from nb)
6a (10)	I-678 S, Whitestone Bridge
5b (9)	Castle Hill Ave, W 🅖 Sunoco, 🍴 McDonald's, 🅞 GNC

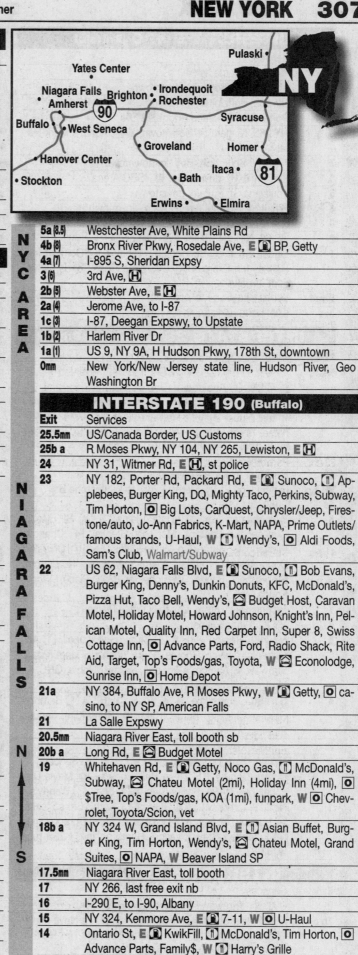

Exit	Services
5a (8.5)	Westchester Ave, White Plains Rd
4b (8)	Bronx River Pkwy, Rosedale Ave, E 🍴 BP, Getty
4a (7)	I-895 S, Sheridan Expsy
3 (6)	3rd Ave, Ⓗ
2b (5)	Webster Ave, E Ⓗ
2a (4)	Jerome Ave, to I-87
1c (3)	I-87, Deegan Expswy, to Upstate
1b (2)	Harlem River Dr
1a (1)	US 9, NY 9A, H Hudson Pkwy, 178th St, downtown
0mm	New York/New Jersey state line, Hudson River, Geo Washington Br

INTERSTATE 190 (Buffalo)

Exit	Services
25.5mm	US/Canada Border, US Customs
25 b a	R. Moses Pkwy, NY 104, NY 265, Lewiston, E Ⓗ
24	NY 31, Witmer Rd, E Ⓗ, st police
23	NY 182, Porter Rd, Packard Rd, E 🅖 Sunoco, 🍴 Applebees, Burger King, DQ, Mighty Taco, Perkins, Subway, Tim Horton, 🅞 Big Lots, CarQuest, Chrysler/Jeep, Firestone/auto, Jo-Ann Fabrics, K-Mart, NAPA, Prime Outlets/famous brands, U-Haul, W 🍴 Wendy's, 🅞 Aldi Foods, Sam's Club, Walmart/Subway
22	US 62, Niagara Falls Blvd, E 🅖 Sunoco, 🍴 Bob Evans, Burger King, Denny's, Dunkin Donuts, KFC, McDonald's, Pizza Hut, Taco Bell, Wendy's, 🛏 Budget Host, Caravan Motel, Holiday Motel, Howard Johnson, Knight's Inn, Pelican Motel, Quality Inn, Red Carpet Inn, Super 8, Swiss Cottage Inn, 🅞 Advance Parts, Ford, Radio Shack, Rite Aid, Target, Top's Foods/gas, Toyota, W 🛏 Econolodge, Sunrise Inn, 🅞 Home Depot
21a	NY 384, Buffalo Ave, R Moses Pkwy, W 🅖 Getty, 🅞 casino, to NY SP, American Falls
21	La Salle Expswy
20.5mm	Niagara River East, toll booth sb
20b a	Long Rd, E 🛏 Budget Motel
19	Whitehaven Rd, E 🅖 Getty, Noco Gas, 🍴 McDonald's, Subway, 🛏 Chateu Motel (2mi), Holiday Inn (4mi), 🅞 $Tree, Top's Foods/gas, KOA (1mi), funpark, W 🅞 Chevrolet, Toyota/Scion, vet
18b a	NY 324 W, Grand Island Blvd, E 🍴 Asian Buffet, Burger King, Tim Horton, Wendy's, 🛏 Chateu Motel, Grand Suites, 🅞 NAPA, W Beaver Island SP
17.5mm	Niagara River East, toll booth
17	NY 266, last free exit nb
16	I-290 E, to I-90, Albany
15	NY 324, Kenmore Ave, E 🅖 7-11, W 🅞 U-Haul
14	Ontario St, E 🅖 KwikFill, 🍴 McDonald's, Tim Horton, 🅞 Advance Parts, Family$, W 🍴 Harry's Grille

The map in the upper right shows cities including Pulaski, Yates Center, Niagara Falls, Brighton, Irondequoit, Rochester, Amherst, Buffalo, West Seneca, Syracuse, Groveland, Homer, Hanover Center, Itaca, Bath, Stockton, Erwins, Elmira, with Interstate 90 and Interstate 81, and NY state outline.

[🅐] = gas [🍴] = food [🛏] = lodging [⭕] = other   Copyright 2011 - The Next Exi

NY

INTERSTATE 190 (Buffalo)

Exit	Services
13	(from nb) same as 14
12	Amherst St, (from nb), downtown
11	NY 198, Buffalo, E [🅐] Sunoco
9	Porter Ave, to Peace Bridge, Ft Erie
8	NY 266, Niagara St downtown, E [🛏] Adam's Mark Hotel
7	NY 5 W, Church St, Buffalo, downtown
6	Elm St, E [H], downtown, W HSBC Arena
5	Louisiana St, Buffalo, downtown
4	Smith St, Fillmore Ave, Buffalo, downtown
3	NY 16, Seneca St, from sb, W [⭕] CarQuest
2	US 62, NY 354, Bailey Ave, Clinton St
1	Ogden St, E [🅐] Sunoco, [🍴] Wendy's, [🛏] Comfort Inn, Holiday Inn Express, [⭕] CVS Drug, Tops Foods, Volvo/GMC Trucks
.5mm	toll plaza nb
0mm	I-90. I-190 begins/ends on I-90, exit 53.

INTERSTATE 287 (New York City)

Exit	Services
12	I-95, N to New Haven, S to NYC. I-287 begins/ends on I-95, exit 21.
11	US 1, Port Chester, Rye, N [🅐] BP, Mobil, Sunoco, [🍴] Burger King, Domino's, Dunkin Donuts, KFC, McDonald's, Port Chester Diner, Subway, Wendy's, [⭕] [H], Goodyear/auto, Kohl's, Mavis Discount Tire, Nissan, Petsmart, Staples, Verizon
10	Bowman Ave, Webb Ave
9N S	Hutchinson Pkwy, Merritt Pkwy, to Whitestone Br
9a	I-684, Brewster
8	Westchester Ave, to White Plains, S [🅐] BP, Mobil, Cheesecake Factory, Morton's Steaks, PF Chang's, Westchester Burger Co, White Plains Diner, [⭕] Chrysler/Dodge/Jeep, Hyundai, Neiman Marcus, Nordstrom, Stop&Shop Foods, Westchester Mall Place, Whole Foods Mkt
7	Taconic Pkwy (from wb), to N White Plains
6	NY 22, White Plains
5	NY 100, Hillside Ave, S [🅐] Citgo, Gulf, Lukoil, [🍴] Applebee's, Dunkin Donuts, Papa John's, Planet Pizza, Subway, [⭕] Aamco, AutoZone, Barnes&Noble, GNC, K-Mart, Lexus, Mazda, Radio Shack, vet
4	NY 100A, Hartsdale, N [🅐] Shell, [⭕] [H], S [🍴] Bamboo Garden Chinese, Burger King, [⭕] BMW/Mini, Jaguar, Staples, Volvo
3	Sprain Pkwy, to Taconic Pkwy, NYC
2	NY 9A, Elmsford, N [🅐] BP, Citgo, Mobil, Sunoco, [🍴] Dunkin Donuts, KFC/Taco Bell, Subway, [⭕] Mavis Discount Tire, NAPA, Sam's Club, S [🅐] Shell, [🍴] Wendy's
1	NY 119, Tarrytown, N [🅐] Gulf/dsl, [🍴] Ruth's Chris Steaks, [🛏] Marriott, Sheraton, S [🅐] Gulf/dsl, [🍴] El Dorado Diner, [🛏] Extended Stay America, Hampton Inn, I-287 runs with I-87 N.

INTERSTATE 290 (Buffalo)

Exit	Services
8	I-90, NY Thruway, I-290 begins/ends on I-90, exit 50.
7b a	NY 5, Main St, N [🅐] Mobil, Sunoco, [🍴] La Nova Pizza/Wings, McDonald's, Pizza Plant, Subway, Tim Horton, Wendy's, [⭕] Quality Mkt Foods, Walgreens, S [🅐]

Exit	Services
7b a	Continued Valero, [🍴] Sonoma Grille, [🛏] Amherst Motel, [⭕] vet
6	NY 324, NY 240, N [🅐] Getty, [🛏] Courtyard, S [🅐] Valero, [🍴] China Star, ChuckeCheese, Subway, [⭕] Chrysler/Jeep, CVS Drug, Hyundai/Subaru, KIA/Mazda, Lexus, Nissan
5b a	NY 263, to Millersport, N [🍴] Houlihan's, [🛏] Comfort Inn, Marriott, Red Roof Inn, S [🅐] Mobil, [🛏] Homewood Suites, [⭕] Scion/Toyota, VW, Walgreens
4	I-990, to St U
3b a	US 62, to Niagara Falls Blvd, N [🅐] Citgo, Valero, [🍴] Bob Evans, Dunkin Donuts, Just Pizza, Max's Grill, Pancake House, Ted's Hot Dogs, [🛏] Blvd Inn, Econolodge, Extended Stay America, Holiday Inn, Knight's Inn, Red Carpet Inn, Sleep Inn, [⭕] Buick/GMC, CarQuest, Dodge, Home Depot, Honda, Walmart/auto, vet, S [🅐] Delta Sonic, Mobil, [🍴] Applebee's, Arby's, BoneFish Grill, Burger King, Carrabba's, Chili's, Denny's, Dibella's Subs, John's Pizza, McDonald's, Moe's SW Grill, Montana's Grill, Outback Steaks, Panera Bread, Pizza Hut, Starbucks, Subway, Swiss Chalet Grill, TGIFriday, Tim Horton, Tulley's, [🛏] Days Inn, Royal Inn, [⭕] Barnes&Noble, Best Buy, $Tree, Firestone, Goodyear/auto, JC Penney, Jo-Ann Fabrics, Lowes Whse, Macy's, Michael's, PetCo, PetsMart, Sears/auto, Target, mall
2	NY 425, Colvin Blvd, N [🍴] Athena's Rest., KFC, McDonald's, Subway, Texas Roadhouse, Tim Horton, Wendy's, [⭕] [H], Big Lots, BJ's Whse/gas, Family$, Gander Mtn, Goodyear/auto, Top's Foods/gas, S [🅐] KwikFill
1b a	Elmwood Ave, NY 384, NY 265, N [🅐] KwikFill, [🍴] John's Pizza/Subs, Sam's Cafe, [🛏] Microtel, [⭕] [H], $Tree, NAPA, Rite Aid, S [🅐] Mobil/dsl, [🍴] Arby's
0mm	I-190. I-290 begins/ends on I-190 in Buffalo.

INTERSTATE 390 (Rochester)

Exit	Services
20a b (76)	I-490. I-390 begins/ends on I-490 in Rochester
19 (75)	NY 33a, Chili Ave, N [🍴] Wishing Well Rest., S [🅐] Sunoco, [🍴] Burger King, Pizza Hut, Subway, [🛏] Motel 6, Quality Inn, [⭕] $General
18a b (74)	NY 204, Brooks Ave, N [🛏] Holiday Inn, S [🛏] Fairfield Inn, [⭕] [✈]
17 (73)	NY 383, Scottsville Rd, W [🅐] Sunoco/Subway/dsl
16 (71)	NY 15a, to E Henryetta, S [🍴] Basil's Rest., [🛏] Courtyard, Hampton Inn, [⭕] [H]
15 (70)	I-590, Rochester
14 (68)	NY 15a, NY 252, E [🍴] Domino's, Gray's Cafe, McDonald's, Outback Steaks, Papa John's, Perkins, Tully's Rest., [🛏] Extended Stay America, [⭕] Staples, W [🅐] Mobil/dsl, [🍴] Boston Mkt, Dunkin Donuts, Starbucks, Subway, Taco Bell, [🛏] Best Western, DoubleTree Inn, [⭕] Big Lots, Office Depot, Radio Shack, Top's Foods
13 (67)	Hylan Dr., E [🍴] Cracker Barrel, [🛏] Comfort Suites, Homewood Suites, W [🅐] Mobil, [🍴] Bonton, Chicago Grill, ChuckeCheese, IHOP, McDonald's, Panera Bread, Ruby Tuesday, Tony Roma's, Wendy's, [⭕] Best Buy, BJ's Whse, Border's Books, Gander Mtn, Michael's, Lowes Whse, Pep Boys, Sam's Club/gas, Target, Walmart, Wegman's Foods, mall
12 (66)	I-90, NY Thruway, NY 253, W [🅐] Citgo/dsl, Hess, Sunoco/dsl, [🍴] McDonald's, Peppermint's Rest., Tim Horton, Wendy's, [🛏] Country Inn&Suites, Day's Inn, Fairfield Inn,

INTERSTATE 390 CONT'D (Rochester)

Exit	Services
12 (66)	Continued Microtel, Red Carpet Inn, Red Roof Inn, Super 8 🅾 GMC, Jeep
11 (62)	NY 15, NY 251, Rush, Scottsville, **2 mi N** 🍴 McDonald's, Tim Horton, Wendy's, 🛏 Cartwright Inn, Days Inn, Fair- field Inn, Red Roof Inn, RIT Inn
10 (55)	US 20, NY 5, Avon, Lima, **N** ⛽ Sunoco/dsl, 🛏 CrestHill Inn, Stratford Inn, **3 mi S** ⛽ Sugar Creek/dsl, 🍴 Avon Cafe, Dutch Hollow Cafe, McDonald's, Tom Wahls Cafe, Subway, 🛏 Avon Cedar Lodge, 🅾 Chrysler/Dodge/ Jeep, Ford, Sugar Creek Camping
9mm	scenic area wb
9 (52)	NY 15, **N** ⛽ Mobil/dsl, 🍴 Dunkin Donuts, Fratelli's Rest., Lakeville Rest., McDonald's, Tee&Gee Cafe, 🛏 Conesus Motel, 🅾 Chevrolet
8 (48)	US 20a, Geneseo, **N** 🍴 Arby's, 🛏 Oak Valley Inn, 🅾 Conesus Camping, **S** 🍴 Denny's, Dunkin Donuts, KFC/ Taco Bell, McDonald's, Wendy's, 🛏 Quality Inn
7 (39)	NY 63, NY 408, Geneseo, **S** ⛽ Mobil, KwikFill, 🍴 Bri- an's Diner, McDonald's, 🛏 Alligence B&B, Country Inn, Geneseo Hotel/Rest., Greenway Motel, 🅾 Ridge Camp- ing
38mm	**rest area both lanes, full ♿ facilities, 🚏 litter barrels, vending, petwalk**
6 (33)	NY 36, Mt Morris, Sonyea
5 (26)	NY 36, Dansville, **N** ⛽ KwikFill, Mobil/Subway, 🍴 Arby's, Burger King, Dunkin Donuts, HoHo Chinese, McDonald's, Pizza Hut, Subway, 🅾 Advance Parts, Chevrolet/Cadillac, CVS Drug, Radio Shack, Rite Aid, Top's Foods/gas, **S** ⛽ TA/Mobil/Buckhorn Rest./@, 🛏 Day's Inn
4 (23)	NY 36, Dansville, **N** ⛽ Sunoco/dsl, 🛏 Logan's Inn, 🅾 🏥, Larocca RV Ctr, **S** ⛽ Skybrook Camping, Stony- brook Park Camping, Sugar Creek Camping, Sunvalley Camping
3 (17)	NY 15, NY 21, Wayland, **N** 🍴 Farmer's Kitchen Rest., 🅾 Holiday Hill Campground (7mi), st patrol
2 (11)	NY 415, Cohocton, Naples, **N** ⛽ Mobil, 🅾 Tumble Hill Camping (2mi)
1 (2)	NY 415, I-390 begins/ends, Avoca, **N** truck/auto repair, **S** ⛽ Mobil, 🛏 Caboose Motel (3mi)

I-390 begins/ends on I-86, exit 36.

INTERSTATE 495 (Long Island)

Exit	Services
	I-495 begins/ends on NY 25.
73	rd 58, Old Country Road, to Greenport, Orient, **0-2 mi S** ⛽ Gulf, Hess/dsl, Lukoil/7-11, Mobil/dsl, 🍴 Applebees, Boulder Creek Steaks, Panera Bread, TGIFridays, Taco Bell, Wendy's, 🛏 Hilton Garden, Holiday Inn Express, 🅾 AutoZone, Best Buy, Buick/GMC, Chevrolet, Chrysler/ Jeep, Curves, CVS Drug, Ford/Lincoln/Mercury, Harley- Davidson, Home Depot, Honda, Kia/Mazda, Lowe's, Michael's, Nissan/Hyundai, PetCo, Stop&Shop, Subaru/ VW, Tanger/famous brands, Target, Toyota/Scion, Volvo, Waldbaum's, Walgreens
72	NY 25, (no ez eb return), Riverhead, Calverton, **N** fun- park, **S** ⛽ Hess, 🛏 Hotel Indigo, 🅾 Tanger/famous brands/foodcourt
71	NY 24, to Hampton Bays (no ez eb return), Calverton, **N** ⛽ Hess/Subway/dsl
70	NY 111, to Eastport, Manorville, **S** ⛽ Mobil/dsl,

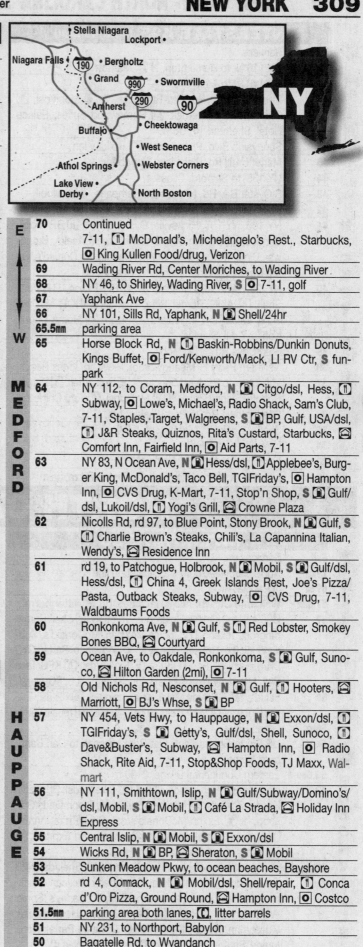

Exit	Services
70	Continued 7-11, 🍴 McDonald's, Michelangelo's Rest., Starbucks, 🅾 King Kullen Food/drug, Verizon
69	Wading River Rd, Center Moriches, to Wading River
68	NY 46, to Shirley, Wading River, **S** 🅾 7-11, golf
67	Yaphank Ave
66	NY 101, Sills Rd, Yaphank, **N** ⛽ Shell/24hr
65.5mm	parking area
65	Horse Block Rd, **N** 🍴 Baskin-Robbins/Dunkin Donuts, Kings Buffet, 🅾 Ford/Kenworth/Mack, LI RV Ctr, **S** fun- park
64	NY 112, to Coram, Medford, **N** ⛽ Citgo/dsl, Hess, 🍴 Subway, 🅾 Lowe's, Michael's, Radio Shack, Sam's Club, 7-11, Staples, Target, Walgreens, **S** ⛽ BP, Gulf, USA/dsl, 🍴 J&R Steaks, Quiznos, Rita's Custard, Starbucks, 🛏 Comfort Inn, Fairfield Inn, 🅾 Aid Parts, 7-11
63	NY 83, N Ocean Ave, **N** ⛽ Hess/dsl, 🍴 Applebee's, Burg- er King, McDonald's, Taco Bell, TGIFriday's, 🅾 Hampton Inn, 🅾 CVS Drug, K-Mart, 7-11, Stop'n Shop, **S** ⛽ Gulf/ dsl, Lukoil/dsl, 🍴 Yogi's Grill, 🛏 Crowne Plaza
62	Nicolls Rd, rd 97, to Blue Point, Stony Brook, **N** ⛽ Gulf, **S** 🍴 Charlie Brown's Steaks, Chili's, La Capannina Italian, Wendy's, 🛏 Residence Inn
61	rd 19, to Patchogue, Holbrook, **N** ⛽ Mobil, **S** ⛽ Gulf/dsl, Hess/dsl, 🍴 China 4, Greek Islands Rest, Joe's Pizza/ Pasta, Outback Steaks, Subway, 🅾 CVS Drug, 7-11, Waldbaums Foods
60	Ronkonkoma Ave, **N** ⛽ Gulf, **S** 🍴 Red Lobster, Smokey Bones BBQ, 🛏 Courtyard
59	Ocean Ave, to Oakdale, Ronkonkoma, **S** ⛽ Gulf, Suno- co, 🛏 Hilton Garden (2mi), 🅾 7-11
58	Old Nichols Rd, Nesconset, **N** ⛽ Gulf, 🍴 Hooters, 🛏 Marriott, 🅾 BJ's Whse, **S** ⛽ BP
57	NY 454, Vets Hwy, to Hauppauge, **N** ⛽ Exxon/dsl, 🍴 TGIFriday's, **S** ⛽ Getty's, Gulf/dsl, Shell, Sunoco, 🍴 Dave&Buster's, Subway, 🛏 Hampton Inn, 🅾 Radio Shack, Rite Aid, 7-11, Stop&Shop Foods, TJ Maxx, Wal- mart
56	NY 111, Smithtown, Islip, **N** ⛽ Gulf/Subway/Domino's/ dsl, Mobil, **S** ⛽ Mobil, 🍴 Café La Strada, 🛏 Holiday Inn Express
55	Central Islip, **N** ⛽ Mobil, **S** ⛽ Exxon/dsl
54	Wicks Rd, **N** ⛽ BP, 🛏 Sheraton, **S** ⛽ Mobil
53	Sunken Meadow Pkwy, to ocean beaches, Bayshore
52	rd 4, Commack, **N** ⛽ Mobil/dsl, Shell/repair, 🍴 Conca d'Oro Pizza, Ground Round, 🛏 Hampton Inn, 🅾 Costco
51.5mm	parking area both lanes, 🚻, litter barrels
51	NY 231, to Northport, Babylon
50	Bagatelle Rd, to Wyandanch

Along the left margin: N ↑ S

Along the right vertical (I-495): E W, MEDFORD, HAUPPAUGE

Along the left vertical (I-390): RIVERHEAD

🛢 = gas 🍴 = food 🏨 = lodging 🅾 = other   Copyright 2011 - The Next Ex

INTERSTATE 495 (Long Island)

Exit	Services
49N	NY 110 N, to Huntington, N 🏨 Marriott
49S	NY 110 S, to Amityville
48	Round Swamp Rd, Old Bethpage, S 🛢 Mobil/dsl, 🍴 Old Country Pizza/deli, 🏨 Homewood Suites, Palace Hotel, Sheraton, 🅾 USPO
46	Sunnyside Blvd, Plainview, N 🏨 Holiday Inn
45	Manetto Hill Rd, Plainview, Woodbury
44	NY 135, to Seaford, Syosset
43	S Oyster Bay Rd, to Syosset, Bethpage, N 🛢 Mobil
42	Northern Pkwy, rd N, Hauppauge
41	NY 106, NY 107, Hicksville, Oyster Bay, S 🛢 BP, Mobil, Sunoco, 🍴 Boston Mkt, Boulder Creek Steaks, Broadway Diner, Burger King, Dunkin Donuts, McDonald's, On the Border, 🅾 Goodyear/auto, Sears/auto
40	NY 25, Mineola, Syosset, S 🛢 BP, Exxon, Hess/dsl, Shell, 🍴 A&W, Burger King, Friendly's, IHOP, McDonald's, Wendy's, 🏨 Howard Johnson, 🅾 Home Depot, Kohl's, 7-11, Staples
39	Glen Cove Rd, N 🛢 Mobil
38	Northern Pkwy E, Meadowbrook Pkwy, to Jones Beach
37	Willis Ave, to Roslyn, Mineola, N 🛢 Gulf, Shell, 🍴 Dunkin Donuts, Skinny Pizza, S 🛢 Mobil/dsl, 🍴 Tofu Chinese
36	Searingtown Rd, to Port Washington, S 🏥
35	Shelter Rock Rd, Manhasset, S 🏥
34	New Hyde Park Rd
33	Lakeville Rd, to Great Neck, N 🏥
32	Little Neck Pkwy, N 🛢 Gulf, 🍴 Centre Pizza, Jain

Exit	Services
32	Continued Rest., KFC/Taco Bell, Panera Bread, Starbucks
31	Douglaston Pkwy, S 🛢 BP/service, 🍴 Burger King, Grimaldi's Pizza, Pinecourt Chinese, Subway, 🅾 DP Drug, Macy's, USPO, Verizon, Waldbaum's Foods
30	E Hampton Blvd, Cross Island Pkwy
29	Springfield Blvd, S 🛢 Citgo, Gulf/Dunkin Donuts, 🍴 McDonald's
27	I-295, Clearview Expswy, Throgs Neck, N 🛢 Gulf, 7-11 🍴 Blue Bay Diner, 🅾 drugstore
26	Francis Lewis Blvd
25	Utopia Pkwy, 188th St, N 🛢 Citgo, Gulf, S 🛢 Mobil Quality/dsl, Savvy, Shell, 🍴 Arby's, Baskin-Robbins Dunkin Donuts, 5 Guys Burgers, Subway, 🅾 Radio Shack, USPO
24	Kissena Blvd, N 🛢 Gulf/dsl, 🍴 Baskin-Robbins, Dunkin Donuts, S 🛢 Mobil
23	Main St, N 🍴 Palace Diner
22	Grand Central Pkwy, to I-678, College Pt Blvd, N 🏨 Holiday Inn Express
21	108th St, N 🛢 BP/7-11, Mobil
19	NY 25, Queens Blvd, Woodhaven Blvd, to Rockaways, N 🍴 McDonald's, 🅾 JC Penney, Macy's, mall, S 🛢 BP 🍴 Applebees, Burger King, Dallas BBQ, 5 Guys Burgers Moe's SW Grill, Subway, 🅾 Aldi Foods, Costco, Kohl's Marshall's, Old Navy, Rite Aid, Sears, TJ Maxx
18.5	69th Ave, Grand Ave (from wb)
18	Maurice St, N 🛢 Exxon S 🛢 BP, 🍴 McDonald's, 🏨 Holiday Inn Express, 🅾 dsl repair
17	48th St, to I-278, N 🏨 Queensboro Hotel, 🅾 ♻
16	I-495 begins/ends in NYC.

NORTH CAROLINA

INTERSTATE 26

Exit	Services
71mm	North Carolina/South Carolina state line
69mm	N Pacolet River
67.5mm	**Welcome Ctr wb, full ♿ facilities, 📞, 🚻, litter barrels**
67	US 74 E, to NC 108, Columbus, Tryon, N 🛢 Shell/Burger King/dsl, Texaco, 🍴 Cocula Mexican, McDonald's, Subway, Waffle House, Wendy's, 🅾 Advance Parts, CVS Drug, Family$, Food Lion, S 🛢 Exxon/dsl, 🍴 KFC/Taco Bell, Mtn View Deli, 🏨 Days Inn, 🅾 🏥, BiLo, $General
59	Saluda, N 🏨 Saluda Motel, 🅾 camping, S 🛢 BP/dsl, Texaco/Subway, 🍴 Schaffer's Grille, 🏨 B&B, 🅾 repair, vet
56mm	Green River
54	US 25, to Greenville, E Flat Rock, access to Carl Sandburg Home
53.5mm	Eastern Continental Divide, 2130 ft
53	Upward Rd, Hendersonville, N 🛢 Texaco/dsl, 🍴 Waffle House, Zaxby's, 🏨 Mtn Inn&Suites, 🅾 Bloomfields Giftshop, S 🛢 Exxon/McDonald's/dsl, Shell/Pizza Inn/dsl, 🍴 Cracker Barrel, Subway, 🏨 Holiday Inn Express, 🅾 RV camping, to Carl Sandburg Home
49b a	US 64, Hendersonville, N 🛢 Chevron/dsl, Shell/dsl/24hr, Texaco/dsl, 🍴 Atlanta Bread Co, Azteca Mexican, Chick-fil-A, Golden Corral, Jack-in-the-Box, O'Charley's, Sonic, Waffle House, Zaxby's, 🏨 Best Western, Hampton Inn, Quality Inn, Ramada Ltd, 🅾 🏥, Advance Parts, $Tree, Ingles, Radio Shack, Sam's Club/gas, Staples, Walmart,

Exit	Services
49b a	Continued World of Clothing, S 🛢 Exxon/dsl/LP, Shell/dsl, 🍴 Applebee's, Arby's, Binion's Roadhouse, Bojangles, Burger King, China Sea, Cici's, Cocula Mexican, Denny's, Fatz Café, Hardee's, Honeybaked Ham, KFC, Krispy Kreme LJ Silver, McDonald's, Outback Steaks, Pizza Hut, Subway, Taco Bell, Wendy's, 🏨 Comfort Inn, Days Inn, Red Roof Inn, 🅾 🏥, Aldi Foods, Belk, BigLots, BiLo Foods CVS Drug, Family$, Home Depot, JC Penney, K-Mart Lowe's, NAPA, Tuesday Morning, Verizon, mall
46mm	**weigh sta both lanes, 📞**
44	US 25, Fletcher, N 🛢 Exxon/dsl, 🍴 Hardee's, Subway, 🅾 flea mkt campground, vet, S 🛢 Citgo/dsl, Shell/Bojangles, Huddle House/dsl/scales/24hr, United/dsl, 🍴 Burger King Jalapeno's Mexican, 🏨 Mountain Inn Suites, 🅾 🏥, Todd's RV/marine, USPO
41mm	**rest area both lanes, full ♿ facilities, 📞, 🚻, litter barrels, vending**
40	NC 280, Arden, N 🛢 Exxon/dsl, Shell/Arby's/dsl, 🍴 Carrabba's, Chili's, Cracker Barrel, Lonestar Steaks, McDonald's, Ruby Tuesday, Waffle House, 🏨 Budget Motel, Clarion Inn, Comfort Inn, Days Inn, EconoLodge, Hampton Inn 🅾 Acura/Honda, Best Buy, Lowe's, Marshall's, Michael's Old Navy, PetsMart, Ross, Target, World Mkt, S 🛢 BP/dsl 🍴 Circle B Ranch BBQ, J&S Cafeteria, 🏨 Fairfield Inn, 🅾 Asheville ♻, BMW, Rutledge Lake Camping
37	NC 146, Skyland, N 🛢 Exxon, 🍴 Arby's, McDonald's, PF Changs, Shoney's, Waffle House, 🏨 Hilton, Quality Inn,

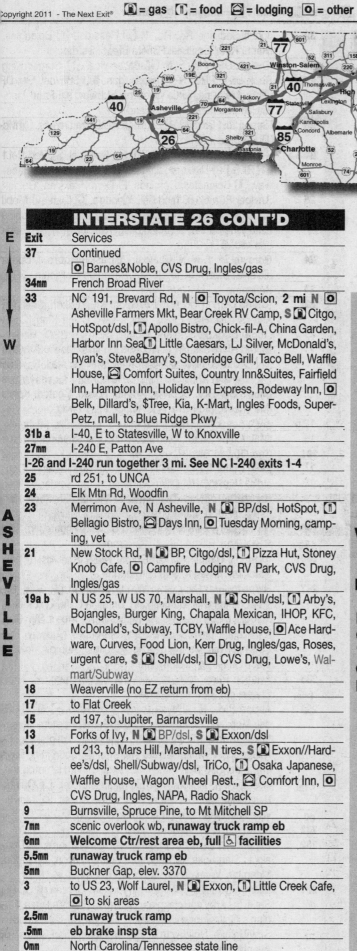

NC

INTERSTATE 26 CONT'D

E ↕ W

ASHEVILLE

Exit	Services
37	Continued
	🅾 Barnes&Noble, CVS Drug, Ingles/gas
34mm	French Broad River
33	NC 191, Brevard Rd, N 🅾 Toyota/Scion, **2 mi** N 🅾 Asheville Farmers Mkt, Bear Creek RV Camp, S 🅾 Citgo, HotSpot/dsl, 🍴 Apollo Bistro, Chick-fil-A, China Garden, Harbor Inn Sea🍴 Little Caesars, LJ Silver, McDonald's, Ryan's, Steve&Barry's, Stoneridge Grill, Taco Bell, Waffle House, 🏠 Comfort Suites, Country Inn&Suites, Fairfield Inn, Hampton Inn, Holiday Inn Express, Rodeway Inn, 🅾 Belk, Dillard's, $Tree, Kia, K-Mart, Ingles Foods, Super-Petz, mall, to Blue Ridge Pkwy
31b a	I-40, E to Statesville, W to Knoxville
27mm	I-240 E, Patton Ave
I-26 and I-240 run together 3 mi. See NC I-240 exits 1-4
25	rd 251, to UNCA
24	Elk Mtn Rd, Woodfin
23	Merrimon Ave, N Asheville, N 🅾 BP/dsl, HotSpot, 🍴 Bellagio Bistro, 🏠 Days Inn, 🅾 Tuesday Morning, camping, vet
21	New Stock Rd, N 🅾 BP, Citgo/dsl, 🍴 Pizza Hut, Stoney Knob Cafe, 🅾 Campfire Lodging RV Park, CVS Drug, Ingles/gas
19a b	N US 25, W US 70, Marshall, N 🅾 Shell/dsl, 🍴 Arby's, Bojangles, Burger King, Chapala Mexican, IHOP, KFC, McDonald's, Subway, TCBY, Waffle House, 🅾 Ace Hardware, Curves, Food Lion, Kerr Drug, Ingles/gas, Roses, urgent care, S 🅾 Shell/dsl, 🅾 CVS Drug, Lowe's, Walmart/Subway
18	Weaverville (no EZ return from eb)
17	to Flat Creek
15	rd 197, to Jupiter, Barnardsville
13	Forks of Ivy, N 🅾 BP/dsl, S 🅾 Exxon/dsl
11	rd 213, to Mars Hill, Marshall, N tires, S 🅾 Exxon//Hardee's/dsl, Shell/Subway/dsl, TriCo, 🍴 Osaka Japanese, Waffle House, Wagon Wheel Rest., 🏠 Comfort Inn, 🅾 CVS Drug, Ingles, NAPA, Radio Shack
9	Burnsville, Spruce Pine, to Mt Mitchell SP
7mm	scenic overlook wb, **runaway truck ramp eb**
6mm	**Welcome Ctr/rest area eb, full ♿ facilities**
5.5mm	**runaway truck ramp eb**
5mm	Buckner Gap, elev. 3370
3	to US 23, Wolf Laurel, N 🅾 Exxon, 🍴 Little Creek Cafe, 🅾 to ski areas
2.5mm	**runaway truck ramp**
.5mm	**eb brake insp sta**
0mm	North Carolina/Tennessee state line

INTERSTATE 40

E ↕ W

WILMINGTON

Exit	Services
420mm	I-40 begins/ends at Wilmington, **Services on US 17 N** 🏠 Hampton Inn, 🅾 Ford/Lincoln/Mercury, Land Rover, Hyundai, Home Depot, Mazda, Nissan, Subaru, Suzuki, Toyota/Scion, Volvo, S 🅾 BP, Carolina Petro, Dodge's Store/dsl, Exxon/dsl/24hr, Hugo's, Murphy USA/dsl, 🍴 Arby's, Bojangles, Buffalo Wild Wings, Carrabba's, Chick-fil-A, China Buffet, Church's, Cracker Barrel, Dunkin Donuts, Hardee's, Hieronymous Sea🍴 Hooters, IHOP, Jeanette's Pizza, McDonald's, O'Charley's, Old Chicago Grill, Olive Garden, Panaderia, Ruby Tuesday, Sonic, Sticky Fingers Rest., Subway, Taco Bell, Waffle House, Whitey's Rest., 🏠 Best Value Inn, Comfort Suites, Days Inn, EconoLodge, Elizabeth's Pizza, Extended Stay America, GreenTree Inn, Holiday Inn, Innkeeper, MainStay Suites, Motel 6, Quality Inn, Ramada Inn, Red Roof Inn, Sleep Inn, Super 8, Travelodge, Travel Inn, Wingate Inn, 🅾 Advance Parts, AutoZone, Cadillac, Costco/gas, Batteries+, CVS Drug, Family$, Hyundai, Marshall's, PetsMart, Radio Shack, Rite Aid, Target, VW, Walmart, **Services 2-4 mi S on NC 132** 🅾 BP, Exxon/dsl, 🍴 Applebee's, Bojangles, Burger King, Checker's, Chili's, Cici's Pizza, Cookout, Domino's, Golden Corral, Hardee's, Hibachi Bistro, HoneyBaked Ham, KFC, Little Caesars, McAlister's Deli, McDonald's, Outback Steaks, Quiznos, Starbucks, Taco Bell, Wendy's, 🏠 Baymont Inn, Comfort Inn, Courtyard, Holiday Inn Express, 🅾 Acura/Honda, Best Buy, Buick/GMC, Chevrolet, Dodge/Jeep, $Tree, Harris-Teeter/24hr, K-Mart, Lowe's Foods, Lowe's Whse, Mercedes, Old Navy, PetCo, Sam's Club, Staples, TJ Maxx, Tuesday Morning, Verizon, urgent care, to UNCW
420b a	Gordon Rd, NC 132 N, **2 mi** N 🅾 Hess/dsl, Kangaroo/dsl, 🍴 Andy's Custard, Hardees, KFC, McDonald's, Smithfield's Chicken/BBQ, Waffle House, Zaxby's, 🅾 CVS Drug, KOA (4mi), Rite Aid, Walgreens, S 🅾 BP/dsl, Kangaroo/dsl, Go Gas/dsl, 🍴 Carolina BBQ, China Wok, Subway, 🅾 Family$, Lowe's Foods, Rite Aid
416b a	I-140, US 17, to Topsail Island, New Bern, & Myrtle Beach
414	to Brunswick Co beaches, Castle Hayne, S 🅾 BP/24hr, GoGas/dsl, Kangaroo, 🍴 Andy's Custard, Hardee's, Subway, 🅾 Bo's Foods, CVS Drug, $General, USPO
413mm	NE Cape Fear River

E / W

NC

INTERSTATE 40 CONT'D

Exit	Services
408	NC 210, **N** Mack/Volvo/International Trucks, **S** 🛢 Hess/Wendy's/dsl/cafe/scales/24hr, Phoenix TC/dsl/scales, Shell/Noble Roman's, 🍴 Hardee's, Noble Roman's, Subway, ⊙ Food Lion, to Moore's Creek Nat Bfd/camping
398	NC 53, Burgaw, **2 mi S** 🍴 Andy's Rest., CW's Cafe, Hardee's, McDonald's, Subway, 🛏 Burgaw Motel, ⊙ H, camping
390	to US 117, Wallace
385	NC 41, Wallace, **N** 🛢 Exxon, 🍴 Mad Boar Rest., 🛏 Holiday Inn Express, ⊙ Lake Leamon Camping
384	NC 11, Wallace
380	Rose Hill, **S** 🛢 BP/dsl (1mi), Pure
373	NC 903, Magnolia, **N** 🛢 BP/dsl/24hr., 🛏 B&B, ⊙ H, Cowan Museum
369	US 117, Warsaw
364	NC 24, to NC 50, Clinton, **rest area both lanes, full** ♿ **facilities,** 🚻, 🏧, **litter barrels, vending, petwalk, N** 🛢 Wilco/Hess/Arby's/Stuckey's/dsl/24hr, **S** 🛢 BP/dsl, Kangaroo/dsl, Marathon, Sunoco/Bojangles, 🍴 KFC, McDonald's, Smithfield's BBQ, Subway, Waffle House, Wendy's, 🛏 Days Inn, Holiday Inn Express
355	NC 403, to US 117, to Goldsboro, Faison, **3 mi N** 🛢 Pure
348	Suttontown Rd
343	US 701, Newton Grove, **1 mi N** 🛢 Exxon/dsl, to Bentonville Bfd
341	NC 50, NC 55, to US 13, Newton Grove, **1.5 mi N** 🛢 Exxon/dsl, 🍴 Hardee's, **S** 🛢 BP/McDonald's, Shell/Subway, 🍴 Smithfield BBQ
334	NC 96, Meadow, **S** 🛢 BP/dsl (1mi)
328b a	I-95, N to Smithfield, S to Benson
325	NC 242, to US 301, to Benson, **S** 🛢 Citgo/dsl
324mm	**rest area both lanes, full** ♿ **facilities,** 🚻, 🏧, **litter barrels, vending, petwalk, no overnight parking**
319	NC 210, McGee's Crossroads, **N** 🛢 Citgo/Papa's Subs & Pizza/dsl, Shell/BBQ/dsl/24hr, 🍴 McDonald's, ⊙ H, vet, **S** 🛢 Mobil/CW's Cafe, 🍴 Bojangles, China Star, Italian Pizza/Pasta, KFC/Taco Bell, Subway, Wendy's, ⊙ AutoZone, Food Lion, $General, USPO
312	NC 42, to Clayton, Fuquay-Varina, **N** 🛢 Wilco/Hess/Wendy's/dsl/24hr, Murphy Express/dsl, 🍴 Andy's Rest., Applebee's, China King, Cookout, Cracker Barrel, Fiesta Mexicana, Golden Corral, Jersey Mike's Subs, King Chinese, Marko's Pizza, Ruby Tuesday, Papa Subs/Pizza, Pizza Inn, Smithfield BBQ, 🛏 Comfort Inn, Holiday Inn Express, Super 8, ⊙ CarQuest, $Tree, JustTires, Lowe's, Wal-Mart, USPO, **S** 🛢 Exxon/Burger King, BP/Subway/dsl/24hr, Citgo/dsl, Shell/dsl, 🍴 Bojangles, DQ, Domino's, Jumbo China, KFC/Taco Bell, McDonald's, Waffle House, 🛏 Hampton Inn, Sleep Inn, ⊙ CVS Drug, Food Lion, Walgreens, vet
309	US 70 E, Goldsboro, Smithfield
306b a	US 70 E bus, to Smithfield, Garner, Goldsboro, **1 mi N** 🛢 Kangaroo/Subway/dsl, Shell/dsl, ⊙ Chrysler/Dodge/Jeep, **S** 🍴 Buffalo Wild Wings, Chili's, Chick-fil-A, Coldstone, Kaze Steaks, La Cocina Mexican, McDonald's, Moe's SW Grill, New Japan Express, Logan's Roadhouse, Moe's SW Grill, Subway, TGIFriday's, Wendy's, ⊙ AT&T, Best Buy, BJ's Whse/gas, GNC, Kohl's, Michaels, PetsMart, Ross, Staples, Target, TJ Maxx

RALEIGH

Exit	Services
303	Jones Sausage Rd, Rd, **N** 🛢 Hess/dsl, 🍴 Bojangles, Burger King, Smithfield BBQ, **S** 🛢 Hess/dsl
301	I-440 E, US 64/70 E, to Wilson
300b a	Rock Quarry Rd, **N** ⊙ Kroger/gas, **S** 🛢 BP/dsl, Exxon, 🍴 Burger King, Little Caesars, Subway, ⊙ Food Lion, Rite Aid
299	Person St, Hammond Rd, Raleigh (no EZ return eb), **1 mi N** 🛢 Exxon/dsl, ⊙ to Shaw U
298b a	US 401 S, US 70 E, NC 50, **N** 🛢 Shell/dsl, 🛏 Red Roof Inn, **S** 🛢 BP, Exxon/dsl, Hess/Wilco/dsl, Hugo's, Raceway, 🍴 Bojangles, Dominos, El Cerro Mexican, Golden Seafood&Chicken, Taco Bell, Wendy's, 🛏 Claremont Inn, Super 8, ⊙ AutoZone, CarQuest, Sam's Club/gas
297	Lake Wheeler Rd, **N** 🛢 Exxon, 🍴 Subway, ⊙ H, Farmer's Mkt, **S** 🛢 Citgo
295	Gorman St, **1 mi N** 🛢 Exxon/dsl, 🍴 Hardee's, McDonald's, Subway, ⊙ to NCSU, Reynolds Coliseum, **S** 🛢 Kangaroo
293	to I-440, US 1, US 64 W, Raleigh, **S** 🛢 Exxon, Shell, 🍴 Astor's Grill, Bob Evans, Chick-fil-A, China King, Coldstone, Cookout, Golden Corral, Dickey's BBQ, Honey-Baked Ham, Jasmin Bistro, McDonald's, Moe's SW Grill, Noodles&Co, Olive Garden, Panera Bread, Qdoba, Red Lobster, Red Robin, Remington Grill, Ruby Tuesday, Starbucks, Subway, Taco Bell, Waffle House, 🛏 Best Western, Red Roof Inn, ⊙ BJ's Whse, Ford, GNC, Home Depot, Jo-Ann Fabrics, Kohl's, Lowe's, Marshall's, Michael's, NTB, Office Depot, Old Navy, PetsMart, Steinmart, mall
291	Cary Towne Blvd, Cary, **1 mi S** 🛢 Circle K, 🍴 Burger King, China 1, DQ, Jersey Mike's, Macaroni Grill, McDonald's, Mimi's Cafe, Olive Garden, On-the-Border, Peiwei, Ragazzi's, Tomyum Thai, ⊙ Belk, Dillards, Firestone, Harris Teeter, JC Penney, Macy's, Sears, TJ Maxx
290	NC 54, Cary, **1 mi N** ⊙ Comfort Suites, Wingate Inn, **2 mi S** 🛢 Citgo, Exxon, Shell, 🛏 Hampton Inn
289	to I-440, Wade Ave, to Raleigh, **N** ⊙ H, Carter-Finley Stadium, museum, **S** to fairgrounds
287	Harrison Ave, Cary, **N** to Wm B Umstead SP, **S** 🛢 BP, 🍴 Bonefish Grill, Burger King, Carolina Cafe, Chick-fil-A, Maggie Moo's Ice Cream, McDonald's, Moe's SW Grill, NY Pizza, Ruth's Chris Steaks, Starbucks, Subway, Thai Cuisine, Wendy's, 🛏 Embassy Suites, Studio+, TownePlace Suites, ⊙ Colony Tire
285	Aviation Pkwy, to Morrisville, Raleigh/Durham ✈, **N** 🛢 Sheetz/dsl, 🛏 Hilton Garden
284	Airport Blvd, **N** 🛏 Hyatt Place, ⊙ to RDU ✈, **S** 🛢 BP/dsl, Mobil, 🍴 Bojangles, Cracker Barrel, Hooters, Jersey Mike's Subs, KFC/Taco Bell, Quizno's, Schlotsky's, TX Roadhouse, Waffle House, Wendy's, 🛏 Courtyard, Days Inn, Extended Stay America, Fairfield Inn, Hampton Inn, Holiday Inn, Holiday Inn Express, Microtel, La Quinta, Residence Inn, Sheraton, Staybridge Suites, ⊙ Morrisville Outlets/famous brands/food court
283	I-540, to US 70, Aviation Pkwy
282	Page Rd, **S** 🍴 Arby's, Bojangles, Jimmy John's, McDonald's, Starbucks, 🛏 Comfort Suites, Hilton, Sheraton, Sleep Inn, Wingate Inn, ⊙ World Trade Ctr
281	Miami Blvd, **N** 🛏 Marriott, Wyndham Garden, **S** 🛢 BP, Shell, 🍴 Arby's, Bojangles, Quizno's, Randy's Pizza, Rudino's Grill, Subway, Wendy's, Wok'n Grill, 🛏 Extended Stay Deluxe, Holiday Inn Express, Homewood Suites, ⊙ Atlantic Tire

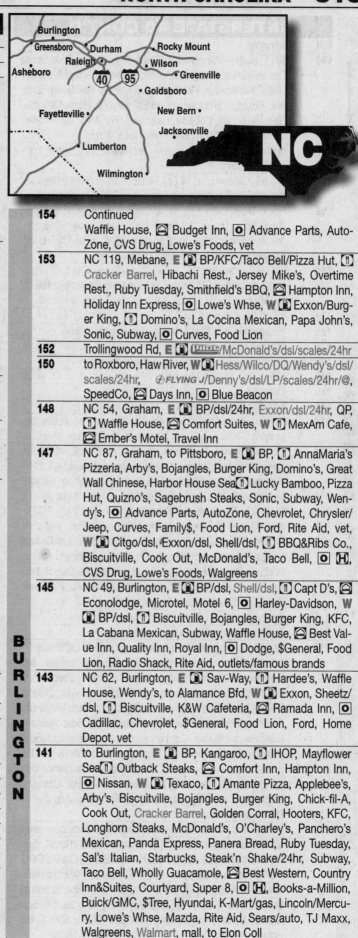

INTERSTATE 40 CONT'D

Exit	Services
280	Davis Dr, **N** to Research Triangle, **S** 🛏 Radisson
279b a	NC 147, Durham Fwy, to Durham, **N** 🅗
278	NC 55, to NC 54, World Trade Ctr, Apex, Foreign Trade Zone 93, **N** 🅖 Citgo, 🍴 Sansui Grill, Waffle House, 🛏 Best Value Inn, Comfort Inn, Doubletree, La Quinta, Red Roof Inn, **S** 🅖 Exxon/dsl, Mobil/dsl (1mi), 🍴 Arby's, Backyard BBQ, Bojangles, Chick-fil-A, Cpt D's, El Dorado Mexican, Golden Corral, Hardee's, McDonald's, Oh'Brian's, Papa John's, Pizza Hut, Quizno's, Starbucks, Subway, Taco Bell, Wendy's, Zorba's Grill, 🛏 Candlewood Suites, Courtyard, Crossland Suites, Homestead Suites, Residence Inn, ⊙ Aamco, Alltune/Lube, AutoZone, BigLots, CVS Drug, $Tree, Food Lion, Jiffy Lube, tires
276	Fayetteville Rd, **N** 🅖 Circle K/dsl, Exxon/dsl, 🍴 McDonald's, Orient Garden, Quizno's, Ruby Tuesday, Rudino's Pizza, Souper Salad, Starbucks, Waffle House, Wendy's, Wing Stop, ⊙ Harris-Teeter, Kroger, Walgreens, to NC Central U, **S** 🍴 Carino's Italian, Chili's, Cold Stone Creamery, Melting Pot, Moe's SW Grill, PF Chang's, Starbucks, Ted's MT Grill, 🛏 Hilton Garden, ⊙ Belks, Best Buy, Macy's, JC Penney, Nordstrom's, Old Navy, Sears/auto, mall
274	NC 751, to Jordan Lake, **1-2 mi N** 🅖 BP, 🍴 Burger King, McDonald's, Waffle House, Wendy's, **S** 🅖 BP, 🍴 Chick-fil-A, Subway
273	NC 54, to Durham, UNC-Chapel Hill, **N** 🅖 Shell/dsl, **S** 🅖 BP, Shell/dsl, 🍴 Hardee's, Nantucket Cafe, New China, 🛏 Courtyard (2mi), Hampton Inn, Holiday Inn Express, ⊙ vet
270	US 15, US 501, Chapel Hill, Durham, **N** 🍴 Bob Evans, Carrabbas, Dickey's BBQ, Firehouse Subs, Jason's Deli, Kanki Japanese, Lonestar Steaks, Longhorn Steaks, Moes' SW Grill, Outback Steaks, Philly Steaks, Reb Robin, Starbucks, Subway, 🛏 Comfort Inn, Homewood Suites, Springhill Suites, Staybridge Suites, ⊙ 🅗, Barnes&Noble, Best Buy, $Tree, Home Depot, Kohl's, Kroger, Marshall's, Michael's, Old Navy, Petsmart, Saab, Walmart, to Duke U, **S** 🅖 Exxon, 🍴 Applebee's, Boston Mkt, Golden Corral, Hardee's, La Hacienda Mexican, McDonald's, Subway, Wendy's, 🛏 Hampton Inn, Red Roof Inn, Residence Inn, Sheraton, ⊙ Acura, Advance Parts, BMW, Chevrolet, Food Lion, Lowe's Whse, Subaru
266	NC 86, to Chapel Hill, **2 mi S** 🅖 BP, Exxon, Wilco/Hess/dsl, 🍴 Pop's Pizza, Quizno's, Subway
263	New Hope Church Rd
261	Hillsborough, **1.5 mi N** 🅖 BP, Citgo/dsl, Shell, 🍴 Hardee's, KFC/Taco Bell, McDonald's, Subway, Waffle House, Wendy's, 🛏 Holiday Inn Express, Microtel
259	I-85 N, to Durham
I-40 & I-85 run together 30 mi. See Interstate 85, exits 131-161.	
161	to US 70 E, NC 86 N
160	Efland, **W** 🅖 Exxon/dsl
158	**weigh sta both lanes**
157	Buckhorn Rd, **E** 🅖 BP/dsl, Petro/Mobil/Iron Skillet/dsl/scales/24hr/@, **W** 🅖 PopShoppe
154	Mebane-Oaks Rd, **E** 🅖 Murphy USA, Shell/dsl/24hr, Sheetz/dsl, 🍴 Andy's Rest., Ciao Pizza, Subway, ⊙ $Tree, Walmart, **W** 🅖 BP, Hess/Wilco/dsl, Shell/dsl/24hr, 🍴 Biscuitville, Bojangles, La Fiesta Mexican, McDonald's, Quizno's, Roma Pizza, Sake Japanese, Stir King,

Exit	Services
154	Continued Waffle House, 🛏 Budget Inn, ⊙ Advance Parts, AutoZone, CVS Drug, Lowe's Foods, vet
153	NC 119, Mebane, **E** 🅖 BP/KFC/Taco Bell/Pizza Hut, 🍴 Cracker Barrel, Hibachi Rest., Jersey Mike's, Overtime Rest., Ruby Tuesday, Smithfield's BBQ, 🛏 Hampton Inn, Holiday Inn Express, ⊙ Lowe's Whse, **W** 🅖 Exxon/Burger King, 🍴 Domino's, La Cocina Mexican, Papa John's, Sonic, Subway, ⊙ Curves, Food Lion
152	Trollingwood Rd, **E** 🅖 🚛/McDonald's/dsl/scales/24hr
150	to Roxboro, Haw River, **W** 🅖 Hess/Wilco/DQ/Wendy's/dsl/scales/24hr, ✈ FLYING J/Denny's/dsl/LP/scales/24hr/@, SpeedCo, 🛏 Days Inn, ⊙ Blue Beacon
148	NC 54, Graham, **E** 🅖 BP/dsl/24hr, Exxon/dsl/24hr, QP, 🍴 Waffle House, 🛏 Comfort Suites, **W** 🍴 MexAm Cafe, 🛏 Ember's Motel, Travel Inn
147	NC 87, Graham, to Pittsboro, **E** 🅖 BP, 🍴 AnnaMaria's Pizzeria, Arby's, Bojangles, Burger King, Domino's, Great Wall Chinese, Harbor House Sea🍴 Lucky Bamboo, Pizza Hut, Quizno's, Sagebrush Steaks, Sonic, Subway, Wendy's, ⊙ Advance Parts, AutoZone, Chevrolet, Chrysler/Jeep, Curves, Family$, Food Lion, Ford, Rite Aid, vet, **W** 🅖 Citgo/dsl, Exxon/dsl, Shell/dsl, 🍴 BBQ&Ribs Co., Biscuitville, Cook Out, McDonald's, Taco Bell, ⊙ 🅗, CVS Drug, Lowe's Foods, Walgreens
145	NC 49, Burlington, **E** 🅖 BP/dsl, Shell/dsl, 🍴 Capt D's, 🛏 Econolodge, Microtel, Motel 6, ⊙ Harley-Davidson, **W** 🅖 BP/dsl, 🍴 Biscuitville, Bojangles, Burger King, KFC, La Cabana Mexican, Subway, Waffle House, 🛏 Best Value Inn, Quality Inn, Royal Inn, ⊙ Dodge, $General, Food Lion, Radio Shack, Rite Aid, outlets/famous brands
143	NC 62, Burlington, **E** 🅖 Sav-Way, 🍴 Hardee's, Waffle House, Wendy's, to Alamance Bfd, **W** 🅖 Exxon, Sheetz/dsl, 🍴 Biscuitville, K&W Cafeteria, 🛏 Ramada Inn, ⊙ Cadillac, Chevrolet, $General, Food Lion, Ford, Home Depot, vet
141	to Burlington, **E** 🅖 BP, Kangaroo, 🍴 IHOP, Mayflower Sea🍴 Outback Steaks, 🛏 Comfort Inn, Hampton Inn, ⊙ Nissan, **W** 🅖 Texaco, 🍴 Amante Pizza, Applebee's, Arby's, Biscuitville, Bojangles, Burger King, Chick-fil-A, Cook Out, Cracker Barrel, Golden Corral, Hooters, KFC, Longhorn Steaks, McDonald's, O'Charley's, Panchero's Mexican, Panda Express, Panera Bread, Ruby Tuesday, Sal's Italian, Starbucks, Steak'n Shake/24hr, Subway, Taco Bell, Wholly Guacamole, 🛏 Best Western, Country Inn&Suites, Courtyard, Super 8, ⊙ 🅗, Books-a-Million, Buick/GMC, $Tree, Hyundai, K-Mart/gas, Lincoln/Mercury, Lowe's Whse, Mazda, Rite Aid, Sears/auto, TJ Maxx, Walgreens, Walmart, mall, to Elon Coll

🅖 = gas   🍴 = food   🛏 = lodging   🅞 = other   Copyright 2011 - The Next Exi

NC

GREENSBORO

WINSTON · SALEM

CLEMMONS

INTERSTATE 40 CONT'D

Exit	Services
140	W 🍴 Buffalo Wing Wings, Chick-fil-A, Chili's, Cold Stone Creamery, Little Italy, McDonald's, Mimi's Cafe, Moe's SW Grill, Olive Garden, Peking House, Qdoba, Red Bowl Asian, Red Robin, Starbucks, TX Roadhouse, 🅞 Barnes&Noble, Belk, Best Buy, Dillard's, Discount Tire, GNC, JC Penney, Michael's, Old Navy, Petsmart, Ross, Target
139mm	**rest area both lanes, full ♿ facilities, 🚻, 🅿️litter barrels, vending**
138	NC 61, Gibsonville, W 🅖 TA/BP/Burger King/Popeye's/dsl/scales/@
135	Rock Creek Dairy Rd, W 🅖 Citgo, Exxon, 🍴 Bojangles, Ciao Pizza,China 1, Domino's, Guacamole Mexican, Jersey Mike's Subs, McDonald's, 🅞 Curves, CVS Drug, $General, Food Lion, Midtown Drug, vet
132	Mt Hope Church Rd, E 🅖 Citgo/Subway/dsl, 🍴 Pascalli's Pizza, W 🅖 Shell/dsl, Hess/Wendy's/dsl/24hr, 🛏 Hampton Inn
131	to US 70, Loop 85
129	Youngsmill Rd, W 🛏 Holiday Inn Express (3mi)
128	Alamance Church Rd
122c b a	US 220, to Greensboro, Asheboro (from sb)
220	US 220 S, to Greensboro
219	Loop 85 N, US 29 N, US 70 E, Greensboro
218	I-85 S, US 29 S, US 70 W, High Point, Charlotte
214	Wendover Ave, N 🍴 Applebee's, Arby's, Biscuitville, Bojangles, Calabash Sea🍴 Chick-fil-A, Chipotle Mexican, Cracker Barrel, Fuddrucker's, Golden Corral, IHOP, Imperial Gourmet, Jimmy John's, Kabuto Japanese, La Hacienda Mexican, Logan's Roadhouse, Longhorn Steaks, McDonald's, O'Charley's, Panda Express, Papa John's, Quizno's, Red Lobster, Steak'n Shake, Subway, TGIFriday, Taco Bell, Tripp's Rest., Vilarosa Italian, Wendy's, 🛏 Best Western, Courtyard, Hyatt Place, La Quinta, Lodge America, SpringHill Suites, Suburban Lodge, Wingate Inn, 🅞 Best Buy, Goodyear, Home Depot, Hummer, Kohl's, K-Mart/gas, Lowe's Whse, Macy's, Petsmart, Ross, Sam's Club/gas, Target, Walmart
212b a	Loop 40, US 241 S, to Bryan Blvd, N to ✈
211	Gallimore Dairy Rd, N 🅞 Freightliner
210	NC 68, to High Point, Piedmont Triad, N 🅖 Shell, 🍴 Arby's, 🛏 Days Inn, Embassy Suites, Fairview Inn, Homewood Suites, Sleep Inn, Wyndham Garden, 🅞 Ford Trucks, Kenworth, to ✈, S 🅖 Exxon/dsl, 🍴 Bojangles, Fatz Cafe, McDonald's, Pizza Hut/Taco Bell, Ruby Tuesday, Shoney's, Subway, Wendy's, 🛏 Best Western, Candlewood Suites, Comfort Suites, Courtyard, Extended Stay Deluxe, Fairfield Inn, Hampton Inn, Holiday Inn Express, Motel 6, Quality Inn, Red Roof Inn, Residence Inn
208	Sandy Ridge Rd, N 🅖 Wilco/Hess/dsl, 🅞 Camping World RV Ctr, S 🅖 Citgo/dsl, 🅞 Farmer's Mkt, Out Of Doors Mart/Airstream
206	Lp 40 (from wb), to Kernersville, Winston-Salem, downtown
203	NC 66, to Kernersville, N 🅖 Citgo/McDonald's/dsl, Exxon/Subway, Hess/dsl, 🍴 Capt Tom's Sea🍴 Clark's BBQ, Out West Steaks, Wendy's, 🛏 Sleep Inn, 🅞 Ford, Merchant Tire/repair, S 🅖 Shell/dsl, 🛏 Holiday Inn Express
201	Union Cross Rd, N 🅖 BP, Citgo/dsl, QM/dsl, 🍴 Blue Naples Pizza, Burger King, China Café, 🅞 CVS Drug, Food Lion

196	US 311 S, to High Point
195	US 311 N, NC 109, to Thomasville, S 🅖 Citgo, Wilco/Hess/dsl
193b a	US 52, NC 8, to Lexington, S 🅖 Hess/dsl, Shell, 🍴 Hardee's
193c	Silas Creek Pkwy (from eb), same as 192
192	NC 150, to Peters Creek Pkwy, N 🅖 Wilco/Hess, Texaco, 🍴 Bojangles, Burger King, Checker's, China Buffet, China Wok, Hong Kong Buffet, IHOP, KFC, Little Caesar's, Mayflower Sea🍴 Monterrey Mexican, Sonic, Subway, Taco Bell, Tokyo Japanese, 🛏 Innkeeper, 🅞 Acura/Subaru/Isuzu, Audi, AutoZone, BigLots, $General, $Tree, Ford, Hyundai, Lincoln/Mercury, Mazda, NAPA, Office Depot, Radio Shack, Rite Aid, VW, S 🅖 BP, QM, 🍴 Arby's, Baskin-Robbins/Dunkin Donuts, Cook Out, McDonald's, K&W Cafeteria, Pizza Hut, Waffle House, Wendy's, 🛏 Holiday Inn Express, 🅞 Advance Parts, BMW/Mini, CVS Drug, Food Lion, Hancock Fabrics, Honda, K-Mart, Mock Tire, Toyota
190	Hanes Mall Blvd (from wb, no re-entry), N 🍴 Chipotle Mexican, Jimmy John's, McDonald's, O'Charley's, Quizno's, Ruby Tuesday, TGIFriday, Tripp's Rest., 🛏 Days Inn, Quality Inn, 🅞 🅷, Belk, Dillard's, Firestone/auto, JC Penney, Macy's, Marshall's, Sears/auto, mall, same as 189, S 🍴 ChuckeCheese, Lonestar Steaks, Outback Steaks, Starbucks, Subway, 🛏 Comfort Suites, Microtel, 🅞 Office Depot
189	US 158, Stratford Rd, Hanes Mall Blvd, N 🅖 BP, Exxon, 🍴 Bojangles, Chili's, Golden Corral, Olive Garden, Red Lobster, Taco Bell, TX Roadhouse, 🛏 Courtyard, Fairfield Inn, 🅞 🅷, Belk, Chevrolet, Dillard's, JC Penney, Jo-Ann Fabrics, Macy's, Michael's, Sears/auto, Walgreens, mall, S 🅖 BP, Shell, 🍴 Applebee's, Bleu Rest., Buffalo Wild Wings, Burger King, Chick-fil-A, Dynasty Buffet, 5 Guys Burgers, Fuddruckers, Hooters, Jason's Deli, Jimmy's Sea🍴 KFC/LJ Silver, Longhorn Steaks, Macaroni Grill, Moe's SW Grill, Panera Bread, Subway, TX Land&Cattle, Wild Wing Cafe, 🛏 Extended Stay America, Hampton Inn, Hilton Garden, La Quinta, Sleep Inn, SpringHill Suites, 🅞 Barnes&Noble, Best Buy, Costco/gas, CVS Drug, Discount Tire, $Tree, Food Lion, Home Depot, Kohl's, Lowe's Whse, Petsmart, Ross, Sam's Club, Target
188	US 421, to Yadkinville, to WFU (no EZ wb return), Winston-Salem, 1/2mi N off US 421...🅖 BP, Exxon, Kangaroo, Shell, 🍴 Arby's, Boston Mkt, Burger King, McDonald's, Starbucks, Subway, Waffle House, Wendy's, 🅞 CarMax, Mercedes, Walmart
184	to US 421, Clemmons, N 🅖 Mobil, Shell, 🍴 Applebee's, Bambini Italian, Donato's Pizza, Eastern Pearl Chinese, IHOP, KFC, K&W Cafe, Marble Slab Creamery, Panera Bread, 🛏 Holiday Inn Express, S 🅖 BP/dsl, Exxon/dsl, Kangaroo, 🍴 Arby's, Biscuitville, Brick Oven Pizza, Burger King, Cozumel Mexican, Cracker Barrel, Dockside Sea🍴 Domino's, Kimono Japanese, McDonald's, Mi Pueblo Mexican, Mtn Fried Chicken, Pizza Hut, Quizno's, Ruby Tuesday, Sagebrush Steaks, Sonic, Starbucks, Subway, Taco Bell, Time to Eat Cafe, Waffle House, Wendy's, 🛏 Super 8, Village Inn, 🅞 Advance Parts, BigLots, CVS Drug, $Tree, K-Mart, Lowe's Foods, Merchant Tire, Parts+, Southern Mkt, Staples, TrueValue, Walgreens, USPO, vet
182	Bermuda Run (from wb, no re-entry), Tanglewood, S 🍴 Chang Thai, Lee's Chinese, Libby Hill Chicken&Sea🍴 Papa John's, 🅞 Harris-Teeter
182mm	Yadkin River

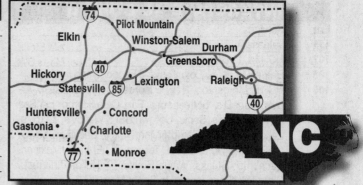

INTERSTATE 40 CONT'D

Exit	Services
180	NC 801, Tanglewood, N 🍴 Capt's Galley Sea🍴 Cicciones Rest., Domino's, Saratogo Steaks, Subway, 🅾 Lowe's Foods, Rite Aid, S 🅿 BP/McDonald's/dsl, Hess/dsl, 🍴 Bojangles, DQ, Jimmy's Greek, Venezia Italian, View Chinese, Wendy's, 🅾 Ace Hardware, CVS Drug, $General, Food Lion, Radio Shack, Walgreens, vet
177mm	**rest areas both lanes, full ♿ facilities, 🚻 vending, ⛽ litter barrels, petwalk**
174	Farmington Rd, N 🅿 Shell/dsl, 🅾 antiques, S 🅾 vineyards
170	US 601, Mocksville, N 🅿 Citgo, Murphy USA/dsl, Pure/Horn's Rest/DQ/Jersey Mike's/dsl/24hr, 🍴 JinJin Chinese, La Carreta Mexican, Moe's BurgerHouse, Subway, 🅾 $Tree, RV Superstore, Walmart, S 🅿 BP/dsl, Exxon, Shell/Taco Bell, 🍴 Arby's, Bojangles, Burger King, Chile Verde, China Grill, KFC, Marco's Pizza, McDonald's, Pier 601, Pizza Hut, Sagebrush Steaks, Shiki Japanese, Wendy's, 🏨 Comfort Inn, HighWay Inn, Quality Inn, Scottish Inn, 🅾 Ⓗ, Advance Parts, $General, Ford/Mercury, Lowe's Whse, Walgreens, USPO, vet
168	US 64, to Mocksville, N 🅿 Exxon/dsl, 🅾 Lake Myers RV Resort (3mi), S 🅿 BP/dsl, 🅾 Ⓗ
162	US 64, Cool Springs, N 🅾 Lake Myers RV Resort (5mi), S 🅿 Shell, 🅾 KOA
161mm	S Yadkin River
154	to US 64, Old Mocksville Rd, N Ⓗ, S 🅿 Citgo/dsl, 🍴 Jaybee's Hotdogs, 🅾 repair/tires
153	US 64 (from eb), **1/2 mi** S 🅿 Citgo/dsl, 🍴 Jaybee's Hotdogs, 🅾 repair/tires
152b a	I-77, S to Charlotte, N to Elkin
151	US 21, E Statesville, N 🅿 Hess/Wilco/24hr, Texaco/dsl, 🍴 Applebee's, Bojangles, Chick-fil-A, Chili's, Cook Out, Cracker Barrel, Dunkin Donuts, Golden Corral, Hooters, Jack-in-the-Box, KFC, K&W Cafeteria, Little China, Logan's Roadhouse, McDonald's, Mi Pueblo Café, Pizza Hut/Taco Bell, Quizno's, Red Lobster, Ruby Tuesday, Sagebrush Steaks, Sakura Japanese, Sorrento Pizza, Wendy's, Zaxby's, 🏨 Days Inn, Sleep Inn, 🅾 Advance Parts, Aldi Foods, AutoZone, BigLots, Bi-Lo, Cadillac/Chevrolet, Chrysler/Jeep, Curves, CVS Drug, $Tree, GNC, Home Depot, Lowe's Whse, Radio Shack, Russell Stover, Staples, Tire Kingdom, Walmart, S 🅿 Exxon, 🍴 Lonestar Steaks, Ming Court, Sonic, Waffle House, 🏨 Econolodge, Holiday Inn Express, Masters Inn, Quality Inn, 🅾 URGENT CARE, $General
150	NC 115, Statesville, N 🅿 BP/dsl, Citgo, Sheetz, Shell/Subway, 🍴 Amalfi's Italian, Little Caesar's, Ol'Bob's BBQ, 🅾 CVS Drug, Food Lion, Fred's Drug, museum
148	US 64, NC 90, W Statesville, N 🅿 Citgo/dsl, QP, Shell, 🍴 Arby's, BoxCar Grille, Burger King, McDonald's, Shiki Japanese, Subway, Village Inn Pizza, 🏨 Economy Inn, 🅾 CVS Drug, $General, Ingles Foods
146	Stamey Farm Rd
144	Old Mountain Rd, N 🅿 BP/dsl/repair, 🍴 Troy's Rest., S 🅿 BP/dsl, Shell/dsl
143mm	**weigh sta both lanes**
141	Sharon School Rd, N 🅿 Citgo
140mm	Catawba River
138	Oxford School Rd, to Catawba, N 🅿 Exxon/dsl/24hr
136mm	**rest areas both lanes, full ♿ facilities, 🚻 ⛽ vending, litter barrels, petwalk**

Exit	Services
135	Claremont, S 🅿 Shell, 🍴 BoxCar Grille, Burger King, Hannah's BBQ, Raffie's Subs, 🏨 Super 8, 🅾 Carolina Coach RV Ctr, $General, Lowe's Foods, TCS LP
133	Rock Barn Rd, N 🅿 Shell/dsl, S 🅿 Wilco/Hess/Stuckey's/Subway/Godfather's Pizza/dsl/scales/24hr
132	to NC 16, Taylorsville, N 🅿 BP, Shell/dsl, 🍴 Burger King, Zaxby's, 🏨 Holiday Inn Express, 🅾 Walmart
130	Old US 70, N 🍴 Domino's, Jack-in-the-Box, Subway, 🅾 $General, K-Mart, NAPA, vet, S 🅿 Citgo, Pure, Texaco, 🅾 repair, USPO
128	US 321, Fairgrove Church Rd, Hickory, N 🅿 BP, Shell, Solo/dsl, 🍴 McDonald's, Waffle House, 🅾 Ⓗ, to Catawba Valley Coll, S 🅿 Citgo/dsl, 🍴 Bennett's Smokehouse, Harbor Inn Sea🍴 Shoney's, Wendy's, 🏨 Days Inn, Ramada Inn, 🅾 Chrysler/Dodge/Jeep, GMC/Volvo
126	to US 70, NC 155, S 🅿 Citgo, Exxon, Shell, 🍴 Applebee's, Bob Evans, IHOP, Libby Hill Sea🍴 McDonald's, O'Charley's, Olive Garden, Taco Bell, Subway, 🏨 Holiday Inn Express, 🅾 Barnes&Noble, $Tree, Hickory Furniture Mart, Lowe's Whse, Michael's, Office Depot, Sam's Club, TJ Maxx, Walmart
125	Hickory, N 🅿 Raceway, 🍴 Bojangles, Golden Corral, Quizno's, Rancho Viejo Mexican, Starbucks, Texas Roadhouse, Tripp's Rest., Yewei Guan Chinese, 🏨 Red Roof Inn, 🅾 Advance Parts, BMW/Mercedes, S 🅿 Hess, Shell/dsl, 🍴 Arby's, Atlanta Bread, Carraba's, Chick-fil-A, ChuckeCheese, CiCi's, Cracker Barrel, Firebonz Rest., Fuddrucker's, Hooters, Jack-in-the-Box, Judge's BBQ, J&S Cafeteria, KFC, Kobe Japanese, Longhorn Steaks, Mamma's Pizza, Outback Steaks, Panda Express, Quizno's, Red Lobster, Ruby Tuesday, Waffle House, Wendy's, Zaxby's, 🏨 Comfort Suites, Courtyard, Crowne Plaza, Fairfield Inn, Hampton Inn, Sleep Inn, 🅾 Aldi Foods, Belk, Best Buy, Bottom$ Foods, Carmax, Dillards, $Tree, Ford, Hancock Fabrics, Harley-Davidson, Home Depot, Honda, JC Penney, Kohl's, Marshall's, Mazda, Mitsubishi, Office Depot, Old Navy, O'Reilly Parts, Petsmart, Porsche/VW, Scion/Toyota, Sears/auto, Suzuki, Target, Tire Kingdom, TJ Maxx, Tuesday Morning, dsl repair, mall
123	US 70/321, to NC 127, Hickory
121	Long View, N 🅾 Kenworth
119b a	Hildebran, N 🅿 Shell, 🍴 Bojangles, Hardee's, 🅾 $General
118	Old NC 10, N 🅿 Pure, Shell/dsl
116	Icard, S 🅿 Marathon/McDonald's/dsl, 🍴 Burger King, Granny's Kitchen, 🏨 Icard Inn/rest.
113	Connelly Springs, N 🅿 Citgo, Southern Star/dsl, 🍴 Subway, 🅾 Ⓗ, CVS Drug, Ford/Hyundai
112	Mineral Springs Mtn Rd, Valdese

E ⬆ **W**

MOCKSVILLE

STATESVILLE

HICKORY

NC

INTERSTATE 40 CONT'D

MORGANTON

E ↕ W

NC

Exit	Services
111	Valdese
107	NC 114, to Drexel
106	Bethel Rd, **S** 🅿 Exxon/dsl, 🛏 Economy Inn
105	NC 18, Morganton, **N** 🅿 Wilco/dsl, 🍴 Abele's Rest., Arby's, Capt D's, Coffeehouse, Fatz Café, Harbor Inn Sea McDonald's, Sonic, Uptown BBQ, Wendy's, Zaxby's, Zeko's Italian, 🛏 Hampton Inn, ⊙ 🅷, Cadillac/Chevrolet/GMC, **S** 🅿 Shell/dsl, Texaco, 🍴 El Paso Mexican, Sagebrush Steaks, Waffle House, 🛏 Holiday Inn/rest., Plaza Inn, Sleep Inn, ⊙ to South Mtns SP
104	Enola Rd, **S** 🅿 Citgo, 🍴 Chick-fil-A, Jersey Mike's Subs, ⊙ Belk, BigLots, $Tree, Food Lion, Staples, st patrol
103	US 64, Morganton, **N** 🅿 Exxon/dsl/24hr, 🍴 Allison's Rest., Village Inn Pizza, 🛏 Days Inn, **S** 🅿 Marathon, RaceWay, 🍴 Butch's BBQ, Checker's, Denny's, Dragon Chinese, Hardee's, KFC, Subway, Taco Bell, 🛏 Comfort Inn, ⊙ Clarks Tire, Food Lion, GNC, Ingles Foods, Lowe's Whse, Radio Shack, Walmart/drugs
100	Jamestown Rd, **N** 🅿 BP/dsl/24hr, 🍴 Waffle Shop, ⊙ Chrysler/Dodge/Jeep, Ford/Lincoln/Mercury, **2 mi N** 🍴 KFC, Taco Bell, 🛏 Eagle Motel
98	Causby Rd, to Glen Alpine, **S** B&B/food
96	Kathy Rd
94	Dysartsville Rd
90	Nebo, **N** 🅿 Country Cookin'/dsl/rest, ⊙ to Lake James SP, **S** 🅿 BP/dsl, ⊙ Springs Creek RV Ctr
86	NC 226, to Spruce Pine, Marion, **N** 🅿 Exxon, ♥Loves♥/Subway/Godfather's/dsl/scales/24hr, 🍴 Hardee's, KFC, Waffle House, ⊙ Jellystone RV Park (1mi)
85	US 221, Marion, **N** 🛏 Hampton Inn, ⊙ to Mt Mitchell SP, **S** 🅿 Shell/dsl/24hr, 🍴 Legends Roadhouse, 🛏 Days Inn, Super 8
83	Ashworth Rd
82mm	**rest area both lanes, full ♿ facilities, 🅒, 🚻, vending, litter barrels, petwalk**
81	Sugar Hill Rd, to Marion, **N** 🅿 BP/dsl, 🍴 Andy's Burgers, TX Pizza, ⊙ 🅷, Chrysler/Dodge/Jeep, $Tree, Walmart, **S** 🅿 Exxon/rest/dsl/24hr
76mm	Catawba River
75	Parker Padgett Rd, **S** 🅿 Exxon/Stuckey's/DQ/dsl
73	Old Fort, **N** 🅿 BP/dsl, 🍴 Hardee's, 🛏 B&B, ⊙ Mtn Gateway Museum, NAPA, **S** 🅿 Super Test/dsl, 🍴 McDonald's, ⊙ Auto+
72	US 70 (from eb), Old Fort, **N** B&B
71mm	Pisgah Nat Forest, eastern boundary
67.5mm	truck rest area eb
66	Ridgecrest, **N** 🛏 B&B
65	(from wb), to Black Mountain, Black Mtn Ctr
64	NC 9, Black Mountain, **N** 🅿 Exxon, Shell/Subway/24hr, 🍴 Pizza Hut, ⊙ BiLo/café, **S** 🅿 BP/dsl, 🍴 Denny's, Huddle House, KFC, McDonald's, Phil's BBQ, Taco Bell, Wendy's, 🛏 Comfort Inn, ⊙ Ingles Foods/gas, Rite Aid
63mm	Swannanoa River
59	Swannanoa, **N** 🅿 BP/Subway, Exxon/dsl, 🍴 Athens Pizza, Burger King, Okies Dokies Smokehouse, ⊙ Ace Hardware, Harley-Davidson, Ingles Foods/gas, KOA (2mi), Miles RV Ctr/Park, to Warren Wilson Coll, USPO, **S** ⊙ Mama Gertie's Camping
55	E Asheville, US 70, **N** 🅿 BP, Citgo/Subway, Mobil,

ASHEVILLE

Exit	Services
55	Continued 🍴 Arby's, Bojangles, Cocula Mexican, Waffle House, Zaxby's, 🛏 B&B, Days Inn, Holiday Inn, Motel 6, Quality Inn, ⊙ VA 🅷, Go Groceries, Top's RV park, to Mt Mitchell SP, Folk Art Ctr
53b a	I-240 W, US 74, to Asheville, Bat Cave, **N** 🍴 Burger King, China Buffet, Fat Buddy's BBQ, KFC, J&S Cafeteria, McDonald's, Subway, 🛏 Ramada Inn, ⊙ Advance Parts, BiLo, CVS Drug, $General, Hamrick's, Hancock Fabrics, **1-2 mi N on US 74** 🅿 BP, Citgo, Exxon/dsl, 🍴 Applebee's, Burger King, Carrabba's, Chili's, Chick-fil-A, Damon's, IHOP, O'Charley's, Olive Garden, Red Lobster, Subway, Waffle House, 🛏 Courtyard, Day's Inn, Econolodge, Extended Stay America, Hampton Inn, Ramada Ltd, ⊙ Barnes& Noble, Best Buy, Dillard's, Home Depot, Ingles Foods, K-Mart, Lowe's, Michael's, Office Depot,, Radio Shack, Ross, Sears/auto, mall, **S** 🅿 BP/dsl/LP, 🍴 Subway, ⊙ to Blue Ridge Pkwy
51	US 25A, Sweeten Creek Rd, **S** 🍴 Subway, 🛏 Brookstone Lodge, ⊙ Fun Depot
50	US 25, Asheville, **N** 🅿 CitiStop/dsl, Shell/dsl, 🍴 Arby's, Asaka Japanese, Chapala Mexican, Hardee's, LJ Silver, McDonald's, Moe's SW Grill, Red Stag Grill, Ruth's Chris Steaks, Starbucks, Subway, TX Roadhouse, TGIFriday's, Wendy's, 🛏 Baymont Inn, Doubletree Inn, Grand Bohemian Hotel, Guesthouse Inn, Howard Johnson, Sleep Inn, ⊙ 🅷, to Biltmore House, **S** 🅿 Hess/dsl, 🍴 Apollo Flame Rest., Atl Bread Co, Huddle House, Province Rest., 🛏 Forest Manor Inn
47mm	French Broad River
47	NC 191, W Asheville, **N** ⊙ Bear Creek RV Camping, **S** 🅿 BP/Subway, 🍴 Moose Cafe, ⊙ Audi/Porsche/VW, Farmer's Mkt, Ford/Lincoln/Mercury, Nissan, **2 mi S** 🛏 Comfort Inn, Country Inn&Suites, Fairfield Inn, Hampton Inn, Holiday Inn Express, Rodeway Inn
46b a	I-26 & I-240 E, **2 mi N** multiple services from I-240
44	US 19, US 23, W Asheville, **N** 🅿 BP, Hess/dsl, Shell/DQ/dsl, 🍴 Applebee's, Asiana Buffet, Burger King, Dunkin Donuts, Cracker Barrel, El Chapala Mexican, Fatz Cafe, Hardee's, IHOP, Pizza Hut, Waffle House, Wendy's, 🛏 Comfort Inn, Country Inn&Suites, Ramada Inn, Red Roof Inn, Rodeway Inn, Sleep Inn, Whispering Pines Motel, ⊙ Chevrolet, Chrysler/Dodge/Jeep, Family$, Ingles Foods, Lowe's, Mazda/Mercedes, **S** 🍴 McDonald's, Shoney's, 🛏 Budget Motel, Holiday Inn, ValuePlace Inn, ⊙ Bi-Lo Foods, CVS Drug, Home Depot
41mm	**weigh sta both lanes**
37	Candler, **N** 🅿 BP, TA/Buckhorn Rest./dsl/scales/24hr/@, ⊙ Goodyear, tires, **S** 🅿 Exxon/dsl, 🛏 Days Inn, Plantation Motel, ⊙ KOA
33	Newfound Rd, to US 74, **S** 🅿
31	Rd 215, Canton, **N** 🍴 Sagebrush Steaks, 🛏 Days Inn, **S** 🅿 BP/dsl, Marathon/DQ, Shell/dsl, 🍴 Arby's, Bojangles, Burger King, McDonald's, Subway, Taco Bell, Waffle House, 🛏 Comfort Inn, ⊙ Ford, Ingles Foods/gas, RV/truck repair
27	US 19/23, to Waynesville, Great Smokey Mtn Expsway, **3 mi S** 🅿 Shell/Burger King, 🍴 Shoney's, Subway, Taco Bell, 🛏 Super 8, ⊙ 🅷, $Tree, Food Lion, GNC, Lowe's, to WCU (25mi)
24	NC 209, to Lake Junaluska, **N** 🅿 Pilot/Subway/dsl/scales/24hr/@, 🛏 Midway Motel, **S** 🅿 Shell/cafe/dsl/24hr, ⊙ 🅷

INTERSTATE 40 CONT'D

Exit	Services
20	US 276, to Maggie Valley, Lake Junaluska, **S** 📷 BP/dsl, Exxon/dsl, Marathon (2mi), ⊙ Creekwood RV Park, Pride RV Resort, Winngray RV Park
16mm	Pigeon River
15	Fines Creek
13mm	Pisgah NF eastern boundary
10mm	**rest area both lanes, full** 🚻 **facilities,** 🕿, **vending,** 🛉, **litter barrels, petwalk**
7	Harmon Den
4mm	tunnel both lanes
0mm	North Carolina/Tennessee state line

INTERSTATE 77

Exit	Services
105mm	North Carolina/Virginia state line
105mm	**Welcome Ctr sb, full** 🚻 **facilities, info,** 🕿, **vending,** 🛉, **litter barrels, petwalk**
103mm	**weigh sta both lanes**
101	I-74 E, to Mt Airy, Winston-Salem, Greensboro, **E** 🛏 Hampton Inn, ⊙ 🏥 (12mi)
100	NC 89, to Mt Airy, **E** 📷 BP/Brintle's/rest/dsl/scales/24hr/@, Exxon/dsl, Marathon/Subway/dsl, 🍴 Wagon Wheel Rest., 🛏 Best Western, ⊙ 🏥 (12mi), clothing outlet
93	to Dobson, Surry, **E** 📷 BP/DQ/dsl, Marathon/dsl, 🛏 Hampton Inn, Surry Inn, ⊙ camping
85	NC 118, CC Camp Rd, to Elkin, **1-3 mi W** 📷 Murphy Express/dsl, Neighbor's, Shell/Blimpie/Stuckey's/dsl, Wilco/Hess/dsl, 🍴 Burger King, KFC, Mazzini's Italian, McDonald's, Sonic, 🛏 Elk Inn, Fairfield Inn, ⊙ AT&T, BigLots, $Tree, Food Lion, Lowe's Whse, Rite Aid, Walmart/Subway
83	US 21 byp, to Sparta (from nb)
82.5mm	Yadkin River
82	NC 67, Elkin, **E** 📷 BP/Backyard Burger/dsl, BP/Case Outlet/dsl, Exxon/dsl, 🍴 Arby's, Cracker Barrel, Jordan's Rest., 🛏 Holiday Inn Express, ⊙ Holly Ridge Camping (8mi), **W** 📷 Wilco/Hess/dsl, 🍴 Bojangles, Capt Galley, McDonald's, Valentino's Pizza, Waffle House, Wendy's, 🛏 Comfort Inn, Days Inn, Hampton Inn, Rose's Motel, ⊙ AutoValue Parts, Buick/GMC, Curves, D-Rex Drug, Food Lion, vet
79	US 21 S, to Arlington, **E** 📷 Citgo/Subway/dsl, 🛏 Super 8, **W** 📷 BP/dsl, 🍴 Glenn's BBQ, 🛏 Best Value Inn
73b a	US 421, to Winston-Salem (20mi), **E** 📷 Shell/Subway/dsl (1mi), USPO
72mm	**rest area nb, full** 🚻 **facilities,** 🕿, **vending,** 🛉, **litter barrels, petwalk**
65	NC 901, to Union Grove, Harmony, **E** ⊙ Van Hoy Farms Camping, **W** 📷 BP/dsl, Shell/Subway/dsl/24hr, 🍴 Burger Barn, 🛏 B&B, ⊙ Ace Hardware, Fiddler's Grove Camping (2mi)
63mm	**rest area sb, full** 🚻 **facilities,** 🕿, **vending,** 🛉, **litter barrels, petwalk**
59	Tomlin Mill Rd, **W** 📷 Valero/dsl
56.5mm	S Yadkin River
54	US 21, to Turnersburg, **E** 📷 Citgo, **W** 📷 Shell/dsl, 🍴 Arby's, **2mi W** 📷 Chick-fil-A, CookOut, Dunkin Donuts, Golden Corral, Zaxby's
51b a	I-40, E to Winston-Salem, W to Hickory
50	E Broad St, Statesville, **E** 📷 BP, Citgo, Kangaroo/dsl,

50	Continued Shell, 🍴 Arby's, Bojangles, Burger King, Charenda Mexican, CiCi's Pizza, Domino's, Golden Dragon, IHOP, Jack-in-the-Box, Little Caesar's, McDonald's, Papa John's, Pizza Hut, Shanghai Buffet, Shoney's, Starbucks, Subway, Wendy's, 🛏 Brookwood Inn, Red Roof Inn, ⊙ URGENT CARE, Ace Hardware, AT&T, Belk, Bi-Lo, $General, $Tree, Food Lion, JC Penney, JR Outlet, K-Mart, Rite Aid, Sears/auto, USPO
49b a	US 70, G Bagnal Blvd, to Statesville, **E** 📷 BP, Citgo/dsl, Kangaroo, Shell, Solo, 🍴 Brewsters, KFC, Outback Steaks, Rice Fun Chinese, Subway, Waffle House, 🛏 Baymont Inn, Best Western, Courtyard, Hampton Inn, Motel 6, Ramada Inn, Super 8, ⊙ Camping World RV Ctr, Chrysler/Dodge/Jeep, Ford/Lincoln/Mercury, Harley-Davidson, Honda, Nissan, Scion/Toyota, **W** 📷 Citgo, Exxon, 🍴 Carolina BBQ, 🛏 Best Value Inn, Microtel
45	to Troutman, Barium Springs, **E** 🛏 KOA, RV Repair, **W** 📷 4 Bros (3mi)
42	US 21, NC 115, to Troutman, Oswalt, **E** 📷 Hess/Wilco/Subway/dsl/scales/24hr, 🍴 McDonald's, Wendy's, ⊙ Lowe's Whse, **W** 📷 Citgo, 🍴 Arby's, ⊙ to Lake Norman SP, camping
39mm	**rest area both lanes, full** 🚻 **facilities,** 🕿, 🛉, **litter barrels, petwalk, vending**
36	NC 150, Mooresville, **E** 📷 Accel/dsl, Exxon, Shell/dsl/24hr, 🍴 Applebee's, Bob Evans, CiCi's Pizza, CookOut, Denny's, FatBoy's Cafe, Jack-in-the-Box, Pizza Hut, Quizno's, Sonny's BBQ, Taco Bell, Waffle House, Wendy's, 🛏 Days Inn, Fairfield Inn, Holiday Inn Express, Ramada Ltd, ⊙ URGENT CARE, AT&T, Belk, $Tree, Gander Mtn, GNC, Kohl's, Tuesday Morning, Walmart/Subway, **W** 📷 BJ's Whse, BP/dsl, Hess, Marathon, Shell/dsl/24hr, 🍴 Arby's, Baskin-Robbins/Dunkin Donuts, Bojangles, Chick-fil-A, Chili's, Cracker Barrel, Domino's, Donato's Pizza, Duckworth's Rest., 5 Guys Burgers, Golden Corral, Hardee's, Hickery Tavern Grill, Hooters, Joe Fish Rest, KFC, Kyoto Japanese, LoneStar Steaks, McAlister's Deli, McDonald's, Monterrey Mexican, O'Charley's, Panda Express, Panera Bread, Poppa's Hotdogs, Red Robin, Sonic, Starbucks, Steak'n Shake, Subway, TX Steaks, 🛏 Hampton Inn, Sleep Inn, Super 8, Wingate Inn, ⊙ Advance Parts, AutoZone, Best Buy, Bloom Foods, CVS Drug, Discount Tire, Lowe's Whse, Michael's, Old Navy, PetCo, Petsmart, Staples, Target, Tire Kingdom, Verizon, Walgreens
33	US 21 N, **E** 📷 Shell, 🍴 Big League Hotdogs, China Express, DQ, Jeffrey's Rest, McDonald's, Quizno's, Showmar's Rest, Starbucks, Subway, 🛏 Hilton Garden, SpringHill Suites, TownePlace Suites, ⊙ 🏥, AT&T, **W** 📷 BP,

Side labels: **E** ↕ **W** / **N** ↕ **S** / **ELKIN** / **STATESVILLE** / **MOORESVILLE** / **NC**

Ⓖ = gas Ⓕ = food Ⓛ = lodging Ⓞ = other

INTERSTATE 77 CONT'D

N ↑ S

Exit	Services
33	Continued
	Citgo/dsl, Ⓕ Arby's, Baskin-Robbins/Dunkin Donuts, Sauza's Mexican, Ⓞ Food Lion, Lake Norman RV Resort (13mi), vet
31	Langtree
30	Davidson, E Ⓖ Exxon/dsl, Ⓕ Donato's Pizza, Ming's Chinese, Subway, Ⓛ Homewood Suites, Ⓞ Harris-Teeter, to Davidson College, W Ⓕ North Harbor Rest
28	US 21 S, NC 73, Cornelius, Lake Norman, E Ⓖ Cashion/dsl, Citgo/24hr, Ⓕ Acropolis Cafe, Gilligan's Rest, Ⓛ Days Inn, Hampton Inn, Ⓞ NAPA, W Ⓖ Texaco, Ⓕ Bojangles, Domino's, Dragon Buffet, Gator's Grill, HoneyBaked Ham, Jersey Mike's, KFC, Kobe Japanese, K&W Cafeteria, Mac's Grill, McAlister's Deli, McDonald's, Pizza Hut, Starbucks, Subway, Taco Bell, Waffle House, Wendy's, Ⓛ Clarion, Comfort Inn, EconoLodge, Ⓞ Chrysler/Dodge/Jeep, Fresh Mkt, Goodyear/auto, Rite Aid, SteinMart, Walgreens, USPO
25	NC 73, Concord, Lake Norman, E Ⓖ Shell/dsl, Ⓕ Buffalo Pizza, Burger King, Chick-fil-A, Chili's, Donato's Pizza, Fuddrucker's, IHOP, Longhorn Steaks, McDonald's, Moe's SW Grill, Panda Express, Panera Bread, Starbucks, Wendy's, Ⓛ Country Inn&Suites, Hawthorn Suites, Quality Inn, Ⓞ AT&T, GNC, Harris-Teeter, Kohl's, Lowe's Whse, Marshall's, PetCo, Staples, Target, Tuffy Auto, Verizon, W Ⓖ Shell/dsl, Ⓕ Arby's, Bob Evans, Bojangles, Carrabba's, Cold Stone, DQ, Jason's Deli, Hickery Tavern Grill, Kabuto Japanese, Max&Erma's, Outback Steaks, Qdoba, Quiznos, Red Rock's Cafe, Starbucks, Subway, Ⓛ Candlewood Suites, Courtyard, Residence Inn, Sleep Inn, Ⓞ Barnes&Noble, Food Lion/deli, Walgreens, to Energy Explorium
23	Gilead Rd, to US 21, Huntersville, E Ⓖ BP, Citgo, Shell/24hr, Ⓕ Baskin-Robbins/Dunkin Dounuts, Chico's Mexican, CookOut, Hardee's, Palace of China, Subway, Waffle House, Wendy's, Ⓛ Holiday Inn Express, Red Roof Inn, Ⓞ AutoZone, Buick/GMC, Food Lion, Ford, Goodyear/auto, Hancock Fabrics, Honda, O'Reilly Parts, Rite Aid, Toyota, Tuesday Morning, VW, USPO, W Ⓖ Shell, Ⓕ CiCi's Pizza, Firehouse Subs, 5 Guys Burgers, Friendly's, Pizza Hut, Quizno's, Starbucks, Vocelli's Pizza, Ⓞ Ⓗ, Batteries+, Bi-Lo, CVS Drug, GNC, Harris-Teeter, Walgreens
19b a	S I-485 Outer, Rd 115, to Spartanburg
18	Harris Blvd, Reames Rd, E Ⓖ BP/Arby's, Shell/dsl, Ⓕ Azteca, Bangkok Square, Bob Evans, Hickory Tavern, Jack-in-the-Box, Lin's Buffet, Pilly Connection, Quizno's, Waffle House, Ⓛ Comfort Suites, Fairfield Inn, Hilton Garden, Suburban Lodge, Ⓞ Ⓗ, Advance Parts, Staples, to UNCC, Univ Research Park, W Ⓕ Bravo Italian, Chick-fil-A, Chili's, Cold Stone, Edomae Grill, Firehouse Subs, 5 Guys Burgers, Fox&Hound, Mimi's Cafe, Moe's SW Grill, Olive Garden, On-the-Border, Panera bread, PF Chang's, Red Robin, Shane's Rib Shack, TGI Friday's, Wendy's, Ⓛ Drury Inn, Ⓞ AT&T, Belk, Best Buy, Dillard's, Lowe's Whse, Macy's, Old Navy, Petsmart, Target, mall
16b a	US 21, Sunset Rd, E Ⓖ 76/Circle K, Shell, Ⓕ Capt D's, Hardee's, KFC, McDonald's, Papa John's, Subway, Taco Bell, Wendy's, Ⓛ Days Inn, Super 8, Ⓞ AutoZone, NAPA, W Ⓖ Citgo/dsl, Shell/dsl/scales/24hr,

C O N C O R D

NC

C H A R L O T T E

Exit	Services
16b a	Continued
	76/Circle K, Ⓕ Baskin-Robbins/Dunkin Donuts, Bojangles, Bubba's BBQ, CookOut, Denny's, Domino's, Jack-in-the-Box, Waffle House, Ⓛ Microtel, Sleep Inn, Ⓞ Advance Parts, Aldi Foods, CVS Drug, Family$, Food Lion, Walgreens
13b a	I-85, S to Spartanburg, N to Greensboro
12	La Salle St, W Ⓖ Shell/dsl, Texaco/dsl
11b a	I-277, Brookshire Fwy, NC 16
10b	Trade St, 5th St, E Ⓞ to Discovery Place, W Ⓖ Texaco, Ⓕ Bojangles
10a	US 21 (from sb), Moorhead St downtown
9	I-277, US 74, to US 29, John Belk Fwy, downtown, E Ⓗ, stadium
8	Remount Rd (from nb, no re-entry)
7	Clanton Rd, E Ⓖ Texaco/dsl, Ⓕ Chick-fil-A, McDonald's, Wendy's, Ⓛ Days Inn, EconoLodge, Super 8, Ⓞ AutoZone, W Ⓖ BP, Shell/dsl
6b a	US 521, Billy Graham Pkwy, E Ⓖ BP, Citgo, Shell/dsl, Sunoco/dsl, Ⓕ Arby's, Azteca Mexican, Bojangles, Capt D's, Carolina Prime Steaks, Domino's, Dragon House, Firehouse Subs, HoneyBaked Ham, IHOP, KFC, Papa John's, Waffle House, Ⓛ Best Western, Days Inn, Howard Johnson, Ramada Ltd, Sheraton, Tres Pesos, Ⓞ CVS Drug, Family$, Home Depot, TJ Maxx, Walgreens, to Queens Coll, W Ⓖ Texaco, Ⓕ Omaha Steaks, Ⓛ Embassy Suites, Holiday Inn, Hyatt Place, InTown Suites, La Quinta, Sleep Inn, Ⓞ Ⓒ
5	Tyvola Rd, E Ⓖ Shell, Texaco, Ⓕ Chili's, China King, Kabuto Japanese, McDonald's, Royal Buffet, Sonny's BBQ, Subway, Ⓛ Candlewood Suites, Comfort Inn, Hilton, Marriott, Quality Inn, Residence Inn, Studio+, Ⓞ Aldi Foods, Costco/gas, Jaguar, Buick/GMC, Verizon, services E of blvd, W Ⓛ Extended Stay America, Wingate Inn
4	Nations Ford Rd, E Ⓖ Citgo, 76/Circle K/24hr, Ⓕ New England Sea Ⓕ Ⓛ Best Value Inn, Knights Inn, La Casa Inn, Motel 6, W Ⓖ Shell/Burger King
3	Arrowood Rd, E Ⓕ Jack-in-the-Box, McDonald's, Sonic, Starbucks, Wendy's, Ⓛ Courtyard, Fairfield Inn, Holiday Inn Express, Hyatt Place, Mainstay Suites, Staybridge Suites, TownePlace Suites, W Ⓕ Ruby Tuesday, Ⓛ Hampton Inn
2	I-485
1.5mm	**Welcome Ctr nb, full Ⓓ facilities, info, Ⓒ, vending, ☕, litter barrels, petwalk**
1	Westinghouse Blvd, to I-485 (from nb), E Ⓖ BP/dsl, Ⓕ Jack-in-the-Box, Subway, Waffle House, Ⓛ Super 8, W Ⓖ Shell/dsl, Ⓕ Burger King
0mm	North Carolina/South Carolina state line

INTERSTATE 85

N ↑ S

Exit	Services
234mm	North Carolina/Virginia state line
233	US 1, to Wise, E Ⓖ Citgo/dsl, Ⓕ Budget Inn
231mm	**Welcome Ctr sb, full Ⓓ facilities, Ⓒ, ☕, litter barrels, petwalk**
229	Oine Rd, to Norlina, E Ⓖ BP, W SRA
226	Ridgeway Rd, W Ⓞ to Kerr Lake, to SRA
223	Manson Rd, E Ⓖ BP/dsl, Ⓞ camping, W to Kerr Dam
220	US 1, US 158, Fleming Rd, to Middleburg, E Ⓖ BP/dsl, W Ⓖ Exxon/dsl/scales/truck wash, Ⓛ Chex Motel/rest.
218	US 1 S (from sb exits left), to Raleigh

INTERSTATE 85 CONT'D

Exit	Services
217	Nutbush Bridge, **E** 🅖 BP/dsl, 🅞 auto repair, **W** 🅖 Exxon/dsl, 🅞 Kerr Lake RA
215	US 158 BYP E, Henderson (no EZ return from nb), **E** 🅖 Shell, Sunoco, 🍴 Burger King, Forsyth's BBQ, Nunnery-Freeman BBQ, Subway, 🏨 Ambassador Inn, Budget Host, EconoLodge, Scottish Inn, 🅞 $General, Food Lion, Roses, repair/tires, services on US 158
214	NC 39, Henderson, **E** 🅖 BP, 🍴 Waffle House, 🅞 TrueValue, Verizon, **W** 🅖 BP/dsl, Shell/HotStuff Pizza, 🅞 to Kerr Lake RA
213	US 158, Dabney Dr, to Henderson, **E** 🅖 BP, Texaco, 🍴 Bamboo Garden, Big Cheese Pizza, Bojangles, Denny's, Ichibar Chinese, KFC, Lam's Garden, McDonald's, Papa John's, Pizza Inn, Sonic, Subway, Wendy's, 🅞 Family$, Food Lion, Radio Shack, Roses, **W** 🅖 Shell, 🍴 Chick-fil-A, Golden Corral, Mayflower Sea🍴 Pizza Hut, Ruby Tuesday, Smithfields BBQ, Taco Bell, 🏨 Holiday Inn Express, 🅞 Advance Parts, Buick/Chevrolet/GMC, Chrysler/Dodge/Jeep, Ford/Lincoln/Mercury, Lowe's, Rite Aid, Staples, Verizon
212	Ruin Creek Rd, **E** 🅖 Shell/dsl, 🍴 Cracker Barrel, Mazatlan Mexican, SiLo Rest., Waffle House, 🏨 Days Inn, 🅞 Toyota/Scion, **W** 🅖 BP/Burger King, 🍴 Chick-fil-A, Pizza Hut, Western Sizzlin, 🏨 Hampton Inn, Holiday Inn Express, Jameson Inn, Sleep Inn, 🅞 🅷, Belk, $Tree, JC Penney, Walmart, mall
209	Poplar Creek Rd, **W** Vance-Granville Comm Coll
206	US 158, Oxford, **E** 🅖 Exxon, **W** 🅖 BP/dsl, 🅞🅚
204	NC 96, Oxford, **E** 🅖 BP/dsl, 🏨 Comfort Inn, King's Inn, 🅞 Buick/Chevrolet/GMC, Ford, Honda, Meineke, **W** 🅖 Great Stops/DQ, Hess, Shell/Pizza Hut/24hr, 🍴 Burger King, China Wok, Cookout, Domino's, KFC/Taco Bell, McDonald's, 96 Buffet, Subway, Wendy's, 🏨 EconoLodge, 🅞 🅷, GNC, Lowe's Foods
202	US 15, Oxford, **W** 🅖 Murphy Express/dsl, 🍴 Andy's Burgers, Bojangles, 🏨 Crown Motel (2mi), 🅞 $Tree, Verizon, Walmart
199mm	**rest area both lanes, full ♿ facilities, 🚻, 🛓, litter barrels, petwalk**
198mm	Tar River
191	191 NC 56, Butner, **E** 🅖 BP/dsl, Hess/dsl, 🍴 Bob's BBQ, Bojangles, Burger King, El Rio Mexican, KFC/Taco Bell, McDonald's, Pizza Hut, Sonic, Subway, Wendy's, 🏨 Comfort Inn, 🅞 Ace Hardware, Advance Parts, AutoZone, Curves, $General, $Tree, Food Lion, M&H Tires, Rite Aid, vet, to Falls Lake RA, **W** 🅖 Exxon/dsl/24hr, Shell/dsl, 🍴 Hardee's, 🏨 Best Western, EconoLodge, Ramada Ltd, 🅞 auto repair
189	Butner, **W** 🅖 BP/dsl
186b a	US 15, to Creedmoor
185mm	Falls Lake
183	Redwood Rd
182	Red Mill Rd, **E** 🅖 Exxon/dsl, 🅞 Kenworth/Isuzu Trucks
180	Glenn School Rd
179	E Club Blvd, **E** 🅖 Exxon
178	US 70 E, to Raleigh, Falls Lake RA, Research Triangle, RDU 🅚
177	Avondale Dr, NC 55, **W** 🅖 BP, Shell, 🍴 American Hero, Arby's, Danny's Pizzaria, Hong Kong Buffet, Los Comales, McDonalds, Subway, 🅞 Advance Parts, Big-Lots, Family$

Exit	Services
176b a	Gregson St, US 501 N, **E** 🅖 Hugo's, 🍴 Biscuitville, Boston Mkt, Burger King, PanPan Diner, Randy's Pizza, Ruby Tuesday, Tripp's Diner, 🅞 Macy's, Museum of Life&Science, Office Depot, Sears/auto, mall, **W** 🅞 🅷, museum
175	Guess Rd, **E** 🅖 Citgo/dsl, 🍴 Hog Heaven BBQ, 🏨 Best Value Inn, Holiday Inn Express, Super 8, 🅞 Rite Aid, **W** 🅖 BP/dsl, Pure/dsl, 🍴 Bojangles, Honey's Diner/24hr, IHOP, JJ Fish&Chicken, TX Steaks, 🏨 Red Roof Inn, 🅞 CVS Drug, Home Depot, Kroger, PetsMart, Ross, vet
174a	Hillandale Rd, **W** 🅖 BP/dsl, 🍴 El Corral, Papa's Grille, Pomodoro Italian, 🏨 Comfort Inn, Courtyard, 🅞 Kerr Drug
174b	US 15 S, US 501 S, **E** 🏨 Forest Inn
173	US 15, US 501, US 70, Colemill Rd, W Durham, **E** 🅖 BP, Exxon/dsl, Mobil, Shell, 🍴 Arby's, Bojangles, Chick-fil-A, Cookout, Cracker Barrel, DogHouse Rest., Domino's, KFC/Taco Bell, McDonald's, Subway, Waffle House, Wendy's, 🏨 Budgetel, Days Inn, Hilton, Quality Inn, 🅞 🅷, Advance Parts, Autozone, CVS Drug, $General, Hancock Fabrics, Kroger, O'Reilly Parts, Rite Aid
172	NC 147 S, to US 15 S, US 501 S (from nb), Durham, from nb
170	to NC 751, to Duke U (no EZ return from nb), **E** 🏨 Durham Skyland Inn, Scottish Inn, **W** to Eno River SP
165	NC 86, to Chapel Hill, **E** 🅖 Eagles/Burger King/dsl, 🍴 Andy's Rest., China Fuji, Papa John's, Subway, 🅞 Home Depot, Walmart, **W** 🅖 BP/dsl
164	Hillsborough, **E** 🅖 BP, Citgo/dsl, 🍴 McDonald's, 🏨 Holiday Inn Express, **W** 🅖 Exxon/dsl, Shell, 🍴 Bojangles, Casa Ibarra Mexican, Domino's, Hardee's, KFC/Taco Bell, Mayflower Sea🍴 Pizza Hut, Subway, Waffle House, Wendy's, 🏨 Microtel, 🅞 AutoZone, CarQuest, $General, $Tree, Food Lion, Ford, Goodyear/auto, Lowe's Foods
163	I-40 E, to Raleigh. **I-85 S and I-40 W run together 38 mi.**
161	to US 70 E, NC 86 N
160	to NC 86 N, Efland, **W** 🅖 Exxon/dsl
158mm	**weigh sta both lanes**
157	Buckhorn Rd, **E** 🅖 BP/dsl, Petro/Mobil/Iron Skillet/dsl/scales/24hr/@, **W** 🅖 PopShoppe
154	Mebane, Oaks Rd, **E** 🅖 Murphy USA, Shell/dsl/24hr, Sheetz/dsl, 🍴 Andy's Rest., Ciao Pizza, Subway, 🅞 $Tree, Walmart, **W** 🅖 BP, Hess/Wilco/dsl, Shell/dsl/24hr, 🍴 Biscuitville, Bojangles, La Fiesta Mexican, McDonald's, Quizno's, Roma Pizza, Sake Japanese, Stir King, Waffle House, 🏨 Budget Inn, 🅞 Advance Parts, AutoZone, CVS Drug, Lowe's Foods, vet
153	NC 119, Mebane, **E** 🅖 BP/KFC/Taco Bell/Pizza Hut, 🍴 Cracker Barrel, Hibachi Rest., Jersey Mike's, Overtime Rest., Ruby Tuesday, Smithfield's BBQ, 🏨 Hampton Inn, Holiday Inn Express, 🅞 Lowe's Whse, **W** 🅖 Exxon/Burger King, 🍴 Domino's, La Cocina Mexican, Papa

Side tabs (top to bottom): HENDERSON · N↕S · OXFORD · BUTNER · DURHAM · MEBANE

NC

INTERSTATE 85 CONT'D

N

S

BURLINGTON

NC

Exit	Services
153	Continued
	John's, Sonic, Subway, 🅞 Curves, Food Lion
152	Trollingwood Rd, E 🅖 ▭▭/McDonald's/dsl/scales/24hr
150	Haw River, to Roxboro, W 🅖 Hess/Wilco/DQ/Wendy's/dsl/scales/24hr, ✈FLYING J/Denny's/dsl/LP/scales/24hr, SpeedCo, 🛏 Days Inn, 🅞 Blue Beacon
148	NC 54, Graham, E 🅖 BP/dsl/24hr, Exxon/dsl/24hr, QP, 🍴 Waffle House, 🛏 Comfort Suites, W 🍴 MexAm Cafe, 🛏 Ember's Motel, Travel Inn
147	NC 87, to Pittsboro, Graham, E 🅖 BP, 🍴 AnnaMaria's Pizzeria, Arby's, Bojangles, Burger King, Domino's, Great Wall Chinese, Harbor House Sea🍴 Lucky Bamboo, Pizza Hut, Quizno's, Sagebrush Steaks, Sonic, Subway, Wendy's, 🅞 Advance Parts, AutoZone, Chevrolet, Chrysler/Jeep, Curves, Family$, Food Lion, Ford, Rite Aid, vet, W 🅖 Citgo/dsl, Exxon/dsl, Shell/dsl, 🍴 BBQ&Ribs Co., Biscuitville, Cook Out, McDonald's, Taco Bell, 🅞 H, CVS Drug, Lowe's Foods, Walgreens
145	NC 49, Burlington, E 🅖 BP/dsl, Shell/dsl, 🍴 Capt D's, 🛏 Econolodge, Microtel, Motel 6, 🅞 Harley-Davidson, W 🅖 BP/dsl, 🍴 Biscuitville, Bojangles, Burger King, KFC, La Cabana Mexican, Subway, Waffle House, 🛏 Best Value Inn, Quality Inn, Royal Inn, 🅞 Dodge, $General, Food Lion, Radio Shack, Rite Aid, outlets/famous brands
143	NC 62, Burlington, E 🅖 Sav-Way, 🍴 Hardee's, Waffle House, Wendy's, to Alamance Bfd, W 🅖 Exxon, Sheetz/dsl, 🍴 Biscuitville, K&W Cafeteria, 🛏 Ramada Inn, 🅞 Cadillac, Chevrolet, $General, Food Lion, Ford, Home Depot, vet
141	to Burlington, E 🅖 BP, Kangaroo, 🍴 IHOP, Mayflower Sea🍴 Outback Steaks, 🛏 Comfort Inn, Hampton Inn, 🅞 Nissan, W 🅖 Texaco, 🍴 Amante Pizza, Applebee's, Arby's, Biscuitville, Bojangles, Burger King, Chick-fil-A, Cook Out, Cracker Barrel, Golden Corral, Hooters, KFC, Longhorn Steaks, McDonald's, O'Charley's, Panchero's Mexican, Panda Express, Panera Bread, Ruby Tuesday, Sal's Italian, Starbucks, Steak'n Shake/24hr, Subway, Taco Bell, Wholly Guacamole, 🛏 Best Western, Country Inn&Suites, Courtyard, Super 8, 🅞 H, Books-a-Million, Buick/GMC, $Tree, Hyundai, K-Mart/gas, Lincoln/Mercury, Lowe's Whse, Mazda, Rite Aid, Sears/auto, TJ Maxx, Walgreens, Walmart, mall, to Elon Coll
140	University Dr, Elon, W 🍴 Buffalo Wing Wings, Chick-fil-A, Chili's, Cold Stone Creamery, Little Italy, McDonald's, Mimi's Cafe, Moe's SW Grill, Olive Garden, Peking House, Qdoba, Red Bowl Asian, Red Robin, Starbucks, TX Roadhouse, 🅞 Barnes&Noble, Belk, Best Buy, Dillard's, Discount Tire, GNC, JC Penney, Michael's, Old Navy, Petsmart, Ross, Target
139mm	**rest area both lanes, full ♿ facilities, 🚰, 🛏, litter barrels, vending**
138	NC 61, Gibsonville, W 🅖 TA/BP/Burger King/Popeye's/dsl/scales/@
135	Rock Creek Dairy Rd, W 🅖 Citgo, Exxon, 🍴 Bojangles, Ciao Pizza, China 1, Domino's, Guacamole Mexican, Jersey Mike's Subs, McDonald's, 🅞 Curves, CVS Drug, $General, Food Lion, Midtown Drug, vet
132	Mt Hope Church Rd, E 🅖 Citgo/Subway/dsl, 🍴 Pascalli's Pizza, W 🅖 Shell/dsl, Hess/Wendy's/dsl/24hr, 🛏 Hampton Inn
131	to US 70, Loop 85, Loop 40

GREENSBORO

THOMASVILLE

Exit	Services
129	Youngsmill Rd, W 🛏 Holiday Inn Express (3mi)
128	Alamance Church Rd
126b a	US 421, to Sanford, E 🅖 Exxon/dsl, Kangaroo/dsl, 🅞 Hagan Stone Park Camping
124	S Elm, Eugene St, W 🍴 Bojangles, Cracker Barrel, McDonald's, Starbucks, Starbuck, Subway, Wendy's, Wing Stop, 🅞 Lowe's Whse, Walmart
122c b a	US 220, to Greensboro, Asheboro (from sb)
121	I-40 W, I-73 N, to Winston-Salem
120	N US 29, E US 70, to I-40 W
119	Groometown Rd, from nb, W 🅖 Citgo/dsl
118	US 29 S, US 70 W, to High Point, Jamestown, W 🛏 Grandover Resort, 🅞 H
115mm	Deep River
114mm	new exit
113	NC 62, Archdale, E 🅖 Citgo/dsl, W 🅖 BP/dsl, 🛏 Quality Inn
111	US 311, to High Point, Archdale, E 🍴 Amici Pizza, Bamboo Garden, Bojangles, Carolina Diner, Hardee's, Subway, Wendy's, 🛏 Innkeeper, 🅞 Curves, CVS Drug, $General, $City, Food Lion, Lowe's Foods/24hr, W 🅖 Circle K/dsl, Exxon/McDonald's, Marathon/dsl, Shell/dsl, 🍴 Biscuitville, Kosta's Rest, Waffle House, 🛏 Comfort Inn, Country Inn&Suites, Fairfield Inn, Hampton Inn, Holiday Inn Express, 🅞 H, O'Reilly Parts, USPO, tires
108	Hopewell Church Rd, Trinity
106	Finch Farm Rd, E 🅖 BP/dsl, W 🍴 Subway (1mi)
103	NC 109, to Thomasville, E 🅖 Murphy USA/dsl, Shell, Texaco/dsl, 🍴 Arby's, Chen's Kitchen, Cookout Burgers, Taco Bell, 🛏 ValuePlace, 🅞 CVS Drug, $Tree, Ingles Foods, K-Mart, Radio Shack, Walmart, W 🅖 Exxon/Subway/dsl, RaceWay, Hess/Wilco/dsl, Shell, 🍴 BBQ Shack, Biscuitville, Bojangles, Burger King, Captain Tom's, China Garden, Denny's, Dino's Italian, Hardee's, Hunan Chinese, KFC, La Carreta Mexican, Mandarin Express, Mazatlan Mexican, McDonald's, Mr Gatti's, Papa John's, Ruby Tuesday, Sonic, Sunrise Diner, Waffle House, Wendy's, 🛏 Country Hearts Inn, Quality Inn, 🅞 Advance Parts, Aldi Foods, AutoZone, Family$, Food Lion, Merchant's Tire, Mighty$, NAPA, O'Reilly Parts, Peebles, Rite Aid, Walgreens
102	Lake Rd, W 🅖 Marathon, Sunoco, 🛏 Days Inn/rest., Microtel, 🅞 H
100mm	**rest area both lanes, full ♿ facilities, 🚰, vending, 🛏, litter barrels, petwalk**
96	US 64, to Asheboro, Lexington, E 🅖 Exxon/dsl, 🅞 Modern Tire, W 🅖 Citgo/dsl, Texaco/dsl, 🍴 Randy's Rest., 🅞 to Davidson Co Coll, NC Zoo
94	Old US 64, E 🅖 Shell, 🅞 Timber Lake Gallery
91	NC 8, to Southmont, E 🅖 BP/dsl, Citgo, Shell/dsl, 🍴 Biscuit King, Burger King, Christo Rest., Hunan Express, Jimmy's BBQ, KFC, Mayberry Rest., McDonald's, Ocean View Sea🍴 Subway, Wendy's, 🛏 Comfort Suites, Highway 8 Motel, 🅞 Food Lion, High Rock Lake Camping (7mi), Kerr Drug, Mock Tire, W 🅖 Exxon/dsl, Murphy USA/dsl, QM/dsl, 🍴 Applebee's, Arby's, Burger King, Cracker Barrel, Golden Corral, King House, La Carreta Mexican, Little Ceasar's, Mi Pueblo, Pizza Hut (1mi), Taco Bell, Zaxby's, 🛏 Country Hearth Inn, Quality Inn, 🅞 H, Belk, $Tree, GNC, Lowe's Whse (1mi), Radio Shack, Walmart (1mi)
88	Linwood, W 🅖 Texaco/dsl, 🅞 H
87	US 29, US 70, US 52 (from nb), High Point, W 🅞 H, ▸
86	Belmont Rd, W 🅖 Bill's Trkstp/dsl/scales/24hr/@

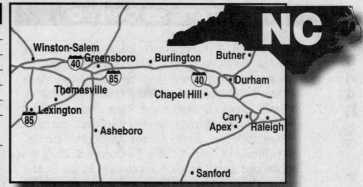

INTERSTATE 85 CONT'D

Exit	Services
85	Clark Rd, to NC 150
83	NC 150 (from nb), to Spencer
82	US 29, US 70 (from sb), to Spencer
81.5mm	Yadkin River
81	Spencer, E 🅶 Liberty, 🅾 camping
79	Spencer Shops SHS, Spencer, E Spencer, W 🍴 Subway (1mi)
76b a	US 52, to Albemarle, Salisbury, E 🅶 BP, Pop Shoppe, 🍴 Applebee's, Capriano's, China Rainbow, Cold Stone Creamery, IHOP, LoneStar Steaks, Mr Gatti's Pizza, Pancho Villa Mexican, Top China, Zaxby's, 🛏 Days Inn, Economy Inn, Happy Traveler Inn, Super 8, 🅾 Aldi Foods, CVS Drug, $Tree, Food Lion, GNC, Harley-Davidson, Lowe's Whse, Marshall's, Old Navy, Radio Shack, Rite Aid, Staples, Tire Kingdom, Walgreens, W 🅶 Murphy Express/dsl, Shell/Circle K/dsl, Wilco/Hess/dsl, 🍴 Beijing Chinese, Blue Bay Sea 🍴 Bojangles, Burger King, Capt D's, Chick-fil-A, China Buffet, Christo's Rest., Cookout, Cracker Barrel, Hardee's, HoneyBaked Ham, Jade Express, KFC, McDonald's, O'Charley's, Outback Steaks, Papa John's, Pizza Hut, Starbucks, Subway, Taco Bell, Tokyo Express, Wendy's, 🛏 Comfort Suites, 🅾 H, Advance Parts, AutoZone, Family$, Firestone/auto, Goodyear/auto, K-Mart, Office Depot, USPO, Walmart
75	US 601, Jake Alexander Blvd, E 🍴 Arby's, Farmhouse Rest., 🛏 Travelodge, 🅾 NAPA, to Dan Nicholas Park, W 🅶 BP, Citgo, Shell/dsl, 🍴 Casa Grande Mexian, Ichiban Japanese, Ryan's, Sagebrush Steaks, Subway, Waffle House, Wendy's, 🛏 Hampton Inn, Holiday Inn, Quality Inn, 🅾 Cadillac/Chevrolet, Chrysler/Dodge/Jeep, Ford, Honda, Kia, Magic Mart, Nissan, Toyota
74	Julian Rd, W 🍴 Longhorn Steaks, Olive Garden, 🅾 Kohl's
72	Peach Orchard Rd
71	Peeler Rd, E 🅶 Derrick TravelCtr/Shell/CW's Cafe/dsl/24hr/scales, W 🅶 Hess/Wilco/Bojangles/Subway/dsl/scales/24hr, 🅾 auto/dsl repair
70	Webb Rd, E flea mkt, W 🍴 Mikey's, 🅾 st patrol
68	US 29, US 601, to Rockwell, China Grove, 1 mi W 🅶 BP, 🍴 Domino's, Gary's BBQ, Hardee's, Pizza Hut, Subway, 🅾 AutoZone, $General, Family$, Food Lion, Rite Aid
63	Kannapolis, E 🅶 🅿/Subway/dsl/scales, 🍴 Waffle House, 🛏 Best Value Inn
60	Earnhardt Rd, Copperfield Blvd, E 🅶 BP, Exxon/dsl, 🍴 Bob Evans, Bojangles, Cracker Barrel, 🛏 Hampton Inn, Sleep Inn, 🅾 H, Discount Tire, W 🅶 BP/dsl, 🍴 Bruster's, Carino's Italian, Casa Grande Mexican, Dragon Wok, Firehouse Subs, Logan's Roadhouse, McDonald's, Ruby Tuesday, Steak'n Shake, Subway, Taco Bell, Unique Pizza, Wendy's, Yamayi Japanese, 🛏 Holiday Inn Express, 🅾 Hobby Lobby, Kohl's, Lowe's Whse, NAPA, Sam's Club/gas, Walmart, visitor info
59mm	**rest area both lanes, full ♿ facilities, 🚻, vending, 🖼, litter barrels, petwalk**
58	US 29, US 601, Concord, E 🅶 BP, Shell/dsl, Texaco, 🍴 Applebee's, Capt D's, Chick-fil-A, Chili's, El Vallarta Mexican, Golden Corral, Mayflower Sea🍴 McDonald's, Moe's SW Grill, Mr C's Rest., O'Charley's, Starbucks, Taco Bell, Wendy's, 🛏 Best Value Inn, Howard

Exit	Services
58	Continued Johnson, Mayfair Motel, 🅾 H, Belk, Harris-Teeter, JC Penney, Lowe's Whse, Rite Aid, Sears/auto, Staples, Tire Kingdom, U-Haul, Walgreens, mall, st patrol, W 🅶 BP, Hess, 🍴 CiCi's, Domino's, Hibachi Grill, IHOP, 🛏 Comfort Inn, Econolodge, Fairfield Inn, Microtel, 🅾 $General, Ford/Lincoln/Mercury, Hancock Fabrics, Home Depot, vet
55	NC 73, to Davidson, Concord, E 🅶 Exxon/dsl, Shell, 🍴 McDonald's, Waffle House, W 🅶 Shell/Punchy's Diner, 76/Circle K/dsl, World Gas, 🛏 Days Inn
54	Kannapolis Pkwy, George W Lyles Pkwy, E 🅶 Citgo, 🅾 Backyard Burger, Bojangles, China Bowl, China Garden, Noodles & Co, Off-the-Grill, Quizno's, 🅾 AutoZone, CVS Drug, Food Lion, Harris Teeter, Walgreens, vet, W 🅶 Exxon, 🍴 Arby's, Asian Cafe, Buffalo Wild Wings, Chick-fil-A, Dickey's BBQ, Fatz Cafe, McDonald's, 🅾 Best Buy, $Tree, Goodyear/auto, Marshall's, Steinmart, Petsmart, Super Target
52	Poplar Tent Rd, E 🅶 Shell/dsl, Texaco/dsl, 🍴 R&R BBQ, 🅾 to Lowe's Speedway, museum, W 🅶 Accel/dsl, Exxon/24hr
49	Bruton Smith Blvd, Concord Mills Blvd, E 🅶 BP/McDonalds, Shell/dsl, 🍴 Arby's, Bob Evans, Bojangles, Carrabbas, ChuckeCheese, Cinco de Mayo Mexican, Cookout, Cracker Barrel, Firehouse Subs, 5 Guys Burgers, Hooters, KFC/Taco Bell, Quaker Steak, Quizno's, Jack-in-the-Box, Ruby Tuesday, Sonic, Starbucks, Subway, Sonny's BBQ, Taco Bell, TX Roadhouse, Waffle House, Wendy's, Zaxby's, 🛏 Comfort Suites, Courtyard, Embassy Suites, Hampton Inn, Hilton Garden, Holiday Inn Express, Residence Inn, Sleep Inn, SpringHill Suites, Suburban Lodge, Wingate Inn, 🅾 BJ's Whse/gas, Fleetwood RV camping (1.5mi), Harley-Davidson, Honda, Scion/Toyota, Tom Johnson RV Ctr (1.5mi), to Lowe's Motor Speedway, W 🅶 Texaco, 🍴 Applebee's, Burger King, Charanda Mexican, Chick-fil-A, Foster's Grille, Mayflower Sea🍴 McAlisters Deli, Olive Garden, On-the-Border, Panera Bread, Razzoo's Cafe, Red Lobster, Ryan's, Steak'n Shake, Sticky Fingers, TGI Friday, 🅾 URGENT CARE, BassPro Shops, BooksAMillion, Discount Tire, $Tree, Concord Mills Mall, Goodyear/auto, Lowe's Whse, Old Navy, PetCo, Radio Shack, Ross, TJ Maxx, Walmart
48	I-485, to US 29, to Rockhill
46	Mallard Creek Church Rd, E 🅶 Exxon/24hr, Texaco/dsl, 🍴 China Cafe, Giacolos Pizza, Jack-in-the-Box, K&W Cafeteria, Utopia Rest, 🅾 Research Park, W 🅶 Circle K/Blimpie/dsl, Texaco/dsl, 🍴 Firehouse Subs, 5 Guys Burgers, Hickory Tavern, Quizno's, Rita's, Starbucks, Thai Taste, 🅾 Trader Joes

🅖 = gas 🍴 = food 🛏 = lodging 🔵 = other   Copyright 2011 - The Next Ex

INTERSTATE 85 CONT'D

Exit	Services
45	Harris Blvd, **E** 🍴 Applebee's, Bikini's Grill, Bojangles, Burger King, Cheddar's, Chick-fil-A, Chili's, China Palace, Ham's Rest, HoneyBaked Ham, IHOP, Jersey Mike's Subs, Max&Erma's, McDonald's, Melting Pot, Nakto's, Panda Express, Panera Bread, Papa John's, Picasso's Pizza, Qdoba, Quizno's, Shane's Rib Shack, Shoney's, Showmar's Rest, Smokey Bones, Starbucks, Taco Bell, TGIFriday, TX Land & Cattle, 🛏 Courtyard, Drury Inn, Extended Stay America, Hampton Inn, Hilton, Holiday Inn, Homewood Suites, Residence Inn, Sleep Inn, 🔵 🅷, Best Buy, Bloom Foods, Kohl's, Michael's, Office Depot, Old Navy, Ross, Sam's Club, TJ Maxx, Walgreens, Walmart/auto, mall, to UNCC, to Miz Scarlett's, U Research Park, **0-2 mi W** 🅖 Citgo, Shell, 🍴 Longhorn Steaks, Maccaroni Grill, Red Robin, Tony's Pizza, 🛏 Springhill Suites, TownePlace Suites, 🔵 Harris Teeter, Rite Aid
43	to City Blvd
42	US 29 (nb only)
41	Sugar Creek Rd, **E** 🅖 RaceWay, Shell/dsl, 🍴 Bojangles, McDonald's, Taco Bell, Wendy's, 🛏 Best Value Inn, Brookwood Inn, Continental Inn, Economy Inn, Garden Inn, Microtel, **W** 🅖 Shell/Circle K, 🍴 Cookout, Dominic's Cafe, Sugar's Rest., Texas Ranch Steaks, 🛏 Comfort Inn, Country Hearth Inn, Days Inn, Ramada Inn, Rodeway Inn, Super 8
40	Graham St, **E** 🅖 Exxon/dsl, 🛏 Budget Inn, 🔵 UPS, Volvo, Western Star, **W** 🅖 Texaco, 🔵 Freightliner
39	Statesville Ave, **E** 🅖 🚛/Subway/dsl/scales/24hr, 🔵 CarQuest, **W** 🅖 Citgo, Shell/dsl, 🍴 Bojangles, 🔵 Family$
38	I-77, US 21, N to Statesville, S to Columbia
37	Beatties Ford Rd, **E** 🅖 Marathon, Shell/Chester's/dsl, 🍴 Burger King, McDonald's, Subway, 🔵 CVS Drug, Family$, Food Lion, USPO, **W** 🅖 BP
36	NC 16, Brookshire Blvd, **E** 🛏 Brookshire Inn, 🔵 🅷, repair, **W** 🅖 Hari/dsl, RaceWay, Shell/dsl, Sunoco, 🍴 Burger King, Jack-in-the-Box, Kennedy Chicken/Pizza, La Unica Mexican, Subway, 🔵 Family$, Griffin Tire
35	Glenwood Dr, **E** 🛏 Knights Inn, **W** 🅖 Shell/dsl
34	NC 27, Freedom Dr, **E** 🅖 Shell, Walkers, 🍴 Beauregard's Rest, Bojangles, Capt D's, Cookout, KFC, McDonald's, Mr C's Rest, Pizza Hut, Showmar's, Subway, Taco Bell, Wendy's, 🔵 Advance Parts, Aldi Foods, AutoZone, $Tree, Family$, Goodyear, K-Mart, Rite Aid, Save-A-Lot Foods, Walgreens, urgent care, vet, **W** 🛏 Charlotte Express, 🔵 JiffyLube
33	US 521, Billy Graham Pkwy, **E** 🅖 Shell, 🍴 Bojangles, KFC/Taco Bell, McDonald's, Wendy's, 🛏 Comfort Suites, Days Inn, Royal Inn, Sheraton, SpringHill Suites, 🔵 ☕, **W** 🅖 Exxon/dsl, 🍴 Cracker Barrel, Ichiban, Waffle House, 🛏 Best Value Inn, EconoLodge, La Quinta, Microtel, Motel 6, Quality Inn, Red Roof Inn
32	Little Rock Rd, **E** 🅖 Shell/dsl, 🛏 🚰 Inn, Courtyard, Hampton Inn, Holiday Inn, **W** 🅖 Citgo, Exxon/dsl, Shell/dsl, 🍴 Arby's, Hardee's, Showmar's Rest., Shoney's, Subway, 🛏 Country Inn&Suites, Ramada Inn, Wingate Inn, 🔵 Family$, Food Lion, Griffin Tire, Rite Aid
30	I-485, to 1-77, Pineville
29	Sam Wilson Rd, **E** 🅖 BP (1mi), 🔵 camping, **W** 🅖 Shell/dsl
28mm	**weigh sta both lanes**

27.5mm	Catawba River
27	NC 273, Mt Holly, **E** 🅖 Exxon/Dunkin Donuts/dsl, Murphy USA/dsl, 🍴 Chick-fil-A, KFC, Pizza Hut, Sake Japanese, Subway, Taco Bell, Waffle House, Wendy's, 🔵 CVS Drug, Family$, Firestone, Food Lion, Lowe's, NAPA, Rite Aid, Walgreens, Walmart/Subway, **W** 🅖 Citgo/dsl, 🛏 Holiday Inn Express
26	NC 7, **E** 🅖 BP, Marathon/dsl, 🍴 Bojangles, Hardee's, King Buffet, McDonald's, New China, Papa John's, 🛏 Hampton Inn, 🔵 Advance Parts, Aldi Foods, BiLo, Curves, Ford, Verizon, **W** Belmont Abbey Coll
24mm	South Fork River
23	NC 7, McAdenville, **W** 🅖 Exxon/dsl, Shell/Subway, 🍴 Hardee's, Hillbilly's BBQ/Steaks
22	Cramerton, Lowell, **E** 🅖 Hess, Marathon, 🍴 Applebee's, Burger King, Chick-fil-A, Gator's Rest., Hooters, Jack-in-the-Box, Jersey Mike's Subs, Moe's SW Grill, Portofino's, Saurka Japanese, Schlotzsky's, Thai House, Zaxby's, 🔵 Books-A-Million, Buick/Cadillac/Chevrolet/GMC, Honda, Kia, K-Mart, Kohl's, Lowe's, Old Navy, Petsmart, Sam's Club/gas, U-Haul
21	Cox Rd, **E** 🅖 Marathon, 🍴 Akropolis Cafe, Buffalo Wild Wings, Chili's, ChuckeCheese, Cookout, Dynasty Buffet, Golden Corral, Krispy Kreme, La Fuente, Logan's Roadhouse, Longhorn Steaks, McAlister's Deli, McDonald's, Olive Garden, On-the-Border, Panera Bread, Peking Garden, Ruby Tuesday, Qdoba, Quiznos, Ryan's, Ruby Tuesday, Steak'n Shake, 🔵 AAA, AT&T, Best Buy, Chrysler/Dodge/Jeep, Dick's, Discount Tire, $Tree, Ford/Subaru, GNC, Harris-Teeter, Home Depot, Office Depot, Mary Jo's Cloth, Michael's, Nissan, O'Reilly Parts, PepBoys, Ross, Target, Tire Kingdom, TJ Maxx, Verizon, Walgreens, Walmart/Subway, vet, **W** 🅖 Marathon, 🍴 Arby's, Brixx Pizza, IHOP, 🛏 Super 8, 🔵 🅷, $General, Medical Ctr Drug
20	NC 279, New Hope Rd, **E** 🅖 World Gas, 🍴 Capt D's, McDonald's, O'Charley's, Pizza Hut, Red Lobster, Sake Japanese, Showmar's Rest, Taco Bell, Wendy's, 🛏 Knights Inn, 🔵 Advance Parts, AutoZone, Belk, Dillard's, Family$, Firestone, Hobby Lobby, JC Penney, Office Depot, Sears/auto, Target, Tuesday Morning, **W** 🍴 Bojangles, Cracker Barrel, KFC, Outback Steaks, TX Roadhouse, Waffle House, 🛏 Best Western, Comfort Suites, Courtyard, Fairfield Inn, Hampton Inn, 🔵 🅷, CarMax
19	NC 7, E Gastonia, **E** 🅖 Shell
17	US 321, Gastonia, **E** 🅖 Citgo/dsl/LP, 🍴 Los Arcos Mexican, 🛏 Days Inn, ValuePlace, 🔵 Family$, **W** 🅖 Marathon/dsl, 🍴 Hardee's, 🛏 Holiday Inn Express, Motel 6, Red Carpet Inn
14	NC 274, E Bessemer, **W** 🅖 BP/Subway, Citgo/dsl, 🍴 Bojangles, Waffle House, 🛏 Express Inn
13	Edgewood Rd, Bessemer City, **E** to Crowders Mtn SP, **W** 🅖 Exxon/dsl, 🛏 Best Inn
10b a	US 74 W, US 29, Kings Mtn
8	NC 161, to Kings Mtn, **E** 🛏 Holiday Inn Express, 🔵 camping, **W** 🅖 BP, 🍴 Big E BBQ, McDonald's, Subway, Taco Bell, Waffle House, Wendy's, 🛏 Quality Inn, 🔵 🅷
5	Dixon School Rd, **E** 🅖 Citgo/Subway/dsl/24hr, 🔵 truck/tire repair
4	US 29 S (from sb)
2.5mm	**Welcome Ctr nb, full** ♿ **facilities, info,** ⓒ **vending,** 🖼 **litter barrels, petwalk**
2	NC 216, Kings Mtn, **E** to Kings Mtn Nat Military Park
0mm	North Carolina/South Carolina state line

Side labels: **CHARLOTTE** (N ↑↓ S), **CHARLOTTE**, **NC**, **GASTONIA**

INTERSTATE 95

Exit	Services
181mm	North Carolina/Virginia state line, **Welcome Ctr sb, full facilities, , , litter barrels, vending, petwalk**
180	NC 48, to Gaston, to Lake Gaston, Pleasant Hill, W Pilot/Subway/dsl/scales/24hr
176	NC 46, to Garysburg, W Shell, Burger King, Best Western
174mm	Roanoke River
173	US 158, Roanoke Rapids, Weldon, E BP/dsl, Shell/dsl, Frazier's Rest., Ralph's BBQ, Waffle House, Days Inn, Orchard Inn, H, W BP/dsl, Exxon/DQ/Stuckey's, Murphy USA/dsl, Shell, Applebee's, Arby's, Burger King, Chick-fil-A, Cookout, Cracker Barrel, Hardee's, Ichiban, KFC, Little Caesar's, Logan's Roadhouse, Mayflower Sea, McDonald's, New China, Pizza Hut, Ruby Tuesday, Ryan's, Starbucks, Subway, Taco Bell, TX Steaks, Waffle House, Wendy's, Comfort Suites, Hampton Inn, Jameson Inn, Motel 6, Quality Inn, Sleep Inn, urgent care, Advance Parts, AutoZone, Belk, BigLots, Buick/GMC, $General, $Tree, Firestone/auto, Food Lion, GNC, Harley-Davidson, Lowe's, O'Reilly Parts, Radio Shack, Rite Aid, Save a Lot Foods, Staples, Toyota, Verizon, Walgreens, Walmart
171	NC 125, Roanoke Rapids, E Hilton Garden, Carolina Crossroads RV Resort, Roanoke Rapids Theater, W Shell/dsl, Holiday Inn Express, st patrol
168	NC 903, to Halifax, E Exxon/Subway/dsl, Shell/Burger King/dsl, W Oasis/Dunkin Donuts/LP/dsl
160	NC 561, to Brinkleyville, E Exxon/24hr, W Citgo/dsl/rest.
154	NC 481, to Enfield, **1mi** W KOA
151mm	**weigh sta both lanes**
150	NC 33, to Whitakers, E golf, W BP/Subway/DQ/Stuckey's/dsl
145	NC 4, to US 301, Battleboro, E BP/dsl, Exxon/DQ, Marathon/dsl, Shell, Denny's, Hardee's, Shoney's, Waffle House, Ashburn Inn, Best Value Inn, Best Western, Comfort Inn, Days Inn, Deluxe Inn, Gold Rock Inn, Howard Johnson, Quality Inn, Red Carpet Inn
142mm	**rest area both lanes, full facilities, , , litter barrels, vending, petwalk**
141	NC 43, Red Oak, E BP/dsl, Exxon/dsl/LP, $General, Smith's Foods, W Red Carpet Inn
138	US 64, **1 mi E on Winstead** Hess/dsl, Bicuitville, Bojangles, Cracker Barrel, Gardner's BBQ, Hardee's, Highway Diner, KFC, Outback Steaks, TX Steaks, Candlewood Suites, Comfort Inn, Country Inn&Suites, Courtyard, Doubletree, Hampton Inn, Holiday Inn, Residence Inn, H, Buick/GMC, Harley-Davidson, Honda, to Cape Hatteras Nat Seashore
132	to NC 58, E Pitstop/dsl, 1 mi W BP/dsl
128mm	Tar River
127	NC 97, to Stanhope, E
121	US 264a, Wilson, **0-4 mi** E BP, Citgo/Subway/dsl, Exxon, Hess/dsl, Kangaroo/dsl/LP, Marathon, Murphy USA/dsl, Shell, Applebee's, Arby's, Buffalo Wild Wings, Burger King, Chick-fil-A, Chili's, CiCi's Pizza, Cookout, Denny's, Domino's, El Tapatio, Golden Corral, Hardee's, KFC/LJ Silver, McDonald's, Moe's SW Grill, Quizno's, Ruby Buffet, Ruby Tuesday, Sonic, Starbucks, Subway, TX Steaks, Waffle House, Wendy's, Candlewood Suites, Hampton Inn, H, Aldi Foods,
121	Continued AT&T, Belk, Best Buy, BooksAMillion, Chevrolet, Chrysler/Dodge/Jeep, $General, Harris-Teeter, Honda, Lowe's, Marshall's, O'Reilly Parts, Petsmart, Ross, Scion/Toyota, Staples, Target, Tuesday Morning, Verizon, Walmart, White's Tires, W BP/dsl, Bojangles, Burger King, Cracker Barrel, McDonald's, Pino's Pizza, Comfort Suites, Country Inn&Suites, Fairfield Inn, Hampton Inn, Holiday Inn Express, Jameson Inn, Microtel, Sleep Inn, to Country Dr Museum
119b a	US 264, US 117
116	NC 42, to Clayton, Wilson, E Shell/dsl, H, W BP/dsl, Rock Ridge Camping
107	US 301, Kenly, E BP/dsl, Exxon/McDonald's/dsl, Fuel Doc, PitStop, Andy's Cafe, Golden China, Nik's Pizza, Norman's BBQ, Subway, Budget Inn, Deluxe Inn, EconoLodge, CarQuest, $General, Food Lion, Ford, Family$, Piggly Wiggly, Tobacco Museum
106	Truck Stop Rd, Kenly, E FLYING J/Denny's/dsl/LP/scales/24hr, W Petro/Subway/Wendy's/dsl/scales/24hr/@, Wilco/Hess/Arby's/dsl/scales/24hr, Waffle House, Days Inn, Super 8, Blue Beacon, Speedco Lube, Truck-o-Mat
105.5mm	Little River
105	Bagley Rd, Kenly, E Big Boys/Shell/105 Pizza/dsl/scales/24hr, Lowell Mill Rest.
102	Micro, W Shop'N-Go, Backdoor Cafe, $General, city park, USPO
101	Pittman Rd
99mm	**rest area both lanes, full facilities, vending, , , litter barrels, petwalk, hist marker**
98	to Selma, E RVacation
97	US 70 A, to Pine Level, Selma, E Kings/dsl/24hr, Mobil/dsl, Denny's, Days Inn, J&R Outlet, W BP/dsl, Exxon/dsl/24hr, Shell/dsl, Bojangles, Cookout, Golden China, KFC, McDonald's, Shoney's, Waffle House, Hampton Inn, Masters Inn, Quality Inn, Regency Inn, Royal Inn, H
95	US 70, Smithfield, E Best Value Inn, Log Cabin Motel/rest., Village Motel, Ava Gardner Museum, W Hess/dsl, Sunoco, Bob Evans, Burger King, Checker's, CiCi's Pizza, Coldstone, Cracker Barrel, Golden Corral, El Sombrero Mexican, Outback Steaks, Ruby Tuesday, Smithfield BBQ (2mi), Subway, TX Steaks, Waffle House, Zaxby's, Best Western, Comfort Inn, Jameson Inn, Sleep Inn, Super 8, Harley-Davidson, Carolina Premium Outlets/famous brands
93	Brogden Rd, Smithfield, W BP/dsl, Citgo
91.5mm	Neuse River

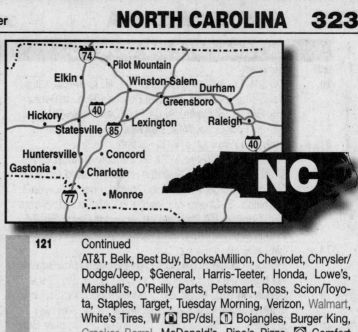

🅶 = gas   🍴 = food   🛏 = lodging   🅾 = other   Copyright 2011 - The Next E

INTERSTATE 95 CONT'D

Exit	Services
90	US 301, US 701, to Newton Grove, E 🅶 BP/dsl, Citgo/dsl, 🛏 Travelers Inn, 🅾 KOA, Ronnie's Tires, to Bentonville Bfd, W 🅶 Exxon/dsl, 🛏 Four Oaks Motel/RV Park
87	NC 96, Four Oaks, W 🅶 BP/dsl, 🍴 Subway
81 b a	I-40, E to Wilmington, W to Raleigh
79	NC 50, to NC 27, to NC 242, Benson, Newton Grove, E 🅶 BP/dsl, Citgo, 🍴 Waffle House, 🅾 auto repair, W 🅶 Exxon/Burger King, Mule City/dsl, Pure, 🍴 China 8, Domino's, El Charro Mexican, KFC, McDonald's, Pizza Hut, Subway, 🛏 Days Inn, 🅾 Advance Parts, Family$, Food Lion, Kerr Drug, auto repair
78 mm	Neuse River
77	Hodges Chapel Rd, E 🅶 Loves/Subway/dsl/scales/RV dump/24hr
75	Jonesboro Rd, W 🅶 Exxon/Milestone Diner, Sadler's/Shell/DQ/Quiznos/dsl/scales/24hr/@
73	US 421, NC 55, to Dunn, Clinton, E 🍴 Cracker Barrel, Panda House Chinese, Wendy's, 🅾 Buick/Chevrolet, Chrysler/Dodge/Jeep, Family$, Food Lion, W 🅶 Exxon/dsl, Hess/dsl, Shell, 🍴 Bojangles, Burger King, Dairy Freeze, El Charro Mexican, Hot Dog&Hamburger Heavan, Sagebrush Steaks, Subway, Taco Bell, Triangle Waffle, 🛏 Hampton Inn, Holiday Inn Express, Jameson Inn, Quality Inn, Super 8, 🅾 IGA Foods, to Campbell U., museum
72	Pope Rd, E 🅶 Atex, 🛏 Comfort Inn, Royal Inn, W 🅶 BP, Pure/dsl, 🍴 Brass Lantern Steaks, 🛏 Valley Motor Inn, 🅾 Cadillac/GMC
71	Longbranch Rd, E 🅶 Kangaroo/Hardee's/dsl/scales/24hr, 🅾 dsl repair, W to Averasboro Bfd
70	SR 1811
65	NC 82, Godwin, E Falcon Children's Home, W 🅶 Epco/dsl
61	to Wade, E 🅶 61 Trkstp/dsl, 🅾 KOA (1mi), W 🅶 BP/dsl/24hr
58	US 13, to Newton Grove, I-295 to Fayetteville, E 🅶 Eastgate, Shell, 🍴 Quiznos, Waffle House, 🛏 Days Inn
56	Lp 95, to US 301 (from sb), Fayetteville, W 🅶 Epco/dsl, Kangaroo/24hr, 🛏 Easterner Inn, 🅾 H, to Ft Bragg, Pope AFB
55	NC 1832, Murphy Rd, W 🅶 Epco/dsl, Kangaroo/24hr, 🛏 Easterner Inn
52	NC 24, Fayetteville, W 🅾 to Ft Bragg, Pope AFB, botanical gardens, museum
49	NC 53, NC 210, Fayetteville, E 🅶 BP, Exxon, Kangaroo/dsl, Marathon, 🍴 Burger King, McDonald's, Pizza Hut, Taco Bell, Waffle House, 🛏 Days Inn, Deluxe Inn, Motel 6, Travelers Inn, W 🅶 BP/Subway/dsl, Exxon/dsl, Shell/dsl, 🍴 Cracker Barrel, Ruby Tuesday, Shoney's, 🛏 Comfort Inn, Country Hearth Inn, Doubletree, EconoLodge, Fairfield Inn, Hampton Inn, Holiday Inn, Quality Inn, Red Roof Inn, Sleep Inn, Super 8
48mm	rest area both lanes, full ♿ facilities, 🅲, 🛏, litter barrels, vending, petwalk
47mm	Cape Fear River
46 b a	NC 87, to Fayetteville, Elizabethtown, W 🅾 H, museum, Civic Ctr, to Agr Expo Ctr
44	Claude Lee Rd, W 🅾 Lazy Acres Camping, to 🗏
41	NC 59, to Hope Mills, Parkton, E 🅶 Kangaroo/24hr, W 🅶 BP/dsl, 🅾 Lake Waldo's Camping, Spring Valley RV Park

Exit	Services
40	Lp 95, to US 301 (from nb), to Fayetteville, **services on US 301** (5-7mi)
33	US 301, St Pauls, E 🅶 BP/dsl/repair/24hr
31	NC 20, to St Pauls, Raeford, E 🅶 BP, Marathon/Huddle House/Quiznos/dsl, Mobil/McDonald's, Pit Row, 🍴 Burger King, Hardee's, 🛏 Days Inn, 🅾 Volvo Trucks, W 🅶 Exxon/dsl, Sunoco, 🍴 Taco Bell, 🅾 Food Lion
25	US 301, E 🅶 BP/dsl
24mm	weigh sta both lanes
22	US 301, E 🅶 Exxon, Marathon, Shell/DQ, 🍴 Burger King, China Wok, DQ, Denny's, Friendly's, Golden Corral, Hardee's, Huddle House, Outback Steaks, Papa John's, Pizza Hut, Quiznos, Ruby Tuesday, Shogun, Smithfield BBQ, Subway, TX Steaks, Waffle House, Wendy's, Zaxby's, 🛏 Best Western, Comfort Suites, Hampton Inn, Holiday Inn, Redwood Inn, Super 8, 🅾 urgent care, Chrysler, Dodge/Jeep, $Tree, Goodyear, Honda, Lowe's Foods, Lowe's, Office Depot, Toyota, Verizon, Walmart, st patrol, W 🅶 Quality, Sun-Do/dsl, Sunoco/dsl, 🍴 Uncle George's Rest., 🅾 Ford/Lincoln/Mercury, Sam's Club/gas
20	NC 211, to NC 41, Lumberton, E 🅶 Citgo, Exxon/dsl Liberty/dsl, 🍴 Arby's, Bojangles, Buger King, Capt D's, CiCi's Pizza, Cook Out, Del Sol Mexican, Golden City Chinese, Hardee's, Hong Kong Chinese, Kami Japanese, KFC, Little Caesar's, McDonald's, Pizza Inn, Shoney's, Sonic, Subway, Taco Bell, Tokyo Japanese, 2 Guys Grille, Village Sta. Rest., Waffle House, 🛏 Deluxe Inn, Howard Johnson, Ramada Inn, 🅾 H, Advance Parts, AutoZone, Belk, CVS Drug, Food Lion/deli, JC Penney, K-Mart, Nissan, O'Reilly Parts, Walgreens, city park, W 🅶 Marathon, Sun-do/dsl, 🍴 Cracker Barrel, Fuller's BBQ Buffet, San Jose Mexican, 🛏 Best Value Inn, Comfort Inn, Country Inn&Suites, Days Inn/rest., Fairfield Inn, Quality Inn
19	Carthage Rd, Lumberton, E 🅶 BP/dsl, 🛏 Travelers Inn, W 🅶 Exxon/dsl, 🛏 Knights Inn, Motel 6
18mm	Lumber River
17	NC 72, Lumberton, Pembroke, E 🅶 Atkinson's/dsl, BP, dsl, Dobb's/Stuckey's/Wendy's, Go-Gas/dsl, Mobil/dsl, 🍴 Burger King, Hardee's, Huddle House, McDonald's, Ruby Tuesday, Subway, Waffle House, 🛏 Atkinson Inn, Budget Inn, Economy Inn, Southern Inn, 🅾 Advance Parts, AutoZone, CVS Drug, Food Lion, $General, Family$, W 🅾 Sleepy Bear's RV Park (3mi)
13	I-74, US 74, Rockingham, Wilmington, E 🅾 U.S.S Wilmington, SE NC Beaches
10	US 301, to Fairmont
7	to McDonald, Raynham
5mm	Welcome Ctr nb, full ♿ facilities, 🅲, 🛏, litter barrels, vending, petwalk
2	NC 130, to NC 904, Rowland
1 b a	US 301, US 501, Dillon, E 🅶 Exxon, Mobil, 🍴 Hot Tamale Rest., Peddler Steaks, Pedro's Diner, Porky's Truckstp, 🛏 Budget Motel, South-of-the-Border Motel, 🅾 Pedro's Campground, W 🅶 Shell/dsl, 🍴 Waffle House, 🛏 Knights Inn, Super 8
0mm	North Carolina/South Carolina state line

INTERSTATE 240 (Asheville)

Exit	Services
9mm	I-240 begins/ends on I-40, exit 53b a.
8	Fairview Rd, N 🅶 Shell/dsl, 🍴 Burger King, Cheddar's, China Buffet, J&S Cafeteria, KFC, La Posada Mexican, Little Caesar's, Little Venice, McDonald's, Subway, 🛏 Ramada Inn, 🅾 Advance Parts, Aldi Foods, Bi-Lo Foods,

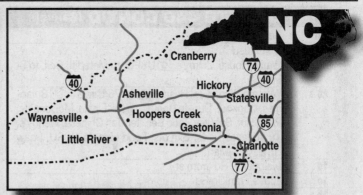

INTERSTATE 240 CONT'D (Asheville)

Exit	Services
8	Continued
	CVS Drug, $General, Hamrick's, Hancock Fabrics, Kohl's, Petsmart, U-Haul, Walmart, S 🅖 Citgo, 🍴 Pizza Hut, 🅾 Home Depot
7.5mm	Swannanoa River
7	US 70, N 🛏 Best Western, 🅾 KIA, Subaru, Suzuki, S 🅖 Shell/dsl, 🍴 Applebee's, Bonefish Grill, Buffalo Wild Wings, Burger King, Cancun Mexican, Chick-fil-A, Chili's, China Palace, ChuckeCheese, Cici's Pizza, Cook Out, Cornerstone Rest., Cracker Barrel, DQ, East Buffet, Firehouse Subs, Guadalajara Mexican, Hooters, IHOP, Longhorn Steaks, McAlister's Deli, McDonald's, Mikado, Mike's Subs, Mountaineer Inn, O'Charley's, Olive Garden, Outback Steaks, Red Lobster, Subway, Taco Bell, Waffle House, 🛏 Country Inn&Suites, Courtyard, Days Inn, EconoLodge, Hampton Inn, Holiday Inn, Homewood Suites, InTown Motor Inn, SpringHill Suites, Super 8, 🅾 Barnes&Noble, Belk, Best Buy, BigLots, Books-A-Million, Dick's, Dillards, $General, $Tree, Ingles Foods/gas, JC Penney, K-Mart, Lowe's, Michael's, Mtn View Tire, Office Depot, Old Navy, Radio Shack, Ross, Sears/auto, Target, TJ Maxx, Tuesday Morning, Verizon, Walgreens
6	Tunnel Rd (from eb) same as 7
5b	US 70 E, US 74A, Charlotte St, N 🅖 BP, Pure, 🍴 Charlotte St. Grill, Fuddruckers, Starbucks, Two Guys Hogi, 🛏 B&B, 🅾 vet, S 🍴 Chop House Rest., Tripp's Rest., 🛏 Renaissance Hotel, Sheraton, 🅾 Civic Ctr
5a	US 25, Merrimon Ave, N 🅖 Exxon/dsl, Shell/dsl, 🍴 Bojangles, La Carreta, 🅾 Green Life Foods, Staples
4c	Haywood St (no EZ return to eb), Montford, S 🍴 3 Bros Rest., 🛏 B&B
4b	Patton Ave (from eb), downtown
4a	US 19 N, US 23 N, US 70 W, to Weaverville
3b	Westgate, N 🍴 Jason's Deli, Oriental Pavillion, Tomato Latina, 🛏 Crowne Plaza, 🅾 CVS Drug, EarthFare Foods, NTB, Sam's Club/gas
3a	US 19 S, US 23 S, W Asheville, N 🅖 BP, 🍴 A&W/LJ Silver, Arby's, Bojangles, Burger King, Denny's, Green Tea Japanese, KFC, Krispy Kreme, Little Caesar's, McDonald's, New 1 China, Nona Mia Italian, Pizza Hut, Ryan's, Sonic, Subway, Taco Bell, Vera Cruz Mexican, Wendy's, Yoshida Japanese, 🅾 Advance Parts, Aldi Foods, AutoZone, Buick/Cadillac/GMC, Curves, $General, Family$, Ingles Foods, Kerr Drug, K-Mart, Mtn View Tire, Radio Shack, Sav-Mor Foods, vet
2	US 19, US 23, W Asheville, N 🅾 B&B Drug, S 🅖 Haywood Quickstop/dsl
1c	Amboy Rd (from eb)
1b	NC 191, to I-40 E, Brevard Rd, S 🅾 farmers mkt, camping
1a	I-40 W, to Knoxville
0mm	I-240 begins/ends on I-40, exit 46b a.

INTERSTATE 440 (Raleigh)

Exit	Services
16	I-40
15	Poole Rd, E 🅖 Exxon, 🍴 Quiznos, W 🅖 BP/dsl, Citgo/dsl, 🍴 Burger King, McDonald's, KFC/Taco Bell, Subway, 🍴 Family$, Food Lion
14	US 64, to Rocky Mount, limited access hwy
13b a	US 64, US 264 E, New Bern Ave, to Wilson, 0-2 mi

Exit	Services
13b a	Continued
	E 🅖 BP, Caroco/dsl, Exxon, Micro Mart, Murphy USA/dsl, 76/Circle K, Shell/dsl, 🍴 Bojangles, Burger King, Golden Corral, Jumbo China, McDonald's, Papa John's, Quiznos, Roh Buffet, Ruby Tuesday, Starbucks, Subway, Waffle House, Wendy's, 🛏 Best Western, Comfort Suites, Holiday Inn Express, Microtel, Super 8, 🅾 Advance Parts, AutoZone, CVS Drug, Firestone/auto, Food Lion, Kroger, Office Depot, O'Reilly Parts, RV Ctr, U-Haul, Walgreens, Walmart, W Ⓗ
12	Yonkers Rd, Brentwood Rd
11b a	US 1, US 401, Capital Blvd N, N 🅖 BP, Citgo, Exxon, Kangaroo/dsl, Mobil, Shell, 🍴 Baskin-Robbins/Dunkin Donuts, Buffalo Bro's, Burger King, ChuckeCheese, Cici's, Cookout, IHOP, Mayflower Sea🍴 McDonald's, Outback Steaks, Perkins, Taco Bell, Vallerta Mexican, Waffle House, 🛏 Best Western, Days Inn, EconoLodge, Holiday Inn, Lodge America, Quality Inn, Sleep Inn, Super 8, Wingate Inn, 🅾 Aamco, AutoZone, Food Lion, Pepboys, Rite Aid, Walgreens, U-Haul
10	Wake Forest Rd, N 🍴 Bahama Breeze, Denny's, 🛏 Days Inn, Hilton, Homestead Suites, Hyatt Place, 🅾 Ⓗ, CVS Drug, S 🅖 BP, 🍴 Applebee's, Arby's, Biscuitville, Burger King, Courtney's Cafe, Jersey Mike's, Jimmy John's, Jumbo China, KFC/Taco Bell, McDonald's, Melting Pot Rest., Papa John's, Pizza Hut, Qdoba, Quiznos, Subway, 🛏 Courtyard, Extended Stay America, Hampton Inn, Studio+, 🅾 Advance Parts, AutoZone, Buick/GMC, Costco/gas, Curves, Discount Tire, Hancock Fabrics, Hyundai, Mazda, Nissan, Staples, Subaru, Trader Joe's, VW
8b a	6 Forks Rd, North Hills, N 🅖 Exxon/repair, 🍴 Bonefish Grill, Chick-fil-A, Firebirds Grill, 5 Guys Burgers, Fox&Hound Grille, Moe's SW Grill, Panera Bread, Pig Shack, Ruths Chris Steaks, Starbucks, Tiola Pizza, Zoe's Kitchen, 🛏 Renaissance, 🅾 AT&T, GNC, Harris Teeter, JC Penney, Kerr Drug, Target
7b a	US 70, NC 50, Glenwood Ave, Crabtree Valley, N 🅖 BP, Shell, 🍴 Brio Grill, Cheesecake Factory, Fleming's, McDonald's, PF Chang's, 🛏 Crabtree Inn, Embassy Suites, Holiday Inn, Marriott, Residence Inn, Windsor Inn, 🅾 Barnes&Noble, Belk, Best Buy, Macy's, McCormick&Shmicks, Just Tires, Old Navy, Sears/auto, mall
6	Ridge Rd (from nb), same as 7
5	Lake Boone Tr, W 🅖 Circle K, 🍴 McDonald's, Starbucks, Subway, Wendy's, 🅾 Ⓗ, Food Lion, Tuesday Morning
4b a	to I-40 W, Wade Ave, W to I-40, RDU ✈
3	NC 54, Hillsboro St, E 🅖 BP, Exxon, Hugo's, Pure, 🍴 Applebee's, Arby's, Bean Sprout Chinese, Burger King, Marco's Pizza, Quiznos, Snoopy's Hotdogs, Subway,

NC ND

INTERSTATE 440 CONT'D (Raleigh)

Exit	Services
3	Continued Waffle House, Zaxby's, 🅞 USPO, to Meredith Coll, to St Mary's
2b a	Western Blvd, E 🅖 Hess, Hugo's, 76/Circle K, 🍴 Bojangles, Cookout, Dunkin Donuts, Greek Fiesta, McDonalds, Pizza Hut, Subway, Taco Bell, Ten Ten Chinese, Wendy's, 🅞 Advance Parts, BigLots, Food Lion, to NCSU, Shaw U, W 🅞 K-Mart
1d	Melbourne Rd (from sb)
1c	Jones-Franklin Rd
1b a	I-40. I-440 begins on I-40., 1-2 mi W on Walnut St 🅖 Exxon, Shell, 🍴 Astor's Grill, Bob Evans, Chick-fil-A, China King, Coldstone, Cookout, Golden Corral, Dickey's BBQ, HoneyBaked Ham, Jasmin Bistro, McDonald's, Moe's SW Grill, Noodles&Co, Olive Garden, Panera Bread, Qdoba, Red Lobster, Red Robin, Remington Grill, Ruby Tuesday, Starbucks, Subway, Taco Bell, Waffle House, 🛏 Best Western, Red Roof Inn, 🅞 BJ's Whse, Ford, GNC, Home Depot, Jo-Ann Fabrics, Kohl's, Lowe's, Marshall's, Michael's, NTB, Office Depot, Old Navy, PetsMart, Steinmart, mall

INTERSTATE 485 (Charlotte)

Exit	Services
61	US 251, Johnston Rd, N 🍴 Eddie's Place Rest, Global Rest, Hickory Tavern, Quizno's, Red Robin, Ruby Tuesday, Sticky Fingers, 🛏 SpringHill Suites, 🅞 Earth Fare Foods, S 🅖 Texaco/dsl, 🍴 Buffalo's SW Cafe, 5 Guys Burgers, Flat Rock Grille, Moe's SW Grill, Smoothie King, Tony's Pizza, 🛏 Ballantyne Hotel, Courtyard, Staybridge Suites, 🅞 CVS Drug
64b a	Rd 51, N 🅖 Exxon, Shell/Circle K, 🍴 Bojangles, Donato's Pizza, KFC/Pizza Hut, McDonald's, Pier 57 Sea 🍴 Wendy's, 🛏 Extended Stay America, Extended Stay Deluxe, 🅞 🅷 Bi-Lo, Firestone/auto, S 🅖 Shell, 🍴 Applebee's, Buca Italian, Burger King, China Buffet, IHOP, Jason's Deli, Red Lobster, Subway, Taco Bell, Tony Roma's, 🛏 Holiday Inn Express, Quality Inn, 🅞 Belk, Dillard's, $General, Food Lion, Home Depot, JC Penney, K-Mart, Office Depot, Petsmart, Rite Aid, Sear/auto, SteinMart, TJ Maxx
65	South Blvd, N 🅖 Texaco, 🍴 Chick-fil-A, Golden Corral, Hooters, McDonald's, Rafferty's, Sonny's BBQ, Steak'n Shake, TX Roadhouse, Wendy's, 🅞 Advance Parts, Chevrolet, Discount Tire, $Tree, Kohl's, Nissan, Old Navy, PetCo, Ross, Target, VW, World Mkt, S 🅞 Cadillac, CarMax, Pineville Tires, vet
67	I-77, US 21, to Charlotte, Columbia, I-485 begins/ends
61b a	US 521 S, Johnston Rd, E 🅖 Exxon, 🍴 Applebee's, Chick-fil-A, China Bistro, 1511 Cantina, JoJo China Bistro, Firebird's Grill, Marble Slab, Miro Spanish Grill, Noodles Rest, Pizza Inn, Starbucks, Wendy's, 🛏 Residence Inn, 🅞 GNC, Goodyear/auto, Harris-Teeter, Radio Shack, Target, vet
59	Rea Rd
57	Providence Rd, Rd 16, E 🅖 Texaco/Wendy's, 🍴 Hickory Tavern, Penn Sta, The Wok, 🅞 Curves, Harris-Teeter, USPO, W 🅖 Exxon, Shell, 🍴 BBQ Shack, Cold Stone, Macaroni Grill, Red Bowl Rest, Starbucks, 🅞 CVS Drug, Home Depot, Lowes Foods, Rite Aid, Staples, SteinMart, vet
52	to Matthews
51b a	US 74, to Charlotte, Monroe, E 🅖 76/Circle K/dsl,

Exit	Services
51b a	Continued Shell, Sunoco/dsl, 🛏 Country Inn&Suites, Holiday Inn Express, InTown Suites, 🅞 Country Camping RV Ctr, Scion/Toyota, W 🅖 Exxon, Shell, 🍴 Bojangles, Pizza Hut, Taco Bell, Wendy's, 🛏 Courtyard, EconoLodge, Microtel, 🅞 🅷, Aamco, AutoZone, Firestone/auto, Goodyear/auto, Radio Shack, Tuesday Morning
49	Idlewild Rd, E 🅖 Exxon/dsl, 🍴 China Cafe, El Maguey Mexican, Mama's Pizza, 🅞 Lowe's Foods, Rite Aid
47	Lawyers Rd, E 🅖 Gate, 🍴 Aladdin's, Bellacino's Pizza, Best China, Domino's, McDonald's, 🅞 CVS Drug, Harris-Teeter, vet, 2 mi W 🍴 Dunkin Donuts, Wendy's
44	Rd 218, to Mint Hill, W 🅖 BP/dsl
43	Rd 51, to Mint Hill
41	Rd 24, Rd 27, to Albemarle, 2 mi W 🍴 Chick-fil-A, Taco Bell
39	Harrisburg Rd, W 🅖 BP, 🍴 China Garden, Papa John's, Wendy's, 🅞 Food Lion
36	Rocky River Rd, N 🅖 Citgo/dsl, Gate, 🍴 Best China, Bojangles, Capriccio's Pizza, Subway, 🅞 CVS Drug, Discount Tire, Harris-Teeter, Tuffy Auto
33	Rd 49, to Harrisburg, N 🅖 Hess/dsl, 🍴 Cici's Pizza, 🅞 Food Lion, S 🅖 BP, Exxon, 76/Circle K, Sunoco, 🍴 Little Caesar's, Wendy's, 🅞 Family$
32	US 29, N 🅞 CVS Drug, S 🅖 Texaco, 🍴 Jack-in-the-Box, 🅞 🅷
23c	Rd 115, to Huntersville, I-485 begins/ends on I-85
23b a	I-77, to Charlotte, Statesville
21	Rd 24, Harris Blvd, S 🍴 Bravo Italian, Chick-fil-A, Chili's, Cold Stone, Edomae Grill, Firehouse Subs, 5 Guys Burgers, Fox&Hound, Mimi's Cafe, Moe's SW Grill, Olive Garden, On-the-Border, Panera bread, PF Chang's, Red Robin, Shane's Rib Shack, TGI Friday's, Wendy's, 🛏 Drury Inn, 🅞 AT&T, Belk, Best Buy, Dillard's, Lowe's Whse, Macy's, Old Navy, Petsmart, Target, mall
16	Rd 16, to Newton, Brookshire Blvd, W 🍴 Bojangles, Bull&Barrister Rest, Chick-fil-A, CiCi's Pizza, McDonald's, Pizza Hut, Red Bowl Asian, Subway, Wendy's 🅞 Harris-Teeter, Rite Aid, Walmart
14	Rd 27, to Mt Holly Rd, W 🅖 BP (2mi)
12	Moores Chapel Rd, E 🍴 Jin Jin Chinese, 🅞 Advance Parts, CVS Drug, Food Lion
10	I-85, to Spartanburg, Greensboro
9	US 29, US 74, Wilkinson Blvd, S 🅖 BP
4	Rd 160, to Fort Mill, N 🅖 Exxon/dsl, 🅞 CVS Drug
3	Arrowood Rd, S 🅖 Quizno's
1	S Tryon St, Rd 49, N 🅖 Exxon, Shell, Texaco, 🍴 Bojangles, Dragon Buffet, McDonald's, O'Charley's, Panera Bread, Qdoba, 🅞 Bi-Lo, Lowe's Whse, Walmart, S 🅖 Texaco/dsl, 🍴 Applebee's, Baskin-Robbins/Dunkin Donuts, Burger King, Domino's, Don Pedro Mexican, Firehouse Subs, Fortune Cookie, Hungry Howie's, McAlister's Deli, Moe's SW Grill, Pan China, Starbucks, Subway, Wild Wing Cafe, 🛏 Hilton Garden, Yorkshire Inn, 🅞 AT&T, AutoZone, Discount Tire, $Tree, Food Lion, NAPA, Office Depot, Tire Kingdom, Tuffy Auto

NORTH DAKOTA

INTERSTATE 29

Exit	Services
218mm	North Dakota state line, US/Canada border
217mm	US Customs sb
216mm	historical site nb, tourist info sb

opyright 2011 - The Next Exit®

N ↕ S

GRAND FORKS

INTERSTATE 29 CONT'D

Exit	Services
215	ND 59, rd 55, Pembina, **E** Gastrak/DutyFree Store/dsl, Gastrak/pizza/dsl/scales/24hr, Pembina State Museum/info
212	no services
208	rd 1, to Bathgate
203	US 81, ND 5, to Hamilton, Cavalier, **W** to Icelandic SP (25 mi), weigh sta both lanes
200	no services
196	rd 3, Bowesmont
193	no services
191	rd 11, to St Thomas
187	ND 66, to Drayton, **E** Cenex/pizza/dsl, Tesoro/dsl, Rte 44 Café, Motel 66, USPO, city park
184	to Drayton, **2 mi E** /dsl, USPO
180	rd 9
179mm	**rest area both lanes (both lanes exit left), full facilities, litter barrels, vending, petwalk**
176	ND 17, to Grafton, **10 mi W** AmericInn
172	no services
168	rd 15, to Minto, Warsaw
164	no services
161	ND 54, rd 19, to Ardoch, Oslo
157	no services
152	US 81, to Gilby, Manvel, **W** Manvel/dsl/food
145	US 81 bus, N Washington St, to Grand Forks
141	US 2, Gateway Dr, Grand Forks, **E** Cenex, Loaf'N Jug/dsl, Stamart, Univ. Sta/dsl, Al's Grill, Burger King, Greatwall Buffet, McDonald's, Best Value Inn, Budget Inn, Clarion, Econolodge, Ramada Inn, Select Inn, Super 8, Ford/Lincoln/Mercury, O'Reilly Parts, transmissions, to U of ND, **1 mi E** DQ, Domino's, Taco John's, H, Freightliner, U-Haul, auto repair, **W** Simonson/dsl/café/24hr/@, StaMart/Tesoro/dsl/RV dump/scales/@, Emerald Grill, Perkins, Settle Inn, Budget RV Ctr, GMC/Volvo, **port of entry/weigh sta**, dsl repair, to AFB
140	DeMers Ave, **E** Cenex, Loaf'N Jug, Valley Dairy, Red Pepper Cafe, Canada Inn, Hilton Garden, H, Alerus Ctr, to U of ND

Exit	Services
138	US 81, 32nd Ave S, **E** Cenex, Holiday/dsl, Arby's, Buffalo Wild Wings, Burger King, China Garden, Coldstone Creamery, Culver's, DQ, Denny's, Golden Corral, Grizzly's Steaks, Ground Round, Jimmy John's, McDonald's, Papa Murphy's, Pizza Hut, Qdoba Mexican, Quizno's, Red Lobster, Space Alien's Rest, Starbucks, Taco Bell, Texas Roadhouse, Village Inn, Wendy's, C'mon Inn, Comfort Inn, Country Inn&Suites, Days Inn, Fairfield Inn, Holiday Inn Express, Lakeview Inn, Roadking Inn, SpringHill Suites, Best Buy, Chrysler, CVS Drug, $Tree, Ford/Lincoln/Mercury, Gordman's, Hugo's Foods, JC Penney, Jo-Ann Fabrics, Kohl's, Lowe's Whse, Macy's, Menards, Michael's, Old Navy, PetCo, Sam's Club/gas, Scion/Toyota, Super 1 Foods, Target, Tires+, TJ Maxx, Walmart, mall, **W** Sinclair/Subway/dsl, Grand Forks Camping
130	ND 15, rd 81, Thompson, **1 mi W** , food
123	to Reynolds, **E** to Central Valley School
119mm	no services
118	to Buxton
111	ND 200 W, to Cummings, Mayville, **W** Big Top Fireworks, to Mayville St U
104	Hillsboro, **E** Cenex/Burger King/dsl/LP/24hr, Tesoro/Stop-n-Go/dsl/24hr, Country Hearth Rest., Pizza Ranch, Subway, Hillsboro Inn, H, RV park, USPO
100	ND 200 E, ND 200A, to Blanchard, Halstad
99mm	**rest area both lanes, full facilities, litter barrels, vending, petwalk**
92	rd 11, Grandin, **E** Co-op/dsl, **W** Stop&Shop/dsl
86	Gardner
79	Argusville
74.5mm	Sheyenne River
73	rd 17, rd 22, Harwood, **E** Cenex/pizza/dsl/LP/café/24hr
69	rd 20
67	US 81 bus, 19th Ave N, **E** Homewood Suites, VA H, Hector Int
66	12th Ave N, **E** StaMart/Tesoro/dsl/24hr/scales, Stop'n Go, H, tuck wash, to ND St U, **W** Cenex/dsl, Arby's, Super 8
65	US 10, Main Ave, W Fargo, **E** Tesoro/dsl/24hr, NAPA, OK Tire, True Value, vet, **W** Cenex/Subway/

NC
ND

INTERSTATE 29 CONT'D

Exit	Services
65	Continued dsl, Simonson/dsl, Stop-n-Go, ⓕ Hardee's, O'Kelly's Rest., ⓛ Kelly Inn, ⓞ CarQuest, Buick/Cadillac/Chevrolet/Honda, CarQuest, Chrysler/Dodge/Jeep, Hyundai, Isuzu/Volvo/GMC, Mac's Hardware, Lincoln/Mercury, O'Reilly Parts, Scion/Toyota, Subaru
64	13th Ave, Fargo, **E** ⓖ All-Stop, Don's, Kum&Go, StaMart/dsl, ⓕ Acapulco Mexican, Applebee's, Arby's, Buck's Rest., Burger King, ChuckeCheese, DQ, Erbert & Gerbert's Subs, Giant Panda Chinese, GreenMill Rest., Ground Round, Hooters, Little Caesar's, Perkins/24hr, Quizno's, Subway, Taco John's, Wendy's, ⓛ AmericInn, Best Western, Comfort Inn, Comfort Suites, Country Inn&Suites, Econolodge, Grand Inn, Hampton Inn, Motel 6, Super 8, ⓞ CashWise Foods/drug/24hr, CVS Drug, Family$, Goodyear/auto, O'Reilly Parts, Tires+/transmissions, White Drug, auto repair, **W** ⓖ All-Stop/dsl, Cenex, Tesoro, ⓕ Applebee's, Arby's, Buffalo Wild Wings, Caribou Coffee, Chili's, Culver's, DQ, Denny's, Domino's, Grizzly's, Godfather's, Happy Joe's Pizza, KFC, Kroll's Diner, LoneStar Steaks, McDonald's, Olive Garden, Paradiso Mexican, Pizza Hut, Red Lobster, Ruby Tuesday, Schlotsky's, Spitfire Grill, Subway, Taco Bell, Taco John's, Texas Roadhouse, TGIFriday, TimberLodge Steaks, ⓛ Comfort Inn, Days Inn, Fairfield Inn, Holiday Inn Express, Kelly Inn, Ramada Inn, Red River Lodge, Select Inn, ⓞ Barnes&Noble, Best Buy, BigLots, Chevrolet, Chrysler/Dodge/Jeep, $Tree, GNC, Gordman's, Hancock Fabrics, Herberger's, Hobby Lobby, Honda, Hornbacher's Foods, JC Penney, Jo-Ann Fabrics, Kohl's, Lowe's Whse, Macy's, Menards, Michael's, Office Depot, Old Navy, PetCo, Petsmart, Sam's Club/gas, Savers Foods, Sears/auto, SunMart Foods, Target, TJ Maxx, Walmart, Walgreens, USPO, mall
63b a	I-94, W to Bismarck, E to Minneapolis
62	32nd Ave S, Fargo, **E** ⓖ F&F/dsl, Holiday, Tesoro, ⓕ Arby's, Country Kitchen, Culver's, KFC, Little Caesar's, Moe's SW Grill, Papa John's, Quizno's, Starbucks, Subway, Taco John's, Village Inn, ⓞ Ⓗ, Buick/GMC, Ford, Freightliner, JiffyLube, SunMart Foods, **W** ⓖ ⊕FLYING J /Denny's/dsl/LP/motel/24hr/@, ♥Loves/McDonald's/Subway/dsl/scales/24hr, ⓞ Goodyear/auto, Peterbilt, Volvo
60	52nd Ave S, to Fargo, **W** ⓞ Walmart
56	to Wild Rice, Horace
54	rd 16, to Oxbow, Davenport
50	rd 18, Hickson
48	ND 46, to Kindred
44	to Christine, **1 mi E** ⓖ
42	rd 2, to Walcott
37	rd 4, to Abercrombie, Colfax, **E** to Ft Abercrombie HS, **3 mi W** ⓖ
31	rd 8, Galchutt
26	to Dwight
24mm	**weigh sta both lanes exit left**
23b a	ND 13, to Wahpeton, Mooreton, **10 mi E** Ⓗ, ND St Coll of Science
15	rd 16, to Mantador, Great Bend
8	ND 11, to Hankinson, Fairmount, **E** ⓖ Tesoro/dsl, **3 mi W** camping

Exit	Services
3mm	Welcome Ctr nb, full ♿ facilities, Ⓒ, 🛢, litter barrels, petwalk
2	rd 22
1	rd 1E, **E** Dakota Magic Casino/Hotel/rest./gas/dsl
0mm	North Dakota/South Dakota state line

INTERSTATE 94

Exit	Services
352mm	North Dakota/Minnesota state line, Red River
351	US 81, Fargo, **N** ⓖ Loaf'n Jug, Stop'n Go, ⓕ Duane's Pizza, Great Harvest Breads, Great Wall Chinese, Santa Lucia Pizza, Taco Shop, ⓞ Ⓗ, Hornbacher's Foods, Medicine Shoppe, vet, **S** ⓖ Stop'n Go, Tesoro/dsl, ⓕ A&W/LJ Silver, Burger King, Happy Joe's Pizza, KFC, McDonald's, N American Steaks, Papa Murphy's, Pepper's Café, Randy's Diner, Subway, Taco Bell, ⓛ Rodeway Inn, Vista Inn, ⓞ Hornbacher's Foods, K-Mart, Verizon, USPO
350	25th St, Fargo, **N** ⓖ Stop'n Go, **S** ⓖ Cenex/dsl, Loaf'n Jug/dsl, ⓕ Dolittle's Grill, Ruby Tuesday
349b a	I-29, **N** to Grand Forks, **S** to Sioux Falls, **services 1 mi N**, exit 64
348	45th St, **0-2 mi N Visitor Ctr/full facilities, litter barrels**, 🛢, ⓖ Holiday, Petro/dsl/LP/24hr/@, ⓕ Carino's, Coldstone, Culver's, Denny's, Dunn Bros Coffee, IHOP, Kroll's Diner, Little Caesar's, McDonald's, Pizza Hut, Qdoba, Quiznos, Papa Murphy's, Space Aliens Grill, Subway, Wendy's, ⓛ Best Western, C'mon Inn, Expressway Suites, Hilton Garden, MainStay Suites, Ramada Inn, Sleep Inn, Staybridge Suites, Wingate Inn, ⓞ Blue Beacon, Hobby Lobby, Home Depot, Kohl's, Office Depot, NAPA, Sam's Club, Scheel's Sports, Target, Verizon, Walmart, **S** ⓖ Clark/dsl, Stop'n Go, Tesoro/DQ/dsl, ⓕ Applebee's, Famous Dave's BBQ, 5 Guys Burgers, Golden Corral, Mexican Village, Old Chicago Pizza, Pizza Ranch, Taco John's, Taco Shop, ⓛ La Quinta, Settle Inn, ⓞ Gander Mtn, Red River Zoo
347	9th St E
346b a	to Horace, W Fargo, **S** ⓖ Tesoro/dsl, repair
343	US 10, Lp 94, W Fargo, **N** ⓖ Cenex/dsl, ⓛ Sunset Motel, ⓞ Adventure RV Ctr, Harley-Davidson, Pioneer Village
342	no services
342mm	**weigh sta wb**
340	to Kindred
338	Mapleton, **N** ⓖ Petro/dsl
337mm	truck parking wb, litter barrels
331	ND 18, to Leonard, Casselton, **N** ⓖ Tesoro/Subway/dsl, ⓕ Country Kitchen, ⓛ Governors Inn/RV park, ⓞ NAPA, repair
328	to Lynchburg
327mm	truck parking eb, litter barrels
324	Wheatland, to Chaffee
322	Absaraka
320	to Embden
317	to Ayr
314	ND 38 N, to Alice, Buffalo, **3 mi N** ⓖ, food
310	no services
307	to Tower City, **N** ⓖ Cenex/café/dsl/RV Park/24hr, motel
304mm	**rest area both lanes (both lanes exit left), full ♿ facilities, info, Ⓒ, 🛢, litter barrels, vending, petwalk**
302	ND 32, to Fingal, Oriska, **1 mi N** city park
298	no services

ND

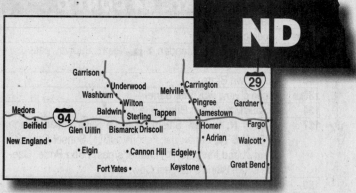

INTERSTATE 94 CONT'D

Exit	Services
296	no services
294	Lp 94, to Kathryn, Valley City, N 🅷, camping
292	Valley City, N 🅖 Tesoro/café/dsl/24hr, 🍴 Sabir's Rest., 🛏 AmericInn, Super 8, Wagon Wheel Inn/rest., 🅞 🅷, to Bald Hill Dam, camping, S 🅞 Ft Ransom SP (35mi)
291	Sheyenne River
290	Lp 94, Valley City, N 🅖 Tesoro/dsl, 🍴 Burger King, Kenny's Rest., Pizza Hut, Roby's Rest., Subway, 🅞 🅷, Chrysler/Dodge/Jeep, Family$, Firestone/auto, Ford, NAPA, Pamida, Radio Shack
288	ND 1 S, to Oakes, S Fort Ransom SP (36 mi)
283	ND 1 N, to Rogers
281	to Litchville, Sanborn, **1-2 mi** N 🅖, 🍴 lodging
276	Eckelson, S 🅞 Prairie Haven Camping/gas/dsl
275mm	continental divide, elev 1490
272	to Urbana
269	Spiritwood
262	Bloom, N 🖂
260	Jamestown, N 🅖 Stop'n Go, Tesoro/café/dsl/@, 🛏 Starlite Motel, 🅞 to St 🅷, camping
259mm	James River
258	US 281, Jamestown, N 🅖 Clark/TCBY/dsl, Tesoro/dsl, 🍴 Arby's, DQ, Hardee's, McDonald's, Pizza Ranch, Subway, Taco Bell, 🛏 Comfort Inn, Days Inn, Holiday Inn Express, 🅞 🅷, Buffalo Herd/museum, Cadillac/GMC, Firestone/auto, NW Tire, O'Reilly Parts, Toyota, vet, S 🅖 Sinclair/dsl/24hr, 🍴 Applebee's, Burger King, Grizzly's Rest., Hong Kong Buffet, La Carreta Mexican, Paradiso Mexican, Perkins, 🛏 Quality Inn, Super 8, 🅞 Chrysler/Dodge/Jeep, $Tree, Ford/Lincoln/Mercury, Harley-Davidson, JC Penney, K-Mart, Sears, Walmart, mall, USPO, vet
257	Lp 94 (from eb), to Jamestown, N dsl repair
256	US 52 W, US 281 N, S 🅞 Wiest truck/trailer repair, **1 mi** S Jamestown Campground/RV dump
254mm	**rest area both lanes, full** ♿ **facilities,** 🅒, 🅐, **litter barrels, petwalk, vending**
251	Eldridge
248	no services
245	no services
242	Windsor, N 🅖
238	to Gackle, Cleveland
233	no services
230	Medina, **1 mi** N 🅖 Famer's Union/dsl/LP, 🍴 DairyTreat, 🅞 Medina RV Park, USPO, city park
228	ND 30 S, to Streeter
224mm	**rest area wb, full** ♿ **facilities,** 🅒, 🅐, **litter barrels, vending, petwalk**
221	Crystal Springs
221mm	**rest area eb, full** ♿ **facilities,** 🅒, 🅐, **litter barrels, vending, petwalk**
217	Pettibone
214	Tappen, S gas/dsl/food
208	ND 3 S, Dawson, N RV camping, **1/2 mi** S 🅖, 🍴 to Camp Grassick, RV camping
205	Robinson
200	ND 3 N, to Tuttle, Steele, S 🅖 Cenex/dsl/24hr, 🍴 Beary Tweet&Tasty, Lone Steer Café, 🛏 OK Motel, 🅞 truckwash
195	no services

Exit	Services
190	Driscoll, S food
182	US 83 S, ND 14, to Wing, Sterling, S 🅖 Cenex/dsl/24hr, 🛏 Top's Motel (1mi)
176	McKenzie
170	Menoken, S to McDowell Dam, RV Park
168mm	**rest area both lanes, full** ♿ **facilities,** 🅒, 🅐, **litter barrels, vending, petwalk**
161	Lp 94, Bismarck Expswy, Bismarck, N 🅖 Cenex/dsl/LP/24hr, Clark/Quiznos/dsl, 🅞 Toyota/Scion, S 🅖 Tesoro/Oasis/rest./dsl/24hr, 🍴 McDonald's, 🛏 Ramada Ltd, 🅞 Capital RV Ctr, Dakota Zoo, Freightliner, Kenworth, OK Tires, Volvo, dsl repair
159	US 83, Bismarck, N 🅖 Simonson/dsl, 🍴 Applebee's, Arby's, Burger King, China Star, China Town, Golden Corral, Hooters, KFC, Kroll's Diner, McDonald's, Olive Garden, Papa Murphy's, Paradiso Mexican, Perkins, Red Lobster, Ruby Tuesday, Schlotzsky's, Space Alien Grill, Subway, Taco Bell, TCBY, Wendy's, 🛏 AmericInn, Candlewood Suites, Comfort Inn, Country Suites, Fairfield Inn, Hampton Inn, Holiday Inn Express, Motel 6, 🅞 Chevrolet, CVS Drug, Dan's Foods, Hancock Fabrics, Hobby Lobby, Jo-Ann Fabrics, K-Mart, Menards, NW Tire, Sears/auto, U-Haul, Verizon, Walmart, mall, USPO, S 🅖 Conoco/dsl, StaMart/dsl, Tesoro, 🍴 DQ, Hardee's, Minerva's Rest., North American Steaks, Pizza Hut, Starbucks, Subway, Taco John's, Woodhouse Rest., 🛏 Best Western, Days Inn, Kelly Inn, La Quinta, Select Inn, Super 8, 🅞 🅷, O'Reilly Parts
157	Divide Ave, Bismarck, N 🅖 Conoco/dsl/LP/24hr, 🍴 Carino's, Coldstone, Cracker Barrel, Goodtimes Grill/Taco John's, McDonald's, Pancheros Mexican, Quiznos, Starbucks, TX Roadhouse, Wendy's, 🅞 Best Buy, $Tree, Kohls, Lowe's, Old Navy, Petsmart, TJ Maxx, Verizon, S 🅖 Cenex/dsl/E85/LP/RV Dump, 🅞 Central Mkt Foods
156mm	Missouri River
156	I-194, Bismarck Expswy, Bismarck City Ctr, **1/2 mi** S Dakota Zoo
155	to Lp 94 (exits left from wb), Mandan, City Ctr, same as 153
153	ND 1806, Mandan Dr, Mandan, **1/2 mi** S 🅖 Cenex/dsl, StaMart/dsl, Tesoro, 🍴 Bonanza, Burger King, DQ, Domino's, Hardee's, Papa Murphy's, Pizza Ranch, Subway, Taco John's, 🛏 North Country Inn, 🅞 Central Mkt Foods, Chevrolet, Family$, Goodyear/auto, NAPA, NW Tire, O'Reilly Parts, Subaru, Dacotah Centennial Park, Ft Lincoln SP (5mi)
152	Sunset Dr, Mandan, N 🅖 Conoco/dsl, 🍴 MT Mike's Steaks, 🛏 Best Western, S 🅖 Tesoro/RV dump, 🍴 Fried's Rest., 🅞 🅷

INTERSTATE 94 CONT'D

E → W **HEBRON**

Exit	Services
152mm	scenic view eb
147	ND 25, to ND 6, Mandan, **S** ⛽ Tesoro/Subway/cafe/dsl/scales/24hr
140	to Crown Butte
135mm	scenic view wb, litter barrel
134	to Judson, Sweet Briar Lake
127	ND 31 N, to New Salem, **N** Knife River Indian Village (35mi), **S** ⛽ Cenex/dsl, Tesoro/dsl, 🍴 Sunset Cafe, 🏨 Arrowhead Inn/café, ⓞ Farmer's/gas, Food Pride, Gaebe Drug, World's Largest Cow, vet
123	to Almont
120	no services
119mm	**rest area both lanes, full ♿ facilities, 🚻, 🏕, litter barrels, petwalk**
117	no services
113	no services
110	ND 49, to Glen Ullin
108	to Glen Ullin, Lake Tschida, **3 mi S** ⛽, 🍴 lodging, camping
102	Hebron, to Glen Ullin, to Lake Tschida, **3 mi S** ⛽, 🍴 lodging, camping
97	Hebron, **2 mi N** ⛽, 🍴 lodging
96.5mm	central/mountain time zone
90	no services
84	ND 8, Richardton, **N** ⛽ Cenex/dsl, ⓞ Ⓗ, to Assumption Abbey, Schnell RA
78	to Taylor
72	to Enchanted Hwy, Gladstone
64	Dickinson, **S** ⛽ Cenex/Tiger Truckstop/dsl/rest./24hr, 🍴 Dakota Diner, ⓞ Ford/Lincoln/Mercury, Honda, NW Tire, Toyota/Scion, dsl repair
61	ND 22, Dickinson, **N** ⛽ Cenex/dsl/LP/24hr, Simonson/dsl, 🍴 Applebee's, Arby's, Bonanza, Burger King, DQ, El Sombrero Mexican, Happy Joe's Pizza, Papa Murphy's, Pizza Ranch, Sanford's Rest., Taco Bell, Taco John's,

DICKINSON

Exit	Services
61	Continued Wendy's, 🏨 AmericInn, Best Western, Comfort Inn, Holiday Inn Express, Ramada, ⓞ Dan's Foods, Goodyear/auto, Herberger's, JC Penney, K-Mart, NAPA, O'Reilly Parts, Verizon, Walmart/Subway, White Drug, USPO, **S** ⛽ Cenex/dsl, Conoco/repair, Holiday/dsl/24hr, Tesoro, 🍴 A&W/KFC, Country Kitchen, Domino's, King Buffet, McDonald's, Perkins, Subway, 🏨 Quality Inn, Select Inn, Super 8, Travel Host, ⓞ Ⓗ, Ace Hardware, museum, visitor info
59	Lp 94, to Dickinson, **S** to Patterson Lake RA, camping, **3 mi S** services in Dickinson
51	South Heart
42	US 85, to Grassy Butte, Belfield, Williston, **N T** Roosevelt NP (52mi), **S** info, ⛽ Cenex/dsl/24hr, Conoco/dsl, 🍴 DQ, 🏨 Trapper's Inn/rest., ⓞ NAPA
36	Fryburg
32	T Roosevelt NP, **Painted Canyon Visitors Ctr, N rest area both lanes, full ♿ facilities, 🚻, 🏕, litter barrels, petwalk**
27	Lp 94, Historic Medora (from wb), T Roosevelt NP
24.5mm	Little Missouri Scenic River
24	Medora, Historic Medora, Chateau de Mores HS, T Roosevelt NP, **S visitors ctr**
23	West River Rd (from wb)
22mm	scenic view eb
18	Buffalo Gap, **N** Buffalo Gap Camping (seasonal), food/lodging
10	Sentinel Butte, Camel Hump Lake, **S** ⛽
7	Home on the Range
1	ND 16, Beach, **N** 🏨 Outpost Motel, ⓞ camping, **S** ⛽ Cenex/dsl/LP/24hr, ⛽FLYING J/Denny's/dsl/scales/LP/24hr, Buckboard Inn, ⓞ Ⓗ, Beach RV Park, **Welcome/Visitor Ctr, full handicapped facilities, litter barrels, petwalk,** 🏕
1mm	**weigh sta eb, litter barrel**
0mm	North Dakota/Montana state line

ND OH

OHIO

INTERSTATE 70

E → W **BLAINE**

Exit	Services
225.5mm	Ohio/West Virginia state line, Ohio River
225	US 250 W, OH 7, Bridgeport, **N** ⛽ Marathon, StarFire, Sunoco/24hr, 🍴 KFC, Papa John's, Pizza Hut, Wendy's (1mi), ⓞ Advance Parts, AutoZone, Family$, NAPA, **S** ⛽ Exxon, Gulf, 🍴 Domino's
220	US 40, rd 214, **N** ⛽ Marathon, Sunoco/dsl, 🍴 Mehlman Cafe, **S** ⛽ Chevron/dsl, 🏨 Days Inn, ⓞ vet
219	I-470 E, to Bel-Aire, Washington PA, (from eb)
218	Mall Rd, to US 40, to Blaine, **N** ⛽ BP, Exxon, 🍴 Applebee's, Arby's, Buffalo Wild Wings, Burger King, DeFelice Pizza, Denny's, Eat'n Park, King Buffet, Little Caesars, Outback Steaks, Pizza Hut, Red Lobster, Steak'n Shake, Subway, Taco Bell, Undo's Rest., Wendy's, W Texas Steaks, 🏨 Best Value Inn, EconoLodge, Hampton Inn, Holiday Inn Express, Red Roof Inn, Super 8, ⓞ AAA, Aldi Foods, AutoZone, Buick/Cadillac/Chevrolet, $General, $Tree, Kroger, Lowe's, Sam's Club, Staples, Verizon, Walmart/McDonald's, **S** 🍴 Bob Evans, Bonanza, Cracker Barrel, Garfield's Rest., KFC/LJ Silver,
218	Continued Longhorn Steaks, McDonald's, Panera Bread, Quiznos, Starbucks, 🏨 Fairfield Inn, ⓞ CVS Drug, Elder-Beerman, JC Penney, Jo-Ann Fabrics, K-Mart, Macy's, NTB, Sears/auto, mall
216	OH 9, St Clairsville, **N** ⛽ BP
215	National Rd, **N** 🍴 Burger King, Domino's, WenWu Chinese, ⓞ NAPA, Riesbeck's Foods, USPO
213	OH 331, Flushing, **S** ⛽ BP, Marathon/Subway/dsl, Sunoco/dsl, 🏨 Twin Pines Motel
211mm	**rest area both lanes, full ♿ facilities, 🚻, 🏕, litter barrels, petwalk, vending**
208	OH 149, Morristown, **N** ⛽ BP/McDonald's/dsl, 🍴 Schlepp's Rest., 🏨 Arrowhead Motel (1mi), ⓞ Cannonball Speedway, $General, Ford/Lincoln/Mercury, **S** ⛽ Marathon/Quiznos/dsl, ⓞ Harley-Davidson, Barkcamp SP
204	US 40 E (from eb, no return), National Rd
202	OH 800, to Barnesville, **S** ⛽ 202 Gas/dsl, ⓞ Ⓗ
198	rd 114, Fairview
193	OH 513, Middlebourne, **N** ⛽ BP, FuelMart/dsl, ⓞ fireworks

OH

INTERSTATE 70 CONT'D

Exit	Services
189mm	**rest area eb, full** ♿ **facilities,** ⑪, ⌂, **litter barrels, pet-walk, vending**
186	US 40, OH 285, to Old Washington, N ■ BP, S ■ Go-Mart/dsl
180b a	I-77 N, to Cleveland, to Salt Fork SP, I-77 S, to Charleston
178	OH 209, Cambridge, **0-1 mi** N ■ BP/dsl, Sheetz/dsl, Starfire, ⑪ Bob Evans, China Village, Coldstone/Tim Horton's, Cracker Barrel, Denny's, DQ, Forum Rest, KFC, McDonald's, Papa John's, Pizza Hut, Ruby Tuesday, Subway, USA Steaks, Wendy's, ⌂ Best Western, Comfort Inn, Days Inn, Hampton Inn, Super 8, ◉ Ⓗ, Advance Parts, AutoZone, BigLots, Buick/Cadillac/GMC, $General, Family$, U-Haul, Value-Fresh Foods, Verizon, S ■ Murphy USA/dsl, ▦/Subway/dsl/scales/24hr, ⑪ Arby's, Burger King, Great Chinese, Little Caesars, Taco Bell, Tlaquepaque Mexican, ⌂ Baymont Inn, ◉ Aldi Foods, $Tree, $Zone, K-Mart/gas, Radio Shack, Spring Valley RV Park, Verizon, Walmart/Subway
176	US 22, US 40, to Cambridge, N ■ Sunoco/dsl, ⌂ Budget Inn, ◉ Western Shop, RV camping, st patrol
173mm	**weigh sta both lanes**
169	OH 83, to Cumberland, New Concord, N ◉ John&Annie Glen Historic Site, RV camping, to Muskingum Coll
164	US 22, US 40, Norwich, N ■ BP, ⌂ Baker's Motel, Zane Gray Museum, S ◉ antiques, pottery
163mm	**rest area wb, full** ♿ **facilities,** ⑪, ⌂, **litter barrels, pet-walk, vending**
160	OH 797, Airport Rd, N ■ ⬤Loves/Arby's/dsl/scales/24hr, S ■ BP, Exxon/Subway/dsl, ⑪ Denny's, McDonald's, Wendy's, ⌂ Best Value Inn, Best Western, Ramada Inn, ◉ ✆, st patrol
157	OH 93, Zanesville, N ■ BP, S ■ Marathon, Shell/dsl, st patrol
155	OH 60, OH 146, Underwood St, Zanesville, N ⑪ Bob Evans, Olive Garden, Oriental Buffet, Red Lobster, Steak'n Shake, Tumbleweed Grill, ⌂ Comfort Inn, Fairfield Inn, Hampton Inn, Holiday Inn Express, ◉ Ⓗ, Pick'n Save Foods, USPO, visitor info, S ■ Exxon/dsl, ⑪ Adornetto Pizza, Cracker Barrel, Subway, Wendy's, ⌂ Baymont Inn, EconoLodge, Travelodge, ◉ Rite Aid
154	5th St (from eb)
153b	Maple Ave (no EZ return from wb), N ■ BP, ⑪ DQ, Italian Eatery, Papa John's, Tee Jaye's Rest, ◉ Ⓗ, CVS Drug, Family$
153a	State St, N ■ Speedway/dsl, ◉ to Dillon SP (8mi), S ■ Marathon
153mm	Licking River

Left margin: E ↑ ↓ W C A M B R I D G E

Right margin (between columns): Z A N E S V I L L E

= gas = food = lodging = other

INTERSTATE 70 CONT'D

E ↕ W

Exit	Services
152	US 40, National Rd, N Exxon/A&W/Blimpie/dsl, Starfire/dsl, McDonald's, Super 8
142	US 40 (from wb, no EZ return), Gratiot, N RV camping
141	OH 668, US 40 (from eb, no return), to Gratiot, same as 142
132	OH 13, to Thornville, Newark, N Dawes Arboretum (3mi), S BP, Shell, Subway (2mi), RV camping
131mm	**rest area both lanes, full facilities, litter barrels, petwalk, vending**
129b a	OH 79, to Buckeye Lake, Hebron, N Best Western, S BP, Valero, Donato's Pizza, McDonald's, Pizza Hut/Taco Bell, Wendy's, Super 8, CarQuest, KOA (2mi), Blue Goose Marina (2mi)
126	OH 37, to Granville, Lancaster, N Marathon/dsl, Pilot/Chester's/Subway/dsl/scales/24hr, Sunoco/dsl, S TA/BP/Popeye's/Sbarro's/dsl/scales/24hr/@, Valero/dsl, Deluxe Inn, Red Roof Inn, IA 80 Truckomat/truckwash, KOA
122	OH 158, to Baltimore, Kirkersville, N Regal Inn, S FLYING J/Denny's/dsl/LP/scales/24hr, fireworks
118	OH 310, to Pataskala, N BP/McDonald's, Shell/dsl, Speedway/dsl, DQ, S BP/Duke's/Subway/dsl, RCD RV Ctr
112c	OH 204, to Blecklick Rd (from eb)
112	OH 256, to Pickerington, Reynoldsburg, N BP, Shell/McDonald's, Chipotle Mexican, Culver's, 5 Guys Burgers, IHOP, Logan's Roadhouse, Noodles&Co, O'Charley's, Olive Garden, Panera Bread, Penn Sta, Rotolo's Pizza, Smokey Bones BBQ, Subway, TGIFriday's, Tim Horton's, Fairfield Inn, Holiday Inn Express, AT&T, Best Buy, Gander Mtn, Jo-Ann Fabrics, Marshall's, NTB, Radio Shack, Sam's Club/gas, Staples, Target, Tire Discounters, Verizon, Walgreens, Walmart/Subway, S Speedway/dsl, Arby's, Bob Evans, CiCi's Pizza, Classic's Diner, Cold Stone, Cracker Barrel, Dragon China, Feta Greek Cafe, Graffiti Burger, Iron Chef, KFC, La Fogata Mexican, LJ Silver, Longhorn Steaks, Skyline Chili, Steak'n Shake, Uno, Wendy's, Best Western, Comfort Inn, Hampton Inn, Barnes&Noble, Kohl's, Kroger/E85, Tuesday Morning, urgent care
110	Brice Rd, to Reynoldsburg, N Speedway, Sunoco, Burger King, Donato's, Genji Japanese, Golden China, Popeye's, Subway, TeeJaye's Rest., Tim Horton's, Waffle House, Days Inn, Extended Stay America, La Quinta, Red Roof Inn, Super 8, BigLots, Goodyear/auto, Home Depot, O'Reilly Parts, S BP, Speedway/dsl, Applebee's, Arby's, Asian Star, Big Boy, Boston Mkt, Burger King, Chipotle Mexican, Ichiban Steaks, KFC, McDonald's, Ruby Tuesday, Starbucks, Taco Bell, Waffle House, White Castle, Best Value Inn, Comfort Suites, EconoLodge, Motel 6, Acura, Advance Parts, Aldi Foods, Discount Tire, Family$, Fiat, Firestone/auto, GNC, Hobby Lobby, Honda, Lowe's, Michael's, NTB, Old Navy, Toyota/Scion, Walgreens
108b a	I-270 N to Cleveland, access to H, I-270 S to Cincinnati
107 ba	OH 317, Hamilton Rd, to Whitehall, S Shell/dsl, Valero/dsl, Arby's, Burger King, Capt D's, ChuckeCheese, Eastland Buffet, Ichiban Japanese, McDonald's, Papa John's, Pizza Hut, Red Lobster, Steak'n Shake,

COLUMBUS AREA

Exit	Services
107 ba	Continued Taco Bell, Fort Rapids Resort, Hampton Inn, Hawthorn Inn, InTown Suites, Knights Inn, AT&T, $General, JC Penney, Kohl's, Macy's, PepBoys, Staples
105a	US 33, to Lancaster, **2 mi** N Tat Italian
105b	US 33, James Rd, Bexley, N Tat Italian
103b a	Livingston Ave, to Capital University, N Exxon, Speedway/dsl, Mr Hero Subs, Peking Dynasty, Popeye's, Subway, Taco Bell, Wendy's, auto repair, S Marathon, Shell, McDonald's, Rally's, White Castle
102	Kelton Ave, Miller Ave
101a	I-71 N, to Cleveland
100b	US 23, to 4th St, downtown
99c	Rich St, Town St (exits left from eb), N Sunoco, Ford
99b	OH 315 N downtown
99a	I-71 S, to Cincinnati
98b	Mound St (from wb, no EZ return), S Speedway, Little Caesars, McDonald's, Rally's, Aldi Foods
98a	US 62, OH 3, Central Ave, to Sullivant, same as 98b
97	US 40, W Broad St, N Valero/dsl, Arby's, Burger King, KFC, McDonald's, Pizza Hut/Taco Bell, Subway, Tim Horton's, Wendy's, White Castle, Knights Inn, Aamco, CVS Drug, U-Haul, USPO
96	I-670 (exits left from eb), to ✈
95	Hague Ave (from wb), S Sunoco
94	Wilson Rd, N Marathon/Circle K/Subway/dsl, Mobil, S BP, Pilot/Wendy's/dsl/scales/24hr, Shell/dsl, Speedway, McDonald's, Waffle House, White Castle, EconoLodge
93b a	I-270, N to Cleveland, S to Cincinnati
91b a	to Hilliard, New Rome, N GetGo, Shell, Speedway/dsl, AA China, Applebee's, Arby's, Big Boy, Buffalo Wild Wings, Burger King, Cracker Barrel, Chick-fil-A, Cold Stone/Tim Horton's, Culver's, Donato's Pizza, El Vaquero Mexican, Fazoli's, 5 Guys Burgers, Golden Chopsticks, Hooters, KFC, McDonald's, Outback Steaks, Panera Bread, Perkins, Pizza Hut/Taco Bell, Red Robin, Ruby Tuesday, Salvi's Bistro, Skyline Chili, Smoothie King, TX Roadhouse, White Castle, Wendy's, Best Value Inn, Comfort Suites, Fairfield Inn, Hampton Inn, Hawthorn Inn, Holiday Inn, La Quinta, Motel 6, Red Roof Inn, Advance Parts, AT&T, Dick's, Discount Tire, Firestone/auto, Ford, Gander Mtn, Giant Eagle Foods/gas, GNC, Kohl's, Marshall's, Meijer/dsl, Michael's, Midas, Old Navy, Petsmart, Sam's Club/gas, Radio Shack, Target, Verizon, Walmart/Subway, urgent care, S BP/dsl, Marathon/dsl, Bob Evans, Handel's Icecream, Steak'n Shake, Best Western, Country Inn&Suites, Super 8
85	OH 142, to Plain City, W Jefferson, N Prairie Oaks SP, S Battelle Darby SP
80	OH 29, to Mechanicsburg, S hwy patrol
79	US 42, to London, Plain City, N Pilot/Arby's/dsl/scales/24hr, Waffle House, Raber's RV Ctr, truck/auto repair, S Speedway/Subway/dsl, TA/BP/Pizza Hut/Popeye's/dsl/scales/24hr/@, McDonald's, Taco Bell, Wendy's, Holiday Inn Express, Motel 6, H, truckwash
72	OH 56, to London, Summerford, N Marathon, **4 mi** S H, lodging
71mm	**rest area both lanes, full facilities, litter barrels, vending, petwalk**

OH

INTERSTATE 70 CONT'D

Exit	Services
66	OH 54, to Catawba, South Vienna, **N** 🔋 Fuelmart/dsl/scales, **S** 🔋 Speedway/dsl
62	US 40, Springfield, **N** 🛏 Harmony Motel, ⊙ Harmony Farm Mkt, antiques, auto repair, to Buck Creek SP, **S** Beaver Valley Camping
59	OH 41, to S Charleston, **N** ⊙ [H], Harley-Davidson, st patrol, **S** 🔋 BP, Clark/dsl, antiques
54	OH 72, to Cedarville, Springfield, **N** 🔋 BP/dsl, Shell, Speedway/dsl, Sunoco/dsl, 🍴 A&W/LJ Silver, Arby's, Bob Evans, Cassano's Pizza/subs, Cracker Barrel, Domino's, El Toro Mexican, Hardee's, Lee's Chicken, Little Caesars, McDonald's, Panda Chinese, Rally's, Rudy's Smokehouse, Subway, Taco Bell, Wendy's, 🛏 Comfort Suites, Days Inn, Hampton Inn, Quality Inn, Ramada Ltd, Red Roof Inn, Super 8, ⊙ [H], Advance Parts, BigLots, Family$, Kroger/deli, Rite Aid, Walgreens, **S** 🔋 Marathon/dsl, Swifty
52b a	US 68, to Urbana, Xenia, **S** to John Bryan SP
48	OH 4 (from wb), to Enon, Donnelsville, **N** 🔋 Speedway, ⊙ camping
47	OH 4 (from eb), to Springfield, **N** 🔋 Speedway, ⊙ RV Camping
44	I-675 S, Spangler Rd, to Cincinnati
43mm	Mad River
41b a	OH 4, OH 235, to Dayton, New Carlisle, **1 mi N** 🔋 BP/dsl, 🍴 KFC/LJ Silver, McDonald's, Wendy's, ⊙ Freightliner, Kenworth
38	OH 201, Brandt Pike, **N** 🔋 Marathon/dsl, ⊙ Meijer/dsl/E85, **S** 🔋 Shell, UDF/dsl, 🍴 Bob Evans, Sonic, Tim Horton's, Waffle House, Wendy's, 🛏 Best Value Inn, Comfort Inn, ⊙ WalmartMcDonald's, vet
36	OH 202, Huber Heights, **N** 🔋 Speedway/dsl, 🍴 Applebee's, Big Boy, Dragon City, El Toro Grill, Fazoli's, Steak'n Shake, Taco Bell, Waffle House, 🛏 Baymont Inn, ⊙ AT&T, Dick's, $Tree, Elder Beerman, Gander Mtn., GNC, Hobby Lobby, Kia, Kohl's, Lowe's, Marshall's, Petsmart, Target, Verizon, urgent care, vet, **S** 🔋 BP/dsl, Marathon/dsl, 🍴 Arby's, Buffalo Wild Wings, Burger King, Cadillac Jack's, Chipotle Mexican, CiCi's Pizza, El Dorado Mexican, La Rosa's Pizza, McDonald's, Skyline Chili, Subway, TGIFriday's, TX Roadhouse, White Castle, 🛏 Days Inn, Hampton Inn, Holiday Inn Express, ⊙ Kroger/gas
33b a	I-75, N to Toledo, S to Dayton
32	to US 40, Vandalia, **N** to Dayton Intn'l ✈
29	OH 48, to Dayton, Englewood, **N** 🔋 BP, Speedway/dsl, Sunoco/dsl, Valero, 🍴 Arby's, Big Boy, Bob Evans, Company BBQ, Hot Head Burrito, KFC, Lee's Chicken, Perkins, Ponderosa, Skyline Chili, Taco Bell, Tim Horton's, Tony's Italian, Wendy's, Yen Ching Chinese, 🛏 Best Value Inn, Best Western, Hampton Inn, Holiday Inn, Super 8, ⊙ Advance Parts, Aldi Foods, BigLots, Family$, O'Reilly Parts, vet, **S** 🍴 McDonald's, Steak'n Shake, Tumbleweed SW Grill, Waffle House, 🛏 Comfort Inn, Motel 6, ⊙ [H], Meijer/dsl/E85
26	OH 49 S, **N** 🔋 Murphy USA/dsl, 🍴 Bob Evans, La Rosa's Pizza, Sonic, ⊙ Radio Shack, Walmart/Subway, urgent care, **S** 🍴 Wendy's
24	OH 49 N, to Greenville, Clayton, **N** 🔋 Sunoco/dsl, ⊙ KOA (seasonal)

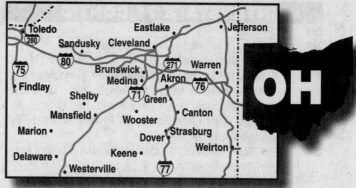

Exit	Services
21	Arlington Rd, Brookville, **N** 🔋 GA/Subway, **S** 🔋 Speedway/dsl, Swifty, 🍴 Arby's, Brookville Grill, DQ, Great Wall Chinese, K's Rest., KFC/Taco Bell, McDonald's, Pizza Hut, Rob's Rest., Subway, Waffle House, Wendy's, 🛏 Best Value Inn, Holiday Inn Express, ⊙ Brookville Parts, Chevrolet, Curves, $General, Family$, IGA Foods, Rite Aid
14	OH 503, to West Alexandria, Lewisburg, **N** 🔋 Marathon/Subway/dsl, 🍴 Dari Twist, 🛏 Super Inn, ⊙ IGA Foods, **S** 🔋 Valero/dsl
10	US 127, to Eaton, Greenville, **N** 🔋 TA/BP/Burger King/Subway/dsl/scales/24hr/@, st patrol, **S** 🔋 🏪/Subway/dsl/scales/24hr, 🛏 Budget Inn
3mm	Welcome Ctr eb/rest area both lanes, **full** ♿ **facilities,** 🅲, vending, 🛓, litter barrels, petwalk
1	US 35 E (from eb), to Eaton, New Hope
0mm	Ohio/Indiana state line, **Welcome Arch, weigh sta eb**

INTERSTATE 71

Exit	Services
247b	I-90 W, I-490 E. I-71 begins/ends on I-90, exit 170 in Cleveland.
247a	W 14th, Clark Ave
246	Denison Ave, Jennings Rd (from sb)
245	US 42, Pearl Rd, **E** 🔋 BP, Sunoco, ⊙ [H], zoo
244	W 65th, Denison Ave
242b a	W 130th, to Bellaire Rd, **W** 🔋 Sunoco, 🍴 Burger King (1/2mi)
240	W 150th, **E** 🔋 Marathon, Speedway/dsl, 🍴 Denny's, 🛏 Marriott, **W** 🔋 BP/Subway/dsl, 🍴 Burger King, MacKenzie's Grill, Somers Rest., Taco Bell, 🛏 Holiday Inn, La Quinta
239	OH 237 S (from sb), **W** to ✈
238	I-480, Toledo, Youngstown, **W** ✈
237	Snow Rd, Brook Park, **E** 🔋 BP, Marathon, Shell, 🍴 Bob Evans Cafe, KFC, McDonald's, Suwaby, 🛏 Best Western, Holiday Inn Express, Howard Johnson, ⊙ AutoZone, Top's Foods, **W** to ✈
235	Bagley Rd, **E** 🍴 Bob Evans, **W** 🔋 BP/dsl, Shell, Speedway, 🍴 Burger King, Caribou Coffee, Chipotle Mexican, Damon's, Denny's, Friendly's, McDonald's, Olive Garden, Panera Bread, Perkins, Pizza Hut, Roadhouse Grill, Taco Bell, 🛏 Comfort Inn, Courtyard, Motel 6, Plaza Motel, Radisson, Ramada Inn, Red Roof Inn, Studio+, TownePlace Suites, ⊙ [H], Aldi Foods, Buick, GMC, K-Mart
234	US 42, Pearl Rd, **E** 🔋 Sunoco/dsl, 🍴 Hunan Chinese, Katherine's Rest., Wendy's, ⊙ Audi/Porsche, Honda, Hyundai, **W** 🔋 AP/dsl, 🍴 Buffalo Wild Wings, Jennifer's Rest., Mad Cactus Mexican, 🛏 Day's Inn, Kings Inn, La Siesta Motel, Metrick's Motel, Village Motel, ⊙ Circle K, Home Depot, Lowes Whse, Walmart, vet,

SPRINGFIELD

E ↕ W

DAYTON

N ↕ S

CLEVELAND

🅖 = gas 🍴 = food 🛏 = lodging 🅞 = other   Copyright 2011 - The Next Exit

INTERSTATE 71 CONT'D

N ↕ S

Exit	Services
233	I-80 and Ohio Tpk, to Toledo, Youngstown
231	OH 82, Strongsville, E 🅖 Shell, 🛏 Holiday Inn, Motel 6, W 🅖 BP/Subway/dsl, Marathon/dsl, Sunoco/dsl, 🍴 Applebee's, Buca Italian, Demetrio's Rest., Longhorn Steaks, Macaroni Grill, Panera Bread, Red Lobster, 🅞 Dillard's, Giant Eagle Foods, JC Penney, Kohl's, NTB, Sears/auto, Target, mall
226	OH 303, Brunswick, E 🅖 Shell/dsl/24hr, 🍴 Pizza Hut, 🅞 Chrysler/Jeep/Toyota, W 🅖 BP, GetGo, Marathon/dsl, Sunoco/dsl, 🍴 Arby's, Bob Evans, Burger King, CiCi's Pizza, McDonald's, Starbucks, Steak'n Shake, Subway, Taco Bell, Wendy's, 🛏 Howard Johnson, Sleep Inn, 🅞 Ford, Giant Eagle 🍴 K-Mart
225mm	rest area nb, full ♿ facilities, 🚻, 🔀, litter barrels, petwalk
224mm	rest area sb, full ♿ facilities, 🚻, 🔀, litter barrels, petwalk
222	OH 3, W st patrol
220	I-271 N, (from nb) to Erie, Pa
218	OH 18, to Akron, Medina, E 🅖 BP/dsl/24hr, Marathon/dsl, Shell/dsl, Sunoco/dsl, 🍴 Alexandri's Rest., Baskin-Robbins/Dunkin Donuts, Burger King, DQ, Lou's Rest., Stricklands Drive-thru, 🛏 Super 8, 🅞 $General, Kia, Nissan, W 🅖 Speedway/dsl, 🍴 Arby's, Bob Evans, Buffalo Wild Wings, Denny's, McDonald's, Pizza Hut, Quiznos, Rocknes Rest., Tres Potrillos, Waffle House, Wendy's, 🛏 Hampton Inn, Motel 6, Red Roof Inn, 🅞 H, Aldi Foods, Buehler's Foods, Buick/Cadillac/GMC, Dodge, Harley-Davidson, Honda, NTB
209	I-76 E, to Akron, US 224, W 🅖 📠/Subway/dsl/scales/24hr, TA/BP/Burger King/Popeye's/dsl/scales/24hr/@, 🍴 Arby's, McDonald's, 🛏 Super 8, 🅞 Blue Beacon, Chippewa Valley Camping (1mi), SpeedCo
204	OH 83, Burbank, E 🅖 BP/dsl, Duke/dsl, 💟Loves/Hardee's/dsl/scales/24hr, 🛏 Plaza Motel, W 🅖 📠/Wendy's/dsl/scales/24hr, 🍴 Bob Evans, Burger King, KFC/Taco Bell, McDonald's, 🅞 H, Lodi Outlets/famous brands
198	OH 539, W Salem
196mm	rest area both lanes, full ♿ facilities, 🚻, vending, 🔀, litter barrels, petwalk
196	OH 301 (from nb, no re-entry), W Salem
186	US 250, Ashland, E 🅖 Marathon, 🍴 Perkins, Grandpa's Village/cheese/gifts, 🅞 Hickory Lakes Camping (7mi), W 🅖 Goasis/BP/Pizza Hut/Popeye's/Starbucks/Taco Bell/dsl/24hr, Marathon, 🍴 Brian Buffet, Denny's, Donato's Pizza, Jake's Rest., McDonald's, Wendy's, 🛏 Ashland Inn, Days Inn, Holiday Inn Express, Super 8, 🅞 H, Aldi Foods, Buehler's Foods, GNC, Home Depot, Walmart, st patrol, to Ashland U
176	US 30, to Mansfield, E 🛏 EconoLodge, 🅞 fireworks
173	OH 39, to Mansfield
169	OH 13, Mansfield, E 🅖 Marathon/dsl, Murphy USA/dsl, 🍴 Applebee's, Cracker Barrel, HillTop Dairy Bar, Steak'n Shake, Subway, Wendy's, 🛏 Best Western, La Quinta, 🅞 Walmart, Mohican SP, W 🅖 Marathon, 🍴 Arby's, Bob Evans, Burger King, El Compasino Mexican, McDonald's, Taco Bell, 🛏 Hampton Inn, Super 8, Travelodge, 🅞 H, st patrol

MANSFIELD

OH

Exit	Services
165	OH 97, to Bellville, E 🅖 BP, Speedway/dsl, Shell/dsl, 🍴 Burger King, Dutch Heritage Rest., KC's Rib House, McDonald's, 🛏 Days Inn, Comfort Inn, Knights Inn, Quality Inn, 🅞 to Mohican SP, W 🍴 Wendy's
151	OH 95, to Mt Gilead, E 🅖 Duke/BP/deli, Marathon, 🍴 Gathering Place Rest., McDonald's, Wendy's, 🛏 Best Western, 🅞 st patrol, W 🅖 Shell/dsl, Sunoco/dsl/E85, 🍴 Subway, 🛏 Knights Inn, 🅞 H, Mt Gilead SP (6mi)
149mm	truck parking both lanes
140	OH 61, Mt Gilead, E 🅖 📠/Arby's/dsl/scales/24hr, W 🅖 BP/Taco Bell, Sunoco, 🍴 Farmstead Rest., 🅞 Cardinal Ctr Camping
131	US 36, OH 37, to Delaware, E 🅖 ⊕FLYING J/Denny's/dsl/LP/scales/24hr, 📠/Subway/dsl/scales/24hr, 🍴 Burger King, 🅞 Harley-Davidson, W 🅖 BP/dsl, Shell/Tim Hortons, 🍴 Arby's, Bob Evans, Cracker Barrel, KFC/LJ Silver, McDonald's, Starbucks, Taco Bell, Waffle House, Wendy's, White Castle, 🛏 Days Inn, Hampton Inn, Holiday Inn Express, 🅞 H, Alum Cr SP, Cross Creek Camping (6mi)
128mm	rest area both lanes, full ♿ facilities, 🚻, vending, 🔀, litter barrels, petwalk
121	Polaris Pkwy, to Gemini Pl, E 🅖 BP, Mobil, Shell, 🍴 Bonefish Grill, Buffalo Wild Wings, Canes, Carfagna's, 5 Guys Burgers, McDonald's, Mellow Mushroom Pizza, Pei Wei, Polaris Grill, Skyline Chili, Starbucks, Steak'n Shake, 🛏 Best Western, Fairfield Inn, Hampton Inn, Wingate Inn, 🅞 Firestone/auto, Polaris Ampitheatre, W 🅖 BP, Marathon/Circle K, Shell/Tim Horton, 🍴 Applebee's, Arby's, Benihana, BJ's Rest., Brio Grille, Caribou Coffee, Carrabba's, Charley Subs, CheeseCake Factory, Chick-fil-A, Chipotle Mexican, City BBQ, Claddagh Rest., Coldstone, Cosi Cafe, Dave&Buster's, Domino's, El Vaquero Mexican, Hoggy's Grill, Honey Baked Ham, Hooters, House of Japan, Jimmy John's, Krispy Kreme, Marcella's Italian, Max&Erma's, McDonald's, Merlot's Rest., MiMi's Cafe, Mitchell Steaks, Noodles&Co, O'Charley's, Olive Garden, Panera Bread, Papa John's, Penn Sta Subs, Pizza Hut/Taco Bell, Planet Smoothie, Potbelly, Qdoba, Quaker Steak, Red Lobster, Red Robin, Rudedog Grill, Smokey Bones BBQ, Sonic, Starbucks, Subway, Tequilas Mexican, TGIFriday's, TX Roadhouse, Waffle House, Wendy's, 🛏 Cambria Suites, Candlewood Suites, Comfort Inn, Extended Stay Deluxe, Hilton, Hilton Garden, 🅞 URGENT CARE, AutoZone, Barnes&Noble, Best Buy, BigLots, Costco/gas, Dick's, GNC, JC Penney, Jo-Ann Etc, Kroger/gas, Lowe's, Macy's, NTB, Old Navy, Petsmart, Sears/auto, Target, TireDiscounters, TJ Maxx, Walgreens, Walmart (3mi), World Mkt, funpark, mall
119 a	I-270, to Indianapolis, Wheeling
117	OH 161, to Worthington, E 🅖 BP/dsl, Shell, Speedway/dsl, Sunoco/dsl, 🍴 Burger King, Carfagna's, China Dynasty, Chipotle Mexican, KFC, LJ Silver, Max&Erma's, McDonald's, Rally's, Red Lobster, Subway, Super Seafood Buffet, Wendy's, White Castle, 🛏 Comfort Inn, Days Inn, Knights Inn, Motel 6, Red Roof Inn, 🅞 URGENT CARE, CVS Drug, Family$, Staples, TireDiscounters, Walgreens, auto repair, vet, W 🅖 GetGo, Shell, Speedway/dsl, 🍴 Bob Evans, China Jade, Domino's, McDonald's, Pizza Hut, Skyline Chili, Starbucks, Subway, Tim Hortons, Waffle House, Wendy's, 🛏 Baymont Inn, Best Western, Clarion, Continental Inn, Country Inn&Suites, Crowne Plaza, Extended Stay America, Hawthorn Suites, Rodeway Inn, Super 8, Travelodge, ValuePlace, 🅞 Advance Parts, Chevrolet, Family$, Giant Eagle Foods, NTB, Walgreens

COLUMBUS AREA

INTERSTATE 71 CONT'D

Exit	Services
116	Morse Rd, Sinclair Rd, **E** 🅿 BP, Marathon/dsl, Shell, Speedway, 🍴 McDonald's, Subway, Taco Bell, ⛺ Howard Johnson, ⊙ Buick/GMC, CVS Drug, $General, Firestone/auto, Ford, Kia, Kohl's, Kroger, PepBoys, Save-A-Lot Foods, **W** 🅿 Sunoco, ⛺ Best Value Inn, Motel 6, Ramada, ⊙ NTB
115	Cooke Rd
114	N Broadway, **W** 🅿 Sunoco, 🍴 Broadway Mkt Cafe, Subway
113	Weber Rd, **W** 🅿 Speedway/dsl, ⊙ CarQuest
112	Hudson St, **E** 🅿 Marathon, Shell/dsl, 🍴 Wendy's, ⛺ Holiday Inn Express, **W** 🍴 Big Boy, ⊙ Aldi Foods, Lowe's, NTB
111	17th Ave, **W** 🍴 McDonald's, ⛺ Comfort Inn, Days Inn
110b	11th Ave
110a	5th Ave, **E** 🅿 Sunoco, 🍴 Royal Fish&Chicken, White Castle, **W** 🅿 Valero, 🍴 Church's, KFC, Popeye's, Rally's, Wendy's, ⊙ AutoZone
109a	I-670
109b	OH 3, Cleveland Ave
109c	Spring St (exits left from sb)
108b	US 40, Broad St, downtown
108 a	Main St
101a [70]	I-70 E, US 23 N, to Wheeling
100ba [70]	US 23 S, Front St, High St, downtown
106a	I-70 W, to Indianapolis
106b	OH 315 N, Dublin St, Town St
105	Greenlawn, **W** 🅿 Marathon, 🍴 Wingin'It Grille, ⊙ 🅗
104	OH 104, Frank Rd
101b a	I-270, Wheeling, Indianapolis
100	Stringtown Rd, **E** 🅿 BP, 🍴 Bob Evans, Charley's Grilled Subs, Chick-fil-A, Chipotle Mexican, CiCi's Pizza, Coldstone, DQ, 5 Guys Burgers, Jalapeno's Mexican, Longhorn Steaks, O'Charley's, Olive Garden, Panda Express, Red Robin, Smokey Bones BBQ, Sonic, Starbucks, Steak'n Shake, White Castle, ⛺ Best Western, Drury Inn, Hampton Inn, Holiday Inn Express, Hilton Garden, La Quinta, Microtel, Red Roof Inn, ⊙ Best Buy, Dick's, Firestone/auto, Home Depot, Michael's, Petsmart, Staples, Target, TJ Maxx, Walmart, **W** 🅿 BP, GetGo, Speedway/dsl, Sunoco/Subway/dsl, 🍴 Applebee's, Arby's, Burger King, Cane's Chicken Fingers, China Bell, Cracker Barrel, El Mesquite Mexican, Fazoli's, Golden Corral, KFC, Mariachi Mexican, McDonald's, Papa John's, Rally's, Ruby Tuesday, Starbucks, Taco Bell, TeeJaye's Rest., Tim Horton, Waffle House, Wendy's, ⛺ Comfort Inn, Days Inn, Motel 6, Travelodge, ⊙ Ace Hardware, Advance Parts, Aldi Foods, AutoZone, BigLots, CVS Drug, Giant Eagle Foods, K-Mart, Kroger/24hr, Radio Shack, Tuffy Auto, Walgreens
97	OH 665, London-Groveport Rd, **E** 🅿 Marathon/Circle K, 🍴 Arby's, McDonald's, Peking House, Quiznos, Sunny St Cafe, Tim Horton/Wendy's, ⊙ URGENT CARE, CVS Drug, Kroger/gas/e-85, Meijer/e-85, TireDiscounters, to Scioto Downs, **W** ⊙ Eddie's Repair
94	US 62, OH 3, Orient, **W** 🅿 Sunoco/dsl
84	OH 56, Mt Sterling, **E** 🅿 BP/Subway, ⛺ Royal Inn, ⊙ to Deer Creek SP (9mi)
75	OH 38, Bloomingburg, **E** fireworks, **W** 🅿 Sunoco/dsl

Exit	Services
69	OH 41, OH 734, Jeffersonville, **E** 🅿 ⓙFLYING J/Denny's/dsl/scales/LP/24hr, ⊙ 🅗, Walnut Lake Camping, **W** 🅿 BP, Shell/Subway, 🍴 Arby's, Wendy's, ⛺ Quality Inn, ⊙ Family$
68mm	**rest area both lanes, full ♿ facilities, ☎, vending, 🏧, litter barrels, petwalk**
65	US 35, Washington CH, **E** 🅿 Shell, TA/BP/Pizza Hut/Popeye's/dsl/scales/24hr/@, 🍴 A&W/KFC, Bob Evans, Chipotle Mexican, LJ Silver/Taco Bell, McDonald's, Waffle House, Wendy's, Werner's BBQ, ⛺ Baymont Inn, Hampton Inn, ⊙ 🅗, AT&T, Prime Outlets/famous brands, **W** 🅿 Loves/Hardee's/dsl/scales/24hr, ⛺ EconoLodge
58	OH 72, to Sabina
54mm	**weigh sta sb**
50	US 68, to Wilmington, **E** ⊙ 🅗, **W** 🅿 BP/dsl, 🚛/Subway/dsl/scales/24hr, Shell/dsl/24hr, 🍴 Max&Erma's, McDonald's, Wendy's, ⛺ Budget Inn, Holiday Inn, Robert's Center, repair/tires
49mm	**weigh sta nb**
45	OH 73, to Waynesville, **E** 🅿 BP, Shell, 🍴 73 Grill, ⊙ 🅗, camping (3mi), RV Park, **W** Caesar Creek SP (5mi)
36	Wilmington Rd, **E** to Ft Ancient St Mem, RV camping
35mm	Little Miami River
34mm	**rest area both lanes, full ♿ facilities, scenic view, ☎, vending, 🏧, litter barrels, petwalk**
32	OH 123, to Lebanon, Morrow, **E** 🅿 BP, Valero, 🍴 Country Kitchen, ⊙ Morgan's Riverside Camping, **3 mi W** 🍴 Bob Evans, Skyline Chili, ⛺ Knights Inn
28	OH 48, S Lebanon, **E** 🅿 Marathon/dsl, ⛺ Countryside Inn, ⊙ Kohl's, Lowe's, Target, **W** ⊙ Lebanon Raceway (6mi), hwy patrol
25	OH 741 N, Kings Mills Rd, **E** 🅿 Shell/Popeye's, Speedway/dsl, 🍴 McDonald's, Ruby Tuesday, Taco Bell, Outback Steaks, ⛺ Comfort Suites, Great Wolf Lodge, Kings Island Resort, ⊙ Harley-Davidson, **W** 🅿 BP, Exxon/Subway, 🍴 Arby's, Big Boy, Bob Evans, Burger King, Perkins, Pizza Hut, Skyline Chili, Tabby's Grill, Waffle House, Wendy's, ⛺ Baymont Inn, Hampton Inn, Microtel, Super 8, ⊙ CarX, CVS Drug, GNC, Kroger
24	Western Row, King's Island Dr (from nb), **E** 🅿 Sunoco, 🍴 Fantastic Wok, MVPizza, ⛺ King's Island Resort, ⊙ Jellystone Camping, funpark
19	US 22, Mason-Montgomery Rd, **E** 🅿 Speedway/dsl, 🍴 Arby's, Asian Fusion, Big Boy, Boston Mkt, Burger King, Cracker Barrel, Fiesta Brava, Golden Corral, HoneyBaked Ham, Iron Chef Grill, KFC, McDonald's, Olive Garden, Quiznos, Taco Bell, Taz Mediterranean Grill, TGIFriday's, Wendy's, White Castle, ⛺ Clarion, Comfort Inn, SpringHill Suites, TownePlace Suites, ⊙ Aldi Foods, AT&T,

COLUMBUS AREA N ↕ S

OH

INTERSTATE 71 CONT'D

N ↕ S

C I N C I N N A T I   A R E A

Exit	Services
19	Continued
	AutoZone, Barnes&Noble, Best Buy, BigLots, Buick/GMC, Chevrolet, Chrysler/Dodge/Jeep, Costco/gas, Firestone/auto, Ford, GNC, Goodyear/auto, Hobby Lobby, Honda, Infiniti, JC Penney, KIA, Kohl's, Kroger, Lexus, Lincoln/Mercury, Mazda, Meijer/dsl, Michael's, Nissan, Old Navy, O'Reilly Parts, Porsche, Radio Shack, Sam's Club/gas, Target, TireDiscounters, Toyota/Scion, Tuffy Auto, Verizon, Walgreens, USPO, vet, W ⛽ BP/dsl, Marathon/dsl/24hr, 🍴 Abuelo's Mexican, Applebee's, BD Mongolian Grill, Bravo Italian, Burger King, Claddagh Irish, Carrabba's, Chipotle Mexican, China City, Dao Asian, 5 Guys Burgers, Fox&Hound Grill, Graeter's Cafe, IHOP, Jimmy John's, LoneStar Steaks, McAlister's Deli, MiMi's Cafe, O'Charley's, Panera Bread, Polo Grill, Qdoba, Red Robin, River City Grill, Steak'n Shake, Skyline Chili, Subway, Waffle House, Wendy's, 🛏 Best Western, Days Inn, Hilton Garden, Holiday Inn Express, Hyatt Place, La Quinta, Marriott, Motel 6, Red Roof Inn, ⊙ Bigg's Foods, Dick's, Home Depot, Lowe's, NAPA, Staples, Walmart, Whole Foods Mkt, vet
17b a	I-275, to I-75, OH 32
15	Pfeiffer Rd, E 🛏, W ⛽ BP, Shell/dsl, Sunoco/dsl/24hr, 🍴 Applebee's, Bob Evans, Buffalo Wild Wings, Subway, Watson Bro's Bistro, 🛏 Courtyard, Crowne Plaza, Embassy Suites, Hampton Inn, Holiday Inn Express, Red Roof Inn, ⊙ Office Depot
14	OH 126, Reagan Hwy, Blue Ash
12	US 22, OH 3, Montgomery Rd, E ⛽ BP/dsl, Shell/24hr, 🍴 Arby's, Bob Evans, Chipotle Mexican, Ember's, Jalapeno Cafe, KFC, LJ Silver, Outback Steaks, Panera Bread, Red Lobster, Ruby Tuesday, Subway, Taco Bell, TGIFriday, Wendy's, 🛏 Best Western, ⊙ Dodge, Firestone, Goodyear, Hyundai, PepBoys, Staples, Tuesday Morning, W ⛽ Chevron, 🍴 Cheesecake Factory, IHOP, KFC, Johnny Rocket's, Macaroni Grill, Max&Erma's, McDonald's, Potbelly's, Starbucks, Wendy's, ⊙ 🛏, Barnes&Noble, Dillard's, Firestone/auto, Fresh Mkt Foods, Macy's, Old Navy, Staples, mall
11	Kenwood Rd, (from nb), W 🛏, same as 12
10	Stewart Rd (from nb), to Silverton, W ⛽ Marathon/dsl
9	Redbank Rd, to Fairfax, (no ez sb return), E ⛽ Mobil, Speedway, ⊙ BMW
8	Kennedy Ave, Ridge Ave W, E ⛽ Meijer/dsl, 🍴 IHOP, 🛏 Motel 6, ⊙ Dodge, Sam's Club/gas, Target, W ⛽ Marathon/dsl, Shell/Subway, Speedway, 🍴 Denny's, Golden Corral, Gold Star Chili, KFC, LJ Silver, McDonald's, Old Country Buffet, Pizza Hut, Rally's, Taco Bell, White Castle, Wendy's, ⊙ Bigg's Foods, Big Lots, Ford, Goodyear, Home Depot, Lowes Whse, Office Depot, Tire Discounter, Walmart, transmissions
7b a	OH 562, Ridge Ave E, Norwood, E ⛽ BP, 🍴 Ponderosa, ⊙ AutoZone
6	Edwards Rd, E ⛽ BP, Shell, Speedway, 🍴 Boston Mkt, Buca Italian, Donato's, Don Pablo, Fuddrucker's, GoldStar Chili, J Alexander's Rest., Longhorn Steaks, Max&Erma's, Noodles, PF Chang's, Starbucks, ⊙ GNC, SteinMart, W ⛽ Shell
5	Dana Ave, Montgomery Rd, W ⊙ Xavier Univ, Zoo

Exit	Services
3	Taft Rd (from sb), U of Cincinnati
2	US 42, Reading Rd, Gilbert ave (from sb), W ⊙ 🛏, art Museum, ballpark stadium arena, downtown
1k j	I-471 S
1d	Main St, downtown
1c b	Pete Rose Way, Fine St, stadium, downtown
1a	I-75 N, US 50, to Dayton
I-71 S and I-75 S run together	
0mm	Ohio/Kentucky state line, Ohio River

INTERSTATE 74

C I N C I N N A T I   A R E A

E ↕ W

Exit	Services
20	I-75 (from eb), N to Dayton, S to Cincinnati, I-74 begins/ends on I-75.
19	Gilmore St, Spring Grove Ave
18	US 27 N, Colerain Ave
17	Montana Ave (from wb), N ⛽ Circle K
14	North Bend Rd, Cheviot, N ⛽ Shell, Speedway/dsl, 🍴 DQ, Dunkin Donuts, McDonald's, Papa John's, Perkins Skyline Chili, Subway, Wendy's, White Castle, ⊙ Curves, Family$, Kroger, Sam's Club/gas, Tire Discounters, Walgreens, S ⛽ BP, 🍴 Bob Evans, ⊙ vet
11	Rybolt Rd, Harrison Pike, S ⛽ BP, 🍴 Longhorn Steaks, Marco's Pizza, McDonald's, Sakura Steaks, Skyline Chili, Wendy's, White Castle, 🛏 Holiday Inn Express, ⊙ Kohl's, Meijer/gas,
9	I-275 N, to I-75, N to Dayton, (exits left from eb)
8mm	Great Miami River
7	OH 128, to Hamilton, Cleves, N ⛽ BP/dsl, Marathon/dsl, 🍴 Wendy's
5	I-275 S, to Kentucky
3	Dry Fork Rd, N ⛽ BP, S ⛽ Marathon/dsl, Shell/Dunkin Donuts/dsl
2mm	weigh sta eb
1	New Haven Rd, to Harrison, N ⛽ BP/dsl, 🍴 Buffalo Wild Wings, Chipotle Mexican, Cracker Barrel, GoldStar Chili, Little Caesars, O'Charley's, Subway, 🛏 Comfort Inn, ⊙ Biggs Foods, Ford, Home Depot, Kia, Staples, Tires+, Verizon, S ⛽ Shell/Circle K, Speedway/dsl, Sunoco/White Castle, 🍴 A&W/KFC, Arby's, Big Boy, Burger King, DQ, Happy Garden, McDonald's, Perkins, Pizza Hut, Skyline Chili, Taco Bell, Waffle House, Wendy's, 🛏 Holiday Inn Express, Howard Johnson, ⊙ Advance Parts, AutoZone, BigLots, CVS Drug, $General, Family$, Firestone, GNC, Jo-Ann Fabrics, K-Mart, Kroger/dsl, NAPA, O'Reilly Parts, Radio Shack, Tire Discounters, Walgreens
0mm	Ohio/Indiana state line

INTERSTATE 75

N ↕ S

Exit	Services
211mm	Ohio/Michigan state line
210	OH 184, Alexis Rd, to Raceway Park, W ⛽ BP/Circle K dsl, 🚚/Subway/dsl/scales/24hr, 🍴 Arby's, Bob Evans, Burger King, McDonald's, Taco Bell, Wendy's, 🛏 Fairfield Inn, Hampton Inn, ⊙ AutoZone, Meijer/dsl, Menards, urgent care
210mm	Ottawa River
209	Ottawa River Rd (from nb), E ⛽ BP, Sunoco, 🍴 China King, Little Caesars, Marco's Pizza, River Diner, ⊙ Family$, Kroger/E85, Rite Aid, vet
208	I-280 S, to I-80/90, to Cleveland
207	Stickney Ave, Lagrange St, E ⛽ BP, 🍴 Arby's, McDonald's, Wendy's, ⊙ Family$, K-Mart, Rite Aid,

INTERSTATE 75 CONT'D

Exit	Services
207	Continued Save-A-Lot Foods, USPO
206	to US 24, Phillips Ave, **W** transmissions
205b	Berdan Ave, **E** 🄷, **W** 🅖 Marathon/dsl, 🍴 Burger King, Subway
205a	to Willys Pkwy, to Jeep Pkwy
204	I-475 W, to US 23 (exits left fom nb), to Maumee, Ann Arbor
203b	US 24, to Detroit Ave, **W** 🅖 AP/dsl, BP, 🍴 KFC, McDonald's, Rally's, Wendy's, 🅞 Rite Aid, Save-A-Lot Foods, U-Haul
203a	Bancroft St, downtown
202	Washington St, Collingwood Ave (from sb, no EZ return), **E** 🅖 BP, 🅞 🄷, Art Museum, **W** 🍴 McDonald's
201 b a	OH 25, Collingwood Ave, **W** Toledo Zoo
200	South Ave, Kuhlman Dr
200mm	Maumee River
199	OH 65, Miami St, to Rossford, **E** 🏠 Days Inn
198	Wales Rd, Oregon Rd, to Northwood, **E** 🅖 Shell/Subway/dsl, Sunoco/dsl, 🍴 Arby's, China Wok, Coney Is. 🏠 Baymont Inn, Comfort Inn
197	Buck Rd, to Rossford, **E** 🅖 Shell/dsl, 🍴 Tim Horton's, Wendy's, **W** 🅖 BP, Sunoco/dsl, 🍴 Denny's, McDonald's, 🏠 American Inn, Knights Inn
195	to I-80/90, OH 795, OH Tpk (toll), Perrysburg, **E** 🅖 BP/Subway/dsl, 🏠 Country Inn&Suites, Courtyard, Hampton Inn, 🅞 Bass Pro Shops
193	US 20, US 23 S, Perrysburg, **E** 🅖 BP/dsl, GetGo, Sunoco, 🍴 Arby's, Big Boy, Bob Evans, Burger King, Chili's, China City, Coldstone, Cracker Barrel, 1st Wok, 5 Guys Burgers, Dragon Chef, Fricker's, IHOP, Jimmy John's, KFC, Mancino's Pizza, Ok Patron, Panera Bread, Penn Sta Subs, Sonic, Subway, Taco Bell, 🏠 Candlewood Suites, Comfort Suites, EconoLodge, Holiday Inn, Holiday Inn Express, Quality Inn, 🅞 Belle Tire, Best Buy, Discount Tire, $Tree, Giant Eagle Foods, GNC, Hobby Lobby, Home Depot, Kohl's, Kroger/gas/E85, KOA (7mi), Lowe's, Meijer/dsl, Michael's, Petsmart, Radio Shack, Target, TJ Maxx, Tuffy, Walgreens, Walmart/Subway, **W** 🅖 Speedway/dsl, 🏠 La Quinta, 🅞 AutoZone, Harley-Davidson
192	I-475, US 23 N (exits left from nb), to Maumee, Ann Arbor
187	OH 582, to Luckey, Haskins
181	OH 64, OH 105, to Pemberville, Bowling Green, **E** 🏠 Holiday Inn Express, 🅞 Meijer/dsl/E85, **W** 🅖 BP/Circle K/Subway/dsl, Speedway, 🍴 Big Boy, Bob Evans, Buffalo Wild Wings, Burger King, Chipotle Mexican, Cinco de Mayo, Coldstone/Tim Horton's, Domino's, El Zarape Mexican, Fricker's Rest., Hunan Buffet, Jimmy John's, McDonald's, Padrone's Pizza, Starbucks, Waffle House, Wendy's, 🏠 Best Western, Days Inn, Hampton Inn, Quality Inn, Victory Inn, 🅞 🄷, Verizon, USPO, to Bowling Green State U
179	US 6, to Fremont, Napoleon, **W** museum
179mm	**rest area both lanes, full ♿ facilities, 🅲, 🛉, litter barrels, vending, petwalk**
175mm	**weigh sta nb**
171	OH 25, Cygnet
168	Eagleville Rd, Quarry Rd, **E** 🅖 FuelMart/dsl
167	OH 18, to Fostoria, North Baltimore, **E** 🅖 Petro/BP/Iron Skillet/dsl/scales/24hr/@, 🍴 McDonald's, 🅞 Blue Beacon, truck repair, **W** 🅖 Loves/Arby's/dsl/scales/24hr, Sunoco, 🏠 Crown Inn, 🅞 $General, Great Scot Mkt

Exit	Services
165mm	Rocky Ford River
164	OH 613, to McComb, Fostoria, **E** 🅞 KOA, Van Buren SP, **W** 🅖 📦/Subway/Taco Bell/dsl/scales/24hr
162mm	**weigh sta sb, 🅲**
161	rd 99, **E** 🅖 Speedway/dsl, Shell/Subway, 🏠 Comfort Suites, 🅞 Ford/Lincoln/Mercury, Kia, hwy patrol, **W** antiques
159	US 224, OH 15, Findlay, **E** 🅖 BP/dsl, Speedway/dsl, Swifty, 🍴 Archie's Ice Cream, Burger King, Culver's, Dakota Grill, Fin's Seafood Grill, Jimmy John's, KFC/LJ Silver, McDonald's, Ming's Great Wall, Pizza Hut, Ralphie's, Spaghetti Shop, Steak'n Shake, Subway, Taco Bell, Wendy's, 🏠 Drury Inn, Red Roof Inn, Rodeway Inn, Motel 6, 🅞 🄷, auto/truck repair, **W** 🅖 Murphy USA/dsl, Shell/dsl, 🍴 Bob Evans, China Garden, Coldstone/Tim Horton's, Cracker Barrel, Denny's, Hokkaido Steaks, Jac&Do's Pizza, Landing Pad, Max&Erma's, Outback Steaks, Tony's Rest., TX Roadhouse, Waffle House, 🏠 Country Inn&Suites, Hampton Inn, Holiday Inn Express, Quality Inn, 🅞 Best 1 Tires/repair, Chrysler/Dodge/Jeep, Peterbilt, Verizon, Walmart/Subway
158mm	Blanchard River
157	OH 12, Findlay, **E** 🅖 GA/dsl, Marathon/Blimpie/Noble Roman's/dsl, 🅞 Findlay Convention Ctr, **W** 🍴 Fricker's Rest., 🏠 EconoLodge, 🅞 vet
156	US 68, OH 15, to Carey, **E** 🄷
153mm	**rest area both lanes, full ♿ facilities, 🅲, 🛉, litter barrels, vending, petwalk**
145	OH 235, to Ada, Mount Cory, **E** TwinLakes Camping
142	OH 103, to Arlington, Bluffton, **E** 🏠 Knights Inn, **W** 🅖 BP/dsl, Marathon/Circle K/dsl, 🍴 Arby's, Burger King, KFC, McDonald's/rv parking, Subway, Taco Bell, 🏠 Comfort Inn, 🅞 $General, auto repair, vet, to Bluffton Coll
140	Bentley Rd, to Bluffton, **W** 🄷
135	OH 696, to US 30, to Delphos, Beaverdam, **E** 🅖 Speedway/dsl/24hr, **W** 🅖 FLYING J/Denny's/dsl/scales/LP/24hr/@, 📦/McDonald's/Subway/dsl/24hr/@, 🍴 Waffle House, 🅞 Blue Beacon, SpeedCo, tires, truck repair
134	Napolean Rd (no nb re-entry), to Beaverdam
130	Bluelick Rd, **E** 🏠 Best Value Inn
127b a	OH 81, to Ada, Lima, **W** 🅖 BP/dsl, Marathon/Subway/dsl, 🍴 Waffle House, 🏠 Comfort Inn, Days Inn/rest., 🅞 Best 1 Tires/repair
126mm	Ottawa River
125	OH 309, OH 117, Lima, **E** 🅖 BP/dsl, Murphy USA/dsl, Speedway/dsl, 🍴 Applebee's, Arby's, Bob Evans, Burger King, Capt D's, China Buffet, Cracker Barrel, Hunan Garden, J's Grill, McDonald's, Olive Garden,

🆐 = gas 🍴 = food 🛏 = lodging 🅾 = other Copyright 2011 - The Next Ex

INTERSTATE 75 CONT'D

LIMA

Exit	Services
125	Continued Panera Bread, Pizza Hut, Ralphie's, Red Lobster, Skyline Chili, Subway, Taco Bell, TX Roadhouse, Wendy's, 🛏 Courtyard, Hampton Inn, Howard Johnson, Motel 6, 🅾 BigLots, Ford, K-Mart, Radio Shack, Ray's Foods, Sam's Club/gas, Verizon, Walgreens, Walmart/McDonald's, **W** 🆐 Shell, 🍴 Kewpee Hamburger's, Yamato Steaks, 🛏 Country Inn&Suites, Holiday Inn, Travelodge, 🅾 🏨, Advance Parts, Best 1 Tires/repair, Curves, $General, Rite Aid, Save-A-Lot Foods
124	4th St, **E** hwy patrol
122	OH 65, Lima, **E** 🆐 Speedway/dsl, **W** 🆐 Marathon/Subway/dsl, 🅾 Freightliner, GMC, Mack, Volvo, truck repair, vet
120	Breese Rd, Ft Shawnee, **W** 🆐 AP Trkstp/dsl, 🅾 Harley-Davidson
118	to Cridersville, **W** 🆐 Fuelmart/Subway/dsl, Speedway/dsl, 🍴 Dixie Ley Diner, 🅾 $General
114mm	**rest area both lanes, hadicapped facilities, 🚻, litter barrels, pet walk, 📞, vending**
113	OH 67, to Uniopolis, Wapakoneta
111	Bellefontaine St, Wapakoneta, **E** 🆐 TA/Marathon/rest./dsl/scales/@, 🍴 Country Charm Rest., 🛏 Knights Inn, 🅾 KOA, truck tires, **W** 🆐 BP/dsl, Murphy USA/dsl, Shell, 🍴 Arby's, Bob Evans, Burger King, Capt D's, Comfort Zone, DQ, El Azteca, King Buffet, Lucky Steer Rest., McDonald's, Pizza Hut, Taco Bell, Waffle House, Wendy's, 🛏 Best Western, Comfort Inn, Super 8, Western Inn, 🅾 Advance Parts, Aldi Foods, CVS Drug, Lowe's, Neil Armstrong Museum, O'Reilly Parts, Radio Shack, Verizon, Walmart, st patrol
110	US 33, to St Marys, Bellefontaine, **E** KOA, hwy patrol
104	OH 219, , **W** 🆐 Marathon/dsl, Shell/Circle K/Subway/dsl, 🍴 Larry's Pizza, 🛏 Budget Host
102	OH 274, to Jackson Ctr, New Breman, **E** bicycle museum, **W** air stream tours
99	OH 119, to Minster, Anna, **E** 🆐 99/dsl, **W** 🆐 GA/Taco Bell, Shell, 🍴 Subway, Wendy's, 🅾 lube/wash/repair
94	rd 25A, Sidney, **E** 🆐 Marathon/deli
93	OH 29, to St Marys, Sidney, **W** Lake Loramie SP, RV camping
92	OH 47, to Versailles, Sidney, **E** 🆐 Shell, Speedway/dsl, 🍴 Arby's, China Garden, Coldstone, Subway, Time Horton, Wendy's, 🅾 🏨, AutoZone, CVS Drug, $General, DM, NAPA, Save-A-Lot Foods, Walgreens, urgent care, **W** 🆐 Murphy USA/dsl, Sunoco/dsl, Valero, 🍴 A&W/LJ Silver, Applebee's, Bob Evans, Buffalo Wild Wings, Burger King, Cazadores Mexican, Culver's, Highmarks Rest., KFC, McDonald's, Perkins, Pizza Hut, Quiznos, Smokin Joe's BBQ, Sonic, Taco Bell, Waffle House, 🛏 Comfort Inn, Country Hearth Inn, Days Inn, Travel Inn, 🅾 Aldi Foods, AT&T, Best 1 Tires/repair, Buick/Cadillac/Chevrolet/GMC, Chrysler/Dodge/Jeep, $Tree, Ford, Lincoln/Mercury, Kroger/dsl, Lowe's, Menards, Radio Shack, Staples, Walmart/McDonald's
90	Fair Rd, to Sidney, **E** 🆐 Sunoco/dsl, **W** 🆐 Marathon/DQ/dsl, 🛏 Hampton Inn
88mm	Great Miami River
83	rd 25A, Piqua, **W** 🆐 Marathon/MaidRite Cafe/Noble Roman's/dsl, 🛏 Red Carpet Inn, 🅾 Chrysler/Dodge/Jeep, Sherry RV Ctr, to Piqua Hist Area

N ↕ S

SIDNEY

OH

TROY

Exit	Services
82	US 36, to Urbana, Piqua, **E** 🆐 Murphy USA/dsl, Valero, 🍴 A&W/LJ Silver, Arby's, China East, China Garden, DQ, KFC, Pizza Hut/Taco Bell, Subway, Waffle House, Wendy's, 🅾 Aldi Foods, BigLots, $Tree, Harley-Davidson, Home Depot, JoAnn Fabrics, Radio Shack, Verizon, Walmart/Subway, st patrol, vet, **W** 🆐 Speedway, 🍴 Bob Evans, Cracker Barrel, El Tapatio Mexican, McDonald's, Red Lobster, 🛏 Comfort Inn, Knights Inn, La Quinta, 🅾 JC Penney
81mm	**rest area both lanes, full 🚻 facilities, 📞s, 🚻, litter barrels, vending**
78	rd 25A, **E** 🏨
74	OH 41, to Covington, Troy, **E** 🆐 BP/dsl, 🍴 Al's Pizza, China Garden, Donato's Pizza, Fox's Pizza, Little Caesars, McDonald's, Pizza Hut, Subway, Taco Bell, 🅾 🏨, Radio Shack, Super Petz, to Hobart Arena, **W** 🆐 Shell, Speedway/dsl, 🍴 Applebee's, Big Boy, Bob Evans, Buffalo Wild Wings, Burger King, Chipotle Mexican, Culver's, Fazoli's, Friendly's, KFC, Logan's Roadhouse, Los Pitayos Mexican, Outback Steaks, Panera Bread, Penn Sta Subs, Ruby Tuesday, Saka Japanese, Skyline Chili, Sonic, Steak'n Shake, 🛏 Best Inn, Comfort Suites, Fairfield Inn, Hampton Inn, Holiday Inn Express, Residence Inn, 🅾 AT&T, AutoZone, $General, $Tree, GNC, Goodyear, Kohl's, Lowe's, Meijer/dsl, Staples, Tire Discounters, Verizon, Walmart/Subway
73	OH 55, to Ludlow Falls, Troy, **E** 🆐 BP, Shell, 🍴 Boston Stoker Coffee House, Hot Head Burrito, Lincoln Sq Rest. Papa John's, Subway, Waffle House, Wendy's, 🛏 Quality Inn, Royal Inn, Super 8, 🅾 🏨, $General, Kroger/e85
69	rd 25A, **E** 🆐 BP/Circle K/Subway/dsl, Starfire/dsl, 🅾 Arbogast RV Ctr, Buick/GMC, Chrysler/Dodge/Jeep, Ford
68	OH 571, to West Milton, Tipp City, **E** 🆐 BP/dsl, Shell, Speedway/dsl, 🍴 Burger King, Cassano's Pizza, Hickory River BBQ, Hong Kong Kitchen, McDonald's, Subway, Taco Bell, 🅾 AutoValue Parts, CVS Drug, Family$, Food Town, Goodyear, Honda, Verizon, **W** 🆐 Speedway/dsl, 🍴 Arby's, Big Boy, Bob Evans, Tipp' O the Town Rest., Wendy's, 🛏 Holiday Inn Express, La Quinta, 🅾 Main S Parts, Menards, vet
64	Northwoods Blvd, **E** 🍴 El Toro Mexican, Emperial Palace, 🅾 $Tree, Kroger/dsl
63	US 40, to Donnelsville, Vandalia, **E** 🆐 Speedway/dsl, 🍴 Bunker's Grill, Dragon China, Fricker's, 🅾 repair, **W** 🆐 BP/dsl, Shell, Speedway/dsl, 🍴 Arby's, Burger King, Domino's, Hot Head Burrito, KFC/LJ Silver, McDonald's, Pizza Hut, Rib House, Subway, Taco Bell, Waffle House, Wendy's, 🛏 Super 8, 🅾 Goodyear/auto, Rexall Drug, Rite Aid
61b a	I-70, E to Columbus, W to Indianapolis, to Dayton Int 🏧
59	Wyse Rd, Benchwood Rd, **E** 🍴 El Rancho Grande, Little York Pizza, Mr Lee's, 🛏 Dayton Inn, Hawthorn Suites, 🅾 BMW/Volvo/VW, Discount Tire, **W** 🆐 Speedway/dsl, Valero, 🍴 Arby's, Asian Buffet, Big Boy, Bob Evans, Cassano's Pizza, Chick-fil-A, Chipotle Mexican, Coldstone, Cracker Barrel, Fricker's, Golden Corral, Hooters, LoneStar Steaks, Max&Erma's, McDonald's, O'Charley's, Olive Garden, Outback Steaks, Panera Bread, Pop's Diner, Red Lobster, Ruby Tuesday, Sake Japanese, Skyline Chili, SmashBurger, SmokeyBones BBQ, Steak'n Shake, Subway, Tim Horton, 🛏 Best Value Inn, Comfort Inn, Country Inn&Suites, Courtyard, Days Inn, Drury Inn, Extended Stay America, Fairfield Inn, Hampton Inn, Knights Inn, Red Roof Inn, Residence Inn, Rodeway Inn, TownePlace Suites, 🅾 Batteries+, Office Depot, Radio Shack, Sam's Club/gas, Verizon, Walmart, Subway

INTERSTATE 75 CONT'D

Exit	Services
58	Needmore Rd, to Dayton, **E** 🅶 BP/dsl, Shell/McDonald's, 🍴 Hardee's, 🛏 🅾 Goodyear/auto, to AF Museum, **W** 🅶 Marathon/dsl, Speedway/dsl, Sunoco/dsl, Swifty, 🍴 A&W/LJ Silver, Church's, Domino's, Subway, Tim Horton, Waffle House, Wendy's, 🅾 Advance Parts, AutoZone, $Tree, Kroger/gas, O'Reilly Parts, Walgreens, USPO, repair/transmissions
57b	Wagner Ford Rd, Siebenthaler Rd, Dayton, **E** 🅶 Sunoco, 🛏 Ramada Inn
57a	Neva Rd
56	Stanley Ave, Dayton, **E** 🅶 Shell, **W** 🅶 Clark, 🍴 Dragon City Chinese, Gold Star Chili, McDonald's, Taco Bell, 🛏 Dayton Motel, 🅾 truck repair
55b a	Keowee St, Dayton, downtown
54c	OH 4 N, Webster St, to Springfield, downtown
54mm	Great Miami River
54b	OH 48, Main St, Dayton, **E** 🅶 Cadillac, Chevrolet, Honda, **W** 🅶 BP, 🅾 Ⓗ
54a	Grand Ave, Dayton, downtown
53b	OH 49, 1st St, Salem Ave, Dayton, downtown
53a	OH 49, 3rd St, downtown
52b a	US 35, E to Dayton, W to Eaton
51	Edwin C Moses Blvd, Nicholas Rd, **E** 🛏 Courtyard, 🅾 Ⓗ, to U of Dayton, **W** 🅶 BP/dsl, 🍴 McDonald's, Wendy's, 🛏 EconoLodge, 🅾 SunWatch Indian Village
50b a	OH 741, Kettering St, Dryden Rd, **E** Ⓗ, vet, **W** 🅶 Marathon/dsl, 🛏 Days Inn, Super 8, 🅾 U-Haul
47	Dixie Dr, Kettering, Moraine, **E** 🅶 Sunoco, Valero, 🍴 Big Boy, Waffle House, 🅾 auto repair, transmissions, **W** 🅶 Shell, Speedway/dsl, 🍴 Ele Cake Co., El Mason, KFC, McDonald's, Pizza Hut, Sonic, Taco Bell, Wendy's, 🅾 $General, USPO
44	OH 725, to Centerville, Miamisburg, **E** 🅶 BP/dsl, Shell, Speedway, 🍴 Applebee's, Baskin-Robbins, Big Boy, Bonefish Grill, Bravo Italiana, Burger King, Dunkin Donuts, El Toro Mexican, Fazoli's, Friendly's, Golden Corral, Hardee's, Jimmy John's, KFC, Logan's Roadhouse, Lonestar Steaks, McDonald's, O'Charley's, Olive Garden, Panera Bread, PF Chang's, Red Lobster, Rooster's Grill, Rusty Bucket Grill, Sake Japanese, Skyline Chili, SmashBurger, Starbucks, Steak'n Shake, Subway, Taco Bell, TGIFriday's, Waffle House, Wendy's, 🛏 Comfort Suites, Courtyard, DoubleTree Suites, Garden Inn, Homewood Suites, InTowne Suites, SpringHill Suites, Studio 6, 🅾 Ⓗ, Advance Parts, Aldi Foods, AT&T, Barnes&Noble, Best Buy, Cub Foods, Dick's, $Tree, Elder Beerman, Hobby Lobby, Home Depot, Honda/Nissan/Mazda, JC Penney, JoAnn Fabrics, Kia, Lowe's, Macy's, Michael's, NTB, Office Depot, PepBoys, Petsmart, Sears/auto, Super Petz, Target, Tire Discounters, TJ Maxx, Toyota/Scion, Verizon, Walmart, mall, urgent care, **W** 🅶 BP, Marathon, Shell/dsl, 🍴 Bob Evans, LJ Silver, Perkins, Tim Horton, 🛏 Knights Inn, Quality Inn, Red Roof Inn, Super 8, 🅾 Ⓗ, Aamco, CarMax, Chevrolet, $General, Ford, NAPA
43	I-675 N, to Columbus
41	Austin Blvd, **E** Kohl's
38	OH 73, Springboro, Franklin, **E** 🅶 Shell, Speedway, 🍴 Applebee's, Arby's, Bob Evans, Burger King, China Garden, Chipotle Mexican, KFC, LJ Silver, McDonald's,

Exit	Services
38	Continued
	Papa John's, Pizza Hut, Skyline Chili, Subway, Taco Bell, Tim Horton, Wendy's, 🛏 Comfort Inn, Hampton Inn, 🅾 K-Mart, Kroger, Radio Shack, Tire Discounters, vet, **W** 🅶 Murphy USA/dsl, Road Ranger, Shell, Swifty, 🍴 A&G Pizza, Big Boy, Cazadore's Mexican, Domino's, GoldStar Chili, Lee's Chicken, McDonald's, 🛏 EconoLodge, Holiday Inn Express, Knights Inn, 🅾 Advance Parts, AutoZone, Clark's Drug, $General, $Tree, Kemper Auto, Main St Mkt, NAPA, Walgreens, Walmart, USPO
36	OH 123, to Lebanon, Franklin, **E** 🅶 BP, 🍴/Subway/Pizza Hut/dsl/scales/24hr/@, Shell, 🍴 McDonald's, Waffle House, 🛏 Quail Inn, **W** 🅶 Marathon/White Castle/dsl, Sunoco
32	OH 122, Middletown, **E** 🍴 McDonald's, 🛏 Best Value Inn, Days Inn, Super 8, Reyton Inn, 🅾 Ⓗ, CVS Drug, **W** 🍴 Applebee's, Arby's, Big Boy, Bob Evans, Cracker Barrel, El Rancho Grande, Golden Corral, GoldStar Chili, Hot Head Burrito, KFC, La Rosa's Pizza, LoneStar Steaks, O'Charley's, Olive Garden, Schlotzsky's, Sonic, Steak'n Shake, Wendy's, White Castle, 🛏 Country Hearth Inn, Drury Inn, Fairfield Inn, Holiday Inn Express, 🅾 Aldi Foods, AT&T, AutoZone, BigLots, Elder Beerman, Kohl's, Kroger/dsl, Lowe's, Meijer/dsl, PetMart, Sears/auto, Staples, Target, Tire Discounters, Verizon, Walmart, urgent care
29	OH 63, to Hamilton, Monroe, **E** 🅶 Shell/Popeye's/dsl, Stony Ridge/dsl, 🍴 Burger King, GoldStar Chili, Tim Horton/Wendy's, Waffle House, 🛏 Comfort Inn, 🅾 Premium Outlets/Famous Brands, Tire Discounters, Trader's World, **W** 🅶 Speedway/dsl, 🍴 Froggy Blue's, McDonald's, Richard's Pizza, Sara Jane's Rest., Subway, 🛏 Hampton Inn, Howard Johnson, 🅾 Honda
27.5mm	rest area both lanes, full ♿ facilities, info, 🔂, 🚮, litter barrels, vending, petwalk
24	OH 129 W, to Hamilton, **W** Cincinnati Gardens
22	Tylersville Rd, to Mason, Hamilton, **E** 🅶 Sunoco, Thornton's/dsl, 🍴 Arby's, Bob Evans, BoneFish Grill, Burger King, Caribou Coffee, Chick-fil-A, Chopsticks, City BBQ, Firehouse Subs, 5 Guys Burgers, Geisha, GoldStar Chili, IHOP, Jimmy John's, KFC, LJ Silver, Longhorn Steaks, McAlister's Deli, McDonald's, Noodles&Co, Panera Bread, Perkins, Pizza Hut, Qdoba, Ruby Tuesday, Skyline Chili, SmashBurger, Soho Japanese, Starbucks, Subway, Taco Bell, TGIFriday's, Twin Dragon, Wendy's, 🛏 Economy Inn, 🅾 Ⓗ, AT&T, BigLots, Firestone, GNC, Goodyear/auto, Home Depot, Kohl's, Kroger, Michael's, Office Depot, Petsmart, Radio Shack, Target, Tires+, TJ Maxx, Verizon, Walgreens, **W** 🅶 Shell, Speedway/dsl,

MIDDLETOWN

OH

INTERSTATE 75 CONT'D

Exit	Services
22	Continued 🍽 O'Charley's, 🛏 Wingate Inn, ⊙ Aldi Foods, CarX, Lowe's, Meijer/dsl, Tire Discounters
21	Cin-Day Rd, **E** 🍽 Big Boy, 🛏 Holiday Inn Express, **W** 🚗 Marathon/dsl, Mobil/Subway/dsl, Speedway/dsl, 🍽 Arby's, Domino's, Guenther's Steaks, La Rosa's Pizza, Las Copas Mexican, Papa John's, Sonic, Waffle House, Wendy's, White Castle, ⊙ Ace Hardware, AutoZone, Curves, PetMart, Walgreens, Walmart/Subway
19	Union Centre Blvd, to Fairfield, **E** 🍽 Bravo Italiana, Champps Rest., Mitchell's Fish Mkt, Original Pancakes, Panera Bread, PF Chang's, Red Robin, Smokey Bones BBQ, Steak'n Shake, ⊙ Barnes&Noble, Verizon, **W** 🚗 BP/Subway/dsl, Marathon/Circle K, Shell, 🍽 Aladdin's Eatery, Applebee's, Bob Evans, Buffalo Wild Wings, Burger King, Chipotle Mexican, Jag's Steaks, Jimmy John's, McDonald's, Qdoba, Quiznos, Rafferty's, Skyline Chili, Starbucks, Tazza Mia, Uno, Wendy's, 🛏 Comfort Inn, Courtyard, Hampton Inn, Marriott, Residence Inn, Staybridge Suites, ⊙ Mercedes, Volvo
16	I-275 to I-71, to I-74
15	Sharon Rd, to Sharonville, Glendale, **E** 🚗 Sunoco, Thornton's/dsl, 🍽 Big Boy, Bob Evans, Cracker Barrel, Jim Dandy BBQ, Ruby Tuesday, Skyline Chili, Subway, Waffle House, 🛏 Baymont Inn, Country Inn&Suites, Drury Inn, Hawthorn Suites, Hilton Garden, Holiday Inn Express, La Quinta, Red Roof Inn, Travel Inn, Travelodge, Wyndham, **W** on Kemper...🚗 Sunoco, 🍽 Burger King, Chick-fil-A, Chili's, ChuckeCheese, 5 Guys Burgers, IHOP, LJ Silver, Macaroni Grill, McDonald's, Panera Bread, Pizza Hut, Taco Bell, Subway, Tokyo Japanese, Vincenzo's, Wendy's, 🛏 Crowne Plaza, EconoLodge, Extended Stay Deluxe, Extended Stay America, Fairfield Inn, LivInn Suites, Residence Inn, ⊙ Best Buy, Costco/gas, Dick's, Lowe's, Nissan, Sam's Club, Sears, Target
14	OH 126, to Woodlawn, Evendale, **E** GE Plant, 🛏 Wingate Inn (3mi), **W** 🚗 Swifty
13	Shepherd Lane, to Lincoln Heights, **E** GE Plant, **W** 🍽 Taco Bell, Wendy's, ⊙ Advance Parts
12	Wyoming Ave, Cooper Ave, to Lockland, **W** 🚗 Marathon, 🍽 DQ, Subway
10a	OH 126, Ronald Reagan Hwy
10b	Galbraith Rd (exits left from nb), Arlington Heights
9	OH 4, OH 561, Paddock Rd, Seymour Ave, **E** to Cincinnati Gardens, **W** fairgrounds
8	Towne St, Elmwood Pl (from nb)
7	OH 562, to I-71, Norwood, Cincinnati Gardens
6	Mitchell Ave, St Bernard, **E** 🚗 Marathon, Shell, Sunoco, 🍽 White Castle, 🛏 Holiday Inn Express, ⊙ Walgreens, to Cincinnati Zoo, to Xavier U, **W** 🚗 BP/Subway/dsl, 🍽 McDonald's, Rally's, ⊙ Advance Parts, Family$, Ford, Honda, Hyundai, Kia, Kroger, Tires+
4	I-74 W, US 52, US 27 N, to Indianapolis
3	to US 27 S, US 127 S, Hopple St, U of Cincinnati, **E** 🚗 BP/Subway/dsl, 🍽 Camp Washington Chili, Isador Italian, White Castle, ⊙ 🏥, Family$, **W** 🚗 Shell, 🍽 Wendy's
2b	Harrison Ave, industrial district, **W** 🚗 BP, 🍽 McDonald's

2a	Western Ave, Liberty St (from sb)
1g	Ezzard Charles Dr, **W** 🛏 Ramada Inn
1f	US 50W, Freeman Ave, **W** 🚗 Sunoco, 🍽 Big Boy, Pizza Hut/Taco Bell, Wendy's, White Castle, 🛏 Ramada Inn, ⊙ Ford, GMC, NAPA, USPO
1e	7th St (from sb), downtown
1c	5th St, downtown, **E** 🛏 Crowne Plaza, Hyatt, Millenia Hotel, Sheraton, ⊙ Macy's, to Duke Energy Center
1a	I-71 N, to Cincinnati, downtown, to stadium
0mm	Ohio/Kentucky state line, Ohio River

INTERSTATE 76

Exit	Services
	Ohio/Pennsylvania state line, Exits 232-235 are on the Ohio Turnpike.
235	I-680 (from wb), to Youngstown
232	OH 7, to Boardman, Youngstown, **N** 🚗 Sheetz, Valero/dsl, 🍽 DQ, Los Gallos Mexican, Rita's Custard, Steamer's Stonewall Tavern, 🛏 Best Value Inn, Budget Inn, Holiday Inn Express, Super 8, ⊙ antiques, **S** 🚗 🍽 /McDonald's/dsl/scales/24hr, Sunoco/dsl, 🍽 Ambrozini's Rest., Road House Diner, 🛏 Davis Motel, Liberty Inn, ⊙ truck repair
60mm	I-76 eb joins Ohio TPK (toll)
57	to OH 45, Bailey Rd, to Warren
54	OH 534, to Newton Falls, Lake Milton, **N** RV camping, **S** 🚗 BP, ⊙ to Berlin Lake, camping
52mm	Lake Milton
48	OH 225, to Alliance, **N** to W Branch SP, camping, **S** to Berlin Lake, to Lake Milton SP
45mm	**rest area both lanes, full ♿ facilities, 🚻, 🍽, litter barrels, petwalk**
43	OH 14, to Alliance, Ravenna, **N** to W Branch SP, **S** Marathon/dsl, ⊙ fireworks
38b a	OH 5, OH 44, to Ravenna, **N** 🚗 BP, Speedway/dsl, 🍽 Arby's, McDonald's/rv parking, Wendy's, ⊙ 🏥, **S** 🚗 Marathon/Circle K/Subway, 🍽 Cracker Barrel, ⊙ $General, Giant Eagle Foods, auto repair/parts, RV camping
33	OH 43, to Hartville, Kent, **N** 🚗 BP/dsl, Sunoco, 🍽 Salsita's Mexican, 🛏 Best Value Inn, Comfort Inn, Days Inn, EconoLodge, Hampton Inn, Holiday Inn Express, Super 8, ⊙ to Kent St U, **S** 🚗 Speedway/dsl, 🍽 Gemini Pizza, Giomino's Pizza, McDonald's, Pizza Hut, Subway, Wendy's, ⊙ Curves, $General, vet
31	rd 18, Tallmadge, **N** 🍽 Applebee's, Arabica/Strickland Cafe, Beef'O'Brady's, La Terraza Mexican, ⊙ AT&T, $Tree, GNC, Kohl's, Lowe's, Verizon, Walmart/Subway
29	OH 532, Tallmadge, Mogadore
27	OH 91, Canton Rd, Gilchrist Rd, **N** 🍽 Bob Evans, **S** 🚗 Marathon/Subway/dsl, 🍽 Hardee's, 🛏 Quality Inn
26	OH 18, E Market St, Mogadore Rd, **N** 🚗 Marathon/dsl, ⊙ Goodyear/auto, **S** 🍽 Arby's, McDonald's, Subway, Wendy's, ⊙ $General
25b a	Martha Ave, General St, Brittain, **N** 🚗 Circle K, ⊙ Goodyear HQ, Mercedes, Toyota/Scion
24	Arlington St, Kelly Ave, **N** Goodyear HQ
23b	OH 8, Buchtell Ave, to Cuyahoga (exits left from eb), to of Akron
23a	I-77 S, to Canton
22b	Grant St, Wolf Ledges, Akron, downtown, **S** 🚗 BP, 🍽 McDonald's, ⊙ Family$
22a	Main St, Broadway, downtown

OH

CINCINNATI AREA

AKRON

INTERSTATE 76 CONT'D

Exit	Services
21c	OH 59 E, Dart Ave, N🄷
21b	Lakeshore St, Bowery St (from eb)
21a	East Ave (from wb)
20	I-77 N (from eb), to Cleveland
19	Battles Ave, Kenmore Blvd
18	I-277, US 224 E, to Canton, Barberton
17b a	OH 619, Wooster Rd, State St, to Barberton (no eb return), S🅖 Sunoco/dsl, 🄾🄷, NAPA, tires/repair
16	Barber Rd, S🅖 Rocky's/dsl/E85, 🍴 Tomaso's Italian, 🄾 Chrysler/Dodge/Jeep, Nissan, Suzuki
14	Cleve-Mass Rd, to Norton, S🅖 BP, Marathon/Circle K, 🍴 Subway, 3 Sons Rest. 🄾 Ace Hardware, Advance Parts, Acme Mkt, CVS Drug, $General, Radio Shack, Ritzman Drug
13b a	OH 21, N to Cleveland, S to Massillon
11	OH 261, Wadsworth, N🅖 Speedway/dsl, S🅖 Giant Eagle, GetGo/E85, 🍴 Arabica Cafe, Beef'O'Brady's, 🄾 GNC, Kohl's, Lowe's, MC Sports, PetCo, Target, Verizon
9	OH 94, to N Royalton, Wadsworth, N🅖 Marathon/Circle K, 🍴 Applebee's, Arby's, Bob Evans, Burger King, China Buffet, China Express, Chipotle Mexican, Galaxy Rest., KFC, Marie's Cafe., McDonald's, Panera Bread, Pizza Hut, Subway, Taco Bell, Wendy's, 🛏 Holiday Inn Express, Rodeway Inn, 🄾 AT&T, BigLots, Buehler's Foods, $General, $Tree, DrugMart, Goodyear/auto, Home Depot, NTB, Radio Shack, Verizon, Walmart, S🅖 Convenient/gas, Marathon/DQ/dsl, Sunoco/dsl, 🍴 Casa Del Rio, Dunkin Donuts, 🛏 Legacy Inn, 🄾 Advance Parts, AutoZone, CVS Drug, NAPA, Rite Aid, auto repair, vet
7	OH 57, to Rittman, Medina, N🅖 Marathon/dsl, S🄾 🄷, 🕑
6mm	**weigh sta both lanes**
2	OH 3, to Medina, Seville, N🅖 Marathon/Circle K, 🍴 DQ, Hardee's, Huddle House, Pizzazo's, Subway, 🛏 Comfort Inn, Hawthorn Suites, 🄾 Maple Lakes Camping (seasonal), S🅖 Shell/dsl, Sunoco, 🍴 E of Chicago Pizza, El Patron Mexican, #1 Chinese, 🄾 Curves, $General, Ritzman Drug
1	I-76 E, to Akron, US 224, W on US 224 🅖 🚛/Subway/dsl/scales/24hr, TA/BP/Burger King/Popeye's/dsl/scales/24hr/@, 🍴 Arby's, McDonald's, 🛏 Super 8, 🄾 Blue Beacon, SpeedCo, Chippewa Valley Camping (1mi), SpeedCo
0mm	I-76 begins/ends on I-71, exit 209.

INTERSTATE 77

Exit	Services
	I-77 begins/ends on I-90 exit 172, in Cleveland.
163c	I-90, E to Erie, W to Toledo
163b	E 9th St, Tower City
162b	E 22nd St, E 14th St (from nb)
162a	E 30th St, Woodland Ave, Broadway St (from nb), W USPO
161b	I-490 W, to I-71, E 55th, E🄷
161a	OH 14 (from nb), Broadway St
160	Pershing Ave (from nb), W🄷
159b	Fleet Ave, E🅖 BP/Subway/dsl
159a	Harvard Ave, Newburgh Heights, W🅖 BP/Subway/dsl/24hr, Marathon
158	Grant Ave, Cuyahoga Heights

Exit	Services
157	OH 21, OH 17 (from sb), Brecksville Rd
156	I-480, to Youngstown, Toledo
155	Rockside Rd, to Independence, E🅖 Shell, Sunoco, 🍴 Aladdin's, Bob Evans, Bonefish Grill, Chipotle Mexican, Del Monico's Steaks, Denny's, McDonald's, Outback Steaks, Quizno's, Red Robin, Shula's Steaks, Starbucks, Wendy's, Zoup, 🛏 Comfort Inn, Doubletree, Embassy Suites, Holiday Inn, La Quinta, Red Roof Inn, 🄾 Drugmart, NTB, Verizon, Walgreens, to Cuyahoga Valley NP, W🅖 BP/dsl, 🍴 Applebee's, Damon's, Longhorn Steaks, 🛏 Courtyard, Hampton Inn, Hyatt Place, Residence Inn, Skyline Hotel
153	Pleasant Valley Rd, to Independence, 7 Hills
151	Wallings Rd
149	OH 82, to Broadview Heights, Brecksville, **1 mi** E🅖 BP, Shell, 🍴 Creek Side Rest., McDonald's, Panera Bread, Simons Cafe, Starbucks, Subway, 🄾 Curves, CVS Drug, Walgreens, vet, W🅖 BP, 🍴 Coco's, Domino's, 🛏 Tally-ho-tel
147	to OH 21, Miller Rd (from sb)
146	I-80/Ohio Tpk, to Youngstown Toledo
145	OH 21 (from nb), E🅖 🚛/Wendy's/dsl/scales, 🍴 DQ, Memories Rest., Richfield Rest., Subway, 🛏 Days Inn, Hampton Inn, Holiday Inn Express, Motel 6, Super 8
144	I-271 N, to Erie
143	OH 176, to I-271 S, W🅖 Sunoco, 🍴 Arabica Café, McDonald's, Panda Chinese, Subway, Teresa's Pizza, 🄾 Curves
141mm	**rest area both lanes, full ♿ facilities, 🕑, 🚻, litter barrels, vending, petwalk**
138	Ghent Rd, W🅖 Circle K/dsl, 🍴 Gasoline Ally, Lanning's Rest.
137b a	OH 18, to Fairlawn, Medina, E🅖 BP, Circle K, GetGo, Shell, Speedway, 🍴 Applebee's, Bob Evans, Boston Mkt, Chick-fil-A, Chili's, Chipotle Mexican, Coldstone Creamery, Cracker Barrel, Cusina Italian, Donato's Pizza, 5 Guys Burgers, Fleming's Steaks, Friendly's, Golden Corral, HoneyBaked Ham, Hyde Park Grille, Macaroni Grill, Max&Erma's, McDonald's, Olive Garden, Pad Thai, Panera Bread, PF Chang, Pot Belly, Quizno's, Red Lobster, Starbucks, Steak'n Shake, Swenson's Rest., Taco Bell, Wendy's, 🛏 Best Value Inn, Courtyard, EconoLodge, Hampton Inn, Hilton, Holiday Inn, Motel 6, Sheraton, 🄾 Acme Foods, Aldi Foods, AT&T, Barnes&Noble, Best Buy, Firestone/auto, Ford, Dillard's, $Tree, Giant Eagle Foods, Goodyear/auto, Home Depot, JC Penney, Jo-Ann Fabrics, Lowe's, Macy's, Michael's, Old Navy, Petsmart, Sam's Club, Staples, TJ Maxx, Verizon, Walgreens, Walmart, World Mkt, W🍴 Burger King, Longhorn Steaks,

🅖 = gas 🍽 = food 🏨 = lodging 🄾 = other   Copyright 2011 - The Next Ex

INTERSTATE 77 CONT'D

N ↕ S

Exit	Services
137b a	Continued Outback Steaks, Steak on a Stone, TGIFriday's, Tres Patrilios, Wasabi Grill, 🏨 Best Western, Comfort Inn, Extended Stay America, Radisson, Studio+, 🄾 🅗
136	(exits left from nb), OH 21S, to Massillon
135	Cleveland-Massillon Rd (from nb, no return)
133	Ridgewood Rd, Miller Rd, E 🅖 Circle K/dsl, W 🍽 Tiffany's Bakery, Old Carolina BBQ
132	White Pond Dr, Mull Ave
131	OH 162, Copley Rd, E 🅖 Circle K, 🍽 Church's, 🄾 Sav-A-Lot Foods, Walgreens, USPO, W 🅖 BP/dsl/24hr, 🍽 McDonald's, Pizza Hut
130	OH 261, Wooster Ave, E 🅖 Circle K, Marathon/dsl, Valero, 🍽 Ann's Place, Burger King, Church's, Rally's, Subway, 🄾 Acme Foods, Advance Parts, AutoZone, Family$, W 🍽 KFC, 🄾 Chevrolet, Dodge, Toyota/Scion, U-Haul
129	I-76 W, to I-277, to Kenmore Blvd, Barberton
21a	East Ave (from nb)
I-77 S and I-76 E run together	
21b	Lakeshore (from sb), to Bowery St
21c	OH 59 E, Dart Ave, downtown, E 🅗
22a	Main St, Broadway St, downtown, W auto parts
22b	Grant St, Wolf Ledges, W 🅖 BP, 🍽 McDonald's, 🄾 Family$
125b	I-76 E, to Youngstown
I-77 and I-76 run together	
125a	OH 8 N, to Cuyahoga Falls, U of Akron
124b	Lover's Lane, Cole Ave
124a	Archwood Ave, Firestone Blvd (from sb), E BP
123b	OH 764, Wilbeth Rd, E 🍽 DQ, 🄾 to 🎞
123a	Waterloo Rd (from sb), W 🅖 GetGo, Marathon, 🍽 Burger King, Hungry Howies, Papa John's, Rally's, Subway, 🄾 $Tree, Giant Eagle Foods, Goodyear/auto, Rite Aid, Walgreens
122a b	I-277, US 224 E, to Barberton, Mogadore
120	Arlington Rd, to Green, E 🅖 Speedway/dsl, 🍽 Applebee's, Church's/White Castle, Denny's, Friendly's, Golden Corral, IHOP, Ryan's, Starbucks, Subway, Waffle House, 🏨 Comfort Inn, Quality Inn, Red Roof Inn, 🄾 AutoZone, $General, Home Depot, Kohl's, Staples, Walmart/auto, W 🅖 BP, 🍽 Bob Evans, Burger King, Chipotle Mexican, CiCi's Pizza, Lion Garden, Mariachi Mexican, McDonald's, Panera Bread, Subway, Taco Bell, TGIFriday's, Wendy's, 🏨 Fairfield Inn, Hampton Inn, Holiday Inn Express, ValuePlace Inn, 🄾 Acura, Buick/GMC, Chevrolet, Goodyear/auto, Honda, Hyundai, Lexus, Lowe's, Mazda, Nissan, Sirpilla RV Ctr/Camping World, Subaru, Target
118	OH 241, to OH 619, Massillon, E 🅖 Sheetz, Speedway/dsl, 🍽 Gionino's Pizza, Handel's Icecream, Subway, W 🅖 BP/Circle K, GetGo, 🍽 Arby's, Grille 39, Hungry Howie's, Lucky Star Chinese, McDonald's, Menche's Rest., Quizno's, 🏨 Cambria Suites, Super 8, 🄾 🅗, AT&T, Giant Eagle Foods, vet
113	Akron-Canton 🛫, W 🏨 Hilton Garden, 🄾 General RV Ctr (2mi)
112	Shuffel St new exit
111	Portage St, N Canton, E 🅖 Circle K, Marathon, Sunoco/dsl, TA/Country Pride/dsl/scales/24hr/@, 🍽 Burger

C A N T O N

111	Continued King, Geisen Haus, Jimmy's Rest., KFC, Palombo's Italian, Quaker Steak, Subway, Sylvester's Italian, 🄾 TrueValue, W 🅖 BP/dsl, Speedway/dsl, 🍽 Baskin-Robbins/Dunkin Donuts, Carrabba's, ChuckeCheese, Coldstone Creamery, Cracker Barrel, Donato's Pizza, Don Pablo, Dunkin Donuts, Baskin-Robbins, Heavenly Ham, Hungry Howie's, IHOP, Longhorn Steaks, Lucky Star Chinese, McDonald's, Panera Bread, Philly Connection, Pizza Hut, Red Robin, Rockne's Cafe, Samantha's Rest., Subway, Taco Bell, Wasabi Japanese, Wendy's, 🏨 Best Western, Microtel, Motel 6, 🄾 AT&T, Best Buy, BJ's Whse, Chevrolet, DrugMart, Gander Mtn, Giant Eagle Foods, GNC, Goodyear/auto, Harley-Davidson, Home Depot, Lowe's, Marshall's, Old Navy, Sam's Club/gas, Walgreens, Walmart/Subway/auto
109b a	Everhard Rd, Whipple Ave, E 🅖 Marathon/Subway Speedway/dsl, 🍽 Denny's, Fazoli's, McDonald's, Taco Bell, Waffle House, 🏨 Comfort Inn, Fairfield Inn, Hampton Inn, La Quinta, Residence Inn, 🄾 Ford, W 🅖 Marathon 🍽 Applebee's, Arby's, Bob Evans, Bravo Italian, Buffalo Wild Wings, Buffet Dynasty, Chick-fil-A, Chili's, Chipotle Mexican, Chips&Salsa Mexican, Cheeseburger Paradise CiCi's Pizza, Damon's, Fox&Hound Grill, Friendly's, Golden Corral, HomeTown Buffet, HoneyBaked Ham, Jimmy John's, KFC, LoneStar Steaks, Macaroni Grill, Manchu Cafe, Max&Erma's, Mulligan's, Olive Garden, Outback Steaks, Panera Bread, Panini's Grill, Papa Bear's, Papa Gyros, Penn Sta. Subs, Perkin's, Red Lobster, Rita's Custard, Roadhouse Cafe, Robek's Cafe, Ruby Tuesday, Sahara Grill, Starbucks, Steak'n Shake, TGIFriday's, Wendy's, 🏨 Courtyard, Days Inn, Holiday Inn, Knights Inn, Magnuson Hotel, Red Roof Inn, 🄾 Aamco, Advance Parts, Alc Foods, AT&T, Dillard's, $Tree, Firestone/auto, Goodyear auto, Jo-Ann Fabrics, Kohl's, Macy's, Marc's Foods, NTB Petsmart, Radio Shack, Sears/auto, Target, TJ Maxx, Tuesday Morning, Verizon, World Mkt, mall, USPO
107b a	US 62, OH 687, Fulton Rd, to Alliance, E 🅖 Marathon Circle K/Subway, 🄾 City Park, W 🅖 Circle K, 🄾 Pro Football Hall of Fame
106	13th St NW, E 🅗
105b	OH 172, Tuscarawas St, downtown
105a	6th St SW (no EZ return from sb), E 🍽 McDonald's, W 🍽 Subway, 🄾 🅗, AutoZone
104	US 30, US 62, to E Liverpool, Massillon
103	OH 800 S, E 🅖 Marathon/Subway, Speedway, 🍽 Arby's, DQ, McDonald's, Peking Chinese, Taco Bell, Waffle House, 🄾 Advance Parts, Goodyear/auto, Rite aid, Save-a-Lot Foods
101	OH 627, to Faircrest St, E 🅖 Gulliver's Trvl Plaza/dsl rest./scales, Speedway/McDonald's, 🍽 Wendy's
99	Fohl Rd, to Navarre, W 🅖 Sunoco, 🄾 KOA (4mi)
93	OH 212, to Zoar, Bolivar, E 🅖 Speedway/Subway, 🍽 McDonald's, Pizza Hut, Wendy's, 🏨 Sleep Inn, 🄾 $General, Giant Eagle Foods, NAPA, Zoar Tavern (3mi), vet, t Lake Atwood Region, W 🅖 Marathon/DQ, 🄾 KOA
92mm	**weigh sta both lanes**
87	US 250W, to Strasburg, E 🍽 Arby's (2mi), W 🅖 Marathon Quizno's/dsl, 🍽 Damon's Pizza, Hardee's, Manor Rest McDonald's, Subway, 🏨 Ramada Ltd, Twins Motel
83	OH 39, OH 211, to Sugarcreek, Dover, E 🅖 BP, Speedway/Subway/dsl, 🍽 Bob Evans, KFC, McDonald's Shoney's, Wendy's, 🏨 Best Value Inn, 🄾 🅗, Chrysler

C A N T O N

OH

INTERSTATE 77 CONT'D

Exit	Services
83	Continued Dodge/Jeep, Flynn's Tires, Ford, Honda, Lincoln/Mercury, Nissan, W 🛏 Comfort Inn
81	US 250, to Uhrichsville, OH 39, New Philadelphia, E ⛽ KwikFill, Sheetz/dsl, Speedway, 🍴 Burger King, Denny's, El San Jose Mexican, Hog Heaven BBQ, LJ Silver, McDonald's, Pizza Hut, Quizno's, Taco Bell, TX Roadhouse, 🛏 Best Western, Hampton Inn, Knights Inn, Motel 6, Schoenbrunn Inn, ⊡ Advance Parts, Aldi Foods, BigLots, $General, $Tree, Walmart/Subway, W ⛽ Auto TP/rest./dsl/scales/24hr, ⊡ Harley-Davidson
73	OH 751, to rd 21, Stone Creek, W ⛽ Marathon
65	US 36, Port Washington, Newcomerstown, W ⛽ BP, Duke TP/rest./dsl, Speedway/Wendy's/24hr, 🍴 McDonald's, 🛏 Hampton Inn, Super 8
64mm	Tuscarawas River
54	OH 541, rd 831, to Plainfield, Kimbolton, W ⛽ BP, 🍴 Jackie's Rest.
47	US 22, to Cadiz, Cambridge, E to Salt Fork SP (6mi), lodging, RV camping, W ⛽ BP/repair, ⊡ 🅷, to Glass Museum, info
46b a	US 40, to Old Washington, Cambridge, W ⛽ BP/24hr, Exxon/Wendy's/dsl, Speedway/dsl/24hr, 🍴 Burger King, Lee's Rest., LJ Silver, McDonald's, Wally's Pizza, ⊡ Riesbeck's Food/deli, vet
44b a	I-70, E to Wheeling, W to Columbus
41	OH 209, OH 821, Byesville, W ⛽ BP/dsl, Circle K, Starfire, 🍴 McDonald's, ⊡ Byesville Drug, $General, Family$
39mm	**rest area nb, full** ♿ **facilities,** ⊙, 🚮, **litter barrels, petwalk, vending**
37	OH 313, Buffalo, E ⛽ BP, Duke, 🍴 Coutos Pizza, Subway, ⊙ truck repair, to Senecaville Lake, UPSO
36mm	**rest area sb, full** ♿ **facilities,** ⊙, 🚮, **litter barrels, petwalk, vending**
28	OH 821, Belle Valley, E ⛽ Sunoco/dsl, ⊡ USPO, to Wolf Run SP, RV camping
25	OH 78, Caldwell, E ⛽ BP, 🛢Arby's/dsl/scales/24hr, Sunoco/Subway/dsl, 🍴 DQ, Lori's Rest., McDonald's, 🛏 Best Western, ⊡ Buick/Chevrolet
16	OH 821, Macksburg, E 🍴 ⊡ antiques
6	OH 821, to Devola, E ⛽ Exxon, W ⛽ BP/dsl/LP, ⊡ 🅷, RV camping
3mm	**rest area nb, full** ♿ **facilities, info,** ⊙, **vending,** 🚮, **litter barrels, petwalk**
1	OH 7, to OH 26, Marietta, E ⛽ GoMart/dsl/24hr, 🍴 CiCi's, DQ, River City Grill, Ryan's, Subway, 🛏 Comfort Inn, Econolodge, Holiday Inn, ⊡ Aldi Foods, Buick/GMC, Cadillac/Chevrolet, Chrysler/Jeep, Dodge, Ford/Lincoln/Mercury, Harley-Davidson, Lowes Whse, Toyota/Scion, Walmart, W ⛽ BP/dsl, Duke/dsl, GetGo, Marathon/dsl, Speedway/dsl, 🍴 Applebees, Arby's, Bob Evan's, Bruster's, Bob Evans, Burger King, Capt D's, China Fun, E Chicago Pizza, Empire Buffet, LJ Silver, McDonald's, Napoli's Pizza, Papa John's, Pizza Hut, Quizno's, Shoney's, Subway, Taco Bell, Tim Horton, Wendy's, 🛏 Hampton Inn, Microtel, Super 8, ⊡ AutoZone, $General, Food4Less, Jo-Ann Crafts, K-Mart, Kroger/24hr, Sav-a-Lot Foods, TrueValue, Walgreens, museum, st patrol
0mm	Ohio/West Virginia state line, Ohio River

INTERSTATE 80

Exit	Services
237mm	Ohio/Pennsylvania state line
237mm	**Welcome Ctr wb, full** ♿ **facilities, info,** ⊙, 🚮, **litter barrels, vending, petwalk**
234b a	US 62, OH 7, Hubbard, to Sharon, PA, , N ⛽ ✈FLYING J /Denny's/dsl/LP/scales/24hr, Shell/rest./dsl/scales/motel/24hr/@, 🍴 Arby's, Burger King, McDonald's, Waffle House, 🛏 Best Western, ⊡ Blue Beacon, Homestead RV Ctr., RV camping (2mi), tire/dsl repair, S ⛽ ♥Loves /Chester's/Subway/dsl/scales/24hr, ⊡ Chevrolet
232mm	weigh sta wb
229	OH 193, Belmont Ave, to Youngstown, N ⛽ GetGo, Speedway/dsl, 🍴 Handl's Ice Cream, Rotelli Italian, Subway, 🛏 Hampton Inn, Motel 6, Super 8, ⊡ Giant Eagle Foods, Verizon, S ⛽ BP/dsl, Shell, 🍴 Antone's Italian Grille, Arby's, Armondo's Rest., Arthur Treacher's, Bob Evans, Casa Ramirez Mexican, Charley's Subs, Denny's, Golden Hunan Chinese, Ianazones Pizza, Jimmy's Italian, KFC, Little Caesars, LJ Silver, McDonald's, Papa John's, Pizza Hut, Subway, Taco Bell, Uptown Pizza, Wendy's, Westfork Steaks, Youngstown Crab Co, 🛏 Days Inn, Quality Inn, ⊡ Advance Parts, Aldi Foods, AT&T, AutoZone, BigLots, $General, Family$, Firestone/auto, Goodyear/auto, Radio Shack, Rite Aid, Walgreens, Walmart/Subway, vet
228	OH 11, to Warren (exits left from eb), Ashtabula
227	US 422, Girard, Youngstown, N ⛽ Shell/dsl, 🍴 Burger King, DQ, JibJab Hotdogs, Subway
226	Salt Springs Rd, to I-680 (from wb), N ⛽ BP/Dunkin Donuts/dsl, Sheetz, 🍴 McDonald's, Waffle House, ⊡ vet, S ⛽ Mr Fuel/Road Rocket Diner/dsl/24hr, Petro/rest./dsl/scales/24hr/@, 🛢/Subway/dsl/scales/24hr, ⊡ Blue Beacon, SpeedCo, dsl repair
224b	I-680 (from eb), to Youngstown
224a	OH 11 S, to Canfield
223	OH 46, to Niles, N ⛽ Country Fair, 🛢/McDonald's/dsl/scales/24hr, 🍴 Bob Evans, Burger King, Dunkin Donuts, IceHouse Rest., Salsita's Mexican, 🛏 Comfort Inn, Economy Inn, Holiday Inn Express, S ⛽ BP/dsl, FuelMart/dsl/scales, Sunoco/Subway, TA/Counry Pride/dsl/scales/24hr/@, 🍴 Arby's, Cracker Barrel, LJ Silver/Taco Bell, Quaker Steak&Lube, Perkins, Starbucks, Wendy's, 🛏 Best Western, Country Inn&Suites, EconoLodge, Fairfield Inn, Hampton Inn, Sleep Inn, Super 8, ⊡ Blue Beacon, Freightliner/24hr, Harley-Davidson
221mm	Meander Reservoir
219mm	I-80 wb joins Ohio Tpk (toll)

For I-80 exits 2-218, see Ohio Turnpike.

☐ = gas ☐ = food ☐ = lodging ☐ = other   Copyright 2011 - The Next Ex

INTERSTATE 90

Exit	Services
E ↑ W	
244mm	Ohio/Pennsylvania state line
242mm	**Welcome Ctr/weigh sta wb, full** ⚐ **facilities, info,** ☐, ⚐, **litter barrels, petwalk**
241	OH 7, to Andover, Conneaut, **N** ☐ Burger King, McDonald's (2mi), ☐ Days Inn, ☐ H, AutoZone, Evergreen RV Park, K-Mart, **S** ☐ Loves/McDonald's/Subway/dsl/scales/24hr, ☐ Beef&Beer Café
235	OH 84, OH 193, to Youngstown, N Kingsville, **N** ☐ Grab&Go/gas, Marathon/Circle K, ☐ Dav-Ed Motel, ☐ Village Green Camping (2mi), **S** ☐ Circle K/Subway/dsl, TA/BP/Burger King/dsl/scales/24hr/@, ☐ Kay's Place Diner, ☐ Kingsville Motel, ☐ tire repair
228	OH 11, to Ashtabula, Youngstown, **N** H (4mi)
223	OH 45, to Ashtabula, **N** ☐ FLYING J/Denny's/Shell/dsl/LP/scales/24hr, ☐ Mr C's Rest., ☐ Best Value Inn, Comfort Inn, Holiday Inn Express, Sleep Inn, ☐ Buccaneer Camping, **S** ☐ ▦/Subway/dsl/scales/24hr, SpeedCo, ☐ Burger King, McDonald's, Waffle House, ☐ Hampton Inn
218	OH 534, Geneva, **N** ☐ GetGo, ☐ Best Friend's Grill, Chop's Grille, McDonald's, Pizza Hut, Wendy's, ☐ Motel 6, ☐ H, Goodyear/repair, Indian Creek Camping (8mi), to Geneva SP, **S** ☐ KwikFill/dsl/rest./scales/24hr, ☐ Quiznos, ☐ Kenisse's Camping
212	OH 528, to Thompson, Madison, **N** ☐ McDonald's, Quinn's Rest., ☐ Mentor RV Ctr, **S** ☐ Marathon/dsl, ☐ Heritage Hills Camping (4mi), radiator repair
205	Vrooman Rd, **S** ☐ Indian Point Park, Masons Landing Park, **0-2 mi S** ☐ BP/dsl, Clark, Marathon/dsl, ☐ Capps Eatery, Subway
200	OH 44, to Painesville, Chardon, **S** ☐ BP/Subway/dsl, Sunoco/dsl, ☐ Bellacino's, CK Steakhouse, McDonald's, Palmer's Bistro, Red Hawk Grille, Teresa's Pizzaria, Waffle House, ☐ Baymont Inn, Quail Hollow Resort, ☐ H, Curves, Reider's Foods, hwy patrol
198mm	**rest area both lanes, full** ⚐ **facilities,** ☐, ⚐, **litter barrels, vending, petwalk**
195	OH 615, Center St, Kirtland Hills, Mentor, **1-2 mi N** ☐ BP, ☐ El Rodeo Mexican, Yours Truly Rest., ☐ Best Western
193	OH 306, to Mentor, Kirtland, **0-2 mi N** ☐ BP/Subway, Speedway, ☐ McDonald's, ☐ Best Value Inn, Comfort Inn, Super 8, **S** ☐ Marathon, ☐ Burger King, Dino's Rest., ☐ Days Inn, Red Roof Inn, ☐ H, Kirtland Temple LDS Historic Site
190	Express Lane to I-271 (from wb)
189	OH 91, to Willoughby, Willoughby Hills, **N** ☐ BP/dsl, Shell/24hr, ☐ Arby's (1mi), Bob Evans, Café Europa, Cracker Barrel, Damon's, Eat'n Park, Peking Chef, Subway, TX Roadhouse, Wendy's, ☐ Courtyard, Motel 6, Radisson (2mi), Travelodge, ☐ H, CVS Drug, Walgreens, **S** ☐ Lexus
188	I-271 S, to Akron
187	OH 84, Bishop Rd, to Wickliffe, Willoughby, **S** ☐ BP/dsl, Shell, ☐ Baker's Square, Burger King, Manhattan Deli, McDonald's, Golden Mountain Chinese, Mr Hero, Subway, Tony's Pizza, ☐ Ramada Inn, ☐ H, Curves, CVS Drug, Chevrolet, Giant Eagle Foods, Marc's Foods, Mazda/VW, NTB
186	US 20, Euclid Ave, **N** ☐ Sunoco, ☐ McDonald's, ☐ Comfort Inn, Mosley Suites, ☐ Ford, Subaru, radiator repair, **S** ☐ Shell, ☐ Arby's, KFC, Popeye's, R-Ribs, Sidewalk Cafe, Taco Bell, ☐ Advance Parts, $General, Family$, Firestone/auto, NAPA, Save-a-Lot Foods
185	OH 2 E (exits left from eb), to Painesville
184b	OH 175, E 260th St, **N** ☐ USPO, **S** ☐ NTB, Ruff's RV Ctr, transmissions, vet
184a	Babbitt Rd, same as 183
183	E 222nd St, **N** ☐ Sunoco/dsl, tires, **S** ☐ BP, Sunoco
182b a	185 St, 200 St, **N** ☐ Subway ☐ Home Depot, Honda, Hyundai, **S** ☐ Marathon/dsl, Shell, Speedway
181b a	E 156th St, **S** ☐ BP/24hr
180b a	E 140th St, E 152nd St
179	OH 283 E, to Lake Shore Blvd
178	Eddy Rd, to Bratenahl
177	University Circle, MLK Dr, **N** ☐ Cleveland Lake SP, **S** ☐ H, Rockefeller Park
176	E 72nd St
175	E 55th St, Marginal Rds
174b	OH 2 W, to Lakewood, downtown, Rock&Roll Hall of Fame, Browns Stadium
174a	Lakeside Ave
173c	Superior Ave, St Clair Ave, downtown, **N** ☐ BP
173b	Chester Ave, **S** ☐ BP
173a	Prospect Ave (from wb), downtown
172d	Carnegie Ave, downtown, **S** ☐ Burger King, ☐ Cadillac
172c b	E 9th St, **S** ☐ H, to Cleveland St U
172a	I-77 S, to Akron
171b a	US 422, OH 14, Broadway St, Ontario St, **N** ☐ BP, ☐ Hilton Garden, ☐ to Browns Stadium
171	Abbey Ave, downtown
170c b	I-71 S, to I-490
170a	US 42, W 25th St, **S** ☐
169	W 44th St, W 41st St, **N** H
167b a	OH 10, West Blvd, 98th St, to Lorain Ave, **N** H, **S** ☐ BP, dsl, ☐ CVS Drug
166	W 117th St, **N** ☐ BP/dsl, Get Go, Shell, ☐ KFC, ☐ Advance Parts, Giant Eagle Foods, Home Depot, Staples Target, **S** ☐ Church's/White Castle
165	W 140th St, Bunts Rd, Warren Rd, **N** ☐ Marathon, ☐ H
164	McKinley Ave, to Lakewood
162	Hilliard Blvd (from wb), to Westway Blvd, Rocky River, **S** ☐ BP, Shell
161	OH 2, OH 254 (from eb, no EZ return), Detroit Rd, Rocky River
160	Clague Rd (from wb), **S** ☐ H, same as 159
159	OH 252, Columbia Rd, **N** ☐ Carrabba's, Clubhouse Grille, Dave&Busters, Manero's, Outback Steaks, ☐ Courtyard, TownePlace Suites, Super 8, ☐ H, **S** ☐ BP, ☐ Houlihan's, KFC, McDonald's, Taco Bell, ☐ Chevrolet, NTB
156	Crocker Rd, Bassett Rd, Westlake, Bay Village, **N** ☐ BP, Shell, ☐ Extended Stay Deluxe, Holiday Inn, Red Roof Inn, Residence Inn, **S** ☐ BP, Speedway, ☐ Applebee's, Baskin-Robbins, Blake's Sea ☐ Bob Evans, Cabin Club Steaks, Caribou Coffee, Cheesecake Factory, Chicago Grill, Chipotle Mexican, El Rodeo Mexican, 5 Guys Burgers, Max&Erma's, McDonald's, Starbucks, Subway, TGI Friday's, Vieng's Asian, Wendy's, ☐ Hampton Inn, ☐ H, Aldi Foods, CVS Drug, Giant Eagle, GNC, Marc's Foods, Radio Shack, Sears Grand, Trader Joes, mall

OH

CLEVELAND

INTERSTATE 90 CONT'D

E ↑
W ↓

Exit	Services
153	OH 83, Avon Lake, **N** 🅶 GetGo/dsl, Marathon/Dunkin Donuts/dsl, 🍴 Arby's, Bubba's BBQ, Buffalo Wild Wings, Perkins, 🅾 AutoZone, Best Buy, Firestone/auto, JC Penney, Lowe's, PetCo, Walmart/auto, **S** 🍴 Applebees, Bob Evans, Burger King, Caribou Coffee, CiCi's Pizza, Coldstone, 5 Guys Burgers, Hot Dog Heaven, IHOP, Mandarin House, Moe's SW Grill, Panera Bread, Quiznos, Red Robin, Subway, Wendy's, 🅾 AT&T, Costco/gas, Curves, CVS Drug, GNC, Home Depot, Kohl's, Marc's Foods, Marshall's, Michael's, Old Navy, Radio Shack, Target, World Mkt
151	OH 611, Avon, **N** 🅶 BP/dsl, 🍴 Subway/dsl/24hr, 🍴 McDonald's, 🛏 Fairfield Inn, Value Place Hotel, 🅾 Goodyear/repair, Harley Davidson, **S** 🍴 BJ's Whse/gas, 🍴 Mulligan's Grille
148	OH 254, Sheffield, Avon, **N** 🍴 Quaker Steak&Lube, 🅾 Ford, GMC, KIA, Mazda, Mitsubishi, Nissan, **S** 🅶 BP, GetGo, Sheetz, Speedway, 🍴 Arby's, Burger King, China Star, Cracker Barrel, KFC, McDonald's, Pizza Hut, Ruby Tuesday, Sedona Grill, Steak'n Shake, Subway, Taco Bell, Wendy's, 🅾 Aldi Foods, CVS Drug, $General, $Tree, Drug Mart, Gander Mtn, Giant Eagle, NTB, Sam's Club/gas
147mm	Black River
145	OH 57, to Lorain, I-80/Ohio Tpk E, Elyria, **N** 🅶 Speedway, 🍴 George's Rest., Hunan King, Red Lobster, Wendy's, 🛏 Country Inn&Suites, 🅾 Chevrolet, Save-a-Lot, U-Haul, vet, **S** 🅶 Speedway, 🍴 Applebee's, Arby's, Bob Evans, Buffalo Wild Wings, Burger King, Chipotle Mexican, Denny's, Eat'n Park, Golden Corral, Harry Buffalo, McDonald's, #1 Buffet, Old Century Buffet, Olive Garden, Red Lobster, Subway, Wasabi Grill, Wendy's, 🛏 Best Western, Comfort Inn, Country Inn&Suites, EconoLodge, Red Carpet Inn, Red Roof Inn, Super 8, 🅾 AT&T, Best Buy, Curves, Dick's, $General, Firestone/auto, Giant Eagle, Home Depot, Honda, Hyundai, JC Penney, Jo-Ann Fabrics, Lowe's, Macy's, Marc's Foods, NTB, Petsmart, Radio Shack, Sears, Staples, Target, Tuffy Repair, Verizon, Walmart/auto
144	OH 2 W (from wb, no return), to Sandusky, **1 mi N** on Broadway Ave **E** 🅶 Marathon, Shell/24hr, 🍴 McDonald's, 🅾 🅷
143	I-90 wb joins Ohio Tpk
	WB exits to Ohio/Indiana state line are on Ohio Turnpike. See Ohio Turnpike exits 142-0.
142	I-90 (from eb), OH 2, to W Cleveland
139mm	**Middle Ridge Service Plaza wb, Vermilion Service Plaza eb,** Sunoco/dsl/24hr, FoodCourt, gifts, 🅲, RV parking
135	rd 51, Baumhart Rd, to Vermillion
132mm	Vermilion River
118	US 250, to Norwalk, Sandusky, **N** 🅶 DM/dsl, Marathon, Speedway, 🍴 4Monks Italian, McDonald's, Subway, 🛏 Comfort Inn, Day's Inn, Hampton Inn, Motel 6, Ramada Ltd, Super 8, 🅾 Oulet/famous brands, **5 mi N** 🍴 Perkins, Roadhouse Grill, 🛏 Econolodge, Fairfield Inn, Red Roof Inn, **S** 🛏 Colonial Inn, Homestead Inn/rest., 🍴 Race Café, 🅾 Chevrolet, to Edison's Birthplace
110	OH 4
100mm	**Erie Islands Service Plaza wb, Commodore Perry Service Plaza eb,** 🅶 Sunoco/dsl/24hr, 🍴 Burger King, Cinnabon, Max&Erma's, Sbarro's, Starbucks, 🅾 🅲

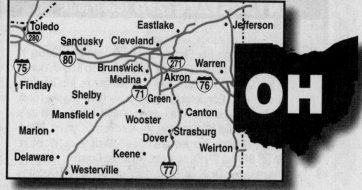

93mm	Sandusky River
91	OH 53, to Fremont, Port Clinton, **N** 🍴 Z's Diner, 🛏 Best Budget Inn, Day's Inn, **S** 🅶 Shell/dsl/24hr, 🍴 Applebee's (2mi), 🛏 Fremont Tpk Motel, Holiday Inn, 🅾 🅷
81	OH 51, Elmore, Woodville, Gibsonburg
80.5mm	Portage River
77mm	**Blue Heron Service Plaza wb, Wyandot Service Plaza eb,** Sunoco/dsl/24hr, Hardee's/chicken, 🅲
71	I-280, OH 420, to Stony Ridge, Toledo, **N** 🅶 Petro/Mobil/dsl/rest./24hr/@, ✈FLYING J/Denny's/dsl/24hr/LP/@, 🍴 Charter House Rest., Country Diner, 🛏 Howard Johnson, Pizza Hut, Knight's Inn, Ramada Ltd, Stony Ridge Inn/truck plaza/dsl/@, 🅾 Blue Beacon, **S** 🅶 FuelMart/dsl/@, 🍴 /dsl/24hr/@, TA/BP/Burger King/Taco Bell/dsl/24hr/@, 🍴 McDonald's, Wendy's, 🅾 truckwash
64	I-75 N, to Toledo, Perrysburg
63mm	Maumee River
59	US 20, to I-475, Maumee, Toledo, **N** 🅶 Amoco, BP/dsl, Speedway/dsl, 🍴 Arby's, Bob Evans, China Gate Rest., Church's, Dominic's Italian, Indian Cuisine, Max's Diner, McDonald's, Pizza Hut, 🛏 Budget Inn, Econolodge, Holiday Inn, Motel 6, Quality Inn, 🅾 Advance Parts, Goodyear/auto, Jo-Ann Fabrics, K-Mart/Little Caesar's, NAPA, Radio Shack, Savers Foods, Sears/auto, to Toledo Stadium, **S** 🅶 Meijer/dsl/24hr, Speedway, 🍴 Big Boy,'s, Fazoli's, Fricker's, Friendly's, Ralphie's Burgers, Red Lobster, Schlotsky's, Taco Bell, 🛏 Best Western, Comfort Inn, Cross Country Inn, Day's Inn, Hampton Inn, Red Roof Inn, Super 8, 🅾 Ames, Chevrolet, Ford/Lincoln/Mercury, Honda, Toyota
52	OH 2, to Toledo, **S** 🛏 Days Inn, Quality Inn (6mi), Super 8, 🅾 RV/truck repair
49mm	**service plaza both lanes,** Valero/dsl/24hr, gifts/ice cream
39	OH 109, Delta, **N** 🅶 Valero, 🍴 Country Lion's
34	OH 108, to Wauseon, **S** 🅶 Shell/Subway/dsl/24hr, 🍴 Smith's Rest., 🛏 Arrowhead Motel, Best Western, Holiday Inn Express, Super 8, 🅾 🅷, Toledo RV Ctr, Woods Trucking/repair (1mi), **2 mi S** on US 20A 🅶 BP/Circle K, 🍴 Burger King, DQ, McDonald's, Pizza Hut, Taco Bell, Wendy's, 🅾 Ace Hardware, Rite Aid, Walmart/dsl
25	OH 66, Burlington, **3 mi S** 🅾 Sauder Village Museum
24.5mm	Tiffin River
13	OH 15, to Bryan, Montpelier, **S** 🅶 Marathon/Subway/dsl, Sunoco, 🍴 Country Fair Rest., 🛏 Econolodge, Holiday Inn Express, Rainbow Motel, Ramada Inn, 🅾 Hutch's dsl Repair
11.5mm	St Joseph River
3mm	toll plaza, 🅲
2	OH 49, to US 20, **N** 🍴 Burger King, 🅾 tire repair
0mm	Ohio/Indiana state line

OH

INTERSTATE 270 (Columbus)

Exit	Services
55	I-71, to Columbus, Cincinnati
52b a	US 23, High St, Circleville, **N** 🅖 Marathon/Circle K, Speedway/dsl, 🍽 A&W/KFC, Arby's, Bob Evans, Burger King, China Town, LJ Silver, Los Campero's, McDonald's, Pizza Hut, Ponderosa, Roadhouse Grill, Skyline Chili, Subway, Taco Bell, Tim Horton, Waffle House, Wendy's, White Castle, 🛏 Kozy Inn, 🅞 AutoZone, Curves, $General, Firestone, Kroger/gas, Lowe's, Walgreens, Walmart, **S** 🅖 BP/dsl, 🛏 Budget Inn, 🅞 Kioto Downs
49	Alum Creek Dr, **N** 🅖 Duke/dsl, Sunoco/dsl, 🍽 Donato's Pizza, KFC/LJ Silver, Subway, **S** 🅖 BP/dsl, 🍽 Arby's, McDonald's, Taco Bell, Wendy's, 🛏 Comfort Inn, Sleep Inn
46b a	US 33, Bexley, Lancaster
43b a	I-70, E to Cambridge, W to Columbus
41b a	US 40, **E** 🅖 BP, Shell, 🍽 Bob Evans, Boston Mkt, Hooters, McDonald's, Outback Steaks, Rally's, Steak'n Shake, Texas Roadhouse, 🅞 Walgreens, **W** 🅖 Mobil, Shell, Speedway, 🍽 Fuddruckers, Golden Corral, Hunan Chinese, LoneStar Steaks
39	OH 16, Broad St, **E** 🅖 Meijer/dsl, Speedway/dsl, 🍽 Arby's, Chipotle Grill, Church's, Quizno's, Waffle House, White Castle, 🛏 Country Inn&Suites, 🅞 🅗, **W** 🅖 Shell, 🍽 Applebee's, 🛏 Ramada Inn
37	OH 317, Hamilton Rd, **E** 🅖 BP/dsl, Marathon, Speedway/dsl, 🍽 Big Boy, Bob Evans, Burger King, Chinese Express, Damon's, Donato's Pizza, Hickory House, KFC, Pizza Hut/Taco Bell, Starbucks, 🛏 Holiday Inn Express, SpringHill Suites, 🅞 Firestone, GNC, Kroger, 2 mi **W** 🛏 Comfort Suites, Hampton Inn, Hilton Garden
35b a	I-670W, US 62, **E** 🅖 Speedway/dsl, 🍽 City BBQ, Donato's Pizza, McDonald's, Tim Horton, 🅞 CVS Drug, **W** I-670
33	no services
32	Morse Rd, **E** 🅖 Marathon/DM, Speedway/dsl, 🍽 Donato's Pizza, 🅞 Mazda, Toyota, **W** 🅖 BP, Mobil/dsl, Shell/Subway, 🍽 Applebee's, Champp's Grill, HomeTown Buffet, Kobe Japanese, Logan's Roadhouse, McDonald's, On-the-Border, Pizza Hut/Taco Bell, Steak'n Shake, Wendy's, 🛏 Extended Stay America, Hampton Inn, 🅞 Best Buy, BMW, Cadillac, Carmax, Discount Tire, Jo-Ann Fabrics, Lexus, Lowe's Whse, Macy's, Mercedes, Nordstrom's, NTB, Sam's Club, Target, Walmart, mall
30	OH 161 E to New Albany, W to Worthington
29	OH 3, Westerville, **N** 🅖 BP/dsl, Shell, 🍽 Applebee's, Arby's, Chipotle Mexican, McDonald's, Fazoli's, Pizza Hut, Tim Horton, 🛏 Baymont Inn, Knight's Inn, 🅞 CarQuest, Firestone/auto, Kroger, **S** 🅖 Speedway/dsl, Sunoco/dsl, 🍽 Carsoni's Italian, China House, Domino's, Subway, 🅞 Aldi Foods, Family$, Midas
27	OH 710, Cleveland Ave, **N** 🅖 Speedway, 🍽 Subway, Tim Horton, Wendy's, 🛏 Quality Inn, Ramada Inn, Signature Inn, 🅞 CVS Drug, NAPA, Tuffy, **S** 🍽 Bob Evans, McDonald's, O'Charley's, Steak'n Shake, 🛏 Embassy Suites, 🅞 Home Depot
26	I-71, S to Columbus, N to Cleveland
23	US 23, Worthington, **N** 🍽 Alexander's, Amazon Grill, Bob Evans, Bravo Italian, Buffalo Wild Wings, Champp's Grill, Chipotle Mexican, Columbus Fish Mkt,

COLUMBUS

Exit	Services
23	Continued El Acapulco, Gilbert's Steaks, Lotus Grill, Mitchell's Steaks, Panera Bread, Quizno's, Ruth's Chris Steaks, Starbucks, Sushiko Japanese, Tutt's Italian, 🛏 AmeriSuites, Courtyard, Days Inn, DoubleTree, Extended Stay America, Motel 6, Homewood Suites, Red Roof Inn, Residence Inn, Sheraton, **S** 🅖 BP, 🍽 Buca Italian, Cosi Grill, Jimmy John's, McDonald's, 🛏 Econolodge, Holiday Inn
22	OH 315, **N** 🅖 Marathon/dsl
20	Sawmill Rd, **N** 🅖 BP, Marathon/dsl, 🍽 Burger King, McDonald's, Olive Garden, Subway, Taco Bell, Wendy's, 🅞 Buick/GMC, CVS Drug, Ford, Hyundai, Lincoln-Mercury, Mazda, NTB, Subaru, Tire Kingdom, **S** 🅖 Meijer, Shell, Speedway, 🍽 Applebee's, Asian Star, Arby's, BajaFresh, Bob Evans, Boston Mkt, Burger King, Charlie's Subs, Chili's, Chipotle Mexican, Cosi Grill, Don Pablo, Golden Corral, HoneyBaked Cafe, Joe's Crabshack, KFC, Krispy Kreme, McDonald's, Mongolian BBQ, Steak'n Shake, Red Lobster, Ruby Tuesday, Ted's MT Grill, 🛏 Hampton Inn, Quality Inn, Woodfin Suites, 🅞 Barnes&Noble, Big Lots, Cadillac/Honda, Discount Tire, $Tree, Firestone, Jo-Ann Fabrics, Kohl's, Lowe's Whse, PetCo, Sam's Club, Staples, SteinMart, Target, Toyota/Scion, Trader Joe's
17b a	US 33, Dublin-Granville Rd, **E** 🅖 Marathon, Sunoco, 🍽 Bob Evans, Donato's, Max&Erma's, McDonald's, Subway, 🛏 Best Value Inn, Courtyard, Crowne Plaza, Embassy Suites, Hilton Garden, Red Roof Inn, Residence Inn, 🅞 BMW/Mini, CVS Drug, Kroger, Mitsubishi, Mr Tire, USPO
15	Tuttle Crossing Blvd, **E** 🅖 BP, Mobil, 🍽 Bob Evans, Boston Mkt, Chipotle Mexican, Cozymel's, Longhorn Steaks, Macaroni Grill, McDonald's, PF Chang's, Pizza Hut/Taco Bell, River City Grill, TGIFriday, Wendy's, 🛏 Drury Inn, Homewood Suites, Hyatt Place, La Quinta, Marriott, 🅞 JC Penney, Macy's, Sears/auto, mall, **W** 🅖 Exxon/Subway/dsl, Shell, 🍽 Quizno's, Steak'n Shake, Uno Pizzaria, 🛏 Staybridge Suites, 🅞 Best Buy, NTB, Walmart/auto, World Mkt
13	Cemetery Rd, Fishinger Rd, **E** 🅖 Shell/Subway, Speedway, 🍽 Burger King, CheeseBurger Paradise, Chili's, Chiotle Mexican, Damon's, Dave&Buster's, Donato's Pizza, KFC, Panera Bread, Quizno's, Skyline Chili, Spaghetti's, TGIFriday, Tropical Bistro, 🛏 Comfort Suites, Homewood Suites, 🅞 CVS Drug, Home Depot, Lowe's Whse, Radio Shack, Staples, Target, Tire Dicounters, **W** 🅖 BP, Mobil, Speedway, Sunoco, 🍽 Bob Evans, Max&Erma's, McDonald's, Tim Horton, Wendy's, 🛏 Hampton Inn, Motel 6, 🅞 Nissan
10	Roberts Rd, **E** 🅖 Marathon, Thornton's/dsl, 🍽 Subway, Tim Horton, Wendy's, **W** 🅖 Speedway, 🍽 Waffle House, 🛏 Courtyard, Quality Inn, Royal Inn, 🅞 Kroger/gas
8	I-70, E to Columbus, W to Indianapolis
7	US 40, Broad St, **E** 🅖 BP, Speedway, 🍽 Bob Evans, Boston Mkt, Burger King, McDonald's, Popeye's, TeeJay's, Wendy's, White Castle, 🅞 Buick/GMC, Chevrolet, Chrysler/Jeep, Family$, Firestone/auto, Kohl's, NTB, Pepboys, Sears/auto, Staples, Suzuki, Target, Tuffy, **W** 🅖 GetGo, Speedway/dsl, Thornton's, 🍽 A&W/LJ Silver, Arby's, Big Boy, KFC, Papa John's, Waffle House, 🛏 Holiday Inn Express, Hometown Inn, 🅞 🅗, CVS Drug, Giant Eagle Foods, Goodyear, Home Depot, Jo-Ann Fabrics
5	Georgesville, **E** 🅖 Marathon, Mobil, Sunoco/dsl, 🅞 Walmart, **W** 🍽 Applebee's, Arby's, Bob Evans,

INTERSTATE 270 CONT'D (Columbus)

Exit	Services
5	Continued
	Buffalo Wild Wings, Chipotle Mexican, DQ, Fazoli's, Fiesta Mariachi, KFC/LJ Silver, LoneStar Steaks, McDonald's, O'Charley's, Red Lobster, Steak'n Shake, Subway, Wendy's, White Castle, ⊡ Advance Parts, GNC, Hyundai/Isuzu/Subaru, KIA, Kroger/gas, Lowe's Whse, NTB, Toyota/Scion, VW
2	US 62, OH 3, Grove City, N ⛽ BP, S ⛽ Shell, Speedway, Sunoco, 🍴 Big Boy, Brewster's, Burger King, Domino's, Donato's Pizza, McDonald's, Quizno's, Subway, Tim Horton/Wendy's, Waffle House, 🏨 Knight's Inn
0mm	I-71

INTERSTATE 271 (Cleveland)

Exit	Services
39mm	I-271 begins/ends on I-90, exit 188
38mm	I-271/I-480, Express Lanes
36	Wilson Mills Rd, Highland Hts, Mayfield, E 🍴 Austin's Steaks, 🏨 Hilton Garden, Holiday Inn, ⊡ vet, W ⛽ BP, Marathon/dsl, 🍴 Denny's, Panera Bread, Qdoba, ⊡ Dick's, DrugMart, Home Depot, Kohl's, Tuesday Morning
34	US 322, Mayfield Rd, E ⛽ BP, Sunmart, 🍴 5 Guys Burgers, Fox&Hound Grille, Jimmy John's, Starbucks, Subway, Wendy's, ⊡ CVS Drug, Marc's Foods, Michael's, Mr Tire, Rite Aid, Target, Walgreens, Walmart, W ⛽ Marathon, Shell, Speedway, 🍴 Arby's, Bob Evans, Burger King, Caribou Coffee, El Rodeo Mexican, McDonald's, Panini's Grill, Penn Sta Subs, Subway, TGI Friday's, Tucky's Burgers, 🏨 Baymont Inn, ⊡ H, AT&T, Best Buy, Costco/gas, Ford, Giant Eagle Foods, GNC, Lincoln/Mercury, Marshall's, Midas, Murray's Parts, Nissan, Old Navy, Petsmart, Radio Shack, World Mkt, vet
32	Brainerd Rd, E 🍴 Champp's Rest., J Alexander's, ⊡ H
29	US 422 W, OH 87, Chagrin Blvd, Harvard Rd, E ⛽ Shell, Speedway, Sunoco, 🍴 Bahama Breeze, Bob Evans, Bravo Italian, Corky&Lenny's Rest., Houlihan's, McDonald's, Mitchelo's Fish Mkt, Paladar Latan Kitchen, Red Lobster, Starbucks, Stone Oven, Wasabi Japanese, Wendy's, 🏨 Courtyard, Extended Stay America, Fairfield Inn, Hampton Inn, Homestead Suites, Super 8, ⊡ H, AT&T, Barnes&Noble, CVS Drug, Rite Aid, TJ Maxx, Trader Joe's, Verizon, Whole Foods Mkt, W ⛽ BP/Subway, Shell, 🍴 Hyde Park Steaks, PF Chang's, Yours Truly, 🏨 Clarion, Embassy Suites, Hilton, Homewood Suites, Residence Inn, ⊡ Buick/GMC, Cadillac, NTB
28b	Harvard Rd, E 🍴 Red Robin, W 🍴 Abuelo's, Chick-fil-A, Chipotle Mexican, DiBella's Subs, 5 Guys Burgers, Olive Garden, Panera Bread, River City Grille, Robeks Cafe, 🏨 Marriott, ⊡ H
28a	OH 175, Richmond Rd, Emery Rd, E ⛽ BP, GetGo, Marathon/Circle K/Subway/dsl, 🍴 Baskin-Robbins/Dunkin Donuts, Jimmy John's, Marianne's Bakery, McDonald's, Quiznos, W 🍴 BJ's Whse
27b	I-480 W
27a	US 422 E, E ⊡ Lowe's
26	Rockside Rd, E ⛽ Speedway/dsl, Sunoco, 🍴 Burger King, Subway
23	OH 14 W, Forbes Rd, Broadway Ave, E ⛽ Sunoco, 🍴 Double Dragon Chinese, McDonald's, Subway, Wendy's, 🏨 Holiday Inn Express, ⊡ Sam's Club/gas, W ⛽ Marathon/Circle K, ⊡ H

Exit	Services
21	I-480 E, OH 14 E (from sb), to Youngstown
19	OH 82, Macedonia, E ⛽ Speedway/dsl, 🍴 Papa John's, W ⛽ Sunoco, 🍴 Applebee's, Arby's, Chick-fil-A, Chili's, Chipotle Mexican, Coldstone, Fuji Japanese, Golden Corral, KFC, McDonald's, Outback Steaks, Panera Bread, Pizza Hut, Steak'n Shake, Subway, Taco Bell, Wendy's, ⊡ Best Buy, Chevrolet, Giant Eagle Foods, GNC, Hobby Lobby, Home Depot, Kohl's, Lowe's, NTB, PetCo, Petsmart, Radio Shack, Target, Walgreens, Walmart
18b a	OH 8, Boston Hts, to Akron, (exits left from sb), E ⛽ BP/ Subway/dsl, Speedway/dsl, 🍴 Bob Evans, Dos Coronas Mexican, 🏨 Country Inn&Suites, Days Inn, Knights Inn, La Quinta, Motel 6, W same as 19
12	OH 303, Richfield, Peninsula
10	I-77, to I-80, OH Tpk (from nb), to Akron, Cleveland
9	I-77 S, OH 176 (from nb), to Richfield
8mm	**rest area both lanes, full ♿ facilities, 🍴, 📞, litter barrels, petwalk**
3	OH 94, to I-71 N, Wadsworth, N Royalton, W ⛽ Marathon/dsl
0mm	I-271 begins/ends on I-71, exit 220.

INTERSTATE 275 (Cincinnati)

See Kentucky Interstate 275

INTERSTATE 280 (Toledo)

Exit	Services
13	I-280 begins/ends on I-75, exit 208
12	Manhattan Blvd, E ⛽ Sunoco, 🏨 Classic Inn, W ⛽ Sunoco, 🍴 Arby's, McDonald's
11	OH 25 S, Eerie St, W ⊡ Huntington Ctr
10mm	Maumee River
9	OH 65, Front St, E ⛽ Sunoco, W ⛽ Sunoco
8	Starr Ave, (from sb only)
7	OH 2, Oregon, E ⛽ Sunoco, 🍴 Arby's, Burger King, Coldstone/Tim Horton's, Empire Chinese, McDonald's, Wendy's, 🏨 Comfort Inn, ⊡ H, Ford, K-Mart, Walgreens, to Maumee Bay SP
6	OH 51, Woodville Rd, Curtice Rd, E ⛽ BP/dsl, 🍴 Bob Evans, Burger King, ⊡ Menards, W ⛽ Meijer/dsl, Speedway/dsl, 🍴 Applebee's, Arby's, Big Boy, Gino's Pizza, KFC, LJ Silver, McDonald's, Pizza Hut, Subway, Taco Bell, 🏨 Sleep Inn, ⊡ H, Advance Parts, $General, $Tree, Jo-Ann Fabrics, O'Reilly Parts, Rite Aid, Tires+
4	Walbridge
2	OH 795, Perrysburg, W ⛽ Sunoco/Subway/dsl
1b	Bahnsen Rd, E ⛽ FLYING J/Denny's/dsl/LP/ scales/24hr, 🏨 Crown Inn, Executive Inn, Regency Inn, W ⛽ Loves/Arby's/dsl/scales/24hr, Petro/BP/Iron

OH

INTERSTATE 280 CONT'D (Toledo)

Exit	Services
1b	Continued
	Skillet/dsl/scales/24hr/@, [T] McDonald's, [O] Super 8, [O] Blue Beacon, SpeedCo
1a	I-280 begins/ends on I 80/90, Ohio Tpk, Exit 71. **services** S [R] FuelMart/Subway/dsl/scales, [food]/McDonald's/dsl/scales/24hr, TA/BP/Burger King/Taco Bell/dsl/scales/24hr/@, [T] Sunrise Cafe

INTERSTATE 475 (Toledo)

Exit	Services
20	I-75. I-475 begins/ends on I-75, exit 204.
19	Jackman Rd, Central Ave, S [R] Shell, [O] [H]
18b	Douglas Rd (from wb)
18a	OH 51 W, Monroe St
17	Secor Rd, N [R] BP, Shell/dsl, [T] Applebee's, Bob Evans, Boston Mkt, Burger King, China 1 Buffet, Famous Dave's BBQ, Hooters, KFC, Penn Sta. Subs, Red Lobster, Red Robin, Rudy's Hot Dogs, Tim Horton, [O] Best Buy, Kroger, Murray's Parts, PharmX Drug, Walgreens, S [R] BP, [T] Big Boy, El Vaquero, McDonald's, Original Pancakes, Pizza Hut, Ponderosa, Popeye's, Taco Bell, Uncle John's Pancakes, [L] Clarion Hotel, Comfort Inn, Red Roof Inn, [O] Costco/gas, Home Depot, Radio Shack, Sears/auto, Steinmart, U of Toledo
16	Talmadge Rd (from wb, no return), N [R] BP/dsl, Speedway, [T] Arby's, Panera Bread, [O] JC Penney, mall
15	Corey Rd (from eb, no return)
14	US 23 N, to Ann Arbor
13	US 20, OH 120, Central Ave, E [R] Speedway, Sunoco, [T] Big Boy, Bob Evans, Magic Wok, McDonald's, Rally's, Wendy's, [O] BMW, Cadillac, Chrysler/Jeep, Ford, Honda, Kia, Mitsubishi, Nissan, Subaru, Toyota/Scion, W [R] BP, Shell, Speedway, [O] Lowes Whse
8b a	OH 2, E [R] BP/dsl, [T] Don Pablo, Texas Roadhouse, [L] Extended Stay America, Knight's Inn, Red Roof Inn, Residence Inn, [O] [H], Home Depot, Kohl's, Old Navy, to OH Med Coll, W [R] BP, Speedway, Sunoco/dsl, [T] Arby's, Big Boy, Bob Evans, Boston Mkt, Brewhouse Rest., Burger King, Chili's, Empire Chinese, Little Caesar's, Mancino's Pizza, McDonald's, Rally's, Subway, Wendy's, [L] Courtyard, Econolodge, Quality Inn, [O] Best Buy, Big Lots, Firestone/auto, Kroger, PetsMart, Rite Aid, Sam's Club/gas, Target, Walmart
6	Dussel Dr, Salisbury Rd, to I-80-90/tpk, E [R] Barney's/BP, Speedway, [T] Applebee's, Arby's, Bankok Kitchen, Bluewater Grill, Buffalo Wild Wings, Burger King, Coldstone Creamery, Cracker Barrel, Gino's Pizza, Ground Round, Jimmy John's, Longhorn Steaks, Marie's Diner, Max&Erma's, McDonald's, Panera Bread, Wendy's, Subway, Yoko Japanese, [L] Country Inn&Suites, Courtyard, Fairfield Inn, Homewood Suites, Residence Inn, Studio+, Super 8, W [R] BP, [T] Abuelo's, Bob Evans, Briarfield Café, Carraba's, Fox's Pizza, Ground Round, Mancino's Pizza, [L] Baymont Inn, [O] Churchill's Foods, vet
4	US 24, to Maumee, Napolean, N [O] [H], Toledo Zoo
3mm	Maumee River
2	OH 25, to Bowling Green, Perrysburg, N [R] BP/dsl, Circle K, Shell, [T] Arby's, Buffalo Wild Wings, Beaner's Coffee, Café Marie, Charlie's Rest., El Vaquero, Gino's Pizza, Hungry Howie, Marco's Pizza, McDonald's, Papa

OH · E ↑↓ W · TOLEDO

INTERSTATE 480 (Cleveland) — second column

Exit	Services
2	Continued
	John's, Subway, Wendy's, [O] Bassett's Mkt Foods, Compounding, Goodyear/auto, GMC, Saab/VW, Toms Tire/repair, Volvo, Young's RV Ctr, S [R] Speedway/dsl, [T] Biaggi's, Bob Evans, Chicago Pizza, Johnny Rockets, Louie's Grill, Maggi's Rest., Max&Erma's, Starbucks, TeaTree Asian, Waffle House, [L] Economy Inn, [O] Books-a-Million, Tire Man, vet
0mm	I-475 begins/ends on I-75, exit 192.

INTERSTATE 480 (Cleveland)

Exit	Services
42	I-80, PA Tpk, I-480 begins/ends, 0-2mi S [R] BP, Marathon/Circle K, Sheetz/24hr, Shell, Speedway, [T] Applebees, Arby's, Baskin Robbins/Dunkin Dounts, Big Boy, Bob Evans, Brown Derby Roadhouse, Buffalo Wild Wings, Burger King, CiCi's Pizza, Denny's, DQ, Eat'n Park, KFC, McDonald's, Mr Hero, New Peking Chinese, Pizza Hut, Quizno's, Rockney's Grill, Ruby Tuesday, Sonic, Steak'n Shake, Taco Bell, Wendy's, Zeppe's Pizza, [L] Best Value Inn, Comfort Inn, Econolodge, Fairfield Inn, Hampton Inn, Holiday Inn Express, Microtel, TownePlace Suites, Wingate Inn, [O] [H], Aldi Foods, AutoZone, Buick/GMC, Curves, Defer Tire, $General, Giant Eagle, Home Depot, Honda, Hyundai, K-Mart, Lowes Whse, Midas, NAPA, NTB, Save-a-Lot Foods, Staples, Target, U-Haul, Van's Tires, Walgreens, Walmart, mall, USPO, vet, to Kent St U
41	Frost Rd, Hudson-Aurora
37	OH 91, Solon, Twinsburg, N [T] Arby's, Pizza Hut, Taco Bell, [O] Comfort Suites, [O] Giant Eagle, S [R] BP
36	OH 82, Aurora, Twinsburg, N [R] BP/dsl, Get'n Go, [T] Burger King, [L] Super 8, S [R] Marathon, Bob Evans, Cracker Barrel, Damon's, Donato's Pizza, McDonald's, Wendy's, [L] Hilton Garden
26	I-271, to Erie, PA
25a b c	OH 8, OH 43, Northfield Rd, Bedford, N [O] Harley-Davidson, S [T] McDonald's, Rally's, White Castle
23	OH 14, Broadway Ave, N [R] Gulf/dsl, [T] Burger King, KFC
22	OH 17, Garanger, Maple Hts, Garfield Hts
21	Transportation Blvd, to E 98th St, S [O] Giant Eagle Foods, JoAnn Fabrics, Walmart
20b a	I-77, Cleveland
17	OH 176, Cleveland
16	OH 94, to OH 176 S, State Rd, N [O] Convenient Mart, transmissions, S [R] BP, Sunoco/dsl, [O] KIA
15	US 42, Ridge Rd, N [R] BP, [T] Applebee's, Baskin-Robbins/Dunkin Donuts, Boston Mkt, CiCi's Pizza, Coldstone Creamery, Hong Kong Buffet, McDonald's, Quizno's, Rockney's Rest., Starbucks, TX Roadhouse, [O] Chevrolet, GNC, Lowe's, Marc's Foods, Radio Shack, TJMaxx, S [R] Speedway, [T] Arby's, DQ, Denny's, Wendy's, [O] K-Mart, Best Buy, $Tree, Hyundai, Staples
13	Teideman Rd, Brooklyn, S [R] BP, Speedway, [T] Burger King, Carrabba's, Chipotle Mexican, Cracker Barrel, Don Pablo's, IHOP, LJ Silver, Panera Bread, Perkin's, Pizza Hut, Steak 'n Shake, TGIFriday's, Wild Ginger China Bistro, [L] Extended Stay America, Hampton Inn, [O] Aldi Foods, Home Depot, Jaguar, LandRover, Mazda, Sam's Club/gas, Volvo, Walmart
12	W 150th, W130th, Brookpark, N [T] Subway, S [R] Marathon, Shell, [T] Arby's, Big Boy, Bob Evans, [L] Best Value

E ↑↓ W

🅖 = gas 🍴 = food 🏠 = lodging 🅞 = other   **OHIO 349**

INTERSTATE 480 (Cleveland)

Exit	Services
12	Continued
	Inn, Park Brook Inn, 🅞 Acura, Lexus, Infiniti, Toyota, U-Haul
11	I-71, Cleveland, Columbus
10	S rd 237, 🍴 Blvd, (wb only)
9	OH 17, Brookpark Rd, N 🏠 Hilton Garden, 🅞 🅷, S 🏠 Sheraton, 🍴
7	(wb only)Clague Rd, to WestLake
6	OH 252, Great Northern Blvd, to N Olmsted, N 🅖 BP, Shell, Speedway, 🍴 Applebee's, Arby's, Bamboo Garden, Boston Mkt, Brown Bag Burgers, Burger King, Chick-fil-A, Chili's, ChuckeCheese, Daishin Japanese, Great Wall Buffet, Famous Dave's, Fat Burger, Harry Buffalo, Jimmy John's, Lonestar Steaks, Macaroni Grill, Moe's SW Grill, Olive Garden, Panera Bread, Penn Sta Subs, Red Lobster, Red Robin, Ruby Tuesday, Smokey Bones BBQ, Wendy's, 🏠 Candlewood Suites, Courtyard, Homestead Suites, La Quinta, Radisson, Studio+, 🅞 Aldi Foods, AT&T, Best Buy, Chipotle Mexican, Dillard's, $Tree, Firestone/auto, Home Depot, JC Penney, Jo-Ann Etc, Macy's, Marc's Foods, Mr Tire, NTB, Petsmart, Radio Shack, Sears/auto, Target, TJ Maxx, Toyota, Walmart, mall
3	Stearns Rd, N 🅷, 2 mi S 🍴 Razzle's Cafe
2	OH 10, Lorain Rd, to OH Tpk, S 🅖 BP, Sheetz/24hr, Speedway/dsl, 🍴 Ace's Grille, Gourme Rest., McDonald's, Pizza Pan, 🏠 Motel 6, Super 8
2	OH 10, Lorain Rd, to OH Tpk, S 🅖 BP, Sheetz/24hr, Speedway/dsl, 🍴 Ace's Grille, Gourme Rest., McDonald's, Pizza Pan, 🏠 Motel 6, Super 8
1	OH 10 W, to US 20 (from wb), Oberlin
0mm	OH 10, to ClevelandI-480 begins/ends on exit 151, OH Tpk

INTERSTATE 680 (Youngstown)

Exit	Services
14	OH 164, to Western Reserve Rd, I-680 begins/ends on OH Tpk, exit 234, S 🅖 Shell/Subway/dsl, 🍴 Dunkin Donuts, McDonald's, Pizza Hut, Wendy's, 🅞 🅷
11b a	US 224, S 🅖 BP, GetGo, Shell, 🍴 Applebee's, Burger King, Carabba's, Dunkin Donuts, KFC, LJ Silver, Longhorn Steaks, McDonald's, O'Charley's, Olive Garden, Outback Steaks, Papa John's, Red Lobster, Springfield Grill, Starbucks, Subway, Taco Bell, TGIFriday's, 🏠 Days Inn, Fairfield Inn, Hampton Inn, Holiday Inn, Red Roof Inn, Residence Inn, 🅞 🅷, Giant Eagle, K-Mart, Lowe's, Marc's Foods, Radio Shack, Sam's Club/gas, Walmart/Subway, urgent care
9b a	OH 170, Midlothian Blvd, Struthers, S 🍴 McDonald's
8	Shirley Rddowntown
7	US 62, OH 7, South Ave, downtown
6b a	US 62, OH 7, Mkt St, downtown
5	Glenwood Ave, Mahoning Ave, downtown
4b a	OH 193, to US 422, Salt Springs Rd, S 🅷, museum
3c b	Belle Vista Ave, Connecticut Ave
3a	OH 711 E, to I-80 E
2	Meridian Rd, S 🅖 Marathon, 🅞 Ford
1	OH 11

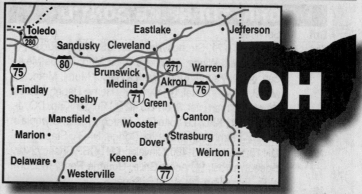

OHIO TURNPIKE

Exit	Services
241mm	Ohio/Pennsylvania state line
239mm	toll plaza, 🅞
237mm	**Mahoning Valley Travel Plaza eb**, Glacier Hills Travel Plaza wb, Valero/dsl/24hr, McDonald's, gifts, 🅞
234	I-680 (from wb), to Youngstown
232	OH 7, to Boardman, Youngstown, N 🅖 Sheetz, Valero/dsl, 🍴 DQ, Los Gallos Mexican, Rita's Custard, Steamer's Stonewall Tavern, 🏠 Best Value Inn, Budget Inn, Holiday Inn Express, Super 8, 🅞 antiques, S 🅖 🚛/McDonald's/dsl/scales/24hr, Sunoco/dsl, 🍴 Ambrozini's Rest., Road House Diner, 🏠 Davis Motel, Liberty Inn, 🅞 truck repair
218	I-80 E, to Youngstown. OH Tpk runs with I-76 eb, I-80 wb., Niles, services S on Mahoning
216	Lordstown (from wb), N GM Plant
215	Lordstown (from eb), N GM Plant
210mm	Mahoning River
209	OH 5, to Warren, N 🏠 Rodeway Inn, S 🅖 Marathon/dsl, 🏠 Econolodge, Holiday Inn Express
197mm	**Portage Service Plaza wb, Bradys Leap Service Plaza eb**, Valero/dsl/24hr, FoodCourt, McDonald's, gifts, 🅞
193	OH 44, to Ravenna
192mm	Cuyahoga River
187	OH 14 S, I-480, to Streetsboro, 0-2mi S 🅖 BP, Marathon/Circle K, Sheetz/24hr, Shell, Speedway, 🍴 Applebees, Arby's, Baskin Robbins/Dunkin Dounts, Big Boy, Bob Evans, Brown Derby Roadhouse, Buffalo Wild Wings, Burger King, CiCi's Pizza, Denny's, DQ, Eat'n Park, KFC, McDonald's, Mr Hero, New Peking Chinese, Pizza Hut, Quizno's, Rockney's Grill, Ruby Tuesday, Sonic, Steak'n Shake, Taco Bell, Wendy's, Zeppe's Pizza, 🏠 Best Value Inn, Comfort Inn, Econolodge, Fairfield Inn, Hampton Inn, Holiday Inn Express, Microtel, TownePlace Suites, Wingate Inn, 🅞 🅷, Aldi Foods, AutoZone, Buick/GMC, Curves, Defer Tire, $General, Giant Eagle, Home Depot, Honda, Hyundai, K-Mart, Lowes Whse, Midas, NAPA, NTB, Save-a-Lot Foods, Staples, Target, U-Haul, Van's Tires, Walgreens, Walmart, mall, USPO, vet, to Kent St U
180	OH 8, to I-90 E, N 🏠 Comfort Inn, Holiday Inn, 🅞 Harley-Davidson, S 🅖 BP/dsl, 🅞 to Cuyahoga Valley NRA
177mm	Cuyahoga River
173	OH 21, to I-77, N 🅖 🚛/Wendy's/dsl/scales, 🏠 Holiday Inn Express, Motel 6, S 🍴 DQ, Memories Rest., Richfield Rest., Subway, 🏠 Days Inn, Hampton Inn, Super 8
170mm	**Towpath Service Plaza eb, Great Lakes Service Plaza wb**, 🅖 Valero/dsl/24hr, 🍴 Burger King, FoodCourt, Panera Bread, Pizza Hut, 🅞 gifts, 🅞

OHIO TURNPIKE CONT'D

Exit	Services
161	US 42, to I-71, Strongsville, **N on US 42** ⛽ AP/dsl, 🍴 Buffalo Wild Wings, Jennifer's Rest, Mad Cactus Mexican, 🏨 Day's Inn, Kings Inn, La Siesta Motel, Metrick's Motel, Village Motel, ⊙ Circle K, Home Depot, Lowes Whse, Walmart, vet, **S on US 42** 🍴 Burger King, DQ, J-Bella Rest., KFC, La Volte Grill, Marco's Pizza, Olympia's Cafe, 🏨 Elmhaven Motel, ⊙ Dodge, NAPA, Staples
152	OH 10, to Oberlin, I-480, Cleveland, **N** ⛽ BP, Sheetz/24hr, Speedway/dsl, 🍴 Ace's Grille, Gourme Rest., McDonald's, Pizza Pan, 🏨 Motel 6, Super 8
151	I-480 E (from eb), to Cleveland⌂
146mm	Black River
145	OH 57, to Lorain, to I-90, Elyria, **N** ⛽ Speedway 🍴 Applebee's, Arby's, Bob Evans, Buffalo Wild Wings, Burger King, Chipotle Mexican, Denny's, Eat'n Park, Golden Corral, Harry Buffalo, Hunan King, Old Century Buffet, Olive Garden, McDonald's, Qdoba Mexican, Red Lobster, Subway, Wasabi Grill, Wendy's, 🏨 Best Western, Comfort Inn, Country Inn&Suites, EconoLodge, Holiday Inn, Red Carpet Inn, Red Roof Inn, ⊙ AT&T, Best Buy, Curves, $Tree, $General, Firestone/auto, Home Depot, Honda, JC Penney, Jo-Ann Fabrics, Lowe's, Macy's, Marc's Foods, NTB, Petsmart, Radio Shack, Sears/auto, Staples, Target, Walmart/auto, **S** ⛽ Shell, Speedway, 🏨 Howard Johnson
142	I-90 (from eb, exits left), OH 2, to W Cleveland
140	OH 58, Amherst, **0-2 mi N** ⛽ BP, GetGo, Speedway, Sunoco/Subway/dsl, 🍴 Blue Sky Rest., Bob Evans, DQ, Donato's Pizza, KFC, Marco's Pizza, McDonald's, Moosehead Grill, Mr Hero, Taco Bell, Wendy's, 🏨 Days Inn, Motel 6, ⊙ Advance Parts, Aldi Foods, Chevrolet, Chrysler/Dodge, Drug Mart, Giant Eagle Foods, K-Mart, Rite Aid, VW, Walgreens, repair, USPO, **S** ⊙ Ford
139mm	**Service Plaza both lanes,** ⛽ Valero/dsl/24hr, 🍴 Burger King, Great Steak, Hershey's, Panera Bread, Popeye's, Starbucks, TCBY, ⊙ gifts, ⓒ, RV parking
135	rd 51, Baumhart Rd, to Vermilion
132mm	Vermilion River
118	US 250, to Norwalk, Sandusky, **N** ⛽ BP/Circle K/Dunkin Donuts, Marathon/dsl, 🍴 Italian Gardens, McDonald's, Subway, 🏨 Comfort Inn, Days Inn, Hampton Inn, Motel 6, Red Roof Inn, Super 8, ⊙ RV Park, to Edison's Birthplace, **S** 🍴 Homestead Inn Rest., 🏨 Colonial Inn, ⊙ Hyundai
110	OH 4, to Bellevue
100mm	**Service Plaza both lanes,** ⛽ Valero/dsl/24hr, 🍴 Burger King, Cinnabon, Sbarro's, Starbucks, ⊙ ⓒ
93mm	Sandusky River
91	OH 53, to Fremont, Port Clinton, **N** 🏨 Days Inn, **0-2 mi S** ⛽ BP/Subway/dsl/24hr, Murphy USA, 🍴 Applebee's, Bob Evans, Burger King, Fricker's, McDonald's, Pizza Hut, Ryan's, Subway, Taco Bell, 🏨 Clarion, Comfort Inn, Delux Inn, Hampton Inn, ⊙ Ⓗ, Aldi Foods, $Tree, Ford/Lincoln/Mercury, Lowe's, Staples, Walmart, Rutherford B. Hayes Library, USPO, vet
81	OH 51, Elmore, Woodville, Gibsonburg
80.5mm	Portage River
77mm	**Service Plaza both lanes,** ⛽ Valero/dsl/24hr, 🍴 Hardee's, Mancino's, Red Burrito, ⓒ
71	I-280, OH 420, to Stony Ridge, Toledo, **N** ⛽ Mobil/Iron Skillet/dsl/scales/24hr/@, ⚡FLYING J/Denny's/dsl/scales/LP/24hr, Petro/BP/Iron Skillet/dsl/scales/24hr/@,

Exit	Services
71	Continued 🏨 Crown Inn, Super 8, ⊙ Blue Beacon, KOA, SpeedCo, **S** ⛽ FuelMart/Subway/dsl/scales, 🍴 McDonald's/dsl/scales/24hr, TA/BP/Burger King/Taco Bell/dsl/scales/24hr/@, ⊙ truckwash
64	I-75 N, to Toledo, Perrysburg, **S** ⊙ BP/Subway/dsl, 🏨 Country Inn&Suites, Courtyard, Hampton Inn, ⊙ Bass Pro Shops
63mm	Maumee River
59	US 20, to I-475, Maumee, Toledo, **N** ⛽ Shell, Speedway/dsl, 🍴 Bob Evans, McDonald's, Nick's Cafe, Olive Garden, Pizza Hut, Steak'n Shake, Subway, Waffle House, 🏨 Clarion, Motel 6, ⊙ Family$, Goodyear/auto, Jo-Ann Fabrics, K-Mart, Murray's Parts, NAPA, Radio Shack, Rite Aid, Savers, Walgreens, to Toledo Stadium, **S** ⛽ Speedway/dsl, 🍴 Big Boy, Chipotle Mexican, Donato's Pizza, El Azteca, Fricker's, Friendly's, Jed's BBQ, Red Lobster, Schlotzsky's, Taco Bell, Tim Horton, 🏨 Comfort Inn, Days Inn, EconoLodge, Hampton Inn, Holiday Inn, Red Roof Inn, ⊙ AT&T, Ford, Honda, Meijer/gas, Toyota
52	OH 2, to Toledo, **S** 🏨 Days Inn, ⊙ RV/truck repair, ⌂
49mm	**service plaza both lanes,** ⛽ Valero/dsl/24hr, 🍴 Nathan's, UNO Grill, gifts/ice cream
39	OH 109, **S** ⛽ Country Corral/Valero/Winchesters Rest/dsl/scales/wi-fi/24hr
34	OH 108, to Wauseon, **S** ⛽ Shell/Subway/dsl/24hr, 🍴 Smith's Rest., 🏨 Arrowhead Motel, Best Western, Holiday Inn Express, Super 8, ⊙ Ⓗ, Woods Trucking/repair (1mi), **2 mi S on US 20A** ⛽ BP/Circle K, Circle K, Marathon, Murphy USA/dsl, Valero, 🍴 A&W/KFC, Arby's, Burger King, DQ, Grasshopper Rest., Kamwa Chinese, McDonald's, Pizza Hut, Subway, Taco Bell, Wendy's, ⊙ Ace Hardware, AutoZone, $General, O'Reilly Parts, Rite Aid, Walmart, Wood Trucking
25	OH 66, Burlington, **N** ⊙ Harrison Lake SP, **3 mi S** ⊙ Sauder Village Museum
24.5mm	Tiffen River
13	OH 15, to Bryan, Montpelier, **S** ⛽ Marathon/dsl, Sunoco, 🍴 4Seasons Rest., 🏨 EconoLodge, Holiday Inn Express, Rainbow Motel, Ramada Inn, ⊙ Hutch's dsl Repair
11.5mm	St Joseph River
3mm	toll plaza, ⓒ
2	OH 49, to US 20, **N** 🍴 Burger King, Subway, ⊙ info, truck tires
0mm	Ohio/Indiana state line

OKLAHOMA

INTERSTATE 35

Exit	Services
236mm	Oklahoma/Kansas state line
231	US 177, Braman, **E** ⛽ Conoco/deli/dsl
230	Braman Rd
229mm	Chikaskia River
225mm	**Welcome Ctr sb, rest area nb, full** ♿ **facilities,** ⓒs, 🏨, **litter barrels, vending, petwalk, RV dump**
222	OK 11, to Blackwell, Medford, Alva, Newkirk, **E** ⛽ Conoco/dsl, Shell/dsl, 🍴 Braum's, KFC/Taco Bell, Los Potros Mexican, McDonald's, Plains Man Rest., Subway, 🏨 Best Way Inn, Best Western, Comfort Inn, ⊙ Ⓗ
218	Hubbard Rd

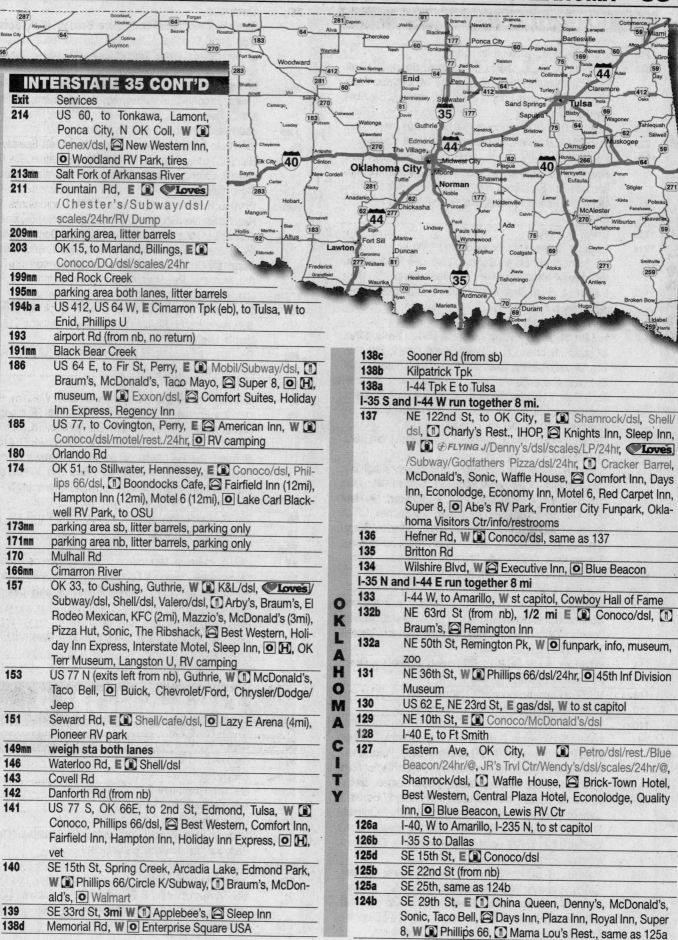

N ↕ S

GUTHRIE

INTERSTATE 35 CONT'D

Exit	Services
214	US 60, to Tonkawa, Lamont, Ponca City, N OK Coll, **W** 🅖 Cenex/dsl, 🛏 New Western Inn, ⊙ Woodland RV Park, tires
213mm	Salt Fork of Arkansas River
211	Fountain Rd, **E** 🅖 ♥Loves /Chester's/Subway/dsl/ scales/24hr/RV Dump
209mm	parking area, litter barrels
203	OK 15, to Marland, Billings, **E** 🅖 Conoco/DQ/dsl/scales/24hr
199mm	Red Rock Creek
195mm	parking area both lanes, litter barrels
194b a	US 412, US 64 W, **E** Cimarron Tpk (eb), to Tulsa, **W** to Enid, Phillips U
193	airport Rd (from nb, no return)
191mm	Black Bear Creek
186	US 64 E, to Fir St, Perry, **E** 🅖 Mobil/Subway/dsl, 🍴 Braum's, McDonald's, Taco Mayo, 🛏 Super 8, ⊙ 🅗, museum, **W** 🅖 Exxon/dsl, 🛏 Comfort Suites, Holiday Inn Express, Regency Inn
185	US 77, to Covington, Perry, **E** 🛏 American Inn, **W** 🅖 Conoco/dsl/motel/rest./24hr, ⊙ RV camping
180	Orlando Rd
174	OK 51, to Stillwater, Hennessey, **E** 🅖 Conoco/dsl, Phillips 66/dsl, 🍴 Boondocks Cafe, 🛏 Fairfield Inn (12mi), Hampton Inn (12mi), Motel 6 (12mi), ⊙ Lake Carl Blackwell RV Park, to OSU
173mm	parking area sb, litter barrels, parking only
171mm	parking area nb, litter barrels, parking only
170	Mulhall Rd
166mm	Cimarron River
157	OK 33, to Cushing, Guthrie, **W** 🅖 K&L/dsl, ♥Loves /Subway/dsl, Shell/dsl, Valero/dsl, 🍴 Arby's, Braum's, El Rodeo Mexican, KFC (2mi), Mazzio's, McDonald's (3mi), Pizza Hut, Sonic, The Ribshack, 🛏 Best Western, Holiday Inn Express, Interstate Motel, Sleep Inn, ⊙ 🅗, OK Terr Museum, Langston U, RV camping
153	US 77 N (exits left from nb), Guthrie, **W** 🍴 McDonald's, Taco Bell, ⊙ Buick, Chevrolet/Ford, Chrysler/Dodge/Jeep
151	Seward Rd, **E** 🅖 Shell/cafe/dsl, ⊙ Lazy E Arena (4mi), Pioneer RV park
149mm	**weigh sta both lanes**
146	Waterloo Rd, **E** 🅖 Shell/dsl
143	Covell Rd
142	Danforth Rd (from nb)
141	US 77 S, OK 66E, to 2nd St, Edmond, Tulsa, **W** 🅖 Conoco, Phillips 66/dsl, 🛏 Best Western, Comfort Inn, Fairfield Inn, Hampton Inn, Holiday Inn Express, ⊙ 🅗, vet
140	SE 15th St, Spring Creek, Arcadia Lake, Edmond Park, **W** 🅖 Phillips 66/Circle K/Subway, 🍴 Braum's, McDonald's, ⊙ Walmart
139	SE 33rd St, **3mi W** 🍴 Applebee's, 🛏 Sleep Inn
138d	Memorial Rd, **W** ⊙ Enterprise Square USA

OKLAHOMA CITY

Exit	Services
138c	Sooner Rd (from sb)
138b	Kilpatrick Tpk
138a	I-44 Tpk E to Tulsa
I-35 S and I-44 W run together 8 mi.	
137	NE 122nd St, to OK City, **E** 🅖 Shamrock/dsl, Shell/dsl, 🍴 Charly's Rest., IHOP, 🛏 Knights Inn, Sleep Inn, **W** 🅖 ⊕FLYING J/Denny's/dsl/scales/LP/24hr, ♥Loves /Subway/Godfathers Pizza/dsl/24hr, 🍴 Cracker Barrel, McDonald's, Sonic, Waffle House, 🛏 Comfort Inn, Days Inn, Econolodge, Economy Inn, Motel 6, Red Carpet Inn, Super 8, ⊙ Abe's RV Park, Frontier City Funpark, Oklahoma Visitors Ctr/info/restrooms
136	Hefner Rd, **W** 🅖 Conoco/dsl, same as 137
135	Britton Rd
134	Wilshire Blvd, **W** 🛏 Executive Inn, ⊙ Blue Beacon
I-35 N and I-44 E run together 8 mi	
133	I-44 W, to Amarillo, **W** st capitol, Cowboy Hall of Fame
132b	NE 63rd St (from nb), **1/2 mi E** 🅖 Conoco/dsl, 🍴 Braum's, 🛏 Remington Inn
132a	NE 50th St, Remington Pk, **W** ⊙ funpark, info, museum, zoo
131	NE 36th St, **W** 🅖 Phillips 66/dsl/24hr, ⊙ 45th Inf Division Museum
130	US 62 E, NE 23rd St, **E** gas/dsl, **W** to st capitol
129	NE 10th St, **E** 🅖 Conoco/McDonald's/dsl
128	I-40 E, to Ft Smith
127	Eastern Ave, OK City, **W** 🅖 Petro/dsl/rest./Blue Beacon/24hr/@, JR's Trvl Ctr/Wendy's/dsl/scales/24hr/@, Shamrock/dsl, 🍴 Waffle House, 🛏 Brick-Town Hotel, Best Western, Central Plaza Hotel, Econolodge, Quality Inn, ⊙ Blue Beacon, Lewis RV Ctr
126a	I-40, W to Amarillo, I-235 N, to st capitol
126b	I-35 S to Dallas
125d	SE 15th St, **E** 🅖 Conoco/dsl
125b	SE 22nd St (from nb)
125a	SE 25th, same as 124b
124b	SE 29th St, **E** 🍴 China Queen, Denny's, McDonald's, Sonic, Taco Bell, 🛏 Days Inn, Plaza Inn, Royal Inn, Super 8, **W** 🅖 Phillips 66, 🍴 Mama Lou's Rest., same as 125a

INTERSTATE 35 CONT'D

Exit	Services
124a	Grand Blvd, E 🏠 Suburban Lodge
123b	SE 44th St, E 🛢 Shell, 🍴 Dominos, Sonic, 🏠 Best Value Inn, Courtesy Inn, W 🍴 Pizza 44, Subway, Taco Mayo, 🅾 Bi-4-Less Foods, $General, Family$, SavALot Foods, USPO
123a	SE 51st St, E 🛢 Conoco/dsl, 🏠 Best Value Inn
122b	SE 59th St, E 🛢 Phillips 66/dsl, W 🛢 Shell, Valero/dsl
122a	SE 66th St, E 🍴 Luby's, McDonald's, Subway, Taco Bell, Texas Roadhouse, Zeke's Rest., 🏠 Fairfield Inn, Ramada Inn, Residence Inn, 🅾 Best Buy, Dillard's, Firestone, JC Penney, Macys, Tires+, mall, W 🛢 7-11, 🍴 Arby's
121b	US 62 W, I-240 E
121a	SE 82nd St, (from sb), W 🏠 Baymont Inn
120	SE 89th St, E 🛢 Valero/dsl/scales, 🏠 Ford, W 🛢 ♥Loves/Subway/dsl/24hr, 🅾 Classic Parts
119b	N 27th St, E 🛢 Shell/Circle K/dsl, 🍴 Pickles Rest., 🅾 Harley-Davidson
119a	Shields Blvd (exits left from nb)
118	N 12th St, E 🍴 Mazzio's, Peking Buffet, 🏠 Super 8, W 🛢 7-11, Shell, 🍴 A&W/LJ Silver, Arby's, Braum's, DQ, Grandy's, Harry Bear's Grill, KFC, La Fajitas, Mamma Lou's, Mazzio's, McDonald's, Papa John's, Subway, Taco Bell, Wendy's, Western Sizzlin, 🏠 Best Western, Candlewood Suites, Comfort Inn, SpringHill Suites, 🅾 Ace Hardware, AutoZone, Family$
117	OK 37, S 4th St, W 🛢 Valero, 🍴 China Wok, Van BBQ, 🅾 USPO
116	S 19th St, E 🛢 Conoco, Shell, 🍴 Braum's, Capt D's, Carl's Jr, DQ, McDonald's, Popeye's, Sara's Rest., Taco Bell, Waffle House, Whataburger, 🏠 Microtel, 🅾 Best Buy, Firestone/auto, Goodyear/auto, JC Penney, Office Depot, PetsMart, Ross, W 🍴 Arby's, Alfredo's Mexican, Applebees, Arby's, Buffalo Wild Wings, Buffet King, Burger King, Chick-fil-A, Earl's Ribs, Freddy's Frozen Custard, Furr's Buffet, IHOP, Jimmy's Egg, Louie's Grill, McAlister's Deli, Panda Express, Quizno's, Sonic, Subway, 🏠 La Quinta, 🅾 Aldi Foods, Discount Tire, $Tree, Gordman's, Harley-Davidson, Home Depot, Kohl's, Lowe's Whse, Radio Shack, Russell Stover Candies, Tires+, Walmart/gas
114	Indian Hill Rd, E 🍴 Bill's Fishhouse, Indian Hills Rest., 🏠 ValuePlace Hotel, 🅾 Guy RV Ctr
113	US 77 S (from sb, exits left), Norman
112	Tecumseh Rd, E 🅾 Nissan, Toyota/Scion
110b a	Robinson St, E 🍴 Carl's Jr, Cheddar's, Logan's Roadhouse, Sonic, Taco Bell, Teimei Asian Buistro, 🏠 Days Inn, Embassy Suites, 🅾 🎗, Chrysler/Jeep, Ford, GMC, Homeland Foods/drug, Honda, Hyundai, Kohl's, Lincoln/Mercury/Mazda, PetCo, Subaru, Super Target, Tires+, TJ Maxx, W 🛢 Conoco/Subway, 🍴 Arby's, Braum's, Cafe Escondido, Cracker Barrel, Golden Chef, Outback Steaks, Papa John's, Rib Crib, Saltgrass Steaks, Santa Fe Cattle Co, Waffle House, 🏠 Comfort Inn, Courtyard, Hilton Garden, Holiday Inn, 🅾 Kia/Isuzu
109	Main St, E 🛢 Phillips 66, Shell, 🍴 Arby's, Braum's, CiCi's, Denny's, Golden Corral, JR's Rest., Krispy Kreme, LJ Silver, Panera Bread, Prairie Kitchen, Subway, Taco Cabana, Waffle House, Wendy's, 🏠 Days Inn, Econolodge, Guest Inn, Quality Inn, Ramada Inn,

Exit	Services
109	Continued Super 8, Thunderbird Lodge, Travelodge, 🅾 AutoZone, Best Buy, Cadillac, Chevrolet, Dodge/Jeep, Hastings Books, Lowe's Whse, Nissan, Subaru, Tires+, Walmart/gas, W 🛢 Conoco/Circle K/dsl, 🍴 Applebee's, BJ's Brewhouse, Burger King, Don Pablo, Charleston's Rest. Chili's, Escondido Mexican, Marie Callender's, McDonald's, Olive Garden, On the Border, Outback Steaks, Piccadilly's, Red Lobster, Red River Steaks, Rio Cafe, Village Inn Rest., 🏠 Fairfield Inn, Hampton Inn, La Quinta, 🅾 Barnes&Noble, Dillard's, IGA Foods, JC Penney, Kia, Michael's, Old Navy, Saab, Sam's Club, Sears/auto, Stein-Mart, mall
108b a	OK 9 E, Norman, E 🛢 Conoco, 🍴 Arby's, Braum's, Del Rancho Steaks, Schlotzsky's, Taco Bell, 🏠 Residence Inn, Sooner Legends Inn, 🅾 to U of OK, W 🍴 Carino's Italian, IHOP, Jasons Deli, Othello's Italian, Red Robin, Souper Salad, 🏠 Country Inn&Suites, La Quinta, 🅾 Home Depot, Michaels, PetsMart, Ross
107mm	Canadian River
106	OK 9 W, to Chickasha, E 🅾 Casino, W 🛢 ♥Loves/Subway/dsl/24hr, Shell, 🍴 McDonald's, Sonic, 🏠 Sleep Inn, 🅾 casino
104	OK 74 S, Goldsby, E 🅾 Floyd's RV Ctr, W 🛢 Shamrock/dsl, Sinclair/dsl, 🍴 Libby's Cafe
101	Ladd Rd
98	Johnson Rd, E 🛢 Shamrock/dsl
95	US 77 (exits left from sb), Purcell, **1-3 mi** E 🛢 Shell, 🍴 Braum's, KFC, Mazzio's, Pizza Hut, Subway, 🅾 🎗, Ford
91	OK 74, to OK 39, Maysville, E 🛢 Conoco/dsl, Murphy USA/dsl, Phillips 66/dsl, 🍴 Braum's, McDonald's, New China, Subway, Taco Mayo, 🏠 EconoLodge, Executive Inn, Ruby's Inn/rest., 🅾 Ace Hardware, American RV Park (1mi), Walmart, W 🛢 Shell/dsl, 🍴 A&W/LJ Silver
86	OK 59, Wayne, Payne, E 🅾 American RV Park
79	OK 145 E, Paoli, E 🛢 Phillips 66
76mm	Washita River
74	OK 19, Kimberlin Rd
72	OK 19, Paul's Valley, E 🛢 Conoco/dsl, Murphy USA/dsl, Valero/dsl/rest./24hr, 🍴 Arby's, Baby D's Cafe&Creamery, Braum's, Chicken Express, Green Tea Chinese, Happy Days Diner, KFC/Taco Bell, Little Ben's Pizza, McDonald's, Sonic, Stevenson BBQ, Subway, Taco Mayo, 🏠 American Inn, Comfort Inn, Days Inn, Garden Inn, Holiday Inn Express, Relax Inn, 🅾 AT&T, Buick/Cadillac/GMC, Chrysler/Dodge/Jeep, Ford/Lincoln/Mercury, Walmart, W 🛢 ♥Loves/Godfather's/dsl/24hr, Phillips 66/dsl/24hr, 🅾 truckwash
70	Airport Rd, E 🎗
66	OK 29, Wynnewood, W 🛢 Kent's Fuel/dsl, Shell/dsl
64	OK 17A E, to Wynnewood, E GW Exotic Animal Park
60	Ruppe Rd
59mm	**rest area both lanes, full** ♿ **facilities, 🚻, 🛢, litter barrels, petwalk, RV dump**
55	OK 7, Davis, E 🛢 Conoco, Phillips 66/A&W/dsl/24hr, 🅾 Microtel, 🅾 casino, to Chickasaw NRA, W 🅾 Oak Hill RV Park/gas/deli, to Arbuckle Ski Area
54.5mm	Honey Creek Pass
53mm	**weigh sta both lanes**
51	US 77, Turner Falls, E 🏠 Arbuckle Mtn Motel, Mtnview Inn (3mi), 🅾 to Arbuckle Wilderness, RV camping, W 🛢 Sinclair/grill, 🅾 Botanic Gardens

INTERSTATE 35 CONT'D

N ↕ S

Exit	Services
49mm	scenic turnout both lanes
47	US 77, Turner Falls Area
46mm	scenic turnout both lanes
42	OK 53 W, Springer, Comanche, **W** ⛽ Exxon/dsl
40	OK 53 E, Gene Autry, **E** ⛽ Shell/dsl/café/24hr, 🍴 Broaster Rest, ◻ Gene Autry Museum (8mi)
33	OK 142, Ardmore, **E** ⛽ Phillips 66/dsl/24hr, 🍴 IHOP, Ponder's Rest., 🛏 Guest Inn, La Quinta, SpringHill Suites, Super 8, **W** ⛽ FLYING J/Denny's/dsl/scales/LP
32	12th St, Ardmore, **E** ⛽ Conoco/dsl, 🍴 Braum's, Quizno's, Santa Fe Steaks, Whataburger, 🛏 Candlewood Suites, La Quinta, ◻ $Tree, Lowe's Whse, PetCo, Toyota, **W** ⛽ Loves/Godfather's/Subway/dsl/24hr/@, 🍴 McDonald's, 🛏 Microtel
31b a	US 70 W, OK 199 E, Ardmore, **E** ⛽ Shell/dsl, Valero/dsl, 🍴 Applebee's, Burger King, Cattle Rustlers, Denny's, El Chico, Jack-in-the-Box, KFC, Mazzio's, McDonald's, Pizza Hut, Polo's Mexican, Prairie Kitchen, 2Frogs Grill, 🛏 Best Western, Days Inn, Hampton Inn, Holiday Inn, Motel 6, Rodeway Inn, ◻ AutoZone, Honda, O'Reilly Parts, **W** ⛽ Conoco/dsl, ◻ Ardmore RV Park, Chrysler/Dodge/Jeep, Ford/Lincoln/Mercury, Nissan, vet
29	US 70 E, Ardmore, **E** 🛏 Economy Inn (1mi), ◻ to Lake Texoma SP, **W** ◻ Hidden Lake RV Park
24	OK 77 S, **E** ◻ Red River Livestock Mkt, to Lake Murray SP
22.5mm	Hickory Creek
21	Oswalt Rd, **W** ⛽ Valero, ◻ KOA
15	OK 32, Marietta, **E** ⛽ Valero/dsl/24hr, 🍴 Carl's Jr, McDonald's, Pizza Hut, Robertson's Sandwiches, Sonic, ◻ Ⓗ, $General, to Lake Texoma SP, **W** ⛽ Phillips 66/24hr, 🍴 Hickory House BBQ
5	OK 153, Thackerville, **W** ◻ Shorty's Foods/gas, Red River Ranch RV Park
3.5mm	**Welcome Ctr nb, full ♿ facilities, ✆, ⛱, litter barrels, vending, petwalk**
1	US 77 N, **E** ⛽ Phillips 66/dsl, 🍴 River Ridge Rest., 🛏 Best Western, Mictotel, ◻ Winstar Casino, **W** ◻ Red River RV Resort (3mi)
0mm	Oklahoma/Texas state line, Red River

INTERSTATE 40

E ↕ W

Exit	Services
331mm	Oklahoma/Arkansas state line
330	OK 64D S (from eb), Ft Smith
325	US 64, Roland, Ft Smith, **N** ⛽ Cherokee Trkstp/Valero/Subway/dsl/scales/24hr, 🍴 Four Star Diner, 🛏 Cherokee Inn, Travelodge, ◻ casino, **S** ⛽ Pilot/Wendy's/dsl/scales/24hr, Shell/dsl/scales, Valero/dsl, 🍴 Arby's, El Celaya Mexican, McDonald's, Mazzio's, Sonic, Subway, Taco Bell, 🛏 Interstate Inn, ◻ $General, Marvin's Foods
321	OK 64b N, Muldrow, **N** 🍴 Sonic (1mi), **S** ⛽ Shell/dsl, 🛏 Best Value Inn, ◻ auto/dsl repair
316mm	**rest area eb, full ♿ facilities, info, ✆, ⛱, litter barrels, vending, petwalk**
313mm	**rest area wb, full ♿ facilities, info, ✆, ⛱, litter barrels, vending, petwalk, RV dump**
311	US 64, Sallisaw, **N** ⛽ Cox's/dsl, Ed's Truckstop/Phillips 66/diner/dsl, 🍴 Hardee's, KFC/Taco Bell, Pizza

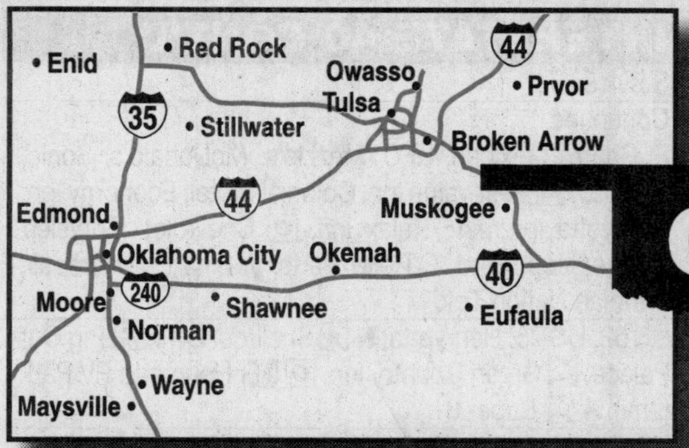

SALLISAW

Exit	Services
311	Continued Hut, Taco Mayo, 🛏 Motel 6, Sallisaw Inn, ◻ Ⓗ, AutoZone, Brushy Lake SP (10mi), $General, NAPA, Sequoya's Home (12mi), city park, USPO
308	US 59, Sallisaw, **N** ⛽ Murphy USA/dsl, Phillips 66/dsl, 🍴 A&W/LJ Silver, Arby's, Braum's, China Panda, Gino's Pizza, Mazzio's, McDonald's, Roma's Italian, Sonic, Subway, Taco Pronto, Western Sizzlin, 🛏 Best Value Inn, Blue Ribbon Inn, Days Inn, Golden Spur Motel, Super 8, ◻ Ⓗ, AT&T, $General, $Tree, Verizon, Walmart, antiques, casino, **S** ⛽ Shell/dsl, 🍴 Emma B's Diner, ◻ Buick/Chevrolet/GMC, Chrysler/Dodge/Jeep, Ford, KOA, to Kerr Lake, truck/tire repair
303	Dwight Mission Rd
297	OK 82 N, Vian, **N** ⛽ FL/dsl, 🍴 Subway, ◻ Cherokee Landing SP (24 mi), IGA Foods, to Tenkiller Lake RA (12 mi), USPO, **S** ◻ Sequoia NWR
291	OK 10 N, to Gore, **N** ◻ Greenleaf SP (10mi), Tenkiller SP (21mi)
290mm	Arkansas River
287	OK 100 N, to Webbers Falls, **N** ⛽ Loves/Subway/dsl/24hr, 🍴 Charlie's Chicken, Godfather's Pizza, 🛏 Sleepy Traveler Motel, ◻ Greenleaf SP, Tenkiller SP, parts/tires/repair
286	Muskogee Tpk, to Muskogee
284	Ross Rd
283mm	parking area both lanes, litter barrels
278	US 266, OK 2, Warner, **N** ⛽ Conoco, Phillips 66/dsl, Sinclair/McDonald's/dsl, 🍴 Duke's Diner, Simon's Pizza, Subway, 🛏 Sleepy Traveler Motel, ◻ $General, Parts+, city park
270	Texanna Rd, to Porum Landing, **S** ⛽ Sinclair
265	US 69 bus, Checotah, **N** ⛽ Quick'n Easy, 🍴 Pizza Hut, Sonic, **S** ⛽ Shell/dsl, 🛏 Budget Inn, ◻ Chevrolet/Chrysler/Dodge/Jeep
264b a	US 69, to Eufaula, 1 mi **N** ⛽ FLYING J/dsl/LP/scales/24hr, Phillips 66/dsl/24hr, 🍴 Charlie's Chicken, El Jarocho Pizza, McDonald's, Simple Simon's Pizza, Subway, 🛏 Best Value Inn, ◻ Ace Hardware, $General, O'Reilly Parts, TrueValue, Walmart/Subway, repair
262	to US 266, Lotawatah Rd, **N** ⛽ Sinclair
261mm	Lake Eufaula
259	OK 150, to Fountainhead Rd, **S** ⛽ Shell, 🛏 Lake Eufaula Inn, ◻ to Lake Eufaula SP
255	Pierce Rd, **N** KOA
251mm	rest area both lanes, no facilities
247	Tiger Mtn Rd, **S** ◻ Quilt Barn/antiques
240b a	US 62 E, US 75 N, Henryetta, **N** ⛽ Conoco/dsl, Loves/dsl, Phillips 66, Shell, Sinclair, 🍴 Arby's, Braum's,

INTERSTATE 40 CONT'D

H E N R Y E T T A   E ↕ W

Exit	Services
240b a	Continued
	El Charro Mexican, KFC, Mazzio's, McDonald's, Sonic, Subway, 🏠 Best Value Inn, Colonial Motel, Economy Inn, Henryetta Inn/rest., Relax Inn, 🅞 Chevrolet, Chrysler/Dodge/Jeep, Ford, O'Reilly Parts, Walmart, tires/repair, **S** Indian Nation Tpk
237	US 62, US 75, Henryetta, **N** 🅖 Shell/dsl/24hr, 🍴 Pig Out Palace, 🏠 Green Country Inn, 🅞 H, Henryetta RV Park (2mi), **S** 🏠 Super 8
231	US 75 S, to Weleetka, **N** 🅖 Phillips 66/dsl, 🍴 Cowpoke's Cafe
227	Clearview Rd, **S** casino
221	US 62, OK 27, Okemah, **N** 🅖 Shamrock, Valero/Subway/dsl/24hr, 🍴 Mazzio's, Sonic, 🏠 Days Inn, 🅞 H, Chevrolet, $General, Homeland Foods, NAPA, TrueValue, **S** 🅖 Loves/Chester Fried/dsl/24hr, Shell/dsl, 🍴 Kellogg's Rest; 🅞 casino, truck repair
217	OK 48, to Bristow, Bearden, **S** 🅖
216mm	N Canadian River
212	OK 56, to Cromwell, Wewoka, **N** 🅞 auto/tire repair, **S** 🅖 Shell/cafe/dsl, to Seminole Nation Museum
208mm	Gar Creek
202mm	Turkey Creek
200	US 377, OK 99, to Little, Prague, **N** 🅖 Bar H Bar TC/Shell/dsl/RV park, **S** 🅖 Conoco/dsl/24hr, Loves/Subway/dsl/24hr, Sinclair/dsl, 🍴 Robertson's Ham Sandwiches, Roundup Rest/RV Park, 🅞 H
197mm	**rest area both lanes, full ♿ facilities, 🅲, 🅰, litter barrels, petwalk**
192	OK 9A, Earlsboro, **S** 🅖 Shell/dsl
189mm	N Canadian River
186	OK 18, to Shawnee, **N** 🅖 Phillips 66, Sinclair, 🍴 Denny's, 🏠 American Inn, Best Value Inn, Comfort Inn, Days Inn, La Quinta, Motel 6, Super 8, **S** 🍴 Sonic, Van's BBQ, 🅞 Cadillac/Chevrolet/GMC, Chrysler/Dodge/Jeep, Ford, Homeland Foods, vet
185	185 OK 3E, Shawnee Mall Dr, to Shawnee, **N** 🅖 Murphy USA/dsl, 🍴 Buffalo Wild Wings, Chili's, KFC, Red Lobster, Santa Fe Steaks, Taco Bueno, Wendy's, 🏠 Holiday Inn Express, 🅞 AT&T, Dillard's, $Tree, JC Penney, Old Navy, Radio Shack, Ross, Sears/auto, Walgreens, Walmart/McDonald's, mall, **S** 🅖 Phillips 66/Circle K/Quiznos/dsl, 🍴 Braum's, Burger King, Cracker Barrel, Delta Cafe, Garfield's Rest., IHOP, Mazzio's, McAlister's Deli, McDonald's, Popeye's, Sonic, Starbucks, Subway, Taco Bell, Whataburger, 🏠 Hampton Inn, 🅞 CVS Drug, Kwik Kar, Lowe's, Staples
181	US 177, US 270, to Tecumseh, **S** 🏠 Budget Inn
180mm	N Canadian River
178	OK 102 S, Dale, **N** 🅖 Firelake/dsl/casino
176	OK 102 N, McLoud Rd, **S** 🅖 Loves/Subway/dsl/24hr, Sinclair/dsl, 🍴 Curtis Watson Rest.
172	Newalla Rd, to Harrah
169	Peebly Rd
166	Choctaw Rd, to Woods, **N** 🅞 KOA, **S** 🍴 Sonic, 🅞 to Lake Thunderbird SP (11mi)
165	I-240 W (from wb), to Dallas
162	Anderson Rd, **N** Leisure Time RV Ctr, LP
159b	Douglas Blvd, **N** 🅖 Conoco, Shell, 🍴 Denny's, LJ Silver, McDonald's, Sonic, Subway, Taco Bell, 🅞 Eastland Hills RV Park, **S** 🅞 Tinker AFB, H

S H A W N E E

O K L A H O M A   C I T Y

Exit	Services
159a	Hruskocy Gate, **N** 🅖 Shell, 🍴 Denny's, McDonald's, Taco Bell, 🅞 Dodge, Family$, Nissan, U-Haul, same as 157, **S** Gate 7, Tinker AFB
157c	Eaker Gate, Tinker AFB, same as 159
157b	Air Depot Blvd, **N** 🅖 Shell/Circle K, 🍴 Chick-fil-A, Chili's, Logans Roadhouse, Old Chicago Grill, Panda Express, Pizza Inn, Qdoba Grill, Santa Fe Steaks, Starbucks, Steak & Shake, 🏠 Super 8, 🅞 Best Buy, Target, Firestone, JC Penney, Kohl's, Lowe's Whse, Marshall's, O'Reilly Parts, PetsMart, Target, **S** Gate 1, Tinker AFB
157a	SE 29th St, Midwest City, **N** 🅖 Conoco/dsl, Shell, 🏠 Best Western, Super 8, 🅞 O'Reilly Parts, **S** 🅞 Ford, Sam's Club/gas
156b a	Sooner Rd, **N** 🅖 Conoco/Circle K, 🍴 Primo's Rest., Waffle House, 🏠 Comfort Inn, Hampton Inn, Hawthorn Suites, Holiday Inn Express, La Quinta, Sheraton, Studio 6, 🅞 Home Depot, Nissan, Radio Shack, Walmart/Subway, **S** 🍴 Buffalo Wild Wings, 🏠 Motel 6, 🅞 Chevrolet/GMC, Tires+, Toyota/Scion
155b	SE 15th St, Del City, **N** 🅖 Shell, 🅞 Family$, **S** 🍴 Madison's Kitchen
155a	Sunny Lane Rd, Del City, **N** 🅖 Conoco/dsl, 🅞 Hyundai, U-Haul, **S** 🅖 Shell, Shamrock, 🍴 Braum's, Dunkin Donuts, Sonic, 🅞 Ace Hardware, $General
154	Reno Ave, Scott St, **N** 🅖 Sinclair, 🏠 Value Place Motel, **S** 🅖 Phillips 66/dsl, 7-11/gas
152	(153 from wb)I-35 N, to Wichita
127	Eastern Ave (from eb), Okla City, **N** 🅖 Petro/Mobil/dsl/scales/rest./@, JR's Trvl Crt/Corky's Grill/dsl/24hr, Shamrock, 🍴 Waffle House, 🏠 Bricktown Hotel, Econolodge, Quality Inn, 🅞 Blue Beacon, Lewis RV Ctr
151b c	I-35, S to Dallas, I-235 N, to downtown, st capitol
151a	Lincoln Blvd, **N** 🅖 Conoco/Subway/Circle K/dsl, 🍴 Earl's Rib Palace, Falcon's Pizza, IHOP, Sonic, 🏠 Residence Inn, Hampton Inn, 🅞 Bass Pro Shop, Bricktown Stadium
150c	Robinson Ave (from wb), OK City, **N** 🍴 Spaghetti Whse, Zio's Italian, 🏠 Courtyard, Residence Inn, Westin Hotel, 🅞 U-Haul, Ford Ctr
150b	Harvey Ave (from eb), downtown, **N** 🏠 Courtyard, Renaissance Hotel, Sheraton, Westin Hotel, 🅞 Ford
150a	Walker Ave (from eb), **N** 🍴 La Luna Mexican, 🅞 Ford/Lincoln/Mercury, **S** transmissions
149b	Classen Blvd (from wb), same as 149a, to downtown
149a	Western Ave, Reno Ave, **N** 🅖 Valero/Subway/dsl, 🍴 China Queen, McDonald's, Sonic, Taco Bell, **S** 🅖 Conoco/dsl, Shell, 🍴 Sweis Gyros
148c	Virginia Ave (from wb), to downtown
148b	Penn Ave (from eb), **N** 🅖 Shamrock, **S** 🅞 Isuzu Trucks
148a	Agnew Ave, Villa Ave, **N** 🅖 Phillips 66/dsl
147c	May Ave
147b a	I-44, E to Tulsa, W to Lawton
146	Portland Ave (from eb, no return), **N** 🅖 Conoco/Subway/dsl, 🅞 water funpark
145	Meridian Ave, OK City, **N** 🅖 Conoco/Circle K/dsl, Shell/Circle K/dsl, 🍴 Cimarron Steakhouse, Denny's, Jin Wei Aisan, Louie's Grill, Mango's, McDonald's, On the Border, Portofinos Italian, Shorty Small's Rest., Trapper's Rest., 🏠 Best Western, Biltmore Hotel, Days Inn, Extended Stay America, Howard Johnson, Red Roof Inn, Residence Inn, Super 8, 🅞 USPO, **S** 🅖 Phillips 66/Circle K/dsl, Sinclair, 🍴 Arby's, Burger King, Charleston Rest., Chili's,

OK

🅶 = gas 🍴 = food 🛏 = lodging 🅾 = other

INTERSTATE 40 CONT'D

Exit	Services
145	Continued

Cracker Barrel, El Sombrero, Golden Palace Chinese, IHOP, Kona Ranch Steaks, Mackie's Steaks, Panera Bread, Pearl's Fish House, Poblano's, Quiznos, Rib Crib, Riggin's Grill, Sonic, Subway, Taco Bell, Taco Bueno, Waffle House, Whataburger, Zapata's, Zio's Italian, 🛏 Baymont Inn, Best Value Inn, Candlewood Suites, Clarion Hotel, Comfort Suites, Caountry Inn&Suites, Courtyard, Embassy Suites, Fairfield Inn, Governors Suites, Hampton Inn, Hilton Garden, Holiday Inn, Holiday Inn Express, Hyatt Place, La Quinta, Meridian Inn, Motel 6, Oak Tree Inn, Ramada Ltd, Regency Inn, Sleep Inn, Staybridge Suites, Wingate Inn, Wyndham Garden, 🅾 Celebration Sta., Shepler's

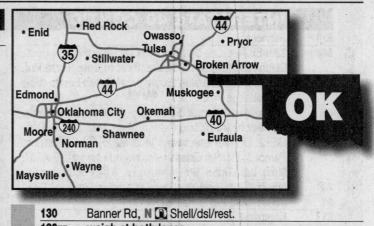

Exit	Services
144	MacArthur Blvd, N 🅶 Shell/Circle K/dsl, 🍴 Applebee's, Coldstone, Golden Corral, Jack-in-the-Box, KFC, Lin's Buffet, McDonald's, Panda Express, Quizno's, Ryan's, Sonic, Starbucks, Steak'n'Shake, Taco Cabana, TX Roadhouse, 🛏 SpringHill Suites, 🅾 AT&T, $Tree, GNC, Hobby Lobby, Office Depot, Petsmart, Radio Shack, Ross, Walmart, S 🛏 Comfort Inn, Green Carpet Inn, Microtel, Super 10 Motel, Travelers Inn, 🅾 Kenworth, Sam's Club/gas, dsl repair
143	Rockwell Ave, N 🅶 Shell/dsl, 🍴 Buffalo Wild Wings, Mike's Subs, Taco Bell, 🛏 Homewood Suites, Rodeway Inn, 🅾 Best Buy, Camping World/McClain's RV Ctr, Discount Tire, Harley Davidson, Home Depot, Tires+, S 🛏 Sands Motel/RV Park/LP, 🅾 Rockwell RV Park, A-OK RV Park
142	Council Rd, N 🅶 Shell, Sinclair, 🍴 Braum's, McDonald's, Subway, Taco Bell, 🛏 Super 40 Inn, 🅾 Goodyear/auto, S 🅶 TA/Country Pride/dsl/scales/24hr/@, 🛏 EconoLodge, 🅾 Council Rd RV Park, Ford/Peterbilt, dsl repair, truckwash
140	Morgan Rd, N 🅶 🅿/McDonald's/dsl/24hr/@, TA/Popeye's/dsl/24hr/@, 🅾 Blue Beacon, S 🅶 ✈FLYING J /dsl/LP/scales/24hr, ❤Loves/Subway/dsl/scales/24hr, 🍴 Ricky's Cafe, Sonic, 🅾 Speedco
139	Kilpatrick Tpk
138	OK 4, to Yukon, Mustang, N 🛏 Best Value Inn, Comfort Suites, 🅾 Chrysler/Dodge/Jeep, S 🅶 Conoco/Circle K/dsl, 🍴 Braum's, Burger King, Hunan Express, IHOP, Interurban Grill, McDonald's, Sonic, Subway, 🛏 Best Western, La Quinta, 🅾 URGENT CARE, CVS Drug, Homeland Food/drug, Cottman Transmissions
137	Cornwell Dr, Czech Hall Rd, N Homeland Food/drug
136	OK 92, Garth Brooks Blvd, Yukon, N 🅶 Murphy USA/dsl, Shell/Circle K, 🍴 A&W/LJ Silver, Braum's, CiCi's Pizza, Harry's Rest., KFC, McDonald's, Primo's Italian, Subway, Taco Mayo, Waffle House, Wendy's, Yukon Buffet, 🛏 Hampton Inn, 🅾 AutoZone, Big Lots, Big O Tire, $Tree, GNC, Hancock Fabrics, Hastings Books, Radio Shack, Tuesday Morning, Verizon, Walmart, Walgreens, USPO, repair, S 🍴 Alfredo's, Carino's Italian, Chick-fil-A, Chili's, Jimmy's Egg Café, Logan's Roadhouse, Louie's Grill, Mike's Subs, Pizza Hut, Quiznos, Rib Crib, Santa Fe Steaks, Starbucks, Taco Bueno, 🛏 Holiday Inn Express, 🅾 🅷, Discount Tire, Ford, Kohl's, Kwik Kar, Lowe's, PetsMart, Staples, Target, Tires+
132	Cimarron Rd, S 🛏

Exit	Services
130	Banner Rd, N 🅶 Shell/dsl/rest.
129mm	**weigh st both lanes**
125	US 81, to El Reno, N 🅶 Conoco/dsl, ❤Loves/Subway/dsl, 🍴 China King, Serapio's Mexican, Taco Mayo, 🛏 Deluxe Inn, Economy Express, Super 8, 🅾 Buick/GMC, Chevrolet, Chrysler/Dodge/Jeep, $General, Ford/Lincoln/Mercury, S truck repair
123	Country Club Rd, to El Reno, N 🅶 Phillips 66, Murphy USA/dsl, Shell, Valero, 🍴 Arby's, Braum's, Burger King, Greatwall Chinese, KFC, Little Caesar's, Mazzio's, McDonald's, Pizza Hut, Subway, Taco Bell, 🛏 Motel 6, 🅾 🅷, AutoZone, Radio Shack, Walmart, Walgreens, S 🅶 🍴 Denny's, MT Mikes Steaks, 🛏 Baymont Inn, Best Western/RV Park, Days Inn, Regency Motel
119	Lp 40, to El Reno
115	US 270, to Calumet
111mm	picnic area eb, 🛏, litter barrels
108	US 281, to Geary, N 🅶 Shell/Subway/dsl/24hr, 🅾 KOA, Indian Trading Post, to Roman Nose SP, S 🅶 Phillips 66/dsl
105mm	S Canadian River
104	Methodist Rd
101	US 281, OK 8, Hinton, N to Roman Nose SP, S 🅶 ❤Loves/Chester's/Godfather's/Sonic/dsl/scales, 🍴 Subway, 🛏 Hinton Travel Inn, 🅾 Chevrolet, casino, picnic area, to Red Rock Canyon SP
95	Bethel Rd
94.5mm	picnic area wb, 🛏, litter barrels
88	OK 58, to Hydro, Carnegie
84	Airport Rd, N 🅶 Phillips 66/dsl/scales/24hr, 🍴 Lucille's Roadhouse, 🛏 Holiday Inn Express, Travel Inn, 🅾 🅷, Buick/Cadillac/Chevrolet/GMC, Chrysler/Dodge/Jeep, S Stafford Aerospace Museum
82	E Main St, Weatherford, N 🅶 Conoco/dsl, Phillips 66/dsl, Shell/dsl, Sinclair, Valero/dsl, 🍴 Arby's, Braum's, Carl's Jr, Jerry's Rest., KFC/Taco Bell, Little Caesars, Mark Rest., Mazzio's, McDonald's, Pizza Hut, Quiznos, Sonic, Subway, Taco Mayo, T-Bone Steaks, Vinicio's Mexican, 🛏 Best Western, Comfort Inn, Fairfield Inn, Scottish Inn, 🅾 🅷, Ace Hardware, $General, GNC, O'Reilly Parts, Walgreens, to SW OSU, S 🅾 Walmart
80a	(from eb), N 🅶 Conoco, 🅾 Ford
80	W Main St, Mountainview, Thomas, N 🛏 Best Value Inn
71	Custer City Rd, N 🅶 ❤Loves/Subway/dsl/24hr, 🅾 Cherokee Trading Post/rest.
69	Lp 40 (from wb), to Clinton, **2 mi** N 🍴 DQ, 🛏 Travel Inn
67.5mm	Washita River
66	US 183, Clinton, S 🅶 Shell/dsl, 🅾 Buick/Chevrolet/GMC, Ford

OK

INTERSTATE 40 CONT'D

Exit	Services
65a	10th St, Neptune Dr, Clinton, **N** 🍴 Branding Iron Rest., China King, Oakwood Steaks, Picante Grille, Pizza Hut, 🅑 Days Inn, Relax Inn, Super 8, 🅞 United Foods, **S** 🅑 EconoLodge
65	Gary Blvd, Clinton, **N** 🅖 Conoco, Shell/dsl, 🍴 Braum's, Del Rancho, KFC/Taco Bell, LJ Silver, Mazzio's, McDonald's, MT Mike's, Subway, Taco Mayo, 🅑 Budget Inn, Hampton Inn, Ramada Inn, Tradewinds Inn, 🅞 Ⓗ, AT&T, $General, K-Mart, Rte 66 Museum, **S** 🅑 Holiday Inn Express
62	Parkersburg Rd, **S** Hargus RV Ctr
61	Haggard Rd
57	Stafford Rd
53	OK 44, Foss, **N** to Foss RA, **S** gas/dsl
50	Clinton Lake Rd, **N** 🅞 KOA/LP/dsl
47	Canute, **S** 🅖 Shell, 🅑 Sunset Inn
41	OK 34 (exits left from eb), Elk City, **N** 🅖 Loves/Subway/dsl, Shell, 🍴 Home Cooking Rest., 🅑 Best Value Inn (3mi), Best Western (3mi), Economy Express, Elk City Motel, HomeTowne Inn, Motel 6, Super 8, Travel Inn, 🅞 Ⓗ, Elk Run RV Park, Rte 66 Museum
40	E 7th St, Elk City, **N** 🍴 Portobello Grill, **S** 🅑 Hampton Inn, 🅞 Walmart, same as 41
38	OK 6, Elk City, **N** 🅖 Conoco/dsl, Phillips 66/dsl, 🍴 Arby's, China Super Buffet, Denny's, LJ Silver, McDonald's, Quizno's, Western Sizzlin, 🅑 Bedford Inn, Days Inn, 🅞 Ace Hardware, Elk Creek RV Park, tires, vet, **S** 🅖 Phillips 66/dsl, 🅑 Clarion Inn, Comfort Inn, Ramada Inn, Rodeway Inn, 🅞 to Quartz Mtn SP
34	Merritt Rd
32	OK 34 S (exits left from eb), Elk City
26	Cemetery Rd, **N** dsl repair, **S** 🅖 TA/Taco Bell/Subway/dsl/scales/24hr/@
25	Lp 40, Sayre, **1 mi N** 🅖 Shell/dsl, 🅑 Western Motel, 🅞 Ⓗ, Chevrolet/GMC, Deep Creek RV Park, $General, Ford
23	OK 152, Sayre, **S** 🅖 Shell/dsl
22.5mm	N Fork Red River
20	US 283, Sayre, **N** 🅖 ✈FLYING J/Denny's/dsl/LP/RV dump/scales/24hr, 🅑 AmericInn, 🅞 truckwash, to Washita Bfd Site (25mi)
14	Hext Rd
13.5mm	**check sta both lanes, litter barrels**
11	Lp 40, to Erick, Hext
10mm	**Welcome Ctr/rest area both lanes, full ♿ facilities, Ⓒ, 🚻, litter barrels, petwalk, RV dump**
7	OK 30, Erick, **N** 🅑 Premier Inn, **S** 🅖 Loves/Subway/dsl/scales, 🍴 Simple Simon's Pizza, 🅑 Days Inn
5	Lp 40, Honeyfarm Rd
1	Texola, **S** 🅖 gas/dsl/rest., 🅞 RV camping
0mm	Oklahoma/Texas state line

INTERSTATE 44

Exit	Services
329mm	Oklahoma/Missouri state line
321mm	Spring River
314mm	**Oklahoma Welcome Ctr, info, restrooms**
313	OK 10, Miami, **N** 🅖 Conoco, Loves/dsl/24hr, Phillips 66, SnakAtak/dsl, 🍴 Donut Palace, Okie Burger, 🅑 Best Western/rest., Deluxe Inn, Econolodge, Hampton

Exit	Services
313	Continued Inn, Holiday Inn Express, Microtel, Super 8, 🅞 Ⓗ, Miami RV Park, to NE OK A&M Coll, vet, **S** 🅞 Chrysler/Dodge/Jeep, casino
312mm	Neosho River
302	US 59, US 69, Afton, **S** 🅖 Conoco/dsl, 🍴 Subway, **3 mi S** 🅑 OK 66 Motel
299mm	**rest area eb, rest rooms, 🚻, litter barrel**
289	US 60, Vinita, **N** 🅖 Murphy USA/dsl, 🍴 Braum's, Clanton's Cafe, McDonald's, Pizza Hut, Sonic, Subway, Woodshed Deli, 🅑 Holiday Inn Express, 🅞 Ⓗ, Ace Hardware, AT&T, Chevrolet, O'Reilly Parts, Walmart, st patrol
288mm	**service plaza both lanes**, Phillips 66/dsl/24hr, McDonald's, Ⓒ
286mm	toll plaza
283	US 69, Big Cabin, **N** 🅖 Shell/Big Cabin/dsl/rest./scales/24hr/@/repair, 🅑 Super 8, 🅞 rv park, trk repair
271mm	picnic eb, 🚻, litter barrel
269	OK 28 (from eb, no re-entry), to Adair, Chelsea
269mm	**rest area eb, rest rooms, 🚻, litter barrel**
256mm	**rest area wb, rest rooms, 🚻, litter barrel, Ⓒ**
255	OK 20, to Pryor, Claremore, **0-2 mi N** 🅖 Kum&Go, Murphy USA/dsl, 🍴 Carl's Jr, Chili's, Woody's Cafe, 🅑 Best Western, Clairmore Inn, Super 8, Travel Inn, Will Rogers Inn, 🅞 Ⓗ, Curves, Walgreens, Walmart, to Rogers U, Will Rogers Memorial, museum
248	to OK 266, Port of Catoosa, **N** 🅖 QT, 🅑 Comfort Inn, Will Rogers Inn
244mm	Kerr-McClellan Navigation System
241mm	Will Rogers Tpk begins eb, ends wb, Ⓒ
241	OK 66 E, to Catoosa
240b	US 412 E, Choteau
240a	OK 167 N, 193rd E Ave, **N** 🍴 KFC, McDonald's, Taco Bell, Taco Bueno, Waffle House, Wendy's, 🅑 Cherokee Inn/Casino, Hampton Inn, Hardrock Hotel/Casino, 🅞 KOA, Walgreens, **S** 🅖 QT, 🍴 Mazzio's, PortCity Diner, Sonic, Subway, 🅑 Holiday Inn Express, 🅞 $General, O'Reilly Parts, tires/repair
238	161st E Ave, **N** 🅖 Sinclair/dsl/scales/rest./24hr, 🅞 Goodyear Trk Tires, truckwash, **S** 🅖 QT/dsl/scales/24hr, 🍴 Arby's, Burger King, 🅑 Microtel, 🅞 OK Welcome Ctr, Walker RV Ctr
236b	I-244 W, to downtown Tulsa ↘
236a	129th E Ave, **N** 🅖 ✈FLYING J/Denny's/dsl/LP/24hr, **S** 🍴 McDonald's
235	E 11th St, Tulsa, **N** 🍴 Big Daddy's BBQ, Mazzio's, Rioberto's Mexican, Sonic, Subway, 🅑 Executive Inn, Garnett Inn, Motel 6, Super 8, 🅞 $General, Drug Whse, O'Reilly Parts, **S** 🅖 QT, 🍴 Braum's, Denny's, Taco Bueno, 🅑 Econolodge, 🅞 Whse Foods
234b a	US 169, N to Owasso, to ↘, S to Broken Arrow, **N** 🅖 QT, 🍴 Braum's, Mazzio's, 🅑 Motel 6, 🅞 $General, May's Drug, **S** 🅞 Whse Mkt
233	E 21st St, **S** 🍴 El Chico, 🅑 Comfort Suites, 🅞 K-Mart, Dean's RV Ctr, vet
231	(232 from wb), US 64, OK 51, to Muskogee, E 31st St, Memorial Dr, **N** 🍴 Whataburger, 🅑 Days Inn, Georgetown Plaza Hotel, Regency Inn, Tulsa Inn, **S** 🅖 Shell, 🍴 Cracker Barrel, IHOP, McDonald's, Pizza Hut, Ruby Tuesday, Village Inn, 🅑 Best Western, Comfort Suites, Courtyard, Econolodge, Embassy Suites, Fairfield Inn, Hampton Inn, Holiday Inn Express, Quality Inn, Sleep Inn, Super 8, 🅞 Cavender's Boots, Chevrolet, Harley-Davidson, Nissan

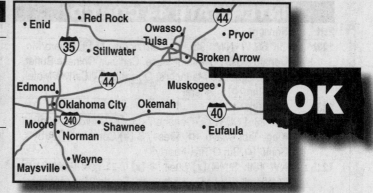

INTERSTATE 44 CONT'D

Exit	Services
230	E 41st St, Sheridan Rd, **N** 🍴 Carl's Jr, El Chico, On-the-Border, Panera Bread, Quizno's, Subway, TGIFriday, Whataburger/24hr, ⊙ AT&T, Barnes&Noble, Curves, Dillard's, JC Penney, Jo-Ann Fabrics, Michael's, Old Navy, Petsmart, Robertson Tire, Ross, **S** 🍴 Carino's Italian, 🛏 La Quinta, ⊙ Batteries+, Home Depot
229	Yale Ave, Tulsa, **N** ⛽ Shell, 🍴 McDonald's, ⊙ Firestone/auto, JC Penney, Macy's, Michael's, Old Navy, PetCo, Ross, mall, **S** ⛽ Phillips 66/dsl, QT/24hr, 🍴 Applebee's, Arby's, Braum's, Delta Cafe, Outback Steaks, Qdoba, Red Lobster, Smoothie King, Sonic, Taco Bell, Village Inn, 🛏 Baymont Inn, Days Inn, Red Roof Inn, Tulsa Select Hotel, ⊙ Ⓗ, Best Buy, Kia, vet
228	Harvard Ave, Tulsa, **N** 🍴 El Tequila Mexican, NYC Pizza, 🛏 Best Western, Tradewinds Motel, **S** 🍴 A&W/LJ Silver, Chili's, Chimi's Mexican, Freckle's Frozen Custard, Jamil's Rest, LoneStar Steaks, Marie Callender's, Mario's Pizza, Osaka Steaks, Papa John's, Piccadilly Cafeteria, Starbucks, Subway, ⊙ $Tree, Food Pyramid, Hobby Lobby, K-Mart, SteinMart
227	Lewis Ave, Tulsa, **S** ⛽ Phillips 66, 🍴 El Chico, ⊙ Walgreens
226b	Peoria Ave, Tulsa, **N** ⛽ Kum&Go, QT, 🍴 Arby's, Biga Italian, Burger St., CiCi's, Egg Roll, La Hacienda Mexican, Mazzio's, KFC, Pizza Hut, Ron's Burgers/Chili, Subway, Taco Bell, Taco Buenco, Waffle House, 🛏 Peoria Inn, ⊙ Hancock Fabrics, Harley-Davidson, O'Reilly Parts, Radio Shack, Robertson Tire, vet, Walmart Mkt, **S** 🍴 Braum's, Golden Palace, ⊙ AutoZone, $General, Family$, May's Drug
226a	Riverside Dr
225mm	Arkansas River
225	Elwood Ave, **N** ⊙ Chevrolet, Ford, **S** 🛏 Budget Inn
224b a	US 75, to Okmulgee, Bartlesville, **N** ⛽ QT/dsl, 🍴 KFC, Mazzio's, Sonic, Subway, ⊙ $General, Whse Mkt, **S** 🛏 Royal Inn, ⊙ RV park
223c	33rd W Ave, Tulsa, **N** 🍴 Braum's, Domino's, **S** ⛽ Conoco, 🍴 Rib Crib BBQ, ⊙ U-Haul
223b	51st St (from wb)
223a	I-244 E, to Tulsa, downtown
222c	(from wb), **S** 🛏 Value Inn
222b	55th Place, **N** 🛏 Capri Motel, Crystal Motel, **S** 🛏 Days Inn, Economy Inn
222a	49th W Ave, Tulsa, **N** 🍴 Carl's Jr, Kelly's Country Cooking, Monterey Mexican, 🛏 Gateway Motel, Interstate Inn, Motel 6, Rest Inn, ⊙ BigLots, $General, **S** ⛽ QT/Wendy's/dsl/scales/24hr, 🍴 Arby's, McDonald's, Taco Bueno, Village Inn, Waffle House, 🛏 Super 8, ⊙ Buick/GMC, Freightliner, Peterbilt, Volvo Trucks
221a	57th W Ave, (from wb), **S** 🍴 Avalon Steaks, ⊙ Buick/GMC
221mm	Turner Tkp begins wb, ends eb
218	Creek Tpk E (from eb)
215	OK 97, to Sand Sprgs, Sapulpa, **S** ⛽ Kum&Go, 🍴 Arby's, Freddy's, Subway, Whataburger, 🛏 Super 8, ⊙ Ⓗ, Hunter RV Ctr, Route 66 RV Park
211	OK 33, to Kellyville, Drumright, Heyburn SP, **S** ⛽ Shell/dsl
207mm	service plaza wb, ⛽ Phillips 66/dsl
204mm	picnic area eb, litter barrels, 🚻

Exit	Services
197mm	service plaza eb, 🍴 McDonald's
196	OK 48, Bristow, **S** ⛽ Conoco/dsl, Phillips 66, 🍴 Mazzio's, Pizza Hut, Steak'nEgg Rest, Taco Mayo, 🛏 Carolyn Inn, ⊙ Ⓗ, Buick/Chevrolet, Ford, Walmart
190mm	picnic area eb, litter barrels, 🚻
182mm	toll plaza
179	OK 99, to Drumright, Stroud, **N** 🛏 Best Western/rest, **S** ⛽ Kids/dsl, Phillips 66/Subway/dsl, 🍴 5Star BBQ, Mazzio's, McDonald's, Mi Casa Mexican, Sonic, Vallarta's Rest, 🛏 Sooner Motel, ⊙ Ⓗ, auto/tire repair
178mm	**Hoback Plaza** (exits left), ⛽ Phillips 66/dsl, 🍴 McDonald's
171mm	picnic area eb, litter barrels, 🚻
167mm	service plaza (from eb), **S** ⛽ Phillips 66/dsl
166	OK 18, to Cushing, Chandler, **N** ⊙ Chrysler/Dodge/Jeep, **S** ⛽ Phillips 66, 🍴 Sonic, 🛏 Econolodge, Lincoln Motel, ⊙ Chandler Tire
166mm	picnic area wb, 🚻s, litter barrels, 🚻
158	OK 66, to Wellston, **N** ⛽ Kum&Go/Subway/dsl/24hr
157	service plaza (from wb), **N** 🍴 McDonald's ⊙ museum info
138d	to Memorial Rd, to Enterprise Square
138a	I-35, I-44 E to Tulsa, Turner Tpk
I-44 and I-35 run together 8 mi. See Interstate 35, exits 137-134.	
130	I-35 S, to Dallas, access to services on I-35 S
129	MLK Ave, Remington Park, **N** 🍴 County Line BBQ, 🛏 Garden Inn, ⊙ Cowboy Museum, **S** 🍴 McDonald's, ⊙ Family$
128b	Kelley Ave, OK City, **N** ⛽ Conoco, Valero/Subway/dsl, 🍴 Sonic
128a	Lincoln Blvd, st capitol, **S** 🛏 Oxford Inn, Whitten Inn
127	I-235 S, US 77, City Ctr, Broadway St, **1 exit N** ⛽ Conoco, Phillips 66/dsl, Shell, 🛏 Best Western, Holiday Inn
126	Western Ave, **N** 🍴 Camille's Cafe, Deep Fork Rest., Sonic, Flip's Rest.
125c	NW Expressway (exits left from sb)
125	Classen Blvd, (exits left from wb), OK City, **N** ⛽ Shell, 🍴 Cheesecake Factory, Chili's, Elephant Bar Rest., Moe's SW Grill, Olive Garden, ⊙ Acura, Dillard's, JC Penney, Macy's, Old Navy, Radio Shack, Ross, Walmart, **S** 🍴 IHOP, McDonald's, 🛏 AmeriSuites, Courtyard, Hawthorn Suites
125a	OK 3A, Penn Ave, to NW Expswy, **N** ⛽ Conoco/dsl/24hr, **S** ⛽ Shell, 🍴 Braum's, Coit's Cafe, 🛏 Habana Inn, ⊙ Homeland Foods,
124	N May, **W** ⛽ Shell/Subway, 🍴 San Marco's Mexican, 🛏 Comfort Inn, Day's Inn, Super 8, ⊙ Dodge, O'Reilly Parts, **S** ⊙ Aamco, Ford, Lowes Whse

Left margin: **E** ↑ ↓ **W**

Right margin: **OK** / **OKLAHOMA CITY**

INTERSTATE 44 CONT'D

Exit	Services
123b	OK 66 W, NW 39th, to Warr Acres, **N** 🅖 Valero/McDonald's/dsl, 🍴 Asian Palace, Carl's Jr, Chinese Buffet, Jimmy's Egg, Los Mariachi's, Quizno's, 🛏 Carlyle Motel, 🅗ity Inn, 🔵 $General
123a	NW 36th St
122	NW 23rd St, **N** 🅖 Conoco/7-11, 🍴 Church's, EggRoll King, Taco Mayo, 🔵 Tires+, **S** 🅖 Conoco, 🍴 Arby's, Sonic, 🔵 Big O Tire, Family$
121b a	NW 10th St, **N** 🅖 Shell, **S** 🅖 7-11/gas, Sinclair, 🔵 $General, Family$, Whittaker's Foods/24hr, antiques, fairgrounds
120b a	I-40, W to Amarillo, E to Ft Smith
119	SW 15th St
118	OK 152 W, SW 29th St, OK City, **E** 🅖 7-11/gas, 🔵 city park, 🍴 A&W/LJ Silver, Burger King, CiCi's Pizza, KFC/Taco Bell, McDonald's, Sonic, Subway, Taco Bueno, 🔵 Advance Parts, AutoZone, Buy-4-Less Foods, $General, $Tree, O'Reilly Parts, Walgreens, **W** 🅖 Shell, 🔵 U-Haul/LP, transmissions
117	SW 44th St, **W** auto repair
116b	Airport Rd (exits left from nb), **W**✈
116a	SW 59th St, **E** 🅖 Conoco, **W** Will Rogers ✈
115	I-240 E, US 62 E, to Ft Smith
114	SW 74th St, OK City, **E** 🅖 TK, Valero, 🍴 Braum's, Burger King, Perry's Rest., 🛏 Cambridge Inn, Ramada Ltd, 🔵 $General
113	SW 89th St, **E** 🅖 Loves/Subway/dsl/24hr, OG, 7-11/gas, Valero/dsl, 🍴 McDonald's, Sonic, Taco Mayo, 🔵 🅗, CVS Drug
112	SW 104th St, **E** 🅖 Valero, **W** 🅖 Shell/rest./dsl
111	SW 119th St, **E** 🍴 Sonic, 🔵 Walker RV Ctr
110	OK 37 E, to Moore, **E** 🅖 Sinclair/dsl, 🍴 Sonic
109	SW 149th St, **E** 🍴 JR's Grill
108mm	S Canadian River
108	OK 37 W, to Tuttle, **W** 🅖 Conoco/Subway/dsl, Phillips 66, 🍴 Braum's, Carlito's Mexican, Carl's Jr, Little Caesar's, Mazzio's, McDonald's, New China, Sonic, 🔵 $General, O'Reilly Parts, Walmart
107	US 62 S (no wb return), to Newcastle, **E** casino/gas, 🛏 Newcastle Motel, 🔵 Newcastle RV, Walker RV
99	H E Bailey Spur, rd 4, to Blanchard, Norman
97mm	toll booth, 🔵
95.5mm	picnic area wb, 🎇, litter barrels
85.5mm	**service plaza**, both lanes exit left, Phillips 66/dsl, McDonald's
83	US 62, Chickasha, **W** 🅖 Jay's/dsl, Valero/dsl, 🔵 Indian Museum
80	US 81, Chickasha, **E** 🅖 Conoco/dsl, Phillips 66/dsl, Shell/dsl, 🍴 Eduardo's Mexican, Western Sizzlin, 🛏 Day's Inn, Holiday Inn Express, Royal American Inn, Super 8, 🔵 🅗, Buick/Chevrolet/Cadillac, Chrysler/Dodge/Jeep, $Tree, , **W** 🅖 Conoco, Loves, Valero, 🍴 Arby's, Braum's, China Moon, Denny's, Domino's, El Rancho Mexican, KFC, LJ Silver, Mazzio's Pizza, McDonald's, Napoli's Rest., New China, Pizza Hut, Quizno's, Sonic, Taco Bell, Taco Mayo, 🛏 Best Western, Budget Motel, Ranch House Motel, 🔵 AutoZone, CVS Drug, Family$, Ford/Lincoln/Mercury, O'Reilly Parts, Radio Shack, Staples, Walmart/Subway/gas

Exit	Services
78mm	toll plaza, 🔵
63mm	picnic area wb, 🎇, litter barrels
62	to Cyril (from wb)
60.5mm	picnic area eb, tables, litter barrels
53	US 277, Elgin, Lake Ellsworth, **E** 🅖 Shamrock, 🍴 Goodcents Subs, Sonic, Taco Tico, **W** 🅖 Fina/dsl
46	US 62 E, US 277, US 281, to Elgin, Apache, Comanche Tribe, last free exit nb
45	OK 49, to Medicine Park, **W** 🅖 Loves/Subway/dsl/24hr, 🍴 Burger King, Sonic, 🔵 Whichita NWR
41	to Ft Sill, Key Gate, **W** Ft Sill Museum
40c	Gate 2, to Ft Sill
40a	US 62 W, to Cache, **E** 🅖 Fina/dsl, **W** 🛏 Super 8
39b	US 281 (from sb), **W** 🛏 Ramada Inn
39a	US 281, Cache Rd (exits left from nb), Lawton, **1-3 mi** 🅖 Phillips 66, Valero/dsl, 🍴 Applebee's, Braum's, Chili's, Chick-fil-A, Fire Mtn Grill, Golden Corral, KFC, Ryan's, Subway, Wendy's, 🛏 Baymont Inn, Holiday Inn, Super 8, Super 9 Motel, 🔵 $General, U-Haul, transmissions
37	Gore Blvd, Lawton, **E** 🅖 Conoco, 🍴 Braum's, Los Tres Amigos, Sonic, Taco Mayo, Woody's Mexican, 🛏 Best Western, 🔵 Curves, casino, **W** 🍴 Arby's (3mi), Cracker Barrel, Mike's Grille, 🛏 Fairfield Inn, Holiday Inn Express, Ramada Inn (2mi), SpringHill Suites, 🔵 Harley-Davidson, Lincoln/Mercury
36a	OK 7, Lee Blvd, Lawton, **E** 🅖 Phillips 66, **W** 🅖 Fina/dsl, repair, Shamrock/dsl, Suncountry/dsl, Welch/dsl, 🍴 Big Chef Rest., KFC/Taco Bell, Leo&Ken's Rest., Popeye's, Salas Mexican, Sonic, 🛏 Motel 6, 🔵 🅗, $General, ✈, vet
33	US 281, 11th St, Lawton, **W** 🔵 🅗, 🅖, 🍴 lodging, ✈, to Ft Sill
30	OK 36, Geronimo
20.5mm	**Elmer Graham Plaza**, both lanes exit left, Phillips 66/dsl, McDonald's, info
20	OK 5, to Walters, **E** 🍴 BBQ
19.5mm	toll plaza
5	US 277 N, US 281, Randlett, last free exit nb, **E** 🅖 Shamrock/dsl
1	OK 36, to Grandfield
0mm	Oklahoma/Texas state line, Red River

INTERSTATE 240 (Oklahoma City)

Exit	Services
16mm	I-240 begins/ends on I-40.
14	Anderson Rd, **S** 🅖 Conoco
11b a	Douglas Blvd, **N** Tinker AFB
9	Air Depot Blvd
8	OK 77, Sooner Rd, **N** 🅖 Shell/dsl, 🍴 Sonic, **S** 🅖 Phillips 66/Popeye's/dsl, Valero/McDonald's/dsl, 🔵 🅗
7	Sunnylane Ave, **S** 🅖 Valero/Subway/dsl, 🛏 Value Place Motel
6	Bryant Ave
5	S Eastern Ave
4c	Pole Rd, **N** 🍴 Burger King, Subway, TX Roadhouse, Zeke's Grill, 🛏 Fairfield Inn, Ramada Inn, Residence Inn, 🔵 URGENT CARE, Best Buy, Tires+
4b a	I-35, N to OK City, S to Dallas, US 77 S, US 62/77 N
3b	S Shields, **N** 🅖 Valero/dsl, 🔵 Dodge, Home Depot, **S** 🔵 Discount Tire, Nissan, Subaru
3a	S Santa Fe, **S** 🅖 Murphy USA/dsl, Shell, 🍴 Chili's, IHOP, Mike's Subs, 🔵 Buick, Staples, Lowe's, Walmart

E ▲ **W** (I-44 margin: LAWTON, CHICKASHA, OK)
E ▲ **W** (I-240 margin)

INTERSTATE 240 CONT'D (Oklahoma City)

Exit	Services
2b	S Walker Ave, N 📌 7-11, Shell/Circle K, 🍴 Rib Crib, S 🍴 Carino's, ChuckeCheese, City Bites, Coach's Grill, Jimmy's Egg Grill, On-the-Border, Primo's Italian, ⊡ URGENT CARE, PepBoys
2a	S Western Ave, N 📌 Conoco, 7-11, 🍴 Burger King, CiCi's Pizza, House of Szechwan, Nino's Mexican, Taste of China, ⊡ Advance Parts, $General, Hyundai, Tires+, vet, S 📌 7-11, Valero/dsl, 🍴 A&W/LJ Silver, Arby's, Grandy's, Hibachi Buffet, KFC, Krispy Kreme, McDonald's, Red Lobster, 🛏 Best Western, Comfort Inn, Hampton Inn, Quality Inn, ⊡ Big O Tire, Chevrolet, Home Depot, Honda, Office Depot, Tire Factory

OKLAHOMA CITY

1c	S Penn Ave, N 📌 Conoco, 🍴 Carl's Jr, Charleston's Rest., Denny's, Golden Corral, Harrigan's Rest., Hooters, Old Chicago Pizza, Olive Garden, Outback Steaks, Pioneer Pies, SaltGrass Steaks, Santa Fe Grill, Schlotsky's, ⊡ AT&T, BigLots, GNC, Hobby Lobby, Marshall's, Michaels, Old Navy, Radio Shack, Ross, Verizon, S 📌 Shell/Circle K, 🍴 August Moon, Hunan Buffet, Joe's Crabshack, Mazzio's, Pancho's Mexican, Papa John's, Starbucks, Subway, Taco Bueno, Wendy's, Western Sizzlin, ⊡ $Tree, Hancock Fabrics
1b	S May Ave, N 📌 7-11/gas, 🍴 Abel's Mexican, Durango Mexican, Taco Bell, Waffle House, ⊡ O'Reilly Parts, S 📌 Valero, 🍴 Burger King, Perry's Rest., 🛏 Cambridge Inn, Ramada Ltd, ⊡ $General
1a	I-44, US 62, I-240 begins ends on I-44.

OREGON

INTERSTATE 5

Exit	Services
308.5mm	Oregon/Washington state line, Columbia River
308	Jansen Beach Dr, E 📌 Chevron/dsl, 🍴 Burger King, Hooters, Starbucks, Taco Bell, 🛏 Oxford Suites, Red Lion, ⊡ Safeway, W 🍴 BJ's Rest., Bradley's Grill, Denny's, McDonald's, Original Joe's, Stanford's Rest., Starbucks, Subway, ⊡ Barnes&Noble, Best Buy, Home Depot, Jansen Beach RV Park, Michael's, Office Depot, Old Navy, PetCo, Ross, Michael's, Staples, Target
307	OR 99E S, MLK Blvd, Union Ave, Marine Dr (sb only), E 📌 Jubitz Trvl Ctr/rest/dsl/@, 76/dsl, 🍴 Portland Cascade Grill, 🛏 Courtyard, Fairfield Inn, Portlander Inn, Residence Inn, ⊡ Blue Beacon, Expo Ctr, truck repair
306b	Interstate Ave, Delta Park, E 📌 76, 🍴 Burger King, Elmer's, Mars Meadows Chinese, Shari's, 🛏 Best Western, Days Inn, Motel 6, ⊡ Baxter Parts, Dick's, Lowe's, Portland Meadows
306a	Columbia (from nb), same as 306b
305b a	US 30, Lombard St (from nb, no return), E 🍴 Little Caesar's, ⊡ Knecht's Parts, W 📌 Astro/dsl, Shell/dsl, 🍴 Panda Express, Subway, Wendy's, ⊡ Fred Meyer
304	Rosa Parks Way, U of Portland, W 📌 Arco, 76/dsl, 🍴 Nite Hawk Cafe, Taco Time, 🛏 Viking Motel
303	Alberta St, Swan Island, E 🄷, W 🍴 Subway, Taco Bell, 🛏 Monticello Motel, Westerner Motel, ⊡ CarQuest
302b	I-405, US 30 W, W to ocean beaches, zoo
302a	Rose Qtr, City Ctr, E 📌 76/Circle K/dsl, Shell/dsl, 🍴 Bellagio's Pizza, Burger King, Chipotle Mexican, McDonald's, Qdoba Mexican, Starbucks, Taco Bell, Wendy's, 🛏 Crowne Plaza, Shiloh Inn, ⊡ 🄷, KIA, Toyota/Scion, Schwab Tire, 7-11, Walgreens, W ⊡ coliseum
301	I-84 E, US 30 E, services E off I-84 exits
300	US 26 E (from sb), Milwaukie Ave, W 🛏 Hilton, Marriott
299b	I-405, US 26 W, to city ctr
299a	US 26 E, OR 43 (from nb), City Ctr, to Lake Oswego
298	Corbett Ave
297	Terwilliger Blvd, W 🍴 Baja Fresh, KFC, La Costita, Starbucks, ⊡ 🄷, Fred Meyer, to Lewis and Clark Coll.
296b	Multnomah Blvd (from sb), same as 296a
296a	(from sb), Barbur, W 📌 Chevron, 76/dsl, 🍴 Bellagio's Pizza, Original Pancake House, Subway, Taco Del Mar, 🛏 Aladdin Inn, Budget Lodge, Capitol Hill Motel, ⊡ 7-11, Schwab Tire

295	Capitol Hwy (from sb), Taylors Ferry Rd (from nb), E 📌 Shell/dsl, 🍴 Juan Colorado Mexican, Koji Japanese, McDonald's, RoundTable Pizza, Starbucks, 🛏 ℍity Inn, W 🍴 Taco Time, Wendy's
294	Barbur Blvd, OR 99W, to Tigard, E 🛏 Comfort Suites, W 📌 Chevron, Shell, 🍴 Arby's, Baja Fresh, Banning's Rest., Baskin-Robbins, Burger King, Buster's BBQ, Chang's Mongolian Grill, Gators Eatery, King's Buffet, Little Caesar's, Mazatlan Mexican, McDonald's, Newport Bay Rest., Quiznos, Starbucks, Subway, Taco Bell, TCBY, 🛏 Quality Inn, Regency Inn, ⊡ Americas Tire, Baxter Parts, Costco, Fred Meyer, JoAnn Fabrics, NAPA, PetCo, Radio Shack, Schwab Tire, U-Haul, Winco Foods, transmissions, vet
293	Haines St, W ⊡ Ford/Lincoln/Mercury
292	OR 217, Kruse Way, Lake Oswego, E 📌 Shell/dsl, 🍴 Applebee's, Chevy's Mexican, Olive Garden, Oswego Grill, Quiznos, Stanford's Rest., Starbucks, Taco Del Mar, 🛏 Crowne Plaza, Fairfield Inn, Hilton Garden, Phoenix Inn, Residence Inn, ⊡ AAA, Curves, LDS Temple, W 🛏 Homestead Suites, ⊡ Lowe's
291	Carman Dr, , W 📌 Chevron, 76/dsl, 🍴 Burgerville, Domino's, El Sol De Mexico, Starbucks, Subway, Sweet Tomatoes, 🛏 Courtyard, Holiday Inn Express, ⊡ Home Depot, Office Depot
290	Lower Boonsferry Rd, Lake Oswego, E 📌 Chevron/dsl, Space Age/dsl/LP, 🍴 Arby's, Baja Fresh, Baskin-Robbins, Burger King, Carl's Jr., Fuddruckers, Miller's Rest., Panda Express, Starbucks, Subway, Taco Bell, Wu's Kitchen, 🛏 Motel 6, ⊡ Dick's, Safeway Foods, Walgreens, W 🍴 CA Pizza Kitchen, Claim Jumper, Jamba Juice, Jimmy John's, Macaroni Grill, McCormick&Schmick's, Pastini Pastaria, PF Chang's, Qdoba Mexican, Royal Panda, Starbucks, Village Inn, 🛏 Grand Hotel, ⊡ Verizon, Whole Foods Mkt
289	Tualatin, E 📌 76, Shell/dsl, 🍴 Chipotle Mexican, Famous Dave's BBQ, McDonald's, Panera Bread, Subway, ⊡ Best Buy, GNC, Old Navy, Petsmart, Portland RV Park, 7-11, W 🍴 Applebee's, Coldstone, Hayden's Grill, Jack-in-the-Box, Outback Steaks, Pizza Hut, Quiznos, Starbucks, Taco Bell, Thai Bistro, Wendy's, 🛏 Century Hotel, ⊡ 🄷, Fred Meyer, Haggen's Foods, K-Mart, Michael's, O'Reilly Parts, Radio Shack, camping
288	I-205, to Oregon City
286	Elligsen Rd, Boonsferry Rd, Stafford, E 📌 76/dsl, 🍴

OK

OR

W I L S O N V I L L E

N ↑ ↓ S

S A L E M

OR

INTERSTATE 5 CONT'D

Exit	Services
286	Continued
	Burger King, Moe's SW Grill, Panda Express, Pizza Schmizza, Starbucks, Subway, 🛏 La Quinta, Super 8, ⊙ Costco/gas, Mercedes, Office Depot, Petsmart, Pheasant Ridge RV Resort, Target, Verizon, **W** ⛽ Chevron, 🍴 Big Town Hero, 🛏 Holiday Inn/rest., ⊙ Audi, Camping World RV Ctr, Chevrolet, Dodge, Nissan, Toyota/Scion
283	Wilsonville, **E** ⛽ 76/dsl, 🍴 Abella Italian, Arby's, Bellagio's Pizza, Boston's Grill, Denny's, Jamba Juice, Juan Colorado, McDonald's, Papa Murphy's, Red Robin, Shari's, Starbucks, Subway, Taco Bell, Taco Del Mar, Wanker's Café, Wendy's, Wong's Chinese, 🛏 GuestHouse Inn, Quality Inn, SnoozInn, ⊙ AT&T, Fry's Electronics, GNC, Honda, Lamb's Foods, NAPA, Rite Aid, Schwab Tire, USPO, funpark, **W** ⛽ Chevron, 🍴 Baskin-Robbins, Burger King, Domino's, Hunan Kitchen, Sonic, Starbucks, Wilsonville Grill, 🛏 Wilsonville Inn, ⊙ Albertson's, Fred Meyer, 7-11, Walgreens, auto repair
282.5mm	Willamette River
282	Charbonneau District, **E** 🍴 Langdon Farms Rest., ⊙ Langdon Farms Golf
281.5mm	**rest area both lanes, full ♿ facilities, 📞, info, 🚮, litter barrels, petwalk, vending, coffee**
278	Donald, **E** ⛽ 76/dsl/LP, ⊙ Aurora Acres RV Park, **W** ⛽ Shell/dsl, TA/Country Pride/Popeye's/dsl/scales/24hr/@, ⊙ SpeedCo Lube, truckwash, to Champoeg SP
274mm	**weigh sta both lanes**
271	OR 214, Woodburn, **E** ⛽ Arco/dsl, Chevron, 76/repair, 🍴 Burger King, Country Cottage Rest., DQ, Denny's, KFC, McDonald's/playplace, Subway, Taco Bell, 🛏 Best Western, Super 8, ⊙ Fairway Drug, Walgreens, Walmart/McDonald's, vet, **W** ⛽ Shell, 🍴 Arby's, Elmer's, Jack-in-the-Box, Jamba Juice, Quiznos, Starbucks, 🛏 La Quinta, ⊙ Ford, Tire Factory, Woodburn RV Park, Woodburn Outlets/famous brands
263	Brooks, Gervais, **E** ⛽ 76/dsl, ⊙ Brooks Mkt/deli, **W** ⛽ 🍴/Subway/Taco Bell/dsl/LP/scales/24hr, 🍴 Chalet Rest., ⊙ Freightliner, Willamette Mission SP (4mi)
260b a	OR 99E, Chemawa Rd, Keizer, **2 mi E** camping, **W** 🍴 Burger King, Jamba Juice, Panda Express, RoundTable Pizza, Starbucks, Subway, Taco Del Mar, ⊙ AT&T, Lowe's, Marshall's, Michael's, Old Navy, PetCo, Ross, Staples, Target, Verizon, World Mkt
259mm	45th parallel, halfway between the equator and N Pole
258	N Salem, **E** ⛽ 76/Circle K, 🍴 Figaro's Italian, Guesthouse Rest., McDonald's, Original Pancake House, 🛏 Best Western, Rodeway Inn, ⊙ Al's RV Ctr, 5 RV Park, Hwy RV Ctr, Roth's Foods, **W** ⛽ Arco, 76/Circle K, Pacific Pride/dsl, Shell/dsl, 🍴 Don Pedro Mexican, Jack-in-the-Box, LumYuen Chinese, 🛏 Budget Lodge, Travelers Inn, ⊙ Stuart's Parts, to st capitol
256	to OR 213, Market St, Salem, **E** 🍴 Alberto's Mexican, Chalet Rest., Denny's, Elmer's, 🛏 Cozzzy Inn, Days Inn, ⊙ Fred Meyer/dsl, **E on Lancaster** ⛽ 76/dsl, 🍴 Arby's, Baja Fresh, Blue Willow Rest., Carl's Jr, China Buffet, El Mirador Mexican, 5 Guys Burgers, Izzy's Rest., Jack-in-the-Box, Olive Garden, Outback Steaks, Quiznos, Sizzler, Skipper's, Subway, Taco Bell, ⊙ Americas Tire, BigLots, Sears/auto, Schwab Tires, Walgreens,

Exit	Services
256	Continued
	W ⛽ Arco, Pacific Pride/dsl, Shell/dsl, Texaco/dsl, 🍴 Almost Home Rest., Baskin-Robbins, DQ, McDonald's, Newport Bay Sea🍴 Pietro's Pizza, Rockin-Rogers Diner, Subway, 🛏 Comfort Inn, Holiday Lodge, Motel 6, Phoenix Inn, Red Lion Hotel, Shilo Inn, Super 8, ⊙ Mazda, Nissan, Save-A-Lot Foods
253	OR 22, Salem, Stayton, **E** ⛽ Chevron/repair, Shell/dsl, Space Age/dsl, 🍴 Burger King, Carls Jr, Las Polomas Mexican, McDonalds/playplace, Shari's, Subway, ⊙ $Tree, Home Depot, ShopKO, Salem Camping/RV Park, WinCo Foods, to Detroit RA, **W** ⛽ Shell/dsl, 🍴 DQ, Denny's, Jack-in-the-Box, Panda Express, Sybil's Omelette, Taco Del Mar, 🛏 Best Western, Comfort Suites, La Quinta, Residence Inn, ⊙ 🄷, AAA, Cadillac/Chevrolet/Subaru, Chrysler/Jeep, Costco/gas, K-Mart, Lowe's, Schwab Tire, Toyota/Scion, Walmart, st police
252	Kuebler Blvd
249	to Salem, **2 mi W** ⛽ Arco, 76, 🍴 Arby's, Burger King, Carl's Jr, Kwan's Cuisine, 🛏 Phoenix Inn, ⊙ Safeway
248	Sunnyside, **E** ⊙ Enchanted Forest Themepark, Willamette Valley Vineyards, **W** ⛽ Pacific Pride/dsl
244	to N Jefferson, **E** Emerald Valley RV Park
243	Ankeny Hill
242	Talbot Rd
241mm	**rest area both lanes, full ♿ facilities, info, 📞, 🚮, litter barrels, petwalk**
240.5mm	Santiam River
239	Dever-Conner
238	S Jefferson, to Scio
237	Viewcrest (from sb)
235	Viewcrest (from nb), Millersburg, **E** ⊙ Harley-Davidson
234	OR 99E, Albany, **E** 🛏 Comfort Suites, Holiday Inn Express, ⊙ Knox Butte Camping/RV dump, 🌐, **W** ⛽ Chevron, 🍴 Burger King, Carl's Jr, China Buffet, DQ, McDonald's, Subway, Taco Bell, 🛏 Budget Inn, La Quinta, Motel 6, Super 8, ⊙ 🄷, Costco/gas, K-Mart, Kohl's, to Albany Hist Dist
233	US 20, Albany, **E** ⛽ Chevron/dsl/LP, 76/dsl, 🍴 Denny's, LumYuen Chinese, 🛏 EconoLodge, Phoenix Inn, Quality Inn, ⊙ Chevrolet, Home Depot, Honda, RV camping, Toyota/Scion, st police, **W** ⛽ 76/dsl, Shell, 🍴 Abby's Pizza, Arby's, Baskin-Robbins, Burgerville, Carl's Jr, Elmer's, Figaro's, Fox Den Pizza, Jack-in-the-Box, Los Dos Amigos, Los Tequilos Mexican, Original Breakfast Cafe, Skipper's, Starbucks, Sweetwaters Rest., Taco Time, Wendy's, 🛏 Valu Inn, ⊙ 🄷, Albertson's, Bi-Mart, CarQuest, Chrysler/Dodge/Hyundai/Jeep/Subaru, Curves, Fred Meyer/dsl, JoAnn Fabrics, Knechts's Parts, NAPA, O'Reilly Parts, PetCo, Rite Aid, Schwab Tires, Staples, Target, Walgreens
228	OR 34, to Lebanon, Corvallis, **E** ⛽ Leather's/dsl, 76/dsl, 🍴 Pine Cone Cafe, ⊙ Mallard Creek Golf/RV Resort, **W** ⛽ Arco/dsl, Chevron/CFN/A&W/dsl, Shell/dsl, ⊙ to OSU, KOA (5mi)
222mm	Butte Creek
216	OR 228, Halsey, Brownsville, **E** ⛽ Pioneer Villa TrkStp/76/Blimpie/dsl/24hr/@, 🛏 Travelodge, ⊙ parts/repair/towing, **W** ⛽ Shell/dsl
209	to Jct City, Harrisburg, **W** ⊙ Diamond Hill RV Park
206mm	**rest area both lanes, full ♿ facilities, info, 📞, 🚮, litter barrels, petwalk**

A L B A N Y

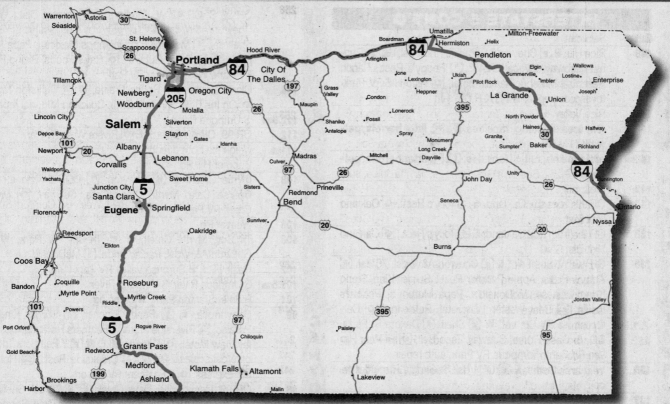

	INTERSTATE 5 CONT'D
Exit	**Services**
199	Coburg, **E** 📷 Fuel'n Go/dsl, 🅾 Premier RV Resort, **W** 📷 Shell/dsl, TA/Country Pride/Truck'n'Travel Motel/dsl/scales/24hr/@, 🅾 Armitage Park Camping, Evert RV Ctr, Freightliner, Volvo, dsl repair, hist dist
197mm	McKenzie River
195b a	N Springfield, **E** 📷 Arco, Chevron, 🍴 Applebee's, Cafe Yummi, Carl's Jr, China Sun, Ciao Pizza, ChuckeCheese, Denny's, Elmer's Rest., FarMan Chinese, 5 Guys Burgers, Gateway Chinese, HomeTown Buffet, IHOP, Jack-in-the-Box, Jimmy John's, KFC, McDonald's, Outback Steaks, Quiznos, Roadhouse Grill, Shari's, Sizzler, Starbucks, Subway, Taco Bell, Taco Time, 🛏 Best Western, Comfort Suites, Courtyard, Hilton Garden, Holiday Inn Express, Holiday Inn, Motel 6, Quality Inn, Shilo Inn/rest., Super 8, 🅾 H, Best Buy, Cabela's, Kohl's, Michael's, Sears/auto, Staples, Target, USPO, mall, st police, **W** 🍴 Taco Bell, 🅾 Costco/gas, Office Depot, Petsmart, ShopKO, to 🖂
194b a	OR 126 E, I-105 W, Springfield, Eugene, **1 mi** **W** 📷 Chevron, 76/repair, 🍴 Carl's Jr, PF Chang's, Quiznos, Starbucks, 🛏 La Quinta, Red Lion Inn, Residence Inn, 🅾 Albertson's/gas, Nissan, Subaru, Trader Joe's, U Of O
193mm	Willamette River
192	OR 99 (from nb), to Eugene, **W** 📷 76, 🍴 Boulevard Grill, House Of Chen, Subway, Wendy's, 🛏 Best Western, Days Inn, Holiday Inn Express, University Inn, 🅾 Mkt Of Choice, to U of O
191	Glenwood, **W** 📷 Shell/dsl/LP, 🍴 Denny's, 🛏 Comfort Suites, Motel 6
189	30th Ave S, Eugene, **E** 📷 Shell/dsl/LP, 🅾 Harley-Davidson, Shamrock RV Park, marine ctr, **W** 📷 76/dsl
188b	OR 99 S (nb only), Goshen

N ↑ ↓ S

SPRINGFIELD

EUGENE

188a	OR 58, OR 99 S to Oakridge, **E** 🅾 Deerwood RV Park, **W** 📷 Pacific Pride/dsl, 🅾 tires
186	Dillard Rd, to Goshen (from nb)
182	Creswell, **E** 🍴 Subway, 🛏 Comfort Inn, 🅾 Bi-Mart, OR RV Ctr, Ray's Foods/drug, golf, **W** 📷 Arco, 76/dsl, 🍴 China Wok, Dari Mart, Figaro's Pizza, Hawaiian BBQ, TJ's Rest., 🛏 Super 8, 🅾 Knecht's Parts, Sherwood Forest RV Park
180mm	Coast Fork of Willamette River
178mm	**rest area both lanes, full** ♿ **facilities,** 📞 🚻 **litter barrels, petwalk, coffee**
176	Saginaw
175mm	Row River
174	Cottage Grove, **E** 📷 Chevron/dsl/repair, Pacific Pride, 🍴 El Paraiso Mexican, Subway, Taco Bell, 🛏 Village Resort/RV park, 🅾 H, Brad's RV Ctr, Chevrolet/GMC, Chrysler/Dodge/Jeep, Walmart, **W** 📷 Chevron/dsl/LP, 76/dsl, Shell/dsl, 🍴 Arby's, Burger King, Carl's Jr, Figaro's Pizza, KFC, McDonald's/RV parking, Torero's Mexican, Vintage Rest., 🛏 Best Western, City Ctr Motel, Comfort Inn, Relax Inn, 🅾 H, Bi-Mart Foods, $Tree, Save-A-Lot Foods, Village Green Motel/RV Park
172	6th St (from sb), Cottage Grove Lake, **2 mi** **E** Cottage Grove RV Village
170	to OR 99, London Rd (nb only), Cottage Grove Lake, 6 mi **W** Cottage Grove RV Village
163	Curtin, Lorane, **E** 🛏 Stardust Motel, 🅾 antiques, **W** 🅾 Pass Creek RV Park,
162	OR 38, OR 99, to Drain, Elkton
161	Anlauf (from nb)
160	Salt Springs Rd
159	Elk Creek, Cox Rd
154	Yoncalla, Elkhead
150	OR 99, to OR 38, Yoncalla, Red Hill, **W** 🅾 Trees of Oregon RV Park

OR

INTERSTATE 5 CONT'D

Exit	Services
148	Rice Hill, E 🅰 Chevron/LP, Pacific Pride/dsl, 🍴/Denny's/Subway/dsl/scales/24hr, 🍴 Peggy's Rest., Ranch Rest., 🏨 Motel 6, Ranch Motel, 🅾 Rice Hill RV Park, towing/dsl repair, W 🍴 K-R Drive-In
146	Rice Valley
144mm	**rest area sb, full ♿ facilities, 🚻, 🅿, litter barrels, petwalk**
143mm	**rest area nb, full ♿ facilities, 🚻, 🅿, litter barrels, petwalk**
142	Metz Hill
140	OR 99 (from sb), Oakland, E 🍴 Tolly's Rest., 🅾 Oakland Hist Dist
138	OR 99 (from nb), Oakland, E 🍴 Tolly's Rest., 🅾 Oakland Hist Dist
136	OR 138W, Sutherlin, E 🅰 Chevron/A&W/dsl, 76/dsl, 🍴 Abby's Pizza, Apple Peddler Rest., Burger King, Hong Kong Chinese, McDonald's, Papa Murphy's, Pedotti's Italian, 🏨 Best Western, Microtel, Relax Inn, 🅾 CarQuest, I-5 RV Ctr, vet, W 🅰 Shell, 🍴 Dakota St Pizza, DQ, Si Casa Flores, Subway, Taco Bell, 🅾 Hi-Way Haven RV Camp, Umpqua RV Park, auto repair
135	Wilbur, Sutherlin, E 🅰 CFN/dsl, Shell/dsl/LP, muffler repair
129	OR 99, Winchester, E 🅰, 🍴 camping, dsl repair, RV Ctr (1mi)
129mm	N Umpqua River
127	Stewart Pkwy, Edenbower Rd, N Roseburg, E 🅰 Shell, 🍴 Shari's Rest., 🏨 Motel 6, Super 8, 🅾 Home Depot, Lowe's, Mt Nebo RV Park, W 🅰 Texaco/Taco Maker/dsl, 🍴 Applebee's, Jack-in-the-Box, McDonald's/playplace, Red Robin, Subway, 🏨 Sleep Inn, 🅾 🅷, Albertson's/gas, Big O Tire, K-Mart, Macy's, Office Depot, Sherm's Foods, Walmart, vet
125	Garden Valley Blvd, Roseburg, E 🅰 Texaco, 🍴 Brutke's Rest., Casey's Rest., Elmer's, Friday BBQ, Gilberto's Mexican, Jack-in-the-Box, KFC, Los Dos Amigo's Mexican, McDonald's, Papa Murphy's, Sonic, Subway, Taco Bell, 🏨 Comfort Inn, Quality Inn, Windmill Inn/rest., 🅾 AT&T, BigLots, Buick/Chevrolet/GMC, Ford/Lincoln/Mercury, NAPA, Safeway/dsl, Toyota, U-Haul, Verizon, Walgreens, transmissions, W 🅰 Chevron/dsl, Shell/LP/repair, 🍴 Arby's, Burger King, Carl's Jr, Fox Den Pizza, Quiznos, Rodeo Steaks, RoundTable Pizza, Si Casa Flores Mexican, Sizzler, Starbucks, TomTom Rest., Wendy's, 🏨 Best Value Inn, Best Western, 🅾 🅷, Bi-Mart Foods, $Tree, Fred Meyer, JC Penney, JoAnn Fabrics, Michael's, O'Reilly Parts, PetCo, Rite Aid, Ross, Sears/auto, Staples, Walgreens, mall
124	OR 138, Roseburg, City Ctr, E 🅰 76/dsl, Texaco/dsl, 🍴 Chi's Chinese, Denny's, 🏨 Dunes Motel, Holiday Inn Express, Travelodge, 🅾 Honda, Rite Aid, W 🅰 76/dsl, Shell/dsl, 🍴 Charley's BBQ, Gay 90's Deli, KFC/LJ Silver, Pete's Drive-In, Subway, Taco Time, 🅾 Grocery Outlet, Harvard Ave Drug, Hometown Drug
123	Roseburg, E 🅾 to Umpqua Park, camping, museum
121	McLain Ave
120.5mm	S Umpqua River
120	OR 99 N (no EZ nb return), Green District, Roseburg, E 🏨 Shady Oaks Motel, W 🅾 auto repair
119	OR 99 S, OR 42 W, Winston, E 🅾 Ingram Dist., W 🅰 Chevron/A&W/dsl, 🔷Loves/Arby's/dsl/scales/LP/24hr, Shell/dsl, 🍴 McDonald's, Ocampos Mexican, Papa Murphy's, Rae's Diner, Subway, 🅾 Ray's Foods, Rising River RV Park, Western Star RV Park
113	Clarks Branch Rd, Round Prairie, W 🏨 Quikstop Motel, 🅾 On the River RV Park (2mi), Quikstop Mkt, dsl repair
112.5mm	S Umpqua River
112	OR 99, OR 42, Dillard, E 🅾 Rivers West RV Park
111mm	weigh sta both directions
110	Boomer Hill Rd
108	Myrtle Creek, E 🅰 Chevron, 🍴 DQ, El Azteca, Golf Course Cafe, Myrtle Creek Cafe, Subway, 🅾 Myrtle Creek RV Park
106	Weaver Rd
103	Tri City, Myrtle Creek, E 🅾 Tri-City RV Park, W 🅰 Chevron/A&W/dsl, Pacific Pride, 🍴 McDonald's
102	Gazley Rd, E Surprise Valley RV Park (1mi)
101.5mm	S Umpqua River, S Umpqua River
101	Riddle, Stanton Park, W camping
99	Canyonville, E 🅰 Penny Pincher, 🍴 Burger King, El Paraiso, 🏨 Riverside Motel, 7 Feathers Hotel/casino, Valley View Motel, 🅾 Canyon Mkt, W 🅰 7 Feathers Trkstp/café/dsl/scales/24hr/@, 🍴 Creekside Rest., 🏨 Holiday Inn Express, 🅾 7 Feathers RV Resort
98	OR 99, Canyonville, Days Creek, E 🅰 76/dsl, Shell/dsl, 🍴 Canyon Cafe, Ken's Cafe, Marla Kay's Cafe, Serafino's Italian, 🏨 Leisure Inn, 🅾 Ace Hardware, NAPA, Ray's Foods, auto repair, vet, W 🅾 Bill's Tire/repair, museum
95	Canyon Creek
90mm	Canyon Creek Pass, elev 2020
88	Azalea
86	Barton Rd, Quine's Creek, E 🅰 Quine's Creek/dsl/LP, 🅾 Heaven on Earth Rest./rest., Meadow Wood RV Park (3mi)
83	Barton Rd (from nb), E 🅾 Meadow Wood RV Park/camping
82mm	**rest area both lanes, full ♿ facilities, 🚻, 🅿, litter barrels, petwalk**
80	Glendale, W 🅰 Country Jct./LP, 🍴 Village Inn Rest.
79.5mm	Stage Road Pass, elev 1830
78	Speaker Rd (from sb)
76	Wolf Creek, W 🅰 Pacific Pride/dsl, 76/deli/dsl, Texaco/dsl, 🍴 Wolf Creek Inn Rest., 🅾 Creekside RV park, auto repair
74mm	Smith Hill Summit, elev 1730
71	Sunny Valley, E 🏨 Sunny Valley Motel, 🅾 Covered Bridge Store/gas, W 🅾 Sunny Valley RV Park
69mm	Sexton Mtn Pass, elev 1960
66	Hugo, E 🅾 Joe Creek Waterfalls RV Park, W 🅾 Pottsville Museum
63mm	**rest area both lanes, full ♿ facilities, 🚻, info, 🅿, litter barrels, vending, petwalk**
61	Merlin, W 🅰 Shell/dsl, 🅾 Almeda RV Park, Beaver Creek RV Resort (2mi), OR RV Ctr, Ray's Foods, Rouge Valley RV Ctr, repair
58	OR 99, to US 199, Grants Pass, W 🅰 CFN/dsl, Chevron, 76/dsl/RV dump, Shell/dsl/repair, Texaco/dsl, TownePump Gas, 🍴 Angela's Mexican, Beacon Cafe, Black Bear Diner, Burger King, Carl's Jr, China Hut, Della's Rest., DQ, Denny's, Jack-in-the-Box, McDonald's, Muchas Gracias Mexican, Papa Murphy's, Sizzler, Subway, Taco Bell,

Side markers (vertical): N / S ... SUTHERLIN ... ROSEBURG ... OR ... CANYONVILLE

INTERSTATE 5 CONT'D

Exit	Services
58	Continued
	Wendy's, ☐ Best Way Inn, Comfort Inn, Hawks Inn, La Quinta, Motel 6, Redwood Motel, Royal Vue Motel, Shilo Inn, Sunset Inn, Super 8, SweetBreeze Inn, Travelodge, Wild River Inn, ☐ ☐, AutoZone, Chevrolet/Honda, Chrysler/Dodge/Jeep, Curves, $Tree, Jack's RV Resort, NAPA, Nissan, Radio Shack, Ray's Foods, Rouge Valley RV Park, Schwab Tire, st police, towing
55	US 199, Redwood Hwy, E Grants Pass, W ☐ Arco/dsl, CFN/dsl, ☐ Applebee's, Abby's Pizza, Carl's Jr, Elmer's, JJ North's Grand Buffet, Las Fajitas, McDonald's, Quiznos, Shari's, Si Casa Flores Mexican, Subway, Taco Bell, ☐ Best Western, Holiday Inn Express, ☐ ☐, Albertson's/gas, AT&T, BigLots, $Tree, Fred Meyer/dsl, Grocery Outlet, Moon Mtn RV Park (2mi), RiverPark RV Park (4mi), Ross, Schuck's Parts, Siskiyou RV Ctr, Tehama Tire, Walmart
48	Rogue River, E ☐ Chevron/dsl, ☐ Abby's Pizza, Homestead Rest., Tarasco Mexican, ☐ Ace Hardware, Rogue River RA, auto repair, W ☐ ☐ Bella Rosa Inn, Best Western, Weasku Inn, ☐ Chinook Winds RV Park, Bridgeview RV Park, Whispering Pines RV Park, visitors ctr/info
45b	W ☐ Valley of the Rogue SP/rest area both lanes, full ☐ facilities, ☐, ☐, litter barrels, petwalk, camping
45mm	Rogue River
45a	OR 99, Savage Rapids Dam, E ☐ Cypress Grove RV Park
43	OR 99, OR 234, to Crater Lake, Gold Hill, E ☐ Lazy Acres Motel/RV Park, RoadRiver B&B
40	OR 99, OR 234, Gold Hill, E ☐ Figaro's Pizza, Patti's Kitchen, ☐ Gold Hill Auto Ctr/gas, KOA, Lazy Acres Motel/RV Park, Running Salmon RV Park, USPO, to Shady Cove Trail, W Dardanelle's RV Ctr/gas, Dardanelle's Trailer Park
35	OR 99, Blackwell Rd, Central Point, 2-4 mi W ☐, ☐ lodging, st police, Jacksonville Nat Hist Landmark
33	Central Point, E ☐ Chevron, ☐/Subway/Taco Bell/dsl/scales/24hr, ☐ Burger King, KFC, Quiznos, Shari's Rest., Sonic, ☐ Candlewood Suites (2mi), Courtyard (2mi), Fairfield Inn, Holiday Inn Express, Super 8, ☐ funpark, W ☐ 76/Circle K/dsl, Shell/dsl, ☐ Abby's Pizza, Mazatlan Grill, McDonald's, ☐ Albertson's, USPO
30	OR 62, to Crater Lake, Medford, E ☐ Chevron, Witham Trkstp/rest./dsl/24hr/@, ☐ Abby's Pizza, Applebee's, Asian Grill, Burger King, Carl's Jr, DQ, Del Taco, Elmer's, Marie Callender's, McDonald's, Olive Garden, Outback Steaks, Panda Express, Papa John's, Pizza Hut, Quiznos, Red Robin, Si Casa Flores Mexican, Sizzler, Sonic, Starbucks, Subway, Taco Bell, Taco Delite, Thai Bistro, Wendy's, ☐ Comfort Inn, Hampton Inn, Motel 6, Quality Inn, Ramada, Rogue Regency Hotel, Shilo Inn, ☐ Ace Hardware, Affordable RV Ctr, AT&T, Barnes&Noble, Best Buy, BigLots, BiMart Foods, Costco/gas, $Tree, Ford/Lincoln/Mercury, Fred Meyer/dsl, Food4Less, JoAnn, Lowe's, Mazda, Mercedes, Michael's, Office Depot, Old Navy, Petsmart, Ross, Safeway, Schuck's Parts, Schwab Tire, Sears/auto, TJ Maxx, USPO, Verizon, Walmart, st police, vet, W ☐ 76/dsl, Shell/dsl, Spirit/dsl, ☐ Jack-in-the-Box, KFC, King Wah Chinese, Red Lobster, Wendy's, ☐ ☐, CarQuest, JC Penney, Kohl's, Macy's, Target, Toyota/Scion, mall

Exit	Services
27	Barnett Rd, Medford, E ☐ Blackbear Diner, DQ, ☐ Best Western, Days Inn/rest., Homewood Suites, Motel 6, Travelodge, ☐ ☐, W ☐ Chevron, 76/Circle K/dsl, Shell/dsl, Texaco/dsl, ☐ Abby's Pizza, Arby's, Burger King, Carl's Jr, HomeTown Buffet, Jack-in-the-Box, KFC, McDonald's, McGrath's FishHouse, Pizza Hut, Quiznos, Rooster's Rest., Senor Sam's Mexican, Shari's, Starbucks, Subway, Taco Bell, Wendy's, ☐ Capri Motel, Comfort Inn, Holiday Inn Express, Medford Inn, Royal Crest Motel, SpringHill Suites, TownePlace Suites, ☐ Fred Meyer/dsl, Grocery Outlet, Harry&David's, Office Depot, Radio Shack, Schucks Parts, Staples, Walgreens, WinCo Foods
24	Phoenix, E ☐ Petro/Iron Skillet/dsl/scales/RV dump/24hr/@, ☐ Best Inn/PearTree RV park, ☐ Home Depot, Peterbilt, W ☐ 76/Circle K/dsl, ☐ Angelo's Pizza, Debby's Diner, Jack-in-the-Box, McDonald's, Si Casa Flores Mexican, Taste of Orient, ☐ Bavarian Inn, ☐ Ray's Foods, Holiday RV Park
22mm	rest area sb, full ☐ facilities, ☐, ☐, litter barrels, vending, petwalk
21	Talent, W ☐ Chevron/dsl, ☐ Avalon Grill, Figaro's Italian, ☐ GoodNight Inn, ☐ American RV Resort, Walmart/auto, repair
19	Valley View Rd, Ashland, W ☐ Pacific Pride/dsl, 76/dsl, Shell/dsl/LP, ☐ Burger King, El Tapatio Mexican, ☐ EconoLodge, La Quinta, ☐ Acura, Chevrolet, Ford, Suzuki
18mm	weigh sta both lanes
14	OR 66, to Klamath Falls, Ashland, E ☐ Chevron/dsl, 76/dsl/LP, Shell/dsl, ☐ El Pariso Mexican, OakTree Rest., ☐ Best Western, Holiday Inn Express, Relax Inn, Windmill Inn, ☐ Emigrant Lake Camping (3mi), Glenyan RV Park (3mi), Nat Hist Museum, W ☐ Arco, Texaco, ☐ Korean BBQ, Panda Garden Chinse, Subway, Taco Bell, Wendy's, Wild Goose Cafe, Yuan Yuan Chinese, ☐ Knights Inn/rest., Rodeway Inn, Super 8, ☐ ☐, Albertson's, Bi-Mart, NAPA, Radio Shack, Rite Aid, Schwab Tire, U-Haul, vet
11	OR 99, Siskiyou Blvd (nb only, no return), services 2-4 mi W
6	to Mt Ashland, E ☐ Callahan's Siskiyou Lodge/rest., ☐ ☐, ski area
4mm	Siskiyou Summit, elev 4310, brake check both lanes
1	to Siskiyou Summit (from nb, no return)
0mm	Oregon/California state line

INTERSTATE 84

Exit	Services
378mm	Oregon/Idaho state line, Snake River
377.5mm	Welcome Ctr wb, full ☐ facilities, info, ☐, ☐, litter barrels, vending, petwalk
376b a	US 30, to US 20/26, Ontario, Payette, N ☐ Chevron/dsl, ☐ A&W/KFC, Burger King, Carl's Jr, China Buffet, Country Kitchen, DQ, Denny's, Domino's, McDonald's,

Side markers:
GRANTS PASS
N ↕ S
MEDFORD
ASHLAND
E ↕ W
OR

O N T A R I O

E ↕ W

B A K E R

OR

INTERSTATE 84 CONT'D

Exit	Services
376b a	Continued
	Primo's Pizza, Quizno's, Taco Del Mar, Wingers, 🛏 Best Western, Colonial Inn, Holiday Inn, Motel 6, Sleep Inn, Super 8, ⬛ Chrysler/Dodge/Jeep, Curves, $Tree, Home Depot, K-Mart, Radio Shack, Staples, Toyota/Scion, Walgreens, Walmart, st police, S ⛽ CFN, 🍴Arby's/dsl/scales/24hr, Shell/dsl, 🍴 DJ's, Far East Chinese, Ogawa's Japanese, Rusty's Steaks, Sizzler, Subway, Taco Bell, Wendy's, 🛏 Economy Inn, Holiday Inn Express, OR Trail Motel, Rodeway Inn, Stockman's Motel, ⬛ 🅷, Commercial Tire, NAPA, Radio Shack, Schwab Tire, 4 Wheeler Museum
374	US 30, OR 201, to Ontario, N to Ontario SP, S ⛽ 💚Loves/Subway/dsl/scales/24hr/@, Pacific Pride, 🛏 Budget Inn, ⬛ 🅷
373.5mm	Malheur River
371	Stanton Blvd, **2 mi S** to correctional institution
362	Moores Hollow Rd
356	OR 201, to Weiser, ID, **3 mi N** Catfish Junction RV Park, Oasis RV Park
354.5mm	**weigh sta eb**
353	US 30, to Huntington, N **weigh sta wb**, ⛽ Joy Travel Plaza/Texaco/rest./dsl, 🛏 Farewell Bend Motel, ⬛ to Farewell Bend SP, truck repair, RV camping, info
351mm	Pacific/Mountain time zone
345	US 30, Lime, Huntington, **1 mi N** ⛽, 🍴 lodging, to Snake River Area, Van Ornum BFD
342	Lime (from eb)
340	Rye Valley
338	Lookout Mountain
337mm	Burnt River
335	to Weatherby, **N rest area both lanes, full ♿ facilities, Oregon Trail Info, 🚮, litter barrels, vending, petwalk**
330	Plano Rd, to Cement Plant Rd, **S** cement plant
329mm	pulloff eb
327	Durkee, N ⛽ Co-op/dsl/LP/café
325mm	Pritchard Creek
321mm	Alder Creek
317	to Pleasant Valley (from wb)
315	to Pleasant Valley (from wb)
313	to Pleasant Valley (from eb)
306	US 30, Baker, **2-3 mi S** ⛽ Chevron/dsl, 🍴 DQ, 🛏 Baker City Motel/RV Park, Bridge Street Hotel, OR Trail Motel/rest., ⬛ 🅷, Schwab Tire, to st police, same as 304
304	OR 7, Baker, N ⛽ Chevron/dsl, 🛏 Super 8, Welcome Inn, S ⛽ Shell/dsl/24hr, Sinclair/dsl/rest./scales/24hr, 🍴 Arceo's Mexican, Domino's, DQ, Fong's Chinese, Golden Crown, McDonald's, Papa Murphy's, Starbucks, Subway, Sumpter Jct Rest., Taco Time, 🛏 Best Western, Budget Inn, Eldorado Inn, Geyser Grand Motel, Rodeway Inn, Western Motel, ⬛ 🅷, Albertson's/gas, Bi-Mart, CarQuest, $Tree, Ford, Mtn View RV Park (3mi), Rite Aid, Safeway Foods, museum, transmissions, to hist dist
302	OR 86 E to Richland, S ⬛ 🅷, OR Tr RV Park/LP, st police
298	OR 203, to Medical Springs
297mm	Baldock Slough
295mm	**rest area both lanes, full ♿ facilities, info, 🚻, 🚮, litter barrels, vending, petwalk**
289mm	Powder River

L A G R A N D E

Exit	Services
287.5mm	45th parallel - halfway between the equator and north pole
286mm	N Powder River
285	US 30, OR 237, North Powder, N🛏 North Powder Motel/cafe, S ⬛ to Anthony Lakes, ski area
284mm	Wolf Creek
283	Wolf Creek Lane
278	Clover Creek
273	Frontage Rd
270	Ladd Creek Rd (from eb, no return)
269mm	**rest area both lanes, full ♿ facilities, info, 🚻, 🚮, litter barrels, vending, petwalk**
268	Foothill Rd
265	OR 203, LaGrande, N ⬛ Eagles Hot Lake RV Park, 🔁, S ⛽ ⓕFLYING J/Shell/dsl/rest./scales/24hr, 🍴 SmokeHouse Rest. (2mi), ⬛ Freightliner
261	OR 82, LaGrande, N ⛽ Chevron/dsl, Shell/dsl, 🍴 Denny's, Pizza Hut, Quizno's, Starbucks, Taco Bell, 🛏 LaGrande Inn, ⬛ Chrysler/Dodge/Jeep, Ford/Lincoln/Mercury, Grocery Outlet, Thunder RV Ctr, Walmart, st police, vet, S ⛽ Chevron, 76/Subway/dsl, Texaco/dsl, 🍴 Bear Mtn. Pizza, China Buffet, Cinco de Mayo Mexican, DQ, Dutch Bro's Coffee, KFC, La Fiesta Mexican, McDonald's, Moy's Dynasty, Nell's Steakburger, Papa Murphy's, Smokehouse Rest., Taco Time, 🛏 Best Value Inn, Best Western, Moon Motel, Orchard Motel, Royal Motel, Sandman Inn, Super 8, Travelodge, ⬛ 🅷, Albertson's, $Tree, Parts+, Rite Aid, Safeway/gas, Schwab Tire, vet, E OR U, Wallowa Lake
260mm	Grande Ronde River
259	US 30 E (from eb), to La Grande, **1-2 mi S** ⛽ Chevron, Shell, 🍴 Burger King, 🛏 All-American Motel, Greenwell Motel/rest., Royal Motel, ⬛ Safeway/gas, same as 261
257	Perry (from wb)
256.5mm	**weigh sta eb**
256	Perry (from eb)
255mm	Grande Ronde River
254mm	scenic wayside
252	OR 244, to Starkey, Lehman Springs, S ⬛ Hilgard SP, camping, chainup area
251mm	Wallowa-Whitman NF, eastern boundary
248	Spring Creek Rd, to Kamela, **3 mi N** Oregon Trail Visitors Park
246mm	Wallowa-Whitman NF, western boundary
243	Summit Rd, Mt Emily Rd, to Kamela, Oregon Trail info, **2 mi N** ⬛ Emily Summit SP
241mm	Summit of the Blue Mtns, elev 4193
238	Meacham, **1 mi N** 🍴 ⬛ Oregon Trail info
234	Meacham, S ⬛ Emigrant Sprs SP, RV camping
231.5mm	Umatilla Indian Reservation, eastern boundary
228mm	Deadman Pass, Oregon Trail info, **rest area both lanes, full ♿ facilities, 🚻 (wb), 🚮, litter barrel, petwalk, vending, RV Dump (wb)**
227mm	**weigh sta wb, brake check area**
224	Poverty Flats Rd, Old Emigrant Hill Rd, to Emigrant Springs SP
223mm	wb viewpoint, no restrooms
221.5mm	eb viewpoint, no restrooms
220mm	wb runaway truck ramp
216	Mission, McKay Creek, N ⛽ Arrowhead Trkstp/Pacific Pride/McDonald's/dsl/24hr, ⬛ Wildhorse Casino/RV Park
213	US 30 (from wb), Pendleton, **3-5 mi N** ⛽ Chevron/dsl, Shell, 🛏 Travelers Inn, ⬛ 🅷, Pendleton NHD

INTERSTATE 84 CONT'D

Exit	Services
212mm	Umatilla Indian Reservation western boundary
210	OR 11, Pendleton, **N** 🅾 🅷, museum, st police, **S** 🖪 Chevron/Circle K/dsl, Shell/dsl/LP, 🍴 Shari's/24hr, 🛏 Best Western, Hampton Inn, Holiday Inn Express, Motel 6, Red Lion Inn/rest., Super 8, 🅾 KOA
209	US 395, Pendleton, **N** 🖪 Arco, 🍴 A&W/Taco Bell, DQ, Jack-in-the-Box, KFC, 🛏 Oxford Suites, Travelodge, 🅾 Dean's Mkt, $Tree, Radio Shack, Rite Aid, Safeway/dsl, Schuck's Parts, Walmart/Subway, **S** 🖪 Astro Gas, 76/dsl, 🍴 Abby's Pizza, Burger King, Denny's, McDonald's, Rooster's Rest, Starbucks, Subway, Wendy's, 🛏 Econolodge, 🅾 Buick/Chevrolet, Honda, Schwab Tire, Thompson RV Ctr
208mm	Umatilla River
207	US 30, W Pendleton, **N** 🖪 Shell/dsl/LP, 🅾 Lookout RV Park, truck repair
202	Barnhart Rd, to Stage Gulch, **N** Woodpecker Truck Repair, **S** 🛏 Rodeo Inn, 🅾 Oregon Trail info
199	Stage Coach Rd, Yoakum Rd
198	Lorenzen Rd, McClintock Rd, **N** 🅾 trailer/reefer repair
193	Echo Rd, to Echo, Oregon Trail Site
188	US 395 N, Hermiston, **N** 🖪 Chevron/dsl (1mi), 🅿/Subway/McDonald's/dsl/24hr/RV park, **5 mi N** 🍴 Denny's/24hr, Jack-in-the-Box, McDonald's, Shari's/24hr, 🛏 Best Western, Economy Inn, Oak Tree Inn, Oxford Suites, 🅾 🅷, **S** 🅾 Henrietta RV Park (1mi), Echo HS
187mm	**rest area both lanes, full ♿ facilities, 🅲, info, 🚻, litter barrels, petwalk**
182	OR 207, to Hermiston, **N** 🅾 Space Age/A&W/dsl/LP/24hr, 🍴 Macario's Mexican, 🛏 Comfort Inn
180	Westland Rd, to Hermiston, McNary Dam, **N** 🅾 Freightliner, trailer repair, **S** 🖪 Shell/Western Express/dsl/24hr
179	I-82 W, to Umatilla, Kennewick, WA
177	Umatilla Army Depot
171	Paterson Ferry Rd, to Paterson
168	US 730, to Irrigon, **8 mi N** 🅾 Green Acres RV Park, Oasis RV Park, Oregon Trail info
165	Port of Morrow, **S** 🖪 Pacific Pride/dsl
164	Boardman, **N** 🖪 Chevron/Circle K/dsl, Shell/dsl, 🍴 C&D Drive-In, Lynard's Cafe, 🛏 Dodge City Motel, Riverview Motel, 🅾 Boardman Drug, Boardman RV/Marina Park, USPO, **S** 🖪 Shell/dsl, 🛏 Rodeway Inn, 🅾 NAPA, Family Foods, Oregon Trail Library, tires
161mm	**rest area both lanes, full ♿ facilities, 🅲, 🚻, litter barrels, vending, petwalk**
159	Tower Rd
151	Threemile Canyon
147	OR 74, to Ione, Blue Mtn Scenic Byway, Heppner, Oregon Trail Site
137	OR 19, Arlington, **S** 🖪 Shell/dsl, 🍴 Happy Canyon Cafe, Pheasant Grill, Village Inn, 🅾 Ace Hardware, Arlington RV Park, Thrifty Foods, city park, USPO
136.5mm	view point wb, 🚻, litter barrels
131	Woelpern Rd (from eb, no return)
129	Blalock Canyon, Lewis&Clark Trail
123	Philippi Canyon, Lewis&Clark Trail
114.5mm	John Day River, 114, **S** LePage Park
112	parking area, both lanes, litter barrels, **N** John Day Dam
109	Rufus, **N** **John Day Visitor Ctr**, **S** 🖪 Shell/dsl, 🍴 Bob's T-Bone, 🛏 Hillview Motel, Tyee Motel, 🅾 Ed's RV Park, Rufus RV Park

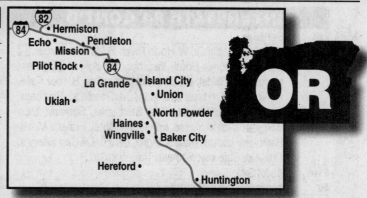

104	US 97, Biggs, **N** 🅾 Des Chutes Park Bridge, **S** 🖪 76/Circle K/Noble Roman's/dsl/24hr, 🅿/McDonald's/dsl/scales/24hr, Linda's/Shell/Subway/rest./dsl, 🛏 Biggs Motel/café, Dinty's Motel, 3 Rivers Inn, 🅾 Maryhill Museum, dsl repair
100mm	Deschutes River, Columbia River Gorge Scenic Area
97	OR 206, Celilo, **N** 🅾 Celilo SP, restrooms, **S** 🅾 Deschutes SP, Indian Village
92	pullout, eb, 88, **N** to The Dalles Dam
87	US 30, US 197, to Dufur, **N** 🖪 Chevron, 76/dsl/24hr, 🍴 McDonald's, Portage Grill, 🛏 Comfort Inn, Shilo Inn/rest., 🅾 Columbia Hills RV Park, Lone Pine RV Park, st police, **S** 🍴 Big Jim's Drive-In, 🛏 Riverview Inn, 🅾 Schwab Tire
85	The Dalles, **N** **Riverfront Park, restrooms, 🅲, 🚻, litter barrels, playground, marina**, **S** 🖪 Chevron, 76/dsl, Shell, 🍴 Burgerville, Domino's, Taco Del Mar, 🛏 Dalles Inn, Oregon Motel, 🅾 🅷, AJ's Radiators, Dalles Parts, NAPA, Toyota/Scion, TrueValue, camping, USPO, to Nat Hist Dist
83	(84 from wb)W The Dalles, **N** 🍴 Casa El Mirador, Orient Café, 🅾 Tire Factory, **S** 🖪 Shell/dsl, 🍴 Arby's, Burger King, Denny's, DQ, Dutch Bro's Coffee, Ixtapa Mexican, KFC, McDonald's, Papa Murphy's, Quizno's, Shari's Rest., Skipper's, Starbucks, Subway, Taco Bell, Taco Time, Wendy's, 🛏 Cousin's Inn/rest., Motel 6, Super 8, 🅾 🅷, Buick/GMC, Chevrolet, Chrysler/Dodge/Jeep, $Tree, Ford, Fred Meyer, Grocery Outlet, Jo-Ann Fabrics, K-Mart, Nissan, Oil Can Henry's, PetCo, Radio Shack, Rite Aid, Safeway, Schuck's Parts, Staples, Subaru, Walgreens
82	Chenowith Area, **S** 🖪 Astro/dsl/24hr, 76/dsl, 🍴 Spooky's Café, 🅾 Bi-Mart Foods, Columbia Discovery Ctr, Home Depot, museum, same as 83
76	Rowena, **N** 🅾 Mayer SP, Lewis & Clark info, windsurfing
73mm	**Memaloose SP, rest area both lanes, full ♿ facilities, 🚻, litter barrels, 🅲, petwalk, RV dump, camping**
69	US 30, Mosier, **S** 🍴 Goodriver Rest. 10 Speed East Rest., 🅾 USPO,
66mm	**N** **Koberg Beach SP, rest area wb, full facilities, 🚻, litter barrels**
64	US 30, OR 35, to White Salmon, Hood River, **N** 🖪 Chevron, Shell/24hr, 🍴 McDonald's, Riverside Grill, Starbucks, 🛏 Best Western, 🅾 marina, museum, st police, **visitors info**
63	Hood River, City Ctr, **N** 🖪 76/dsl, **S** 🍴 Andrew's Pizza, Annz Cafe, Crazy Pepper Mexican, Horse Feathers Grill, Pietro's Pizza, Sage's Cafe, Taco Del Mar, 3 River's Grill, 🛏 Hood River Hotel/rest., Oakstreet Hotel, 🅾 🅷, USPO, same as 64

Left margin (top to bottom): **PENDLETON**   E↕W

Right margin (top to bottom): **THE DALLES**   **HOOD RIVER**   **OR**

INTERSTATE 84 CONT'D

Exit	Services
62	US 30, Westcliff Dr, W Hood River, N 🍴 Charburger, 🛏 Columbia Gorge Hotel, Vagabond Lodge, S 🛢 Chevron/dsl/LP, 76/dsl, 🍴 Domino's, DQ, Egg Harbor Cafe, HoHo Rest., Ixtapa Mexican, McDonald's, Pizzicato, Quizno's, Red Carpet Cafe, Starbucks, Subway, Taco Bell, 🛏 Comfort Suites, Lone Pine Motel, Prater's Motel, Riverview Lodge, Sunset Motel, Ⓞ Ⓗ, Oil Can Henry's, Rite Aid, Safeway, Schwab Tire, Walmart
61mm	pulloff wb
60	service rd wb (no return)
58	Mitchell Point Overlook (from eb)
56	N Ⓞ Viento SP, RV camping, Ⓒ
55	Starvation Peak Tr Head (from eb), restrooms
54mm	**weigh sta wb**
51	Wyeth, S camping
49mm	pulloff eb
47	Forest Lane, Hermon Creek (from wb), camping
45mm	**weigh sta eb**
44	US 30, to Cascade Locks. **1-4 mi** N 🛢 CFN, Shell/dsl, 🍴 Charburger, Pacific Crest Pub, 🛏 Best Western, Bonneville Hot Spring Hotel, Bridge of the Gods Motel, Cascade Motel, Econolodge, Skamania Springs Hotel, Ⓞ to Bridge of the Gods, KOA, Stern Wheeler RV Park
41	Eagle Creek RA (from eb), to fish hatchery, 40, N Ⓞ Bonneville Dam NHS, info, to fish hatchery
37	Warrendale (from wb)
35	Historic Hwy, Multnomah Falls, S Ⓞ Ainsworth SP, scenic loop highway, waterfall area, Fishery RV Park
31	Multnomah Falls (exits left from both lanes), S Multnomah Falls Lodge/Rest. (hist site), camping
30	S Benson SRA (from eb)
29	Dalton Point (from wb)
28	to Bridal Veil (7 mi return from eb), S USPO
25	N Rooster Rock SP
23mm	viewpoint wb, hist marker
22	Corbett, **2 mi** S 🛢 Corbett Mkt, 🍴 View Point Rest., Ⓞ Crown Point RV Camping
19mm	Columbia River Gorge scenic area
18	Lewis&Clark SP, to Oxbow SP lodging, 🍴 RV camping
17.5mm	Sandy River
17	Marine Dr, Troutdale, N 🍴 Wendy's, 🛏 Holiday Inn Express, S 🛢 Chevron/24hr, 🛢Loves/deli/dsl/LP/scales/24hr, TA/Buckhorn Rest./Popeye's/Subway/dsl/scales/24hr/@, Shell/dsl, 🍴 Arby's, McDonald's, Shari's/24hr, Subway, Taco Bell, Troutdale Diner, 🛏 Comfort Inn, Motel 6, Ⓞ Premium Outlets/famous brands, Sandy Riverfront RV Resort
16	238th Dr, Fairview, N 🛢 Arco/dsl/24hr, 🍴 Bronx Eatery, Burger King, Jack-in-the-Box, Quizno's, Taco Del Mar, 🛏 Travelodge, Ⓞ Camping World, Walmart, S 🛢 76, Best Western, Ⓞ Ⓗ
14	207th Ave, Fairview, N 🛢 Shell/Taco Time/dsl, 🍴 Gin-Sun Chinese, Ⓞ American Dream RV Ctr, NAPA, Portland RV Park, Rolling Hills RV Park, auto repair
13	181st Ave, Gresham, N 🛢 Chevron/dsl, 🛏 Hampton Inn, S 🛢 Arco, Texaco, 🍴 Burger King, Carl's Jr, Jung's Chinese, McDonald's, PlumTree Rest., Quizno's, Round-Table Pizza, Shari's/24hr, Starbucks, Tom's Pizza, Wendy's, Xavier's, 🛏 Comfort Suites, Days Inn,

Exit	Services
13	Continued Extended Stay America, Quality Inn, Sheraton, Ⓞ Albertson's, Candy Basket Chocolates, Curves, Rite Aid, Safeway, 7-11, 76, auto repair, vet
10	122nd Ave (from eb)
9	I-205, S to Salem, N to Seattle, to ✈, (to 102nd Ave from eb)
8	I-205 N (from eb), N to ✈
7	Halsey St (from eb), Gateway Dist
6	I-205 S (from eb)
5	OR 213, to 82nd Ave (eb only), N 🛏 Days Inn, S 🍴 Eastern Cathay, 🛏 Comfort Inn
4	68th Ave (from eb), to Halsey Ave
3	58th Ave (from eb), S 🛢 Shell, Ⓞ Ⓗ, Fred Meyer
2	43rd Ave, 39th Ave, Halsey St, N 🛢 Chevron, 76, Shell, Texaco, 🍴 Baja Fresh, Burger King, China Kitchen, McDonald's, Panera Bread, Quizno's, Poor Richard's Rest., Subway, 🛏 Banfield Motel, Rodeway Inn, Ⓞ Radio Shack, Rite Aid, Trader Joe's, S Ⓞ Ⓗ, Buick/Jeep, same as 1
1	33rd Ave, Lloyd Blvd (eb only), downtown, same as 2, N 🍴 Applebee's, 🛏 DoubleTree Inn, Residence Inn, Ⓞ $Tree, Macy's, Marshall's, JC Penney, Sears, S 🍴 Pizza Hut, Ⓞ Cadillac
1	to downtown (wb only)
0mm	I-84 begins/ends on I-5, exit 301.

INTERSTATE 205 (Portland)

Exit	Services
37mm	I-205 begins/ends on I-5. Exits 36-27 are in Washington.
36	NE 134th St (from nb), E 🛢 Arco, 7-11, 76, TrailMart/dsl, 🍴 Applebee's, Billygan's Roadhouse, Booster Juice, Burger King, Burgerville, Jack-in-the-Box, McDonald's, Muchas Gracias, Panda Express, Round Table Pizza, Starbucks, Subway, Taco Bell, Taco Del Mar, 🛏 Comfort Inn, Holiday Inn Express, Olympia Motel, Red Lion, Salmon Creek Inn, Shilo Inn, Ⓞ Ⓗ, Albertson's/gas, Long's Drugs, Safeway/gas, Zupan's Mkt, 99 RV Park, to Portland ✈, W 🛢 Shell, 🍴 Baskin-Robbins, Coldstone, El Tapatio, Papa Murphy's, PizzaSchmitzza, Quizno's, Starbucks, The Great Impasta, 🛏 La Quinta, Ⓞ Fred Meyer
32	NE 83rd St, Andreson Rd, Battle Ground, W 🛢 Shell/dsl/24hr, 🍴 Burger King, Emporor Chinese, Krispy Kreme, Panda Express, Starbucks, Subway, Wendy's, Weinerschnitzel, Ⓞ Costco/gas, Home Depot
30c b a	WA 500, Orchards, Vancouver, E 🛢 76, Shell/24hr, 🍴 ABC Buffet, Applebee's, Burger King, Burgerville, DQ, Imperial Palace, McDonald's, Papa Murphy's, Starbucks, Subway, Wendy's, Ⓞ Jo-Ann Crafts, Office Depot, PetCo, Sportsman's Whse, Toyota, Tuesday Morning, Walgreens, W 🛢 Chevron/24hr, Shell/dsl, 🍴 A&W, Azteca Mexican, Buffet City, Burgerville, Chevy's Mexican, ChuckeCheese, Elmer's Rest., Golden Tent BBQ, IHOP, Jamba Juice, Muchas Gracias, Newport Bay Sea🍴 Olive Garden, Outback Steaks, Red Lobster, Red Robin, RoundTable Pizza, Shari's/24hr, Starbucks, Subway, Taco Bell, TCBY, TGIFriday, 🛏 Best Western, Comfort Suites, Ramada, Residence Inn, Rodeway Inn, Staybridge Inn, Ⓞ Americas Tire, Big Lots, $Tree, Ford, JC Penney, Lincoln/Mercury, Macy's, Old Navy, Ross, Sears/auto, Target, VW, mall, RV park
28	Mill Plain Rd, E 🛢 Chevron, 76/Circle K, Shell/dsl, 🍴

(side bars) E / W ; OR ; PORTLAND ; N / S PORTLAND AREA

INTERSTATE 205 CONT'D (Portland)

N ↑ S

PORTLAND AREA

Exit	Services
28	Continued
	Baskin-Robbins, Burger King, Burgerville, DQ, Elmer's Rest., Irishtown Grill, Kings Buffet, McDonald's, Muchas Gracias Mexican, Pizza Hut, Quiznos, Shari's, Starbucks, Taco Bell, 🏠 Best Western, Extended Stay America, Motel 6, 🅾 $Tree, Fred Meyer, PetCo, Schuck's Parts, Schwab Tire, 7-11, W 🅿 Arco, 76, 7-11, 🍴 Arby's, Jack-in-the-Box, Subway, Taco Del Mar, 🅾 🅗, Chevrolet, Walmart, Walgreens, auto/tire repair, vet, transmissions
27	WA 14, Vancouver, Camas, Columbia River Gorge
25mm	Oregon/Washington state line. Columbia River. **Exits 27-36 are in Washington.**
24	122nd Ave, ⤴ Way, E 🍴 Burger King, China Wok, CoffeeHouse, Jack-in-the-Box, McDonald's, Shari's, Subway, 🏠 Clarion, Comfort Suites, Courtyard, Fairfield Inn, Hilton Garden, Holiday Inn Express, La Quinta, Residence Inn, Shilo Inn/rest., SpringHill Suites, Staybridge Suites, Super 8, 🅾 Home Depot, W 🏠 Embassy Suites, Hampton Inn, Loft Hotel, Sheraton/rest., 🅾 Best Buy, PetsMart, Ross, Staples, ⤴
23b a	US 30 byp, Columbia Blvd, E 🅿 Leather's Fuel/dsl, Shell/dsl, 🍴 Bill's Steaks, Elmer's Rest., 🏠 Best Western, Carolina Motel, Comfort Inn, Econolodge, Quality Inn, Rodeway Inn, 🅾 🅗, W 🅿 Shell, 🏠 Best Value Inn, Holiday Inn, Radisson, Ramada Inn, 🅾 camping
22	I-84 E, US 30 E, to The Dalles
21b	I-84 W, US 30 W, to Portland
21a	Glisan St, E on NE 102nd St 🅿 Arco, 76, 🍴 Applebee's, Carl's Jr, Jamba Juice, Quizno's, McDonald's, 🅾 Fred Meyer, Kohl's, Office Depot, Ross, WinCo Foods
20	Stark St, Washington St, E 🅿 Chevron/dsl, 🍴 Arby's, Baja Fresh, Burger King, Denny's, Elmer's Rest., Jack-in-the-Box, McMenamin's Rest., Old Chicago Pizza, Olive Garden, Panda Express, Pizza Shmizza, Red Robin, Saylor's, Starbucks, Village Inn, 🏠 Chestnut Tree Inn, Holiday Inn Express, 🅾 Big Lots, Home Depot, Target, Tuesday Morning, mall, W 🍴 Stark St Pizza, Taco Bell, 🏠 Motel 6, 🅾 7-11
19	US 26, Division St, E 🅿 Space Age/dsl, 🅾 🅗, W 🅿 76, 🍴 Burgerville, Campbell's BBQ, ChuckeCheese, McDonald's, Subway, 🅾 Jo-Ann Fabrics, 7-11, Walmart
17	Foster Rd, **1 mi** W 🅿 Chevron, 76, Shell, 🍴 Arby's, Burger King, IHOP, McDonald's, Wendy's, 🏠 Econolodge, Home Depot, 🅾 U-Haul
16	Johnson Creek Blvd, W 🅿 76, 🍴 Applebee's, Arby's, Bajio, Burger King, Carl's Jr, Jack-in-the-Box, Krispy

PORTLAND AREA

Exit	Services
16	Continued
	Kreme, McDonald's, Outback Steaks, Pizza Shmizza, Quizno's, Ron's Café, RoundTable Pizza, Starbucks, Subway, Taco Bell, WeiWei, 🅾 Best Buy, Fred Meyer/gas, Home Depot, Knecht's Parts, PetsMart, RV Ctrs, Schuck's Parts, 7-11, Trader Joe's, Walgreens, Walmart
14	Sunnyside Rd, E 🅿 76, 🍴 A&W/KFC, Baja Fresh, Chen's Kitchen, Domino's, Gustav's Grill, Izzy's Pizza, KFC, McMenamin's, Quizno's, Starbucks, Subway, TCBY, 🏠 Best Western, Days Inn, 🅾 🅗, Office Depot, W 🅿 Texaco/dsl/24hr, 🍴 Burger King, CA Pizza Kitchen, Chevy's Mexican, Chili's, Claim Jumper, Denny's, DQ, Macaroni Grill, McDonald's, Noodles&Co, Old Spaghetti Factory, Olive Garden, Pizza Hut, Red Robin, Stanford's Rest., Taco Time, Wendy's, 🏠 Courtyard, Monarch Hotel/rest., 🅾 America's Tire, Barnes&Noble, JC Penney, Kohl's, Macy's, Nordstroms, Old Navy, PetCo, Sears/auto, Target, U-Haul, Walgreens, World Mkt, mall
13	OR 224, to Milwaukie, W 🅾 K-Mart, Lowe's Whse
12	OR 213, to Milwaukie, E 🅿 Chevron/24hr, Pacific Pride, Shell, 🍴 Denny's, Elmer's, KFC, McDonald's, Subway, Taco Bell/24hr, Wendy's, 🏠 Clackamas Inn, Hampton Inn, 🅾 Fred Meyer, 7-11, W 🏠 Comfort Suites
11	82nd Dr, Gladstone, W 🅿 Arco/24hr, Chevron, 🍴 McDonald's, 🏠 Oxford Suites, 🅾 Harley-Davidson, Safeway, Starbucks
10	OR 213, Park Place, E 🅿 76/Pacific Pride/dsl, 🅾 🅗, Home Depot, to Oregon Trail Ctr
9	OR 99E, Oregon City, E 🅿 Chevron, 76, 🍴 KFC, 🅾 🅗, NAPA, Subaru, W 🍴 La Hacienda Mexican, McDonald's, Shari's, Starbucks, Subway, Thai Rest., 🏠 Best Western Rivershore, 🅾 Coastal Ranch Store, $Tree, Firestone/auto, Michael's, Rite Aid
8.5mm	Willamette River
8	OR 43, W Linn, Lake Oswego, E 🅾 museum, W 🅿 76, Shell/dsl/24hr, 🍴 Blue Sage Cafe, Centanni's Pizza, Coldstone Creamery, Starbucks, Taco Del Mar, 🅾 Mkt of Choice, USPO
7mm	viewpoint nb, hist marker
6	10th St, W Linn St, E 🅿 Chevron/LP, 76, 🍴 5 Guys Burgers, Ixtapa Mexican, McDonald's, McMenamin's Rest., Papa Murphy's, Rose's Rest., Shari's/24hr, Wilamet Coffee House, 🅾 Oil Can Henry's, Schwab Tire, W 🍴 Jack-in-the-Box, Starbucks, Subway, 🅾 Albertsons/Sav-On
4mm	Tualatin River
3	Stafford Rd, Lake Oswego, W 🍴 Corner Saloon, 🅾 🅗
0mm	I-205 begins/ends on I-5, exit 288.

OR / PA

PENNSYLVANIA

INTERSTATE 70

E ↑ W

Exit	Services
171mm	Pennsylvania/Maryland state line, **Welcome Ctr wb, full ♿ facilities, info, 📞, vending, 🧺 litter barrels, petwalk**
168	US 522 N, Warfordsburg, N 🅿 Exxon/dsl, S fireworks
163	PA 731 S, Amaranth
156	PA 643, Town Hill, N 🏠 Day's Inn, 🅾 NAPA
153mm	**rest area eb, full ♿ facilities, 📞, 🧺, litter barrels, vending, petwalk**
151	PA 915, Crystal Spring, N 🍴 CornerStone Family

Exit	Services
151	Continued
	Rest., 🅾 auto repair, S 🅾 Country Store/USPO
149	US 30 W, to Everett, S Breezewood (no immediate wb return), **3 mi** S 🍴 McDonald's, 🏠 Penn Aire Motel, Redwood Motel, Wildwood Motel
147	US 30, Breezewood, **Services on US 30** 🅿 BP/dsl, Citgo, Exxon/dsl, Mobil/dsl/24hr, Sheetz/24hr, Shell, Sunoco/dsl/café, TA/dsl/rest./24hr/@, Texaco/Subway, 🍴 Arby's, Big John's Buffet, Bob Evans, Burger King, DQ, Denny's, Domino's, Family House Rest., Hardee's, KFC, McDonald's, Perkins, Pizza Hut, Taco Bell,

INTERSTATE 70 CONT'D

Exit	Services
147	Continued
	Wendy's, 🏨 Best Western, Breezewood Motel, Comfort Inn/rest., Econolodge, Holiday Inn Express, Penn Aire Motel, Quality Inn, Ramada Inn, Wiltshire Motel, 🅾 museum I-70 W and I-76/PA Turnpike W run together

I-70 and I-76/PA Turnpike run together 71 mi. For I-70 and I-76/PA TPK exits 146-75, see Pennsylvania Interstate 76/PA TPK.

Exit	Services
57b a	I-70 W, US 119, PA 66 (toll), New Stanton, N 🛢 Exxon, Sheetz, 🍴 Bob Evans, Campy's Pizza, Eat'n Park, McDonald's, Pagano's Rest., Pizza Hut, Subway, Szechuan Wok, Wendy's, 🏨 Best Value Inn, Budget Inn, Comfort Inn, Days Inn, EconoLodge, Fairfield Inn, Howard Johnson, Super 8, S 🛢 BP/7-11/dsl, Sunoco, 🍴 Cracker Barrel, La Tavola Risorante, TJ's Rest., 🅾 USPO
54	Madison, N KOA, S truck repair
53	Yukon
51b a	PA 31, West Newton, S Volvo/Mack
49	Smithton, N 🛢 Citgo/rest./dsl/scales/@, ⛽FLYING J/Denny's/dsl/LP/scales/24hr/@
46b a	PA 51, Pittsburgh, N 🛢 BFS/dsl, 🍴 Burger King, 🏨 Comfort Inn, 🅾 Buick/Cadillac/Chevrolet, Ford/Kia, S 🛢 GetGo/dsl, PP/dsl, 🍴 Clubhouse Grille, 🏨 Belle Vernon Hotel, Knotty Pine Motel, 🅾 golf
44	Arnold City
43b a	(43 from eb)PA 201, to PA 837, Fayette City, S 🛢 Exxon/dsl, 🍴 A&W/LJ Silver, Burger King, China 88 Buffet, Denny's, Eat'n Park, Hoss' Rest., Italian Village Pizza, KFC, Little Bamboo, McDonald's, Old Mexico, Pizza Hut, Ponderosa, Sonny's Grille, Starbucks, Subway, Wendy's, 🏨 Hampton Inn, 🅾 Advance Parts, Aldi Foods, AT&T, BigLots, Curves, CVS Drug, $General, $Tree, Giant Eagle Foods, GNC, Jo-Ann Fabrics, K-Mart, Lowe's, Radio Shack, Rite Aid, Staples, Walmart
42a	Monessen
42	N Belle Vernon, S 🛢 BP/McDonald's/7-11, Sunoco/dsl, 🍴 DQ
41	PA 906, Belle Vernon
40mm	Monongahela River
40	PA 88, Charleroi, N 🛢 BP, Gulf, PP/dsl, Sunoco, 🍴 La Fiesta, McDonald's, Subway/TCBY, 🅾 🏥, Rite Aid, Save-A-Lot Foods, Valley Tire
39	Speers, N 🍴 Lorraine's Rest., S 🛢 Exxon/dsl
37b a	PA 43 (toll), N to Pittsburgh, S to CA
36	Lover (from wb, no re-entry)
35	PA 481, Centerville
32b a	PA 917, Bentleyville, S 🛢 BP/dsl, 🚚/DQ/Subway/dsl/scales/24hr, 🍴 Burger King, King Rest., King of the Hill Steaks, McDonald's, Pizza Hut, 🏨 Best Western, Holiday Inn Express, 🅾 Advance Parts, Blue Beacon, $General, Ford, Giant Eagle Foods, Rite Aid
31	to PA 136, Kammerer, N 🏨 Carlton Motel
27	Dunningsville, S 🏨 Avalon Motel
25	PA 519, to Eighty Four, S 🛢 BP/7-11 Diner/dsl/24hr, Sunoco/dsl
21	I-79 S, to Waynesburg.

I-70 W and I-79 N run together 3.5 mi.

Exit	Services
20	PA 136, Beau St, S to Washington&Jefferson Coll
19b a	US 19, Murtland Ave, N 🛢 GetGo, 🍴 Applebee's,

Exit	Services
19b a	Continued
	Arby's, Bruster's, Cracker Barrel, Fusion Steaks, Jimmy John's, Krispy Kreme, Max&Erma's, McDonald's, Moe's SW Grill, Outback Steaks, Panera Bread, Ponderosa, Quiznos, Red Lobster, Red Robin, Rita's Custard, Starbucks, Subway, TX Roadhouse, TGIFriday's, Wong's Wok, 🏨 SpringHill Suites, 🅾 Aldi Foods, AT&T, Dick's, $Tree, Ford, Giant Eagle Foods, GNC, Honda, Hyundai, Kohl's, Lowe's, Mercedes, Michael's, Nissan, PetCo, Petsmart, Radio Shack, Sam's Club/gas, Save-A-Lot Foods, Target, Toyota/Scion, Walmart/McDonald's, urgent care, vet, S 🛢 BP/dsl, Exxon/dsl, Sunoco, Valero, 🍴 A&W/LJ Silver, Bob Evans, CiCi's Pizza, Donut Connection, Eat'n Park, Evergreen Chinese, Grand China, KFC, Old Mexico, Papa John's, Pizza Hut, Waffle House, 🏨 Hampton Inn, Motel 6, 🅾 🏥, BigLots, Buick/GMC, Chevrolet, Curves, Firestone/auto, Home Depot, JC Penney, Jo-Ann Fabrics, Staples, Subaru
18	I-79 N, to Pittsburgh.

I-70 E and I-79 S run together 3.5 mi.

Exit	Services
17	PA 18, Jefferson Ave, Washington, N 🛢 GetGo/dsl, 🍴 DQ, McDonald's, 🅾 Family$, Rite Aid, S 🛢 Valero/dsl, 🍴 Burger King, China Express, Domino's, 4Star Pizza, Little Caesars, Subway, 🅾 Advance Parts, AutoZone, CVS Drug, $General, Shop'n Save Foods, Walgreens, USPO
16	Jessop Place, Jessop Place, N 🛢 Citgo, S auto/truck repair
15	US 40, Chesnut St, Washington, N 🍴 USA Steaks, 🅾 Food Land, S 🛢 Exxon, Sunoco/dsl, Valero, 🍴 Bob Evans, Denny's, El Paso Mexican, Garfield's Rest., LJ Silver, McDonald's, Pizza Hut, Taco Bell, Wendy's, 🏨 Comfort Suites, Days Inn, Ramada Inn, Red Roof Inn, 🅾 BonTon, Gander Mtn, Macy's, Rite Aid, Sears/auto, mall
11	PA 221, Taylorstown, N 🛢 BP/dsl, 🅾 truck repair
6	PA 231, to US 40, Claysville, N 🛢 Exxon, S 🛢 Petro/BP/Huddle House/Subway/dsl/scales/24hr/@
5mm	Welcome Ctr/weigh sta eb, full ♿ facilities, 🚻, vending, 🗑 litter barrels, petwalk
1	W Alexander
0mm	Pennsylvania/West Virginia state line

INTERSTATE 76

Exit	Services
354mm	Pennsylvania/New Jersey state line, Delaware River, Walt Whitman Bridge
351	Front St, I-95 (from wb), N to Trenton, S to Chester
350	Packer Ave, 7th St, to I-95 (fromeb), S 🏨 Holiday Inn, 🅾 to sports complex
349	to I-95, PA 611, Broad St, N 🛢 Citgo
348	PA 291, W to Chester (exits left from wb)
347a	to I-95 S (exits left from wb)
347b	Passyunk Ave, Oregon Ave, N 🍴 Burger King, McDonald's, 🅾 BJ's Whse, Home Depot, Ross, ShopRite, S 🅾 sports complex
346c	28th St, Vare Ave, Mifflin St (from wb)
346b	Grays Ferry Ave, University Ave, N 🍴 Little Caesars, McDonald's, 🅾 PathMark Foods, Radio Shack, USPO, S 🛢 Citgo, Hess/dsl, 🅾 🏥
346a	South St (exits left from wb)
345	30th St, Market St, downtown
344	I-676 E, US 30 E, to Philadelphia (no return from eb)
343	Spring Garden St, Haverford

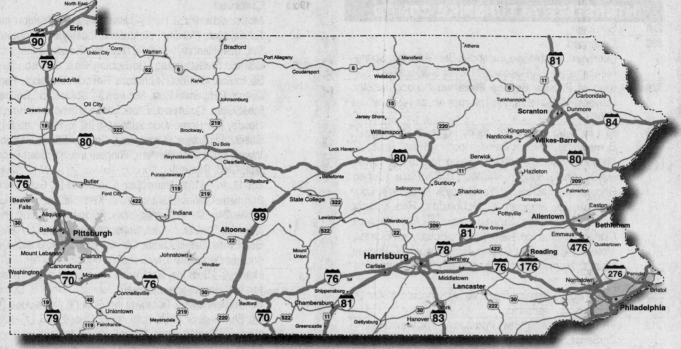

INTERSTATE 76 CONT'D	**E**

E
↑
↓
W

INTERSTATE 76 CONT'D

Exit	Services
342	US 13, US 30 W, Girard Ave, **S** Philadelphia Zoo, E Fairmount Park
341	Montgomery Dr, W River Dr, **S** W Fairmount Park
340b	US 1 N, Roosevelt Blvd, to Philadelphia
339	US 1 S, **S** 🍴 CA Pizza Kitchen, Chipotle Mexican, Houlihans, PeiWei Asian, Potbelly's, Starbucks, TGIFriday's, 🛏 Crowne Plaza, 🄾 Target, Verizon
340a	Lincoln Dr, Kelly Dr, to Germantown
338	Belmont Ave, Green Lane, **S** 🅿 Sunoco, 🄾 WaWa, St Police
337	Hollow Rd (from wb), Gladwyne
332	PA 23 (from wb), Conshohocken, **N** 🛏 Marriott
331b a	I-476, PA 28 (from eb), to Chester, Conshohocken
330	PA 320, Gulph Mills, **S** to Villanova U
329	Weadley Rd (from wb), **N** 🅿 Exxon
328b a	US 202 N, to King of Prussia, **N** 🅿 Citgo, Exxon/dsl, Lukoil, Shell, Sunoco, WaWa, 🍴 Bahama Breeze, Baja Fresh, Burger King, CA Pizza Kitchen, Capital Grille, Champp's, Cheesecake Factory, Chili's, Fox&Hound, Gino's, Joe's Crabshack, Lonestar Steaks, Maggiano's, Morton's Steaks, Panera Bread, Red Lobster, Ruby's Diner, Sullivan's Steaks, TGIFriday's, Uno Grill, 🛏 Best Western, Clarion, Comfort Inn, Crowne Plaza, Fairfield Inn, Hampton Inn, Holiday Inn, Hotel Sierra, Motel 6, 🄾 Acme Foods, Best Buy, Bloomingdale's, Costco, Home Depot, JC Penney, Lord&Taylor, Macy's, Neiman Marcus, Nordstrom, Old Navy, Sears/auto, mall, vet
327	US 202 S, to US 420 W, Goddard Blvd Valley Forge Park
326	I-76 wb becomes I-76/PA Tpk to Ohio
	For I-76 westbound to Ohio, see I-76/PA Turnpike.

INTERSTATE 76 TURNPIKE

Exit	Services
	PA Tpk runs wb as I-276.
359	I-276 continues to NJ, connecting with NJ TPK,

359	Continued Pennsylvania/New Jersey state line, Delaware River Bridge
358	US 13, Delaware Valley, **N** 🅿 BP, WaWa, 🍴 Dallas Diner, 🛏 Comfort Inn, Day's Inn, Ramada Inn, 🄾 auto repair, 7-11, U-Haul, vet, **S** 🅿 LukOil/dsl, Sunoco/dsl, Valero, 🍴 Burger King, Gigi's Pizza, Golden Eagle Diner, Italian Family Pizza, 🛏 Villager Lodge, 🄾 Buick, $General, Mr. Transmission
352mm	**Neshaminy Service Plaza, wb Welcome Ctr,** 🅿 Sunoco/dsl/24hr, 🍴 Burger King, Nathan's, 🄾 Starbucks, **eb** 🅿 Sunoco/dsl, 🍴 Breyer's, HotDog Co, McDonald's, Nathan's
351	US 1, to I-95, to Philadelphia, **N** 🍴 Bob Evans, Chick-fil-A, Cracker Barrel, Longhorn Steaks, On The Border, 99, Red Robin, Ruby Tuesday, Starbucks, Wendy's, 🛏 Courtyard, Hampton Inn, Holiday Inn Select, 🄾 Buick/GMC, Home Depot, Lowes Whse, Macy's, Sears/auto, Target, Walmart, mall, **S** 🅿 Exxon/Subway, LukOil, Sunoco/dsl, 🍴 Dunkin Donuts, 🛏 Comfort Inn, Howard Johnson, Knight's Inn, Neshaminy Inn, Radisson, Red Roof Inn, Sunrise Inn, 🄾 Toyota/Scion
343	PA 611, Willow Grove, **N** 🅿 Shell, 🍴 Carrabba's, 🛏 Candlewood Suites (5mi), Courtyard, 🄾 H, **S** 🅿 Hess/dsl, Shell, Sunoco, 🍴 Bonefish Grill, China Garden, Domino's, Dunkin Donuts, Friendly's, McDonald's, Nino's Pizza, Ooka Japanese, Starbucks, Williamson Rest., 🛏 Hampton Inn, 🄾 Audi/Infiniti, Best Buy, PepBoys, 7-11, Staples, repair, transmissions
340	to VA Dr, EZ tagholder only, no trucks, no return eb
339	PA 309, Ft Washington, **N** 🅿 Gulf, LukOil/dsl, 🍴 Dunkin Donuts, Friendly's, Subway, 🛏 Best Western, Hilton Garden, Holiday Inn, 🄾 BMW, Mercedes, Volvo, WaWa
334	PA Tpk NE Extension, I-476, **S** to Philadelphia, **N** to Allentown
333	Germantown Pike, to Norristown, **N** 🅿 LukOil/dsl, Sunoco/Dunkin Donuts, 🍴 California Pizza Kitchen, Houlihan's, PF Chang's, Red Stone Grill, Starbucks, 🛏

PA

INTERSTATE 76 TURNPIKE CONT'D

Exit	Services
E ↕ W	
333	Continued Courtyard, DoubleTree, Extended Stay America, Spring-Hill Suites, 🅾 🏥, Boscov's, Macy's, S 🛢 LukOil
328mm	**King of Prussia Service Plaza wb** Sunoco/dsl/24hr, Breyer's, McDonald's, PA Tpk runs eb as I-276, wb as I-76.
326	I-76 E, to US 202, I-476, Valley Forge, N 🛢 Shell, 🍴 Burger King, Cracker Barrel, Hooters, Hoss' Rest., 🏨 MainStay Suites, Radisson, Sleep Inn, S 🛢 Exxon, LukOil, Shell, Sunoco, WaWa, 🍴 CA Pizza Kitchen, Cheesecake Factory, Chili's, Denny's, Houlihan's, Lone Star Steaks, Maggiano's, McDonald's, Red Lobster, Ruth's Chris Steaks, Sullivan Steaks, 🏨 Best Western, Clarion, Comfort Inn, Hampton Inn, Holiday Inn Express, Motel 6, 🅾 Best Buy, Costco, Home Depot, JC Penney, Macy's, Neiman Marcus, Nordstrom, Sears/auto, Walmart, mall
325mm	**Valley Forge Service Plaza eb** 🛢 Sunoco/dsl/24hr, 🍴 Burger King, Starbucks
312	PA 100, to Downingtown, Pottstown, N 🛢 WaWa/dsl, 🅾 CarSense, Harley-Davidson, S 🛢 Sunoco/dsl, WaWa, 🍴 Applebee's, Chick-fil-A, Hoss's, Isaac's Deli, Red Robin, Starbucks, Uno Grill, 🏨 Comfort Suites, Extended Stay America, Fairfield Inn, Hampton Inn, Residence Inn, 🅾 🏥, Genuardi's Foods, Giant Foods, Walgreens
305mm	**Camiel Service Paza wb** Sunoco/dsl/24hr, Roy Rogers, Sbarro's, Starbucks
298	I-176, PA 10, to Reading, Morgantown, N 🍴 Arby's, DQ, Dunkin Donuts, Sonic, Subway, 🏨 Economy Lodge, Heritage Motel/rest., 🅾 🏥, $Tree, GNC, Lowe's, Verizon, Walmart, S 🛢 Exxon, Sheetz, 🍴 Heritage Rest., McDonald's, Rita's Custard, 🏨 Holiday Inn, 🅾 Chevrolet, Rite Aid
290mm	**Bowmansville Service Plaza eb** 🛢 Sunoco/dsl/24hr, 🍴 Burger King, Hershey's, Starbucks
286	US 322, PA 272, to Reading, Ephrata, N 🛢 Citgo/dsl, Turkey Hill, 🍴 Baskin-Robbins/Dunkin Donuts, Subway, 🏨 Black Horse Inn/rest., Comfort Inn, Red Carpet Inn, Red Roof Inn, 🅾 S 🏨 Hampton Inn (11mi)
266	PA 72, to Lebanon, Lancaster, N 🛢 Hess/Blimpie/dsl, Sunoco/Chester's, 🍴 Farmer's Hope Inn Rest., 🏨 Holiday Inn Express (17 mi), Penns Woods Inn, Red Carpet Inn, 🅾 🏥, Harley-Davidson, NAPA, auto repair, S 🍴 Hitz Mkt/deli, 🏨 Hampton Inn, 🅾 Mt Hope Winery, Pinch Pond Camping
259mm	**Lawn Service Plaza wb** 🛢 Sunoco/dsl/24hr, 🍴 Burger King, Starbucks, 🅾 RV dump
250mm	**Highspire Service Plaza eb** 🛢 Sunoco/dsl/24hr, 🍴 Hershey's Ice Cream, Sbarro's, Starbucks
247	I-283, PA 283, to Harrisburg, Harrisburg East, Hershey, N 🛢 Exxon/dsl, Sunoco, 🍴 Bob Evans, Capitol Diner, Eat'n Park, McDonald's, Taco Bell, Wendy's, 🏨 Best Western, Courtyard, Days Inn, EconoLodge, Holiday Inn Express, Howard Johnson, La Quinta, Red Roof Inn, Rodeway Inn, Sheraton, Super 8, Travelodge, Wingate Inn, Wyndham, 🅾 Harrisburg East Camping, JC Penney, Kia, Target
246mm	Susquehannah River
242	I-83, Harrisburg West, N 🛢 Shell/dsl, Hess/Dunkin Donuts, 🍴 Bob Evans, Doc Holliday's Rest., John's Diner,
242	Continued McDonald's, Pizza Hut, 🏨 Best Western, Comfort Inn, Fairfield Inn, Holiday Inn, Motel 6, Quality Inn, Rodeway Inn, Travel Inn, 🅾 vet, S 🏨 Days Inn, Keystone Inn
236	US 15, to Gettysburg, Gettysburg Pike, Harrisburg, N 🛢 Exxon, Gulf/dsl, 🍴 Isaac's Rest, McDonald's, Papa John's, Peppermill Rest, Subway, 🏨 Comort Inn, Country Inn&Suites, Courtyard, EconoLodge, Hampton Inn/rest., Holiday Inn, Homewood Suites, 🅾 🏥, U-Haul, vet, S 🛢 Sheetz, 🍴 Arby's, Burger King, Cracker Barrel, Quiznos, Wendy's, 🏨 Best Western, Wingate Inn, 🅾 Giant Food/gas, GNC, Rite Aid
226	US 11, to I-81, to Harrisburg, Carlisle, N 🛢 Gulf, Petro/Iron Skillet/dsl/scales/24hr/@, ✈FLYING J/Denny's/dsl/LP/scales/24hr/@, 🌑Loves/Wendy's/dsl/scales/24hr, Pioneer/dsl, Shell/dsl/scales, Sunoco/Subway/dsl, 🍴 Arby's, Bob Evans, Carelli's Subs, Country Club Diner, Dunkin Donuts, Embers Steaks, McDonald's, Middlesex Diner, Waffle House, 🏨 Best Inn, Best Value Inn, EconoLodge, Hampton Inn, Hotel Carlisle, Howard Johnson, Motel 6, Quality Inn, Residence Inn, Rodeway Inn, Super 8, Travelodge, 🅾 🏥, Blue Beacon, S 🛢 Rutter's/dsl, Sheetz/E85, 🍴 Hoss' Rest., 🏨 Best Western, Motel 6, 🅾 🏥, U-Haul, vet
219mm	**Plainfield Service Plaza eb** 🛢 Sunoco/dsl/24hr, 🍴 Hershey's Ice Cream, Roy Rogers, 🅾 gifts
203mm	**Blue Mtn Service Plaza wb** 🛢 Sunoco/dsl/24hr, 🍴 Hershey's Ice Cream, Nathan's, Roy Rogers, Uno
201	PA 997, to Shippensburg, Blue Mountain, S 🏨 Johnnie's Motel/rest., Kenmar Motel
199mm	Blue Mountain Tunnel
197mm	Kittatinny Tunnel
189	PA 75, Willow Hill, S 🏨 Willow Hill Motel/rest.
187mm	Tuscarora Tunnel
180	US 522, Mt Union, Ft Littleton, N 🛢 Gulf/dsl, Noname/dsl, 🍴 The Family Rest., 🏨 Downes Motel, 🅾 🏥, st police
172mm	**Sideling Hill Service Plaza both lanes** S 🛢 Sunoco/dsl/24hr, 🍴 Burger King, Famiglia Pizza, Hershey's Ice Cream, Popeye's, Starbucks, 🅾 gifts, RV dump
161	US 30, Breezewood, **Services on US 30** 🛢 TA/Gateway Rest/rest./dsl/24hr/@, BP/dsl, Exxon/dsl, Petro/Blue Beacon, Sheetz, Shell/Blimpie, Sunoco/café/dsl, Valero/dsl, 🍴 Bob Evans, DQ, Denny's, Domino's, Family House Rest., Hardee's, KFC, McDonald's, Perkins, Pizza Hut, Quiznos, Starbucks, Subway, Taco Bell, Wendy's, 🏨 Best Western, Breezewood Motel, Holiday Inn Express, Howard Johnson, Penn Aire Motel, Quality Inn, Ramada Inn, Village Motel, Wiltshire Motel, 🅾 Radio Shack, camping, museum, truck/tire repair
161mm	I-70 W and I-76/PA Turnpike W run together
148mm	**Midway Service Plaza both lanes**, Sunoco/dsl/24hr, Hershey's Ice Cream, Quiznos, Sbarro's, Starbucks, gifts
146	I-99, US 220, Bedford, N 🛢 Gulf/dsl, PP/dsl, Sheetz/dsl/24hr, Shell/Subway/dsl, 🍴 Arena Rest., Bedford Diner, Carriage House Rest., Denny's, Ed's Steaks, Hoss' Rest., LJ Silver, McDonald's, Pizza Hut, Wendy's, 🏨 Best Value Inn, Best Western, Budget Host, Fairfield Inn, Hillcrest Motel, Quality Inn, Relax Inn, 🅾 to Shawnee SP (10mi), Blue Knob SP (15mi), S 🏨 Hampton Inn
123mm	Allegheny Tunnel
112mm	**Somerset Service Plaza both lanes** Sunoco/dsl/24hr, 🍴 Famiglia Pizza, Hershey's Ice Cream, Quiznos, Roy Rogers, Starbucks, 🅾 gifts

PA

HARRISBURG

BREEZEWOOD

INTERSTATE 76 TURNPIKE CONT'D

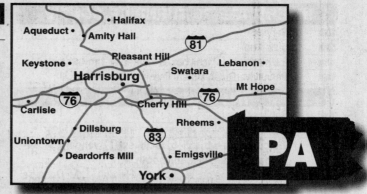

Exit	Services
110	PA 601, to US 219, Somerset, N KwikFill/dsl, Sheetz, Hog Father's BBQ, Hoss' Rest., King's Rest., Pizza Hut, $Inn, Economy Inn, Advance Parts, Chrysler/ Jeep, Ford, tires, S Somerset TravelCtr/dsl/@, Turkey Hill, Arby's, Bruster's Ice Cream, DQ, Donut Connection, Eat'n Park, KFC, LJ Silver, Maggie Mae's Café, McDonald's, Pine Grill, Ruby Tuesday, Starbucks, Subway, Summit Diner, Wendy's, Best Value Inn, Best Western, Budget Host, Budget Inn, Comfort Inn, Days Inn, Hampton Inn, Holiday Inn, Quality Inn, Super 8, Dodge, Harley-Davidson, Volvo
91	PA 711, PA 31, to Ligonier, Donegal, N Tall Cedars Rest., S BP/McDonald's, Exxon/Subway/dsl, Sunoco/dsl, DQ, Days Inn, camping, golf
78mm	**New Stanton Service Plaza wb** Sunoco/dsl/24hr, Burger King, Hershey's Ice Cream, Quiznos, Starbucks, , I-70 E runs with I-76/PA Turnpike eb.
75	I-70 W, US 119, PA 66 (toll), New Stanton, S BP/7-11/dsl, Exxon, Sheetz, Sunoco, Bob Evans, Campy's Pizza, Cracker Barrel, Eat'n Park, La Tavola Risorante, McDonald's, Pagano's Rest., Pizza Hut, Subway, Szechuan Wok, TJ's Rest., Wendy's, Best Value Inn, Budget Inn, Comfort Inn, Days Inn, EconoLodge, Fairfield Inn, Howard Johnson, Super 8, USPO
74.6mm	**Hemphill Service Plaza eb** Sunoco/dsl/24hr, Breyer's, McDonald's, atm
67	US 30, to Greensburg, Irwin, N BP/dsl, Sheetz/24hr, H, Ford, tires, vet, S Marathon/7-11, Sunoco/24hr, Arby's, Bob Evans, Burger King, CiCi's Pizza, Denny's, DQ, Dunkin Donuts, Eat'n Park, KFC, LJ Silver, Los Campesinos Mexican, McDonald's, Panera Bread, Pizza Hut, Subway, Taco Bell, Teddy's Rest., Wendy's, Conley Inn, Holiday Inn Express, Advance Parts, Aldi Foods, CarQuest, $Tree, Giant Eagle Foods/24hr, GNC, Kohl's, Radio Shack, Rite Aid, Target
61mm	parking area eb
57	I-376, US 22, to Pittsburgh, Monroeville, S Citgo/ dsl, Exxon, Sheetz, Sunoco, A&W/LJ Silver, Arby's, Baskin-Robbins, Bob Evan's, Chick-fil-A, China Palace, ChuckeCheese, CiCi's Pizza, Damon's, Denny's, Golden Corral, Honeybaked Ham, Max&Erma's, McDonald's, Olive Garden, Outback Steaks, Panera Bread, Park Diner, Pizza Hut, Primanti Bro's, Quizno's, Red Lobster, Starbucks, Taco Bell, TGIFridays, Wendy's, Comfort Suites, Courtyard, Day's Inn, Extended Stay America, Hampton Inn, Holiday Inn, Radisson Inn, Red Roof Inn, Springhill Suites, H, Aamco, Big Lots, Border's Books, Firestone/auto, Honda, Jaguar/Land Rover, Jo-Ann Fabrics, Marshall's, Michael's, Lowes Whse, NTB, Office Depot, Old Navy, PetCo, Pet Land, Radio Shack, Rite Aid, to Three Rivers Stadium
49mm	**Oakmont Service Plaza eb** Sunoco/dsl/24hr, FoodCourt, litter barrels,
48.5mm	Allegheny River
48	PA 28, to Pittsburgh, Allegheny Valley, New Kensington, N Shell/24hr, Sunoco, Pizza Hut, Subway, CarQuest, Rite Aid, S Exxon/dsl, GetGo, Bob Evans, Bruster's, Denny's, Gino Bro's Pizza, KFC, King's Rest., McDonald's, Ponderosa, Primanti Bros, Subway, Taco

Exit	Services
48	Continued Bell, Wendy's, Comfort Inn, Day's Inn, Holiday Inn Express, Super 8, Valley Motel, Advance Parts, Ford, Target
41mm	parking area/call box eb
39	PA 8, to Pittsburgh, Butler Valley, 0-1 mi N Exxon/7-11/dsl, GetGo, Sheetz/24hr, Sunoco, Applebees, Atria's Rest., Bruno's Pizza, Buffalo Wild Wings, Eat'n Park, King's Rest., Max&Erma's, McDonald's, Sonic, Starbucks, Taco Bell, Wendy's, Comfort Inn, Pittsburgh N Motel/rest, Advance Parts, Curves, Dodge, $Tree, Giant Eagle Foods, GNC, Kohl's, Lowes Whse, Rite Aid, Shop'n Save Foods, Target, TJ Maxx, Walmart/auto/ drugs, S BP, Sunoco/dsl, Arby's, Brusters, Burger King, China Bistro, KFC, McDonald's, Pasquales Pizza, Panera Bread, Pizza Hut, Subway, Vocelli Pizza, Wendy's, H, AutoZone, Firestone/auto, Goodyear/auto, Home Depot, Mr. Tire, Radio Shack, Rite Aid, USPO
31mm	**Toll Plaza wb**
28	to I-79, to Cranberry, Pittsburgh, N BP/dsl, Exxon/dsl/24hr, GetGo, Sheetz/24hr, Sunoco/dsl, A&W/LJ Silver, Adrian's Pizza, Arby's, Bob Evans, Boston Mkt, Bravo Italian, Burger King, Chipotle Mexican, CiCi's Pizza, DQ, Denny's, Dominichi's Rest., Dunkin Donuts, Dynasty, Eat'n Park, 5 Guys Burgers, Hartner's Rest., HotDog Shoppe, Houlihan's, Ichiban Steakhouse, King's Rest., Krispy Kreme, LoneStar Steaks, Mad Mex, Max&Erma's, McDonald's, Montecello's Grill, Panera Bread, Perkins, Pizza Hut, Pizza Roma, Primanti Bros, Quaker Steak, Saga Steaks, Subway, UNO, Vocelli Pizza, Wendy's, Comfort Inn, Fairfield Inn, Hampton Inn, Holiday Inn Express, Hyatt Place, Motel 6, Red Roof Inn, Residence Inn, Sheraton, Super 8, Barnes&Noble, Best Buy, Costco/ gas, Dick's, $Tree, GNC, Giant Eagle Foods, Home Depot, Jo-Ann Fabrics, Kuhn's Foods, Marshall's, Michael's, NAPA, Old Navy, PepBoys, PetCo, Radio Shack, Rite Aid, Toyota/Scion, Tuesday Morning, Walgreens, Walmart, mall, transmissions, USPO, vet
23.5mm	pulloff eb
22mm	**Zelienople Service Plaza eb Welcome Ctr,** Sunoco/ dsl/24hr, FoodCourt, crafts, gifts
17mm	parking area eb
13.4mm	parking area eb
13mm	Beaver River
13	PA 8, to Ellwood City, Beaver Valley, N Al's Corner, Subway, Alpine Inn, Beaver Falls Motel, HillTop Motel, Holiday Inn, Lark Motel, H, S Super 8
10	PA 60 (toll), to New Castle, Pittsburgh, S services (6mi), to
6mm	pulloff eb

INTERSTATE 76 TURNPIKE CONT'D

Exit	Services
2mm	pulloff eb
1mm	toll plaza eb, [C], call boxes located at 1 mi intervals
0mm	Pennsylvania/Ohio state line

INTERSTATE 78

E ↕ W

Exit	Services
77mm	Pennsylvania/New Jersey state line, Delaware River
76mm	**Welcome Ctr wb, full [&] facilities, [C], vending, [A], litter barrels, petwalk, toll booth wb**
75	to PA 611, Easton, N [g] TurkeyHill/dsl, [f] McDonald's (1mi), [l] Quality Inn, [o] Crayola Factory, S [g] Exxon
71	PA 33, to Stroudsburg, **1 mi N on Freemansburg Ave** [f] Frank's Pizza, JJ Wong's, Panera Bread, Ruby Tuesday, TX Roadhouse, TGIFriday's, [l] Courtyard, [o] Barnes&Noble, Dick's, Lowe's, Michael's, Pet Supplies+, Staples
67	PA 412, Hellertown, N [g] TurkeyHill/gas, [l] Comfort Suites (3mi), [f] Wendy's, [o] [H], Chevrolet, S [g] Citgo, Exxon/dsl, Lukoil, Sunoco, [f] Antonio's Brick Oven, Rocco's Pizza, Rita's Shakes, Vassi's Drive-In, Waffle House, [l] Holiday Inn Express, [o] CVS Drug, Firestone, 7-11, repair
60b a	PA 145 N, PA 309 S, South Fort St, Quakertown
59	to PA 145 (from eb), Summit Lawn
58	Emaus St (from wb), S [g] Gulf, Sunoco
57	Lehigh St, N [g] Hess/dsl, WaWa, [f] Arby's, Dragon Pond Chinese, IHOP, Palumbo Pizza, Queen City Diner, Subway, Willy Joe's Rest., [l] Best Value Inn, [o] BigLots, CVS Drug, $Tree, Family$, Ford/Lincoln/Mercury, Home Depot, Kia, NSA Mkt, Radio Shack, Redner's Whse, STS Tires/repair, Toyota/Scion, VW, S [g] Lukoil, Pipeline/dsl, Sunoco, TurkeyHill, [f] Brass Rail Rest., Domino's, Dunkin Donuts, McDonald's, Papa John's, Perkins, Pizza Hut/Taco Bell, Rossi's Pizza, Starbucks, Subway, Wendy's, [o] Acura, AT&T, Audi/Mercedes/Porsche, BonTon, Buick/GMC, Cadillac/Chevrolet, Chrysler/Dodge/Jeep, Honda, Hyundai, Mazda, PetCo, Staples, SteinMart, Verizon, Volvo
55	PA 29, Cedar Crest Blvd, N [g] Shell, S [H]
54b a	US 222, Hamilton Blvd, N [g] Hess, [f] Baskin-Robbins/Dunkin Donuts, Boston Mkt, Burger King, Cali Burrito, Carrabba's, Friendly's, Ice Cream World, King George Rest., Mango's Rest, McDonald's, Perkins, Subway, Teppan Steaks, TGIFriday's, Wendy's, [l] Comfort Suites/rest., Holiday Inn Express, Howard Johnson, [o] Dorney Funpark, Dorneyville Drug, Office Depot, Rite Aid, Weis Foods, S [g] WaWa, [f] Dunkin Donuts, Pizza Hut, [l] Wingate Inn, [o] Queen City Tire, Subaru, repair
53	PA 309 (wb only)
51	to I-476, US 22 E, PA 33 N (eb only), Whitehall
49b a	PA 100, Fogelsville, N [f] Arby's, Cracker Barrel, Joe's Pizza, LJ Silver, Panda&Fish Chinese, Pizza Hut, [l] Comfort Inn, Hawthorn Inn, [o] KOA, Rite Aid, STS Tire/repair, S [g] Shell, Sunoco, WaWa, [f] Boston's Grill, Burger King, Florence Italian, Starlite Diner, Taco Bell, Yocco's Hotdogs, [l] Hampton Inn, Hilton Garden, Holiday Inn, Sleep Inn, Staybridge Suites, [o] Clover Hill Winery, Toyota/Scion, st police
45	PA 863, to Lynnport, N [g] Exxon/Subway/dsl, Sunoco/New Smithville Diner/dsl, S [l] Super 8

A L L E N T O W N (vertical, left margin)

PA (left margin box)

Exit	Services
40	PA 737, Krumsville, N [o] Pine Hill Campground, Robin Hill RV Park (4mi), S [g] Shell/dsl, [l] Skyview Rest.
35	PA 143, Lenhartsville, **3 mi S** Robin Hill Park
30	Hamburg, S [f] Hamburg Mkt
29b a	PA 61, to Reading, Pottsville, N [g] Shell/dsl, WaWa/dsl, [f] Baskin-Robbins/Dunkin Donuts, Burger King, Campfire Rest., Cracker Barrel, JA Buffet, LJ Silver/Taco Bell, Logan's Roadhouse, McDonald's, Pappy T's, Pizza Hut, Red Robin, Wendy's, [l] Microtel, [o] AT&T, Boat'n RV Ctr RV, Cabela's Outdoor, GNC, Harley-Davidson (8mi), Hyundai, Lowe's, Pet Supplies+, Toyota/Scion, Verizon, Walmart/Subway
23	Shartlesville, N [g] [Loves]/McDonald's/Subway/dsl/scales/24hr, [l] Dutch Motel, [o] Appalachian Campsites, S [f] Blue Mtn Family Rest., [l] Scottish Inn, [o] Dutch Haus/gifts, antiques, camping, USPO
19	PA 183, Strausstown, N [g] Lukoil, [l] Sheepskin Motel, S [g] Power/dsl
17	PA 419, Rehrersburg, N truck/tire repair
16	Midway, N [g] Exxon/dsl, Sunoco/dsl, [f] Midway Diner, [l] Comfort Inn, S auto/truck repair
15	Grimes
13	PA 501, Bethel, N [g] Shell/dsl, S [g] Exxon/dsl, [o] dsl repair
10	PA 645, Frystown, S [g] [TA]/rest./dsl/scales/24hr/@, Gulf/dsl, [l] Travel Inn
6	(8 from wb, US 22)PA 343, Fredricksburg, **1 mi S** [g] PP/dsl, Redner's Whse/mkt, [f] Esther's Rest., [o] KOA (5mi)
1	I-81. I-78 begins/ends on I-81, exit 89.

INTERSTATE 79

N ↕ S

Exit	Services
183b a	PA 5, 12th St, Erie, E [g] Shell, [o] [H], Valley Tire, W [g] Country Fair, Sunoco, [f] Applebee's, Backyard Burger, Bob Evans, Eat'n Park/24hr, El Canelo Mexican, Hibachi Japanese, KFC, McDonald's, Panera Bread, Pizza Hut, Taco Bell, Taki Rest., Tim Hortons, Wendy's, [l] Comfort Inn (2mi), [o] Advance Parts, Aldi Foods, BigLots, CVS Drug, $General, Dunn Tire, Family$, Giant Eagle Foods, GNC, NAPA, Rite Aid, Tires-4-Less, Tuesday Morning, U-Haul, transmissions, vet, to Presque Isle SP
182	US 20, 26th St, E [g] Country Fair, KwikFill, [f] Subway, [o] [H], CVS Drug, Family$, Tops Foods/gas/24hr, W [g] Country Fair, GetGo, [f] Arby's, Burger King, Hoss's Steaks, LJ Silver, McDonald's, Subway, Super Buffet, Tim Hortons, Vocelli's Pizza, [l] Glass House Inn, [o] Aamco, AT&T, AutoZone, $General, Family$, Ford, Giant Eagle Foods, K-Mart/Little Caesar's, Radio Shack, TrueValue, Volvo, vet
180	US 19, to Kearsarge, E [f] Aoyama Japanese, Arby's, Buffalo Wild Wings, Fox&Hound, KFC, Max&Erma's, McDonald's, Moe's SW Grill, O'Charley's, Olive Garden, Outback Steaks, Ponderosa, Red Lobster, Ruby Tuesday, Smokey Bones BBQ, Wendy's, [l] Fairfield Inn, Homewood Suites, SpringHill Suites, TownePlace Suites, [o] [H], Audi/Cadillac, Barnes&Noble, Bon-Ton, Chrysler/Jeep, Dick's, Firestone/auto, Gander Mtn, Goodyear/auto, JC Penney, Macy's, Michael's, Old Navy, PetCo, Sears/auto, TJ Maxx, Toyota/Scion, mall, W [g] Country Fair, [o] camping
178b a	I-90, E to Buffalo, W to Cleveland
174	to McKean, E access to gas/dsl, W camping
166	US 6N, to Edinboro, E [g] Country Fair, Sheetz, [f] Burg

INTERSTATE 79 CONT'D

Exit	Services
166	Continued er King (3mi), McDonald's (3mi), Perkins (2mi), Subway, Wendy's, 🛏 Comfort Suites, Edinboro Inn, 🅾 Walmart, vet, **W** 🅾 Liana's Lake Park Camping
163mm	**rest area both lanes, full** 🅰 **facilities,** 🅲, **vending,** 🅰, **litter barrels, petwalk**
154	PA 198, to Saegertown, Conneautville, **E** Erie NWR (7mi)
147b a	US 6, US 322, to Meadville, **E** 🅶 All American Gas/wash, Country Fair, GetGo, Sheetz/dsl/24hr, 🍽 Applebee's, Arby's, Chovy's Italian, Cracker Barrel, DQ, 5 Guys Burgers, Hoss's Rest., KFC, Perkins, Pizza Hut, Super Buffet, Taco Bell, 🛏 Best Value Inn, Days Inn/rest., Holiday Inn Express, 🅾 🅷, Advance Parts, Giant Eagle Foods/24hr, Jo-Ann Fabrics, Home Depot, Radio Shack, **W** 🅶 Sheetz, 🍽 Burger King, Compadres Mexican, King's Rest./24hr, McDonald's, Ponderosa, Red Lobster, Subway, Tim Hortons, Yuen's Garden, 🛏 Hampton Inn, Quality Inn, 🅾 Aldi Foods, AutoZone, Buick/Cadillac/GMC, Chevrolet, $Tree, GNC, K-Mart, Staples, Toyota/Scion, Walmart, to Pymatuning SP, st police, visitor info
141	PA 285, to Geneva, **E** to Erie NWR (20mi), **W** 🍽 Aunt Bee's Rest./dsl
135mm	**rest area/weigh sta both lanes, full** 🅰 **facilities,** 🅲, **vending,** 🅰, **litter barrels, petwalk**
130	PA 358, to Sandy Lake, **W** 🅾 🅷 (13mi), to Goddard SP
121	US 62, to Mercer, **E** 🅾 Valley Tire, **W** 🅶 Sunoco/dsl, 🅾 st police
116b a	I-80, **E** to Clarion, **W** to Sharon
113	PA 208, PA 258, to Grove City, **E** 🅶 BP, Country Fair/dsl/24hr, 🍽 Compadres Mexican, 🅾 🅷, **W** 🅶 KwikFill/Subway, Sheetz/24hr, 🍽 Eat'n Park/24hr, Elephant&Castle Rest., Hoss' Rest., King's Rest., McDonald's, My Bros Place, Wendy's, 🛏 Best Western, Comfort Inn, Hampton Inn, Holiday Inn Express, Microtel, Super 8, 🅾 KOA (3mi), Prime Outlets/famous brands, fireworks, tires
110mm	**rest area/weigh sta sb, full** 🅰 **facilities,** 🅲, **vending,** 🅰, **litter barrels, petwalk**
107mm	**rest area/weigh sta nb, full** 🅰 **facilities,** 🅲, **vending,** 🅰, **litter barrels, petwalk**
105	PA 108, to Slippery Rock, **E** 🍽 DQ, 🛏 Evening Star Motel, 🅾 Slippery Rock Camping, to Slippery Rock U
99	US 422, to New Castle, **E** to Moraine SP, **W** 🅶 🍽 Pilot/McDonald's/Subway/dsl/scales/24hr, 🅾 Coopers Lake Camping, to Rose Point Camping
96	PA 488, Portersville, **E** Bear Run Camping, Moraine SP, **W** 🍽 Brown's Country Kitchen, McConnell's Mill SP (3mi), gas/dsl
88	(87 from nb), to US 19, PA 68, (no ez return), Zelienople, **W** 🅶 Exxon, 🍽 Burger King, Pizza Hut
85	(83 from nb), PA 528 (no quick return), to Evans City, **W** 🅾 Buick
80mm	**weigh sta both lanes**
78	(76 from nb, exits left from nb), US 19, PA 228, to Mars, access to I-76, PA TPK, **E** 🅶 Gulf/7-11/dsl, 🍽 Applebee's, Chick-fil-A, Coldstone, DiBella's Subs, Jimmy Wan's Chinese, Longhorn Steaks, McDonald's, Moe's SW Grill, Olive Garden, On-the-Border, Quiznos, Red Robin, Smokey Bones BBQ, Starbucks, Subway,

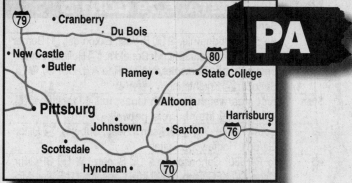

Exit	Services
78	Continued 🛏 Marriott, 🅾 🅷, AT&T, GNC, Kohl's, Lowe's, Petsmart, Staples, Target, TJ Maxx, **W on US 19** 🅶 BP/dsl, Exxon/dsl/24hr, GetGo, Sheetz/24hr, Sunoco/dsl, 🍽 A&W/LJ Silver, Adrian's Pizza, Arby's, Bob Evans, Boston Mkt, Bravo Italian, Burger King, Chipotle Mexican, CiCi's Pizza, DQ, Denny's, Dominichi's Rest., Dunkin Donuts, Dynasty, Eat'n Park, 5 Guys Burgers, Hartner's Rest., HotDog Shoppe, Houlihan's, Ichiban Steakhouse, King's Rest., Krispy Kreme, LoneStar Steaks, Mad Mex, Max&Erma's, McDonald's, Montecello's Grill, Panera Bread, Perkins, Pizza Hut, Pizza Roma, Primanti Bros, Quaker Steak, Saga Steaks, Subway, UNO, Vocelli Pizza, Wendy's, 🛏 Comfort Inn, Fairfield Inn, Hampton Inn, Holiday Inn Express, Hyatt Place, Motel 6, Red Roof Inn, Residence Inn, Sheraton, Super 8, 🅾 Barnes&Noble, Best Buy, Costco/gas, Dick's, $Tree, GNC, Giant Eagle Foods, Home Depot, Jo-Ann Fabrics, Kuhn's Foods, Marshall's, Michael's, NAPA, Old Navy, PepBoys, PetCo, Radio Shack, Rite Aid, Toyota/Scion, Tuesday Morning, Walgreens, Walmart, mall, transmissions, USPO, vet
77	I-76/Tpk, to Youngstown, **E** 🍽 Quiznos
75	US 19 S (from nb), to Warrendale, services along US 19
73	PA 910, to Wexford, **E** 🅶 BP/24hr, 🍽 Eat'n Park, King's Family Rest./24hr, Starbucks, 🛏 Best Inn, 🅾 **W** 🅶 Exxon/Subway/dsl/24hr, 🍽 Carmody's Rest.
72	I-279 S (from sb), to Pittsburgh
68	Mt Nebo Rd, **W** 🅷
66	to PA 65, Emsworth
65	to PA 51, Coraopolis, Neville Island, **E** 🅶 Gulf, 🛏 Fairfield Inn, 🅾 Penske Trucks, **W** 🍽 Subway
64.5mm	Ohio River
64	PA 51 (from nb), to Coraopolis McKees Rocks
60	PA 60, Crafton, **E** 🅶 Exxon/dsl/24hr, 🍽 King's Rest./24hr, Primanti Bros, 🛏 Carefree Inn, Comfort Inn, EconoLodge, Motel 6, 🅾 🅷, **W** 🍽 Juliano's Rest.
59b	I-376 W, US 22 W, US 30 (from nb), **W** 🅰
59a	I-376 E, to Pittsburgh
57	to Carnegie, **1-3 mi E** 🅶 BP, Exxon, 🍽 LJ Silver, McDonald's, 🛏 Ford, Lowe's, Radio Shack, Shop'n Save, Walgreens, Walmart, mall
55	PA 50, **to Heidelberg E on PA 50** 🅶 Sunoco, 🍽 Arby's, Bob Evans, ChuckeCheese, CiCi's Pizza, Damon's, Eat'n Park, KFC, King's Rest., Pizza Hut, Firestone/auto, Sonic, Starbucks, Subway, Taco Bell, TX Roadhouse, Vocelli Pizza, Wendy's, 🅾 BigLots, $Tree, Firestone/auto, Giant Eagle Foods, GNC, Home Depot, Jo-Ann Fabrics, K-Mart/Little Caesar's, Mr Tire, TJ Maxx, Tuesday Morning, auto repair

N ↑ **S** ↓   **M E A D V I L L E**

PA

INTERSTATE 79 CONT'D

Exit	Services
54	PA 50, to Bridgeville, **E** 🅖 BP/dsl, Exxon/dsl, 🍴 Burger King, King's Rest./24hr, McDonald's, 🛏 Holiday Inn Express, ⊡ Ⓗ, Chevrolet, NAPA, Rite Aid, USPO, **W** 🅖 Sunoco, 🛏 Knights Inn
50mm	**rest area/weigh sta both lanes, full** ♿ **facilities,** 🚻**, vending,** 🛒**, litter barrels, petwalk**
48	South Pointe, **W** 🍴 Jackson's Rest., Subway, 🛏 Hilton Garden, Homewood Suites
45	to PA 980, Canonsburg, **E** 🅖 Sheetz, **W** 🅖 BP/24hr, Citgo, 🍴 KFC/Taco Bell, Little Caesar's, LJ Silver, McDonald's, Papa John's, Pizza Hut, Quiznos, Starbucks, Subway, WaiWai Grill, Wendy's, 🛏 Super 8, ⊡ Advance Parts, Walgreens
43	PA 519, Houston, **E** 🅖 BP/dsl, **W** 🅖 Sunoco/24hr, ⊡ Freightliner
41	Race Track Rd, **E** 🅖 Exxon, RaceTrack, 🍴 Buger King, McDonald's, Waffle House, Wendy's, 🛏 Cambria Suites, Candlewood Suites, Comfort Inn, Country Inn&Suites, Hampton Inn, Holiday Inn, ⊡ Audi, Old Navy, Tanger Outlets/famous brands, **W** 🅖 BP/dsl, ⊡ Trolley Museum
40	Meadow Lands (from nb, no re-entry), **W** ⊡ Trolley Museum (3mi), golf, racetrack
38	I-70 W, to Wheeling
19b a	(I-77), US 19, Murtland Ave, **E** 🅖 GetGo, 🍴 Applebee's, Arby's, Bruster's, Cracker Barrel, Fusion Steaks, Jimmy John's, Krispy Kreme, Max&Erma's, McDonald's, Moe's SW Grill, Outback Steaks, Panera Bread, Ponderosa, Quiznos, Red Lobster, Red Robin, Rita's Custard, Starbucks, Subway, TX Roadhouse, TGIFriday's, Wong's Wok, 🛏 SpringHill Suites, ⊡ Aldi Foods, AT&T, Dick's, $Tree, Ford, Giant Eagle Foods, GNC, Honda, Hyundai, Kohl's, Lowe's, Mercedes, Michael's, Nissan, PetCo, Petsmart, Radio Shack, Sam's Club/gas, Save-A-Lot Foods, Target, Toyota/Scion, Walmart/McDonald's, urgent care, vet, **W** 🅖 BP/dsl, Exxon/dsl, Sunoco, Valero, 🍴 A&W/LJ Silver, Bob Evans, CiCi's Pizza, Donut Connection, Eat'n Park, Evergreen Chinese, Grand China, KFC, Old Mexico, Papa John's, Pizza Hut, Waffle House, 🛏 Hampton Inn, Motel 6, ⊡ Ⓗ, BigLots, Buick/GMC, Chevrolet, Curves, Firestone/auto, Home Depot, JC Penney, Jo-Ann Fabrics, Staples, Subaru
20	(I-77) PA 136, to Beau St, **S** to Washington&Jefferson Coll
34	I-70 E, to Greensburg
33	US 40, to Laboratory, **W** ⊡ KOA
31mm	**parking area/weigh sta sb**
30	US 19, to Amity, **W** 🅖 Exxon/Subway/dsl
23	to Marianna, Prosperity
19	PA 221, to US 19, Ruff Creek, **W** 🅖 BP/dsl
14	PA 21, to Waynesburg, **E** 🅖 Sunoco, 🍴 Bob Evans, 🛏 Comfort Inn, Microtel, ⊡ Walmart, visitor info, **W** 🅖 BP/dsl/24hr, Exxon/dsl, GetGo, Marathon, Sheetz, 🍴 Burger King, China 88, DQ, Golden Wok, Hardee's, KFC, McDonald's, Pizza Hut, Scotty's Pizza, Subway, Vocelli Pizza, Wendy's, 🛏 EconoLodge, Super 8, ⊡ Ⓗ, Ace Hardware, Advance Parts, Aldi Foods, AutoZone, BigLots, Cadillac/Chevrolet/Subaru, Chrysler/Dodge/Jeep, CVS Drug, $General, $Tree, Giant Eagle Foods, Family$, Radio Shack, Rite Aid, Walgreens, st police
7	to Kirby
6mm	**Welcome Ctr/weigh sta nb, full** ♿ **facilities,** 🚻**,** 🛒**, litter barrels, vending, petwalk**
1	Mount Morris, **E** 🅖 Citgo/rest./dsl/scales, ⊡ Honda/Mazda, **W** 🅖 BP/dsl, Marathon, ⊡ Mt Morris Campground
0mm	Pennsylvania/West Virginia state line

INTERSTATE 80

Exit	Services
311mm	Pennsylvania/New Jersey state line, Delaware River
310.5	toll booth wb, 🚻
310	PA 611, Delaware Water Gap, **S Welcome Ctr/rest area, full services, info,** 🅖 Fuel On, Gulf/repair, 🍴 Doughboys Pizza, Village Farmer Bakery, Water Gap Diner
309	US 209 N, PA 447, to Marshalls Creek, **N** 🅖 Exxon/dsl, Gulf, 🍴 Blue Tequila Mexican, DQ, Dunkin Donuts, Landmark Cafe, Wendy's (2mi), 🛏 Days Inn, ⊡ Ⓗ
308	East Stroudsburg, **N** 🅖 Exxon/Subs Now, ⊡ Ⓗ, WaWa, vet, **S** 🍴 JR's Grill, 🛏 Budget Motel, Super 8, **1 mi S** 🍴 Arby's, Burger King, CiCi's, Friendly's, Holy Guacamole, KFC, McDonald's, ⊡ K-Mart, NAPA, Radio Shack, ShopRite Foods, Walmart/McDonald's
307	PA 191, Broad St, **N** 🛏 Hampton Inn, ⊡ Ⓗ, **S** 🅖 Sunoco, 🍴 Compton's Rest., 🛏 Budget Host
306	Dreher Ave (from wb, no EZ return), **N** 🅖 WaWa
305	US 209, Main St, **N** 🅖 Gulf, Shell, 🍴 Perkins, 🛏 Quality Inn, **S** 🅖 Exxon/dsl
304	US 209, to PA 33, 9th St (from wb), same as 303
303	9th St, (from eb), **N** 🅖 🍴 Burger King, Dunkin Donuts, 5 Guys Burgers, Fulay Chinese, Garfield's Rest., McDonald's, Olive Garden, Panera Bread, Pizza Hut, Popeye's, Ruby Tuesday, Starbucks, TX Roadhouse, ⊡ Best Buy, Buick/GMC, Cadillac, Chevrolet, Chrysler/Dodge, CVS Drug, $Tree, JC Penney, Old Navy, Petsmart, Subaru, Walgreens, Weis Foods/gas
302	PA 611, to Bartonsville, **N** 🅖 Exxon/dsl, 🍴 Big Daddy's BBQ, Chili's, Dunkin Donuts, Frank's Pizza, Ichiban Steaks, Longhorn Steaks, Moe's SW Grill, Red Lobster, Red Robin, Sonic, Subway (2mi), 🛏 Comfort Inn, Howard Johnson, Knights Inn, ⊡ Advance Parts, AT&T, $Tree, Giant Foods/gas, Kohl's, Lowe's, Nissan, Peterbilt, Verizon
299	PA 715, Tannersville, **N** 🅖 Chohan, Shell, Turkey Hill, 🍴 Pocono Diner, 🛏 Ramada Ltd, ⊡ CVS Drug, The Crossing Factory Outlet/famous brands, Weis Foods, **1-4 mi N** 🍴 Barley Creek Brewing, 5 Guys Burgers, Friendly's, Subway, Wendy's, ⊡ camping, **S** 🅖 Sunoco, 🍴 Tannersville Diner, 🛏 Days Inn, Summit Resort, ⊡ to Camelback Ski Area, to Big Pocono SP
298	PA 611 (from wb), to Scotrun, **N** 🅖 Sunoco/dsl, 🍴 Brick Oven Pizza, Plaza Deli, 🛏 Great Wolf Lodge, Scotrun Diner/motel, ⊡ to Mt Pocono
295mm	**rest area eb, full** ♿ **facilities,** 🚻**,** 🛒**, litter barrels, vending, petwalk**
293	I-380 N, to Scranton, (exits left from eb)
284	PA 115, to Wilkes-Barre, Blakeslee, **N** 🅖 WaWa (1mi), 🛏 Best Western, Blakeslee Inn (2mi), ⊡ Fern Ridge Camping, st police, **S** 🅖 Exxon/dsl, ⊡ to Pocono Raceway
277	PA 940, to PA Tpk (I-476), to Pocono, Lake Harmony, Allentown, **N** 🅖 WaWa, 🍴 A&W/LJ Silver, Arby's, McDonald's, 🛏 Comfort Inn, EconoLodge, Holiday Inn Express, Knights Inn, Mtn Laurel Resort, Pocono Inn/Resort, Split Rock Resort

N ↕ S

WASHINGTON

STROUDSBURG

PA

INTERSTATE 80 CONT'D

Exit	Services
274	PA 534, **N** ⛽ Fuel On/Subs Now/dsl/24hr, Hickory Run/Valero/rest./dsl/scales/24hr, ⊙ towing/repair, **S** ⊙ to Hickory Run SP (6mi)
273mm	Lehigh River
273	PA 940, PA 437, to Freeland, White Haven, **N** ⛽ Exxon, Fuel On, **S** 🍴 Powerhouse Eatery, ⊙ Sandy Valley Campground
270mm	**rest area eb, full ♿ facilities, info, 🅦, 🚮, litter barrels, vending, petwalk**
262	PA 309, to Hazleton, Mountain Top, **N** ⛽ Safari, 🍴 Mary's Rest., Wendy's, 🛏 EconoLodge, ⊙ auto/truck repair, **S** 🛏 Holiday Inn Express, ⊙ Nescopeck SP (5mi)
260 b a	I-81, N to Wilkes-Barre, S to Harrisburg
256	PA 93, to Nescopeck, Conyngham, **N** ⛽ 🏪/Subway/dsl/scales/24hr, Sunoco/repair, 🛏 Lookout Motel, **S** 🍴 Tom's Kitchen (2mi), 🛏 Best Value Inn, Hampton Inn (4mi), ⊙ 🅷, towing/truck repair
251mm	Nescopeck River
246mm	**rest area/weigh sta both lanes, full ♿ facilities, weather info, 🅦, 🚮, litter barrels, vending, petwalk**
242	PA 339, to Mainville, Mifflinville, **N** ⛽ ♥Loves/Arby's/dsl/scales/24hr, Sunoco/Subway/dsl, 🍴 McDonald's, 🛏 Super 8, **S** ⛽ Universal/dsl, 🛏 Comfort Inn
241mm	Susquehanna River
241 b a	US 11, to Berwick, Lime Ridge, Bloomsburg, **N** 🛏 Red Maple Inn (2mi), ⊙ 🅷, **S** ⛽ Exxon, 🍴 Morris Rest., Taste of Italy, 🛏 Budget Host, **2-5 mi S** ⛽ Sheetz/dsl, 🍴 Applebee's, Arby's, Burger King, China Queen, Domino's, Dunkin Donuts, McDonald's, New China Buffet, Pizza Hut, Playa Cancun, Rita's Custard, Subway, Taco Bell, Terrapins Cantina, Wendy's, ⊙ Ace Hardware, Advance Parts, BigLots, Cadillac/Chevrolet, CVS Drug, $Tree, Ford/Honda, Giant Foods/gas, Kost Tire, Rite Aid, Staples, U-Haul, Weis Foods/gas
236	PA 487, to Bloomsburg, Lightstreet, **S** ⛽ Sunoco, 🍴 Denny's, 🛏 Hampton Inn, Tennytown Motel (2mi), Turkey Hill Inn, ⊙ 🅷, to Bloomsburg U
232	PA 42, Buckhorn, **N** ⛽ Exxon, TA/Subway/dsl/scales/24hr/@, 🍴 Burger King, Cracker Barrel, KFC, Perkins, Quaker Steak&Lube, Ruby Tuesday, Wendy's, 🛏 EconoLodge, Holiday Inn Express, ⊙ AT&T, BonTon, Home Depot, JC Penney, Sears/auto, mall, **S** 🍴 Carini's Italian, Gourmet Buffet, Panera Bread, 🛏 Comfort Suites, ⊙ $Tree, Indian Head Camping (3mi), Lowe's, PetCo, Verizon, Walmart/McDonald's
224	PA 54, to Danville, **N** ⛽ Shell/Subway/dsl, 🛏 Quality Inn, **S** 🍴 Friendly's, McDonald's, Mom's Dutch Kitchen, 🛏 Best Western, Days Inn, Hampton Inn, Red Roof Inn, Super 8, ⊙ 🅷
219mm	**rest area both lanes, full ♿ facilities, info, 🅦, 🚮, litter barrels, vending, petwalk**
215	PA 254, Limestonevill, **N** ⛽ Milton 32 Trkstp/rest./dsl/24hr, **S** ⛽ Penn 80/Shell/Subway/dsl/scales/24hr/@
212 b a	I-180 W, PA 147 S, to Muncy, Williamsport, **S** ⛽ Sunoco (1mi)
210.5mm	Susquehanna River
210 b a	US 15, to Williamsport, Lewisburg, **S** ⛽ Citgo, 🍴 Bonanza, 🛏 Comfort Inn, Holiday Inn Express, ⊙ 🅷, KOA (5mi)

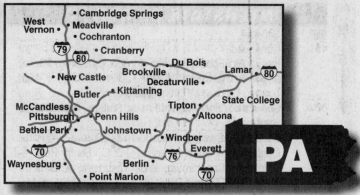

Exit	Services
199	Mile Run
194mm	**rest area/weigh sta both lanes, full ♿ facilities, 🅦, 🚮, litter barrels, vending, petwalk**
192	PA 880, to Jersey Shore, **N** ⛽ Citgo/dsl, 🍴 Pit-Stop Rest., **S** ⛽ Valero/dsl, ⊙ 🅷, towing/truck repair
185	PA 477, Loganton, **N** ⛽ Valero, ⊙ camping, **S** 🍴 Twilight Diner, RB Winter SP (12mi)
178	US 220, Lock Haven, **5 mi N** ⛽ KwikFill/dsl, Sheetz, 🍴 Ruby Tuesday, Subway, ⊙ Advance Parts, K-Mart, Lowe's, Walmart
173	PA 64, Lamar, **N** ⛽ 🏪/Subway/dsl/scales/24hr, 🍴 Cottage Rest., McDonald's, Perkins, 🛏 Comfort Inn/rest., Hampton Inn, **S** ⛽ Citgo, ✈FLYING J/Denny's/dsl/LP/scales, TA/Country Pride/Subway/dsl/scales/24hr/@, 🍴 DQ, ⊙ auto repair
161	I-99, US 220 S, PA 26, to Bellafonte, **N** ⊙ KOA (2mi), **S** ⊙ to PSU
158	US 220 S, PA 150, to Altoona, Milesburg, **N** ⛽ Bestway/rest./dsl/motel/24hr/@, B&B Mkt/dsl, TA/dsl/scales/24hr/@, 🍴 Buckhorn Rest., McDonald's, Subway, 🛏 Quality Inn, **S** st police
147	PA 144, to Snow Shoe, **N** ⛽ Citgo/dsl/24hr, Exxon/dsl/repair/24hr, 🍴 Snow Shoe Sandwich Shop, Subway, ⊙ Hall's Foods, repair
146mm	**rest area both lanes, full ♿ facilities, 🅦, 🚮, litter barrels, vending, petwalk**
138mm	Moshannon River
133	PA 53, to Philipsburg, Kylertown, **N** ⛽ KwikFill/motel/dsl/scales, Sunoco/dsl, 🍴 Roadhouse Rest., ⊙ USPO, dsl repair, Black Moshannon SP (9mi), **S** ⊙ 🅷
123	PA 970, to Shawville, Woodland, **S** ⊙ Woodland Camping, **S** ⛽ Gio's BBQ/dsl (2mi), PP/dsl, ⊙ st police, USPO
120mm	Susquehanna River, W Branch
120	PA 879, Shawville, Clearfield, **N** ⛽ Sapp Bros/rest./dsl/scales/24hr/@, 🛏 Country Hearth Inn, **S** ⛽ BP, Sheetz, Snappy's, 🍴 Arby's, Burger King, Dunkin Donuts, Dutch Pantry, KFC/Taco Bell, McDonald's, 🛏 Comfort Inn, Days Inn, Hampton Inn, Holiday Inn Express, Super 8, ⊙ 🅷, Lowe's, Walmart/Subway
111mm	highest point on I-80 east of Mississippi River, 2250 ft
111	PA 153, to Penfield, **N** to Parker Dam, to SB Elliot SP, **S** 🅷
101	PA 255, Du Bois, **N** ⛽ Snappy's/Quiznos/dsl, ⊙ camping, **S** ⊙ 🅷, st police, **1-2 mi S** ⛽ Sheetz/dsl, 🍴 A&W/LJ Silver, Arby's, Burger King, Domino's, Eat'n Park, Italian Oven, KFC, McDonald's, Perkins, Pizza Hut, Ponderosa, Red Lobster, Ruby Tuesday, Subway, Taco Bell, Valley Dairy Rest., Wendy's, 🛏 Best Western, Hampton

E / W (margin arrows)

LAMAR (vertical margin text)

DU BOIS (vertical margin text)

🅖 = gas 🍴 = food 🛏 = lodging 🅞 = other   Copyright 2011 - The Next Ex

INTERSTATE 80 CONT'D

Exit	Services
101	Continued Inn, 🅞 Aldi Foods, BigLots, BonTon, CVS Drug, $General, $Tree, Hyundai, JC Penney, Jo-Ann Fabrics, K-Mart, Lowe's, Old Navy, PetCo, Radio Shack, Rite Aid, Ross, Sears/auto, Shop'n Save Foods, Staples, Walmart/Subway, mall
97	US 219, to Brockway, Du Bois, S 🅖 ▨▨▨/Arby's/dsl/scales/24hr, Sheetz/dsl/24hr, 🍴 Dutch Pantry Rest., 🛏 Clarion, Holiday Inn Express, 🅞 🅷, Freightliner, st police, 2 mi S 🍴 Hoss' Rest., Pizza Hut, 🛏 Best Western, 🅞 Advance Parts
90	PA 830 E,, N Du Bois Regional 🛬
87.5mm	rest area both lanes, full ♿ facilities, 🍴, 🛒, litter barrels, vending, petwalk
86	PA 830, to Reynoldsville
81	PA 28, to Brookville, Hazen, S Brookville, hist dist (2mi)
78	PA 36, to Sigel, Brookville, N 🅖 ⓕFLYING J/Denny's/dsl/LP/scales/24hr, TA/BP/Taco Bell/dsl/scales/Howard Johnson/24hr/@, 🍴 DQ, KFC, McDonald's, Pizza Hut, 🛏 Super 8, 🅞 NAPA, to Cook Forest SP, S 🅖 Country Fair, Sheetz, USA, 🍴 Arby's, Burger King, China Wok, Plyler's Buffet, Subway, 🛏 Budget Host, Quality Inn, Travelodge, 🅞 Chrysler/Dodge/Jeep, Family$
73	PA 949, Corsica, N 🅞 to Clear Creek SP, S USPO
70	US 322, to Strattanville
64	PA 66 S, to New Bethlehem, Clarion, N to Clarion U
62	PA 68, to Clarion, N 🅖 BP, KwikFill/dsl, 🍴 A&W/LJ Silver, Applebee's, Arby's, Eat'n Park, Hunan King, McDonald's, Perkins, Pizza Hut, RRR Roadhouse, Subway, Taco Bell, 🛏 Comfort Inn, Hampton Inn, Holiday Inn/rest., Microtel, Quality Inn, Super 8, 🅞 🅷, Advance Parts, Aldi Foods, AT&T, AutoZone, $Tree, JC Penney, K-Mart, Radio Shack, Staples, Walmart/Subway, mall
61mm	Clarion River
60	PA 66 N, to Shippenville, N 🍴 Jiffy, 🅞 to Cook Forest SP, camping
56mm	weigh sta both lanes
53	to PA 338, to Knox, N 🅖 Satterlee Gas/dsl (cardlock), 🍴 BJ's Eatery, 🅞 Countryside Crafts/Quilts, Wolf's Camping Resort, S 🅞 Good Tire Service
45	PA 478, to St Petersburg, Emlenton, 4 mi S 🅞 Golf Hall of Fame
44.5mm	Allegheny River
42	PA 38, to Emlenton, N 🅖 Exxon/Subway/dsl, Roady's Trkstp/rest./dsl/scales/24hr, 🍴 Fat Chaps Rest., 🛏 Deluxe Motel, 🅞 Gaslight RV Park, truck/RV repair
35	PA 308, to Clintonville
30.5mm	rest area both lanes, full ♿ facilities, 🍴, 🛒, litter barrels, vending, petwalk
29	PA 8, to Franklin, Barkeyville, N 🍴 Arby's, Burger King, King's Rest., 🛏 Comfort Inn, Motel 6, 🅞 Freightliner, S 🅖 Citgo, KwikFill/dsl/scales/motel/24hr, TA/BP/Subway/dsl/scales/24hr/@, 🅞 truckwash, to Slippery Rock U
24	PA 173, to Grove City, Sandy Lake, S 🅞 🅷, Grove City Coll, Wendell August Forge/gifts (3mi), truck repair
19b a	I-79, N to Erie, S to Pittsburgh
15	US 19, to Mercer, N 🅖 BP, PP/dsl, 🍴 Charlie B's Rest., Burger King, McDonald's/rv parking, 🛏 Comfort Inn, 🅞 st police, 2 mi S 🍴 Iron Bridge Rest., 🅞 KOA (4mi)
4b a	I-376, PA 60, to PA 18, to Sharon-Hermitage, New

Exit	Services
4b a	Continued Castle, N 🅖 Sheetz, Sunoco/Subway/dsl, 🛏 EconoLodge, Holiday Inn Express, Quality Inn, Park Inn, Red Roof Inn, Super 8, S 🍴 DQ, MiddleSex Diner, 🅞 $General
2.5mm	Shenango River
1mm	Welcome Ctr eb, full ♿ facilities, 🍴, 🛒, litter barrels, vending, petwalk
0mm	Pennsylvania/Ohio state line

INTERSTATE 81

Exit	Services
233mm	Pennsylvania/New York state line
232mm	Welcome Ctr/weigh sta sb, full ♿ facilities, 🍴, 🛒, litter barrels, petwalk
230	PA 171, Great Bend, E 🅖 Valero/24hr, W 🅖 Exxon, Arby's/dsl/24hr, Sunoco/dsl, 🍴 Burger King, Dobb's Country Kitchen, Dunkin Donuts, McDonald's, Subway, 🛏 Colonial Brick Motel, 🅞 Big M Foods, Ford, Reddon's Drugs, Rob's Mkt
223	PA 492, New Milford, W 🅖 Gulf/dsl, Sunoco, Valero/24hr, 🍴 Blue Ridge Motel, Green Gables Rest.
219	PA 848, to Gibson, W 🅖 Exxon/McDonald's/dsl/24hr, ⓕFLYING J/Denny's/dsl/scales/24hr, 🛏 Holiday Inn Express, st police
217	PA 547, Harford, E 🅖 Exxon/Subway/dsl/24hr, Getty's, dsl/rest./24hr
211	PA 92, Lenox, E Elk Mtn Ski Area, Shady Rest Camping (3mi), W 🅖 Lukoil/dsl/24hr, Shell/dsl, 🍴 Bingham's Rest. Mamasita's Mexican, 🅞 Lenox Drug
209mm	rest area sb, full ♿ facilities, 🍴, 🛒, litter barrel, vending, petwalk
206	PA 374, to Glenwood, Lenoxville, E to Elk Mountain Sk Resort
203mm	rest area nb, full ♿ facilities, 🍴, 🛒, litter barrels, vending, petwalk
202	PA 107, to Fleetville, Tompkinsville
201	PA 438, East Benton, W 🅖 Duchniks/dsl/repair
199	PA 524, Scott, E 🅖 BP/dsl, W 🅖 Exxon/Subway, 🛏 Motel 81, 🅞 to Lackawanna SP
197	PA 632, Waverly, E 🅞 Mr Z's Foods, Rite Aid, W 🅖 Sunoco/24hr, 🍴 Doc's Deli/24hr
194	US 6, US 11, to I-476/PA Tpk, Clarks Summit, W 🅖 Shell, dsl, Sheetz/24hr, Sunoco/dsl, 🍴 Burger King, Damon's Dino&Francesco's, Domino's, Dunkin Donuts, Euro Cafe, Friendly's, Krispy Kreme, Kyoto, McDonald's, New Century Chinese, Pizza Hut, Quizno's, Starbucks, Subway, Taco Bell, Waffle House, Wendy's, 🛏 Comfort Inn Econolodge, Hampton Inn, Nichols Village Inn, Ramada Inn, 🅞 Advance Parts, $Bazaar, Kost Tire, Radio Shack Rite Aid, Weis Foods
191b a	US 6, US 11, to Carbondale, E 🅖 Shell/dsl, Sheetz/dsl 🍴 A&W/LJ Silver, Applebees, Arby's, Burger King, Chicago Grill, China Wok, ChuckeCheese, Denny's, Don Pablo, Eastern Buffet, 5 Guys Cafe, Fresno's, La Tonalateca, McDonald's, Old Country Buffet, Olive Garden, Perkins, Pizza Hut Red Lobster, Red Robin, Ruby Tuesday, Smokey Bones BBQ, Subway, TCBY, TX Roadhouse, TGIFriday, 🛏 Days Inn, 🅞 Aldi Foods, Firestone/auto, Harley-Davidson, Home Depot, Hyundai, JC Penney, Jo-Ann Crafts, K-Mart, Kohl's Macy's, Marshall's, Michael's, PepBoys, PetsMart, Radio Shack, Sears/auto, Target, TJ Maxx, Walmart, William's Tires, mall, W 🅞 to Anthracite Museum

INTERSTATE 81 CONT'D

Exit	Services
190	Main Ave, Dickson City, **E** 🍴 Charlie Brown's Steaks, Wendy's, 🛏 Fairfield Inn, Residence Inn, 🅞 Best Buy, Gander Mtn, Lowes Whse, Sam's Club/gas, Staples, **W** 🅞 Toyota/Scion
188	PA 347, Throop, **E** 🅖 Sheetz/24hr, Sunoco/dsl, 🍴 China World Buffet, McDonald's, Quizno's, Wendy's, 🛏 Day's Inn, Sleep Inn, Super 8, 🅞 Advance Parts, Big Lots, Kost Tire, PriceChopper Foods, st police, **W** 🅖 Exxon, 🍴 Burger King, Dunkin Donuts, Friendly's, New China Star, Subway
187	to I-84, I-380, US 6 (no return from nb)
186	PA 435, Drinker St (from nb) **E** 🅖 Valero, 🛏 Holiday Inn, **W** 🅖 Exxon
185	Central Scranton Expwy (exits left from nb), **W** 🅷
184	to PA 307, River St, **W** 🅖 Citgo, Shell, USA/Subway/dsl, Valero, 🍴 Dunkin Donuts, House of China, 🛏 Clarion, 🅞 🅷, CVS Drug, $Tree, Gerrity Foods
182	Davis St, Montage Mtn Rd, **E** 🅖 USA/Coldstone/Subway, 🍴 Johnny Rockets Cafe, Longhorn Steaks, Mugg's Rest., Panchero's Mexican, Panera Bread, Quizno's, Ruby Tuesday, Starbucks, 🛏 Comfort Suites, Courtyard, Hampton Inn, TownePlace Suites, 🅞 GNC, **W** 🅖 Sunoco, 🍴 Dunkin Donuts, Waffle House, Wendy's, 🅞 CVS Drug, USPO
180	to US 11, PA 502, to Moosic, (exits left from nb) **W on US 11** 🅖 Exxon, Shell/Subway/dsl/24hr, Sunoco, 🍴 McDonalds, Moosic Diner, 🛏 Rodeway Inn
178b a	to US 11, Avoca, **E** 🛏 Holiday Inn Express, **W** 🅖 Petro/Sunoco/dsl/rest./24hr/@
175b a	PA 315 S, to I-476, Dupont, **E** 🅖 Exxon, Sunoco/24hr, 🍴 Arby's, McDonald's, Perkins, 🛏 Knights Inn, Super 8, 🅞 Suzuki, **W** 🅖 Getty/repair, 🚛/Wendy's/dsl/scales/24hr, 🛏 Quality Inn, 🅞 Walmart
170b a	PA 115, PA 309, Wilkes-Barre, **E** 🅖 Exxon/Subway/dsl, Sunoco/dsl, 🛏 Best Western, 🅞 to Pocono Downs, **W** 🅖 Sunoco/24hr, Valley Mart, 🍴 Burger King, Denny's, Friendly's, LJ Silver, Lonestar Steaks, McDonald's, Pizza Hut, Sonic, TGIFriday's, Wendy's, 🛏 Days Inn, Extended Stay Deluxe, Fairfield Inn, Holiday Inn Express, Quality Inn, Red Roof Inn, 🅞 🅷, BonTon, Chevrolet, JC Penney, Goodyear, Macy's, Sears/auto, mall, tires
168	Highland Park Blvd, Wilkes-Barre, **W** 🅖 Sheetz/24hr, Sunoco, TurkeyHill, 🍴 Applebee's, Arby's, Bob Evans, Chili's, ChuckeCheese, Coldstone, Cracker Barrel, King's Buffet, La Tolteca Mexican, Logan's Roadhouse, Louie's Rest., Lucky's SportHouse, Olive Garden, Outback Steaks, Panera Bread, Quizno's, Red Robin, Smokey Bones BBQ, Subway, Starbucks, Wendy's, 🛏 Hampton Inn, Hilton Garden, 🅞 URGENT CARE, AT&T, Barnes&Noble, Best Buy, Dick's, Firestone/auto, Home Depot, Kohl's, Kost Tire, Lowe's, Marshall's, Michael's, Nissan, Old Navy, PepBoys, PetCo, Petsmart, PriceChopper, Radio Shack, Ross, Sam's Club/gas, Staples, Target, TJ Maxx, U-Haul, Verizon, Walgreens, Walmart, Wegman's Foods
165b a	PA 309 S, exits left from nb, Wilkes-Barre, **W** 🅖 UniMart/dsl, Gulf, 🍴 Abe's Hotdogs, Dunkin Donuts, Mark II Rest., McDonald's, Perkins, Taco Bell, 🛏 Comfort Inn, EconoLodge, 🅞 Advance Parts, $Tree, K-Mart
164	PA 29, to Nanticoke, Ashley
159	Nuangola, **W** 🅖 UniMart/Subs Now, 🅞 Council Camping (10mi)
157mm	**rest area/weigh sta sb, full ♿ facilities, vending, ☎, 🚻, litter barrels, petwalk**
156mm	**rest area/weigh sta nb, full ♿ facilities, vending, ☎, 🚻, litter barrels, petwalk**
155	to Dorrance, **E** 🅖 Sunoco/dsl/24hr, 🛏 EconoLodge (2mi), **W** 🛏 Blue Ridge Plaza/dsl
151b a	I-80, E to Mountaintop, W to Bloomsburg
145	PA 93, W Hazleton, **E** 🅖 Sunoco/dsl/24hr, TurkeyHill, 🍴 Bonanza, Damon's, 5 Stars Chinese, Friendly's, LJ Silver, McDonald's, Perkins, Pizza Hut, Taco Bell, Wendy's, 🛏 Best Western (2mi), Comfort Inn, Fairfield Inn, Forest Hill Inn, Ramada Inn (2mi), 🅞 🅷, Aldi Foods, Buick/Cadillac/GMC, Chrysler/Dodge/Jeep, $Tree, JC Penney, K-Mart, Mazda, Old Navy, Radio Shack, st police, **W** 🍴 Top of the 80's, 🛏 Candlewood Suites, Hampton Inn
143	PA 924, to Hazleton, **W** 🅖 Fuelon/Subs Now/dsl, Shell/Subway, TurkeyHill/dsl, 🍴 Burger King, Sonic, 🛏 Residence Inn
141	PA 424, S Hazleton Beltway, **E** 🛏 Mt. Laurel Motel
138	PA 309, to McAdoo, **2 mi E** 🛏 Pines Motel
134	to Delano
132mm	**parking area/weigh sta both lanes**
131b a	PA 54, Mahanoy City, **E** 🅞 to Tuscarora/Locust Lake SP, **W** 🅖 Exxon, Shell/dsl
124b a	PA 61, to Frackville, **E** 🍴 China Palace, Cracker Barrel, McDonald's, 🛏 Holiday Inn Express, 🅞 BigLots, BonTon, K-Mart, Sears/auto, mall, **W** 🅖 Exxon, Gulf, Hess, 🍴 Anthony's Pizza, Dutch Kitchen, Subway, 🛏 EconoLodge, Granny's Motel, Rodeway Inn, 🅞 🅷, Rite Aid, st police
119	High Ridge Park Rd, to Gordon, **E** 🛏 Country Inn&Suites, 🅞 🅷
116	PA 901, to Minersville, **E** 🍴 901 Rest.
112	PA 25, to Hegins, **W** 🍴 Fountain Rest (3mi), 🅞 camping
107	US 209, to Tremont
104	PA 125, Ravine, **E** 🅖 Exxon/Pizza Hut/Quizno's/dsl/24hr, 🅞 Echo Valley Campground
100	PA 443, to Pine Grove, **E** 🅖 Exxon/dsl, 🍴 Arby's, McDonald's, 🛏 Comfort Inn, EconoLodge, 🅞 $General, **W** 🅖 Cheap/dsl, 🚛/DQ/Subway/dsl/scales/24hr, 🍴 Gooseberry Farms Diner, 🛏 Hampton Inn, 🅞 KOA (5mi), truckwash
90	PA 72, to Lebanon, **E** 🅖 Exxon/Subway, Hess/Blimpie/dsl, 🅛Loves/McDonald's/dsl/scales/24hr, 🍴 DQ, Sbarro's, Wendy's, 🛏 Best Western, Days Inn, 🅞 Curves, KOA (5mi) Lickdale Camping, st police, **W** 🛏 Quality Inn
89	I-78 E, to Allentown

Map of Pennsylvania showing locations:
West Vernon, Meadville, Cambridge Springs, Cochranton, Cranberry, Du Bois, Lamar, New Castle, Brookville, Decaturville, Butler, Kittanning, Tipton, State College, McCandless, Pittsburgh, Penn Hills, Johnstown, Altoona, Bethel Park, Windber, Everett, Waynesburg, Berlin, Point Marion

Highways: 79, 80, 70, 76

PA

Side labels: **N S SCRANTON HAZLETON LEBANON**

INTERSTATE 81 CONT'D

N ↕ S

Exit	Services
85b a	PA 934, to Annville, **2 mi W** 🅐 Exxon/dsl, 🍽 Funck's Rest., 🅞 to IndianTown Gap Nat Cem
80	PA 743, Grantville, **E** 🅐 LukOil/dsl, 🛏 Days Inn, Hampton Inn, **W** 🅐 Exxon/dsl, 🍽 Italian Delight, 🛏 Comfort Suites, Holiday Inn, 🅞 camping, racetrack
79mm	**rest area/weigh sta both lanes, full &♿; facilities, 🅲, vending, 🚯, litter barrels, petwalk**
77	PA 39, to Hershey, **E** 🅐 Exxon/dsl, ⛽/Pizza Hut/dsl/scales/24hr, Valero/dsl, 🛏 Country Inn&Suites, Howard Johnson, Motel 6, Scottish Inn, 🅞 to Hershey Attractions, st police, **W** 🅐 Citgo/Sub Shop/dsl, TA/Country Pride/motel/dsl/scales/24hr/@, Wilco/Hess/Perkins/Stuckey's/dsl/24hr/@, 🍽 McDonald's, 🛏 Comfort Inn, 🅞 Goodyear, SpeedCo
72	to US 22, Linglestown, **E** 🅐 Hess/dsl, Sheetz, Sunoco/dsl, 🍽 Bro Joe's Pizza, Burger King, Chipotle Mexican, 5 Guys Burgers, Great Wall Chinese, Hong Kong City, McDonald's, Old Country Buffet, Red Robin, Starbucks, Subway, Tonino's Pizza, 🛏 Holiday Inn Express, Quality Inn, 🅞 Advance Parts, Chrysler/Dodge/Jeep, Costco/gas, CVS Drug, Giant Foods, Harley-Davidson, Karn's Foods, Target, Toyota/Scion, U-Haul, Weis Foods, **W** 🍽 Mikado Japanese, 🛏 Best Western, Candlewood Suites
70	I-83 S, to York, 🔀 69 Progress Ave, **E** 🍽 Cracker Barrel, Damon's, Macaroni Grill, Sandella's Flat Bread Cafe, Starbucks, Tonino's Grille, 🅞 AT&T, CVS Drug, 7-11, Susquehanna Shoppes, st police, **W** 🅐 Turkey Hill, 🍽 Arby's, YP Rest., 🛏 Capital Plaza Inn, Red Roof Inn, SpringHill Suites
67b a	US 22, US 322 W, PA 230, Cameron St, to Lewistown
66	Front St, **E** 🅗, **W** 🅐 Exxon, Sunoco, 🍽 Bro's Pizza, Jade Buffet, McDonald's, Pizza Hut, Taco Bell, Wendy's, 🛏 Budget Inn, Days Inn
65	US 11/15, to Enola, **1 mi E** 🅐 Sunoco/dsl/24hr, Tom's, 🍽 Al's Pizza, China Tasty, DQ, Dunkin Donuts, McDonald's, Panther Jungle Pizza, Subway, Summerdale Diner, Wendy's, 🛏 Quality Inn, 🅞 Advance Parts, $Tree, Fischer Parts, K-Mart, Radio Shack, Rite Aid
61	PA 944, to Wertzville, **E** 🛏 Comfort Suites, **W** 🅐 Turkey Hill/dsl, 🛏 Microtel
59	PA 581, to US 11, to I-83, Harrisburg, **3 mi E** 🅐 Sunoco, 🍽 Bob Evans, Burger King, Carrabba's, Dunkin Donuts, Denny's, Friendly's, Hooters, McDonald's, Old Country Buffet, Outback Steaks, Quizno's, TGIFriday's, Wendy's, 🛏 Comfort Inn, Hampton Inn, Holiday Inn, 🅞 AutoZone, Dick's, GNC, Home Depot, K-Mart, Lowe's, Petsmart, Radio Shack, Staples, TJ Maxx
57	PA 114, to Mechanicsburg, **2 mi E** 🅐 Sheetz, 🍽 Alfredo's Pizza, Arby's, Great Wall Chinese, Isaac's Rest., McDonald's, Pizza Hut, Red Robin, Silver Spring Diner, Subway, Taco Bell, 🛏 Ramada Ltd, 🅞 Giant Foods/gas, Marshall's, Walmart
52b a	US 11, to I-76/PA Tpk, Middlesex, **E** 🅐 ✈FLYING J/Denny's/dsl/scales/24hr/@, Pioneer/dsl, 🍽 Bob Evans, Denny's, Dunkin Donuts, Ember's Steaks, Middlesex Diner, 🛏 Best Inn, Best Value Inn, Hotel Carlisle, Motel 6, Super 8, 🅞 🅗, **W** 🅐 Gulf, Loves/Wendy's/dsl/24hr, Petro/dsl/24hr/@, Shell/dsl/scales, Sunoco/Subway, 🍽 Arby's, Carelli's Subs, Country Club Diner,

HARRISBURG / CARLISLE

Exit	Services
52b a	Continued Country Oven Rest, McDonald's, Waffle House, 🛏 Best Western, Hampton Inn, Howard Johnson, Quality Inn, Residence Inn, Rodeway Inn, Super 8, Travelodge, 🅞 🅗, Blue Beacon, truckwash
49	PA 74 (no EZ sb return), **E** 🅐 Sheetz, same as 48, **W** 🅐 Citgo
48	PA 74, York St (no EZ nb return), **E** 🍽 Coldstone, Red Robin, Starbucks, Subway, 🅞 Aldi Foods, $Tree, Kohl's, Michael's, Old Navy, Petsmart, Rite Aid, Target, Verizon, **W** 🅐 Gulf/dsl, Hess, KwikFill, 🍽 Brick House Rest, Burger King, McDonald's, Pizza Hut, Quizno's, Taco Bell, 🅞 BonTon, CVS Drug, Dunkin Donuts, Ford, Lowe's, Radio Shack, Weis Foods
47	PA 34, Hanover St, **E** 🍽 Chili's, Cracker Barrel, 🛏 Sleep Inn, 🅞 Home Depot, **W** 🅐 Gulf, 🍽 Al's Pizza, Applebee's, Bruster's/Nathan's, DQ, Palace China, Panera Bread, Papa John's, Subway, Super Buffet, Vinny Rest, Wendy's, 🅞 AT&T, CVS Drug, Rite Aid, Ross, Staples, TJ Maxx, Walmart
45	College St, **E** 🅐 BP/dsl, 🍽 Alfredo Pizza, Arby's, Bonanza, Friendly's, Great Wall Buffet, McDonald's, 🛏 Days Inn Super 8, 🅞 🅗, K-Mart, Nell's Foods, Tire Pros
44	PA 465, to Plainfield, **E** 🛏 Country Inn&Suites, Fairfield Inn, 🅞 st police, **W** 🅐 Sheetz/24hr, 🍽 Subway
38.5mm	**rest area both lanes, full &♿; facilities, 🅲, 🚯, litter barrels, petwalk**
37	PA 233, to Newville, **E** Pine Grove Furnace SP, **W** Col Denning SP
29	PA 174, King St, **E** 🅐 Sunoco/dsl, 🛏 Rodeway Inn, **W** 🅐 Rutter's/dsl, 🍽 Bro's Pizza, Burger King, China House, KFC, Little Caesar's, McDonald's (2mi), Subway, Taco Bell, Wendy's, 🛏 Best Western, Theo's Motel, 🅞 Advance Parts, Cadillac/Chevrolet, CVS Drug, Ford, K-Mart, Lowe's, Walmart, vet
24	PA 696, Fayette St, **W** 🅐 Exxon/dsl, Pacific Pride
20	PA 997, Scotland, **E** 🅐 Exxon/dsl, 🍽 Bonanza, McDonald's, 🛏 Comfort Inn, Super 8, 🅞 BonTon, Gander Mtn, JC Penney, Sears/auto, mall, **W** 🅐 BP/dsl, Sunoco/24hr, 🛏 Sleep Inn
17	Walker Rd, **W** 🅐 Sheetz/24hr, 🍽 Aki Steaks, Bruster's, Nathan's, Fox's Pizza, Fuddrucker's, Jerry's Subs, Moe's SW Grill, Panera Bread, Quizno's, Red Robin, TGIFriday's, 🛏 Country Inn&Suites, 🅞 Ford, Giant Foods/gas, Kohl's, Michael's, Mr Tire, Petsmart, Staples, Target
16	US 30, to Chambersburg, **E** 🅐 Exxon, Fuel Ctr, Lincoln Way/dsl, Sheetz/24hr, 🍽 Arby's, Bro's Pizza, Burger King, Chris' Country Kitchen, Ginger House Chinese, Hoss' Rest., Jade Garden, KFC, Meadow's Custard, Montezuma Mexican, Perkins, Popeye's, Quizno's, Rita's Custard, Ryan's, Waffle House, Wendy's, 🛏 Days Inn, 🅞 AAA, Aldi Foods, AT&T, Curves, $Tree, Harley-Davidson, Hobby Lobby, Jo-Ann Fabrics, Lowe's, NAPA, Nissan/Scion/Toyota, Radio Shack, U-Haul, Walmart/Subway, st police, vet, **W** 🅐 Hess/dsl, 🍽 Burger King, Copper Kettle, Fox's Pizza, Hardee's, LJ Silver, McDonald's, Pat&Carla Italian, Pizza Hut, Ponderosa, Ruby Tuesday, Starbucks, Taco Bell, 🛏 Best Western, La Quinta, Sheraton, Travelodge, 🅞 🅗, AutoZone, Ford, Lincoln/Mercury, Walgreens
14	PA 316, Wayne Ave, **E** 🍽 Bob Evans, Cracker Barrel, 🛏 Fairfield Inn, Hampton Inn, Red Carpet Inn, **W** 🅐 BP, Exxon/Dunkin Donuts, KwikFill, Sheetz, Shell, 🍽

CHAMBERSBURG

PA

INTERSTATE 81 CONT'D

Exit	Services
14	Continued
	Applebee's, Arby's, China Buffet, China Wok, Denny's, Mario's Italian, Montezuma Mexican, Papa John's, Red Lobster, Subway, Twin Dragon Chinese, Wendy's, 🛏 EconoLodge, Holiday Inn Express, Quality Inn, 🅾 AT&T, CVS Drug, $Tree, Giant Foods/gas, GNC, K-Mart, Verizon, Weis Foods
12mm	**weigh sta sb**
10	PA 914, Marion
7mm	**weigh sta nb**
5	PA 16, Greencastle, **E** 🖭 TA/BP/Buckhorn/dsl/scales/24hr/@, Sunoco/grill/dsl, 🍴 Arby's, McDonald's, Subway, 🛏 Rodeway Inn, Star Inn, 🅾 Whitetail Ski Resort, **W** 🖭 Exxon/dsl, 🛏 Castle Green Motel/rest
3	US 11, **E** 🖭 Sunoco, 🍴 Bro's Pizza, 🛏 Comfort Inn, 🅾 Goodyear/auto
2mm	**Welcome Ctr nb, full** ♿ **facilities,** 🚻, 🏞, **litter barrels, vending, petwalk**
1	PA 163, Mason-Dixon Rd, **W** 🛏 Knights Inn, Stateline Motel, 🅾 Keystone RV Ctr
0mm	Pennsylvania/Maryland state line, Mason-Dixon Line

INTERSTATE 83

Exit	Services
51 b a	I-83 begins/ends on I-81, exit 70.
50b a	US 22, Jonestown Rd, Harrisburg, **E** 🖭 Hess/dsl, Sunoco/dsl, USA, 🍴 Applebee's, Arby's, Atlanta Bread, Chipotle Mexican, Cold Stone, Colonial Park Diner, Domino's, El Rodeo Mexican, 5 Guys Burgers, Gilligan's Grill, Grand Buffet, LJ Silver, McDonald's, Old Country Buffet, Olive Garden, Pizza Hut, Red Lobster, Red Robin, Starbucks, Subway, Taco Bell, Tonino's Pizza, Wendy's, 🅾 Aamco, Advance Parts, Best Buy, BonTon, Boscov's, Coscto/gas, CVS Drug, Dick's, Ford, Gander Mtn, Giant Foods, Goodyear/auto, Home Depot, K-Mart, Kohl's, Marshall's, Michael's, NAPA, NTB, Old Navy, PepBoys, PetCo, Radio Shack, Ross, Sears/auto, Super Petz, Target, Tires+, U-Haul, Verizon, Weis Foods, William's Tires/repair, mall, urgent care, **W** 🖭 Capital, 🍴 DQ, Dunkin Donuts, Friendly's, Gabriella's Italian, KFC, Roberto's Pizza, 🅾 Rite Aid
48	Union Deposit Rd, **E** 🖭 Sunoco, 🍴 Arby's, Burger King, Evergreen Chinese, Panera Bread, 🛏 Best Western, Hampton Inn, 🅾 Ⓗ, $Tree, Giant Foods/gas, Rite Aid, Staples, mall, **W** 🖭 Gulf/dsl, 🍴 ChuckeCheese, Empire Asian Bistro, Great Wall Chinese, Jimmy John's, JoJo's Pizza, Maple's Pizza, McDonald's, Mulligan's Grill, New China, Outback Steaks, Rita's Ice Cream, Starbucks, Subway, TX Roadhouse, TGIFriday's, Waffle House, Wendy's, YP Rest., 🛏 Country Inn&Suites, Fairfield Inn, Holiday Inn Express, Motel 6, 🅾 BigLots, Curves, $Tree, Family$, Hancock Fabrics, Lowe's, PriceRite Foods, Tuesday Morning, Weis Foods
47	(46b from nb), US 322 E, to Hershey, Derry St, **E** 🖭 Hess, 🍴 Papa John's, 🅾 Home Depot, Petsmart
46b a	I-283 S, to I-76/PA Tpk, **services E off I-283** **S** 🖭 Exxon/dsl, Sunoco, 🍴 Bob Evans, Capitol Diner, Doc Holliday's Steaks, Domino's, Eat'n Park, McDonald's, Waffle House, 🛏 Courtyard, EconoLodge, Holiday Inn, Howard Johnson, La Quinta, Red Roof Inn, Sheraton, Super 8,

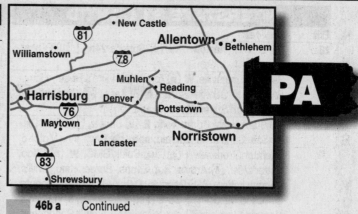

Exit	Services
46b a	Continued
	Travelodge, Wyndham, 🅾 Buick, JC Penney, LandRover, Target, VW/Audi, **W** 🖭 Sunoco, 🍴 Taco Bell, Wendy's, 🛏 Best Western, Days Inn
45	Paxton St, **E** 🖭 Sheetz/dsl, 🍴 Applebees, Burger King, Dunkin Donuts, Fuddrucker's, Isaac's Rest., Pizza Hut, Ruby Tuesday, Starbucks, Wendy's, 🛏 Hilton Garden, Homewood Suites, Towneplace Suites, 🅾 Bass Pro Shops, Barnes&Noble, JC Penney, Macy's, Mazda/Subaru/Toyota, Nissan, mall
44b	17th St, 19th St, **E** 🖭 Sunoco, 🍴 Bankok Thai Cuisine, Benihana Japanese, Dunkin Donuts, Hardee's, 🅾 Advance Parts, AutoZone, Buick/GMC, Firestone/auto, Honda, Hyundai/Suzuki, Nissan, Tires+
44a	PA 230, 13th St, Harrisburg, downtown, **W** 🅾 Chevrolet
43	2nd St, Harrisburg, downtown, st capitol, **W** 🛏 Crowne Plaza, Hilton, 🅾 Ⓗ
42.5mm	Susquehanna River
42	Lemoyne
41b	Highland Park, **E** 🖭 Hess, Turkey Hill, 🍴 Burger King, KFC, **E** 🖭 Sunoco, 🍴 Ciao Pizza, 🅾 Ace Hardware, Family$, Weis Foods
41a	US 15, PA 581 W, to Gettysburg
40b	New Cumberland, **W** 🖭 Gulf/dsl, 🍴 JoJo's Pizza, McDonald's, New China, Sidoti's Italian, Subway, 🅾 CVS Drug, $General
40a	Limekiln Rd, to Lewisberry, **E** 🖭 Shell/dsl, Tom's, 🍴 Bob Evans, Doc Holliday's, John's Diner, McDonald's, Pizza Hut, 🛏 Comfort Inn, Fairfield Inn, Holiday Inn/rest, Quality Inn, Rodeway Inn, **W** 🖭 Hess, 🛏 Best Western, Motel 6, Travel Inn, 🅾 vet
39b	I-76/PA Tpk
39a	PA 114, Lewisberry Rd, **E** 🖭 Rutter's/dsl, 🛏 Days Inn, Highland Inn, Keystone Inn, Red Carpet Inn
38	Reesers Summit
36	PA 262, Fishing Creek, **E** 🖭 Hess/Dunkin Donuts, 🍴 Bruster's, Mamma's Pizza, 🅾 CVS Drug
35	PA 177, Lewisberry, **E** 🍴 Hillside Café, **W** 🖭 Exxon, 🍴 Francescos, Summit Rest., 🛏 Alpine Inn
34mm	**parking area/weigh sta sb**
34	Valley Green (from nb), same as 33
33	PA 392, Yocumtown, **E** 🖭 Hess/Dunkin Donuts/dsl, Rutter's, 🍴 Burger King, Hong Kong Buffet, KFC/Taco Bell, Maple Donuts, McDonald's, NewBerry Diner, New China Buffet, 2 Bro's Pizza, 🛏 Super 8, 🅾 $Tree, Family$, GNC, Radio Shack, Rite Aid, Verizon, Walmart/Subway
33mm	**parking area/weigh sta nb**
32	PA 382, Newberrytown, **E** 🖭 Rutter's/deli/dsl/24hr, **W** Exxon/dsl

PA

PA

INTERSTATE 83 CONT'D

Exit	Services
28	PA 295, Strinestown, **W** 🅖 Rutter's/24hr, 🍴 83 Diner, Wendy's
24	PA 238, Emigsville, **W** 🅖 Tom's, 🍴 4 Bro's Rest.
22	PA 181, N George St, **E** 🅖 Rutter's, 🛏 Comfort Inn, Homewood Suites, **W** same as 21b
21b a	US 30, Arsenal Rd, to York, **E** 🅖 Sheetz, 🍴 Clock Diner, San Carlo's Rest., Starbucks, 🛏 Days Inn, Motel 6, Sheraton, Yorkview Hotel, 🄾 Buick/GMC, **W** 🅖 Citgo, Rutter's/dsl, 🍴 Arby's, Bob Evans, Burger King, Chili's, China Kitchen, DQ, Denny's, Domino's, Dunkin Donuts, El Rodeo Mexican, 5 Guys Burgers, Friendly's, Hardee's, Hooters, Hoss's, KFC, Little Caesars, Logan's Roadhouse, LJ Silver, McDonald's, Old Country Buffet, Olive Garden, Panera Bread, Pizza Hut, Popeye's, Quiznos, Rita's Custard, Ruby Tuesday, Smokey Bones BBQ, Subway, Taco Bell, TGIFriday's, Wendy's, 🛏 Best Western, Red Roof Inn, Rodeway Inn, Super 8, Wingate Inn, 🄾 Acura, Advance Parts, AT&T, AutoZone, BJ's Whse, BMW, BonTon, Cadillac/Chevrolet, Chrysler/Dodge/Jeep, Curves, CVS Drug, Dick's, $General, $Tree, Giant Foods/gas, Harley-Davidson, Honda, Kia, Kohl's, Lowe's, Macy's, NTB, Office Depot, Old Navy, PepBoys, PetCo, Petsmart, Radio Shack, Ross, Staples, Subaru, Target, TJ Maxx, Verizon, Walmart/McDonald's, Weis Foods/gas, transmissions
19	PA 462, Market St, **E** 🅖 Hess, 🍴 Applebee's, Arby's, ChuckECheese's, Coldstone, DQ, Fuddruckers, Outback Steaks, Papa John's, Perkins, Rita's Custard, Taco Bell, Tokyo Diner, Wendy's, 🛏 Quality Inn, 🄾 🛉, Advance Parts, Aldi Foods, $General, $Tree, Giant Foods, Home Depot, Lowe's, Nissan, NTB, Sam's Club, Walgreens, Walmart, Weis Foods
18	PA 124, Mt Rose Ave, Prospect St, **E** 🅖 Pacific Pride, Rutters, 🍴 Al Dente Italian, Burger King, 5 Guys Burgers, Nino's Pizza, Pizza Hut, Subway, Sweet House Chinese, Uncle Nick's Diner, 🛏 Budget Host, 🄾 Curves, K-Mart, Nello Tire
16b a	PA 74, Queen St, **E** 🅖 Tom's, 🍴 Baskin-Robbins/Dunkin Donuts, Bella's Italian, China Buffet, Cracker Barrel, Isaac's Rest., Ruby Tuesday, 🛏 Country Inn&Suites, 🄾 Giant Foods/gas, Lincoln, **W** 🅖 LukOil, Sheetz, 🍴 Infinito's Pizza, McDonald's, Pizza Hut/Taco Bell, Quiznos, S Yorke Diner, Subway, 🄾 BonTon, CVS Drug, $General, $Tree, Jo-Ann Fabrics, Price Rite Foods, Tuesday Morning, Walgreens
15	S George St, I-83 spur into York, **W** 🛉
14	PA 182, Leader Heights, **E** 🍴 Domino's, First Wok, Subway, 🄾 vet, **W** 🅖 Rutter's, 🍴 McDonald's, 🛏 Holiday Inn Express, 🄾 Rite Aid
10	PA 214, Loganville, **W** 🍴 Elsie's Rest., Mamma's Pizza, 🛏 Midway Motel, 🄾 TrueValue, st police
8	PA 216, Glen Rock, **E** 🛏 Rocky Ridge Motel, **W** 🄾 Amish Farmers Mkt (2mi)
4	PA 851, Shrewsbury, **E** 🅖 Tom's/dsl/24hr, 🍴 Cracker Barrel, Ruby Tuesday, 🛏 Hampton Inn, 🄾 Home Depot, TrueValue, **W** 🅖 Exxon/dsl, 🍴 Arby's, Chick-fil-A, Coachlight Rest., Emerald Garden Chinese, KFC/Taco Bell, McDonald's, Quiznos, Rita's Custard, Starbucks, Subway, Szechuan Chinese, Wendy's, 🄾 Advance Parts, Curves, $Tree, Giant Foods, GNC, Mr Tire, Radio Shack, Sauble's Foods, Walmart
2mm	Welcome Ctr nb, full 🦽 facilities, 🄲 vending, ⛽ litter barrels, petwalk
0mm	Pennsylvania/Maryland state line

INTERSTATE 84

Exit	Services
54mm	Pennsylvania/New York state line, Delaware River
53	US 6, PA 209, Matamoras, **N** **Welcome Ctr/both lanes, full 🦽 facilities, 🄲 vending, ⛽ litter barrels, petwalk,** 🅖 Exxon, Go24, Shell, TurkeyHill/dsl, 🍴 Stewart's Drive-Inn, The Grill, 🛏 Appl Inn, 🄾 AutoZone, PriceChopper, auto repair, fireworks, **S** 🅖 Sunoco, 🍴 Dunkin Donuts, McDonald's, Perkins, Roma Pizza, Subway, Village Diner, Wendy's, 🛏 Best Western, Hampton Inn, Scottish Inn, 🄾 Home Depot, K-Mart, Lowe's, Staples, Tristate RV Park, Walmart/Subway
46	US 6, to Milford, **N** 🅖 Sunoco/dsl, **0-2 mi S** 🅖 Exxon/dsl, Gulf, TurkeyHill, Xtra, 🍴 Apple Valley Rest., 🛏 Black Walnut B&B, Chang Mao Chinese, 🛏 Red Carpet Inn, 🄾 Grand Union Foods, NAPA, Rite Aid, USPO
34	PA 739, to Lords Valley, Dingmans Ferry, **S** 🅖 Sunoco/Dunkin Donuts/dsl, Xtra/dsl, 🍴 Bruno's Pizza, China Dynasty, ChuckeCheese, McDonald's, Panda Chinese, Subway, 🄾 Curves, Family$, Rite Aid, Weis Foods, USPO
30	PA 402, to Blooming Grove, **N** st police, to Lake Wallenpaupack
26	PA 390, to Tafton, **N** Exxon/dsl, Tanglewood Ski Area (4mi), to Lake Wallenpaupack, **S** 🄾 to Promised Land SP
26mm	**rest area/weigh sta both lanes, full 🦽 facilities, 🄲 vending, ⛽ litter barrels, petwalk**
20	PA 507, Greentown, **N** 🅖 Exxon/dsl, Shell/Subway, 🍴 John's Italian, 🄾 Animal Park (5mi)
17	PA 191, to Newfoundland, Hamlin, **N** 🅖 Howe's/Exxon/dsl/scales/24hr, 🍴 Twin Rocks Rest., 🛏 Comfort Inn, 🄾 dsl repair
8	PA 247, PA 348, Mt Cobb, **N** 🅖 Gulf/dsl/24hr, 🍴 Cobb Rest., **S** 🅖 Exxon/Subway/dsl
4	I-380 S, to Mount Pocono
2	PA 435 S, to Elmhurst
1	Tigue St, **N** 🛏 Holiday Inn, **S** 🅖 Valero/dsl
0mm	I-84 begins/ends on I-81, exit 54.

INTERSTATE 90

Exit	Services
46mm	Pennsylvania/New York state line, **Welcome Ctr/weigh sta wb, full 🦽 facilities, 🄲 vending, ⛽ litter barrels, petwalk**
45	US 20, to State Line, **N** 🅖 KwikFill/dsl/scales, 🍴 McDonald's, **S** 🅖 BP/Subway/dsl, 🛏 Red Carpet Inn, 🄾 Niagara Falls Info, fireworks
41	PA 89, North East, **N** 🅖 Shell/repair, 🍴 New Harvest Rest., 🛏 Holiday Inn Express, Super 8, Vineyard B&B, **S** 🄾 Family Affair Camping (4mi), winery
37	I-86 E, to Jamestown
35	PA 531, to Harborcreek, **N** 🅖 TA/BP/Pizza Hut/Subway/dsl/rest./scales/24hr/@, 🛏 Rodeway Inn, 🄾 Blue Beacon, dsl repair
32	PA 430, PA 290, to Wesleyville, **N** 🅖 Country Fair, st police, **S** 🄾 camping
29	PA 8, to Hammett, **N** 🅖 Country Fair, 🍴 Wendy's, 🄾 🛉, 🛏 Travelodge, 🄾 Peterbilt, dsl repair
27	PA 97, State St, Waterford, **N** 🅖 Country Fair/dsl/24hr, Kwikfill, 🍴 Arby's, Barbato's Italian, Doc Holiday's Grill,

N ↕ S YORK

E ↕ W

E ↕ W

INTERSTATE 90 CONT'D

Exit	Services
27	Continued
	McDonald's, 🛏 Days Inn, La Quinta, Red Roof Inn, Tallyho Inn, ⊙ ℍ, S 🍴 ⛽/Subway/dsl/scales/24hr, Shell/dsl, 🛏 Quality Inn, Super 8, ⊙ casino
24	US 19, Peach St, to Waterford, N 🍴 Country Fair, Delta Sonic, KwikFill, 🍴 Applebee's, Burger King, Chick-fil-A, ChuckeCheese, Cracker Barrel, Eat'n Park, Golden Corral, KFC, Krispy Kreme, Longhorn Steaks, McDonald's, Old Country Buffet, Olive Garden, Panera Bread, Quaker Steak&Lube, Quiznos, Safari Grill, S&S Buffet, Steak'n Shake, Subway, Taco Bell, TX Roadhouse, TGIFriday's, Tim Horton, Torero's Mexican, 🛏 Courtyard, Hilton Garden, ⊙ ℍ, Advance Parts, Best Buy, Curves, $Tree, Giant Eagle Foods, Home Depot, Jo-Ann Fabrics, Kohl's, Lowe's, Marshall's, PetsMart, Sam's Club/gas, Staples, Target, Walmart, Wegman's Foods, urgent care, S 🍴 BP/dsl, Country Fair, Shell/dsl, 🍴 Bob Evans, Boston's Rest., 🛏 Comfort Inn, Country Inn&Suites, EconoLodge, Hampton Inn, Holiday Inn Express, Microtel, Residence Inn, Wingate Inn, ⊙ waterpark
22b a	I-79, N to Erie, S to Pittsburgh, **3-5 mi** N services in Erie
18	PA 832, Sterrettania, N 🍴 Marathon/dsl/24hr, 🍴 Burger King, ⊙ Hill's Family Camping, to Presque Isle SP, S 🍴 Beechwood Rest., 🛏 Quality Inn, ⊙ KOA
16	PA 98, to Franklin Center, Fairview, S ⊙ Follys Camping (2mi), Mar-Da-Jo-Dy Camping (5mi)
9	PA 18, to Girard, Platea, N 🍴 Gulf/dsl/repair, st police, S 🛏 Green Roof Inn (2mi)
6	PA 215, to Albion, E Springfield, N lodging, S 🍴 Sunoco, lodging, repair
3	US 6N, to Cherry Hill, West Springfield, N lodging on US 20, S 🍴 BP/dsl/rest./scales/24hr
2.5mm	**Welcome Ctr/weigh sta eb, full** ♿ **facilities, info,** 🚻, 🏞, **litter barrels, vending, petwalk**
0mm	Pennsylvania/Ohio state line

INTERSTATE 95

Exit	Services
51mm	Pennsylvania/New Jersey state line, Delaware River
51	PA 32, to New Hope, **W** Washington Crossing Hist Park
50mm	**Welcome Ctr sb, full** ♿ **facilities, vending,** 🚻, 🏞, **litter barrels, petwalk**
49	PA 332, to Yardley, Newtown, W 🍴 Dunkin Donuts, 🛏 Hampton Inn, ⊙ ℍ, to Tyler SP
46b a	US 1 to I-276, PA TPK, Langhorne, Oxford Valley, E ℍ
44	US 1, PA 413, to Penndel, Levittown, E 🍴 Shell/7-11/dsl, 🍴 Arrano Hibachi Steaks, Blue Fountain Diner, Buffalo Wild Wing, ChuckECheese's, Dunkin Donuts, Friendly's, Great American Diner, Hong Kong Pearl, Langhorne Ale House, Ming's Asian, Olive Garden, Panera Bread, Red Lobster, Ruby Tuesday, Subway, Wendy's, 🛏 Sheraton, ⊙ ℍ, Acura, Chrysler/Dodge/Jeep, $Tree, Firestone/auto, Ford, Goodyear/auto, Harley-Davidson, Honda, Hyundai/Suzuki, Kia, K-Mart, Lincoln, Lowe's, Marshall's, Mazda, PepBoys, Redner's Whse Mkt, Sam's Club, Staples, Subaru, Target, TJ Maxx, VW/Volvo, W 🍴 LukOil/dsl, 🍴 Denny's, McDonald's, ⊙ Toyota/Scion, U-Haul
40	PA 413, I-276, to Bristol Bridge, Burlington, E 🍴 Hess/Dunkin Donuts/dsl, WaWa, 🍴 Fish Factory Rest., Golden Eagle Diner, KFC, McDonald's, ⊙ ℍ, Chevrolet

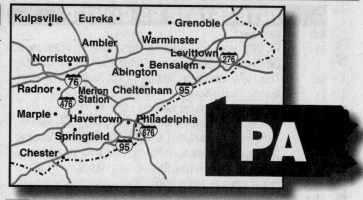

37	PA 132, to Street Rd, W 🍴 BP/dsl, Sunoco/dsl, 🍴 Burger King, Chili's, China Sun Buffet, Dunkin Donuts, Gino's Burgers/Chicken, Golden Corral, IHOP, McDonald's, Old Country Buffet, Popeye's, Sonic, TX Roadhouse, Wendy's, ⊙ Advance Parts, Aldi Foods, $Tree, Giant Foods, GNC, Goodyear/auto, K-Mart, Kohl's, PepBoys, Radio Shack, Ross, Save-A-Lot, 7-11, U-Haul, Walgreens, WaWa
35	PA 63, to US 13, Woodhaven Rd, Bristol Park, W 🍴 Liberty, 🍴 Bob Evans, Champs Pizza, Dunkin Donuts, McDonald's, Old Haven Pizza, Rita's Custard, 🛏 Hampton Inn, ⊙ ℍ, Acme Foods, Home Depot, Verizon, WaWa, **1 mi** W 🍴 BP, Exxon, LukOil, Sunoco/dsl, 🍴 Arby's, Boston Mkt, Burger King, Dave&Buster's, Dynasty Rest., Grand China Buffet, Hibachi Buffet, Joe Santucci's, KFC, McDonald's, Mr V's Steaks, Panda King, Pizza Hut, Ruby Tuesday, Supreme Buffet, Taco Bell, Uno, Wendy's, ⊙ BigLots, Burlington Coats, Dick's, $Tree, Marshall's, NTB, Old Navy, Pathmark Foods, Rite Aid, Sam's Club, Tires+, Walmart
32	Academy Rd, W ⊙ ℍ, K-Mart
30	PA 73, Cottman Ave, W 🍴 Sunoco
27	Bridge St, W 🍴 BP, Exxon, LukOil, 7-11, 🍴 Dunkin Donuts, ⊙ ℍ, Rite Aid
26	to NJ 90, Betsy Ross Brdg, W 🍴 BP, Hess, Sunoco/dsl, 🍴 Applebee's, Burger King, KFC, McDonald's, Wendy's, ⊙ Home Depot, Lowe's, ShopRite Foods, Target
25	Allegheny Ave, W 🍴 Sunoco, ⊙ ℍ, WaWa
23	Lehigh Ave, Girard Ave, E casino, W 🍴 Exxon, 🍴 Applebee's, Arby's, Coldstone, Dunkin Donuts, Pizza Hut, Rita's Custard, ⊙ ℍ, AutoZone, CVS Drug, Family$, GNC, PepBoys, Radio Shack, Rite Aid, WaWa
22	I-676, US 30, to Central Philadelphia, Independence Hall
20	Columbus Blvd, Penns Landing, **1-2 mi** E **on Columbus** 🍴 BP, Liberty/WaWa/dsl, LukOil/dsl, 🍴 Burger King, Dave&Buster's, Champp's Rest., ChartHouse Rest., Chick-fil-A, Famous Dave's BBQ, IHOP, La Veranda Italian, Longhorn Steaks, McDonald's, Moshulu Rest., Ruby Buffet, Wendy's, 🛏 Comfort Inn, Sheraton, Hyatt Hotel (1mi), ⊙ Best Buy, $Tree, Home Depot, Lowe's, Marshall's, PepBoys, ShopRite Foods, Staples, Target, Verizon, Walmart
19	I-76 E, to Walt Whitman Bridge, E 🛏 Holiday Inn, to stadiums, **W on Front St** E 🍴 BP, Exxon/dsl, Sunoco, 🍴 Burger King, Dunkin Donuts, KFC, Little Caesars, McDonald's, Pizza Hut, ⊙ Aldi Foods
17	PA 611, to Broad St, Pattison Ave, W ⊙ ℍ, to Naval Shipyard, to stadium
15mm	Schuykill River
15	Enterprise Ave, Island Ave (from sb)
14	Bartram Ave, Essington Ave (from sb)

ERIE E ↕ W

N ↕ **S** **LEVITTON** N

PHILADELPHIA AREA

PA

🅖 = gas 🍴 = food 🏨 = lodging 🅞 = other Copyright 2012 - The Next Exit

INTERSTATE 95 CONT'D

Exit	Services
13	PA 291, to I-76 W (from nb), to Central Philadelphia, **E** 🅖 Exxon/dsl, 🏨 Days Inn, Guest Quarters, Hilton, Marriott, Renaissance Inn, Residence Inn, Sheraton, Sheraton Suites, Westin Suites
12	**E** Philadelphia Intl 🛬, services same as 10
10	PA 291, Bartrom Ave, (from nb), Cargo City, **E** 🏨 Marriott, Renaissance Hotel, **W** 🅖 WaWa/dsl, 🍴 Ruby Tuesday, 🏨 Courtyard, Embassy Suites, Extended Stay America, Extended Stay Deluxe, Fairfield Inn, Hampton Inn, Microtel, Studio+, 🅞 Heins NWR
9b a	PA 420, to Essington, Prospect Park, **E** 🅖 Sunoco/dsl, Valero/dsl, 🍴 Denny's, Lehmans Rest., Mel's Diner, Philly Diner, 🏨 Comfort Inn, Motel 6, Ramada Inn, Red Roof Inn, Residence Inn, SpringHill Suites, Wyndham Garden, 🅞 USPO, WaWa
8	to Chester Waterfront, Ridley Park, **W on US 13** 🍴 Stargate Diner
7	I-476 N, to Plymouth, Meeting
6	PA 352, PA 320, to Edgmont Ave, **1 mi E on US 13** 🍴 McDonald's, Popeye's, 🅞 Radio Shack, Walmart/Subway, **W** 🏨 Days Inn/Dawn's Diner
5	Kerlin St (from nb), **E** 🅖 Gulf
4	US 322 E, to NJ, to Barry Bridge, **W** 🏨 Highland Motel
3	(from nb, no EZ return) US 322 W, Highland Ave, **E** 🅖 Sunoco/dsl, 🅞 Ford, Goodyear
2	PA 452, to US 322, Market St E, **W** 🅖 Exxon, 🍴 McDonald's, Subway
1	Chichester Ave, **E** 🅖 Sunoco, 🅞 fireworks, **W** 🅖 BP, 🅞 WaWa, transmissions
0mm	**Pennsylvania/Delaware state line, Welcome Ctr/weigh sta nb, full ♿ facilities, 🅒, 🚻, litter barrels, petwalk**

INTERSTATE 99

Exit	Services
83	PA 350, (I-99 begins/ends on I-80, exit 161), Bellafonte, **E** 🅖 Weis Foods, **W** 🅖 Lyken's Mkt, 🍴 Bonfatto's Rest., Burger King, Pizza Hut, 🅞 Rite Aid, TrueValue
81	PA 26 S, to PA 64, to Pleasant Gap
80	Harrison Rd (no re-entry nb)
78b a	PA 150, to Bellafonte, **W** 🅖 Sheetz/dsl, 🍴 Bro's Pizza, EconoLodge, 🅞 Bumper Parts, Ford, auto repair, Vistors Ctr
76	Shiloh Rd, **E** 🅖 Sheetz, 🍴 Garfields, LJ Silver, McDonald's, Rey Azteca, 🏨 Best Western, 🅞 Barnes&Noble, BigLots, BonTon, Chevrolet, JC Penney, Jo-Ann Fabrics, Macy's, Office Depot, Ross, Sam's Club, Sears, Subaru, Walmart/Subway
74	Innovation Park, Penn State U, Beaver Stadium
73	US 322 E, Lewiston State College
71	Woodycrest, Tofftrees, **E** 🍴 Applebee's, Chick-fil-A, Cracker Barrel, Eat'n park, Hoss', KFC, McDonald's, Olive Garden, Outback Steaks, TX Roadhouse, Wendy's, 🏨 Hampton Inn, Holiday Inn Express, Quality Inn, SpringHill Suites, 🅞 Dick's, Kohl's, Michael's, PetCo, Target, Wegman's Foods, Walmart
69	US 322 E, Valley Vista Dr, **E** 🅖 Exxon
68	Skytop Mtn Rd, Grays Woods, Waddle
62	US 322 W, to Phillipsburg (from sb)
61	US 322 W, Port Matilda, **E** 🅖 Best, 🍴 Brother's Pizza, Subway, 🏨 Port Matilda Hotel, 🅞 USPO

Exit	Services
52	PA 350, **E** 🅖 BP/Subway
48	PA 453, Tyrone, **W** 🅖 Choice, 🍴 Burger King, 🅞 🅗, Rite Aid
45	Tipton, Grazierville, **W** 🍴 Pizza Hut (2mi), Sammy's BBQ, 🅞 🅗, DelGrosso's Funpark
41	PA 865 N, Bellwood, **E** Ft Roberdeau HS, **W** 🅖 Martin Gen Store/dsl, Sheetz/dsl, 🅞 DelGrosso's Funpark
39	PA 764 S, Pinecroft, **W** Oak Spring Winery
33	17th St, Altoona, **E** same as 32, **W** 🅖 Sheetz, 🍴 Hoss' Rest., Subway (2mi), 🅞 Lowe's, Railroader Museum, U-Haul
32	PA 36, Frankstown Rd, Altoona, **E** 🅖 GetGo, 🍴 Chili's, Panera Bread, 🅞 Barnes&Noble, Best Buy, Boscov's, Giant Eagle Foods, GNC, Home Depot, Kohl's, Michael's, PetCo, Ross, Staples, Canoe Cr SP, **W** 🅖 Gulf, Sheetz, 🍴 ChuckeCheese, Dunkin Donuts, HongKong Buffet, McDonald's, Olive Garden, Papa John's, Perkins, Pizza Hut, Red Lobster, Subway, Uno, Wendy's, 🏨 EconoLodge, Holiday Inn Express, Quality Inn, Super 8, 🅞 🅗, AutoZone, Cadillac, CVS Drug, Dodge, $Tree, Jo-Ann Fabrics, NAPA, Nissan, Rite Aid, Save-A-Lot, Walgreens, USPO
31	Plank Rd, Altoona, **E** 🍴 Cici's Pizza, Friendly's, Hoss' Rest., Jethro's Rest., King's Rest., Krispy Kreme, Outback Steaks, Ruby Tuesday, TGIFriday's, 🏨 Comfort Inn, Ramada Inn, 🅞 Firestone/auto, Radio Shack, Sam's Club/gas, Target, TJ Maxx, Walmart, st police, **W** 🅖 Shell/Subway, 🍴 Applebee's, Arby's, Burger King, Cracker Barrel, Denny's, Eat'n Park, Hooters, KFC, Little Ceasars, LJ Silver, Ponderosa, Taco Bell, 🏨 Hampton Inn, Motel 6, 🅞 Advance Parts, BigLots, $General, Giant Eagle Foods, JC Penney, K-Mart, Macy's, PharMor, Sears/auto, Weis Foods
28	US 22, to Ebensburg, Holidaysburg
23	PA 36, PA 164, Roaring Spring, Portage, **E** 🅖 GetGo/dsl, Sheetz/24hr, Turkey Hill, 🍴 Backyard Burger, 🅞 🅗, Walmart, truck repair
15	Claysburg, King, **W** 🍴 Subway, 🅖
10	to Imler, **W** 🅖, 🍴 Blue Knob SP (8mi)
7	PA 869, Osterburg, St Clairsville, **W** 🅖, 🍴 Blue Knob SP
3	PA 56, Johnstown, Cessna, **E** 🅞 truck parts
1	I-70/76, I-99 begins/ends on US 220., **E** 🅖 BP/dsl, Pacific Pride, Sheetz/dsl, 🍴 Arena Rest., Denny's, Ed's Steaks, Hoss' Rest., LJ Silver, McDonald's, Pizza Hut, Subway, Wendy's, 🏨 Best Western, Budget Host, Hampton Inn, Hillcrest Motel, Holiday Inn Express, Quality Inn, Relax Inn, Super 8

INTERSTATE 476

Exit	Services
131	US 11, US 6. I-476 begins/ends on I-81, services same as I-81, exit 194.
122	Keyser Ave, Old Forge, Taylor
121mm	toll plaza
115	I-81, PA 315, Wyoming Valley, Pittston, **W** 🅖 Mobil, 🍴 Wendy's/dsl/scales/24hr, Sunoco, 🍴 Arby's, McDonald's, Perkins, 🏨 Knight's Inn, Ramada Inn, 🅞 Chevrolet
112mm	toll plaza
105	PA 115, Wilkes-Barre, Bear Creek, **E** 🅖 BP, Exxon, PSC
97mm	parking areas both lanes
95	I-80, PA 940, Pocono, Hazleton, **W** 🅖 WaWa, 🍴 A&W/LJ Silver, Arby's, McDonald's, 🏨 Comfort Inn, EconoLodge, Holiday Inn Express, Knights Inn, Mtn Laurel Resort, Pocono Inn/Resort, Split Rock Resort

INTERSTATE 476 CONT'D

Exit	Services
90mm	parking area sb
86mm	**Hickory Run Service Plaza both lanes,** 🅶 Sunoco/dsl, 🍴 Breyer's, McDonald's, hot dogs
74	US 209, Mahoning Valley, Lehighton, Stroudsburg, **W** 🅶 Shell/Subway/dsl, 🍴 Trainer's Inn Rest., 🏨 Country Inn&Suites, Hampton Inn
71mm	Lehigh Tunnel
56	I-78, US 22, PA 309, Lehigh Valley, **E** 🅶 Gulf, 🍴 Dunkin Donuts, Quiznos, Red Robin, Trivet Diner, Wendy's, 🏨 Comfort Inn, Days Inn, McIntosh Inn, 🅾 BMW, CVS Drug, Infiniti, Jaguar, K-Mart, Land Rover, Staples, **W on US 22** 🅶 Mobil, Sunoco, 🍴 Chris Rest., Parma Pizza, 🏨 Best Western, 🅾 CVS Drug
56mm	**Allentown Service Plaza both lanes,** 🅶 Sunoco/dsl, 🍴 Big Boy, Hershey's Ice Cream, Pizza Hut, Roy Rogers
44	PA 663, Quakertown, Pottstown, **E** 🅶 BP, Mobil/dsl, 🍴 Avanti Grill, Faraco's Pizza, 🏨 Best Western (3mi), Comfort Suites, Hampton Inn, Holiday Inn Express, Rodeway Inn, 🅾 🄷
37mm	parking area sb
31	PA 63, Lansdale, **E** 🅶 Exxon, Lukoil, WaWa 🍴 Bones Grill, 🏨 Best Western, Courtyard, Lansdale Motel, Residence Inn, 🅾 🄷

RHODE ISLAND

INTERSTATE 95

Exit	Services
43mm	Rhode Island/Massachusetts state line
30 (42)	East St, to Central Falls, **E** 🍴 Dunkin Donuts, Subway
29 (41)	US 1, Cottage St, **W** 🍴 d'Angelo's
28 (40)	RI 114, School St, **E** 🅶 Sunoco, 🅾 🄷, Car Pros, Yarn Outlet, to hist dist
27 (39)	US 1, RI 15, Pawtucket, **W** 🅶 Shell/repair, Sunoco/dsl/24hr, 🍴 Burger King, Dunkin Donuts, Ground Round, 🏨 Comfort Inn
26 (38)	RI 122, Lonsdale Ave (from nb), **E** 🅾 U-Haul
25 (37)	US 1, RI 126, N Main St, Providence, **E** 🅶 Gulf, Hess, Shell, 🍴 Chili's, Dunkin Donuts, Gregg's Rest., Subway, 🅾 🄷, PepBoys, Rite Aid, Walgreens, urgent care, **W** 🅶 Gulf/dsl, Hess, 🍴 Burger King, Chelo's Rest., 🅾 AAA, Aamco, Suzuki
24 (36.5)	Branch Ave, Providence, downtown, **W** 🅶 Mobil, 🍴 Wendy's, 🅾 Stop&Shop, Walmart/Subway, urgent care
23 (36)	RI 146, RI 7, Providence, **E** 🅶 Mobil/dsl, 🏨 Marriott, 🅾 🄷, **W** USPO
22 (35.5)	US 6, RI 10, Providence, **E** 🍴 Cheesecake Factory, Dave&Buster's, 🅾 CVS Drug, JC Penney, Macy's, Nordstrom's, mall
21 (35)	Broadway St, Providence, **E** 🏨 Hilton, Regency Plaza
20 (34.5)	I-195, to E Providence, Cape Cod
19 (34)	Eddy St, Allens Ave, to US 1, **W** 🍴 Wendy's, Dunkin Donuts, 🄷
18 (33.5)	US 1A, Thurbers Ave, **W** 🅶 Shell/dsl, 🍴 Burger King, 🅾 🄷
17 (33)	US 1 (from sb), Elmwood Ave, **W** 🅾 Cadillac, Tires Whse
16 (32.5)	RI 10, Cranston, **W** Williams Zoo/park
15 (32)	Jefferson Blvd, **E** 🅶 Mobil, 🍴 Bugaboo Creek Steaks, Dunkin Donuts, Shogun Steaks, 🏨 Courtyard, La Quinta, Motel 6, **W** 🅾 Ryder Trucks

PHILADELPHIA

Exit	Services
20	Germantown Pike W, to I-276 W, PA Tpk W
19	Germantown Pike E
18b a	(18 from sb), Conshohocken, Norristown, **E** 🅶 Lukoil, Sunoco, 🍴 Andy's Diner, Baja Fresh, Burger King, Domino's, Dunkin Donuts, Illiano's Pizza, McDonald's, Outback Steaks, Panera Bread, Rita's Ice Cream, Salad Works, Starbucks, 🅾 Giant Foods, Genuradi's Foods, Marshall's, Toyota/Scion, **E on Chemical Rd** 🍴 Cracker Barrel, Ruby Tuesday, 🏨 Hampton Inn, 🅾 Barnes&Noble, Best Buy, Dick's, Giant Foods, Lowe's, Office Depot, Old Navy, Petsmart, Ross, Target, **W** 🍴 Papa John's, Uno, Wendy's, 🅾 BJ's Whse, Ford, Home Depot, Honda, Hyundai, Kia, Mazda, Michael's, Nissan, Porsche
16b a	(16 from sb), I-76, PA 23, to Philadelpia, Valley Forge
13	US 30, **E** 🅶 Shell, 🍴 Campus Pizza, Nova Grill, Winger's, 🅾 🄷, Staples, USPO, to Villanova U
9	PA 3, Broomall, Upper Darby, **E** 🍴 Barnaby's Rest., 🅾 🄷
5	US 1, Lima, Springfield, **E** 🍴 Dragon Garden, Mesa Mexican, 🅾 AT&T, Giant Foods, Jo-Ann Fabrics, Marshall's, Old Navy, Petsmart, Verizon, Walmart
3	Baltimore Pike, Media, Swarthmore, **E** 🅶 Lukoil, 🍴 Ruby Tuesday, 🅾 🄷, Macy's, Target, Swarthmore Coll
1	McDade Blvd, **E** 🅶 Exxon, 🍴 Dunkin Donuts, KFC, McDonald's, Panda Chinese, 🅾 CVS Drug, Rite Aid
0mm	I-476 begins/ends on I-95, exit 7.

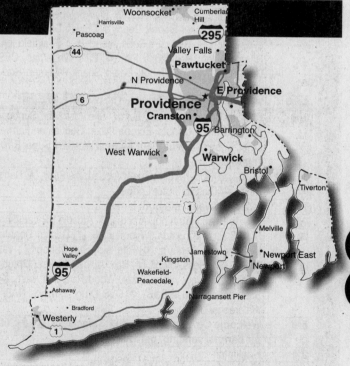

Exit	Services
14 (31)	RI 37, Post Rd, to US 1, **W** 🅶 Shell, Sunoco 🍴 Burger King, 🅾 🄷, CVS Drug, Ford/Lincoln/Mercury, Mazda, Volvo
13 (30)	1 mi **E** TF Green ✈, 🅶 Shell, Sunoco/Dunkin Donuts, 🍴 Chelo's Grill, Legal Sea 🍴 Wendy's, 🏨 Best Western, Comfort Inn, Hampton Inn, Hilton Garden, Holiday Inn

PA

RI

INTERSTATE 95 CONT'D

Exit	Services
13 (30)	Continued
	Express, Homestead Suites, Homewood Suites, Radisson, Residence Inn
12b (29)	RI 2, I-295 N (from sb)
12a	RI 113 E, to Warwick, E 🅖 Shell/Dunkin Donuts/dsl, 🛏 Crowne Plaza Hotel, 🄾 Lowe's, Stop&Shop, W 🅖 Sunoco, 🍽 ChuckeCheese, Wendy's, 🄾 Kohl's, Sears/auto, Walmart/Subway, mall
11 (29)	I-295 N (exits left from nb), to Woonsocket
10b a (28)	RI 117, to Warwick, W 🄷
9 (25)	RI 4 S, E Greenwich
8b a (24)	RI 2, E Greenwich, E 🅖 Shell/dsl, 🍽 China Buffet, Coldstone, Dunkin Donuts, McDonald's, Outback Steaks, Panera Bread, Ruby Tuesday, TX Roadhouse, 🛏 Extended Stay America, 🄾 AT&T, CVS Drug, Dave's Mkt, Walgreens, 0-2 mi W 🅖 Citgo, Sunoco/dsl, 🍽 Agave's Mexican, Applebee's, Carrabba's, Chili's, Denny's, 5 Guys Burgers, KFC, Olive Garden, PapaGino's Pizza, Smokey Bones BBQ, TGIFriday's, Wendy's, 🛏 SpringHill Suites, 🄾 Acura, Aldi Foods, Arlington RV Ctr, Audi/Bentley/BMW/Inifinti/Lexus/Mini/Porsche/Smart, Barnes&Noble, Best Buy, Cadillac, Dick's, GNC, Goodyear/auto, Home Depot, Honda, Hyundai, Jaguar, Jo-Ann Fabrics, Land Rover, Lowe's, Mercedes, Michael's, Nissan, PepBoys, Petco, Petsmart, Staples, Stop&Shop, Target, VW, mall, vet
7 (21)	to Coventry, E 🅖 Mobil/dsl, W 🍽 Applebee's, Cilantro Mexican, Cracker Barrel, Denny's, Dunkin Donuts, Honeydew Donuts, Riccotti's Subs, Wendy's, 🛏 Fairfield Inn, Hampton Inn, Residence Inn, 🄾 BJ's Whse/gas, CVS Drug, GNC, Home Depot, Radio Shack, Walmart/Subway
6a (20)	Hopkins Hill Rd, W 🍽 Dunkin Donuts, 🄾 park&ride
6 (18)	RI 3, to Coventry, W 🅖 Lukoil, Shell/dsl/24hr, Sunoco/dsl, 🍽 Dunkin Donuts, Europa Pizza, Gentleman Farmer Diner, Subway, Venus Pizza, 🛏 Best Western, Super 8, 🄾 TrueValue
5b a (15)	RI 102, W 🅖 R.I.'s Only Trkstp/dsl/scales/24hr, 🍽 Dan's Rest., 🛏 Classic Motor Lodge
10mm	rest area/weigh sta both lanes
4 (9)	RI 3, to RI 165 (from nb), Arcadia, W Arcadia SP, camping
3b a (7)	RI 138 E, to Kingston, Wyoming, E 🍽 Dunkin Donuts, McDonald's, Wendy's, 🄾 Rite Aid, Stop&Shop/🅖, vet, W 🅖 Gulf, Hess, Mobil, 🍽 Bali Village Chinese, Dragon Palace, Subway, Village Pizza, Wood River Inn Rest., 🛏 Stagecoach House B&B, 🄾 CVS Drug, Family$, NAPA, Walgreens, USPO
6mm	Welcome Ctr/rest area nb, full ♿ facilities, 🚻, 🛗, litter barrels, vending, petwalk
2 (4)	Hopkinton
1 (1)	RI 3, to Hopkinton, Westerly, E 🄾 🄷, to Misquamicut SP, RV camping, beaches
0mm	Rhode Island/Connecticut state line

INTERSTATE 295 (Providence)

Exit	Services
2b a (4)	I-95, N to Boston, S to Providence. I-295 begins/ends on I-95, exit 4 in MA. Exits 2-1 are in MA.
1b a (2)	US 1, E 🅖 Mobil/Dunkin Donuts/dsl, 🍽 d'Angelo's, Chicago Grill, ChuckeCheese, Friendly's, Hearth'n Kettle, Longhorn Steaks, 99 Rest., Panera Bread, PapaGino's Italian, Ruby Tuesday, TGIFriday's, 🄾 Best Buy,

Exit	Services
1b a (2)	Continued
	BJ's Whse, Buick/Chevrolet/GMC, CVS Drug, Dick's, $Tree, JC Penney, Jo-Anne Fabrics, Lowe's, Macy's, Marshalls, Michael's, Office Depot, Old Navy, Petsmart, Sears/auto, Staples, Stop&Shop, Target, TJMaxx, Walmart, mall, W 🅖 Emerald/dsl, Gulf, Shell/dsl, 🍽 Applebee's, Dunkin Donuts, 🛏 Holiday Inn Express, Pineapple Inn, Super 8, 🄾 CVS Drug, Nissan, Toyota/Scion
0mm	Rhode Island/Massachusetts state line. Exits 1-2 are in MA.
11 (24)	RI 114, to Cumberland, E 🅖 Shell/dsl, Sunoco, 🍽 Dunkin Donuts, HoneyDew Donuts, 🄾 CVS Drug, Dave's Foods, USPO, W 🍽 J's Deli, Pizza Pasta&More, Saki's Pizza/subs, 🄾 Diamond Hill SP
10 (21)	RI 122, E 🅖 Gulf, Lukoil, 🍽 Burger King, Dunkin Donuts, Forno Pizza, Jacky's Rest., McDonald's, Ronzio Pizza, 🄾 Verizon, W 🍽 Forno Pizza, Fortune House Chinese, Pamfilios Deli, Subway, 🄾 Ace Hardware, Curves, CVS Drug, Rite Aid, Seabra Foods, urgent care
20mm	Blackstone River
19.5mm	weigh sta/rest area (full facilities) nb, Baskin-Robbins, Dunkin Donuts
9b a (19)	RI 146, Woonsocket, Lincoln, E 🛏 Courtyard
8b a (16)	RI 7, N Smithfield, E 🍽 European Cafe, W 🅖 7-11/dsl, Shell, 🍽 Decarlo's Italian, Dunkin Donuts, House of Pizza, Parentes Rest., 🛏 Comfort Suites, Hampton Inn, Holiday Inn Express, 🄾 Smith-Appleby House
7b a (13)	US 44, Centerdale, E 🅖 Hess, Valero, 🍽 Ball's Grill, Cancun Mexican, La Cocina Italian, 🄾 🄷, NAPA, CarQuest repair, W 🅖 Gulf/dsl, Mobil, Shell, 🍽 A&W, Applebee's, Burger King, Chelo's Grill, Chicago Grill, Chili's, D'angelo's, Dominos, Dunkin Donuts, KFC/Taco Bell, McDonald's, Panera Bread, PapaGino's, Subway, TinTsin Chinese, Wendy's, Yamato Steaks, 🄾 AAA, AT&T, Barnes&Noble, Curves, CVS Drug, Dave's Foods, Dick's, $Tree, Home Depot, Kohl's, Michael's, Old Navy, Radio Shack, Rite Aid, Staples, Stop&Shop, Target, TJ Maxx, Verizon, urgent care, to Powder Mill Ledges WR
6b c (10)	US 6, to Providence, E 🅖 7-11, Shell, 🍽 Atwood Grill, Burger King, D'Angelo's, Dunkin Donuts, Jacky's Rest., KFC, Newport Creamery, Noble House Chinese, Ruby Tuesday, Subway, Wendy's, 🄾 AT&T, BJ's Whse, Buick/Chevrolet/GMC, Chrysler/Dodge/Jeep, CVS Drug, Honda, Kia, Office Depot, PetsMart, Rite Aid, Saab, Stop&Shop, USPO
6a (9)	US 6 E Expswy, 1 mi E 🍽 McDonald's, Ribs&Co, Ruby Tuesday, Taco Bell, 🄾 BJ's Whse, Home Depot, Petsmart
5 (8)	RI Resource Recovery Industrial Park
4 (7)	RI 14, Plainfield Pk, E 🅖 Hess, W 🅖 Gulf, Mobil/dsl/24h, 🍽 Dunkin Donuts, Palmieri Pizza, 🄾 CVS Drug, repair
3b a (4)	rd 37, Phenix Ave, E TF Green ✈
2 (2)	RI 2 S, to Warwick, E 🍽 Chicago Grill, Longhorn Steaks, Red Robin, 🄾 JC Penney, Macy's, Marshalls, Old Navy, Verizon, Walgreens, mall, W 🅖 Mobil, Sunoco, 🍽 Burger King, Chili's, Chipotle Mexican, ChuckeCheese, Dunkin Donuts, Hometown Buffet, McDonald's/playplace, Olive Garden, On-the-Border, Panera Bread, Starbucks, Taco Bell, Subway, Wendy's, 🄾 AT&T, Barnes&Noble, Best Buy, Chrysler/Dodge/Keep/Kia, Home Depot, Jaguar, Kohl's, Price Rite Foods, PetsMart, Rite Aid, Sears/auto, Staples, Subaru, Target, TJMaxx, TownFair Tire, Trader Joe's, Verizon, Walmart/Subway, mall
1 (1)	RI 113 W, to W Warwick, same as 2
0mm	I-295 begins/ends on I-95, exit 11.

INTERSTATE 20

Exit	Services
141b a	I-95, N to Fayetteville, S to Savannah. I-20 begins/ends on I-95, exit 160. See Interstate 95, exit 160a for services.
137	SC 340, to Timmonsville, Darlington, N 🅖 BP (1mi), S 🅖 Marathon
131	US 401, SC 403, to Hartsville, Lamar, N 🅖 Exxon/dsl, 🅾 to Darlington Int Raceway, S 🍴 Subway (3mi)
129mm	rest area, no facilities both lanes, commercial vehicles only
123	SC 22, N Lee SP
121mm	Lynches River
120	SC 341, Bishopville, Elliot, N 🏠 Bishopville Motel (3mi), S 🅖 Exxon/dsl, 🍴 Taste of Country Rest., 🏠 Best Value Inn, 🅾 🅷
116	US 15, to Sumter, Bishopville, Shaw AFB, N 🅖 Shell/KFC/dsl/24hr, 🍴 McDonald's, Pizza Hut, Subway (1mi), Waffle House, Zaxby's, 🏠 EconoLodge, S 🅖 Wilco/Hess/DQ/Wendy's/dsl/scales/24hr, 🍴 Huddle House
108	SC 34, to SC 31, Manville, N 🅖 BP/dsl, S 🅖 Citgo/dsl
101	rd 329
98	US 521, to Camden, N 🅖 BP/dsl, Citgo, Exxon/McDonald's, Shell, 🍴 Fatz Cafe, 🏠 Comfort Suites, Holiday Inn Express, 🅾 🅷, 3-5 mi N 🍴 Golden Corral, 🏠 Colony Inn, Greenleaf Inn, Knights Inn, 🅾 Revolutionary War Pk
96mm	Wateree River
93mm	**rest area both lanes, full ♿ facilities, 🚻s, vending, ☕, litter barrels, petwalk**
92	US 601, to Lugoff, N 🅖 BP, ▦/DQ/Subway/dsl/scales/24hr, Shell/Bojangles/dsl, 🍴 Hardee's, Waffle House, 🏠 EconoLodge, Ramada Ltd, 2-3 mi N 🍴 KFC, McDonald's, Shoney's, 🏠 Best Western, Travel Inn, 🅾 Ace Hardware, S Camden RV Park (1mi)
87	SC 47, to Elgin, N 🅖 BP/dsl, Shell/dsl
82	SC 53, to Pontiac, N 🅖 Mobil, Shell, 🍴 Blimpie, Burger King, loding: Value Place Inn, 🅾 $General, Harley-Davidson, S 🅖 BP, 🅾 Clothing World Outlet
80	Clemson Rd, N 🅖 Exxon/dsl, 76/Circle K, Shell/Bojangles/dsl, 🍴 Brick Oven Pizza, D's Rest, Groucho's Deli, Maurice's BBQ, McDonald's, San Jose Mexican, Subway, Sumo Japanese, Tokyo Grill, Travinia Italian, Waffle House, Zaxby's, 🏠 Hampton Inn, Holiday Inn Express, 🅾 CVS Drug, Firestone/auto, S 🍴 Wendy's, 🅾 Chevrolet, Hyundai
76b	Alpine Rd, to Ft Jackson, N Sesquicentennial SP
76a	(76 from eb), I-77, N to Charlotte, S to Charleston
74	US 1, Two Notch Rd, to Ft Jackson, N 🅖 Mobil/dsl, 🍴 Chili's, Fazoli's, Hooters, IHOP, Lizard's Thicket, Outback Steaks, Waffle House, 🏠 Comfort Inn, Comfort Suites, Fairfield Inn, InTown Suites, Jameson Suites, La Quinta, Microtel, Motel 6, Ramada Inn, Red Roof Inn, 🅾 Home Depot, USPO, to Sesquicentennial SP, S 🅖 BP, Exxon, Shell/dsl, 🍴 Applebees', Bojangles, Capt D's, Church's, Crabhouse, Harbor Sea 🍴 Hardee's, Honeybaked Ham, Longhorn Steaks, Maurice's BBQ, McDonald's, Monterrey Mexican, Nick's Gyros, Piccadilly's, Schlotzsky's, Splendid China, Substaion II, 🏠 Days Inn, 🅾 Advance Parts, AutoZone, Best Buy, Dillard's, Family$, Firestone/auto, K-Mart, Lowe's, Macy's, Marshall's, NAPA, Sears/auto, Staples, mall
73b	SC 277 N, to I-77 N
73a	SC 277 S, to Columbia, S 🅷
72	SC 555, Farrow Rd

COLUMBIA

SC

COLUMBIA (vertical side label)

SC (side tab)

INTERSTATE 20 CONT'D

Exit	Services
71	US 21, N Main, to Blythewood, Columbia, N 🅖 Gaz-Bah/dsl, TravelPlaza/Pizza Hut/Subway/dsl/scales/24hr/@, Save-a-Ton/dsl, 🍴 McDonald's, 🛏 Days Inn, 🅞 truckwash, tires, S 🅖 Shell
70	US 321, Fairfield Rd, S 🅖 Exxon, ⊘FLYING J/Denny's/dsl/LP/24hr, 🍴 Hardee's, 🛏 Super 8
68	SC 215, Monticello Rd, to Jenkinsville, N 🅖 Exxon/dsl, Shell/dsl, S 🅖 Shell/dsl, 🍴 Big Daddy's Café
66mm	Broad River
65	US 176, Broad River Rd, to Columbia, N 🅖 BP, Exxon, 76/Circle K, 🍴 Applebee's, Bojangles, Chop Stix Chinese, Monterrey Mexican, Rush's BBQ, Sonic, Subway, Waffle House, 🛏 Rodeway Inn, 🅞 Aamco CVS Drug, U-Haul, Walgreens, S 🅖 Hess/Godfather's Pizza, RaceWay, 🍴 Arby's, Baskin-Robbins/Dunkin Donuts, Blimpie, Chick-fil-A, Church's, KFC, Lizard's Thicket, McDonald's, Ruby Tuesday, Sammi Deli, Sandy's HotDogs, Schlotzsky's, Taco Bell, Wendy's, Zaxby's, 🛏 American Inn, InTown Suites, Quality Inn, Ramada Ltd, Royal Inn, 🅞 Advance Parts, Belk, $General, Office Depot, PepBoys, Rite Aid, mall
64b a	I-26, US 76, E to Columbia, W to Greenville, Spartanburg
63	Bush River Rd, N 🅖 76/Circle K/dsl, 🍴 Cracker Barrel, Real Mexican, Subway, 🛏 Travelodge, 🅞 CVS Drug, Hamrick's, S 🅖 Citgo, Murphy USA, RaceWay, Sunoco, 🍴 El Chico, Fuddrucker's, Pizza Hut, Waffle House, 🛏 Best Inn, Best Western, Courtyard, Knights Inn, Radisson, Sleep Inn, 🅞 GNC, Walmart
61	US 378, W Columbia, N 🅖 Exxon/Hardee's, 🍴 Chili's, Taco Bell, 🛏 Wingate Inn, 🅞 Honda, S 🅖 BP/dsl/24hr, 🍴 Waffle House
58	US 1, W Columbia, N 🅖 Exxon, Shell/Subway/dsl, 🍴 Waffle House, 0-2 mi S 🅖 BP, Shell, 🍴 Burger King, KFC, Lizard's Thicket, McDonald's, San Jose Mexican, Subway, 🛏 Value Place Inn, 🅞 Advance Parts, Barnyard RV Park/Flea Mkt, Piggly Wiggly, to 🍴
55	SC 6, to Lexington, N 🅖 Shell, 🛏 Hampton Inn (2mi), 🅞 CarQuest, John's RV Ctr, S 🅖 BP/dsl, Citgo, Kangaroo/DQ/dsl, Pops, 🍴 Bojangles, Golden Town Chinese, Great Wall Chinese, Maurice's BBQ, McDonald's, Subway, Waffle House, Wendy's, 🛏 Ramada Ltd, 🅞 CVS Drug, $General, Piggly Wiggly
52.5mm	weigh sta wb
51	SC 204, to Gilbert, N 🅖 Exxon/dsl, Shell/Stuckey's/Subway/dsl/24hr, 🍴 Burger King, S 🅖 Mobil/dsl, 🅞 $General
44	SC 34, to Gilbert, N 🅖 BP/Blimpie/dsl, 44Trkstp/dsl/rest./24hr
39	US 178, to Batesburg, N 🅖 Exxon/dsl, 🍴 Hillview Rest. S 🅖 BP/dsl/24hr
35.5mm	weigh sta eb
33	SC 39, to Wagener, N 🅖 El Cheapo/dsl, S 🅖 BP/Huddle House/dsl/scales
29	SC 49, Wire Rd
22	US 1, to Aiken, S 🅖 BP/dsl, RaceWay, 76/Circle K/dsl, Shell/dsl, 🍴 Baynham's, Hardee's, McDonald's, Waffle House, 🛏 Days Inn, Quality Inn, 🅞 $General, RV Camping (5mi), to USC Aiken
20mm	parking area, both lanes (commercial vehicles only)
18	SC 19, to Aiken, S 🅖 Exxon/Subway/dsl, Shell/dsl, 🍴 Waffle House, 🛏 Deluxe Inn, Guesthouse Inn, 🅞 🅗

Exit	Services
11	SC 144, Graniteville, N 🅖 BP/dsl/scales/24hr, 🍴 Huddle House
6	I-520 to N Augusta
5	US 25, SC 121, N 🅖 BP/dsl, Circle K/DQ, 76/Circle K/Blimpie/dsl/24hr, Shell/Bojangles/dsl/24hr, 🍴 Burger King, Checker's, Huddle House, Sonic, Subway, 🅞 Advance Parts, $General, Food Lion, S 🅖 Citgo/dsl, Murphy USA/dsl (5mi), 🍴 Bojangles, Waffle House, 🛏 Sleep Inn, 🅞 Walmart (5mi)
1	SC 230, Martintown Rd, N Augusta, S 🅖 76/Circle K/Blimpie/dsl/24hr, 🍴 Waffle House, 🅞 to Garn's Place
.5mm	Welcome Ctr eb, full 🚻 facilities, (🅒, 🚮, litter barrels, vending, petwalk
0mm	South Carolina/Georgia state line, Savannah River

INTERSTATE 26

CHARLESTON (vertical side label)

Exit	Services
221	Meeting St, Charleston, 2 mi E 🍴 Church's, KFC, 🛏 Hampton Inn, 🅞 Visitors Ctr, Family$, Piggly Wiggly
221b	US 17 N, to Georgetown, I-26 begins/ends on US 17 in Charleston, SC.
221a	US 17 S, to Kings St, to Savannah, N 🅗
220	Romney St (from wb)
219b	Morrison Dr, East Bay St (from eb), N 🅖 Exxon
219a	Rutledge Ave (from eb, no EZ return), to The Citadel C o l- lege of Charleston
218	Spruill Ave (from wb), N Charleston
217	N Meeting St (from eb)
216b a	SC 7, Cosgrove Ave, 1 mi S 🍴 Burger King, McDonald's, S&S Cafeteria, SunFire Grill, Wendy's, 🅞 to Charles Towne Landing
215	SC 642, Dorchester Rd, N Charleston, N 🅖 El Cheapo, 🛏 Deluxe Inn, S 🅖 BP/dsl, 🍴 Alex's Rest./24hr, 🅞 Best Value Inn
213b a	Montague Ave, Mall Dr, N 🍴 Piccadilly's, Red Lobster, 🛏 Courtyard, Sheraton, 🅞 Charles Towne Square, Firestone, S 🅖 BP/dsl, Hess/Bojangles/dsl, Mobil, 🍴 Kamille's Cafe, McDonald's, Panera Bread, Waffle House, 🛏 Comfort Inn, Day's Inn, Econolodge, Embassy Suites, Extended Stay America, Hampton Inn, Hilton Garden, HomePlace Suites, Homewood Suites, InTown Suites, N Charleston Inn, Quality Inn, Residence Inn, Sleep Inn, Super 8, 🅞 vet
212c b	I-526, E to Mt Pleasant, W to Savannah, 🍴
212a	Remount Rd (from wb, no EZ return), Hanahan, N on US 52/78 🅖 Exxon, Hess/dsl, 🍴 KFC, Pizza Hut/Taco Bell, 🅞 AutoZone, Dodge, Ford
211b a	Aviation Pkwy, N on US 52/78 🅖 BP, Exxon, Hess, Sunoco, 🍴 Andolini's Pizza, Arby's, Burger King, Capt D's, C&W Buffet, China Town, Church's, Domino's, Golden River Chinese, Hilliard's Rest., McDonald's, Pizza Hut, Pizza Inn, Popeye's, Quizno's, Schlotsky's, Shoney's, Sonic, Subway, Taco Bell, Zaxby's, 🛏 Masters Inn, Radisson, 🅞 Batteries+, Big Lots, $General, $Tree, Goodyear, PepBoys, Radio Shack, Super Pets, U-Haul, USPO, S 🅖 Citgo/dsl, 🍴 Waffle House, 🛏 Budget Inn, Howard Johnson, Palace Inn
209	Ashley Phosphate Rd, to US 52, N 🅖 Exxon, Kangaroo, 🍴 Applebee's, Carraba's, Chick-fil-A, China Buffet, Chucke-Cheese, Denny's, Fazoli's, Hardee's, Hooters, Jason's Deli, Larry's Subs, Longhorn Steaks, Moe's SW Grill, Noisy Oyster Grill, O'Charley's, Olive Garden, Outback Steaks, Perkins, Pizza Hut, Ryan's, Smokey Bones BBQ, Starbucks, Sticky Fingers Rest., Subway, Taco Bell, Thai Rest.,

INTERSTATE 26 CONT'D

Exit	Services
209	Continued Waffle House, Wendy's, Wild Wing Cafe, 🛏 Candlewood Suites, Country Hearth Inn, Country Inn&Suites, Holiday Inn Express, Ramada Inn, Red Roof Inn, Residence Inn, Studio+, Suburban Lodge, 🅾 HOSPTIAL, Barnes&Noble, Best Buy, BooksAMillion, Dillard's, Firestone/auto, Hancock Fabrics, Home Depot, JC Penney, Lowe's Whse, Marshall's, Michael's, Nissan, Office Depot, Old Navy, Ross, Sears/auto, Target, Tire Kingdom, Toyota, Walmart, mall, **S** 🅖 BP, Hess, RaceWay, 🍴 Bojangles, Cracker Barrel, Domino's, IHOP, McDonald's, Ruby Tuesday, Waffle House, 🛏 Best Western, Hampton Inn, InTown Suites, La Quinta, Motel 6, Quality Inn, Relax Inn, Sleep Inn, Value Place Inn
209a	to US 52 (from wb), to Goose Creek, Moncks Corner
205b a	US 78, to Summerville, **N** 🅖 BP, Hess/dsl, 🍴 Arby's, Atl Bread Co, Bruster's, Dunkin Donuts, Sonic, Subway, Waffle House, Wendy's, Zaxby's, 🛏 Fairfield Inn, Wingate Inn, 🅾 H, DENTIST, Kerr Drug, Charleston Southern U, **S** 🅖 Sunoco, 🍴 KFC, 🅾 KOA
204mm	**rest area eb, full ♿ facilities, vending, 🅒, 🛱, litter barrels, petwalk**
203	College Park Rd, Ladson, **N** 🅖 BP, Sunoco, 🍴 McDonald's, Waffle House, 🛏 Best Western, Day's Inn, **2 mi S** 🅾 KOA (2mi)
202mm	**rest area wb, full ♿ facilities, vending, 🅒, 🛱, litter barrels, petwalk**
199b a	US 17 A, to Moncks Corner, Summerville, **N** 🅖 BP, Hess/dsl, ▦/McDonald's/dsl/24hr, Shell, Texaco/dsl, 🍴 KFC, Pizza Hut, Subway, 🅾 Advance Parts, AutoZone, BiLo, Buick/GMC, $General, Family$, vet, **S** 🅖 Shell, 🍴 Applebee's, Atlanta Bread, Bojangles, Burger King, Coldstone Creamery, Domino's, Fazoli's, Hardee's, IHOP, La Hacienda, Logan's Roadhouse, McAlisters Deli, Moe's SW Grill, O'Charleys, Papa John's, Perkins/24hr, Ryan's, Shoney's, Waffle House, Zaxby's, 🛏 Comfort Suites, Country Inn&Suites, Econolodge, Hampton Inn, Holiday Inn Express, Sleep Inn, 🅾 Best Buy, Belk, Chevrolet, Chrysler/Jeep, GNC, Home Depot, Kohl's, Lowe's Whse, PetsMart, Radio Shack, Staples, Superpetz, Target, Tire Kingdom, TJ Maxx, Walmart, Walgreens
194	SC 16, to Jedburg, access to Foreign Trade Zone 21
187	SC 27, to Ridgeville, St George, **N** 🅖 Shell, **S** 🅖 BP/dsl, **10 mi S** 🅾 Francis Beidler Forest
177	SC 453, to Holly Hill, Harleyville, **S** 🅖 Shell/dsl/LP
174mm	**weigh sta both lanes**
172b a	US 15, to Santee, St George, **S** 🅖 Horizon/Subway/dsl/scales/24hr
169b a	I-95, N to Florence, S to Savannah
165	SC 210, to Bowman, **N** 🅖 Exxon/dsl, **S** 🅖 BP/dsl/rest.
159	SC 36, to Bowman, **N** 🅖 Li'l Cricket/Stuckey's, ▦/McDonald's/dsl/scales/@
154b a	US 301, to Santee, Orangeburg, **N** 🛏 Days Inn, **S** 🅖 Exxon/dsl, ♥Loves/Subway/dsl/scales/24hr, Shell, 🍴 Waffle House
152mm	**rest area wb, full ♿ facilities, vending, 🅒, 🛱, litter barrels, petwalk**
150mm	**rest area eb, full ♿ facilities, vending, 🅒, 🛱, litter barrels, petwalk**
149	SC 33, to Cameron, to SC State Coll, Orangeburg, Claflin Coll
145b a	US 601, to Orangeburg, St Matthews, **S** 🅖 BP/24hr, Exxon, Shell, Sunoco/dsl, 🍴 Burger King, Cracker Barrel, Fatz Café, Hardee's, KFC, McDonald's, Mediterranean Grill, Ruby Tuesday, Subway, Waffle House, Zaxby's, 🛏 Best Western, Carolina Lodge, Comfort Inn, Country Inn&Suites, Fairfield Inn, Hampton Inn, Holiday Inn Express, Howard Johnson, Sleep Inn, Southern Lodge, Traveler's Inn, 🅾 H, 🅾 Cadillac/Chevrolet, Chrysler/Dodge, Nissan, Toyota/Scion
139	SC 22, to St Matthews, **S** 🅖 Horizon, Li'l Cricket, Wilco/Hess/Arby's/dsl/scales/24hr, 🅾 Sweetwater Lake Camping (2.5mi)
136	SC 6, to North, Swansea, **N** 🅖 Exxon/dsl/LP/rest./24hr
129	US 21, **N** 🅖 Shell/grill/dsl
125	SC 31, to Gaston, **N** 🅾 Sandy Run Store/gas, Wolfe's Truck/trailer repair
123mm	**rest area both lanes, full ♿ facilities, vending, 🅒, 🛱, litter barrels, petwalk**
119	US 176, US 21, to Dixiana, **S** 🅖 BP/Subway/dsl, Exxon/Stuckey's/dsl
116	I-77 N, to Charlotte, US 76, US 378, to Ft Jackson
115	US 176, US 21, US 321, to Cayce, **N** 🅖 BP, Raceway/24hr, Texaco, 🍴 Waffle House, 🅾 Advance Parts, Bi-Lo, $General, Harley-Davidson, **S** 🅖 ▦/DQ/Wendy's/dsl/scales/24hr, Shell, 🍴 Bojangles, Great China, Hardee's, McDonald's, Subway, 🛏 Country Hearth Inn, 🅾 Firestone, Piggly Wiggly
113	SC 302, Cayce, **N** 🅖 Exxon, Mobil/Burger King, Sunoco, 🍴 Waffle House, 🛏⊕ Inn, Cambridge Plaza, Knight's Inn, Masters Inn, 🅾 O'Reilly Parts, **S** 🅖 BP, Raceway, Shell/Circle K, 🍴 Lizard's Thicket, Shoney's, Subway, Waffle House/24hr, 🛏 Carolina Lodge, Comfort Inn, Country Inn& Suites, Sleep Inn, Travelers Inn, 🅾 NAPA, ⊕
111b a	US 1, to W Columbia, **N** 🅖 Murphy USA/dsl, Raceway/dsl, Shell/Circle K, 🍴 Chick-fil-A, Domino's, Dragon City Chinese, Hardee's, Maurice's BBQ, Ruby Tuesday, Sonic, Subway, TCBY, Waffle House, Zaxby's, 🛏 Holiday Inn, Quality Inn, 🅾 BiLo Foods, $General, $Tree, GNC, Kroger, Pet Supplies+, Walgreens, Walmart, to USC, **S** 🅖 Hess, 🍴 Applebee's, Popeye's, Wendy's, 🅾 Aldi Foods, Big Lots, Family$, Lowe's Whse, U-Haul
110	US 378, to W Columbia, Lexington, **N** 🍴 Burger King, Grecian Garden, Lizard's Thicket, Maurice's BBQ, McDonald's, Rush's Rest., Subway, Waffle House, 🛏 Best Value Inn, Day's Inn, Hampton Inn, Holiday Inn, 🅾 CVS Drug, Food Lion, Rite Aid, U-Haul, **S** 🅖 Li'l Cricket/dsl, 76/Circle K, 🍴 Atlanta Bread, Bojangles, Pizza Hut, 🛏 Executive Inn, SpringHill Suites, 🅾 H

E
W

COLUMBIA

SC

INTERSTATE 26 CONT'D

Exit	Services
108b a	I-126 to Columbia, Bush River Rd, N 🅖 Shell/dsl, 🍴 Blimpie, Capt D's, Chick-fil-A, Hardee's, Peking Palace, Ruby Tuesday, Schlotsky's, Shoney's, Super China, Wendy's, Zaxby's, 🛏 Day's Inn, Scottish Inn, Villager Lodge, Western Inn, 🅞 Advance Parts, Belk, $General, Firestone/auto, K-Mart, Office Depot, Rite Aid, mall, S 🅖 City Gas, RaceWay, Sunoco/dsl, 🍴 Cracker Barrel, Fuddrucker's, Villa Italian, Waffle House, 🛏 Best Inn, Courtyard, Knight's Inn, Radisson, Sleep Inn, 🅞 Walmart, **multiple services 1-3 mi N** off I-126, **Greystone Blvd**, N 🅖 BP, Exxon, 🍴 Waffle House, 🛏 Embassy Suites, Extended Stay America, Homewood Suites, Residence Inn, Studio+, 🅞 Chrysler/Jeep, Dodge, Ford, Honda, Hyundai, KIA, Lincoln/Mercury, Mazda, S Riverbanks Zoo
107b a	I-20, E to Florence, W to Augusta
106b a	St Andrews Rd, N 🅖 Exxon/dsl, 🍴 Chick-fil-A, IHOP, Papa John's, Sonic, Top China Buffet, 🛏 Motel 6, 🅞 BiLo Foods, Buick/GMC, Camping World RV Ctr, CVS Drug, Infiniti, Jaguar, Kroger/deli, Nissan, Walgreens, S 🅖 BP/dsl, Hess/dsl, Shell, 🍴 Domino's, King Buffet, Maurice's BBQ, McDonald's, Pizza Hut, Substation II, Thai Lotus, Waffle House, WG's Wings, Zaxby's, 🛏 EconoLodge, Red Roof Inn, 🅞 $General, Food Lion, Tire Kingdom
104	Piney Grove Rd, N 🅖 Sunoco/dsl, 🍴 Hardee's, San Jose Mexican, Waffle House, 🛏 Quality Inn, 🅞 Sportsman's Whse, S 🅖 Exxon/dsl, Shell, 🛏 Country Inn&Suites, Microtel, 🅞 Carmax, Land Rover
103	Harbison Blvd, N 🍴 Applebee's, Hooters, Wendy's, 🛏 Hampton Inn, 🅞 Chevrolet, Home Depot, Lowe's, funpark, S 🅖 Shell, 🍴 Bailey's Grill, Blimpie, Bojangles, BoneFish Grill, Bruster's, Carolina Alehouse, Carrabba's, Casa Linda, Chili's, Chick-fil-A, Coldstone, Columbiana Buffet, Copper River Grill, Denny's, Fazoli's, Firehouse Subs, 5 Guys Burgers, HoneyBaked Ham, Hudson's Smokehouse, Inyabi, Longhorn Steaks, Macaroni Grill, McAlister's, McDonald's, Miyabi Japanese, Miyo's, O'Charley's, Olive Garden, Outback Steaks, Panera Bread, Ruby Tuesday, Rush's Rest., Ryan's, Sonic, Subway, Super Buffet, TX Roadhouse, Tokyo Grill, Tsunami Steaks, Which Wich, Yamato Japanese, 🛏 Comfort Suites, Country Inn&Suites, Fairfield Inn, Hilton Garden, Holiday Inn Express, InTown Suites, TownePlace Suites, Wingate Inn, 🅞 AT&T, Barnes&Noble, Belk, Best Buy, Books-A-Million, Dillard's, $Tree, Goodyear, Hancock Fabrics, JC Penney, Kohl's, Marshall's, Michael's, Midas, Office Depot, Old Navy, PetsMart, Publix, Rite Aid, Ross, Sam's Club/gas, Sears/auto, Staples, Target, Tire Kingdom, Verizon, Walmart, mall
102	SC 60, Ballentine, Irmo, N 🍴 Cracker Barrel, 🛏 Extended Stay America, Hyatt Place, S 🅖 JP/dsl, 76/Circle K, Shell, 🍴 Arby's, Bellacino's Pizza, Groucho's Deli, Maurice's BBQ, Moe's SW Grill, New China, Papa John's, TCBY, Zaxby's, 🅞 AAA, CVS Drug, Jiffy Lube, tires, same as 103
101b a	US 76, US 176, to N Columbia, **1/2 mi N** 🅖 Exxon/Subway/dsl, 🍴 China House, Fatz Café, HotDog Heaven, Zorba's, 🅞 AutoZone, $General, Food Lion, Harley Davidson, Publix, Rite Aid, Walgreens, S 🅖 BP, Mobil, 🍴 Burger King, Oyster House Grill, Waffle House, 🅞 Toyota/Scion

97	US 176, to Ballentine, Peak, N 🍴 China 1, Happy Frog Cafe, Subway, 🅞 Food Lion, Woodsmoke Camping, S 🅖 Exxon/dsl
94mm	weigh sta wb
91	SC 48, to Chapin, S 🅖 BP/dsl, Exxon/Taco Bell/Blimpie/dsl, Shell/dsl, 🍴 Bojangles, Farm Boys BBQ, McDonald's, Waffle House, 🅞 urgent care, to Dreher Island SP
85	SC 202, Little Mountain, Pomaria, S to Dreher Island SP
82	SC 773, to Prosperity, Pomaria, N 🅖 BP/Subway/dsl/24hr, Wilco/Hess/Wendy's/dsl/scales, 🍴 Waffle House, 🅞 Flea Mkt Campground
81mm	weigh sta eb
76	SC 219, to Pomaria, Newberry, N 🅖 Loves/McDonald's/Chester's/dsl/scales/24hr, **0-2 mi** S 🅖 BP, Murphy USA, 🍴 Burger King, Wendy's, 🛏 Hampton Inn, Holiday Inn Express, 🅞 Walmart, to Newberry Opera House
74	SC 34, to Newberry, N 🅖 BP, Shell/dsl/24hr, 🍴 Bill&Fran's Café, 🛏 Best Value Inn, S 🅖 Citgo/dsl, 🍴 Arby's, Capt D's, Waffle House, 🛏 Days Inn, 🅞 H, to NinetySix HS, **2-4 mi** S 🍴 Hardee's, McDonald's, 🛏 Comfort Inn, Economy Inn, Holiday Inn Express
72	SC 121, to Newberry, S 🅖 Citgo/dsl, 🅞 H, to Newberry Coll
66	SC 32, to Jalapa
63.5mm	rest area both lanes, full 🅥 facilities, 🅒, vending, 🅐, litter barrels, petwalk
60	SC 66, to Joanna, S 🅖 BP, 🅞 Magnolia Camping
54	SC 72, to Clinton, N 🅖 BP, S 🅖 Citgo/dsl/24hr, 🍴 Fatz Cafe, 🛏 Hampton Inn, 🅞 H, to Presbyterian Coll, Thornwell Home
52	SC 56, to Clinton, N 🅖 Pilot/Subway/dsl/scales/24hr, 🍴 Blue Ocean Rest., McDonald's, 🛏 Comfort Suites, Quality Inn, S 🅖 Citgo/dsl, 🍴 Hardee's, Waffle House, Wendy's, 🛏 Days Inn, Howard Johnson, 🅞 H
51	I-385, to Greenville (from wb)
45.5mm	Enoree River
44	SC 49, to Cross Anchor, Union
41	SC 92, to Enoree, N 🅖 Valero
38	SC 146, to Woodruff, N 🅖 HotSpot/Shell/Hardee's/Stuckey's/dsl/scales/24hr
35	SC 50, to Woodruff
33mm	S Tyger River
32mm	N Tyger River
28	US 221, to Spartanburg, N 🅖 Kangaroo/Aunt M's/Quiznos/dsl/24hr, Shell/Subway/dsl/24hr, 🍴 Bojangles, Burger King, J-Bones BBQ, Waffle House, 🅞 H, Pine Ridge Camping (3mi), to Walnut Grove Plantation
22	SC 296, Reidville Rd, to Spartanburg, N 🅖 BP/Kangaroo, dsl, Exxon, Spinx, 🍴 Arby's, Blue Bay Rest., Bruster's, Chief's Rest., Fatz Cafe, Fuddrucker's (1mi), Little Caesar's, McDonald's, Outback Steaks, Quiznos, Waffle House, Wasabi Japanese, Zaxby's, 🅞 Advance Parts, $General, vet, to Croft SP, S 🅖 Hickory Point/dsl, Sunoco, 🍴 Apollo's Pizza, Burger King, Clock Rest., Denny's, Domino's, Hardee's, Hong Kong Express, Panda Garden, Papa John's, Subway, 🛏 Sleep Inn, Southern Suites, Super 8, 🅞 BiLo, BMW, CVS Drug, $General, Food Lion, Hyundai, Rite Aid, Toyota/Scion, Walgreens, vet
21b a	US 29, to Spartanburg, N 🅖 BP, Sphinx, 🍴 A&W/LJ Silver, Blue Fin Grill, Bojangles, Burger King, Chick-fil-A, Chuck eCheese, CiCi's, City Range Grill, Corona Mexican, DQ, Firehouse Subs, Fuji Japanese, Garfield's Rest., Golden

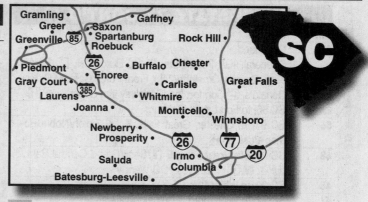

INTERSTATE 26 CONT'D

Exit	Services
21b a	Continued

SPARTANBURG

Corral, Hooters, Jack-in-the-Box, Jason's Deli, Kantai Tokyo, KFC, Marble Slab, McAlister's Deli, Moe's SW Grill, O'Charley's, Olive Garden, Pizza Hut, Red Lobster, Ruby Tuesday, Ryan's, Souper Salad, Substation II, Subway, Wendy's, 🏠 Comfort Suites, Hampton Inn, Holiday Inn Express, 🅾 AT&T, Barnes&Noble, Belk, Best Buy, Costco/gas, Curves, Dillard's, Discount Tire, $General, Firestone/auto, Goodyear, Hamricks, Home Depot, JC Penney, Lowe's, Michael's, Office Depot, Old Navy, PetsMart, Rite Aid, Ross, Sears/auto, TJ Maxx, Tuesday Morning, Walmart, mall, USPO, S 🅰 Citgo/Aunt M's/dsl, Texaco/dsl, 🍴 Applebee's, IHOP, McDonald's, Piccadilly's, Pizza Inn, Sahara Grill, Shogun Japanese, Taco Bell, Taste of Thai, Waffle House, 🅾 Advance Parts, CarQuest, $Tree, Hobby Lobby, Ingles Foods/gas, Kohl's, Sam's Club/gas, Target, TrueValue

19b a	Lp I-85, Spartanburg, N 🍴 Cracker Barrel, 🏠 Country Hearth Inn, Radisson, Residence Inn, S 🏠 Brookwood Inn
18b a	I-85, N to Charlotte, S to Greenville
17	New Cut Rd, S 🅰 Chevron/dsl, 🍴 Burger King, Fatz Café, McDonald's, Waffle House, 🏠 Days Inn, EconoLodge, Howard Johnson, Red Roof Inn
16	John Dodd Rd, to Wellford, N 🅰 Citgo/Aunt M's/dsl, 🅾 Camping World RV Ctr
15	US 176, to Inman, N 🅰 Breakers, 76/Circle K/dsl, 🍴 Waffle House, 🅾 H S 🅰 Citgo/dsl
10	SC 292, to Inman, N 🅰 Shell/Subway/dsl/24hr
7.5mm	Lake William C. Bowman
5	SC 11, Foothills Scenic Dr, Chesnee, Campobello, N 🅰 Kangaroo/Aunt M's Café/dsl/scales, S 🅰 Marathon/Li'l Cricket
3mm	**Welcome Ctr eb, full ♿ facilities, info, 🚻s, 🛢, litter barrels, vending, petwalk**
1	SC 14, to Landrum, S 🅰 HotSpot/gas (2mi), Shell/Burger King/dsl, 🍴 Bojangles, China Cafe, Pizza Hut (1mi), Subway, 🅾 BiLo Foods, $General, Ingles/café/gas/24hr, vet
0mm	South Carolina/North Carolina state line

INTERSTATE 77

Exit	Services
91mm	South Carolina/North Carolina state line
90	US 21, Carowinds Blvd, E 🅰 Gulf, Rocket Stop/fireworks, 🍴 Bojangles, 🅾 H, RV camping (4mi), W 🅰 Exxon/café, Shell/Circle K/Wendy's/dsl, Texaco/Subway, 🍴 Cracker Barrel, El Cancun Mexican, KFC, Papa Pino's, Shoney's, 🏠 Best Western, Comfort Inn, Holiday Inn Express, Motel 6, Plaza Motel, Sleep Inn, 🅾 Carowinds Funpark, Carolina Pottery/outlet mall/famous brands
89.5mm	**Welcome Ctr sb, full ♿ facilities, info, 🚻, vending, 🛢, litter barrels, petwalk/weigh sta nb**
88	Gold Hill Rd, to Pineville, E 🅾 urgent care, W 🅰 Gate (2mi), Shell/dsl, Valero, 🍴 Bojangles (2mi), 🅾 Chrysler/Dodge/Jeep, Ford, Hyundai, KOA
85	SC 160, Ft Mill, Tega Cay, E 🅰 Exxon, 🍴 Subway, 🅾 Bi-Lo, Ft Mill Drug, W 🅰 BP/dsl, Shell/Circle K, 🍴 Backyard Burger, Beef O'Brady's, Burger King, Chick-fil-A, Fratelli's Italian, Papa John's, Pizza Hut, Quizno's, Starbucks, Wendy's, 🅾 CVS Drug, Goodyear/auto, Harris-Teeter, Lowe's Whse, Walgreens

ROCK HILL

84.5mm	weigh sta sb
83	SC 49, Sutton Rd, W 🅰 Loves/Chester/Subway/dsl/scales/24hr
82.5mm	Catawba River
82c	US 21, SC 161, Rock Hill, Ft Mill, E 🅰 Exxon, 🍴 IHOP, Sonny's BBQ, Steak'n Shake, Zaxby's, 🅾 Home Depot, Petsmart, museum, W 🅰 Citgo, Shell, Texaco, 🍴 Delicacy Chinese, Empire Sta Pizza, Hooters, Outback Steaks, Sonic, Starbucks, 🏠 Courtyard, 🅾 H, Toyota, Tuffy Auto, U-Haul
82b a	E 🅰 Exxon, 🏠 Motel 6, W 🅰 RaceWay, Sunoco/dsl, Texaco, 🍴 Arby's, Bojangles, Burger King, Burk's BBQ, Capt's Galley, Chick-fil-A, CiCi's Pizza, Denny's, Firebonez, Golden Corral, Happy Garden, HoneyBaked Ham, Jack-in-the-Box, KFC, Little Caesar's, Marco's Pizza, McDonald's, Penn Sta., Pizza Hut, Sakura Japanese, Shoney's, Subway, Taco Bell, TCBY, Waffle House, Wendy's, 🏠 Baymont Inn, Best Value Inn, Country Inn&Suites, Days Inn, EconoLodge, Microtel, Quality Inn, Regency Inn, Super 8, 🅾 Aamco, Advance Parts, Aldi Foods, AutoZone, BigLots, Bi-Lo, Cadillac/Chevrolet, Compare Mkt, $General, Family$, Firestone/auto, Hancock Fabrics, K-Mart, NAPA, Nissan, Office Depot, O'Reilly Parts, PepBoys, Verizon, city park
79	SC 122, Dave Lyle Blvd, to Rock Hill, E 🅰 BP, Murphy USA/dsl, 🍴 Applebee's, Chick-fil-A, Cracker Barrel, DQ, Hardee's, Longhorn Steaks, Maurice's BBQ, O'Charley's, Ryan's, Ruby Tuesday, 🏠 Comfort Suites, Hampton Inn, Holiday Inn, TownePlace Suites, Wingate Inn, 🅾 Belk, Discount Tire, $Tree, Food Lion, Harley-Davidson, Hobby Lobby, Honda, JC Penney, Kohl's, Lowe's Whse, Sears/auto, Staples, Tire Kingdom, Walmart, mall, W 🅰 Texaco/dsl, 🍴 Baskin-Robbins/Dunkin Donuts, Bob Evans, Chili's, Jack-in-the-Box, McAlister's Deli, McDonald's, Moe's SW Grill, Olive Garden, Panera Bread, Quizno's, Stagebrush Steaks, Subway, Taco Bell, Wendy's, 🏠 Hilton Garden, 🅾 URGENT CARE, Best Buy, Books-a-Million, Ford/Lincoln/Mercury, Michael's, Ross, Target, TJ Maxx, visitor ctr
77	US 21, SC 5, to Rock Hill, E 🅰 BP/Subway/dsl, Cone/dsl/24hr, 🅾 to Andrew Jackson SP (12mi), W 🅰 Exxon/dsl, Pride/dsl/scales, 🍴 Bojangles, KFC (1mi), McDonald's (1mi), Subway (1mi), Waffle House, 🅾 to Winthrop Coll
75	Porter Rd, E 🅰 Sunoco/dsl
73	SC 901, to Rock Hill, York, E 🅰 Exxon/dsl, 🛢FLYING J/Denny's/dsl/scales/LP/24hr, W H
66mm	**rest area both lanes, full ♿ facilities, 🚻, 🛢, litter barrels, vending, petwalk**
65	SC 9, to Chester, Lancaster, E 🅰 BP/24hr, Citgo/dsl, Liberty/Subway/dsl, 🍴 Bojangles, China Wok, Waffle House, 🏠 Days Inn, EconoLodge, Relax Inn, 🅾 $Express,

SC

INTERSTATE 77 CONT'D

Exit	Services
65	Continued $General, IGA Foods/gas, **W** 🅖 Exxon/dsl, 🍴 Burger King, Country Omelette/24hr, Front Porch Cafe, KFC, McDonald's, 🛏 Comfort Inn, Rodeway Inn, Super 8, 🅞 🅗
62	SC 56, to Fort Lawn, Richburg
55	SC 97, to Chester, Great Falls, **E** 🅖 Exxon/Noble Roman's/dsl, **W** 🅗
48	SC 200, to Great Falls, **E** 🅖 Shell/Grand Central Rest./dsl/@, **W** 🅖 Wilco/Hess/DQ/Wendy's
46	SC 20, to White Oak
41	SC 41, to Winnsboro, **E** to Lake Wateree SP
34	SC 34, to Winnsboro, Ridgeway, **E** 🛏 Ridgeway Motel (1mi), 🅞 camping (1mi), **W** 🅖 Exxon/dsl, 🍴 Waffle House, 🛏 Ramada Ltd.
32	Peach Rd, Ridgeway
27	Blythewood Rd, **E** 🅖 BP/dsl, Exxon/Bojangles/dsl/24hr, 🍴 Blythewood Pizza, Carolina Wings, Hardee's, KFC/Pizza Hut, McDonald's, San Jose Mexican, Southern Pig BBQ, Subway, Waffle House, Wendy's, 🛏 Comfort Inn, Days Inn, Holiday Inn Express, 🅞 Curves, $General, IGA Foods, repair/tires, **W** 🍴 Lizard's Thicket, 🅞 AT&T, Food Lion, Groucho's Deli
24	US 21, to Wilson Blvd., **E** 🅖 BP, Shell/Subway/dsl, 🅞 auto repair, vet
22	Killian Rd, **E** 🅖 Mobil/Burger King/dsl, Murphy USA/dsl, 🍴 Bojangles, Zaxby's (2mi), 🅞 Acura, AutoZone, CVS Drug, Discount Tire, Firestone, Honda, Kia, Lowe's, Mazda, Rite Aid, Scion/Toyota, VW, Walgreens, **W** 🍴 China Dragon, Monterrey's Mexican, 🅞 AT&T, Lexus, Verizon, Walmart/McDonald's
19	SC 555, Farrow Rd, **E** 🅖 BP, Exxon, Shell, 🍴 Bojangles, Cracker Barrel, Wendy's, 🛏 Courtyard, Residence Inn, 🅞 🅗, Longs Drug, **W** 🅖 Shell/dsl, 🍴 Waffle House, 🅞 SC Archives
18	to SC 277, to I-20 W (from sb), Columbia
17	US 1, Two Notch Rd, **E** 🅖 BP, Citgo, Kangaroo, Shell/Circle K, 🍴 Arby's, Burger King, TX Roadhouse, Waffle House, 🛏 Holiday Inn, InTown Suites, Quality Inn, Wingate Inn, 🅞 Rite Aid, U-Haul, USPO, to Sesquicentennial SP, **W** 🅖 Mobil, 🍴 Chili's, Fazoli's, Hooters, IHOP, Lizard's Thicket, Outback Steaks, Waffle House, 🛏 Comfort Inn, Fairfield Inn, Hampton Inn, Jameson Suites, La Quinta, Microtel, Motel 6, Ramada Ltd, Red Roof Inn, 🅞 Home Depot, PepBoys, Walgreens, mall, vet
16 b a	I-20, **W** to Augusta, **E** to Florence, Alpine Rd
15 b a	SC 12, to Percival Rd, **W** 🅖 El Cheapo/gas, Shell, **1/2 mi W** 🅖 Exxon
13	Decker Blvd (from nb), **W** 🅖 El Cheapo
12	Forest Blvd, Thurmond Blvd, **E** to Ft Jackson, **W** 🅖 BP/dsl, 76/dsl, Shell/dsl/24hr, 🍴 Bojangles, Chick-fil-A, Fatz Café, Golden Corral, Hardee's, McDonald's, RedBone Rest., Steak&Ale, Subway, Wendy's, 🛏 Extended Stay America, Marlboro Inn, Super 8, 🅞 🅗, $Tree, Sam's Club/gas, Walmart, museum
10	10 SC 760, Jackson Blvd, **E** to Ft Jackson, **2 mi W** 🅖 BP, 🍴 Applebee's, Bojangles, Burger King, Maurices BBQ, Ruby Tuesday, Subway, 🛏 EconoLodge, Liberty Inn
9 b a	US 76, US 378, to Sumter, Columbia, **0-2 mi E** 🅖 BP, Citgo, Murphy USA/dsl, Shell/Burger King, Sunoco/

COLUMBIA

9 b a	Continued dsl, United, 🍴 Arby's, Bojangles, Capt D's, Chick-fil-A, Domino's, Hibachi Grill, KFC, Lizard's Thicket, McDonald's, Pizza Hut, Popeye's, Ruby Tuesday, Rush's Rest., Shoney's, Subway, Taco Bell, Waffle House, 🛏 Best Western, Candlewood Suites, Comfort Inn, Country Inn&Suites, Days Inn, Holiday Inn Express, La Quinta, Microtel, Quality Inn, Sleep Inn, TownePlace Suites, 🅞 Advance Parts, Aldi Foods, AutoZone, Buick/Cadillac/GMC, CVS Drug, $Tree, Family$, Firestone/auto, Interstate Batteries, Lowe's, NAPA, O'Reilly Parts, Piggly Wiggly, Tire Kingdom, USPO, Walgreens, Walmart, **W** 🅖 Circle K, Shell, 🍴 CiCi's Pizza, Eric's Mexican, Hardee's, Jimmy John's, Panera Bread, Sonic, Starbucks, Wendy's, 🛏 Best Value Inn, 🅞 🅗, BigLots, $General, Jo-Ann Fabrics, Radio Shack, Rite Aid, Sav-A-Lot Foods, Target
6 b a	Shop Rd, **W** to USC Coliseum, fairgrounds
5	SC 48, Bluff Rd, **1 mi E** 🅖 76, **W** 🅖 Shell/Burger King/dsl, 🍴 Bojangles (2mi)
3mm	Congaree River
2	Saxe Gotha Rd
1	US 21, US 176, US 321 (from sb), Cayce, **W** accesses same as SC I-26, exit 115.
0mm	I-77 begins/ends on I-26, exit 116.

INTERSTATE 85

N / S

Exit	Services
106.5mm	South Carolina/North Carolina state line
106	US 29, to Grover, **E** 🅖 BP/dsl, **W** 🅖 Exxon/dsl, Hickory Point/gas, Wilco/Hess/DQ/Wendy's/dsl/scales/24hr
104	SC 99, Tribal Rd, **E** 🅖 Loves/McDonald's/Subway/dsl/scales/24hr, **W** fireworks
103mm	**Welcome Ctr sb, full ♿ facilities, info, 🅒, 🅟, litter barrels, vending, petwalk**
102	SC 198, to Earl, **E** 🅖 BP/dsl, Shell, 🍴 Hardee's, **W** 🅖 Citgo/dsl, ✈FLYING J/Denny's/dsl/scales/LP/24hr, 🍴 McDonald's, Waffle House
100mm	Buffalo Creek
100	SC 5, to Blacksburg, Shelby, **W** 🅖 Citgo, Sunoco/Subway/dsl/scales/24hr
98	Frontage Rd (from nb), **E** 🍴 Broad River Café
97mm	Broad River
96	SC 18, **E** 🅖 Kangaroo/Krystal/dsl
95	SC 18, to Gaffney, **E** 🅖 Kangaroo/Aunt M's Rest./dsl, PetroMax/dsl, 🛏 Gaffney Inn, Shamrock Inn, 🍴 Mr Waffle 🅞 🅗, to Limestone Coll
92	SC 11, to Gaffney, **E** 🅖 Marathon/Subway, Murphy USA/dsl, 🍴 Aegean Pizza, Applebee's, Bojangles, Burger King, Chick-fil-A, Daddy Joe's BBQ, Domino's, Fuji, KFC, King Buffet, Little Caesars, McDonald's, Olive Garden, Papa John's, Pizza Hut, Santiago's Mexican, Sonic, Taco Bell, Waffle House, Wendy's, Zaxby's, 🛏 Jameson Inn, Super 8, 🅞 Advance Parts, Aldi Foods, Belk, BigLots, BiLo, $General, $Tree, Ingles Foods, Lowe's, O'Reilly Parts, Radio Shack, Rite Aid, Walgreens, Walmart, USPO, to Limestone Coll, **W** 🅖 BP, 🍴 Fatz Cafe, 🛏 Homestead Lodge, Quality Inn, 🅞 to The Peach, Foothills Scenic Hwy
90	SC 105, SC 42, to Gaffney, **E** 🅖 BP/DQ/dsl, Loves/Arby's/dsl/scales/24hr, 🍴 Bronco Mexican, Clock Rest., Starbucks, Subway, Waffle House, 🛏 Red Roof Inn, Sleep Inn, **W** 🅖 Citgo/dsl, Kangaroo/Burger King, 🍴 Cracker Barrel, FoodCourt, Outback Steaks, 🛏 Hampton Inn, 🅞 Hamrick's, Prime Outlets/famous brands, fruit stand

GAFFNEY

SC

🅶 = gas 🍽 = food 🏨 = lodging 🅾 = other   **SOUTH CAROLINA**   **391**

INTERSTATE 85 CONT'D

N ↑ S

S P A R T A N B U R G

Exit	Services
87	SC 39, **E** 🅾 KOA, **W** 🅾 Rug Outlet, fruit stand/peaches/fireworks
83	SC 110, **E** 🅶 Hot Spot/dsl, 🅾 NAPA, fruit stand, truck repair, **W** 🅶 Auto Trkstp/Mr Waffle/dsl/24hr/@, 🅾 to Cowpens Bfd, fruitstand
82	Frontage Rd (from nb)
80.5mm	Pacolet River
80	SC 57, to Gossett, **E** 🅶 Hot Spot/Shell/dsl
78	US 221, Chesnee, **E** 🅶 Citgo/dsl, 🍽 Hardee's, 🏨 Motel 6, 🅾 fruit stand, **W** 🅶 BP/Subway, QT/dsl, RaceWay/dsl, Sunoco/Burger King/dsl, 🍽 Arby's, Bojangles, McDonald's, Southern BBQ, Subway, Waffle House, Wendy's, 🏨 Hampton Inn, Holiday Inn Express, 🅾 Advance Parts, $General, Harley-Davidson, Ingles Foods/cafe/dsl
77	Lp 85, Spartanburg, services along Lp 85 exits E
75	SC 9, Spartanburg, **E** 🍽 Denny's, 🏨 Best Value Inn, **W** 🅶 BP/Burger King/dsl, Pure, QT/dsl, RaceWay/dsl, 🍽 Bruster's, Capri's Italian, Copper River Grill, Fatz Café, Grapevine Rest, Jade House Asian, La Paz Mexican, McDonald's, Pizza Hut, Waffle House, Zaxby's, 🏨 Days Inn, Comfort Inn, 🅾 CVS Drug, Ingles/cafe/gas, USPO
72	US 176, to I-585, **E** 🅾 to USCS, Wofford/Converse Coll, **W** 🅶 Kangaroo, RaceWay, 🍽 Subway, Waffle House, 🅾 $General, Ingles Foods/cafe/gas, Masters RV Ctr
70b a	I-26, E to Columbia, W to Asheville
69	Lp 85, SC 41 (from nb), to Fairforest
68	SC 129, to Greer
67mm	N Tyger River
66	US 29, to Lyman, Wellford, **E** 🅶 Exxon/Subway/dsl, 🍽 Waffle House
63	SC 290, to Duncan, **E** 🅶 Circle K/dsl, Citgo/dsl, Spinx/Dunkin Donuts/dsl, 🍽 Arby's, Clock Rest., Cracker Barrel, Firehouse Subs, KFC, Paisanos Italian, Pizza Inn, Sake Japanese, Taco Bell, Thai Cuisine, Waffle House, Zaxby's, 🏨 Hampton Inn, Jameson Inn, Microtel, 🅾 Curves, **W** 🅶 BP, Marathon/dsl, 🛢/Wendy's/dsl/scales/24hr, TA/BP/DQ/rest./dsl/scales/24hr/@, 🍽 Bojangles, Hardee's, La Molcajete Mexican, McDonald's, Waffle House, 🏨 Holiday Inn Express, Quality Inn, Sheridan Inn, ValuePlace Inn, 🅾 Blue Beacon, Speedco
62.5mm	S Tyger River
60	SC 101, to Greer, **E** 🅶 Grand/dsl, Marathon, Sunoco/dsl, 🍽 Senor Garcia's Mexican, Subway, Theo's Rest, **W** 🅶 Exxon/Burger King, 🍽 Waffle House, 🏨 Super 8, 🅾 BMW Visitor Ctr
58	Brockman-McClimon Rd
57	**W** 🅾 Greenville-Spartanburg ✈
56	SC 14, to Greer, **E** 🅶 Citgo/dsl, **W** 🅶 Spinx/dsl, 🅾 🅷, Goodyear, Outdoor World RV Ctr
55mm	Enoree River
54	Pelham Rd, **E** 🅶 BP/dsl, 🍽 Burger King, Corona Mexican, Skin's Hotdogs, Waffle House, 🏨 Best Western, **W** 🅶 BP/dsl, Spinx, 🍽 Acropolis Rest, American Pie Factory, Atlanta Bread Co, Bojangles, Bertolos Pizza, California Dreaming Rest., Chick-fil-A, China Wok, Chophouse 47, Chops Cajun, Dunkin Donuts, 5 Guys Burgers, Hardee's, Jack-in-the-Box, Joe's Crabshack, Joy of Tokyo, Logan's Roadhouse, Macaroni Grill, McDonald's, MidTown Deli, Moe's SW Grill, On the Border, Rita's Custard, Ruby

G R E E N V I L L E

Exit	Services
54	Continued Tuesday, Schlotsky's, Starbucks, Subway, Wendy's, 🏨 Courtyard, Extended Stay America, Fairfield Inn, Hampton Inn, Holiday Inn Express, Mainstay Suites, Marriott, Microtel, Wingate Inn, 🅾 BiLo, CVS Drug, EarthFare Foods, Radio Shack, Walgreens, Walmart
52mm	weigh sta nb
51	I-385, SC 146, Woodruff Rd, **E** 🅶 Blue Jay/dsl, 🍽 Brixx Pizza, Buffalo Wild Wings, Chipotle Mexican, Coldstone, Cracker Barrel, Fatz Café, Fuddrucker's, IHOP, Lieu's Bistro, Longhorn Steaks, Mimi's Cafe, Monterrey Mexican, Nihao Buffet, Oriental House, Panera Bread, PF Chang's, Red Robin, Sticky Fingers, Wasabi, 🏨 Drury Inn, Hampton Inn, Hilton Garden, Homewood Suites, Staybridge Suites, 🅾 Barnes&Noble, Best Buy, Dick's, Goodyear/auto, Hamrick's Outlet, Lowe's, Marshall's, Petsmart, Ross, Verizon, Whole Foods Mkt, vet **W** 🅶 BP, RaceWay, 🍽 Atlanta Bread Co, Capri's Italian, Carraba's, Flatrock Grill, Jack-in-the-Box, Krystal, McDonald's, MidTown Deli, Ruby Tuesday, Ruth's Chris Steaks, TGIFriday, 🏨 Crowne Plaza, Days Inn, Embassy Suites, Fairfield Inn, Holiday Inn Express, La Quinta, Marriott (3mi), Microtel, 🅾 Costco/gas, Firestone/auto, Home Depot, Old Navy, Target, U-Haul
48b a	US 276, Greenville, **E** 🍽 Waffle House, 🏨 Red Roof Inn, 🅾 CarMax, to ICAR, **W** 🅶 Exxon/dsl, Murphy USA, Sunoco, 🍽 Arby's, Bojangles, Burger King, Hooters, Jack-in-the-Box, McDonald's, Olive Garden, Pizza Hut/Taco Bell, Ryan's, 🏨 Comfort Inn, Embassy Suites, Relax Inn, 🅾 Acura, Advance Parts, Audi/Porsche/VW, AutoZone, Bi-Lo, BMW/Mini, Books-A-Million, Buick, Dodge, $Tree, Ford, GMC, Hancock Fabrics, Honda, Infiniti, Isuzu, Jaguar, Kia, Lexus, Marshall's, Mazda, Mercedes, Michael's, Nissan, Office Depot, Pepboys, Petsmart, Saab, SteinMart, Subaru, Suzuki, Toyota, Volvo
46c	rd 291, Pleasantburg Rd, Mauldin Rd, **W** 🅶 BP, Citgo/dsl, 🍽 Jack-in-the-Box, Papa John's, Steak-Out, Subway, 🏨 InTown Suites, Quality Inn, Super Lodge, Value Place, 🅾 Aamco, Advance Parts, BiLo/gas, Bloom Foods, CVS Drug, Home Depot, Tire Kingdom, same as 46ba
46b a	US 25 bus, Augusta Rd, **E** 🅶 Mike&Jack, Spinx, Vgo, 🍽 Burger King, Waffle House, 🏨 Camelot Inn, Holiday Inn, Motel 6, Southern Suites, **W** 🏨 Economy Inn, Traveler's Inn, 🅾 Home Depot, same as 46c
44	US 25, White Horse Rd, **E** 🅶 Spinx/Subway/dsl, **W** 🅶 Citgo/McDonald's, RaceWay, 🍽 Waffle House, 🅾 🅷, Freightliner
44a	SC 20 (from sb), to Piedmont
42	I-185 toll, US 29, to Greenville, **W** 🅷
40	SC 153, to Easley, **E** 🅶 Breakers/dsl, 🍽 Waffle House,

SC

SC

🖪 = gas   🍴 = food   🛏 = lodging   ◉ = other   Copyright 2012 - The Next Exit

INTERSTATE 85 CONT'D

Exit	Services
40	Continued
	W 🖪 BP, Citgo/dsl, RaceWay, 🍴 Arby's, Bojangles, Burger King, Cracker Barrel, El Sureno Mexican, Huddle House, KFC, McDonald's, Pizza House, Pizza Hut/Taco Bell, Sonny's BBQ, Subway, Zaxby's, 🛏 Best Western, Executive Inn, Hampton Inn, Super 8, ◉ Advance Parts, BiLo, $General, GNC, Rite Aid
39	SC 143, to Piedmont, E 🖪 Vgo/dsl, W 🖪 Shell/dsl, ◉ antiques
35	SC 86, to Easley, Piedmont, E 🖪 ▭▭▭/McDonald's/dsl/scales/24hr, 🍴 Hardee's (1.5mi), Mozzerelli's Pizza, Subway (1.5mi), Sweet P's, W 🖪 BP/grill/dsl
34	US 29 (from sb), to Williamston
32	SC 8, to Pelzer, Easley, E 🖪 Hickory Point/dsl, Shell/dsl
27	SC 81, to Anderson, E 🖪 BP/dsl, Exxon, Zooms, 🍴 Arby's, KFC/Pizza Hut, McDonald's, Waffle House, 🛏 Hampton Inn, Holiday Inn Express, ◉ Ⓗ, W 🍴 Charlie's Wings
23mm	**rest area sb, full 🅿 facilities, 🚰, vending, ♻ litter barrels, petwalk**
21	US 178, to Anderson, E 🖪 QT/dsl, Shell/dsl, 🍴 Waffle House, **2 mi E** 🍴 Applebee's, Chick-fil-A, Chili's, Longhorn Steaks, O'Charley's, 🛏 HomeTowne Suites, Quality Inn, ◉ Publix/deli
19b a	US 76, SC 28, to Anderson, E 🖪 Exxon/dsl, 🍴 Fuddruckers, Hardee's, 🛏 Days Inn, Hilton Garden, Royal American Motel, ◉ Russell Stover, **2 mi E** 🖪 QT/dsl, Shell, 🍴 Applebee's, Chick-fil-A, Chili's, CookOut, 5 Guys Burgers, Golden Corral, Grand China, Hardee's, Jack-in-the-Box, Logan's Roadhouse, Longhorn Steaks, O'Charley's, Olive Garden, Panera Bread, Red Lobster, Rita's Custard, Ryan's, Sonny BBQ, TX Roadhouse, Zaxby's, 🛏 Best Value Inn, Holiday Inn, La Quinta, Super 8, ◉ Advance Parts, Aldi Foods, AT&T, Best Buy, Chrysler/Dodge/Jeep, Dick's, $General, $Tree, Ford/Mazda, Goodyear, Hancock Fabrics, Harley-Davidson, Hobby Lobby, Home Depot, Honda, K-Mart, Kohl's, Lowe's, Michael's, Nissan, Office Depot, Old Navy, O'Reilly Parts, Petsmart, Publix/deli, Ross, Sam's Club/gas, Staples, Target, Toyota/Scion, Verizon, Walmart, vet, W 🖪 HotSpot/McDonald's, RaceWay/dsl, 🍴 Arby's, Cracker Barrel, Fatz Cafe, Hooters, Outback Steaks, Subway, Waffle House, Wendy's, Wild Wing Cafe, 🛏 Comfort Suites, Country Inn&Suites, Fairfield Inn, Hampton Inn, Holiday Inn Express, Jameson Inn, Microtel, ◉ to Clemson U
18mm	**rest area nb, full 🅿 facilities, 🚰, vending, ♻ litter barrels, petwalk**
15mm	Lake Hartwell
14	SC 187, to Clemson, Anderson, E 🖪 Marathon/dsl, 🍴 Huddle House, ◉ camping (1mi), W 🖪 Hickory Point/dsl, 🍴 Famous Pizza Grill, 🛏 Budget Inn, ◉ to Clem Research Pk
12mm	Seneca River, Lake Hartwell
11	SC 24, SC 243, to Townville, E 🖪 Exxon/dsl, Sunoco/dsl/24hr, 🍴 Subway, ◉ to Savannah River Scenic Hwy, W 🖪 Shell/dsl, 🍴 Townville Cafe, ◉ RV camping
9mm	**weigh sta nb**
4	SC 243, to SC 24, Fair Play, E 🖪 ◆Love's/Arby's/dsl/scales/24hr, Mobil/dsl/scales/LP/24hr

Exit	Services
2	SC 59, to Fair Play, W fireworks
1	SC 11, to Walhalla, W 🍴 Gazebo Rest., ◉ fireworks, to Lake Hartwell SP
.5mm	**Welcome Ctr nb, full 🅿 facilities, info, 🚰, ♻ litter barrels, vending, petwalk**
0mm	South Carolina/Georgia state line, Lake Hartwell, Tagaloo River

INTERSTATE 95

Exit	Services
198mm	South Carolina/North Carolina state line
196mm	**Welcome Ctr sb, full 🅿 facilities, info, 🚰, vending, ♻ litter barrels, petwalk**
195mm	Little Pee Dee River
193	SC 9, SC 57, to N Myrtle Beach, Dillon, E 🖪 Exxon, Mobil/dsl, Murphy Express/dsl, Sunoco/dsl, 🍴 B&C Steak/BBQ, Burger King, Huddle House, Pizza Hut, Shoney's, Subway, Tokyo Cafe, Waffle House, Wendy's, Zaxby's, 🛏 Best Value Inn, Comfort Inn, Days Inn, Quality Inn, Royal Regency Inn, ◉ Ⓗ, Advance Parts, CVS Drug, $General, $Tree, Food Lion, O'Reilly Parts, Walgreens, Walmart, fireworks, W 🖪 BP/dsl, 🛏 EconoLodge, Super 8, ◉ Bass Lake RV Camp/LP
190	SC 34, to Dillon, W 🖪 ◆Love's/Arby's/dsl/scales/24hr
181	SC 38, Oak Grove, E 🖪 BP/Subway/dsl/24hr, ◆FLYING J/Subway/dsl/LP/scales/24hr, Shell/McDonald's/dsl/24hr, ◉ fireworks, W 🖪 Wilco/Hess/DQ/Wendy's/dsl/scales/24hr, 🛏 Best Western, ◉ auto/truck repair
175mm	Pee Dee River
170	SC 327, E 🖪 BP, ▭▭▭/Wendy's/dsl/scales/24hr, 🍴 McDonald's, Waffle House, Zaxby's, 🛏 Holiday Inn Express, ◉ to Myrtle Beach, Missile Museum
169	TV Rd, to Florence, E ◉ Florence RV Park, dsl repair, W 🖪 BP/dsl, ◆FLYING J/Shell/rest./dsl/scales/24hr/@, 🛏 Best Value Inn, ◉ Blue Beacon, Peterbilt, dsl repair
164	US 52, to Darlington, Florence, E 🖪 Exxon/dsl, RaceWay/24hr, Shell/Huddle House/dsl, 🍴 Angelo's Seafood Rest., Cracker Barrel, Hardee's, McDonald's, Quincy's, Quiznos, Ruby Tuesday, Waffle House, Wendy's, 🛏 Baymont Inn, Best Western, EconoLodge, Motel 6, Ramada Inn, Suburban Lodge, Super 8, Travel Inn, ◉ Ⓗ, Chrysler/Dodge/Jeep, Hyundai, W 🖪 TA/BP/Popeye's/dsl/scales/@, ▭▭▭/Subway/Taco Bell/dsl, 🍴 Arby's, Bojangles, Fatz Café, Krispy Kreme, La Fogata Mexican, Shoney's, Young's Pecans, Zaxby's, 🛏 Comfort Suites, Country Inn&Suites, Days Inn, Hampton Inn, Howard Johnson, Microtel, Sleep Inn, Thunderbird Inn, Travel House Inn, Wingate Inn, ◉ transmissions, to Darlington Raceway
160b	I-20 W, to Columbia
160a	Lp 20, to Florence, E 🍴 Arby's, Bruster's Ice Cream, Burger King, Chick-fil-A, Chili's, ChuckeCheese, IHOP, Indigo Joe's Rest., Longhorn Steaks, Olive Garden, Outback Steaks, Percy & Willy, Red Lobster, Ruby Tuesday, Shoney's, Waffle House, Western Sizzlin, 🛏 Courtyard, Fairfield Inn, Hampton Inn, Hilton Garden, Holiday Inn Express, Quality Inn, Red Roof Inn, Residence Inn, SpringHill Suites, ◉ Barnes&Noble, Belk, Best Buy, $Tree, Hobby Lobby, Hamricks, Home Depot, JC Penney, Kohl's, Lowes Whse, Sam's Club, Sears/auto, Target, Walmart, mall
157	US 76, Timmonsville, Florence, E 🖪 BP/dsl/repair, Exxon, McDonald's/dsl, Kangaroo/dsl, Marathon, 🍴 La Palmas Mexican, Waffle House, 🛏 Day's Inn, Howard Johnson Express, Swamp Fox Inn, Travelodge, W 🖪 Sunoco, 🛏 Ramada/rest., Tree Top Inn, Swamp Fox Camping (1mi)

SC

INTERSTATE 95 CONT'D

Exit	Services
153	Honda Way, **W** 💽 Exxon, 🍴 Hardees (2mi), ⊙ Honda Plant
150	SC 403, to Sardis, **E** 💽 BP/scales/dsl, 🍴 Hotplate Cafe, 🛏 Econolodge, **W** 💽 Exxon/dsl
147mm	Lynches River
146	SC 341, to Lynchburg, Olanta, **E** 💽 Moneysaver/dsl, 🛏 Relax Inn
141	SC 53, SC 58, to Shiloh, **E** 💽 Exxon/dsl, ⊙ DonMar RV Ctr, to Woods Bay SP, **W** 💽 Shell
139mm	**rest area both lanes, full ♿ facilities, 🚻, vending, 🏧, litter barrels, petwalk**
135	US 378, to Sumter, Turbeville, **E** 💽 BP, Citgo/dsl/24hr, 🍴 Compass Rest., 🛏 America's Inn, Day's Inn, **W** 💽 Exxon/Subway/dsl, ⊙ Pineland Golf Course
132	SC 527, to Sardinia, Kingstree
130mm	Black River
122	US 521, to Alcolu, Manning, **W** 💽 Exxon/dsl, 🍴 Paradise Cafe
119	SC 261, to Paxville, Manning, **0-1 mi E** 💽 Mobil, Murphy USA/dsl, Shell/24hr, TA/BP/Pizza Hut/Popeye's/dsl/scales/24hr/@, 🍴 Arby's, Bojangles, Burger King, Huddle House, KFC, Mariachi Mexican, McDonald's, Shoney's, Sonic, Subway, Waffle House, Wendy's, Yucatan Mexican, Zaxby's, 🛏 Days Inn, Hampton Inn, Holiday Inn Express, Quality Inn, Ramada Inn, ⊙ 🅷, AutoZone, Chrysler/Dodge/Jeep, CVS Drug, $General, Ford, Radio Shack, Walmart, **W** 💽 Horizon/dsl/E85, Paxville/24hr, 🛏 Super 8, ⊙ auto repair
115	US 301, to Summerton, Manning, **W** 💽 Shell/dsl/24hr, 🍴 Georgio's Greek, 🛏 Executive Inn
108	SC 102, Summerton, **E** 💽 BP/DQ/Stuckey's, TawCaw/dsl, ⊙ TawCaw RV Park (6m), **W** 🛏 Best Inn, Day's Inn, Deluxe Inn, Knight's Inn
102	US 15, US 301 N, to Santee, **E** 💽 StopSpot/dsl, 🍴 Arista Rest., 🛏 Santee Resort/Motel, ⊙ Bigwater RV Camping, Santee Lakes Camping, **W** 💽 Horizon/dsl/E85, ⊙ to Santee NWR
100mm	Lake Marion
99mm	**rest area both lanes, full ♿ facilities, 🚻, info, vending, 🏧, litter barrels, petwalk**
98	SC 6, to Eutawville, Santee, **E** 💽 BP/Bojangles, Chevron/LP, Citgo, Mobil, 🍴 Captains Quarters Rest., Coaster's Sea🍴 Huddle House, KFC, La Fogata Mexican, LT's Rest., Pizza Hut, Shoney's, Subway, 🛏 Best Western, Hampton Inn, Howard Johnson, Super 8, Travelodge, Whitten Inn, ⊙ $General, Piggly Wiggly, Russell Stover Candy, Santee Outlets/famous brands, **W** 💽 Citgo, Exxon, Hess/dsl, Horizon/Noble Roman's/dsl/24hr, 🍴 Burger King, Cracker Barrel, Maurice's BBQ, McDonald's, Peking Chinese, Waffle House, Wendy's, 🛏 Clark Inn/rest., Country Inn&Suites, Holiday Inn, Lake Marion Inn, Motel 6, Quality Inn, ⊙ CarQuest, CVS Drug, Family$, Food Lion, USPO, to Santee SP (3mi)
97	US 301 S (from sb, no return), to Orangeburg
93	US 15, to Santee, Holly Hill
90	US 176, to Cameron, Holly Hill, **W** 💽 Exxon/dsl
86b a	I-26, W to Columbia, E to Charleston
82	US 178, to Bowman, Harleyville, **E** 💽 BP, Wilco/Hess/Stuckey's/Wendy's/DQ/dsl/scales/24hr, 🛏 Peachtree Inn, **W** 💽 Shell/dsl, ⊙ tires/truck repair

Exit	Services
77	US 78, to Bamberg, St George, **E** 💽 Exxon/KFC, Monoco, Horizon/Subway/TCBY, Sunoco, 🍴 Georgio's Rest., Hardee's, McDonald's, Mi Rancho Mexican, Pizza Hut, Skynyrd's Grill, Waffle House, 🛏 Best Value Inn, Comfort Inn/RV Park, Econolodge, Quality Inn, ⊙ Chevrolet/GMC, CVS Drug, $General, Family$, Ford, Jolly Acres RV Park, Radio Shack, Ried's Foods, USPO, **W** 💽 BP, Shell/Taco Bell/dsl, 🍴 Huddle House, 🛏 Country Hearth Inn, Day's Inn, Southern Inn, Super 8
68	SC 61, Canadys, **E** 💽 BP, El Cheapo/scales, Shell/Subway/dsl, ⊙ truck lube/repair, to Colleton SP (3mi)
62	SC 34
57	SC 64, Walterboro, **E** 💽 Horizon, Shell/DQ, Mobil/dsl, Sunoco/dsl, 🍴 Arby's, Burger King, Capt D's, Dimitrio's Rest., Domino's, Huddle House, KFC, McDonald's, Olde House Café, Subway, Waffle House, Wendy's, 🛏 Carolina Lodge, Sleep Inn, Southern Inn, ⊙ 🅷, Ace Hardware, Advance Parts, AutoZone, $General, Family$, Ford/Mercury, GNC Nutrition, Piggly Wiggly, Reid's Foods, **W** 💽 BP/dsl, Murphy USA, 🍴 China Buffet, Zaxby's, 🛏 Super 8, ⊙ $Tree, PetCo, Walmart
53	SC 63, to Varnville, Walterboro, Hampton, **E** 💽 BP/McDonald's, El Cheapo, Exxon, Shell/DQ, Texaco/dsl, 🍴 Glasshouse Rest., KFC, Longhorn Steaks, Ruby Tuesday, Shoney's, Waffle House, 🛏 Best Western, Comfort Inn/rest., Econo Inn, Motel 6, Quality Inn, Ramada Inn, Royal Inn, Rice Planter's Inn, ⊙ fireworks, **W** 💽 Horizon, 🍴 Cracker Barrel, 🛏 Country Hearth Inn, Day's Inn, Hampton Inn, Holiday Inn Express, Microtel, ⊙ Green Acres Camping
47mm	**rest area both lanes, full ♿ facilities, 🚻, vending, 🏧, litter barrels, petwalk**
42	US 21, to Yemassee, Beaufort
40mm	Combahee River
38	SC 68, to Hampton, Yemassee, **E** 💽 Horizon/dsl/E85, ⊙ Family$, **W** 💽 BP/Subway/TCBY, Exxon/dsl, Shell/dsl, 🍴 Courtney Bay Sea🍴 J's Rest., 🛏 Palmetto Lodge/rest., Super 8
33	US 17 N, to Beaufort, **E** 💽 BP/dsl, Exxon/McDonald's, Shell, Texaco/TCBY/Subway, 🍴 Denny's, Country Kitchen, Waffle House, Wendy's, 🛏 Best Western, Budget Inn, Hampton Inn, Holiday Inn Express, Knight's Inn, ⊙ Confederate Railroad Museum, KOA, Oaks RV Camping
30.5mm	Tullifinny River
29mm	Coosawhatchie River
28	SC 462, to Coosawhatchie, Hilton Head, Bluffton, **W** 💽 Chevron/dsl, Citgo, Exxon/Chester Fried/dsl
22	US 17, Ridgeland, **W** 💽 Sunoco, 🛏 Ridgeland Inn, ⊙ 🅷
21	SC 336, to Hilton Head, Ridgeland, **E** 🍴 Wendy's,

🖾 = gas 🍴 = food 🏨 = lodging 🄾 = other   Copyright 2012 - The Next Exit

INTERSTATE 95 CONT'D

Exit	Services
21	Continued
	🄾 Boat'n RV Whse, **W** 🖾 BP/DQ/dsl, Exxon, Gulf/dsl, Shell, 🍴 Bella Pizza, Burger King, Hong Kong Chinese, Huddle House, Jasper's Porch, KFC, Subway, Waffle House, 🏨 Carolina Lodge, Comfort Inn/rest., Days Inn, Quality Inn, 🄾 🅷, Curves, $General, Harvey's Foods, Rite Aid
18	SC 13, to US 17, US 278, to Switzerland, Granville, Ridgeland
17mm	parking area both lanes, commercial vehicles only
8	US 278, to Bluffton, Hardeeville, **E** 🖾 BP/Wendy's/dsl/scales, Exxon, Kangaroo/McDonald's, 🄾 🅷, **W** 🖾 Horizon/Subway/Dominos/dsl, Mobil/Kangaroo/dsl, 🏨 Holiday Inn Express, Motel 6
5	US 17, US 321, to Savannah, Hardeeville, **E** 🖾 Citgo, Exxon/Blimpie, Gulf/dsl, Shell/24hr, 🍴 Mi Tierrita Mexican, Waffle House, 🏨 Days Inn, Economy Inn, Sleep Inn, 🄾 fireworks, to Savannah NWR, **W** 🖾 BP/dsl, Butlers/dsl/repair, Marathon, Sunoco/dsl, 🍴 Burger King, Shoney's, Wendy's, 🏨 Comfort Motel, Country Hearth Inn, Deluxe Inn, Knights Inn, Quality Inn, Red Roof Inn, Super 8, 🄾 $General, NAPA
4.5mm	**Welcome Ctr nb, full ♿ facilities, info, 📞, 🚮, litter barrels, vending, petwalk**
4mm	**weigh sta both lanes**
0mm	South Carolina/Georgia state line, Savannah River

INTERSTATE 385 (Greenville)

Exit	Services
42	US 276, Stone Ave, to Travelers Rest., to Greenville Zoo, **E** 🍴 Pete's Gyros, 🄾 CarQuest, **W** 🖾 Spinx/dsl, **1-2 mi W** multiple services on US 276, I-385 begins/ends on US 276.
40b a	SC 291, Pleasantburg Dr, **E** 🖾 Sunoco, 🍴 Jack-in-the-Box, Little Caesar's, Olive Tree, S&S Cafeteria, Sonic, Starbucks, Subway, Taco Casa, Wendy's, 🄾 CVS Drug, $Tree, Walgreens, to BJU, Furman U, **W** 🖾 Citgo/dsl, 🍴 Domino's, Krispy Kreme, 🏨 Quality Inn, Phoenix Inn/Rest., Sleep Inn, 🄾 Cottman Transmissions
39	Haywood Rd, **E** 🖾 BP, Spinx, 🍴 Noodleville, Outback Steaks, Portofino's, Tony's Pizzeria, 🏨 Clarion, Courtyard, Hawthorn Inn, Hilton, Hyatt Place, La Quinta, 🄾 Firestone/auto, TJ Maxx, **W** 🖾 BP, Pumpers, 🍴 Arby's, Applebee's, Backyard Burger, Burger King, Chick-fil-A, Chili's, ChuckeCheese, CiCi's Pizza, CityRange Steaks, Copper River Grill, Don Pablo, Fried Green Tomatoes, Harbor Inn Sea 🍴 Honeybaked Ham, Italian Mkt/grill, Jason's Deli, Jimmy John's, Kanpai Tokyo, McAlister's Deli, Miabi Japanese, Moe's SW Grill, Monterrey Mexican, Panera Bread, Quiznos, Rafferdi's, Starbucks, Steak'n Shake, Waffle House, 🏨 Studio+, 🄾 AT&T, Barnes&Noble, Belk, Dillard's, Discount Tire, JC Penney, Macy's, NTB, Sears/auto, mall
37	Roper Mtn Rd, **W** 🖾 BP/dsl, RaceWay/dsl, 🍴 Atl Bread Co, Capri's Italian, Carrabba's, Cracker Barrel, El Patron Mexican, 5 Guys Burgers, FlatRock Grille, Harry&Jean's Rest., Krystal, McDonald's, Ruby Tuesday, Ruths Chris Steaks, Steak'n Shake, Strossner's Cafe, Subway, TGI Friday's, Waffle House, 🏨 Days Inn, Comfort Inn, Crowne Plaza, Embassy Suites, Holiday Inn Express, La Quinta, Vintel, 🄾 AT&T, Costco/gas, Firestone/auto, Home Depot, Hyundai, Lincoln/Mercury, Lowe's, Old Navy, Target, Trader Joe's

Exit	Services
36b a	I-85, N to Charlotte, S to Atlanta
35	SC 146, Woodruff Rd, **0-2 mi E** 🖾 BP, Spinx, 🍴 Applebee's, AZ Steaks, Bojangles, Bone Fish Grill, Boston Pizzeria, Bruster's, Burger King, Chick-fil-A, Chili's, Chin Chin Chinese, China Buffet, Dunkin Donuts, Great Harvest Bread, Green Tomato, Hardee's, Hibachi Grill, Jersey Mike's, KFC, Little Caesar's, McAlister's Deli, McDonald's, Mimi's Japanese Steaks, Moe's SW Grill, Perkins, Pizza Inn, Quiznos, Sonic, Starbucks, Stevi B's, Subway, Taco Bell, Topper's Rest., Travinia Italian, Waffle House, Wendy's, Zaxby's, 🄾 URGENT CARE, Ace Hardware, Aldi Foods, Bi-Lo Foods, BigLots, Curves, Discount Tire, $Tree, GNC, Hobby Lobby, Kohl's, Publix, Radio Shack, Rite Aid, Sam's Club/gas, Save-a-Lot Foods, Staples, Tire Kingdom, USPO, Walmart, **W** 🖾 Blue Jay/dsl, 🍴 Brixx Pizza, Buffalo Wild Wings, Chipotle Mexican, Coldstone, Cracker Barrel, Fatz Café, Fuddrucker's, IHOP, Lieu's Bistro, Longhorn Steaks, Mimi's Cafe, Monterrey Mexican, Nihao Buffet, Oriental House, Panera Bread, PF Chang's, Red Robin, Sticky Fingers, Wasabi, 🏨 Drury Inn, Hampton Inn, Hilton Garden, Homewood Suites, Staybridge Suites, 🄾 Barnes&Noble, Best Buy, Dick's, Goodyear/auto, Hamrick's Outlet, Lowe's, Marshall's, Petsmart, Ross, Verizon, Whole Foods Mkt, vet
34	Butler Rd, Mauldin, **E** 🖾 Exxon, 🍴 Arby's, 🄾 CVS Drug, **W** 🍴 Dino's Rest., Moretti's Pizzeria, Sub Sta. 2, 🄾 $General
33	Bridges Rd, Mauldin
31	I-185 toll, SC 417, to Laurens Rd, **E** 🖾 BP, 🍴 Hardee's, McDonald's
30	I-185 toll, US 276, Standing Springs Rd
29	Georgia Rd, to Simpsonville, **W** 🏨 ValuePlace Inn
27	Fairview Rd, to Simpsonville, **E** 🍴 Carolina Rest., CoachHouse Rest., Little Caesar's, McDonald's, Milano Pizzeria, Mojo's Burgers, New China Buffet, Subway, 🏨 Palmetto Inn, 🄾 🅷, Advance Parts, AutoZone, CVS Drug, $General, O'Reilly Parts, **W** 🖾 Exxon, Murphy USA, Spinx, 🍴 Anthony's Pizza, Applebee's, Arby's, AZ Steaks, Baskin-Robbins, Bellacino's, Bruster's, Burger King, Chick-fil-A, Cracker Barrel, Dragon Den Chinese, Hungry Howie's, Jack-in-the-Box, Jersey Mike's, KFC, La Fogata Mexican, McDonald's, Moe's SW Grill, O'Charley's, Panera Bread, Pizza Hut, Quiznos, Ruby Tuesday, Ryan's, Sonic, Starbucks, Subway, Taco Bell, Tequila's Mexican, Waffle House, Wendy's, Zaxby's, 🏨 Comfort Suites, Days Inn, Hampton Inn, Holiday Inn Express, Quality Inn, 🄾 AT&T, Belk, Bi-Lo, CVS Drug, $Tree, GNC, Goodyear/auto, Home Depot, Ingles Foods, Kohl's, Lowe's, Publix, Radio Shack, Ross, Target, Tire Kingdom, TJ Maxx, Verizon, Walgreens, Walmart, USPO
26	Harrison Bridge Rd, **W** same as 27
24	Fairview St, **E** 🖾 Marathon, 🍴 Hardee's, Waffle House, 🄾 carwash
23	SC 418, to Fountain Inn, Fork Shoals, **E** 🖾 Exxon/pizza/subs, 🄾 $General, USPO, **W** 🖾 Sunoco/dsl
22	SC 14 W, Old Laurens Rd, to Fountain Inn
19	SC 14 E, to Gray Court, Owings
16	SC 101, to Woodruff, Gray Court
10	rd 23, Barksdale, Ora
9	US 221, to Laurens, Enoree, **E** 🖾 Citgo/Subs/dsl, 🍴 Waffle House, 🏨 Budget Lodge, **W** Walmart Dist Ctr
6mm	**rest area both lanes (both lanes exit left), full ♿ facilities, 📞, vending, 🚮, litter barrels, petwalk**

Vertical margin text (left): N S HARDEEVILLE GREENVILLE N S — SC

Vertical margin text (right): SIMPSONVILLE

INTERSTATE 385 CONT'D (Greenville)

Exit	Services
5	SC 49, to Laurens, Union
2	SC 308, to Clinton, Ora, W ◻ Ⓗ, to Presbyterian Coll in Clinton
0mm	I-26 S to Columbia, I-385 begins/ends on I-26 at 52mm.

INTERSTATE 526 (Charleston)

Exit	Services
33mm	I-526 begins/ends.
32	US 17, 0-1 mi N ⛽ Hess/dsl, Shell, 🍴 Benito's Pizza, Burger King, Chili's, IHOP, LongHorn Steaks, Mama Fu's Asian, On The Border, Starbucks, TGIFriday, 🛏 Courtyard, ◻ Advance Parts, Barnes&Noble, Belk, Chevrolet, CVS Drug, Firestone, Lowes Whse, Midas, Old Navy, Rite Aid, Tire Kingdom, TrueValue, Walgreens, 0-1 mi S ⛽ Exxon/Dunkin Donuts, Mobil, Shell/Circle K, Sunoco, 🍴 Applebees, Arby's, Chick-fil-A, Cici's, Domino's, Hardee's, Huddle House, KFC, La Hacienda Mexicana, McDonald's, Outback Steaks, Papa John's, Sticky Fingers, Subway, Wendy's, Zeus Grill, 🛏 Best Western, Day's Inn, Extended Stay America, Hampton Inn, Holiday Inn, Masters Inn, Quality Inn, Red Roof Inn, River Inn, ◻ Aamco, Bi-Lo, Cadillac, $General, Ford, Harris Teeter, Jiffy Lube, K-Mart, Marshall's, Office Depot, Radio Shack, Staples, TJ Maxx, USPO, VW, Walmart, Whole Foods Mkt, vet
30	Long Point Rd, N ⛽ BP, Exxon, 🍴 Bamboo Garden, Beef'o Brady's, McAlister's, Moe's SW Grill, Sonic, Starbucks, Subway, Waffle House, Wendy's, ◻ CVS Drug, Food Lion, Harris Teeter Foods, PetsMart, Ross, Steinmart,.Charles Pinckney NHS
26mm	Wando River
24	Daniel Island, S ⛽ Texaco, 🍴 Dragon Palace, Lana's Mexican, Queen Anne's Steaks/sea🍴 Subway, 🛏 Hampton Inn, ◻ Publix
23b a	Clements Ferry Rd
21mm	Cooper River
20	Virginia Ave (from eb), S ⛽ Hess Depot

CHARLESTON

Exit	Services
19	N Rhett Ave, N ⛽ Hess, Kangaroo/Subway/dsl, 🍴 Hardee's, ◻ Family$, Food Lion, Rite Aid, S ⛽ BP
18b a	US 52, US 78, Rivers Ave, N ⛽ BP/dsl, Hess, Kangaroo/dsl, 🍴 KFC, Peking Gourmet, Pizza Hut/Taco Bell, ◻ AutoZone, Dodge, Family$, Ford, H&L Foods, auto repair, S ⛽ Exxon
17b a	I-26, E to Charleston, W to Columbia
16	Montague Ave, 🔄 Rd, S ⛽ Sunoco, 🍴 Chili's, La Hacienda, Panera Bread, Quizno's, Starbucks, Wendy's, 🛏 Comfort Inn, Embassy Suites, Extended Stay America, Hilton Garden, Holiday Inn, Homewood Suites, Quality Inn, Residence Inn, Wingate Inn, ◻ Sam's Club, Staples, Tanger Outlet/famous brands, Walmart
15	SC 642, Dorchester Rd, Paramount Dr, N ⛽ BP, 🍴 Pizza Roma (1mi), Wendy's (1mi), S ⛽ Citgo/dsl, Sunoco, 🍴 Burger King, Checker's, Domino's, East Bay Deli, Huddle House, Pizza Hut, 🛏 🔄 Inn, ◻ Bi-Lo Foods, CVS Drug, Family$, Food Lion, Harley-Davidson, U-Haul
14	Leeds Ave, S 🛏 Value Place Inn, ◻ Ⓗ, boat marina
13mm	Ashley River
11b a	SC 61, Ashley River Rd, N 🍴 Chick-fil-A, McDonald's, O'Charley's, Subway, ◻ Ⓗ, Food Lion, Home Depot, Lowes Whse, Rite Aid
10	US 17, SC 7, **services from US 17** E ⛽ BP, 🍴 Alex's Rest., Burger King, Capt D's, Checker's, CiCi's, Dunkin Donuts, 5 Guys Burgers, Hopsing's, IHOP, McDonald's, Messengers BBQ, Pizza Hut, Red Lobster, Ruby Tuesday, Shoney's, Taco Bell, 🛏 Best Western, Holiday Inn Express, Motel 6, Sleep Inn, ◻ Buick/GMC, Chevrolet, Dillards, Ford, Honda, Hyundai, Jaguar, Kerr Drug, K-Mart, Mazda, Mini, Mitsubishi, Nissan, Dodge, Pepboys, Piggly Wiggly, Sears/auto, Tire Kingdom, vet, W ⛽ Exxon, Hess, Shell/Circle K, 🍴 Halligan's Rest., Hardees, Subway, Waffle House, 🛏 Econolodge, Hampton Inn, InTown Suites, ◻ Acura, Audi, Advance Parts, Carmax, Chrysler/Jeep, Costco/gas, CVS Drug, Family$, Food Lion, KIA, Subaru, Toyota, I-526 begins/ends on US 17.

SOUTH DAKOTA

INTERSTATE 29

Exit	Services
253mm	South Dakota/North Dakota state line
251mm	**Welcome Ctr sb, full ♿ facilities, info, 🚻, 🧺, litter barrels, petwalk**
246	SD 127, to Rosholt, New Effington, **3 mi** W ⛽, 🍴 RV camping, Sica Hollow SP (24mi)
242	no services
235mm	**weigh sta sb**
232	SD 10, Sisseton, E ⛽ Dakota Connection/dsl/casino/24hr, 🍴 Crossroads Cafe, **1-3 mi** W ⛽ Amstar/dsl, FuelMax/dsl, Sinclair/dsl, Tesoro, 🍴 Cottage Rest, DQ, Pizza Hut, Subway, Taco John's, West Inn Grille, 🛏 Holiday Motel, I-29 Motel, Super 8, Viking Motel, ◻ Alco, Camp Dakotah, Buick/Chevrolet, Family$, NAPA, SuperValu Foods/gas, to Roy Lake SP (25mi), Ft Sisseton SP (35mi)
224	Peever, Sioux Tribal Hqtrs, E ⛽ Sunoco/dsl, W Pickerel Lake (16mi)
213	SD 15, to Wilmot, **rest area both lanes, full ♿ facilities, 🚻, 🧺, litter barrels, petwalk, RV dump**, st patrol, **7 mi** E ⛽, 🍴 to Hartford Beach SP (17mi)

WATERTOWN

Exit	Services
207	US 12, Summit, E ⛽ Sinclair/dsl/24hr, 🍴 County Line Rest (1mi), W Blue Dog Fish Hatchery (15mi), Waubay NWR (19mi)
201	to Twin Brooks
193	SD 20, to South Shore, Stockholm
185	to Waverly, **4 mi** W ◻ Dakota Sioux Casino/rest.
180	US 81 S, to Watertown, **5 mi** W ⛽ Sinclair, ◻ Bramble Park Zoo, 🔄
177	US 212, Watertown, E ⛽ Tesoro/Grainery Cafe/dsl/24hr, 🛏 Holiday Inn Express, ◻ Volvo, WW Tires, truck wash, W ⛽ Shell/dsl, 🍴 Applebee's, Culver's, IHOP, Jimmy John's, KFC/LJ Silver, Lonepine BBQ, McDonald's, Starbucks, 🛏 Comfort Inn, Country Inn&Suites, Days Inn, Hampton Inn, ◻ Ⓗ, $Tree, Redlin Art Ctr, Walmart/Subway, **1-2 mi** W ⛽ Cenex/dsl, Clark/dsl, Freedom, Sinclair, Tesoro, 🍴 Arby's, Burger King, Cici's Pizza, Domino's, DQ, Dragon Wall Chinese, Godfather's, Guadalajara Mexican, McDonald's, Papa Murphy's, Perkins, Pizza Hut, Quizno's, Senor Max's Mexican, Subway/TCBY, Taco John's, 🛏 Drake Hotel, Travelers Inn, ◻ Advance Parts, Buick, Chrysler/Dodge/Jeep, EconoFoods, Ford, Goodyear/auto,

SC

SD

=gas **=food** **=lodging** **=other** Copyright 2012 - The Next Exit®

INTERSTATE 29

N ↕ S

BROOKINGS

SIOUX FALLS

Exit	Services
177	Continued Harley-Davidson, Herberger's, Hy-Vee Foods, JC Penney, Menards, NAPA, O'Reilly Parts, Pronto Parts, ShopKO, Target, Tires+, Walgreens, mall, to Sandy Shore RA (10mi)
164	SD 22, to Castlewood, Clear Lake, **9 mi E** Cenex/dsl, H
161mm	**rest area both lanes, full facilities, , , litter barrels, vending, petwalk**
157	to Brandt
150	SD 28, SD 15 N, to Toronto, **7 mi W** , lodging, **24 mi W** Lake Poinsett RA, SD Amateur Baseball Hall of Fame
140	SD 30, to White, Bruce, **W** Oakwood Lakes SP (12mi)
133	US 14 byp, Brookings, **E** WW Tires, **W** to SD St U, museums, Laura Ingalls Wilder Home
132	US 14, Lp 29, Brookings, **E** Cenex/Burger King/dsl, Applebee's, Fairfield Inn, Hampton Inn, Holiday Inn Express, Super 8, **W** BP, Cenex, Shell, Arby's, Burger King, Culver's, DQ, Jimmy John's, KFC, King's Wok, McDonald's, Papa John's, Papa Murphy's, Pavillion Grill, Perkins, Pizza Ranch, Qdoba Mexican, Quizno's, Subway, Z'Kota Grill, Comfort Inn, Days Inn, Staurolite Inn, H, Advance Parts, CarQuest, Buick/Cadillac/Chevrolet/GMC, Lowe's Whse, Radio Shack, Walmart, city park
127	SD 324, to Elkton, Sinai
124mm	Big Sioux River
121	to Nunda, Ward, **E rest area both lanes, full facilities, , , litter barrels, vending, petwalk, RV dump,** st patrol, **W** RV camping
114	SD 32, to Flandreau **7 mi E** Cenex, Subway, Sioux River Motel/RV park, Santee Tribal Hqtrs
109	SD 34, to Madison, Colman, **W** BP/dsl/rest., Shell/dsl/rest., **20 mi W** to Lake Herman SP, Dakota St U, museum
104	to Trent, Chester
103mm	parking area both lanes
98	SD 115 S, Dell Rapids, **E** Chevrolet, **3 mi E** Cenex, Shell, DQ, Pizza Ranch, Bilmar Inn, H
94	SD 114, to Baltic, **10 mi E** to EROS Data Ctr, US Geological Survey
86	to Renner, Crooks
84b a	I-90, **W** to Rapid City, **E** to Albert Lea
83	SD 38 W, 60th St, **E** FLYING J/Denny's/dsl/scales/24hr/@, Quality Suites, Freightliner Trucks, Harley-Davidson, Northview Campers, repair, **W** fireworks
82	Benson Rd
81	SD 38 E, Russell St, Sioux Falls, **E** BP/24hr, Food'n Fuel, Michael's Steaks, Roll'n Pin Rest., Arena Motel, Best Western/Ramkota, Brimark Inn, Kelly Inn, Knight's Inn, Motel 6, Ramada Inn, Sheraton, Sleep Inn, Schaap's RV Ctr, st patrol, **W** Subway
80	Madison St, **E** Sinclair/dsl, to fairgrounds
79	SD 42, 12th St, **E** BP/24hr, Freedom, Burger King, Burger Time, Golden Harvest Chinese, KFC, McDonald's, Pizza Hut, Subway, Taco Bell, Taco John's, Tomacelli's Pizza, Wendy's, Ramada Ltd, ValuePlace Inn, H, Ace Hardware, Buick, Chevrolet, $General, K-Mart, Lewis Drug, NAPA, Scion/Toyota, Sunshine Foods, Walgreens, city park, USPO, to Great Plains Zoo/museum, **W** BP/dsl, Cenex/dsl, Food'n Fuel, Tower RV Park
78	26th St, Empire St, **E** BP, Carino's Italian, Carnival Brazillian Grill, Coldstone Creamery, Chevy's Mexican, ChuckeCheese, Cracker Barrel, Culver's, Domino's, Granite City Rest, Outback Steaks, Puerto Vallarta, Ruby Tuesday, Clubhouse Suites, Hampton Inn, Holiday Inn Express, StayBridge Suites, Home Depot, Petsmart, Sam's Club/gas, USPO, World Mkt, **W** Boss' Pizza, DQ, Dynasty Chinese, Oscar's Coffee, Papa John's, Quizno's, Referee Grill, Starbucks, TownePlace Suites, Curves, Hy-Vee Foods/gas, Lowe's Whse
77	41st St, Sioux Falls, **E** BP/24hr, Sinclair/dsl, SA/dsl, Arby's, Burger King, Champp's Grill, Chili's, Fry'n Pan Rest., Fuddrucker's, HuHot Mongolian, KFC, McDonald's, Old Chicago Pizza, Olive Garden, Pancake House, Papa Murphy's, Perkins, Pizza Hut, Pizza Ranch, Qdoba Mexican, Quizno's, Red Lobster, Starbucks, Subway, Szechwan Chinese, Taco Bell, Taco John's, Texas Roadhouse, TimberLodge Steaks, Wendy's, Comfort Suites, Courtyard, Fairfield Inn, Microtel, Residence Inn, Rodeway Inn, SpringHill Suites, Super 8, Advance Parts, Barnes&Noble, Best Buy, Curves, Ford/Lincoln/Mercury, Goodyear/auto, Hancock Fabrics, Hy-Vee Foods, Hyundai/Nissan, JC Penney, Macy's, Mazda, Old Navy, PetCo, Radio Shack, Sears/auto, ShopKO, Target, Tires+, Walgreens, Walmart, Younkers, mall, **W** Shell/dsl, Burger King, Denucci's Pizza, Godfather's, IHOP, Peking Chinese, Perkins/24hr, Subway, AmericInn, Baymont Inn, Days Inn, Red Roof Inn, Lewis Drug, USPO
75	I-229 E, to I-90 E
73	Tea, **E** Sinclair/dsl, Marlin's Rest, **1.5mi W** Red Barn Camping
71	to Harrisburg, Lennox, **W** RV camping
68	to Lennox, Parker
64	SD 44, Worthing, **W** Buick/Chevrolet, Great Plains RV Ctr
62	US 18 E, to Canton, **E** Shell/pizza/dsl, Countryside RV park/motel, **W** repair
59	US 18 W, to Davis, Hurley
56	to Fairview, **E** to Newton Hills SP (12mi)
53	to Viborg
50	to Centerville, Hudson
47	SD 46, to Irene, Beresford, **E** BP/Burger King, Casey's, Sinclair/dsl, Emily's Café, Subway, Crossroads Motel, Super 8, Chevrolet, $General, Fiesta Foods, repair, **W** Cenex/cafe/dsl/24hr
42	to Alcester, Wakonda
41mm	truck check (from sb)
38	to Volin, **E** to Union Grove SP (3mi)
31	SD 48, to Akron, Spink
26	SD 50, to Vermillion, **E Welcome Ctr/rest area both lanes, full facilities, info, , , litter barrels, petwalk, RV dump, W** BP/dsl, **6-7 mi W** Burger King, Godfather's Pizza, Subway, Taco John's, Comfort Inn, Holiday Inn Express, Super 8, Westside Inn, H, Hy-Vee Foods, Walmart/deli, to U of SD, to Lewis & Clark RA
18	Lp 29, to Burbank, Elk Point, **E** BP/dsl, Casey's, Cody's Rest., HomeTowne Inn
15	to Elk Point, **1 mi E** Kum&Go/Subway/dsl, **W** fireworks
13mm	**weigh sta nb**, parking area sb
9	SD 105, Jefferson, **E** BP/Choice Cut Rest./dsl
4	McCook, **1 mi W** KOA (seasonal), Adams Homestead/nature preserve

SD

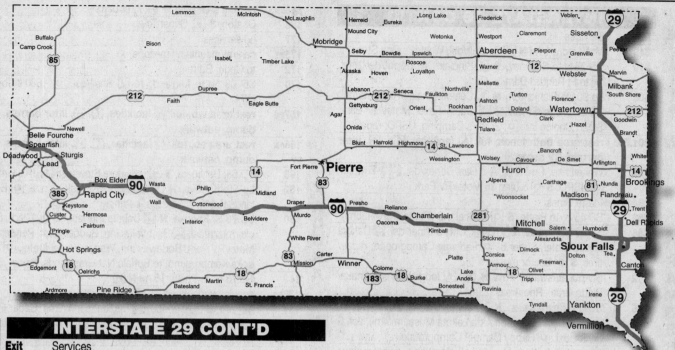

INTERSTATE 29 CONT'D

Exit	Services
2	N Sioux City, **E** 🅖 Cenex, Goode/dsl/rest/casino, 🍴 Glass Palace Rest. (1mi), McDonald's, Taco John's, 🄾 USPO, fireworks, **W** 🅖 Casey's/gas, Clark, 🛏 Comfort Inn, Hampton Inn, Red Carpet Inn, Super 8, 🄾 KOA, to Sodrac Dogtrack
1	**E** 🄾 Dakota Dunes Golf Resort, **W** 🅖 Dunes Gen. Store/dsl, 🍴 Graham's Grill, 🛏 Country Inn&Suites
0mm	South Dakota/Iowa state line, Big Sioux River

INTERSTATE 90

Exit	Services
412.5mm	South Dakota/Minnesota state line
412mm	**Welcome Ctr wb/rest area eb, full ♿ facilities, info, ⓒ, 🚻, litter barrels, petwalk, RV dump (wb), weigh sta (wb)**
410	Valley Springs, **N** Palisades SP (7mi), **S** Beaver Creek Nature Area, 🅖, food
406	SD 11, Brandon, Corson, **N** Palisades SP (10mi), **S** 🅖 BP/dsl, Shell, Sinclair/McDonald's/dsl, 🍴 Brandon Steaks, DQ, Great Wall, Pizza Ranch, Subway, Taco John's, Tailgater's Grill, 🛏 Comfort Inn, Holiday Inn Express, 🄾 Curves, Lewis Drug, Sunshine Foods, TrueValue, Verizon, to Big Sioux RA (4mi)
402	EROS Data Ctr, **N** 🄾 Jellystone RV Park, tires
400	I-229 S
399	SD 115, Cliff Ave, Sioux Falls, **N** 🅖 TC's/BP/dsl, 🄾 Spader RV Ctr, KOA, **S** 🅖 BP, Holiday/dsl/E-85, ◆Loves/Grandma Max's/Subway/dsl/scales/24hr/@, Shell/dsl, Sinclair, 🍴 Arby's, Burger King, McDonald's/truck parking, Perkins, Taco Bell, Taco John's, 🛏 Cloud Nine Motel, Days Inn, EconoLodge, Super 8, 🄾 🄷, Blue Beacon, Graham Tire, Kenworth, Peterbilt, Volvo
398mm	Big Sioux River
396b a	I-29, N to Brookings, S to Sioux City
395	Marion
390	SD 38, Hartford, **N** 🍴 Pizza Ranch, 🄾 Camp Dakota RV Park, Goos RV Ctr, **S** 🄾 Cowboy Town/dsl
387	rd 17, Hartford, **N** 🅖 BP/dsl, 🍴 Pizza Ranch
379	SD 19, Humboldt, **N** 🅖 Mobil/dsl, Shell/Town&Country Store/dsl (1mi), 🄾 USPO

Exit	Services
375mm	E Vermillion River
374	to SD 38, Montrose, 5 mi **S** 🄾 Battle Creek Res., Lake Vermillion RA, RV camping
368	Canistota, 4 mi **S** 🛏 Best Western
364	US 81, to Yankton, Salem, 4 mi **N** 🅖 Cenex, 🛏 Home Motel, 🄾 Camp America
363.5mm	W Vermillion River
363mm	**rest area both lanes, full ♿ facilities, ⓒ, 🚻, litter barrels, vending, petwalk, RV dump**, st patrol
357	to Bridgewater, Canova
353	Spencer, Emery, **S** 🅖 FuelMart/Subway/dsl/casino/24hr
352mm	Wolf Creek
350	SD 25, Emery, Farmer, **N** to DeSmet, Home of Laura Ingalls Wilder
344	SD 262, to Fulton, Alexandria, **S** 🅖 Shell/dsl
337mm	parking area both lanes
335	Riverside Rd, **N** 🄾 KOA (1mi)
334.5mm	James River
332	SD 37 S, to Parkston, Mitchell, **N** 🅖 Cenex/DQ/dsl, Clark, Mobil, ▮▮▮/Shell/Marlin's Rest./Subway/dsl/scales/24hr, Sinclair, 🍴 Arby's, Corona Village Mexican, McDonald's, Perkins, Pirogue's BBQ, Pizza Hut, Pizza Ranch, Twin Dragon Chinese, 🛏 AmericInn, Best Western, Days Inn, Quality Inn, Super 8/truck parking, Thunderbird Motel, 🄾 🄷, Advance Parts, Chrysler/Dodge/Jeep, K-Mart, O'Reilly Parts, Rondee's Campground, Walgreens, transmissions, **1-2 mi N** 🄾 to Corn Palace, Museum of Pioneer Life, **S** 🅖 Shell/Godfather's/Taco Bell/dsl/24hr, 🍴 Culver's, Hardee's, Quiznos, Ruby Tuesday, Whiskey Creek Grill, 🛏 Comfort Inn, Hampton Inn, Holiday Inn Express, Kelly Inn, 🄾 Cabela's, $Tree, Menards, Radio Shack, Walmart/Subway
330	SD 37 N, Mitchell, **N** 🅖 Cenex/dsl/24hr, Shell/dsl, Sinclair/dsl, 🍴 DQ, 🛏 Budget Inn, EconoLodge, Motel 6, Ramada Inn, Siesta Motel, 🄾 🄷, County Fair Foods, Jack's Campers/RV Ctr, Mr. Tire, to Corn Palace, museum, transmissions, **weigh sta**, **S** 🄾 Dakota RV Park
325	Betts Rd, **S** Famil-e-Fun Camping

INTERSTATE 90 CONT'D

E / W / CHAMBERLAIN / MURDO (left margin)

Exit	Services
319	Mt Vernon, **1 mi N** 🅰 Sinclair/dsl, Westey's One Stop
310	US 281, to Stickney, **S** 🅰 Sinclair/Deli Depot/dsl/24hr, 🅾 to Ft Randall Dam
308	Lp 90, to Plankinton, **N** 🅰 Cenex, Sinclair/Al's Cafe/dsl, 🍴 Commerce St Grille, 🛏 Cabin Fever Motel/RV Park, Smart Choice Inn, 🅾 Gordy's Camping, USPO, repair
301.5mm	**rest area both lanes, full ♿ facilities, 🚻s, 🏕, litter barrels, RV dump**
296	White Lake, **1 mi N** 🅰 A-Z Gas, Cenex/dsl, 🛏 A-Z Motel, 🅾 USPO, **S** 🅾 Siding 36 Motel/RV Park
294mm	Platte Creek
289	SD 45 S, to Platte, **S** 🅾 to Snake Cr/Platte Cr RA (25mi)
284	SD 45 N, Kimball, **N** 🅰 Clark, Ditty's/Diner/dsl, 🛏 Dakota Winds Motel, Super 8, 🅾 Parkway Campground, repair/tires, **S** 🅾 tractor museum
272	SD 50, Pukwana, **2 mi N** 🅰, 🍴, lodging, **S** 🅾 Snake/Platte Creek Rec Areas (25mi)
265	SD 50, Chamberlain, **N** 🅰 Cenex/DQ/dsl, 🛏 AmericInn, 🅾 🏥, Alco, St Joseph Akta Lakota Museum (4mi), vet, **S** 🅰 SA/dsl, 🅾 Happy Camper Campground
264mm	**rest area both lanes, full ♿ facilities, scenic view, info, 🚻s, 🏕, litter barrels**
263	Chamberlain, **N** 🅰 Sinclair/dsl, 🍴 Casey's Café, McDonald's, Pizza Hut, Subway (1mi), Taco John's, 🛏 Best Western (1mi), Bel Aire Motel (1mi), Riverview Inn, Super 8, 🅾 Crow Creek Sioux Tribal Hqtrs, SD Hall of Fame
262mm	Missouri River
260	SD 50, Oacoma, **N** 🅰 Cenex/Arby's/dsl, Clark/dsl, Shell/dsl, 🛏 Al's Oasis/Motel/Camping/cafe/mkt, Cedar Shore Motel/Camping (3mi), Days Inn, Howard Johnson, Quality Inn, 🅾 Buick/Chevrolet, Old West Museum, antiques
251	SD 47, to Winner, Gregory
248	SD 47, Reliance, **N** 🅰 Cenex (1mi), Farmer's Union/dsl (1mi), 🅾 Sioux Tribal Hqtrs, to Big Bend RA
241	to Lyman
235	SD 273, Kennebec, **N** 🅰 Clark/dsl, 🍴 Hot Rods Steaks, 🛏 Budget Host, Kings Inn, 🅾 KOA
226	US 183 S, Presho, **N** 🅰 Cenex/dsl, Sinclair/dsl, 🛏 Hutch's Motel/café, 🅾 New Frontier RV Park, repair, vet
225	lp 90, Presho, same as 226
221mm	**rest area wb, full ♿ facilities, info, 🚻, 🏕, litter barrels, RV dump, petwalk**
220	no services
218mm	**rest area eb, full ♿ facilities, info, 🚻, 🏕, litter barrels, RV dump, petwalk**
214	Vivian
212	US 83 N, SD 53, to Pierre, **N** 🅰 Sinclair/dsl, 🍴 Vivian Jct Rest., 🅾 🏥 (34mi)
208	no services
201	Draper, **N** 🅰 Farmer's Oil/Cafe
194mm	parking area both lanes
192	US 83 S, Murdo, **N** 🅰 HHH/Shell/dsl, Pioneer/dsl, Sinclair/dsl, 🍴 Buffalo Rest., Murdo Drive-In, The Diner, Prairie Pizza, Rusty Spur Steaks, 🛏 American Inn, Anchor Inn, Best Western, Days Inn, Iversen Inn, Lee Motel, Sioux Motel, Super 8, 🅾 American RV Park/camping, Ford, Murdo Foods, auto museum, city park, USPO, **S** 🛏 Country Inn, 🅾 to Rosebud
191	Murdo, **N** same as 192

KADOKA / WALL (right margin)

Exit	Services
188mm	parking area both lanes, litter barrels
183	Okaton, **S** 🅰, Ghost Town
177	no services
175mm	central/mountain timezone
172	to Cedar Butte
170	SD 63 N, to Midland, **N** 🅰 Shell/dsl, 🅾 1880's Town, KOA
167mm	**rest area wb, full ♿ facilities, 🚻, 🏕, litter barrels, RV dump, petwalk**
165mm	**rest area eb, full ♿ facilities, 🚻, 🏕, litter barrels, RV dump, petwalk**
163	SD 63, Belvidere, **S** 🅰 Belvidere Store/dsl, 🍴 JR's Grill
152	Lp 90, Kadoka, **N** 🅰 Conoco/rest./dsl/24hr, **S** 🅾 Badlands Petrified Gardens, camping
150	SD 73 S, Kadoka, **N** 🛏 Dakota Inn/rest., 🅰 Clark, Sinclair/pizza/dsl, 🛏 Best Value Inn, Budget Host, Ponderosa Motel/RV Park, Rodeway Inn, Wagon Wheel Motel, 🅾 Kadoka Kampground, to Buffalo Nat Grasslands, repair
143	SD 73 N, to Philip, **15 mi N** 🏥
138mm	scenic overlook wb
131	SD 240, **S** 🅰 Conoco, 🛏 Badlands Inn (9mi), Cedar Pass Lodge/rest. (9mi), 🅾 Circle 10 Camping, Prairie Home NHS, KOA (11mi), to Badlands NP
129.5mm	scenic overlook eb
127	no services
121	Bigfoot Rd
116	239th St
112	US 14 E, to Philip
110	SD 240, Wall, **N** 🅰 Conoco/dsl, Exxon, Phillips 66/Subway, 🍴 DQ, Elkton House Rest., Red Rock Rest., Wall Drug Rest., 🛏 Ann's Motel, Best Value Inn, Best Western, Days Inn, EconoLodge, Fountain Hotel, Motel 6, Sunshine Inn, Super 8, The Wall Motel, Welsh Motel, 🅾 Ace Hardware, Arrow Campground, NAPA, National Grasslands Visitor Ctr, Sleepy Hollow RV Park/Camping, Wall Drug, Wall Foods, Wounded Knee Museum, **S** to Badlands NP, RV camping
109	W 4th Ave, Wall, **1-2 mi N** access to same as 110
107	Cedar Butte Rd
101	Jensen Rd, to Schell Ranch
100mm	**rest area both lanes, full ♿ facilities, info, 🚻, 🏕, litter barrels, RV dump, vending, petwalk**
99.5mm	Cheyenne River
98	Wasta, **N** 🅰 Mobil/dsl, 🛏 Redwood Motel, 🅾 24 Express RV Camping, USPO
90	173rd Ave, to Owanka
88	171st Ave (from eb, no re-entry)
84	167th Ave, **N** Olde Glory Fireworks
78	161st Ave, New Underwood, **1/2 mi S** 🅾 Boondocks Camping, Steve's General Store/dsl/motel/rest.
69mm	parking area both lanes
67	to Box Elder, Ellsworth AFB, **N** 🅰 Loaf'n Jug, 🅾 Air&Space Museum
63	(eb only) to Box Elder, Ellsworth AFB
61	Elk Vale Rd, **N** 🅰 FLYING J/Conoco/CountryMkt/dsl/e-85/LP/RV dump/scales/24hr/@, 🅾 Cabela's, Dakota RV Ctr, **S** 🅰 Conoco, Mobil/dsl, 🍴 Arby's, McDonalds, 🛏 Comfort Inn, Fairfield Inn, La Quinta, Sleep Inn, 🅾 I-90 RV Ctr, KOA (2mi, seasonal), transmissions
60	Lp 90, to Mt Rushmore, Rapid City, **S** 🍴 Pizza Ranch, Qdoba Mexican, 🅾 🏥, $Tree, Gordman's, Menards, Michael's, PetCo, Sam's Club/gas, Scheel's Sports, Target, TJ Maxx, Verizon, Nat Coll of Mines/Geology

⛽ = gas 🍴 = food 🏠 = lodging ⊙ = other

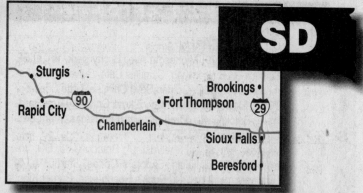

INTERSTATE 90 CONT'D

Exit	Services
59	La Crosse St, Rapid City, **N** ⛽ Mobil/24hr, Phillips 66, 🍴 Boston's Rest, Burger King, Denny's, Fuddrucker's, Minerva's Rest., Outback Steaks, Starbucks, TGIFriday's, 🏠 Best Western, Country Inn&Suites, EconoLodge, Hilton Garden, Holiday Inn Express, Super 8, ⊙ Hobby Lobby, Sears/auto, mall, st patrol, **S** ⛽ Exxon/24hr, Sinclair, 🍴 Arnold's Diner, China Wok, Golden Corral, Mongolian Grill, MillStone Rest., Perkins/24hr, Schlotzsky's, Subway, 🏠 AmericInn, Comfort Inn, Days Inn, Fair Value Inn, Foothills Inn, Grand Gateway Hotel, Hampton Inn, Microtel, Motel 6, Quality Inn, Thrifty Motel, Travelodge, ⊙ Walgreens, Walmart/McDonald's
58	Haines Ave, Rapid City, **N** ⛽ SPF, 🍴 Applebee's, Chili's, Hardee's, IHOP, Olive Garden, Red Lobster, 🏠 Best Value Inn, Grand Stay Motel, ⊙ Best Buy, $Discount, Hancock Fabrics, Herbergers, JC Penney, Kohl's, Lowe's, Petsmart, Sewing Ctr/Bernina, Tires+, to Rushmore Mall, **S** ⛽ Loaf'n Jug, 🍴 ChuckeCheese, Dickey's BBQ, Jimmy John's, Papa John's, Taco John's, Wendy's, ⊙ 🅷, Family$, ShopKO
57	I-190, US 16, to Rapid City, Mt Rushmore, **1 mi S on North St** ⛽ Exxon, 🏠 Holiday Inn, Howard Johnson, Radisson, ⊙ Ace Hardware, Family Thrift Foods, Office Depot
55	Deadwood Ave, **N** ⊙ Dakota RV Ctr, Harley-Davidson/cafe, **S** ⛽ 🚚 Sinclair/Subway/dsl/scales/24hr/@, 🍴 Marlin's Rest., Windmill Rest., ⊙ Cadillac/Chevrolet, dsl repair
52	Peaceful Pines Rd, Black Hawk, **N** ⊙ Three Flags Camping (1mi), **S** 🍴 BJ's/dsl, 🍴 Godfather's Pizza, Longhorn Rest., Pizza Hut, ⊙ Curves, Family$, USPO
48	Stagebarn Canyon Rd, **N** ⊙ RV camping, **S** ⛽ PitStop/dsl, Sinclair/Haggar's Mkt/🍴 🍴 Pizza Hut, Sacora Sta Rest., Summerset Bistro, 🏠 Ramada, ⊙ Mid-States RV Ctr, auto repair
46	Piedmont Rd, Elk Creek Rd, **N** ⊙ Elk Creek RV Park, to Petrified Forest, camping, **S** ⛽ Conoco/Country Corner Cafe/dsl, 🍴 Sacora Sta Rest.
44	Bethlehem Rd, **S** ⊙ Jack's RV Ctr (2mi)
42mm	**rest area both lanes, full** ♿ **facilities, info, 🅲s, 🏠, litter barrels, RV dump, petwalk, vending**
40	Tilford, **S** RV Park
39mm	**weigh sta eb**
37	Pleasant Valley Rd, **N** ⊙ Elkview Camp, **S** ⊙ Bulldog Camping, Rush-No-More Camping
34	**S** ⊙ Black Hills Nat Cemetary, No Name City RV Park
32	SD 79, Jct Ave, Sturgis, **N** ⛽ Conoco/dsl, Exxon/dsl, 🍴 Si Senor Mexican, Taco John's, 🏠 Best Western, Star-Lite Motel, ⊙ 🅷, Ford, Grocery Mart, NAPA, Rodney RV Park, motorcycle museum, vet, to Bear Butte SP
30	US 14A W, SD 34E, to Deadwood, Sturgis, **N** ⛽ Cenex/dsl, Fresh Start/dsl, 🍴 McDonald's, Pizza Hut, Sturgis Doghouse, ⊙ Back to Nature Foods, CarQuest, Famliy$, Mr Tire, O'Reilly Parts, Pamida/drug, Radio Shack, Day's End Camping, **S** ⛽ Conoco/dsl, RanchMart, 🍴 Burger King, DQ, Pizza Ranch, Subway, 🏠 Holiday Inn Express, Days Inn, Super 8, ⊙ Chevrolet
23	SD 34 W, to Belle Fourche, Whitewood, **N** ⊙ Northern Hills RV Ctr, **S** ⛽ Howdy's/dsl, 🍴 Whitewood Rest., 🏠 Iron Horse Inn, Tony's Motel, ⊙ USPO

Exit	Services
17	US 85 S, to Deadwood, **9-17 mi S in Deadwood** 🍴 Brown Rock, Deadwood Grill, Silverado Café, 🏠 AmericInn, Deadwood Lodge, Elkhorn Ridge Motel, Franklin Motel, Holiday Inn Express, Mineral Palace Motel, Super 8, ⊙ Deadwood NLH, Elkhorn Ridge RV Resort, Whistler Gulch Camping
14	US 14A, Spearfish Canyon, **N** ⛽ FreshStart/dsl, 🍴 Applebee's, Culver's, Subway, 🏠 Comfort Suites, Fairfield Inn, Holiday Inn/rest., Quality Inn, ⊙ Walmart/Papa John's, **S** ⛽ Phillips 66/dsl, 🍴 KFC/LJ Silver, Perkins, Pizza Ranch, Roma's Rest., 🏠 Howard Johnson, Rodeway Inn, Super 8, ⊙ Ace Hardware, Ford/Lincoln/Mercury, K-Mart, auto museum, camping
12	Jackson Blvd, Spearfish, **S** ⛽ Conoco/dsl, Exxon, Loaf'n Jug, Phillips 66/dsl, 🍴 Arby's, Barbacoa's, Domino's, Emperial China, McDonald's, Millstone Rest., Papa John's, Papa Murphy's, Pizza Hut, Quiznos, Taco John's, 🏠 Best Western, Travelodge, ⊙ 🅷, CarQuest, Chrysler/Dodge/Jeep, Curves, Radio Shack, Black Hills St U, historic fish hatchery, same as 10
10	US 85 N, to Belle Fourche, **S** 🍴 Burger King, Cedar House Rest., Golden Dragon Chinese, McDonald's, Subway, Taco Bell, 🏠 Days Inn, ⊙ 🅷, Buick/Chevrolet, Cadillac/GMC, KOA, Safeway/drug/gas, Walgreens, USPO, same as 12
8	McGuigan Rd, W Spearfish, **S** KOA (1mi)
2	**1 mi N** McNenny St Fish Hatchery
1mm	**Welcome Ctr eb, full** ♿ **facilities, info, 🅲, 🏠, litter barrels, RV dump, petwalk**
0mm	South Dakota/Wyoming state line

INTERSTATE 229 (Sioux Falls)

Exit	Services
10 b a	I-90 E and W. I-229 begins/ends on I-90, exit 400.
9	Benson Rd, **W** ⛽ BP/pizza, 🍴 Marlin's Rest., ⊙ Ford Trucks, Western Star
7.5mm	Big Sioux River
7	Rice St, **E** winter sports, **W** to stockyards
6	SD 38, 10th St, **E** ⛽ Mobil, Sinclair, 🍴 A&W, Applebee's, Arby's, Boston's Rest., Denny's, DQ, Domino's, Fryn' Pan Rest., IHOP, KFC, Pizza Hut, Pizza Ranch, Quizno's, Sonic, Taco Bell, Tomacelli's Italian, 🏠 Super 8, ⊙ AutoZone, Family$, Hy-Vee Foods, K-Mart, ShopKO, Sunshine Foods, Sturdevant's Parts, Valvoline, USPO, vet, **W** ⛽ BP, Corner, Shell, 🍴 Burger King, BurgerTime, Godfather's, Little Caesar's, McDonald's, Pizza Inn, Puerto Vallarta, Steak-Out, Subway, Taco John's, 🏠 Rushmore Motel, ⊙ Lewis Drug, vet
5.5mm	Big Sioux River
5	26th St, **E** ⛽ Shell/dsl, 🍴 Burger King, Cherry Creek Grill, Dario's Pizza, McDonald's, SaiGon Panda, ⊙ city park, **W** ⊙ 🅷

SD (tab markers in left and right margins)

INTERSTATE 229 CONT'D (Sioux Falls)

Exit	Services
4	Cliff Ave, **E** ⛽ BP/dsl
3	SD 115, Lp 229, Minnesota Ave, **E** city park, **W** ⛽ BP, Sinclair, 🍴 Burger King, Camilles Cafe, Culver's, DQ, Famous Dave's BBQ, Golden Bowl Chinese, Little Caesar's/TCBY, McDonald's, Subway, Z'kota Grille, ⊡ Ace Hardware, Buick/GMC, $Tree, Hy-Vee Foods/gas, Kia, Lewis Drug, Staples, tire, USPO
2	Western Ave, **E** ⛽ Shell/dsl, 🍴 Bracco Cafe, DQ, Joey's Grill, Nucci Italian, Scooters Coffee, Starbucks, **W** ⛽ Cenex/dsl, Shell, 🍴 Buck's Roadhouse, Burger King, Champp's Café, China Buffet, Huhot Mongolian,

SIOUX FALLS (side tab)

Exit	Services
2	Continued Papa Murphy's, Qdoba Mexican, Quizno's, Redrossa Pizza, Scheell's, ⊡ H, Advance Parts, Best Buy, Goodyear/auto, Hancock Fabrics, Radio Shack
1.5mm	Big Sioux River
1c	Louise Ave, **E** 🛏 Homewood Suites, ⊡ H, Dodge, **W** ⛽ BP, Phillips 66/dsl, 🍴 Applebee's, Arby's, Burger King, Cici's Pizza, Jimmy John's, McDonald's, Panera Bread, Qdoba Mexican, Red Lobster, Royal Palace, Spezia's Rest, Taco John's, Wendy's, 🛏 Hilton Garden Inn, ⊡ Barnes&Noble, Honda, Hy-Vee Foods/gas, JC Penney, Jo-Ann Fabrics, Kohl's, Target, Walgreens, mall
1b a	I-29 N and S. I-229 begins/ends on I-29, exit 75.

TENNESSEE

INTERSTATE 24

Exit	Services
185b a	I-75, N to Knoxville, S to Atlanta. I-24 begins/ends on I-75, exit 2 in Chattanooga.
184	Moore Rd, **S** 🍴 Chef Lin Buffet, Provino's Italian, ⊡ $Tree, Radio Shack
183	(183a from wb), Belvoir Ave, Germantown Rd
181a	US 41 S, to East Ridge (from eb), **S** 🍴 Sugar's Ribs, 🛏 King's Lodge, ⊡ Ford Trucks
181	Fourth Ave, to TN Temple U, Chattanooga, **N** ⛽ Citgo/dsl, Exxon/dsl, Hi-Tech Fuel, Stop'n Save, 🍴 Bojangles, Burger King, Capt D's, Central Park, Hardee's, Krystal, Subway, Waffle House, 🛏 Villager Lodge, ⊡ BiLo, $General, Family$, Goodyear, Mr Transmission, O'Reilly Parts, repair, vet, **S** ⛽ Citgo
180b a	US 27 S, TN 8, Rossville Blvd, **N** ⊡ U-Haul, to Chickamauga, UT Chatt, **S** ⛽ Exxon, RaceWay/dsl, 🛏 Hamilton Inn, ⊡ NTB
178	US 27 N, Market St, to Lookout Mtn, Chattanooga, **N** ⛽ BP/dsl, Citgo, 🛏 Days Inn, La Quinta, Marriott, Ramada Inn, Staybridge Suites, ⊡ Ford, Nissan, U-Haul, to Chattanooga ChooChoo, **S** 🍴 KFC, 🛏 Comfort Suites, Hampton Inn, Motel 6
175	Browns Ferry Rd, to Lookout Mtn, **N** ⛽ BP, Exxon/dsl, 🍴 China Gourmet, Country Diner, 🛏 Best Value Inn, ⊡ CVS Drug, $General, Food Lion, vet, **S** ⛽ Market/dsl, Shell/dsl, 🍴 Hardee's, McDonald's, 🛏 Comfort Inn, EconoLodge, Quality Inn
174	US 11, US 41, US 64, Lookout Valley, **N** 🍴 Waffle House, 🛏 Days Inn, ⊡ Racoon Mtn Camping (1mi), **S** ⛽ BP/dsl, Kangaroo, 🍴 Cracker Barrel, Logan's Roadhouse, New China, Taco Bell, Waffle House, Wendy's, 🛏 Baymont Inn, Best Western, Budget Motel, Country Inn&Suites, Fairfield Inn, Hampton Inn, Holiday Inn Express, Knights Inn, Ramada Ltd, Super 8, ⊡ Ace Hardware, $Tree, Lookout Valley Camping, Walmart/Subway, st patrol
172mm	**rest area eb, full ♿ facilities, 🛢, 🛢, litter barrels, vending, petwalk**
171mm	Tennessee/Georgia state line
169	GA 299, to US 11, **N** ⛽ Exxon/dsl, **S** ⛽, BP/Krispy Chicken/dsl/24hr, Pilot/Subway/dsl/scales/24hr, RaceWay, 🍴 Granny's Rest., ⊡ repair
167	I-59 S, to Birmingham
167mm	Tennessee/Georgia state line, Central/Eastern time zone
161	TN 156, to Haletown, New Hope, **N** ⛽ BP/dsl (1mi), ⊡

E / W CHATTANOOGA (side tab)

Exit	Services
161	Continued Hales RV Park, **S** ⛽ Chevron/fireworks, ⊡ On The Lake Camping
160mm	Tennessee River/Nickajack Lake
159mm	**Welcome Ctr wb/rest area eb, full ♿ facilities, 🛢, vending, 🛢, litter barrels, petwalk**
158	US 41, TN 27, Nickajack Dam, **S** ⛽ BP/dsl/fireworks, ⊡ Shellmound Camping (2.5mi)
155	TN 28, Jasper, **N** ⛽ BP/dsl (1mi), Exxon/dsl, 🍴 Dairy Queen (1mi), Hardee's, Western Sizzlin, 🛏 Acuff Country Inn, **S** ⛽ BP/Quizno's/dsl, ⊡ H
152	US 41, US 64, US 72, Kimball, S Pittsburg, **N** ⛽ BP/fireworks, RaceWay, Shell/dsl, 🍴 A&W/LJ Silver, Arby's, China Buffet, Cracker Barrel, Domino's, KFC, Krystal, McDonald's, Mi Jacal Mexican, Pizza Hut, Shoney's, Subway, Taco Bell, Waffle House, Wendy's, 🛏 Best Value, Comfort Inn, Country Hearth Inn, Holiday Inn Express, ⊡ H, Chevrolet/Buick, $Tree, Lowe's Whse, Radio Shack, Walmart, to Russell Cave NM, **3 mi S** ⊡ Lodge Cast Iron
143	Martin Springs Rd, **N** ⛽ Chevron/dsl/fireworks
135	US 41 N, Monteagle, **N** ⛽ Citgo/dsl/rest./24hr, Mystik/dsl, 🍴 Shan Chinese, Smok'n B's BBQ, ⊡ S Cumberland RV Park, USPO, **S** Days Inn
134	US 64, US 41A, to Sewanee, Monteagle, **N** ⛽ BP/McDonald's, Papa Ron's Grill, 🛏 American Eagle Inn, ⊡ Monteagle Winery, to S Cumberland SP, **S** ⛽ Citgo, Shell/dsl, 🍴 Hardee's, Monteagle Diner, Pizza Hut, Smokehouse BBQ, Subway, Waffle House, 🛏 Best Western, Regency Inn, ⊡ $General, Fred's Drugs, Piggly Wiggly, to U of The South
133mm	**rest area both lanes, full ♿ facilities, 🛢, 🛢, litter barrels, vending, petwalk**
128mm	Elk River
127	US 64, TN 50, to Winchester, Pelham, **N** ⛽ BP, Phillips 66, Texaco/Stuckey's, **S** ⛽ Gulf/dsl, ⊡ to Tims Ford SP/RV camping
119mm	trucks only parking area both lanes
117	to Tullahoma, USAF Arnold Ctr, UT Space Institute
116mm	**weigh sta both lanes**
114	US 41, Manchester, **N** ⛽ BP/24 Truckers/scales/dsl, Marathon, Shell/dsl, 🍴 Domino's, Huddle House, O'Charley's, Panda Express, Starbucks, 🛏 Comfort Inn, Holiday Inn Express, Ramada Ltd, Scottish Inn, Sleep Inn, Super 8, ⊡ Country Cabin Camping, Dollar Stop, Home Depot, KOA, Nissan, Toyota, Truck/tire repair, Walmart/gas, museum, **S** ⛽ Citgo, Kangaroo, RaceWay, 🍴 Arby's, Burger King, Capt D's, KFC, Krystal, McDonald's/playplace, Pizza Hut, Shoney's, Subway, Taco Bell, Waffle House, Wendy's, 🛏

MONTEAGLE / MANCHESTER (side tab)

SD / TN (side tab)

M A N C H E S T E R	

INTERSTATE 24 CONT'D

Exit	Services
114	Continued
	Country Inn Suites, Day's Inn, Royal Inn, 🅞 Advance Parts, AutoZone, Chevrolet, Curves, Family$, Ford/Lincoln/Mercury, Fred's Drug, Goodyear, Napa, O'Reilly Parts, Russell Stover, USPO, carwash
111	TN 55, Manchester, N 🅖 BP/dsl, Citgo/dsl/24hr, Co-op gas/dsl, 🅞 to Rock Island SP, S 🅖 BP, 🍴 Hardee's, J&G Pizza/Steaks, Sonic, 🅞 🎗 to Jack Daniels Dist HS, Old Stone Fort
110	TN 53, Manchester, N 🅖 BP, Kangaroo, Shell/dsl, 🍴 Coconut Bay Cafe, Cracker Barrel, D Crockett's Roadhouse, Emma's Rest., Oak Rest., 🛏 Ambassador Inn, Economy Inn, Hampton Inn, S 🅖 Shell/dsl/24hr, 🍴 Los 3 Amigos Mexican, Waffle House, 🅞 🎗 U-Haul
110mm	Duck River
105	US 41, N 🅖 BP/dsl/24hr, Shell/dsl, 🍴 RanchHouse Rest., S tire/repair, to Normandy Dam, Dickle HS
97	TN 64, to Shelbyville, Beechgrove, N 🅞 auto parts/repair, S 🅖 Citgo
89	Buchanan Rd, N 🅖 ⬭Loves/McDonald's/scales/dsl, Texaco/Outpost Rest/dsl, S 🅖 Shell/dsl/rest./24hr, 🍴 Huddle House, 🅞 A&L RV Ctr
84	Joe B. Jackson Pkwy
81	US 231, Murfreesboro, N 🅖 BP/dsl/24hr, Exxon, RaceWay/24hr, Shell, 🍴 Cracker Barrel, King's Table Rest., Krystal, Parthenon Steaks, Shanghai Chinese, Shoney's, Waffle House/24hr, Wendy's, 🛏 Best Value, Knight's Inn, Quality Inn, Ramada Ltd, Regal Inn, Scottish Inn, 🅞 🎗 Dodge, Honda, Mazda, S 🅖 Citgo/24hr, Kangaroo, Mapco/dsl/24hr, Phillips 66/dsl/24hr/@, ⬭Arbys/scales/dsl/24hr, 🍴 La Siesta Mexican, McDonald's/playplace, Pizza Hut/Taco Bell, Quizno's, Sonic, Subway, Waffle House, Zaxby's, 🛏 Howard Johnson, Safari Inn, Vista Inn, 🅞 Gateway Tire, Rite Aid, Toyota/Scion
80	New Salem Hwy, rd 99, S 🍴 Domino's
78	TN 96, to Franklin, Murfreesboro, N 🅖 BP, Citgo, Phillips 66/Church's/White Castle/dsl, Shell/Jack-in-the-Box, Texaco/24hr, 🍴 Arby's, Applebee's, Bellacino's Pizza, Bonefish Grill, Buffalo Wild Wings, Chick-fil-A, Chuck-eCheese, Coconut Bay Cafe, Cracker Barrel, Fazoli's, IHOP, Jason's Deli, Jim'n Nick's BBQ, KFC, McDonald's, Olive Garden, Outback Steaks, Panera Bread, Quizno's, Red Lobster, Red Robin, Ryan's, Santa Fe Steaks, Starbucks, Steak'n Shake, Subway, TGI Friday's, The Chophouse, Waffle House, Wendy's, Zaxby's, 🛏 Baymont Inn, Best Western, Comfort Inn, Country Inn Suites, Day's Inn, DoubleTree, Econolodge, Fairfield Inn, Hampton Inn,

E ⬍ W	
M U R F R E E S B O R O	

N A S H V I L L E

Exit	Services
78	Continued
	Holiday Inn, Microtel, Motel 6, Red Roof Inn, Sleep Inn, Super 8, Wingate Inn, 🅞 Aldi Foods, Belk, BooksAMillion, Dillard's, Discount Tire, Home Depot, JC Penney, Lowe's Whse, Marshall's, Michael's, Old Navy, PetsMart, Ross, Sears/auto, Staples, Target, TJ Maxx, Walmart/gas, mall, to Stones River Bfd, S 🅖 BP/dsl/24hr, Chevron/24hr, Kangaroo/dsl, 🍴 Corky's BBQ, China Garden, Hardee's, Las Palmas, McDonald's, O'Charley's, Papa Murphy's, Pizza Hut, Sonic, Subway, Taco Bell, Waffle House, 🅞 AutoZone, $General, Kohl's, Kroger, Old Time Pottery, Sam's Club/gas, Walgreen
76	Manson Pike, Medical Center Pkwy, N 🅞 🎗 to Stones River Nat. Bfd
74b a	TN 840, to Lebanon, Franklin
70	TN 102, Lee Victory Pkwy, Almaville Rd, to Smyrna, N 🅖 Shell/dsl/scales, S 🅖 BP, Kangaroo/Quizno's/dsl, Mapco, 🍴 McDonald's, Legends Steaks, Ringalino's, Sonic, 🛏 Deerfield Inn, 🅞 $General, Tennessee Expo
66	TN 266, Sam Ridley Pkwy, to Smyrna, N 🅖 Citgo/dsl/24hr, Shell/dsl, 🍴 Arby's, A&W/LJ Silver, Blue Coast Burrito, Catfish House, Chili's, Famous Dave's, Hickory Falls Cafe, Jim'n Nick's BBQ, Logan's Roadhouse, Papa John's, Sonic, Starbucks, Subway, Wendy's, 🅞 CVS Drug, Kohl's, Kroger/gas, PetsMart, Publix, Staples, Target, Nashville I-24 Camping (3mi), S 🍴 Cracker Barrel, O'Charley's, Ruby Tuesday, 🛏 Comfort Suites, Fairfield Inn, Hampton Inn, Hilton Garden, Holiday Inn Express, Sleep Inn, 🅞 I-24 Expo
64	Waldron Rd, to La Vergne, N 🅖 Kangaroo, Kwik Sak, ⬭/Subway/dsl/24hr/scales, 🍴 Arby's, Hardee's, Krystal/24hr, McDonald's, Waffle House, 🛏 Comfort Inn, Holiday Inn Express, Super 8, 🅞 Music City Camping (3mi), RV service, S 🅖 Mapco/dsl/24hr, 🛏 Motel
62	TN 171, Old Hickory Blvd, N 🅖 Chevron, Citgo/Subway, Shell/dsl/24hr, TA/BP/Burger King/Popeye's/dsl/24hr/scales/@, 🍴 El Arroyo Mexican, Waffle House, 🛏 Best Western
60	Hickory Hollow Pkwy, N 🅖 BP, Mapco, Shell, 🍴 Applebee's, Arby's, Bailey's Grill, Burger King, ChuckeCheese, Cracker Barrel, KFC, Logan's Roadhouse, McDonald's/Playplace, O'Charley's, Outback Steaks, Pizza Hut, Red Lobster, Starbucks, Subway, Taco Bell, TGIFriday, Wendy's, 🛏 Country Inn Suites, Hampton Inn, Holiday Inn, 🅞 Best Buy, Chevrolet, Dillard's, Dodge, $Tree, Firestone/auto, Kroger/gas, Macy's, Mazda, NTB, Office Depot, Rite Aid, Sears, mall, transmissions, S 🅖 BP/dsl, Shell, 🍴 Camino Royale Mexican, Casa Fiesta Mexican, Evergreen Chinese, IHOP, Olive Garden, Shoney's, Steak'n Shake, Waffle House/24hr, 🛏 Knight's Inn, Super 8,

TN

INTERSTATE 24 CONT'D

Exit	Services
60	Continued
	Vista Inn, 🅾 Acura, Goodyear/auto, Home Depot, KIA, Target
59	TN 254, Bell Rd, same as 60
57	Haywood Lane, **N** ⛽ Kwik Sak, Marathon, 🍴 Hardee's, Pizza Hut, 🅾 CarQuest, $General, Food Lion, Walgreen, **S** ⛽ Kangaroo, Shell
56	TN 255, Harding Place, **N** ⛽ Chevron/dsl, Exxon, Mapco, Shell/dsl/24hr, 🍴 Applebee's, KFC, McDonald's, Mikado Japanese, Pizza Hut/Taco Bell, Waffle House, Wendy's, 🛏 Executive Inn, Knight's Inn, Motel 6, Stay Lodge, Thrifty Inn, 🅾 Sam's Club/gas, **S** ⛽ Mapco, Shell, 🍴 Burger King, Fiesta Mexican, Hooters, Jack-in-the-Box, 🛏 Best Value Inn, Motel 6, 🅾 H
54b a	TN 155, Briley Pkwy to Opryland
53	I-440 W, to Memphis
52	US 41, Murfreesboro Rd, **N** ⛽ Shell, Texaco, 🍴 Jack-in-the-Box, Piccadilly's, Pizza Hut, Taco Bell, Waffle House, 🛏 Day's Inn, Economy Inn, Econolodge, Executive Inn, Holiday Inn Express, Howard Johnson, Quality Inn, Ramada Inn, Rodeway Inn, Scottish Inn, Sunrise Inn, 🅾 CarQuest, Office Depot, **S** 🅾 Chevrolet, Dodge
52b a	I-40, E to Knoxville, W to Memphis
I-24 & I-40 run together 2 mi. See Interstate 40 exits 212-213.	
50b	I-40 W
49	Shelby Ave, (from wb only), to LP Field
48	James Robertson Pkwy, **N** ⛽ Citgo, **S** ⛽ Exxon, TA/Subway/dsl/24hr/@, 🍴 Shoney's, 🛏 Ramada, Stadium Inn, 🅾 LP Stadium, st capitol
47a	US 31E
47	N 1st St, Jefferson St, **N** ⛽ BP/Subway, Phillips 66, 🅾 Family$, **S** ⛽ Mystic Gas, 🛏 Days Inn, Knights Inn, 🅾 U-Haul
I-24 and I-65 run together. See Interstate 65 exit 87 b a.	
87b a	US 431, Trinity Lane, **N** ⛽ BP, 💛Loves/Subway/dsl/scales/24hr, 🍴 Church's/White Castle, Krystal, Sonic, 🅾 Piggly Wiggly, 🛏 Cumberland Inn, Delux Inn, **S** ⛽ BCP/dsl, BP, Exxon, Mapco, 🍴 Fat Mo's, Jack-in-the-Box, Jack's BBQ, McDonald's, Subway, Taco Bell, Waffle House, 🛏 Best Value Inn, Comfort Inn, Days Inn, EconoLodge, Halmark Inn, Howard Johnson, King's Inn, Quality Inn, Ravin Hotel, Regency Inn, Rodeway Inn, 🅾 $General, Family$
44b a	I-65, N to Louisville, S to Nashville
43	TN 155, Briley Pkwy, Brick Church Pike
40	TN 45, Old Hickory Blvd, **N** ⛽ BP/Subway/dsl, Phillips 66/dsl/24hr, Shell/dsl, 🛏 Super 8
35	US 431, to Joelton, Springfield, **N** H, **S** ⛽ Heritage TC/DQ/Subway/dsl, Shell, 🍴 Family Rest., Mazatlan Mexican, McDonald's, 🛏 Days Inn, 🅾 Curves, Family$, OK Camping, auto repair
31	TN 249, New Hope Rd, **N** ⛽ Shell/Taco Tico/dsl, **S** ⛽ BP/dsl, Shell/dsl/24hr
24	TN 49, to Springfield, Ashland City, **N** ⛽ BP/dsl, Mapco/dsl/24hr, Phillips 66/dsl/24hr, 🅾 H, repair, **S** ⛽ Shell/dsl, SS/Dunkin Donuts/Wendy's, 🍴 Dragon Buffet, KFC/Taco Bell, Sonic, Subway, 🅾 $General, Hill Foods, USPO, city park, vet
19	TN 256, Maxey Rd, to Adams, **N** ⛽ BP/dsl, **S** ⛽ Shell

11	TN 76, to Adams, Clarksville, **N** ⛽ Shell/dsl/24hr, **S** ⛽ BP/dsl/24hr, 🍴 McDonald's, Subway, Waffle House, 🛏 Days Inn, Holiday Inn Express, Quality Inn, Super 8, 🅾 H
9mm	Red River
8	TN 237, Rossview Rd, **S** Dunbar Cave SP
4	US 79, to Clarksville, Ft Campbell, **N** ⛽ BP/dsl/24hr, Exxon/dsl, 🍴 Cracker Barrel, 🛏 Hilton Garden, 🅾 Sam's Club/gas, Spring Creek Camping (2mi), **S** ⛽ BP/dsl/24hr, Murphy USA/dsl, Shell/dsl, 🍴 Applebee's, Arby's, Baskin-Robbins, Buffalo Wild Wings, Burger King, Capt D's, Chili's, Chopsticks, ChuckeCheese, Church's/White Castle, DQ, Fazoli's, Golden Corral, Harbor Cafe, IHOP, KFC, Krystal, Logan's Roadhouse, LJ Silver, Longhorn Steaks, McDonald's, O'Charley's, Old Chicago Pizza, Olive Garden, Outback Steaks, Papa Murphy's, Quiznos, Rafferty's, Red Lobster, Ryan's, Shogun Japanese, Shoney's, Starbucks, Steak'n Shake, Subway, Taco Bell, Waffle House, Wendy's, Zaxby's, 🛏 AT&T, Best Inn, Best Value Inn, Best Western, Candlewood Suites, Comfort Inn, Country Inn&Suites, Courtyard, Days Inn, EconoLodge, Fairfield Inn, Guesthouse Inn, Hampton Inn, Hawthorn Suites, Hometowne Suites, Mainstay Suites, Microtel, Quality Inn, Ramada Ltd, Red Roof Inn, Super 8, ValuePlace Hotel, Wingate Inn, 🅾 H, Advance Parts, Belk, Best Buy, Books-A-Million, Buick/GMC, Dick's, Dillard's, $Tree, Firestone/auto, Goodyear/auto, Hancock Fabrics, Hobby Lobby, Home Depot, Hyundai, JC Penney, Kohl's, Kroger/dsl, K-Mart, Lowe's, Mazda, Office Depot, Petsmart, Sears/auto, Subaru, Target, TJ Maxx, Verizon, U-Haul, Walmart, mall, winery, to Austin Peay St U, to Land Between the Lakes
1	TN 48, to Clarksville, Trenton, **N** ⛽ Shell/dsl, 🅾 Clarksville RV Camping, **S** ⛽ BP, 🍴 Coldstone, El Tapatio Mexican, Gatti's Pizza, Sonic, Wendy's, 🅾 AutoZone, $General, Walgreens
.5mm	**Welcome Ctr eb, full** ♿ **facilities,** 🚻, **vending,** 🗑, **litter barrels, petwalk**
0mm	Tennessee/Kentucky state line

INTERSTATE 26

Exit	Services
54.5mm	Tennessee/North Carolina state line
54mm	**runaway truck ramp wb**
52mm	scenic overlook eb (no trucks)
50	Flag Pond Rd
47.5mm	scenic overlook wb (no trucks)
46mm	**N Welcome Ctr/rest area both lanes, full** ♿ **facilities,** 🗑, **litter barrels,** 🚻, **petwalk**
44mm	S Indian Creek
43	US 19 W, rd 352, Temple Hill Rd
42mm	S Indian Creek
40	Jackson-Love Hwy, Erwin, Jonesborough, **N** ⛽ Appco Gas/A&W/LJ Silver, 🛏 Clayton's Dogwood B&B, Holiday Inn Express, 🅾 H, Nolichucky Gorge Camping (2mi)
37	TN 81, rd 107, Erwin, Jonesborough, **N** ⛽ Shell/dsl/24hr, 🍴 Huddle House/24hr, McDonald's, Sonic, 🅾 H, NAPA, Walgreens, **S** 🛏 Super 8, 🅾 River Park Camping (5mi)
36	Main St, Erwin, **N** ⛽ Appco/dsl/e-85, BP/dsl/24hr, 🍴 Azteca Mexican, Hardee's, KFC, Little Caesar's, Pizza Hut, Subway, Wendy's, 🅾 Advance Parts, AutoZone, $General, Firestone, Rite Aid, White's Foods
34	Tinker Rd, **N** ⛽ Murphy USA/dsl, 🅾 Walmart
32	rd 173, Unicoi Rd, to Cherokee NF, **N** ⛽ Unicoi Mkt, 🍴

Side labels: E N A S H V I L L E W (westbound/Nashville direction, I-24)
C L A R K S V I L L E
E W / E R W I N (I-26)

TN

INTERSTATE 26 CONT'D

Exit	Services
32	Continued
	Maple Grove Café, Melony's Italian, 🅾 Grandview Ranch Camping (7mi), S Woodsmoke Camping
27	rd 359 N, Okolona Rd, N 🔋 BP, 🍴 Kozy Kitchen, 🏨 Budget Inn (3mi)
24	US 321, TN 67, Elizabethton, N 🔋 Shell/dsl, S 🔋 BP/dsl, 🍴 Arby's, Burger King, Little Caesars, LJ Silver, Subway, 🏨 Comfort Inn, 🅾 Advance Parts, CVS Drug, Food City/gas, IGA Foods, Walgreens, to ETSU, Roan Mtn SP
23	rd 91, Market St, N 🍴 DQ, McDonald's, 🏨 Americinn, S 🅾 museum
22	rd 400, Unaka Ave, Watauga Ave
20 b a	US 11 E, US 19 N, to Roan St, N 🔋 Chevron/dsl, Sunoco, 🍴 Arby's, Cootie Brown's Rest., DQ, Empire Buffet, Harbor House Sea🍴 Hardee's, Little Caesars, LJ Silver, Mellow Mushroom Pizza, Moto Japanese, Peerless Rest., Perkins, Sonic, 🏨 Best Western, Holiday Inn, Ramada Ltd, Super 8, 🅾 Acura, AutoZone, BigLots, Ford, Honda, Mazda, O'Reilly Parts, Subaru, Tuesday Morning, S 🍴 Applebees, Bailey's Grille, Burger King, Carino's Italian, Fazoli's, 5 Guys Burgers, Hooters, Jack's City Grill, KFC, McDonald's, O'Charley's, Olive Garden, Papa Murphy's, Red Lobster, Ryan's, Shoney's, Smokey Bones BBQ, Starbucks, Subway, Taco Bell, TCBY, TX Roadhouse, Zaxby's, 🏨 Days Inn, DoubleTree Inn, Quality Inn, Red Roof Inn, 🅾 Belk, Books-A-Million, CVS Drug, $General, $Tree, Hancock Fabrics, JC Penney, Kroger, Office Depot, Sears/auto, Target, TJ Maxx, Walgreens
19	TN 381, to St of Franklin Rd, to Bristol, N 🔋 Appco/McDonald's, Murphy USA, 🍴 Golden Corral, Honeybaked Ham, Logan's Roadhouse, Outback Steaks, Subway, 🏨 Comfort Suites, 🅾 Hyundai, Radio Shack, VW, Walmart, **0-2 mi** S 🍴 Atlanta Bread, Barberito's Grille, Carrabba's, Cheddar's, Chick-fil-A, Chili's, ChuckeCheese, CiCi's, Fuddruckers, IHOP, Jason's Deli, Marble Slab, Panera Bread, Rita's Custard, Stir Fry Cafe, Wendy's, 🏨 Courtyard, Hampton Inn, Sleep Inn, 🅾 AT&T, Barnes&Noble, Best Buy, Home Depot, K-Mart, Kohl's, Lowe's, Michael's, Natural Foods Mkt, Old Navy, PetsMart, Ross, Sam's Club/gas, Steinmart, USPO, Verizon, vet
17	Boone St, N 🔋 BP, 🍴 Beef'o Brady's, Bob Evans, Burger King, Kemosabe's BBQ, Lil Chicago Pizza, Pizza+, 🅾 Ingles Foods, S 🔋 Appco/e-85, Shell, 🍴 Cracker Barrel, Domino's, El Matador Mexican, Waffle House, Wendy's, 🏨 Jameson Inn, Value Place, 🅾 Wilson Drugs
13	Rd 77, Bobby Hicks Hwy, N 🔋 BP, Shell, 🍴 Burger King, China Luck, DQ, Gino's Italian, McDonald's, Pal's HotDogs, Papa John's, Pizza Hut, Subway, Taco Bell, Yong Asian, 🅾 Advance Parts, $General, Firestone/auto, Food City/gas, O'Reilly Parts, Rite Aid, Walgreens, USPO, S 🔋 Appco
10	Eastern Star Rd, N 🍴 Phil's Dream Pit
8 b a	I-81, to Bristol, Knoxville
6	rd 37, Rock Springs Rd, S 🔋
4	TN 93, Wilcox Dr, N 🔋 BP/Subway, Shell/McDonald's/dsl, 🍴 Burger King, Hardee's, La Carreta Mexican, Pizza Hut, Wendy's, 🏨 Comfort Suites, Hampton Inn, Holiday Inn Express, Jameson Inn, 🅾 Cave's Drug, $General, IGA Foods, S 🔋 BP, Zoomerz/Arby's/dsl, 🍴 Pizza+
3	Meadowview Pkwy, N 🏨 Marriott

Exit	Services
1	West Stone Dr, N 🔋 Shell, 🍴 Little Caesar's, Molcajete's Mexican, 🏨 Super 8, 🅾 🏥, Walgreens, S 🔋 BP, Murphy USA, 🍴 Bojangles, China Star, Fatz Cafe, Sonic, Subway, 🅾 $Tree, Lowe's, Walmart
0mm	I-26 begins/ends on US 23.

INTERSTATE 40

Exit	Services
451mm	Tennessee/North Carolina state line
451	Waterville Rd
447	Hartford Rd, N 🔋 Citgo/dsl, S 🔋 BP/dsl, 🍴 Bean Tree Cafe, Pigeon River Smokehouse, 🅾 Foxfire Camping, Shauan's Riverside RV Park, whitewater rafting
446mm	**Welcome Ctr wb, full ♿ facilities, 🚰, vending, 🗑, litter barrels, petwalk, NO TRUCKS**
443	Foothills Pkwy, to Gatlinburg, Great Smoky Mtns NP, S camping
443mm	Pigeon River
440	US 321, to Wilton Spgs Rd, Gatlinburg, S 🔋 BP, 🍴 Krispy Krunchy Chicken, 🅾 Arrow Creek Camping (14mi), CrazyHorse Camping (14mi), Jellystone Camping (12mi)
439mm	Pigeon River
435	US 321, to Gatlinburg, Newport, N 🔋 Exxon/Biodsl/e-85, Mobil, Shell/dsl/24hr, Stop'n Go, 🍴 Arby's, Burger King, Hardee's, KFC, La Carreta Mexican, McDonald's, Pizza Hut, Pizza+, SageBrush Steaks, Shoney's, Subway, Taco Bell, 🏨 Motel 6, Parkway Inn, 🅾 🏥, CVS Drug, O'Reilly Parts, Town&Country Drug, S 🔋 BP, Murphy USA/dsl, 🍴 Bojangles, Blue Smokey BBQ, Cracker Barrel, Monterrey Mexican, New China, Papa John's, Quiznos, Ruby Tuesday, Waffle House/24hr, Wendy's, 🏨 Best Western, Days Inn, Family Inn, Holiday Inn Express, Mountain Crest Inn, 🅾 $General, $Tree, Lowe's, Save-A-Lot Foods, Verizon, Walmart
432b a	US 70, US 411, US 25W, to Newport, N 🔋 BP/dsl, Exxon/dsl/24hr, TimeOut Travel Ctr/Huddle House/dsl/scales/, Phillips 66, 🍴 Country Kitchen, Osaka Japanese, 🏨 Comfort Inn, Relax Inn, 🅾 Buick/Chevrolet, Chrysler/Dodge/Jeep, Ford, KOA (2mi), TMC Camping, Westgate Tire, S 🔋 BP/pizza/dsl, Citgo/dsl/24hr, Marathon, Shell, 🏨 Family Inn/rest.
426mm	**rest area wb, full ♿ facilities, 🚰, vending, 🗑, litter barrels, petwalk**
425mm	French Broad River
424	TN 113, Dandridge, N 🔋 BP/dsl
421	I-81 N, to Bristol
420mm	**rest area eb, full ♿ facilities, 🚰, vending, 🗑, litter barrels, petwalk**
417	TN 92, Dandridge, N 🔋 BP, Pilot/Subway/dsl/

Side labels (left margin): E ← W, JOHNSON CITY, KINGSPORT

Side labels (right margin): E ← W, NEWPORT

TN

🅖 = gas 🍽 = food 🛏 = lodging 🅞 = other Copyright 2012 - The Next Exit

INTERSTATE 40 CONT'D	

DANDRIDGE E→W / KNOXVILLE

Exit	Services
417	Continued scales/24hr/@, 🍽 Capt's Galley, Hardee's, McDonald's, Perkins, Ruby Tuesday, 🛏 EconoLodge, S 🅖 Shell/Wendy's/dsl, Marathon/KFC/dsl, Weigel's, 🍽 Arby's, LJ Silver/Taco Bell, Shoney's, Waffle House, 🛏 Hampton Inn, Holiday Inn Express, Jefferson Inn, Quality Inn, Super 8, 🅞 Advance Parts
415	US 25W, US 70, to Dandridge, S 🅖 Marathon/dsl, 🍽 Sonic (3mi)
412	Deep Sprgs Rd, to Douglas Dam, N 🅖 ♥Loves/Chester's/Subway/dsl/scales/24hr, S 🅖 TR Trkstp/rest/dsl/scales/24hr/@
407	TN 66, to Sevierville, Pigeon Forge, Gatlinburg, N 🅖 Shell/Huddle House/dsl, 🍽 Chophouse, Cracker Barrel, Marble Slab, McDonald's, 🛏 Fairfield Inn, Hampton Inn, Holiday Inn Express, Motel 6, 🅞 Bass Pro Shops, RV Camping, Smoky Mtn Visitor's Ctr, S 🅖 BP/Dunkin Donuts, Exxon/Subway/dsl, Shell/Krystal/dsl, 🍽 FlapJack's, Wendy's, 🛏 Comfort Suites, Days Inn, Knights Inn, Quality Inn, 🅞 Chrysler/Dodge/Jeep, Russell Stover, RV Camping, USPO, flea mkt, **3-10 mi** S multiple services/outlets
402	Midway Rd
398	Strawberry Plains Pk, N 🅖 BP/dsl, Exxon/dsl, Shell/dsl, 🍽 McDonald's, Outback Steaks, Quality Inn, Ruby Tuesday, Waffle House, Wendy's, 🛏 Baymont Inn, EconoLodge, Hampton Inn, Holiday Inn Express, Quality Inn, Ramada Ltd, Red Roof Inn, Super 8, 🅞 Camping World/TN RV Ctr, S 🅖 ▦/Subway/dsl/scales/24hr, Weigel's, 🍽 Arby's, Burger King, Cracker Barrel, Golden Wok Chinese, KFC, Krystal, Puleo's Grille, Taco Bell, 🛏 Best Western, Comfort Suites, Fairfield Inn, La Quinta, Motel 6
395mm	Holston River
394	US 70, US 11E, US 25W, Asheville Hwy, N 🅖 Marathon, Mobil/dsl, ▦/dsl, 🍽 Subway, Wendy's, 🛏 Gateway Inn, 🅞 Advance Parts, AutoZone, city park, S 🅖 Exxon, Shell/dsl, 🍽 Penson Rest., Scott's Place, Waffle House/24hr, 🛏 Days Inn, 🅞 CVS Drug, Family$, Kroger/gas, Walgreens, vet
393	I-640 W, to I-75 N
392	US 11W, Rutledge Pike, N 🅖 Citgo/dsl, 🅞 $General, U-Haul, truck repair, S 🅖 BP, 🍽 Buddy's BBQ, Hardee's, Shoney's, 🛏 Family Inn, 🅞 NAPA, Sav-A-Lot Foods, transmissions, to Knoxville Zoo
390	Cherry St, Knoxville, N 🅖 Marathon/dsl, Top Fuel Mart, Weigel's/Subway, 🍽 Country Table Rest., Happy Garden Chinese, 🛏 Red Carpet Inn, 🅞 tires, S 🅖 Exxon, 🍽 Arby's, KFC, Little Caesar's, LJ Silver, McDonald's, WishBone's Wings, 🛏 Regency Inn, 🅞 Advance Parts, Family$, O'Reilly Parts, Walgreens, vet
389	US 441 N, Broadway, 5th Ave, N 🅖 BP, ▦/dsl, Star, 🍽 Burger King, Capt D's, KFC, Krystal, McDonald's, Sonic, Subway, Taco Bell, Wendy's, 🅞 Belew Drug, CVS Drug, $General, Family$, Firestone/auto, Kroger/gas, Radio Shack, Save-A-Lot Foods, Walgreens/24hr, USPO
388	US 441 S (exits left from wb) downtown, S 🛏 Hilton, Holiday Inn, Crowne Plaza, 🅞 to Smokey Mtns, to U of TN
387b	TN 62, 17th St, N 🅖 Gas'N Go, ▦/dsl, 🛏 Economy Inn, Royal Inn, 🅞 $General, Food City/gas
387a	I-275 N, to Lexington

KNOXVILLE

Exit	Services
386b a	US 129, University Ave, to UT
385	I-75 N, I-640 E
I-40 W and I-75 S run together 17 mi.	
383	Papermill Rd, N 🛏 Red Roof Inn, S 🅖 BP, Citgo, ▦/dsl, Spur Gas, 🍽 Buddy's BBQ, Burger King, 5 Guys Burgers, Krispy Kreme, Sonic, TGIFriday's, Waffle House, 🛏 Super 8, 🅞 Food City, Walgreens, same as 380
380	US 11, US 70, West Hills, S 🅖 Shell, Weigel's, 🍽 Applebee's, Arby's, Chick-fil-A, Chili's, Brazeiro's Brazilian Steaks, Brixx Pizza, Dunkin Donuts, Firehouse Subs, Hardee's, Honeybaked Ham, Jet's Pizza, Macaroni Grill, McAlister's Deli, McDonald's, Mr Gatti's, O'Charley's, Olive Garden, Papa John's, Petro's Chili, PF Chang's, Pizza Hut, PlumTree Chinese, Puleo's Grille, Qdoba Mexican, Ray's Grille, Red Lobster, Salsarita's Cantina, Spice Rack Grill, Starbucks, Subway, Taco Bell, TX Roadhouse, Tropical Smoothie Cafe, Wishbone Wings, 🛏 Extended Stay America, Magnuson Hotel, Ramada Inn, 🅞 AT&T, Barnes&Noble, Belk, Dillards, $Tree, Food City, JC Penney, Kohl's, NTB, Office Depot, Old Navy, O'Reilly Parts, Petsmart, Ross, Sears/auto, Staples, Steinmart, Target, TJ Maxx, U-Haul, Walgreens, mall, st patrol
379	Bridgewater Rd, N 🅖 Exxon/Subway, ▦/McDonald's, Shell, 🍽 McDonald's, Taco Bell, 🅞 Sam's Club/gas, Walmart, S 🅖 BP/dsl, Citgo/dsl, Conoco, 🍽 Buddy's BBQ, Burger King, China Buffet, ChuckeCheese, CiCi's Pizza, Krystal, Makino's Japanese, Shoney's, Sonic, Wendy's, 🛏 InTown Suites, 🅞 Aamco, Advance Parts, AutoZone, Books-A-Million, Buick/GMC, Chrysler/Dodge/Jeep, Firestone/auto, Ford/Lincoln/Mercury, Hyundai, Mazda, Nissan, Saab, Subaru, Tire Barn, Transmission World
378	Cedar Bluff Rd, N 🅖 ▦/Taco Bell, Shell, Weigel's, 🍽 Arby's, Burger King, Cracker Barrel, Dunkin Donuts, KFC, Little Caesar's, McDonald's, Old Mill Bread Co., Papa John's, Quiznos, Starbucks, Subway, Waffle House, Wendy's, 🛏 Country Inn&Suites, Days Inn, Hampton Inn, Holiday Inn, Ramada Inn, Sleep Inn, 🅞 ⓗ, $General, S 🅖 Exxon, Phillips 66, 🍽 Applebee's, Bob Evans, Carrabba's, Corky's Ribs/BBQ, Denny's, Fazoli's, Famous Dave's BBQ, Firehouse Subs, Friendly's, Fuddrucker's, Grady's Grill, IHOP, Krystal, Outback Steaks, Panera Bread, Parkside Grill, Peerless Grill, Penn Sta. Subs, Pizza Hut, Puleo's Grill, Rafferty's, Rubio's Grill, Sunny's BBQ, 🛏 Best Western, Clubhouse Inn, Comfort Inn, Courtyard, Extended Stay America, Guesthouse Suites, Hilton Garden, Jameson Inn, La Quinta, Microtel, Red Roof Inn, Residence Inn, Signature Inn, Towne Place Suites, 🅞 Best Buy, Cadillac, Celebration Sta, Chevrolet, Chrysler, CVS Drug, Dick's, Food City, Ford, Jo-Ann Fabrics, KIA, Lowe's, Michael's, Staples, Tuesday Morning, Walgreens
376	I-140 E, TN 162 N, to Maryville, N to Oak Ridge Museum
374	TN 131, Lovell Rd, N 🅖 Shell/dsl, TA/Country Pride/dsl/scales/24hr/@, 🍽 Bojangles, McDonald's, Subway, Waffle House, 🛏 Guesthouse Inn, Travelodge, 🅞 Harley-Davidson, S 🅖 ▦/Wendy's/dsl/24hr, 🍽 Arby's, Baskin-Robbins, Bonefish Grill, Brixx Pizza, Buffalo Wild Wings, Calhoun's Rest., Chick-fil-A, Connor's Rest., Flemings, Genghis Grill, Jim'N Nick's BBQ, IHOP, Jimmy John's, Kabuki Japanese, Krystal, Mangia Pizza, Marble Slab, McAlister's Deli, McDonald's, Mike's Subs, Mimi's Cafe, Noodles&Co, O'Charley's, Olive Garden, Pei Wei, Pimento's Cafe, Red Robin, Salsarita's Cantina, Shoney's, Smokey Mtn

TN

INTERSTATE 40 CONT'D

Exit	Services
374	**Continued** Brewery, Sonic, Starbucks, Steak'n Shake, Subway, TX Roadhouse, Wasabai Japanese, 🛏 Candlewood Suites, Homewood Suites, Motel 6, SpringHill Suites, 🅾 Advance Parts, Belk, Best Buy, BMW/Mini, CarMax, $Tree, EarthFare Foods, GNC, Hobby Lobby, Honda, Lexus, Marshall's, Mercedes, Old Navy, Petsmart, Radio Shack, Ross, Target, Toyota/Scion, Walgreens, Walmart
373	Campbell Sta Rd, **N** 🚪 Shell/dsl, Marathon/dsl, 🛏 Comfort Suites, Country Inn&Suites, Holiday Inn Express, Super 8, 🅾 Buddy Gregg RV Ctr, **S** 🚪 BP, 🏨 Weigel's, 🍴 Border Tacos, Capt Ernie's Fishouse, Cracker Barrel, Dunkin Donuts, Gatti's Pizza, Hardee's, Kasumi Japanese, Mellow Mushroom, Newk's Grill, Vietnamese Bistro, Wild Wings Cafe, 🛏 Baymont Inn, EconoLodge, Hampton Inn, 🅾 AT&T, Gander Mtn, JC Penney, Verizon, Walgreens
372mm	**weigh sta both lanes**
369	Watt Rd, **N** 🚪 ⚡FLYING J/Denny's/dsl/LP/scales/RV dump/24hr, Speedco, **S** 🚪 Exxon/dsl, Petro/Iron Skillet/dsl/scales/24hr/@, TA/BP/Burger King/Pizza Hut/Popeye's/Subway/dsl/24hr/@, 🅾 Blue Beacon, Knoxville Coach/RV

I-40 E and I-75 N run together 17 mi.

Exit	Services
368	I-75 and I-40
364	US 321, TN 95, Lenoir City, Oak Ridge, **N** 🚪 Melton Hill Mkt/gas, 🅾 Crosseyed Cricket Camping (2mi), **4-5 mi S** 🍴 KFC, Krystal, Ruby Tuesday, 🛏 Comfort Inn, Days Inn, EconoLodge, Hampton Inn, Holiday Inn Express, Ramada Ltd
362	Industrial Park Rd
360	Buttermilk Rd, **N** Soaring Eagle RV Park
356	TN 58 N, Gallaher Rd, to Oak Ridge, **N** 🚪 BP/dsl, Weigels/dsl, 🍴 Gallaher Grill, 🛏 Budget Inn, Motel 6, 🅾 4 Seasons Camping
355	Lawnville Rd, **N** 🚪 🏨/Subway/dsl
352	TN 58 S, Kingston, **N** 🛏 Knights Inn, **S** 🚪 Exxon/dsl, RaceWay, Shell, 🍴 Buddy's BBQ, Hardee's, McDonald's, Sonic, Subway, Taco Bell, 🛏 Super 8, 🅾 Family$, Marina RV Park, Piggly Wiggly, USPO, to Watts Bar Lake
351mm	Clinch River
350	US 70, Midtown, **N** 🅷, **S** 🍴 Gondolier Italian, 🅾 Caney Creek Camping (3mi), Kroger, Lowe's, Patterson RV Supplies, Walgreens
347	US 27, Harriman, **N** 🚪 Phillips 66/dsl, 🍴 Hardee's, KFC, Los Primos Mexican, LJ Silver, McDonald's, Pizza Hut, Ruby Tuesday, Subway, Taco Bell, Wendy's, 🛏 Days Inn, 🅾 Verizon, to Frozen Head SP, Big S Fork NRA, **S** 🚪 BP, Shell/Krystal/dsl/24hr, Sunoco/dsl, 🍴 Cancun Mexican, Cracker Barrel, Shoney's, 🛏 Comfort Inn, Holiday Inn Express, Quality Inn, Rodeway Inn, **2-3 mi S** 🚪 Murphy USA/dsl, 🍴 Capt D's, China King, Domino's, Sonic, 🅾 🅷, Ace Hardware, BigLots, Radio Shack, Walmart/Subway, vet
340	TN 299 N, 🅿 Rd
339.5mm	eastern/central time zone line, eastern/central time zone line
338	TN 299 S, Westel Rd, **N** 🚪 BP/dsl, **S** 🚪 Shell/dsl, 🅾 Boat-N-RV Ctr/Park
336mm	**parking area/weigh sta eb, litter barrel**
329	US 70, Crab Orchard, **N** 🚪 BP/dsl, Liberty/dsl, 🅾 KOA (4mi), **S** 🅾 Cumberland Trails SP, Wilson SP

Exit	Services
327mm	**rest area wb, full ♿ facilities, 🍴, 🏨, litter barrels, petwalk, vending**
324mm	**rest area eb, full ♿ facilities, 🍴, 🏨, litter barrels, petwalk, vending**
322	TN 101, Peavine Rd, Crossville, **N** 🚪 BP/Bean Pot Rest., Exxon/dsl, Volunteer/dsl, 🍴 Hardee's, McDonald's, Quiznos, Subway, 🛏 Holiday Inn Express, 🅾 Deer Run RV Resort, KOA Camping, Roam-Roost RV Campground, to Fairfield Glade Resort, **S** 🚪 Phillips 66/dsl, 🍴 Cancun Mexican, Taco Bell, 🛏 Comfort Suites, Hampton Inn, Super 8, 🅾 🅷, Chestnut Hill Winery, Cumberland Mtn SP, RV Camping, Vallyhoo
320	TN 298, Crossville, **N** 🚪 🏨/Wendy's/dsl/scales/24hr, 🍴 Halcyon Days Rest., 🅾 antiques, golf, winery, **S** 🚪 BP/DQ/Pizza Hut/dsl, Shell/dsl, 🅾 🅷, Crossville Outlet/famous brands, Save-A-Lot Foods, antiques, auto repair/tires
318mm	Obed River
317	US 127, Crossville, **N** 🚪 Exxon/dsl/24hr, Shell/dsl, 🍴 Shoney's, Subway, 🛏 Best Western, La Quinta, Motel 6, 🅾 repair, to Big South Fork RA, to York SP, **0-2 mi S** 🚪 Citgo/dsl, Jiffy, Marathon, Murphy USA/dsl, Shell, 🍴 Arby's, Burger King, Cancun Mexican, Cracker Barrel, La Costa Mexican, McDonalds, Papa John's, Peking Buffet, Ruby Tuesday, Ryan's, Sonic, Subway, Taco Bell, Vegas Steaks, Waffle House, Zaxby's, 🛏 Best Value Inn, Days Inn, Economy Inn, 🅾 🅷, AT&T, Buick/Cadillac/Chevrolet/GMC, Chrysler/Dodge/Jeep, $General, $Tree, GNC, Lowe's, Rite Aid, Shadden Tires, Staples, Verizon, Walmart, Walgreens, vet, to Cumberland Mtn SP
311	Plateau Rd, **N** 🚪 Sunoco/Papa Lorenzo's Pizza/dsl, **S** 🚪 BP/dsl, Exxon/Hunt Bro's Pizza, 🅾 rv service
307mm	**parking area/weigh sta wb, litter barrels**
301	US 70 N, TN 84, Monterey, **N** 🚪 Phillips 66, Shell, 🍴 Burger King, DQ, Subway, 🛏 Super 8
300	US 70, Monterey, **N** 🚪 Citgo/dsl, 🍴 DQ, Hardee's
291mm	Falling Water River
290	US 70, Cookeville, **N** 🚪 BP (1mi), **S** 🚪 Citgo, 🛏 Alpine Suites
288	TN 111, to Livingston, Cookeville, Sparta, **N** Hull SP, **S** 🚪 Sunoco/dsl, TN TravelCtr/dsl/24hr, 🍴 Mona's Rest., 🛏 Knights Inn
287	TN 136, Cookeville, **N** 🚪 BP, Exxon, Murphy USA, 🍴 Applebee's, Arby's, Baskin-Robbins, Bully's Rest., Burger King, Capt D's, Cheddars, Chick-fil-A, Chili's, Cracker Barrel, DQ, Fazoli's, Golden Corral, IHOP, King Buffet, Krystal, LJ Silver, Logan's Roadhouse, Longhorn Steaks, Mandarin Palace, McDonald's, Mike's Subs, Nick's Rest., O'Charley's, Olive Garden, Outback Steaks, Papa Murphy's, Pizza Hut, Puleo's Grill, Quiznos, Red Lobster,

TENNESSEE

Oneida • Elk Valley • Tazewell • La Follette • Caryville • Washburn Bulls Gap 81 • 75 • Norris • Luttrell • Morristown • Strawberry Plains • White Pine • Oak Ridge • Knoxville • Newport • Kingston 40 • Farragut • Sevierville • Loudon • Maryville Gatlinburg 40 • Sweetwater • Englewood • TN

(left margin, vertical) E ↕ W

(left margin, vertical) H A R R I M A N

(right margin, vertical) CROSSVILLE

(right margin, vertical) COOKEVILLE

(right margin) TN

	INTERSTATE 40 CONT'D
Exit	**Services**
287	Continued
	Ruby Tuesday, Shoney's, Sonic, Starbucks, Steak'n Shake, Subway, Taco Bell, Wendy's, 🛏 Best Value Inn, Best Western, Clarion, Comfort Inn&Suites, Days Inn, Hampton Inn, Red Roof Inn, Super 8, 🅞 Aldi Foods, Big-Lots, Firestone/auto, Harley-Davidson, JC Penney, K-Mart, Kroger/gas, Lowe's, Nissan, Radio Shack, Verizon, Walmart, st patrol, transmissions, **S** 🅖 Marathon/dsl, 🛢/dsl, 🍴 Gondola, KFC, Waffle House, 🛏 Baymont Inn, Country Hearth Inn, Country Inn&Suites, Fairfield Inn, Holiday Inn Express, 🅞 URGENT CARE, Sam's Club/gas
286	TN 135, Burgess Falls Rd, **N** 🅖 BP, Exxon, RaceWay/dsl, Shell/dsl, 🍴 Arby's, Beef'O'Brady's, Christy's Cafe, Hardee's, Waffle House, 🅞 H, Chrysler/Dodge/Jeep, Ford/Lincoln/Mercury, Goodyear/auto, Hyundai, KIA, Toyota/Scion, USPO, to TTU, vet, **S** 🅖 Sunoco/dsl, 🛏 Star Motor Inn, 🅞 Burgess Falls SP (8mi)
280	TN 56 N, Baxter, **N** 🅖 Loves/McDonalds/Subway/dsl/scales/24hr, 🍴 Huddle House, 🅞 Camp Discovery (2mi), Twin Lakes RV Park (2mi)
276	Old Baxter Rd
273	TN 56 S, to Smithville, **S** 🅖 BP/dsl, Phillips 66, 🍴 Rose Garden Rest., 🅞 USPO
268	TN 96, Buffalo Valley Rd, **N** Grandville Marina Camping (11mi), **S** to Edgar Evins SP/RV camping
267mm	Caney Fork River
267mm	**rest area both lanes, full ♿ facilities, info, 🚰, 🛢, litter barrels, petwalk, vending**
266mm	Caney Fork River
263mm	Caney Fork River
258	TN 53, Gordonsville, **N** 🅖 Exxon/KFC/Taco Bell, Shell/dsl, 🍴 McDonald's, Timberloft Café, Waffle House, 🛏 Comfort Inn, 🅞 to Cordell Hull Dam, **S** 🅖 Hess/Wendy's/dsl/scales/24hr, Mobil/dsl, 🍴 Arby's, Cornerstone Cafe, El Corral Mexican, 🅞 $General
254	TN 141, to Alexandria
252mm	parking area/truck sta both lanes, 🛢, litter barrels
245	Linwood Rd, **N** 🅖 BP/dsl
239	US 70, Lebanon, **N** 🅖 Citgo/dsl, RaceWay, **S** 🅖 Phillips 66/Uncle Pete's/dsl/scales, 🍴 Jalisco Mexican
238	US 231, Lebanon, **N** 🅖 Exxon, Mapco, Shell, 🍴 Applebee's, Arby's, Cici's Pizza, Cracker Barrel, Demo's Steaks, El Molino Mexican, Gondola Rest., Hardee's, Jack-in-the-Box, KFC, King Buffet, McDonald's, Pizza Hut, Ponderosa, Ryan's, Shoney's, Sunset Rest., Subway, Taco Bell, Waffle House, Wendy's, White Castle, Whitt's BBQ, Zaxby's 🛏 Best Value Inn, EconoLodge, Executive Inn, Holiday Inn Express, Quality Inn, Ramada, 🅞 H, Aldi Foods, $Tree, Discount Tire, Lowe's, Walgreens, Walmart, to Bledsoe SP, **S** 🅖 Citgo/Pizza Inn/Quiznos/dsl, 🛢/Chester's/Subway/dsl/scales/24hr, Shell/dsl, 🍴 O'Charley's, Sonic, 🛏 Comfort Suites, Country Inn&Suites, Days Inn, Knights Inn, Super 8, 🅞 Family RV Ctr, Lebanon Outlets/famous brands, Shady Acres Camping, Timberline Campground, to Cedars of Lebanon SP, RV camping
236	S Hartmann Dr, **N** 🅖 Mapco, Shell/dsl, 🍴 Chili's, Outback Steaks, Pizza Inn, Ruby Tuesday, Sonic, Subway, 🛏 Hampton Inn, 🅞 H, Home Depot, Rose Tire

235	TN 840 W, to Murfreesboro
232	TN 109, to Gallatin, **N** 🅖 Citgo, Mapco/Quiznos/dsl, Shell/McDonald's/dsl/24hr, Thornton's/dsl, 🍴 Bellacino's Pizza, Coach's Grill, Sonic, Subway, Waffle House, Wendy's, 🛏 Sleep Inn, ValuePlace Inn, **2 mi S** 🅞 Countryside Resort Camping
228mm	truck sta, wb only
229b a	Beckwitch Rd
226mm	truck sta
226	TN 171, Mt Juliet Rd, **N** 🅖 BP/McDonald's/dsl, Exxon/dsl, Shell/dsl/24hr, 🍴 Arby's, Capt D's, Cheddars, Don Pancho Mexican, Far East Buffet, 5 Guys Burgers, Subway, 🛏 Comfort Suites, 🅞 Aldi Foods, $Tree, Lowe's, NTB, Walmart, **S** 🅖 Mapco/Quiznos/dsl, 🍴 Buffalo Wild Wings, Chick-fil-A, Cori's Dog House, Cracker Barrel, Fulin's Asian, Hacienda Del Sol, Logan's Roadhouse, NY Pizza, O'Charley's, Olive Garden, Panera Bread, Red Lobster, Red Robin, Ruby Tuesday, Salsarita's Cantina, Sonic, Steak'n Shake, Taco Bell, Waffle House, Wasabi Steaks, Wendy's, Zaxby's, 🛏 Hampton Inn, Holiday Inn Express, Quality Inn, 🅞 AT&T, Belk, Best Buy, Books-A-Million, Curves, Dick's, Discount Tire, Ford, GNC, JC Penney, JoAnn Fabrics, Kroger/dsl, Old Navy, Petsmart, Publix, Ross, Staples, Target, TJ Maxx, Verizon, Walgreens, to Long Hunter SP
221	TN 45 N, Old Hickory Blvd, to The Hermitage, **0-2 mi N** 🅖 BP, Exxon, Mapco/dsl, RaceWay/dsl, Shell/24hr, 🍴 Applebee's, Baskin-Robbins/Dunkin Donuts, Buffalo Wild Wings, Burger King, Chick-fil-A, Chili's, DQ, Famous Dave's, Fazoli's, Firehouse Subs, Golden Corral, Hardee's, IHOP, Jack-in-the-Box, Mike's Subs, O'Charley's, Outback Steaks, Panera Bread, Qdoba Mexican, Starbucks, Steak'n Shake, Subway, Waffle House, 🛏 Best Value Inn, Suburban Lodge, Super 8, Vista Inn, 🅞 H, Hobby Lobby, Home Depot, Kroger, Lowe's, PetCo, Staples, Walgreens, **S** 🅖 Phillips 66/White Castle, Shell/McDonald's, Qwiksak/dsl
219	Stewart's Ferry Pike, **N** 🅖 Mapco, **S** 🅖 Mapco/dsl, Shell/dsl, Thornton's/dsl, 🍴 China King, Cracker Barrel, Epic Pizza, La Hacienda Mexican, Sal's Pizza, Subway, Waffle House, 🛏 Best Western, Comfort Suites, Country Inn&Suites, Days Inn, EconoLodge, Family Inn, Sleep Inn, 🅞 $General, Food Lion, Fred's, vet
216	(216 c from eb) TN 255, Donaldson Pk, **N** 🅖 BP/dsl, Mapco, RaceWay/dsl, Shell/dsl/24hr, 🍴 Arby's, Backyard Burger, Bar-B-Cutie, Darfon's, Domino's, Jalisco Mexican, KFC, McDonald's, New China, Pizza Hut/Taco Bell, Ruby Tuesday, Shoney's, Subway, Waffle House, Wendy's, 🛏 Country Inn&Suites, Drury Inn, Fairfield Inn, Hampton Inn, Holiday Inn Express, Hyatt Place, La Quinta, Radisson, Red Roof Inn, SpringHill Suites, Super 8, Wingate Inn, 🅞 Advance Parts, K-Mart, Walgreens, USPO, **S** 🅞 ✈
216b a	(from eb), **S** Nashville Intn'l ✈
215b a	TN 155, Briley Pkwy, to Opryland, **N on Elm Hill** 🅖 Citgo, Mapco, 🍴 Casta Fiesta Mexican, Jack-in-the-Box, Waffle House, 🛏 Alexis Inn, Baymont Inn, Comfort Suites, Courtyard, Embassy Suites, Extended Stay, Hilton Garden, Holiday Inn, Homestead Suites, Homewood Suites, La Quinta, Marriott, Ramada, Residence Inn, Sheraton, Studio+, **S** 🅖 Phillips 66/dsl, 🍴 Dunkin Donuts, Mazatlan Mexican, Panda House, Subway, 🛏 Hamilton Inn, Hotel Preston
213b	I-24 W
213a	I-24 E/I-440, E to Chattanooga
213	US 41 (from wb no return), to Spence Lane, **N** 🅞

NASHVILLE

LEBANON

TN

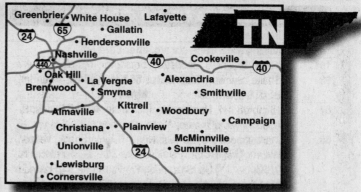

INTERSTATE 40 CONT'D

Exit	Services
213	Continued
	Kenworth, **S** ⓖ Phillips 66/dsl, Shell, ⓕ Waffle House, ⓛ Days Inn, Holiday Inn Express, Rodeway Inn, Super 8, same as 212
212	Fessler's Lane (from eb, no return), **N** ⓞ Freightliner, Harley-Davidson, **S** ⓖ Mapco/dsl, Shell/Dunkin Donuts, ⓕ Burger King, McDonald's, Sonic, Wendy's, ⓛ Scottish Inn, ⓞ Chevrolet, same as 213
211mm	Cumberland River
211b	I-24 W
211a	I-24E, I-40 W
210c	US 31 S, US 41A, 2nd Ave, 4th Ave, **N** ⓛ Hilton, Sheraton, Stouffer Hotel, **S** museum
210b a	I-65 S, to Birmingham
209b a	US 70 S, Charlotte Ave, Nashville, **N** ⓖ Exxon, ⓕ McDonald's, ⓛ Sheraton, ⓞ Firestone, Country Music Hall of Fame, Conv Ctr, transmissions, **S** ⓖ Exxon, ⓕ Burger King, Krystal, Sonic, Subway, White Castle, ⓛ Comfort Inn, Guesthouse Inn, ⓞ Walgreens, urgent care
208b a	I-65, N to Louisville, S to Birmingham
207	28th Ave, Jefferson St, Nashville, **N** ⓖ BP, Citgo, ⓕ Subway, Wendy's, Wing Zone, ⓞ ⓗ, Family$, to TN St U
206	I-440 E, to Knoxville
205	46th Ave, W Nashville, **N** ⓞ Harley-Davidson, **S** ⓖ Mapco, Shell, ⓕ McDonald's, Mrs. Winners
204	TN 155, Briley Pkwy, **S** ⓖ BP/dsl, Citgo, ⓕ Burger King, China Buffet, Church's/White Castle, Cinco De Mayo, Domino's, Jack-in-the-Box, KFC, Krystal, Las Palmas, Papa John's, Shoney's, Subway, Waffle House, ⓛ Baymont Inn, Best Western, Comfort Inn, Days Inn, ⓞ CarQuest, CVS Drug, Firestone/auto, Kroger/gas, NTB, O'Reilly Parts, PepBoys, Sav-a-lot Foods, Walgreens
201b a	US 70, Charlotte Pike, **N** ⓖ Exxon, Shell/dsl/24hr, ⓕ Bojangles, China Buffet, Cracker Barrel, Jim 'N Nick's BBQ, Krystal, Subway, Waffle House, Wendy's, ⓛ Super 8, ⓞ $Tree, GNC, Kwik Kar, Lowe's Whse, Radio Shack, Walmart, **S** ⓖ BP, Mapco, Shell, ⓕ Arby's, McDonald's, Pizza Hut, Red Robin, Taco Bell, ⓞ Best Buy, Big Lots, Books-A-Million, BigLots, Costco/gas, Firestone/auto, Marshall's, Old Navy, PetsMart, Ross, Staples, Target, Uhaul, World Mkt
199	rd 251, Old Hickory Blvd, **N** ⓖ Shell, **S** ⓖ BP, Mapco, ⓕ Sonic, Subway, ⓞ Sam's Club/gas
196	US 70, to Bellevue, Newsom Sta, **N** ⓖ Mapco/dsl, ⓕ Shoney's, **S** ⓖ BP, Mapco/dsl, Shell/dsl/24hr, ⓕ Arby's, Asihi Asian, O'Charley's, Pizza Hut, Sir Pizza, Sonic, Subway, Taco Bell, Waffle House, Wendy's, ⓛ Hampton Inn, Microtel, ⓞ $Tree, Firestone/auto, Home Depot, Michael's, PetCo, Publix, Sears/auto, Staples, USPO, Walgreens
195mm	Harpeth River
192	McCrory Lane, to Pegram, **N** ⓖ Eddie's Mkt (1mi), **4 mi S** ⓕ Loveless Cafe, ⓞ Natchez Trace Pkwy
190mm	Harpeth River
188mm	Harpeth River
188	rd 249, Kingston Springs, **N** ⓖ BP, Mapco/Quiznos/dsl, Shell/Arby's/dsl, ⓕ El Jardin Mexican, McDonald's/playplace, Sonic, Subway, ⓛ Best Western, Mid-Town Inn, Relax Inn, ⓞ CB Foods, USPO, **S** ⓖ Petro/BP/Quick Skillet/dsl/scales/showers/24hr/@, ⓞ vet

Exit	Services
182	TN 96, to Dickson, Fairview, **N** ⓖ BP/dsl, ⓛ Fairview Inn, ⓞ M Bell SP (16mi), **S** ⓖ 🚚FLYING J/Denny's/dsl/LP/scales/24hr, Shell/Backyard Burger/Dunkin Donuts/dsl, ⓛ Deerfield Inn
176	TN 840
172	TN 46, to Dickson, **N** ⓖ Citgo/Subway, Exxon, 🚛/Wendy's/dsl/scales/24hr, Shell, ⓕ Arby's, Cracker Barrel, Farmer's Rest., Logan's Roadhouse, McDonald's, Ruby Tuesday, Waffle House/24hr, Wang's China, ⓛ Best Western, Comfort Inn, EconoLodge, Hampton Inn, Motel 6, Quality Inn, South-Aire Inn, Super 8, ⓞ ⓗ, Chappell's Foods, Chevrolet, Dickson RV Park, Ford, Nissan, truck repair, to M Bell SP, **S** ⓖ BP, Shell/dsl, ⓕ O'Charley's, Sonic, ⓛ Days Inn, Dickson Inn, Holiday Inn Express
170	**rest area both lanes, full ♿ facilities, ⓣ, ⚠, litter barrels, vending, petwalk**
166mm	Piney River
163	rd 48, to Dickson, **N** ⓖ Phillips 66/dsl, ⓞ tire repair, **S** ⓖ Shell, ⓞ Pinewood Camping (7mi), Tanbark Camping
152	rd 230, Bucksnort, **N** ⓖ Citgo, ⓕ Rudy's Rest., ⓛ Travel Inn
149mm	Duck River
148	rd 50, Barren Hollow Rd, to Turney Center
143	TN 13, to Linden, Waverly, **N** ⓖ BP, 🚛/Arby's/dsl/scales/24hr, Shell, ⓕ Hot Spot BBQ, Log Cabin Rest., Loretta Lynn's Kitchen, McDonald's, Subway, ⓛ Best Western, Days Inn, Holiday Inn Express, Knights Inn, ⓞ KOA/LP, tires, **S** ⓖ Fast Fuel/dsl, ⓛ Scottish Inn
141mm	Buffalo River
137	Cuba Landing, **N** ⓞ TN River RV Park, **S** ⓕ Cuba Landing Rest./gas
133mm	Tennessee River
133	rd 191, Birdsong Rd, **9 mi N** ⓛ Birdsong RV Resort/marina, Good Sam RV Park
131mm	**rest area both lanes, full ♿ facilities, ⓣ, vending, ⚠, litter barrels, petwalk**
126	US 641, TN 69, to Camden, **N** ⓖ Marathon/Subway/dsl, Phillips 66/North 40/dsl, Shell/dsl, ⓞ Paris Landing SP, tire/truck repair, to NB Forrest SP, **S** ⓖ BP/dsl, Shell/dsl, ⓛ Days Inn, ⓞ ⓗ, Mouse-tail Landing SP (24mi)
116	rd 114, **S** ⓞ to Natchez Trace SP, RV camping
110mm	Big Sandy River
108	TN 22, to Lexington, Parkers Crossroads, **N** ⓖ BP/McDonald's/24hr/dsl, Citgo/dsl/24hr, Phillips 66/dsl, ⓕ Bailey's Rest., DQ, Subway, ⓛ Knights Inn, ⓞ USPO, city park, **S** ⓖ Exxon, ⓕ Po' Boys Pizza, ⓛ Best Value Inn, ⓞ ⓗ, RV camping, Parkers Crossroads Bfd Visitors Ctr, to Shiloh NMP (51mi)
103mm	**parking area/truck sta eb, litter barrels**

Exit	Services

INTERSTATE 40 CONT'D

Exit	Services
102mm	parking area/truck sta wb, litter barrels
101	rd 104, N ⬛ 101 TP/rest/dsl/tires/24hr, ⬛ golf (3mi)
93	rd 152, Law Rd, N ⬛ Phillips 66/deli/dsl/24hr, S ⬛ BP/dsl, Super Way/dsl
87	US 70, US 412, Huntingdon, McKenzie, N ⬛ Coastal/dsl, S ⬛ BP/dsl, ⬛Loves⬛/Hardee's/dsl/scales/24hr
85	Christmasville Rd, to Jackson, N ⬛ BP/dsl, Exxon/dsl/24hr, ⬛/Denny's/dsl/scales/24hr, ⬛ Comfort Inn, ⬛ $General, S ⬛ Horizon/Baskin-Robbins/Pizza Pro, ⬛ Jiang Jun Chinese, Lenny's Subs, Los Portales, McDonald's, Reggi's BBQ, Sonic, Sparky's, Taco Bell, ⬛ Holiday Inn Express, ⬛ $Tree, Food Giant
83	Campbell st, N ⬛ Exxon/Old Madina Mkt/dsl, ⬛ Residence Inn, S ⬛ Courtyard, Hampton Inn
82b a	US 45, Jackson, N ⬛ BP, ⬛ Cracker Barrel, ⬛ Knights Inn, Microtel, ⬛ Batteries+, Curves, Smallwoods RV Ctr (4mi), S ⬛ BP, Clark/dsl, Exxon, ⬛ Baskin-Robbins, Burger King, Catfish Galley, ChuckeCheese, DQ, KFC, Krystal, Little Caesar's, LJ Silver, McDonald's/playplace, Niko's Creek, Pizza Hut, Popeye's, Sakura Japanese, Shoney's, Sonic, Subway, Taco Bell, Tulum Mexican, Waffle House, Wendy's, ⬛ Executive Inn, La Quinta, Ramada Ltd, Super 8, Travellers Motel, ⬛ Advance Parts, AT&T, AutoZone, BigLots, $General, $Tree, Firestone/auto, Fred's, Goodyear/auto, JC Penney, Kroger/24hr, Macy's, Office Depot, Radio Shack, Sears/auto, TJ Maxx, mall, vet
80b a	US 45 Byp, Jackson, 0-2 mi N ⬛ BP, Exxon, ⬛ Arby's, Asahi Japanese, Backyard Burger, Baskin-Robbins, Buffalo Wild Wings, Capt D's, Chili's, Chick-fil-A, El Comal Mexican, Fazoli's, Fujiyama Japanese, HoneyBaked Ham, IHOP, Jason's Deli, KFC, Lenny's Subs, Longhorn Steaks, Los Portales, Maggie Moo's, McAlisters Deli, Moe's SW Grill, Olive Garden, Outback Steaks, Panera Bread, Peking Chinese, Perkins, Popeye's, Quiznos, Red Robin, Ruby Tuesday, Sonic, Starbucks, Steak'n Shake, Subway, TGIFriday's, Wendy's, Zaxby's, ⬛ Baymont Inn, Jameson Inn, SigNature Hotel, ⬛ AT&T, Best Buy, Books-A-Million, Buick/Cadillac/Chevrolet/GMC, Dick's, Firestone/auto, Gateway Tires/repair, Hobby Lobby, Home Depot, JoAnn Fabrics, Kohl's, Lowe's, Marshall's, Mazda, Nissan, Old Navy, Petsmart, Ross, Sam's Club/gas, Steinmart, Target, Verizon, Walmart/gas, S ⬛ BP/Circle K, G/dsl, Phillips 66/dsl, ⬛ Arby's, Asia Garden, Barnhill's Buffet, Burger King, Double D Ranch Rest., Heavenly Ham, Logan's Roadhouse, McDonald's, Mrs Winner's, O'Charley's, Old Hickory Steakhouse, Old Town Spaghetti, Red Bones Grill, Subway, Taco Bell, Waffle House, ⬛ Best Western, Casey Jones Motel, Comfort Suites, Days Inn, DoubleTree, EconoLodge, Guesthouse Inn, Holiday Inn, Motel 6, Old Hickory Inn, Quality Inn, ⬛ ⬛, Chrysler/Dodge/Jeep, $General, Ford/Lincoln/Mercury, Harley-Davidson, Honda, Hyundai, K-Mart, Toyota/Scion, Tuesday Morning, to Pinson Mounds SP, Chickasaw SP
79	US 412, Jackson, N ⬛ Gander Mtn., S ⬛ BP/dsl, Citgo/dsl, Exxon, ⬛ Days Inn, ⬛ Jackson RV Park
78mm	Forked Deer River
76	rd 223, S ⬛ McKenzie BBQ, ⬛ McKellar-Sites ⬛, Whispering Pines RV Park
74	Lower Brownsville Rd
73mm	rest area both lanes, full ⬛ facilities, info, ⬛, ⬛, litter barrels, vending, petwalk

Exit	Services
68	rd 138, Providence Rd, N ⬛ BP/dsl, ⬛ Ole South Inn, S ⬛ TA/Citgo/Subway/dsl/scales/24hr/@, Valero/dsl, ⬛ Joy-O RV Park
66	US 70, to Brownsville, N ⬛ Ft Pillow SHP (51mi), S ⬛ Exxon/dsl, ⬛ Motel 6
60	rd 19, Mercer Rd
56	TN 76, to Brownsville, N ⬛ BP, Shell/dsl/24hr, ⬛ DQ, KFC, McDonald's/playplace, Pizza Hut/Taco Bell, ⬛ Best Value Inn, Comfort Inn, Days Inn, Econolodge, S ⬛ Exxon/Huddle House/dsl/24hr
55mm	Hatchie River
52	TN 76, rd 179, Koko Rd, to Whiteville, S ⬛ Koko/dsl
50mm	weigh sta both lanes, ⬛
47	TN 179, to Stanton, Dancyville, S ⬛ Exit 47 Trkstp/dsl
42	TN 222, to Stanton, N ⬛ Best Value Inn, S ⬛ Exxon/dsl, ⬛/Chester's/Subway/dsl/scales/24hr, ⬛ Deerfield Inn
35	TN 59, to Somerville, S ⬛ BP/dsl/scales, ⬛ Longtown Rest.
29.5mm	Loosahatchie River
25	TN 205, Airline Rd, to Arlington, N ⬛ Shell/dsl, S ⬛ Exxon/Backyard Burger/dsl, ⬛ vistor ctr
24	TN 385, rd 204, to Arlington, Millington, Collierville
20	Canada Rd, Lakeland, N ⬛ BP/McDonald's, Shell, ⬛ Cracker Barrel, Waffle House, ⬛ Motel 6, Relax Inn, Super 8, S ⬛ Exxon/Subway/dsl, foo: TCBY, ⬛ Memphis East Camping
18	US 64, to Bartlett, N ⬛ Shell, ⬛ Abuelo's, Bob Evans, Buffalo Wild Wings, El Porton Mexican, Firebird's Grill, Hooters, McAlister's Deli, Longhorn Steaks, O'Charley's, Olive Garden, Steak'n Shake, TGI Friday's, TX Roadhouse, ⬛ Best Western, Fairfield Inn, Holiday Inn, La Quinta, SpringHill Suites, ⬛ Buick/GMC, Firestone/auto, Goodyear/auto, Lowe's, Sam's Club/gas, Walmart, same as 16, S ⬛ BP/Circle K, Citgo/dsl, ⬛ Backyard Burger, KFC, Lenny's Subs, Papa John's, Pizza Hut, Subway, Zaxby's, ⬛ Kroger, Schnuck's Foods/gas, Walgreens, Zaxby's
16b a	TN 177, to Germantown, N ⬛ BP/Circle K, Shell/Circle K, ⬛ Abuelo's, Arby's, Bahama Breeze, Burger King, Casa Mexicana, Chili's, Chick-fil-A, Danver's, IHOP, J. Alexander's, Joe's Crabshack, Logan's Roadhouse, Macaroni Grill, McDonald's/playplace, On-the-Border, Red Lobster, Taco Bell, TCBY, Tellini's Italian, Waffle House, Wendy's, ⬛ Extended Stay Deluxe, Hampton Inn, Hyatt Place, ⬛ ⬛, Barnes&Noble, Best Buy, BigLots, Chevrolet, Chrysler/Dodge/Jeep, Dillard's, $Tree, Ford, Hancock Fabrics, Hobby Lobby, Home Depot, Honda, JC Penney, Macy's, Michael's, Nissan, Office Depot, Old Navy, Petsmart, Sears/auto, Target, TJ Maxx, Walgreens, mall, 0-2 mi S ⬛ BP/Circle K, Shell/Circle K, ⬛ Abbay's Rest., Arby's, Backyard Burger, Burger King, ChuckeCheese, Corky's BBQ, El Porton Mexican, Genghis Grill, Honeybake Ham, Howard's Doughnuts, Jason's Deli, Jim'n Nick's BBQ, Jimmy John's, Lenny's Subs, McDonald's, Newk's Cafe, Pei Wei Chinese, Qdoba Mexican, Shogun Japanese, Slim Skillets, Smoothie King, Waffle House, Wendy's, ⬛ Comfort Suites, Microtel, Quality Inn, Quality Suites, Studio+, Wingate Inn, ⬛ Aldi Foods, AT&T, AutoZone, Costco/gas, Dick's, GNC, Gordman's, Kroger/gas, Kohl's, Marshall's, Rite Aid, Ross, Steinmart, Toyota/Scion, Tuesday Morning, Verizon, vet
15b a	Appling Rd, N ⬛ BP/Circle K/dsl, Shell/dsl, ⬛ ⬛
14	Whitten Rd, N ⬛ Citgo/dsl, Mapco, Shell/Burger King,

E / W

J A C K S O N

TN

INTERSTATE 40 CONT'D

Exit	Services
14	Continued
	🍴 McDonald's, Sidecar Café, ⊙ Harley-Davidson, **S** ⊕ BP/Circle K, Shell/Backyard Burger/dsl, 🍴 Dunkin Donuts, Subway, Supreme Hot Wings, ⊙ Walgreens
12	Sycamore View Rd, **N** ⊕ Citgo/dsl, Texaco/dsl, 🍴 Cajun Catfish Co., Capt D's, Church's, Cracker Barrel, IHOP, McDonald's, Mrs Winner's, Perkins, Ruby Tuesday, Shoney's, Sonic, Starbucks, Taco Bell, Waffle House, 🛏 Baymont Inn, Best Value Inn, Clarion, Drury Inn, EconoLodge, Extended Stay America, Memphis Plaza, Red Roof Inn, ⊙ AutoZone, $General, Family$, Fred's, Walgreens, **S** ⊕ BP/Circle K/dsl, Exxon, Mapco, 🍴 Beijing Chinese, Burger King, Popeye's, Subway, Tops BBQ, Wendy's, 🛏 Best Western, Budgetel, Comfort Inn, Days Inn, Fairfield Inn, La Quinta, Memphis Inn, Motel 6, Super 8, ⊙ Bass Pro Shops, Parts+
10.5mm	Wolf River
10 b a	(from wb)I-240 W around Memphis, I-40 E to Nashville
12c	(from eb)I-240 W, to Jackson, I-40 E to Nashville
12b	Sam Cooper Blvd (from eb)
12a	US 64/70/79, Summer Ave, **N** ⊕ Mapco/dsl, Shell, 🍴 Asian Palace, Waffle House, 🛏 Welcome Inn, ⊙ U-Haul, **S** ⊕ Exxon, 🍴 Arby's, McDonald's, ⊙ $Tree, Firestone/auto, Fred's, Goodyear/auto, Sav-A-Lot Foods
10	TN 204, Covington Pike, **N** ⊕ BP/Circle K, 🍴 McDonald's, Wendy's, ⊙ Audi/VW, Buick/GMC, Chevrolet, Chrysler/Dodge/Jeep, Honda, Hyundai, KIA, Mazda, Nissan, Sam's Club, Subaru, Suzuki, SuperLo Food/gas, Volvo
8 b a	TN 14, Jackson Ave, **N** ⊕ Citgo/dsl, Shell, 🛏 Motel 6, Sleep Inn, ⊙ Raleigh Tire, vet, **S** ⊕ Citgo/dsl, Mapco, ⊙ AutoZone, Family$, O'Reilly Parts, transmissions
6	Warford Rd
5	Hollywood St, **N** ⊕ BP, Q-Mart/dsl, 🍴 Burger King, Mother's Rest., **S** ⊙ Memphis Zoo
3	Watkins St, **N** ⊕ BP, Chevron/dsl, Coastal/dsl, Oil City USA/dsl, Texaco/dsl, ⊙ Family$, U-Haul
2a	rd 300, to US 51 N, Millington, **N** ⊙ Meeman-Shelby SP
2	Smith Ave, Chelsea Ave, **N** ⊕ Citgo, **S** ⊕ BP
1e	I-240 E
1 d c b	US 51, Danny Thomas Blvd, **N** ⊕ Exxon, 🍴 KFC, Wendy's, ⊙ Ronald McDonald House, St Jude Research Ctr
1a	2nd St (from wb), downtown, **S** 🛏 Crowne Plaza, Holiday Inn, Marriott, Sheraton, Wyndham Garden, ⊙ Conv Ctr
1	Riverside Dr, Front St (from eb), Memphis, **S** 🛏 Comfort Inn, ⊙ Conv Ctr, Riverfront, Welcome Ctr
0mm	Tennessee/Arkansas state line, Mississippi River

INTERSTATE 55

Exit	Services
13mm	Tennessee/Arkansas state line, Mississippi River
12c	Delaware St, Memphis, **W** 🛏 Super 8
12b	Riverside Dr, downtown Memphis, **E** TN Welcome Ctr
12a	E Crump Blvd (from nb), **E** ⊕ BP, Exxon, 🍴 Capt D's, Wendy's, ⊙ museum
11	McLemore Ave, Presidents Island, industrial area
10	S Parkway, **1/2 mi E** ⊕ BP/dsl
9	Mallory Ave, industrial area
8	Horn Lake Rd (from sb)
7	US 61, 3rd St, **E** ⊕ BP, Exxon/mart, 🍴 Church's,

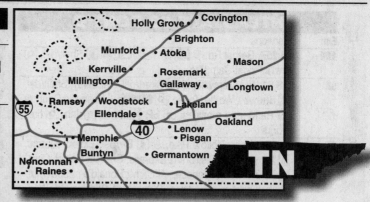

7	Continued
	Interstate BBQ, ⊙ AutoZone, Family$, Kroger, Walgreens, **W** ⊕ MapCo, 🍴 KFC, McDonald's, Subway, 🛏 Rest Inn, ⊙ Fuller SP, Indian Museum
6 b a	I-240
5b	US 51 S, Elvis Presley Blvd, to Graceland, **0-2 mi W on US 51** ⊕ BP, Citgo/dsl, Dodge's/dsl, Exxon, Phillips 66, 🍴 Alexander's Rest, BJ's Wings, Capt D's, Checker's, Exline Pizza, Kettle Rest., KFC, McDonald's, Piccadilly's, Taco Bell, 🛏 American Inn, Days Inn, Heartbreak Hotel/RV Park, Scottish Inn, Value Place Inn, ⊙ 🄷, Advance Parts, Aldi Foods, D&N RV Ctr, $Tree, Family$, Harley-Davidson, Piggly Wiggly, Presley RV Park, Radio Shack, Walgreens, transmissions, to Graceland
5a	Brooks Rd, **E** ⊕ BP, Exxon, MapCo, 🍴 Blimpie, Popeye's, 🛏 Inn, Best Value Inn, Budget Lodge, Memphis Plaza, Quality Inn, ⊙ Freightliner, Peterbilt
3mm	Welcome Ctr nb, full ♿ facilities, 🄲, vending, 🛈, litter barrels, petwalk
2 b a	TN 175, Shelby Dr, Whitehaven, **E** ⊕ BP/dsl, Citgo/Subway, Exxon, Shell/dsl, Texaco, 🛏 Colonial Inn, **W** ⊕ BP, Exxon, 🍴 Burger King, Dixie Queen, IHOP, McDonald's, Popeye's, ⊙ $General, Family$, Goodyear/auto, Macy's, Save-a-Lot Foods, Schnuck's Foods, Sears, Toyota/Scion, U-Haul, Walgreens
0mm	Tennessee/Mississippi state line

INTERSTATE 65

Exit	Services
121.5mm	Tennessee/Kentucky state line
121mm	Welcome Ctr sb, full ♿ facilities, 🄲, 🛈, litter barrels, vending, petwalk
119mm	weigh/insp sta both lanes
117	TN 52, Portland, **E** ⊕ BP/Godfather's/Quiznos/dsl, Shell/dsl/fireworks, 🛏 Comfort Suites, ⊙ 🄷, Bledsoe Cr SP, **W** ⊕ BP/dsl, 🛏 Budget Host, ⊙ fireworks
116mm	Red River
113mm	Red River
112	TN 25, Cross Plains, **E** ⊕ BP/dsl, 🍴 Sad Sam's Deli, ⊙ Bledsoe Cr SP, antiques, fireworks **W** ⊕ Mapco/dsl, Shell/Godfather's/dsl, 🍴 Sweet&Savory Diner
108	TN 76, White House, **E** ⊕ Nervous Charlie's/dsl, Shell, 🍴 A&W/KFC, China Spring, Cracker Barrel, Hardee's, Little Caesars, Los Agave's, McDonald's, Mr Wok, Sonic, Subway, Taco Bell, Waffle House, Wendy's, 🛏 Best Western, Comfort Inn, Holiday Inn Express, Quality Inn, ⊙ Ace Hardware, $Tree, Kroger/gas, O'Reilly Parts, Rite Aid, Walgreens, Walmart/Subway, USPO, city park/playground, **W** ⊕ BP/dsl, 🍴 Greek Gyro, 🛏 Days Inn

INTERSTATE 65 CONT'D

Exit	Services
104	rd 257, Bethel Rd, E 🅶 BP/rest./dsl, W 🅶 Shell/dsl, 🅾 Owl's Roost Camping
98	US 31 W, Millersville, E 🅶 Citgo/dsl, RaceWay, Shell/dsl, ⑪ Subway, Waffle House, 🅾 $General, Nashville Country RV Park, auto repair, W 🅶 BP, 🅰 Economy Inn, 🅾 fireworks
97	rd 174, Long Hollow Pike, E 🅶 BP/dsl, Exxon, Mapco, ⑪ Arby's, Capt D's, China Express, Cracker Barrel, Domino's, Kabuto Japanese, KFC, McDonald's, Papa Murphy's, Quiznos, Shoney's, Subway, Waffle House, Wendy's, 🅰 Best Western, Courtyard, Days Inn, Executive Inn, Hampton Inn, Quality Inn, Red Roof Inn, 🅾 K-Mart, Kroger, Walgreens, W 🅶 Shell/dsl, ⑪ Buck's BBQ, DQ, Hardee's, Krystal, Poncho Villa Grill, Sonic, 🅰 Holiday Inn Express, Motel 6, 🅾 Rite Aid, Walgreens, vet
96	Rivergate Pky, E 🅶 Citgo/dsl, Shell/dsl, ⑪ Bailey's Grill, Dougie Ray's Grill, El Chico, Fuji Steaks, HoneyBaked Ham, Hooters, Las Palmas Mexican, McDonald's, Pizza Hut, Subway, Waffle House, Wendy's, 🅰 Baymont Inn, Best Value Inn, Comfort Suites, Rodeway Inn, 🅾 Ⓗ, Best One Tires, Dillard's, Macy's, JC Penney, Sears/auto, mall, E on Gallatin N ⑪ A&W/LJ Silver, Arby's, Bar-B-Cutie, Burger King, Calhoun's Cafe, Checker's, Chick-fil-A, Chili's, ChuckeCheese, Fazoli's, IHOP, Krispy Kreme, Las Fiestas, Logan's Roadhouse, Longhorn Steaks, Olive Garden, Outback Steaks, Panera Bread, Popeye's, Rafferty's, Ryan's, Sonic, Starbucks, Steak'n Shake, TGI Friday's, Taco Bell, 🅾 AAA, AT&T, Best Buy, Books-A-Million, CarMax, Chevrolet, Chrysler/Dodge/Jeep, CVS Drug, Dick's, Discount Tire, $General, Firestone/auto, Goodyear/auto, Harley-Davidson, Hobby Lobby, Home Depot, Honda, JoAnn's Etc, Kia, Lexus, Lincoln/Mercury, Lowe's, Mazda, Michael's, Nissan, Office Depot, Old Navy, PepBoys, Petsmart, Sam's Club/gas, Staples, Target, TJ Maxx, Toyota/Scion, Verizon, VW, Walgreens, Walmart, urgent care, W 🅶 Marathon, Volunteer
95	TN 386, Vietnam Veterans Blvd (from nb)
92	rd 45, Old Hickory Blvd, E 🅾 Ⓗ, to Old Hickory Dam
90 b	TN 155 E, Briley Pkwy, E to Opreyland
90a	US 31W, US 41, Dickerson Pike, E 🅶 Citgo/dsl, Exxon/dsl, Mapco/dsl, Shell, ⑪ Arby's, Capt D's, Chicago Gyros, China King, Church's, Domino's, Jay's Rest., KFC, McDonald's, Pizza Hut, Subway, Taco Bell, Waffle House, Wendy's, 🅰 Days Inn, EconoLodge, Sleep Inn, Super 8, 🅾 Advance Parts, AutoZone, CVS Drug, $General, Family$, Kroger, O'Reilly Parts, Walgreens, W 🅾 Lowe's, Walmart
88b a	I-24, W to Clarksville, E to Nashville
87b a	US 431, Trinity Lane, E 🅶 BP, 🌊Loves/Subway/dsl/scales/24hr, ⑪ Church's/White Castle, Krystal, Sonic, 🅾 Piggly Wiggly, 🅰 Cumberland Inn, Delux Inn, W 🅶 BCP/dsl, BP, Exxon, Mapco, ⑪ Fat Mo's, Jack-in-the-Box, Jack's BBQ, McDonald's, Subway, Taco Bell, Waffle House, 🅰 Best Value Inn, Comfort Inn, Days Inn, EconoLodge, Halmark Inn, Howard Johnson, King's Inn, Quality Inn, Ravin Hotel, Regency Inn, Rodeway Inn, 🅾 $General, Family$
86	I-24 E, to I-40 E, to Memphis
86mm	Cumberland River
85	US 41A, 8th Ave, E 🅶 BP, 🅾 O'Reilly Parts, tires, to st capitol, W 🅶 Exxon, ⑪ Arby's, Jersey Mike's,

Exit	Services
85	Continued McDonald's, Pizza Hut, Starbucks, Subway, Taco Bell, Wendy's, Wise Burger, 🅰 Millennium Hotel, SpringHill Suites, 🅾 Cadillac/Honda
84b a	I-40, E to Knoxville, W to Memphis
209[I-40]	US 70, Charlotte Ave, Church St, E 🅶 Exxon, ⑪ McDonald's, 🅾 Firestone, W 🅶 Exxon, Shell, ⑪ Burger King, Krystal, Sonic, Subway, White Castle, 🅰 Comfort Inn, 🅾 Walgreens, urgent care
82b a	I-40, W to Memphis, E to Nashville
81	Wedgewood Ave, W 🅶 BP, Exxon, Shell, ⑪ Burger King, Subway 🅾 $General, U-Haul
80	I-440, to Memphis, Knoxville
79	Armory Dr, E on Powell 🅶 Shell, ⑪ Applebee's, Jersey Mike's, Logan's Roadhouse, Panda Express, Panera Bread, Rafferty's, Subway, Wendy's, 🅾 BMW, CarMax, Home Depot, Michael's, Petsmart, Ross, Staples, TJ Maxx
78b a	rd 255, Harding Place, E 🅶 Mapco, Pure, Shell, ⑪ Beijing Chinese, Cracker Barrel, Mama Mia's Italian, Sub House, Waffle House, 🅰 La Quinta, Red Roof Inn, Traveler's Rest Hist Home, 🅾 CVS Drug
74	TN 254, Old Hickory Blvd, to Brentwood, E ⑪ Capt D's, Coldstone, Longhorn Steaks, Panera Bread, Qdoba Mexican, Shoney's, Waffle House, 🅰 Best Western, Holiday Inn Express, Hyatt Place, Sheraton, 🅾 GNC, Target, W 🅶 BP, Gulf, Shell/dsl, ⑪ Backyard Burger, Chick-fil-A, Chili's, Chipotle Mexican, Church's, Corky's BBQ, 5 Guys Burgers, Jimmy John's, Maggie Moo's, Mazatlan Mexican, McAlister's Deli, McDonald's, Moe's SW Grill, Mrs Winner's, O'Charley's, Papa John's, Pei Wei, Pizza Hut, Ruby Tuesday, Starbucks, Subway, Taco Bell, Wendy's, 🅰 Courtyard, Extended Stay America, Hampton Inn, Hilton Suites, Homestead Suites, Studio+, 🅾 Cadillac, CVS Drug, Fresh Mkt Foods, Harris-Teeter, Land Rover, Office Depot, PetCo, Publix, Rite Aid, SteinMart, TJ Maxx, USPO, Walgreens
71	TN 253, Concord Rd, to Brentwood
69	rd 441, Moores Lane, Galleria Blvd, E 🅶 MapCo/dsl, Shell, ⑪ Amerigo's Grill, Baskin-Robbins, Cozymel's, Dunkin Donuts, Fuji Japanese, Greek Cafe, Outback Steaks, Papa Murphy's, Shogun Japanese, Sonic, Starbucks, 🅰 Hilton Garden, Hyatt Place, Red Roof Inn, Wingate Inn, 🅾 Acura/Lexus, CVS Drug, Home Depot/gas, Michael's, Petsmart, Publix, Walgreens, W 🅶 BP, Shell/dsl, ⑪ Backyard Burger, Buca Italian, Burger King, Capt D's, Chili's, Cracker Barrel, Famous Dave's, HoneyBaked Ham, J Alexander's Rest., Krispy Kreme, Logan's Roadhouse, Macaroni Grill, McDonald's, Peking Palace, Pizza Hut/Taco Bell, Red Lobster, Schlotzsky's, Stoney River Steaks, 🅰 Sleep Inn, 🅾 Barnes&Noble, Belk, Best Buy, Costco/gas, Dillard's, Discount Tire, $Tree, JC Penney, Macy's, NTB, Old Navy, Ross, Sears/auto, Target, mall
68b a	Cool Springs Blvd, E ⑪ Jersey Mike's, 🅰 Courtyard, Embassy Suites, Marriott, Residence Inn, W 🅶 Exxon, Shell, ⑪ BoneFish Grill, Bread&Co, Canton Buffet, Carrabba's, Chick-fil-A, ChuckeCheese, Chuy's Mexican, 5 Guys Burgers, Genghis Grill, Golden Corral, Greek Cafe, Jack-in-the-Box, Jason's Deli, J Christopher's, Jersey Mike's, KFC, McAlister's Deli, McDonald's, Moe's SW Grill, Newk's Cafe, Omikoshi Japanese, Otter's Chicken Tenders, Panera Bread, PF Chang's, Pizza Hut, Quiznos, Royal Thai, Starbucks, Subway, TGIFriday's, Wendy's, 🅰 ALoft, Country Inn&Suites, Hampton Inn, 🅾 Acura, AT&T, Dick's,

INTERSTATE 65 CONT'D

N ↑↓ S

F R A N K L I N

Exit	Services
68b a	Continued GNC, Harley-Davidson, Jo-Ann Fabrics, Kohl's, Kroger, Lowe's, Marshall's, Office Depot, Sam's Club/gas, Staples, TJ Maxx, Verizon, Walgreens, to Galleria Mall
67	McEwen Dr, **W** 🍴 Blue Coast Burrito, Brick Top's, Little Caesars, Marco's Pizza, Sonic, Subway, Tazikis Mediterranean Cafe, 🛏 Drury Inn, 🅾 Toyota/Scion, Walmart/Blimpie, Whole Food Mkt
65	TN 96, to Murfreesboro, Franklin, **E** 🅿 Mapco, Shell/Krystal, 🍴 Cracker Barrel, Sonic, Steak'n Shake, 🛏 Best Value Inn, Comfort Inn, Days Inn, Holiday Inn Express, La Quinta, Ramada Inn, 🅾 Chevrolet, Honda, Kia, Subaru, Volvo, Walgreens, auto repair, urgent care, **W** 🅿 BP/dsl, Shell/dsl, 🍴 Arby's, Backyard Burger, Hardee's, KFC, McDonald's, Nashville Pizza, O'Charley's, Papa John's, Poncho's Mexican, Shoney's, Starbucks, Subway, Taco Bell, Waffle House, Wendy's, Zaxby's, 🛏 Best Western, Quality Inn, 🅾 Aldi Foods, BigLots, Chrysler/Dodge/Jeep, Discount Tire, $General, Ford/Mercury, Hobby Lobby, Home Depot, Kroger, K-Mart, Publix/gas, Radio Shack, Rite Aid, SteinMart, USPO, Verizon, Walgreens, to Confederate Cem at Franklin, vet
64mm	Harpeth River
61	TN 248, Peytonsville Rd, to Spring Hill, **E** 🅿 TA/BP/rest./dsl/scales/24hr/@, **W** 🅿 Mapco, Shell/dsl, 🅾 Goose Creek Inn/rest.
59b a	TN 840, to Nashville
58mm	W Harpeth River
53	TN 396, Saturn Pkwy, Spring Hill, Columbia, TN Scenic Pkwy
48mm	truck insp/weigh sta nb, litter barrels
46	US 412, TN 99, to Columbia, Chapel Hill, **E** 🅿 BP/dsl, Loves/Arbys/dsl/scales/24hr, 🅾 Harley-Davidson, Henry Horton SP, **W** 🅿 Citgo/dsl, Phillip 66/Subway/dsl, Shell, TJ's/Burger King, 🍴 Cracker Barrel, Waffle House, Wendy's, 🛏 Best Value Inn, Comfort Inn, Hampton Inn, Holiday Inn Express, Relax Inn, Super 8, 🅾 🄷
40.5mm	Duck River
37	TN 50, to Columbia, Lewisburg, **E** 🅾 🄷, TN Walking Horse HQ, **W** 🅿 Shell/dsl, 🅾 to Polk Home
32	rd 373, to Lewisburg, Mooresville
27	rd 129, to Lynnville, Cornersville, **E** 🅾 Texas T Camping
25mm	parking area sb, litter barrels
24mm	parking area nb, litter barrels
22	US 31A, to Pulaski, **E** 🅿 Tennesseean Trkstp/Exxon/Pop's BBQ/dsl/scales/24hr/@, 🍴 McDonald's, Subway, 🛏 EconoLodge, **W** 🅿 dsl/scales/24hr, Shell/dsl
14	US 64, to Pulaski, **E** 🅿 BP/dsl, Shell/dsl, 🍴 Sarge's Shack Rest., 🛏 Super 8, 🅾 to Jack Daniels Distillery, **W** 🄷, to David Crockett SP
6	rd 273, Bryson, **E** 🅿 Phillips 66/rest./dsl, 🛏 Best Value Inn, 🅾 dsl repair, **W** 🅿 Marathon (2mi)
5mm	weight sta nb
4mm	Elk River
3mm	Welcome Ctr nb, full ♿ facilities, info, 🅲, 🚬, litter barrels, petwalk
1	US 31, rd 7, Ardmore, **E** 🅿 Chevron/dsl, Exxon/Chicken Express/dsl, **1-2 mi E** 🅿 Shell/repair, 🍴 DQ, Hardee's, McDonald's, Subway
0mm	Tennessee/Alabama state line

INTERSTATE 75

N ↑↓ S

B E T H E L

Exit	Services
161.5mm	Tennessee/Kentucky state line
161mm	**Welcome Ctr sb, full ♿ facilities, 🅲, vending, 🚬, litter barrels, petwalk**
160	US 25W, Jellico, **E** 🅿 BP, Exxon/dsl, Marathon/dsl, 🛏 Jellico Motel, **W** 🅿 BP/Wendy's, Shell/Arby's/dsl, 🍴 Hardee's, Heritage Pizza, Subway, 🛏 Best Value Inn, Days Inn/rest., 🅾 🄷, camping, fireworks, to Indian Mtn SP
156	Rarity Mtn Rd
144	Stinking Creek Rd, **4 mi E** 🛏 Ride Royal Blue Camping
141	TN 63, to Royal Blue, Huntsville, **E** 🅿 Shell/Stuckey's/dsl, 🍴 El Rey Mexican, **W** 🅿 Subway/dsl/scales/24hr, Shell/dsl, 🛏 Comfort Inn, 🅾 fireworks, repair/truckwash, to Big South Fork NRA
134	US 25W, TN 63, Caryville, **E** 🅿 Shell, 🍴 Quik Stop BBQ, Takumi Japanese, Waffle House, 🛏 Hampton Inn, Motel 6, Super 8, 🅾 🄷, to Cove Lake SP, Cumberland Gap NHP, **W** 🅿 BP/dsl, 🍴 Shoney's, Scotty's Hamburgers, 🛏 Budget Host, 🅾 USPO
129	US 25W S, Lake City, **W** 🅿 BP/Sonic, Exxon/dsl, dsl/scales/24hr, Shell/dsl, 🍴 Cracker Barrel, Domino's, Glen's Pizza, KFC/Taco Bell, La Fiesta Mexican, McDonald's, Subway, 🛏 Days Inn, Blue Haven Motel, Lamb's Inn/rest., Scottish Inn, 🅾 $General, Family$, fireworks, same as 128
128	US 441, to Lake City, **E** 🅿 BP, Sunoco, 🅾 Mtn Lake Marina Camping (4mi), **W** 🅿 Exxon/dsl, Marathon, Weigel's/dsl, 🛏 Blue Haven Motel, 🅾 Advance Parts, $General, Family$, antique cars, to Norris Dam SP, same as 129
126mm	Clinch River
122	TN 61, Bethel, Norris, **E** 🅿 Shell/dsl, Wiegel's/dsl, 🍴 Shoney's, 🅾 Fox Inn Camping, Suzuki, Toyota/Scion, Museum of Appalachia, antiques, **W** 🅿 BP, Exxon/Burger King/Subway/dsl, Git'n Go, Phillips 66, Shell/Baskin-Robbins, 🍴 Arby's, Golden Girls Rest., Hardee's, Harrison's Grill, Krystal, LJ Silver, McDonald's, Waffle House, Wendy's, Zaxby's, 🛏 Comfort Inn, Country Inn&Suites, Holiday Inn Express, Red Roof Inn, Super 8, Travelodge, 🅾 Ford, Verizon, Walgreens, Walmart/McDonald's, Big Pine Ridge SP
117	rd 170, Racoon Valley Rd, **E** 🅿 dsl/scales/24hr, **W** 🛏 Valley Inn, 🅾 Volunteer RV Park
112	rd 131, Emory Rd, to Powell, **E** 🅿 BP/Buddy's BBQ/dsl, DQ/Taco Bell/dsl, 🍴 Arby's, Aubrey's Rest., Bruster's, Firehouse Subs, 5 Guys Burgers, McDonald's/playplace, Krystal, Ruby Tuesday, Starbucks, Steak'n Shake, Subway, 3 Amigos Mexican, Wendy's, Zaxby's, 🛏 Comfort Inn, Country Inn&Suites, Holiday Inn Express, 🅾 🄷, CVS Drug, Family$, Ingles/gas, O'Reilly Parts, Rigg's Drug, Verizon, **W** 🅿 Exxon/dsl, Shell/dsl, Weigel's/dsl, 🍴 Hardee's,

INTERSTATE 75 CONT'D

KNOXVILLE N ↕ S

Exit	Services
112	Continued
	Shoney's, Waffle House, 🛏 Super 8
110	Callahan Dr, **E** 🅖 Weigel's, 🍴 Asian Cafe, 🛏 Express Inn, Quality Inn/rest., ◎ Honda, **W** 🅖 BP, 🛏 Scottish Inn, ◎ Kia, Mack/Volvo
108	Merchants Dr, **E** 🅖 BP/dsl, Citgo/dsl, 🅟/dsl, Shell/dsl, 🍴 Applebee's, Cracker Barrel, El Chico's, Hooters, Monterrey Mexican, O'Charley's, Pizza Hut, Puelo's Grill, Ramsey's Rest., Starbucks, Waffle House, Wok Hay Asian, 🛏 Best Western, Comfort Suites, Days Inn, Hampton Inn, Mainstay Suites, Quality Inn, Red Roof Inn, Sleep Inn, ◎ Ingles, Valvoline, **W** 🅖 Conoco/dsl, Exxon/dsl, 🅟/dsl, 🍴 Baskin-Robbins, Burger King, Capt D's, Great American Steaks, IHOP, Mandarin House, McDonald's, Nixon's Deli, Outback Steaks, Quaker Steak, Red Lobster, Subway, 🛏 Best Value Inn, Clarion Inn, EconoLodge, Motel 6, Super 8, ◎ CVS Drug, Radio Shack, Walgreens
107	I-640 & I-75
3b [I-640]	US 25W, (from nb), **W** ◎ Chevrolet, Dodge, Ford, Nissan
1 [I-640]	rd 62, Western Ave, **E** 🍴 Hardee's, Krystal, ◎ Advance Parts, O'Reilly Parts, **W** 🅖 Exxon/dsl, Marathon/dsl, RaceWay/dsl, 🍴 Central Park, KFC, Little Caesars, LJ Silver, McDonald's, Panda Chinese, Shoney's, Subway, Taco Bell, Wendy's, ◎ CVS Drug, Kroger/gas, Walgreens
	I-75 and I-40 run together 17 mi. See Interstate 40, exits 369 through 385.
84 ba [368]	I-40, W to Nashville, E to Knoxville
81	US 321, TN 95, to Lenoir City, **E** 🅖 BP/Buddy's BBQ/TCBY/dsl, Exxon/Subway/dsl, Marathon/dsl, Mobil, Murphy USA/dsl, Shell/dsl, 🍴 Angelo's Brick Oven, Bojangles, Burger King, Capt D's, Chili's, China Buffet, Cracker Barrel, Dunkin Donuts, 5 Guys Burgers, Hardee's, KFC, McDonald's, Monterrey Mexican, Panda Buffet, Pizza Hut, Quiznos, Shoney's, Snappy Tomato Pizza, Taco Bell, Waffle House, Wendy's, Zaxby's, 🛏 Days Inn, Hampton Inn, Holiday Inn Express, King's Inn/rest., ◎ Advance Parts, AutoZone, AT&T, CVS Drug, $General Mkt, $Tree, Food City/gas, Ford, Home Depot, Lazy Acres RV Park (7mi), O'Reilly Parts, Radio Shack, Verizon, Walmart/Subway, Great Smokies NP, Ft Loudon Dam, **W** 🅖 Citgo/dsl, Shell/dsl, 🍴 Krystal, Ruby Tuesday, 🛏 Comfort Inn, EconoLodge, Knights Inn, ◎ Crosseyed Cricket Camping (6mi), Matlock Tires/Repair
76	rd 324, Sugar Limb Rd, **W** to TN Valley Winery
74mm	Tennessee River
72	TN 72, to Loudon, **E** 🅖 BP/McDonald's, Shell/Wendy's, 🍴 Cabin Rest., KFC, Taco Bell, 🛏 Country Inn&Suites, Super 8, ◎ Weigel's/dsl, to Ft Loudon SP, **W** 🅖 Marathon, 🛏 Best Value Inn, ◎ Express RV Park
68	rd 323, to Philadelphia, **E** 🅖 BP/dsl, Sunoco (2mi), 🍴 cheese factory/store (2mi)
62	RD 322, Oakland Rd, to Sweetwater, **E** 🍴 Dinner Bell Rest., **W** ◎ KOA
60	TN 68, Sweetwater, **0-2 mi E** 🅖 BP, RaceWay, Shell/dsl, 🍴 A&W/LJ Silver, Bradley's BBQ, Burger King, Hardee's, KFC, McDonald's, Pizza Hut, Sonic, Subway, Taco Bell, 🛏 Comfort Inn, Days Inn, EconoLodge, Economy Inn, Hilltop Motel, ◎ 🅷, Ace Hardware, Advance Parts, $General, O'Reilly Parts, $General, Family$, Ford/Lincoln/Mercury,

SWEETWATER

TN

ATHENS CLEVELAND

Exit	Services
60	Continued
	K-Mart, Verizon, Walgreens, to Lost Sea Underground Lake, **W** 🅖 Marathon, Kangaroo/dsl, 🛏 Magnuson Hotel, Quality Inn, ◎ flea mkt, to Watts Bar Dam, tires/repair, vet
56	rd 309, Niota, **E** 🅖 Wilco/Stuckey's/Wendy's/dsl/scales/24hr, ◎ TN Country Camping, **W** tires
52	rd 305, Mt Verd Rd, to Athens, **E** 🅖 Marathon/dsl (2mi), 🍴 Subway (2mi), ◎ Overniter RV Park, **W** 🅖 BP, 🛏 Athens Lodge
49	TN 30, to Athens, **E** 🅖 BP, Marathon, Murphy USA/dsl, Kangaroo, RaceWay, Shell/dsl, 🍴 Applebee's, Arby's, Buddy's BBQ, Burger King, Capt D's, China Wok, Firehouse Subs, Hardee's, KFC, Krystal, McDonald's, Monterrey Mexican, Papa John's, Pizza Hut, Ruby Tuesday, Shoney's, Sonic, Subway, Taco Bell, Waffle House, Wendy's, Western Sizzlin, Zaxby's, 🛏 Days Inn, Hampton Inn, Holiday Inn Express, Homestead Inn, Motel 6, Scottish Inn, Super 8, ◎ 🅷, Advance Parts, Athens I-75 Camping, Big Lots, $General, Food Lion, K-Mart, Lowe's, Russell Stover, Staples, Verizon, Walgreens, Walmart/Subway, to TN Wesleyan Coll, **W** 🅖 Shell, 🍴 Cracker Barrel, 🛏 Best Value Inn, Comfort Inn
45mm	**rest areas, both lanes, full ♿ facilities, 🛏 litter barrels, 🅲, petwalk, vending**
42	rd 39, Riceville Rd, **E** 🅖 Citgo/dsl, 🛏 Relax Inn, Rice Inn (2mi)
36	rd 163, to Calhoun, **E** 🍴 Hardee's (3mi), ◎ Hiwassee/Ocoee River SP
35mm	Hiwassee River
33	rd 308, to Charleston, **E** 🅖 Marathon/dsl, **W** 🅖 Loves/McDonald's/Subway/dsl/scales/24hr, Shell/rest./dsl
27	Paul Huff Pkwy, **1 mi E** 🅖 Murphy USA, Phillips 66, 🍴 Applebee's, Capt D's, Chili's, CiCi's, DQ, Fazoli's, Firehouse Subs, 5 Guys Burgers, Golden Corral, IHOP, McDonald's, O'Charley's, Outback Steaks, Panera Bread, Pizza Hut, Ryan's, Sonic, Steak'n Shake, Taco Bell, Takoyaki, 🛏 Jameson Inn, ◎ Aldi Foods, AutoZone, Belk, Buick/Cadillac/GMC, CVS Drug, $Tree, Food Lion, Hobby Lobby, Home Depot, JC Penney, K-Mart, Lowe's, PetCo, Radio Shack, Rite Aid, Sears, Staples, TJ Maxx, Verizon, Walgreens, Walmart, auto repair/tires, mall, **W** 🅖 BP/dsl, Exxon/dsl, Shell/Subway, 🍴 Denny's, Fulin's Asian, Hardee's, Shane's Ribshack, Stevi B's Pizza, Waffle House, Wendy's, 🛏 Classic Suites, Hampton Inn, Quality Inn, Ramada Ltd, Royal Inn, Super 8, ◎ AT&T, Books-A-Million, Kohl's, Michael's, Ross, Target
25	TN 60, Cleveland, **E** 🅖 Chevron/dsl, RaceWay/dsl, Shell/dsl, 🍴 Bojangles, Burger King, Checker's, Cracker Barrel, Hardee's, McDonald's, Sonic, Waffle House, Wendy's, Zaxby's, 🛏 Colonial Inn, Days Inn, Douglas Inn, EconoLodge, Economy Inn, Fairfield Inn, Howard Johnson, Knights Inn, Travel Inn, ◎ 🅷, Ace Hardware, BigLots, Cherokee Drug, $General, Tuesday Morning, vet, to Lee Coll, **W** 🅖 Shell, 🛏 Comfort Inn, Mtn View Inn, Wingate Inn
23mm	**truck/weigh sta nb**
20	US 64 byp, to Cleveland. **1-4 mi E** 🅖 FuelMart, ◎ Ford, Honda, **W** 🅖 BP/DQ/Pizza Hut/dsl, Exxon/dsl, ◎ KOA (1mi), Toyota/Scion, fireworks
16mm	scenic view sb
13mm	**truck/weigh sta, litter barrels sb**
11	US 11 N, US 64 E, Ooltewah, **E** 🅖 BP, Murphy USA/dsl, RaceWay/dsl, Shell, 🍴 Arby's, Bojangles, Burger King,

INTERSTATE 75 CONT'D

Exit	Services
11	Continued

Cracker Barrel, Capt D's, China Rose, El Matador Mexican, Hardee's, Little Caesars, McDonald's, Sonic, Subway, Taco Bell, Wendy's, Zaxby's, 🏨 Hampton Inn, Holiday Inn Express, ⊙ Ace Hardware, Bi-Lo, GNC, O'Reilly Parts, Verizon, Walgreens, Walmart/Subway, **W** ⛽ BP/Quiznos/dsl, 🍴 Krystal, Waffle House, 🏨 Super 8, ⊙ Publix, to Harrison Bay SP

9	Volkswagon Dr
7b a	US 11, US 64, Lee Hwy, **E** ⛽ Exxon/dsl, **W** ⛽ Shell, 🍴 City Cafe, Waffle House, 🏨 Best Inn, Best Value Inn, Best Western, Comfort Inn, EconoLodge, Motel 6, ⊙ Harley-Davidson, Jaguar/Land Rover/Porsche, repair
5	Shallowford Rd, **E** 🍴 Alexander's, Arby's, Capt. D's, Chili's, Chophouse Rest., CiCi's, Country Place Rest., DQ, Famous Dave's, J. Alexanders, Krystal, Logan's Roadhouse, Macaroni Grill, McAlister's Deli, McDonald's/playplace, Outback Steaks, Smokey Bones BBQ, Starbucks, Steak'n Shake, Souper Salad, Taco Bell, Zaxby's, 🏨 Courtyard, Quality Inn, Wingate Inn, ⊙ AAA, Barnes&Noble, Best Buy, Books-A-Million, Firestone/auto, Ford, FreshMkt Foods, Hobby Lobby, Home Depot, Lowe's, Office Depot, Old Navy, Petsmart, SteinMart, Target, Walgreens, Walmart/Subway, World Mkt, **W** ⛽ BP, Citgo/dsl, Exxon, Shell, 🍴 Applebee's, Blimpie, Cracker Barrel, Fazoli's, Fuji Steaks, GlenGene Deli, O'Charley's, Papa John's, Shoney's, Sonic, Subway, TX Roadhouse, Waffle House, Wendy's, 🏨 Clarion, Comfort Inn, Country Inn&Suites, Fairfield Inn, Guesthouse Inn, Hampton Inn, Hilton Garden, Homewood Suites, Knights Inn, La Quinta, MainStay Suites, Microtel, Ramada Ltd, Red Roof Inn, Residence Inn, Sleep Inn, Staybridge Suites, Super 8, ⊙ 🏥, Bi-Lo, CVS Drug, Goodyear/auto, U of TN/Chatt, same as 4a
4a	(from nb)Hamilton Place Blvd, **E** 🍴 Abuelo's, Acropolis, Big River Grille, BoneFish Grill, Carraba's, DQ, El Mason, Firehouse Subs, 5 Guys Burgers, Fox&Hound Grill, Golden Corral, Jason's Deli, Moe's SW Grill, Olive Garden, Outback Steaks, Panera Bread, PF Chang's, Piccadilly's, Red Lobster, Ruby Tuesday, Salsarita's Mexican, Shogun Japanese, Starbucks, Sticky Fingers BBQ, Kampai Of Tokyo, 🏨 InTown Suites, ⊙ AAA, Belk, Dillard's, Firestone, JC Penney, Kohl's, Marshall's, Michael's, Ross, Sears/auto, Staples, Target, TJ Maxx, mall, same as 5
4	TN 153, Chickamauga Dam Rd, 🍴
3b a	TN 320, Brainerd Rd, **E** ⛽ BP, 🍴 Baskin-Robbins, Subway, **W** ⊙ BMW
2	I-24 W, to I-59, to Chattanooga, Lookout Mtn
1.5mm	**Welcome Ctr nb, full ♿ facilities, 🚰 vending, 🛱, litter barrels, petwalk**
1b a	US 41, Ringgold Rd, to Chattanooga, **E** ⛽ BP, Texaco/dsl, 🍴 Wendy's, 🏨 Best Value Inn, Comfort Inn, Country Hearth Inn, Crown Inn, Knights Inn, Motel 6, Ramada Ltd, ⊙ Bi~Lo Foods, Camping World RV Ctr/park, Family$, **W** ⛽ Conoco/dsl, Mapco, 🍴 A&W/LJ Silver, Arby's, Baskin-Robbins, Burger King, Central Park Burger, Cracker Barrel, Hardee's, Krystal, McDonald's, PortoFino Italian, Shoney's, Subway, Taco Bell, Teriyaki House, Uncle Bud's Catfish, Waffle House, Wally's Rest., 🏨 Day's Inn,

1b a	Continued
	Fairfield Inn, Holiday Inn Express, Super 8, Superior Creek Lodge, Waverly Motel, ⊙ Holiday Travel Park, O'Reilly Parts, U-Haul
0mm	Tennessee/Georgia state line

INTERSTATE 81

Exit	Services
75mm	**Tennessee/Virginia state line, Welcome Ctr sb, full ♿ facilities, info, 🚰, vending, 🛱, litter barrels, petwalk**
74b a	US 11W, to Bristol, Kingsport, **E** 🏨 Hampton Inn, ⊙ 🏥, **W** ⛽ Valero, 🏨 Bristol Inn
69	TN 394, to Blountville, **E** ⛽ BP/Subway/dsl, 🍴 Arby's, Burger King (1mi), McDonald's, ⊙ Advance Parts, Bristol Int Speedway, Lakeview RV Park (8mi)
66	TN 126, to Kingsport, Blountville, **W** ⛽ Chevron/24hr, 🍴 McDonald's
63	rd 357, Tri-City 🛬, **E** ⛽ BP/Krystal/dsl, Shell/Subway/dsl/24hr, 🍴 Cracker Barrel, Wendy's, 🏨 La Quinta, Sleep Inn, ⊙ Hamricks, **W** ⛽ Citgo/dsl, 🏨 Red Carpet Inn, ⊙ KOA, Rocky Top Camping
60mm	Holston River
59	RD 36, to Johnson City, Kingsport, **E** ⛽ BP/dsl, 🏨 Super 8, **W** ⛽ BP/TCBY/LP, Shell/dsl, Sunoco, Zoomerz, 🍴 Arby's, Crazy Tomato, Hardee's, HotDog Hut, La Carreta Mexican, Little Caesar's, McDonald's, Pal's Drive-Thru, Perkins, Pizza Hut, Sonic, Subway, 🏨 Best Western, Comfort Inn, ⊙ Advance Parts, Curves, CVS Drug, $General, $Tree, Firestone/auto, Food City/gas, Ingles/deli, Walgreens, USPO, vet, to Warrior's Path SP
57b a	I-26
56	Tri-Cities Crossing
50	TN 93, Fall Branch, **W** ⊙ auto auction, st patrol
44	Jearoldstown Rd, **E** ⛽ Marathon
41mm	**rest area sb, full ♿ facilities, 🚰, vending, 🛱, litter barrels, petwalk**
38mm	**rest area nb, full ♿ facilities, 🚰, vending, 🛱, litter barrels, petwalk**
36	RD 172, to Baileyton, **E** ⛽ ▦/Subway/dsl/scales, **W** ⛽ BP/dsl/24hr, Shell/Subway/dsl/24hr, TA/Country Pride/dsl/scales/24hr/@, 🍴 Pizza+, 🏨 36 Motel, ⊙ Around Pond RV Park, Baileyton Camp (2mi), $General, Family$
30	TN 70, to Greeneville, **E** ⛽ Exxon/DQ/Stuckey's/dsl
23	US 11E, to Greeneville, **E** ⛽ BP/Wendy's, Zoomerz/Subway, ⊙ Tri-Am RV Ctr, to Andrew Johnson HS, Crockett SP, **W** ⛽ Exxon/DQ, dsl, Phillips 66/dsl/rest./scales, 🍴 McDonald's, Pizza+, Taco Bell, Tony's BBQ, 🏨 Best Western, Super 8
21mm	**weigh sta sb**

CHATTANOOGA

KINGSPORT

N S

INTERSTATE 81 CONT'D

Exit	Services
15	RD 340, Fish Hatchery Rd
12	TN 160, to Morristown, **E** 🫰 Phillips 66, **W** 🫰 Shell/dsl, 🛏 Days Inn (6mi), Hampton Inn (12mi), Motel 6 (6mi), ⊙ to Crockett Tavern HS
8	US 25E, to Morristown, **E** 🫰 Shell/dsl/repair, 🍽 Sonic (2mi), 🛏 Twin Pines Motel (3mi), **W** 🫰 BP/dsl, 🍽 Cracker Barrel, Hardee's, 🛏 Holiday Inn/rest., Parkway Inn, Super 8, ⊙ to Cumberland Gap NHP
4	rd 341, White Pine, **E** 🫰 ⛽/McDonald's/dsl/scales/24hr, 🛏 Crown Inn, **W** 🫰 Wilco/Hess/Wendy's/dsl/scales/24hr, 🛏 Days Inn, ⊙ to Panther Cr SP
2.5mm	**rest area sb, full** 🦽 **facilities,** ⊙, 🛗, **litter barrels, vending, petwalk**
1b a	I-40, E to Asheville, W to Knoxville. I-81 begins/ends on I-40, exit 421.

INTERSTATE 640 (Knoxville)

Exit	Services
9mm	I-640 begins/ends on I-40, exit 393.
8	Millertown Pike, Mall Rd N, **N** 🫰 Exxon/DQ/24hr, Shell, 🍽 Applebee's, Burger King, Don Pablos, Gunthor's, KFC, Krystal, McDonald's, Pizza Hut, Taco Bell,

Left margin: N ↕ S

Right margin (I-81/640): K N O X V I L L E   E ↕ W

8	Continued TX Roadhouse, Wendy's, ⊙ Belk, $General, Food City, JC Penney, Kohl's, Marshall's, NTB, Old Navy, Ross, Sam's Club, Sears/auto, Target, Walmart, mall, **S** 🫰 Shell, 🍽 Cracker Barrel, Little Caesars, O'Charley's, Subway, ⊙ Food Lion, Home Depot, Lowe's Whse, PepBoys
6	US 441, to Broadway, **N** 🫰 Citgo, Phillips 66, ⛽/dsl, Shell, 🍽 Arby's, Austin's Steaks, Cancun Mexican, Chop House, CiCi's, Fazoli's, Hardee's, Krispy Kreme, Lenny's Subs, LJ Silver, Marble Slab, McDonald's, Panera Bread, Papa John's, Ruby Tuesday, Sonic, Subway, Taco Bell, ⊙ Advance Parts, AutoZone, BigLots, CVS Drug, $General, Firestone, Food City/gas, Kroger/24hr, Walgreens, repair/tires, **S** 🍽 Buddy's BBQ, Little Caesars, Shoney's, ⊙ $General, Food City, K-Mart, Office Depot
3a	I-75 N to Lexington, I-275 S to Knoxville
3b	US 25W, Clinton Hwy, (from eb), **N** ⊙ Chevrolet, Dodge, Ford, Nissan, services on frontage rds
1	TN 62, Western Ave, **N** 🫰 Exxon/dsl, Marathon/dsl, Raceway/dsl, 🍽 Central Park, KFC, Little Caesars, LJ Silver, McDonald's, Panda Chinese, Shoney's, Subway, Taco Bell, Wendy's, ⊙ CVS Drug, Kroger/gas, Walgreens, **S** 🍽 Hardee's, Krystal, ⊙ Advance Parts, O'Reilly Parts,
0mm	I-640 begins/ends on I-40, exit 385.

TEXAS

INTERSTATE 10

Exit	Services
880.5mm	Texas/Louisiana state line, Sabine River
880	Sabine River Turnaround, RV camping
870mm	**Welcome Ctr wb, full** 🦽 **facilities,** ⊙, 🛗, **litter barrels, vending, petwalk**
878	US 90, Orange, **N** 🫰 Mobil/dsl, ⊙ airboat rides, RV Park, **S** ⊙ Western Store
877	TX 87, 16th St, Orange, **N** 🫰 Exxon/dsl, Shamrock/dsl, 🍽 Pizza Hut, Subway, 🛏 Hampton Inn, ⊙ Ace Hardware, $General, Market Basket/deli, **S** 🫰 Exxon, Kwik Stop, Shell/dsl, Valero/dsl, 🍽 Casa Ole, Church's, DQ, General Wok, Jack-in-the-Box, McDonald's, Popeye's, Sonic, Taco Bell, 2 Amigo's Mexican, ⊙ CVS Drug, Goodyear/auto, HEB Foods, Kroger/dsl, Modica Tires, O'Reilly Parts, Verizon, Walgreens
876	Adams Bayou, frontage rd, Adams Bayou, **N** 🫰 Mobil/dsl, 🍽 Cajun Cookery, Gary's Café, Taste of Orange Rest., Waffle House, 🛏 Best Value, Days Inn, EconoLodge, Executive Inn, Ramada Inn, Super 8, ⊙ Toyota, **S** 🫰 Chevron/dsl, 🛏 Holiday Inn Express, same as 877
875	FM 3247, MLK Dr, **S** ⊙ Ⓗ, Chrysler/Dodge/Jeep
874	US 90, Womack Rd, to Orange, **S** Ⓗ
873	TX 62, TX 73, to Bridge City, **N** 🫰 Exxon/dsl/24hr, ✈FLYING J/Denny's/dsl/LP/scales/24hr, 🛏 Studio 6, ⊙ Oak Leaf RV Park, **S** ⛽/Subway/Wendy's/dsl/scales/24hr, Shell/Church's/dsl, Valero, 🍽 Jack-in-the-Box, McDonald's, Sonic, Waffle House, Whataburger, 🛏 Comfort Inn, La Quinta, Sleep Inn
872	N Mimosa Ln, Jackson Dr, from wb
870	FM 1136
869	FM 1442, to Bridge City, **S** 🫰 Chevron, ⊙ Lloyd's RV Ctr
868.5mm	**rest areas both lanes, full** 🦽 **facilities, vending,** 🛗, **litter barrels**

Left margin (I-10): E ↕ W   O R A N G E

867	frontage rd (from eb)
865	Doty Rd (from wb), frontage rd
864	FM 1132, FM 1135, **N** 🛏 Budget Inn, ⊙ TX Star RV Park
862	Lakeside St, Timberlane Dr, **N** 🫰 Conoco
861	FM 105, Deweyville, Mauriceville, **N** 🫰 Chevron/dsl, Conoco/dsl, Shell, Valero, 🍽 Casa Ole, Church's, DQ, Domino's, Jack-in-the-Box, Little Caesars, McDonald's/playplace, Ming's Buffet, Popeye's, Waffle House, ⊙ Family$, Mktbasket Foods, O'Reilly Parts, Radio Shack, Walgreens, **S** 🫰 Exxon/dsl, Texaco, 🍽 Burger King, Pizza Hut, Sonic, Subway, Taco Bell, Whataburger, 🛏 Holiday Inn, La Quinta, ⊙ Family$, auto repair, tires
860	Dewitt Rd, frontage rd, W Vidor, **S** 🫰 Exxon/dsl, Texaco, 🍽 Burger King, Sonic, Subway, Taco Bell, Whataburger, 🛏 Holiday Inn Express, La Quinta, ⊙ Family$, repair
859	Bonner Turnaround (from eb), Asher Turnaround (from wb), **N** ⊙ Boomtown RV Park, **S** 🫰 Chevron/Spindletop/dsl/24hr
858	Rose City
856	Old Hwy 90 (from eb), Rose City
855b	Magnolia St (from wb)
855a	US 90 bus, to downtown, Port of Beaumont
854	ML King Pkwy, Beaumont, **N** 🍽 Jack-in-the-Box, **S** 🫰 Exxon, Shamrock/dsl, 🍽 McDonald's
853b	11th St, **N** 🫰 Valero, 🍽 Cafe Del Rio, Red Lobster, Waffle House, 🛏 Best Value, Days Inn, Motel 6, Red Carpet Inn, Sleep Inn, Studio 6, Super 8, Travel Inn, ⊙ MktBasket, **S** 🫰 Shamrock, Texaco/dsl, 🍽 Checker's, Chula Vista Mexican, Dunkin Donuts, Luby's, Popeye's, 🛏 Howard Johnson Express, Rodeway Inn, ⊙ Ⓗ
853a	US 69 N, to Lufkin
852	Harrison Ave, Calder Ave, Beaumont, **N** 🫰 Shell/dsl, Valero/dsl, 🍽 Casa Ole Mexican, Chili's, Frankie's Italian, Olive Garden, Saltgrass Steaks, Willie Ray's BBQ, **S** 🍽 Church's, McDonald's, 🛏 EconoLodge, La Quinta, ⊙ Ⓗ

Right margin (I-10): V I D O R

Lower left tab: **TN** / **TX**

B E A U M O N T

E ↑ ↓ W

INTERSTATE 10 CONT'D

Exit	Services
851	US 90, College St, **N** 🅖 Chevron/dsl, Exxon/dsl, Raceway, 🍴 Acapulco Mexican, Carrabba's, Floyd's Cajun Cafe, Golden Corral, Hooters, Outback Steaks, Tokyo Japanese, Waffle House, 🛏 Best Value, Best Western, Quality Inn, Ramada, Red Roof Inn, 🅾 Advance Parts, AutoZone, GMC, Harley-Davidson, Honda, Nissan, O'Reilly Parts, Volvo Trucks, **S** 🅖 Exxon, Mobil, Shell, 🍴 Baytown Sea🍴 China Garden, IHOP, Issac Lee's Crabs, Jason's Deli, KFC, Pizza Hut, Quiznos, Sonic, Taco Bell, Wendy's, Whataburger, 🛏 Courtyard, Economy Inn, Elegante Motel, Fairfield Inn, Motel 6, ValuePlace Hotel, 🅾 🏥, BMW, Chrysler/Jeep, CVS Drug, Discount Tire, Dodge, $Tree, Firestone/auto, GMC/Cadillac, HEB Foods, Honda, Jeep, Mercedes, Nissan, NTB, Office Depot, Radio Shack, Sam's Club/gas, U-Haul, Walgreens
850	wb only, same as 851
849	US 69 S, Washington Blvd, to Port Arthur 🔄
848	Walden Rd, **N** 🅖 Shell, 🍴 Pappadeaux Sea🍴 Sonic, 🛏 Comfort Suites, Holiday Inn/rest., La Quinta, 🅾 USPO, **S** 🅖 Petro/Mobil/dsl/scales/24hr/@, Shell, 🍴 Carino's Italian, Cheddar's, Cracker Barrel, Jack-in-the-Box, Joe's Crabshack, Waffle House, 🛏 Candlewood Suites, Courtyard, Hampton Inn, Homewood Suites, Hilton Garden, Knights Inn, Residence Inn, Super 8, 🅾 Blue Beacon
847	Brooks Rd (from wb), (845 from eb), **S** 🅾 Gulf Coast RV Resort
843	Smith Rd
838	FM 365, Fannett, **N** 🍴 Alligator Park/Rest., Bar-H BBQ, 🅾 T&T RV Park
837.5mm	cmv sta wb
833	Hamshire Rd, **N** 🅖 Chevron/dsl, 🍴 Bergerons Rest.
829	FM 1663, Winnie, **N** 🅖 Exxon/dsl, Shell/dsl/24hr, Texaco/Burger King/dsl, 🍴 McDonald's, Taco Bell,

W I N N I E

829	Continued Whataburger/24hr, 🛏 Days Inn, 🅾 RV Park, **S** 🅖 Chevron/Chester's/dsl, Mobil/Pizza Hut/Subway/dsl/scales, 🍴 Al-T's Sea🍴 Hart's Chicken, Jack-in-the-Box, Subway, Waffle House, 🛏 Comfort Inn, EconoLodge, Hampton Inn, Holiday Inn Express, Home Suites, La Quinta, Motel 6, Studio 6, Winnie Inn/RV Park, 🅾 🏥
828	TX 73, TX 124 (from eb), to Winnie, **S** 🏥, same as 829
827	FM 1406
822	FM 1410
819	Jenkins Rd, **S** 🅖 Exxon/Stuckey's/Chester's/dsl
817	FM 1724
814	frontage rd, from eb
813	TX 61 (from wb), Hankamer, **N** 🅖 Shell/dsl, 🛏 Days Inn, **S** 🅖 Exxon/DJ's Diner/dsl, 🍴 McDonald's, same as 812
812	TX 61, Hankamer
811	Turtle Bayou Turnaround, **S** 🅖 Gator Jct/dsl, 🅾 Turtle Bayou RV Park
810	FM 563, to Anahuac, Liberty, **S** 🅖 Chevron/dsl, Texaco/Jack-in-the-Box/dsl
807	to Wallisville, **S** 🅾 Heritage Park
805.5mm	Trinity River
804mm	Old, Lost Rivers
803	FM 565, Cove, Old River-Winfrey, **N** 🅾 Paradise Cove RV Park, **S** 🅖 Valero/dsl

TX

INTERSTATE 10 CONT'D

BAYTOWN · E → W · HOUSTON

Exit	Services
800	FM 3180, N 🅖 Exxon/dsl
799	TX 99, Grand Pkwy
797	(798 from wb) TX 146, 99 toll, Baytown, N 🅖 Chevron, Conoco/Subway/dsl/scales, Shell/dsl, 🍴 DQ, McDonald's, Waffle House, 🛏 Crystal Inn, Motel 6, Super 8, 🅞 L&R RV Park, Value RV Park, S 🅖 Exxon, Texaco/Popeye's/dsl, RaceWay/dsl, 🍴 Baytown Sea🍴 Jack-in-the-Box, KFC/Taco Bell, Sonic, 🅞 🏥, Houston East RV Park, RV Service, vet
796	frontage rd, N 🅖 Chevron/Phillips/Chemical Refinery
795	Sjolander Rd
793	N Main St, S 🅖 Valero/Hartz Chicken/dsl/24hr
792	Garth Rd, N 🅖 Chevron/dsl, 🍴 Cracker Barrel, Denny's, Jack-in-the-Box, Red Lobster, Richard's Cajun, Sonic, Starbucks, Tuscany Italian, Waffle House, Whataburger, 🛏 Comfort Suites, Days Inn, EconoLodge, Hampton Inn, La Quinta, SpringHill Suites, 🅞 Buick/GMC, Chrysler/Jeep/Dodge, Honda, Hyundai, Kia, Lincoln/Mercury, Nissan, O'Reilly Parts, Toyota/Scion, Walgreens, S 🅖 RaceWay/dsl, Shell/dsl, 🍴 Bravos's Mexican, Buffalo Wild Wings, Carino's Italian, Chili's, Chinese Buffet, McDonald's, Olive Garden, Outback Steaks, Pizza Hut/Taco Bell, Popeye's, Subway, Tortuga Mexican, Wendy's, 🛏 Candlewood Suites, Palace Inn, Sleep Inn, ValuePlace Hotel, 🅞 🏥, $General, JC Penney, Kohl's, Macy's, Marshall's, Michael's, Sears/auto, Tuesday Morning, Verizon
791	John Martin Rd, S 🍴 Cheddars, 🅞 Cadillac/Chevrolet, Ford
790	Ellis School Rd, N 🛏 Super 8
789	Thompson Rd, N 🅖 Loves/McDonald's/dsl/scales/@, Valero/dsl, S 🅖 FLYING J/Denny's/dsl/LP/scales/RV dump/24hr, TA/SpeedCo Lube/dsl/rest./24hr/scales/@, 🅞 Blue Beacon
788.5mm	**rest area eb, full ♿ facilities, 🍴, 🚻, litter barrels, petwalk**
788	sp 330 (from eb), to Baytown
787	sp 330, Crosby-Lynchburg Rd, to Highlands, N 🅖 Texaco/Domino's/dsl, 🅞 RV Camping (1mi), S 🅖 Phillips 66/dsl, 🍴 Four Corners BBQ, 🅞 to San Jacinto SP, camping
786.5mm	San Jacinto River
786	Monmouth Dr
785	Magnolia Ave, to Channelview, N 🅖 Shell/dsl, S 🅖 Exxon/dsl, truckwash
784	Cedar Lane, Bayou Dr, N 🅖 Valero/dsl, 🛏 Budget Lodge, Knights Inn
783	Sheldon Rd, N 🅖 Shell, Texaco/dsl, Valero, 🍴 Burger King, Church's, Jack-in-the-Box, Pizza Hut, Popeye's, Subway, Taco Bell, Whataburger, 🛏 Best Value, Days Inn, Economy Inn, Holiday Inn, Leisure Inn, Parkway Inn, Travelers Inn, 🅞 Advance Parts, AutoZone, Discount Tire, Family$, FoodFair, USPO, S 🅖 Chevron, Texaco/dsl, 🍴 McDonald's, Scottish Inn, Wendy's, 🛏 Deluxe Inn, Fairfield Inn, Scottish Inn
782	Dell-Dale Ave, N 🅖 Exxon, 🛏 Dell-Dale Motel, Economy Inn, Palace Inn, 🅞 🏥, S 🅞 Channelview RV Ctr
781b	Market St, N 🛏 Clarion, 🅞 🏥
781a	TX 8, Sam Houston Pkwy
780	(779a from wb)Uvalde Rd, Freeport St, N 🅖 Chevron/dsl, Texaco, 🍴 Capt Tom's Sea🍴 China Dragon, IHOP,

HOUSTON

Exit	Services
780	Continued Jack-in-the-Box, KFC, Panda Express, Shipley Donuts, Sonic, Subway, Taco Bell, Taco Cabana, 🅞 🏥, Aamco, Ace Hardware, $Tree, Office Depot, S 🍴 Baytown Sea🍴 Golden Corral, 🅞 Firestone, Home Depot, Sam's Club/gas, Walmart/McDonald's
779b	N 🅖 Mobil, Valero, 🍴 China Dragon, IHOP, Jack-in-the-Box, KFC, Panda Express, Shipley's Donuts, Sonic, Subway, Taco Cabana, 🛏 Interstate Motel, 🅞 Ace Hardware, $Tree, Office Depot
778b	Normandy St, N 🅖 Shell/Jack-in-the-Box, Texaco/dsl, 🍴 Golden Corral, 🛏 La Quinta, S 🅖 Citgo, Shell, 🍴 Church's, 🛏 Normandy Inn, Scottish Inn, 🅞 Verizon
778a	FM 526, Federal Rd, Pasadena, N 🅖 Shell, 🍴 Burger King, Casa Ole Mexican, Denny's, Jack-in-the-Box, KFC/Taco Bell, Pizza Hut, Popeye's, Subway, Wendy's, 🛏 La Quinta, 🅞 CVS Drug, HEB Foods, Kroger/gas, Target, 🍴 Joe's Crabshack, McDonald's, Sonic, 🛏 Lamplight Inn, 🅞 AutoZone, Discount Tire
776b	John Ralston Rd, Holland Ave, N 🅖 Chevron, 🍴 Chinese Buffet, Denny's, Fuddruckers, Luby's, Mambo Sea🍴 Pappasito's Cantina, Rancho Del Viejo, Subway, 🛏 Best Western, Candlewood Suites, Comfort Inn, Day Inn, La Quinta, Palace Inn, Regency Inn, 🅞 Family$, Fiesta Foods, Kroger/deli, NTB, S same as 778
776a	Mercury Dr, N 🍴 Aranda's Mexican, Burger King, McDonald's, TX Grill, 🛏 Baymont Inn, Best Western, Days Inn, Premier Inn, Quality Inn, 🅞 Volvo Trucks, S 🅖 Shell/dsl, Valero, 🍴 Chili's, Chula's Mexican, Cici's Pizza, James Coney Island, Murphy's Deli, Pappa's Sea🍴 Peking Bo Chinese, Saltgrass Steaks, 🛏 Holiday Inn Express, Super 8, 🅞 CVS Drug, O'Reilly Parts
775b a	I-610
774	Gellhorn (from eb) Blvd, Anheuser-Busch Brewery
773b	McCarty St, N 🅖 Mobil/dsl, Shell
773a	US 90A, N Wayside Dr, N 🅖 Speedy/dsl, 🍴 Jack-in-the-Box, Whataburger, S 🅖 Chevron/dsl, Shell, Texaco, 🍴 Church's, 🅞 HEB Foods, NAPA, dsl repair
772	Kress St, Lathrop St, N 🅖 Conoco, Exxon, 🍴 Popeye's, S 🍴 Burger King, Seafood Rest.
771b	Lockwood Dr, N 🅖 Chevron/Subway/dsl, 🍴 McDonald's, 🅞 Family$, Walgreens, S 🅖 Shell/dsl, 🛏 Palace Inn
771a	Waco St
770c	US 59 N
770b	Jenson St, Meadow St, Gregg St
770a	US 59 S, to Victoria
769c	McKee St, Hardy St, Nance St downtown
769a	Smith St (from wb), to downtown
768b a	I-45, N to Dallas, S to Galveston
767b	Taylor St
767a	Studemont Dr, Yale St, Heights Blvd, S 🅖 Shell/dsl, 🍴 Arby's, Chili's, Jason's Deli, Subway, 🅞 Petsmart, Staples, Target
766	(from wb), Heights Blvd, Yale St
765b	N Durham Dr, N Shepherd Dr, N 🅖 Shell/dsl, 🍴 Wendy's, 🛏 Howard Johnson, 🅞 vet, S 🅖 Valero/dsl
765a	TC Jester Blvd, N 🍴 Wendy's, S 🅖 Exxon/dsl, Texaco/dsl, 🍴 Quiznos, Starbucks
764	Westcott St, Washington Ave, Katy Rd, N 🍴 Denny's, 🛏 Comfort Inn, S 🅖 Chevron, 🍴 IHOP, 🛏 Scottish Inn
763	I-610
762	Silber Rd, Post Oak Rd, N 🍴 Cafe Adobe, Panda

INTERSTATE 10 CONT'D

Exit	Services
762	Continued
	Express, Quiznos, Red Robin, SteaKountry, Wings&More, 🄾 Dodge, Firestone/auto, **S** 🅰 Shell, 🍴 Jack-in-the-Box, 🏨 Best Western, Holiday Inn Express, Plaza Hotel, Ramada Inn, 🄾 Chevrolet, NTB, carwash
761b	Antoine Rd, **N** 🍴 Hunan Chinese, **S** 🅰 Exxon, Shell, 🍴 Blue Oyster Grill, McDonald's, Papa John's, Subway, Whataburger/24hr, 🏨 Wellesley Inn, 🄾 Chrysler/Dodge/Jeep, CVS Drug, NTB
761a	Wirt Rd, Chimney Rock Rd, **S** 🅰 Chevron, Exxon/TCBY, Shell, 🍴 McDonald's
760	Bingle Rd, Voss Rd, **N** 🍴 Hunan Chef, Starbucks, Subway, 🄾 AT&T, Home Depot, **S** 🅰 Citgo, Mobil, Shell, 🍴 Goode Co BBQ, Marie Callender, Mason Jar Rest., Pappy's Café, Redwood Grill, SaltGrass Steaks, Sweet Tomatos, 🄾 Ⓗ
759	Campbell Rd (from wb), same as 758b
758b	Blalock Rd, Campbell Rd, **N** 🍴 Ciro's Italian, Sonic, 🄾 Adam's Automotive, Lowe's, LubeStop, Mail It, cleaners, **S** 🅰 Chevron/McDonald's/dsl, Exxon, Texaco, 🄾 Ⓗ, Kroger, Walgreens
758a	Bunker Hill Rd, **N** 🅰 Exxon, 🍴 Arby's, Boudreaux's Cajun, CiCi's, Dennys, Five Guys Burgers, Olive Garden, Panda Express, Quiznos, 🄾 Best Buy, Costco/gas, HEB Foods, Lowe's, Michael's, PepBoys, Radio Shack, **S** 🅰 Texaco/dsl, Circle K, 🍴 Charlie's Burgers, Guadalajara Mexican, Quiznos, Subway, 🏨 Days Inn, Howard Johnson, Super 8, 🄾 Ford, Goodyear/auto, Marshall's, Nissan, Ross, Target
757	Gessner Rd, **N** 🍴 Chili's, Cici's, DQ, McDonald's, Olive Garden, Schlotsky's, Taco Bell, SteaKountry, Wendy's, Whataburger/24hr, 🄾 CVS Drug, Hobby Lobby, Home Depot, NAPA, Petsmart, Radio Shack, Sam's Club/gas, U-Haul, **S** 🍴 59 Diner, Fuddrucker's, Goode Co. Sea🍴 Jason's Deli, Pappasito's, Papadeaux Sea🍴 Perry's Steaks, Taste of TX Rest., 🏨 Sheraton, 🄾 Ⓗ, Firestone/auto, Ford, Goodyear, Macy's, Office Depot, Target, mall
756	TX 8, Sam Houston Tollway
755	Willcrest Rd, **N** 🄾 Buick, Discount Tire, Mazda, Lincoln/Mercury, NTB, U-Haul, **S** 🅰 Citgo/dsl, Exxon/McDonald's/24hr, Phillips 66, 🍴 Carabbas, China View, Denny's, Dimassi Mediterranean, IHOP, McDonald's, Steak&Ale, Subway, Taco Cabana, 🏨 Extended Stay America, Hampton Inn, La Quinta, Radisson, Sheraton
754	Kirkwood Rd, **N** 🏨 Embassy Suites, 🄾 Lexus, Lincoln/Mercury, Toyota/Scion, same as 753b, **S** 🅰 Chevron/dsl, Shell/24hr, 🍴 Carrabba's, IHOP/24hr, Kingfish Mkt, Mesa Grill, Original Pasta Co, Subway, Taco Cabana, 🏨 Extended Stay America, 🄾 Chevrolet, Discount Tire, Subaru
753b	Dairy-Ashford Rd, **N** 🄾 Buick, Chrysler/Dodge, Infiniti, Lexus, Nissan, Toyota, Volvo, **S** 🅰 Exxon/dsl, Shell, 🍴 Beck's Prime Rest., Subway, TX Cattle Steaks, Whataburger, 🏨 Courtyard, Hilton Garden, Holiday Inn Express, 🄾 Cadillac, Chevrolet
753a	Eldridge Pkwy, **N** 🅰 Conoco/dsl, 🏨 Omni Hotel, **S** 🅰 Valero
751	TX 6, to Addicks, **N** 🅰 Shell, 🍴 Bro.'s Pizza, Cattlegard Rest., Waffle House, 🏨 Crowne Plaza, Drury Inn, Homewood Suites, Red Roof Inn, Studio 6, 🄾 Sam's Club/gas, **S** 🏨 Extended Stay Deluxe, Fairfield Inn, Holiday

Exit	Services
751	Continued
	Inn, Hyatt Suites, La Quinta, Motel 6, Summerfield Suites, Super 8, TownePlace Suites, 🄾 Acura, BMW
750	Park Ten Blvd, eb only, **S** 🄾 Hoover RV Ctr, Hyundai, Subaru
748	Barker-Cypress Rd, **N** 🅰 Texaco/Subway, 🍴 Coaches Grill, Firehouse Subs, Panchero's Mexican, Ruby Tuesday, 🄾 Ⓗ, **S** 🍴 Cracker Barrel, 🄾 Dodge, GMC, Hyundai, Subaru, VW
747	Fry Rd, **N** 🅰 Mobil/dsl, Murphy USA, Shell/24hr, 🍴 Applebee's, Arby's, Buffalo Wild Wings, Burger King, DQ, Denny's, 5 Guys Burgers, McDonald's, Murphy's Deli, Panda Express, Pizza Hut, Sonic, Souper Salad, Subway, Taco Bell, Waffle House, Whataburger, 🄾 Best Buy, HEB Food/gas, Hobby Lobby, Home Depot, Kohl's, Kroger/gas, O'Reilly Parts, Ross, Sam's Club/gas, Walgreens, Walmart, **S** 🅰 Valero, 🍴 Capt Tom's Sea🍴 Fazoli's, IHOP, McDonald's, Omar's Mexican, Outback Steaks, Quiznos, Wendy's, Willie's, 🏨 ValuePlace Hotel, 🄾 Ⓗ, Ford, Lowe's, Petsmart, Radio Shack, Target, U-Haul
746	W Green Blvd, wb only, **N** 🍴 Chang's Chinese, Cheddar's, Coldstone, NY Pizza, Springcreek BBQ, Tequila Mexican, TX Roadhouse, Wild Wings Cafe, 🏨 Holiday Inn Express, **S** 🄾 CVS Drug, Honda
745	Mason Rd, **S** 🅰 Chevron/dsl, Exxon, Shell, Valero, 🍴 Babin's Sea🍴 Blackeyed Pea, Burger King, Carino's Italian, Chick-fil-A, Chili's, CiCi's, DQ, Fuzzy's Pizza, Hartz Chicken, Jack-in-the-Box, Jason's Deli, KFC, Landry's Sea🍴 Luby's, McDonald's, Panda Express, Papa John's, Pizza Hut, Popeye's, SaltGrass Steaks, Schlotsky's, Subway, Taco Bell, Taco Cabana, Whataburger, 🏨 Comfort Inn, Hampton Inn, Holiday Inn Express, La Quinta, Super 8, 🄾 Discount Tire, Dodge, $Tree, Fiesta Foods, Firestone/auto, Goodyear/auto, Hancock Fabrics, HEB Food/gas, Kroger, Randall's 🍴 Toyota/Scion, Walgreens, transmissions
743	TX 99, Grand Pkwy, Peek Rd, **N** 🅰 Shell, 🍴 La Madeleine, 🄾 JC Penney, **S** 🅰 Exxon, Shell/dsl, 🍴 A&W, Arrandas Mexican, Hooters, Popeye's, 🏨 Best Western, Holiday Inn Express, La Quinta, Super 8, 🄾 Chevrolet, CVS Drug, Kia, Kroger
741	(742 from wb)Katy-Fort Bend County Rd, Pin Oak Rd, **S** 🅰 Murphy USA, Shell, Texaco, 🍴 ChuckeCheese, Cici's Pizza, Dennys, Fuddruckers, Jack-in-the-Box, LJ Silver/Taco Bell, Los Cucos, Red Lobster, Subway, TGIFriday's, 🏨 Hilton Garden, Residence Inn, SpringHill Suites, 🄾 Ⓗ, BassPro Shops, Discount Tire, Katy Mills Outlet/famous brands, Walgreens, Walmart
740	FM 1463, **N** 🍴 McDonald's, Sonic, 🄾 RV World of TX, Yamaha, **S** 🅰 Chevron, 🍴 RainForest Café, 🄾 Books-A-Million

TX

INTERSTATE 10 CONT'D

Exit	Services
737	Pederson Rd, N 🅖 Loves/Arby's/dsl/scales/24hr, S 🅞 Camping World RV Super Ctr, Holiday World RV Ctr
735	Igloo Rd, new exit
732	FM 359, to Brookshire, N 🅖 Exxon/Chester's/dsl, ⓕFLYING J/Denny's/dsl/LP/scales/24hr/@, Shell, 🍴 Church's, Orlando's Pizza, Subway, 🛏 Executive Inn, 🅞 RV camping, S 🅖 Chevron/dsl, Exxon/Burger King/dsl/24hr, Shell/McDonald's/dsl, 🍴 Jack-in-the-Box, 🛏 Super 8, 🅞 truckwash
731	FM 1489, to Koomey Rd, N 🅖 Exxon/dsl, 🍴 Ernesto's Mexican, 🛏 Days Inn, 🅞 RV Park, S 🛏 La Quinta
729	Peach Ridge Rd, Donigan Rd (730 from wb)
726	Chew Rd (from eb), S golf
725	Mlcak Rd (from wb)
724mm	**check sta wb**
723	FM 1458, to San Felipe, N 🅖 Exxon/Subway/dsl/scales/24hr, 🅞 to Stephen F Austin SP (3mi), S 🅞 Riverside Tire
721	(from wb) US 90, N 🅖 Shell/Chester's/dsl, 🅞 Ford
720a	Outlet Ctr Dr, N 🅖 Shell/Chester's/dsl
720	TX 36, to Sealy, N 🅖 Shell/dsl, 🍴 China Buffet, DQ, Hartz Chicken, McDonald's, Sonic, Tony's Rest., 🅞 Chevrolet/Buick/GMC, $General, Jones RV Ctr, O'Reilly Parts, Walgreens, S 🅖 Chevron/dsl, Mobil/dsl, Murphy USA/dsl, Shell/dsl, 🍴 Cazadore's Mexican, Hinze's BBQ, Jack-in-the-Box, Pizza Hut, Whataburger, 🛏 Best Value Inn, Countryside Inn, Holiday Inn Express, Super 8, 🅞 Verizon, Walmart/Subway
718	US 90 (from eb), to Sealy
716	Pyka Rd, N 🅖 Exxon/dsl/rest./showers/24hr/@
713	Beckendorff Rd
709	FM 2761, Bernardo Rd
704	FM 949, N Happy Oaks RV Park (3mi)
699	FM 102, to Eagle Lake, N 🅞 Happy Oaks RV Park, antiques, S 🅞 Eagle Lake SP (14mi)
698	Alleyton Rd, N 🍴 Mikeska's BBQ, 🛏 Red Carpet Inn, S 🅖 Shell/Taco Bell/dsl, 🅞 Chrysler/Dodge/Jeep, Ford
697mm	Little Colorado River
696	TX 71, Columbus, N 🅖 Chevron/dsl, Shell/dsl, 🍴 Cantus Rest., El Ray Mexican, Jack-in-the-Box, #1 Buffet, Pizza Hut, Schobel's Rest., Whataburger, 🛏 Columbus Inn, Holiday Inn Express, 🅞 ⒽH, AT&T, AutoZone, HEB Foods, Walmart, S 🅖 Citgo/Church's/dsl, Valero/dsl, 🍴 Los Cabos Mexican, McDonald's, Nancy's Steaks, Sonic, Subway, 🛏 Country Hearth Inn, LaQuinta, 🅞 Columbus RV Park
695	TX 71 (from wb), to La Grange
693	FM 2434, to Glidden
692mm	**rest areas both lanes, full ♿ facilities, vending, Ⓒ, ☕, litter barrels, RV dump, petwalk**
689	US 90, to Hattermann Lane, N KOA
682	FM 155, to Wiemar, N 🅖 Exxon/dsl, Shell/BBQ/dsl, 🍴 DQ, McDonald's, Subway/Texas Burger, 🛏 Days Inn, 🅞 ⒽH, $General, Tire Pros, S 🅖 Chevron/dsl/24hr, 🅞 Buick/Chevrolet/GMC
678mm	E Navidad River
677	US 90
674	US 77, Schulenburg, N 🅖 Chevron/dsl, Exxon/dsl, 🍴 McDonald's, Oak Ridge Smokehouse, 🛏 Executive Inn, Oak Ridge Motel, 🅞 Ford, Potter Country Store,

Exit	Services
674	US 77, S 🅖 Citgo, Shell/dsl, Valero/Subway, 🍴 DQ, Frank's Rest., Guadalajara Mexican, Paddy's TX Kitchen, Whataburger, 🛏 Best Western, 🅞 $General, Schulenberg RV Park
672mm	W Navidad River
668	FM 2238, to Engle
661	TX 95, FM 609, to Flatonia, N 🅖 Citgo/dsl, 🍴 Joel's, BBQ, San Jose Mexican, 🅞 Flatonia RV Ranch (1mi), S 🅖 Exxon/dsl, Shell/McDonald's/Grumpy's Rest./motel/dsl, Valero, 🍴 DQ, 🛏 Carefree Inn, 🅞 $General, NAPA
658mm	picnic areas both lanes, tables, litter barrels
653	US 90, Waelder, N 🅖 Shell/dsl/cafe
649	TX 97, to Waelder
642	TX 304, to Gonzales
637	FM 794, to Harwood
632	US 90/183, to Gonzales, N 🅖 Loves/Subway/dsl/scales/24hr, 🛏 Coachway Inn (2mi), S 🅖 Shell/Buc-ee's/dsl, 🅞 to Palmetto SP, camping
630mm	San Marcos River
628	TX 80, to Luling, N 🅖 Exxon (2mi), Valero/Church's/dsl/24hr, 🍴 DQ (2mi), 🅞 ⒽH, Riverbend RV Park
625	Darst Field Rd
624.5mm	Smith Creek
621mm	**weigh sta, both lanes**
620	FM 1104
619mm	**rest area both lanes, full ♿ facilities, Ⓒ, ☕, petwalk**
617	FM 2438, to Kingsbury
614.5mm	Mill Creek
612	US 90
611mm	Geronimo Creek
610	TX 123, to San Marcos, N 🅖 Exxon/dsl, Shell/Subway/dsl, 🍴 Bella Sera Italian, Chili's, IHOP, Los Cucos Mexican, 🛏 Comfort Inn, Days Inn, Hampton Inn, Holiday Inn Express, 🅞 Carters Tires, S 🅖 Valero/dsl, 🍴 Taco Cabana, 🅞 ⒽH
609	TX 123, Austin St, S 🅖 Phillips 66/dsl, 🅞 Chevrolet, Home Depot
607	TX 46, FM 78, to New Braunfels, N 🅖 Valero/Jack-in-the-Box/dsl, 🛏 Motel 6, S 🅖 Chevron/dsl, Exxon/DQ/dsl, Valero/dsl, 🍴 Dixie Grille, McDonald's, Whataburger, 🛏 La Quinta, Super 8, 🅞 Chrysler/Dodge
605	FM 464, N 🅞 Twin Palms RV Park
605mm	Guadalupe River
604	FM 725, to Lake McQueeney, N 🅖 Loves/Arby's/dsl/scales/24hr, 🅞 Explore USA RV Ctr, Twin Palms RV Park
603	US 90 E, US 90A, to Seguin, N 🅞 Explore USA RV Sales
601	FM 775, to New Berlin, N 🅖 Chevron/Subway/dsl/scales/24hr
600	Schwab Rd
599	FM 465, to Marion
599mm	Santa Clara Creek
597	Santa Clara Rd, N auto racetrack
595	Zuehl Rd
594mm	Cibolo Creek
593	FM 2538, Trainer Hale Rd, N 🅖 Texaco/dsl, 🅞 tires, S 🅖 Exxon/Lucille's Rest./dsl/24hr
593mm	Woman Hollering Creek
591	FM 1518, to Schertz, N Alamo Trvl Ctr/Shell/dsl, 🅞 repair
589	Pfeil Rd, Graytown Rd
589mm	Salatrillo Creek
587	LP 1604, Randolph AFB, to Universal City
585.5mm	Escondido Creek

INTERSTATE 10 CONT'D

Exit	Services
585	FM 1516, to Converse, **N** ⓖ Shell/Church's/dsl/scales/24hr, ⓛ Best Western, **S** ⓞ Kenworth, Peterbilt/GMC/Freightliner
585mm	Martinez Creek
583	Foster Rd, **N** ⓖ ⊛FLYING J/Denny's/dsl/LP/scales/24hr/@, Valero/Subway/dsl/24hr, ⓕ Jack-in-the-Box, ⓛ La Quinta, ⓞ Blue Beacon, Speedco Lube, T&W Tire, Tire Mart, **S** ⓖ TA/Chevron/Burger King/Pizza Hut/Popeye's/dsl/24hr/@
582.5mm	Rosillo Creek
582	Ackerman Rd, Kirby, **N** ⓖ ⓖ/Subway/dsl/scales/24hr, ⓞ Blue Beacon, **S** ⓖ Petro/Iron Skillet/dsl/scales/24hr/@, ⓕ El Rodeo Mexican, ⓛ Knights Inn, ⓞ Petrolube, Blue Beacon
581	I-410
580	LP 13, WW White Rd, **N** ⓖ Chevron/dsl, Fina/dsl, ⓕ El Jacalito, La Playa Sea ⓕ Wendy's, ⓛ Motel 6, Red Roof Inn, Rodeway Inn, ⓞ RV camping, tires, **S** ⓖ Exxon/dsl, ⓕ Bill Miller BBQ, La Vina Mexican, Lazaritas Mexican, McDonald's, Popeye's, Pizza Hut, Sonic, Subway, ⓛ EconoLodge, Quality Inn, Rosepark Inn, Super 8, ⓞ $General, Ford/Volvo Trucks, tires/repair
579	Houston St, **N** ⓖ Valero/dsl, ⓛ Travelodge, **S** ⓖ Chevron, ⓛ Comfort Inn, Days Inn, Passport Inn
578	Pecan Valley Dr, ML King Dr, **N** ⓖ
577	US 87 S, to Roland Ave, **S** ⓕ Whataburger, ⓛ Super 8
576	New Braunfels Ave, Gevers St, **S** ⓖ Valero, ⓕ McDonald's
575	Pine St, Hackberry St, **S** ⓕ Little Red Barn Steaks, Pizza Hut
574	I-37, US 281
573	Probandt St, **N** ⓕ Jack-in-the-Box, Miller's BBQ, **S** ⓖ Valero, ⓞ to SA Missions HS, tires
572	**I-10 and I-35 run together 3 miles**
154a	Nogalitos St
154b	S Laredo St, Cevallos St, **E** ⓖ Exxon, Shell, ⓕ April's Chinese, Church's, McDonald's, Piedra's Negras, Pizza Hut, Wendy's, ⓛ Best Western, Candlewood Suites, Days Inn, Holiday Inn Express, Ramada Ltd, ⓞ USPO, **W** ⓖ Conoco, ⓛ Microtel
155a	South Alamo St, same as 154b
155b	Durango St, downtown, **E** ⓕ Bill Miller BBQ, ⓛ Best Western, Comfort Suites, Courtyard, Fairfield Inn, Holiday Inn, La Quinta, Residence Inn, ⓞ Ⓗ, **W** ⓕ McDonald's, ⓛ Microtel, Motel 6, Radisson
156	I-10 E, US 90 W, US 87, to Kelly AFB, Lackland AFB
570	**I-10 and I-35 run together 3 miles**
569c	Santa Rosa St, downtown, to Our Lady of the Lake U
568	spur 421, Culebra Ave, Bandera Ave, **S** to St Marys U
567	Lp 345, Fredericksburg Rd (from eb upper level accesses I-35 S, I-10 E, US 87 S, lower level accesses I-35 N)
566b	Fresno Dr, **S** ⓖ Exxon, ⓛ Galaxy Inn
566a	West Ave, **N** ⓖ Exxon, ⓕ DQ, Subway, Whataburger, ⓞ CarCare
565c	(from wb), access to same as 565 a b, **S** ⓖ Shell, ⓕ Guadalahara Mexican, Starbucks, ⓛ La Quinta
565b	Vance Jackson Rd, **N** ⓖ Murphy USA, ⓕ Bill Miller BBQ, IHOP, ⓛ Comfort Inn, Days Inn, EconoLodge, ⓞ Walmart, **S** ⓖ Shell, ⓛ La Quinta

Exit	Services
565a	Crossroads Blvd, Balcone's Heights, **N** ⓖ Exxon, Shell/dsl, ⓕ Denny's, Whataburger, ⓛ Comfort Suites, Howard Johnson, Rodeway Inn, **S** ⓕ Dave&Buster's, El Pollo Loco, McDonald's, ⓛ SpringHill Suites, Super 8, ⓞ Firestone/auto, Mazda, Office Depot, RV Ctr, Target, Toyota, mall, transmissions
564b a	I-410, services off of I-410 W, Fredericksburg Rd
563	Callaghan Rd, **N** ⓖ Valero, ⓕ Las Palapas Mexican, Philly Connection, Subway, ⓛ Embassy Suites, Marriott, ⓞ $General, Ford, Lexus, Mazda, Sun Harvest Foods, Toyota, **S** ⓖ Exxon, ⓕ Mamacita's Rest., ⓞ Lowe's
561	Wurzbach Rd, **N** ⓖ Texaco/dsl, ⓕ Bolo's Grille, County Line BBQ, Egg&I, Fuddrucker's, Honeybaked Ham, Jason's Deli, Pappasito's Cantina, Popeye's, Quiznos, Sea Island Shrimphouse, Taste Of China, TX Land&Cattle, Wasabi Grill, ⓛ Homewood Suites, Hyatt Place, Knights Inn, Omni Hotel, Staybridge Suites, Studio+, ⓞ AutoZone, BigLots, Ford, HEB Food/gas, Office Depot, Toyota/Scion, **S** ⓖ Shell/dsl, ⓕ Alamo Café, Arby's, Benihana, Chester's Burgers, China Sea, Church's, Denny's, El Taco Tote, IHOP, Jack-in-the-Box, Mamma Margie's Mexican, McDonald's, Pizza Hut, Taco Bell, Wendy's, ⓛ Baymont Inn, Best Western, Candlewood Suites, Drury Inn, Holiday Inn Express, La Quinta, Motel 6, Residence Inn, Sleep Inn, ⓞ Ⓗ, CarMax
560b	frontage rd (from eb), **N** ⓕ Water St Seafood
560a	Huebner Rd, **N** ⓕ Carrabba's, Champp's, La Madeleine, Macaroni Grill, On the Border, Panera Bread, SaltGrass Steaks, ⓞ Acura, Cadillac/Hummer, Chrysler/Jeep/Dodge, Old Navy, Ross, Smart Car, **S** ⓖ Chevron, Exxon, ⓕ Burger King, Cracker Barrel, Jim's Rest., ⓛ Days Inn, Hampton Inn, Homestead Village
559	Lp 335, US 87, Fredericksburg Rd, **N** ⓕ Brew Wok, La Madeleine, Macaroni Grill, On-the-Border, Outback Steaks, Panera Bread, Pearl Inn, Saltgrass Steaks, Starbucks, ⓞ Acura, Ross Old Navy, **S** ⓖ Shell, Texaco, ⓕ Cracker Barrel, Jack-in-the-Box, Krispy Kreme, ⓛ Days Inn, Hampton Inn, HomeGate Studios, Motel 6, SpringHill Suttes, ⓞ Infinity
558	De Zavala Rd, **N** ⓖ Chevron, Shell/Subway, ⓕ Bill Miller BBQ, Burger King, Carrabba's, Chick-fil-A, Chili's, Joe's Crabshack, KFC/Taco Bell, Logan's Roadhouse, McDonald's, Outback Steaks, Papa Murphy's, Sonic, Taco Cabana, The Earl of Sandwich, Wendy's, ⓛ Super 8, ⓞ GNC, HEB Food/gas, Home Depot, Hyundai, Marshall's, PetCo, Petsmart, Steinmart, Target, **S** ⓕ Cracker Barrel, IHOP, Schlotzsky's, ⓛ Hampton Inn, Sleep Inn, SpringHill Suites, Studio6, ⓞ Buick, Discount Tire, Sam's Club, Walmart
557	Spur 53, Univ of TX at San Antonio, **N** ⓖ Exxon/dsl, ⓛ Best Western, EconoLodge, Howard Johnson, Super 8,

TX

INTERSTATE 10 CONT'D

SAN ANTONIO E↕W

Exit	Services
557	Continued 🔘 Audi, Chevrolet, Hyundai, Jaguar/Mazerati/Ferrari, S 🍴 A&W/LJ Silver, Cici's Pizza, Huhot Chinese, IHOP, Matamoro's Cantina, My Sam Chinese, Quiznos, TGIFriday's, Zio's Italian, Whataburger, 🔘 Costco/gas, Land Rover, Sams Club/gas, Walmart
556b	frontage rd
556a	to Anderson Lp, S 🛏 Comfort Inn, 🔘 to Seaworld
555	La Quintera Pkwy, N 🍴 Chick-fil-A, Little Italy, McDonald's/playplace, Mimi's Cafe, Red Robin, 🛏 Courtyard, Residence Inn, 🔘 Bass Pro Shops, Best Buy, Dick's, JC Penney, Lowe's, Ross, Target, S 🍴 Olive Garden, Red Lobster, 🛏 Drury Inn, La Quinta, Motel 6, 🔘 Honda, to La Cantera Pkwy
554	Camp Bullis Rd, N 🅡 Citgo, 🍴 TGIFriday's, 🔘 Lowe's, Old Navy, Russell CP, TJ Maxx, S 🅡 Shell, 🛏 Rodeway Inn
551	Boerne Stage Rd (from wb), to Leon Springs, N 🅡 Shamrock/dsl, 🍴 Rudy's BBQ, Sonic, S 🍴 Las Palapas Mexican, Longhorns Rest., Pappa Nacho's, Quiznos, Starbucks, 🔘 GNC, HEB Foods/gas, vet
550	FM 3351, Ralph Fair Rd, N 🅡 Exxon/McDonald's/dsl, Valero/dsl, 🍴 Leon Creek Steaks, 🛏 La Quinta, S 🅡 Shell/Domino's/dsl
546	Fair Oaks Pkwy, Tarpon Dr, N 🍴 Papa John's, 🔘 American Dream RV Ctr, Harley-Davidson, vet, S 🅡 Chevron/dsl/café, Exxon/dsl/café, 🔘 Goodyear/auto, Hoover RV Ctr
543	Boerne Stage Rd, to Scenic LP Rd, N 🅡 Valero/Subway/dsl, 🛏 Caverns Inn/rest., Fairfield Inn, 🔘 Ancira RV Ctr, Buick/GMC, Chevrolet, Chrysler/Dodge/Jeep, Ford, NAPA, Buick/GMC, W&W Tires, to Cascade Caverns, S 🔘 Explore USA RV Ctr, Mercedes, Toyota/Scion
542	(from wb), N 🅡 Shamrock, 🍴 Domino's, Pizza Hut, Wendy's, 🔘 Alamo Fiesta RV Park, $Tree, same as 540
540	TX 46, to New Braunfels, N 🅡 Exxon/Taco Bell/dsl, Murphy USA, Shell/dsl/24hr, 🍴 Baskin-Robbins, Burger King, Church's, DQ, Denny's, El Rio Mexican, Guadalajara Mexican, Little Caesars, Marble Slab Creamery, Margarita's Café, Pizza Hut, Quiznos, Shanghai Chinese, Sonic, Taco Cabana, Wendy's, 🛏 Best Value, Comfort Inn, Key to the Hills Motel, 🔘 AutoZone, HEB Food/gas, Radio Shack, Walgreens, Walmart, S 🍴 Chili's, Starbucks, Whataburger, 🛏 Hampton Inn, 🔘 Home Depot
539	Johns Rd, N 🛏 La Quinta, S 🅡 Valero/dsl/LP
538mm	Cibolo Creek
538	Ranger Creek Rd
537	US 87, to Boerne
533	FM 289, Welfare, N 🍴 Po-Po Family Rest., 🔘 Top of the Hill RV Park (1mi)
532mm	Little Joshua Creek
531mm	picnic area wb, tables, litter barrels
530mm	Big Joshua Creek
529.5mm	picnic area eb, tables, litter barrels
527	FM 1621 (from wb), to Waring
526.5mm	Holiday Creek
524	TX 27, FM 1621, to Waring, N vet, S 🅡 Shell
523.5mm	Guadalupe River
523	US 87 N, to Comfort, N 🅡 Chevron/dsl, ♥Loves/McDonald's/Subway/dsl/scales/24hr, S 🅡 Exxon/dsl,

KERRVILLE JUNCTION

Exit	Services
523	Continued 🍴 Comfort BBQ, DQ, 🛏 Executive Inn, 🔘 $General, RV Park/LP
521.5mm	Comfort Creek
520	FM 1341, to Cypress Creek Rd
515mm	Cypress Creek
514mm	rest areas both lanes, full ♿ facilities, vending, 🍴, 🅡 litter barrels, RV dump, petwalk, playground, wireless internet
508	TX 16, Kerrville, N 🅡 Exxon/dsl, 🔘 Buick/Cadillac/Chevrolet, RV camping, 0-2 mi S 🅡 Exxon, Shell/McDonald's/dsl/24hr, Stripes/dsl, Valero/dsl, 🍴 Acapulco Mexican, Bamboo Asian, Cracker Barrel, DQ, IHOP, KFC, Jack in-the-Box, Little Caesars, McDonald's, Santo Coyote, Schlotzsky's, Sonic, Taco Bell, Taco Casa, 🛏 Best Value Inn, Best Western, Big Texas Inn, Comfort Inn, Days Inn, Hampton Inn, Holiday Inn Express, La Quinta, Motel 6, Super 8, Yo Ranch Hotel, 🔘 🏥, Advance Parts, AT&T, Big Lots, $Tree, Hastings Books, Home Depot, Kerrville RV Ctr, Lowe's, NAPA, O'Reilly Parts, Walgreens, vet
505	FM 783, to Kerrville, S 🅡 Exxon/dsl, 3 mi S on TX 27 🅡 Chevron/dsl, Exxon, Phillips 66/dsl, Stripes/dsl, 🍴 Chili's, CiCi's, Culver's, DQ, Fuddruckers, Mamcita's, McDonald's, Pizza Hut, Quiznos, Starbucks, Sonic, Subway, Taco Casa, Wendy's, Whataburger, 🛏 Inn of the Hills, 🔘 AutoZone, Chrysler/Dodge/Jeep, Curves, CVS Drug, Discount Tire, $General, HEB Foods/gas, Walmart/McDonald's
503.5mm	scenic views both lanes, litter barrels
501	FM 1338, N 🔘 Buckhorn RV Resort, S 🔘 KOA (2mi)
497mm	picnic area both lanes, tables, litter barrels
492	FM 479
490	TX 41
488	TX 27, to Ingram, Mountain Home
484	Midway Rd
477	US 290, to Fredericksburg
476.5mm	service rd eb
472	Old Segovia Rd
465	FM 2169, to Segovia, S 🅡 Phillips 66/rest./dsl, 🛏 EconoLodge/RV park
464.5mm	Johnson Fork Creek
462	US 83 S, to Uvalde
461mm	picnic area eb, tables, litter barrels
460	(from wb), to Junction
459mm	picnic area wb, tables, litter barrels
457	FM 2169, to Junction, N 🅡 Shell/dsl, S 🛏 Days Inn, 🔘 RV camping, S. Llano River SP
456.5mm	Llano River
456	US 83/377, Junction, N 🅡 Chevron/dsl, Fina/dsl, Valero/McDonald's/dsl/24hr, 🍴 Cooper's BBQ, JR's Rest., Tia Nina's Mexican, 🛏 Motel 6, S 🅡 Big Star/dsl, Exxon, Church's, Shell/dsl, 🍴 DQ, Isaack Rest., La Familia Mexican, Lum's BBQ, Sonic, Subway, 🛏 Best Western, Lazy T Motel, Legends Inn, Rodeway Inn, The Hills Motel, 🔘 🏥, Best Hardware, CarQuest, $General, Family$, KOA (.5mi), Plumley's Store, Radio Shack, Super S Foods, to S Llano River SP
452.5mm	Bear Creek
451	RM 2291, to Cleo Rd
448mm	North Creek
445	RM 1674, S camping
444.5mm	Stark Creek
442mm	Copperas Creek

TX

INTERSTATE 10 CONT'D

Exit	Services
442	RM 1674, to Ft McKavett, **N** to Ft McKavett SHS
439mm	N Llano River
438	Lp 291 (from wb), to Roosevelt same as 437
437	Lp 291 (from eb, no EZ return), to Roosevelt, **1 mi N** ⛽ Simon Bros Mercantile/dsl, ⊡ USPO
429	RM 3130, to Harrell
423mm	parking area both lanes, litter barrels
420	RM 3130, to Baker Rd
412	Allison Rd, RM 3130
404	RM 3130, RM 864, **N** to Ft McKavett St HS, **3 mi S** ⛽ Stripes/dsl, 🏨 Holiday Host Motel, ⊡ 🅗
400	US 277, Sonora, **N** ⛽ Shell/dsl, 🍴 Sutton Co Steaks, 🏨 Days Inn, ⊡ vet, **S** ⛽ Chevron/dsl, Exxon/dsl, Fina/7-11/dsl, Stripes/dsl, 🍴 DQ, La Mexicana Rest., Pizza Hut, Sonic, Taco Grill, 🏨 Best Western, Comfort Inn, Economy Inn, ⊡ Alco, CarQuest, Family$, NAPA, USPO
399	(from eb)LP 467, Sonora, **N** ⛽ Days Inn, **S** ⛽ Chevron/dsl, Fina, Exxon/dsl, Stripes, 🍴 DQ, Subway, ⊡ 🅗, RV camping
394mm	**rest area both lanes, full ♿ facilities, ⬚, 🪑, litter barrel, petwalk, RV dump**
392	RM 1989, Caverns of Sonora Rd, **8 mi S** ⊡ Caverns of Sonora Camping, ⬚
388	RM 1312 (from wb)
381	RM 1312 (from eb)
372	Taylor Box Rd, **N** ⛽ Exxon/rest./dsl/scales/24hr, 🏨 Super 8, ⊡ Circle Bar RV Park, auto museum
368	LP 466, **N** same as 365 & 363
365	TX 163, Ozona, **N** ⛽ Chevron/dsl, Stripes/Godfather's/Taco Co/dsl, 🍴 DQ, Sonic, Subway, 🏨 Best Value Inn, Best Western, Economy Inn/RV Park, Hillcrest Inn, Holiday Inn Express, ⊡ 🅗, Best Hardware, $General, NAPA, to David Crockett Mon, **S** ⛽ Chevron, 🍴 El Chato's
363	Lp 466, to Ozona
361	RM 2083, Pandale Rd
357mm	Eureka Draw
351mm	Howard Draw
350	FM 2398, to Howard Draw
349mm	parking area wb, litter barrels
346mm	parking area eb, litter barrels
343	TX 290 W, **S** Ft. Lancaster Historic Site
337	Live Oak Rd
336.5mm	Live Oak Creek
328	River Rd, Sheffield
327.5mm	Pecos River
325	TX 290, TX 349, to Iraan, Sheffield, **N** 🅗
320	frontage rd
314	frontage rd
309mm	**rest area both lanes, full ♿ facilities, ⬚, 🪑, litter barrels, petwalk, wireless internet**
307	US 190, FM 305, to Iraan, **N** 🅗
298	RM 2886
294	FM 11, Bakersfield, **N** ⛽ Exxon, **S** ⛽ Chevron/café/dsl, ⊡ ⬚
288	Ligon Rd, **N** many windmills
285	McKenzie Rd, **S** ⊡ Domaine Cordier Ste Genevieve Winery
279mm	picnic area eb, tables, litter barrels
277	FM 2023
273	US 67/385, to McCamey, 🪑 wb, tables, litter barrels

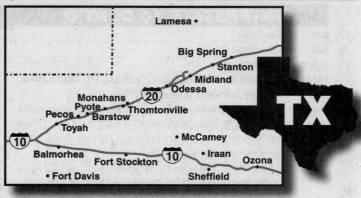

Exit	Services
272	University Rd
264	Warnock Rd, **N** ⊡ Fort Stockton RV Park/BBQ/cafe
261	US 290 W, US 385 S, **N** ⛽ Exxon/dsl, **1-2 S** ⛽ Stripes/dsl, 🏨 Budget Inn, Deluxe Inn, EconoLodge, 🍴 DQ, Pizza Hut, Sonic, Subway, ⊡ 🅗, RV camping, to Big Bend NP
259b a	(259 from eb) TX 18, FM 1053, Ft Stockton, **N** ⛽ Apache Fuel Ctr/dsl, Fina/dsl, Shell/Burger King/dsl, ⊡ I-10 RV Park, tires
257	US 285, to Pecos, Ft Stockton, **N** ⊡ Comanche Land RV Park, golf, **S** ⛽ Chevron/dsl, Exxon/rest./dsl, Fina/dsl, Shell, 🍴 DQ, IHOP, KFC/Taco Bell, McDonald's, Pizza Hut, Pizza Pro, Sonic, Steak House, Subway, 🏨 Atrium Inn, Candlewood Suites, Days Inn, Hampton Inn, Quality Inn, Texan Inn, ⊡ Ace Hardware, AutoZone, Buick/Chevrolet, $General, Firestone/auto, Lowe's Foods, McKissick Tires, O'Reilly Parts, Radio Shack
256	to US 385 S, Ft Stockton, **N** ⊡ HillTop RV, **1 mi S** ⛽ Shell/dsl, 🍴 Dragon Buffet, Howard's Drive-In, K-Bob's Steaks, Subway, 🏨 Comfort Suites, Holiday Inn Express, Motel 6, Sleep Inn, Super 8, Swiss Clock Inn, ⊡ 🅗, Ford, Walmart, to Ft Stockton Hist Dist, Big Bend NP, auto/RV repair, vet
253	FM 2037, to Belding
248	US 67, FM 1776, to Alpine, **S** to Big Bend NP
246	Firestone
241	Kennedy Rd
235	Mendel Rd
233mm	**rest area both lanes, full ♿ facilities, ⬚, 🪑, litter barrels, petwalk**
229	Hovey Rd
222	Hoefs Rd
214	(from wb), FM 2448
212	TX 17, FM 2448, to Pecos, **N** picnic area, litter barrels, **S** ⛽ I-10 Fuel/café/dsl, Saddleback RV Camping
209	TX 17, **S** ⊡ to Balmorhea SP, to Davis Mtn SP, Ft Davis NHS
206	FM 2903, to Balmorhea, Toyah, **S** to Balmorhea SP
192	FM 3078, to Toyahvale, **S** ⊡ to Balmorhea SP
188	Giffin Rd
187	I-20, to Ft Worth, Dallas
186	I-10, E to San Antonio (from wb)
185mm	picnic area both lanes, tables, litter barrels
184	Springhills
181	Cherry Creek Rd, **S** ⛽ Chevron/dsl
176	TX 118, FM 2424, to Kent, **S** ⊡ to McDonald Observatory, Davis Mtn SP, Ft Davis
173	Hurd's Draw Rd
166	Boracho Sta
159	Plateau, **N** ⛽ Exxon/rest./dsl/24hr
153	Michigan Flat

🅖 = gas 🍴 = food 🛏 = lodging 🅞 = other Copyright 2012 - The Next Ex

INTERSTATE 10 CONT'D

Exit	Services
146	Wild Horse Rd
146mm	weigh sta wb
145mm	**rest area both lanes, full ♿ facilities, ⛱, litter barrels, petwalk, wireless internet**
140b	Ross Dr, Van Horn, **N** 🅖 Chevron/dsl, Exxon/dsl, ▨Loves/Subway/dsl/scales/24hr, 🛏 Days Inn, Desert Inn, Sands Motel/rest., 🅞 El Campo RV Park, repair, **S** 🅞 Mountain View RV Park/dump
140a	US 90, TX 54, Van Horn Dr, **N** 🅖 Phillips 66/dsl, 🛏 Hotel El Capitan, 🅞 🅗, NAPA, TrueValue, USPO, **S** 🅖 Exxon, ▨/Wendy's/dsl/scales/24hr, 🍴 Papa's Pantry, 🅞 KOA, RV Dump, dsl/tire repair
138	Lp 10, to Van Horn, **N** 🍴 Chuy's Rest., DQ, 🛏 Budget Inn, EconoLodge, Economy Inn, King's Inn, Knights Inn, Motel 6, Ramada Ltd, Value Inn, 🅞 $General, Eagles Nest RV Park, Pueblo Foods, auto/dsl repair, UPSO, visitor info, **S** 🅖 Chevron/dsl/24hr, 🍴 McDonald's, 🛏 Hampton Inn, Holiday Inn Express, Super 8, 🅞 tires/repair
137mm	weigh sta eb
136mm	scenic overlook wb, ⛱, litter barrels
135mm	Mountain/Central time zone line, Mountain/Central time zone line
133	(from wb) frontage rd
129	to Hot Wells, Allamore
108	to Sierra Blanca (from wb), same as 107
107	FM 1111, Sierra Blanca Ave, **N** 🅖 Exxon/dsl/24hr, 🍴 Curly's BBQ, Michael's Rest., 🅞 truck/tire repair, USPO, to Hueco Tanks SP, **S** 🅖 Chevron/dsl, 🛏 Americana Inn, 🅞 Stagecoach Trading Post
105	(106 from wb) Lp 10, Sierra Blanca, same as 107
102.5mm	insp sta eb
99	Lasca Rd, **N** 🅞 **picnic area both lanes, ⛱, litter barrels, no restrooms**
98mm	picnic area eb, tables, litter barrels, no restrooms
95	frontage rd (from eb)
87	FM 34
85	Esperanza Rd
81	FM 2217
78	TX 20 W, to McNary
77mm	truck parking area wb
72	spur 148, to Ft Hancock, **S** 🅖 Shell/dsl, 🍴 Angie's Rest., 🛏 Ft Hancock Motel, 🅞 USPO
68	Acala Rd
55	Tornillo
51mm	**rest area both lanes, full ♿ facilities, ⛱, litter tables, petwalk**
49	FM 793, Fabens, **S** 🅖 FastTrac/dsl, 🛏 Fabens Inn/Cafe, **1 mi S** 🍴 Church's, McDonald's, Subway, 🅞 Family$, San Eli Foods
42	FM 1110, to Clint, **S** 🅖 gas/dsl, 🍴 Cotton Eyed Joe's, Mamacita's Rest., 🛏 Adobe Inn, Cotton Valley Motel/RV Park/rest./dump, Super 8
37	FM 1281, Horizon Blvd, **N** 🅖 ✦FLYING J/Denny's/dsl/scales/24hr/@, ▨Loves/Chester's/Subway/dsl/scales/24hr, 🛏 Americana Inn, 🅞 Freightliner, Speedco Lube, **S** 🅖 Petro/Valero/Iron Skillet/Subway/dsl/scales/24hr/@, 🍴 McDonald's, 🛏 Deluxe Inn, 🅞 Blue Beacon
35	Eastlake Blvd.

34	TX 375, Americas Ave, **N** 🅖 Chevron/dsl, Valero/dsl, 🛏 Microtel, ValuePlace, 🅞 GMC, Mission RV Camping, Peterbilt, **S** 🅞 RV camping, El Paso Museum of Hist
32	FM 659, Zaragosa Rd, **N** 🅖 Fina/7-11, 🍴 Arby's, Barrigos Mexican, BJ's Grill, Cheddar's, Chico's Tacos, Famous Daves, Furr's Buffet, Great American Steaks, IHOP, Krispy Kreme, LJ Silver/Taco Bell, Logan's Roadhouse, Macaroni Grill, Outback Steaks, Pei Wei, Peter Piper Pizza, San Francisco Oven, Sonic, Starbucks, Subway, Taco Bell, Village Inn, Whataburger, 🛏 Holiday Inn Express, 🅞 Chevrolet, Discount Tire, Kohl's, Lowe's, Michael's, Nissan, Office Depot, Ross, Walgreens, World Mkt, **S** 🅖 Fina/7-11, Shamrock/dsl, 🍴 Gallego's Mexican, 🅞 Volvo/Mac
30	Lee Trevino Dr, **N** 🅖 Circle K, Exxon, 🍴 Chili's, Denny's, Jack-in-the-Box, La Ganadas Mexican, Taco Cabana, Whataburger, 🛏 La Quinta, Motel 6, Red Roof Inn, Studio 6, 🅞 Discount Tire, Firestone, Ford, Isuzu, Home Depot, Lexus, Mazda, NTB, Sears/auto, Toyota/Scion, mall, **S** 🅞 Chrysler/Dodge/Jeep
29	Lomaland Dr, **N** 🍴 Denny's, 🛏 Hyatt Place, **S** 🅖 Fina/7-11, 🛏 Ramada, 🅞 Harley-Davidson
28b	Yarbrough Dr, El Paso, **N** 🅖 Murphy USA, Shell/Coldstone, 🍴 Beijing Lili, Buffalo Wild Wings, Burger King, Grandy's, Dunkin Donuts, El Ciro's, Hong Kong Buffet, LJ Silver, McDonald's, Peter Piper Pizza, Quiznos, Sonic, Subway, TX Roadhouse, Wendy's, Whataburger, Wienerschnitzel, 🛏 Days Inn, 🅞 Marshall's, PepBoys, Petsmart, Radio Shack, Ross, Walmart, **S** 🅖 Shamrock, 🍴 Applebee's, Fuddrucker's, Julio's Cafe, La Malinche Mexican, Lin's Buffet, Pizza Hut, Rudy's BBQ/gas, Shangri-La, Villa Del Mar, 🛏 Comfort Inn, InTown Suites, La Quinta, 🅞 🅗
28a	FM 2316, McRae Blvd, **N** 🅖 Texaco/dsl, Valero, 🍴 Chuck-eCheese, Grand China, Jack-in-the-Box, KFC, La Hacienda, Pizza Hut, Red Barrel Grill, Taco Bell, Taco Campero, 🛏 La Quinta, 🅞 🅗, Barnes&Noble, Best Buy, BigLots, $General, $Tree, Family$, Firestone/auto, Goodyear/auto, Jo-Ann Fabrics, K-Mart, Michael's, Office Depot, Walgreens, **S** 🅖 Circle K/dsl, 🍴 Fuddruckers, Gabriel's Mexican, 🛏 Comfort Inn, La Quinta, 🅞 Tuesday Morning
27	Hunter Dr, Viscount Blvd, **N** 🅖 Fina/7-11, Valero, 🍴 Carrow's Rest., Grand China Buffet, K-Bob's, Red Lobster, Taco Bell, 🛏 La Quinta, 🅞 Barnes&Noble, Best Buy, Firestone, **S** 🅖 Exxon/dsl, Fina/7-11, 🍴 Whataburger, 🅞 Family$, Food City
26	Hawkins Blvd, El Paso, **N** 🅖 Chevron, Murphy USA, Shamrock, Shell, 🍴 Anadele Rest., Arby's, Burger King, Country Kitchen, DQ, Golden Corral, IHOP, Landry's Sea🍴 Luby's, Olive Garden, Red Lobster, Taco Cabana, Wyatt's Cafeteria, 🛏 Howard Johnson, 🅞 Dillard's, JC Penney, Macy's, Office Depot, Pennzoil, Sam's Club/gas, Sears/auto, Walmart, **S** 🅖 Shamrock/dsl, 🍴 China King's, McDonald's, Village Inn, 🛏 Best Western, 🅞 Tony Lama Boots
25	Airway Blvd, El Paso 🛬, **N** 🅖 Shell/dsl, 🍴 Jack-in-the-Box, Landry's Sea🍴 Starbucks, Whataburger, 🛏 Courtyard, Hampton Inn, Holiday Inn, Radisson, Residence Inn, 🅞 VW/Volvo/Mercedes, **S** 🅖 Chevron/Subway/dsl/24hr
24b	Geronimo Dr, **N** 🍴 El Taco Tote, Taco Cabana, 🛏 Wingate Inn, 🅞 Dillard's, Kohl's, Office Depot, Marshall's, Ross, Target, Walgreens, mall, **S** 🅖 Circle K, Fina/7-11/dsl, 🍴 IHOP, Denny's, El Nido Mexican, 🛏 Embassy Suites, Hilton Garden, Homewood Suites, Hyatt Place, La Quinta, 🅞 urgent care

VAN HORN

E ⇕ **W**

EL PASO

EL PASO

EL PASO

TX

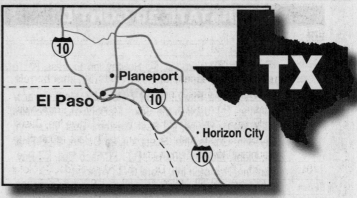

INTERSTATE 10 CONT'D

Exit	Services
24a	Trowbridge Dr, N 🅿 Fina, Thunderbird Gas, ⑪ Alexandrio's Mexican, Luby's, McDonald's, Steak&Ale, Whataburger, 🏠 Budget Inn, 🅾 Ford, Nissan, Toyota
23b	US 62/180, to Paisano Dr, N ⑪ Jack-in-the-Box, McDonald's, Whataburger, 🏠 Budget Inn, Sleep Inn, 🅾 Ford, U-Haul, to Carlsbad
23a	Raynolds St, S ⑪ Arby's, 🏠 Motel 6, Super 8, 🅾 Ⓗ
22b	US 54, Patriot Fwy
22a	Copia St, El Paso, N 🅿 Shamrock, ⑪ KFC
21	Piedras St, El Paso, N ⑪ Burger King, McDonald's, 🅾 Family$
20	Dallas St, Cotton St, N 🅿 Valero, ⑪ Church's, Subway
19	TX 20, El Paso, downtown, N 🅿 Chevron, S 🏠 DoubleTree Inn, Holiday Inn Express
18b	Franklin Ave, Porfirio Diaz St
18a	Schuster Ave, N Sun Bowl, S to UTEP
16	Executive Ctr Blvd, N 🅿 Valero, 🏠 Best Value Inn
13b a	US 85, Paisano Dr, to Sunland Park Dr, N 🅿 Shamrock, ⑪ Barrigo's Café, Carino's Italian, ChuckeCheese, Grand China, IHOP, Olive Garden, PF Chang's, Quiznos, Red Lobster, Sonic, Whataburger, 🅾 Barnes&Noble, Best Buy, Dillard's, JC Penney, K-Mart, Macy's, Michael's, Office Depot, Old Navy, Petsmart, Sears/auto, Target, Verizon, mall, S 🅿 Shamrock/dsl/24hr, Shell, ⑪ Bob-O's Rest., La Malinche Mexican, McDonald's, Sonic, Subway, 🏠 Best Western, Comfort Suites, Holiday Inn, Sleep Inn, Studio+, 🅾 Buick/GMC, Chrysler/Dodge/Jeep, Family$, Sunland Park RaceTrack, funpark
12	Resler Dr (from wb)
11	TX 20, to Mesa St, Sunland Park, N 🅿 Chevron/dsl, Circle K, Mobil, Valero, ⑪ AJ's Diner, Aloha BBQ, Chili's, CiCi's, Coldstone, Cracker Barrel, El Taco Tote, Famous Dave's BBQ, Fuddruckers, Golden Corral, Jaxon's Rest/brewery, Krispy Kreme, Leo's Mexican, PacoWong's Chinese, Papa John's, Pei Wei, Popeye's, Rancher's Grill, Subway, Taco Bell, TX Roadhouse, Wienerschnitzel, Wendy's, 🏠 Comfort Suites, EconoLodge, Fairfield Inn, La Quinta, Red Roof Inn, SpringHill Suites, 🅾 Albertson's, BigLots, Curves, $General, Family$, Firestone/auto, GNC, Goodyear/auto, Home Depot, PepBoys, SteinMart, Verizon, Walmart/McDonald's, USPO, S 🅿 Chevron/dsl, Valero/dsl, ⑪ Ay Caramba Mexican, Burger King, Church's, Golden Buddha, Jack-in-the-Box, KFC, McDonald's, Peter Piper Pizza, Pizza Hut, Starbucks, Subway, Taco Cabana, Village Inn, 🏠 Days Inn, Motel 6, Super 8, Travelodge, 🅾 AutoZone, Big 8 Foods, $Tree, Hobby Lobby, Martin Tires, Radio Shack, Sam's Club/gas, Walgreens
9	Redd Rd, N 🅿 Valero, ⑪ Applebee's, Baskin-Robbins, Burger King, Double Dave's Pizza, Pizza Hut, Starbucks, Subway, 🅾 Albertson's/gas, Ford, Kohl's, Lowe's, O'Reilly Parts, S 🅿 Circle K, Shamrock, 🅾 Chevrolet, Honda
8	Artcraft Rd, S 🅿 Shell/dsl, ⑪ Carl's Jr, Rudy's BBQ, 🏠 Hampton Inn, Holiday Inn Express, Microtel
6	Lp 375, to Canutillo, N 🅿 Shell/DQ/dsl, 🅾 to Trans Mountain Rd, Franklin Mtns SP, S 🅿 Chevron/McDonald's, Shorty's/Mama's Mexican/dsl, Whataburger, 🅾 Discount Tire, El Paso Shops/Famous Brands, RV camping
5mm	truck check sta eb
2	Westway, Vinton, N 🅿 Petro/Valero/Subway/dsl/

Exit	Services
2	Continued scales/24hr/@, 🅾 American RV Park, Camping World (1mi), PetroLube/tires, S 🅿 gas, 🅾 Mack, truck repair/tires
1mm	Welcome Ctr eb, full ♿ facilities, info, Ⓒ, 🅿, litter barrels, petwalk, weigh sta wb
0	FM 1905, Anthony, N 🅿 ⊘FLYING J/Denny's/dsl/LP/RV dump/24hr, ⑪ Carl's Jr, 🏠 Super 8, S 🅿 Fina/7-11/dsl, Pilot/Subway/Wendy's/dsl/24hr/@, ⑪ Great American Steaks, 🏠 Best Western, Burger King, KFC, Taco Bell, 🅾 Anthony RV Ctr, Big 8 Foods, $General, Walgreens, funpark, truckwash, tires
0mm	Texas/New Mexico state line

INTERSTATE 20

Exit	Services
636mm	Texas/Louisiana state line
635.5mm	full ♿ facilities, Ⓒ, 🅿, litter barrels, petwalk
635	TX 9, TX 156, to Waskom, N 🅿 Chevron/Burger King/dsl, Exxon/dsl, ⑪ DQ, Jim's BBQ, 🅾 Family$, USPO
633	US 80, FM 9, FM 134, to Waskom, N 🅿 Shell, ⑪ Catfish Village Rest., S 🅾 Miss Ellie's RV Park
628	to US 80, to frontage rd
624	FM 2199, to Scottsville
620	FM 31, to Elysian Fields, N Marshall RV Park (2mi)
617	US 59, Marshall, 0-2 mi N 🅿 Exxon/dsl, Shell, ⑪ Applebee's, Burger King, Cafe Italia, Catfish Express, Golden Corral, Gucci's Pizza, IHOP, KFC, LJ Silver, McDonald's, Pizza Hut, Porky's Smokehouse, Sonic, Subway, Taco Bell, Waffle House, Wendy's, Whataburger, 🏠 Best Western, Comfort Suites, Fairfield Inn, Hampton Inn, La Quinta, Quality Inn, 🅾 Cadillac/Chevrolet, Chrysler/Dodge/Jeep, $General, Ford/Lincoln/Mercury, Scion/Toyota, Country Pines RV Park (8mi), S 🅿 Chevron/dsl, Pony Express, Rudy's, Valero/dsl, ⑪ Varsity Diner, 🏠 Best Value Inn, EconoLodge, Holiday Inn Express, Motel 6, Super 8, 🅾 Holiday Springs RV Park (2mi)
614	TX 43, to Marshall, S to Martin Creek Lake SP
610	FM 3251
604	FM 450, Hallsville, N 🅿 Shamrock/dsl, 🅾 450 Hitchin' Post RV Park, to Lake O' the Pines
600mm	Mason Creek
599	FM 968, Longview, N 🏠 Comfort Suites, Fairfield Inn (8mi), Wingate Inn (8mi), 🅾 Kenworth Trucks, truck/rv wash, S 🅿 Chevron/Natl TrkStp/Quizno's/dsl/scales/@, Exxon/Sonic/dsl, 🅾 Goodyear, truck repair
596	US 259 N, TX 149, to Lake O' Pines, N 🅿 Exxon/Grandy's/dsl, Shell/Sonic/TX Smokehouse, ⑪ Burger King, Whataburger, 🏠 Comfort Suites, Microtel, Super 8,

EL PASO · E · N · EL PASO · MARSHALL · E W

TX

INTERSTATE 20 CONT'D

Exit	Services
596	Continued
	🅞 🅗 **S** 🅟 Valero/dsl, 🅰 Holiday Inn Express, 🅞 to Martin Lake SP
595b a	TX 322, Estes Pkwy, **N** 🅟 Exxon, EZ Mart, Texaco/dsl/24hr, 🍴 Jack-in-the-Box, McDonald's, Mitchell's BBQ, Waffle House, 🅰 Best Western, Best Value Inn, Days Inn, Express Inn, Guest Inn, La Quinta, **S** 🅟 Fina/dsl, Mobil, Murphy USA/dsl, 🍴 KFC/Taco Bell, 🅰 Baymont Inn, Hampton Inn, Motel 6, 🅞 Walmart
593mm	Sabine River
591	FM 2087, FM 2011
589b a	US 259, TX 31, Kilgore (exits left from both lanes), **1-3 mi S** 🍴 Kilgore Café, 🅰 Budget Inn, Comfort Inn, Days Inn, Holiday Inn Express, Homewood Suites, Ramada Inn, **S** 🅞 E Texas Oil Museum
587	TX 42, Kilgore, **N** 🅟 Valero, 🍴 Bodacious BBQ, **S** 🅟 Shell/Wendy's/dsl, 🍴 Denny's, 🅞 E TX Oil Museum, **3 mi S** 🅞 Walmart
583	TX 135, to Kilgore, Overton, **N** 🅟 Exxon/dsl, 🅞 Shallow Creek RV Resort
582	FM 3053, Liberty City, **N** 🅟 Exxon/Subway/dsl, Shell/Whataburger/dsl, 🍴 Bob's BBQ, DQ, Java House, Sonic
579	Joy-Wright Mtn Rd
575	Barber Rd
574mm	**picnic area both lanes, 🚻, litter barrels, ♿ accessible**
571b	FM 757, Omen Rd, to Starrville
571a	US 271, to Gladewater, Tyler, **S** 🅟 Shell/Sonic/Texas Smokehouse/dsl/scales/24hr
567	TX 155, **N** 🅟 Valero/dsl/24hr, **S** 🅰 Best Value Inn, 🅞 🅗
565	FM 2015, to Driskill-Lake Rd
562	FM 14, **N** 🍴 Bodacious BBQ, 🅞 Northgate RV Park, Whispering Pines RV Park (6mi), to Tyler SP, **S** 🅟 Pilot/McDonald's/dsl/scales/24hr
560	Lavender Rd, **S** 🅞 5 Star RV Park (2 mi)
557	Jim Hogg Rd
556	US 69, to Tyler, **N** 🅟 Murphy USA, RaceWay/dsl, Shamrock/dsl, 🍴 Burger King, Chicken Express, Chili's, Domino's, Eastern Buffet, KFC\LJ Silver, Juanita's Mexican, McDonald's, Pizza Hut, Pizza Inn, Posado's Cafe, Sonic, Subway, Taco Bell, TX BBQ, 🅰 Best Western, Comfort Suites, Days Inn, Hampton Inn, La Quinta, 🅞 Lowe's, Walmart, vet, **S** 🅟 Chevron, Exxon, 🍴 Cracker Barrel, DQ, Wendy's, 🅰 Best Value Inn
554	Harvey Rd, **S** 🅞 Yellow Rose RV Park
552	FM 849, **N** 🅟 Shell
548	TX 110, to Grand Saline, **N** 🅟 Exxon/dsl, **S** 🅟 Valero/dsl
546mm	**check sta eb**
544	Willow Branch Rd, **N** 🅟 Conoco/dsl/rest., 🅞 Willow Branch RV Park
540	FM 314, to Van, **N** 🅟 Loves/Carl's Jr/dsl/24hr, 🍴 DQ, Sonic, Soul Mans BBQ, 🅰 Van Inn
538mm	**rest area both lanes, full ♿ facilities, 🅲, vending, 🚻, litter barrels, petwalk**
537	FM 773, FM 16
536	Tank Farm Rd
533	Oakland Rd, to Colfax, **N** 🅟 Shell/dsl
530	FM 1255

C A N T O N

Exit	Services
528	FM 17, to Grand Saline
527	TX 19, **N** 🅟 Exxon/dsl/24hr, 🍴 Burger King, Whataburger/24hr, 🅰 Comfort Inn, Motel 6, Super 8, **S** 🅟 Circle K/dsl/24hr, Shell/Subway/dsl, 🍴 Baker's Ribs, DQ, Dairy Palace, Juanita's Mexican, KFC/Taco Bell, McDonald's, Senorita's Mexican, 🅰 Best Western, Days Inn, 🅞 Ford/Mercury, Mule Creek Ranch RV Resort, to First Monday SP, LP
526	FM 859, to Edgewood
523	TX 64, to Canton
521	Myrtle Springs Rd, **N** trailer sales, **S** 🅞 Explore USA RV Ctr, RV camp/dump, U-Haul
519	Turner-Hayden Rd, **S** Canton RV Park
516	FM 47, to Wills Point, **N** to Lake Tawakoni, **S** 🅟 Texaco/24hr, 🍴 Robertson's Café/gas, 🅰 Interstate Motel
512	FM 2965, Hiram-Wills Point Rd
512mm	**weigh sta both lanes**
509	Hiram Rd, **S** 🅟 Shell/dsl/cafe/24hr
506	FM 429, FM 2728, College Mound Rd, **S** Blue Bonnet Ridge RV Park
503	Wilson Rd, **S** 🅟 TA/Shell/Country Fair/Pizza Hut/Subway/dsl/LP/24hr/@

T E R R E L L

Exit	Services
501	TX 34, to Terrell, **N** 🅟 Exxon/dsl, 🍴 Capt D's, Schlotsky's, Sonic, Starbucks, Waffle House, 🅰 Best Value Inn, Best Western, Comfort Inn, Days Inn, La Quinta, Motel 6, 🅞 🅗, Home Depot, **S** 🅟 Circle K, Valero/dsl/24hr, 🍴 Applebee's, Carmona's Cantina, IHOP, McDonald's, Wendy's, 🅰 Holiday Inn Express, Super 8, 🅞 Tanger Outlet/famous brands
499b	Rose Hill Rd, to Terrell
499a	to US 80, W to Dallas, same as 498
498	FM 148, to Terrell, **N** 🅟 Exxon/Denny's/Subway/dsl, Shell/dsl
493	FM 1641, **S** 🅟 Exxon/Pizza Inn/Sonic/dsl
491	FM 2932, Helms Tr, to Forney, **N** 🅟 Shell/Subway/dsl
490	FM 741, to Forney
487	FM 740, to Forney, **S** Forney RV park
483	Lawson Rd, Lasater Rd
482	Belt Line Rd, to Lasater, **N** 🅟 Exxon/dsl, 🍴 Smokehouse, Sonic, **S** 🅟 Shell/KFC/Pizza Hut/Subway, 🅞 RV park
481	Seagoville Rd, **N** 🅟 Valero/dsl, Shell/Church's, 🅰 La Quinta, **S** 🍴 Lindy's Rest.
480	I-635, **N** to Mesquite
479b a	US 175, **S** 🅟 Shell/dsl
477	St Augustine Rd, **S** 🅟 Shell/dsl, 🍴 Sonic
476	Dowdy Ferry Rd
474	TX 310 N, Central Expsy
473b a	JJ Lemmon Rd, I-45, **N** to Dallas, **S** to Houston

D A L L A S

Exit	Services
472	Bonnie View Rd, **N** 🅟 FLYING J/Denny's/dsl/LP/24hr, Shell, 🍴 Jack-in-the-Box, 🅰 Ramada Ltd, 🅞 Blue Beacon, Kenworth, Speedco Lube, **S** 🅟 TA/Exxon/Burger King/Taco Bell/dsl/scales/24hr/@
470	TX 342, Lancaster Rd, **N** 🅟 Chevron, USA/Texaco/Popeye's/dsl/scales/24hr, 🍴 Big Bruce's BBQ, **S** 🅟 Pilot/Wendy's/dsl/scales/24hr, Shell, 🍴 LJ Silver/Taco Bell, McDonald's, Sonic, Subway, Whataburger, William's Chicken, 🅰 Days Inn
468	Houston School Rd, **S** 🅟 Exxon/dsl, 🍴 Whataburger
467b a	I-35E, **N** to Dallas, **S** to Waco, **1 mi N** off of I-35E 🅟 Shell, 🍴 McDonald's
466	S Polk St, **N** 🅟 Exxon, Texaco, 🍴 DQ, Sonic, Subway, **S** 🅟 Loves/Carl's Jr/dsl/scales/24hr

TX

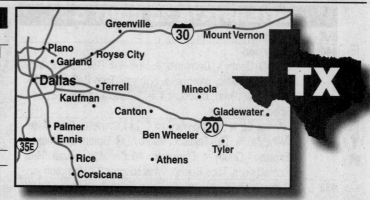

INTERSTATE 20 CONT'D

Exit	Services
465	Wheatland/S Hampton Rds, **N** 🍴 Chick-fil-A, Chili's, ⊙ CVS Drug, Target, **S** 📶 Chevron/McDonald's, Murphy USA, RaceWay, 🍴 Arby's, Cheddar's, Jack-in-the-Box, Popeye's, Sonic, Spring Creek BBQ, Taco Bell, Wendy's, 🛏 Super 8, ⊙ H, Buick/GMC, Home Depot, Honda, Hyundai, Kia, Lincoln/Mercury, Lowe's, Mazda, Petsmart, Sam's Club/gas, Suzuki, Toyota, Walmart
464b a	US 67, Love Fwy
463	Camp Wisdom Rd, **N** 📶 Chevron, Exxon, 🍴 Catfish King Rest., Denny's, Taco Bell/LJ Silver, Taco Cabana, 🛏 Hotel Suites of America, Motel 6, Royal Inn, Suburban Lodge, ⊙ Nissan, **S** 📶 Shamrock, 🍴 Burger King, Chubby's Rest., Dave's BBQ, Jack-in-the-Box, McDonald's, Olive Garden, Red Lobster, Subway, Tortilla Factory, Wendy's, ⊙ K-Mart
462b a	Duncanville Rd (no EZ wb return), **S** 📶 Exxon, QT, Shell/dsl, 🍴 Arby's, Church's, KFC, Los Lupes Mexican, Mr Gatti's, Popeye's, Whataburger, 🛏 Hilton Garden, Motel 6, ⊙ Goodyear, Kroger, Radio Shack
461	Cedar Ridge Rd
460	TX 408
458	Mt Creek Pkwy
457	FM 1382, to Grand Prairie, **N** 📶 Shell/7-11/dsl, Valero/dsl, 🍴 Waffle House, **S** 📶 RaceTrac, 🍴 Jack-in-the-Box, ⊙ to Joe Pool Lake
456	Carrier Pkwy, to Corn Valley Rd, **N** 📶 QT, 🍴 Chick-fil-A, Don Pablo, Starbucks, Taco Cabana, Whataburger, ⊙ Home Depot, Kohl's, Radio Shack, Target, **S** 📶 Shell, 🍴 Baskin-Robbins, Boston Mkt, Chapp's Cafe, Cheddar's, Chili's, Denny's, IHOP, Little Caesar's, McDonald's, Spring Creek BBQ, Subway, 🛏 Holiday Inn Express, ⊙ Albertsons/gas, CVS Drug, GNC, Tom Thumb Foods/gas, Walgreens, vet
455	TX 151
454	Great Southwest Pkwy, **N** 📶 Chevron/24hr, Conoco/dsl, Exxon, 🍴 Beto's, Carino's Italian, China Dragon, Chuck-eCheese, Golden Corral, KFC, McDonald's, Taco Bell, Taco Bueno, TX Roadhouse, Waffle House, Wendy's, Wienerschnitzel, 🛏 Heritage Inn, La Quinta, Quality Inn, ⊙ H, Goodyear, Harley-Davidson, U-Haul, **S** 📶 7-11, Shell/Subway/dsl, Valero/dsl, 🍴 Applebee's, Arby's, Buffalo Wild Wings, Burger King, Schlotzsky's, Sonic, 🛏 Comfort Inn, La Quinta, Super 8, ⊙ AT&T, Discount Tire, Dodge, $Tree, Kroger, Office Depot, Petsmart, Sam's Club/gas, Walgreens, Walmart, to Joe Pool Lake
453b a	TX 360
452	Frontage Rd
451	Collins St, New York Ave, **N** 📶 Exxon/dsl, RaceTrac, 🍴 Jack-in-the-Box, Whataburger, ⊙ Acura, Chrysler/Jeep, Kia/Mazda/VW, Subaru, **S** 📶 E-Z, QT, Valero, 🍴 Chicken Express, KFC, McDonald's, Sonic, Subway, Taco Bell, Taco Bueno, 🛏 Hampton Inn, ⊙ Buick/GMC, Lincoln/Mercury, Nissan
450	Matlock Rd, **N** 📶 QT, 🍴 BJ's Rest., Bone Daddy's, Boudreaux's Cajun, Chey's Mexican, Coldstone Creamery, Dave&Buster's, Fat Fish Blue, Genghis Grill, Gloria's Cafe, Hoffbrau Steaks, Houlihan's, IHOP, Jamba Juice, Kincade's Burgers, India Grill, Italian Mkt, Keg Steaks, Melting Pot, Mendela's Italian, Mercado Juarez, Mimi's

Exit	Services
450	Continued Cafe, PF Changs, Pluckers's Wings, Pot Belly, Ralph's BBQ, Red Robin, Sweet Tomatoes, Wendy's, 🛏 Quality Inn, ⊙ H, AT&T, Costco/gas, Jo-Ann Fabrics, Lowe's, Michael's, Old Navy, Petsmart, Staples, **S** 📶 7-11, RaceTrac, Shamrock, Shell/7-11, 🍴 Joe's Pizza, Starbucks, ⊙ Fry's Electronics, NTB
449	FM 157, Cooper St, **N** 📶 Mobil, Shell, 7-11, Texaco, 🍴 Abuelo's Mexican, Atlanta Bread, Blackeyed Pea, Cheesecake Factory, Chili's, China Café, CiCi's, Corner Bakery, Don Pablo, Golden Corral, Grandy's, Hong Kong Cafe, Jason's Deli, KFC, McDonald's, On-the-Border, Outback Steaks, Razzoo's Cajun Café, Red Lobster, Rock Fish Grill, Salt Grass Steaks, Schlotsky's, Souper Salad, Spaghetti Whse, Starbucks, Thai Cuisine, Wendy's, Whataburger, 🛏 Best Western, Days Inn, Holiday Inn Express, Homestead Village, La Quinta, Studio 6, ⊙ Barnes&Noble, Best Buy, Dillard's, Discount Tire, Hancock Fabrics, Hyundai, JC Penney, Office Depot, PetCo, Sears/auto, Subaru, Target, TJ Maxx, mall, **S** 📶 Chevron, Conoco, Shell, 🍴 Applebee's, Arby's, Boston Mkt, Burger King, Burger St, Chick-fil-A, Denny's, El Fenix Mexican, LJ Silver, Luby's, Macaroni Grill, McDonald's, Olive Garden, Panda Express, Popeye's, Ryan's, Sonic, Subway, Taco Bueno, TGIFriday, 🛏 InTown Suites, ⊙ Acura, $Tree, Ford, GMC, Hobby Lobby, Home Depot, Honda, Hyundai, Isuzu, Kia, K-Mart, Kroger, Ross, Suzuki, Toyota, Walmart
448	Bowen Rd, **N** 📶 QT, RaceTrac, 🍴 Cracker Barrel, **S** 📶 Shell
447	Kelly-Elliott Rd, Park Springs Blvd, **N** 📶 Lonestar Express, 7-11, **S** 📶 Exxon, Fina/Blimpie, ⊙ camping
445	Green Oaks Blvd, **N** 📶 Conoco/dsl, Shell, 🍴 Arby's, Boston Mkt, Braum's, Burger St, Church's, Colter's BBQ, Hooters, Jack-in-the-Box, KFC, Mac's Grill, Papa John's, Popeye's, Quizno's, Schlotzsky's, Starbucks, Taco Bell, Taco Cabana, Whataburger, ⊙ Ace Hardware, Albertsons, CVS Drug, Firestone, Office Depot, Radio Shack, **S** 📶 Chevron/24hr, Murphy Express/dsl, 7-11, Valero, 🍴 Cheddar's, IHOP, Fazoli's, Khaki's, McDonald's, Pancho's Mexican, Panda Express, Sonic, Steak&Ale, Subway, Taco Bueno, Waffle House, ⊙ AutoZone, BigLots, Discount Tire, $General, NTB, O'Reilly Parts, Walmart, vet
444	US 287 S, to Waxahatchie, same as 445, from eb
443	Bowman Springs Rd (from wb)
442b a	I-820 to Ft Worth, US 287 bus, **N** 📶 Valero, 🛏 Great Western Inn, Super 8, **S** 📶 Chevron/dsl
441	Anglin Dr, Hartman Lane, **S** 📶 Conoco/dsl
440b	Forest Hill Dr, **N** 📶 Value Place Inn, **S** 📶 Chevron/24hr, Conoco, Shell/7-11/dsl, 🍴 Braum's, Capt D's, CiCi's Piz

INTERSTATE 20 CONT'D

Exit	Services
440b	Continued
	za, DQ, Denny's, Domino's, Jack-in-the-Box, Luby's, McDonald's, Sonic, Starbucks, Subway, Taco Bell, ⊙ AutoZone, CVS Drug, Discount Tire, $General, $Tree, Super 1 Foods, Walgreens
440a	Wichita St, N ⛽ Chevron/dsl, 🍴 #1. Chinese, Taco Casa, Wendy's, S ⛽ Texaco, Valero, 🍴 Braum's, Chicken Express, Denny's, Domino's, McDonald's, Pizza Hut, Schlotzsky's, Taco Bueno, Whataburger, 🏠 Hampton Inn
439	Campus Dr, N ⊙ Chrysler/Jeep, Ford, S ⊙ Sam's Club/gas
438	Oak Grove Rd, **1 mi** N ⛽ Shell, 🍴 Burger King, Denny's, Jack-in-the-Box, McDonald's, Whataburger, 🏠 Days Inn, S ⛽ Valero
437	I-35W, N to Ft Worth, S to Waco
436b	Hemphill St, N ⛽ Shell/dsl, S ⊙ Chevrolet
436a	FM 731 (from eb), to Crowley Ave, N ⛽ Valero, ⊙ $General, Sav-a-Lot Foods, S 🍴 BurgerBox, Pizza Hut/Taco Bell, Subway, ⊙ transmissions
435	McCart St, N ⛽ Shell, S ⛽ Mobil
434b	Trail Lakes Dr, S ⛽ Shell, 🍴 Sonic, Starbucks, ⊙ CVS Drug
434a	Granbury rd, S 🍴 Pancho's Mexican, Wendy's, ⊙ JoAnn Fabrics
433	Hulen St, N ⛽ Shell/dsl, 🍴 ChuckeCheese, Grady's Grill, Hooters, Olive Garden, Souper Salad, Subway, TGIFriday, 🏠 TownePlace Suites, ⊙ Albertsons, Home Depot, Office Depot, Petsmart, TJ Maxx, S ⛽ Shamrock, Valero, 🍴 Denny's, Jack-in-the-Box, McDonald's, Red Lobster, Taco Bell, 🏠 Hampton Inn, ⊙ Dillard's, Macy's, Ross, mall
431	(432 from wb), TX 183, Bryant-Irvin Rd, N ⛽ Chevron, Valero, 🍴 Chipotle Mexican, Genghis Grill, Mimi's Café, On-the-Border, Taste of Asia, ⊙ Best Buy, Cavender's Boots, Kohl's, Lowe's, Petsmart, Sam's Club/gas, S ⛽ Chevron/24hr, Exxon, QT, Shell, Texaco, 🍴 Blackeyed Pea, Chicken Express, Chick-fil-A, Cousin's BBQ, Fuddruckers, IHOP, Lonestar Oysters, Outback Steaks, Quizno's, Razzoo's Cajun, Rio Mambo, SaltGrass Steaks, Schlotzsky's, Sonic, Starbucks, Subway, 🏠 Courtyard, Extended Stay America, Holiday Inn Express, Hyatt Place, La Quinta, ⊙ H, AT&T, Buick, Costco/gas, Ford, Goodyear/auto, Lexus, Mazda, PetCo, Suzuki, Staples, Target, Tom Thumb/gas, Verizon, Walgreens, transmissions/repair
430mm	Clear Fork Trinity River
429b	Winscott Rd, N ⛽ Circle K/dsl, 🍴 Cracker Barrel, 🏠 Best Western, Comfort Suites
429a	US 377, to Granbury, S ⛽ RaceTrac/24hr, Valero, 🍴 Arby's, Burger King, Chicken Express, Domino's, DQ, Jack-in-the-Box, KFC/Taco Bell, McDonald's, Sonic, Starbucks, Waffle House, Whataburger/24hr, 🏠 Motel 6, ⊙ Albertsons, AutoZone, $General, Walgreens
428	I-820, N around Ft Worth
426	RM 2871, Chapin School Rd
425	Markum Ranch Rd
421	I-30 E (from eb), to Ft Worth
420	FM 1187, Aledo, Farmer parking
419mm	**weigh sta eb**
418	Ranch House Rd, Willow Park, Willow Park, N ⛽ Exxon, Shell/dsl, 🍴 Los Vaqueros, Pizza Hut, Sonic, Subway,

Exit	Services
418	Continued
	Taco Casa, Whataburger, ⊙ Ace Hardware, S ⛽ Shell/ChickenExpress/dsl, 🍴 Domino's, McDonald's, Milano's Italian, Mr Jim's Pizza, Railhead BBQ, 🏠 Knights Inn, ⊙ Ace RV Ctr., Brookshire Foods, Cowtown RV Park, Curves, $General
417mm	no services
415	FM 5, Mikus Rd, Annetta, S ⛽ Chevron/dsl, Shell/dsl, ⊙ 415 RV Ctr
413	(414 from wb), US 180 W, Lake Shore Dr, N ⛽ Murphy USA/dsl, RaceTrac, Shell, Texaco/dsl, 🍴 DQ, McDonald's, Sonic, Subway, Waffle House, ⊙ Buick/GMC, Cadillac/Chevrolet, Ford, Lincoln/Mercury, Nissan, Scion/Toyota, Suzuki, Walgreens, Walmart, S ⛽ Chevron/dsl, Valero/dsl
410	Bankhead Hwy, S ⛽ 🔶Loves/Subway/dsl/24hr
409	FM 2552 N, Clear Lake Rd, N ⛽ Petro/Mobil/dsl/rest./24hr/@, 🍴 Antonio's Mexican, Granny's Kitchen, Jack-in-the-Box, 🏠 Best Western, Sleepgo, ⊙ H, Blue Beacon, S ⛽ Shell/dsl
408	TX 171, FM 1884, FM 51, Tin Top Rd, Weatherford, N ⛽ Chevron, Exxon/24hr, Mobil, Murphy USA/dsl, 🍴 Applebee's, Baker's Ribs, Braum's, Buffalo Wild Wings, Chicken Express, Cici's Pizza, Cotton Patch Cafe, Country Cafe, Denny's, Golden Corral, IHOP, Kincade's Burgers, LJ Silver, Logan's Roadhouse, McAlister's Deli, McDonald's, MT Rest., Olive Garden, Rosa's Cafe, Schlotzsky's, Starbucks, Subway, Taco Bell, Taco Bueno, Wendy's, Whataburger, Wild Mushroom Steaks, 🏠 La Quinta, Sleep Inn, Super 8, ⊙ AT&T, AutoZone, Belk, $Tree, Firestone/auto, Home Depot, JC Penney, Michael's, Radio Shack, Sears, Super Sav Foods, Tuesday Morning, Walgreens, Walmart, S ⛽ Exxon/Subway/dsl, Shell/Burger King/dsl/24hr, 🍴 Chick-fil-A, Chili's, Coldstone Creamery, Cracker Barrel, On-the-Border, Waffle House, 🏠 Candlewood Suites, Comfort Suites, Express Inn, Fairfield Inn, Hampton Inn, Holiday Inn Express, Motel 6, Super Value Inn, ⊙ Best Buy, GNC, Kohl's, Lowe's, NTB, Petsmart, Ross, Target
407	Tin Top Rd (from eb), S ⊙ Serenity Ranch RV Park, same as 408
406	Old Dennis Rd, N ⛽ Truck&Travel/dsl, 🍴 Chuck Wagon Rest., 🏠 Quest Inn, S ⛽ 🔶/Wendy's/dsl/scales/24hr, 🏠 EconoLodge, Quality 1 Motel, ⊙ Rip Griffin Repair
402	(403 from wb), TX 312, to Weatherford
397	FM 1189, to Brock, N ⛽ Valero/dsl, ⊙ Oak Creek RV Park
394	FM 113, to Millsap
393mm	Brazos River
391	Gilbert Pit Rd
390mm	**rest area both lanes, full ♿ facilities, 🔌, vending, 🏕 litter barrels, petwalk**
386	US 281, to Mineral Wells, N ⛽ Shell/Subway/dsl, ⊙ Coffee Creek RV Resort
380	FM 4, Santo, S ⊙ Windmill Acres RV Park
376	Blue Flat Rd, Panama Rd
373	TX 193, Gordon
370	TX 108 S, FM 919, Gordon, N ⛽ Texaco/Bar-B/dsl, S ⛽ Exxon/dsl, ⊙ Cactus Rose RV Park, Longhorn Inn/Country Store
367	TX 108 N, Mingus, N 🍴 Smoke Stack Café, ⊙ Thurber Sta, S 🍴 NY Hill Rest.
364mm	Palo Pinto Creek
363	Tudor Rd, picnic area, tables, litter barrels

FT WORTH · E · W · **FT WORTH**

WEATHERFORD

TX

INTERSTATE 20 CONT'D

E ↑ ↓ **W**

Exit	Services
362mm	Bear Creek, picnic area both lanes, tables, litter barrels
361	TX 16, to Strawn
358	(from wb), frontage rd
356mm	Russell Creek
354	Lp 254, Ranger
351	(352 from wb), College Blvd
349	FM 2461, Ranger, N 🅖 Loves/Godfather's/Subway/dsl/scales/24hr, 🍴 DQ, 🛏 Best Value Inn, ⊡ RL RV Park, S 🅖 Shell/dsl, repair
347	FM 3363 (from wb), Olden, S ⊡ TX Steakhouse
345	FM 3363 (from eb), Olden, S 🍴 TX Steakhouse
343	TX 112, FM 570, Eastland, Lake Leon, N 🅖 Conoco/dsl, Fina/7-11/Subway, Murphy USA/dsl, 🍴 Chicken Express, DQ, Mav Pizza, McDonald's, Sonic, Taco Bell, 🛏 Holiday Inn Express, La Quinta, Super 8/RV park, ⊡ AT&T, AutoZone, Buick/Cadillac/Chevrolet/GMC, Chrysler/Dodge/Jeep, Curves, $General, Ford/Mercury, O'Reilly Parts, TrueValue, Walmart, S 🅖 Exxon/dsl/24hr, 🍴 Pulido's Mexican, 🛏 Budget Host, Days Inn
340	TX 6, Eastland, N 🅖 Chevron/dsl, ⊡ H, S 🅖 Shell/dsl
337	spur 490, N ⊡ The Wild Country RV Park
332	US 183, Cisco, N 🅖 Cow Pokes, Exxon/dsl, 🍴 DQ, Pizza Heaven, Sonic, Subway, 🛏 Executive Inn, Knights Inn, ⊡ $General, Parts+, Hilton Mon (1mi)
330	TX 206, Cisco, N 🛏 Best Value Inn, ⊡ H
329mm	picnic area wb, tables, litter barrels, ♿ accessible
327mm	picnic area eb, tables, litter barrels, ♿ accessible
324	Scranton Rd
322	Cooper Creek Rd
320	FM 880 N, FM 2945 N, to Moran
319	FM 880 S, Putnam, N 🅖 gas/dsl/café, ⊡ USPO
316	Brushy Creek Rd
313	FM 2228
310	Finley Rd
308	Lp 20, Baird
307	US 283, Clyde, N 🍴 DQ, 🛏 Baird Motel/RV park/dump, S 🅖 Conoco/dsl, Fina/7-11, 🍴 Robertson's Café
306	FM 2047, Baird, N ⊡ Chevrolet/GMC, Chrysler/Dodge/Jeep, Hanner RV Ctr
303	Union Hill Rd
301	FM 604, Cherry Lane, N 🅖 Exxon/Subway/dsl, 🍴 Sonic, Whataburger/24hr, S 🅖 Fina/7-11/dsl, Shell/dsl/24hr, 🍴 DQ, Pizza House, ⊡ Family$
300	FM 604 N, Clyde, N ⊡ Chrysler/Dodge/Jeep, S 🅖 Conoco/dsl, ⊡ White's RV Park/dump
299	FM 1707, Hays Rd
297	FM 603, Eula Rd
296.5mm	**rest area both lanes, full ♿ facilities, 🚻, 🅿, litter barrels, petwalk, wireless internet**
294	Buck Creek Rd, N Big Counry RV Ctr, RV Dump, S Abeline RV Park
292b	Elmdale Rd
292a	Lp 20 (exits left from wb)
290	TX 36, Lp 322, S 🚭, zoo
288	TX 351, N 🅖 Fina/7-11/dsl, Murphy USA/dsl, 🍴 Chili's, Cracker Barrel, DQ, Jack-in-the-Box, Oscar's Mexican, Subway, Wendy's, 🛏 Comfort Suites, Days Inn, Executive Inn, Holiday Inn Express, Quality Inn, Residence Inn, Whitten Inn, ⊡ $Tree, Lowe's, Radio Shack, Walmart, S 🛏 Super 8, ⊡ H

A B I L E N E

286c	FM 600, Abilene, N 🅖 Exxon/dsl, Fina/7-11/dsl, 🍴 Denny's, 🛏 Best Western, Hampton Inn, La Quinta, S 🅖 Fina/7-11/dsl, 🛏 Sleep Inn, ⊡ Russell Stover's Candies
286	US 83, Pine St, Abilene, S 🅖 Fina, 🛏 Frontier Inn, ⊡ H
285	Old Anson Rd, N 🅖 Exxon/dsl, 🛏 Travel Inn, ⊡ The American Wash, S 🅖 Exxon/dsl, 🛏 Best Value Inn
283b	N US 277, U83, Anson
283a	US 277 S, US 83 (exits left from wb)
282	FM 3438, Shirley Rd, S 🛏 Motel 6, ⊡ KOA
280	Fulwiler Rd, to Dyess AFB
279	US 84 E, to Abilene, **1-3 mi S** access to facilities
278	Lp 20, N 🅖 Conoco/dsl/24hr, ⊡ dsl repair, S 🅖 Conoco/dsl/rest./scales/@, ⊡ Mac Trucks/Volvo
277	FM 707, Tye, N 🅖 FLYING J/Denny's/dsl/LP/24hr, ⊡ Tye RV Park, truck tire, S 🅖 Fina/7-11/dsl
274	Wells Lane
272	Wimberly Rd
270	FM 1235, Merkel, N 🅖 Conoco/dsl, Shell/dsl/café/24hr
269	FM 126, N 🍴 Sonic, Subway, 🛏 Scottish Inn, S 🅖 Fina/7-11/dsl/24hr, Shell, 🍴 Skeet's BBQ, ⊡ CarQuest, Family$
267	Lp 20, Merkel, **1 mi S** access to 🅖, 🍴 lodging
266	Derstine Rd
264	Noodle Dome Rd
263	Lp 20, Trent
262	FM 1085, S 🅖 Fina/7-11/dsl/24hr
261	Lp 20, Trent
259	Sylvester Rd
258	White Flat Rd, oil wells
257mm	**rest area both lanes, full ♿ facilities, 🚻, vending, 🅿, litter barrels, petwalk**
256	Stink Creek Rd
255	Adrian Rd
251	Eskota Rd
249	FM 1856, N ⊡ Lonestar RV Park
247	TX 70 N, Sweetwater, N 🍴 Whataburger
246	Alabama Ave, Sweetwater
245	Arizona Ave (from wb), same as 244
244	TX 70 S, Sweetwater, N 🅖 Chevron/dsl, Fina/7-11/dsl/24hr, Murphy USA/dsl, 🍴 Domino's, DQ, Jack-in-the-Box, McDonald's, Subway, Wendy's, 🛏 Best Western, La Quinta, Motel 6, ⊡ H, AutoZone, Medicine Place Drug, Verizon, Walmart, S 🅖 Shell, 🍴 Big Boy's BBQ, Buck's BBQ, Golden Chick, Great Wall Buffet, Schlotzsky's, Skeet's Grill, Taco Bell, 🛏 Country Hearth Inn, Hampton Inn, Holiday Inn Express, Ranch House Motel/rest., ⊡ Buick/Cadillac/Chevrolet/GMC, Chaparral RV Park, K-Mart, Rainboat RV Park
243	Hillsdale Rd, Robert Lee St
242	Hopkins Rd, S 🅖 TA/Conoco/Pizza Hut/Popeye's/dsl/

S W E E T W A T E R

TX

INTERSTATE 20 CONT'D

E ↑ ↓ W

Exit	Services
242	Continued scales/24hr/@, 🄾 Rolling Plains RV Park, truck/tire repair, truck wash
241	Lp 20, Sweetwater, N 🅖, 🍴 lodging, S RV camping
240	Lp 170, N ⊙, camping
239	May Rd
238b a	US 84 W, Blackland Rd
237	Cemetery Rd
236	FM 608, Roscoe, N 🅖 Shell, TC/Country Cookin/dsl, 🄾 NAPA, N 🍴 Retta Mae's Rest
235	to US 84, Roscoe, S repair
230	FM 1230 many wind turbines
229mm	picnic area wb, tables, litter barrels, ♿ accessible
228mm	picnic area eb, tables, litter barrels, ♿ accessible
227	Narrell Rd
226b	Lp 20 (from wb), Loraine
226a	FM 644 N, Wimberly Rd
225	FM 644 S, 1 mi S access to 🅖, food
224	Lp 20, to Loraine, 1 mi S 🅖, food
223	Lucas Rd, S 🄾 223 RV Park
221	Lasky Rd
220	FM 1899
219	Lp 20, Country Club Rd, Colorado City
217	TX 208 S
216	TX 208 N,, N 🅖 Chevron/Subway/dsl, 🍴 DQ, 🛏 Days Inn, S 🅖 TC/Country Cookin/dsl, 🍴 Pizza Hut, Sonic, 🛏 American Inn, 🄾 ⊞, Alco, $General, Health Mart Drugs, Parts+
215	FM 3525, Rogers Rd, 2 mi S ⊞, access to 🅖, food
214.5mm	Colorado River
213	Lp 20, Enderly Rd, Colorado City
212	FM 1229
211mm	FM 1229, Morgan Creek
210	FM 2836, S 🅖 Just Stop/dsl, 🄾 to Lake Colorado City SP, picnic area, camping
209	Dorn Rd
207	Lp 20, Westbrook
206	FM 670, to Westbrook
204mm	**rest area wb, full ♿ facilities, ⓒ, ⊞, litter barrels, petwalk**
200	Conaway Rd
199	Iatan Rd
195	frontage rd (from eb)
194a	E Howard Field Rd
192	FM 821, many oil wells
191mm	**rest area eb, full ♿ facilities, ⓒ, ⊞, litter barrels, petwalk**
190	Snyder Field Rd
189	McGregor Rd
188	FM 820, Coahoma, N 🅖 TC/Country Cookin/dsl, 🍴 DQ, Vickie's Cafe, 🄾 USPO
186	Salem Rd, Sand Springs
184	Moss Lake Rd, Sand Springs, N 🅖 Fina/dsl, S RV camping
182	Midway Rd
181b	Refinery Rd, N 🅖 Fina Refinery
181a	FM 700, N ⊙, RV camping, 2 mi S ⊞
179	US 80, Big Spring, S 🅖 Fina/7-11, 🍴 DQ, Denny's, 🛏 Camlot Inn, Quality Inn, Super 8, 🄾 Buick/Cadillac/Chevrolet, $General
178	TX 350, Big Spring, N 🅖 Shell/dsl, S 🄾 truck repair

BIG SPRING

177	US 87, Big Spring, N 🅖 Exxon/dsl, TA/Country Fare/Popeye's/dsl/scales/24hr/@, 🍴 Texas Cajun Cafe, 🛏 Advantage Inn, La Quinta, Motel 6, Plaza Inn, S 🅖 Chevron/dsl, Fina/dsl, 🍴 Casa Blanca Mexican, DQ, 🛏 Best Western, Hampton Inn, Holiday Inn Express
176	TX 176, Andrews
174	Lp 20 E, Big Springs, S 🅖 Shell/dsl, 🄾 ⊞, Big Springs SP, ⊙
172	Cauble Rd
171	Moore Field Rd
169	FM 2599
168mm	picnic area both lanes, tables, littter barrels
165	FM 818
158	Lp 20 W, to Stanton, N RV camping
156	TX 137, Lamesa, S 🅖 Phillips 66/Country Cookin/Subway/dsl/24hr, 🍴 Sonic, 🛏 Baymont Inn
154	US 80, Stanton, 2 mi S access to 🅖, 🍴 lodging
151	FM 829 (from wb)
144	Loop 250 2-3 mi N facilities in Midland
143mm	frontage rd (from eb)
142mm	picnic area both lanes, tables, litter barrels, hist marker
140	FM 307 (from eb)
138	TX 158, FM 715, Greenwood, N 🅖 Shell/dsl, United/dsl, 🍴 KD's BBQ, Whataburger/24hr, S 🅖 Stripes/Subway/dsl
137	Old Lamesa Rd

MIDLAND

136	TX 349, Midland, N 🅖 Murphy USA, Stripes/tacos/dsl, 🍴 Cici's Pizza, Domino's, IHOP, Jack-in-the-Box, Little Caesar's, McAlister's Deli, Sonic, Starbucks, 🛏 Comfort Inn, Country Inn&Suites, Holiday Inn Express, West Texas Inn, 🄾 Advance Parts, AutoZone, Chavez Tires, Discount Tire, $General, $Tree, Family$, Petroleum Museum, Verizon, Walmart, S 🅖 Exxon/Burger King/dsl, Daves Gas/NAPA, Stripes/tacos
135	Cotton Flat Rd, S ⊞
134	Midkiff Rd, 0-1 mi (Wall St) N 🅖 Fina/7-11, Exxon/dsl, Shell, Stripes/Subway/dsl, 🍴 Denny's, DQ, 🛏 Best Value Inn, Bradford Inn, Days Inn, Executive Inn, Knights Inn, La Quinta, Studio 6, Super 8, 🄾 ⊞, Bo's RV Ctr, Chevrolet, Chrysler/Dodge/Jeep, Honda, Ford, Mercedes/Volvo, Midland RV Park, Nissan, Scion/Toyota, Subaru
131	TX 158, Midland, N 🛏 Travelodge, S 🄾 Midland RV Park
126	FM 1788, N 🅖 Chevron/tacos/dsl, ▭/McDonald's/dsl/scales, Warfield/Texaco/Subway/dsl/scales/@, 🄾 Western Auto, museum, ⊙

ODESSA

121	Lp 338, Odessa, 0-3 mi (TX 191) N 🅖 Fina/7-11, Stripes/tacos/dsl, 🍴 Carino's, Chili's, Fazoli's, Golden Corral, Hooters, Logan's Roadhouse, McDonald's, Pizza Hut, Pizza Patron, Red Lobster, Rosa's Cafe, Schlotzsky's, Sonic, Subway, Wendy's, Whataburger, 🛏 Days Inn, Comfort Suites, Elegante Hotel, Fairfield Inn, Hampton Inn Express, Hilton Garden, Holiday Inn, La Quinta, Studio 6, Super Inn, 🄾 Albertsons, AT&T, Buick/GMC, Chevrolet, Dillard's, $Gerneral, $Tree, Hobby Lobby, Home Depot, Honda, Hyundai, Lowe's, Nissan, Sears/auto, Sam's Club/gas, Scion/Toyota, Staples, Target, Walmart, U of TX Permian Basin
120	JBS Pkwy, N 🛏 Super 8, Comfort Inn, 🄾 Mac/Volvo
118	FM 3503, Grandview Ave, N 🅖 Fina/dsl, 🄾 Freightliner/Peterbilt
116	US 385, Craine, Andrews, N 🅖 Chevron/dsl, Stripes/tacos, 🍴 DQ, 🛏 Best Western, Delux Inn, Villa West Inn, 🄾 ⊞, S 🅖 Fina/dsl, Shell/dsl, 🛏 Motel 6, 🄾 city park

TX

INTERSTATE 20 CONT'D

Exit	Services
115	FM 1882, **N** 🚗 Stripes/tacos/dsl/24hr, **S** 🚗 ♥Loves/ McDonald's/Subway/dsl/scales/24hr
113	TX 302, Odessa
112	FM 1936, Odessa, **N** 🚗 Drivers/dsl
108	Moss Ave, Meteor Crater
104	FM 866, Meteor Crater Rd, **weigh st both directions**
103.5mm	**weigh sta wb/parking area eb, litter barrels**
101	FM 1601, Penwell
93	FM 1053
86	TX 41, **N** Monahans Sandhills SP, camping
83	US 80, Monahans, **2 mi N** ⊙ H, RV camping
80	TX 18, Monahans, **N** 🚗 Chevron/dsl/24hr, 🍴 Bar-H Steaks, DQ, Great Wall Buffet, McDonald's, Pappy's BBQ, Pizza Hut, Sonic, ⊙ H, Alco, $General, Family$, Kwik Lube, Lowe's Foods, O'Reilly Parts, RV Park, Verizon, **S** 🚗 Fina/dsl/24hr, Kent, TC/Subway/dsl/24hr, 🍴 Huddle House, 🏨 Best Value Inn, Best Western, Comfort Inn, Texan Inn, ⊙ Buick/Chevrolet/GMC, Chrysler/Dodge/Jeep
79	Lp 464, Monahans
76	US 80, Monahans, **2 mi N** ⊙ to Million Barrel Museum, RV camping
73	FM 1219, Wickett, **N** 🚗 Shell/Allsup's/dsl, **S** 🚗 Texaco/Subway/dsl/24hr
70	TX 65
69.5mm	**rest area both lanes, full** 🦽 **facilities,** 🚻, 🏨, **litter barrels, petwalk**
66	FM 1927, to Pyote
58	frontage rd, multiple oil wells
52	Lp 20 W, to Barstow
49	FM 516, to Barstow
48mm	Pecos River
44	Collie Rd
42	US 285, Pecos, **N** 🚗 Chevron/24hr, Fina, ⊕FLYING J/Denny's/dsl/scales/24hr, Shell/dsl, 🍴 Alfredo's Mexican, DQ, El Rodeo Mexican, Pizza Hut, 🏨 Country Inn, Holiday Inn Express, Motel 6, Quality Inn, OakTree Inn, ⊙ AutoZone, Walmart, museum, tire repair
40	Country Club Dr, **N** st patrol, **S** 🚗 Chevron/Subway, 🏨 Best Western/rest., ⊙ RV camping, municipal park
39	TX 17, Pecos, **S** 🏨 Hampton Inn, ⊙ H, Buick/Cadillac/Chevrolet/GMC, Trapark RV Park
37	Lp 20 E, **2 mi N** 🍴 Sonic
33	FM 869
29	Shaw Rd, **S** to TX AM Ag Sta
25mm	**picnic area both lanes, tables, litter barrels,** 🦽 **accessible**
22	FM 2903, to Toyah
13	McAlpine Rd
7	Johnson Rd
3	Stocks Rd
0mm	I-20 begins/ends on I-10, 187mm.

INTERSTATE 27

Exit	Services
	I-27 begins/ends on I-40, exit 70 in Amarillo.
123b	I-40, W to Albuquerque, E to OK City
123a	26th Ave, **E** 🚗 Discount Gas, **W** 🍴 DJ Burgers, La Campana Mexican
122c	from sb only

Exit	Services
122a	34th Ave, Tyler St, **E** 🚗 Shell, Valero, 🍴 Sonic
122b	FM 1541, Washington St, Parker St, Moss Lane, **W** 🍴 Hungry Howie's, Taco Bell, Thai Express
121a	Hawthorne Dr, Austin St, **E** 🏨 Amarillo Motel, ⊙ Honda Motorcycles, Main Auto Parts, **W** ⊙ Scottie's Transmissions
121b	Georgia St, **E** 🚗 Murphy USA/dsl, ⊙ Buick/GMC, Honda, Kia, Nissan, Subaru, Walmart/McDonald's
120b	45th Ave, **E** 🍴 Waffle House, ⊙ O'Reilly Parts, repair, **W** 🚗 Exxon, Shell, Valero, 🍴 Abuelo's Mexican, Burger King, Donut Stop, Gatti's Pizza, Grand Burger, McDonald's, Whataburger, ⊙ Advance Parts, BMW, Dodge, $General, Drug Emporium
120a	Republic Ave
119b	Western St, 58th Ave, **E** 🚗 Phillips 66, 🍴 Sonic, Subway, ⊙ $General, **W** 🚗 Shell/dsl, Valero, 🍴 Arby's, Braum's, LJ Silver, Pizza Hut, Thai Palace, Wendy's, ⊙ Aamco, U-Haul, USPO
119a	W Hillside
117	Bell St, Arden Rd, **W** 🚗 Shell/24hr, 🍴 Popeye's, Sonic, ⊙ $General
116	Lp 335, Hollywood Rd, **E** 🚗 ♥Loves/Subway/dsl/24hr, Phillips 66/dsl, 🍴 McDonald's, Waffle House, Whataburger, 🏨 Comfort Suites, Days Inn, **W** 🏨 Holiday Inn Express, ⊙ H (8mi)
115	Sundown Lane
113	McCormick Rd, **E** ⊙ Ford, **W** ⊙ Family Camping Ctr
112	FM 2219, **E** ⊙ Stater's RV Ctr, transmissions
111	Rockwell Rd, **W** ⊙ Buick/GMC
110	(from sb), US 87 S, US 60 W, Canyon
109	Buffalo Stadium Rd, **W** stadium
108	FM 3331, Hunsley Rd
106	TX 217, to Palo Duro Cyn SP, Canyon, **E** ⊙ Palo Duro Canyon SP, RV camping, **W** 🏨 Holiday Inn Express (2mi), ⊙ Plains Museum, to WTA&M
103	FM 1541 N, Cemetery Rd
99	Hungate Rd
98mm	parking area both lanes, litter barrels
96	Dowlen Rd
94	FM 285, to Wayside
92	Haley Rd
90	FM 1075, Happy, **W** gas/dsl, 🍴 Happy Place Cafe
88b a	US 87 N, FM 1881, Happy, same as 90
83	FM 2698
82	FM 214
77	US 87, Tulia, **1-2 mi E** 🚗 Phillips 66, Shell, 🍴 Pizza Hut, Sonic, 🏨 Lasso Inn, Liberty Suites, ⊙ H, Ford, ☞
75	NW 6th St, Tulia, **1 mi E** 🚗 Phillips 66, Shell, 🍴 Pizza Hut, Sonic, 🏨 Lasso Motel, **W** same as 74

Vertical left margin labels: E / W, MONAHANS, PECOS

Vertical center margin labels: N / S, AMARILLO

TX

INTERSTATE 27 CONT'D

N ↕ S

PLAINVIEW

Exit	Services
74	TX 86, Tulia, E 🛏 Lasso Motel, 🅾 🅷, W ⛽ Rip Griffin/Phillips 66/Subway/Chester's/dsl/scales/24hr, 🛏 Executive Inn
70mm	parking area both lanes, litter barrels
68	FM 928
63	FM 145, Kress, **1 mi** E gas/dsl, 🍴 🅾
61	US 87, County Rd
56	FM 788
54	FM 3183, to Plainview, W truck service
53	Lp 27, Plainview, E 🅾 🅷, access to ⛽, camping, 🍴 lodging
51	Quincy St
50	TX 194, Plainview, E ⛽ Phillips 66, 🅾 🅷, to Wayland Bapt U, W 🛏 RH Hotel
49	US 70, Plainview, E ⛽ Allstar Fuel/dsl, Conoco, Fina/dsl, Shell/dsl, 🍴 A&W/LJ Silver, Carlito's Mexican, China Dragon, Cotton Patch Café, El Patron, Furr's Café, Kettle, Leal's Mexican, Pizza Hut, 🛏 Best Western, Comfort Suites, Days Inn, 🅾 Beall's, $Tree, Ford/Lincoln/Mercury/Toyota, GNC, Hastings Books, NAPA, O'Reilly Parts, Radio Shack, United Foods, W ⛽ Chevron, Murphy USA/dsl, Phillips 66/dsl, 🍴 Burger King, Chicken Express, Chili's, Empire Buffet, IHOP, Little Mexico, McDonald's, Sonic, Subway, Taco Bell, 🛏 Holiday Inn Express, Knights Inn, Super 8, 🅾 JC Penney, Verizon, Walmart
45	Lp 27, to Plainview
43	FM 2337
41	County Rd
38	Main St
37	FM 1914, Cleveland St, E ⛽ Co-op, W 🅷, Lowe's Foods
36	FM 1424, Hale Center
32	FM 37 W
31	FM 37 E
29mm	**rest area both lanes, full ♿ facilities, 🍴 🅰, litter barrels, petwalk, tornado shelter**
27	County Rd
24	FM 54, W RV park/dump
22	Lp 369, Abernathy, W Filling Sta Cafe/dsl
21	FM 597, Main St, Abernathy, W ⛽ Conoco/dsl, 🍴 Antelope Corner, DQ, 🅾 $General, USPO
20	Abernathy (from nb)
17	CR 53
15	Lp 461, to New Deal same as 14
14	FM 1729, E ⛽ Fina/rest/dsl/scales/24hr
13	Lp 461, to New Deal
12	access rd (from nb)
11	FM 1294, Shallowater
10	Keuka St, E 🅾 Fed Ex
9	Airport Rd, E ✈, W ⛽ Lubbock RV Park/LP/dump
8	FM 2641, Regis St
7	Yucca Lane, E Pharr RV Ctr
6 b a	Lp 289, Ave Q, Lubbock, E 🅾 Pharr RV
5	B. Holly Ave, Municipal Dr, E 🅾 Mackenzie Park, W 🅾 Civic Ctr
4	US 82, US 87, 4th St, to Crosbyton, W ⛽ ⛽FLYING J/Subway/dsl/LP/scales/24hr, 🅾 to TTU
3	US 62, TX 114, 19th St, Floydada
2	34th St, E ⛽ Phillips 66, 🍴 Pete's Drive Inn, W 🍴 Simple Simon's Pizza, 🅾 AutoZone, Raff&Hall Drug

LUBBOCK

Exit	Services
1c	50th St, E ⛽ Buddy's, 🍴 El Jalapeno Café, W ⛽ Bolton Fuel/dsl, Conoco, Fina /7-11, Valero, 🍴 Bryan's Steaks, Burger King, China Star, Church's, Domino's, KFC, McDonald's, Pizza Hut/Taco Bell, Subway, Taco Villa, Whataburger, Wienerschnitzel, 🛏 Howard Johnson, 🅾 $General, Family$, O'Reilly Parts, United Food/drug/gas, USPO, Walgreens, Woody Tire
1b	US 84, E 🛏 Best Value, Days Inn, W 🛏 Best Western, Comfort Inn, Holiday Inn Express, Motel 6, Quality Inn, Red Roof Inn, Super 8, Value Place
1a	Lp 289
1	82nd St, W ⛽ Phillips 66, I-27 begins/ends on US 87 at 82nd St in S Lubbock.

INTERSTATE 30

E ↕ W

TEXARKANA

Exit	Services
223mm	Texas/Arkansas state line
223b a	US 59, US 71, State Line Ave, Texarkana, N ⛽ EZ Mart, Mobil, Shell, 🍴 Denny's, IHOP, Pizza Inn, Waffle House, 🛏 Baymont Inn, Best Western, Budget Host, Holiday Inn Express, Holiday Inn Express, LaCrosse Hotel, Quality Inn, Ramada Inn, Super 8, 🅾 Cooper Tire, KOA, S ⛽ Exxon, EZ Mart, RaceWay/dsl, Shell, 🍴 Burger King, Cattleman's Steaks, China Inn, China King, Dixie Diner, Hooters, KFC, La Carreta Mexican, Little Caesars, LJ Silver, Marble Slab, McDonald's, Papa John's, Pizza Hut, Pizza Inn, Popeye's, Quizno's, Subway, Taco Bell, Taco Tico, Wendy's, Whataburger/24hr, 🛏 Ambassador Inn, Best Value Inn, Best Western, Comfort Inn, Days Inn, Econolodge, Economy Inn, Executive Inn, La Quinta, Rodeway Inn, 🅾 Albertson's/Sav-On, $General, Hancock Fabrics, KIA, O'Reilly Parts, Radio Shack, Walgreens, Walmart
223mm	**Welcome Ctr wb, full ♿ facilities, info, 🍴, 🅰, litter barrels, vending, petwalk**
222	TX 93, FM 1397, Summerhill Rd, N ⛽ EZ Mart, Shell, Valero/Subway/dsl, 🍴 Applebee's, McDonald's, Shogun Steaks, Waffle House, 🛏 Motel 6, 🅾 AT&T, Freightliner, Hyundai, S ⛽ Shell/24hr, 🍴 Bryce's Rest., Catfish King, 🅾 Chrysler/Dodge, Discount Tire, Ford, Gateway Tires, Lincoln/Mercury, Mercedes, Nissan, Toyota
220b	FM 559, Richmond Rd, N ⛽ Chevron, Exxon, Shell, 🍴 Asian Grill, Burger King, Carino's Italian, Cracker Barrel, Chick-fil-A, Cici's Pizza, Coldstone Creamery, DQ, Domino's, Little Caesars, McAlister's Deli, On-the-Border, Pizza Hut, Randy's BBQ, Red Lobster, Ruby Tuesday, Smokey Joe's BBQ, Sonic, Starbucks, Taco Bell, TaMolly's Mexican, TX Roadhouse, Wendy's, 🛏 Comfort Suites, Courtyard, TownePlace Suites, 🅾 AT&T, Best Buy, Chevrolet, Discount Tire, $Tree, Gander Mtn, Home Depot, Honda, Kohls, Kwik Kar, Old Navy, PetsMart, Sam's Club/gas, Staples, Super 1 Food/gas, Target, TJ Maxx, S ⛽ Valero/dsl, 🍴 Arby's, Chili's, ChuckeCheese, Golden Corral, Grandy's, McDonald's, Olive Garden, Outback Steaks, Quizno's, Subway, Taco Bueno, 🛏 Candlewood Suites, Fairfield Inn, Hampton Inn, Holiday Inn Express, 🅾 AT&T, Albertson's/Sav-On, Books-A-Million, Buick/GMC, Cadillac, Cavender's Boots, Dillard's, Hobby Lobby, JC Penney, Jeep, Mazda, Michael's, Office Depot, Ross, Sears/auto, Tuesday Morning, Walgreens, mall
220a	US 59 S, Texarkana, S ⛽ Exxon/Wendy's, Murphy USA, 🍴 DQ, Subway, 🅾 Lowe's Whse, Radio Shack, Walmart, mall

TX

INTERSTATE 30 CONT'D

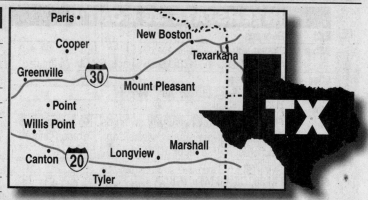

Exit	Services
218	FM 989, Nash, **N** 🅰 Road Runner/dsl, 🍴 Dixie Diner, **S** 🅰 Exxon/Burger King/dsl, 🅾 GMC/Peterbilt, to Lake Patman
213	FM 2253, Leary, **N** 🅾 Palma RV Ctr
212	spur 74, Lone Star Army Ammo Plant, **S** 🅰 Shell
208	FM 560, Hooks, **N** 🍴 Old Farm Mkt/BBQ, 🅾 Hooks Camper Ctr., **S** 🅰 Texaco/Subway/dsl/scales/24hr, 🍴 DQ, Noble Roman's, Sonic, TasteeHouse Rest., 🅾 $General, Family$, Hooks Tire
206	TX 86, **S** 🅾 Red River Army Depot
201	TX 8, New Boston, **N** 🅰 Shell/dsl, Valero/dsl, 🍴 Pitt Grill, 🛏 Tex Inn, 🅾 Chevrolet, Chrysler/Dodge/Jeep, **S** 🅰 Murphy USA/dsl, Shell/dsl, 🍴 Catfish King, Church's, DQ, KFC/Taco Bell, McDonald's, Nana's Diner, Pizza Hut, Randy's BBQ, Sonic, 🛏 Best Value Inn, Bostonian Inn, Holiday Inn Express, 🅾 Ⓗ, Brookshire's Foods/gas, Curves, Ford/Mercury, O'Reilly Parts, Walmart/Subway, RV park
199	US 82, DeKalb, 1/2 mi **N** 🅰 Shell
198	TX 98, 1/2 mi **N** 🅰 Shell
193mm	Anderson Creek
192	FM 990, **N** 🅰 FuelStop/Culpeppers Rest/dsl
186	FM 561
181mm	Sulphur River
178	US 259, to DeKalb, Omaha
174mm	White Oak Creek
170	FM 1993
165	FM 1001, **S** 🅰 Exxon/dsl
162b a	US 271, FM 1402, FM 2152, Mt Pleasant, **N** 🅰 Exxon/dsl/24hr, 🍴 Applebee's, Blalock BBQ, Pitt Grill, 🛏 Holiday Inn Express, Super 8, 🅾 KOA, **S** 🅰 Shell/dsl, Valero/Subway/dsl, 🍴 Burger King, McDonald's, Pizza Inn, Sonic, 🛏 Best Western, 🅾 Ⓗ, Cadillac/Chevrolet, Family$, Ford, vet
160	US 271, FM 1734, Mt Pleasant, **N** 🅰 Texaco/dsl, 🍴 Senorita's Mexican, 🛏 La Quinta, 🅾 Buick/GMC (1mi), Lowe's Whse, Ramblin Fever RV Park, Toyota, Verizon, **S** 🅰 Exxon/dsl, Shell/dsl, 🍴 El Chico, IHOP, Western Sizzlin, 🛏 Comfort Inn, Days Inn, Executive Inn, Hampton Inn, 🅾 Sandlin SP
158mm	**weigh sta both lanes**
156	frontage rd
153	spur 185, to Winfield, Millers Cove, **N** 🅰 I-30, Phillips 66, Winfield/dsl, **S** 🅰 Shamrock/dsl
150	Ripley Rd, **N** 🅾 Lowe's Distribution
147	spur 423, **N** 🅰 Loves/Chester's/Subway/dsl/scales/24hr, 🛏 American Inn, Economy Inn, 🅾 tires/repair
146	TX 37, Mt Vernon, **N** 🅰 Shell/dsl, 🍴 Sonic, 🅾 Alco, 🅾 Ⓗ, **S** 🅰 Exxon/dsl, Fina/dsl/24hr, 🍴 Burger King, DQ, Mi Casita, Mt Vernon Cafe, 🛏 Super 8, 🅾 to Lake Bob Sandlin SP, auto repair, antiques
143	**rest area both lanes, full ♿ facilities, 🍴, 🛏, litter barrels, vending, petwalk**
142	County Line Rd (from eb)
141	FM 900, Saltillo Rd
136	FM 269, Weaver Rd
135	US 67 N
131	FM 69
127	US 67, Lp 301, **N** 🛏 Comfort Suites, Quality 1 Inn, Super Hotel, 🅾 Ⓗ, **S** 🅰 Shell, 🍴 Burton's Rest./24hr, 🛏 Best Western

Exit	Services
126	FM 1870, College St, **S** 🅰 Exxon, 🍴 Burton's Rest./24hr, 🛏 Best Western, 🅾 Firestone/auto, same as 127
125	Bill Bradford Rd, same as 124
124	TX 11, TX 154, Sulphur Springs, **N** 🅰 Exxon, 🍴 Bodacious BBQ, Chicken Express, Dominos, Juan Pablo's Mexican, Pitt Grill, Pizza Hut, San Remo Italian, Subway, 🛏 Holiday Inn Express, La Quinta, Royal Inn, 🅾 Ⓗ, AutoZone, Buick/Chevrolet/GMC, CVS Drug, $General, Family$, Ford, FSA Outlet/famous brands, O'Reilly Parts, Walgreens, USPO, **S** 🅰 Exxon/dsl, Murphy USA/dsl, Shell, 🍴 Braum's, Burger King, Chili's, Dominos, Furr's Rest., Jack-in-the-Box, LJ Silver/Taco Bell, McDonald's, Pizza Inn, Sonic, Tierra Del Sol, Whataburger, 🅾 Discount Tire, Lowe's Whse, Radio Shack, Verizon, Walmart
123	FM 2297, League St, **N** 🅰 Shamrock, Shell
122	TX 19, to Emory, **N** 🅰 Shamrock, 🅾 Ⓗ, Chrysler/Dodge/Jeep, **S** 🅰 🍴 Arby's/dsl/scales/24hr, 🅾 RV Park, vet, to Cooper Lake
120	US 67 bus
116	FM 2653, Brashear Rd
112	FM 499 (from wb)
110	FM 275, Cumby, **N** 🅰 Phillips 66, **S** 🅰 Shell/24hr
104	FM 513, FM 2649, Campbell, **S** to Lake Tawakoni
101	TX 24, TX 50, FM 1737, to Commerce, **N** 🅰 Valero/dsl, 🅾 to E TX St U
97	Lamar St, **N** 🅰 Exxon/dsl, 🛏 Budget Hotel, Dream Lodge Motel
96	Lp 302
95	Division St, **S** 🅾 Ⓗ, Puddin Hill Fruit Cakes
94b	US 69, US 380, Greenville, **N** 🅰 Valero/dsl, 🍴 Ninja's Grill, Senorita's Mexican, 🛏 Best Value Inn, Days Inn, Royal Inn, **S** 🅰 Exxon, Fina/dsl, 🍴 Arby's, Catfish Cove Rest., McDonald's, 🛏 Econolodge, Economy Inn, Motel 6, Quality Inn, Super 8
94a	US 69, US 380, Greenville, **S** 🅰 Valero, 🅾 Chrysler/Dodge/Jeep, Hyundai, Nissan
93b a	US 67, TX 34 N, **N** 🅰 Chevron, Exxon, Texaco, 🍴 Applebee's, Chick-fil-A, Chicken Express, CiCi's, DQ, Grandy's, IHOP, Jack-in-the-Box, KFC, Little Caesars, Pizza Hut, Schlotsky's, Sonic, Starbucks, Steak Angus, Subway, Taco Bell, Taco Bueno, Tony's Italian, Wendy's, Whataburger/24hr, 🛏 Hampton Inn, 🅾 Ⓗ, Ace Hardware, AT&T, Belk, BigLots, Brookshire's Foods, Buick/GMC, Cadillac, Discount Tire, JC Penney, Lowes Whse, O'Reilly Parts, Staples, Walgreens, USPO, mall, transmissions, **S** 🅰 Exxon/dsl/24hr, Valero/dsl, 🍴 Chili's, Cracker Barrel, Eastrock Buffet, Paesano Italian, Papa Murphy's, Red Lobster, Subway, TaMolly's Mexican, 🛏 Best Western, Holiday Inn Express, 🅾 $Tree, Ford/Lincoln/Mercury, Home

Left margin: E ↕ W · N E W B O S T O N

Right margin: S U L P H U R S P R I N G S · G R E E N V I L L E · TX

INTERSTATE 30 CONT'D

E ↑ ↓ W

Exit	Services
93b a	Continued Depot, Mitsubishi, NTB, Radio Shack, RV Ctr, Walmart
90mm	Farber Creek
89	FM 1570, S 🛏 Luxury Inn
89mm	E Caddo Creek
87	FM 1903, N 🅖 Chevron/Pizza Inn/dsl, 🅞 fireworks, S 🅖 🍽/McDonald's/dsl/scales/24hr, Texaco/Pancake House/dsl, 🅞 tire repair
87mm	Elm Creek
85	FM 36, Caddo Mills, N KOA
85mm	W Caddo Creek
83	FM 1565 N, N 🅖 Exxon/dsl
79	FM 2642, N Budget RV Ctr, S vet
77b	FM 35, Royse City, N 🅖 Exxon/dsl, Texaco/Subway/dsl/scales/24hr, 🍽 Soulman's BBQ, 🅞 Family$
77a	TX 548, Royse City, N 🅖 Shell/dsl, 🍽 Jack-in-the-Box, McDonald's, 🛏 Sun Royse Inn, 🅞 AutoZone, tires, S 🅖 Exxon/KFC/Quizno's, 🍽 Denny's, Sonic, Wingdingers, 🛏 Holiday Inn Express
73	FM 551, Fate
70	FM 549, N 🅞 Happy Trails RV Ctr, Hyundai, McLains RV Ctr, S 🅖 ❤Loves/Carl's Jr./dsl/scales/24hr 🅞 KIA
69	(from wb), frontage rd, N 🛏 Super 8, S 🅞 Toyota/Scion
68	TX 205, to Rock Wall, N 🅖 RaceWay, Shell, 🍽 Braum's, DQ, Jowilly's Grill, KFC, Luigi's Italian, Pizza Hut, Pizza Inn, Subway, Taco Casa, Whataburger, 🛏 Holiday Inn Express, Super 8, Value Place, 🅞 Chevrolet, Dodge, Ford/Mercury, Hobby Lobby, S 🅖 TA/Burger King/Starbucks/dsl/rest./24hr/scales/@, Valero/dsl, 🅞 Belk, Costco/gas
67	FM 740, Ridge Rd, N 🅖 Chevron, Murphy USA/dsl, 🍽 Arby's, Burger King, Carabba's, Culver's, Dominos, Grandy's, IHOP, Logan's Roadhouse, McDonald's, Popeye's, Schlotsky's, Smoothie King, Starbucks, Steak'n Shake, Taco Bueno, Taco Cabana, Waffle House, Wendy's, 🛏 Hampton Inn, 🅞 Firestone/auto, Goodyear/auto, Kwik Kar, Walmart, S 🅖 Exxon, Shell, Valero, 🍽 Applebee's, Bahama Buck's Ice Cream, Blackeyed Pea, Buffalo Wild Wings, Carino's Italian, Chick-fil-A, Chili's, Chipotle Mexican, ChuckeCheese, CiCi's, Cotton Patch Cafe, El Chico, Jack-in-the-Box, La Madelein, McDonald's, On-the-Border, Pizza Hut/Taco Bell, Quizno's, Shogun Steaks, Sonic, Soulman's BBQ, Starbucks, Subway, TGIFriday's, 🛏 La Quinta, 🅞 Albertson's, AT&T, Best Buy, CVS Drug, Discount Tire, $Tree, GNC, Home Depot, Kohl's, Lowe's Whse, Michael's, Office Depot, Old Navy, PetCo, PetsMart, Radio Shack, Ross, Staples, SteinMart, Target, Walgreens, to Lake Tawakoni, vet
67a	Horizon Rd, Village Dr, N 🅖 Valero, 🍽 Genghis Grill, Kyoto Japanese, Saltgrass Steaks, Starbucks, 🛏 Hampton Inn, S 🛏 Hilton
66mm	Ray Hubbard Reservoir
64	Dalrock Rd, Rowlett, N 🅖 Exxon, Valero/dsl, 🛏 Comfort Suites, 🅞 H, Express Drug
63mm	Ray Hubbard Reservoir
62	Bass Pro Rd, N 🛏 Best Western, 🅞 to Hubbard RA, S 🅖 Shell, Texaco, Valero, 🍽 CiCi's, Flying Saucer Grill, Primo's Grill, Sonic, TX Land&Cattle, Whataburger, 🅞 Bass Pro Shops
61	Zion Rd (from wb), N 🅖 Exxon/dsl, 🛏 Discovery Inn
60b	Bobtown Rd (eb only), N 🅖 Exxon, 🍽 Jack-in-the-Box, 🛏 La Quinta, S 🅖 Shell, 🍽 Subway

ROCK WALL

Exit	Services
60a	Rose Hill Dr
59	Beltline Rd, Garland, N 🅖 QT, 7-11, 🍽 Chili's, China City, Denny's, India Garden, KFC, McDonald's, Papa John's, Pizza Hut/Taco Bell, Quizno's, Starbucks, Subway, Taco Casa, Taco Cabana, Whataburger, Wendy's, 🅞 Albertson's, GNC, Radio Shack, Tuesday Morning, Walgreens, Walmart, S 🍽 Buffet King, DQ, Sonic, Waffle House, Williams Chicken, 🛏 Best Value Inn, Motel 6, Super 8, 🅞 Kroger
58	Northwest Dr, N 🅖 Shell, Valero/dsl, 🅞 Hyundai, Nissan, S 🅖 Fina, 🍽 Jack-in-the-Box, 🅞 Lowe's Whse
56c b	I-635 S-N
56a	Galloway Ave, Gus Thomasson Dr (from eb), N 🅖 Texaco, Valero, 🍽 KFC, McDonald's, Sonic, 🅞 AutoZone, Walgreens, USPO, S 🅖 Chevron, 7-11, 🍽 Arby's, Celebration Sta, Church's, Dicky's BBQ, Domino's, El Fenix, Grandy's, Hooters, Jack-in-the-Box, Luby's, Olive Garden, Outback Steaks, Outback Steaks, Posades Cafe, Quizno's, Sports City Cafe, Razzoo's Cajun, Red Lobster, TGIFriday's, Luby's, Olive Garden, Subway, Wendy's, 🛏 Courtyard, Crossland Suites, Delux Inn, Fairfield Inn, 🅞 H, Aldi Foods, BigLots, Firestone/auto, Kroger, Nichols RV Ctr, NTB
55	Motley Dr, N 🅖 Shell/dsl, 🛏 Astro Inn, Executive Inn, S 🅖 Chevron, 🛏 Microtel, 🅞 H, to Eastfield Coll
54	Big Town Blvd, N 🅖 Texaco, Valero/dsl, 🛏 Mesquite Inn, S 🅞 Explore RV Ctr, Holiday World RV Ctr, dsl repair
53b	US 80 E (from eb), to Terrell
53a	Lp 12, Buckner, N 🅖 RaceTrac, Texaco, 🍽 Burger King, 🛏 Lamplighter Inn, Luxury Inn, Super 8, 🅞 Chevrolet, Toyota/Scion, S 🅖 7-11, 🍽 CiCi's, Enrique's Cafe, Taco Cabana, Whataburger, 🛏 Holiday Inn Express, 🅞 $Tree, Sam's Club, Staples, Walmart/gas
51	(52 a from wb), Highland Rd, Jim Miller Blvd, N 🅖 Exxon, 🍽 Country China, Denny's, Luby's, McDonald's, 🛏 Holiday Inn Express, La Quinta, S 🅖 RaceWay, Shell/dsl, 🍽 Burger King, Capt D's, Furr's Cafe, Grandy's, KFC, Pizza Hut, Popeye's, Subway, Taco Bell, Wendy's, 🛏 Howard Johnson, Super 7 Inn, 🅞 AutoZone, CVS Drug, O'Reilly Parts
50b a	Ferguson Rd, N 🅖 Texaco, S 🅞 Brake-O, U-Haul
49b	Dolphin Rd, Lawnview Ave, Samuell Ave, N 🅖 Shell, 🛏 Best Value Inn
49a	Winslow St, N 🅖 Circle K/gas, Shell/dsl/repair, Texaco, 🍽 McDonald's, S 🅖 Shell/24hr
48b	TX 78, E Grand, S fairpark, arboretum
48a	Carroll Ave, Central Ave, Peak St, Haskell Ave, N 🅖 7-11, Shamrock, 🅞 H, Hamm's Tires, S 🅖 Fina, 🍽 Joe's Rest
47	2nd Ave, S 🍽 McDonald's, 🅞 Cotton Bowl, fairpark
46b	I-45, US 75, to Houston
46a	Central Expswy, downtown
45	I-35E, N to Denton, to Commerce St, Lamar St, Griffin St, S 🅖 Fuel City, 🍽 McDonald's, 🛏 Ambassador Inn
44b	I-35E S, Industrial Blvd
44a	I-35E N, Beckley Ave (from eb)
43b a	Sylvan Ave (from wb), N 🅖 Valero/Quizno's/dsl, 🅞 H, Family$, USPO
42	Hampton Rd
41	Westmorland Ave
39	Cockrell Hill Rd, N 🍽 KFC/Taco Bell, IHOP, Luckio's BBQ, Polo Cantero, Sonic, Wing Stop, 🛏 Comfort Suites, Hampton Inn, 🅞 Staples, S 🅖 Murphy USA, 🍽 Chili's, Golden Corral, Lucky Rice, McDonald's, Panda Express, Starbucks, Subway, Taco Cabana, Wendy's, Whataburger,

GARLAND DALLAS

DALLAS

TX

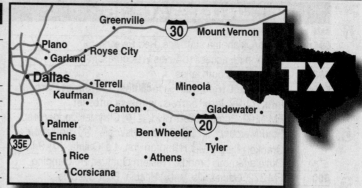

INTERSTATE 30 CONT'D

Exit	Services
39	Continued
	🛏 Holiday Inn Express, ⊙ AT&T, Best Buy, $Tree, Lowe's Whse, Radio Shack, Ross, Walmart
38	Lp 12, **1 mi** N 📟 Exxon, Fina, 🍴 Burger King, Popeye's
36	MacArthur Blvd, S ⊙ U-Haul
34	Belt Line Rd, N 📟 Chevron, RaceTrac, 🛏 Studio 6, Super 8, ⊙ Ford, Ripley's Museum, S 📟 RaceTrac/dsl, Shell/Subway, Valero, 🍴 Burger King, Popeye's, Schlotzky's, Starbucks
32	NW 19th, N 📟 Shamrock, S 📟 Texaco, 🍴 Church's, Denny's, Whataburger, 🛏 La Quinta
30	TX 360, Six Flags Dr, Arlington Stadium, N 📟 Mobil, Shell, 🍴 China Sea, Cracker Barrel, Grand Buffet, Saltgrass Steaks, Steak'n Shake, TrailDust Steaks, Wendy's, 🛏 Best Value Inn, Budget Suites, Crowne Plaza, Executive Inn, Fairfield Inn, Hilton, Hilton Garden, Homestead Suites, Studio+, S 📟 Conoco/dsl, Shell/7-11/dsl, Valero, 🍴 Denny's, Jack-in-the-Box, McDonald's, Mariano's Mexican, Pancho's Mexican, Patomino's, 🛏 Baymont Inn, Holiday Inn Express, Knight's Inn, La Quinta, Motel 6, ⊙ Ford/Lincoln/Mercury, Office Depot, Six Flags Funpark
29	Ball Park Way, N 📟 Chevron, QT, Valero, 🍴 Dicky's BBQ, Sonic, 🛏 Springhill Suites, Towneplace Suites, ⊙ Toyota, S 📟 Fina/dsl, 🍴 On-the-Border, Texas Land&Cattle, 🛏 Howard Johnson, Sheraton, ⊙ Six Flags Funpark
28b	TX 157, Nolan Ryan Expswy, N 📟 Chevron, 🍴 Boston Mkt, Waffle House, 🛏 Country Inn&Suites, ⊙ Cadillac, Chrysler/Dodge/Jeep, S 🛏 EconoLodge, Holiday Inn Express, ⊙ Barnes&Noble, TX Stadium
28a	FM 157, Collins St, N 🍴 Whataburger, ⊙ 🅗, Dodge, S 🍴 Blackeyed Pea, Chick-fil-A, Colter's BBQ, Jason's Deli, Marble Slab, Olen Jack's Grill, Panera Bread, Pappasito's Cantina, Souper Salad, Taco Bueno, TGIFriday's, Wendy's, 🛏 Comfort Suites, ⊙ Best Buy, Curves, $Tree, Home Depot, Pepboys, PetsMart, Ross, Sav-a-Lot Foods, SteinMart
27	Lamar Blvd, Cooper St, N 📟 Texaco, 🍴 Jack-in-the-Box, ⊙ BigLots, Family$, Kroger/gas, vet, S 📟 7-11, Shell, 🍴 Burger King, Denny's, Tom's Burgers
26	Fielder Rd, S ⊙ to Six Flags (from eb)
25mm	Village Creek
24	Eastchase Pkwy, N 🍴 Jack-in-the-Box, Panda Express, 🛏 La Quinta, ⊙ CarMax, Lowe's Whse, Sam's Club/gas, Walmart, S 📟 Chevron/dsl, RaceTrac, Shell/7-11/dsl, 🍴 Asian Grill, Burger King, Chicken Express, IHOP, McDonald's, No Frills Grill, Schlotzky's, Subway, Taco Bell, Wendy's, Whataburger, ⊙ GNC, Office Depot, Radio Shack, Ross, Target
23	Cooks Lane, S 📟 Shell
21a	Bridgewood Dr, N 📟 Chevron, 🍴 Church's, KFC, Jack-in-the-Box, Luby's, Subway, Wendy's, ⊙ Albertson's, Braums Foods, Discount Tire, Home Depot, Kroger, U-Haul, S 📟 Conoco, QT, Shamrock, 🍴 Taco Bueno, Whataburger/24hr
21c b	I-820
19	Brentwood Stair Rd (from eb), N 📟 Chevron, Shell/dsl, S 📟 Shamrock
18	Oakland Blvd, N 📟 Circle K, Shell/dsl, 🍴 Taco Bell,

Exit	Services
18	Continued
	Waffle House, 🛏 Motel 6
16c	Beach St, S 📟 7-11, 🛏 Quality Inn, Inn Suites
16b a	Riverside Dr (from wb), S 🛏 Great Western Inn
15b a	I-35W N to Denton, S to Waco
14b	Jones St, Commerce St, Ft Worth, downtown
14a	TX 199, Henderson St, Ft Worth, downtown
13b	TX 199, Henderson St, N 🛏 Omni, Sheraton
13a	8th Ave, N 🛏 Holiday Inn Express
12d	Forest Park Blvd, N 🍴 Pappa's Burgers, Pappadeaux Café, Pappasito's, S ⊙ 🅗
12b	Rosedale St
12a	University Dr, City Parks, S 🛏 SpringHill Suites
11	Montgomery St, S 📟 Shell/7-11/dsl, 🍴 Whataburger, ⊙ visitor info
10	Hulen St, Ft Worth, S 🍴 Chick-fil-A, Coldstone, Republic Grill, Smoothie King, ⊙ WorldMkt
9b	US 377, Camp Bowie Blvd, Horne St, N 🍴 Uncle Julio's Mexican, S 📟 Exxon, 7-11, Texaco/dsl, 🍴 Jack-in-the-Box, Mexican Inn, Pizza Hut/Taco Bell, Qdoba, Subway, Taco Bueno, Wendy's, ⊙ Batteries+, Radio Shack
9a	Bryant-Irvin Rd, S 📟 Shell, same as 9b
8b	Ridgmar, Ridglea, N 📟 Valero/dsl
8a	TX 183, Green Oaks Rd, N 🍴 Applebee's, Arby's, Chili's, Don Pablo, Grand Buffet, Jack-in-the-Box, New Grand Buffet, Olive Garden, Quizno's, Subway, Starbucks, Taco Bueno, 🛏 Courtyard, ⊙ Albertson's, AT&T, Best Buy, $Tree, Dillard's, Firestone/auto, JC Penney, Jo-Ann Fabrics, Lowe's Whse, Macy's, Neiman Marcus, NTB, Office Depot, PetsMart, Radio Shack, Ross, Sam's Club/gas, Sears/auto, Target, U-Haul, Walmart, S 🍴 Tommy's Burgers, 🛏 Comfort Suites, Hampton Inn
7b a	Cherry Lane, TX 183, spur 341, to Green Oaks Rd, N 📟 Shell/7-11, Texaco/dsl, Valero/dsl, 🍴 ChuckeCheese, IHOP/24hr, Popeye's, Ryan's, Subway, Taco Bell, Wendy's, 🛏 La Quinta, Super 8, ⊙ BigLots, O'Reilly Parts, Suzuki, U-Haul, S 🛏 Holiday Inn Express, Quality Inn, ⊙ Nissan
6	Las Vegas Trail, N 📟 Chevron/McDonald's, 🍴 Jack-in-the-Box, Waffle House, 🛏 Days Inn, ⊙ Hyundai, Lincoln/Mercury, Mitsubishi, S 📟 Fina, Shell/7-11/dsl, Valero/dsl, 🛏 Best Budget Suites, Best Value Inn, Motel 6, ⊙ AutoZone, Kia
5b c	I-820 S and N
5a	Alemeda St (from eb, no EZ return)
3	RM 2871, Chapel Creek Blvd, S 📟 Exxon/Church's/Subway, 🍴 Sonic
2	spur 580 E
1b	Linkcrest Dr, S 📟 Mobil/dsl
0mm	I-20 W. I-30 begins/ends on I-20, exit 421.

TX

INTERSTATE 35

Exit	Services
504mm	Texas/Oklahoma state line, Red River
504	frontage rd, access to Texas Welcome Ctr
503mm	parking area both lanes
502mm	**Welcome Ctr sb, full ♿ facilities, TX Tourist Bureau/ info, 🚻, 🛗, litter barrels, wireless internet**
501	FM 1202, Prime Outlets Blvd, **E** 🅾 Chrysler/Dodge/Jeep, Ford/Mercury, **W** 🅶 Conoco/dsl/café, 🍴 Applebee's, Cracker Barrel, 🛏 Hampton Inn, La Quinta, 🅾 Prime Outlets/famous brands, Western Outfitter, RV camping
500	FM 372, Gainesville, **W** 🅶 Hitchin' Post/Shell/dsl
498b a	US 82, to Wichita Falls, Gainesville, Sherman, **E** 🅶 Exxon, Phillips 66/dsl, Shell/dsl, Valero/dsl, 🍴 Catfish Louie's, CiCi's, Subway, Whatburger/24hr, 🛏 Bed&Bath Inn, Budget Host, Comfort Inn, Delux Inn, Super 8, 12 Oaks Inn, 🅾 🅗, Firestone, **W** 🅶 Exxon/dsl, 🛏 Bed&Bath Inn, Comfort Suites, Days Inn, Fairfield Inn, Rodeway Inn
497	frontage rd, **W** 🅶 Valero/dsl
496b	TX 51, FM 51, California St, Gainesville, **E** 🅶 Chevron, Conoco/dsl, 🍴 Arby's, Braum's, IHOP, McDonald's, Starbucks, Taco Bell, Taco Casa, Sonic, Starbucks, Wendy's, 🛏 Holiday Inn Express, Quality Inn, 🅾 Cadillac, Dodge, Goodyear/auto, Mkt Place Foods, N Central TX Coll, **W** 🅶 Valero, 🍴 Chili's
496a	to Weaver St
496mm	Elm Fork of the Trinity River
495	frontage rd
494	FM 1306
492mm	picnic area sb, tables, litter barrels
491	Spring Creek Rd
490mm	picnic area nb, 🛗, litter barrels
489	(488 from nb), FM 1307, to Hockley Creek Rd,
487	FM 922, Valley View, **W** 🅶 Chevron/dsl/24hr, 🍴 Big Fatty's BBQ, DQ, 🅾 USPO
486	Fm 1307, **W** 🅶 Texaco/dsl, 🛏 Valley View Inn, 🅾 $General
485	frontage rd (from sb)
483	FM 3002, Lone Oak Rd, **E** 🅶 Shell/Subway/dsl, 🅾 Roberts Lake SP
482	Chisam Rd
481	View Rd, **W** 🅾 TX Sundown Ranch RV Park
480	Lois Rd, **E** 🅾 Walmart Dist Ctr
479	Belz Rd, Sanger, same as 478
478	FM 455, to 🅿 Pt, Bolivar, **E** 🅶 QuikTrack, Shell, Valero, 🍴 DQ, Migualito's Mexican, Sonic, Subway, 🛏 Sanger Inn, 🅾 Indian Village Campground, USPO, **W** 🅶 Chevron/24hr, Fuel 4 TX/Chicken Express/dsl, 🍴 Jack-in-the-Box, McDonald's, 🅾 Chevrolet, Family$, IGA Foods, Kwikar Lube, O'Reilly Parts, RV Park, Ray Roberts Lake and SP
477	Keaton Rd, **E** 🍴 Smokey's BBQ, 🅾 Curves, **W** 🅶 Shamrock/dsl, 🅾 Select Choice RV Ctr
475b	Rector Rd
475a	FM 156, to Krum (from sb)
474	Cowling rd (from nb)
473	FM 3163, Milam Rd, **E** 🅶 ❤Love's/Subway/dsl/24hr
472	Ganzer Rd, **W** RV sales
471	US 77, FM 1173, Lp 282, to Denton, Krum, **E** 🅶 TA/ Pizza Hut/Taco Bell/dsl/scales/24hr/@, 🍴 Good Eats Café, 🅾 🅗, **W** 🅶 Fina/dsl/café/scales/24hr, Texaco/ dsl/scales/24hr/@, 🅾 Foster's Western Shop, to Camping World RV Supply
470	Lp 288, same services as 469 from sb
469	US 380, University Dr, to Decatur, McKinney, **E** 🅶 Chevron/Subway, RaceTrac, 🍴 Braum's, Catfish King, ChinaTown Café, Cracker Barrel, Luigi's Pizza, McDonald's, 🛏 Best Western, Fairfield Inn, 🅾 Albertson's/Sav-On, **W** 🅶 Conoco/dsl, Shell/dsl, Valero, 🍴 DQ, Denny's, Sonic, Waffle House, 🛏 Comfort Inn, Holiday Inn Express, Howard Johnson, Motel 6, Travelodge, ValuePlace Inn, 🅾 🅗, Camping World RV Supply, to TX Woman's U
468	FM 1515, 🔄 Rd, W Oak St, **E** 🅗
467	I-35W, S to Ft Worth
	I-35 divides into E and W sb, converges into I-35 nb. See Texas I-35 W.
466b	Ave D, **E** 🅶 Exxon/dsl, 🍴 Central Grill, Chicken Express, IHOP, McDonald's, NY Sub Hub, Pancho's Mexican, Taco Cabana, 🛏 Comfort Suites, 🅾 $General, Sack'n Save Foods, to NTSU
466a	McCormick St, **E** 🅶 Phillips 66, Shell/dsl, 🛏 Royal Inn, **W** 🅶 Fina/dsl/U-Haul
465b	US 377, Ft Worth Dr, **E** 🅶 RaceTrac, Valero, 🍴 Michael's Kitchen, Taco Bueno, Whataburger/24hr, 🛏 La Quinta, **W** 🅶 Conoco, QuickTrack, 🍴 Outback Steaks, Sonic, 🛏 Day's Inn
465a	FM 2181, Teasley Ln, **E** 🅶 7-11, 🍴 Applebee's, Braum's, Carino's, ChuckeCheese, Hooters, KFC, Little Caesar's, Pizza Hut, 🛏 Hampton Inn, Holiday Inn, Quality Inn, 🅾 Brookshires Foods, bank, **W** 🅶 Exxon, Shell, 🍴 Rudy's BBQ/gas, 🛏 Best Value Inn, Super 8
464	US 77, Pennsylvania Dr, Denton, same as 463
463	Lp 288, to McKinney, **E** 🅶 RaceTrac, 🍴 Arby's, Burger King, Chick-fil-A, Colter's BBQ, Grandy's, Jason's Deli, KFC/Taco Bell, McAlister's Deli, Pizza Hut, On-the-Border, Sonic, Starbucks, Texas Roadhouse, Wendy's, Wienerschnitzel, 🅾 Barnes&Noble, Big Lots, Burlington Coats, Dillards, Discount Tire, $Tree, Hastings Books, Home Depot, JC Penney, Kroger, Macy's, Office Depot, Old Navy, Ross, Sears/auto, Staples, PetCo, **W** 🅶 Chevron/dsl, 🍴 Blackeyed Pea, Chili's, Jack-in-the-Box, Luby's, Red Lobster, Red Pepper's Rest., Schlotsky's, 🅾 Albertson's, vet, same as 464
462	State School Rd, Mayhill Rd, **E** 🅶 QT, Texaco/dsl, 🍴 Dickey's BBQ, Olive Garden, 🅾 🅗, Hyundai, **W** 🅶 Chevron, Exxon/café, 🍴 Shogun Japanese, Sonic, 🅾 Albertsons, Buick/GMC, Cadillac, Chevrolet, Dodge, Honda, Toyota/Scion
461	Sandy Shores Rd, Post Oak Dr, **E** 🅾 Ford, McClain RV Ctr **W** 🅾 Chrysler/Jeep/Kia, Lincoln/Mercury/Mazda, Nissan
460	Corinth Pkwy, **E** 🅶 Chevron/dsl/repair, 🅾 McClain RV Ctr camping, **W** 🅾 Harley-Davidson
459	frontage rd, **W** 🅾 Destiny RV Resort
458	FM 2181, Swisher Rd, **E** 🅶 Circle K, 🛏 Best Western 🅾 O'Reilly Parts, **W** 🅶 Chevron/McDonald's, Exxon, 🍴 Burger King, Chick-fil-A, IHOP, Jack-in-the-Box, JC China KFC/Pizza Hut/Taco Bell, McDonald's, Quizno's, Starbucks Subway, Wendy's, Whataburger, 🅾 Albertson's, AutoZone Discount Tire, GNC, Radio Shack, Walmart/gas
457b	Denton Rd, Hundley Dr, Lake Dallas, **E** 🅶 Shell, 🍴 Chili's Hickory Creek BBQ, Subway, TX L&C Steaks, vet
457a	Hundley Dr (from nb), Lake Dallas
456	Highland Village
456mm	Lewisville Lake
454b	Garden Ridge Blvd, **W** 🅶 Fuel 4 TX, 🅾 city park

N ← S

G A I N E S V I L L E

D E N T O N

TX

INTERSTATE 35 CONT'D

Exit	Services

N ↑↓ S

454a FM 407, Justin, **E** 🛢 Valero, 🍴 BBQ, **W** 🛢 QT, Texaco, 🍴 McDonald's

453 Valley Ridge Blvd, **E** 🛢 Ford, **W** 🛢 Chevron, 🍴 Burger King, Subway, ⊙ Home Depot, Kohl's, Lowes Whse, Staples

452 FM 1171, to Flower Mound, **E** 🍴 IHOP, Taco Bueno, 🛏 Days Inn, ⊙ H, **W** 🛢 Chevron, Exxon/dsl, Shell, 🍴 Burger King, Chick-fil-A, Chipotle Mexican, CiCi's Pizza, Golden Corral, Grandy's, Panda Express, Taco Bell, Whataburger/24hr, ⊙ Sam's Club/gas, Staples, U-Haul, Walmart same as 451

451 Fox Ave, **E** 🛢 Shell/dsl, 🍴 Braum's, **W** 🛢 Chevron/24hr, Conoco/dsl, QuickTrack Gas, 🍴 Cracker Barrel, El Chico, 🛏 Econolodge, Hampton Inn, ⊙ transmissions, VW

450 TX 121, Lewisville, **E** 🛢 Citgo/7-11, RaceTrac, 🍴 China Dragon, Owens Rest., Sugarbaby's BBQ, 🛏 Ramada Ltd, Rodeway Inn, ⊙ Chevrolet/Subaru, Dodge, **W** 🛢 Chevron, Conoco/dsl, 7-11, Texaco/dsl, 🍴 Burger King, Chili's, Church's, IHOP, KFC, LJ Silver, McDonald's, Pancho's Mexican, Pizza Hut, Subway, Taco Bell, Waffle House, Whataburger/24hr, 🛏 Best Value Inn, Crossroads Inn, Super 8, ⊙ Chief Parts, Firestone/auto, Food Lion, KIA, Kroger, Mitsubishi, Nissan, Toyota, transmissions

449 Corporate Drive, **E** 🛢 Conoco, 🍴 China Dragon, Hooters, On-the-Border, 🛏 Extended Stay America, Hearthside Inn, Motel 6, ⊙ Cavender's Boots, Honda, Ross, Target, **W** 🛢 Texaco, 🍴 Chili's, 🛏 Best Western, La Quinta, Sun Suites, ⊙ Honda, Kia, NTB

448b a FM 3040, Round Grove Rd, **E** 🛢 7-11, 🍴 Abuelo's Mexican, Cane's, Jack-in-the-Box, Joe's Crabshack, Mimi's Cafe, Olive Garden, Peiwei Chinese, 🛏 Homewood Suites, ⊙ Honda, Ross, Target, **W** 🛢 Exxon, 🍴 Applebee's, BJ's Grill, Buffalo Wild Wings, Cantina Laredo, Carino's Italian, Chick-fil-A, Chipotle Mexican, Denny's, Don Pablo, Logan's Roadhouse, Macaroni Grill, McDonald's, Outback Steaks, Red Lobster, Schlotsky's, Sonic, Spring Creek BBQ, Steak'n Shake, Taco Bueno, Taco Cabana, TGIFriday, Tony Roma, Wendy's, 🛏 Comfort Suites, Country Inn&Suites, Courtyard, Fairfield Inn, Hilton Garden, Holiday Inn Express, Old Country Inn, ⊙ Barnes&Noble, Best Buy, Costco/gas, Dillard's, Discount Tire, JC Penney, Macy's, Marshall's, Michael's, Office Depot, Old Navy, Sears/auto, Target, mall

446 Frankford Rd, **E** 🛢 RaceTrac, 🍴 La Hacienda Ranch Grill, ⊙ Buick/GMC, Volvo

445b Pres Geo Bush Tpk

444 Whitlock Lane, Sandy Lake Rd, **E** 🛢 Shell, 🍴 Pizza Pasta, 🛏 Rodeway Inn, ⊙ RV camping, **W** 🍴 McDonald's, Starbucks, 🛏 Delux Inn, ⊙ Harley-Davidson

443 Belt Line Rd, Crosby Rd, **E** 🛢 RaceTrac, ⊙ Ford, Hyundai, NTB, **W** 🛢 Shell, ⊙ U-Haul

442 Valwood Pkwy, **E** 🛢 Chevron/Subway, 🍴 El Chico, Grandy's, Jack-in-the-Box, Redline Burgers, Taco Bueno, Waffle House, 🛏 Comfort Inn, Guest Inn, LoneStar Inn, Royal Inn, **W** 🛢 Fina/dsl, ⊙ transmissions

441 Valley View Lane, **W** 🛢 Mobil, Shell, 🍴 Michael's Rest., 🛏 Best Value Inn, Day's Inn, Econolodge, La Quinta

440b I-635 E

440c I-635 W, to DFW ✈

439 Royal Lane, **E** 🛢 Fina, Shell, 🍴 McDonald's, Wendy's,

D A L L A S

439 Continued
Whataburger/24hr, ⊙ Daewoo, **W** 🛢 Chevron, Conoco, 🍴 Jack-in-the-Box

438 Walnut Hill Lane, **E** 🛢 Chevron, Shell, Valero, 🍴 Burger King, Church's, Dave&Buster's, Denny's, Porter House Steaks, Trail Dust Steaks, Wild Turkey Grill, 🛏 Comfort Inn, Hampton Inn, Quality Inn, ⊙ Isuzu, **W** 🛢 Chevron, Shell/dsl, ⊙ RV Ctr

437 Manana Rd (from nb), same as 438

436 TX 348, to DFW, Irving, **E** 🛢 Exxon/dsl, Shell, 🍴 IHOP, Luby's, Waffle House, 🛏 Courtyard, Days Inn, Elegante Hotel, Holiday Inn Express, La Quinta, Springhill Suites, Studio 6, Suburban Lodge, **W** 🛢 Fina, Mobil, Shell, 🍴 Chili's, Don Pablo, Ghengis Grill, Jack-in-the-Box, Jason's Deli, Joe's Crabshack, McDonald's, Olive Garden, Outback Steaks, Papadeaux Sea🍴 Pappasito's Mexican, Red Lobster, Taco Bell/Pizza Hut, Tony Roma's, TX L&C, Wendy's, Wing House, 🛏 Budget Lodge, Century Inn

435 Harry Hines Blvd (from nb), **E** 🛢 RaceTrac, 🍴 Arby's, ⊙ U-Haul, same as 436

434b Regal Row, **E** 🛢 Texaco/Grandy's, 🍴 Denny's, Whataburger/24hr, 🛏 Econolodge, **W** 🛏 Ramada Inn

434a Empire, Central, **E** 🛢 Chevron/McDonald's, 🍴 Sonic, Tony's Grill, Wendy's, 🛏 Budget Suites, Candlewood Suites, InTown Suites, Wingate Inn, ⊙ Office Depot, **W** 🛢 Texaco, 🍴 Burger King, Pizza Hut/Taco Bell, Schlotsky's

433b Mockingbird Lane, Love Field ✈, **E** 🛢 Shell, 🍴 Jack-in-the-Box, 🛏 Budget Suites, Comfort Inn, Crowne Plaza, InTown Suites, Sheraton, Radisson, Residence Inn

433a (432b from sb)TX 356, Commonwealth Dr, **W** 🛏 Delux Inn

432a Inwood Rd, **E** 🛢 Exxon, ⊙ H, Chevrolet, **W** 🛢 Texaco/Subway/dsl, Shell, 🍴 Whataburger/24hr, 🛏 Embassy Suites, Homewood Suites

431 Motor St, **E** 🛢 Chevron, 🍴 Denny's, ⊙ H, **W** 🛢 Shell, 🍴 Pepe's Grill, 🛏 Marriott Suites

430c Wycliff Ave, **E** 🍴 JoJo's Rest., 🛏 Holiday Inn, Renaissance Hotel, ⊙ Intn'l Apparel Mart, **W** 🛏 Hilton Anatole, Hilton Garden

430b Mkt Ctr Blvd, **E** ⊙ World Trade Ctr, **W** 🛢 Shell, 🍴 Denny's, 🛏 Courtyard, Fairfield Inn, Ramada Inn, Sheraton, Wilson World Hotel, Wyndham Garden

430a Oak Lawn Ave, **E** 🛏 Holiday Inn, **W** 🛢 Shell, Texaco/dsl, 🍴 Denny's, Medieval Times Rest., ⊙ to Merchandise Mart

429c HiLine Ave (from nb)

429b Continental Ave, Commerce St, W downtown, **E** 🍴 Hooters, **W** 🛢 Exxon, Shell, 🍴 McDonald's

429a to I-45, US 75, to Houston

428e Commerce St E, Reunion Blvd, Dallas, downtown

LEWISVILLE

DALLAS

TX

Exit	Services
	INTERSTATE 35 CONT'D
428d	I-30 W, to Ft Worth
428a	I-30 E, to I-45 S
428b	Industrial Blvd, E 🅖 Chevron, W 🅖 Fina, KwikStop/dsl, Shamrock
427b	I-30 E
427a	Colorado Blvd, E 🄷
426c	Jefferson Ave, E 🅖 Shell/dsl
426b	TX 180 W, 8th St, E 🅖 Shell/dsl
426a	Ewing Ave, E 🍴 McDonald's, Popeye's
425c	Marsalis Ave, E 🛏 Dallas Inn, W 🅖 Chevron, Valero
425b	Beckley Ave, 12th St, sb only, W 🅖 Shell, Valero, 🍴 Wendy's
425a	Zang Blvd same as 425b
424	Illinois Ave, E 🅖 Chevron, 🍴 William's Chicken, 🅞 🄷, W 🅖 Exxon, 🍴 Jack-in-the-Box, Pancake House, Sonic, Taco Bell, 🅞 Kroger, Ross, Walgreens
423b	Saner Ave
423a	(422b from nb)US 67 S, Kiest Blvd, W 🅖 Shell/repair, 🍴 McDonald's, Subway, Taco Del Mar, 🛏 Dallas Inn
421b	Ann Arbor St
421a	Lp 12E W, E 🅖 RaceWay, 🛏 Delux Inn
420	Laureland, W 🅖 Conoco, Texaco, 🛏 Linfield Inn
419	Camp Wisdom Rd, E 🅖 Exxon, 🛏 Oak Cliff Inn, W 🅖 Chevron, Shell/24hr, 🍴 McDonald's, 🛏 Suncrest Inn, 🅞 U-Haul
418c	Danieldale Rd (from sb)
418b	I-635/I-20 E, to Shreveport
418a	I-20 W, to Ft Worth
417	Wheatland Rd (from nb)
416	Wintergreen Rd, E 🅞 repair, W 🅖 Citgo/7-11, 🍴 Cracker Barrel, Golden Corral, Waffle House, 🛏 Holiday Inn Express, Red Roof Inn
415	Pleasant Run Rd, E 🅖 Chevron/24hr, RaceTrac, Shell/Blimpie/dsl, 🍴 Bienvenidos Mexican, Evergreen Buffet, Subway, Waffle House, 🛏 Great Western Inn, Royal Inn, Spanish Trails Motel, Super 8, 🅞 Chrysler/Jeep, PepBoys, transmissions, W 🅖 Chevron, Exxon, 🍴 Burger King, El Chico, Golden Corral, KFC, LJ Silver, Luby's, McDonald's, On the Border, Outback Steaks, Pizza Inn, Taco Bueno, Wendy's, 🛏 Best Western, 🅞 🄷, Chevrolet, Discount Tire, Ford, Kroger, K-Mart, Office Depot, Ross
414	FM 1382, Desoto Rd, Belt Line Rd, E 🍴 Chili's, Whataburger, 🅞 Walmart/gas
413	Parkerville Rd, W 🅖 Exxon/Subway, 🅞 U-Haul
412	Bear Creek Rd, W 🅖 Shell/dsl, 🍴 Bubba's BBQ, Jack-in-the-Box, Whataburger, 🅞 HiHo RV Park, transmissions
411	FM 664, Ovilla Rd, E 🅖 Exxon/TCBY/24hr, RaceTrac/24hr, 🍴 LJ Silver/Taco Bell, McDonald's, Whataburger, 🛏 Comfort Inn, 🅞 Brookshire's Foods, CVS Drug, W 🅖 Exxon/Subway, Shamrock
410	Red Oak Rd, E 🅖 Citgo/dsl, Nock's/Shell/Pizza Inn/Subway/dsl, 🍴 Denny's, Merryland Chinese, 🛏 Day's Inn, W 🅞 Hilltop Travel Trailers
408	US 77, TX 342, to Red Oak, E golf
406	Sterrett Rd, E fireworks
405	FM 387, E 🅖 Phillips 66/dsl
404	Lofland Rd, industrial area
403	US 287, to Ft Worth, E 🍴 Jack-in-the-Box, McDonald's, Taco Bell, Waffle House, 🛏 Hampton Inn, 🅞 Chevrolet/Cadillac, Jeep, W 🅞 Buick/GMC, Chrysler/Dodge, Ford/Mercury

Exit	Services
401b	US 287 bus, Waxahatchie, E 🛏 Best Western, Super 8
401a	Brookside Rd, E 🛏 Best Value Inn, Days Inn
399b	FM 1446
399a	FM 66, FM 876, Maypearl, E 🛏 Texas Inn, W 🅖 Chevron/dsl, StarMart/dsl/24hr
397	to US 77, to Waxahachie
393mm	**rest area both lanes, full ♿ facilities, 🍴, 🚻, litter barrels, vending, petwalk**
391	FM 329, Forreston Rd
386	TX 34, Italy, E 🅖 Shell/dsl, 🍴 DQ, Smokehouse BBQ, Sonic, 🅞 $General, W 🅖 Exxon/Grandy's/Mcdonald's/Subway/Pizza Inn/dsl, 🛏 Italy Inn, 🅞 truckwash
384	Derrs Chapel Rd
381	FM 566, Milford Rd
377	FM 934
374	FM 2959, Carl's Corner, W 🅖 Carl's Trkstp/dsl/rest.,
371	I-35 W. I-35 divides into E and W nb, converges sb, **See Texas I-35 W.**
370	US 77 N, FM 579, Hillsboro
368b	FM 286, E 🍴 LoneStar Café, Taco Bell, Wendy's, 🛏 Hampton Inn, 🅞 Prime Outlets/famous brands, W 🅖 Exxon/Domino's, Valero/dsl, 🍴 Braum's, Domino's, DQ, El Conquistador Mexican, El Taco Jalisco, McDonald's, Pizza Hut, 🛏 Best Western, Comfort Inn, La Quinta, 🅞 🄷
368a	TX 22, TX 171, to Whitney, E 🅖 7-11, 🅛 Loves/Chester's/Subway/dsl/scales/24hr, 🍴 Arby's, Blackeyed Pea, Harvest Buffet, IHOP, McDonald's, Starbucks, 🛏 Comfort Suites, Days Inn, Holiday Inn Express, Motel 6, Super 8, W 🅖 Chevron, Mobil, Murphy USA/dsl, Shell/dsl, 🍴 Chicken Express, Jack-in-the-Box, KFC, Schlotsky's, Whataburger/24hr, 🛏 Thunderbird Motel/rest., 🅞 Cadillac/Chevrolet, Ford/Mercury, Radio Shack, Walmart/Subway
367	Old Bynum Rd (from nb)
364b	TX 81 N, to Hillsboro (exits left from nb)
364a	FM 310
362	Chatt Rd
359	FM 1304, W 🅖 Mobil/dsl/24hr, 🅞 truckwash
358	FM 1242 E, Abbott, E 🅖 Exxon/dsl, 🍴 Up in Smoke BBQ
356	Co Rd 3102
355	County Line Rd, E 🅞 KOA
354	Marable St, E 🅞 KOA
353	FM 2114, West, E 🅖 Chevron, Fina/dsl, Shell/Czech Bakery, 🍴 Bush's Chicken, Sonic, Subway, 🅞 Ford, W 🅖 Exxon, Texaco, 🛏 Czech Inn, 🅞 Chevrolet
351	FM 1858, E tires/repair
349	Wiggins Rd
347	FM 3149, Tours Rd
346	Ross Rd, E 🅖 Shell/dsl/24hr, W 🅖 Exxon/Church's/dsl/24hr, 🅞 I-35 RV Park/LP, antiques
345	Old Dallas Rd, E 🅞 antiques, W 🅞 I-35 RV Park/LP
345a	frontage rd, same as 345
343	FM 308, Elm Mott, E 🅖 Exxon/DQ, Shell/Jct Cafe/dsl/scales/24hr, W 🅖 Chevron/dsl/24hr, 🍴 El Mezcal, Heitmiller Steaks
342b	US 77 bus, W North Crest RV Park
342a	FM 2417, Crest Dr, W 🅖 Valero/dsl, 🍴 Bush's Chicken, DQ, 🛏 Everyday Inn, 🅞 Family$, auto repair
341	Craven Ave, Lacy Lakeview, W 🅖 Chevron, Shell
340	Myers Lane (from nb)
339	to TX 6 S, FM 3051, Lake Waco, E 🅖 Valero/dsl, 🍴 Casa Ole, Cici's, Domino's, El Conquistador, Jack-in-the-Box, Luby's, Pizza Hut, Popeye's, Sonic, Wendy's,

N ↑↓ S

TX

H I L L S B O R O

INTERSTATE 35 CONT'D

Exit	Services
339	Continued Whataburger/24hr, 🛏 Holiday Inn, 🅞 Advance Parts, Discount Tire, $General, Home Depot, Radio Shack, Walmart/24hr, **W** 🅖 Chevron, Citgo, 🍴 Burger King, Cracker Barrel, KFC, McDonald's, Papa John's, Starbucks, Taco Bell, 🛏 Fairfield Inn, Hampton Inn, 🅞 to 🏥
338b	Behrens Circle (from nb), **E** 🍴 Jack-in-the-Box, Sonic, same as 339, **W** 🅖 Shell/dsl/LP, 🍴 Cracker Barrel, 🛏 Comfort Inn, Country Inn, Days Inn, Delta Inn, Hampton Inn, Knight's Inn, Motel 6
337	(338a from nb)US 84, to TX 31, Waco Dr, **E** 🅖 Phillips 66, 🍴 ChopStix, 🛏 Value Place Suites, 🅞 AutoZone, Family$, HEB Food/gas, O'Reilly Parts, Sam's Club/gas, **W** 🛏 Radisson, 🅞 🅷
335c	Lake Brazos Dr, MLK Blvd, **E** 🛏 Hotel Waco, **W** 🍴 Buzzard Billy's, 🛏 Scottish Inn, Victorian Inn, 🅞 🅷
335mm	Brazos River
335b	FM 434, University Parks Dr, **E** 🍴 China Grill, Jim's Rest., Quizno's, Thai Cuisine, 🛏 Best Western, 🅞 Baylor U, TX Ranger Museum, **W** 🍴 Arby's, Jack-in-the-Box, Magic China, 🛏 Best Value Inn, Residence Inn
335a	4th St, 5th St, **E** 🅖 Exxon/Subway/dsl, 🍴 Denny's, IHOP, Lupito's Mexican, Pizza Hut, 🛏 Best Western, La Quinta, 🅞 Baylor U, **W** 🅖 Chevron, Valero, 🍴 Fazoli's, LJ Silver, McDonald's, Taco Bell, Taco Bueno, Taco Cabana, Wendy's, Whataburger/24hr, 🛏 Clarion
334b	US 77 S, 17th St, 18th St, **E** 🅖 Shell/dsl, 🍴 Burger King, Popeye's, Schlotsky's, Vitek's BBQ, 🛏 Budget Inn, EconoLodge, Super 8, **W** 🅖 Phillips 66/dsl, Shell, 🍴 Arranda's Mexican, 🅞 🅷
333a	Lp 396, Valley Mills Dr, **E** 🍴 El Chico, Elite Café, Rudy's BBQ, TX Roadhouse, Trujillo's Mexican, 🛏 Comfort Suites, La Quinta, Motel 6, 🅞 Isuzu/Mazda, KIA, Suzuki, **W** 🅖 RaceWay, Valero, 🍴 Bush's Chicken, Catfish King, Church's, Jack-in-the-Box, Little Caesars, Papa John's, Sonic, Subway, 🅞 Aamco, Advance Parts, AutoZone, CVS Drug, Family$, Freightliner, HEB Foods, Lincoln/Mercury, Walgreens
331	New Rd, **E** 🛏 New Road Inn, Relax Inn, Rodeway Inn, **W** 🅖 FLYING J/Denny's/dsl/scales/24hr, 🍴 Hooters, IHOP, 🛏 Quality Inn, 🅞 Harley Davidson
330	Lp 340, TX 6, 0-2 mi **E** 🅖 Chevron, 🍴 Bush's Chicken, Camille's Cafe, Coldstone, Don Carlo's Mexican, Logan's Roadhouse, Outback Steaks, Panera Bread, TGIFridays, Subway, 🛏 Extended Stay America, Fairfield Inn, Hampton Inn, Homewood Suites, 🅞 Belk, Best Buy, Books-A-Million, Ford, Honda, Hyundai, Kohl's, Lowe's Whse, Marshall's, Nissan, Office Depot, Ross, Old Navy, Toyota/Scion, Verizon, Walmart
328	FM 2063, FM 2113, Moody, **E** 🅖 🚂/Subway/Wendy's/dsl/scales/24hr/@, 🍴 McDonald's, 🛏 La Quinta, 🅞 Kenworth, **W** 🅖 Shell/24hr, Valero/dsl, 🛏 Sleep Inn
325	FM 3148, Moonlight Dr, **W** 🅖 Conoco/dsl, 🅞 Walkabout RV Ctr
323	FM 2837 (from sb), Lorena, **W** 🅖 Brookshire Bros/Conoco, 🍴 Pizza House, Sonic
322	Lorena, **E** 🅖 Phillips 66/dsl, 🍴 Baytown Sea 🍴 **W** 🍴 Bush's Chicken, Ruthy's Mexican, 🅞 $General
319	Woodlawn Rd
318b a	Bruceville, **E** 🅖 Conoco/dsl, 🅞 picnic area both lanes, litter barrels

Exit	Services
315	TX 7, FM 107, Eddy, **1 mi E** RV Park, **W** 🅖 Shell/Subway/dsl/24hr, Texaco, 🅞 Family$, to Mother Neff SP
314	Old Blevins Rd
311	Big Elm Rd, **E** fireworks, **W** picnic area
308	FM 935, Troy, **E** 🅖 Shell, 🅞 Troy Foods, **W** 🅖 Exxon, 🅞 dsl repair
306	FM 1237, Pendleton, **W** 🅖 Loves/Subway/dsl/24hr, 🅞 Temple RV Park/LP
305	Berger Rd, **W** 🅖 Exxon/dsl/scales/24hr, 🛏 Sharon Jean's Rest., 🅞 Lucky's RV Park, Temple RV Park, repair
304	Lp 363, Dodgen Loop, **W** 🅖 Shell/Wendy's/dsl, Valero/dsl/24hr, 🅞 Freightliner
303	spur 290, N 3rd St, Temple, **E** 🅖 S-2 Gas, 🛏 Texas Inn, **W** 🛏 Continental Inn
302	Nugent Ave, **E** 🅖 Exxon/dsl, Texaco, 🛏 Comfort Suites, EconoLodge, Quality Inn, Red Roof Inn, **W** 🅖 Pay Less Gas, Shell, 🍴 Denny's, 🛏 Best Western, Days Inn, Knight's Inn, Motel 6, Stratford House Inn
301	TX 53, FM 2305, Adams Ave, **E** 🅖 Valero, 🍴 Arby's, Chick-fil-A, KFC, LJ Silver, McDonald's, Pizza Hut, Starbucks, Subway, Taco Bell, Wendy's, Whataburger, 🛏 La Quinta, 🅞 🅷, Advance Parts, Ford/Lincoln/Mercury, HEB Foods, **W** 🍴 TX Roadhouse, 🛏 Best Western
300	Ave H, 49th–57th Sts, **E** 🅖 Shell, 🍴 Clem Mikeskas BBQ, **W** 🅖 Shell
299	US 190 E, TX 36, **E** 🅖 Shell, 🍴 Cracker Barrel, Jack-in-the-Box, Luby's, Olive Garden, 🛏 Best Value Inn, Residence Inn, 🅞 🅷, Ancira RV Ctr, Chrysler/Dodge/Jeep, **W** 🍴 BJ's Rest., Chili's, IHOP, McDonald's, Taco Cabana, 🅞 Batteries+, Best Buy, Home Depot, PetsMart, Target
298	nb only, to frontage rd, **E** 🛏 Residence Inn
297	FM 817, Midway Dr, **E** 🅖 Phillips 66, 🛏 Holiday Inn, Super 8/rest., 🅞 Nissan, Suzuki, **W** 🅖 Valero, 🅞 Buick/GMC, Fed Ex, VW
294b	FM 93, 6th Ave, **E** 🅖 Shell/dsl, 🍴 McDonald's, 🅞 Chevrolet, Toyota/Scion, **W** 🍴 Subway, 🛏 River Forest Inn, 🅞 Harley-Davidson, U of Mary Hardin Baylor
294a	Central Ave, **W** 🅖 Shell/dsl, 🍴 Burger King, Mexicano Grill, Pizza Hut, Schlotzky's, Sonic, Taco Bell, Whataburger, 🛏 Knight's Inn, 🅞 AutoZone, Goodyear, O'Reilly Parts, Parts+
293b	TX 317, FM 436, Main St
293a	US 190 W, to Killeen, Ft Hood
292	Lp 121 (same as 293a), **E** 🅖 Valero/dsl/rest./24hr, 🛏 Budget Host, **W** 🅖 Mobil/dsl/24hr, 🍴 Oxbow Steaks, 🛏 La Quinta, 🅞 Belton RV Park, Family$, Ford, Sunbelt RV Ctr, auto/tire repair
290	Shanklin Rd
289	Tahuaya Rd, **E** 🅞 Hi-Way Parts

INTERSTATE 35 CONT'D

N ↑ ↓ S

Exit	Services
287	Amity Rd
286	FM 2484, **E** 🛏 Best Western, Holiday Inn Express, **W** 🅞 to Stillhouse Hollow Lake, vet
285	FM 2268, Salado, **E** 🅖 Conoco/Brookshire Foods, 🍴 Subway, 🛏 Holiday Inn Express, **W** 🅖 Pay Less, 🍴 Cowboys BBQ, Robertson's Rest., Sonic
284	Stagecoach Rd, **E** 🅖 Exxon/Arby's, 🍴 Roy T's, **W** 🅖 Texaco/dsl, 🍴 DQ, 🛏 Super 8
283	FM 2268, FM 2843, to Holland, Salado, **E** 🛏 Stagecoach Inn
282	FM 2115, **E** 🅖 Valero/dsl, 🅞 **RV camping, rest area sb, full** ♿ **facilities,** 🅲, 🏖, **litter barrels, vending, pet-walk, RV dump**
281mm	**rest area nb, full** ♿ **facilities,** 🅲, 🏖, **litter barrels, vending, petwalk, RV dump**
280	Prairie Dell
279	Hill Rd, **W** 🅞 RV Park
277	Yankee Rd
275	FM 487, to Florence, Jarrell, **E** 🅖 Exxon/dsl, **W** 🅖 Shell, 🅞 USPO
274	Rd 312, **E** 🅖 Chevron/dsl, Exxon/Subway, ⊛FLYING J/dsl, 🍴 Burger King, Denny's, McDonald's
271	Theon Rd, **E** 🅖 Explore USA RV Ctr, **W** 🅖 Shell/Subway/dsl/24hr
268	fm 972, Walburg, **E** 🅞 Crestview RV Ctr
266	TX 195, **E** 🅖 Phillips 66/dsl
265	TX 130 S, to Austin
264	Lp 35, Georgetown
262	RM 2338, Lake Georgetown, **E** 🅖 Valero, 🍴 Burger King, Chipotle Mexican, Keva Juice, KFC, McDonald's, Pizza Hut, Quizno's, Shangahi Express, Sonic, Starbucks, Subway, 🅞 URGENT CARE, CVS Drug, $Tree, Parts+, Radio Shack, **W** 🅖 Shell, 🍴 DQ, La Tapatia, Placa Greek, Whataburger, 🛏 Georgetown Inn, Holiday Inn Express, La Quinta
261	TX 29, Georgetown, **E** 🅖 Shell/dsl, 🍴 Applebee's, Chili's, Luby's, Schlotsky's, Taco Bell, 🛏 Comfort Suites, Holiday Inn Express, 🅞 Albertson's, HEB Foods, Hobby Lobby, Tuesday Morning, same as 262, **W** 🅖 Murphy USA/dsl, 🍴 Casa Ole, Chick-fil-A, CiCi's, Genghis Grill, Ichyban Buffet, IHOP, Mama Fu's, McAlister's Deli, MT Mike's, Panda Express, Souper Salad, Taco Cabana, 🅞 AT&T, Beall's, Best Buy, Home Depot, Kohl's, Office Depot, Old Navy, PetsMart, Target, TJ Maxx, Walgreens, Walmart, antiques
260	RM 2243, Leander, **E** 🅞 🏥, USPO, **W** 🅖 Chevron, Exxon, Texaco, 🍴 Jack-in-the-Box, 🛏 Quality Inn
259	Lp 35, **W** 🅞 RV Outlet Ctr, to Interspace Caverns
257	Westinghouse Rd, **E** 🅞 Buick/Chevrolet, Ford, Hummer, Kia, Mazda, Mercedes, Mitsubishi, Volvo, VW
256	RM 1431, Chandler Rd, **E** 🍴 Chili's, Jamba Juice, La Madeline, Mimi's Cafe, 🅞 Round Rock Outlet, Hummer, Mazda, JC Penney, Jo-Ann Fabrics, PetsMart, Ross, Volvo
254	FM 3406, Round Rock, **E** 🅖 Chevron, 🍴 Arby's, Garcia's Mexican, Gatti's Pizza, McDonald's, 🛏 Best Western, 🅞 CVS Drug, $General, Firestone, Harley-Davidson, Honda, Hyundai, Smart Car, Toyota, **W** 🅖 Phillips 66/dsl, Shell, 🍴 Carino's Italian, Chuy's Mexican, Cracker Barrel, Dave's Pizza, Denny's, La Margarita Mexican,

G E O R G E T O W N

R O U N D   R O C K

Exit	Services
254	Continued Mesa Rosa Mexican, Rudy's BBQ, SaltGrass Steaks, Summer Palace, 🛏 Country Inn&Suites, Courtyard, Hilton Garden, Holiday Inn, La Quinta, Round Rock Inn, Red Roof Inn, SpringHill Suites, ValuePlace, 🅞 GMC, Nissan
253b	US 79, to Taylor, **E** 🅖 Chevron, Shell, Texaco, 🍴 Arby's, Baskin-Robbins, DQ, Famous Sam's Café, Fuddrucker's, KFC, LoneStar Café, LJ Silver, Que Pasa Mexican, Sirloin Stockade, 🛏 Wingate Inn, 🅞 🏥, AutoZone, Beall's, Cottman Transmissions, HEB/deli, **W** 🅖 Exxon/dsl, Shell/dsl/24hr, 🍴 Gatti's Pizza, Hunan Lion, IHOP, Popeye's, Starbucks, Taco Bell, 🛏 Country Inn&Suites, La Quinta, Red Roof Inn, Sleep Inn, ValuePlace, 🅞 CVS Drug, $Tree, Tuesday Morning, USPO
253a	Frontage Rd, same as 253 b
252b a	RM 620, **E** 🅖 Shell/dsl/24hr, 🛏 Candlewood Suites, Extended Stay America, 🅞 NAPA, **W** 🅖 Texaco/dsl, 🍴 Little Caesar's, McDonald's, Quizno's, Starbucks, Wendy's, 🛏 Comfort Suites, Staybridge Suites
251	Lp 35, Round Rock, **E** 🅖 Valero, 🍴 CiCi's Pizza, Outback Steaks, Whataburger, 🛏 Residence Inn, 🅞 Aamco, Big-Lots, Brake Check, $General, **W** 🅖 Shell, 🍴 Burger King, Jack-in-the-Box, Lucky Dog Grill, Luby's, Taco Cabana, 🛏 Mariott, 🅞 GNC, Hastings Books, NTB, Walgreens
250	FM 1325, **E** 🍴 Chick-fil-A, Chili's, El Chico, Jason's Deli, Joe's Crabshack, Macaroni Grill, McDonald's, Panda Express, Subway, Twin Peaks Rest., 🛏 Hampton Inn, Residence Inn, 🅞 Best Buy, Discount Tire, Home Depot, PetsMart, Radio Shack, Target, Walmart, **W** 🅖 Shell, 🍴 Applebee's, Fast Eddie's, Hooters, Jimmy John's, Mongolian Grille, Olive Garden, Starbucks, 🛏 Extended Stay America, La Quinta, 🅞 AT&T, Barnes&Noble, Hobby Lobby, Kohl's, Lowe's Whse, Marshall's, Michael's, Office Depot, Old Navy, PetCo, Ross, Sam's Club/gas, Steinmart, World Mkt
248	Grand Ave Pkwy, **E** 🅖 Citgo, Shell, Texaco/Subway/dsl, 🍴 Cheddar's, Chucho's Mexican, Fish Daddy's Grill, Jack-in-the-Box, Taco Cabana, Thundercloud Subs, TX Roadhouse, 🛏 Comfort Suites, 🅞 URGENT CARE, Firestone, **W** 🅖 Chevron/McDonald's
247	FM 1825, Pflugerville, **E** 🅖 RaceTrac, 🍴 Jack-in-the-Box, Sonic, Taco Cabana, Wendy's, 🅞 Firestone/auto, HEB Foods, cinema, **W** 🅖 Exxon, Shell/Church's, 🍴 KFC, Miller's BBQ, Whataburger, 🛏 Holiday Inn Express
246	Howard Lane, **E** 🅖 Citgo, Shell/dsl, 🍴 Arby's, Baby Acapulco, Carino's, Chili's, McDonald's, Subway, Wings'n More, 🅞 Home Depot, Kohl's, NTB, **W** 🅖 Valero/dsl, 🍴 IHOP, Whataburger
245	FM 734, Parmer Lane, to Yager Lane (244 from nb), **E** 🍴 Carino's, Chick-fil-A, Chili's, Schlotzsky's, Subway, 🛏 Courtyard, 🅞 HEB Food/gas, JC Penney, Kohl's, PetsMart, Radio Shack, Ross, Sears Grand, Target, **W** 🅖 Conoco/dsl, Murphy USA, 🍴 Hoho Chinese, Red Robin, Starbucks, 🛏 Fairfield Inn, Hilton Garden, Residence Inn, SpringHill Suites, 🅞 CarMax, Discount Tire, Lowe's Whse, Walmart
243	Braker Lane, **E** 🅖 Valero, 🍴 Jack-in-the-Box, Whataburger/24hr, 🅞 U-Haul, **W** 🅖 Citgo, Shell/dsl, 🛏 Austin Motel, ValuePlace, 🅞 $General
241	Rundberg Lane, **E** 🅖 Exxon, 🍴 Grand China Buffet, Jack-in-the-Box, Mr Gatti's, Old San Francisco Steaks, 🛏 Extended Stay Deluxe, Ramada Inn, 🅞 Albertson's, Chevrolet, $General, U-Haul, Walmart, **W** 🅖 Chevron, Shell,

INTERSTATE 35 CONT'D

Exit	Services
241	Continued
	🛏 Austin Suites, Austin Village, Budget Inn, Economy Inn, Holiday Inn Express, Motel 6, Red Roof Inn, Super 8, Wingate Inn
240a	US 183, Lockhart, **E** 🅖 Exxon, 🍴 DQ, Jack-in-the-Box, Old San Francisco Steaks, 🛏 Days Inn, Ramada Inn, **W** 🅖 Chevron/dsl/24hr, Texaco/dsl, 🛏 Motel 6, Red Roof Inn, Super 8, Wingate Inn
239	St John's Ave, **E** 🅖 Shell, 🍴 Burger King, Chili's, Fuddruckers, Japon Japanese, Jim's Rest., Pappadeaux, Pappasito's Mexican, Steak&Egg, 🛏 Budget Host, Crowne Plaza, Days Inn, DoubleTree, Drury Inn, Hampton Inn, Red Lion Hotel, Studio 6, 🅞 Dodge, Home Depot, KIA, Volvo, Walmart, USPO, **W** 🅖 Conoco, Exxon, Valero, 🍴 Antonio's Texmex, Applebee's, Carrabba's, Denny's, IHOP, Panda Express, Quizno's, Wendy's, 🛏 Baymont Inn, Best Value Inn, Comfort Inn, Country Inn&Suites, Courtyard, Holiday Inn Express, Hyatt Place, La Quinta, Radisson, Ramada Inn, Sheraton, Sumner Suites, 🅞 Office Depot
238b	US 290 E, RM 222, same as 238a, frontage rds connect several exits
238a	51st St, **E** 🅖 Exxon, Chevron, Shell, 🍴 Burger King, Chili's, Fuddrucker's, LJ Silver, McDonald's, Sonic, Subway, TX Steaks, Whataburger, 🛏 Doubletree Hotel, Drury Inn, Econolodge, Embassy Suites, Holiday Inn, 🅞 Advance Parts, Best Buy, $Tree, Firestone, FoodLand, Home Depot, Jo-Ann Crafts, Marshall's, Old Navy, PetsMart, Ross, Staples, Target, Volvo, Walgreens, **W** 🅖 Shell, 🍴 Baby Acapulco, Capt Benny's Sea 🍴 Carrabba's, IHOP, Outback Steaks, Quizno's, 🛏 Capital Inn, Courtyard, Drury Inn, Fairfield Inn, Hilton, La Quinta, Motel 6, Quality Inn, Ramada Ltd, Super 8, 🅞 Dillard's, Ford, Office Depot
237b	51st St, same as 238a
237a	Airport Blvd, **E** 🍴 BBQ, **W** 🍴 Jack-in-the-Box, Wendy's, 🅞 GNC, Goodyear, HEB Foods, Old Navy, PetCo, Sears/auto, upper level is I-35 thru, lower level accesses downtown
236b	39th St, **E** 🅖 Chevron/dsl, 🍴 Short Stop Burgers, Subway, 🅞 Fiesta Foods, HiLo Parts, O'Reilly Parts, U-Haul, **W** 🅖 Shell/dsl, 🅞 Tune&Lube, tires, to U of TX
236a	26th-32nd Sts, **E** 🍴 Los Altos Mexican, Subway, 🛏 Days Inn, **W** 🛏 Rodeway Inn, 🅞 🄷
235b	Manor Rd same as 236a, **E** 🍴 Denny's, 🛏 DoubleTree, **W** 🛏 Rodeway Inn, 🅞 U of TX, st capitol, vet
235a	MLK, 15th St, **W** 🄷, upper level is I-35 thru, lower level accesses downtown
234c	11th St, 12th St, downtown, **E** 🅖 Chevron, Shell, 🍴 Denny's, Wendy's, 🛏 DoubleTree Hotel, Super 8, 🅞 CVS Drug, **W** 🅖 Chevron, Shell, Texaco, 🍴 Wendy's, 🛏 Crowne Plaza, Marriott, Hilton Garden, Omni Motel, Radisson, Sheraton, 🅞 🄷, museum, st capitol
234b	8th-3rd St, **W** 🍴 IHOP
234a	Cesar Chavez St, Holly St, downtown
233	Riverside Dr, Town Lake, **E** 🅖 Citgo, 🛏 Extended Stay America, **W** 🅖 Chevron/dsl, 🛏 Holiday Inn
232mm	Little Colorado River
232b	Woodland Ave
232a	Oltorf St, **E** 🅖 Shell/dsl, 🍴 Luby's, 🛏 Best Value Inn, Country Garden Inn, Howard Johnson, La Quinta,

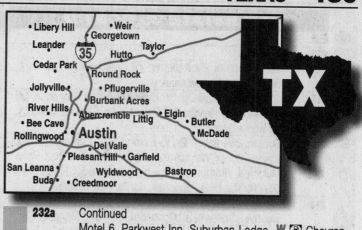

Exit	Services
232a	Continued
	Motel 6, Parkwest Inn, Suburban Lodge, **W** 🅖 Chevron, Exxon, 🍴 Denny's, Mesa Ranch Grill, Starbucks, 🛏 Clarion, Quality Inn
231	Woodward St, **E** 🅖 Shell/dsl, 🍴 Country Kitchen, 🛏 Wyndham Garden, same as 232, **W** 🅞 Home Depot
230b a	US 290 W, TX 71, Ben White Blvd, St Elmo Rd, **E** 🅖 Shell, 🍴 Domino's, Jim's Rest., McDonald's, Sigon Kitchen, Subway, Western Choice Steaks, 🛏 Best Western, Comfort Suites, Courtyard, Fairfield Inn, Hampton Inn, Marriott, Omni Hotel, Red Roof Inn, Residence Inn, SpringHill Suites, 🅞 Acura, Sam's Club/gas, **W** 🍴 Burger King, Furr's Cafeteria, IHOP, Pizza Hut, Taco Cabana, 🛏 Candlewood Suites, Days Inn, Hawthorn Suites, La Quinta, 🅞 🄷, BMW, Carmax, Chrysler/Dodge/Jeep, Ford, GMC, Honda, Hyundai, Kia, Lincoln/Mercury, Mazda, Nissan, NTB, Suzuki/Kia, Toyota/Scion
229	Stassney Lane, **W** 🍴 Chili's, Krispy Kreme, Logan's Roadhouse, Macaroni Grill, Pizza Hut, Rockfish Grill, TX Cattle Co Steaks, Twin Peaks Rest., 🅞 Albertson's/gas, Fiesta Foods, KIA, Lowe's Whse
228	Wm Cannon Drive, **E** 🅖 Exxon, Valero, 🍴 Applebee's, McDonald's, Taco Bell, 🅞 Brake Check, Chrysler, Discount Tire, HEB Foods, Hyundai/Subaru, Mitsubishi, Nissan, Radio Shack, Target, **W** 🅖 Texaco, Shell/dsl, 🍴 Arby's, Burger King, China Harbor, Gatti's Pizza, Jack-in-the-Box, KFC, LJ Silver, Peter Piper Pizza, Taco Cabana, Wendy's, Whataburger/24hr, 🅞 Advance Parts, BigLots, Chevrolet, CVS Drug, $General, Firestone
227	Slaughter Lane, Lp 275, S Congress, **E** 🅖 Shell/dsl, 🍴 IHOP, 🅞 Home Depot, Lone Star RV Resort, U-Haul, **W** 🅖 Murphy USA, Texaco, Valero/dsl, 🍴 Carino's, Chili's, Chipotle Mexican, Miller BBQ, Sonic, Starbucks, Steak'n Shake, Subway, Jack-in-the-Box, TGIFriday's, TX Roadhouse, Whataburger, 🅞 Border's Books, Hobby Lobby, JC Penney, Marshall's, PetsMart, Ross, Target, Walmart
226	Slaughter Creek Overpass
225	FM 1626, Onion Creek Pkwy, **E** 🅖 Shell, Texaco, 🅞 Harley-Davidson
224	frontage rd (from nb)
223	FM 1327
221	Lp 4, Buda, **E** 🅖 Chevron/McDonald's, Shell/dsl, 🍴 Starbucks, 🛏 Best Value Inn, Comfort Suites, Holiday Inn Express, 🅞 Ford, **W** 🅖 Chevron/24hr, Murphy USA, Shell, 🍴 Arby's, Chili's, Cracker Barrel, Culver's, Dan's Hamburgers, Jack-in-the-Box, KFC/LJ Silver, Sonic, Subway, Taco Bell, loding: Hampton Inn, 🅞 AT&T, Cabela's, HEB Food/gas, Radio Shack, Walgreens, Walmart
220	FM 2001, Niederwald, **E** 🅖 Shell, 🅞 Camper Clinic RV

TX

INTERSTATE 35 CONT'D

N ↕ **S**

SAN MARCOS

Exit	Services
220	Continued
	Ctr, Marshall's RV Park, W 🅞 Crestview RV Ctr/Park, GMC/Peterbilt, auto repair
217	Lp 4, Buda, E 🅖 Conoco/dsl/24hr, 🛏 La Quinta, W 🅖 Exxon/dsl, Valero/dsl, 🍴 Burger King, 🛏 Best Western, 🅞 Home Depot
215	Bunton Overpass, E 🅖 Exxon/KFC/LJ Silver, 🅞 Ⓗ, Lowe's Whse, Walgreens, W 🍴 Jack-in-the-Box, Papa Murphy's, Starbucks, Subway, Whataburger, 🅞 Explore USA RV Ctr, HEB Foods/dsl, Kohl's, PetCo, Target
213	FM 150, Kyle, E 🅖 Valero/dsl, 🍴 DQ, 🅞 AutoZone, Goodyear/auto, W 🅖 Conoco/dsl, 🅞 CVS Drug, repair
210	Yarrington Rd, E 🅞 Hyundai, W 🅞 Plum Creek RV Park
208mm	Blanco River
208	insp sta
207	Frontage Rd, Blanco River Rd, W 🅞 GM
206	Lp 82, Aquarena Springs Rd, E 🅖 Conoco, Valero, 🅞 San Marcos RV Park, W 🅖 Citgo/dsl, Exxon/dsl, Shell, Texaco, 🍴 Pancake House, Popeye's, Sonic, 🛏 Best Value Inn, Comfort Inn, Howard Johnson, La Quinta, Motel 6, Ramada Ltd, River Inn, Rodeway Inn, Super 8, 🅞 to SW TX U
205	TX 80, TX 142, Bastrop, E 🅖 Exxon, Quix, RaceWay, Shell/dsl, Valero, 🍴 Arby's, DQ, Fazoli's, Jason's Deli, Subway, Wing Stop, 🛏 Executive Inn, 🅞 AutoZone, CVS Drug, $General, Hastings Books, Hobby Lobby, Walmart, vet, W 🅖 Valero, 🍴 A&W/LJ Silver, Burger King, Church's, CiCi's, Furr's Cafe, IHOP, KFC, Kobe Japanese, Logan's Roadhouse, McDonald's, Pizza Hut, Taco Cabana, Wendy's, 🛏 Best Western, Budget Inn, Days Inn, Gateway Inn, Knight's Inn, Red Roof Inn, Rodeway Inn, 🅞 Brake Check, GNC, JC Penney, Office Depot, Radio Shack
204mm	San Marcos River
204b	CM Allen Pkwy, W 🅖 Shell/dsl, Spirit, 🍴 DQ, Mazatlan Mexican, Plucker's Grill, Sonic, 🛏 Best Western, Econolodge, 🅞 AutoZone, O'Reilly Parts
204a	Lp 82, TX 123, to Seguin, E 🅖 Conoco, Valero, 🍴 Burger King, Carino's, Chili's, FasTaco, Golden Corral, Luby's, McDonald's, Red Lobster, Whataburger/24hr, 🛏 Comfort Suites, Hampton Inn, Holiday Inn Express, 🅞 Ⓗ, Ford/Mercury, Jeep/Chrysler, transmissions
202	FM 3407, Wonder World Dr, E 🅖 Exxon, Shell/Church's, 🍴 Fuschaks BBQ, Hardees, Jack-in-the-Box, Taco Bueno, Taste of China, Wienerschnitzel, 🅞 Ⓗ, Best Buy, Discount Tire, $Tree, Lowe's Whse, Marshalls, PetsMart, Ross, Sams Club/gas, W 🅖 Valero/dsl, 🍴 TX Roadhouse, 🛏 Country Inn&Suites, 🅞 repair, transmissions
201	McCarty Lane, E 🛏 Embassy Suites, W 🅞 Beall's, Chrysler/Dodge, JC Penney, Nissan, Target
200	Centerpoint Rd, E 🍴 Cracker Barrel, Food Court, Outback Steaks, River City Grill, Subway, Taco Bell, Wendy's, 🅞 Cavender's Boots, GNC, Old Navy, Prime Outlets/famous brands, Tanger Outlet/famous brands, W 🅖 Valero/dsl, 🍴 Craig O's Pizza, McDonald's, Quizno's, Starbucks, Whataburger/24hr, 🛏 Baymont Inn, 🅞 Honda
199	Posey Rd, E 🅞 Tanger Outlets/famous brands, Toyota/Scion, same as 200
196	FM 1106, York Creek Rd, W 🅞 King&Trail RV Park
195	Watson Lane, Old Bastrop Rd
193	Conrads Rd, Kohlenberg Rd, W 🅖 TA/Country

NEW BRAUNFELS

Exit	Services
193	Continued
	Fare Rest/Popeye's/Subway/dsl/scales/24hr/@, 🅞 Camping World RV Ctr
191	FM 306, FM 483, Canyon Lake, E 🅞 AT&T, Best Buy, I-35 RV Camping, JC Penney, Ross, Target, Verizon, Walmart Dist Ctr, W 🅖 Chevron, Exxon/dsl, 🍴 Burger King, 🛏 Wingate Inn, 🅞 transmissions
190c	Post Rd
190b	frontage rd
190a	frontage rd, same as 189
189	TX 46, Seguin, E 🅖 Shell/dsl, 🍴 Chili's, Denny's, Olive Garden, Oma's Haus Rest., Quizno's, Taco Bueno, 🛏 Best Value Inn, Econolodge, Hampton Inn, La Quinta, Super 8, 🅞 Discount Tire, Home Depot, K-Mart, Kohl's, Office Depot, vet, W 🅖 Texaco, 🍴 Applebee's, Garden Buffet, IHOP, McDonald's, Pizza Hut, Taco Bell, Taco Cabana, Wendy's, 🛏 Days Inn, Edelweiss Inn, Fairfield Inn, Hilton Garden, Holiday Inn, Howard Johnson, Motel 6, Rodeway Inn, Quality Inn, Sleep Inn, 🅞 Ⓗ, Walgreens
188	Frontage Rd, W 🍴 Mamacita's Rest., Ryan's, 🛏 River Ranch Resort, 🅞 Hastings Books
188mm	Guadalupe River
187	FM 725, Lake McQueeny Rd, E 🍴 A&W/LJ Silver, Arby's, Burger King, CiCi's, Schobell's Rest., Subway, Whataburger/24hr, 🅞 Aamco, BigLots, Family$, Ford/Lincoln/Mercury, Hobby Lobby, Jeep, W 🅖 Shell/dsl, 🍴 Adobe Café, DQ, Jack-in-the-Box, Jason's Deli, Mesquite Pit BBQ, Steaks to Go, 🛏 Budget Inn, 🅞 Ⓗ, CVS Drug, River Ranch RV Resort, transmissions
186	Walnut Ave, E 🅖 Exxon/Subway, Murphy USA/dsl, Valero, 🍴 Chick-fil-A, McDonald's, Popeye's, Schlotsky's, Taco Bell, 🛏 Red Roof Inn, 🅞 Lowe's Whse, Walmart, W 🅖 Shell/dsl, 🍴 Baskin-Robbins, KFC, Mr Gatti's, Panda Express, Papa John's, Starbucks, 🅞 AT&T, AutoZone, Brake Check, $Tree, GNC, HEB Foods/gas, Radio Shack, U-Haul, Walgreens
185	FM 1044
184	FM 482, Lp 337, Ruekle Rd, E 🅖 Shell/dsl, 🅞 Buick/GMC, Kia, Mazda, RV Camping, W 🅖 💲/McDonald's/dsl/scales, 🅞 Suzuki
183	Solms Rd, W 🅖 Exxon
182	Engel Rd, E 🅞 Stamann RV Ctr
180	Schwab Rd
179mm	**rest area both lanes, full ♿ facilities, 🚻, 🅿, litter barrels, vending, petwalk**
178	FM 1103, Cibolo Rd, Hubertus Rd, E 🅖 Shell/dsl, 🅞 Walgreens
177	FM 482, FM 2252, E 🅞 Stone Creek RV Park
176	Weiderstein Rd, same as 175
175	FM 3009, Natural Bridge, E 🅖 Valero, 🍴 Chili's, IHOP, La Pasadita Mexican, McDonald's, Miller's BBQ, Schlotsky's, Sonic, Taco Cabana, 🛏 Fairfield Inn, Hampton Inn, 🅞 HEB Food/gas, Lowe's Whse, W 🅖 Chevron, Murphy USA/dsl, Shell/dsl, Valero/Subway/dsl, 🍴 Abel's Diner, Arby's, Bellacino's, Denny's, Domino's, Jack-in-the-Box, KFC/Taco Bell/Pizza Hut, Marble Slab, McDonald's, Panda Express, Pazzo Italian, Quizno's, Wendy's, Whataburger, Wing Stop, 🛏 La Quinta, 🅞 AT&T, $Tree, Factory Shoestore, Walmart
174b	Schertz Pkwy, E 🅖 Shell
174a	FM 1518, Selma, E 🅖 Phillips 66, 🍴 Ruddy's BBQ, 🅞 Honda/Mitsubishi, Subaru, W 🛏 Comfort Inn, 🅞 Tex-Al RV Ctr

TX

INTERSTATE 35 CONT'D

N ↑ ↓ S

Exit	Services
173	Old Austin Rd, Olympia Pkwy, E 🍴 Baskin Robbins, Chick-fil-A, Chili's, Chipotle Mexican, Firehouse Subs, Freddy's Custard, Hooters, IHOP, Macaroni Grill, Outback Steaks, Panda Express, Peter Piper Pizza, Red Robin, Sea Island Srimp, Starbucks, Subway, TGIFriday's, Wendy's, 🏨 Holiday Inn Express, 🅞 AT&T, Beall's, Best Buy, Costco/gas, Discount Tire, GNC, Hobby Lobby, Home Depot, Kohl's, NTB, Old Navy, PetsMart, Ross, Verizon, Target, TJ Maxx, WorldMkt, W 🍴 ChuckeCheese, Chuy's Mexican, Houlihan's, 🅞 Retama Park RaceTrack
172	TX 218, Anderson Lp, P Booker Rd, E 🍴 Buffalo Wild Wings, Coldstone Creamery, IHOP, Krystal, On-the-Border, Outback Steaks, TX Roadhouse, Zio's, 🏨 Comfort Inn, ValuePlace, 🅞 Ford, Nissan, Home Depot, Hyundai, Kohls, Target, to Randolph AFB, W to SeaWorld
171	Topperwein Rd, same as 170
170	Judson Rd, to Converse, E 🍴 Denny's, Subway, Whataburger/24hr, 🏨 Great Value Inn, La Quinta, 🅞 H, Chevrolet, Chrysler, Ford, Hyundai, Nissan, GMC, Toyota, W 🅖 Exxon, 🏨 Best Western, 🅞 Kia, Mazda, Sam's Club/gas
169	O'Conner Rd, Wurzbach Pkwy, E 🅖 Exxon/dsl, 🍴 McDonald's, Quizno's, Subway, Taco Cabana, 🏨 Comfort Suites, 🅞 Chrysler/Jeep, Lowe's Whse, Walgreens, W 🅖 Shell/dsl, Valero, 🍴 Jack-in-the-Box, Jim's Rest., Mi Casa Mexican, Sonic, 🅞 Mazda
168	Weidner Rd, E 🅖 Citgo/dsl, 🏨 Days Inn, Comfort Suites, W 🅖 Chevron, 🏨 Park Inn, Super 8, 🅞 Harley-Davidson, Volvo Trucks
167b	Thousand Oaks Dr, Starlight Terrace, E 🅖 Valero/dsl
167a	Randolph Blvd, E 🅖 Valero, W 🏨 Continental Inn, Days Inn, Motel 6, Rodeway Inn, Ruby Inn
166	I-410 W, Lp 368 S, W 🅞 to Sea World
165	FM 1976, Walzem Rd, E 🅖 Shell, Valero/dsl, 🍴 Applebee's, Bill Miller BBQ, Burger King, China Harbor, ChuckeCheese, Church's, Domino's, Firehouse Grill, IHOP, Jack-in-the-Box, KFC/Taco Bell, Las Palapas Mexican, LJ Silver, Luby's, McDonald's, Marie Callender's, Olive Garden, Pizza Hut, Red Lobster, Shoneys, Starbucks, Subway, Taco Cabana, Wendy's, Whataburger, 🏨 Drury Inn, PearTree Inn, 🅞 AutoZone, Cavender's Boots, CVS Drug, Discount Tire, $World, Firestone/auto, Home Depot, Michael's, 99cent Store, PepBoys, PetsMart, Radio Shack, W 🍴 Sonic, 🅞 NTB
164b	Eisenhauer Rd, E 🅖 Exxon/dsl, 🏨 Hawthorn Suites, ValuePlace Inn, 🅞 $General
164a	Rittiman Rd, E 🅖 Exxon, Shell/dsl, Valero/dsl, 🍴 Burger King, Church's, Cracker Barrel, Denny's, Guadalajara Mexican, Jack-in-the-Box, McDonald's, Taco Cabana, Whataburger/24hr, 🏨 Best Western, Comfort Suites, La Quinta, Motel 6, Rittiman Inn, 🅞 HEB Foods, dsl repair, W 🅖 Chevron/dsl, Valero, 🍴 Bill Miller BBQ, Popeye's, Sonic
163	I-410 S (162 from nb, exits left from sb)
161	Binz-Engleman Rd (from nb), same as 160
160	Splashtown Dr, E 🅖 Valero/Subway/dsl/24hr, 🏨 Delux Inn, 🅞 funpark, W 🍴 Grady's BBQ, 🏨 Best Value Inn, Clarion, Days Inn, Howard Johnson, Microtel, Super 8, Travelodge
159b	Walters St, E 🍴 McDonald's, W 🏨 Econolodge, 🅞 to Ft Sam Houston

SAN ANTONIO

Exit	Services
159a	New Braunfels Ave, E 🅖 Shell/dsl, Texaco/Burger King, W 🅖 Chevron, Valero/dsl/24hr, 🍴 Bill Miller BBQ, Sonic, 🏨 Antonian Suites, 🅞 to Ft Sam Houston
158c	N Alamo St, Broadway
158b	I-37 S, US 281 S, to Corpus Christi, to Alamo
158a	US 281 N (from sb), to Johnson City
157b a	Brooklyn Ave, Lexington Ave, N Flores, downtown, E 🏨 Super 8, 🅞 H, W 🍴 Luby's
156	I-10 W, US 87, to El Paso
155b	Durango Blvd, downtown, E 🏨 Best Western, Courtyard, Fairfield Inn, Holiday Inn, La Quinta, Residence Inn, Woodfield Suites, 🅞 H, W 🍴 McDonald's, 🏨 Motel 6, Radisson
155a	South Alamo St, E 🅖 Exxon, Shell, 🍴 Church's, Denny's, McDonald's, Piedras Negras Mexican, Pizza Hut, Wendy's, 🏨 Best Western, Comfort Inn, Days Inn, Holiday Inn, La Quinta, Ramada Ltd, Residence Inn, 🅞 USPO, W 🅖 Conoco, 🏨 Microtel
154b	S Laredo St, Ceballos St, same as 155b
154a	Nogalitos St
153	I-10 E, US 90 W, US 87, to Kelly AFB, Lackland AFB
152b	Malone Ave, Theo Ave, E 🍴 Taco Cabana/24hr, W 🅖 Shamrock, Shell
152a	Division Ave, E 🅖 Chevron, 🍴 Bill Miller BBQ, Las Cazuelas Mexican, Whataburger/24hr, 🏨 Quality Inn, W 🍴 Sonic, 🅞 transmissions
151	Southcross Blvd, E 🅖 Exxon, Shell, W 🅖 Shell/dsl, 🍴 Mazatlan Mexican
150b	Lp 13, Military Dr, E 🅖 Valero, 🍴 Applebee's, Arby's, Denny's, Don Pedro Mexican, KFC, Pizza Hut, Sonic, Starbucks, Subway, Taco Cabana, 🏨 La Quinta, 🅞 AutoZone, Discount Tire, U-Haul, W 🅖 Exxon, 🍴 Chili's, Coyote Canyon, Freddy's Custard, Hungry Farmer Rest, Jack-in-the-Box, KFC, LJ Silver, Luby's, Moma Margie's Mexican, McDonald's, Mr Gatti, Olive Garden, Panda Express, Pizza Hut, Sea Island Shrimp House, Wendy's, Whataburger, 🏨 La Quinta, 🅞 Best Buy, $Tree, Firestone/auto, HEB Foods, Home Depot, JC Penney, Lowe's Whse, Macy's, Office Depot, Old Navy, Sears/auto, Walgreens, mall,
150a	Zarzamora St (149 fom sb), same as 150b
149	Hutchins Blvd (from sb), E 🅖 Valero/dsl, 🏨 Motel 6, ValuePlace, 🅞 H, W 🅞 Chevrolet, Ford, Honda, Hyundai, Kia
148b	Palo Alto Rd, W 🅖 Valero
148a	TX 16 S, spur 422 (from nb), Poteet, E 🅖 Chevron, 🏨 Days Inn, W 🍴 Phillips 66, 🅞 $General
147	Somerset Rd, E 🅖 Shell/dsl, W 🅞 Dodge
146	Cassin Rd (from nb)
145b	Lp 353 N

TX

🅖 = gas 🍴 = food 🛏 = lodging 🅞 = other Copyright 2012 - The Next Exit®

INTERSTATE 35 CONT'D

N ↕ S

Exit	Services
145a	I-410, TX 16
144	Fischer Rd, **E** 🅖 Valero/Subway/dsl/scales/24hr, 🛏 D&D Motel, 🅞 lube, RV camping, **W** 🅖 Loves/Carl's Jr/dsl/scales/24hr, 🅞 Scion/Toyota
142	Medina River Turnaround (from nb)
141	Benton City Rd, Von Ormy, **W** 🅖 Shell/dsl/Parador Café
140	Anderson Lp, 1604, **E** 🅖 Exxon/dsl/24hr, 🍴 Burger King, **W** 🅖 Valero/Church's/dsl/scales/24hr, 🅞 Alamo River RV Resort, to Sea World
139	Kinney Rd
137	Shepherd Rd, **E** truck repair, **W** gas/dsl, dsl repair
135	Luckey Rd
133	TX 132 S (from sb), Lytle, same as 131
131	FM 3175, FM 2790, Benton City Rd, **E** 🅞 NAPA, **W** 🅖 Conoco/dsl/24hr, 🍴 Bill Miller BBQ, DQ, McDonald's, Eatza Pizza, Sonic, Topis Mexican, 🛏 Days Inn, 🅞 AutoZone, Crawford Drug, $General, HEB Food/dsl
129mm	**rest area both lanes, full ♿ facilities, 🚻, litter barrels, vending, petwalk**
127	FM 471, Natalia
124	FM 463, Bigfoot Rd, **E** Ford
122	TX 173, Devine, **E** 🅖 Exxon/dsl, 🅞 Chevrolet, Chrysler/Dodge/Jeep, **W** 🅖 Chevron/McDonald's/Subway/dsl, Exxon, Shamrock, Shell, 🍴 CCC Steaks, Church's, Pizza Inn, Sonic, Viva Zapatas Mexican, 🛏 Country Corner Inn/rest
121	TX 132 N, Devine
118.5mm	**weigh sta both lanes**
114	FM 462, Yancey, Bigfoot, **E** 🅖 Lucky/dsl
111	US 57, to Eagle Pass, **W** 🅖 Valero/dsl
104	Lp 35, **3 mi E** 🅖 Valero, 🍴 McDonald's, 🛏 Executive Inn, 🅞 🅗
101	FM 140, Pearsall, **E** 🅖 Chevron/dsl, 🍴 Cowpokes BBQ, 🛏 Best Western, Rio Frio Motel, Royal Inn, 🅞 🅗, GMC, **W** 🅖 Exxon/Subway/dsl/24hr, Valero/Porter House Rest/dsl/scales/24hr
99	FM 1581, to Divot, Pearsall
93mm	**parking/picnic area both lanes, litter barrels, ♿ accessible**
91	FM 1583, Derby
90mm	Frio River
86	Lp 35, Dilley
85	FM 117, **E** 🍴 Garcia Café, 🛏 Relax Inn, **W** 🅖 Exxon, 🍴 DQ, 🛏 Budget Inn, Sona Inn, 🅞 RV park
84	TX 85, Dilley, **E** 🅖 Conoco/Burger King/dsl, 🍴 Millie's Mexican, 🅞 🅗, Chevrolet, Super S Foods/dsl, **W** 🅖 Shell/Pollo Grande/dsl/24hr, Valero/Subway/dsl/24hr, 🛏 Executive Inn
82	County Line Rd, to Dilley
77	FM 469, Millett
74	Gardendale
69	Lp 35, Cotulla, **E** Super S Food/gas
67	FM 468, to Big Wells, **E** 🅖 Exxon/Wendy's/dsl/24hr, JJ's/dsl, Valero/deli/dsl/24hr, 🍴 DQ, 🛏 Executive Inn, Village Inn, 🅞 tire repair, **W** 🅖 Chevron/McDonald's/dsl/scales/24hr, 🛏 Best Western, 🅞 rv park
65	Lp 35, Cotulla
63	Elm Creek Interchange
59mm	picnic area both lanes, litter barrels
56	FM 133, Artesia Wells

Exit	Services
48	Caiman Creek Interchange
39	TX 44, Encinal, **E** 🅖 Loves/Chester Fried/Subway/dsl/scales/24hr, **W** 🅖 Exxon/dsl
38	TX 44 (from nb), Encinal
32	San Roman Interchange
29mm	**inspection sta nb**
27	Callaghan Interchange
24	255 toll, Camino Colombia toll rd, to Monterrey
22	Webb Interchange
18	US 83 N, to Carrizo Springs, **E TX Travel Info Ctr (8am-5pm)/rest area, full facilities, 🚻, litter barrels, petwalk, wireless internet, W** RV Camping
14mm	parking area, sb
12b	(13 from sb), Uniroyal Interchange, **E** 🍴 🅖 /McDonald's/Subway/dsl/scales/24hr, 🅞 Blue Beacon, **W** ⊙FLYING J/Denny's/dsl/scales/24hr, TA/Burger King/Subway/Taco Bell/dsl/scales/24hr/@
12a	Port Loredo
10	Port Laredo Carriers Dr (from nb)
9	Industrial Blvd, to Bob Bullock Lp (from sb only)
9	Industrial Blvd, to Bob Bullock Lp (from sb only)
8b	Lp 20 W, to Solidarity Bridge
8a	Lp 20 W, to to World Trade Bridge, Milo
5	San Isidro Pkwy
7	Shilo Dr, Las Cruces Dr, **E** 🅖 Valero/dsl, 🍴 El Pescador Mexican
4	FM 1472, Del Mar Blvd, **E** 🅖 Exxon/Burger King/dsl, Valero, 🍴 Applebee's, Carino's Italian, CiCi's, IHOP, Jack-in-the-Box, McDonald's, Quizno's, Whataburger, 🛏 Extended Stay America, Hampton Inn, Residence Inn, 🅞 Best Buy, HEB Foods/gas, Honda, Lowe's Whse, Marshall's, Old Navy, Radio Shack, Target, **W** 🅖 Shell/dsl, 🛏 Days Inn, 🅞 Harley-Davidson
3b	Mann Rd, **E** 🍴 Buffalo Wild Wings, Krispy Kreme, Lin's Chinese, 🅞 URGENT CARE, Buick/GMC, Dillard's, Ford/Lincoln/Mercury, Honda, Lowe's Whse, Mazda, Toyota, mall, **W** 🍴 Chili's, Danny's Rest, Golden Corral, Hayashi Japanese, Outback Steaks, Kettle Pancake House, Subway, Taco Palenque, Whataburger, 🛏 Family Garden Inn, Gateway Inn, La Hacienda Motel, Monterey Inn, Motel 6, Red Roof Inn, SpringHill Suites, 🅞 $Tree, Home Depot, Kohl's, Michael's, Office Depot, PetCo, Ross, Verizon, Walmart/auto
3a	San Bernardo Ave, **E** 🅖 Shell/dsl, 🍴 Chick-fil-A, El Taco Tote, Emperor Chinese, Fuddrucker's, LJ Silver, Logan's Roadhouse, Luby's, Olive Garden, Peter Piper Pizza, Red Lobster, Sirloin Stockade, Tony Roma's, 🛏 Fairfield Inn, 🅞 Advance Parts, HEB Foods/gas, K-Mart, Macy's, NAPA, PepBoys, Sears/auto, SteinMart, mall, **W** 🅖 Valero, 🍴 Arby's, Burger King, Chick-fil-A, Logan's Roadhouse, McDonald's, Pizza Hut, Popeye's, Taco Bell, Taco Palenque, Tori Cafe, Wendy's, 🅞 O'Reilly Parts, Radio Shack, Sam's Club
2	US 59, Saunders Rd, **E** 🅖 Conoco, Shell, 🍴 Jack-in-the-Box, 🅞 🅗, **W** 🅖 Exxon/Burger King/dsl, Shell, 🍴 Church's, Denny's, 🛏 Courtyard, Holiday Inn, La Quinta, Relax Inn, Super8, 🅞 Advance Parts, AutoZone, Mexico Insurance
1b	Park St, to Sanchez St, **W** 🅖 Conoco/dsl, 🍴 La Mexicana Rest., Popeye's
1a	Victoria St, Scott St, Washington St (from sb), **E** 🅖 Exxon, Shell, Valero, **W** 🅖 Chevron, Exxon/dsl, Shell, Valero, 🍴 KFC, Mariachi Express, McDonald's, Wendy's, 🅞 Firestone/auto, tires/auto repair, transmissions, I-35 begins/ends in Laredo at Victoria St, access to multiple services

P E A R S A L L

L A R E D O

TX

🅖 = gas 🍴 = food 🛏 = lodging 🄾 = other

INTERSTATE 35 WEST

N ↑↓ S

Exit	Services
	I-35W begins/ends on I-35, exit 467.
85b	W Oak St, 🅖 🄷
85a	I-35E S
84	FM 1515, Bonnie Brae St, 🅖 🄷
82	FM 2449, to Ponder
79	Crawford Rd
76	FM 407, to Justin, Argyle, **W** 🅖 Phillips 66/dsl/24hr, 🄾 Corral City RV Park, Paradise Foods
76mm	picnic area both lanes, litter barrels, 🚻
74	FM 1171, to Lewisville
72	Dale Earnhardt Way, **E** same as 70, **W** TX Motor Speedway
70	TX 114, to Dallas, Bridgeport, **E** 🅖 7-11, Shell/Subway/dsl, 🍴 Waffle House/24hr, 🛏 Motel 6, Sleep Inn, 🄾 North Lake RV Park, to DFW ✈, **W** 🄾 TX Motor Speedway
68	Eagle Pkwy, **W** ✈
67	Alliance Blvd, **W** 🄾 to Alliance ✈, FedEx
66	to Westport Pkwy, Keller-Haslet Rd, **E** 🛏 Hampton Inn, Residence Inn, **W** 🅖 Mobil/Wendy's/dsl, 🍴 Bryan's BBQ, Snooty Pig, Subway, Taco Bueno, 🄾 USPO
65	TX 170 E, **E** 🅖 Pilot/McDonald's/dsl/scales/24hr, 🍴 IHOP, 🄾 Cabela's/cafe
64	Golden Triangle Blvd, to Keller-Hicks Blvd, **E** 🄾 Chrysler/Dodge/Jeep
63	Heritage Trace, **E** 🅖 7-11, 🍴 Cheddar's, Jason's Deli, Subway, 🄾 Belk, Best Buy, Hobby Lobby, JC Penney, PetsMart
62	North Tarrant Pkwy, **E** 🍴 Pizza Inn
60	US 287 N, US 81 N, to Decatur
59	Basswood (sb only), **E** 🅖 Chevron/Jack-in-the-Box/dsl, 🍴 Sonic, 🄾 Home Depot
58	Western Ctr Blvd, **E** 🅖 7-11, Shell/Church's, 🍴 Braum's, Casa Rita, Chili's, Denny's, Dublin Square Rest., Flips Grill, Genghis Grill, Macaroni Grill, On-the-Border, Posados Cafe, Quizno's, SaltGrass Steaks, Shady Oak Grill, Wendy's, Wing Stop, Zio's Italian, 🛏 Best Western, Residence Inn, 🄾 AT&T, Kauffman Tire, **W** 🍴 Bardo's Pizza, Boston's, Firehouse subs, Joe's Crabshack, Popeye's, Rosa's Cafe, Starbucks, Subway, Waffle House, Whataburger, 🛏 Holiday Inn Express, 🄾 URGENT CARE, repair
57b a	I-820 E&W
56b	Melody Hills
56a	Meacham Blvd, **E** 🅖 Shell, 🛏 Hilton Garden, Howard Johnson, La Quinta, **W** 🅖 Texaco/dsl, 🍴 Cracker Barrel, McDonald's, Subway, 🛏 Baymont Inn, Holiday Inn, Radisson, Super 8, 🄾 USPO
55	Pleasantdale Ave (from nb)
54c	33rd St, Long Ave (from nb), **W** 🅖 Conoco/dsl, Valero/dsl, 🛏 Motel 6
54b a	TX 183 W, Papurt St, **W** 🅖 QuikStop/dsl, 🍴 Chester's Chicken, 🛏 Classic Inn
53	North Side Dr, Yucca Dr, **E** 🅖 Shell/dsl, **W** 🍴 Mercado Juarez Café, 🛏 Country Inn&Suites
53mm	Trinity River
52e	Carver St (from nb)
52d	Pharr St
52b	US 377N, Belknap
52a	US 377 N, TX 121, to DFW
51a	I-31 E, to Avalene (from nb), downtown Ft Worth

Exit	Services
50c a	I-30 W, E to Dallas
50b	TX 180 E (from nb)
49b	Rosedale St, **W** 🄷
49a	Allen Ave, **E** 🅖 Valero, **W** 🄷
48b	Morningside Ave (from sb), same as 48a
48a	Berry St, **E** 🅖 Chevron/McDonald's, 🍴 Texas Style Rest., 🄾 Autozone, Sack'n Save Foods, **W** 🅖 RaceTrac, 🄾 U-Haul, zoo
47	Ripy St, **E** 🄾 transmissions, **W** 🛏 Astro Inn
46b	Seminary Dr, **E** 🅖 RaceWay, 🍴 Grandy's, Jack-in-the-Box, Rice Bowl, Subway, Taco Cabana, Whataburger, 🛏 Days Inn, Delux Inn, Regency Inn, Super 7 Inn, 🄾 NAPA, **W** 🅖 Shamrock, Shell, 🍴 Denny's, Sonic, Wendy's, 🄾 Fiesta Foods, Firestone/auto, Pepboys
46a	Felix St, **E** 🅖 Valero, 🛏 Dalworth Inn, **W** 🍴 McDonald's, 🄾 Family$, Super Plaza Foods
45b a	I-20, E to Dallas, W to Abilene
44	Altamesa, **E** 🛏 Radisson, **W** 🅖 Prism, 🍴 Rig Steaks, Waffle House, 🛏 Baymont Inn, Best Western, Comfort Suites, Motel 6, South Lp Inn
43	Sycamore School Rd, **W** 🅖 Exxon, 🍴 Chicken Express, Jack-in-the-Box, Sonic, Subway, Whataburger, 🄾 $General, Home Depot, Radio Shack, repair
42	Everman Pkwy, **W** 🅖 QT/dsl/scales, Shell
41	Risinger Rd, **W** 🄾 Camping World RV Service/Supplies, McClain's RV Ctr
40	Garden Acres Dr, **E** 🅖 Loves/Subway/dsl/scales/24hr, 🛏 Microtel, 🄾 🄷, **W** 🍴 Taco Bell
39	FM 1187, McAlister Rd, **E** 🄷, **W** 🅖 Shamrock/dsl/24hr, Shell, 🍴 Buffalo Wild Wings, Firehouse Subs, Logan's Roadhouse, Olive Garden, Panda Express, Red Lobster, TGIFriday's, Waffle House, 🛏 Howard Johnson, 🄾 Best Buy, Kohl's, Staples, Verizon
38	Alsbury Blvd, **E** 🅖 Chevron/24hr, Mobil/dsl, 🍴 Chili's, Cracker Barrel, Hibachi Japanese, IHOP, McDonald's, Mexican Inn Cafe, On-the-Border, Outback Steaks, Over Time Grill, Spring Creek BBQ, 🛏 Hampton Inn, Holiday Inn Express, La Quinta, Super 8, 🄾 Discount Tire, Ford, Lowe's Whse, **W** 🅖 RaceTrac, Shamrock, Shell/24hr, 🍴 Applebees, Arby's, Burger King, Chick-fil-A, Coldstone Creamery, Cotton Patch Cafe, Denny's, Pancho's Mexican, Sonic, Taco Cabana, Wendy's, 🄾 Albertson's, Chevrolet, JC Penney, Kwik Kar, Michael's, PetsMart, Radio Shack, Ross, vet
37	TX 174, Wilshire Blvd, to Cleburne, **W** Walmart (2mi), from sb, same as 36
36	FM 3391, TX 174S, Burleson, **E** 🅖 Chevron, Mobil, 🍴 Miranda's Cantina, Sonic, Waffle House, 🛏 Best Western, Comfort Suites, Days Inn, **W** 🄾 Curves, $General, transmissions

TX

gas = gas   food = food   lodging = lodging   other = other   Copyright 2012 - The Next Exit®

INTERSTATE 35 WEST CONT'D

Exit	Services
35	Briaroaks Rd (from sb), **W** RV camping
33mm	**rest area sb, full ♿ facilities, ☎, ♨, litter barrels**
32	Bethesda Rd, **E** Valero, Best Value Inn, RV Ranch Park, **W** Mockingbird Hill RV Park
31mm	**rest area nb, full ♿ facilities, ☎, ♨, litter barrels**
30	FM 917, Mansfield, **E** Shell/Sonic/dsl, **W** Shell/dsl, RanchHouse Rest.
27	Rd 604, Rd 707
26b a	US 67, Cleburne, **E** Chevron/KFC/dsl, Chicken Express, DQ, McDonald's, Pizza Hut, Sonic, Waffle House, Whataburger, Best Western, Days Inn, La Quinta, Super 8, Ancira RV Ctr, AutoZone, Brookshire Foods, $General, Family$, Motor Home Specialist, Parts+, Walmart
24	FM 3136, FM 1706, Alvarado, **E** Shell/Grandy's/dsl/scales/24hr, Longhorn Grill
21	Rd 107, to Greenfield
17	FM 2258
16	TX 81 S, Rd 201, Grandview
15	FM 916, Maypearl, **W** Chevron/dsl, Mobil/dsl, Subway
12	FM 67
8	FM 66, Itasca, **E** Valero/dsl/café/24hr, **W** DQ, Ford, ♨, litter barrels
7	FM 934, **E** ♨, litter barrels, **W** Exxon/dsl, Golden Chick Cafe
3	FM 2959, **E** to Hillsboro ✈

I-35W begins/ends on I-35, 371mm.

INTERSTATE 37

Exit	Services
142b a	I-35 S to Laredo, N to Austin. I-37 begins/ends on I-35 in San Antonio.
141c	Brooklyn Ave, Nolan St (from sb), downtown
141b	Houston St, **E** Red Roof Inn, tires, **W** Citgo, Denny's, Crockett Hotel, Crowne Plaza, Days Inn, Drury Inn, Hampton Inn, Hyatt Hotel, Marriott, La Quinta, Residence Inn, Macy's, to The Alamo
141a	Commerce St, **E** Staybridge Suites, **W** Denny's, La Quinta, Marriott, Macy's
140b	Durango Blvd, downtown, **E** Bill Miller BBQ, to Alamo Dome
140a	Carolina St, Florida St, **E** Citgo/dsl
139	I-10 W, US 87, US 90, to Houston, **W** to Sea World
138c	Fair Ave, Hackberry St, **E** DQ, Jack-in-the-Box, La Tapatia Mexian, Pimpilo Chicken, Popeye's, Brake Check, Family$, Home Depot, **W** Exxon, Shell
138b	E New Braunfels Ave (from sb), **E** IHOP, Little Caesar's, McDonald's, Taco Cabana, Whataburger, Wendy's, HEB/dsl, Marshall's, **W** Exxon, Sonic
138a	Southcross Blvd, W New Braunfels Ave, **E** McDonald's, Taco Cabana, Wendy's, **W** Exxon, Sonic
137	Hot Wells Blvd, **W** IHOP, Motel 6, Super 8
136	Pecan Valley Dr, **E** Citgo/dsl, KFC/Taco Bell, Pizza Hut, Pecan Valley Inn, AutoZone, O'Reilly Parts, **W** H
135	Military Dr, Lp 13, **E** Shell, Valero, Jack-in-the-Box, Best Western, Mission Trail RV park, **W** Valero/Subway/dsl, A&W/LJ Silver, Buffalo Wild Wings, Burger King, Carino's Italian, Cherry's Buffet, Chick-fil-A, Chili's, IHOP, Little Caesar's, Longhorn Cafe,

Exit	Services
135	Continued Panda Express, Panda Express, Peter Piper Pizza, Quizno's, Sonic, Starbucks, Subway, Whataburger/24hr, La Quinta, Advance Parts, AT&T, Best Buy, BigLots, Discount Tire, $Tree, Hancock Fabrics, HEB Food/gas, Home Depot, Lowe's Whse, Office Depot, PetCo, Radio Shack, Ross, Target, Walgreens, Walmart, to Brooks AFB
133	I-410, US 281 S
132	US 181 S, to Floresville (no SB return), **E** Shell, $General
130	Donop Rd, Southton Rd, **E** Valero/dsl, Tom's Burgers, Guest House Inn, Braunig Lake RV Resort, **W** Shell/dsl, car/truckwash
127	San Antonio River Turnaround (from nb), Braunig Lake
127mm	San Antonio River
125	FM 1604, Anderson Lp, **E** Conoco/dsl/24hr, Burger King, **W** Citgo/dsl, Exxon/dsl, Bill Miller BBQ, Whataburger, tires
122	Priest Rd, Mathis Rd
120	Hardy Rd
117	FM 536
113	FM 3006
112mm	**picnic area both lanes, ♿ accessible, ♨, litter barrels**
109	TX 97, to Floresville, **E** Chevron/dsl/rest., Selly's Mexican, Chrysler/Dodge/Jeep
106	Coughran Rd
104	spur 199, Leal Rd, to Pleasanton (no immediate sb return), same as 103
103	US 281 N, Leal Rd, to Pleasanton, **E** Valero/dsl, DQ, K&K Cafe, Kuntry Inn
98	TX 541, McCoy
92	US 281A, Campbellton, **2 mi W** Kuntry Korner gas, Stetson's Cafe
88	FM 1099, to FM 791, Campbellton
83	FM 99, Whitsett, Peggy, **E** Shell/dsl/cafe, **W** Chevron/dsl, Exxon/dsl
82mm	**rest area sb, full ♿ facilities, ☎, ♨, litter barrels**
78mm	**rest area nb, full ♿ facilities, ☎, ♨, litter barrels**
76	US 281A, FM 2049, Whitsett
75mm	**truck weigh sta sb**
74mm	**truck weigh sta nb**
72	US 281 S, Three Rivers, **4 mi W** Valero, DQ, Staghorn Rest, Subway, Best Western, Econolodge, to Rio Grande Valley
69	TX 72, Three Rivers, **W** Valero/dsl/café/24hr, tires, to Choke Canyon SP
65	FM 1358, Oakville, **E** Van's BBQ
59	FM 799
56	US 59, George West, **E** Valero/dsl/24hr, **W** Shell/Subway/24hr, Valero/Burger King/dsl/24hr
51	Hailey Ranch Rd
47	FM 3024, FM 534, Swinney Switch Rd, **W** Mike's Mkt/gas (1mi), to KOA (4mi)
44mm	parking area sb
42mm	parking area nb
40	FM 888
36	TX 359, to Skidmore, Mathis, **W** Valero/dsl (1mi), Shell/McDonald's/dsl, Texaco/Subway/dsl, Pizza Hut, Best Western, Lake Corpus Christi SRA
34	TX 359 W, **E** Adventure TX RV Ctr/LP, **W** Citgo, Shell, Valero/dsl, Church's, DQ, Pizza Hut, $General,

INTERSTATE 37 CONT'D

Exit	Services
34	Continued
	O'Reilly Parts, to Lake Corpus Christi SP
31	TX 188, to Sinton, Rockport
22	TX 234, FM 796, to Odem, Edroy
20b	Cooper Rd
19.5mm	**picnic area both lanes, accessible, tables, litter barrels**
17	US 77 N, to Victoria
16	LaBonte Park, **W** info, litter barrels
15	Sharpsburg Rd (from sb), Redbird Ln
14	US 77 S, Redbird Ln, to Kingsville, Robstown, **1 mi W on FM 624** RaceWay, Valero/Burger King/dsl, Shell, Bill Miller BBQ, Chili's, CiCi's, Denny's, Good'n Crisp Chicken, Papa John's, Pizza Hut, Popeye's, Sonic, Subway, Whataburger/24hr, Wienerschnitzel, Comfort Inn, Holiday Inn Express, , Beall's, CVS Drug, Firestone/auto, GNC, Hobby Lobby, Home Depot, O'Reilly Parts, Radio Shack, Walmart
13b	Sharpsburg Rd (from nb)
13a	FM 1694, Callicoatte Rd, Leopard St
11b	FM 24, Violet Rd, Hart Rd, **E** Chicken Shack, La Quinta, **W** Exxon/dsl, Valero/dsl, DQ, Domino's, Fliz Amancer Mexican, KFC/LJ Silver, Little Caesar's, McDonald's, Schlotzsky's, Sonic, Subway, Taco Bell, Whataburger/24hr, Best Western, Hampton Inn, AutoZone, Family$, HEB Food/gas, O'Reilly Parts, Walgreens, vet
11a	McKinzie Rd, **E** Shell, Jack-in-the-Box, La Quinta, **W** Valero/dsl
10	Carbon Plant Rd
9	FM 2292, Up River Rd, Rand Morgan Rd, **W** Valero/dsl, Whataburger/24hr
7	Suntide Rd, Tuloso Rd, Clarkwood Rd, **W** Freightliner
6	Southern Minerals Rd, **E** refinery
5	Corn Products Rd, Valero Way, **E** Kenworth, **W** PetroFleet, Jalisco Rest., Super 8, Travelodge, Val-u-Stay
4b	Lantana St, McBride Lane (from sb), **W** Inn, Motel 6
4a	TX 358, to Padre Island, **W** Shell/dsl, Holiday Inn, Plaza Inn, Quality Inn, Walmart (4mi)
3b	McBride Lane (from nb), **W** Gulf Coast Racing
3a	Navigation Blvd, **E** Valero/dsl, Rodeway Inn, **W** Exxon/dsl, BBQ Man, Denny's, Best Western, Days Inn, Hampton Inn, La Quinta, CarQuest
2	Up River Rd, **E** refinery
1e	Lawrence Dr, Nueces Bay Blvd, **E** refinery, **W** Valero, Church's, Red Roof Inn, Aamco, AutoZone, HEB Foods, Firestone, USPO
1d	Port Ave (from sb), **W** Coastal, Shell, Vick's Burgers, EconoLodge, Radio Shack, Port of Corpus Christi
1c	US 181, TX 286, Shoreline Blvd, Corpus Christi, **W**
1b	Brownlee St (from nb), **W** Shell
1a	Buffalo St (from sb), **0-1 mi W on Shoreline** Valero/dsl, Burger King, Joe's Crabshack, Landry's Sea Subway, Whataburger, Bayfront Inn, Best Western, Omni Hotel, Super 8, Curves, U-Haul, USPO, I-37 begins/ends on US 181 in Corpus Christi.

INTERSTATE 40

Exit	Services
177mm	Texas/Oklahoma state line
176	spur 30 (from eb), to Texola
175mm	picnic area wb, litter barrels
169	FM 1802, Carbon Black Rd
167	FM 2168, Daberry Rd
165mm	check sta wb
164	Lp 40 (from wb), to Shamrock, **1 mi S** EconoLodge, , museum, **check sta eb**
163	US 83, to Wheeler, Shamrock, **N** Chevron/Taco Bell/dsl, Mitchell's Rest., Best Western, Irish Inn, Ace Hardware, **S** Conoco/dsl, Phillips 66/Subway/dsl, Cicero's Pizza, DQ, McDonald's, EconoLodge, Holiday Inn Express, Sleep Inn, Western Motel
161	Lp 40, Rte 66 (from eb), to Shamrock, **S** Phillips 66
157	FM 1547, Lela, **1 mi S** West 40 RV Camping
152	FM 453, Pakan Rd
148	FM 1443, Kellerville Rd
146	County Line Rd
143	Lp 40 (from wb), to McLean, to Shell/dsl
142	TX 273, FM 3143, to McLean, **N** Shell/dsl, Red River Steaks, Cactus Inn, RV Camping/dump, USPO
141	Rte 66 (from eb), McLean, same as 142
135	FM 291, Rte 66, Alanreed, **S** Conoco/motel/café/RV park/dump, USPO
132	Johnson Ranch Rd ranch access
131mm	**rest area wb, full facilities, , , litter barrels, pet-walk**
129mm	**rest area eb, full facilities, , , littler barrels, pet-walk, playground**
128	FM 2477, to Lake McClellan, **N** Lake McClellan RA/RV Dump
124	TX 70 S, to Clarendon, **S** RV camping/dump
121	TX 70 N, to Pampa
114	Lp 40, Groom, **N** dsl repair
113	FM 2300, Groom, **S** Phillips 66/dsl, DQ, Chalet Inn
112	FM 295, Groom, **S** Biggest Cross, **1 mi S**
110	Lp 40, Rte 66
109	FM 294
108mm	parking area wb, litter barrels
106mm	parking area eb, litter barrels
105	FM 2880, grain silo
98	TX 207 S (from wb), to Claude
96	TX 207 N, to Panhandle, **N** Loves/Subway/dsl/24hr, **S** Conway Inn/cafe, Executive Inn,
89	FM 2161, to Rte 66
87	FM 2373
87mm	picnic areas both lanes, litter barrels
85	Amarillo Blvd, Durrett Rd, access to camping
81	FM 1912, **N** Phillips 66/dsl

INTERSTATE 40 CONT'D

Exit	Services
80	FM 228, **N** [O] AOK RV Park
78	US 287 S (from eb), FM 1258, Pullman Rd, same as 77
77	FM 1258, Pullman Rd, **N** [G] Travel Plaza/dsl/scales/24hr
76	spur 468, **N** [G] *FLYING J*/Denny's/dsl/LP/RV dump/scales/24hr, Shell/dsl, [T] Buffalo Wild Wings, [L] Holiday Inn Express, [O] Mack/Volvo Trucks, tourist info, **S** [G] Speedco, [O] Custom RV Ctr, TX info
75	Lp 335, Lakeside Rd, **N** [G] [LOVES]/McDonald's/dsl/scales/24hr/@, [T] Waffle House, [L] [⌂] Plaza Hotel, Best Value Inn, Super 8, [O] UPS, Peterbilt Trucks, KOA (2mi), **S** [G] Petro/dsl/rest./scales/@, [O] Blue Beacon
74	Whitaker Rd, **N** [T] Big Texan Inn, [O] RV camping, **S** [G] [LOVES]/Subway/dsl/scales/@, TA/Exxon/FoodCourt/dsl/scales/24hr/@, [L] Budget Inn, [O] Blue Beacon
73	Eastern St, Bolton Ave, Amarillo, **N** [G] Shell/dsl, [L] Dean Motel, Motel 6, Value Place, **S** [G] Chevron/dsl, [L] Best Western
72b	Grand St, Amarillo, **N** [G] Shell, [T] Henk's BBQ, [L] Value Inn, [O] Family$, O'Reilly Parts, **S** [G] Murphy USA/dsl, Phillips 66, Valero, [T] Braum's, Chicken Express, McDonald's, Pizza Hut, Sonic, Starbucks, Subway, Taco Villa, Whataburger, [L] Motel 6, [O] URGENT CARE, Advance Parts, Amigo's Foods, AutoZone, BigLots, $General, Walmart, same as 73
72a	Nelson St, **N** [T] Cracker Barrel, [L] La Kiva Hotel, Luxury Inn, Sleep Inn, Super 8, Travelodge, [O] Qtrhorse Museum, **S** [G] Shell/dsl, [L] Camelot Suites, [O] transmissions
71	Ross St, Osage St, Amarillo, **N** [G] Shell/dsl, Valero, [T] A&W/LJ Silver, Burger King, IHOP, KFC, McDonald's, Schlotsky's, Subway, Wienerschnitzel, [L] Comfort Inn, Days Inn, Holiday Inn, Microtel, Quality Inn, **S** [T] Arby's, Denny's, Fiesta Grande Mexican, Sonic, Taco Bell, Wendy's, [L] Hampton Inn, La Quinta, Magnuson Hotel, [O] Chevrolet, Ford Trucks, Hyundai, Sam's Club/gas, USPO
70	I-27 S, US 60 W, US 87, US 287, to Canyon, Lubbock, to downtown Amarillo
69b	Washington St, Amarillo, **S** [T] DQ, Subway, [O] CVS Drug
69a	Crockett St, access to same as 68b
68b	Georgia St, **N** [G] Shell/Subway, [T] Schlotzky's, TGIFriday, [L] Ambassador Hotel, **S** [G] Valero, [T] Baker Bro's Deli, Burger King, Church's Chicken, Coldstone, Denny's, Furr's Café, LJ Silver, Pizza Hut, Red Lobster, Sonic, Starbucks, Taco Bueno, TX Roadhouse, Whataburger, [L] Baymont Inn, Holiday Inn Express, Quality Inn, Travelodge, [O] [H], Hastings Books, Home Depot, Office Depot, Radio Shack, Walgreens
68a	Julian Blvd, Paramount Blvd, **N** [G] Shell, [T] Arby's, Chili's, Nick's Rest., Pizza Hut, Schlotzky's, TGIFriday's, Wendy's, [L] Ambassador Inn, same as 67, **S** [G] Valero, [T] Baker Bro's Deli, Burger King, Furr's Buffet, Kushiyama, Red Lobster, Ruby Tequila's Mexican, TX Roadhouse, [L] Best Value, Comfort Suites, Holiday Inn Express, Motel 6, Super 8, Travelodge, [O] Home Depot, Office Depot
67	Western St, Amarillo, **N** [G] Phillips 66, Shell, [T] Braum's, Burger King, Cattle Call BBQ, Chili's, McDonald's, Rosa's Cafe, Sonic, Taco Bell, Wendy's, **S** [G] Rudy's/BBQ/dsl, Valero, [T] Blue Sky Rest., Cheddar's, IHOP, Olive

Exit	Services
67	Continued Garden, Waffle House, Willy's Grill, [L] Baymont Inn, [O] Discount Tire, Firestone, Michael's, Petco, same 68
66	Bell St, Amarillo, **N** [G] Shell/dsl, Valero/dsl, [L] Fairfield Inn, Quality Inn, Relax Inn, Residence Inn, [O] Harley-Davidson, **S** [T] Doughnut Stop, King & I Chinese, Taco Bueno, [O] Albertson's/Sav-On
65	Coulter Dr, Amarillo, **N** [G] Phillips 66/dsl, [T] Arby's, Carino's Italian, Country Barn BBQ, Golden Corral, Kabuki Japanese, SaltGrass Steaks, Subway, Taco Bell, Waffle House, [L] Courtyard, Days Inn, Executive Inn, La Quinta, [O] [H], Cadillac/Chevrolet, Cavender's Boots, Discount Tire, Dodge, Firestone/auto, Nissan, **S** [G] Chevron/Chicken Express/dsl, Shell, [T] ChinaStar, CiCi's, Hoffbrau Steaks, Jason's Deli, McDonald's, Outback Steaks, Pizza Hut, Wendy's, Whataburger, [L] Hampton Inn, 5th Season Inn, Sleep Inn, [O] AT&T, Goodyear/auto, Verizon
64	Soncy Rd, to Pal Duro Cyn, **N** [T] Famous Dave's BBQ, Furr's Buffet, Jimmy John's, Red Robin, Lin's Chinese, Logan's Roadhouse, Plaza Rest., [L] Comfort Inn, Country Inn&Suites, Drury Inn, Extended Stay America, Hilton Garden, Holiday Inn, Holiday Inn Express, Homewood Suites, [O] USPO, **S** [G] Valero/dsl/24hr, [T] Applebee's, Baker Bros Deli, ChuckeCheese, DQ, Fazoli's, Hooters, Jake's Grill, Marble Slab Creamery, McAlisters Deli, McDonald's, On-the-Border, Pei Wei, Ruby Tequila's Mexican, Starbucks, Subway, [O] Barnes&Noble, Best Buy, Dillard's, $Tree, Ford, Home Depot, JC Penney, Jo-Ann Fabrics, Kohl's, Lincoln/Mercury, Old Navy, PetsMart, Ross, Sears/auto, Target, World Mkt, mall
62b	Lp 40, Amarillo Blvd, **N** [O] Gander Mtn, **S** [O] Sundown RV Resort
62a	Hope Rd, Helium Rd, **S** [O] RV camping, antiques
60	Arnot Rd, **S** [G] [LOVES]/Subway/dsl, [O] Oasis RV Resort/dump
57	RM 2381, Bushland, **N** grain silos, **S** [G] Phillips 66/dsl, [T] BBQ Barn, [O] USPO, RV camping/dump (1mi)
55mm	parking area wb, litter barrels
54	Adkisson Rd
53.5mm	parking area eb, litter barrels
49	FM 809, Wildorado, **S** [G] Crist Fuel/dsl/LP, [L] Royal Inn
42	Everett Rd
37	Lp 40 W, to Vega, **1 mi N** [L] Bonanza Motel, [O] Walnut RV Park, same as 36
36	US 385, Channing, Hereford, **N** [G] Conoco/dsl/24hr, Fina/dsl, Shamrock, [T] Boothill Grill, DQ, Wooden Spoon Cafe, [L] Days Inn, [O] RV Park, **S** [G] Shell/cafe/dsl
35	to Rte 66, to Vega, **N** [L] Best Western, Bonanza Motel (1mi), [O] Walnut RV Park (1mi), same as 36
32mm	picnic area both lanes, litter barrels
28	to Rte 66, Landergin
23	to Adrian
Vega	same as 22
22	TX 214, Adrian, **N** [T] Midpoint Cafe, [O] USPO, auto repair, **S** [G] Phillips 66/dsl/Tommy's Café
18	FM 2858, Gruhlkey Rd, **S** [G] Shell/Stuckey's/cafe/dsl
15	Ivy Rd
13mm	picnic area both lanes, [♿] litter barrels
5.5mm	turnout
0	Lp 40, to Glenrio
0mm	Texas/New Mexico state line, Central/Mountain time zone

E / **W**

AMARILLO

AMARILLO

VEGA

TX

INTERSTATE 44

E
↕
W

Exit	Services
15mm	Texas/Oklahoma state line, Red River
14	Lp 267, E 3rd St, **W** 🅾 Burk RV Park
13	Glendale St, **W** 🍴 Subway, 🅾 Beall's, Family$, Sav-A-Lot Foods, Walmart
12	Burkburnett, **E** 🛏 Hampton Inn, **W** 🅖 Fina/7-11, 🍴 Braum's, Feedlot Rest., Lite Pan Asian, Mazzio's, McDonald's, Whataburger/24hr, 🅾 CarQuest, Chevrolet, Ford
11	FM 3429, Daniels Rd
9mm	picnic area both lanes, 🪑, litter barrels, petwalk
7	East Rd
6	Bacon Switch Rd
5a	FM 3492, Missile Rd, **E** 🍴 El Mejicano Rest., Hunan Chinese, Pizza Hut, 🅾 st patrol, **W** 🅖 Exxon/dsl
5	Access Rd
4	City Loop St
3c	FM 890, **W** 🍴 Cracker Barrel, KFC/Taco Bell, Subway, 🅾 Walmart/gas, vet
3b	sp 325, Sheppard AFB
3a	US 287 N, to Amarillo, **W** 🅖 Shell, 🍴 Carl's Jr, 🛏 Ramada Ltd
2	Maurine St, **E** 🅖 Fina/7-11/dsl, Shell/dsl, 🛏 Best Value Inn, Comfort Inn, Motel 6, Quality Inn, 🅾 Chevrolet, Mazda, **W** 🅖 Fina/7-11, 🍴 China Star, Denny's, El Chico, LJ Silver, Whataburger/24hr, 🛏 Best Western, Candlewood Suites, La Quinta, Super 8, Travelers Inn
1d	US 287 bus, Lp 370, **W** 🅖 Conoco/dsl, 🛏 Travelodge
1c	Texas Tourist Bureau, **E** 🅖 $Saver, **W** 🛏 The Inn
1b	Scotland Park (from nb)
1a	US 277 S, to Abilene
0mm	I-44 begins/ends in Witchita Falls, **1-2 mi S in Wichita Falls S** 🅖 Valero, 🍴 Arby's, Burger King, Carl's Jr, IHOP, McDonald's, Popeye's, Subway, 🛏 Econolodge, Holiday Inn, Howard Johnson, Knights Inn, 🅾 🅷

INTERSTATE 45

N
↕
S

D
A
L
L
A
S

Exit	Services
286	to I-35 E, to Denton. I-45 begins/ends in Dallas.
285	Bryan St E, US 75 N
284b a	I-30, W to Ft Worth, E to Texarkana, access to 🅷
283b	Pennsylvania Ave, to MLK Blvd, **E** 🅖 Shamrock
283a	Lamar St
281	Overton St (from sb), **W** 🅖 Chevron
280	Illinois Ave, Linfield St, **E** 🛏 Star Motel, **W** 🅖 Shell/dsl
279b a	Lp 12
277	Simpson Stuart Rd, **W** 🅾 to Paul Quinn Coll
276b a	I-20, W to Ft Worth, E to Shreveport
275	TX 310 N (from nb, no re-entry)
274	Dowdy Ferry Rd, Hutchins, **E** 🅖 Exxon/Subway/dsl, Shell/McDonald's/dsl, 🛏 Gold Inn, La Quinta, Super 8, **W** 🍴 DQ, Jack-in-the-Box, Whataburger
273	Wintergreen Rd
272	Fulghum Rd, **E** 🅖 ♥Loves/Carl's Jr/dsl/scales/24hr, **W weigh sta, both lanes**
271	Pleasant Run Rd
270	Belt Line Rd, to Wilmer, **E** 🅖 Texaco/Pizza Inn/dsl, **W** 🅖 Exxon/Sonic/dsl, Shell/Church's/Subway/dsl, 🅾 $General
269	Mars Rd
268	Malloy Bridge Rd
267	Frontage Rd

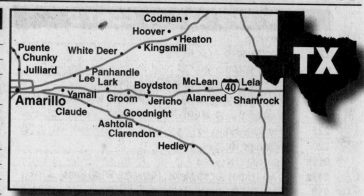

E
N
N
I
S

Exit	Services
266	FM 660, **E** 🍴 Jack-in-the-Box, **W** 🅖 Shamrock/dsl, 🍴 DQ
265	Lp 45, Ferris, nb only
263a b	Lp 561
262	frontage rd
260	Lp 45, **E** 🍴 Trailor RV Park, **W** 🅖 Shell/Sonic/dsl
259	FM 813, FM 878, Jefferson St, **W** 🅾 Goodyear
258	Lp 45, Palmer, **E** 🅖 Exxon/Subway/dsl/scales/24hr, 🅾 golf, **W** 🛏 Palmer Motel
255	FM 879, Garrett, **E** 🅖 Exxon/dsl
253	Lp 45, **W** 🅖 Shell/Subway/dsl
251b	TX 34, Ennis, **E** 🅖 Fina/dsl, Shell/dsl, 🍴 Bubba's BBQ, McDonald's, 🛏 Baymont Inn, Comfort Suites, Days Inn, Holiday Inn Express, La Quinta, 🅾 Ford, **W** 🅖 Chevron/dsl, Exxon/dsl/24hr, Murphy USA/dsl, 🍴 Braum's, Broster Chicken, Burger King, Chili's, Denny's, DQ, Domino's, Grand Buffet, IHOP, Jack-in-the-Box, KFC, Pizza Hut, Sonic, Starbucks, Subway, Taco Bell, Taco Cabana, Vero Pizza, Waffle House, Wall Chinese, Wendy's, Whataburger/24hr, 🛏 Ennis Inn, Quality Inn, 🅾 🅷, AutoZone, Beall's, Chevrolet, Chrysler/Dodge/Jeep, $Tree, Ford/Mercury, Radio Shack, Walmart, RV camping
251a	Creechville Rd, FM 1181, **W** 🅷
249	FM 85, Ennis, **E** 🛏 Budget Inn, **W** 🅖 Exxon/Subway, 🅾 Blue Beacon, 🅾 repair
247	US 287 N, to Waxahatchie
246	FM 1183, Alma, **W** 🅖 Chevron
244	FM 1182
243	Frontage Rd
242	Calhoun St, Rice
239	FM 1126, **W** 🅖 45 Kwik Stop
238	FM 1603, **E** 🅖 Exxon/rest/dsl/24hr, 🅾 Casita RV Trailers
237	Frontage Rd
235b	Lp I-45 (from sb), to Corsicana
235a	Frontage Rd
232	Roane Rd, E 5th Ave
231	TX 31, Corsicana, **E** 🅖 Phillips 66/dsl, 🍴 Jack-in-the-Box, 🛏 Best Western, Colonial Inn, La Quinta, 🅾 Buick/Cadillac/Chevrolet/GMC, **W** 🅖 Chevron, Exxon/Subway/dsl, 🍴 Bill's Fried Chicken, DQ, McDonald's, 🛏 Comfort Inn, 🅾 🅷, Chrysler/Dodge/Jeep, Ford/Lincoln/Mercury, to Navarro Coll
229	US 287, Palestine, **E** 🅖 Exxon/Wendy's/dsl, Shell/dsl/24hr, 🍴 Chili's, Collin St Bakery, Denny's, Russell Stover Candies, Sonic, Taco Bell, 🛏 Hampton Inn, Holiday Inn Express, 🅾 Gander Mtn, Home Depot, Office Depot, VF Outlet/famous brands, **W** 🍴 Waffle House, 🛏 Corsicana Inn, Motel 6, Royal Inn
228b	Lp 45 (exits left from nb), Corsicana, **2 mi W** services

= gas = food = lodging = other Copyright 2012 - The Next Exit®

INTERSTATE 45 CONT'D

Exit	Services
228b	Continued in Corsicana
228a	15th St, Corsicana, **W** Scion/Toyota
225	FM 739, Angus, **E** Conoco/dsl, to Chambers Reservoir, RV park, **W** Camper Depot
221	Frontage Rd
220	Frontage Rd
219b	Frontage Rd
219a	TX 14 (from sb), to Mexia, Richland, **W** Shell
218	FM 1394 (from nb), Richland, **W**. Shell
217mm	**rest area both lanes, full facilities, ,, litter barrels, vending, petwalk**
213	TX 75 S, FM 246, to Wortham, **W** Chevron, Exxon/dsl
211	FM 80, to Streetman, Kirvin
206	FM 833, **3 mi W on frntge rd** I-45 RV Park
198	FM 27, to Wortham, **E** Shell/Pitt BBQ, Gilberto's Mexican, La Quinta, , Cedar Grove RV Park (3mi), **W** Exxon, Loves/Burger King/dsl/scales/24hr, Budget Inn, I-45 RV Park (4mi)
197	US 84, Fairfield, **E** Chevron/dsl, Exxon/dsl, Shell/dsl, DQ, Jack-in-the-Box, McDonald's, Ponte's Diner, Sam's Rest., Sonic, Subway/Texas Burger, Days Inn, Holiday Inn Express, Super 8, Brookshire Foods/gas, Chevrolet, Chrysler/Dodge/Jeep, Fred's Store, Hyundai, **W** Exxon/dsl, Shell/dsl, Texaco/dsl, Dalia's Mexican, I-45 Rest., KFC/Taco Bell, Pizza Hut, Sammy's Rest., Best Value Inn, Regency Inn, Ace Hardware, Ford
189	TX 179, to Teague, **E** Exxon/Chester's/dsl, Citgo/Shirley's Cafe/dsl
187mm	**picnic area both lanes, tables, litter barrels**
180	TX 164, to Groesbeck
178	US 79, Buffalo, **E** Gilliam's/dsl, Shell/dsl, Subway/Texas Burger, Brookshire Foods/gas, Family$, **W** Exxon/Church's/Pizza Inn/dsl/scales, Mobil/dsl, Shamrock/dsl/24hr, Dickey's BBQ, DQ, Longhorn BBQ, Pitt Grill/24hr, Rancho Mexican, Sonic, Best Western, Comfort Inn, Economy Inn, Hampton Inn
175mm	Bliss Creek
166mm	**weigh sta sb**
164	TX 7, Centerville, **E** Chevron, Shell/Woody's BBQ/dsl, Country Cousins BBQ, Subway/Texas Burger, Days Inn, **W** Exxon/24hr, Shell/Woody's BBQ/dsl, DQ, Jack-in-the-Box, Roble's Mexican
160mm	**picnic area sb, tables, litter barrels, hist marker, accessible**
159mm	Boggy Creek
156	FM 977, to Leona, **W** Exxon/dsl
155mm	**picnic area nb, , litter barrels, accessible**
152	TX OSR, to Normangee, **W** Chevron/dsl, Yellow Rose RV Park/café
146	TX 75
142	US 190, TX 21, Madisonville, **E** Exxon/BBQ/dsl, Shell/Buc-ees, Best Western, Carefree Inn, **W** Chevron/Church's, Shell/Subway/24hr, Jack-in-the-Box, McDonald's, Pizza Hut, Sonic, Taco Bell, Texas Burger, Budget Motel, Western Lodge, , Ford, Toyota
136	spur 67, **E** Home on the Range RV camping/LP (3mi)
132	FM 2989

124mm	**rest area both lanes, full facilities, ,, litter barrels, vending, petwalk**
123	FM 1696
118	TX 75, **E** Shell/Hitchin Post/dsl/24hr/@, Texas Prison Museum, truckwash, **W** /Wendy's/dsl/scales/24hr, Rodeo Mexican
116	US 190, TX 30, **E** Phillips 66, Valero/dsl, Arby's, Bandera Grill, Church's, El Chico, Mr Gatti's, Golden Corral, Imperial Garden Chinese, Jct Steaks, McDonald's, Popeye's, Schlotzsky's, Sonic, Whataburger, Days Inn, EconoLodge, Holiday Inn Express, La Quinta, Motel 6, , , AutoZone, Brookshire Foods/gas, Buick/Cadillac/Chevrolet/GMC, Cavander's Boots, CVS Drug, Family$, Firestone/auto, Hastings Books, NAPA, O'Reilly Parts, Walgreens, vet, **W** Exxon/dsl, Murphy USA/dsl, Shell/24hr, Bob Luby's Sea Burger King, Chili's, CiCi's, Denny's, Grand Buffet, IHOP, Jack-in-the-Box, KFC, Pizza Hut, Starbucks, Subway, Taco Bell, Tinsley's Chicken, Wing Stop, Guesthouse Inn, AT&T, Chrysler/Dodge/Jeep, Discount Tire, $Tree, GNC, Home Depot, JC Penney, Kroger, Office Depot, Radio Shack, Target, Walmart, USPO
114	FM 1374, **E** Exxon/dsl, Shell, DQ, Margaritas Rest., Gateway Inn, Super 8, **W** Citgo/dsl, Valero/dsl, Country Inn Steaks, Best Value Inn, Comfort Suites, , , Ford/Lincoln/Mercury, Hyundai
113	TX 19 (from nb), Huntsville
112	TX 75, **E** Citgo, Baker Motel, Houston Statue, to Sam Houston St U, museum
109	Park 40, **W** to Huntsville SP
105mm	picnic area both lanes, tables, litter barrels
103	FM 1374/1375 (from sb), to New Waverly
102	FM 1374/1375, TX 150 (from nb), to New Waverly, **E** Valero/dsl (1mi), **W** Waverly Rest.
101mm	**weigh sta nb**
98	TX 75, Danville Rd, Shepard Hill Rd, **E** Convenience RV Park/repair
95	(from nb, no return), Calvary, Longstreet Rd
94	FM 1097, Longstreet Rd, to Willis, **E** Jack-in-the-Box, Mr Gatti, Quizno's, Sonic, AutoZone, $General, Kroger/gas, **W** Chevron/Popeye's, Shell/Taco Bell/dsl/24hr, McDonald's, Subway, Best Western
92	FM 830, Seven Coves Dr, **W** Omega Farms RV Park, RV Park on the Lake (3mi), Thousand Trails Resort
91	League Line Rd, **E** Chevron/McDonald's, Mamma Juanita's Mexican, Subway, Waffle House, Wendy's, Comfort Inn, La Quinta, Supreme Inn, Conroe Outlets/famous brands, **W** Citgo, Shell/Jack-in-the-Box, Cracker Barrel
90	FM 3083, Teas Nursery Rd, Montgomery Co Park, **E** Exxon/dsl, Applebee's, Buck's Burgers, Buffalo Wild Wings, Popeye's, Fairfield Inn, AT&T, Kohl's, Old Navy, Petsmart, Ross, TJ Maxx, convention center (4mi), **W** Olive Garden, Subway, ValuePlace Inn, JC Penney
88	Lp 336, to Cleveland, Navasota, **E** Mobil/Chester's/dsl, Valero/dsl, Arby's, A&W/LJ Silver, Burger King, Chili's, China Delight, Denny's, Domino's, Los Cucos Mexican, Marble Slab Creamery, Margarita's Mexican, McDonald's, Papa John's, Pizza Hut, Quizno's, Sonic, TX Roadhouse, Whataburger, Wing Stop, Hampton Inn, Holiday Inn Express, Advance Parts, Buick, CVS Drug, Discount Tire, $Tree, GNC, HEB Foods/gas, Hobby Lobby,

TX

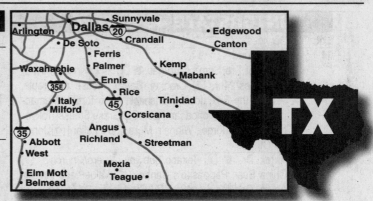

INTERSTATE 45 CONT'D

Exit	Services
88	**Continued**
	Just Brakes, Kroger/gas, Michael's, Walgreens, vet, **W** 🅖 Chevron/24hr, 🍴 Blackeyed Pea, Casa Ole Mexican, El Bosque Mexican, KFC, Ryan's, Subway, 🅞 Hancock Fabrics, Lowe's Whse, 99Cent Store, PetCo, Sam's Club/gas, Tuesday Morning, Walmart
87	TX 105, Conroe, **E** 🍴 Burger King, Jack-in-the-Box, Kettle, Luther's BBQ, McDonald's, Outback Steaks, Popeye's, Sonic, Saltgrass Steaks, Taco Bell, Tast of China, 🛏 Super 8, 🅞 🅷, CVS Drug, $General, Firestone/auto, Hyundai, Kia, NTB, **W** 🅖 Exxon, 🍴 Chick-fil-A, Coney Island, Luby's, Panda Express, Panera Bread, Quizno's, Schlotzsky's, Shogun Japanese, Smoothie King, Starbucks, Subway, Taco Bell, Taco Bueno, Whataburger, 🅞 Best Buy, Buick/GMC, Hastings Books, Home Depot, Office Depot, Radio Shack, Target, Tiremaxx
85	FM 2854, Gladstell St, **E** 🅖 Citgo/dsl, 🛏 Motel 6, 🅞 🅷, Honda, Nissan, **W** 🅖 Shell/dsl, Valero, 🍴 IHOP, 🛏 Baymont Inn, Days Inn, 🅞 Cadillac, Chrysler/Dodge/Jeep, Fun Country RV Ctr, Mazda, Scion/Toyota
84	TX 75 N, Frazier St, **E** 🅖 Chevron, 🛏 Corporate Inn, Ramada Ltd, 🅞 Ford/Mercury, U-Haul, **W** 🅖 Shell, 🍴 China Buffet, Incredible Pizza, Subway, Taco Cabana, Waffle House, 🅞 🅷, Albertson's, Discount Tire, K-Mart, Kroger
83	Crighton Rd, Camp Strake Rd
82	River Plantation Dr
82mm	San Jacinto River
81	FM 1488, to Hempstead, Magnolia, **E** 🅖 Citgo, **W** 🅖 Valero/Subway, 🅞 CamperLand RV Ctr
80	Needham Rd (from sb)
79	TX 242, Needham, **E** 🅖 Shell/McDonald's, 🍴 Mama Juanita's Mexican, Quizno's, 🛏 Best Western, 🅞 Batteries+, **W** 🅖 Chevron, Murphy USA/dsl, 🍴 Adobe Cafe, Arby's, Burger King, ChuckeCheese, Domino's, Outback Steaks, Popeye's, Sonic, Subway, Taco Cabana, Wendy's, Whataburger, Willie's Grill, Wings'N More, 🛏 Country Suites, Fairfield Inn, TownPlace Suites, 🅞 🅷, BMW/Mini, Firestone/auto, Kohl's, Lowe's Whse, Walgreens, Walmart
78	Needham Rd (from sb), Tamina Rd, access to same as 77
77	Woodlands Pkwy, Robinson, Chateau Woods, **E** 🅖 Chevron, Conoco/dsl, 🍴 Babin's Sea🍴 Buca Italian, Buffalo Wild Wings, Church's, Chuy's, Hooters, Lupe Tortilla, Melting Pot, Pancho's Mexican, Pappa's BBQ, Pappadeaux, PeiWei, Pizza Hut, Red Robin, Saltgrass Steaks, Subway, Tom's Steaks, 🛏 Best Value Inn, Budget Inn, 🅞 Discount Tire, Home Depot, Jo-Ann Fabrics, Michael's, NTB, Office Depot, Old Navy, Petsmart, Sam's Club/gas, SteinMart, Walgreens, funpark, vet, **W** 🅖 Exxon, Shell, Texaco, Valero/dsl, 🍴 A&W/KFC, Blackeyed Pea, Cane's, Chick-fil-A, Chili's, Chipotle Mexican, Culver's, Denny's, El Bosque Mexican, Guadalajara Mexican, Jack-in-the-Box, Jason's Deli, Jimmy John's, Kabab House, Kirby's Steakhouse, La Madeliene, Landry's Sea🍴 Luby's, Macaroni Grill, Olive Garden, Red Lobster, Sweet Tomatos, TGIFriday's, 🛏 Comfort Suites, Days Inn, Drury Inn, Hampton Inn, Homewood Suites, La Quinta, Marriott, Shenandoa Inn, 🅞 🅷, Best Buy, Dillard's, HEB Foods, Macy's, Marshall's, Sears, Ross, Target, World Mkt, auto repair, mall
76	Research Forest Dr, Tamina Rd, **E** 🅖 Chevron/dsl, 🍴 LJ Silver, Pappa's BBQ, 🅞 URGENT CARE, Firestone/auto, JustBrakes, Tiremaxx, vet, **W** 🅖 Shell, 🍴 Carrabba's, Denny's, El Chico, IHOP, Jack-in-the-Box, Kyoto Japanese, Macaroni Grill, Olive Garden, TGIFriday's, Tortuga Mexican, 🛏 Crossland Suites, Courtyard, Residence Inn, 🅞 Goodyear/auto, JC Penney, Sears/auto, Woodlands Mall
73	Rayford Rd, Sawdust Rd, **E** 🅖 Conoco, Shell, Valero, 🍴 Hartz Chicken, Jack-in-the-Box, McDonald's, Popeye's, Sonic, Taqueria Arandas, Thomas BBQ, 🛏 Holiday Inn Express, La Quinta, 🅞 Aamco, AutoZone, O'Reilly Parts, U-Haul, **W** 🅖 Mobil/dsl, Shell, Texaco, 🍴 Carrabba's, Cici's Pizza, Grand Buffet, IHOP, Subway, Taipei Chinese, Tortuga, 🛏 Extended Stay America, Red Roof Inn, Super 8, 🅞 Brake Check, Discount Tire, GNC, Goodyear/auto, Harley-Davidson, HEB Foods, Kroger, Walgreens
72a	Spring Crossing Dr, **W** 🅖 Texaco/dsl
72b	to Hardy Toll Rd from sb
70b	Spring-Stuebner Rd, **E** Vaughn RV Ctr
70a	FM 2920, to Tomball, **E** 🅖 Exxon, Murphy USA/dsl, Rudy's BBQ/dsl, Shell, 🍴 Arby's, Chick-fil-A, El Palenque Mexican, Godfather's Pizza, Golden Jade Chinese, Hartz Chicken, McDonald's, Pizza Hut, Subway, Quizno's, Taco Cabana, Wendy's, Whataburger, 🅞 BigLots, $General, $Tree, Kohl's, Kroger, Lincoln/Mercury, Michael's, O'Reilly Parts, Radio Shack, Ross, Scion/Toyota, Vaughn's RV Ctr, Walmart, transmissions, **W** 🅖 Chevron, RaceTrac, Texaco, 🍴 Burger King, Taco Bell, Tuscan Sun Coffee, Whataburger/24hr, 🛏 Travelodge, 🅞 Ford, U-Haul
68	Holzwarth Rd, Cypress Wood Dr, **E** 🅖 Texaco/dsl, 🍴 Burger King, Pizza Hut/Taco Bell, Sonic, Wendy's, 🅞 Albertson's, AT&T, Gander Mtn, GNC, Tiremaxx, **W** 🅖 Chevron/dsl, 🍴 Cheddar's, Denny's, Jack-in-the-Box, Lenny's Subs, Pizza Hut, Popeye's, Starbucks, 🛏 Motel 6, Spring Lodge, 🅞 Advance Parts, Best Buy, Chrysler/Dodge/Jeep, Firestone/auto, Ford, Home Depot, Lowe's Whse, Office Depot, PetCo, Target, Walgreens
66	FM 1960, to Addicks, **E** 🅖 Chevron, RaceTrac, Shell, 🍴 Jack-in-the-Box, Sonic, Subway, TX Roadhouse, 🅞 Acura, AT&T, BMW, Chevrolet, Honda, Mercedes, Mistubishi, Petsmart, Radio Shack, Subaru, **W** 🅖 Exxon, Shell/dsl/24hr, Texaco/dsl, Valero, 🍴 Cici's Pizza, Hooters, Jack-in-the-Box, James Coney Island, McDonald's, Outback Steaks, Panda Express, Red Lobster, Subway, Taco Bell, Taquiera Arendas, 🛏 Baymont Inn, Comfort Suites, Fairfield Inn, Hampton Inn, Studio 6, 🅞 🅷, Audi, Infiniti, Jaguar/LandRover, Lexus, NTB, U-Haul, mall
64	Richey Rd, **E** 🍴 Atchafalaya River Café, 🛏 Best Value Inn, Holiday Inn, Lexington Suites, Ramada, 🅞 CarMax,

N
↕
S

C O N R O E

H O U S T O N

TX

🛢 = gas ⑪ = food ⌂ = lodging ⊙ = other Copyright 2012 - The Next Ex

INTERSTATE 45 CONT'D

Exit	Services
64	**Countinued** Discount Tire, Sam's Club/gas, W 🛢 ⊘FLYING J/Denny's/dsl/scales/24hr, ⑪ Cracker Barrel, House of Creole, Jack-in-the-Box, Joe's Crabshack, Lupe Tortilla, Mamacita's Mexican, Michoacan Rest, SaltGrass Steaks, Tokyohana, Whataburger, Wings'n More, Zio's Italian, ⊙ Jones RV Ctr
63	Airtex Dr, E 🛢 Texaco/Subway, Valero/Church's, ⑪ China Bear, Pappasito's Cantina, ⌂ ValuePlace Inn, ⊙ Acura, Cadillac, LoneStar RV Ctr, Nissan, W ⑪ Cracker Barrel, Jack-in-the-Box, Whataburger, ⌂ Best Western, Guesthouse Suites
62	Rankin Rd, Kuykendahl, E ⌂ Best Classic Inn, Scottish Inn, W 🛢 Chevron/McDonald's, RaceTrac, Shell, ⑪ Luby's, Shiply Donuts, ⌂ Palace Inn, Studio+, SunSuites, ⊙ Buick/GMC, Demontrono RV Ctr, Hummer, Hyundai, Kia, Lamborghini, Mercedes, Volvo, VW
61	Greens Rd, E 🛢 Texaco, ⑪ Brown Sugar's BBQ, IHOP, Imperial Dragon, Luna's, ⌂ Knights Inn, ⊙ Dillard's, JC Penney, Macy's, Sears/auto, mall, W ⑪ Burger King, Luby's, Subway, ⌂ Baymont Inn, Comfort Inn, ⊙ Burlington Coat Factory, $General, Kroger
60c	Beltway E, 60 (b a from nb), TX 525, E 🛢 Shell, ⑪ Burger King, China Border, Denny's, Domino's, Mambo Sea⑪ Michoacan Rest, Moon Palace Chinese, Pizza Hut, Taco Cabana, ⊙ Chrysler/Dodge/Jeep, Family$, Firestone/auto, Honda, Office Depot, W ⑪ Pappas Sea⑪ ⊙ U-Haul
59	FM 525, West Rd, E ⑪ A&W, LJ Silver, McDonald's, ⊙ CarQuest, Fiesta Foods, W 🛢 Exxon, Shell, ⑪ Chili's, Jalisco's Mexican, Panda Express, Papa John's Pizza, Quizno's, Starbucks, Subway, Taco Bell, Taco Cabana, Wendy's, Whataburger, Wing Stop, ⌂ Best Value Inn, Best Western, ⊙ AT&T, Best Buy, Discount Tire, $Tree, Fry's Electronics, Home Depot, Office Depot, NTB, PepBoys, Radio Shack, Ross, Verizon, Walmart
57	(b a from nb), TX 249, Gulf Bank Rd, Tomball, E 🛢 Mobil/dsl, Texaco/Church's, ⑪ Wings'N More, ⊙ Discount Tire, W 🛢 Shell, ⑪ Sonic, Tombico Sea⑪ ⌂ Greenchase Motel, La Quinta, Quality Inn, ⊙ CVS Drug, Family$, Giant$, Mas Club/dsl
56	Canino Rd, E 🛢 Taj Inn Suites, W 🛢 Shell, Texaco, ⑪ Capt D's, Denny's, Jack-in-the-Box, KFC, Luby's, ⌂ Best Value Inn, EconoLodge, Gulfwind Motel, Passport Inn, ⊙ Ford, Isuzu, USPO
55	(b a from nb), Little York Rd, Parker Rd, E 🛢 Chevron, Texaco, ⑪ Burger King, China Panda, McDonald's, Whataburger, ⊙ Advance Parts, FoodTown, W 🛢 Shell, ⑪ Popeye's, ⌂ Symphony Inn, ⊙ Ⓗ, Family$, Walgreens
54	Tidwell Rd, E 🛢 Exxon, ⑪ Aunt Bea's Rest, Chacho's Mexican, China Border, Frenchys, Pancho's Mexican, Thomas BBQ, Wings'N More, ⊙ BigLots, CVS Drug, Discount Tire, Radio Shack, W 🛢 Chevron, ⑪ McDonald's, ⌂ Guest Motel, Scottish Inn, Southwind Motel, Town Inn, ⊙ U-Haul
53	Airline Dr, E 🛢 Citgo, ⑪ Popeye's, ⊙ Fiesta Foods/drug, W 🛢 Citgo, Shell, ⑪ Little Mexico, Wendy's, ⌂ Luxury Inn, Palace Inn
52	(b a from nb), Crosstimbers Rd, E 🛢 Shell/dsl, ⑪

Exit	Services
52	Continued Burger King, China Star, CiCi's, IHOP, Jack-in-the-Box, James Coney Island, KFC, Pappas BBQ, Pizza Hut, Sonic, Subway, Taco Bell, ⊙ AT&T, Discount Tire, $Tree, Firestone, Marshall's, Ross, mall, W 🛢 Chevron/dsl, ⑪ Whataburger/24hr, ⌂ Texan Inn
51	I-610
50	(b a from nb), Patton St, Calvacade St, Link Rd, E 🛢 Citgo, Exxon, ▬Love's/Wendy's/dsl/scales/24hr, Shell, ⌂ Best Value Inn, Luxury Inn, W ⌂ Astro Inn, ⊙ NAPA
49b	N Main St, Houston Ave, E 🛢 Citgo, ⑪ Casa Grande Mexican, ⌂ Best Value Inn, Luxury Inn, W 🛢 Exxon/dsl, ⑪ Domino's, McDonald's, Subway, Whataburger/24hr, ⌂ Sleep Inn, ⊙ O'Reilly Parts
48b a	I-10, E to Beaumont, W to San Antonio
47d	Dallas St, Pierce St (from sb), E ⊙ Ⓗ
47c	McKinney St (from sb, exits left)
47b	Houston Ave, Memorial Dr, downtown, W ⌂ Double Tree Hotel
47a	Allen Pkwy (exits left from sb)
46b a	US 59, N to Cleveland, S to Victoria, E 🛢 Chevron, ⑪ BBQ, W 🛢 Texaco, ⑪ McDonald's, Taco Bell, ⊙ BMW
45b a	South St, Scott St, Houston, E 🛢 Shell, ⊙ Firestone, to TSU
44	Cullen Blvd, Houston, E 🛢 Valero/dsl, to U of Houston
43b	Telephone Rd, Houston, E ⑪ Luby's
43a	Tellepsen St, E ⑪ Luby's, ⌂ Day's Inn, W ⊙ U of Houston
41b	US 90A, Broad St, S Wayside Dr, E 🛢 Phillips 66, ⑪ La Terraza, ⌂ Day's Inn, Red Carpet Inn, W 🛢 Chevron, Exxon, Mobil, ⑪ Jack-in-the-Box, McDonald's, Monterrey Mexican, Subway, Taquiera Mexican, Wings and More, ⊙ $Tree, K-Mart, Sellars Foods
41a	Woodridge Dr, E 🛢 Shell, ⑪ Bonnie's Sea ⑪ Denny's, McDonald's, Pappa's Seafood House, Schlotsky's, W 🛢 Citgo, ⑪ BoneBreak BBQ, IHOP, Pappas BBQ, Sonic, Subway, Whataburger, Wendy's, ⊙ Chevrolet/Buick, Dillard's, HEB Food/gas, Home Depot, Lowe's Whse, Marshall's, Office Depot, Old Navy, Radio Shack, Ross, mall
40c	I-610 W
40b	I-610 E, to Pasadena
40a	Frontage Rd (from nb)
39	Park Place Blvd, Broadway Blvd, E 🛢 Shell, W ⑪ Kelley's Rest., Los Campos, ⊙ Chevrolet, Dodge, Family$
38b	Howard Dr, Bellfort Dr (from sb), E 🛢 Shell, ⑪ Jack-in-the-Box, Wendy's, W 🛢 Citgo, ⑪ Chilo's Sea⑪ ⌂ Camelot Inn, Mustang Inn, Palace Inn, Passport Inn, ⊙ HEB Food/gas, PepBoys
38	TX 3, Monroe Rd, E 🛢 Chevron, Shell, Valero, ⑪ DQ, Jack-in-the-Box, Luther's BBQ, Ninfa, Wendy's, ⊙ Firestone, NTB, U-Haul, W 🛢 Chevron/dsl, Texaco/dsl, ⑪ Luby's, Manny's Sea⑪ Pappa's BBQ, ⌂ Best Western, Holiday Inn Express, Quality Inn, Smile Inn, ⊙ Firestone, Kottman Transmissions, Radio Shack, Suzuki, U-Haul
36	College Ave, Airport Blvd, E 🛢 Shamrock, Shell, ⑪ DQ, Waffle House, ⌂ Best Value, Day's Inn, Fairfield Inn, Rodeway Inn, ⊙ RV Ctr, W 🛢 Exxon, Mobil, Shell, Valero, ⑪ Church's Chicken, Denny's, Taco Cabana, ⌂ AmeriSuites, Baymont Inn, Comfort Inn, Country Inn, Courtyard, Drury Inn, Hampton Inn, Holiday Inn Express, La Quinta, Marriott/Damon's, Motel 6, Red Roof Inn, Regency Inn, SpringHill Suites, Super 8, Travel Inn, ⊙ Discount Tire

H O U S T O N

TX

INTERSTATE 45 CONT'D

Exit	Services
35	Edgebrook Dr, **E** 📳 Chevron, Exxon, RaceTrac, 🍴 Burger King, Aranda's Bakery, Jack-in-the-Box, KFC, Popeye's, Subway, Taco Bell, Taquiera Arrandas, Waffle House, 🛏 ☍ Inn, ⊙, Family$, Fiesta Foods, Firestone, Office Depot, Terry Vaugn's RV Ctr, Walgreens, **W** 📳 Exxon, Shell, Circle K, 🍴 James Coney Island, KFC, LJ Silver, McDonald's, Pizza Hut, Whataburger, ⊙ Academy Sports, Honda, NTB
34	S Shaver Rd, **E** 📳 Conoco, RaceWay, 🍴 McDonald's, 🛏 Island Suites, ⊙ Acura, Honda, Kia, GMC, Toyota, Vaughn's RV Ctr, **W** 📳 Chevron/24hr, Exxon, Mobil, 🍴 Arby's, Burger King, Pancho's Mexican, Wendy's, 🛏 Scottish Inn, ⊙ Best Buy, Discount Tire, $Tree, Honda, Jo-Ann Fabrics, Macy's, Nissan, NTB, Target, Walmart/gas
33	Fuqua St, **E** 📳 Shamrock, 🍴 Chili's, Fuddrucker's, Las Haciendas, Luby's, Olive Garden, Schlotzky's, TGIFriday, 🛏 Studio 6, Sun Suites, ⊙ Chrysler/Jeep, Dodge, Ford, Honda, Hyundai, Isuzu, Lincoln/Mercury, **W** 🍴 Blackeyed Pea, Boston Mkt, Bouderaux's Cajun Kitchen, Casa Mexican, Casa Ole, CiCi's Pizza, Fox&Hound, Golden Corral, Gringo's Mexican, IHOP, Joe's Crabshack, Outback Steaks, Steak&Ale, Subway, Taco Cabana, Taco Bell, TX Cattle Steaks, Whataburger, ⊙ BigLots, CarMax, Chevrolet, Firestone, JC Penney, Kroger, Macy's, Old Navy, Radio Shack, Ross, Sam's Club, Subaru, Tire Station, mall
32	Sam Houston Tollway
31	FM 2553, Scarsdale Blvd, **W** 📳 Shell, ⊙ Chevrolet, Mitsubishi
30	FM 1959, Dixie Farm Rd, Ellington Field, **E** 📳 Shell/dsl, 🍴 Subway, 🛏 Howard Johnson, ⊙ H, Dodge, Infiniti, **W** 📳 RaceWay, Shell/dsl, 🍴 McDonald's, Popeye's, 🛏 Palace Inn, ⊙ Lonestar RV, VW
29	FM 2351, Clear Lake City Blvd, to Clear Lake RA, Friendswood
27	El Dorado Blvd, **E** 📳 Shell, 🍴 DQ, **W** 🍴 Sonic, Texas Roadhouse, Whataburger, ⊙ Cadillac, Hummer, Kohl's, Lexus, Radio Shack, Sam's Club/gas, Walmart
26	Bay Area Blvd, **E** 🍴 Red Lobster, TGI Friday's, ⊙ H, Barnes&Noble, Lowe's Whse, Michael's, Old Navy, Oshman's Sports, Steinmart, to Houston Space Ctr, **W** 📳 Shell, 🍴 Chick-fil-A, Denny's/24hr, McDonald's, Olive Garden, 🛏 Best Western, ⊙ Dillard's, Macy's, Office Depot, Sears/auto, Target, U of Houston, mall
25	FM 528, NASA rd 1, **E** 📳 Conoco, Shamrock, Texaco, 🍴 Cheddar's, Chili's, Hooters, IHOP, Las Haciendas Mexican, Pappasito's Cantina, Saltgrass Steaks, Waffle House, Vito's, 🛏 Best Western, Comfort Suites, La Quinta, Motel 6, ⊙ H, Audi, Best Buy, Big Lots, Fry's Electronics, Home Depot, Honda, Mazda, Volvo, **W** 🍴 Hot Wok Chinese, Pappa's, Subway, ⊙ Fiesta Foods, Radio Shack, Tuesday Morning
23	FM 518, League City, **E** 📳 RaceWay, Shell/dsl, 🍴 Applebee's, Burger King, Jack-in-the-Box, KFC, Little Caesar's, Pepper's Beef, Sonic, Subway, Sudie's Sea🍴 ⊙ Academy Sports, BMW, Just Brakes, Kroger, Mercedes, Walgreens, **W** 📳 Chevron, Exxon/24hr, Mobil, 🍴 Cracker Barrel, Hartz Chicken, McDonald's, Taco Bell, Waffle House, Wendy's, 🛏 Super 8, ⊙ Discount Tire, Space Ctr RV Park, U-Haul

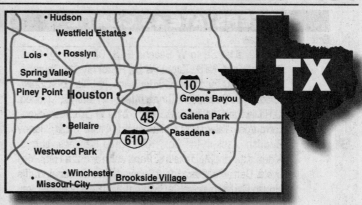

Exit	Services
22	Calder Dr, Brittany Bay Blvd, **E** ⊙ Nissan, Toyota, camping, **W** ⊙ Holiday World RV Ctr
20	FM 646, Santa Fe, Bacliff, **E** 🍴 Denny's, Panda Express, Whataburger, ⊙ Best Buy, Home Depot, JC Penney, Lowes Whse, Radio Shack, Walmart, **W** 📳 Valero/dsl, 🍴 Chili's, Subway, Taco Cabana, ⊙ HEB Foods/gas, Kohl's, PetCo
19	FM 517, Dickinson Rd, Hughes Rd, **E** 🍴 Jack-in-the-Box, Monterey Mexico, Pizza Inn, ⊙ Adventure Out RV Park, Buick/GMC/Subaru, CVS Drug, Family$, Food King, Radio Shack, **W** 📳 Mobil, Shell/dsl, 🍴 Burger King, Dickenson's Sea🍴 Heartbreak Grill, KFC, McDonald's, Pizza Hut, Sonic, Subway, Taco Bell, Wendy's, Whataburger/24hr, 🛏 Day's Inn, El Rancho Motel, ⊙ Ford, Kroger, Subaru, Target, Walgreens
17	Holland Rd, **W** to Gulf Greyhound Park
16	FM 1764 E (from sb), Texas City, same as 15
15	FM 2004, FM 1764, Hitchcock, **E** 📳 Shell, 🍴 Gringo's Cafe, Jack-in-the-Box, Olive Garden, Popeye's, Ryan's, Uncle Chan's, 🛏 Best Western, Fairfield Inn, Hampton Inn, Holiday Inn Express, ⊙ H, Chevrolet/Toyota/RV Ctr, Dillard's, JC Penney, Lowe's Whse, Macy's, Sam's Club/gas, Sears/auto, mall, **W** 📳 Mobil/Subway, Shell, 🍴 IHOP, Sonic, Waffle House, Wendy's, Whataburger, 🛏 Super 8, ⊙ Chevrolet/RV Ctr, Gulf Greyhound Park, Radio Shack, Toyota/Scion, Walmart/gas
13	Century Blvd, Delany Rd, **E** 📳 Valero, **W** 🍴 Acupulco Mexican, 🛏 Super 8, Travelodge, ⊙ VF Factory Outlet/famous brands
12	FM 1765, La Marque, **E** 📳 Chevron/24hr, 🍴 Domino's, Jack-in-the-Box, Kelley's Rest., Sonic
11	Vauthier Rd
10	**E** 📳 Valero, 🍴 McDonald's, **W** 📳 Shell/dsl, ⊙ Oasis RV Park
9	Frontage Rd (from sb)
8	Frontage Rd (from nb)
7c	Frontage Rd
7b	TX 146, TX 6 (exits left from nb), Texas City, **W** 📳 EZ Mart
7a	TX 146, TX 3
6	Frontage Rd (from sb)
5	Frontage Rd
4	Frontage Rd, Village of Tiki Island, **W** 📳 Valero ⊙ public boat ramp
4mm	West Galveston Bay
1c	TX 275, FM 188 (from nb), Port Ind Blvd, Teichman Rd, Port of Galveston, **E** 📳 Exxon, Mobil/dsl, Valero, 🛏 Howard Johnson, Motel 6, ⊙ Chevrolet, Chrysler/Dodge/Jeep, Ford, Honda, Mazda, Mitsubishi, Nissan, Toyota/Scion
1b	71st St (from sb), **E** 📳 EZ Mart/gas, same as 1c

TX

🅖 = gas 🍴 = food 🛏 = lodging 🄾 = other   Copyright 2012 - The Next Ex

INTERSTATE 45 CONT'D

N ↕ S

Exit	Services
1a	TX 342, 61st St, to W Beach, **E** 🅖 Chevron, 🄾 GNC, Home Depot, NTB, Target, **W** 🅖 RaceWay, 🍴 Church's, McDonald's, Taco Bell, 🛏 Day's Inn, 🄾 Big Lots, Chevrolet/Buick/Cadillac, Chrysler/Jeep, Family$, Honda, O'Reilly Parts, U-Haul, USPO, **1-2 mi W** 🅖 Chevron/dsl, Exxon/dsl, Valero, 🍴 China Island, CiCi's Pizza, Happy Buddah, Jack-in-the-Box, KFC, Little Caesar's, Luby's, Mario's Italian, McDonald's, Papa John's, Pizza Hut, Popeye's, Quizno's, Starbucks, Subway, Taco Cabana, Waffle House, Whataburger, 🛏 Baymont Inn, Beachcomber Inn, Best Value Inn, Quality Inn, Super 8, 🄾 Curves, CVS Drug, Firestone/auto, Hastings Books, HEB Foods, Office Depot, Randall's Food/gas, Ross, Walgreens

I-45 begins/ends on TX 87 in Galveston.

INTERSTATE 410 (San Antonio)

N ↕ S

Exit	Services
53	I-35, S to Laredo, N to San Antonio
51	FM 2790, Somerset Rd
49	TX 16 S, spur 422, **N** 🅖 Chevron, Texaco/dsl, 🍴 Church's, Domino's, Sonic, Subway, Whataburger, 🛏 Days Inn, 🄾 🅷, to Palo Alto Coll, **S** 🅖 Valero/dsl, 🍴 Jack-in-the-Box, 🛏 Best Western
48	Zarzamora St
47	Turnaround (from eb)
46	Moursund Blvd
44	US 281 S, spur 536, Roosevelt Ave, **N** 🅖 Shell/McDonald's/dsl, Valero/dsl, **S** 🛏 Holiday Inn Express
43	Espada Rd (from eb)
42	spur 122, S Presa Rd, to San Antonio Missions Hist Park, **S** 🅖 Citgo/dsl
41	I-37, US 281 N
39	spur 117, WW White Rd
37	Southcross Blvd, Sinclair Rd, Sulphur Sprs Rd, **N** 🅖 Valero, 🍴 Capparelli's Pizza, 🄾 🅷
35	US 87, Rigsby Ave, **E** 🅖 Exxon, Murphy USA/dsl, Valero/dsl, 🍴 A&W, BorderTown Mexican, Cici's Pizza, Denny's, Jack-in-the-Box, LJ Silver, McDonald's, Subway, Taco Bell, 🄾 $Tree, Radio Shack, Walmart, **W** 🅖 Chevron, 🍴 Barnacle Bill's Sea🍴 Bill Miller BBQ, Domino's, El Tapito Mexican, Luby's, Sonic, Taco Cabana, Whataburger, 🛏 Days Inn, 🄾 Aamco, Advance Parts, $General, O'Reilly Parts, U-Haul, Walgreens, auto/dsl repair, vet
34	FM 1346, E Houston St, **W** 🅖 Valero/dsl
33	I-10 E, US 90 E, to Houston, I-10 W, US 90 W, to San Antonio
32	Dietrich Rd (from sb), FM 78 (from nb), to Kirby
31b	Lp 13, WW White Rd
31a	FM 78, Kirby, **E** 🅖 Citgo, Valero/dsl, 🄾 Family$
30	Binz-Engleman, Space Center Dr (from nb)

I-410 and I-35 run together 7 mi, See Interstate 35, exits 161 thru 165.

Exit	Services
27	I-35, N to Austin, S to San Antonio
26	Lp 368 S, Alamo Heights
25b	FM 2252, Perrin-Beitel Rd, **N** 🅖 Chevron/dsl, Valero, 🍴 Carl's Jr, KFC/Taco Bell, Quizno's, Schlotsky's, Tastee-Freez/Wienerschnitzel, Wendy's, 🛏 Best Value Inn, 🄾 Brake Check, **S** 🍴 Jim's Rest.
25a	Starcrest Dr, **N** 🅖 Valero, 🍴 Jack-in-the-Box, Los Patios Mexican, 🄾 🅷, Toyota

SAN ANTONIO

SAN ANTONIO

Exit	Services
24	Harry Wurzbach Hwy, **N** 🍴 Taco Cabana, **S** 🅖 Chevron, 🍴 BBQ Sta., 🄾 VW
23	Nacogdoches Rd, **N** 🅖 Shell, 🍴 Bill Miller BBQ, Church's, IHOP, Jack-in-the-Box, Luby's, Mamma's Cafe, Pizza Hut, Sonic, Wendy's, 🛏 Crowne Plaza, **S** 🅖 Chevron
22	Broadway St, **N** 🅖 Shell/dsl, 🍴 Chili's, Las Palapas, McDonald's, 🛏 Cambria Suites, Courtyard, 🄾 vet, **S** 🅖 Citgo, Valero, 🍴 Chesters Hamburgers, Jim's Rest., Little Caesar's, Martha's Mexican, Quizno's, Taco Palenque, Whataburger, 🛏 Residence Inn, TownHouse Motel
21	US 281 S, 🚂 Rd, Jones Maltsberger Rd, **N** 🍴 Applebee's, Bubba's Rest., 🛏 Best Western, Drury Suites, Hampton Inn, Holiday Inn, Holiday Inn Express, PearTree Inn, **S** 🅖 Murphy USA/dsl, 🍴 Pappadeaux, Red Lobster, Texas Land&Cattle, Whataburger, 🛏 Best Western, Courtyard, Days Inn, Fairfield Inn, La Quinta, Renaissance Hotel, Staybridge Suites, TownePlace Suites, 🄾 Hyundai/Kia, Mitsubishi, Subaru, Target, TJ Maxx, Walmart/McDonald's
20	TX 537, **N** 🅖 Valero, 🍴 Arby's, Chick-fil-A, Jack-in-the-Box, Jason's Deli, McDonald's, Subway, TGIFriday's, 🛏 DoubleTree Hotel, Hilton, 🄾 Barnes&Noble, Bealls, Best Buy, Brake Check, Cavender's Boots, Chevrolet, Honda, Jo-Ann Fabrics, Lexus, Lincoln/Mercury, Marshall's, Mazda, Office Depot, PetCo, Ross, WorldMkt, **S** 🍴 Cheesecake Factory, El Pollo Loco, Luby's, La Madeleine, Taco Cabana, 🄾 AT&T, CVS Drug, Dillard's, Dodge, JC Penney, Macy's, Saks 5th, Sears/auto, Target, Verizon, mall
19b	FM 1535, FM 2696, Military Hwy, **N** 🍴 Guajillos Mexican, Souper Salad, **S** 🍴 Denny's, Jim's Rest.
19a	Honeysuckle Lane Castle Hills
17b	(18 from wb), **S** 🅖 Shell, 🍴 Bill Miller BBQ, Subway, 🄾 Firestone/auto, HEB Foods/gas
17	Vance Jackson Rd, **N** 🅖 Valero/dsl, 🍴 Jack-in-the-Box, McDonald's, Sonic, Taco Cabana, Whataburger, 🛏 Embassy Suites, Marriott, 🄾 Aamco, Discount Tire, **S** 🅖 Citgo, Shell, 🍴 Church's, Subway, 🄾 U-Haul
16b a	I-10 E, US 87 S, to San Antonio, I-10 W, to El Paso, US 87 N
15	Lp 345, Fredericksburg Rd, **E** 🅖 Citgo, 🍴 Church's, Dave&Buster's, Denny's, El Pollo Loco, Jack-in-the-Box, Jim's Rest., Luby's, McDonald's, Taco Cabana, Wendy's, Whataburger, 🛏 Best Value Inn, SpringHill Suites, 🄾 AT&T, Family$, Firestone/auto, Hobby Lobby, Jo-Ann Fabrics, SteinMart, Target, transmissions, **W** 🅖 Chevron/dsl, 🄾 CVS Drug
14	(c b a from sb), Callaghan Rd, Babcock Ln, **E** 🅖 Chevron/dsl, Valero, 🍴 Marie Callender's, Popeye's, 🛏 Comfort Inn, Hampton Inn, Travelodge Suites, 🄾 AT&T, GMC, Hyundai, **W** 🅖 Shell, Valero, 🍴 Burger King, Chili's, ChopSticks Chinese, DingHow Chinese, Golden Corral, Henry's Tacos, IHOP, Jack-in-the-Box, Jim's Rest, Joe's Crabshack, Las Palapas Mexican, McDonald's, Quizno's, Red Lobster, Taco Cabana, Wendy's, 🄾 🅷, Cavander's Boots, Chevrolet, Home Depot, NTB, Petsmart, Sam's Club/gas, Walmart/Subway, vet
13	(b a from sb), TX 16 N, Bandera Rd, Evers Rd, Leon Valley, **E** 🍴 Outback Steaks, Panda Express, 🄾 Audi, HEB Foods/dsl, Office Depot, Old Navy, Toyota, U-Haul, **W** 🍴 Bill Miller BBQ, Henry's Tacos, Jim's Rest., Schlotzsky's, Sea Island Rest, Taco Cabana, 🄾 BigLots, Chevrolet
12	(from sb), **W** 🍴 Fortune Cookie Chinese, Jason's Deli, Sea Island Shrimp House, Starbucks, 🄾 AT&T, Barnes&Noble, Best Buy, $Tree, Marshall's, Michael's, Ross

TX

INTERSTATE 410 CONT'D (San Antonio)

Exit	Services
11	Ingram Rd, **E** 🅖 Shell/dsl, 🍴 KFC/Taco Bell, Krystal, Panda Buffet, TX Roadhouse, 🏠 Days Inn, Comfort Suites, Courtyard, EconoLodge, Holiday Inn Express, Red Roof Inn, Residence Inn, 🅞 Aamco, BrakeCheck, Chrysler/Dodge/Jeep, Mazda, **W** 🍴 Applebee's, Casa Real Mexican, Chick-fil-A, ChuckeCheese, Denny's, Fuddrucker's, Jack-in-the-Box, Whataburger, 🏠 Best Western, 🅞 Dillard's, Firestone/auto, JC Penney, Macy's, Sears/auto, mall
10	FM 3487, Culebra Rd, **E** 🍴 Bill Miller BBQ, Denny's, J Anthony's Sea🍴 McDonald's, Wendy's, 🏠 La Quinta, Ramada Ltd, 🅞 Harley-Davidson, to St Mary's U, **W** 🅖 Phillips 66, 🅞 Ford, Mitsubishi
9	(b a from sb), TX 151, **W** 🅖 Murphy USA/dsl, 🍴 Buffalo Wild Wings, Carino's Italian, Cheddar's, Chili's, Chipotle Mexican, IHOP, McAlister's Deli, Panda Express, Starbucks, Taco Bueno, TGIFriday's, Cracker Barrel, 🏠 Alamo City Hotel, Quality Inn, Sleep Inn, 🅞 Home Depot, Lowe's Whse, Office Depot, Petsmart, Ross, Target, Verizon, Walmart, to Sea World
7	(8 from sb), Marbach Dr, **E** 🅖 Exxon, 🍴 Church's, IHOP, 🅞 PepBoys, **W** 🅖 Chevron/dsl, Shell, 🍴 Acadiena Café, Asia Kitchen, Burger King, Coyote Canyon, Golden Wok, Jack-in-the-Box, Jim's Rest., KFC, LJ Silver, McDonald's, Mr Gatti's, Pancho's Mexican, Peter Piper Pizza, Pizza Hut, Red Lobster, Sonic, Subway, Taco Bell, Taco Cabana, Whataburger/24hr, 🏠 Motel 6, Super 8, 🅞 Advance Parts, Bealls, BigLots, BrakeCheck, Discount Tire, $General, $Tree, Firestone/auto, HEB Foods/gas
6	US 90, to Lackland AFB, **E** 🏠 Country Inn Motel, **W** 🅖 Shell/dsl, Valero/dsl, 🍴 Andrea's Mexican, 🏠 Best Western, 🅞 Explore USA RV Ctr
4	Valley Hi Dr, to Del Rio, San Antonio, **E** 🅖 Valero, 🍴 Burger King, Church's, McDonald's, Pizza Hut, Sonic, 🅞 AutoZone, HEB Food/gas, Radio Shack, **W** 🅖 Valero, 🍴 Jack-in-the-Box, 🅞 Walgreens, to Lackland AFB
3	(b a from sb), Ray Ellison Dr, Medina Base, **E** 🅖 Chevron/dsl, **W** 🅖 Valero/Subway/dsl
2	FM 2536, Old Pearsall Rd, **E** 🅖 Shell/dsl, Valero/dsl, 🍴 Bill Miller BBQ, Church's, Mexico Taqueria, McDonald's, Sonic, Subway, 🅞 O'Reilly Parts
1	Frontage Rd, **S** Scion/Toyota

INTERSTATE 610 (Houston)

Exit	Services
38c a	TX 288 N downtown, access to zoo
37	Scott St, **N** 🅖 Citgo, Valero
36	FM 865, Cullen Blvd, **N** 🏠 Crystal Inn, **S** 🅖 Chevron/McDonald's, Mobil, Shell, Valero, 🍴 Timmy Chan, 🏠 Crown Inn, Cullen Inn
35	Calais Rd, Crestmont St, MLK Blvd, **N** 🅖 Exxon, Valero, 🍴 Burger King
34	S Wayside Dr, Long Dr, **N** 🅖 Chevron, Phillips 66, Shell, 🍴 Church's, Wendy's, 🅞 Fiesta Foods, **S** 🅖 Valero, Shell
33	Woodridge Dr, Tele🍴 Rd, **N** 🅖 Shell/dsl, 🍴 IHOP, KFC/Taco Bell, McDonald's, Papa John's, Wendy's, 🏠 South Lp Inn, 🅞 Lowe's Whse, Old Navy, **S** 🅖 Texaco, 🍴 BBQ, Burger King, KFC, Piccadilly's Cafeteria, Spanky's Pizza, Whataburger, 🅞 Dodge, Ford, mall

Exit	Services
32b a	I-45, S to Galveston, N to Houston, to ✈
31	Broadway Blvd, **S** 🅖 Valero/dsl, Texaco/dsl
30c b	TX 225, to Pasadena San Jacinto Mon
29	Port of Houston Main Entrance
28	Clinton Dr to Galina Park
27	Turning Basin Dr, industrial area
26b	Market St
26a	I-10 E, to Beaumont, I-10 W, to downtown
24	(b a from sb), US 90 E, Wallisville Rd, **E** 🅖 Citgo/dsl, Loves/Arby's/dsl/scales/24hr, McDonald's/dsl/scales, Texaco/dsl, Valero/Heart's Chicken/dsl/scales/24hr, 🍴 Luby's, Wendy's, 🅞 Blue Beacon, **W** 🅖 Citgo/dsl
23b	N Wayside, **N** 🅖 Valero
23a	Kirkpatrick Blvd
22	Homestead Rd, Kelley St, **N** 🅖 Shell/dsl, 🍴 Whataburger, 🏠 Super 8, **S** 🅖 Chevron/Subway/dsl/scales
21	Lockwood Dr, **N** 🅖 Chevron/McDonald's, Shell, 🍴 Church's, Popeye's, Timmy Chan Chinese, 🅞 Ⓗ, Family$, Fiesta Foods
20a b	US 59, to downtown
19b	Hardy Toll Rd
19a	Hardy St, Jensen Dr (from eb)
18	Irvington Blvd, Fulton St, **N** 🅖 Chevron, **S** 🅖 Shell/dsl
17b c	I-45, N to Dallas, S to Houston
17a	(eb only) Airline Dr, **S** 🅖 Shell, 🍴 Jack-in-the-Box, 🏠 Western Inn
16	(b a from eb), Yale St, N Main St, Shamrock, **N** 🅖 Exxon, 🅞 Harley-Davidson, **S** 🅖 Texaco, 🍴 Burger King, Church's, KFC/Taco Bell, Starbucks
15	TX 261, N Shepherd Dr, **N** 🍴 Sonic, Taco Cabana, **S** 🅖 Chevron, Shell, 🍴 Wendy's, Whataburger, 🅞 Home Depot, PepBoys
14	Ella Blvd, **N** 🅖 Exxon, Texaco, 🍴 A&W, KFC, McDonald's, Popeye's, Taco Bell, **S** 🅖 Shell, 🍴 Thomas BBQ, 🅞 Ⓗ, BrakeCheck, Lowe's Whse, Office Depot
13c	TC Jester Blvd, **N** 🅖 Mobil, Shell, 🍴 Denny's, Juanita's Mexican, Po' Boys Sandwiches, 🏠 Courtyard, SpringHill Suites, **S** 🅖 Phillips 66/dsl
13b a	US 290 (exits left from nb)
12	W 18th St, **E** 🍴 Applebee's, Whataburger, **W** 🅖 Shell, 🍴 Burger King, 🏠 Sheraton
11	I-10, W to San Antonio, E to downtown Houston
10	Woodway Dr, Memorial Dr, **E** 🅖 Shamrock, 🍴 Steak'n Egg, **W** 🅖 Exxon, Shell, 🍴 Shug's Rest.
9b	Post Oak Blvd, **E** 🏠 Drury Inn, La Quinta, **W** 🍴 Champp's Rest., McCormick&Schmick's Café
9a	San Felipe Rd, Westheimer Rd, FM 1093, **E** 🅖 Mobil, Shell, 🏠 Courtyard, Hampton Inn, La Quinta, 🅞 CVS

TX

INTERSTATE 610 CONT'D (Houston)

Exit	Services
9a	Continued Drug, NTB, Target, **W** 🅰 Shell, ⚟ Champ's Rest., Luke's Burgers, 🅰 Crowne Plaza Hotel, HomeStead Suites, Marriott, Sheraton, 🅾 Best Buy, Dillard's, Nieman-Marcus
8a	US 59, Richmond Ave, **E** 🅰 Holiday Inn, Extended Stay America, 🅾 CVS Drug, **W** 🅰 Shell, 🅾 Dillards,
7	Bissonet St, West Park Dr, Fournace Place, **E** ⚟ Beudreax's Kitchen, 🅰 Candlewood Suites, 🅾 Home Depot, **W** 🅰 Shell/dsl/repair
6	Bellaire Blvd
5b	Evergreen St
5a	Beechnut St, **E** 🅰 Chevron, ⚟ Boston Mkt, IHOP, Lowe's Whse, McDonald's, Outback Steaks, 🅾 bank, **W** 🅰 Citgo, Shell, ⚟ Escalante Mexican Grill, James Coney Island, Saltgrass Steaks, Smoothie King, 🅾 GNC, Marshall's, mall
4a	S Post Oak Rd, Brasswood, **E** 🅰 Citgo, ⚟ Outback

HOUSTON

Exit	Services
4a	Continued Steaks, 🅰 Days Inn, **W** 🅾 Target, Walmart
3	Stella Link Rd, **N** 🅰 Chevron, ⚟ Jack-in-the-Box, 🅾 Discount Tire, Food City, Radio Shack, **S** 🅰 Exxon, Phillips 66/dsl, Shell
2	US 90A, **N** 🅰 Chevron, Conoco, Valero, ⚟ Arby's, Burger King, Church's, Denny's/24hr, KFC, McDonald's, Shoney's, Taco Bell, Wendy's, 🅰 Grand Plaza Hotel, Howard Johnson, Villa Motel, 🅾 CVS Drug, Discount Tire, Ford, Honda, Walgreen, **S** 🅰 Chevron, Shell, ⚟ Golden Corral, Pizza Hut/Taco Bell, Whataburger/24hr, 🅰 CareFree Inn, La Quinta, Motel 6, Super 8, 🅾 Chevrolet, Firestone, Mazda, Nissan, Toyota, U-Haul, to Buffalo Speedway
1c	Kirby Dr (from eb), **N** 🅰 Shell, ⚟ Burger King, 🅰 Radisson, **S** ⚟ Joe's Crabshack, Pappadeaux Sea ⚟ Pappasito's Cantina, 🅾 Cavender's Boots, NTB, GMC, Sam's Club, Toyota
1b a	FM 521, Almeda St, Fannin St, **N** 🅰 Chevron, Shell, ⚟ Burger King, 🅰 Scottish Inn, 🅾 Astro Arena, **S** 🅰 Shell, ⚟ McDonald's, 🅾 Aamco, to Six Flags

UTAH

INTERSTATE 15

Exit	Services
400.5mm	Utah/Idaho state line
398	Portage
392	UT 13 S, Plymouth, **E** 🅰 Sinclair/Subway/dsl
385	UT 30 E, to Riverside, Fielding, **1 mi E** 🅰 Sinclair/Riverside Grill/dsl
381	Tremonton, Garland, 2 mi **E** 🅾 🅷, 🅰, ⚟ lodging
379	I-84 W, to Boise
376	UT 13, to Tremonton, **E** 🅰 Texaco/Arby's/dsl/24hr, **2-3 mi E** ⚟ Arctic Circle, Crossroads Rest., El Parral Mexican, JC'S Diner, Subway, Taco Time, 🅰 Marble Motel, Sandman Motel
372	UT 240, to UT 13, to rec area, Honeyville, **E** 🅾 Crystal Hot Springs Camping
370mm	**rest area sb, full** 🅰 **facilities, info,** 🅲, 🅰, **litter barrels, vending, petwalk**
365	UT 13, Brigham City, **W** 🅾 to Golden Spike NHS
363	Forest St, Brigham City, **W** 🅾 Bear River Bird Refuge
362	US 91, to US 89, Brigham City, Logan, **E** 🅰 Chevron/dsl, ⚟FLYING J/dsl/24hr, 7-11, USA, Sinclair, ⚟ Arby's, Beto's Mexican, Burger King, Hunan Chinese, KFC/Taco Bell, Little Caesar's, McDonald's, Old Grist Mill Bread, Pizza Hut, Pizza Press, Sonic, Subway, Taco Time, Wendy's, Wingers, 🅰 Crystal Inn, Howard Johnson Express, 🅾 🅷, AutoZone, Checker Parts, Buick/Cadillac/Chevrolet, Chrysler/Dodge/Jeep, $Tree, Golden Spike RV Park, KOA, Smith's, Radio Shack, ShopKO, Walmart/Subway, to Yellowstone NP via US 89, **W** 🅰 ⛟/DQ/dsl/scales/24hr, 🅰 Days Inn
361mm	**rest area nb, full** 🅰 **facilities,** 🅲, 🅰, **litter barrels, vending, petwalk**
359	Port of Entry both lanes
357	UT 315, to Willard, Perry, **E** 🅰 ⚟FLYING J/Denny's/dsl/LP/scales/24hr, 🅾 KOA (2mi)
351	UT 126, to US 89, to Utah's Fruit Way, Willard Bay, **W** 🅾 Smith & Edwards Hardware
349	UT 134, N Ogden, Farr West, **E** 🅰 Exxon/Wendy's, Maverik, 7-11, ⚟ Arby's, Domino's, Jumbo Burger,

BRIGHAM CITY

Exit	Services
349	Continued McDonald's, Bella's Mexican, Subway, 🅰 Comfort Inn, 🅾 Kwik Lube, **W** 🅰 Conoco/dsl
346	to Harrisville, **W** 🅰 Chevron/dsl, Maverik, Cal Store, dsl repair
344	UT 39, 12th St, Ogden, **E** 🅰 Chevron, Phillips 66, Shell/dsl, 🅰 Best Western/rest., **1-2 mi E** 🅰 Chevron, ⚟ Denny's, KFC, McDonald's, Sizzler, Village Inn Rest., 🅰 Motel 6, 🅾 to Ogden Canyon RA, **W** 🅰 ⛟/DQ/Subway/Taco Bell/dsl/24hr, ⚟ Iron Pan Bistro, 🅰 Sleep Inn, Western Inn
343	UT 104, 21st St, Ogden, **E** 🅰 Chevron/Arby's/dsl, ⚟FLYING J/Denny's/dsl/LP/24hr, Phillips 66/dsl, ⚟ Cactus Red's Rest., McDonalds, Outlaw Rest., 🅰 Best Western, Comfort Suites, Holiday Inn Express, ValuePlace Inn, 🅾 Justus RV Ctr, RV Repair, **W** 🅰 Texaco, 🅰 Super 8, 🅾 Century RV Park
342	(from nb), UT 53, 24th St, Ogden, **E** 🅰 Sinclair/dsl
341b a	UT 79 W, 31st St, Ogden, **1-2 mi E on Wall St** 🅰 7-11, ⚟ Arby's, Golden Corral, JJ North's Buffet, Sizzler, 🅰 Day's Inn, Hampton Inn, Marriott, 🅾 🅷, Dillard's, Chevrolet, Ford/Lincoln/Mercury, RV Ctr, mall, to Weber St U, **W** 🅾
340	I-84 E (from sb), to Cheyenne, Wyo
339	UT 26 (from nb), to I-84 E, Riverdale Rd, **E** 🅰 Conoco/dsl, Sinclair, ⚟ Applebee's, Arby's, Boston Mkt, Carl's Jr, Chili's, La Salsa Mexican, McDonald's, 🅰 Motel 6, 🅾 Buick/GMC, Chrysler/Jeep, Harley-Davidson, Home Depot, Honda/Nissan, Isuzu, Jo-Ann Fabrics, Lincoln/Mercury/Kia, Mazda, Sam's Club/gas, Target, Toyota, Walmart, Wilderness RV
338	UT 97, Roy, Sunset, **E** 🅾 Air Force Museum, **W** 🅰 Exxon/dsl, Phillips 66, 7-11, Sinclair, ⚟ Arby's, Arctic Circle, Blimpie, Burger King, DQ, KFC, McDonald's, Panda Express, Pizza Hut, Ponderosa, Sonic, Subway, Taco Bell, Village Inn Rest., Wendy's, 🅰 Quality Inn, Motel 6, 🅾 AutoZone, BrakeWorks, Checker Parts, Citte RV Ctr, Discount Tire, Early Tires, Firestone, Goodyear, Radio Shack, RiteAid, Schwab Tires, Smith's/gas, Walgeen, transmissions
335	UT 103, Clearfield, **E** Hill AFB, **W** 🅰 Chevron, Conoco, PetroMart, 7-11, Texaco, Circle K, ⚟ Arby's,

OGDEN

INTERSTATE 15 CONT'D

Exit	Services
335	Continued Carl's Jr, KFC, McDonald's, Skipper's, Subway, Taco Bell, Winger's, 🛏 Days Inn, The Cottage Inn, 🅾 Big O Tire, Sierra RV Ctr
334	UT 193, Clearfield, to Hill AFB, **E** 🅰 Chevron, Maverik, **W** 🅰 Chevron/dsl, 🍴 Wendy's
332	UT 108, Syracuse, **E** 🅰 Chevron, Phillips 66/dsl, Circle K, 🍴 Applebee's, Brick Oven, Carl's Jr, Cracker Barrel, Famous Dave's, Golden Corral, JB's, Marie Callender's, Outback Steaks, Quizno's, Red Robin, TimberLodge Steaks, 🛏 Courtyard, Fairfield Inn, Hampton Inn, Hilton Garden, Holiday Inn Express, La Quinta, TownePlace Suites, 🅾 Barnes&Noble, Lowe's Whse, Office Depot, Old Navy, Target, **W** 🅰 Conoco, 7-11, 🍴 Arby's, McDonald's, 🅾 🅷, to Antelope Island
331	UT 232, UT 126, Layton, **E** 🅰 Mobil, Phillips 66, Texaco, 🍴 Denny's, Garcia's, McDonald's, Olive Garden, Red Lobster, Sizzler, Training Table Rest., Wendy's, 🛏 Comfort Inn, Hilton Garden, 🅾 Dick's, JC Penney, Tuesday Morning, mall, to Hill AFB S Gate, **W** 🅰 Common Cents/dsl, 🍴 Blimpie, Burger King, China Buffet, ChuckeCheese, IHOP, KFC, Krispy Kreme, LoneStar Steaks, McGrath's FishHouse, Taco Bell, 🅾 Batteries+, Cadillac/GMC, Chevrolet, Discount Tire, Dodge, Home Depot, NTB, Jeep, Ream's Foods, Sam's Club/gas, ShopKO, Staples, Walmart
330	Layton Pkwy, to UT 126, Layton, **E** 🍴 Little Orient Chinese, 🅾 repair, **W** 🅰 Texaco, 🅾 Jensen's RV
328	UT 273, Kaysville, **E** 🅰 Chevron/McDonald's, 7-11, Sinclair, 🍴 Arby's, Cutler's Sandwiches, DQ, Joanie's Rest., Gandolfo's, KFC, Quizno's, Subway, Taco Maker, Taco Time, Wendy's, Winger's, 🅾 Checker Parts, Fresh Mkt Foods, Schwab Tire, Walgreens, **W** 🅾 Camping World/Jensen RV Ctr, Kia
325mm	parking area both lanes
325	UT 225, Lagoon Dr, Farmington (from sb), **E** 🍴 Subway, 🅾 funpark, camping, **W** 🅾 Kohls
324	US 89 N, UT 225, Legacy Pkwy (from sb) **1 mi E** 🅰 Conoco/Smith's Foods/dsl, Maverik/gas, 🍴 Arby's, Burger King, Little Caesar's, Subway, 🅾 Aunt Pam's, Goodyear/auto, RV Park, to I-84
322	UT 227 (from nb), Lagoon Dr, to Farmington, **E** 🍴 Subway, 🅾 Lagoon Funpark/RV Park
319	Centerville, **E** 🅰 Chevron/dsl, Phillips 66/dsl, 🍴 Arby's, Arctic Circle, Burger King, Carl's Jr, Chili's, DQ, Del Taco, Fusion of Asia, Gandolfo's, IHOP, In-N-Out, Jake's Shakes, LoneStar Steaks, McDonald's, Subway, Taco Bell, TacoMaker, Wendy's, 🅾 Albertson's, Big O Tire, Checker Parts, Curves, Home Depot, Kohl's, Land Rover, Radio Shack, Schwab Tire, Target/foods, Walmart, **W** 🅾 RV Ctr

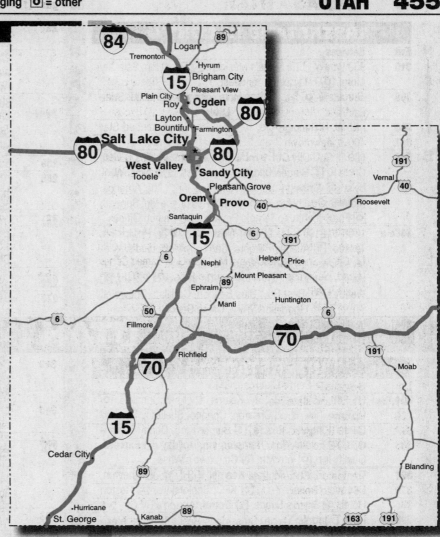

Exit	Services
317	US 89 S (exits left from sb), UT 131, 500W,, S Bountiful, **E** 🅰 Chevron/24hr, Exxon/dsl, Phillips 66/dsl, Sinclair/dsl, 🍴 Alicia's Rest., Starbucks, 🛏 Country Inn Suites, 🅾 Costco/gas, Office Depot, Parts+, PetCo, Goodyear, Jiffy Lube, tires
316	UT 68, 500 S, W Bountiful, Woods Cross, **E** 🅰 Exxon, Texaco, 🍴 Applebee's, Blimpie, Burger King, Carl's Jr, Christopher's Steaks, ChuckaRama, Coldstone, Del Taco, HogiYogi, KFC, La Frontera Mexican, McDonald's, Panda Express, Pizza Hut, Rinny's Rest., Sizzler, Subway, SuCasa Mexican, Taco Bell, Winger's, 🅾 🅷, Albertson's, AutoZone, Barnes&Noble, Big O Tire, Checker Parts, Costco/gas, Firestone/auto, Michael's, Radio Shack, Ross, ShopKO, TJ Maxx, Walgreens, **W** 🅰 Phillips 66/A&W/dsl, 🛏 InTown Suites
315	26th S, N Salt Lake, **E** 🅰 Chevron/dsl, Sinclair, Tesoro, 🍴 Apollo Burger, Arby's, Atlantis Burger, Empire Chinese, McDonald's, Subway, Taco Time, Village Inn, Wendy's, 🛏 Best Western, Comfort Inn, 🅾 Ace Hardware, Chevrolet/Buick/Kia, Discount Tire, Dodge, Ford/Lincoln/Mercury, Honda, K-Mart, Mazda, Nissan, Schwab Tire, Smith's Foods, Toyota, Tunex, U-Haul, **W** 🅰 Conoco, 🍴 Denny's, Lorena's Mexican, 🛏 Hampton Inn, Motel 6, 🅾 Goodyear
314	Center St, Cudahy Lane (from sb), N Salt Lake, **E** 🅰
313	I-215 W (from sb), to ✈
312	US 89 S, to Beck St, N Salt Lake
311	2300 N

UT

INTERSTATE 15 CONT'D

Exit	Services
310	900 W, **W** 🍴 Tia Maria's Mexican, 🏠 Regal Inn, Salt City Motel, 🅞 7-11, Self's conv/rest.
309	600 N, **E** 🅞 **H**, LDS Temple, downtown, to UT State FairPark
308	I-80 W, to Reno ✈
307	400 S, downtown
306	600 S, SLC City Ctr **1 mi E** 🅖 Chevron, Phillips 66/dsl, Circle K, 🍴 Burger King, DQ, Denny's, McDonald's, Wendy's, 🏠 Embassy Suites, Hampton Inn, Little America, Motel 6, Quality Inn, Ramada Inn, Residence Inn, Super 8, 🅞 Ford, Toyota, to Temple Square, LDS Church Offices
305c-a	1300 S, 2100 S UT 201 W, West Valley, **E** 🅖 Phillips 66, Texaco, 🍴 Atlantis Burgers, Carl's Jr, McDonald's, Wienerschnitzel, 🅞 Costco/gas, Home Depot, PetsMart, U-Haul, Walmart, **W** 🅖 ⓕFLYING J/Denny's/dsl/LP/24hr, 🍴 Wendy's, 🅞 Best Buy, Blue Beacon, Cadillac, Chevrolet, $Tree, Ford, Goodyear, NAPA, Office Depot
304	I-80 E, to Denver, Cheyenne
303	UT 171, 3300 S, S Salt Lake, **E** 🅖 7-11, Phillips 66, 🍴 Apollo Diner, Burger King, McDonald's, Taco Bell, 🏠 Bonneville Inn, Day's Inn, Roadrunner Motel, **W** 🅖 Maverik/dsl, 🅞 Sam's Club/gas, GMC
301	UT 266, 4500 S, Murray, Kearns, **E** 🍴 McDonald's, 🅞 UpTown Tire, **W** 🅖 Chevron, Conoco, Shell/dsl, Sinclair/Burger King/dsl, Texaco, 🍴 Burger King, Denny's, Wendy's, 🏠 Fairfield Inn, Hampton Inn, Holiday Inn Express, Quality Inn, 🅞 InterMtn RV Ctr, Lowe's Whse
300	UT 173, 5300 S, Murray, Kearns, **E** **H**, **W** 🅖 Chevron, Conoco, Sinclair, 7-11, 🍴 KFC, Schlotsky's, 🏠 Reston Hotel, 🅞 Smith's Foods, FunDome, Jenson's RV Ctr
298	I-215 E and W
297	UT 48, 7200 S, Midvale, **E** 🅖 Chevron, Conoco, Phillips 66, Sinclair, Texaco/LP, 🍴 Chili's, Denny's, John's Place, KFC, McDonald's, Midvale Mining Café, Sizzler, South Seas Café, Taco Bell, Village Inn Rest., 🏠 Best Western, Day's Inn, Discovery Inn/café, Executive Inn, La Quinta, Motel 6, Rodeway Inn, Sandman Inn, Super 8, 🅞 Cadillac/Buick, carwash, to Brighton, Solitude Ski Areas, Walgreens, **W** 🅖 Sinclair/Subway/dsl
295	UT 209, 9000 S, Sandy, **E** 🅖 Chevron, Sinclair, 🍴 Arby's, Burger King, Fuddrucker's, Hardee's, Johanna's Kitchen, Schlotzsky's, Sconecutter's Rest., Sweet Tomato, 🏠 Comfort Inn, Majestic Rockies Motel, 🅞 Discount Tire, Early Tires, Firestone, Ford, NAPA, to Snowbird, Alta Ski Areas, **W** 🅖 Maverik, Tesoro, 🍴 KFC, Village Inn 🅞 **H**, Aamco
293	106th S, Sandy, S Jordan, **E** 🅖 Conoco, Phillips 66, Tesoro, 🍴 Bennett's BBQ, Carver's Prime Rib, Chili's, Eat a Burger, HomeTown Buffet, Jim's Rest., Johanna's Rest., Subway, TGIFriday, Village Inn, Wendy's, 🏠 Best Western, Courtyard, Extended Stay America, Hampton Inn, Hilton Garden, Hyatt Summerfield, Marriott, Residence Inn, TownePlace Suites, 🅞 Best Buy, Chevrolet, Chrysler/Jeep, Costco/gas, Dillard's, Goodyear, Honda, JC Penney, Nissan, Target, Toyota, mall, **W** 🍴 Denny's, 🏠 Country Inn Suites, Sleep Inn, Super 8, 🅞 Buick/GMC, CarMax, Sam's Club/gas, VW, Walmart
291	UT 71, 12300 S, Draper, Riverton, **E** 🅖 Chevron, Common Cents/dsl, 🍴 Arby's, Arctic Circle, Café Rio Mexican, Carl's Jr, Del Taco, Fazoli's, Guadalahonky's Mexican,

Exit	Services
291	Continued In-N-Out, Jamba Juice, KFC, McDonald's, Panda Express, Pizza Hut, Quizno's, Ruby Tuesday, Sonic, Teriyaki Express, Wendy's, Wienerschnitzel, Wingers Diner, 🏠 Comfort Inn, Fairfield Inn, Ramada Ltd, 🅞 Brown RV, Camping World RV Supplies (1mi), Discount Tire, Goodyear/auto, Greenbax, Kohl's, Mountain Shadows Camping, Smith's Foods, FSA Outlets/famous brands **W** 🅖 Phillips 66, 🅞 Sam's Club/gas, Walmart
289	Bangerter Hwy, **W** 🅖 Exxon, 7-11, 🍴 Quizno's
288	UT 140, Bluffdale, **E** 🅖 Chevron/dsl, 🅞 Kohl's, Camping World RV Supplies (2mi), Quality RV Ctr, **W** 🅖 Common Sense/gas, 7-11, 🅞 st prison
284	UT 92, to Alpine, Highland, **E** 🅞 Cabela's, **W** 🅖 Chevron/Iceberg Café/dsl, Maverik/dsl, 🍴 Del Taco, JCW Burgers, 🏠 Hampton Inn, SpringHill Suites, 🅞 Lone Peak RV Ctr, Thanksgiving Point/café, to Timpanogas Cave
282	US 89 S, 12th W, to UT 73, Lehi, **W** 🅖 Chevron
279	UT 73, to Lehi, **E** 🅖 Texaco/dsl, 🍴 Applebee's, 1 Man Band Diner, Panda Express, TX Roadhouse, Wienershnitzel, 🏠 Motel 6, 🅞 Costco/gas, Lowe's Whse, Home Depot, Petsmart, Schwab Tire, Walgreens, Walmart, **W** 🅖 Chevron/dsl, Phillips 66/Wendy's, 🍴 Arctic Circle, Dutch Oven Rest., KFC/Pizza Hut, McDonald's, Papa Murphy's, Subway, Tepanyki Japanese, Wingers, 🏠 Best Western, Comfort Inn, Day's Inn, Super 8, 🅞 Albertson's, Big O Tire, Checker Parts, GNC, Dave's Chiropractic, USPO, museum
278	Main St, American Fork, **E** 🅖 Phillips 66/dsl, Texaco, 🍴 Chili's, Cobblestone Pizza, Del Taco, In-N-Out, Ottavio's Italian, Pier 49, Sonic, Wendy's, 🅞 **H**, Chevrolet, Chrysler/Dodge/Jeep, $Tree, Home Depot, K-Mart, Kohl's, Office Depot, Old Navy, Smith's Foods, Subaru/Suzuki, Target, Walmart, **W** 🏠 Value Place
276	5th E, Pleasant Grove, **E** 🅖 Conoco/Blimpie, 🍴 Carl's Jr, Denny's, McDonald's, Taco Bell, 🏠 Quality Inn, 🅞 Stewart's RV Ctr, **1-2 mi E** 🅖 Circle K, Phillips 66, Texaco, 🍴 Arby's, Del Taco, Golden Corral, Hardee's, KFC, Subway, Wendy's, 🅞 **H**, American Camping, Chevrolet, **W** 🅞 Buick/GMC, Ford, Land Rover
275	Pleasant Grove, **E** 🍴 Bajio Grill, Panda Express, Sonic, Wienerschnitzel, 🅞 BMW, Macey's Foods
273	Orem, Lindon, **E** 🅖 Exxon/dsl, Holiday, 🍴 Costa Vida Mexican, Del Taco, 🅞 Discount Tire, Home Depot, Lexus, Mercedes, Schwab Tire, **W** 🅞 Harley-Davidson
272	UT 52, to US 189, 8th N, Orem, **E** 🅖 Maverik, Phillips 66, 🏠 La Quinta, **1 mi E** 🍴 Arby's, Cafe Rio, DQ, Denny's, Sonic, 🅞 to Sundance RA
271	Center St, Orem, **E** 🅖 Conoco, 7-11, 🅞 **H**, funpark, **1-2 mi E** 🍴 Burger King, Cafe Rio, KFC, Panda Express, Taco Bell, Wendy's, **W** 🅖 Tesoro, 🍴 La Casita Blanca Mexican, 🏠 Econolodge, 🅞 LP
269	272 UT 265, 12th St S, University Pkwy, **E** 🅖 Texaco/Wendy's/dsl, Sinclair, 🍴 HoneyBaked Ham, IHOP, Krispy Kreme, McDonald's, Subway, Thai Evergreen, 🏠 Comfort Inn, Hampton Inn, La Quinta, 🅞 Ford, JiffyLube, Mazda, Toyota/Scion, Walmart, **1-3 mi E** 🅖 Chevron, 🍴 Applebee's, Arby's, Carrabba's, Chili's, Fuddrucker's, Golden Corral, Noodles & Co., Outback Steaks, Pizza Hut, Sakura Japanese, Sizzler, Starbucks, Village Inn, 🏠 Best Western, Courtyard, 🅞 Barnes&Noble, Best Buy, Honda, JC Penney, Jo-Ann Fabrics, Lowe's Whse, Mazda, Michael's,

UT

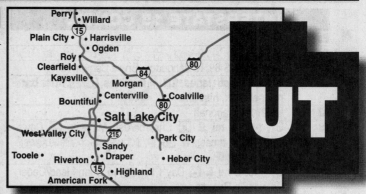

INTERSTATE 15 CONT'D

Exit	Services

P R O V O

269 Continued

Nissan, Office Depot, Old Navy, Petsmart, Ross, Subaru, TJ Maxx, VW, mall, to BYU, many services on US 89, **W** 🅖 Chevron

265b a UT 114, Center St, Provo, **E** 🅖 Conoco, Phillips 66/Wendy's, Shell, Sinclair/dsl, 7-11, ◻ 🅗, Albertson's, Checker Parts, Firestone/auto, auto repair, 1 mi **E** 🏨 Marriott, Travelers Inn, Travelodge, **W** 🅖 Chevron, Shell/dsl, 🍴 Great Steak Rest., Subway, 🏨 Econolodge, ◻ KOA, Lakeside RV, to Utah Lake SP

P R O V O N → S

263 US 189 N, University Ave, Provo, **E** 🅖 Chevron, Conoco/dsl, Maverik, Sinclair, 🍴 A&W/KFC, Arby's, Burger King, ChuckaRama, Fazoli's, Hogi Yogi, McDonald's, Papa Murphy's, Ruby River Steaks, Sizzler, Taco Bell, Taco Time, Village Inn Rest., Wendy's, 🏨 Best Western, Colony Inn, Fairfield Inn, Hampton Inn, La Quinta, Motel 6, National 9 Inn, Sleep Inn, Super 8, ◻ Curves, Dillard's, GoodEarth Foods, Home Depot, JC Penney, K-Mart, Les Schwab, NAPA, Sam's Club/gas, Sears/auto, Staples, Silver Fox RV Camping, mall, to BYU, 1 mi **E** 🍴 Los Three Amigos Mexican, 🏨 Safari Motel, Western Inn, ◻ CarQuest, VW/Audi, auto repair

S P R I N G V I L L E

261 UT 75, Springville, **E** 🅖 ⓙFLYING J/Denny's/dsl/scales/24hr, Maverik, 🍴 McDonald's (1mi), 🏨 Best Western, ◻ E Bay RV Park, RestStop

260 UT 77, Springville, Mapleton, **E** 🅖 Phillips 66/Quizno's/dsl, 🍴 Del Taco, DQ, IHOP, Mongolian Grill, Pizza Hut, Quizno's, Wendy's, ◻ Big O Tire, JiffyLube, Walmart, **W** 🅖 Chevron/Arby's/dsl, 🍴 Cracker Barrel, 🏨 Days Inn, ◻ Quality RV Ctr

258 US 89 S, US 6 E (from sb), to Price, **E** 🅖 Chevron/dsl, Phillips 66, Texaco, 🍴 Arby's, Burger King, Carl's Jr, KFC, McDonald's, Papa Murphy's, Subway, Taco Bell, Wendy's, Winger's, 🏨 Holiday Inn Express, Western Inn, ◻ Albertson's/gas, AutoZone, Checker Parts, Fakler's Tire, K-Mart, Radio Shack, RV Ctr

257 US 6 E, UT 156, Spanish Fork, **E** 🅖 Chevron, Phillips 66, Sinclair, Tesoro, Texaco/dsl/LP, 🍴 Amber Rest., Arby's, Bajio Grill, Burger King, China Wok, Hogi Yogi, Italian Place, KFC, Little Caesar's, McDonald's, One Man Band Diner, Pizza Factory, Sonic, Subway, Taco Bell, Taco Time, Wendy's, ◻ Albertsons, Big O Tire, Cal Store, $Tree, Jo-Anne Fabrics, K-Mart, Macey's Foods, ShopKO, USPO, transmissions, **W** 🅖 Conoco/dsl, ◻ Chevrolet, Chrysler/Jeep, Ford, RV Ctr

253 UT 164, to Spanish Fork

250 UT 115, Payson, **E** 🅖 Chevron/dsl, 🍴 McDonald's, Subway, 🏨 Comfort Inn, ◻ 🅗, Checker Parts, Payson Foods, RiteAid, Mt Nebo Loop, dsl repair

248 Payson, Salem, **E** 🅖 Chevron, Sinclair/Arby's/dsl, 🍴 Tsing Tao Asian, Hunan City, Pizza Hut, Subway, ◻ $Tree, Walmart, **W** 🅖 Phillips 66/Wendy's/dsl

244 US 6 W, Santaquin, **E** 🅖 Maverik, ◻ Tire Factory, TrueValue, **W** 🅖 Conoco/dsl, Sinclair, 🍴 Family Tree Rest., One Man Band Diner, Santa Queen Burgers, Subway, Taco Time, ◻ Family$, Ford, Main St Mkt, Nat Hist Area, USPO, auto/tire care

242 to S Santaquin, **W** Chevron/dsl

233 UT 54, Mona

N E P H I

228 UT 28, to Nephi, **2-4 mi W** services

225 UT 132, Nephi, **E** 🅖 Tesoro/dsl/LP, 🍴 Quizno's, Salt Creek Steaks, Taco Time, One Man Band Rest., ◻ Burn's Bros RV Park (5mi), **W** 🅖 Chevron/Arby's/dsl, Phillips 66/Wendy's/dsl, 🏨 Economy Inn, ◻ 🅗, Big O Tire

222 UT 28, to I-70, Nephi, **E** 🅖 Chevron/dsl, Sinclair/Hogi Yogi/scales/dsl/24hr, Texaco/dsl/24hr, 🍴 Burger King, Mickelson's Rest., Subway, 🏨 Motel 6, Roberta's Cove Motel, Super 8, ◻ dsl repair, **W** 🅖 ⓙFLYING J/Denny's/dsl/LP/scales/24hr, 🍴 Lisa's Country Kitchen, 🏨 Best Western, Safari Motel, ◻ 🅗, Hi-Country RV Park

207 to US 89, Mills

202 Yuba Lake, ◻, access to boating, camping, rec services

188 US 50 E, to I-70, Scipio, **E** 🅖 Sinclair/Subway/dsl, Texaco, 🏨 Super 8, **W** 🅖 ⓙFLYING J/DQ/dsl/rest stop/24hr

184 ranch exit

178 US 50, to Delta, **W** 🅖, ◻, to Great Basin NP

174 to US 50, Holden, to great Basin NP

F I L L M O R E

167 Lp 15, Fillmore, **0-3 mi E** 🅖 Chevron/dsl, Shell, Sinclair/dsl, 🍴 5 Buck Pizza, Old Frontier Steaks, 🏨 Best Western/rest., ◻ 🅗, CarQuest, Goodyear, KOA, WagonsWest RV Park, **W** 🅖 Chevron/Subway/rest stop, Texaco/dsl, 🍴 Carl's Jr

163 Lp 15, to UT 100, Fillmore, **E** 🅖 Chevron/Arby's/dsl, Maverik, 🏨 Comfort Inn, ◻ 🅗, KOA, **W** 🅖 Texaco/Burger King, 🏨 motel

158 UT 133, Meadow, **E** 🅖 Chevron/dsl, Shell/dsl

153mm view area sb

151mm view area nb

146 Kanosh, 2 mi **E** 🅖, chainup area

138 ranch exit

135 Cove Fort Hist Site, **E** 🅖 Chevron/Subway, ◻ **rest stop**

132 I-70 E, to Denver, Capitol Reef NP, Fremont Indian SP

129 Sulphurdale, chainup area

125 ranch exit

120 Manderfield, chainup area nb

B E A V E R

112 to UT 21, Beaver, Manderfield, **E** 🅖 Chevron, Sinclair/dsl, Conoco/dsl, 🍴 Arby's, Arshel's Café, Hunan Chinese, McDonald's, Paradise Canyon Grill, Subway, 🏨 Best Western, Country Inn, Day's Inn, Rodeway Inn, ◻ 🅗, Family$, KOA (1mi), auto repair, **W** 🅖 ⓙFLYING J/cafe/dsl/scales/24hr, 🍴 Wendy's, 🏨 Eagle's Landing Hotel, Super 8, ◻ to Great Basin NP

109 to UT 21, Beaver, **E** 🅖 Phillips 66/dsl, Shell/Burger King/dsl/24hr, 🏨 Best Western, Comfort Inn, ◻ 🅗, Cache Valley Cheese, Camper Land RV Park, Mike's Foodtown, NAPA, auto repair, **W** 🅖 Chevron/DQ/dsl/24hr, 🍴 KanKun Mexican, Timberline Rest., 🏨 Quality Inn, ◻ RV park, truckwash, to Great Basin NP

UT

INTERSTATE 15 CONT'D

Exit	Services
100	ranch exit
95	UT 20, to US 89, to Panguitch Bryce Canyon NP
88mm	**rest area both lanes, full ♿ facilities, 🍴, 🅿, litter barrel, petwalk, hist site**
82	UT 271, Paragonah
78	UT 141, **1 mi E** 🅖 Chevron/dsl, Maverik, 🏨 Day's Inn, 🅞 ski areas, **W** 🍴 TA/Subway/Taco Bell/LP/dsl/scales/24hr/@
75	UT 143, **2 mi E** 🏨 Day's Inn, 🅞 to Brian Head/Cedar Breaks Ski Resorts
71	Summit
62	UT 130, Cedar City, **E** 🅖 Loves/Carl's Jr/Subway/dsl/scales/24hr, Phillips 66/dsl, 🍴 Arctic Circle, Godfather's Pizza, 🅞 Country Aire RV Park, KOA (2mi), st patrol, **W** 🅖 Maverik/dsl, Shell/dsl/24hr/dsl repair, 🏨 Travelodge
59	UT 56, Cedar City, **0-2 mi E** 🅖 Chevron, ✈FLYING J/dsl/rest./24hr, FoodMart/dsl, Maverik, Phillip 66/LP/dsl, 🍴 A&W/KFC, Arby's, Bajio, Burger King, Denny's, Godfather's, Great Harvest Bread Co., IHOP, Little Caesars, McDonald's/playplace, Papa Murphy's, Pizza Factory, Sizzler, Sonic, Taco Bell, Wendy's, 🏨 Abbey Inn, Best Western, Econolodge, Quality Inn, Stratford Hotel, 🅞 Buick/Chevrolet, $Tree, Goodyear/auto, Lin's Mkt, NAPA, Tire Co., USPO, **W** 🅖 Maverik, Sinclair/dsl, 🍴 Bard's Cafe, Subway, 🏨 Crystal Inn, Motel 6, Super 8
57	Lp 15, to UT 14, Cedar City, **0-2 mi E** 🅖 Chevron/repair/24hr, Phillips 66/dsl, Shell, Sinclair/dsl, 🍴 DQ, Domino's, Hogi Yogi, Pizza Hut, Subway, 🏨 Comfort Inn, Days Inn, Holiday Inn Express, Knights Inn, Rodeway Inn, SpringHill Suites, 🅞 🄷, Albertson's, AutoZone, Beall's, Big O Tire, CAL Ranch, Checker Parts, Country Aire RV Park, Family$, KOA, Main 57 Tire, NAPACare, Smith's Food/gas, Staples, to Cedar Breaks, Navajo Lake, Bryce Cyn, Duck Crk, **W** 🅖 Chevron/dsl, USA, 🍴 Applebee's, Chili's, Costa Vida, Del Taco, Lupita's Mexican, Ninja Japanese, Panda Express, Quizno's, Starbucks, Subway, Winger's, 🏨 Hampton Inn, 🅞 GNC, Home Depot, Jiffy Lube, Radio Shack, Tunex, Walgreens, Walmart
51	Kanarraville, Hamilton Ft
44mm	**rest area both lanes, full ♿ facilities, 🍴, 🅿, litter barrels, petwalk, hist site**
42	New Harmony, Kanarraville, **W** 🅖 Texaco/dsl
40	to Kolob Canyon, **E** 🅞 Zion's NP, tourist info/🍴, scenic drive
36	ranch exit
33	ranch exit
31	Pintura
30	Browse
27	UT 17, Toquerville, **E** 🅞 to Zion NP, Grand Canyon, Lake Powell
23	Leeds, Silver Reef (from sb), **3 mi E** 🅞 Leed's RV Park/gas, hist site, museum
22	Leeds, Silver Reef (from nb), same as 23
16	UT 9, to Hurricane, **E** 🅖 Shell/Arby's/dsl, 🏨 Holiday Inn Express, 🅞 Harley-Davidson, Walmart Dist Ctr, **10 mi E** 🅖 Chevron, Shell, 🍴 Calydascope Cafe, Coral Canyon Grille, 🏨 Comfort Inn, Motel 6, Travelodge, 🅞 to Zion NP, Grand Canyon, Lake Powell, RV Camping
13	Washington Pkwy, **E** 🅖 Maverik/dsl
10	Middleton Dr, Washington, **E** 🅖 Mirastar, Phillips 66/dsl,

10	Continued
	Sinclair, 🍴 Arby's, Arctic Circle, Bajio, Burger King, Del Taco, Honeybaked Ham, IHOP, In-N-Out, Jack-in-the-Box, Jimmy John's, Little Caesars, Lucky Buffet, Noble Romans, Pizza Factory, Ruby Tuesday, Sonic, Steak&Sea🍴Subway, TX Roadhouse, Toro Moro Mexican, Wendy's, 🏨 Country Inn&Suites, Red Cliffs Inn, 🅞 AAA, Albertsons/Sav-On, AutoZone, Barnes&Noble, Best Buy, Big Lots, Checker Parts, Costco/gas, Dillard's, Discount Tire, Home Depot, Kohl's, JC Penney, Jiffy Lube, PetCo, Sears/auto, Tunex, Walmart, mall, **W** 🅖 Chevron/dsl/LP, Texaco/24hr, 🅞 auto repair
8	St George Blvd, St George, **E** 🅖 Chevron/Subway/dsl, Freddy's/dsl, Texaco/dsl, 🍴 Applebee's, Arby's, Carl's Jr, Chili's, ChuckaRama, Coldstone, Don Jose Mexican, Fazoli's, Golden Corral, Mongolian BBQ, Olive Garden, Outback Steaks, Pachanga's, Panda Express, Papa John's, Quizno's, Red Lobster, Sharky's Mexican, Starbucks, Village Inn Rest., Winger's, 🏨 Best Inn, Courtyard, Hampton Inn, Ramada Inn, TownePlace Suites, 🅞 🄷, $Tree, Harmon's Foods, Lowes Whse, Michael's, Old Navy, Ross, Staples, Sunrise Tire, Target, TJ Maxx, Zion Factory Stores/famous brands, same as 10, **W** 🅖 Conoco/dsl, Maverik/dsl, Shell, Sinclair/Domino's/LP/dsl, Texaco/dsl, 🍴 A&W/KFC, Burger King, Cafe Rio, Denny's, Fairway Grill, Iceberg Drive-In, Jimmy John's, Larsen's Drive-In, Mandarin Buffet, McDonald's, Panda Garden, Roberto's, Taco Bell, Taco Time, Wendy's, 🏨 Best Western, Coronada Inn, Days Inn, Econolodge, Economy Inn, Motel 6, Rodeway Inn, Sands Motel, SunTime Inn, Super 8, 🅞 Aamco, Big O Tire, Checker Parts, Desert Coach RV Ctr, NAPA, Rite Aid, St Geo RV, to LDS Temple
6	UT 18, Bluff St, St George, **E** 🅖 Chevron/dsl/24hr, Texaco/dsl, 🍴 Cracker Barrel, Jack-in-the-Box, Player's Grill, Subway, 🏨 Ambassador Inn, Comfort Inn, Fairfield Inn, Hilton Garden, 🅞 Buick/GMC, Firestone/auto, Hyundai, U-Haul, **W** 🅖 Shell, Texaco, 🍴 Arby's, Burger King, Claimjumper Steaks, DQ, Denny's, JB's, Jimmy John's, McDonald's, Pizza Hut, SF Pizza, 🏨 Best Value Inn, Best Western, Budget Inn, Claridge Inn, Comfort Suites, Crystal Inn, Desert Palms, Holiday Inn, Howard Johnson, Knight's Inn, Quality Inn, 🅞 🄷, Albertson's, AutoZone, Big O Tire, Cadillac/Chevrolet, Chrysler/Dodge/Jeep, Ford/Lincoln/Mercury, Goodyear/auto, Honda, Jo-Ann Fabrics, K-Mart, KwikLube, Mazda, NAPA, Nissan, Parts+, Radio Shack, Staples, Subaru, TempleView RV Park, Toyota, Vacation World RV Ctr, funpark
4	Brigham Rd, Bloomington, **E** 🅖 Pilot/Burger King/dsl/scales/24hr, 🏨 La Quinta, **W** 🅖 Chevron/Taco Bell, Mirastar/dsl, 🍴 Hungry Howie's, Subway, Taco Time, Wendy's, 🏨 Wingate Inn, 🅞 Walmart
2	UT 7 E, Southern Pkwy, **E** ➦
1	**Port of Entry/weigh sta both lanes**
0mm	Utah/Arizona state line

INTERSTATE 70

Exit	Services
232mm	Utah/Colorado state line
228mm	view area wb, litter barrels
227	Westwater
221	ranch exit
214	to Cisco
204	UT 128, to Cisco
193	Yellowcat Ranch Exit

N ↕ S — CEDAR CITY

ST GEORGE

N ↕ S

UT

N

INTERSTATE 70 CONT'D

Exit	Services
190mm	**Welcome Ctr wb, full ♿ facilities, vending, info, 🚮, litter barrels**
187	Thompson Springs, **N** 🅖 Shell/dsl, 🅞 café, camping, lodging
185mm	parking area eb
182	US 191 S, Crescent Jct, to Moab, **N** 🅖 Papa Joe's, **S** to Arches/Canyonlands NP
181mm	**rest area eb, full ♿ facilities, scenic view, 🚮, litter barrels**
175	ranch exit

N ↑ S

G R E E N R I V E R

164	UT 19, Green River, **1-3 mi N** 🅖 Phillis 66/Burger King/dsl, Silver Eagle/Blimpie/dsl, Westwinds Trkstp/Sinclair/rest/dsl/scales/24hr, 🍴 Tamarisk Rest., 🛏 Bookcliff Motel/rest., Comfort Inn, Holiday Inn Express, Knights Inn, Motel 6, Super 8, Ramada Ltd, River Terrace Inn, 🅞 KOA, Powell River Museum, tires/repair, same as 160
160	UT 19, Green River, **0-2 mi N** 🅖 Chevron/Subway/dsl, Conoco/Arby's/dsl, 🍴 Ben's Cafe, Chowhound, Ray's Rest., 🛏 Budget Inn, Green River Inn, Robbers Roost, Sleepy Hollow Motel, 🅞 Ace Hardware, AG Mkt, Green River SP, NAPA/repair, Shady Acres RV Park, USPO, city park, same as 164
157	US 6 W, US 191 N, to Price, Salt Lake
149	UT 24 W, to Hanksville, to Capitol Reef, Lake Powell, Goblin Valley SP
146	**view area, restrooms wb**
144mm	**runaway truck ramp eb**
143mm	**view area both lanes, restrooms**
142mm	**runaway truck ramp eb**
138mm	**brake test area, restrooms eb**
131	Temple Mt Rd
122mm	Ghost Rock View Area both lanes, restrooms
116	to Moore, **N** view area both lanes
115	**N** view area eb
108	ranch exit
105mm	Salt Wash View Area both lanes
99	ranch exit
91	UT 10 N, UT 72, to Emery, Price, **12 mi N** 🅖, **S** to Capitol Reef NP
86mm	**S rest area both lanes, full ♿ facilities, litter barrels, petwalk**
73	ranch exit
63	Gooseberry Rd
56	US 89 N, to Salina, US 50 W, to Delta, **0-1 mi N** 🅖 Conoco/dsl, Maverik, Phillips 66/dsl, Sinclair/Burger King/dsl, 🍴 Denny's, El Mexicano Mexican, Losta Motsa Pizza, Mom's Cafe, Subway, 🛏 EconoLodge, Rodeway Inn, Super 8, 🅞 Barretts Foods, Butch Cassidy RV Camp, NAPA, truck/RV/auto repair, **NEXT SERVICES 109 MI EB**
48	UT 24, to US 50, Sigurd, Aurora, **1-2 mi S** 🅖, 🍴 to Fishlake NF, Capitol Reef NP
40	Lp 70, Richfield, **0-2 mi S** 🅖 Chevron, ⛽FLYING J/Pepperoni's/dsl/LP/rest./24hr, Maverik, Texaco/dsl, 🍴 Arby's, Frontier Village Rest., South China Rest., Subway, Taco Time, 🛏 Best Western, Budget Host, Days Inn/rest., Holiday Inn Express, Super 8, 🅞 🏥, Big O Tire, Buick/Cadillac/Chevrolet/GMC, Chrysler/Dodge/Jeep, Family$, Fresh Mkt, IFA Store, NAPA, city park, USPO, RV/truck repair
37	Lp 70, Richfield, **S** 🅖 Phillips 66/Wendy's/dsl, 🍴

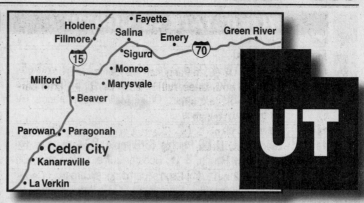

R I C H F I E L D

37	Continued
	KFC/Taco Bell, Wingers, 🛏 Comfort Inn, Fairfield Inn, Hampton Inn, 🅞 Home Depot, golf, **1-2 mi S** 🅖 Silver Eagle/Burger King/dsl, 🍴 JB's Rest., Lotsa Motsa Pizza, McDonald's, Pizza Hut, Rice King Chinese, 🛏 New West Motel, Quality Inn, Royal Inn, Travelodge, 🅞 Ace Hardware, AutoZone, $Tree, Ford, K-Mart, KOA, O'Reilly Parts, Pearson Tire, Verizon, Walmart/Subway, to Fish Lake/Capitol Reef Parks, st patrol
31	Elsinore, Monroe, **S** 🅖 Silver Eagle/gas
25	UT 118, Joseph, Monroe, **S** 🅖 Diamond D Travel Plaza, 🅞 Flying U Country Store/dsl/RV park
23	US 89 S, to Panguitch, Bryce Canyon, Zion
17	**N** 🅞 Fremont Indian SP, museum, info, 🅒, camping, chain-up area (WB)
13mm	brake test area eb
7	Ranch Exit
3mm	Western Boundary Fishlake NF
1	Historic Cove Fort, **N** 🅖 Chevron/Subway/rest stop (2mi)
0mm	I-15, N to SLC, S to St George. I-70 begins/ends on I-15, exit 132.

INTERSTATE 80

E ↑ W

Exit	Services
197mm	Utah/Wyoming state line
193	Wahsatch
189	ranch exit
185	Castle Rock
182mm	Port of Entry/weigh sta wb
180	Emery (from wb)
170	**Welcome Ctr wb/rest area eb, full ♿ facilities, 🅒, vending, 🚮, litter barrels, petwalk, RV dump**
169	Echo, **1 mi N** gas/dsl, 🍴 lodging
168	I-84 W, to Ogden, I-80 E, to Cheyenne
166	view area both lanes, litter barrels
164	164 Coalville, **N** 🅖 Phillips 66/dsl/mart, 🛏 Best Western, 🅞 Holiday Hills RV Camp/LP, CamperWorld RV Park, **S** 🅖 Chevron/dsl, Sinclair, 🅞 Griffith's Foods, NAPA, USPO, to Echo Res RA
155	UT 32 S, Wanship, **N** 🍴 Spring Chicken Café, **S** 🅖 Sinclair/dsl, 🅞 to Rockport SP
150	toll gate promontory
146b a	US 40 E, to Heber, Provo, **N** 🅖 Sinclair/Blimpie/dsl, **S** 🅞 Home Depot
145	UT 224, Kimball Jct, to Park City, **N** 🅞 Chevrolet, Ford/Mercury, RV camping, **S** 🅖 Chevron, 🍴 Arby's, Bajio Grill, Coldstone Creamery, Gandalfo's Deli, Ghidottis Italian, Loco Lizard Cantina, McDonald's, Panda Express, Quizno's, Starbucks, Subway, Ruby Tuesday, Taco Bell,

K I M B A L L J C T

UT

INTERSTATE 80 CONT'D

Exit	Services
145	Continued
	Wendy's, Wild Oats Cafe, Wingers, ⬛ Best Western, Hampton Inn, Holiday Inn Express, ⬛ GNC, Smith's Foods, USPO, Walmart, Outlet Mall/famous brands, RV camping, to ski areas
144mm	view area eb
141	ranch exit, **N** ⬛ Phillips 66/Blimpie, 🍴 Pizza Hut, ⬛ to Jeremy Ranch, **S** 🍴 Booster Juice, Cafe Sabor, Oh Shucks Grill, ⬛ Albertson's, camping, ski area
140	Parley's Summit, **S** ⬛ Sinclair/dsl, 🍴 No Worries Café
137	Lamb's Canyon
134	UT 65, Emigration Canyon, East Canyon Mountaindale RA
133	utility exit (from eb)
132	ranch exit
131	(from eb) Quarry
130	I-215 S (from wb)
129	UT 186 W, Foothill Dr, Parley's Way, **N** 🅷
128	I-215 S (from eb)
127	UT 195, 23rd E St, to Holladay
126	UT 181, 13th E St, to Sugar House, **N** ⬛ Chevron, Texaco, 🍴 Olive Garden, Red Lobster, Sizzler, Training Table Rest., Wendy's, ⬛ ShopKO
125	UT 71, 7th E St, ⬛ Texaco, ⬛ Firestone, **N** 🍴 McDonald's
124	US 89, S State St, **N** ⬛ Citgo/7-11, Chevron, Texaco/dsl, 🍴 Burger King, Skipper's, Taco Bell, Uncle Sid's Rest., Wendy's, Woody's Drive-In, ⬛ Buick, Chrysler/Jeep, Discount Tire, Dodge, Honda, Jeep, Suzuki, transmissions, **S** 🍴 KFC, Pizza Hut, ⬛ Ramada Inn
123mm	I-15, N to Ogden, S to Provo
	I-80 and I-15 run together approx 4 mi. See Interstate 15 exits 308-310.
121	600 S, to City Ctr
120	I-15 N, to Ogden
118	UT 68, Redwood Rd, to N Temple, **0-1 mi N on N Temple E** ⬛ Chevron/Subway/dsl, Maverik, ❤Loves/Arby's/dsl/scales/24hr, Tesoro, 🍴 A&W/KFC, Burger King, Carls Jr, Denny's, Taco Bell, Wendy's, ⬛ ☕ Inn, Candlewood Suites, Comfort Suites, Day's Inn, Holiday Inn Express, Motel 6, Quality Inn, Radisson, Utah St Fairpark, **S** 🅷
117	I-215, N to Ogden, S to Provo
115b a	Bangerter Hwy, **N** to Salt Lake ☕
114	Wright Bros Dr (from wb), **N** same as 113
113	5600 W (from eb), **N** ⬛ Phillips 66/dsl, 🍴 Perkins, Subway, Wingtips Bistro, ⬛ Comfort Inn, Courtyard, Fairfield Inn, Hampton Inn, Hilton, Holiday Inn, Hyatt Place, La Quinta, Microtel, Ramada Inn, Residence Inn, SpringHill Suites, Super 8
111	7200 W
104	UT 202, Saltair Dr, to Magna, **N** ⬛ Great Salt Lake SP, beaches
102	UT 201 (from eb), to Magna
101mm	view area wb
99	UT 36, to Tooele, **S** ⬛ Chevron/Subway/dsl, ✦FLYING J/Denny's/dsl/scales/LP/24hr, TA/Burger King/Taco Bell/dsl/scales/24hr/@, Texaco/dsl, 🍴 Del Taco, McDonald's, ⬛ Comfort Inn/Suites, Oquirrh Motel/RV Park, ⬛ 🅷, Blue Beacon, Mamie's Place, SpeedCo

88	to Grantsville
84	UT 138, to Grantsville, Tooele
77	UT 196, to Rowley, Dugway
70	to Delle, **S** ⬛ Delle/Sinclair/café/dsl
62	to Lakeside, Eagle Range, military area
56	to Aragonite
55mm	**rest area both lanes, full ♿ facilities, ⬛, 🚮, litter barrels, petwalk, vending**
49	to Clive
41	Knolls
26mm	architectural point of interest
10mm	**rest area both lanes, full ♿ facilities, ⬛, 🚮, litter barrels, vending, petwalk, observation area**
4	Bonneville Speedway, **N** ⬛ Sinclair/dsl/café/24hr
3mm	**Port of Entry, weigh sta both lanes**
2	UT 58 (no EZ wb return), Wendover, **S** ⬛ Sinclair/dsl, Shell/Taco Time/dsl, 🍴 Subway, ⬛ Best Western, Bonneville Inn, Days Inn, Knights Inn, Motel 6, Nugget Hotel/casino, Quality Inn, Western Ridge Motel, ⬛ Family$, Fred's Foods, Bonneville Speedway Museum, Montego Bay Hotel/Casino, KOA, USPO, auto repair
0mm	Utah/Nevada state line, Mountain/Pacific time zone

INTERSTATE 84

Exit	Services
120	I-84 begins/ends on I-80, exit 168 near Echo, Utah.
115	Ut 65 S, to Henefer, Echo, **1/2 mi S** ⬛ Grump's Gen Store, USPO, to E Canyon SP
112	UT 86 E, Henefer, **S** ⬛, 🍴, ⬛
111	Croydon
111mm	Devil's Slide Scenic View
108	Taggart
106	ranch exit
103	UT 66, Morgan, E Canyon SP, **N** Ford, **S** ⬛ Phillips 66/7-11, Texaco/dsl, 🍴 Luise's Mexican, Spring Chicken Café, Steph's Drive-In, Subway, ⬛ Ace Hardware, Ridley's Mkt, USPO, city park
96	Peterson, **N** ⬛ Sinclair (3mi), ⬛ to Snow Basin, Powder Mtn, Nordic Valley Ski Areas, **S** ⬛ Phillips 66/dsl
94mm	**rest area wb, full ♿ facilities, 🚮, litter barrels, petwalk**
92	UT 167 (from eb), to Huntsville, **N** ⬛ Sinclair/dsl (2mi), ⬛ trout farm (1mi), to ski areas
91mm	**rest area eb, full ♿ facilities, 🚮, litter barrels, petwalk**
87b a	US 89, to Ogden, Layton, **N** 🍴 McDonald's (2mi), ⬛ Best Western, ⬛ Cheese Outlet, Goodyear/auto **S** to Hill AFB
85	S Weber, Uintah
81	to I-15 S, UT 26, Riverdale Rd, **N** ⬛ Conoco/dsl, Sinclair, 🍴 Applebee's, Arby's, Carl's Jr, Chili's, Del Taco, IHOP, Jamba Juice, Lucky Buffet, McDonald's, Starbucks, ⬛ AT&T, Best Buy, Buick/GMC, Cadillac, $Tree, Good Earth Foods, Harley-Davidson, Home Depot, Honda, Jo-Ann, Kia, Lowe's Whse, Mazda, Nissan, PepBoys, Petsmart, Sam's Club/gas, Schwab Tire, Target, Toyota/Scion, Walmart/McDonald's, **S** ⬛ Motel 6, ⬛ Chrysler/Dodge/Jeep
	I-84 and I-15 run together. See Interstate 15, exits 344 through 376.
41	I-15 N to Pocatello
40	UT 102, Tremonton, Bothwell, **N** ⬛ Chevron/Quizno's/dsl/wash/24hr, Sinclair/Burger King/dsl/scales/@, 🍴 Denny's/24hr, McDonald's, Wendy's, ⬛ Hampton Inn,

INTERSTATE 84 CONT'D

E ↕ W

Exit	Services
40	Continued
	Western Inn, ⊡ Ⓗ (4mi), Jack's RV Ctr, truck/tire repair, **1 mi N** 🔋 Maverik, Phillips 66/dsl, Tesoro, 🛏 Marble Motel, ⊡ Alco, **S** ⊡ to Golden Spike NM, tires/repair
39	to Garland, Bothwell, **N** Ⓗ
32	ranch exit
26	UT 83 S, to Howell
24	to Valley
20	to Blue Creek
17	ranch exit
16	to Hansel Valley
12	ranch exit
7	Snowville, **N** 🔋 Chevron/Subway/dsl, ⚑*FLYING J*/Pepperoni's/dsl/LP/24hr, 🍴 Mollie's Café, Ranch House Diner, 🛏 Outsiders Inn, ⊡ Lotti Dell RV camping
5	UT 30, to Park Valley
0mm	Utah/Idaho state line

INTERSTATE 215 (Salt Lake)

N ↕ S

Exit	Services
29	I-215 begins/ends on I-15.
28	UT 68, Redwood Rd, **W** 🔋 ⚑*FLYING J*/dsl/rest./mart/24hr/@, Maverik/24hr, 🍴 Subway, ⊡ BMW (motorcycles)
26	Legacy Pkwy
25	22nd N
23	7th N, **E** 🔋 Exxon, Maverik, ⬛⬛⬛/Arbys/dsl/scales/24hr (1.5 mi), 🍴 Arby's, KFC, McDonald's, Taco Bell, Wendy's, 🛏 Motel 6, **W** 🛏 🔄 Inn, Baymont Inn, Candlewood Suites, Comfort Suites, Holiday Inn Express, Radisson
22b a	I-80, W to Wendover, E to Cheyenne
21	California Ave, **E** 🔋 Chevron/dsl, Sapp Bros/Sinclair/Burger King/dsl/@, 🍴 Great American Diner, Subway, ⊡ Goodyear
20b a	UT 201, W to Magna, 21st S, **W** ⊡ Goodyear, Kenworth
18	UT 171, 3500 S, W Valley, **E** 🔋 Sinclair, 🍴 Applebee's, Chili's, Costa Vida Mexican, Cowloon Moon, Cracker Barrel, Denny's, IHOP, Training Table, 🛏 Baymont Inn, Country Inn Suites, Crystal Inn, Extended Stay America,

S A L T L A K E C I T Y

Exit	Services
18	Continued
	La Quinta, Ruby Tuesday, Sleep Inn, ⊡ Ⓗ, PepBoys, **W** 🍴 Olive Garden, Pizza Hut, Red Robin, Starbucks, TGI-Friday's, Winger's, ⊡ Big O Tire, Costco/gas, JC Penney, Jubilee Foods, Macy's, Staples, Verizon
15	UT 266, 47th S, **E** 🔋 Conoco/dsl, 🍴 Dee's Rest., KFC, Pizza Hut, Taco Time, Taco Bell, Village Inn, Wendy's, ⊡ Albertson's, Goodyear/auto, Marie Callender's, Rite Aid, Walgreens, **W** 🔋 Chevron, 🍴 Arby's
13	UT 68, Redwood Rd, **E** 🔋 Chevron, Tesoro, 🍴 Applebee's, Apollo Burger, Arby's, Bajio Grill, Burger King, Carl's Jr, Golden China, Great Harvest Bread, Honey Baked Ham, McDonald's/playplace, Old Spaghetti Factory, Panda Express, Papa John's, Souper Salad, Starbucks, Subway, TX Roadhouse, Tuesday Morning, 🛏 Homestead Suites, ⊡ $Tree, Harmon's, Jo-Ann Fabrics, PetsMart, Radio Shack, Ross, ShopKO, Walmart/auto
12	I-15, N to SLC, S to Provo
11	same as 10 (from eb)
10	UT 280 E, **E** ⊡ Sam's Club, **W** 🍴 Applebee's, Arby's, Hooters, Jason's Deli, La Salsa Mexican, Macaroni Grill, Olive Garden, Red Lobster, Taco Bell, Wendy's, Village Inn, ⊡ Ⓗ
9	Union Park Ave, **E** 🍴 Black Angus, Carl's Jr, Chili's, Denny's, Famous Dave's BBQ, LaSalsa Mexican, Marie Callender's, Outback Steaks, Sweet Tomato, Tony Roma, 🛏 Best Western, Crystal Inn, Extended Stay America, Homewood Suites, ⊡ Albertson's, Barnes&Noble, Home Depot, Old Navy, Ross, Smith's Foods, Target, Walmart/auto, **W** 🔋 Tesoro, 🛏 Crystal Inn, Motel 6, Super 8
8	UT 152, 2000 E, **E** 🔋 Chevron, 🍴 KFC, Panda Express, Taco Bell, **W** 🍴 Wendy's
6	6200 S, **E** 🍴 Loco Lizards Café, Mikado Café, Quizno's, ⊡ Alta, Brighton, Snowbird, Solitude/ski areas
5	UT 266, 45th S, Holladay, **W** 🔋 Tesoro
4	39th S, **E** 🔋 Chevron, Sinclair, 🍴 Barbacoa Grill, Rocky Mtn Pizza, ⊡ Ace Hardware, Dan's Foods, **W** Ⓗ
3	33rd S, Wasatch, **W** 🔋 Tesoro, 🍴 Burger King, KFC, McDonald's, Taco Bell, Wendy's
2	I-80 W
	I-215 begins/ends on I-80, exit 130.

VERMONT

INTERSTATE 89

S T A L B A N S

Exit	Services
130mm	I-89 Begins/Ends, US/Canada Border, Vermont state line
22 (129)	US 7 S, Highgate Springs, **E** ⊡ DutyFree, **3 mi E** 🔋 Irving/dsl
129mm	Latitude 45 N, midway between N Pole and Equator
128mm	Rock River
21 (123)	US 7, VT 78, Swanton, **E** 🔋 Shell/dsl, **W** 🔋 Mobil/dsl, Shell, Sunoco/dsl, 🍴 Dunkin Donuts, Jacob's Rest., McDonald's, Pam's Pizza, Shaggy's Snack Bar, ⊡ Hannaford Foods, NAPA
20 (118)	US 7, VT 207, St Albans, **W** 🔋 Mobil/dsl, Shell/dsl, Sunoco, 🍴 Burger King, Dunkin Donuts, KFC/Taco Bell, McDonald's, Oriental Kitchen, Panda China, Pizza Hut, Thai House, ⊡ Ⓗ, Advance Parts, AT&T, Aubuchon Hardware, Chevrolet, Ford, Hannaford Foods, Jo-Ann Fabrics, Kinney Drug, PriceChopper Foods, Radio Shack, Sears, Staples, TJ Maxx, Verizon

N ↕ S

Exit	Services
19 (114)	US 7, VT 36, VT 104, St Albans, **W** 🔋 Mobil/dsl, Shell, 🛏 La Quinta, ⊡ Ⓗ, st police, vet
111mm	**rest area both lanes, full ♿ facilities, info, 🔌, 🛢, litter barrels, vending, petwalk, wifi**
18 (107)	US 7, VT 104A, Georgia Ctr, **E** 🔋 Mobil/dsl, Shell, 🍴 GA Farmhouse Rest., ⊡ GA Auto Parts, Homestead RV Park, USPO, repair
17 (98)	US 2, US 7, Lake Champlain Islands, **E** 🔋 Mobil, Shell/dsl, ⊡ camping (4mi), **W** ⊡ to NY Ferry, camping (6mi)
96mm	**weigh sta both lanes**
16 (92)	US 7, US 2, Winooski, **E** 🔋 Mobil, 🍴 Friendly's, T-Bones Rest., 🛏 Hampton Inn, ⊡ Costco, Osco Drug, Shaw's Foods, **W** 🔋 Citgo, Irving, Shell/dsl, 🍴 Beyo Cafe, Burger King, Jr's Italian, Libby's Diner, McDonald's, Subway, 🛏 Motel 6, Quality Inn
15 (91)	VT 15 (from nb no return), Winooski, **E** 🛏 Days Inn, Handys Extended Stay Suites, ⊡ to St Michael's Coll., **W** 🔋 Mobil/dsl, Shell, ⊡ USPO

VT

VT

BURLINGTON N → S

INTERSTATE 89 CONT'D

Exit	Services
90mm	Winooski River
14 (89)	US 2, Burlington, **E** 🅖 Citgo/repair, Gulf, Mobil, Shell/dsl, Sunoco, 🍴 Al's Cafe, Applebee's, Burger King, CheeseTrader, Chicken Charlie's, Dunkin Donuts, Friendly's, Leonardo's Pizza, Marco's Pizza, McDonald's, Moe's SW Grill, Outback Steaks, Quiznos, Starbucks, Trader Dukes, Wind Jammer Rest., Zachary's Pizza, 🛏 Anchorage Inn, Best Western, Comfort Inn, DoubleTree Hotel, Holiday Inn, La Quinta, University Inn, 🅞 Barnes&Noble, BonTon, Healthy Living Mkt, JC Penney, Jo-Ann Fabrics, Kohl's, PriceChopper, Rite Aid, Sears/auto, mall, USPO, **W** 🅖 Mobil/dsl, Shell, 🛏 Sheraton, 🅞 🅷, Advance Parts, Michael's, PetCo, Staples, Verizon, to UVT
13 (87)	I-189, to US 7, Burlington, **2 mi W on US 7 N** 🅖 Citgo, Gulf, 🍴 Buffalo Wild Wings, China Express, Dunkin Donuts, KFC, Mamma Mia's Pizza, Starbucks, Subway, 🛏 Liberty Inn, 🅞 Bond Parts, Hyundai/Subaru, Kinney Drug, PriceChopper Foods, Radio Shack, Shaw's Foods, TJ Maxx, Walgreens, USPO, **2 mi W on US 7 S** 🅖 Gulf, Mobil, Sunoco, Shell, 🍴 Burger King, Burlington Cafe, Chicago Grill, Denny's, Koto Japanese, Lakeview House Rest.; McDonald's, Olive Garden, Pauline's Cafe, Pizza Hut, Quiznos, Zen Garden, 🛏 Comfort Suites, Ho-Hum Hotel, Holiday Inn Express, Maple Leaf Motel, North Star Motel, Quality Inn, Rodeway Inn, 🅞 Acura/Audi/VW, Advance Parts, Buick/Cadillac/GMC, Chevrolet, Country Curtains, Dodge, Ford, Hannaford Foods, Jeep, K-Mart, Lowe's, Nissan, Tire Whse, Toyota/Scion, repair, vet
12 (84)	VT 2A, to US 2, to Essex Jct, Williston, **E** 🅖 Mobil/24hr, Sunoco/dsl/24hr, 🍴 Chili's, Friendly's, Longhorn Steaks, Moe's SW Grill, 99 Rest., Ponderosa, Starbucks, TX Roadhouse, VT Sandwich, 🛏 Fairfield, TownePlace Suites, 🅞 Best Buy, Dick's, Hannaford Foods, Home Depot, Marshall's, Natural Provisions Mkt, Old Navy, Osco Drug, Petsmart, Shaws Foods, Staples, Walmart, st police, **W** 🛏 Courtyard, Residence Inn
82mm	**rest area both lanes (7am-11pm), full** ♿ **facilities,** 🅲, 🚮 **, litter barrels, vending, petwalk, WiFi**
11 (79)	US 2, to VT 117, Richmond, **E** 🛏 Kitchen Table Rest., **W** 🅖 Mobil/dsl
67mm	**parking area/weigh sta sb**
66mm	**weigh sta nb**
10 (64)	VT 100, to US 2, Waterbury, **E** 🅖 Mobil/dsl/24hr, Shell/dsl, 🍴 Pizza Shoppe, 🛏 Best Western/rest, Thatcher Brook Inn/rest., 🅞 Shaws Foods/Osco Drug, TrueValue, **W** 🅖 Citgo/dsl, 🍴 Maxi's Rest., Zachary's Pizza, 🅞 USPO
9 (59)	US 2, to VT 100B, Middlesex, **W** 🍴 Red Hen Baking Co, 🅞 museum, st police
8 (53)	US 2, Montpelier, **1 mi E** 🅖 Citgo, Gulf/dsl, Mobil, Shell/dsl, Sunoco/repair, 🍴 Al Portego Italian, China Star, Dunkin Donuts, Julio's, Sarducci's Rest., Subway, 🛏 Capitol Plaza Hotel, Montpelier Inn, 🅞 Aubuchon Hardware, Bond Parts, Rite Aid, Shaw's Foods, camping (6mi), to VT Coll
7 (50)	VT 62, to US 302, Barre, **E** 🅖 Irving/dsl, 🍴 Applebee's, 🛏 Comfort Suites, 🅞 Honda, Shaw's Foods, Staples, **1 mi E** 🛏 Hilltop Inn, 🅞 🅷, JC Penney, Jo-Ann Fabrics, Subaru, Toyota/Scion, camping (7mi)
6 (47)	VT 63, to VT 14, S Barre, **4 mi E** 🅖, 🍴 🛏, camping, info

N → S DERBY CTR

Exit	Services
5 (43)	VT 64, to VT 12, VT 14, Williamstown, **6 mi E** gas/dsl, 🍴 🛏, camping, **W** to Norwich U
41mm	highest elevation on I-89, 1752 ft
34.5mm	**weigh sta both lanes**
4 (31)	VT 66, Randolph, **E** 🅞 RV camping (seasonal 1mi), **W** 🅖 Mobil/dsl, 🍴 McDonald's, lodging (3mi), 🅞 🅷, RV camping (5mi)
30mm	parking area sb
3 (22)	VT 107, Bethel, **E** 🅖 Mobil/dsl, 🍴 Eaton's Rest., Village Pizza, 🅞 to Jos Smith Mon (8mi), **1 mi W** 🅖 Irving/dsl/LP, 🅞 Rite Aid, st police, vet
14mm	White River
2 (13)	VT 14, VT 132, Sharon, **W** 🅖 Gulf/dsl, 🍴 Dixie's Kitchen, Sandy's Drive Inn, 🅞 Sharon Country Store, USPO, Jos Smith Mon (6mi)
9mm	**rest area/weigh sta both lanes (7am-11pm), full** ♿ **facilities,** 🅲**, info,** 🚮**, litter barrels, vending, wi-fi**
7mm	White River
1 (4)	US 4, to Woodstock, Quechee, **3 mi E** 🅖 Irving, 🛏 Hampton Inn, Holiday Inn Express, Super 8
1mm	I-91, N to St Johnsbury, S to Brattleboro
0mm	Vermont/New Hampshire state line, Connecticut River

INTERSTATE 91

Exit	Services
178mm	I-91 begins/ends., US/Canada Border, Vermont state line, US Customs
29 (177)	US 5, Derby Line, **E** Dutyfree, **1 mi W** 🅖 Irving/Circle K/dsl, 🅞 city park
176.5mm	**Welcome Ctr sb, full** ♿ **facilities, info,** 🚮**, litter barrels,** 🅲**, petwalk, wi-fi, Midpoint between the Equator and N Pole**
28 (172)	US 5, VT 105, Derby Ctr, **E** 🅖 Gulf, Shell/dsl, Sunoco/repair, 🍴 Cow Palace Rest., 🛏 Border Motel, 🅞 Ace Hardware, USPO, **W** 🅖 Irving/Hoagie's Pizza, Mobil/dsl, 🍴 McDonald's, Roasters Cafe, Sub Sta./Village Pizza, 🛏 4 Seasons, Pepin's Motel, 🅞 🅷, Advance Parts, Bond Parts, Chrysler/Dodge/Jeep, $Tree, Kinney Drug, Parts+, PriceChopper Foods, Rite Aid, Shaw's Foods, Verizon, RV camping, st police
27 (170)	VT 191, to US 5, VT 105, Newport, **3 mi W** 🅞 🅷, Border Patrol, camping, info
167mm	**parking area/weigh sta both directions**
26 (161)	US 5, VT 58, Orleans, **E** 🅖 Irving, Sunoco, 🍴 Subway, 🅞 Austin's Drugs, Family$, Thibaults Mkt, TrueValue, USPO, **W** camping (5mi)
156.5mm	Barton River
25 (156)	VT 16, Barton, **1 mi E** 🅖 Gulf, Irving/Circle K/dsl, 🍴 Ming's Chinese, Parson's Corner Rest., Step Back Cafe, 🅞 Barton Drug, Bond Parts, C&C Foods, USPO, camping (2mi), repair
154mm	parking area nb
150.5mm	highest elevation on I-91, 1856 ft
143mm	scenic overlook nb
141mm	**rest area sb, full** ♿ **facilities, info,** 🚮**, litter barrels,** 🅲
24 (140)	VT 122, Wheelock, **2 mi E** 🅖, 🍴 lodging
23 (137)	US 5, to VT 114, Lyndonville, **E** 🅖 Gulf/dsl, Mobil/Dunkin Donuts, Valero, 🍴 China Moon, Hoagie's Pizza, McDonald's, Miss Lyndonville Diner, Pizza Man, 🛏 Colonnade Inn, 🅞 $General, NAPA, Kinney Drug, Rite Aid, TrueValue, White Mkt Foods, **W** 🛏 Lyndon Motel
22 (132)	to US 5, St Johnsbury, **1-2 mi E** 🅖 Sunoco/dsl, 🍴

INTERSTATE 91 CONT'D

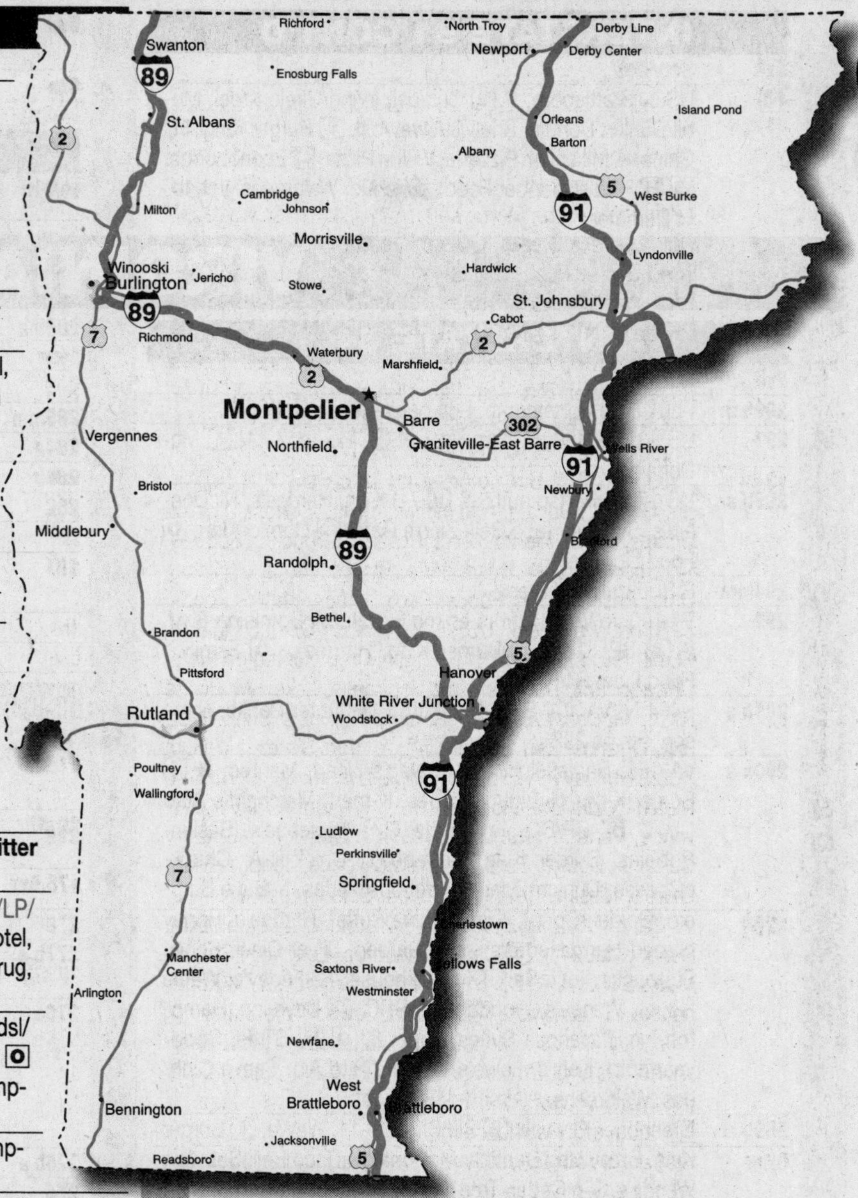

Exit	Services
22 (132)	Continued
	KFC/Taco Bell, Kham's Cuisine, Pizza Hut, ◎ Ⓗ, Aubuchon Hardware, Bond Parts, Buick/GMC, Kinney Drug, PriceChopper Foods, Subaru, repair, **3 mi E** on US 5 ⊠ Irving, ◎ AT&T, Firestone, JC Penney, Radio Shack, Sears
21 (131)	US 2, to VT 15, St Johnsbury, **1-2 mi E** services
20 (129)	US 5, to US 2, St Johnsbury, **E** ⊠ Irving/dsl, Mobil, Shell/dsl, ⊞ Anthony's Diner, Dunkin Donuts, East Garden Chinese, McDonald's, Subway, Winegate Rest., ◎ Family$, Kevin's Repair, Mkt St, Rite Aid, TrueValue, museum, welcome ctr, **W** ⊟ Comfort Inn, ◎ st police
19 (128)	I-93 S to Littleton NH
122mm	scenic view nb
18 (121)	to US 5, Barnet, **E** ◎ camping (5mi), **W** ◎ camping (5mi)
115mm	parking area sb
113mm	parking area nb
17 (110)	US 302, to US 5, Wells River, NH, **E** ⊞ Warner's Rest., **W** ⊠ P&H Trkstp/rest./dsl/scales/24hr, ◎ Ⓗ (5mi), camping (9mi)
100mm	**nb rest area, full** ♿ **facilities,** ☏ **info,** ⊠ **litter barrels, petwalk, sb parking area**
16 (98)	VT 25, to US 5, Bradford, **E** ⊠ Mobil/dsl/LP/café, ⊞ Hungry Bear Grill, ⊟ Bradford Motel, ◎ Bond Parts, Hannafords Foods, Kinney Drug, NAPA, Pierson Farm Mkt, **W** st police
15 (92)	Fairlee, **E** ⊠ Citgo/dsl, Gulf, Irving/dsl, Shell/dsl/LP, ⊞ Baileys Tavern, Fairlee Diner, Subway, ◎ Ace Hardware, Wings Mkt/deli, USPO, camping, **W** ◎ golf
14 (84)	VT 113, to US 5, Thetford, **1 mi E** ◎ ⊞ camping, **W** ◎ camping
13 (75)	US 5, VT 10a, Hanover, NH, **E** ◎ Ⓗ, to Dartmouth, **W** ⊠ Citgo, ⊞ Norwich Inn Rest., ◎ Subaru, USPO
12 (72)	US 5, White River Jct, Wilder, **E** ⊠ Gulf/dsl, Mobil
11 (71)	US 5, White River Jct, **E** ⊠ Mobil/dsl, Shell/Subway/dsl, Sunoco, ⊞ China Moon, Crossroads Country Café, McDonald's, ⊟ Comfort Inn, Regency Inn, ◎ Ford/Lincoln/Mercury, Hyundai, Jct Mktplace, Toyota, USPO, **W** ⊠ Citgo, Irving/Dunkin Donuts, Lukoil/dsl, ⊟ Fairfield Inn, Hampton Inn, Holiday Inn Express, Super 8, White River Inn, ◎ Ⓗ
10N (70)	I-89 N, to Montpelier
10S (70)	I-89 S, to NH, ⊠
68mm	**weigh sta both lanes**
9 (60)	US 5, VT 12, Hartland, **E** Ⓗ, **W** ⊠ Mobil (1mi), info
8 (51)	US 5, VT 12, VT 131, Ascutney, **E** ⊠ Citgo/dsl, Gulf/dsl, Irving/Circle K, Sunoco/Dunkin Donuts/dsl, ⊞ Ascutney House Rest., RedBarn Cafe, ⊟ Yankee Village Motel, ◎ Ⓗ, Getaway Camping (2mi), USPO, **W** auto repair/tires
7 (42)	US 5, VT 106, VT 11, Springfield, **W** ⊠ Irving/Circle K/Subway/dsl/scales/24hr, ⊟ Holiday Inn Express (5mi), ◎ Ⓗ camping
39mm	**weigh sta sb**
6 (34)	US 5, VT 103, to Bellows Falls, Rockingham, **E** ⊠ Shell/dsl, ⊞ Leslie's Rest., ⊟ Every Day Inn, **W** ⊠ Sunoco/dsl, ◎ st police (6mi)
5 (29)	VT 121, to US 5, to Bellows Falls, Westminster, **3 mi E** ⊠, ⊞ ☏, lodging
24mm	parking area both lanes
22mm	**weigh sta sb**
20mm	parking area nb
4 (18)	US 5, Putney, **E** ⊟ Putney Inn/rest., **W** ⊠ Rod's/repair, Sunoco/dsl/LP/24hr, ◎ Putney Grocery/deli, camping (3mi)
3 (11)	US 5, VT 9 E, Brattleboro, **E** ⊠ Agway/dsl, Citgo/dsl, Mobil/dsl, Sunoco, ⊞ China Buffet, Dunkin Donuts, Fast Eddy Cafe, Friendly's, House of Pizza, KFC, McDonald's, 99 Rest., Panda North, Pizza Hut, Steak-Out, Taco Bell, Village Pizza, Wendy's, ⊟ Best Inn, Colonial Motel, Hampton Inn, Holiday Inn Express, Motel 6, Quality Inn, Super 8, ◎ Advance Parts, Bond Parts, Buick/Chevrolet/GMC, $Tree, Ford, Hannaford Foods, Radio Shack, Rite Aid, Staples, Subaru, TrueValue, Verizon, USPO
2 (9)	VT 9 W, to rd 30, Brattleboro, **W** ⊠ Shell, ⊞ VT Country Deli, ◎ to Marlboro Coll, st police

ST JOHNSBURY

N ↑↓ S

BRATTLEBORO

= gas   = food   = lodging   = other   Copyright 2012 - The Next Ex

INTERSTATE 91 CONT'D

Exit	Services
1 (7)	US 5, Brattleboro, E [gas] Gulf/dsl, Irving/Circle K/dsl, Mobil/Dunkin Donuts, Shell/Subway/dsl, [food] Burger King, FC Chinese, Millenium Pizzaria, VT Inn Pizza, [lodging] EconoLodge, [other] [H], PriceChopper Foods, Rite Aid, Walgreens, vet, to Ft Dummer SP

6mm	Welcome Ctr nb, full [handicap] facilities, info, [C], [A], litter barrels, vending, petwalk, playground, wi-fi
0mm	Vermont/Massachusetts state line

INTERSTATE 93
See New Hampshire Interstate 93

VIRGINIA

INTERSTATE 64

Exit	Services
299b a	I-264 E, to Portsmouth. I-64 begins/ends on I-264.
297	US 13, US 460, Military Hwy, N [gas] Exxon, 7-11, [food] McDonald's
296b a	US 17, to Portsmouth, N [gas] 7-11, [food] Hardee's, McDonald's, Subway, Taco Bell, Zino's Cafe, [lodging] Comfort Inn, [other] Food Lion, vet
294mm	S Br Elizabeth River
292	VA 190, to VA 104 (from eb, no EZ return), Dominion Blvd, S [gas] BP, Shell, [food] Burger King, Hardee's, [other] Family$, Food Lion, Rite Aid
291b a	I-464 N, VA 104 S, to Elizabeth City, Outer Banks, same services as 292
290b a	VA 168, Battlefield Blvd, to Nag's Head, Manteo, N [food] Burger King, [other] BigLots, $Tree, K-mart, Merchant's Auto Ctr, S [gas] BP/DQ, 7-11, Shell, [food] Applebee's, Baskin-Robbins, Burger King, Carrabba's, Chick-fil-A, ChuckeCheese, Dunkin Donuts, Firehouse Subs, 5 Guys Burgers, Golden Corral, Grand China Buffet, Hardee's, Honey Glazed Ham, Hooters, Jade Garden, Silver Diner, Sonic, Starbucks, Taco Bell, TX Steakhouse, TGIFriday's, Waffle House, Wendy's, Woodchick's BBQ, [lodging] Days Inn, Hampton Inn, Savannah Suites, Super 8, [other] [H], $Tree, Goodyear/auto, Kohl's, Lowe's, Nissan, Rite Aid, Sam's Club/gas, Walgreens, Walmart, USPO, vet
289b a	Greenbrier Pkwy, N [gas] BP, Citgo, 7-11, WaWa, [food] Burger King, Crazywing Cantina, McDonald's, Taco Bell, Subway, Wendy's, [lodging] Cedar Tree Inn, Extended Stay, Hampton Inn, Marriott, Red Roof Inn, Staybridge Suites, Wingate Inn, [other] Aamco, Acura, Chevrolet, Chrysler/Dodge/Jeep, Ford, Hyundai, Jo-Ann Fabrics, Lincoln/Mercury, Mazda, Scion/Toyota, U-Haul, vet, S [gas] 7-11, [food] Abuelo's Mexican, Baker's Crust, Boston Mkt, Buffalo Wild Wings, China Chef, Chipotle Mexican, Coldstone, Cracker Barrel, Fazoli's, Firehouse Subs, Friendly's, Greenbrier Buffet, Jason's Deli, Jimmy John's, Joe's Crabshack, Kyoto Japanese, LoneStar Steaks, McDonald's, Olive Garden, Panera Bread, Paradocks Grill, Pizza Hut, Pop's Diner, Qdoba Mexican, Quizno's, Ruby Tuesday, Smokey Bones BBQ, Starbucks, Subway, Zoot's Cafe, [lodging] Aloft Hotel, Comfort Suites, Courtyard, Extended Stay America, Fairfield Inn, Hilton Garden, Homewood Suites, Hyatt Place, InTown Suites, Residence Inn, SpringHill Suites, Sun Suites, [other] AT&T, Barnes&Noble, Best Buy, Dillard's, Food Lion, Harris Teeter, Macy's, Marshall's, Michael's, Office Depot, Old Navy, Petsmart, Ross, Sears/auto, Steinmart, Target, TJ Maxx, Verizon, Walgreens, mall
286b a	Indian River Rd, N [gas] BP/dsl, Hess/dsl, Shell, SkyMart/dsl, Texaco, [food] Baskin-Robbins/Dunkin Donuts, Golden China, Hardee's, S [gas] Sunoco/dsl, [food] Capt D's,

Exit	Services
286b a	Continued Oriental Cuisine, Shoney's, Top's China, Waffle House, [lodging] Founder's Inn, [other] 7-11
285mm	E Branch Elizabeth River
284a	I-264, to Norfolk, to VA Beach (exits left from eb)
284b	Newtown Rd
282	US 13, Northampton Blvd, N [lodging] Quality Inn, Sleep Inn, [other] to Chesapeake Bay Br Tunnel
281	VA 165, Military Hwy (no EZ eb return), N [gas] BP, Shell, dsl/24hr, [lodging] EconoLodge, [other] Aamco, Chysler/Dodge/Jeep, S [gas] Citgo, 7-11, [food] Chick-fil-A, El Pollo Loco, Hooters, IHOP, KFC, Max&Erma's, Ruby Tuesday, Wendy's, [lodging] Hampton Inn, Hilton, Holiday Inn Express, Holiday Inn Select, La Quinta, Ramada, Residence Inn, [other] Bottom$ Foods, FarmFresh Foods, Firestone/auto, Home Depot, Nissan, Pep Boys, Petsmart, Target, Walgreens, Walmart/Subway
279	Norview Ave, N [gas] Shell/repair, [food] China House, Golden Corral, Pizza Hut, Wendy's, [other] $General, $Tree, Food Lion, K-Mart/gas, 7-11, Tire City, to airport & botanical garden
278	VA 194 S (no EZ return)
277b a	VA 168, to Tidewater Dr, N [gas] Citgo, 7-11, [food] Hardee's, S [gas] BP
276c	to US 460 W, VA 165, Little Creek Rd, from wb only, N [gas] Flag Gas, S [gas] BP, Shell, [food] McDonald's, KFC, Pizza Hut, Starbucks, Subway, Taco Bell, Wendy's, [other] AutoZone, $Tree, FarmFresh Foods, Kroger, Old Virginia Ham, Rite Aid, Walgreens
276b a	I-564 to Naval Base
274	Bay Ave (from wb), to Naval Air Sta
273	US 60, 4th View St, Oceanview, N [gas] BP/dsl/24hr, [lodging] Ecomony Inn, [other] Oceanview Boathouse/Pier, S [other] to Norfolk Visitors Ctr, info
272	W Ocean View Ave, N [food] Willoughby's Seafood, S [food] Sunset Grill
270mm	Chesapeake Bay Tunnel
269mm	weigh sta eb
268	VA 169 E, to Buckroe Beach, Ft Monroe, N [gas] Citgo, [food] Hardee's, McDonald's, [other] to VA Air&Space Ctr
267	US 60, to VA 143, Settlers Ldg Rd, S [food] Burger King, Golden City Chinese, [other] [H], to Hampton U
265c	(from eb), N [other] Armistead Ave, to Langley AFB
265b a	VA 134, VA 167, to La Salle Ave, N [gas] Citgo, RaceWay, [lodging] Super 8, [other] Home Depot, S [gas] BP, [food] McDonald's, KFC/Taco Bell, [other] [H], Advance Parts, Family$
264	I-664, to Newport News, Suffolk
263b a	US 258, VA 134, Mercury Blvd, to James River Br, N [gas] BP, Exxon/dsl, 7-11, Shell, [food] Abuelo's Mexican, Applebee's, Bojangles, Boston Mkt, Burger King, Chick-fil-A, Chili's, China Wok, Chipotle Mexican, Denny's, Dog House, El Azteca, 5 Guys Burgers, Golden Corral, Hooters, IHOP, Jason's Deli, KFC, McDonald's, Mongolian BBQ,

E   W

N O R F O L K

VA

INTERSTATE 64 CONT'D

Exit	Services

263b a Continued
New Garden Buffet, Olive Garden, Outback Steaks, Panera Bread, Pizza Hut, Quizno's, Rally's, Red Lobster, Starbucks, Subway, Taco Bell, Tokyo Japanese, Waffle House, Wendy's, 🛏 Best Western, Comfort Inn, Courtyard, Days Inn, Embassy Suites, Holiday Inn, Quality Inn, Ramada Inn, Red Roof Inn, 🅞 AT&T, Bottom$ Foods, Chevrolet/Mazda, FarmFresh Foods, Ford, GNC, Goodyear/auto, JC Penney, Jo-Ann Fabrics, Macy's, Marshall's, NAPA, Nissan, Office Depot, PetCo, Ross, Target, U-Haul, Verizon, Volvo, USPO, Walgreens, Walmart, S 🅖 Citgo/dsl, Miller's, 🍴 Chick-fil-A, CiCi's Pizza, Coldstone, Cracker Barrel, El Pollo Loco, Joe's Crabshack, Lone Star Steaks, Pizza Hut, Sonic, Sports Grill, TX Steaks, Waffle House, 🛏 EconoLodge, Hampton Bay Suites, Hilton Garden, La Quinta, Savannah Suites, SpringHill Suites, 🅞 Advance Parts, BassPro Shop, BigLots, BJ's Whse/Subway/gas, CVS Drug, $General, Firestone/auto, Hancock Fabrics, Lowe's, PepBoys, Radio Shack, Scion/Toyota, 7-11, vet

262 VA 134, Magruder Blvd (from wb, no EZ return), N 🅖 Exxon, 7-11, 🛏 Country Inn&Suites, Quality Inn, Suburban Lodge, 🅞 Hyundai, Mercedes

261b a Center Pkwy, to Hampton Roads, N 🛏 Hampton Inn, S 🅖 7-11, Shell, 🍴 Anna's Italian, Fortune Garden Chinese, McDonald's, Peking Chinese, Pizza Hut/Taco Bell, Plaza Azteca, Ruby Tuesday, Subway, 🅞 BooksAMillion, $Tree, FarmFresh Foods, Food Lion, GNC, Rite Aid, TJMaxx

258b a US 17, J Clyde Morris Blvd, N 🅖 BP, Shell/dsl, 🍴 Chatfield's Grill, Domino's, New China, Waffle House, 🛏 BudgetLodge, Country Inn&Suites, Holiday Inn, Host Inn, PointPlaza Hotel, Super 8, 🅞 Advance Parts, Family$, Food Lion, 7-11, S 🅖 BP, Citgo/dsl/24hr, WaWa, 🍴 Angelo's Steaks, Burger King, Cale Cafe, DQ, KFC/Taco Bell, Papa John's, Starbucks, Subway, Vinny's Pizza, 🛏 Marriot (1mi), Motel 6, Omni Hotel/rest., 🅞 🅷, Honda, museum

256b a Victory Blvd, Oyster Point Rd, N 🅖 BP, Citgo/dsl, Murphy USA/dsl, 🍴 Arby's, Blimpie, Burger King, Chick-fil-A, China Ocean, Hardee's, Pizza Hut, Red Circle Grill, Ruby Tuesday, Starbucks, Subway, TX Roadhouse, 3 Amigos Mexican, Uno Grill, 🛏 CandleWood Suites, Courtyard, Hampton Inn, Hilton Garden, Staybridge Suites, TownePlace Suites, 🅞 $Tree, FarmFresh Foods, K-Mart, Kroger, Walmart, vet, S 🛏 Crestwood Suites, Sleep Inn

255b a VA 143, to Jefferson Ave, N 🅖 Shell/dsl, 🍴 Chili's, Golden Corral, Hooters, McDonald's, Moe's SW Grill, Olive Garden, Panera Bread, Papa John's, Red City Buffet, Red Lobster, Silver Diner, Smokey Bones BBQ, Starbucks, 🛏 Comfort Suites, 🅞 🅷, Aamco,

255b a Continued
Acura, Buick/Cadillac/GMC, Chrysler/Dodge/Jeep, Farm-Fresh Foods/deli, Home Depot, Kohl's, Lincoln/Mercury, Lowe's, Michael's, Ross, PetCo, Sam's Club/gas, TJ Maxx, Trader Joe's, Tuesday Morning, Walmart, 🖂, S 🅖 BP/dsl, Citgo/dsl, Exxon/dsl, 🍴 Applebee's, Bailey's Grill, Buffalo Wild Wings, Carrabba's, Cheddar's, Cheeseburger Paradise, Chick-fil-A, Chipotle Mexican, Cracker Barrel, KFC, McDonald's, Melting Pot, Outback Steaks, Red Robin, Ruby Tuesday, Starbucks, Subway, Taco Bell, TGIFriday's, Waffle House, Wendy's, 🛏 Best Western, Comfort Inn, Courtyard, Hampton Inn, Microtel, Residence Inn, Studio+, 🅞 Barnes&Noble, Best Buy, Belk, Costco, Dillard's, JC Penney, Macy's, Old Navy, Petsmart, Sears Auto Ctr, 7-11, Target, Verizon, World Mkt, mall

250b a to US Army Trans Museum, N 🅖 BP/dsl, Exxon/dsl, 7-11/gas, Sunoco, 🍴 Hardee's, 🅞 B&L Auto Repair, Newport News Campground/Park (1mi), to Yorktown Victory Ctr, S 🅖 RaceWay, 🛏 Ft Eustis Inn, Holiday Inn Express, Mulberry Inn, Rodeway Inn, 🅞 7-11

247 VA 143, to VA 238 (no EZ return wb), N 🅖 7-11/gas, 🅞 to Yorktown, S 🅞 to Jamestown Settlement

243 VA 143, to Williamsburg, exits left from wb, S same as 242a

242b a VA 199, to US 60, to Williamsburg, N 🛏 Day's Hotel/rest., 🅞 Best Buy, JC Penney, Kohl's, Target, water funpark, to Yorktown NHS, **1 mi** S 🅖 7-11/gas, Texaco, 🍴 China's Cuisine, KFC, McDonald's, Sportsmans Grille, Starbucks, Subway, Taco Bell, Wendy's, Whaling Co Rest., 🛏 Country Inn&Suites, Courtyard, Marriott/rest., Quality Inn, 🅞 camping, to William&Mary Coll, Busch Gardens, to Jamestown NHS

238 VA 143, to Colonial Williamsburg, Camp Peary, **2-3 mi** S on US 60 🅖 7-11/gas, Shell, Texaco, 🍴 Aberdeen Barn Rest., Black Angus Grill, Cracker Barrel, DQ, Firehouse Subs, 5 Guys Burgers, Golden Corral, Hooter's, IHOP, Jefferson Steaks, KFC, McDonald's, Mirabella's Pizza, Pizza Hut, Plaza Azteca, Red Hot&Blue BBQ, Sal's Rest., Subway, The Gazebo Pancakes, Uno Grille, 🛏 Best Value Inn, Best Western, Comfort Inn, Country Inn&Suites, Days Inn, EconoLodge, Embassy Suites, Fairfield Inn, Hampton Inn, Hilton Garden, Holiday Inn/rest., Homewood Suites,

VA

INTERSTATE 64 CONT'D

E ↕ W

Exit	Services
238	Continued
	La Quinta, Patriot Inn, Quality Inn, 1776 Hotel, Sleep Inn, SpringHill Suites, Travelodge, [⊙] [H], Anvil Camping (4mi), CVS Drug
234	VA 646, to Lightfoot **1-2 mi N** [⊙] KOA, **2-3 mi S** [⛽] BP/dsl, Exxon/dsl, Shell/dsl, [🍴] Burger King, Chick-fil-A, China Wok, Hardee's, IHOP, KFC, McDonald's, Pierce's Pitt, BBQ, Quizno's, Sonic, Starbucks, Subway, [🛏] Days Inn, Greatwolf Lodge, Super 8, [⊙] [H], $Tree, Ford/Lincoln/Mercury, Home Depot, Lowes, PetCo, Pottery Camping (3mi), Radio Shack, Ross, Walmart
231b a	VA 607, to Norge, Croaker, **N** [⛽] 7-11/gas, [⊙] to York River SP, **1-3 mi S on US 60** [⛽] Shell/dsl, [🍴] Candle Light Kitchen, China Star, Daddy-O's Pizza, KFC, Wendy's, [🛏] EconoLodge, [⊙] American Heritage RV Park, Doll Factory, FarmFresh Deli/gas
227	VA 30, to US 60, to West Point, Toano, **S** [⛽] BP/dsl (2mi), Shell/dsl, Star/Subway/dsl, [🍴] Welcome South Rest. (1mi)
220	VA 33 E, to West Point, **N** [⛽] Exxon/dsl
214	VA 155, to New Kent, Providence Forge, **S** [⛽] Exxon/DQ/dsl, [🍴] Antonio's Pizza, Tops China, [⊙] Colonial Downs Racetrack, camping (8mi)
213mm	**rest area both lanes, full [♿] facilities, [C] vending, [♨] litter barrels, petwalk**
211	VA 106, to Talleysville, to James River Plantations, **S** [⛽] [🍴]/Subway/dsl/scales/24hr
205	VA 33, VA 249, to US 60, Bottoms Bridge, Quinton, **N** [⛽] Exxon/dsl, Valero, [🍴] Nada's Subs, Panda Garden, Pearl City Chinese, Pepito's Mexican, Subway, [⊙] Food Lion, Rite Aid, **S** [⛽] FasMart, Shell/dsl, [🍴] McDonald's, Willie's BBQ, [🛏] Star Motel (3mi)
204mm	Chickahominy River
203mm	**weigh sta both lanes**
200	I-295, N to Washington, S to Rocky Mount, to US 60
197b a	VA 156, Airport Dr, to Highland Springs, **N** [⛽] Shell/dsl, Valero, [🍴] Antonio's Pizza, Domino's, Hardee's, Subway, Tops China, [⊙] Advance Parts, CVS Drug, Farmers Foods, 7-11, **S** [⛽] BP, Chubby's/dsl, Citgo/dsl, 7-11, Wawa, [🍴] Arby's, Aunt Sarah's Pancakes, Burger King, Chicago Pizza, Pizza Hut, Waffle House, [🛏] Best Value Inn, Best Western Clarion, Comfort Inn, Courtyard, Days Inn, Double Tree, EconoLodge, Hampton Inn, Hilton Garden, Holiday Inn, Holiday Inn Express, Homewood Suites, Microtel, Motel 6, Red Roof Inn, Super 8, [⊙] to [✈]
195	Laburnum Ave, **N** [⛽] Chevron, [⊙] repair, **S** [⛽] BP/24hr, Exxon, 7-11, [🍴] Applebee's, Asian Buffet, Capt D's, Chick-fil-A, China King, CiCi's Pizza, Cracker Barrel, Firehouse Subs, 5 Guys Burgers, Hardee's, KFC, Longhorn Steaks, McDonald's, Olive Garden, Papa John's, Qdoba Mexican, Red Lobster, Subway, Taco Bell, TGIFriday's, Wendy's, [🛏] Hyatt Place, Wyndham Hotel, [⊙] AT&T, Best Buy, CarQuest, CVS Drug, $General, $Tree, Ford, JC Penney, Kroger, Lowe's, Martin's Foods, Petsmart, Radio Shack, Sam's Club/gas, Target, Walgreens
193b a	VA 33, Nine Mile Rd, **N** [⛽] Exxon/Subway, [🍴] Arby's (1mi), McDonald's (2mi), **S** [H]
192	US 360, to Mechanicsville, **N** [⛽] Citgo/dsl, [🍴] McDonald's, [⊙] Tuffy Repair, **S** [⛽] BP, Citgo, [🍴] Church's

RICHMOND

RICHMOND

Exit	Services
190	I-95 S, to Petersburg, 5th St, **N** [⊙] Richmond Nat Bfd Park **S** [🛏] Marriott, [⊙] st capitol, coliseum.

I-64 W and I-95 N run together. See Virginia Interstate 95, exits 76-78.

| 187 | I-95 N (exits left from eb), to Washington. |

I-64 E and I-95 S run together.

186	I-195, to Powhite Pkwy, from wb, Richmond
185b a	US 33, Staples Mill Rd, Dickens Rd
183c	from wb, US 250 W, Broad St, Glenside Dr N, same as exit 183
183b a	US 250, Broad St E, Glenside Dr S., **N** [⛽] Chevron, Sheetz, [🍴] Bob Evans, Famous Dave's, McDonald's, Olive Garden, Pizza Hut, Taco Bell, TGIFriday's, Waffle House, [🛏] Baymont Inn, Best Western, Embassy Suites, Hampton Inn, Super 8, [⊙] AutoZone, Honda, Hyundai, K-Mart, Volvo, vet, same as 181, **S** [🍴] Denny's, [🛏] Sheraton, Westin, [⊙] [H] Home Depot, to U of Richmond
181b a	Parham Rd, **2 mi N on Broad** [⛽] BP/dsl, Citgo, Exxon, Hess, Shell, Wawa, [🍴] Arby's, Bailey's Grill, Buffalo Wild Wings, Burger King, Casa Grande Mexican, Chick-fil-A, ChuckeCheese, CiCi's Pizza, Coldstone, Domino's, Friendly's, Gyros & Subs, Hooters, KFC, LoneStar Steaks, Ma Ma Wok, McDonald's, Nanking Rest., Outback Steaks, Penn Sta Subs, Piccadilly, Quaker Steak, Red Lobster, Shoney's, Starbucks, Superking Buffet, Valacino's, Wendy's, Zorba's Rest., [🛏] Country Inn&Suites, EconoLodge, Quality Inn, Rodeway Inn, Suburban Lodge, [⊙] [H], Aamco, Acura, Audi/VW, BigLots, BMW/Mini, Books-A-Million, Cadillac, Chrysler/Dodge/Jeep, CVS Drug, $General, $Tree, Food Lion, Hancock Fabrics, Infiniti, Jo-Ann Fabrics, KIA, Marshall's, Merchant's Tire, Mercedes, NAPA, PepBoys, Scion/Toyota, Subaru, Steinmart, TJ Maxx, Tuffy Repair, Verizon, Walgreens
180	Gaskins Rd, **N** [⛽] BP/24hr, Shell/dsl, [🍴] Cracker Barrel, O'Charley's, Starbucks, [🛏] Fairfield Inn, Holiday Inn Express, SpringHill Suites, **N on Broad** [⛽] East Coast/Blimpie, Exxon, 7-11, [🍴] Applebee's, Golden Corral, IHOP, McDonald's, Pizza Hut, Qdoba Mexican, Ruby Tuesday, Subway, Taco Bell, Tripp's Rest., [⊙] Advance Parts, Costco/gas, $Tree, Goodyear/auto, Kroger/gas, Lowe's, Martin's Foods, Mazda, Michael's, Office Depot, Sam's Club/gas, mall
178b a	US 250, Broad St, Short Pump, **N** [⛽] Exxon, Wawa, [🍴] Chipotle Mexican, DQ, Firehouse Subs, 5 Guys Burgers, Leonardo's Pizza, Moe's SW Grill, Panera Bread, Silver Diner, Starbucks, [🛏] Comfort Suites, Courtyard, Hampton Inn, Hilton Garden, Homestead Suites, Hyatt Place, [⊙] CarMax, CVS Drug, Firestone/auto, Ford, Marshall's, Ross, Verizon, **S** [⛽] BP, 7-11, Shell, [🍴] Applebee's, Arby's, Barlouie Grill, Bertucci's, Burger King, Capt D's, Cheesecake Factory, Chick-fil-A, Chili's, Chipotle Mexican, Dave&Buster's, Domino's, Jason's Deli, Jimmy John's, Kanpai, KFC, Kona Grill, Longhorn Steaks, LJSilver, Maggiano's Italian, McDonald's, Mexico Rest., Mimi's Cafe, Panera Bread, Pizza Fusion, Quizno's, Red Robin, Starbucks, Taco Bell, TGIFriday's, Wendy's, [🛏] Candlewood Suites, Hilton, Hotel Sierra, Wingate Inn, [⊙] AT&T, Barnes&Noble, Best Buy, Buick/Chevrolet/GMC, CarQuest, Dillard's, $Tree, Home Depot, Kohl's, Kroger, Lowe's, Macy's, Martin's Foods, Merchant's Tires, Nissan, Nordstrom, Petsmart, Staples, Steinmart, Target, Trader Joe's, Verizon, Walmart, Whole Foods Mkt, World Mkt

RICHMOND

INTERSTATE 64 CONT'D

Exit	Services
177	I-295, to I-95 N to Washington, to Norfolk, VA Beach, Williamsburg
175	VA 288
173	VA 623, to Rockville, Manakin, **0-2 mi S** 🛢 Citgo/dsl, Exxon/dsl, Shell/dsl, Valero, 🍴 Bill's BBQ, CD's BBQ, Sunset Grill, ⊙ $General, Food Lion
169mm	**rest area both lanes, full** ♿ **facilities, vending,** 🍴 🛢 **litter barrels, petwalk**
167	VA 617, to Goochland, Oilville, **N** 🛢 Exxon/dsl, **S** 🛢 BP/Bullets/dsl/24hr
159	US 522, to Goochland, Gum Spring, **N** 🛢 Exxon/dsl, **S** 🛢 BP/DQ/dsl, Citgo
152	VA 629, Hadensville, **S** 🛢 BP (1mi), Liberty
148	VA 605, Shannon Hill
143	VA 208, to Louisa, Ferncliff, **7 mi N** ⊙ Small Country Camping, **S** 🛢 Citgo/dsl, Exxon/dsl
136	US 15, to Gordonsville, Zion Crossroads, **N** 🏠 Best Western, 🍴 IHOP, ⊙ Lowe's, Walmart, **S** 🛢 BP/McDonald's/dsl/24hr, Citgo/Blimpie/dsl/scales, Exxon/Burger King/dsl, 🍴 Crescent Rest.
129	VA 616, Keswick, Boyd Tavern, **S** 🛢 Citgo
124	US 250, to Shadwell, **2 mi N** 🛢 BP, Exxon, Hess, Liberty, Shell, 🍴 Applebee's, Aunt Sarah's Pancakes, Burger King, Guadalajara Mexican, Hardee's, King Chef, McDonald's, Quizno's, Starbucks, Taco Bell, Topeka's Steaks, 🏠 Hilton Garden, ⊙ 🅷 Audi/VW, BMW, CarMax, Ford, Giant Foods, KIA, Mercedes, Porsche, Rite Aid, Scion/Toyota, **S** 🏠 Comfort Inn
123mm	Rivanna River
121	VA 20, to Charlottesville, Scottsville, **S** ⊙ KOA (10mi), to Monticello
120	VA 631, 5th St, to Charlottesville, **N** 🛢 Exxon/dsl, Shell, 🍴 Burger King, Hardee's, Pizza Hut/Taco Bell, Waffle House, 🏠 Hampton Inn (2mi), Holiday Inn, Omni Hotel (2mi), Sleep Inn, ⊙ CVS Drug, Family$, Food Lion, vet
118b a	US 29, to Lynchburg, Charlottesville, **1-4 mi N** 🛢 BP, Citgo/dsl, Exxon, Shell, 🍴 Blimpie, Hardee's, Subway, 🏠 Best Western, Boar's Head Inn, Budget Inn, Comfort Inn, EconoLodge, ⊙ 🅷, UVA
114	VA 637, to Ivy
113mm	**rest area wb, full** ♿ **facilities,** 🍴 **vending,** 🛢 **litter barrels, petwalk**
111mm	Mechum River
108mm	Stockton Creek
107	US 250, Crozet, **1 mi N** 🛢 Exxon, Shell/dsl, **1 mi S** ⊙ Misty Mtn Camping
105mm	**rest area eb, full** ♿ **facilities,** 🍴 **vending,** 🛢 **litter barrels, petwalk**
104mm	scenic area eb, litter barrels, no truck or buses
100mm	scenic area eb, litter barrels, hist marker, no trucks or buses
99	US 250, to Waynesboro, Afton, **N** 🏠 Colony Motel, ⊙ to Shenandoah NP, Skyline Drive, ski area, to Blue Ridge Pkwy, **S** 🏠 Afton Inn
96	VA 622, to Lyndhurst, Waynesboro, **3 mi N** 🍴 Tastee Freez 🏠 Quality Inn, ⊙ Waynesboro Camping
95mm	South River
94	US 340, to Stuarts Draft, Waynesboro, **N** 🛢 Exxon/dsl, RaceTrac, 7-11/dsl, 🍴 Applebee's, Buffalo Wild Wings,

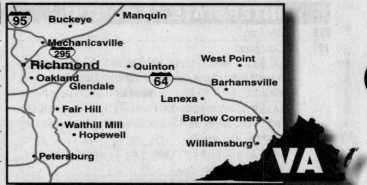

Exit	Services
94	**Continued** Clearwaters Rest., Cracker Barrel, Giovanni's Pizza, Golden Corral, KFC, King Garden, Outback Steaks, Quizno's, Ruby Tuesday, Shoney's, Sonic, South River Grill, Starbucks, Waffle House, Wendy's, 🏠 Best Western, Comfort Inn, Days Inn, Holiday Inn Express, Residence Inn, Super 8, ⊙ 🅷, Home Depot, Lowe's, Martin's Food/Drug, Radio Shack, Waynesboro N 340 Camping (9mi), Walmart, vet, **S** 🛢 Shell/dsl, 🍴 Chick-fil-A, McAlister's Deli, McDonald's, ⊙ AT&T, Books-A-Million, Kohl's, Michael's, Petsmart, Ross, Target, Verizon, museum
91	Va 608, to Stuarts Draft, Fishersville, **N** 🛢 Exxon/Subway (1mi), Texaco/Dunkin Donuts/dsl, 🏠 Hampton Inn, ⊙ 🅷, Eaver's Tires, **S** 🛢 Sheetz/dsl, 🍴 McDonald's, Wendy's, ⊙ Shenadoah Acres Camping (8mi), Walnut Hills Camping (9mi)
89mm	Christians Creek
87	I-81, N to Harrisonburg, S to Roanoke
	**I-64 and I-81 run together 20 miles. See I-81, exits 220-195.**
220	VA 262, to US 11, Staunton, **1 mi S** 🛢 BP, Citgo, Exxon, Shell, 🍴 A&W/LJ Silver, Applebee's, Arby's, Burger King, Country Cookin, El Puerto, KFC, Kline's Dairy Bar/BBQ, McDonald's, Papa John's, Red Chopstix, Red Lobster, Sam's HotDogs, Subway, Taco Bell, Wendy's, 🏠 Budget Inn, Hampton Inn, ⊙ Advance Parts, Belk, Buick/GMC, Cadillac/Chevrolet, CVS Drug, Dodge/Jeep, $Tree, Food Lion, Ford/Lincoln/Mercury, Harley-Davidson, Honda, Hyundai, JC Penney, KIA/Mazda, Merchant's Tire/auto, Nissan, Rule RV Ctr, Staples, Subaru, TJ Maxx, VW
217	VA 654, to Mint Spring, Stuarts Draft, **N** 🛢 BP/Subway/dsl, 🏠 Days Inn, **S** 🛢 Citgo/dsl/24hr, Liberty/LP, 🏠 Relax Inn, ⊙ KOA
213b a	US 11, US 340, Greenville, **N** 🛢 BP/Subway, 🚚 /Arby's/scales/dsl/24hr, Shell, 🍴 Edelweiss Rest., 🏠 Budget Host, ⊙ KOA
205	VA 606, Raphine, **N** 🛢 Exxon/Burger King, Fuel City/Smiley's BBQ/dsl/24hr, Sunoco/dsl, Whites/dsl/24hr/motel/@, **S** 🛢 Wilco/Hess/Wendy's/dsl/scales/24hr, 🏠 Days Inn/rest., ⊙ Koogler RV Ctr, Peterbilt
200	VA 710, Fairfield, **N** 🛢 BP/McDonald's/dsl/24hr, Texaco, **S** 🛢 Exxon/Subway/dsl, Shell/dsl
199mm	**rest area sb, full** ♿ **facilities,** 🍴 **vending,** 🛢 **litter barrels, petwalk**
195	US 11, Lee Highway, **N** 🏠 Maple Hall Country Inn, **S** 🛢 Exxon/dsl, Shell/Berky's Rest./dsl/scales/24hr/@, 🍴 Aunt Sarah's, 🏠 Best Value Inn, Days Inn, Howard Johnson, ⊙ Lee-Hi Camping, NAPA
	**I-64 and I-81 run together 20 miles. See I-81, exits 195-220.**
55	US 11, to VA 39, **N** 🛢 Exxon, 🍴 Burger King, Crystal Chinese, Naples Pizza, Ruby Tuesday, Waffle House,

(L E X I N G T O N — vertical sidebar)

VA

INTERSTATE 64 CONT'D

Exit	Services
55	Continued
	🛏 Best Western, Sleep Inn, Super 8, Wingate Inn, 🔵 $Tree, Radio Shack, Stonewall Jackson Museum, Lowe's, Walmart, **S** 🅖 BP/DQ, Texaco/Subway, 🍴 Applebee's, Country Cookin, Redwood Rest., 🛏 Best Western, Comfort Inn, Country Inn&Suites, Economy Inn, Holiday Inn Express, 🔵 Curves
50	US 60, VA 623, to Lexington, **5 mi S** 🛏 Days Inn
43	VA 780, to Goshen
35	VA 269, VA 850, Longdale Furnace
33mm	truck rest area eb
29	VA 269, VA 850, **S** 🅖 Citgo/dsl/rest.
27	US 60 W, US 220 S, VA 629, Clifton Forge, **N** 🔵 to Douthat SP, **S** 🅖 BP, Citgo/dsl, Exxon, 🍴 Pizza Hut (2mi), 🔵 Alleghany Highlands Arts/crafts
24	US 60, US 220, Clifton Forge, **1 mi S** 🅖 Shell/dsl, 🍴 DQ, Hardee's
21	to VA 696, Low Moor, **S** 🅖 Exxon, 🍴 Penny's Diner, Quiznos, 🛏 Oak Tree Inn, 🔵 HOSPITAL
16	US 60 W, US 220 N, to Hot Springs, Covington, **N** 🅖 BP/Subway, Exxon/dsl, Shell, 🍴 Belly-up Cafe, Burger King, Cucci's, Western Sizzlin, 🛏 Best Value Inn, Best Western, Holiday Inn Express, Pinehurst Hotel, 🔵 to ski area, **S** 🍴 McDonald's, 🛏 Compare Inn, 🔵 K-Mart
14	VA 154, to Hot Springs, Covington, **N** 🅖 Exxon/Arby's, Sunoco, 🍴 Hong Kong Chinese, KFC, Little Caesar's, LJ Silver, Subway, Wendy's, 🔵 Advance Parts, AutoZone, CVS Drug, $General, Family$, Food Lion, **S** 🍴 Applebee's, China House, Mama Pizza, 🔵 $Tree, Walmart
10	US 60 E, VA 159 S, Callaghan, **S** 🅖 Marathon/dsl/LP
7	VA 661
2.5mm	**Welcome Ctr eb, full** ♿ **facilities,** 🄲 🚮 **litter barrels, petwalk**
1	Jerry's Run Trail, **N** to Allegheny Trail
0mm	Virginia/West Virginia state line

INTERSTATE 66

Exit	Services
77mm	Constitution Ave, to Lincoln Mem. I-66 begins/ends in Washington, DC.
76mm	Potomac River, T Roosevelt Memorial Bridge
75	US 50 W (from eb), to Arlington Blvd, G Wash Pkwy, I-395, US 1, **S** Iwo Jima Mon
73	US 29, Lee Hwy, Key Bridge, to Rosslyn, **N** 🛏 Marriott, **S** 🛏 Holiday Inn
72	to US 29, Lee Hwy, Spout Run Pkwy (from eb, no EZ return), **N** 🅖 Shell, 🛏 Virginia Inn, **S** 🍴 Starbucks, Tarbouch Grill, 🔵 CVS Drug, Starbucks, Giant Foods, Rite Aid, Walgreens
71	VA 120, Glebe Rd (no EZ return from wb), **N** HOSPITAL, **S** 🅖 Sunoco, 🍴 Booeymonger Grill, IHOP, Melting Pot, PF Chang's, 🛏 Comfort Inn, Holiday Inn
69	US 29, Sycamore St, Falls Church, **N** 🅖 Exxon/7-11, **S** 🍴 Rock Cafe, 🛏 EconoLodge
68	Westmoreland St (from eb), same as 69
67	to I-495 N (from wb), to Baltimore, Dulles 🛫
66b a	VA 7, Leesburg Pike, to Tysons Corner, Falls Church, **N** 🅖 Exxon, Sunoco, 🍴 Jason's Deli, Ledo's Pizza, Olive Garden (2mi), Starbucks, Subway, Tara Thai, 🔵 7-11, Trader Joe's, Whole Foods Mkt, **S** 🅖 Citgo, 🍴 Baja Fresh,

66b a	Continued
	LJ Silver, McDonald's, Starbucks, 🔵 CVS Drug, Giant Foods, GNC, Kia, Staples, Volvo, vet
64b a	I-495 S, to Richmond
62	VA 243, Nutley St, to Vienna, **S** 🅖 Citgo, 🍴 Starbucks, 🔵 CVS Drug, Michael's, Safeway Foods/gas, Walgreens, **mi S on Lee Hwy** 🅖 Citgo, Liberty, Shell, Sunoco/dsl, 🍴 Chick-fil-A, Dunkin Donuts, IHOP, McDonald's, 🔵 Advance Parts, Chrysler/Dodge/Jeep, Harley-Davidson, Home Depot, Jeep, Radio Shack, 7-11, Subaru
60	VA 123, to Fairfax, **S** 🅖 Exxon, Shell, Sunoco, 🍴 Denny's, Fuddruckers, Hooters, KFC, Outback Steaks, Panera Bread, Red Lobster, 29 Diner, 🛏 Best Western, Hampton Inn, Residence Inn, 🔵 Chevrolet, CVS Drug, Kia, Mazda, NAPA, Rite Aid, Toyota/Scion, to George Mason U
57b a	US 50, to Dulles 🛫, **N** 🍴 Cheesecake Factory, 🛏 Extended Stay America, Marriott, 🔵 JC Penney, Lord&Taylor, Macy's, Sears/auto, mall, access to same as 55, **S** 🅖 BP, Shell/dsl, 🍴 Ruby Tuesday, Wendy's, 🛏 Comfort Inn/rest. Courtyard, SpringHill Suites, 🔵 Ford, Giant Foods, Honda, K-Mart, NRA Museum, Volvo, VW, Walmart
55	Fairfax Co Pkwy, to US 29, **N** 4 Lakes Mall, 🅖 Exxon, Sunoco, 🍴 Applebees, Blue Iguana Café, Burger King, Cantina Italiana, Cooker Rest., Joe's Crabshack, Logan's Roadhouse, Malibu Grill, Olive Garden, Pizza Hut/Taco Bell, Red Robin, Sakura Japanese, Starbucks, Wendy's, 🛏 Hyatt Hotel, Residence Inn, 🔵 🄷, Best Buy, BJ's Whse, Bloom's Foods, GNC, Kohl's, Michael's, Petsmart, Radio Shack, Target, Walmart, Whole Foods Mkt, World Mkt
53b a	VA 28, to Centreville Dulles 🛫, Manassas Museum, S same as 52
52	US 29, to Bull Run Park, Centreville, **N** 🅖 Sunoco/dsl, 🔵 Bull Run Park/RV Dump, Goodyear/auto, **S** 🅖 Exxon, Sunoco/dsl, 🍴 5 Guys Burgers, IHOP, Panda Express, Pizza Hut, Starbucks, Subway, Thai Rest., Tien Asia, 🔵 SpringHill Suites, 🔵 Advance Parts, AT&T, $Tree, Giant Foods, Grand Mart, Radio Shack, Trader Joe's, Walgreens, vet
49mm	**rest area both lanes, full** ♿ **facilities,** 🄲 🚮 **litter barrels, petwalk**
47b a	VA 234, to Manassas, **N** 🅖 Shell/dsl, 🍴 Cracker Barrel, 5 Guys Burgers, Golden Corral, Hershey's Ice Cream, Jerry's Subs, Uno, Wendy's, 🛏 Courtyard, Fairfield Inn, Holiday Inn Express, Sheraton, 🔵 Kohl's, Old Navy, Manassas Nat Bfd, **S** 🅖 BP, Exxon, RaceWay/dsl, 7-11, Shell, repair, Sunoco, 🍴 Arby's, Backyard Grill, Baja Fresh, Bob Evans, Burger King, Cafe Rio, CA Tortilla, Casa Chimayo, Checker's, Chick-fil-A, Chili's, China Jade, Chipotle Mexican, ChuckECheese's, City Grille, Coldstone, Denny's, Domino's, Don Pablo's, El Tolteca, Firehouse Subs, Great American Buffet, Hibachi Buffet, Hooters, KFC, Logan's Roadhouse, Marlin Ray's Grill, McDonald's, Olive Garden, Panda Express, Panera Bread, Papa John's, Pizza Hut, Pollo Campero, Popeye's, Potbelly's, Red Hot&Blue BBQ, Red Lobster, Starbucks, Subway, Taco Bell, TGIFriday's, Wendy's, Wok'n Roll, 🛏 Best Western, Comfort Suites, Hampton Inn, Holiday Inn, Quality Inn, Red Roof Inn, Residence Inn, Super 8, 🔵 Advance Parts, Aldi Foods, AT&T, AutoZone, Barnes&Noble, Best Buy, Bottom$ Foods, Buick/GMC, Burlington Coats, Costco/gas, CVS Drug, Chevrolet, Dick's, $Tree, Family$, Giant Foods, Macy's, Home Depot, Honda, Jo-Ann Fabrics, K-Mart, Lowe's, Macy's, Marshall's, Merchant Auto Ctr, Michael's, NTB,

Vertical text left margin: **E ↕ W C O V I N G T O N E ↕ W D C A R E A**

Vertical text right margin: **M A N A S S A S**

INTERSTATE 66 CONT'D

Exit	Services
47b a	Continued Office Depot, PepBoys, PetCo, Petsmart, Radio Shack, Reines RV Ctr, Ross, Sears/auto, Shopper's Foods, Staples, Toyota, Tuesday Morning, Verizon, Walgreens, Walmart, vet
44	VA 234 S, Manassas, N to Bristoe Sta Bfd SP
43b a	US 29, to Warrenton, Gainesville, N $\boxed{P}$ WaWa, S $\boxed{P}$ 7-11, Sunoco/dsl, WaWa, $\boxed{\text{¶}}$ Burger King, Chick-fil-A, Chili's, Coldstone, Domino's, 5 Guys Burgers, IHOP, Joe's Pizza/Subs, KFC/Pizza Hut/Taco Bell, McDonald's, Mimi's Cafe, MVP Grill, Papa John's, PeiWei, Potbelly, Qdoba, Subway, Wendy's, $\boxed{\triangle}$ Hampton Inn, ValuePlace, $\boxed{O}$ Best Buy, CVS Drug, Giant Food/drug, GNC, Goodyear/auto, Lowe's, Petsmart, Target/food, Walgreens
40	US 15, Haymarket, N $\boxed{O}$ Greenville Farms Camping, S $\boxed{P}$ Sheetz/dsl, $\boxed{\text{¶}}$ Foster's Grill, Giuseppe's Italian, McDonald's, Papa John's, Subway, Young Chow Cafe, $\boxed{O}$ Bloom Foods, CVS Drug
31	VA 245, to Old Tavern, **1 mi N** $\boxed{P}$ BP, $\boxed{O}$ USPO
28	US 17 S, Marshall, N $\boxed{P}$ BP/McDonald's/dsl, 7-11, $\boxed{\text{¶}}$ Anthony's Pizza, Foster's Grille, Great Wall Chinese, Subway, $\boxed{O}$ $\boxed{H}$, Bloom Foods, Radio Shack, vet
27	VA 55 E, Rd 647, Marshall, **1 mi N** $\boxed{P}$ Citgo, Exxon/dsl/LP, $\boxed{\text{¶}}$ Marshall Diner, $\boxed{O}$ IGA Foods
23	US 17 N, VA 55, Delaplane (no eb re-entry)
20mm	Goose Creek
18	VA 688, Markham
13	VA 79, to VA 55, Linden, Front Royal, S $\boxed{P}$ Exxon/dsl, Shell/7-11, $\boxed{\text{¶}}$ Applehouse Rest./BBQ/gifts, $\boxed{O}$ to Shenandoah NP, Skyline Drive
11mm	Manassas Run
7mm	Shenandoah River
6	US 340, US 522, to Winchester, Front Royal, N $\boxed{P}$ Quarle's/Bullet's/dsl, 7-11, $\boxed{\text{¶}}$ Applebee's, Checkers, Cracker Barrel, Foster's Grille, Ledo's Pizza, Los Potrillo's, McAlister's Deli, Mikado, Panda Express, Quiznos, Starbucks, TGIFriday's, Vocelli Pizza, $\boxed{O}$ Buick/GMC, $Tree, Ford, GNC, Lowe's, PetCo, Staples, Target, Walmart, S $\boxed{P}$ Exxon/Dunkin Donuts, 7-11, Shell, $\boxed{\text{¶}}$ McDonald's, $\boxed{\triangle}$ Hampton Inn, $\boxed{O}$ Poe's Southfork Camping (2mi)
1b a	I-81, N to Winchester, S to Roanoke
0mm	I-66 begins/ends on I-81, exit 300.

INTERSTATE 77

Exit	Services
67mm	Virginia/West Virginia state line, East River Mtn
66	VA 598, to East River Mtn
64	US 52, VA 61, to Rocky Gap
62	VA 606, to South Gap
62mm	**Welcome Ctr sb, full** $\boxed{\&}$ **facilities, info,** $\boxed{(\cdot)}$ **vending,** $\boxed{\text{☷}}$ **litter barrels, petwalk**
59mm	**rest area nb, full** $\boxed{\&}$ **facilities,** $\boxed{(\cdot)}$ **vending,** $\boxed{\text{☷}}$ **litter barrels, petwalk**
58	US 52, to Bastian, E $\boxed{P}$ BP/dsl, $\boxed{\text{¶}}$ Front Porch Cafe, W $\boxed{P}$ Citgo/dsl, Exxon/dsl
56mm	**runaway ramp nb**
52	US 52, VA 42, Bland, E $\boxed{P}$ Citgo, $\boxed{\text{¶}}$ Subway, $\boxed{O}$ $General, IGA Foods, W $\boxed{P}$ Kangaroo/DQ/dsl, $\boxed{\triangle}$ Big Walker Motel
51.5mm	**weigh sta both lanes**

(map of Richmond area with I-95, I-64, I-295, I-64 showing Manquin, Buckeye, Mechanicsville, Tuckahoe, Quinton, Richmond, Lee Park, Oakland, Brookbury, Glendale, Beulah, Fair Hill, Chester, Hopewell, Walthall, Colonial Heights, Petersburg, Prince George, Fort Davis, Burgess — VA)

W Y T H E V I L L E

48mm	Big Walker Mtn
47	VA 717, **6 mi W** $\boxed{O}$ to Deer Trail Park/NF Camping
41	VA 610, Peppers Ferry, Wytheville, E $\boxed{\text{¶}}$ Sagebrush Steaks, $\boxed{\triangle}$ Best Western, Sleep Inn, Super 8, W $\boxed{P}$ Kangaroo/dsl/scales/24hr, TA/BP/Country Pride/Popeye's/Subway/Taco Bell/dsl/scales/24hr/@, $\boxed{\text{¶}}$ Southern Diner, $\boxed{\triangle}$ Comfort Suites, Country Inn&Suites, Fairfield Inn, Hampton Inn, Ramada Inn
40	I-81 S, to Bristol, US 52 N

I-77 and I-81 run together 9 mi. See Interstate 81, exits 73-80.

73	US 11 S, Wytheville, W $\boxed{P}$ BP, Citgo, Go-Mart, Kangaroo/dsl, $\boxed{\text{¶}}$ Applebee's, Bob Evans, Cracker Barrel, El Puerto Mexican, Hardee's, LJ Silver, Ocean Bay Rest., Papa John's, Peking Chinese, Shoney's, Sonic, Waffle House, Wendy's, Yamoto Japanese, $\boxed{\triangle}$ Budget Host, Days Inn, EconoLodge, Knights Inn, La Quinta, Motel 6, Quality Inn, Red Roof Inn, Travelodge, $\boxed{O}$ $\boxed{H}$, AutoZone, Buick/Cadillac/Chevrolet/GMC, CVS Drug, $General, Food Lion, Ford, Goodyear/auto, Harley-Davidson, K-Mart, Nissan, Rite Aid, Subaru
32	I-81 N, to Roanoke
26mm	New River
24	VA 69, to Poplar Camp, E $\boxed{P}$ Pure/gas, $\boxed{O}$ to Shot Tower SP, New River Trail Info Ctr, W $\boxed{P}$ Marathon/dsl
19	VA 620, airport
14	US 58, US 221, to Hillsville, Galax, E $\boxed{P}$ Marathon/Subway, $\boxed{\text{¶}}$ Peking Palace, $\boxed{\triangle}$ Red Carpet Inn, $\boxed{O}$ $\boxed{H}$, W $\boxed{P}$ BP/24hr, Exxon/DQ/dsl, Gulf/dsl/24hr, $\boxed{\text{¶}}$ Countryside Rest., McDonald's, Pizza Inn/TCBY, Shoney's, Wendy's, $\boxed{\triangle}$ Best Western, Comfort Inn, Hampton Inn, Holiday Inn Express, Quality Inn, Super 8, $\boxed{O}$ Carrollwood Camping (1mi)
8	VA 148, VA 775, to Fancy Gap, E $\boxed{P}$ Gulf, Marathon/dsl, $\boxed{\text{¶}}$ Fancy Gap Cafe (2mi), $\boxed{\triangle}$ Lakeview Motel/rest., Mountaintop Motel/rest., $\boxed{O}$ Chance's Creek RV Ctr, to Blue Ridge Pkwy, W $\boxed{P}$ BP, Marathon/dsl, $\boxed{\triangle}$ Countryview Inn, Days Inn, $\boxed{O}$ KOA (2mi)
6.5mm	**runaway truck ramp sb**
4.5mm	**runaway truck ramp sb**
3mm	**runaway truck ramp sb**
1	VA 620, E $\boxed{P}$ Loves/McDonald's/Subway/dsl/scales
.5mm	**Welcome Ctr nb, full** $\boxed{\&}$ **facilities, info,** $\boxed{(\cdot)}$ $\boxed{\text{☷}}$ **litter barrels, petwalk**
0mm	Virginia/North Carolina state line

INTERSTATE 81

Exit	Services
324mm	Virginia/West Virginia state line
323	RD 669, to US 11, Whitehall, E $\boxed{P}$ Exxon, W $\boxed{P}$ FLYING J/Denny's/Subway/dsl/LP/scales/24hr

= gas = food = lodging = other Copyright 2012 - The Next E

INTERSTATE 81 CONT'D

Exit	Services
321	RD 672, Clearbrook, E Citgo/Bullets/dsl, vet
320mm	Welcome Ctr sb, full facilities, vending, litter barrels, petwalk
317	US 11, Stephenson, E Chick-fil-A, Guan's Garden, Main St Wings, McDonald's, Sonoma Cafe, Subway, Lowe's, Target, W Exxon/dsl, 7-11/Burger King, Sheetz/dsl/24hr, Sunoco/dsl, Denny's, Pizza Hut/Taco Bell, Comfort Inn, EconoLodge, Holiday Inn Express (3mi), , Candy Hill Camping
315	VA 7, Winchester, E Exxon, Sheetz/24hr, Bamboo Garden, Foster's Grille, Ledo's Pizza, Maggie Moo's, Sonic, Starbucks, Vocelli Pizza, TownePlace Suites, Curves, $Tree, Goodyear/auto, Martin's Foods/gas, PetCo, Walgreens, W Chevron/dsl, Exxon/Dunkin Donuts/Subway, Liberty/dsl, Shell/dsl, Arby's, Camino Real Mexican, China Town, 5 Guys Burgers, George's Pizza, KFC, LJ Silver, McDonald's, Pizza Hut, 3.Pizza, Wendy's, Hampton Inn, Shoney's Inn/rest., AutoZone, CVS Drug, Food Lion, TrueValue
314mm	Abrams Creek
313	US 17/50/522, Winchester, E BP/dsl, Citgo, Exxon/Subway, Shell/dsl, Asian Garden, Baskin-Robbins/Dunkin Donuts, Cracker Barrel, Golden Corral, IHOP, Los Tolteco's Mexican, TX Steaks, Waffle House, Aloft Hotel, Candlewood Suites, Holiday Inn, Fairfield Inn, Quality Inn, Red Roof Inn, Sleep Inn, Super 8, Travelodge, BigLots, Costco/gas, Food Lion, Jo-Ann Fabrics, Nissan, vet, W Sheetz/24hr, Bob Evans, Castiglia's Italian, Checkers, Chick-fil-A, Chili's, China Jade, China Wok, Chipotle Mexican, CiCi's Pizza, Coldstone, 5 Guys Burgers, Glory Days Grill, KFC, McDonald's, Olive Garden, Panera Bread, Perkin's, Pizza Hut/Taco Bell, Quizno's, Rancho Mexican, Red Lobster, Ruby Tuesday, TGIFriday's, Subway, Wendy's, Best Western, Hampton Inn, Hilton Garden, Wingate Inn, AT&T, Belk, Best Buy, Books-A-Million, $Tree, Home Depot, JC Penney, K-Mart, Kohl's, Lowe's, Martin's Foods, Michael's, Old Navy, PepBoys, Petsmart, Radio Shack, Ross, Sears/auto, 7-11, Staples, Target, TJ Maxx, Verizon, Walgreens, Walmart, mall, to Shenandoah U
310	VA 37, to US 50W, W Sunoco/dsl, Bo's Express, McDonald's, Outback Steaks, Subway, Best Value Inn, Budget Motel, Country Inn&Suites, Days Inn, Royal Inn, , Aldi Foods, Camping World, Candy Hill Camping (6mi), CarQuest, Gander Mtn, Honda, Suzuki, VW
307	VA 277, Stephens City, E CB's, 7-11, Shell/Subway/dsl, Arby's, Burger King, Butcher Block Cafe, Domino's, Ginger Asian, KFC/Taco Bell, McCoy's Dairy Bar, McDonald's, Pizza Hut, Roma Italian, Waffle House, Wendy's, Comfort Inn, Holiday Inn Express, Advance Parts, AutoZone, Curves, Food Lion, Martin's Foods/gas, Rite Aid, vet, W Exxon/Dunkin Donuts, Sheetz/24hr
304mm	weigh sta both lanes
302	RD 627, Middletown, E Exxon/dsl, W Liberty/dsl, 7-11, Super 8, Wayside Inn/rest., to Wayside Theatre
300	I-66 E, to Washington, Shenandoah NP, Skyline Dr
298	US 11, Strasburg, E BP/dsl, Exxon/McDonald's/dsl/LP, Arby's, Burger King, Castiglia Italian, Ciro's Pizza, Denny's, Great Wall Buffet, Golden China, Rancho Viejo Mexican, Fairfield Inn, Hotel Strasburg/rest.,
298	Continued Ramada Inn, Family$, Food Lion, Rite Aid, vet, W Battle of Cedar Grove Camping, to Belle Grove Plantation
296	US 48, VA 55, Strasburg, E museums
291	RD 651, Toms Brook, E Sunoco (1mi), Budget In (3mi), W Loves/Arby's/dsl/scales/24hr, Wilcox Hess/DQ/Stuckey's/Subway/dsl/scales/24hr, truck wash/repair
283	VA 42, Woodstock, E Liberty/7-11, Sheetz, Shell Dunkin Donuts, Arby's, Burger King, Hardee's, KFC McDonald's, Pizza Hut, Taco Bell, Wendy's, Comfor Inn, Hampton Inn, Holiday Inn Express, , CVS Drug Family$, Food Lion, NAPA Care, Rite Aid, to Massanutte Military Academy, W Exxon/dsl/24hr, Sunoco, China Wok, Cracker Barrel, Domino's, Subway, $Tree, Lowe's Radio Shack, Walmart
279	VA 185, RD 675, Edinburg, E BP/dsl, Exxon/dsl, Shell dsl/24hr, Sal's Italian Bistro, Ace Hardware, Creek side Camping (2mi), USPO
277	VA 614, Bowmans Crossing
273	VA 292, RD 703, Mt Jackson, E Exxon/dsl, Liberty Blimpie/dsl/scales/24hr, 7-11, Sheetz/Wendy's/ds scales/24hr, Burger King, China King, Denny's, Godfather's, Super 8, $General, Food Lion/24hr, USPO, t Mt Jackson Hist Dist
269	RD 730, to Shenandoah Caverns, E Chevron/dsl
269mm	N Fork Shenandoah River
264	US 211, New Market, E BP/Blimpie/dsl, Chevron/dsl Exxon/Subway/dsl, Shell/dsl, Texaco, Appleseed's Rest., Burger King, Godfather's, Italian Job, McDonald's Budget Inn, Quality Inn, Shenvalee Motel/rest., End less Cavern's Camping, NAPA Care, to Shenandoah NF Skyline Dr, W 7-11, Days Inn, to New Market Bf SHP
262mm	rest area both lanes, full facilities, vending, litter barrels, petwalk
257	US 11, VA 259, to Broadway, E Liberty/Blimpie/Burge King/Godfather's/dsl, 3-5 mi E KOA, Endless Caverns Camping
251	US 11, Harrisonburg, W Exxon/dsl, Economy Inn
247b a	US 33, Harrisonburg, E BP/Blimpie/dsl, Citgo/dsl Exxon/dsl, Royal/dsl, Sheetz, Applebee's, Bob Evans Bruster's, Chick-fil-A, Chili's, China Jade, CiCi's Pizza Domino's, El Charro Mexican, 5 Guys Burgers, Golder Corral, Great Wok, Ham's Rest., IHOP, Jess' Lunch, LJ Sil ver, McAlister's Deli, O'Charley's, Outback Steaks, Panera Bread, Quizno's, Red Lobster, Ruby Tuesday, Shoney's Subway, Taco Bell, TX Roadhouse, TX Steaks, Top China Waffle House, Wendy's, Wood Grill Buffet, Best Western Candlewood Suites, Comfort Inn, Courtyard, EconoLodge Hampton Inn, Holiday Inn, Jameson Inn, Motel 6, Resi dence Inn, Sleep Inn, AT&T, Barnes&Noble, Belk, Bes Buy, Books-A-Million, Chevrolet, $Tree, Firestone/auto Home Depot, JC Penney, K-Mart, Kohl's, Kroger, Lowe's Martin's Foods/gas, Michael's, Nissan, Office Depot, Ol Navy, PetCo, Petsmart, Ross, Staples, Target, TJ Maxx Verizon, Walmart/gas, to Shenandoah NP, Skyline Dr, W Exxon/Dunkin Donuts/dsl, Royal, Sheetz, Texaco, Arby's, DQ, Dragon Palace, Dunkin Donuts, Golden China Hardee's, KFC, Kyoto, L' Italia, Little Caesar's, McDonald's Sam's Hotdogs, , Advance Parts, BigLots, CVS Drug Food Lion

INTERSTATE 81 CONT'D

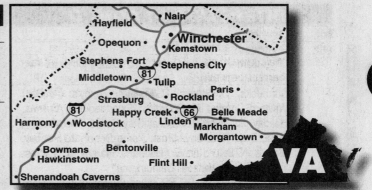

Exit	Services
245	VA 659, Port Republic Rd, **E** 🅿 Campus Corner, Exxon/dsl, Liberty/dsl, Texaco, 🍴 Panchero's Mexican, Subway, 🛏 Days Inn, **W** 🍴 Jimmy John's, Starbucks, 🅾 Ⓗ, to James Madison U
243	US 11, to Harrisonburg, **0-2 mi W** 🅿 BP/dsl, Exxon/dsl, Harrisonburg Travel Ctr/diner/dsl/scales, Liberty, 7-11, Sheetz, 🍴 Burger King, China Gourmet, Cracker Barrel, McDonald's, Pano's Rest., Pizza Hut, Pueblo Grande, Subway, Taco Bell, 🛏 Country Inn&Suites, Hampton Inn, Holiday Inn Express, Ramada Inn, Red Carpet Inn, Super 8, 🅾 Advance Parts, AutoZone, Chrysler/Dodge/Jeep, Family$, Ford, Honda, Hyundai, KIA, Subaru, Toyota
240	VA 257, RD 682, Mount Crawford, **1-3 mi W** 🅿 Exxon/dsl, 🍴 Burger King, Mrs. Rowe's, 🛏 Village Inn
235	VA 256, Weyers Cave, **E** 🅿 Texaco/dsl, **W** 🅿 BP/Subway/dsl, Exxon/dsl, 🅾 Freightliner, antiques, to Grand Caverns
232mm	**rest area both lanes, full ♿ facilities, ⓒ vending, 🗑 litter barrels, petwalk**
227	RD 612, Verona, **E** 🅿 BP/Subway/dsl, 🍴 Waffle Inn, **W** 🅿 Citgo/Wendy's/dsl, Exxon/Dunkin Donuts, Shell/dsl, 🍴 Burger King, China City, Ciro's Pizza, Hardee's, McDonald's, 🛏 Knights Inn, 🅾 Food Lion, Good Sam RV Park (3mi), Rite Aid, antiques
225	VA 275, Woodrow Wilson Pkwy, **E** 🛏 Quality Inn, **W** 🛏 Days Inn, Holiday Inn/rest.
222	US 250, Staunton, **E** 🅿 BP, Texaco/dsl, 🍴 Cracker Barrel, McDonald's, Mrs Rowe's Rest., Shoney's, TX Steaks, 🛏 Best Western, Red Roof Inn, Sleep Inn, **W** 🅿 Hess, Sheetz, Texaco/dsl, 🍴 Burger King, Chili's, Dunkin Donuts, 5 Guys Burgers, Massaki Japanese, Quizno's, Starbucks, Waffle House, 🛏 Comfort Inn, EconoLodge, Microtel, 🅾 AT&T, AutoZone, Lowe's, Martin's Foods/gas, Scion/Toyota, Walmart/Subway, American Frontier Culture Museum, auto repair
221	I-64 E, to Charlottesville, Skyline Dr, Shenandoah NP
220	VA 262, to US 11, Staunton, **1 mi W** 🅿 BP, Citgo, Exxon, Shell, 🍴 A&W/LJ Silver, Applebee's, Arby's, Burger King, Country Cookin, El Puerto, KFC, Kline's Dairy Bar/BBQ, McDonald's, Papa John's, Red Chopstix, Red Lobster, Sam's HotDogs, Subway, Taco Bell, Wendy's, 🛏 Budget Inn, Hampton Inn, 🅾 Advance Parts, Belk, Buick/GMC, Cadillac/Chevrolet, CVS Drug, Dodge/Jeep, $Tree, Food Lion, Ford/Lincoln/Mercury, Harley-Davidson, Honda, Hyundai, JC Penney, KIA/Mazda, Merchant's Tire/auto, Nissan, Rule RV Ctr, Staples, Subaru, TJ Maxx, VW
217	RD 654, to Mint Spring, Stuarts Draft, **E** 🅿 BP/Subway/dsl, 🛏 Days Inn, **W** 🅿 Citgo/dsl/24hr, Liberty/LP, 🛏 Relax Inn, 🅾 KOA
213b a	US 11, US 340, Greenville, **E** 🅿 BP/Subway, 🍴 Arby's/scales/dsl/24hr, Shell, 🍴 Edelweiss Rest., 🛏 Budget Host, 🅾 KOA
205	RD 606, Raphine, **E** 🅿 Exxon/Burger King, Fuel City/Smiley's BBQ/dsl/24hr, Sunoco/dsl, Whites/dsl/24hr/motel/@, **W** 🅿 Wilco/Hess/Wendy's/dsl/scales/24hr, 🛏 Days Inn/rest., 🅾 Koogler RV Ctr, Peterbilt
200	RD 710, Fairfield, **E** 🅿 BP/McDonald's/dsl/24hr, Texaco, **W** 🅿 Exxon/Subway/dsl, Shell/dsl
199mm	**rest area sb, full ♿ facilities, ⓒ vending, 🗑 litter barrels, petwalk**
195	US 11, Lee Hwy, **E** 🛏 Maple Hall Country Inn, **W** 🅿 Exxon/dsl, Shell/Berky's Rest./dsl/scales/24hr/@, 🍴 Aunt Sarah's, 🛏 Best Value Inn, Days Inn, Howard Johnson, 🅾 Lee-Hi Camping, NAPA
191	I-64 W (exits left from nb), US 60, to Charleston
188b a	US 60, to Lexington, Buena Vista, **3-5 mi E** 🅿 BP, Exxon, 🍴 Hardee's, KFC, LJ Silver, McDonald's, Pizza Hut, Taco Bell, Wendy's, 🛏 Budget Inn, Buena Vista Inn, 🅾 Ⓗ, to Glen Maury Park, to Stonewall Jackson Home, Marshall Museum, to Blue Ridge Pkwy, **W** 🅿 Exxon/dsl/24hr, 🅾 to Washington&Lee U, VMI
180	US 11, Natural Bridge, **E** 🅿 Shell/dsl, 🛏 Relax Inn, 🅾 Cave Mtn NF, Jellystone Camping, **W** 🅿 Shell/dsl, 🍴 Pink Cadillac Diner, 🛏 Budget Inn, 🅾 KOA, (180a exits left from sb)
175	US 11 N, to Glasgow, Natural Bridge, **E** 🅿 Exxon, 🛏 Natural Bridge Hotel/rest., 🅾 to James River RA, Jellystone Camping
168	VA 614, US 11, Blue Ridge Pkwy, Arcadia, **E** 🅿 Shell, 🍴 Mtn View Rest., 🛏 Wattstull Inn, 🅾 Middle Creek Camping (6mi), **2 mi W** 🅿 Exxon, 🍴 Burger King
167	US 11 (from sb), Buchanan
162	US 11, Buchanan, **E** 🅿 Exxon/dsl, 🅾 to BR Pkwy, **W** 🅿 Texaco/Subway/24hr
158mm	**rest area sb, full ♿ facilities, ⓒ vending, 🗑 litter barrels, petwalk**
156	RD 640, to US 11, **E** 🅿 Exxon/Brugh's Mill/dsl
150	US 11/220, to Fincastle, **E** 🅿 Citgo/dsl/24hr, Dodge's/dsl, 🍴 Subway/dsl/24hr, TA/BP/Country Pride/dsl/scales/24hr/@, 🍴 Bella Pizza, Country Cookin, Cracker Barrel, Hardee's, McDonald's, Shoney's, Waffle House, 🛏 Comfort Inn, Holiday Inn Express, Quality Inn, Red Roof Inn, Travelodge, 🅾 Berglund RV Ctr, CVS Drug, $General, truckwash, **W** 🅿 BP/dsl, Exxon/dsl/24hr, Sunoco, 🍴 Bojangles, Pizza Hut, Rancho Viejo Mexican, 3 Lil Pigs BBQ, Wendy's, 🛏 Howard Johnson, Super 8, 🅾 Curves, Kroger/gas, Verizon, vet
149mm	**weigh sta both lanes**
146	VA 115, Cloverdale, **E** 🅿 Exxon, Shell/dsl, 🍴 Burger King, El Rodeo Mexican, Hardees, McDonald's, Subway, 🛏 Country Inn&Suites, Days Inn/rest., Fairfield Inn, Hampton Inn, 🅾 Camping World, CVS Drug, Gander Mtn
143	I-581, US 220, to Roanoke, Blue Ridge Pkwy (exits left from sb), **1 mi E** 🅿 Sheetz, 🍴 El Toreo, Subway, Waffle House, 🛏 Hampton Inn, Howard Johnson, Knights Inn, Quality Inn, Super 8, **2-3 mi E on Hershberger** 🅿 BP, Exxon, Murphy USA/dsl, Shell, 🍴 Abuelo's Mexican, Applebee's, Buffalo Wild Wings, Carrabba's, Chick-fil-A, Coldstone, Hardee's, IHOP, Logan's Roadhouse, O'Charley's,

N ↕ S

S T A U N T O N

L E X I N G T O N

VA

ROANOKE · SALEM · N ↕ S

INTERSTATE 81 CONT'D

Exit	Services
143	Continued Olive Garden, Panera Bread, Red Palace Chinese, Red Robin, Ruby Tuesday, Shaker's, Smokey Bones BBQ, Starbucks, TX Steaks, TGIFriday's, Zaxby's, 🛏 Best Western, Comfort Inn, Courtyard, Extended Stay America, Holiday Inn, Hyatt Place, MainStay Suites, Sheraton, 🅞 AT&T, Belk, Best Buy, $Tree, Home Depot, JC Penney, Macy's, NTB, Old Navy, PetsMart, Sears/auto, Staples, Target, U-Haul, Verizon, Walmart, mall
141	VA 419, Salem, **E** 🅖 BP, Liberty/Burger King, Valero/dsl, 🍴 Country Cookin, Hardee's, IHOP, McDonald's, Starbucks, 🛏 Days Inn, Holiday Inn Express, La Quinta, Quality Inn, 🅞 🅷 Chevrolet, GNC, Kroger/gas, **W** 🅖 BP/Subway/dsl, Citgo
140	VA 311, Salem, **1 mi E** 🍴 Mac&Bob's Cafe, **1 mi W** 🍴 Hanging Rock Grill/golf
137	VA 112, VA 619, Salem, **E** 🅖 BP, Chevron, Citgo, Exxon/dsl, Go-Mart, Liberty, Sheetz/24hr, 🍴 Anthony's Cafe, Applebees, Arby's, Bojangles, Burger King, Denny's, Dynasty Buffet, El Rodeo Mexican, Firehouse Subs, Five Guys Burgers, Hardee's, Henry's BBQ, K&W Cafeteria, KFC, Mamma Maria Italian, McDonald's, Omelette Shoppe, Pizza Hut, Quiznos, Sam's HotDogs, Shoney's, Sonic, Starbucks, Subway, Taco Bell, Tokyo Express, Wendy's, Zaxby's, 🛏 Comfort Suites, EconoLodge, Quality Inn, Super 8, 🅞 Aamco, Advance Parts, AutoZone, BigLots, $General, $Tree, Food Lion, Goodyear, K-Mart, Kroger/gas, Lowe's, Merchant's Tire, Mitsubishi, O'Reilly Parts, Radio Shack, Snyder's RV, Walgreens, Walmart, **W** 🛏 Holiday Inn, Howard Johnson
132	VA 647, to Dixie Caverns, **E** 🅖 Citgo, Shell, 🛏 Budget Host, 🅞 Dixie Caverns Camping, st police
129mm	**rest area nb, full** ♿ **facilities,** 🚰 **vending,** 🗑 **litter barrels, petwalk**
128	US 11, VA 603, Ironto, **E** 🅖 Shell, **W** 🅖 Exxon/Dixie's/Subway/dsl/24hr
118c b a	US 11/460, Christiansburg, **E** 🅖 Shell/dsl, 🍴 Denny's, Cracker Barrel, 🛏 Days Inn, Fairfield Inn, Holiday Inn Express, Quality Inn, Super 8, 🅞 Harley-Davidson, **W** 🅖 BP, Exxon/dsl, Kash King, Shell, 🍴 Country Cookin, Hardee's, McDonald's, Pizza Hut, Ruby Tuesday, Subway, Waffle House, Wendy's, 🛏 EconoLodge, Knights Inn, 🅞 🅷 Advance Parts, Chevrolet, Chrysler/Dodge/Jeep, Ford, Honda, Hyundai, KIA, Toyota/Scion, to VA Tech
114	VA 8, Christiansburg, **0-1 mi W** 🅖 Citgo, Sunoco, 🍴 Anthony's Cafe, Burger King, Macado's Rest., Pizza Inn, 🛏 Budget Inn, 🅞 $General, repair
109	VA 177, VA 600, **E** 🅞 🅷, **0-2 mi W** 🅖 BP/dsl, Marathon, 🛏 Best Western, Comfort Inn, La Quinta, Super 8, 🅞 Buick/Chevrolet/GMC
107mm	**rest area both lanes, full** ♿ **facilities,** 🚰 **vending,** 🗑 **litter barrels, petwalk**
105	VA 232, RD 605, to Radford, **W** 🅖 Citgo (2mi), Marathon, 🛏 Executive Motel (4mi), 🅞 museum
101	RD 660, to Claytor Lake SP, **E** 🛏 Claytor Lake Inn, Sleep Inn, **W** 🅖 Citgo/DQ/dsl, Shell/Omelette Shoppe/Taco Bell/dsl/scales/@
98	VA 100 N, to Dublin, **E** 🅖 Exxon/Subway/dsl, 🍴 Bojangles, Shoney's, 🛏 Comfort Inn, Hampton Inn, Holiday Inn Express, **W** 🅖 Bisc-Chic/dsl, Liberty/Blimpie/dsl,

WYTHEVILLE

Exit	Services
98	Continued Marathon/dsl, 🍴 Arby's, Burger King, Fatz Cafe, McDonald's, Subway, Waffle House, Wendy's, 🛏 Super 8, 🅞 🅷 Walmart, vet, to Wilderness Rd Museum
94b a	VA 99 N, to Pulaski, **E** 🛏 Pulaski Motel, **0-3 mi W** 🅖 BP, Exxon/dsl, Hess, 🍴 China Wall, Domino's, Hardee's, KFC, Kimono Japanese, Little Caesars, McDonald's, Pizza Hut, Sonic, Steerhouse, Subway, Taco Bell, Wendy's, 🅞 🅷, Advance Parts, Curves, $General, Family$, Food Lion, Goodyear/auto, O'Reilly Parts, Rite Aid, Save-a-Lot
92	RD 658, to Draper, **E** 🅖 BP, 🅞 to New River Trail SP
89b a	US 11 N, VA 100, to Pulaski, **E** auto/truck repair
86	RD 618, Service Rd, **W** 🅖 Sunoco/Appletree Rest./dsl, 🅞 repair
84	RD 619, to Grahams Forge, **W** 🅖 Kangaroo/DQ/dsl/24hr, 🅖 Loves/Chester Fried/Subway/dsl/scales/24hr, 🛏 Fox Mtn Inn, Trail Motel
81	I-77 S, to Charlotte, Galax, to Blue Ridge Pkwy.
I-81 S and I-77 N run together 9 mi.	
80	US 52 S, VA 121 N, to Ft Chiswell, **E** 🅖 BP/Burger King/dsl, ⛽FLYING J/Denny's/dsl/scales/24hr/@, 🍴 Wendy's, 🛏 Hampton Inn, Super 8, 🅞 Blue Beacon, Ft Chiswell RV Park, NAPA, **W** 🅖 Citgo/Kangaroo/dsl, Valero, 🍴 McDonald's, 🛏 Comfort Inn, 🅞 Speedco
77	Service Rd, **E** 🅖 Citgo/Subway/dsl/24hr, ⛽FLYING J/Denny's/dsl/LP/RV Dump/24hr, Wilco/Hess/dsl/LP, 🍴 Burger King, 🅞 KOA, **W** 🅖 Exxon/dsl, Wilco/Hess/Arby's/DQ/dsl/scales/24hr, 🅞 Truck'o Mat, st police
73	US 11 S, Wytheville, **E** 🅖 BP, Citgo, Go-Mart, Kangaroo/dsl, 🍴 Applebee's, Bob Evans, Cracker Barrel, El Puerto Mexican, Hardee's, LJ Silver, Ocean Bay Rest., Papa John's, Peking Chinese, Shoney's, Sonic, Waffle House, Wendy's, Yamoto Japanese, 🛏 Budget Host, Days Inn, EconoLodge, Knights Inn, La Quinta, Motel 6, Quality Inn, Red Roof Inn, Travelodge, 🅞 🅷, AutoZone, Buick/Cadillac/Chevrolet/GMC, CVS Drug, $General, Food Lion, Ford, Goodyear/auto, Harley-Davidson, K-Mart, Nissan, Rite Aid, Subaru
I-81 N and I-77 S run together 9 mi.	
72	I-77 N, to Bluefield, **1 mi N I-77 exit 41 E** 🍴 Sagebrush Steaks, 🛏 Best Western, Sleep Inn, Super 8, **W** 🅖 Kangaroo/dsl/24hr, TA/Country Pride/Popeye's/Subway/Taco Bell/dsl/scales/24hr/@, 🍴 Southern Diner, 🛏 Comfort Suites, Country Inn&Suites, Fairfield Inn, Hampton Inn, Ramada/rest.
70	US 21/52, Wytheville, **E** 🅖 BP/dsl, Exxon, Sheetz, 🍴 Arby's, China Wok, El Patio Mexican, KFC/Taco Bell, Little Caesar's, McDonald's, Ruby Tuesday, Starbucks, Subway, Wendy's, 🅞 🅷, $Tree, Food Lion, IGA Foods, Lowe's, Verizon, Walmart, **W** 🅖 Kangaroo, 🛏 Comfort Inn
67	US 11 (from nb, no re-entry), to Wytheville
61mm	**rest area nb, full** ♿ **facilities,** 🚰 **vending,** 🗑 **litter barrels, petwalk, NO TRUCKS**
60	VA 90, Rural Retreat, **E** 🅖 Chevron/dsl, 🍴 El Ranchero, McDonald's, Subway, 🅞 to Rural Retreat Lake, camping
54	rd 683, to Groseclose, **E** 🅖 Exxon/dsl, Shell/dsl, 🍴 The Barn Rest., 🛏 Relax Inn, 🅞 Settler's Museum
53.5mm	**rest area sb, full** ♿ **facilities,** 🚰 **vending,** 🗑 **litter barrels, petwalk**
50	US 11, Atkins, **W** 🅖 Citgo/Subway/dsl/24hr, Exxon, 🍴 Atkins Rest., 🛏 Comfort Inn, 🅞 NAPA
47	US 11, to Marion, **W** 🅖 BP/Subway, Chevron/dsl/24hr, 🍴

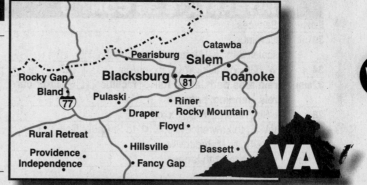

INTERSTATE 81 CONT'D

Exit	Services
47	Continued
	Arby's, KFC/Taco Bell, Little Caesar's, LJ Silver, McDonald's, Pioneer Rest., Pizza Hut, Puerto Mexican, Sonic, Wendy's, 🛏 EconoLodge, VA House Inn, ⊙ 🄷, Advance Parts, AutoZone, Buick/Chevrolet/GMC, CVS Drug, $General, $Tree, Family$, Food City, Food Lion, Ford, Ingles, Marion Drug, O'Reilly Parts, Radio Shack, Rite Aid, Walgreens, Walmart, to Hungry Mother SP (4mi)
45	VA 16, Marion, E 📌 Valero, 🍴 AppleTree Rest., ⊙ to Grayson Highlands SP, Mt Rogers NRA, W 📌 BP, Chevron, 🍴 Hardee's, ⊙ NAPA, USPO
44	US 11, Marion, W 📌 Marathon/dsl
39	US 11, RD 645, Seven Mile Ford, E 🛏 Budget Inn, W ⊙ Interstate Camping
35	RD 107, Chilhowie, E 🍴 Hardees, 🛏 Knights Inn, W 📌 Chevron, Exxon/dsl, Rouse's/dsl, 🍴 McDonald's, Subway, TasteeFreez, 🛏 Budget Inn (1mi), ⊙ Curves, $General, Food City, Greever's Drugs, NAPA
32	US 11, to Chilhowie
29	VA 91, to Damascus, Glade Spring, E 📌 Marathon/Subway/dsl, Petro/dsl/rest./24hr/@, Sunoco/Wendy's, 🍴 Giardino's Italian, Pizza+, 🛏 Swiss Inn, Travel Inn, ⊙ Back Country Camping, $General, Peterbilt, W 📌 Chevron/dsl/24hr, Exxon, Spirit, 🍴 Casa Hispania, ⊙ CarQuest, vet
26	VA 737, Emory, W ⊙ to Emory&Henry Coll
24	VA 80, Meadowview Rd, W auto repair
22	VA 704, Enterprise Rd
19	US 11/58, to Abingdon, E 📌 Shell/Subway/dsl, 🍴 Pizza+, ⊙ Lowe's, vet, to Mt Rogers NRA, W 📌 Chevron/dsl/24hr, Citgo/Huddle House, Exxon/dsl, 🍴 Burger King, Cracker Barrel, DaVinci's Cafe, Harbor House Seafood, Wendy's, 🛏 Alpine Motel, Days Inn, Holiday Inn Express, Quality Inn
17	US 58A, VA 75, Abingdon, E 🍴 Domino's, LJ Silver, 🛏 Hampton Inn, ⊙ Mr Transmission, W 📌 Exxon, Gas'n Go, 🍴 Arby's, China Wok, Hardee's, KFC, Los Arcos Mexican, McDonald's, Papa John's, Pizza Hut, Quiznos, Shoney's, Subway, Taco Bell, Tuscan Grill, Wendy's, 🛏 Super 8, ⊙ 🄷, Advance Parts, Food City, GNC, Kroger, K-Mart, Medicine Shoppe, info
14	US 19, VA 140, Abingdon, W 📌 Chevron/dsl/24hr, Exxon, Shell/dsl, 🍴 McDonald's, Milano's Italian, Pizza Inn, Subway, 🛏 Comfort Inn, Comfort Suites, ⊙ CarQuest, Ford/Lincoln/Mercury, Riverside Camping (10mi), Verizon
13.5mm	**TRUCKERS ONLY rest area nb, full 🖐 facilities, ⬤ vending, 🗑 litter barrels**
13	VA 611, to Lee Hwy, W 📌 Shell/dsl, ⊙ Kenworth, Mack
10	US 11/19, Lee Hwy, W 📌 Appco, BP/dsl, Chevron, 🛏 Beacon Inn, Deluxe Inn, Economy Inn, Evergreen Inn, Red Carpet Inn, Skyland Inn
7	Old Airport Rd, E 📌 Shell/dsl, 🍴 Bojangles, Cracker Barrel, Sonic, 🛏 La Quinta, W 📌 Marathon, Sunoco, Wendy's, Valero/dsl, 🍴 Charlie's Subs, Chili's, Domino's, El Patio Mexican, Fazoli's, Golden Corral, IHOP, Kobe Japanese, Logan's Roadhouse, Los Arco's, O'Charley's,

Exit	Services
7	Continued
	Outback Steaks, Perkins, Pizza Hut, Red Lobster, Ruby Tuesday, Starbucks, Subway, Taco Bell, 🛏 Courtyard, Holiday Inn, Microtel, Motel 6, ⊙ Advance Parts, Best Buy, Books-A-Million, $Tree, $General, Home Depot, Lowe's, Office Depot, Old Navy, PetsMart, Ross, Sam's Club/gas, Target, Walmart, Sugar Hollow Camping
5	US 11/19, Lee Hwy, E 📌 Citgo, Shell, 🍴 Arby's, Burger King, Hardee's, KFC, LJ Silver, McDonald's, Shoney's, 🛏 Budget Inn, Super 8, ⊙ Family$, Food Lion, Harley-Davidson, USPO, W 📌 Exxon, 🛏 Comfort Inn, ⊙ Blevins Tire, Buick/GMC, Lee Hwy Camping
3	I-381 S, to Bristol, 1 mi E 📌 Chevron, Exxon/dsl, 🍴 Applebee's, Arby's, Krystal, Ryan's, 🛏 Days Inn, EconoLodge
1b a	US 58/421, Bristol, 1 mi E 📌 Appco, Chevron, Citgo, Shell, Zoomer's, 🍴 Burger King, Capt D's, Chick-fil-A, KFC, Lighthouse Cafe, McDonald's, Pizza Hut, Sonic, Subway, Taco Bell, Wendy's, 🛏 Howard Johnson, Knight's Inn, ⊙ 🄷, Belk, Chrysler/Dodge/Jeep, CVS Drug, Family$, K-Mart, Kroger, Sears/auto, Toyota/Scion, Verizon, Walgreens, mall, vet
0mm	Virginia/Tennessee state line, **Welcome Ctr nb, full 🖐 facilities, info, ⬤ vending, 🗑 litter barrels, petwalk, NO TRUCKS**

INTERSTATE 85

Exit	Services
69mm	I-85 begins/ends on I-95.
69	US 301, I-95 N, Wythe St, Washington St, Petersburg
68	I-95 S, US 460 E, to Norfolk, Crater Rd
65	Squirrel Level Rd, E ⊙ to Richard Bland Coll, W 📌 BP
63b a	US 1, to Petersburg, E 📌 Chubby's/dsl, Exxon/KFC/dsl/24hr, Shell/Burger King/dsl, 🍴 Hardee's, Waffle House, 🛏 Holiday Inn Express, W 📌 BP, 🍴 McDonald's
61	US 460, to Blackstone, E 📌 EastCoast/Subway/dsl/LP, 🍴 Huddle House, W 📌 Shell/dsl, Valero (1mi), ⊙ 🖂
55mm	**rest area both lanes, full 🖐 facilities, ⬤ 🗑 litter barrels, vending, petwalk**
53	VA 703, Dinwiddie, W 📌 Exxon/dsl, 🍴 Jerry's Rest., ⊙ to 5 Forks Nat Bfd
52mm	Stony Creek
48	VA 650, DeWitt
42	VA 40, McKenney, W 📌 Citgo, Exxon, ⊙ auto repair, 🛏 Economy Inn (1mi)
40mm	Nottoway River
39	VA 712, to Rawlings, E ⊙ VA Battlerama, W 📌 Citgo/dsl, Davis TC/Exxon/Dunkin Donuts/Subway/dsl/

INTERSTATE 85 CONT'D

Exit	Services
39	Continued
	scales/24hr, 🏨 Nottoway Motel/rest.
34	VA 630, Warfield, W 🅿 Exxon/dsl
32mm	**rest area both lanes, full** 🅿 **facilities,** 🅲 🏨 **litter barrels, vending, petwalk**
28	US 1, Alberta, W 🅿 Exxon
27	VA 46, to Lawrenceville, E 🅾 to St Paul's Coll
24	VA 644, to Meredithville
22mm	**weigh sta both lanes**
20mm	Meherrin River
15	US 1, to South Hill, E 🅿 Citgo, W 🅿 Valero/dsl, 🍴 Kahill's Diner, Los Bandito's Mexican
12	US 58, VA 47, to South Hill, E 🅿 BP/Quizno's/Stucky's/dsl, RaceWay, Shell/dsl, 🍴 Applebee's, Arby's, Bojangles, Domino's, Glass House Grill, Sonic, 🏨 Best Western, Comfort Inn, Fairfield Inn, Hampton Inn, 🅾 $Tree, Verizon, Walmart/Subway, W 🅿 Citgo/Shell, Exxon/dsl, Kangaroo/dsl, 🍴 Brian's Steaks, Burger King, Cracker Barrel, Denny's, Down Home Buffet, Hardee's, KFC/Taco Bell, McDonald's, New China, Pizza Hut, Subway, Wendy's, 🏨 Days Inn, Quality Inn, 🅾 🄷, AutoZone, CVS Drug, $General, Family$, Food Lion, Home Depot, Roses
4	VA 903, to Bracey, Lake Gaston, E 🅿 BP/DQ/Subway/dsl, Exxon/Simmon's/dsl/scales/24hr/@, 🍴 Huddle House, 🅾 Americamps Camping (5mi), W 🅿 Shell/Pizza Hut/Quizno's, 🍴 Mayflower Seafood, 🏨 Lake Gaston Inn
3mm	Lake Gaston
1mm	**Welcome Ctr nb, full** 🅿 **facilities,** 🅲 🏨 **phones, litter barrels, vending, petwalk**
0mm	Virginia/North Carolina state line

INTERSTATE 95

Exit	Services
178mm	Virginia/Maryland state line, Potomac River, W Wilson Mem Br
177c b a	US 1, to Alexandria, Ft Belvoir, E 🍴 Great American Steaks, 🏨 Budget Host, Hampton Inn, Red Roof Inn, Relax Inn, 🅾 Chevrolet, Chrysler/Dodge/Jeep, W 🅿 Hess, Liberty/repair
176b a	VA 241, Telegraph Rd, E 🅿 Hess/dsl, W 🏨 Courtyard, Holiday Inn, Homestead Suites, 🅾 Staples
174	Eisenhower Ave Connector, to Alexandria
173	rd 613, Van Dorn St, to Franconia, E 🏨 Comfort Inn, **1 mi** W 🅿 Exxon, Shell, 🍴 Dunkin Donuts, Jerry's Subs, McDonald's, Quizno's, Red Lobster, 🅾 Aamco, Emily&Adam, Giant Foods, NTB
170a	I-495 N, I-495 & I-95 N run together to MD., to Rockville
170b	I-395 N, to Washington
169b a	rd 644, Springfield, Franconia, E 🍴 Bertucci's, Dunkin Donuts, Silver Diner, Starbucks, Subway, TGIFriday's, 🏨 Best Western, Courtyard, Extended Stay America, Hampton Inn, Hilton, 🅾 🄷, AT&T, Barnes&Noble, Best Buy, Border's Books, Family$, Firestone/auto, Ford, Home Depot, JC Penney, Macy's, Michael's, Nissan, Old Navy, Petsmart, Staples, Subaru, Target, mall, W 🅿 BP, Shell, Sunoco, 🍴 Bob Evans, Chipotle Mexican, Deliah's Grill, Domino's, Dunkin Donuts, 5 Guys Burgers, KFC, McDonald's, Outback Steaks, Quizno's, Starbucks,

Exit	Services
169b a	Continued
	Subway, Tokyo Japanese, 🏨 Holiday Inn Express, Motel 6, Residence Inn, TownePlace Suites, 🅾 CarQuest, CVS Drug, Dodge/Jeep, Giant Foods, Goodyear/auto, K-Mart, Mr. Tire, Scion/Toyota, Verizon, VW, vet
167	VA 617, Backlick Rd (from sb), W 🅿 InterFuel/dsl, 🅾 Chevrolet
166b a	VA 7100, Newington, to Ft Belvoir, E 🅿 Pkwy Express, 🍴 Wendy's, 🅾 NTB, U-Haul, W 🅾 Costco
163	VA 642, Lorton, E 🅿 Citgo, Shell/24hr, W 🅿 Shell, 🍴 Antoneli's Pizza, Burger King, McDonald's, 🏨 Comfort Inn
161	US 1 S (exits left from sb, no reentry nb), to Ft Belvoir, Mt Vernon, Woodlawn Plantation, Gunston Hall
160.5mm	Occoquan River
160b a	VA 123 N, Woodbridge, Occoquan, E 🅿 BP, Sunoco, 🍴 Dixie Bones BBQ, Subway, Taco Bell, 🏨 EconoLodge, Hampton Inn, Quality Inn, Rodeway Inn, 🅾 Aldi Foods, Radio Shack, W 🅿 Exxon/dsl, Fast Fuels, Shell, 🍴 KFC, McDonald's, VA Grill, Wendy's, 🅾 7-11, same as 161
158b a	VA 3000, Prince William Pkwy, Woodbridge, W 🅿 Exxon, Shell, 7-11, Sunoco, WaWa, 🍴 Boston Mkt, Chick-fil-A, Chipotle Mexican, ChuckeCheese, Coldstone, Famous Dave's BBQ, Hooters, IHOP, Macaroni Grill, McDonald's, Old Country Buffet, On-the-Border, Panda Express, Panera Bread, Quiznos, Red Lobster, Smokey Bones BBQ, Starbucks, Taco Bell, TGIFriday's, UNO Grill, Wendy's, 🏨 Country Inn&Suites, Courtyard, Fairfield Inn, Holiday Inn Express, Residence Inn, Sleep Inn, 🅾 Advance Parts, Best Buy, Border's Books, Carmax, $Tree, Lowe's, Michael's, Office Depot, Petsmart, Sam's Club/gas, Shopper's Foods, Target, Verizon, Walmart/Subway
156	VA 784, Potomac Mills, E 🅿 Shell, 🍴 Zoe's Kitchen, 🅾 🄷, AT&T, Wegmans, to Leesylvania SP, W 🅿 Chevron, Shell, Sunoco, Texaco, 🍴 Bamboo Buffet, Bob Evans, Burger King, Char Broil Grill, Chili's, China King Buffet, Denny's, DQ, El Charro Mexican, Guapo's, La Azteca Latina, McDonald's, Olive Garden, Outback Steaks, Popeye's, Silver Diner, Subway, Wendy's, 🏨 Best Western, Wytestone Suites, 🅾 Books-A-Million, Costco/gas, Family$, Firestone/auto, JC Penney, Jo-Ann Fabrics, K-Mart, Marshall's, NAPA, Nordstrom's, NTB, Potomac Mills Outlets/Famous Brands, Staples, TJ Maxx, Tuesday Morning, U-Haul, vet
154mm	**rest area/weigh sta both lanes**
152	VA 234, Dumfries, to Manassas, E 🅿 BP/dsl/24hr, Chevron/service, Shell/dsl, Texaco/Subway, 🍴 Applebee's, China One, 5 Guys Burgers, Joe's Place Pizza, KFC, McDonald's, Ruby Tuesday, Taco Bell, 🏨 Sleep Inn, Super 8, 🅾 AutoZone, $Tree, NAPA, Weems-Botts Museum, W 🅿 Exxon, 7-11, 🍴 Cracker Barrel, IHOP, Jerry's Subs, MontClair Rest., Panera Bread, Subway, Tiziano Italian, Waffle House, 🏨 Comfort Inn, Days Inn, EconoLodge, Hampton Inn, Holiday Inn, 🅾 Prince William Camping, Rite Aid, Shoppers Foods, Target
150	VA 619, Quantico, to Triangle, E 🅿 7-11, 🍴 Dunkin Donuts, 🏨 Ramada Inn, 🅾 to Marine Corps Base, W Prince William Forest Park
148	to Quantico, **2 mi** E 🅿 Gulf/dsl, 🏨 Spring Lake Motel, 🅾 to Marine Corps Base

Vertical left margin labels: **VA**, **N ↕ S**, **DC AREA N ↕ S**

Vertical right margin label: **DUMFRIES**

INTERSTATE 95 CONT'D

Exit	Services

N ↕ S

143b a   to US 1, VA 610, Aquia, **E** 🅖 Exxon, Valero, 🍴 Carlos O'Kelly's, El Gran Charro, KFC, McDonald's, Mick's Rest., Pizza Hut, Ruby Tuesday, 🛏 Best Western, Hampton Inn, Staybridge Suites, Towne Place Suites, 🅞 7-11, Tires+, **W** 🅖 BP/dsl, Exxon, 7-11/dsl, WaWa, 🍴 Amici Italian, Applebee's, Baskin-Robbins/Dunkin Donuts, Bob Evans, Bruster's, Burger King, Chick-fil-A, Chili's, China Wok, Firehouse Subs, 5 Guys Burgers, Hardee's, IHOP, Jerry's Subs, Jimmy the Greek, Little Caesar's, Maggie Moo's, Moe's SW Grill, Outback Steaks, Pancho Villa, Panera Bread, Popeye's, Quiznos, Ruby Tuesday, Starbucks, Taco Bell, Wendy's, 🛏 Comfort Inn, Country Inn, Holiday Inn Express, Super 8, Wingate Inn, 🅞 AutoZone, Best Buy, Border's Books, CVS Drug, $General, $Tree, Giant Foods, GNC, Home Depot, Kohl's, Lowe's, Merchant's Tire, Michael's, PetCo, Petsmart, Radio Shack, Ross, Scion/Toyota, Shopper's Foods, Staples, Target, TJ Maxx, Verizon, Walmart/auto, Aquia Pines Camping

140   VA 630, Stafford, **E** 🅖 7-11, Sunoco/dsl, Valero, 🍴 McDonald's, **W** 🅖 Exxon, Shell/dsl

137mm   Potomac Creek

136   rd 8900, Centreport, **W** airport

133b a   US 17 N, to Warrenton, **E** 🅖 Exxon/dsl, Gulf/dsl, 🍴 Arby's, 🛏 Howard Johnson Express, Motel 6, 🅞 CarQuest, 7-11, auto/truck repair, **W** 🅖 EastCoast/Subway/dsl, Shell/dsl, WaWa/dsl, 🍴 Burger King, Foster's Grille, Hardee's, McDonald's, Perkin's, Pizza Hut, Ponderosa, Taco Bell, Waffle House, 🛏 Comfort Inn, Country Inn&Suites, Days Inn, Holiday Inn, Quality Inn, Sleep Inn, Super 8, Super Value Inn, Travelodge, Wingate Inn, 🅞 URGENT CARE, Advance Parts, Blue Beacon, Honda, Petsmart, Target

132.5mm   Rappahannock River

132mm   **rest area sb, full ♿ facilities, 🚻 🖼 litter barrels, petwalk, vending**

130b a   VA 3, to Fredericksburg, **E** 🅖 BP/dsl/24hr, Gulf, Shell, Wawa/24hr, 🍴 Arby's, Bob Evans, Carlos O'Kelly's, Dunkin Donuts, Friendly's, Honeybaked Ham, KFC, King Buffet, Lonestar Steaks, Mexico Lindo, Popeye's, Shoney's, Starbucks, Subway, Wendy's, 🛏 Best Western, Quality Inn, 🅞 Ⓗ, AutoZone, Batteries+, BigLots, Hancock Fabrics, Home Depot, PepBoys, Staples, Tuesday Morning, U-Haul, **W** 🅖 BP, Chevron/dsl, Exxon/dsl/24hr, Murphy USA, 7-11, Sheetz, Valero, WaWa/24hr, 🍴 A&W/LJ Silver, Applebee's, Arby's, Asia Bistro, Aunt Sarah's, Bailey's Grille, Baja Fresh, BoneFish Grill, Bridges Brickoven, Buffalo Wild Wings, Burger King, Caribou Coffee, Carrabba's, Checker's, Cheeseburger Paradise, Chick-fil-A, Chili's, China Jade, Chipotle Mexican, ChuckeCheese, CiCi's Pizza, Cracker Barrel, Denny's, Dunkin Donuts, El Paso Mexican, 5 Guys Burgers, Firehouse Subs, Fuddrucker's, IHOP, Joe's Crabshack, Krispy Kreme, Logan's Roadhouse, Margarita Grill, McDonald's, Melting Pot, Noodles&Co, O'Charley's, Old Country Buffet, Olive Garden, Outback Steaks, Pancho Villa, Panda Express, Panera Bread, Piccadilly, Poncho Villa Mexican, Qdoba, Quizno's, Red Lobster, Rodango's Steaks, Ruby Tuesday, Ryan's, Sam's Pizza, Santa Fe Grill, Smokey Bones BBQ, Starbucks, Subway, Taco Bell, TGIFriday's,

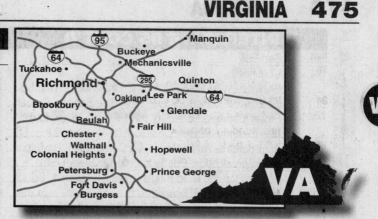

130b a   Continued

🛏 Best Western, Hampton Inn, Hilton Garden, Homewood Suites, Hospitality House, Ramada Inn, Super 8, 🅞 Advance Parts, AT&T, AutoZone, Belk, Best Buy, BJ's Whse, Bloom Foods, Costco, CVS Drug, $General, $Tree, Gander Mtn, Giant Foods, JC Penney, Kohl's, K-Mart, Lowe's, Macy's, Merchants Tire, Michael's, NTB, Office Depot, Old Navy, Petsmart, Radio Shack, Ross, Sears/auto, Shopper's Foods, Target, Walmart, Wegman's Foods, Yankee Candle, mall

126   US 1, US 17 S, to Fredericksburg, **E** 🅖 BP, Chevron/dsl, Citgo, Exxon, Shell/dsl, 🍴 Arby's, Denny's, Friendly's, Golden Corral, Hardee's, Hooters, McDonald's, Pizza Hut, Poncho Villa Mexican, Ruby Tuesday, Subway, Taco Bell, Waffle House, 🛏 Country Inn&Suites, Days Inn/rest., EconoLodge, Fairfield Inn, Hampton Inn, Motel 6, Ramada Inn, Royal Inn, Super 8, TownePlace Suites, 🅞 Ⓗ, Advance Parts, Aldi Foods, AutoZone, Bloom Foods, BMW, Buick/GMC, Cadillac, CVS Drug, Dodge, $General, $Tree, Family$, Nissan, Hyundai, KIA, Mazda, Rite Aid, Subaru, Suzuki, VW, White Tires, **W** 🅖 Exxon, 7-11, Sunoco/dsl, WaWa, 🍴 Applebee's, Arby's, Bob Evans, Burger King, Chick-fil-A, Chili's, China Jade, Chipotle Mexican, Coldstone Creamery, Cracker Barrel, El Charro Mexican, Famous Dave's BBQ, Firehouse Subs, 5 Guys Burgers, Foster's Grill, Glory Days Grill, Golden China, KFC, Lenny's Subs, Longhorn Steaks, McDonald's, Mimi's Cafe, Ozeki Japanese, Panera Bread, Papa John's, Red Robin, Starbucks, Sonic, Subway, Sully's Seafood, Tony's Pizza, Wendy's, 🛏 Comfort Inn, Sleep Inn, WyteStone Suites, 🅞 AT&T, Best Buy, Carmax, CVS Drug, $Plus, Firestone/auto, Jo-Ann Fabrics, Kohl's, Lowe's, Marshall's, Petsmart, Radio Shack, Rite Aid, Ross, Staples, Target, Verizon, Walmart, World Mkt, USPO, vet

118   VA 606, to Thornburg, **E** 🅖 Shell/dsl, 🅞 Safford RV Ctr, to Stonewall Jackson Shrine, **W** 🅖 Citgo/dsl, Exxon, Shell/DQ, Valero, 🍴 Angela's Rest., Burger King, McDonald's, Subway, 🛏 Holiday Inn Express, Lamplighter Motel, Quality Inn, 🅞 KOA (7mi), to Lake Anna SP, USPO

110   VA 639, to Ladysmith, **E** 🅖 Citgo, Shell/dsl, **W** 🅖 Citgo/dsl, Exxon/dsl, 🍴 Domino's, Guiseppe's Rest., Lin's Gormet, Subway, Timbers Rest., VA BBQ, 🅞 Curves, Express Tire/repair, Family$, Food Lion, Lady Smith Drug

104   VA 207, to US 301, Bowling Green, **E** 🅖 Chevron/dsl, Exxon/dsl, Mr Fuel/dsl, Ruther Glen TP/dsl/scales/24hr/@, Loves/DQ/Subway/dsl/scales/24hr,

F R E D E R I C K S B U R G

INTERSTATE 95 CONT'D

N ↑ S

VA

ELMONT

Exit	Services
104	Continued
	Shell/dsl, Valero/dsl, 🅕 Arby's, McDonald's, Wendy's, 🄐 Howard Johnson, Super 8, 🄾 Blue Beacon, Russell Stover Candies, SpeedCo, to Ft AP Hill, **W** 🅖 Exxon/dsl, ⚡FLYING J/Denny's/dsl/scales/RV dump/24hr, 🅕 Aunt Sarah's, Waffle House, 🄐 Comfort Inn, Days Inn/rest., EconoLodge, Quality Inn, 🄾 CarQuest, USPO
98	VA 30, Doswell, **E** to King's Dominion Funpark, 🅖 All American Plaza/Subway/dsl/scales/24hr/@, Exxon, 7-11, 🅕 Burger King, Denny's, 🄐 Best Western, Comfort Suites, Country Inn&Suites, Days Inn, EconoLodge, 🄾 Camp Wilderness, King's Dominion Camping, truckwash
92	VA 54, Ashland, **E** 🅖 Sunoco, **W** 🅖 BP/dsl, TA/dsl/rest./@, EC/Blimpie/Krispy Kreme/dsl, Exxon/Subway, 7-11, Shell/dsl, 🅕 Anthony's Pizza, Applebee's, Arby's, Brickoven Rest., Burger King, Capt D's, China Wok, Cracker Barrel, DQ, El Azteca, Hardee's, Jersey Mike's Subs, KFC/LJ Silver, McDonald's, New China Buffet, Perkin's, Pizza Hut, Ponderosa, Quiznos, Ruby Tuesday, Starbucks, Taco Bell, Waffle House, Wendy's, 🄐 Apple Garden Motel, Days Inn, EconoLodge, Hampton Inn, Holiday Inn Express, Howard Johnson, Motel 6, Quality Inn, Sleep Inn, 🄾 Ace Hardware, Advance Parts, AutoZone, CarQuest, CVS Drug, Family$, Food Lion, Radio Shack, Rite Aid, Tuesday Morning, Ukrop's Foods, Walmart
89	VA 802, to Lewistown Rd, **E** 🅖 Shell, TA/Pizza Hut/Popeye's/dsl/scales/24hr/@, 🄾 Americamps RV Camp, **W** 🄐 Cadillac Motel, 🄾 Bass Pro Shops, Kosmo Village Camping, Rolling Hills RV Ctr
86b a	VA 656, Elmont, to Atlee, **E** 🅖 Sheetz, Valero, 🅕 Burger King, McDonald's, 🄾 CVS Drug, Food Lion, **W** 🅕 CiCi's Pizza, Jade Chinese, Jersey Mike's Subs, 🄾 Gander Mtn, Home Depot, **W on US 1** 🅖 7-11, Shell/dsl, 🅕 Applebee's, Arby's, Buffalo Wild Wings, Burger King, Chick-fil-A, Chili's, Chipotle Mexican, Chophouse, Coldstone Creamery, Famous Dave's BBQ, McDonald's, NY Grill, O'Charley's, Panera Bread, Papa John's, Pizzaro, Quizno's, Red Robin, Roda Japanese, Ruby Tuesday, Shoney's, Sonic, Starbucks, Subway, TX Roadhouse, Vinny's Grill, Wendy's, 🄐 Candlewood Suites, Comfort Suites, Courtyard, Hampton Inn, SpringHill Suites, 🄾 AT&T, Barnes&Noble, Best Buy, Dillard's, $Tree, Firestone/auto, Goodyear/auto, JC Penney, Macy's, Merchant's Tire, Michael's, Petsmart, Sears/auto, Target, Tire America, Ukrop's Foods, Walgreens, mall
84b a	I-295 W, to I-64, to Norfolk
83b a	VA 73, Parham Rd, **W** 🅖 Exxon/DQ, 7-11, Shell/dsl, Texaco/dsl, Wawa, 🅕 Aunt Sarah's, Burger King, Frida's Cafe, Hardee's, Hawks BBQ, KFC, McDonald's, River City Diner, Starbucks, Stuffy's Subs, Subway, Taco Bell, Waffle House, Wendy's, 🄐 Best Western, Broadway Motel, Clarion, EconoLodge, Guest Inn, Knights Inn, Sleep Inn, 🄾 BigLots, CVS Drug, Family$, Food Lion, Kroger, Lowe's, Verizon, Walmart
82	US 301, Chamberlayne Ave, **E** 🅖 Chevron, Exxon/dsl, Sunoco, Texaco, WaWa, 🅕 Arby's, Friendly's, McDonald's, Subway, 🄐 Days Inn, Super 8, 🄾 Food Lion, USPO

RICHMOND

CHESTER

Exit	Services
81	US 1, Chamberlayne Ave (from nb), same as 82
80	Hermitage Rd, Lakeside Ave (from nb, no return), **W** 🅕 EC/Subway, 🄾 Goodyear/auto, Ginter Botanical Gardens
79	I-64 W, to Charlottesville, I-195 S, to U of Richmond
78	Boulevard (no EZ nb return), **E** 🅖 BP, 🄐 Holiday Inn, **W** 🅖 Citgo/dsl, 🅕 Bill's BBQ, 🄐 EconoLodge, 🄾 H, to VA HS, stadium
76	Chamberlayne Ave, Belvidere, **E** 🄾 H, VA Union U
75	I-64 E, VA Beach, to Norfolk, airport
74c	US 33, US 250 W, to Broad St, **W** 🄾 H, st capitol, Museum of the Confederacy
74b	Franklin St, **E** 🄾 Richmond Nat Bfd Park
74a	I-195 N, to Powhite Expswy, downtown
73.5mm	James River
73	Maury St, to US 60, US 360, industrial area
69	VA 161, Bells Rd, **E** Port of Richmond, **W** 🅖 Exxon/dsl/24hr, Shell/dsl, 🅕 McDonald's, Subway, 🄐 Candlewood Suites, Hampton Inn, Holiday Inn, Red Roof Inn
67b a	VA 895 (toll E), VA 150, to Chippenham Pkwy, Falling Creek, **W** 🅖 RaceWay, Shell, 🄾 Food Lion, U-Haul
64	VA 613, to Willis Rd, **E** 🅖 BP, Exxon, 🅕 Waffle House, 🄐 Best Value Inn, EconoLodge, **W** 🅖 Chubby's, Citgo, 7-11, Shell/dsl, Sunoco, 🅕 Bandito's Mexican, Burger King, McDonald's, Subway, 🄐 Country Inn&Suites, Economy House Motel, La Quinta, Sleep Inn, VIP Inn, 🄾 Drewry's Bluff Bfd, flea mkt
62	VA 288 N, to Chesterfield, Powhite Pkwy, to 🄾
61b a	VA 10, Chester, **E** 🅖 RaceWay, 🅕 Don Jose Mexican, Hardee's, 🄐 Comfort Inn, Courtyard, Hampton Inn, Holiday Inn Express, Homewood Suites, Quality Inn, 🄾 H, to James River Plantations, City Point NHS, Petersburg NBF, **W** 🅖 BP, Citgo, Exxon/dsl, 7-11, Texaco/dsl, 🅕 Applebee's, Burger King, Capt D's, Chili's, CiCi's Pizza, Cracker Barrel, Denny's, Don Paba Mexican, 5 Guys Burgers, Friendly's, Hardee's, Hooters, IHOP, KFC, McDonald's, O'Charley's, Panera Bread, Peking Chinese, Pizza Hut, Quizno's, Shoney's, Sonic, Starbucks, Subway, Taco Bell, UNO, Waffle House, Wendy's, 🄐 Clarion, Country Inn&Suites, Days Inn, Fairfield Inn, InTowne Suites, Super 8, 🄾 Aamco, Chevrolet, CVS Drug, $General, $Tree, Food Lion, GNC, Home Depot, K-Mart, Kohl's, Kroger/gas, Lowe's, NAPA, PetCo, Radio Shack, Rite Aid, Target, Tuesday Morning, Ukrops Foods, to Pocahontas SP
58	VA 746, to Ruffinmill Rd, **E** 🅖 🄴/Wendy's/dsl/scales/24hr, 🄾 Honda, Hyundai, Scion/Toyota, **W** 🅖 Exxon, 🅕 Dunkin Donuts, Subway, 🄐 Candlewood Suites
54	VA 144, Temple Ave, Hopewell, to Ft Lee, **E** 🅖 BP/24hr, Exxon/Subway, Sheetz, Shell/Burger King, 🅕 Applebee's, Arby's, Buffalo Wild Wings, China Min's Buffet, CiCi's Pizza, Denny's, El Caporal Mexican, 5 Guys Burgers, Golden Corral, Great China, LoneStar Steaks, McDonald's, Olive Garden, Outback Steaks, Panera Bread, Picadilly, Pizza Hut, Quizno's, Red Lobster, Ruby Tuesday, Sagebrush Steaks, Sonic, Starbucks, Taco Bell, Wendy's, 🄐 Comfort Suites, Hampton Inn, Hilton Garden, Holiday Inn, ValuePlace Inn, 🄾 AT&T, Best Buy, BooksAMillion, Dillard's, $Tree, Macy's, Home Depot, JC Penney, Jo-Ann Fabrics, KIA, K-Mart, Macy's, Marshall's, Merchant's Tire, Michael's, Nissan, Old Navy,

INTERSTATE 95 CONT'D

Exit	Services
54	Continued Petsmart, Radio Shack, Sam's Club/gas, Sears/auto, Staples, Target, Verizon, Walmart, mall, **W** ⛽ Kangaroo/dsl, 🍴 DQ, Hardee's, Waffle House, ⊙ U-Haul, to VSU
53	S Park Blvd (from nb), **E** same as 54
52.5mm	Appomattox River
52	Washington St, Wythe St, **E** ⛽ Exxon/dsl, Valero/dsl, 🍴 Jade Garden, 🛏 Best Value Inn, Red Carpet Inn, Royal Inn, Super 8, Travelodge, ⊙ Petersburg Nat Bfd, **W** ⛽ Liberty, 🛏 Broadway Inn, Ramada Inn, ⊙ HOSPITAL
51	I-85 S, to South Hill, US 460 W
50d	Wythe St, (from nb) same as 52
50 b c	**E** ⛽ 7-11, 🛏 Flagship Inn
50a	US 301, US 460 E, to Crater Rd, County Dr, **E** ⛽ BP, RaceWay, Star Express, 🍴 Hardee's, 🛏 American Inn, Budget Inn, California Inn, EconoLodge, ⊙ HOSPITAL
48b a	Wagner Rd, **W on Crater Rd** ⛽ BP, Wawa, 🍴 Arby's, Bettos, Bojangles, Burger King, Capt D's, KFC, Pizza Hut, Subway, Taste of China, Taco Bell, 🛏 Country Inn&Suites, Super 8, ⊙ Advance Parts, $Tree, $General, PepBoys, Radio Shack, Walgreens, Walmart, USPO
47	VA 629, to Rives Rd, **W** ⛽ Citgo, Texaco/dsl, 🛏 Heritage Motel, **1-2 mi W** 🍴 Mad Italian, Subway, Taco Bell, 🛏 Country Inn&Suites, Crater Inn, ⊙ Softball Hall of Fame Museum, same as 48 on US 301
46	I-295 N (exits left from sb), to Washington
45	US 301, **E** ⛽ Shell/dsl, **W** ⛽ Exxon/dsl, 🍴 Lighthouse Rest., Nanny's Rest., Steven Kent Rest., 🛏 Comfort Inn, Days Inn, Hampton Inn, Holiday Inn Express, Howard Johnson, Quality Inn
41	US 301, VA 35, VA 156, **E** ⛽ US/Exxon/dsl/scales/24hr, 🛏 EconoLodge, ⊙ South 40 camp resort, **W** 🛏 Travelers Inn
40mm	**weigh sta both lanes**
37	US 301, Carson, **W** ⛽ BP/dsl, Shell/dsl
36mm	**rest area nb, full** ♿ **facilities,** 🎟 **vending,** 🗑 **litter barrel, petwalk**
33	VA 602, **W** ⛽ Davis/Exxon/Subway/Starbucks/dsl/scales/24hr, 🍴 Burger King, Denny's, Little Italy, 🛏 Hampton Inn, Sleep Inn
31	VA 40, Stony Creek, to Waverly, **W** ⛽ Shell/dsl/24hr, Sunoco, 🍴 Tastee Hut
24	VA 645
20	VA 631, Jarratt, **W** ⛽ Exxon/Blimpie/dsl/24hr, Race-in/dsl, ⊙ Ford
17	US 301, **1 mi E** 🛏 Knights Inn, Reste Motel, ⊙ Jellystone Park Camping
13	VA 614, to Emporia, **E** ⛽ Exxon/Chester's/dsl, Shell/dsl
12	US 301 (from nb)
11b a	US 58, Emporia, to South Hill, **E** ⛽ BP/Subway/dsl, Citgo/Burger King, Exxon/Blimpie/LJ Silver, Shell/dsl, 🍴 Applebee's, Arby's, Carolina BBQ, Cracker Barrel, Domino's, Hardee's, KFC, McDonald's, Pizza Hut, Taco Bell, Wendy's, Wong's Garden, 🛏 Country Inn&Suites, Fairfield Inn, Rodeway Inn, ⊙ H, Advance Parts, CVS Drug, $Tree, Family$, Food Lion, Lowe's, NAPA, O'Reilly Parts, Radio Shack, Rite Aid, Verizon, Walmart, **W** ⛽ Exxon, Race-In/Quiznos/dsl, 🚛 Sadler/5 Guys Burgers/dsl/scales/24hr/@, 🍴 Bojangles, Pueblo Viejo, Shoney's, 🛏 Best Western, Days Inn, Hampton Inn, Holiday Inn Express, Quality Inn, Sleep Inn

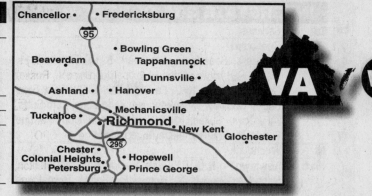

Exit	Services
8	US 301, **E** ⛽ Citgo, Exxon/Huddle House/Simmon's/dsl/scales/24hr, 🛏 Deluxe Inn, Red Carpet Inn, ⊙ truck repair
4	VA 629, to Skippers, **E** ⛽ Loves/McDonald's/dsl/scales/24hr, **W** ⛽ Shell/dsl, 🛏 EconoLodge, ⊙ camping (3mi)
3.5mm	Fountain's Creek
.5mm	**Welcome Ctr nb, full** ♿ **facilities,** 🎟 **vending,** 🗑 **litter barrels, petwalk**
0mm	Virginia/North Carolina state line

INTERSTATE 264 (Norfolk)

Exit	Services
23mm	I-264 begins/ends, BP, Shell, convention ctr
22	Birdneck Rd, I-264 begins/ends, **S** ⛽ Shell, 🍴 Max&Erma's, McDonald's/playplace, 🛏 Double Tree, ⊙ Food Lion, museum
21	VA Beach Blvd, First Colonial Rd, **N** ⛽ BP, 🍴 Applebee's, Arby's, Burger King, Chick-fil-A, DQ, KFC, McDonald's, Outback Steaks, Panera Bread, Pizza Hut, Taco Bell, Wendy's, Virginian Steaks, ⊙ Advance Parts, CVS Drug, Food Lion, K-Mart, Kroger, Michael's, Target, **S** ⛽ Shell, Wawa, ⊙ CarQuest, 7-11, NAPA
20	US 58 E, to VA Beach Blvd (eb only), **N** ⛽ Citgo, Kangaroo, Wawa, 🍴 Capt. George's Seafood, China Moon, Dunkin Donuts, Hardee's, Ruby Tuesday, Subway, ⊙ Family$, Food Lion, KIA/Lincoln/Mercury, Lowe's, PepBoys, 7-11, TJ Maxx, Tuesday Morning
19	Lynnhaven Pkwy, **N** ⛽ 7-11, Wawa, 🍴 Ensenda Mexican, Quizno's, ⊙ URGENT CARE, Audi, Chevrolet, FarmFresh Foods, Ford, Jaguar, Porsche, Subaru, VW, **S** 🍴 McDonald's
18	Rosemont, **N** ⛽ Exxon, 🍴 Bonefish Grill, Burger King, Denny's, Hardee's, KFC, LJ Silver, McDonald's, Mi Casita Mexican, Papa John's, Starbucks, Taco Bell, Wendy's, 🛏 EconoLodge, ⊙ AutoZone, BJ's Whse/gas, CarMax, Chrysler/Dodge/Jeep, $Tree, Food Lion, Harris Teeter, Home Depot, Honda, Kroger, Merchant's Tire/Auto, Nissan, Petsmart, Radio Shack, Rite Aid, Sam's Club/gas, Walgreens, **S** ⛽ Hess/dsl, Shell, Wawa, 🍴 4 Seasons Chinese
17.5mm	wb only, **inspection sta**
17a b	Independance Blvd, **N** ⛽ Exxon, Shell, 🍴 Cheesecake Factory, Fuddruckers, IHOP, Jason's Deli, Macaroni Grill, Max&Erma's, McDonald's, PF Chang's, Ruby Tuesday, Smokey Bones BBQ, Starbucks, Taco Bell, Tripps Rest., Wendy's, Village Inn, 🛏 Candlewood Suites, Crowne Plaza, Days Inn, Extended Stay, Hilton Garden, Motel 6, Westin, ⊙ Barnes&Noble, Best Buy, K-Mart, Kohl's,

VA

INTERSTATE 264 CONT'D (Norfolk)

Exit	Services
17a b	Continued Michael's, Sears/auto, Steinmart, **S** 🅖 Exxon, 7-11, Wawa, 🅕 Arby's, Azteca Mexican, Domino's, Golden Corral, Hardee's, KFC, La Casa Italian, Quizno's, Starbucks, Subway, TX Roadhouse, Wing Zone, Zero Subs, 🅰 InTown Suites, 🅞 $General, Food Lion, Fortune Foods, Mazda, Rite Aid, auto repair, vet
16	Witchduck
15a b	Newtown Rd, **N** 🅖 BP, Citgo, 🅕 Domino's, McDonald's, Shoney's, Wendy's, 🅰 Homewood Suites, TownePlace Suites, 🅞 AutoZone, **S** 🅖 BP, Shell, 🅕 Denny's, Ruby Tuesday, 🅰 Courtyard, Hampton Inn, Holiday Inn, La Quinta, Red Roof Inn, SpringHill Suites 🅞 Rite Aid, 7-11
14b a	I-64, US 13, to Military Hwy
13	US 13, Military Hwy, **N** 🅖 Shell, 🅕 Arby's, Boston Mkt, China Garden, Grate Steak, Lonestar Steaks, Mihogar Mexican, Mongolian BBQ, Norfolk Garden Korean, Piccadilly, Schlotzsky's, 🅰 Best Value, Days Inn, EconoLodge, Motel 6, Ramada Ltd, 🅞 Firestone/auto, JC Penney, Macy's, Ross
12	Ballentine Blvd, **N** 🅞 🅗, Norfolk SU
11b a	US 460, VA 166/168, Brambleton Ave, Campostello Rd, **N** 🅖 7-11, Shell
10	Tidewater Dr, City Hall Ave, exits left from eb, **N** 🅖 7-11, Shell
9	St Paul's Blvd, Waterside Dr, to Harbor Park Stadium
8	I-464 S, to Chesapeake
7.5mm	tunnel
7b a	VA 141, Effingham St, Crawford St, **N** 🅖 7-11, 🅕 Hardee's, 🅞 Naval HOSPITAL, **S** 🅞 Shipyard
6.5mm	**weigh sta eb**
6	Des Moines Ave (from eb)
5	US 17, Frederick Blvd, Midtown Tunnel, **N** HOSPITAL, **S** 🅖 BP, 🅞 Harley-Davidson
4	VA 337, Portsmouth Blvd
3	Victory Blvd, **N** 🅖 Exxon, 7-11, Shell, WaWa, 🅕 Bojangles, Capt D's, DQ, Domino's, KFC, McDonald's, Pizza Hut, Ruby Tuesday, Taco Bell, Wendy's, 🅞 Advance Parts, AutoZone, BigLots, $Tree, FarmFresh Food/drug, Lowe's, PepBoys, Radio Shack, Walgreens, vet, **S** 🅖 Valero/dsl
2b a	Greenwood Dr
0mm	I-264 begins/ends on I-64, exit 299.

INTERSTATE 295 (Richmond)

Exit	Services
53b a	I-64, W to Charlottesville, E to Richmond, to US 250, I-295 begins/ends.
51b a	Nuckols Rd, **1 mi N** 🅖 Miller's/dsl, Valero, 🅕 Bruster's, Casa Grande, Cheeburger, Chen's Chinese, Home Team Grill, McDonald's, Nonna's Pizzaria, Rico's Mexican, Samurai Japanese, Starbucks, Subway, Tropical Smoothie Cafe, 🅞 CVS Drug, Food Lion, Walgreens, vet, **S** 🅖 Exxon/Mkt Cafe, 🅞 USPO
49b a	US 33, Richmond, **2 mi S** 🅕 Carvel's Ice Cream, Little Szechuan, Quiznos, 🅞 Martin's Foods, 7-11
45b a	Woodman Rd, **1-2 mi S** 🅖 7-11, Valero, 🅕 Little Caesar's, 🅞 CVS Drug, $General, Meadow Farm Museum
43	I-95, US 1, N to Washington, S to Richmond (exits left

MECHANICSVILLE

43	Continued from nb), **N** on US 1 🅖 BP, Shell/dsl, 🅕 Applebee's, Arby's, Buffalo Wild Wings, Burger King, Chick-fil-A, Chili's, Chipotle Mexican, Chophouse, Famous Dave's BBQ, McDonald's, O'Charley's, Panera Bread, Papa John's, Pizzaro, Quizno's, Red Robin, Ruby Tuesday, Shoney's, Subway, TX Roadhouse, Vinny's Grill, Wendy's, 🅰 Candlewood Suites, Comfort Suites, Courtyard, Hampton Inn, SpringHill Suites, 🅞 Barnes&Noble, Best Buy, Dillard's, Firestone/auto, Goodyear/auto, Home Depot, JC Penney, Macy's, Martin's Foods, Merchant's Tire, Michael's, Old Navy, PetsMart, Sears/auto, 7-11, Target, Tire America, Walgreens, mall, **1-2 mi S** 🅖 Exxon, EC/Subway/dsl, 7-11, Sheetz, Shell, WaWa/dsl, 🅕 Aunt Sarah's, Burger King, Cesaer's El Pa,so Mexican, Hardee's, McDonald's, Subway, Waffle House, Wendy's, Wings Pizza & Things, 🅰 Broadway Motel, Cavalier Motel, EconoLodge, GuestHouse Inn, Howard Johnson, Knights Inn, Residence Inn, 🅞 Aamco, CVS Drug, Food Lion, Firestone, Lowe's, Rite Aid, Walmart
41b a	US 301, VA 2, **E** 🅖 BP/dsl, Valero/dsl, WaWa/dsl, 🅕 Burger King, McDonald's, Popeye's, Tropical Smoothie Cafe, Zheng's Chinese, 🅞 $General, Kroger/gas, Walgreens, **0-4 mi W** 🅖 Exxon/dsl, 🅕 Friendly's, 🅰 Holiday Inn, Super 8, Travelodge
38b a	VA 627, Pole Green Rd, **0-1mi E** 🅖 BP/Miller's Mkt/dsl, Exxon, 7-11, 🅕 Antonio's Pizza, Bruster's, Chen's Rest., Coffee Lane, Mimmo's Rest., Plaza Tapatia, Subway, 🅞 Curves, Food Lion, vet, **W** 🅖 7-11, Valero, 🅕 Padon's Hams
37b a	US 360, **1 mi E** 🅖 BP, Shell/dsl, Valero, 🅕 Applebee's, Arby's, Buffalo Wild Wings, Burger King, Chick-fil-A, China Buffet, Cracker Barrel, DQ, Gus' Italian, IHOP, KFC, McDonald's, Mexico Rest., Moe's SW Grill, Noodles&Co, Outback Steaks, Panera Bread, Papa John's, Pizza Hut, Ruby Tuesday, Shoney's, Starbucks, Taco Bell, Waffle House, Wendy's, 🅰 Hampton Inn, Holiday Inn Express, 🅞 AT&T, Best Buy, BJ's Whse/gas, $Tree, GNC, Home Depot, Kohl's, Marshall's, Martin's Foods, Old Navy, Petsmart, Radio Shack, Target, Verizon, Walmart, **W** 🅖 7-11, Sunoco/dsl, Valero/dsl, 🅞 $General, to Mechanicsville
34b a	VA 615, Creighton Rd, **E** 🅖 7-11, Valero
31b a	VA 156, **E** 🅖 Citgo/dsl, 🅞 to Cold Harbor Bfd, **4 mi W** 🅖 Shell, Valero, 🅕 Hardee's, 🅰 Courtyard, EconoLodge, Holiday Inn Express, Motel 6
28	I-64, to US 60, **W** 🅞 museum
25	Rd 895 W (toll), to Richmond
22b a	VA 5, Charles City, **E** 🅖 Exxon/dsl, 🅕 DQ, 🅞 Shirley Plantation, **W** 🅖 Valero/dsl, 🅕 China Taste, Portabella's Cafe, 🅞 Food Lion, Rite Aid, Richmond Nat Bfd
18mm	James River
16mm	new exit

HOPEWELL

15b a	VA 10, Hopewell, **E** 🅖 BP/dsl, 🅞 🅗, James River Plantations, **W** 🅖 EC/Subway/dsl, Exxon/McDonald's/dsl, Sheetz, WaWa, 🅕 Cesare's Ristorante, Chen's Rest., Jalapeno's, Wendy's, Wing's Pizza, 🅰 Hyatt Place, Residence Inn, 🅞 Curves, CVS Drug, Food Lion, 7-11
13mm	Appomattox River
9b a	VA 36, Hopewell, **E** 🅖 Gulf, Petrol, WaWa, 🅕 A&W, Bojangles, El Nopal Mexican, Hardee's, Hong Kong's Rest., Huddle House, KFC, Little Caesar's, LJ

= gas ⊓ = food ⌂ = lodging ◻ = other

INTERSTATE 295 CONT'D (Richmond)

Exit	Services
9b a	Continued
	Silver, McDonald's, Rosa's Italian, ⌂ Best Western, EconoLodge, Fairfield Inn, StayOver Suites, ◻ Advance Parts, AutoZone, Family$, O'Reilly Parts, Walgreens, vet, **W** ⓡ BP/dsl/24hr, Shell, Valero/dsl, ⊓ Burger King, DQ, Denny's, Dragon Express, Dunkin Donuts, Kanpai Japanese, McDonald's, Papa John's, Pizza Hut, Ruby Tuesday, Shoney's, Subway, Taco Bell, Top's China, Waffle House, Wendy's, ⌂ Baymont Inn, Candlewood Suites, Hampton Inn, Quality Inn, ◻ Chevrolet, $General, Family$, Farmer's Foods, Food Lion, Rite Aid, U-Haul, US Army Museum, to Petersburg Nat Bfd
5.5mm	Blackwater Swamp
3b a	US 460, Petersburg, to Norfolk, **E** ⓡ EC/Subway/dsl, Wilco/Hess/Wendy's/dsl/scales/24hr, ⊓ Prince George BBQ, **1-2 mi W** ⓡ BP/dsl, ⊓ McDonald's
1	I-95, N to Petersburg, S to Emporium, I-295 begins/ends.

INTERSTATE 495 (DC)

Exit	Services
27	I-95, N to Baltimore, S to Richmond. **I-495 & I-95 S run together.**
28b a	MD 650, New Hampshire Ave, **N** ⓡ Citgo, Exxon/dsl, Shell/repair, ⊓ Domino's, Quizno's, Starbucks, Urban BBQ, ◻ CVS Drug, Radio Shack, Safeway Foods, 7-11
29b a	MD 193, University Blvd
30b a	US 29, Colesville, **N** ⓡ BP, Getty, Oceanic, Shell, ⊓ McDonald's, Papa John's, Starbucks, Subway, ◻ CVS Drug, Safeway Foods, 7-11/Jerry's Subs, Tuesday Morning
31b a	MD 97, Georgia Ave, Silver Springs, **N** Ⓗ, **S** ⓡ C&G, Chevron, Exxon/dsl, Shell, ⊓ Armand's Pizza, Domino's, Mayflower Chinese, ◻ CVS Drug, Snider's Foods, Staples, vet
33	MD 185, Connecticut Ave, **N** ◻ LDS Temple, **S** ⓡ Citgo/repair, Liberty, Sunoco, ⊓ Starbucks, ⊓ Chevy Chase Foods
34	MD 355, Wisconsin Ave, Bethesda
35	(from wb), I-270
36	MD 187, Old Georgetown Rd, **S** ◻ HOSPITAL
38	I-270, to Frederick
39	MD 190, River Rd, Washington, Potomac
40	Cabin John Pkwy, Glen Echo (from sb), no trucks
41	Clara Barton Pkwy, Carderock, Great Falls, no trucks
42mm	Potomac River, Virginia/Maryland state line. **Exits 41-27 are in Maryland.**
43	G Washington Mem Pkwy, no trucks
44	VA 193, Langley
45b a	VA 267 W (toll), to I-66 E, to Dulles Airport
46b a	VA 123, Chain Bridge Rd, **W** ⓡ Hilton, ⌂ Crowne Plaza, ◻ Barnes&Noble, Old Navy
47b a	VA 7, Leesburg Pike, Tysons Corner, Falls Church, **E** ⌂ Westin, **W** ⓡ BP/dsl, Exxon, Shell, ⊓ Chili's, McDonald's, Olive Garden, On-the-Border, Panera Bread, Quizno's, Ruth's Chris Steaks, Starbucks, Subway, Wendy's, ⌂ Best Western, Embassy Suites, Hilton Garden, Marriott, Sheraton, ◻ AT&T, Best Buy, Bloomingdale's, Chevrolet, Dodge/Jeep, Ford, Honda, Infiniti, Lincoln/Mercury, Marshall's, Mr Tire, Nissan, Nordstrom's,

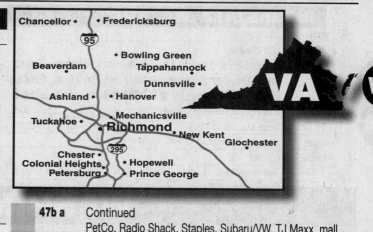

Exit	Services
47b a	Continued
	PetCo, Radio Shack, Staples, Subaru/VW, TJ Maxx, mall
49c b a	I-66 (exits left from both lanes), to Manassas, Front Royal
50b a	US 50, Arlington Blvd, Fairfax, Arlington, **E** ⌂ Marriott, **W** ⓡ Shell, Sunoco, ⊓ Chevy's Mexican, 5 Guys Burgers, Jasmine Garden, KFC, McDonald's, Panda Express, Papa John's, Starbucks, UNO Grill, Wendy's, ⌂ Residence Inn, Sweet Water Tavern Inn, ◻ Ⓗ, CVS Drug, vet
51	VA 657, Gallows Rd, **W** ⓡ Exxon, ◻ Ⓗ, 7-11
52b a	VA 236, Little River Tpk, Fairfax, **E** ⓡ Citgo, Sunoco/repair, ⊓ Chicken Loco, McDonald's, Wendy's, ◻ Safeway Foods, 7-11
54b a	VA 620, Braddock Rd, Ctr for the Arts, Geo Mason U, **S** ⓡ Sunoco, ◻ Curves, NTB, Rite Aid, Safeway Foods, 7-11
57	**I-95 S, I-395 N, I-95 N. I-495 & I-95 N run together. See Virginia I-95 exits 173-177**

INTERSTATE 664 (Norfolk)

Exit	Services
15b a	I-64 to Chesapeake, I-264 E to Portsmouth & Norfolk, I-664 begins/ends on I-64, exit 299.
13b a	US 13, US 58, US 460, Military Hwy, **E** ⓡ Shell/dsl, ⌂ Econolodge
12	VA 663, Dock Landing Rd
11b a	VA 337, Portsmouth Blvd, **E** ⓡ Hess, 7-11, Shell/dsl, ⊓ Applebee's, Arby's, Buffet City, Burger King, Chick-fil-A, ChuckeCheese, Fazoli's, Golden Corral, Japan Samurai, KFC, McDonald's, Olive Garden, Outback Steaks, Piccadilly, Pizza Hut, Red Lobster, Red Robin, Rita's Custard, Subway, Taco Bell, Wendy's, Zero's Subs, ⌂ Hampton Inn, Holiday Inn Express, SpringHill Suites, ◻ AutoZone, Best Buy, BJ's Whse/gas, Buick, Dodge, $Tree, Firestone Auto, Food Lion, Ford, Home Depot, JC Penney, K-Mart, Lukoil, Macy's, Merchant's Auto Ctr, Michael's, Old Navy, Petsmart, Ross, Sears/auto, Target, TJ Maxx, Tuesday Morning,
10	VA 659, Pughsville Rd, **E** ⓡ 7-11, Shell, ⊓ IHOP, McDonald's, Spaghetti Eddie's
9b a	US 17, US 164, **E** ⓡ Hess, 7-11, Wawa, ⊓ Burger King, Capt D's, DQ, Domino's, Dunkin Donuts, Great Wall Chinese, KFC, McDonald's, Miller's, Pizza Hut, Quizno's, Sonic, Taco Bell, Waffle House, Wendy's, ⌂ Budget Lodge, Extended Stay America, Hampton Inn, Sleep Inn, Super 8, ◻ Ⓗ, Chevrolet, $Tree, FarmFresh Foods, Firestone/auto, Honda, Hyundai, NAPA, Nissan, Scion/Toyota, tires, **W** to James River Br, museum
8b a	VA 135, College Dr, **E** ⓡ Exxon, 7-11, ⊓ Applebee's,

N ↑ S (left margin, top)

N ↑ S (left margin, middle)

WASHINGTON DC AREA (left margin)

E ↑ W PORTSMOUTH (right center margin)

INTERSTATE 664 CONT'D (Norfolk)

E ↕ W

Exit	Services
8b a	Continued Arby's, Firehouse Subs, McDonald's, Panera Bread, Ruby Tuesday, Subway, Wendy's, 🅞 Food Lion, Kohl's, Radio Shack, Walmart, **W** 🅝 Riverstone Chophouse, 🅛 Courtyard, TownePlace Suites
11.5mm	insp sta nb
9mm	James River
8mm	tunnel
7	Terminal Ave

Exit	Services
6	25th St, 26th St, E 🅖 7-11, 🅝 McDonald's
5	US 60 W, 35th St, Jefferson Ave, E 🅖 Fast&Easy, 🅝 Church's, King's Pizza, #1 Chinese, 🅞 Hornsby Tire
4	Chesnut Ave, Roanoke Ave
3	Aberdeen Rd, W 🅝 Hardee's, McDonald's, Wendy's
2	Powhatan Pkwy, E 🅖 7-11, **1-2 mi** W 🅝 Cheyenne's Rest., Coldstone, Cracker Barrel, El Pollo Loco, Joe's Crabshack, Lonstar Steaks, 🅛 Hilton Garden, Spring-Hill Suites, 🅞 Bass Pro Shop, BJ's Whse/gas, Lowe's
1b a	I-64, W to Richmond, E to Norfolk. I-664 begins/ends on I-64

WASHINGTON

INTERSTATE 5

N ↕ S

Exit	Services
277mm	USA/Canada Border, Washington state line, customs
276	WA 548 S, Blaine, E 🅖 Shell/dsl, Texaco/dsl, USA/dsl, 🅝 Big Al's Diner, 🅞 Duty Free, NAPA, to Peace Arch SP, W 🅖 Chevron/dsl/repair, 🅝 Chada Thai, Little Red Caboose Cafe, Pizza Factory, Pasa Del Norte, Seaside Bakery Cafe, Subway, Tony's Cafe, 🅛 Anchor Inn, Bay Side Motel, Cottage by the Bay B&B, International Motel, Sunset Inn, 🅞 Blaine Marine Park, USPO
275	WA 543 N (from nb, no return) truck customs, E 🅖 Chevron/dsl, Mkt/dsl, Shell/dsl, 🅝 Burger King, Little Caesars, Subway, 🅞 Ace Hardware, CostCutter Foods, $Tree, Rite Aid, vet
274	Peace Portal Drive (from nb, no return), Blaine, W 🅖 Shell/dsl, 🅝 Hot Spot Burgers, 🅞 Semi-ah-moo Resort, camping
270	Birch Bay, Lynden, W 🅖 Shell/Domino's/Subway/dsl, 🅝 Bob's Burgers, Jack-in-the-Box, 🅛 Semi-ah-moo Resort, 🅞 Birch Bay Mkt, Curves, Thousand Trails Camping, vet
269mm	**Welcome Ctr sb, full ♿ facilities, info, 🅒, 🅟, litter barrels, petwalk, vending**
267mm	**rest area nb, full ♿ facilities, info, 🅒, 🅟, litter barrels, petwalk, vending**
266	WA 548 N, Grandview Rd, Custer, W 🅖 Arco, 🅞 Birch Bay SP
263	Portal Way, E 🅖 Pacific Pride/dsl, Shell/dsl, 🅞 Cedars RV Park
263mm	Nooksack River
262	Main St, Ferndale, E 🅖 76/dsl, Texaco/dsl, 🅝 Denny's, McDonald's, Subway, 🅛 Super 8, 🅞 RV Park, TDS Tires, W 🅖 Gull/dsl, 76, Shell/Pizza Hut/dsl, 🅝 Bob's Burgers, DQ, Domino's, Quiznos, Sonic, Starbucks, 🅛 Scottish Lodge, 🅞 Costcutter Foods, $Tree, Haggen's Foods, NAPA, Schwab Tire, Walgreens, vet
260	Slater Rd, Lummi Island, E 🅖 Arco, 🅞 El Monte RV Ctr, antiques, **4 mi** W 🅖 76, Shell/dsl, 🅛 Silver Reef Hotel/Casino, 🅞 Lummi Ind Res
258	Bakerview Rd, E 🅝 Baskin-Robbins, Chilli Mexican, 5 Guys Burgers, Papa Murphy's, Subway, 🅞 Fred Meyer/dsl, Verizon, W 🅖 Arco, Mkt/dsl, 76, 🅝 Jack-in-the-Box, Mykono's Greek Rest., 🅛 Hampton Inn, Shamrock Motel, 🅞 Bellingham RV Park, ☕, st patrol
257	Northwest Ave, E 🅞 URGENT CARE, Cadillac/Chevrolet

Exit	Services
256b	Bellis Fair Mall Pkwy, E 🅞 JC Penney, Sears, Target, mall
256a	WA 539 N, Meridian St, E 🅖 Shell/dsl, Super Gas/dsl, 🅝 Arby's, Asian 1, Boston's Rest., Burger King, China Palace, Coldstone, Denny's, Lorenzo's Mexican, McHale's Rest., Mi Mexico, Old Country Buffet, Olive Garden, Quiznos, Red Robin, Shari's, Subway, Taco Bell, Taco Time, Thai House Rest., Wendy's, Wonderful Buffet, 🅛 Best Western, Comfort Inn, Holiday Inn Express, La Quinta, Quality Inn, 🅞 AAA, AT&T, Barnes&Noble, Best Buy, Costco/gas, Costcutter Foods, $Tree, Home Depot, JC Penney, Kohl's, Macy's, Michael's, Office Depot, O'Reilly Parts, PetCo, Petsmart, Rite Aid, Ross, Schwab Tire, Sears/auto, Target, TJ Maxx, U-Haul, Walgreens, Walmart/McDonald's, mall, st patrol, to Nooksack Ind Res, W 🅝 Slopitch Grill, 🅛 EconoLodge, Rodeway Inn
255	WA 542 E, Sunset Dr, Bellingham, E 🅖 Chevron/dsl, 76, Shell/Subway/Domino's/dsl, 🅝 A&W/KFC, Applebee's, Hawaii BBQ, Jack-in-the-Box, Panda Express, RoundTable Pizza, Taco Bell, 🅞 Costcutter Foods, Jo-Ann Fabrics, K-Mart, Lowe's, Rite Aid, Tuesday Morning, Walgreens, repair, USPO, to Mt Baker, W 🅞 🅗
254	Iowa St, State St, Bellingham, E 🅖 76, Valero, 🅞 Audi/VW, Buick/GMC, Chrysler/Dodge/Jeep, Honda, Hyundai, KIA, Mercedes, Nissan, Subaru, Toyota/Scion, Volvo, W 🅖 Chevron/dsl, Shell, 🅝 DQ, McDonald's, Subway, 🅞 Ford/Lincoln, NAPA, O'Reilly Parts, repair
253	Lakeway Dr, Bellingham, E 🅝 Lychee Buffet, Little Caesars, Papa Murphy's, Port of Subs, Sol de Mexico, Subway, 🅛 Best Western, Guesthouse Inn, 🅞 Discount Tire, Fred Meyer/dsl, Radio Shack, 7-11, W same as 252
252	Samish Way, Bellingham, E same as 253, W 🅖 Chevron, 76, Shell/dsl, SuperGas/dsl, 🅝 Arby's, Boomers Drive-In, Diego's Mexican, El Agave, Kyoto Steaks, McDonald's, Pizza Hut, Pizza Pipeline, Quiznos, Starbucks, Subway, Taco Time, Thai Cuisine, Wendy's, 🅛 Aloha Motel, Bay City Motel, Cascade Inn, Coachman Inn, Days Inn, Motel 6, Travelodge, Villa Inn, 🅞 Haggen Foods, Rite Aid
250	WA 11 S, Chuckanut Dr, Bellingham, Fairhaven Hist Dist, W 🅖 Arco, Chevron/repair, 🅞 Fairhaven Mkt, to Larrabee SP, to Alaska Ferry
246	N Lake Samish, W 🅖 Shell/dsl, 🅞 Lake Padden RA, RV camping
242	Nulle Rd, S Lake Samish
240	Alger, E 🅖 Shell/dsl/LP/RV dump, 🅝 Alger Grille, 🅛

Copyright 2012 - The Next Exit®   🚹 = gas   🍴 = food   🛏 = lodging   🅾 = other

INTERSTATE 5 CONT'D

N↑S (BURLINGTON)

Exit	Services
240	Continued
	Whispering Firs Motel/RV Parking
238mm	**rest area both lanes, full ♿ facilities, 🚻, 🚮, litter barrels, vending, petwalk**
236	Bow Hill Rd, E Skagit Hotel Casino/rest./dsl/LP
235mm	**weigh sta sb**
234mm	Samish River
232	Cook Rd, Sedro-Woolley, E 🚹 76/Subway/dsl, Shell/dsl, 🍴 Bob's Burgers, Jack-in-the-Box, Starbucks, 🛏 Fairfield Inn, 🅾 🅷, KOA
231	WA 11 N, Chuckanut Dr, E 🅾 Camping World RV Ctr, KIA, st patrol, W to Larrabee SP (14mi)
230	WA 20, Burlington, E 🚹 Shell/dsl, 🍴 Applebee's, Carino's Italian, China Wok, El Cazador, Jack-in-the-Box, Krispy Kreme, Outback Steaks, Papa Murphy's, Pizza Factory, Pizza Hut/Taco Bell, Popeye's, Quiznos, Red Robin, 🛏 Cocusa Motel, Sterling Motel, 🅾 🅷, AutoZone, Fred Meyer/dsl, Haggen Foods, JC Penney, Macy's, Schwab Tire, Sears/auto, 7-11, Target, Walgreens, mall, transmissions, to N Cascades NP, W 🍴 McDonald's, 🛏 Holiday Inn Express, Mark II Motel, 🅾 Harley-Davidson, Hyundai, to San Juan Ferry
229	George Hopper Rd, E 🚹 Arco, USA/dsl, 🍴 Jamba Juice, McDonald's, Olive Garden, Shari's, Starbucks, Subway, Taco Del Mar, Wendy's, 🛏 Hampton Inn, 🅾 Best Buy, Costco/gas, Costcutter Foods, Discount Tire, Home Depot, K-Mart/Little Caesars, Kohl's, Michael's, NAPA, Old Navy, Outlet Shops/famous brands, Petsmart, Ross, See's Candies, Verizon, vet, W 🅾 Chrysler/Jeep/Dodge, Ford, Honda, Nissan, Toyota/Scion, Subaru, Suzuki, VW, RV Ctr
228mm	Skagit River
227	WA 538 E, College Way, Mt Vernon, E 🍴 A&W, Big Scoop Rest., Dragon Inn, Denny's, Domino's, El Gitano, Hong Kong Rest., Jack-in-the-Box, KFC, Papa

MT VERNON

Exit	Services
227	Continued
	Murphy's, Patron Mexican, Pizza Hut/Taco Bell, Quiznos, Riverside Cafe, RoundTable Pizza, Starbucks, Subway, Taco Time, 🛏 Days Inn, West Winds Motel, 🅾 Ace Hardware, AutoZone, Buick/Cadillac/GMC, $Plus, $Tree, Goodyear/auto, Grocery Outlet, Jo-Ann Fabrics, Office Depot, O'Reilly Parts, PetCo, Rite Aid, Safeway/dsl, W 🚹 APP/dsl, Shell/dsl, 🍴 Arby's, Burger King, Cranberry Tree Rest., DQ, Forks&Knives Steaks, Fortune Chinese, Royal Star Buffet, 🛏 Best Western, Quality Inn, Tulip Inn, 🅾 Blade RV Ctr, Chevrolet, Lowe's, Riverbend RV Park, Walmart/Subway
226	WA 536 W, Kincaid St, City Ctr, E 🅾 🅷, RV camping, W 🍴 Old Towne Grainery Rest., Skagit River Brewing Co, 🅾 NAPA, Red Apple Mkt, Valley RV Ctr, antiques
225	Anderson Rd, E 🚹 Fuel Express/dsl, 76/dsl, 🅾 Country Motorhomes, W 🚹 Truck City Trkstp/dsl, Valero, 🍴 Long Haul Cafe, 🅾 Freightliner, Poulsbo RV Ctr, Valley RV Ctr
224	WA 99 S (from nb, no return), S Mt Vernon, E gas/dsl, food
221	WA 534 E, Conway, Lake McMurray, E 🚹 76/dsl, 🅾 farmers mkt, W 🚹 76/dsl, Texaco/dsl/LP, 🍴 Conway Deli, 🛏 Channel Lodge/Rest. (11mi), 🅾 Blake's RV Park/marina (6mi)
218	Starbird Rd
215	300th NW, W 🚹 Interstate/dsl
214mm	**weigh sta nb**
212	WA 532 W, Stanwood, Bryant, W 🚹 76/dsl, Shell/Burger Stop/dsl, 🅾 Camano Island SP (19mi)
210	236th NE, E 🅾 Angel of the Winds Casino/Watershed Rest.
209mm	Stillaguamish River
208	WA 530, Silvana, Arlington, E 🚹 Arco/dsl, 76/Circle K, Shell, Tesoro/dsl, 🍴 Denny's, Patty's Eggnest&Turkeyhouse, 🛏 Arlington Motel, 🅾 🅷, to N Cascades Hwy, W 🚹 76/dsl
207mm	**rest area both lanes, full ♿ facilities, 🚻, 🚮, litter barrels, coffee, vending, RV dump, petwalk**

INTERSTATE 5 CONT'D

Exit	Services
206	WA 531, Lakewood, **E** 🅖 Arco, Shell, 7-11, 🍴 Alfy's Pizza, Buzz Inn Steaks, Domino's, Jack-in-the-Box, KFC, McDonald's, Moose Creek BBQ, Olympia Pizza, Starbucks, Subway, Taco Del Mar, Taco Time, Wendy's, 🛏 Medallion Hotel, Smokey Point Motel, 🅞 AT&T, Buick/GMC, Chrysler/Dodge/Jeep, $Tree, Harley-Davidson, Jo-Ann Fabrics, Lowe's, O'Reilly Parts, Rite Aid, Safeway/gas, Schwab Tire, Smokey Point RV Park, Walmart/Subway, vet, **W** 🍴 Boston's Rest., Burger King, 5 Guys Burgers, Hot Iron Mongolian, IHOP, Jamba Juice, Pizza Hut, Red Robin, Starbucks, Subway, Taco Bell, Wonderful Buffet, 🅞 AT&T, Best Buy, Costco/gas, Discount Tire, Marshall's, Michael's, Office Depot, PetCo, Target, Verizon, to Wenburg SP
202	116th NE, **E** 🅖 76/dsl, Shell/dsl, 🍴 Carl's Jr, Magic Dragon Chinese, Starbucks, Subway, Taco Bell, Tres Hermanos Mexican, 🅞 Albertson's, Kohl's, Petsmart, Rite Aid, Ross, Verizon, WinCo Foods, **W** 🅖 Chevron/dsl, Donna's Trkstp/Gull/dsl/scales/24hr/@, 🍴 McDonald's, Olive Garden, 🅞 Seattle Outlets/famous brands, Tulalip Resort/Casino, st patrol
200	88th St NE, Quil Ceda Way, **E** 🅖 7-11, 76, Shell/dsl/LP, 🍴 Applebee's, Mkt St Cafe, Quiznos, Starbucks, 🛏 Holiday Inn Express, 🅞 Haggen's Foods, **W** 🅖 Mirastar, 🍴 Bob's Burgers, Port of Subs, Taco Del Mar, 🅞 Home Depot, Walmart/McDonald's, casino
199	WA 528 E, Marysville, Tulalip, **E** 🅖 Arco, Chevron/dsl, 76, Shell/dsl, 🍴 Burger King, Don's Rest./24hr, DQ, Jack-in-the-Box, Jumbo Buffet, Las Margaritas Mexican, Maxwell's Rest., 🛏 Village Motel/Rest., 🅞 Albertson's, JC Penney, O'Reilly Parts, PepBoys, Rite Aid, Staples, **W** 🅖 76, 🍴 Arby's, McDonald's, Taco Time, Wendy's, 🛏 Best Western/rest., Comfort Inn, 🅞 Chevrolet/Subaru, Robinson RV Ctr, to Tulalip Indian Res
198	Port of Everett (from sb), Steamboat Slough, st patrol
195mm	Snohomish River
195	Port of Everett (from nb), Marine View Dr
194	US 2 E, Everett Ave City Ctr, **W** 🅖 Shell/dsl, 🅞 Schwab Tire
193	WA 529, Pacific Ave (from nb), **W** 🅖 Chevron, 76, 🍴 Denny's, 🛏 Best Western, Holiday Inn, Travelodge, 🅞 🅷, Lowe's
192	Broadway, to 41st St, City Ctr, **W** 🅖 Arco, Chevron, 76/dsl, Shell, 🍴 Buzz Inn Steaks, IHOP, Iver's Sea 🍴 La Cuesta Mexican, Little Caesars, McDonald's, Quiznos, Starbucks, Subway, 🛏 Days Inn, Travelodge
189	WA 526 W, WA 527, Everett Mall Way, Everett, **E** 🅖 Arco, Chevron, Shell/dsl, 🍴 Alfy's Pizza, Burger King, Buzz Inn Steaks, Subway, Wendy's, 🛏 Travelodge, 🅞 Costco/gas, WinCo Foods, vet, **W** 🅖 Shell, 🛏 Best Western, Days Inn, Extended Stay America, Motel 6, 🅞 Goodyear/auto, Macy's, mall
188mm	**rest area/weigh sta sb, full** ♿ **facilities, info, 🄲, 🚻, litter barrels, coffee, RV dump**
186	WA 96, 128th SW, **E** 🅖 76/dsl, Shell/dsl, Texaco, 🍴 O'Donnells Rest., 🛏 Quality Inn, 🅞 Lakeside RV Park, **W** 🅖 Arco, Chevron, 7-11, Shell, 🍴 A&W/KFC, Acropolis Pizza, DQ, Denny's, McDonald's, Ming Dynasty, Pizza Hut, Skipper's, Subway, Taco Bell, Taco Time, 🛏 Holiday Inn Express, La Quinta, Motel 6, 🅞 Albertson's/Sav-on,

Exit	Services
186	Continued $Tree, Goodyear/auto, Maple RV Park, transmissions, vet
183	164th SW, **E** 🅖 Arco, Shell/dsl, 🍴 Jack-in-the-Box, Panda Express, Quiznos, Starbucks, Subway, Taco Del Mar, Taco Time, 🅞 Curves, Walgreens, Walmart, **W** 🅖 Chevron/dsl, 🍴 5 Guys Burgers, 🅞 Fred Meyer/dsl
182	WA 525, Alderwood Mall Blvd, to Alderwood Mall, **E** I-405 S, to Bellevue, **W** 🅖 Arco, 🍴 Fatburger, Jersey Mike's, Keg Steaks, Macaroni Grill, Panera Bread, PF Chang's, Qdoba Mexican, Red Robin, Subway, TCBY, 🛏 Residence Inn, 🅞 JC Penney, Kohl's, Macy's, Marshall's, Nordstrom, Rite Aid, Ross, Sears/auto, See's Candies, Target, vet
181	44th Ave W, to WA 524, Lynnwood, **E** 🅖 Arco, 76/dsl, Shell, 🍴 Jimmy John's, McDonald's/playplace, Old Spaghetti Factory, Starbucks, 🛏 Embassy Suites, Extended Stay America, Hampton Inn, Holiday Inn Express, 🅞 Barnes&Noble, Best Buy, Jaguar, Land Rover, Lowe's, Old Navy, PetCo, Staples, Verizon, **W** 🅖 Arco, Chevron, 76/dsl, Shell/repair, 🍴 Alfy's Pizza, Applebee's, Arby's, Black Angus, Buca Italian, Celtic Bayou, Chevy's Mexican, Chipotle Mexican, ChuckeCheese, Denny's, Herfy's Burgers, IHOP, Jack-in-the-Box, KFC, McDonald's, Old Country Buffet, Olive Garden, Panda Express, Quiznos, Red Lobster, Rock Woodfire Pizza, Silver Spoon Rest., Starbucks, Subway, Taco Bell, Taco Time, Todo Mexico, Wendy's, 🛏 Best Western, Courtyard, Days Inn, La Quinta, 🅞 URGENT CARE, Fred Meyer/dsl, Goodyear/auto, Radio Shack, Schwab Tire, 7-11, Tuesday Morning, USPO, vet
179	220th SW, Mountlake Terrace, Mountlake Terrace, **W** 🅖 Shell/dsl, 🍴 Azteca Mexican, Port of Subs, Subway, 🅞 🅷
178	236th St SW (from nb), Mountlake Terrace
177	WA 104, Edmonds, **E** 🅖 Chevron/dsl, Shell/dsl, 🍴 Mazatlan Mexican, McDonald's/playplace, Starbucks, Subway, Tagalicci Pizza, Todo Mexico, 🛏 Motel 6, 🅞 Office Depot, O'Reilly Parts, RiteAid, Thriftway Foods, **1-2 mi W on WA 99** 🅖 76/dsl, 🍴 A&W/KFC, Arby's, Barlee's Rest., Scott's Grill, Starbucks, 🛏 Days Inn, 🅞 Costco, Discount Tire, Home Depot, Nissan, PetCo, Radio Shack, Verizon, VW
176	NE 175th St, Aurora Ave N, to Shoreline
175	WA 523, NE 145th, 5th Ave NE
174	NE 130th, Roosevelt Way
173	1st Ave NE, Northgate Way, **E** 🅖 76, 🍴 Azteca Mexican, CA Pizza Kitchen, Chipotle Mexican, 5 Guys Burgers, Macaroni Grill, Marie Callender's, Panera Bread, Quiznos, Ram Rest., Red Robin, Stanford's Rest., Super Buffet, 🅞 Barnes&Noble, Best Buy, JC Penney, Macy's, Nordstrom, Ross, Target, Verizon, mall, **W** 🅖 Chevron, 76, Shell/dsl, 🍴 McDonald's, Pizza Xpress, Saffron Grill, Starbucks, 🛏 Hotel Nexus, 🅞 7-11
172	N 85th, Aurora Ave
171	WA 522, Lake City Way, Bothell
170	(nb only), Ravenna Blvd, **E** 🅖 Shell/dsl
169	NE 45th, NE 50th, **E** 🅖 76, Shell, 🍴 Subway, 🅞 🅷, PetCo, U of WA, **W** 🅞 to Seattle Pacific U, zoo
168b	WA 520, to Bellevue
168a	Lakeview Blvd, downtown
167	Mercer St (exits left from nb), Fairview Ave, Seattle Ctr,

SEATTLE

INTERSTATE 5 CONT'D

N ↕ **S**

S E A T T L E

Exit	Services
167	Continued
	W 🗓 Shell, 🛏 Silver Cloud Inn
166	Olive Way, Stewart St, E 🅾 H, W 🛏 SpringHill Suites, 🅾 Honda
165a	Seneca St (exits left from nb), James St, E 🅾 H
165b	Union St, E 🛏 Homewood Suites, W ⋔ Ruth's Chris Steaks, 🛏 Renaissance Inn
164b	4th Ave S, to Kingdome, downtown
164a	I-90 E, to Spokane, downtown
163	6th Ave, S Spokane St, W Seattle Br, Columbian Way, **1 mi W on 4th Ave S** 🗓 Arco/dsl, Gull/dsl, Shell, ⋔ Arby's, Burger King, Denny's, Jack-in-the-Box, KFC, McDonald's, Quiznos, Starbucks, Subway, Taco Bell, 🅾 Costco/gas, Pepboys, USPO
162	Corson Ave, Michigan St (exits left from nb), same as 161
161	Swift Ave, Albro Place, W 🗓 Shell/dsl, ⋔ Starbucks, Thai Rest., 🛏 Georgetown Inn
158	Pacific Hwy S, E Marginal Way, W 🗓 Chevron, 🅾 NAPA
157	ML King Way
156	WA 539 N, Interurban Ave (no EZ return to sb), Tukwila, E 🗓 Pacific Pride/dsl, ⋔ Billy Baroos Rest., W 🗓 76/dsl, Shell/dsl, ⋔ Emerald Green, Jack-in-the-Box, Quiznos, Starbucks, 🛏 Days Inn
154b	WA 518, Burien, W 🛏 Extended Stay America
154a	I-405, N to Bellevue
153	S Center Pkwy, (from nb), E 🗓 Chevron/dsl, ⋔ Applebee's, Azteca Mexican, Bahama Breeze, BJ's Rest., Cheesecake Factory, Chipotle Mexican, Famous Dave's, IHOP, Jamba Juice, McDonald's, Olive Garden, Outback Steaks, Panda Express, Panera Bread, Qdoba Mexican, Quiznos, Red Robin, Simply Thai, Sizzler, Starbucks, Stanford's Rest., Subway, Zoopa, 🛏 DoubleTree Inn, 🅾 Acura, AT&T, Barnes&Noble, Best Buy, $Tree, JC Penney, Jo-Ann Fabrics, Kohl's, Macy's, Michael's, Nordstrom, Office Depot, Old Navy, PetCo, Petsmart, Ross, Sears/auto, See's Candies, Target, Tuesday Morning, Verizon, World Mkt, mall
152	S 188th, Orillia Rd, W 🗓 76/dsl, 🛏 Motel 6, 🅾 city park, 1 mi W 🗓 Shell, ⋔ Dave's Diner, Denny's, Jack-in-the-Box, Taco Bell, 🛏 DoubleTree Hotel, La Quinta, 🅾 to ✈
151	S 200th, Military Rd, E 🗓 Shell/dsl, 🛏 Motel 6, W 🗓 Chevron, 7-11, 76, ⋔ Bob's Burger, IHOP, 🛏 Best Value Inn, Best Western, Days Inn, Comfort Inn, EconoLodge, Fairfield Inn, Hampton Inn, Holiday Inn Express, Quality Inn, Sleep Inn, Super 8, 🅾 NAPA, O'Reilly Parts, U-Haul, city park
149	WA 516, to Kent, Des Moines, E 🛏 Century Motel, 🅾 Poulsbo RV Ctr, W 🗓 Arco, Chevron, Shell/dsl, ⋔ Burger King, Church's, McDonald's, Pizza Hut, Starbucks, Subway, 🛏 Garden Suites, Kings Arms Motel, New Best Inn, 🅾 $Tree, Lowe's, Radio Shack, 7-11, Walgreens, to Saltwater SP
147	S 272nd, E 🗓 76/Circle K/dsl, **W on Pacific Hwy** 🗓 Arco, Shell/dsl, ⋔ Jack-in-the-Box, Little Caesars, McDonald's, Quiznos, Papa Murphy's, Starbucks, Subway, Taco Bell, 🅾 Ace Hardware, AutoZone, Bartell Drug, Firestone/auto, Safeway

T A C O M A

Exit	Services
143	S 320th, Federal Way, W 🗓 Arco, 76/Circle K/dsl, Shell/dsl, ⋔ Applebee's, Arby's, Azteca Mexican, Black Angus, Chipotle Mexican, Church's, Coldstone, Denny's, Domino's, El Torero Mexican, Grand Buffet, Ivar's Sea⋔ Jasmine Mongolian, Jimmy John's, Main Japanese Buffet, Marie Callender, McDonald's, McGrath's Fishouse, Old Country Buffet, Outback Steaks, Panera Bread, Qdoba Mexican, Red Lobster, Red Robin, Starbucks, Subway, Taco Bell, Taco Time, Tokyo Japanese Steaks, Village Inn, Wendy's, 🛏 Best Western, Clarion, Comfort Inn, Courtyard, Extended Stay America, Hampton Inn, 🅾 AT&T, Barnes&Noble, Best Buy, BigLots, Discount Tire, Jo-Ann Fabrics, Macy's, Michael's, O'Reilly Parts, PetCo, Petsmart, Radio Shack, Rite Aid, Ross, Safeway, See's Candies, Sears/auto, Target, TJ Maxx, Top Foods, Trader Joe's, Verizon, Walmart/McDonald's, mall, to Dash Point SP
142b a	WA 18 E, S 348th, Enchanted Pkwy, E 🅾 funpark, W 🗓 Chevron, Shell/dsl, ⋔ Arby's, Burger King, Del Taco, Denny's, Fatburger, Jack-in-the-Box, Jamba Juice, Jimmy Mac's Roadhouse, KFC, LJ Silver, McDonald's, Olive Garden, Panda Express, Popeye's, Puerta Vallarta, RoundTable Pizza, Shari's, Starbucks, Subway, Taco Bell, Taco Del Mar, The Rock Pizza, Time Out Grill, 🛏 Quality Inn, Super 8, 🅾 H, Chevrolet, Costco/gas, Discount Tire, Home Depot, Lowe's, Office Depot, Schwab Tire, Verizon, Walmart/Subway
140mm	**weigh sta, both lanes. Rest area, nb, full (handicapped) facilities, litter barrels, 🐾, petwalk, RV dump**
137	WA 99, Fife, Milton, E 🗓 Arco, Chevron/dsl, 76/dsl, Shell, ⋔ DQ, Johnny's Rest., 🛏 Motel 6, 🅾 Acura, Cadillac, Hummer, Saab, W 🗓 76/Circle K/dsl, Shell/dsl, ⋔ Arby's, A&W/KFC, Baskin-Robbins, Denny's, Fife Rest., Herfy's Burgers, McDonald's, Mitzel's Kitchen, Pizza Hut/Taco Bell, Poodle Dog, Quiznos, Starbucks, Taco Time, Wendy's, 🛏 Baymont Inn, Days Inn, EQC Motel/casino, Kings Motel, 🅾 Emerald RV Ctr, Holiday RV Ctr, Infiniti, NAPA, O'Reilly Parts, Schwab Tire
136b a	Port of Tacoma, E 🗓 CFN/dsl, 🅾 Baydos RV Ctr, BMW, Costco, Honda, I-5 Motors, Mercedes, Mini, Peterbilt, Tacoma RV Ctr, W 🗓 Chevron/dsl, 🅾 Loves/Chester's/Subway/dsl/scales/LP/RV dump/24hr, Gull/dsl, ⋔ Jack-in-the-Box, Subway, 🛏 Best Night Inn, Extended Stay America, Howard Johnson, Rodeway Inn, Sunshine Motel, Travelodge, 🅾 Goodyear/biodsl, Harley-Davidson, Land Rover/Jaguar/Lexus, Nissan, Volvo, truck repair
135	Bay St, Puyallup, E 🗓 Shell, 🅾 Majestic RV Park (4mi),

INTERSTATE 5 CONT'D

Exit	Services
135	Continued W 🅖 Arco, 🛏 La Quinta, ⊡ to Tacoma Dome
134	Portland Ave (from nb), same as 135
133	WA 7, I-705, City Ctr, W 🛏 Best Western, Courtyard, ⊡ Tacoma Dome, museum
132	WA 16 W, S 38th, Gig Harbor, to Bremerton, W 🍴 Adriatic Grill, Jamba Juice, Jimmy John's, Krispy Kreme, Panera Bread, Quiznos, Red Robin, Subway, Wendy's, ⊡ Best Buy, Costco/gas, $Tree, Firestone/auto, Ford/Toyota, Goodyear/auto, JC Penney, JoAnn Fabrics, Macy's, Nordstrom, PetCo, Sears/auto, Verizon, to Pt Defiance Pk/Zoo, mall
130	S 56th, Tacoma Mall Blvd, W 🅖 Shell/dsl, 🍴 Axteca Mexican, ChuckeCheese, Jack-in-the-Box, Subway, Wingers, 🛏 Extended Stay America
129	S 72nd, S 84th, E 🅖 Chevron, Valero, 🍴 Applebee's, Burger King, DQ, Elmer's, Famous Dave's, IHOP, Jack-in-the-Box, Mongolian Grill, Olive Garden, Red Lobster, RoundTable Pizza, Shari's, Starbucks, Subway, 🛏 Motel 6, Shilo Inn, ⊡ Lowe's, WinCo Foods, W 🍴 Hooters, 🛏 Days Inn, ⊡ Home Depot, to Steilacoom Lake
128	S 84th St (from nb) same as 129, E 🅖 76, Shell/dsl, 🍴 Denny's, Greatwall Chinese, Neo Woodfire Pizza, Subway, 🛏 American Lodge, Comfort Inn, Crossland Suites, Hampton Inn, Holiday Inn Express, King Oscar Motel, Red Lion Hotel, Rodeway Inn, Rothem Inn, Tacoma Inn, W 🅖 Shell, ⊡ Discount Tire
127	WA 512, S Tacoma Way, Puyallup, Mt Ranier, W 🅖 Arco, 7-11, 76/Circle K, 🍴 DQ, Ivar's Sea🍴 Mazatlan Mexican, McDonald's, Sizzler, Starbucks, Subway, Taco Guaynas, Taco Time, Wendy's, 🛏 Best Value Inn, Candlewood Suites, ⊡ Grocery Outlet, O'Reilly Parts, transmissions
125	to McChord AFB, Lakewood, W 🅖 Chevron, 76/Circle K/dsl, 🍴 A&W/KFC, Carr's Rest., Church's, Denny's, Greek Cafe, Pizza Hut, Wendy's, 🛏 La Quinta, ⊡ 🄷 Aamco, Ford, NAPA, O'Reilly Parts, 7-11, U-Haul, tires/repair, vet
124	Gravelly Lake Dr, W 🅖 Arco/repair, 76/Circle K, 🍴 El Toro Mexican, Pizza Casa, Red Robin (2mi), same as 125
123	Thorne Lane, Tillicum Lane
122	Berkeley St, Camp Murray, E ⊡ 🄷, W 🅖 Chevron/repair, 🍴 BBQ Inn, Gertie's Grill, Happy Wok, KFC, McDonald's, Papa John's, Pizza Hut, Subway, Taco Bell, Teryaki Hut, ⊡ AutoZone, 7-11
120	Ft Lewis, E ⊡ Ft Lewis Military Museum
119	Du Pont Rd, Steilacoom, E to Ft Lewis, W 🅖 Chevron, 76, 🍴 Jack-in-the-Box, Starbucks, Subway
118	Center Dr, W 🅖 Chevron/dsl, 🍴 Domino's, Farrelli's Pizza, Fortune Cookie Chinese, Jack-in-the-Box, Koko's Wok, McNamara's Eatery, McDonald's, Quiznos, Starbucks, Subway, Super Buffet, Viva Mexico, 🛏 GuestHouse Inn, Liberty Inn
117mm	weigh sta nb
116	Mounts Rd, Old Nisqually, E Lacy Creek Cafe, golf
115mm	Nisqually River
114	Nisqually, E 🅖 Chevron/repair, Shell/dsl/LP, 🍴 Nisqually Grill, Norma's Burgers, Shipwreck Café, ⊡ Nisqually

Exit	Services
114	Continued RV Park, River Bend RV Park (3mi)
111	WA 510 E, Marvin Rd, to Yelm, E 🅖 Chevron, 76/Circle K, Shell/dsl, 🍴 Burger King, Coldstone, Hawk's Prairie Rest./casino, Jack-in-the-Box, Jamba Juice, KFC/LJ Silver, McDonald's, Panda Express, Panera Bread, Papa Murphy's, Puerto Vallarta, Quiznos, RoundTable Pizza, Starbucks, Super Buffet, Taco Del Mar, Taco Time, 🛏 Best Western, King Oscar Motel, ⊡ Best Buy, BigLots, Costco/gas, $Tree, Harley Davidson, Home Depot, O'Reilly Parts, Radio Shack, Safeway/gas, Schwab Tire, Verizon, Walgreens, Walmart/Subway, W 🅖 Pacific Pride/dsl, 🍴 Mayan Mexican, ⊡ Cabela's, Tolmie SP (5mi), RV camping
109	Martin Way, Sleator-Kenny Rd, E 🍴 Main Chinese Buffet, Taco Bell, The Rock Pizza, ⊡ Discount Tire, ShopKO, Top 🍴 W 🅖 Shell/dsl, 🍴 Casa Mia, Denny's, El Serape Mexican, Red Lobster, Shari's, Subway, 🛏 Comfort Inn, La Quinta, Ramada Inn, Super 8, ⊡ 🄷, Tire Factory
108	Sleater-Kinney Rd, E 🅖 Shell/dsl, 🍴 Applebee's, Arby's, McDonald's/playplace, Starbucks, Wendy's, ⊡ $Tree, Firestone/auto, Fred Meyer, Kohl's, Marshall's, Michael's, Office Depot, Petsmart, Radio Shack, Rite Aid, Sears/auto, Target, Tuesday Morning, Verizon, W 🅖 Shell, 🍴 Casa Mia, Coldstone, Dirty Dave's, El Sarape Mexican, Jack-in-the-Box, Panda Express, Subway, 🛏 Ramada Inn, ⊡ 🄷, K-Mart, Lowe's, Safeway/gas, Tire Factory, same as 109
107	Pacific Ave, E 🅖 Shell/dsl/E-85, 🍴 DQ, Izzy's Pizza, Shari's, Sizzler, Subway, Taco Time, ⊡ 🄷, Albertson's/Sav-on, Home Depot, Ross, vet, W ⊡ Coumbs RV Ctr, Ford
105	St Capitol, W 🅖 Chevron/dsl, Shell/Subway/dsl, 🛏 Quality Inn, ⊡ to St Capitol
104	US 101 N, W Olympia, to Aberdeen, W 🅖 Arco, Chevron, 7-11, 🍴 Jack-in-the-Box, Oly Burgers, 🛏 Extended Stay America, Red Lion Hotel, ⊡ 🄷, to Capitol Mall
103	2nd Ave, Deschutes Ave, to hist dist
102	Trosper Rd, Black Lake, E 🅖 Shell/dsl, 🍴 Arby's, Brewery City Pizza, Burger King, El Sarape Mexican, Happy Teriyaki, Jack-in-the-Box, KFC, McDonald's, Plaza Jalisco Mexican, Starbucks, Subway, Taco Bell, Taco Time, 🛏 Best Western, Motel 6, ⊡ Ace Hardware, Goodyear/auto, O'Reilly Parts, W 🅖 Chevron, 76/Circle K, 🍴 Georgio's Subs, Nickelby's Rest., Panda Express, Papa Murphy's, Port of Subs, Starbucks, Subway, Taco Del Mar, The Brick Rest., ⊡ Albertson's/gas, Alderbrook RV Park, AutoZone, Costco/gas, Fred Meyer, GNC, Home Depot, MegaFoods, Radio Shack, Walmart
101	Tumwater Blvd, E 🅖 Chevron, Shell/dsl, 🍴 DQ (1mi), Inferno's Pizza, Quiznos, Teriyaki Wok, 🛏 Comfort Inn, GuestHouse Inn, Olympia Camping, ⊡ USPO
99	WA 121 S, 93rd Ave, Scott Lake, E 🅖 ▯/McDonald's/Subway/dsl/scales/24hr, ⊡ Ace Hardware, American Heritage Camping, Olympia Camping, W 🅖 Shell/Michael's Rest./dsl/LP, 🛏 Restover Motel
95	WA 121, Littlerock, 3 mi E ⊡ Millersylvania SP, RV camping, W 🅖 Chevron/dsl, 🍴 Farmboy Drive-In
93.5mm	rest area sb, full 🚻 facilities, info, 🄲, ♿, litter barrels, vending, coffee, petwalk

OLYMPIA

ⓖ = gas   Ⓕ = food   Ⓛ = lodging   Ⓞ = other

INTERSTATE 5 CONT'D

N ↕ S

C E N T R A L I A

Exit	Services
91mm	rest area nb, full Ⓗ facilities, info, Ⓒ, Ⓛ, litter barrels, vending, coffee, petwalk
88	US 12, Rochester, **E** Ⓞ I-5 RV Ctr/Service, **W** ⓖ Arco, CFN, Chevron/dsl, 76/dsl, Shell/McDonald's, Ⓕ Burger Claim, DQ, Figaro's Pizza, Little Red Barn Rest., Quiznos, The Grill, Ⓛ Great Wolf Lodge, Ⓞ Curves, Outback RV Park (2mi), truck wash
82	Harrison Ave, Factory Outlet Way, Centralia, **E** ⓖ Arco, Shell/dsl, Ⓕ Burger King, Burgerville, Casa Ramos Mexican, Centralia Deli, DQ, Panda Chinese, Papa Pete's Pizza, Peking House Chinese, Pizza Hut, Quiznos, Thai Dish, Wendy's, Ⓛ Ferryman's Inn, King Oscar Motel, Rodeway Inn, Ⓞ Ⓗ, VF/famous brands, **W** ⓖ Chevron, Shell, Texaco/Circle K, Ⓕ Arby's, Bill&Bea's, Country Cousin Rest., Denny's, Domino's, Jack-in-the-Box, McDonald's, Papa Murphy's, Starbucks, Subway, Taco Bell, Ⓛ Motel 6, Ⓞ Centralia Outlets/famous brands, Midway RV Park, O'Reilly Parts, Rite Aid, Safeway/dsl, Schwab Tire
82mm	Skookumchuck River
81	WA 507, Mellen St, **E** ⓖ Chevron, Shell, Ⓕ PJ's Rest., Subway, Ⓛ Empress Inn, Pepper Tree Motel/RV Park/dump, Travel Inn, **W** Ⓗ
79	Chamber Way, **E** ⓖ Shell/dsl, Ⓕ Jalisco Mexican, Ⓞ Goodyear/auto, museum, visitor info, **W** ⓖ Texaco/dsl/LP, Ⓕ Applebee's, Coldstone, McDonald's, Roobucks Pizza, Starbucks, Subway, Taco Del Mar, Wendy's, Ⓞ $Tree, Ford, GNC, Grocery Outlet, Home Depot, K-Mart/Little Caesar's, Michael's, Radio Shack, Toyota/Scion, Verizon, Walgreens, Walmart/McDonald's, st patrol
77	WA 6 W, Chehalis, **E** ⓖ Cenex/dsl/LP, 76/dsl, Ⓕ Dairy Bar, Ⓛ Holiday Inn Express, Ⓞ NAPA, Schwab Tire, USPO, **W** Ⓞ Rainbow Falls SP (16mi), truck parts, veterans museum
76	13th St, **E** ⓖ Arco, Chevron/dsl, Ⓕ Denny's, Jack-in-the-Box, Kit Carson Rest., South Pacific Bistro, Subway, Ⓛ Best Western, Chehalis Inn, Relax Inn, Ⓞ Baydo's RV Ctr, Uhlmann's I-5 RV Ctr/RV dump, **W** RV park/dump
74	Labree Rd
72	Rush Rd, Napavine, **E** ⓖ Shell/dsl/scales, Ⓕ Burger King, McDonald's, RibEye Rest., Subway, Ⓞ Dave's RV Ctr/repair, RV park, **W** ⓖ Ⓛ Loves/Carl's Jr/dsl/scales/24hr, Shell/dsl
72mm	Newaukum River
71	WA 508 E, Onalaska, Napavine, **E** ⓖ 76/dsl, Ⓞ KC Truck Parts
68	US 12 E, Morton, **E** ⓖ Arco/dsl, Texaco/dsl, Ⓕ Spiffy's Rest., Ⓞ RV Park, to Lewis&Clark SP, Mt Ranier NP, **W** ⓖ 76/rest./dsl, Ⓕ Jammer's Rest.
63	WA 505, Winlock, **W** ⓖ Shell/Chesters/dsl/LP
60	Toledo Vader Rd
59	WA 506 W, Vader, **E** ⓖ Shell/dsl, Ⓕ Beesley's Cafe, **W** ⓖ Chevron/Subway/dsl, Ⓕ Country House Rest.
59mm	Cowlitz River
57	Jackson Hwy, Barnes Dr, **E** Ⓞ R&R Tires, **W** ⓖ GeeCee's/café/dsl/scales/24hr/@, Ⓞ repair, RV camping
55mm	rest area both lanes, full Ⓗ facilities, Ⓒ, Ⓛ, litter barrels, vending, petwalk
52	Barnes Dr, Toutle Park Rd, **E** Ⓞ Paradise Cove RV

K E L S O

K A L A M A

52	Continued Park/general store, **W** Ⓞ Toutle River RV Resort
50mm	Toutle River
49	WA 504 E, Castle Rock, **E** ⓖ Shell/dsl, Texaco/dsl/LP, Ⓕ Burger King, C&L Burgers, El Compadre Mexican, 49er Diner, Papa Pete's Pizza, RoseTree Rest., Subway, Ⓛ Mt St Helens Motel, 7 West Motel, Silver Lake Motel/RV resort, Timberland Inn, Ⓞ Seaquest SP (5mi)
48	Castle Rock, **W** Ⓕ Hattie's Rest. (2mi), Ⓞ Cedars RV Park/dump
46	Pleasant Hill Rd, Headquarters Rd, **E** Ⓞ Cedars RV Park/dump
44mm	weigh sta sb, Ⓒ
42	Bridge Dr, Lexington, **W** ⓖ Chevron/dsl
40	to WA 4, Kelso-Longview
39	WA 4, Kelso, to Longview, **E** ⓖ Arco, Shell, Ⓕ Denny's, Grinder Rest., McDonald's, Shari's, Subway, Taco Time, Ⓛ Motel 6, Red Lion Hotel, Ⓞ Brook Hollow RV Park, Rite Aid, city park, **W** Ⓕ Azteca Mexican, Burger King, ChuckeCheese, DQ, Izzy's Pizza, Red Lobster, Starbucks, Taco Bell, Ⓛ Comfort Inn, GuestHouse Inn, Ⓞ JC Penney, Macys, Safeway/dsl, Sears/auto, Target, mall, museum
36	WA 432 W, to WA 4, to US 30, Kelso, **E** Ⓞ U-Neek RV Ctr, **W** Ⓞ Toyota/Scion, RV Camping
32	Kalama River Rd, **E** Ⓕ Fireside Café, Ⓞ Camp Kalama RV Park/camping/gifts
31mm	Kalama River
30	Kalama, **E** ⓖ Chevron/dsl, Ⓕ Burger Bar, Columbia Rest., Lucky Dragon Chinese, Playa Azul Mexican, Poker Pete's Pizza, Subway, Ⓛ Columbia Motel, Kalama River Inn, Ⓞ Godfrey's Drug, USPO, antiques, **W** ⓖ Spirit/dsl, Ⓞ RV camping
27	Todd Rd, Port of Kalama, **E** ⓖ Rebel/Shell/café/dsl/24hr
22	Dike Access Rd, **E** Ⓞ tires, transmissions, **W** ⓖ CFN/dsl, Ⓞ Columbia Riverfront RV Park
21	WA 503 E, Woodland, **E** ⓖ Arco, Chevron, Pacific Pride, Shell/LP/dsl, Ⓕ America's Diner, Burgerville, Casa Tapatia, DQ, Fat Moose Grill, Figaro's, Guilliano's Pizza, Mali Thai, OakTree Rest., Rosie's Rest., Ⓛ Lewis River Inn, Motel. 6, Woodland Inn, Ⓞ Ace Hardware, Hi-School Drug, Radio Shack, Woodland Shores RV Park, **W** ⓖ Astro, Shell, Ⓕ Guadalajara Mexican, McDonald's, Papa Murphy's, Quiznos, Starbucks, Subway, Ⓛ Hansen's Motel, Scandia Motel, Ⓞ NAPA, Oil Can Henry's, Safeway/dsl, repair
20mm	N Fork Lewis River
18mm	E Fork Lewis River

WA

INTERSTATE 5 CONT'D

N ↕ S

VANCOUVER

Exit	Services
16	NW La Center Rd, La Center, **E** ⛽ Shell/dsl, 🍴 Twin Dragons Rest., 🅾 Paradise Point SP, Tri-Mountain Golf/rest.
15mm	**weigh sta nb**
14	WA 501 S, Pioneer St, Ridgefield, **E** ⛽ Arco, 76/Circle K/dsl, 🍴 Country Café, Papa Pete's Pizza, Subway, 🅾 to Battleground Lake SP (14mi), Big Fir RV Park (4mi), Ridgefield WR, Tri-Mountain RV Park, **W** ⛽ Chevron/dsl
13mm	**rest area sb, full** ♿ **facilities, info,** 🚻, 🛒, **litter barrels, vending, petwalk, RV dump**
11	WA 502, Battleground, **rest area nb, full** ♿ **facilities, info,** 🚻, 🛒, **litter barrels, vending, petwalk, RV dump**
9	NE 179th St, **E** 🍴 Jollie's Rest., **W** ⛽ Chevron/dsl, 🅾 RV Park
7	I-205 S (from sb), to I-84, WA 14, NE 134th St, **E** ⛽ Arco, 7-11, 76, TrailMart/dsl, 🍴 Applebee's, Billygan's Roadhouse, Booster Juice, Burger King, Burgerville, Jack-in-the-Box, McDonald's, Muchas Gracias, Panda Express, Round Table Pizza, Starbucks, Subway, Taco Bell, Taco Del Mar, 🛏 Comfort Inn, Holiday Inn Express, Olympia Motel, Red Lion, Salmon Creek Inn, Shilo Inn, 🅾 🏥, Albertson's/gas, Long's Drugs, Safeway/gas, Zupan's Mkt, 99 RV Park, to Portland ✈, **W** ⛽ Shell, 🍴 Baskin-Robbins, Coldstone, El Tapatio, Papa Murphy's, PizzaSchmitzza, Quizno's, Starbucks, The Great Impasta, 🛏 La Quinta, 🅾 Fred Meyer
5	NE 99th St, **E** ⛽ 7-11, 🍴 Burgerville, Carl's Jr, Del Taco, Domino's, Fat Dave's Rest., Quiznos, 🅾 Harley-Davidson, Nissan/Kia, Walgreens, Walmart/Subway, Winco Foods/gas, **W** ⛽ Arco/dsl, Chevron/dsl, 🍴 Applebee's, Bortolami's Pizza, McDonald's, Papa John's, Primo's Subs, Subway, Taco Del Mar, 🅾 $Tree, Kohl's, Office Depot, PetCo, Target
4	NE 78th St, Hazel Dell, **E** ⛽ 76, 7-11, 🍴 Baja Fresh, Burger King, Don Pedro Mexican, Dragon Buffet, KFC, McDonald's, Pizza Hut, PeachTree Rest., Skipper's, Smokey's Pizza, Steakburger, Subway, Taco Bell, 🛏 Quality Inn, 🅾 Aamco, CarQuest, CostLess Parts, Firestone, Fred Meyer, Dodge, Ford, Mazda, Nissan, Radio Shack, Save-A-Lot Foods, Schuck's Parts, Tire Factory, U-Haul, **W** ⛽ Shell/dsl/LP, 🍴 Jack-in-the-Box, Nick&Willy's Pizza, Panda Express, RoundTable Pizza, Starbucks, Tully's Coffee, Wendy's, 🅾 Petsmart, Ross, Safeway, Tuesday Morning
3	NE Hwy 99, Main St, Hazel Dell, **E** ⛽ 7-11, 🍴 Muchas Gracias Mexican, Pizza Hut, Skippers, 🅾 🏥, Schwab Tire, vet, **W** ⛽ Arco, 76/dsl, 🅾 Safeway, transmissions
2	WA 500 E, 39th St, to Orchards
1d	E 4th, Plain Blvd W, to WA 501, Port of Vancouver
1c	Mill Plain Blvd, City Ctr, **W** ⛽ Chevron, 🍴 Black Angus, Burgerville, 🛏 Comfort Inn, 🅾 Clark Coll, st patrol
1b	6th St, **E** 🍴 Joe's Crabshack, **W** 🛏 EconoLodge, Hilton
1a	WA 14 E, to Camas, **E** 🏥, **W** 🛏 EconoLodge, Hilton
0mm	Washington/Oregon state line, Columbia River

INTERSTATE 82

Exit	Services
11mm	I-82 Oregon begins/ends on I-84, exit 179.
10	Westland Rd, **E** 🅾 to Umatilla Army Depot, 🅾 🏥

E ↕ W

KENNEWICK

SUNNYSIDE

Exit	Services
5	Power Line Rd
1.5mm	Umatilla River
1	US 395/730, Umatilla, **E** 🍴 Jack-in-the-Box (5mi), 🛏 Best Western (8mi), Desert Inn/rest. (2mi), Motel 6 (8mi), Oxford Inn (5mi), 🅾 Hatrock Camping (8mi), to McNary Dam, **W** ⛽ Shell/Crossroads Trkstp/dsl/rest./24hr, Tesoro/Subway/dsl, Texaco, 🛏 Tillicum Motel, Umatilla Inn, 🅾 Harvest Foods, USPO, st police, Umatilla Marina/RV **Park, Welcome Ctr, weigh sta**
132mm	Washington/Oregon state line, Columbia River
131	WA 14 W, Plymouth, **N** 🅾 RV camping, to McNary Dam
130mm	**weigh sta wb**
122	Coffin Rd
114	Locust Grove Rd
113	US 395 N, to I-182, Kennewick, Pasco, **2-4 mi N** ⛽ Chevron, Exxon, Mirastar/dsl, Tesoro/dsl, 🍴 A&W/KFC, Azteca Mexican, Bob's Burgers, Burger King, Carl's Jr, DQ, Denny's, Jack-in-the-Box, Little Caesars, McDonald's, Panda Express, Starbucks, Subway, Taco Bell, 🛏 Baymont Inn, Best Western, Days Inn, EconoLodge, La Quinta, 🅾 🏥, AT&T, $Tree, Fred Meyer/dsl, GNC, Harley-Davidson, Home Depot, PetCo, Radio Shack, Rite Aid, Safeway/dsl, Traveland RV Ctr, Verizon, Walgreens, Walmart/Blimpie, st patrol
109	Badger Rd, W Kennewick, **N** ⛽ Shell/Subway/dsl, 🍴 Chico's Tacos, **3 mi N** 🛏 Guesthouse Suites, Quality Inn, Red Lion Hotel, Super 8
104	Dallas Rd **3 mi N** ⛽ Conoco/dsl
102	I-182, US 12 E, to US 395, Spokane, 🏥, services in Richland, Pasco
96	WA 224 E, Benton City, **N** ⛽ Conoco/cafe/dsl, 🅾 Beach RV Park
93	Yakitat Rd
88	Gibbon Rd
82	WA 22, WA 221, Mabton, **S** ⛽ Conoco, **2 mi S** 🛏 Prosser Motel, 🅾 🏥, to WAS U Research, to Wine Tasting, museum
82mm	Yakima River
80	Gap Rd, **S** ⛽ Chevron/dsl, Pacific Pride/dsl, Shell/dsl/scales, 🍴 Burger King, El Rancho Alegre, Golden Horse Chinese, KFC/Taco Bell, McDonald's, Starbucks, Subway, 🛏 Barn Motel/RV Park/rest., Best Western, Prosser Motel, 🅾 🏥, Ford/Mercury, Wine Country RV Park, **rest area both lanes, full** ♿ **facilities,** 🚻, 🛒, **litter barrels, rv dump**
76mm	**weigh sta eb**
75	County Line Rd, Grandview, **S** ⛽ Cenex/dsl, Conoco/dsl (1mi), **1 mi S** 🛏🅾 Safeway/dsl, same as 73
73	Stover Rd, Wine Country Rd, Grandview, **S** ⛽ Chevron/Subway/dsl, Conoco/dsl, 🍴 DQ, Eli&Kathy's Rest., New Hong Kong, 10-4 Café, 🛏 Apple Valley Motel, Grandview Motel, 🅾 Chrysler/Dodge/Jeep, Grandview Mkt, Safeway, Schwab Tire, auto repair, RV park/dump
69	WA 241, Vernita Bridge, to Sunnyside, **N** ⛽ Arco/dsl, Mirastar, Shell/TacoMaker/dsl/scales/24hr, 🍴 A&W, Burger King, China Buffet, China Grove, El Charrito Mexican, KFC, Little Caesars, McDonald's, Mongolian Grill, Papa Murphy's, Pizza Hut, Skipper's, Subway, Taco Bell, 🛏 Best Western, Rodeway Inn, 🅾 AT&T, AutoZone, Buick/Chevrolet, $Tree, Fiesta Foods, GNC, JC Penney, O'Reilly Parts, Radio Shack, Rite Aid, Walmart/Subway

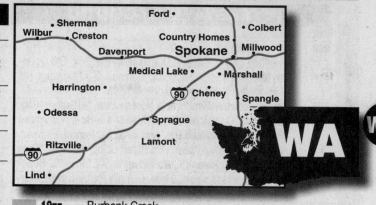

INTERSTATE 82 CONT'D

Exit	Services
67	Sunnyside, Port of Sunnyside, N📷 Chevron/CFN/dsl, Conoco/dsl/e85, 🍴 Jack-in-the-Box, ⊙ 🏥, BiMart Foods, S⊙ DariGold Cheese
63	Sunnyside, Outlook 3 mi N🍴 Snipe's Rest., 🏨 Country Inn&Suites, Travel Inn, ⊙ RV camping
58	WA 223 S, to Granger, S📷 Arco/dsl, Conoco/dsl
54	Division Rd, Yakima Valley Hwy, to Zillah, S⊙ Teapot Dome NHS
52	Zillah, Toppenish, N📷 Chevron/dsl, Shell/dsl, 🍴 El Porton Mexican, McDonald's, Pizza Hut, Subway, Tuscan Sans Rest., 🏨 Comfort Inn
50	WA 22 E, to US 97 S, Toppenish, 3-4 mi S🍴 Legends Buffet/casino, McDonald's, 🏨 Days Inn, Quality Inn, ⊙ 🏥, Murals Museum, RV Park, to Yakima Nation Cultural Ctr
44	Wapato, N📷 Shell/dsl
40	Thorp Rd, Parker Rd, Yakima Valley Hwy, N⊙ Sagelands Vineyard/Winery, S⊙ Windy Point Vineyard
39mm	Yakima River
38	Union Gap (from wb), 1 mi S⊙ 📷, lodging, museum
37	US 97 (from eb), 1 mi S📷 Shell
36	Valley Mall Blvd, Yakima, S📷 Arco/dsl, Cenex/dsl, Shell/Gearjammer/Subway/dsl/scales/24hr/@, 🍴 Applebee's, A&W/KFC, Burger King, Coldstone, Denny's, El Porton Mexican, IHOP, McDonald's, Miner's Drive-In, Old Country Buffet, Outback Steaks, SeaGalley Rest., Shari's, Starbucks, Subway, Taco Bell, 🏨 Best Western, Quality Inn, Super 8, ⊙ Best Buy, Canopy RV Ctr, Gap Autoparts, Kohl's, Lowe's, Office Depot, Old Navy, Macy's, PetCo, Rite Aid, Ross, Sears/auto, ShopKO, Tire Factory, TJ Maxx, Verizon, dsl/repair, mall, st patrol
34	WA 24 E, Nob Hill Blvd, Yakima, N⊙ K-Mart, Sportsman SP, dsl/repair, S📷 Arco/dsl, CFN/dsl, 76/dsl, 7-11, Time/dsl, 🍴 McDonald's, ⊙ 🏥, 19th Hole RV Park, Freightliner, Kenworth, 19th Hole RV Park, O'Reilly Parts, Peterbilt, Volvo
33	Yakima Ave, Yakima, N📷 Chevron/dsl, Shell/Chester's/dsl, 🍴 Burger King, El Mirador Mexican, 🏨 Oxford Inn&Suites, ⊙ Chevrolet, Honda, Walmart/McDonald's, S📷 Arco, 7-11, 🍴 Bob's Burgers, DQ, Pizza Hut, Taco Bell, 🏨 Cedars Suites, Fairfield Inn, Holiday Inn, Holiday Inn Express, Howard Johnson, Ledgestone Hotel, Red Lion Hotel, ⊙ BigLots, Schwab Tire, Target
31b a	US 12 W, N 1st St, to Naches, S📷 Arco/dsl, Shell, 🍴 Arctic Circle, Black Angus Steaks, Golden Moon Chinese, Goody's Rest., Jack-in-the-Box, Mel's Diner, NY Teryaki, Peking Palace, Red Lobster, Subway, Waffle's Cafe, Wendy's, 🏨 All Star Motel, Best Western, Clarion, Days Inn, EconoLodge, Knights Inn, Motel 6, Red Apple Motel, Rodeway Inn, Sun Country Inn, Sunshine Motel, Yakima Inn, ⊙ Harley-Davidson, Trailer Inns RV Park
30	WA 823 N, Rest Haven Rd, to Selah
29	E Selah Rd, N⊙ fruits/antiques
26	WA 821 N, to WA 823, Canyon Rd, N📷 Shell/Noble Romans/Subway/dsl
24mm	**rest area eb, full ♿ facilities, 🚮 litter barrels, RV dump**
23mm	Selah Creek
22mm	**rest area wb, full ♿ facilities, 🚮 litter barrels, RV dump**
21mm	S Umptanum Ridge, 2265 elev

19mm	Burbank Creek
17mm	N Umptanum Ridge, 2315 elev
15mm	Lmuma Creek
11	Military Area
8mm	view point both lanes, Manastash Ridge, 2672 elev
3	WA 821 S, Thrall Rd
0mm	I-90, E to Spokane, W to Seattle. I-82 begins/ends on I-90, exit 110.

INTERSTATE 90

Exit	Services
300mm	Washington/Idaho state line, Spokane River
299	State Line, Port of Entry, N Welcome Ctr/rest area both lanes, full ♿ facilities, 🍴, 🚮, litter barrels, petwalk, N⊙ Cabela's, Walmart
298mm	weigh sta wb
296	Otis Orchards, Liberty Lakes, N📷 Conoco/dsl, 🍴 Legend's Grill, 🏨 Best Western, ⊙ Buick/GMC, Kia, Mercedes, Porsche, S📷 Cenex/dsl, Chevron/LP, 🍴 Barlow's Rest., Carl's Jr, Domino's, Great Harvest Bread, McDonald's, Papa Murphy's, Pizza Hut, Quiznos, Starbucks, Subway, Taco Bell, Taco Time, 🏨 Cedar's Inn, ⊙ URGENT CARE, Albertson's/Sav-On, Home Depot, O'Reilly Parts, Peterbilt, RNR RV Ctr, Safeway, TireRama, Walgreens, Verizon, vet
294	Country Vista Dr, Appleway Ave
293	Barker Rd, Greenacres, N📷 Conoco/dsl, GTS Trkstp/dsl/scales, 🍴 Roadside Grill, Wendy's, ⊙ Freedom RV Ctr, Harley-Davidson, S📷 Exxon/Subway/dsl, Mobil/dsl, ⊙ NW RV Ctr, repair, USPO
291b	Sullivan Rd, Veradale, N🍴 Arby's, Hooters, Krispy Kreme, Outback Steaks, 🏨 Hampton Inn, Oxford Suites, Residence Inn, ⊙ AT&T, Avocado Buffet, Barnes&Noble, Best Buy, Jo-Ann Fabrics, Staples, mall, S📷 Cenex, Chevron/dsl, Conoco/dsl, Tesoro, 🍴 A&W, DQ, 5 Guys Burgers, Jack-in-the-Box, KFC, Little Caesars, McDonald's, Mongolian BBQ, Noodle Express, Panda Express, Pizza Hut, Schlotzsky's, Shari's, Starbucks, Subway, Taco Bell, Wendy's, 🏨 Mirabeau Park Hotel, Ramada Inn, ⊙ Ace Hardware, $Tree, Fred Meyer/dsl, Hancock Fabrics, Hastings Books, Kohl's, Lowe's, Michael's, NAPA, PetCo, Petsmart, Ross, Schwab Tire, Verizon, Walgreens, Walmart, USPO
291a	Evergreen Rd, N🍴 Azteca Mexican, Black Angus, Boston's Rest, IHOP, Red Robin, Wingers, ⊙ Hobby Lobby, JC Penney, Macy's, Old Navy, Sears/auto, TJ Maxx, mall, S📷 Exxon/dsl
289	WA 27 S, Pines Rd, Opportunity, N📷 7-11, 🍴 Black Pearl Rest., Subway, S📷 Cenex, Conoco/dsl,

WA

INTERSTATE 90 CONT'D

Exit	Services
289	Continued
	Holiday, ⓕ Applebee's, DQ, Jack-in-the-Box, Old Country Buffet, Qdoba Mexican, Quiznos, ⓛ Pheasant Hill Inn, ⓞ Ⓗ, Walgreens, repair
287	Argonne Rd, Millwood, N ⓖ Holiday/dsl, ⓕ Burger King, Denny's, Domino's, DQ, Jack-in-the-Box, Longhorn BBQ, Marie Callender's, McDonald's, Panda Express, Papa Murphy's, Pizza Hut, Starbucks, Subway, Taco Time, Timber Creek Grill, Wendy's, ⓛ Motel 6, Super 8, ⓞ Albertson's/gas, $Tree, O'Reilly Parts, Savon, Walgreens, Yoke's Foods, S ⓖ Cenex/dsl, Conoco, ⓕ Casa de Oro Mexican, Little Caesars, Perkins, Starbucks, ⓛ Holiday Inn Express, Quality Inn, ⓞ Curves, Rite Aid, Safeway
286	Broadway Ave, N ⓖ Chevron, ⓕʟʏɪɴɢ ᴊ/Conoco/rest./dsl/LP/scales/24hr/@, ⓕ Smacky's Cafe, Zip's Burgers, Goodyear, ⓛ Rodeway Inn, ⓞ International Trucks, Volvo, Kenworth, Schwab Tire, S ⓞ 7-11
285	Sprague Ave, N ⓕ Dragon Garden Chinese, IHOP, Jack-in-the-Box, McDonald's, Subway, Wendy's, ⓛ ParkLane Motel/RV Park, ⓞ AutoZone, Costco/gas, Grocery Outlet, Freightliner, Home Depot, K-Mart/Little Caesars, Lowe's, O'Reilly Parts, Radio Shack, S ⓖ Conoco, ⓕ Cottage Cafe, Puerta Vallarta Mexican, Starbucks, Stop&Go Rest., Taco Time, Zip's Burger, ⓞ Chrysler/Dodge, Nissan/Saab, Tirerama, Trailer Inn RV Park, transmissions, vet
284	Havana St (from eb, no EZ return), N ⓖ Tesoro/dsl, ⓕ Jack-in-the-Box, McDonald's, Wolf Lodge Steaks, S ⓖ Conoco/dsl, ⓞ Fred Meyer/dsl
283b	Freya St, Thor St, N ⓖ Tesoro/dsl, ⓕ Jack-in-the-Box, McDonald's, Wolf Lodge Steaks, S ⓖ Conoco/dsl, ⓞ Fred Meyer/dsl
283a	Altamont St, S ⓖ Cenex
282b	2nd Ave, N ⓖ Conoco/dsl, ⓛ Comfort Inn, ⓞ Office Depot
282a	WA 290 E, Trent Ave, Hamilton St, N ⓖ Conoco/dsl, ⓛ Comfort Inn, ⓞ Office Depot
281	US 2, US 395, to Colville, N ⓖ Conoco, Exxon, 7-11, Tesoro/dsl, ⓕ Arby's, Dick's Hamburgers, Frankie Doodles Rest., Ichiban Buffet, Starbucks, Subway, Taco Time, ⓛ Days Inn, FairBridge Inn, ⓞ Firestone/auto, Schwab Tire, U-Haul, S ⓛ Quality Inn, ⓞ Ⓗ
280b	Lincoln St, N ⓖ Conoco/dsl, ⓕ Carl's Jr, Domino's, Jack-in-the-Box, McDonald's, Molly's Rest., Taco Bell, Taste of Asia, Thai Cuisine, Zip's Burgers, ⓛ Tradewinds Motel, ⓞ Honda, Lexus, Toyota/Scion, Troy's Tire, S Ⓗ
280a	Spokane, downtown, N ⓖ Chevron/McDonald's/dsl, Conoco/dsl, ⓕ Frank's Diner, ⓛ Select Motel, ⓕ Pizza Hut, Subway, ⓞ AAA, Jaguar, Land Rover, Volvo
279	US 195 S, Pullman, to Colfax
277b a	US 2 W (no ez wb return), to Grand Coulee Dam,, Fairchild AFB, N ⓛ Best Value Inn, Blvd Motel, EconoLodge, Hampton Inn, Motel 6, Sunset Motel, West Wynn Motel
276	Geiger Blvd, N ⓖ ⓕʟʏɪɴɢ ᴊ/dsl/LP/24hr, ⓕ Denny's, Subway, ⓛ Airway Express Inn, Best Western, ⓞ st patrol, S ⓖ Conoco/dsl, ⓞ Hideaway RV Park
272	WA 902, Medical Lake, N ⓖ Mobil/dsl, ⓞ Overland Sta/RV Park, S ⓖ Exxon/Subway/dsl, Petro/Iron Skillet/dsl/scales/24hr/@, ⓕ McDonald's, ⓛ Super 8, ⓞ Freightliner, Ponderosa Falls RV Resort, truck repair

SPOKANE (vertical label, left margin)

CHENEY (vertical label)

Exit	Services
270	WA 904, Cheney, Four Lakes, S ⓖ Exxon, ⓛ Holiday Inn Express (4mi), Willow Springs Motel (6mi), ⓞ Peaceful Pines RV Park (7mi), E WA U
264	WA 902, Salnave Rd, to Cheney, Medical Lake, **2 mi N** camping
257	WA 904, Tyler, to Cheney, S ⓞ Peaceful Pines RV Park (10mi), Tyler Store/RV Park, to Columbia Plateau Trail SP
254	Fishtrap, S ⓞ Fishtrap RV camping/tents
245	WA 23, Sprague, S ⓖ Chevron/dsl, ⓕ Viking Drive-In, ⓛ, Sprague Motel, ⓞ 4 Seasons RV Park (6mi), Sprague Lake Resort/RV Park
242mm	**rest area both lanes, full ♿ facilities, Ⓒ, 🏭, litter barrels, tourist/weather info, petwalk, RV dump (eb)**
231	Tokio, S **weigh sta both lanes**, ⓕ Templin's Café/CFN/dsl, ⓞ RV Park
226	Schoessler Rd
221	WA 261 S, Ritzville, City Ctr, N ⓖ Conoco/dsl, Chevron/McDonald's, Shell/Subway/dsl, ⓕ Perkins, Starbucks, Taco Del Mar, Zip's Rest., ⓛ Best Western, Cedars Inn, The Cottage/RV Park, Empire Motel, Top Hat Motel, ⓞ Ⓗ, Cow Creek Merchantile, hist dist
220	to US 395 S, Ritzville, N ⓖ Pacific Pride/dsl, Texaco/Jake's Rest./dsl, ⓕ Casuela's Grill, ⓛ Top Hat Motel, ⓞ Cedars Inn RV Park, Harvest Foods, Schwab Tire, st patrol
215	Paha, Packard
206	WA 21, Odessa, to Lind
199mm	**rest area both lanes, full ♿ facilities, Ⓒ, 🏭, litter barrels, vending, RV dump, petwalk**
196	Deal Rd, to Schrag
188	U Rd, to Warden, Ruff
184	Q Rd
182	O Rd, to Wheeler
179	WA 17, Moses Lake, N ⓖ Conoco/Subway/dsl, Ernie's Trkstp/Chevron/café/dsl/24hr, Texaco/dsl, ⓕ Arby's, Bob's Cafe, Burger King, Denny's, McDonald's, Shari's, Starbucks, Taco Bell, ⓛ Comfort Suites, Holiday Inn Express, Moses Lake Inn, Ramada Inn, Shilo Inn, ⓞ Ⓗ, Chevrolet, Chrysler/Dodge/Jeep, Lowe's, Nissan, Toyota/Scion, vet, **1 mi N** ⓕ DQ, Subway, ⓛ El Rancho Motel, ⓞ $Tree, Ford/Lincoln/Mercury, Honda, vet, S ⓞ I-90 RV, Mardon RV Park (15mi), Willows RV Park (2mi), Potholes SP (22mi)
177mm	Moses Lake
176	WA 171, Moses Lake, N ⓖ Cenex/dsl, Chevron/dsl, Conoco, Exxon/dsl, 76/dsl, Shell/dsl, ⓕ El Rodeo Mexican, Michael's Rest., Perkins, Subway, Taco Del Mar, ⓛ Best Western/rest., Interstate Inn, Motel 6, Oasis Motel, Super 8, ⓞ Ⓗ, AAA RV Park, Ace Hardware, Harvest Foods, Lake Front RV Park, auto repair, transmissions, vet, S ⓛ Lakeshore Motel
175	Westshore Dr (from wb), N ⓞ Moses Lake SP, to Mae Valley, S ⓞ st patrol
174	Mae Valley, N ⓞ Suncrest Resort/RV, S ⓖ Conoco/dsl, ⓞ Pier 4 RV Park, st patrol
169	Hiawatha Rd
164	Dodson Rd, N ⓞ Sunbasin RV park/camp (1mi)
162mm	**rest area wb, full ♿ facilities, Ⓒ, 🏭, litter barrels, petwalk, RV dump**
161mm	**rest area eb, full ♿ facilities, Ⓒ, 🏭, litter barrels, petwalk, RV dump**

MOSES LAKE (vertical label)

INTERSTATE 90 CONT'D

Exit	Services
154	Adams Rd
151	WA 281 N, to Quincy, **N** 🚗 Shell/pizza/subs/dsl, 🅾 🄷 (12mi), Shady Grove RV park, to Grand Coulee Dam
149	WA 281 S, George, **N** 🄷 (12mi), **S** 🚗 Cenex/dsl, 76/ Subway/dsl, 🅾 RV camp
143	Silica Rd, to The Gorge Ampitheatre
139mm	Wild Horses Mon, scenic view both lanes
137	WA 26 E, to WA 243, Othello, Richland
137mm	Columbia River
136	Huntzinger Rd, Vantage, **N** 🚗 Spirit, Texaco/dsl, 🍴 Blustery's Burger Drive-in, Golden Harvest Rest., 🅾 Riverstone Vantage Resort/RV Park, Vantage Gen. Store, to Ginkgo SP, auto repair, **S** 🅾 to Wanapum SP (3mi)
126mm	Ryegrass, elev 2535, **rest area both lanes, full** ♿ **facilities,** 🚻, 🚭, **litter barrels, petwalk**
115	Kittitas, **N** 🚗 Shell/dsl/LP, 🅾 Olmstead Place SP
110	I-82 E, US 97 S, to Yakima
109	Canyon Rd, Ellensburg, **N** 🚗 Astro/dsl, Chevron, Circle K, Eagle/dsl, 76, Shell, 🍴 Arby's, Baskin Robbins, BoxcCar Burgers, Burger King, East Chinese Buffet, Fiesta Mexican, Golden Dragon Chinese, KFC, Los Cabos Mexican, McDonald's, Papa Murphy's, RanchHouse Rest., Roadhouse Grill, Rodeo City BBQ, Starbucks, Subway, Taco Bell, Taco Del Mar, Wendy's, 🛏 Best Western, Comfort Inn, Goose Creek Inn, Holiday Inn Express, Quality Inn, Super 8, 🅾 🄷, AutoZone, CarQuest, Chevrolet, NAPA, O'Reilly Parts, Rite Aid, Schwab Tire, Super 1 Foods, TrueValue, vet, **S** 🚗 ✈FLYING J/Sak's/. dsl/scales/LP/24hr, 🍴 Buzz Inn Steaks, 🛏 Days Inn/RV park
106	US 97 N, to Wenatchie, **N** 🚗 Chevron/dsl, Conoco/dsl, ⬤Loves/Subway/dsl/scales/24hr, 76/dsl, 🍴 DQ, Perkins, 🛏 Hampton Inn, I-90 Inn, Thunderbird Motel, 🅾 Buick/Cadillac/GMC, Canopy Country RV Ctr, Chrysler/Jeep, Truck/RV Wash, **S** 🅾 KOA, st patrol
101	Thorp Hwy, **N** 🚗 Arco/dsl, 🅾 antiques/fruits/vegetables
93	Elk Heights Rd, Taneum Creek
92.5mm	Elk Heights, elev 2359
89mm	Indian John Hill, elev 2141, **rest area both lanes, full** ♿ **facilities,** 🚻, 🚭, **litter barrels, RV dump, petwalk, vending**
85	WA 970, WA 903, to Wenatchie, **N** 🚗 Gas Save/dsl, 76/dsl, Shell/dsl, 🍴 Cottage Café, Giant Burger, Homestead Rest., 🛏 Aster Inn, Cascade Mtn Inn, Chalet Motel, Cle Elum Traveler's Inn, 🅾 vet
84	Cle Elum (from eb, return at 85), **N** 🚗 Chevron/dsl, Pacific Pride/dsl, Shell/Subway/dsl, 🍴 Beau's Pizza, Burger King, Caboose Grill, DQ, El Caporal Mexican, Lentine's Italian, MaMa Vallones, McDonald's, New Cam Chinese, Quiznos, Sahara Pizza, Sunset Café, Taco Del Mar, 🛏 Best Western Snowcap, Timber Lodge Inn, Stewart Lodge, 🅾 🄷, Cle Elum Drug, Cle Elum Hardware, NAPA AutoCare, Radio Shack, Safeway/dsl, Trailer Corral RV Park, museum
81mm	Cle Elum River
80	Roslyn, Salmon la Sac
80mm	**weigh sta both lanes**
78	Golf Course Rd, **S** 🅾 Sun Country Golf/RV Park

Exit	Services
74	W Nelson Siding Rd
71	Easton, **S** 🚗 CB's Store/dsl/LP, 🅾 John Wayne Tr, Iron Horse SP, USPO
71mm	Yakima River
70	Sparks Rd, Easton, Lake Easton SP, **N** 🚗 Shell/RV Town/dsl/café, 🍴 Mtn High Burger, 🅾 Silver Ridge Ranch RV Park, repair, **S** 🅾 Easton Ridge RV Camping, Lake Easton SP
63	Cabin Creek Rd
62	Stampede Pass, elev 3750, to Lake Kachess, **N** Lake Kachess Lodge
54	Hyak, Gold Creek, **S** Ski Area
53	Snoqualmie Pass, elev 3022, info, **S** 🚗 Chevron, 🍴 Red Mtn Coffee, Xanadu Rest., 🛏 Summit Lodge, 🅾 to rec areas
52	W Summit (from eb), same as 53
47	Tinkham Rd, Denny Creek, Asahel Curtis, **N** 🅾 chain area, **S** 🅾 RV camping/dump
45	USFS Rd 9030, **N** 🅾 to Lookout Point Rd
42	Tinkham Rd, 38, **N** 🅾 fire training ctr
35mm	S Fork Snoqualmie River
34	468th Ave SE, Edgewick Rd, **N** 🚗 76/BBQ/dsl, Shell/cafe/dsl, TA/Country Pride/dsl only/24hr/@, 🛏 Edgewick Inn, 🅾 Norwest RV Park
32	436th Ave SE, Snoqualmie Ranger Sta, **1 mi N** 🚗, 🍴 lodging, **S** Iron Horse SP (3mi)
31	WA 202 W, North Bend, Snoqualmie, **N** 🚗 Chevron/dsl, Shell/dsl, 🍴 Arby's, Baskin-Robbins, Blimpie, Burger King, Los Cabos, McDonald's, Mongolian Grill, Papa Murphy's, Starbucks, Subway, Taco Time, 🛏 North Bend Motel, Sallish Lodge, Sunset Motel, 🅾 🄷, North-Bend Outlets/famous brands, O'Reilly Parts, Safeway/dsl, museum, st patrol
27	North Bend, Snoqualmie (from eb, no return), **N** 🚗 76/dsl, 🍴 Woodman's Steaks, 🅾 🄷
25	WA 18 W, Snoqualmie Pkwy, Tacoma, to Auburn, **N** 🚗 Shell/dsl/e85 (1.5mi), 🅾 weigh sta
22	Preston, **N** 🚗 Shell/dsl, 🍴 Burgers& Teriyaki, Subway, 🅾 LP, NAPA, Snoqualmie River RV Park (4mi), USPO, **S** 🅾 Blue Sky RV Park
20	High Point Way
18	E Sunset Way, Issaquah, **S** 🚗 Shell (1mi), 🍴 Flying Pie Pizza, Front St Mkt, Issaquah Brewhouse, Jack's Grill, Mandarin Garden, Shanghai Garden Chinese, Stan's BBQ, Sunset Alehouse, 🅾 Curves
17	E Sammamish Rd, Front St, Issaquah, **N** 🚗 76, 🍴 Coho Café, Coldstone, Fatburger, Jamba Juice, Krispy Kreme, McDonald's, Qdoba Mexican, Quiznos, Papa John's, Starbucks, Subway, 🅾 URGENT CARE, AT&T,

Side labels: E / W, ELLENSBURG, CLE ELUM, ISSAQUAH

Map: Discovery Bay, Everett, Mukilteo, Edmonds, Shoreline, Lynnwood, Bothell, Bangor, Silverdale, Redmond, Bremerton, Seattle, Bellevue, Issaquah, Shorewood, Renton, Des Moines, Kent, Summit, Gig Harbor, Federal Way, Tacoma, Bonney Lake, Lakewood, Parkland, Lacey, Spanaway, WA, 90, 5

INTERSTATE 90 CONT'D

Exit	Services
17	Continued Bartell Drug, Best Buy, Fred Meyer, Home Depot, Verizon, Walgreens, **S** 🅖 Arco/dsl, Chevron/dsl, Shell/dsl, 🅕 Boehms Chocolates, Domino's, Extreme Pizza, La Costa Mexican, Las Margaritas, Pogacha Rest., Shanghai Garden Rest., Stan's BBQ, Subway, 🅞 Staples, transmissions
15	WA 900, Issaquah, Renton, **N** 🅖 Arco, 🅕 Cocina Cocina, Georgio's Subs, IHOP, O'Char Thai, Red Robin, Tully's Coffee, 🅛 Holiday Inn, Motel 6, 🅞 Barnes&Noble, Costco/gas, Lowe's, Michael's, Office Depot, Petsmart, Trader Joe's, to Lk Sammamish SP, vet, **S** 🅖 Shell/dsl, 🅕 Baskin-Robbins, Burger King, Cascade Garden Chinese, Chipotle Mexican, Denny's, Franky's Pizza, Georgio's Subs, Issaquah Cafe, Jack-in-the-Box, Jamba Juice, KFC/Taco Bell, Lombardi's Italian, McDonald's, Panera Bread, Papa Murphy's, RoundTable Pizza, Starbucks, Subway, Taco Time, Tuttabella Pizza, 🅛 Hilton Garden, 🅞 Chevrolet, Firestone/auto, Ford, GNC, O'Reilly Parts, PetCo, QFC Foods, Radio Shack, Rite Aid, Ross, Safeway, See's Candies, Target, Verizon, USPO
13	SE Newport Way, W Lake Sammamish
11	SE 150th, 156th, 161st, Bellevue, **N** LDS Temple, 🅖 Shell, 🅕 DQ, Greenwood Mandarin Chinese, Lil' Jon's Rest., McDonald's, Starbucks, Subway, Tulley's Coffee, 🅛 Days Inn, Embassy Suites, Hotel Sierra, Silver Cloud Inn, 🅞 Ford, 7-11, Subaru/VW, Safeway, Toyota/Scion, **S** 🅖 Chevron, 76, Shell/dsl, Standard, 🅕 Baskin-Robbins, Domino's, Outback Steaks, Pizza Hut, 🅛 Homestead Suites, 🅞 Albertson's, Honda, Larkspur Landing, O'Reilly Parts, Rite Aid, RV Park
10	I-405, N to Bellevue, S to Renton, facilities located off I-405 S, exit 10
9	Bellevue Way
8	E Mercer Way, Mercer Island
7c	80th Ave SE (exits left from wb)
7b a	SE 76th Ave, 77th Ave, Island Crest Way, Mercer Island, **S** 🅖 Chevron, 76/repair, Shell/dsl/repair, 🅕 McDonald's, Starbucks, Subway, Thai Rest., Tully's Coffee, 🅛 Travelodge, 🅞 Island Foods, TrueValue, Walgreens
6	W Mercer Way (from eb), same as 7
5mm	Lake Washington
3b a	Ranier Ave, Seattle, downtown, **N** 🅖 Shell/dsl, 🅞 VET
2c b	I-5, N to Vancouver, S to Tacoma
2a	4th Ave S, to King Dome
	I-90 begins/ends on I-5 at exit 164.

INTERSTATE 182 (Richland)

Exit	Services
14b a	US 395 N, WA 397 S, OR Ave, **N** 🅖 ✈ FLYING J/dsl/scales/24hr, King City/Shell/rest/dsl/@, 🅕 Burger King, Subway, 🅞 Freightliner, Peterbilt, RV Park, **S** 🅛 Motel 6 I-182 begins/ends on US 395 N.
13	N 4th Ave, Cty Ctr, **N** 🅖 CFN/dsl, 🅛 ♨ Motel, Starlite Motel, **S** 🅖 76/dsl, 🅞 🄷, RV park, museum
12b	N 20th Ave, **N** 🅛 Best Western, Red Lion Hotel
12a	US 395 S, Court St, **S** on Court St. 🅖 Chevron/Domino's, Conoco, Exxon/Jack-in-the-Box, Shell, Tesoro, Texaco, 🅕 Asian Express, A&W/KFC, Baskin-Robbins, Burger King, DQ, Little Caesars, McDonald's, Oriental

Exit	Services
12a	Continued Express, Papa Murphy's, Pizza Hut, Quiznos, RoundTable Pizza, Subway, Super China Buffet, Taco Bell, Wendy's, 🅞 Albertson's/gas, AutoZone, Cadillac/Chevrolet, Chief RV Ctr, $Tree, Ford, Hyundai, Mazda, Nissan, Rite Aid, Save-A-Lot Foods, Subaru, U-Haul, Walgreens
9	rd 68, Trac, **N** 🅖 Maverik/dsl, Shell, Tesoro/dsl, 🅕 Antonio's Pizza, Applebee's, Arby's, Bruchi's, Cousin's Rest., Eatza Pizza, Fiesta Mexican, Figaro's Pizza, Hacienda Mexican, IHOP, Jack-in-the-Box, McDonald's, Panda Express, Pier 39 Sea🅕 Pita Pit, Sonic, Starbucks, Subway, Taco Bell, Teryaki Grill, 🅛 Holiday Inn Express, 🅞 AT&T, Discount Tire, Firestone/auto, Franklin County RV Park, Lowe's, O'Reilly Parts, Schwab Tire, Verizon, Walgreens, Walmart/Subway, Yokes Foods
7	Broadmoor Blvd, **N** 🅛 Sleep Inn, 🅞 Broadmoor Outlets/famous brands, GNC, **S** 🅖 Shell/dsl, 🅞 Broadmoor RV Ctr, KOA
6.5mm	Columbia River
5b a	WA 240 E, Geo Washington Way, to Kennewick, **N** 🅖 Conoco/dsl, 🅕 Applebee's, Jack-in-the-Box, Starbucks, 🅛 Clarion, Courtyard, Days Inn, Economy Inn, Hampton Inn, Red Lion Hotel, Shilo Inn, 🅞 AT&T, $Tree, Winco Foods/gas
4	WA 240 W, **N** 🅖 Shell/dsl, 🅕 McDonald's, Rancho Bonito, 🅞 BMW, Fred Meyer/dsl
3.5mm	Yakima River
3	Keene Rd, Queensgate, **N** 🅖 Mirastar/dsl, Shell, 🅕 A&W/KFC, Burger King, El Rancho Alegre, LJ Silver, McDonald's, Panda Express, Starbucks, Subway, Taco Bell, 🅞 GNC, Home Depot, PetCo, Target, Walmart/Subway, **S** 🅞 RV Park (3mi)
0mm	I-182 begins/ends on I-82, exit 102.

INTERSTATE 405 (Seattle)

Exit	Services
30	I-5, N to Canada, S to Seattle, I-405 begins/ends on I-5, exit 182.
26	WA 527, Bothell, Mill Creek, **E** 🅕 Canyon's Rest., McDonald's, 🅛 Extended Stay Deluxe, 🅞 Lake Pleasant RV Park, **W** 🅖 Shell/dsl, 🅕 Applebee's, Arby's, Bamboo House, Baskin-Robbins, Bonefish Grill, Crystal Creek Cafe, D.Thai, Denny's, Fortune Cookie Chinese, Grazie Ristorante, Imperial Wok, Jack-in-the-Box, Mongolian Grill, Outback Steaks, Papa Murphy's, Qdoba Mexican, Quiznos, Starbucks, Subway, Taco Bell, Taco Time, Tully's Coffee, Wendy's, 🅛 Comfort Inn, Extended Stay America, Hilton Garden, Holiday Inn Express, 🅞 Albertson's, Bartell Drug, Goodyear/auto, QFC Foods, Radio Shack, Rite Aid, 7-11, Verizon
24	NE 195th St, Beardslee Blvd, **E** 🅖 Shell/Quiznos/dsl, 🅕 Subway, Teryaki Etc., 🅛 Country Inn&Suites, Residence Inn
23b	WA 522 W, Bothell
23a	WA 522 E, to WA 202, Woodinville, Monroe
22	NE 160th St, **E** 🅖 Chevron, Shell/dsl, 🅕 Denice's Cafe
20	NE 124th St, **E** 🅖 Chevron, Shell/dsl, 🅕 Denny's, Jack-in-the-Box, KFC, Pizza Hut, Santa Fe Mexican, Subway, Taco Bell, Thai Kitchen, Zaburo's Grill, 🅛 Baymont Inn, Comfort Inn, Motel 6, 🅞 🄷, Big O Tire, Chrysler/Dodge/Jeep, Discount Tire, Fiat, Firestone/auto, Ford, Hyun

INTERSTATE 405 (Seattle)

N ↕ S

SEATTLE

Exit	Services
20	Continued
	dai, Infiniti, O'Reilly Parts, Radio Shack, Rite Aid, Ross, Schwab Tire, 7-11, Toyota/Scion, Verizon, **W** ⛽ Arco, 76, 🍴 Azteca Mexican, Burger King, Hunan Wok, McDonald's, Papa Murphy's, Romio's Pizza, Olive Garden, Starbucks, Subway, Taco Del Mar, Taco Time, Wendy's, 🏨 Courtyard, 🔵 AT&T, Buick/GMC, Fred Meyer, GNC, QFC Foods
18	WA 908, Kirkland, Redmond, **E** ⛽ Chevron, 76/Circle K/dsl, Shell/dsl, 🍴 Baskin-Robbins, Garlic Jim's, McDonald's, Outback Steaks, Starbucks, Subway, Valhalla Grill, 🔵 Chevrolet, Costco, Goodyear/auto, Hancock Fabrics, Honda, KIA, Mazda, O'Reilly Parts, PetCo, Safeway, 7-11, U-Haul, Walgreens, vet, **W** ⛽ Chevron, Shell/dsl, 🍴 Acropolis Pizza, Crab Cracker, Papa John's, Subway, Taco Del Mar, Wendy's, 🔵 QFC Foods, Tire Factory, Verizon
17	NE 70th Pl
14b a	WA 520, Seattle, Redmond
13b	NE 8th St, **E** ⛽ Arco, Chevron/dsl, Shell/dsl, 🍴 Burger King, Denny's, Hunan Garden, 🏨 Coast Hotel, 🔵 🏥, Bartell Drugs, Cadillac, Chevrolet, Chrysler/Dodge/Jeep, Ford/Lincoln/Mercury, Home Depot, Lexus, Mercedes, Nissan, Porsche, Volvo, Whole Foods Mkt, **W** 🍴 Starbucks, Subway, 🏨 Courtyard, Hyatt
13a	NE 4th St, **E** 🏨 Extended Stay America, Residence Inn, 🔵 Ford, Lexus, **W** 🏨 Best Western, Doubletree Hotel, Hilton, Ramada Ltd., Red Lion/Bellevue Inn, Sheraton
12	SE 8th St, **W** 🏨 Residence Inn
11	I-90, E to Spokane, W to Seattle
10	Cold Creek Pkwy, Factoria, **E on Factoria Blvd** ⛽ Chevron, 76, 🍴 Applebee's, Burger King, Coldstone, El Tapatio Mexican, Goldberg's Rest., Great Harvest Bread, Jamba Juice, Keg Steaks, McDonald's, Old Country Buffet, Panda Express, Panera Bread, Quiznos, Red Robin,

Exit	Services
10	Continued
	Ricardo's Mexican, Romio's Pizza, Starbucks, Subway, Taco Bell, Taco Time, Thai Ginger, 🔵 AT&T, Bartell Drug, Old Navy, O'Reilly Parts, PetCo, QFC Foods, Radio Shack, Rite Aid, Safeway, 7-11, Target, Verizon, vet
9	112th Ave SE, Newcastle, 🍴
7	NE 44th St, **E** 🍴 Denny's, McDonald's, Subway, 🏨 EconoLodge
6	NE 30th St, **E** ⛽ Arco, **W** ⛽ Chevron, Shell, 🔵 7-11
5	WA 900 E, Park Ave N, Sunset Blvd NE, **W** 🔵 Fry's Electronics
4	WA 169 S, Wa 900 W, Renton, **E** 🍴 Shari's, 🏨 Quality Inn, 🔵 Aqua Barn Ranch Camping, **W** 🍴 Burger King, Stir Rest., 🏨 Renton Inn, 🔵 7-11,
2	WA 167, Rainier Ave, to Auburn, **E** 🏨 Hilton Garden, Larkspur Landing, SpringHill Suites, TownePlace Suites, 🏥, **W** ⛽ Chevron, 76/dsl, Shell, USA/dsl, 🍴 A&W/KFC, Applebee's, Arby's, Baskin-Robbins, Georgio's Subs, IHOP, Jack-in-the-Box, Jimmy Mack's, King Buffet, Mazatlan Mexican, McDonald's, PanAsia, Panda Express, Papa Murphy's, Pizza Hut, Popeye's, Qdoba Mexican, Starbucks, Subway, Taco Bell, Taco Time, Torero's Mexican, Wendy's, Yankee Grill, 🏨 Holiday Inn, 🔵 Aamco, Buick/Cadillac/GMC, Chevrolet, Chrysler/Jeep, Discount Tire, Dodge, Ford, Fred Meyer, Firestone/auto, Honda/Hyundai/Kia/Mazda, Isuzu, O'Reilly Parts, Radio Shack, Rite Aid, Safeway/gas, Sam's Club/gas, Schwab Tire, Subaru, Toyota/Scion, Walgreens, Walmart, vet
1	WA 181 S, Tukwila, **E** ⛽ Chevron/dsl, 76/dsl, Shell/dsl, 🍴 Barnaby's Rest., Jack-in-the-Box, McDonald's, Sushi&Grill, Taco Bell, Teriyaki Wok, Wendy's, 🏨 Best Western, Courtyard, Embassy Suites, Hampton Inn, Homestead Suites, Residence Inn, 🔵 7-11, mall, **W** ⛽ Shell, 🏨 Comfort Suites, Homewood Suites, 🔵 fun center
0mm	I-5, N to Seattle, S to Tacoma, WA 518 W. I-405 begins/ends on I-5, exit 154.

S E A T T L E

WEST VIRGINIA

INTERSTATE 64

E ↕ W

LEWISBURG

Exit	Services
184mm	West Virginia/Virginia state line
183	VA 311, (from eb, no reentry), Crows
181	US 60, WV 92 (no ez wb return), White Sulphur Springs, **0-2 mi N** ⛽ BP/Godfather's, Exxon/Quiznos, Shell, 🍴 April's Pizzaria, Hardee's, Mason Jar Rest., 🏨 Budget Inn, Greenbrier Resort, Old White Motel, 🔵 Family$, Food Lion, NAPA, Rite Aid, USPO, to Midland Trail, ski area, **S** 🏨 Black Bear Lodge, 🔵 Twilite Camping
179mm	Welcome Ctr wb, info, full ♿ facilities, 🍴, 🔵, litter barrels, petwalk
175	US 60, WV 92, Caldwell, **N** ⛽ Chevron/dsl/24hr, Exxon, Shell/Subway/dsl, 🍴 Granny's House Rest., McDonald's, Wendy's, 🏨 Village Motel, 🔵 $General, **S** 🔵 Greenbrier SF, Mountainaire Camping
173mm	Greenbrier River
169	US 219, Lewisburg, Hist Dist, **N** ⛽ Shell, 🍴 Biscuit World, Blackwell's Rest., 🏨 Relax Inn, 🔵 Federated Parts, **S** ⛽ Exxon/dsl, Gomart, Shell, 🍴 Applebee's, Arby's, Bob Evans, China Palace, Hardee's, Ruby

Exit	Services
169	Continued
	Tuesday, Shoney's, Subway, 🏨 Fairfield Inn, Hampton Inn, Holiday Inn Express, Quality Inn, Super 8, 🔵 🏥, Buick/Chevrolet, $Tree, Ford, Lowe's, Walmart/gas
161	WV 12, Alta, **S** ⛽ Alta Sta/cafe, Exxon, 🔵 Greenbrier River Camping (14mi)
156	US 60, Midland Trail, Sam Black Church, **N** ⛽ Citgo, Exxon/dsl, Shell/dsl, 🍴 Linda's Rest.
150	Dawson, **S** ⛽ Exxon, 🍴 Cheddar's Cafe, 🏨 Dawson Inn, 🔵 RV camping
147mm	runaway truck ramp wb
143	WV 20, Green Sulphur Springs, **N** ⛽ Liberty/dsl
139	WV 20, Sandstone, Hinton, **S** ⛽ Citgo/dsl, 🔵 Blue Stone SP (16mi), Richmonds Store/USPO, to Pipestem Resort Park (25 mi)
138mm	New River
136mm	eb runaway truck ramp
133	WV 27, Bragg Rd, Sandstone Mtn (Elev. 2765), mandatory truck stop eb, **S** 🔵 RV camping
129	WV 9, Shady Spring, **N** 🔵 to Grandview SP, **S** ⛽ Exxon/dsl, Shell/dsl, 🍴 Subway, 🔵 Little Beaver SP

[⛽] = gas   [🍴] = food   [🛏] = lodging   [○] = other   Copyright 2012 - The Next Exit®

INTERSTATE 64 CONT'D

Exit	Services
	E ↑↓ W (Charleston direction marker)
125	WV 307, [○] Rd, Beaver, N [⛽] Shell/dsl, [🍴] Biscuit World, [🛏] Sleep Inn, **1 mi** S [⛽] BP/dsl, Exxon, GoMart/gas, [🍴] DQ, Hardee's, KFC, Little Caesar's, LJ Silver, McDonald's, Pizza Hut, Subway, Wendy's, [○] Advance Parts, Adventure RV Ctr, Curves, Family$, Kroger, Walgreens, USPO
124	US 19, E Beckley, **1-2 mi** N [⛽] BP/dsl, Exxon, GoMart/gas, [🍴] Capt D's, Huddle House, [🛏] Green Bank Motel, Microtel, [○] $General, last exit before toll rd wb
121	I-77 S, to Bluefield
	I-64 and I-77 run together 61 mi. See Interstate 77, exits 42 through 100.
59	I-77 N (from eb), to I-79
58c	US 60, Washington St, N [⛽] BP, Exxon, GoMart/dsl, [🍴] Arby's, [○] Lincoln/Mercury, S [🍴] 5th Quarter Steaks, LJ Silver, Shoney's, Wendy's, [🛏] Embassy Suites, Hampton Inn, Holiday Inn Express, Marriott, [○] [H], Sears, civic ctr, mall
58b	US 119 N (from eb), Charleston, same as 58c, downtown
58a	US 119 S, WV 61, MacCorkle Ave, S [⛽] Exxon/7-11, [🍴] Domino's, [○] vet
56	Montrose Dr, N [⛽] Chevron, Exxon/dsl, Speedway, [🍴] Hardee's, Los Agaves Mexican, [🛏] Microtel, Ramada Inn, Wingate Inn, [○] Acura, Advance Parts, Chevrolet, Dodge, $General, Hyundai, KIA, NAPA, Rite Aid, VW
55	Kanawha Tpk (from wb)
54	US 60, MacCorkle Ave, N [🍴] Burger King, Krispy Kreme, Subway, [○] $Tree, Kroger/gas, TJ Maxx, S [⛽] Citgo, [🍴] Bob Evans, KFC, LJ Silver, McDonald's, Pizza Hut, Schlotzsky's, Taco Bell, Wendy's, [○] [H], Aamco, Family$, Harley-Davidson, Honda, Mazda/Mitsubishi
53	Roxalana Rd, to Dunbar, S [⛽] GoMart/gas, [🍴] BiscuitWorld, Capt D's, Gino's Pizza, McDonald's, Shoney's, Subway, Wendy's, [🛏] Super 8, Travelodge, [○] Advance Parts, Aldi Foods, CVS Drug, Jo-Ann Fabrics, Kroger, NTB, Rite Aid
50	VW 25, Institute, S [⛽] GoMart/gas
47b a	WV 622, Goff Mtn Rd, N [⛽] Chevron/24hr, Exxon, Go-Mart, Speedway/dsl, [🍴] BiscuitWorld, Bob Evans, Capt D's, Cozumel Mexican, Domino's, Gino's Pizza, McDonald's, Papa John's, Pizza Hut, Rice Bowl, Subway, Taco Bell, Tim Horton, Wendy's, [🛏] Motel 6, [○] URGENT CARE, Advance Parts, Kroger/gas, Rite Aid, Walgreens, S [🍴] Arby's, Buffalo Wild Wings, Burger King, Coco's Chinese, Cracker Barrel, Fazoli's, Golden Corral, HoneyBaked Ham, La Roca Mexican, Subway, TGIFriday's, [🛏] Comfort Inn, Sleep Inn, [○] $Tree, Freightliner, Lowe's, Radio Shack, Staples, Walmart
45	WV 25, Nitro, N [⛽] [LLLL]/Arby's/dsl/scales/24hr, [○] Chevrolet, S [⛽] Exxon/dsl, GoMart, Speedway/dsl, [🍴] BiscuitWorld, Checker's, DQ, Gino's Pizza, McDonald's, Subway, Wendy's, [🛏] EconoLodge, Economy Inn, [○] Marty's Tires
44.3mm	Kanawha River
44	US 35, St Albans, S [⛽] Chevron/dsl, [○] 7-11
40	US 35 N, Winfield, Pt Pleasant, S [⛽] Speedway, [🍴] DQ
39	WV 34, Winfield, N [⛽] BP/Arby's, GoMart/dsl, [🍴] Applebee's, Bob Evans, Rio Grande Mexican, Taste of Asia, [🛏] Days Inn, Holiday Inn Express, Red Roof Inn,

Exit	Services
39	Continued [○] Advance Parts, BigLots, $General, Elder-Beerman, GNC, Home Depot, Radio Shack, urgent care, USPO, S [⛽] Exxon/7-11/dsl, GoMart/gas, TA/dsl/rest./scales/24hr/@, [🍴] Biscuit World, Burger King, Capt D's, China Chef, El Rancho Grande, Gino's Pizza, Graziano's Pizza, KFC, McDonald's, Penn Sta., Shoney's, Subway, Taco Bell, TCBY, Wendy's, [🛏] Hampton Inn, [○] AT&T, AutoZone, K-Mart, Kroger/gas, Rite Aid, Verizon
38mm	**weigh sta both lanes**
35mm	**rest area both lanes, full [♿] facilities, [☎], vending, [🦐], litter barrels, petwalk**
34	WV 19, Hurricane, N [🍴] Arby's, KFC, Taco Bell, [○] Chevrolet, Chrysler/Dodge/Jeep, $Tree, Ford, Martin RV Ctr, Walmart/Subway, S [⛽] Exxon/7-11, Go-Mart, Sheetz, [🍴] BiscuitWorld/Gino's Pizza, Little Caesar's, McDonald's, Mi Pueblito, Pizza Hut, Subway, [🛏] American Inn, [○] Rite Aid, Walgreens, vet
28	US 60, Milton, **0-2 mi** S [⛽] Exxon, Go-Mart, Marathon/dsl, Rich Gas, Sheetz, [🍴] Biscuit World, DQ, Gino's Pizza, Jin Long Chinese, McDonald's, Pizza Hut, Subway, Wendy's, [○] Advance Parts, Curves, $General, Family$, Foodland, Jim's Camping (2mi), KOA (3mi), NAPA, Rite Aid, Save-a-Lot foods, USPO
20	US 60, Mall Rd, Barboursville, N [🍴] Alexander's Steaks, Applebee's, Arby's, Bob Evans, Burger King, Chick-fil-A, Chili's, Cici's Pizza, IHOP, Logan's Roadhouse, McDonald's, Old Chicago, Olive Garden, Panera Bread, Qdoba Mexican, Ruby Tuesday, Super China, Wendy's, [🛏] Comfort Inn, [○] Best Buy, Drug Emporium, Elder-Beerman, Firestone/auto, Hobby Lobby, JC Penney, Jo-Ann Fabrics, Kohl's, Lowe's, Macy's, Michael's, NTB, Old Navy, Sears/auto, Walmart, mall, S [⛽] BP, Sheetz, [🍴] Cracker Barrel, 3 Amigos, Famous Dave's BBQ, Johnny's Pizza, Outback Steaks, Shogun Japanese, Sonic, Steak&Shake, Subway, Taco Bell, TCBY, [🛏] Best Western, Hampton Inn, Holiday Inn, [○] Toyota/Scion
18	US 60, to WV 2, Barboursville, N [🍴] Bellacino's, O'Charley's, Starbucks, [○] $Tree, Home Depot, Marshall's, Office Depot, Target, S [⛽] Chevron/7-11, [🍴] Biscuit World, Giovanni's Pizza, Hardee's, Hooters, Papa John's, Pizza Hut, [○] Curves, Food Land, Honda, Kia, Kroger/gas, NAPA, Rite Aid, Walgreens
15	US 60, 29th St E, N [⛽] GoMart/dsl, Speedway/dsl, [🍴] Arby's, Biscuit World, Pizza Hut, Subway, Wendy's, Waffle House, [○] [H], AT&T, BigLots, Curves, $General, NAPA, Save-a-Lot Foods, Verizon, Walmart/McDonald's, st police, S [⛽] Exxon, [🍴] Fazoli's, Golden Corral, KFC, Little Caesar's, McDonald's, Penn Sta., Taco Bell, [🛏] Days Inn, Red Roof Inn, [○] Buick/Cadillac/GMC, CVS Drug, K-Mart, Mitsubishi/Nissan, Subaru
11	WV 10, Hal Greer Blvd, **0-2 mi** N [⛽] BP, Go-Mart, Marathon, [🍴] Arby's, Baskin-Robbins, Biscuit World, Bob Evans, Frostop Drive-In, McDonald's, Papa John's, Ritzy's Cafe, Wendy's, [🛏] Ramada Ltd, Super 8, TownePlace Suites, [○] [H], AutoZone, Rite Aid, S [○] Beech Fork SP (8mi)
10mm	**Welcome Ctr eb, full [♿] facilities, [☎], vending, [🦐], litter barrels, petwalk**
8	WV 152 S, WV 527 N, S [⛽] Speedway
6	US 52 N, W Huntington, Chesapeake, N [⛽] Marathon/dsl, Speedway/24hr, [🍴] Pizza Hut, [○] [H], AutoZone, BigLots, $General, Family$, Save-a-Lot Foods

(left margin vertical labels: **WV**, **CHARLESTON**; right margin vertical label: **HUNTINGTON**)

Copyright 2012 - The Next Exit®   ⛽ = gas   🍴 = food   🛏 = lodging   ⊡ = other

WV

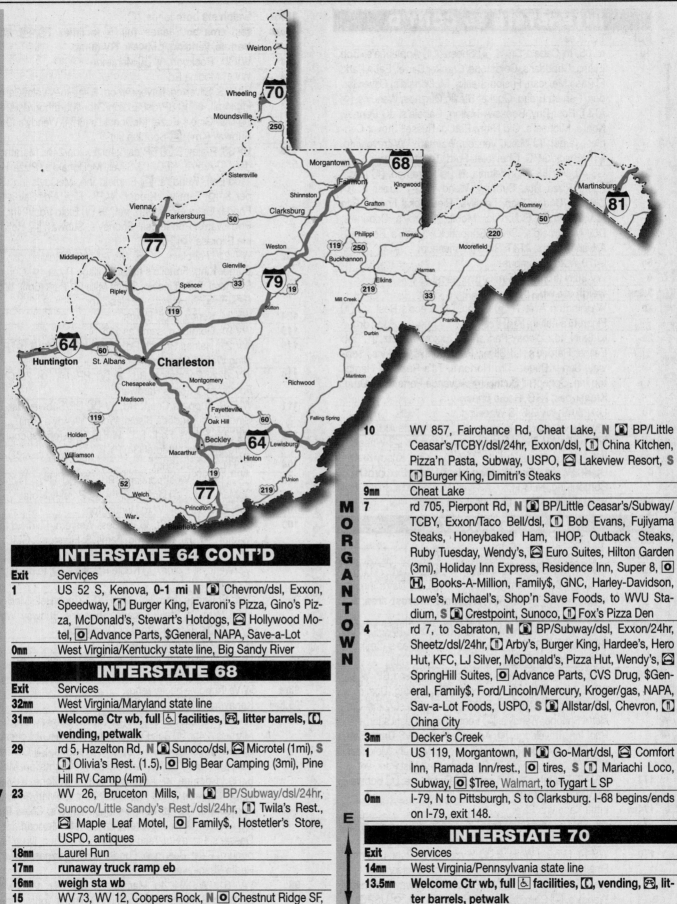

10	WV 857, Fairchance Rd, Cheat Lake, **N** ⛽ BP/Little Ceasar's/TCBY/dsl/24hr, Exxon/dsl, 🍴 China Kitchen, Pizza'n Pasta, Subway, USPO, 🛏 Lakeview Resort, **S** 🍴 Burger King, Dimitri's Steaks
9mm	Cheat Lake
7	rd 705, Pierpont Rd, **N** ⛽ BP/Little Ceasar's/Subway/ TCBY, Exxon/Taco Bell/dsl, 🍴 Bob Evans, Fujiyama Steaks, Honeybaked Ham, IHOP, Outback Steaks, Ruby Tuesday, Wendy's, 🛏 Euro Suites, Hilton Garden (3mi), Holiday Inn Express, Residence Inn, Super 8, ⊡ H, Books-A-Million, Family$, GNC, Harley-Davidson, Lowe's, Michael's, Shop'n Save Foods, to WVU Stadium, **S** ⛽ Crestpoint, Sunoco, 🍴 Fox's Pizza Den
4	rd 7, to Sabraton, **N** ⛽ BP/Subway/dsl, Exxon/24hr, Sheetz/dsl/24hr, 🍴 Arby's, Burger King, Hardee's, Hero Hut, KFC, LJ Silver, McDonald's, Pizza Hut, Wendy's, 🛏 SpringHill Suites, ⊡ Advance Parts, CVS Drug, $General, Family$, Ford/Lincoln/Mercury, Kroger/gas, NAPA, Sav-a-Lot Foods, USPO, **S** ⛽ Allstar/dsl, Chevron, 🍴 China City
3mm	Decker's Creek
1	US 119, Morgantown, **N** ⛽ Go-Mart/dsl, 🛏 Comfort Inn, Ramada Inn/rest., ⊡ tires, **S** 🍴 Mariachi Loco, Subway, ⊡ $Tree, Walmart, to Tygart L SP
0mm	I-79, N to Pittsburgh, S to Clarksburg. I-68 begins/ends on I-79, exit 148.

INTERSTATE 70

Exit	Services
14mm	West Virginia/Pennsylvania state line
13.5mm	**Welcome Ctr wb, full** ♿ **facilities,** ⊡ **vending,** 🛏 **litter barrels, petwalk**
11	WV 41, Dallas Pike, **N** ⛽ TA/rest./dsl/@, 🛏 Comfort Inn, **S** ⛽ Mobil/DQ/dsl, 🛏 EconoLodge, ⊡ RV camping

INTERSTATE 64 CONT'D

Exit	Services
1	US 52 S, Kenova, **0-1 mi N** ⛽ Chevron/dsl, Exxon, Speedway, 🍴 Burger King, Evaroni's Pizza, Gino's Pizza, McDonald's, Stewart's Hotdogs, 🛏 Hollywood Motel, ⊡ Advance Parts, $General, NAPA, Save-a-Lot
0mm	West Virginia/Kentucky state line, Big Sandy River

INTERSTATE 68

	Exit	Services
E ↑ ↓ **W**	32mm	West Virginia/Maryland state line
	31mm	**Welcome Ctr wb, full** ♿ **facilities,** 🛏 **litter barrels,** ⊡ **vending, petwalk**
	29	rd 5, Hazelton Rd, **N** ⛽ Sunoco/dsl, 🛏 Microtel (1mi), **S** 🍴 Olivia's Rest. (1.5), ⊡ Big Bear Camping (3mi), Pine Hill RV Camp (4mi)
	23	WV 26, Bruceton Mills, **N** ⛽ BP/Subway/dsl/24hr, Sunoco/Little Sandy's Rest./dsl/24hr, 🍴 Twila's Rest., 🛏 Maple Leaf Motel, ⊡ Family$, Hostetler's Store, USPO, antiques
	18mm	Laurel Run
	17mm	runaway truck ramp eb
	16mm	weigh sta wb
	15	WV 73, WV 12, Coopers Rock, **N** ⊡ Chestnut Ridge SF, Sand Springs Camping (2mi)
	12mm	runaway truck ramp wb

🅖 = gas 🍴 = food 🛏 = lodging 🅞 = other   Copyright 2012 - The Next Exit®

INTERSTATE 70 CONT'D

E ↕ W

WHEELING

Exit	Services
10	rd 65, to Cabela Dr, N 🅖 Sheetz, 🍴 Applebee's, Bob Evans, Cheddar's, Coldstone, Cracker Barrel, Eat'n Park, El Paso Mexican, Fusion Steaks, McDonald's, Olive Garden, Panera Bread, Quaker Steak, Quiznos, Wendy's, 🅞 AT&T, Best Buy, Books-A-Million, Cabela's, JC Penney, Kohl's, Michael's, Old Navy, PetCo, Russell Stover Candies, Target, TJ Maxx, Verizon, Walmart, WV travel info, S 🅞 Buick/GMC, Chevrolet, Ford, Toyota/Scion
5	US 40, WV 88 S, Tridelphia, N 🅖 Marathon, 🍴 Hoss' Rest., Pizza Hut, Subway, Wendy's, 🛏 Super 8, 🅞 Chrysler/Dodge/Jeep, Family$, Riesbeck's Foods, Rite Aid, vet, S 🅖 Exxon/dsl, Mobil, 🍴 Arby's, Domino's, DQ, McDonald's, Silver Chopsticks, Undo's Rest., 🅞 Advance Parts, AT&T, Rite Aid, museum
5a	I-470 W, to Columbus
4	WV 88 N (from eb), Elm Grove, same as 5
3.5mm	weigh sta wb
2b	Washington Ave, N 🅖 Exxon, 🍴 Greco's Rest., S 🍴 Figaretti's Italian, 🅞 🅷
2a	rd 88 N, to Oglebay Park, N 🅖 Exxon, Sheetz, 🍴 Bob Evans, Hardee's, LJ Silver, Papa John's, Perkins, Subway, Super Buffet, Tim Horton's, TJ's Rest., 🛏 Hampton Inn, SpringHill Suites, 🅞 Advance Parts, CVS Drug, Kroger/gas, NTB, Radio Shack
1b	US 250 S, WV 2 S, S Wheeling
1mm	tunnel
1a	US 40 E, WV 2 N, Main St, downtown, S 🛏 Wheeling Inn
0	US 40 W, Zane St, Wheeling Island, N 🅖 Exxon/dsl, 🍴 Burger King, KFC
0mm	West Virginia/Ohio state line, Ohio River

INTERSTATE 77

N ↕ S

PARKERSBURG

Exit	Services
186mm	West Virginia/Ohio state line, Ohio River
185	WV 14, WV 31, Williamstown, W 🅖 GoMart, 7-11/gas (1mi), 🍴 Dutch Pantry, Subway (1mi), 🛏 Day's Inn, 🅞 Glass Factory Tours, **WV Welcome Ctr/rest area, full facilities, info, 🚻, litter barrels**
179	WV 2 N, WV 68 S, to Waverly, E 🅖 Exxon, 🅞 ☕, W 🅖 BP, Chevron (3mi), 🍴 Burger King, Hardee's (3mi), 🛏 Red Carpet Inn, 🅞 🅷
176	US 50, 7th St, Parkersburg, E to North Bend SP, W 🅖 BP, GoMart, 7-11, 🍴 Bob Evans, Burger King, Domino's, DQ, LJ Silver, McDonald's, Mountaineer Rest./24hr, Omelette Shoppe, Wendy's, 🛏 Econolodge, Knight's Inn, Red Roof Inn, Travelodge, 🅞 Advance Parts, CVS Drug, Family$, Ford, Hyundai, Kroger/dsl, Lincoln/Mercury, Mercedes, NAPA, Rite Aid, Toyota, to Blennerhassett Hist Park, vet
174	WV 47, Staunton Ave, **1 mi** E 🅖 FinishLine, 🍴 Subway, W 🅖 47 Carry Out
174mm	Little Kanawha River
173	WV 95, Camden Ave, E 🅖 Marathon/dsl, **1-4 mi** W 🅖 BP, 🍴 Hardee's, 🛏 Blennerhassett Hotel, 🅞 🅷
170	WV 14, Mineral Wells, E 🅖 BP/dsl/repair/24hr, Chevron, FinishLine Gas, Parkersburg Trkstp/dsl/scales/24hr, Liberty Trkstp/dsl/24hr, 🍴 McDonald's, Subway, Taco Bell, Wendy's, 🛏 Comfort Suites, Hampton Inn, 🅞 USPO, W 🍴 Cracker Barrel, 🛏 AmeriHost, Holiday Inn Express, Microtel

CHARLESTON

Exit	Services
169mm	weigh sta both lanes, 🅞
166mm	**rest area both lanes, full ♿ facilities, 🅞, 🚻, litter barrels, vending, petwalk, RV dump**
161	WV 21, Rockport, W 🅖 Marathon
154	WV 1, Medina Rd
146	WV 2 S, Silverton, Ravenswood, E 🅞 Ruby Lake Camping (4mi), W 🅖 BP/dsl, Exxon/24hr, Marathon/dsl/24hr, 🍴 DQ, Gino's Pizza, McDonald's (3mi), Wendy's (3mi), Subway (4mi), 🛏 Scottish Inn
138	US 33, Ripley, E 🅖 BP/dsl/24hr, Exxon/24hr, Marathon/dsl, 🍴 Arby's, KFC, LJ Silver, McDonald's, Pizza Hut, Taco Bell, Wendy's, 🛏 Fairfield Inn, McCoy's Inn, Super 8, 🅞 Family$, Kroger, NAPA, Rite Aid, Sav-a-Lot Foods, Walmart/Subway, vet, W 🅖 Exxon/dsl/24hr, 🍴 Bob Evan's, Ponderosa, Shoney's, Subway, 🛏 Holiday Inn Express, 🅞 🅷
132	WV 21, Fairplain, E 🅖 BP/7-11/dsl, GoMart/dsl, 🍴 Burger King, Fratello's Italian, Village Pizza, 🅞 Curves, $General, Ford/Lincoln, Statts Mills RV Park (6mi), W 🅖 ❤Loves/Subway/dsl/scales/24hr
124	WV 34, Kenna, E 🅖 Exxon
119	WV 21, Goldtown, same as 116
116	WV 21, Haines Branch Rd, Sissonville, **4 mi** E 🅞 Rippling Waters Camping
114	WV 622, Pocatalico Rd, E 🅖 BP/dsl, 🅞 FasChek Foods/drug, Tom's Hardware
111	WV 29, Tuppers Creek Rd, W 🅖 BP/Subway/dsl, 🍴 Gino's (2mi), Tudor's Biscuit World, Wendy's (2mi)
106	WV 27, Edens Fork Rd, W 🅖 Chevron/dsl/country store, 🛏 Sunset Motel (3mi)
104	I-79 N, to Clarksburg
102	US 119 N, Westmoreland Rd, E 🅖 BP/7-11/24hr, GoMart/24hr, 🍴 Hardee's/24hr, 🛏 Parsley Motel
101	I-64, E to Beckley, W to Huntington
100	Broad St, Capitol St, W 🛏 Best Western, Fairfield Inn, Marriott, 🅞 🅷, CVS Drug, Family$, Firestone, GMC
99	WV 114, Capitol St, E ☕, W 🅖 BP/7-11/Domino's/Rally's/Wendys, Exxon, 🍴 Noble Roman's, 🅞 to museum, st capitol
98	35th St Bridge (from sb), W 🍴 KFC/Taco Bell, McDonald's, Murad's, Steak Escape, Shoney's, Subway, Wendy's, 🅞 🅷, Rite Aid, to U of Charleston
97	US 60 W (from nb), Kanawha Blvd
96	US 60 E, Midland Trail, Belle, W 🍴 Biscuit World, Gino's, 🛏 Budget Host
96mm	W Va Turnpike begins/ends
95.5mm	Kanawha River
95	WV 61, to MacCorkle Ave, E 🅖 BP/Subway/dsl, GoMart/dsl/24hr, 🍴 Bob Evans, China Wok, IHOP, Lonestar Steaks, McDonald's, TX Steaks, Wendy's, 🛏 Comfort Suites, Country Inn&Suites, Days Inn, Knights Inn, Motel 6, Red Roof Inn, 🅞 Advance Parts, AutoZone, K-Mart, W 🅖 Chevron/7-11, Exxon/dsl/24hr, GoMart/24hr, 🍴 Applebee's, Arby's, Burger King, Capt D's, China Buffet, Cracker Barrel, Hooters, La Carreta Mexican, Little Caesar's, Pizza Hut/Taco Bell, 🅞 AT&T, $Tree, Drug Emporium, Elder Beerman, Foodland, Kroger/gas, Lowe's, Radio Shack, vet
89	WV 61, WV 94, to Marmet, E 🅖 Exxon/Subway/dsl/24hr, GoMart, Sunoco/dsl, 🍴 BiscuitWorld, Gino's Pizza, Hardee's, LJ Silver, Wendy's, 🅞 $General, Family$, Kroger/deli, NAPA, Rite Aid, USPO

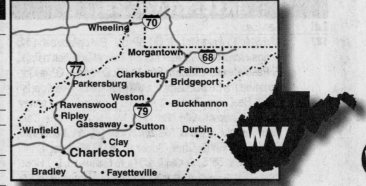

INTERSTATE 77 CONT'D

Exit	Services
85	US 60, WV 61, East Bank, **E** 🅖 Exxon, GoMart, 🍴 Gino's Pizza, McDonald's, Shoney's, 🅞 Chevrolet, $General, Kroger, Rite Aid, tire repair, USPO
82.5mm	toll booth
79	Cabin Creek Rd, Sharon
74	WV 83, Paint Creek Rd
72mm	**Morton Service Area wb,** 🅖 Exxon/dsl, 🍴 Burger King, Hershey's Ice Cream, KFC, Pizza Hut, Starbucks, atm
69mm	**rest area eb, full** ♿ **facilities,** 🅒, 🏞, **litter barrels**
66	WV 15, to Mahan, **1/2 mi W** 🅖 Sunoco/dsl/24hr
60	WV 612, to Mossy, Oak Hill, **1/2 mi E** 🅖 Exxon/dsl/repair/24hr, 🅞 RV camping
56.5mm	toll plaza, 🅒
54	rd 2, rd 23, Pax, **E** 🅖 BP
48	US 19, N Beckley, **1-4 mi E on US 19/WV 16** 🅖 Exxon/Subway, 🍴 Bob Evans, Burger King, Chick-fil-A, Chili's, Garfield's Rest., Logan's Roadhouse, LoneStar Steaks, LJ Silver, McDonald's, Peking Buffet, Rally's, Ryan's, Sonic, Starbucks, Taco Bell, Tumbleweed Grill, Wendy's, 🛏 Days Inn, 🅞 Advance Parts, AT&T, Belk, BigLots, Cadillac/Chevrolet, CVS Drug, $General, $Tree, Food Lion, Goodyear/auto, Hobby Lobby, Honda, Hyundai, JC Penney, Jo-Ann Fabrics, KIA/Subaru, K-Mart, Kohl's, Kroger/gas, Lowe's, NAPA, Nissan, Radio Shack, Rite Aid, Sam's Club/gas, Sears, Staples, Suzuki, TJ Maxx, Toyota, U-Haul, Walgreens, Walmart, RV Ctr
45mm	**Tamarack Service Area both lanes, W** 🅖 Exxon/dsl, 🍴 Burger King, Hershey's Ice Cream, Quiznos, Sbarro's, Starbucks, 🅞 gifts
44	WV 3, Beckley, **E** 🅖 Chevron/dsl, Exxon, Shell/Hardee's/24hr, 🍴 Applebee's, Campestre Mexican, DQ, Hibachi Japanese, Hooters, IHOP, McDonald's, Omelette Shoppe, Outback Steaks, Pizza Hut, 🛏 Best Value Inn, Courtyard, EconoLodge, Fairfield Inn, Howard Johnson, Quality Inn/rest., Super 8, 🅞 Ⓗ,.CVS Drug, Kroger/gas, Rite Aid, Tires, urgent care, **W** 🅖 BP/Subway/dsl, GoMart/dsl, 🍴 Bob Evans, Cracker Barrel, Pasquale Mira Italian, Ruby Tuesday, Sam's Hotdogs, TX Roadhouse, Wendy's, 🛏 Country Inn&Suites, Hampton Inn, Holiday Inn, Microtel, Park Inn
42	WV 16, WV 97, to Mabscott, **2 mi E** 🍴 BiscuitWorld, 🛏 Budget Inn, 🅞 Ⓗ, **W** 🅖 BP/dsl, GoMart, 🍴 Godfather's Pizza, Subway, 🅞 AutoValue Repair, Walmart, USPO
40	I-64 E, to Lewisburg
30mm	toll booth, 🅒
28	WV 48, to Ghent, **E** 🅖 Exxon/dsl, Marathon/dsl, 🍴 Subway, 🛏 Glade Springs Resort (1mi), Appalachian Resort Inn (12mi), 🅞 to ski area, **W** 🛏 Knight's Inn
26.5mm	Flat Top Mtn, elevation 3252
20	US 19, to Camp Creek, **E** 🅖 Exxon/dsl, **W** 🅞 Camp Creek SP/RV camping
18.5mm	scenic overlook/parking area/**weigh sta sb**, Bluestone River
17mm	**Bluestone Service Area/weigh sta nb, full** ♿ **facilities, scenic view,** 🅖 Exxon/dsl, Blimpie, Hershey's Ice Cream, Starbucks, Uno Pizza, atm/fax
14	WV 20, Athens Rd, **E** 🅞 Pipestem Resort SP, to Concord U
9mm	WV Turnpike begins/ends

PRINCETON →

Exit	Services
9	US 460, Princeton, Pearisburg, **E** 🍴 Campestre Mexican, Kimono Japanese, Outback Steaks, Ryan's, Subway, 🛏 Country Inn&Suites, 🅞 Welcome Ctr/Rest Area, pinic tables, little barrels, 🅒s, full facilities, $Tree, Radio Shack, Walmart, urgent care, **W** 🅖 BP/dsl, Exxon/24hr, Marathon, Sheetz, Shell, 🍴 Applebee's, Arby's, Bob Evans, Capt D's, Chili's, Cracker Barrel, DQ, Hardee's, McDonald's, Omelette Spot, Shoney's, Starbucks, TX Steaks, Webb's Sea🍴 Wendy's, 🛏 Comfort Inn, Days Inn, Hampton Inn, Holiday Inn Express, Microtel, Sleep Inn, Turnpike Motel, 🅞 Ⓗ, Hyundai, Lowe's, Suzuki
7	WV 27, Twelve Mile Rd
5	WV 112 (from sb, no re-entry), to Ingleside
3mm	East River
1	US 52 N, to Bluefield, **4 mi W** 🍴 KFC/LJ Silver, Wendy's, 🛏 EconoLodge, Holiday Inn/rest., Knights Inn, 🅞 Ⓗ, to Bluefield St Coll
0mm	West Virginia/Virginia state lineEast River Mtn

INTERSTATE 79

Exit	Services
160mm	West Virginia/Pennsylvania state line
159	**Welcome Ctr sb, full** ♿ **facilities, info,** 🏞, **litter barrels,** 🅒, **vending, petwalk**
155	US 19, WV 7, **0-3 mi E** 🅖 GetGo, Sheetz, 🍴 Burger King, Cheddars, Chili's, CiCi's Pizza, Cracker Barrel, Eat'n Park, Golden Corral, Longhorn Steaks, McDonald's, Olive Garden, Red Lobster, Shoney's, TX Roadhouse, 🛏 Best Western, EconoLodge, Fairfield Inn, Hampton Inn, Quality Inn, 🅞 Ⓗ, Barnes&Noble, Best Buy, CVS Drug, $Tree, Giant Eagle Foods, Old Navy, PetCo, Sam's Club/gas, Target, TJ Maxx, Walmart, to WVU
152	US 19, to Morgantown, **E** 🅖 BFS/dsl, Exxon, Getty, 🍴 Arby's, China Wok, McDonald's, Pizza Hut, Subway, Taco Bell, 🛏 EconoLodge, 🅞 URGENT CARE, Advance Parts, BigLots, Shop'n Save Foods, **W** 🍴 Bob Evans, Burger King, Garfield's Rest., 🛏 Microtel, 🅞 Belk, Elder-Beerman, JC Penney, K-Mart, Lowe's, Sears/auto, mall
150mm	Monongahela River
148	I-68 E, to Cumberland, MD, **1 mi E** 🅖 Go-Mart/dsl, 🍴 Mariachi Loco, Subway, 🛏 Comfort Inn, Morgantown Motel, Ramada Inn, 🅞 $Tree, Walmart, to Tygart Lake SP, tires
146	WV 77, to Goshen Rd
141mm	**weigh sta both lanes**
139	WV 33, E Fairmont, **E** 🅖 Sunoco, **W** 🅖 Exxon/24hr, K&T/BP/dsl, 🅞 RV camping, tires, vet, to Prickett's Ft SP

BECKLEY (vertical left margin)

N / S MORGANTOWN (vertical center margin)

🅖 = gas 🅡 = food 🛏 = lodging 🅞 = other   Copyright 2012 - The Next Exit®

WV

FAIRMONT N ↕ S — CLARKSBURG

INTERSTATE 79

Exit	Services
137	WV 310, to Fairmont, E 🅖 BP/dsl, Exxon/dsl/24hr, 🛏 Holiday Inn, 🅞 to Valley Falls SP, vet, W 🅖 Shell/dsl, 🍴 Domino's, KFC, McDonald's, Subway, Wendy's, 🅞 H, Advance Parts, $General, Family$, Shop'n Save Foods
136	rds 31, 2, County Rt
135	WV 64, Pleasant Valley Rd
133	Kingmont Rd, E 🅖 BFS/Subway/dsl, 🍴 Cracker Barrel, 🛏 Holiday Inn Express, Super 8, W 🅖 King/dsl, Shell/Quiznos/dsl, 🍴 DJ's Diner, 🛏 Comfort Inn
132	US 250, S Fairmont, E 🍴 Applebee's, Arby's, Bob Evans, Colasessano's Italian, Grand China Buffet, Hardee's, Hunan Rest., McDonald's, Subway, Taco Bell, 🛏 Days Inn, Fairfield Inn, Red Roof Inn, 🅞 Ace Hardware, Advance Parts, Chrysler/Dodge/Jeep, $General, GNC, NAPA, Sav-A-Lot Foods, Shop'n Save, Walmart, mall, to Tygart Lake SP, W 🅖 Exxon/dsl/24hr, GoMart/dsl/24hr, Sunoco/dsl, 🛏 Country Club Motel (4mi), 🅞 H, Buick/GMC, Ford/Lincoln/Mercury, Toyota/Scion, Trailer City RV Ctr
125	WV 131, Saltwell Rd, to Shinnston, E 🍴 Oliverio's Rest. (4mi), W 🅖 Exxon/Subway/dsl/24hr
124	rd 279, Jerry Dove Dr, E 🅖 Exxon/Dunkin Donuts/dsl, 🍴 Buffalo Wild Wings, 🛏 Microtel, Wingate Inn, W 🍴 Subway, 🛏 Holiday Inn Express, 🅞 H
123mm	**rest area both lanes, full ♿ facilities, info, ☎, 🖼 litter barrels, vending, petwalk, RV dump**
121	WV 24, Meadowbrook Rd, E 🅖 GoMart/24hr, Sheetz, 🍴 Biscuit World, Bob Evans, Gino's Pizza, Subway, 🛏 Hampton Inn, 🅞 URGENT CARE, Hyundai/Subaru, W 🅖 Exxon/dsl, 🍴 Burger King, Garfield's Rest., Outback Steaks, 🛏 Super 8, 🅞 Dick's, Honda, JC Penney, Jo-Ann Fabrics, Marshall's, NTB, Old Navy, Sears/auto, Target, mall
119	US 50, to Clarksburg, E 🍴 A&W/LJ Silver, Boomerang's Cafe, Brickside Grille, Chick-fil-A, Cici's Pizza, Coldstone, Denny's, Eat'n Park, Grand China, Hank's Deli, KFC, Las Trancas, Little Caesar's, Maxey's Rest., McDonald's, Panera Bread, Pizza Hut, Quiznos, Shogun Japanese, Shoney's, Starbucks, Taco Bell, TX Roadhouse, Wendy's, 🛏 Days Inn, Holiday Inn, Sleep Inn, Sutton Inn, Travelodge, 🅞 H, Advance Parts, BigLots, Family$, GNC, Home Depot, K-Mart, Kohl's, Kroger/dsl, Lowe's, Radio Shack, Sam's Club/gas, Walgreens, USPO
117	WV 58, to Anmoore, E 🅖 BFS/dsl, 🍴 Applebee's, Arby's, Burger King, Ruby Tuesday, Ryan's, Subway, 🛏 Hilton Garden, 🅞 Aldi Foods, AT&T, Staples, Walmart
115	WV 20, Nutter Fort, to Stonewood, E 🅖 BP/7-11/dsl, Exxon/dsl, 🅞 Stonewood Bulk Foods, W 🛏 Greenbrier Motel (5mi)
110	Lost Creek, E 🅖 BP/dsl
105	WV 7, to Jane Lew, E 🅖 I-79 Trkstp/dsl/rest., Valero/dsl, rest, 🛏 Plantation Inn, W 🅖 Exxon, GoMart, 🅞 glass factory tours
99	US 33, US 119, to Weston, E 🅖 BFS/DQ/Little Caesars/dsl, Fuel Ctr, Sheetz/24hr, 🍴 Burger King, Gino's Pizza, McDonald's, Peking Buffet, Steer Steakhouse, Subway, 🛏 Comfort Inn/rest., Hampton Inn (9mi), Holiday Inn Express, Super 8, 🅞 Advance Parts, Curves,

CHARLESTON N ↕ S

Exit	Services
99	Continued Family$, GNC, Kroger, Radio Shack, Walmart, 0-2 mi W 🅖 Exxon/7-11, Go-Mart, Rich Gas, 🍴 Domino's, Hardee's, KFC, LJ Silver, Pizza Hut, Subway, Wendy's, 🅞 H, Chrysler/Dodge, CVS Drug, $General, Ford/Mercury, NAPA, NAPACare, Rite Aid, Save-a-Lot, Twin Lakes Camper Sales, to Canaan Valley Resort, Blackwater Falls
96	WV 30, to S Weston, E 🅞 Broken Wheel Camping, to S Jackson Lake SP
91	US 19, to Roanoke, E 🅖 Marathon, 🍴 Stillwaters Rest, 🅞 to S Jackson Lake SP, camping
85mm	**rest area both lanes, full ♿ facilities, info, 🖼, litter barrels, ☎, vending, petwalk, RV dump**
79.5mm	Little Kanawha River
79	WV 5, Burnsville, E 🅖 Exxon/24hr, 🛏 79er Motel/rest., 🅞 Burnville Dam RA, W 🅖 GoMart, 🍴 Gino's Pizza, 🅞 Cedar Cr SP
76mm	Saltlick Creek
67	WV 4, to Flatwoods, E 🅖 BP/Arby's/dsl, Exxon/dsl, GoMart/dsl, Shell, 🍴 KFC/Taco Bell, McDonald's, Subway, Waffle Hut, 🛏 Day's Hotel, Sutton Lake Motel, 🅞 Buick/Chevrolet, to Sutton Lake RA, antiques, camping, W 🅖 Sunoco/motel/dsl, 🍴 Shoney's, Wendy's, 🅞 Flatwood Factory Stores, farmer's mkt
62	WV 4, Gassaway, to Sutton, E 🍴 Century Rest. (2mi), 🛏 Elk Motel, W 🅖 GoMart, 🍴 Giovanni's Pizza, LJ Silver, Pizza Hut, 🛏 Microtel, 🅞 H, Chrysler/Dodge/Jeep, CVS Drug, Ford, Kroger/deli, Super$
57	US 19 S, to Beckley
52mm	Elk River
51	WV 4, to Frametown, E antiques, food
49mm	**rest area both lanes, full ♿ facilities, 🖼, ☎, litter barrels, vending, petwalk, RV dump**
46	WV 11, Servia Rd
40	WV 16, to Big Otter, E 🅖 GoMart/dsl, W 🅖 Exxon/dsl, 🍴 Antique Cafe
34	WV 36, to Wallback, **10 mi** E 🍴 BiscuitWorld, Gino's Diner, Subway
25	WV 29, to Amma, E 🅖 Exxon/dsl
19	US 119, VW 53, to Clendenin, E 🅖 BP/dsl/24hr, 🍴 BiscuitWorld, Gino's Diner, 🅞 7-11, Shafer's Superstop
9	WV 43, to Elkview, E 🅖 GoMart/dsl, 🍴 Burger King, W 🅖 Exxon/Arby's/dsl, Speedway/dsl/24hr, 🍴 Bob Evans, China Super Buffet, La Carreta, McDonald's, Pizza Hut, Subway, 🛏 Country Inn&Suites, 🅞 Advance Parts, CVS Drug, $Tree, K-Mart, Kroger, Radio Shack
5	WV 114, to Big Chimney, 1 mi E 🅖 Exxon, 🍴 Hardee's, 🅞 Rite Aid, Smith's Foods
1	US 119, Mink Shoals, E 🍴 Harding's Family Rest., 🛏 Sleep Inn
0	I-77, S to Charleston, N to Parkersburg. I-79 begins/ends on I-77, exit 104.

INTERSTATE 81

Exit	Services
26mm	West Virginia/Maryland state line, Potomac River
25mm	**Welcome Ctr sb, full ♿ facilities, info, ☎, 🖼, litter barrels, petwalk**
23	US 11, Marlowe, Falling Waters, **1 mi** E 🅞 Falling Waters Camping, W 🅖 BP/dsl, 🅞 Curves, Outdoor Express RV Ctr, 7-11

INTERSTATE 81 CONT'D

Exit	Services
20	WV 901, Spring Mills Rd, **E** 🅖 Sheetz, 🍴 Barney's Rest., China Spring, McDonald's, Pizza Montese, Tokyo Cafe, 🛏 EconoLodge, 🅞 AT&T, Walmart/Subway, **W** 🅖 Shell/dsl, 🍴 Burger King, Domino's, 🛏 Holiday Inn Express
16	WV 9, N Queen St, Berkeley Springs, **E** 🅖 BP, Citgo, Exxon/Subway/dsl, Sheetz/24hr, 🍴 American Icecream, Arby's, Casa Gonzales Mexican, China King, DQ, Domino's, Dunkin Donuts, East Moon Asian, Hoss's, KFC, LJ Silver, McDonald's, Pizza Hut, Popeye's, Rita's Custard, Subway, Vocelli Pizza, Waffle House, 🛏 Comfort Inn, Knights Inn, Super 8, Rodeway Inn, 🅞 Advance Parts, AT&T, AutoZone, BigLots, CVS Drug, Family$, Food Lion, Walgreens, USPO, **W** 🅖 Citgo, Shell/dsl
14	RD 13, Dry Run Rd, **E** 🅞 🅗, **W** 🅞 Butler's Farm Mkt (1mi)
13	RD 15, Kings St, Martinsburg, **E** 🅖 BP/Subway/dsl, Sheetz/24hr, 🍴 Applebee's, Arkena's Cafe, Asian Garden, Buffalo Wild Wings, Burger King, Cracker Barrel, Daily Grind, Jerry's Subs, Kobe Japanese, Las Trancas, Outback Steaks, Pizza Hut, Shoney's, Wendy's, 🛏 Days Inn, Holiday Inn/rest., 🅞 🅗, Chevrolet/Scion/Toyota, Walmart

MARTINSBURG

Exit	Services
12	WV 45, Winchester Ave, **E** 🅖 Citgo/dsl, Sheetz/24hr, Shell/dsl, 🍴 Arby's, Bob Evans, Chick-fil-A, China City Buffet, McDonald's, Papa John's, Quizno's, Ryan's, Ruby Tuesday, Taco Bell, TX Steaks, Waffle House, 🛏 Hampton Inn, Holiday Inn Express, Kristalite Inn, 🅞 Advance Parts, AutoZone, BonTon, Food Lion, JC Penney, K-mart/Little Caesar's, Lowe's, Martin's Foods/gas, Nahkeeda Camping, Sears/auto, mall, **W** 🍴 Ledo's Pizza, Logan's Roadhouse, Subway, 🅞 AT&T, Best Buy, Books-A-Million, Dick's, Michael's, Petsmart, Staples, Target, TJ Maxx
8	RD 32, Tablers Sta Rd, **2 mi E** 🛏 Pikeside Motel, **W** 🅞 Orr's Farm Mkt
5	WV 51, Inwood, to Charles Town, **E** 🅖 Exxon, Liberty, 7-11, Sheetz, Shell/dsl, 🍴 Burger King, DQ, Domino's, KFC, McDonald's, Pizza Hut, Pizza Oven, Subway, Waffle House, 🛏 Hampton Inn, 🅞 CVS Drug, Family$, Food Lion, NAPA, Rite Aid, **W** 🅞 Lazy-A Camping (9mi)
2mm	**Welcome Ctr/weigh sta nb, full** ♿ **facilities, info, ℂ, vending, ⛽, litter barrels, petwalk**
0mm	West Virginia/Virginia state line

WISCONSIN

INTERSTATE 39

Exit	Services
211	US 51, rd K, Merrill, **2 mi W** 🅖 Cenex, 🍴 Chip's Burgers, Hardee's, Pizza Hut, 🅞 ⊙
208	WI 64, WI 70, Merrill, **E** 🍴 KFC, Taco Bell, **W** 🅖 Kwik-Trip, Mobil/dsl, 🍴 Culver's, McDonald's, Pine Ridge Rest., Pizza Now, Subway, 3's Company Rest., 🛏 Americinn, EconoLodge, Super 8, 🅞 🅗, Chrysler/Dodge/Jeep, $Tree, O'Reilly Parts, Piggly Wiggly, Walmart, to Council Grounds SP
206mm	Wisconsin River
205	US 51, rd Q, Merrill, **E** 🅖 BP/Hwy 51/dsl/rest./24hr, 🅞 Buick/Cadillac/Chevrolet, fireworks
197	rd WW, to Brokaw, **W** 🅖 Citgo/dsl
194	US 51, rd U, rd K, Wausau, **E** 🅖 F&F/dsl, KwikTrip/gas, 🍴 McDonald's, Taco Bell, **W** 🅖 BP/Arby's, 🅞 Ford/Mercury, Toyota/Scion
193	Bridge St, **E** 🍴 Culvers, Starbucks, Subway, 🛏 Plaza Hotel, **W** 🅗
192	WI 29 W, WI 52 E, Wausau, to Chippewa Falls, same as 191
191b a	Sherman St, **E** 🅖 BP, 🍴 Annie's Rest., Applebee's, Buffalo Wild Wings, Coldstone, George's Rest., Great Dane Rest., Hong Kong Buffet, Hudson's Grill, Jimmy John's, King Buffet, Little Caesar's, McDonald's, Noodles&Co, Papa Murphy's, Qdoba, Subway, 🛏 Country Inn&Suites, Courtyard, Hampton Inn, La Quinta, Super 8, 🅞 🅗, County Mkt Foods, **W** 🍴 Hardee's, 2510 Deli, 🅞 Cadillac, Home Depot, Honda, Menards
190mm	Rib River
190	rd NN, **E** 🅖 Mobil/Burger King, 🍴 IHOP, Krumbee's Bakery, 🛏 Howard Johnson, **W** 🅖 The Store/Subway/dsl, 🛏 Best Western, 🅞 Granite Mtn Ski Area, Rib Mtn Ski Area, st patrol
188	rd N, **E** 🅖 BP/dsl/scales/24hr, Phillips 66/dsl, 🍴

N S

WAUSAU

Exit	Services
188	Continued Burracho's Mexican, El Mezcal, Fazoli's, HoneyBaked Ham, Hong Kong Buffet, McDonald's, Rococo Pizza, Starbucks, TX Roadhouse, Wendy's, 🛏 Country Inn&Suites (1mi), Days Inn, 🅞 Aldi Foods, AT&T, Barnes&Noble, Best Buy, Chevrolet, $Tree, GNC, Gordman's, Jo-Ann Fabrics, King's RV Ctr, Kohl's, Michael's, Nissan, PetCo, Peterbilt, Petsmart, Radio Shack, Sam's Club/gas/dsl, TJ Maxx, Tires+, Volvo, Walmart, **W** 🅞 Rib Mtn SP
187mm	I-39 begins/ends. Freeway continues N as US 51.
187	WI 29 E, to Green Bay
186mm	Wisconsin River
185	US 51, Rothschild, Kronenwetter, **E** 🅖 BP/dsl, 🍴 Arby's, Culver's, Denny's, Green Mill Rest., Subway, Tony Roma's, 🛏 Candlewood Suites, Cedar Creek Lodge, Comfort Inn, Holiday Inn, Motel 6, Stoney Creek Inn, 🅞 Cedar Creek Factory Stores/famous brands, Gander Mtn, Harley-Davidson, Pick'n Save Foods, mall, visitor ctr
181	Maple Ridge Rd, Kronenwetter, Mosinee, **E** vet, **W** Kenworth
179	WI 153, Mosinee, **W** 🅖 BP/Subway/dsl, KwikTrip, Shell/dsl/24hr, 🍴 McDonald's, StageStop Rest., 🛏 Mosinee Inn
175	WI 34, Knowlton, to WI Rapids, **1 mi W** 🅞 Mullins Cheese Factory
171	rd DB, Knowlton, **E** camping, **W** 🅞 to 🅖, 🍴 lodging, camping
165	US 10 W, to Marshfield (no nb re-entry)
163	Casimir Rd
161	US 51, Stevens Point, **W** 🅖 BP, KwikTrip/24hr, Quik Mart/dsl, Shell/E85, The Store, 🍴 China Wok, Coldstone, Cousins Subs, 4Star Rest., Hardee's, Jimmy John's, KFC, McDonald's, Michele's Rest., Noodles&Co, Perkins, Pizza Hut, Rococo's Pizza, Starbucks, Subway, Taco Bell,

WV WI

S T E V E N S P O I N T

N ↕ S

WI

INTERSTATE 39 CONT'D

Exit	Services
161	Continued
	Tokyo Steaks, Topper's Pizza, 🅛 Comfort Suites, Country Inn&Suites, Point Motel, Ramada Inn, Stay Inn, Super 8, 🅞 AT&T, $Tree, K-Mart, Radio Shack
159	WI 66, Stevens Point, W 🅕 KwikTrip/dsl, 🅞 H, Dodge/Jeep, Ford, Honda, Hyundai, Nissan, VW
158	US 10, Stevens Point, E 🅕 F&F/dsl, Mobil/dsl/24hr, 🅕 Applebee's, Arby's, Buffalo Wild Wings, Culver's, DQ, El Mezcal Mexican, Fazoli's, Grazie's Italian, Hong Kong Buffet, El Mezcal, McDonald's, Rudy's Grill, Subway, Taco Bell, Wendy's, 🅛 Fairfield Inn, Holiday Inn Express, 🅞 Aldi Foods, Copp's Foods, Frank's Hardware, Hancock Fabrics, Staples, Target, vet, W 🅕 BP/24hr, 🅕 Hilltop Grill, 🅛 La Quinta, Royale Inn
156	rd HH, Whiting, E 🅕 The Store/Subway/dsl, 🅕 Charcoal Grill, Chili's, Golden Corral, Hudson's Grill, McDonald's, Starbucks, Subway, 🅞 Best Buy, $Tree, GNC, Kohl's, Lowe's, Michael's, PetCo, Walmart
153	rd B, Plover, W 🅕 BP, Mobil/dsl, Renew/E85/E20, 🅕 Bamboo House, Burger King, El Patron Mexican, Happy Wok, IHOP, KFC, Taco Bell, 🅛 AmericInn, Comfort Inn, Hampton Inn, 🅞 Copp's Foods, $Tree, Menards, NAPA, ShopKo, Toyota/Scion, Younkers, city park, dsl repair, vet
151	WI 54, to Waupaca, E 🅕 Shell/Arby's/dsl/scales/24hr, 🅕 4Star Family Rest., Shooter's Rest., 🅛 Elizabeth Inn/Conv Ctr, 🅞 tires/repair
143	rd W, Bancroft, to WI Rapids, E 🅕 Citgo/dsl, 🅕 Area 51 Rest
139	rd D, Almond
136	WI 73, Plainfield, to WI Rapids, E 🅕 BP/dsl, 🅕 Hooligan's Grill, 🅞 NAPA Care, W 🅕 Phillips 66/Subway/dsl
131	rd V, Hancock, E 🅕 Citgo, 🅕 Country Kettle
127mm	**weigh sta both lanes** (exits left)
124	WI 21, Coloma, E 🅕 Mobil/A&W/dsl, 🅛 Mecan Inn, 🅞 Caloma Camping, W 🅕 BP/dsl
120mm	**rest area sb, full** ♿ **facilities,** 🚻, 🍽, **vending, litter barrels, petwalk**
118mm	**rest area nb, full** ♿ **facilities,** 🚻, 🍽, **vending, litter barrels, petwalk**
113	rd E, rd J, Westfield, W 🅕 BP/Burger King, Marathon, Mobil/dsl, 🅕 McDonald's, Subway, 🅛 Pioneer Motel/rest., 🅞 Curves, Family$, city park
106	WI 82 W, WI 23 E, Oxford, E 🅛 Crossroads Motel, W 🅕 Citgo/dsl
104	(from nb, no EZ return) rd D, Packwaukee
100	WI 23 W, rd P, Endeavor, E 🅕 BP/dsl, 🅕 Larry's Chicken Inn
92	US 51 S, Portage, E 🅕 KwikTrip/dsl, Mobil, 🅕 Culver's, Dino's Rest., Jimmy John's, KFC, La Tolteca Mexican, McDonald's, Papa Murphy's, Subway, Taco Bell, Wendy's, World Buffet, 🅛 Best Western, Ridge Motel, Super 8, 🅞 H, Ace Hardware, AutoZone, Chrysler/Dodge/Jeep, Curves, $Tree, Ford/Lincoln/Mercury, GNC, K-Mart, Pierce's Foods, Radio Shack, Staples, Verizon, Walgreens, Walmart
89b a	WI 16, to WI 127, Portage, E 🅕 Mobil/dsl, 🅕 Hitching Post Eatery, Murph's Chop Shop
88.5mm	Wisconsin River
87	WI 33, Portage, W ski area

Exit	Services
86mm	Baraboo River
85	Cascade Mt Rd
84	I-39, I-90 & I-94 run together sb.

INTERSTATE 43

N ↕ S

G R E E N B A Y

Exit	Services
192mm	I-43 begins/ends at Green Bay on US 41.
192b	US 41 S, US 141 S, to Appleton, services on Velp Ave, **1 mi S** 🅕 BP/A&W/dsl, Express, Mobil/Arby's, 🅕 Black Forest Rest, Burger King, Kim's Grill, Rite View Diner, Riverside Coffee House, Riverstreet Rest, Taco Bell, Watering Hole Rest, 🅛 AmericInn, 🅞 Bumper Parts, Curves
192a	US 41 N, US 141 N
189	Atkinson Dr, to Velp Ave, Port of Green Bay
188mm	Fox River
187	East Shore Dr, Webster Ave, W 🅕 Shell/dsl/24hr, 🅕 Maria's Italian, McDonald's, Wendy's, 🅞 H
185	WI 54, WI 57, University Ave, to Algoma, W 🅕 Citgo, Mobil, Shell/A&W, 🅕 Green Bay Pizza, Harvest Cafe, Kahn's Mongolian, Lee's Cantonese Chinese, Pizza Hut, Subway, Taco Bell, 🅞 NAPA, SuperValu Foods, Walgreens, U of WI GB
183	Mason St, rd V, E 🅕 Culver's, Ground Round, Makinaw's Grill, Tim Horton, 🅛 Country Inn&Suites, Super 8, 🅞 H, **1 mi W** 🅕 BP, Mobil/dsl, Shell, 🅕 Applebee's, Arby's, Burger King, China Buffet, China Kitchen, Country Kitchen, DQ, Fazoli's, Grand Buffet, Great Lakes Sandwiches, KFC, Little Caesar's, LJ Silver, McDonald's, Papa John's, Papa Murphy's, Perkins, Pizza Hut, Starbucks, Taco Bell, 🅞 Advance Parts, Aldi Foods, AT&T, AutoZone, Batteries+, Cadillac, Chevrolet, Chrysler/Dodge/Jeep, Copps Foods, Dodge, $General, Goodyear/auto, Hobby Lobby, Kohl's, Mazda, PetCo, ShopKO, Subaru, Tires+, Walgreens, Walmart/Subway
181	Eaton Rd, rd JJ, E 🅕 BP/McDonald's/dsl, 🅕 Blimpie, Hardee's, Jimmy John's, K-2 Rest, Luigi's, Taco John's, 🅞 Ford/Kia, Harley-Davidson, Home Depot, W 🅕 Mobil/Subway/dsl, Shell, 🅕 A&W, Ravine Grill, 🅛 AmericInn, 🅞 Farm&Fleet/gas, Festival Foods, Menards
180	WI 172 W, to US 41, 1 exit W 🅕 BP/Taco Bell/24hr, Citgo/Country Express/dsl/scales/24hr, Kwik Trip, Shell, 🅕 Burger King, McDonald's, Subway, Tuscon's Rest., 🅛 Guest House Inn, 🅞 H, Copps Foods, Target, Walgreens, to stadium, **5 mi W** multiple services
178	US 141, to WI 29, rd Mm, Bellevue, E 🅕 Shell/Arby's/dsl, W repair
171	WI 96, rd KB, Denmark, E 🅕 BP/dsl, 🅕 Lorrie's Café, McDonald's, Steve's Cheese, Subway, 🅞 Shady Acres Camping
168mm	**rest area both lanes, full** ♿ **facilities,** 🚻, **vending,** 🍽, **litter barrels, petwalk**
166mm	Devils River
164	WI 147, rd Z, Maribel, W 🅕 BP/dsl, 🅕 Ridge Rest
160	rd K, Kellnersville, **1mi W** 🅕 BP, food
157	rd V, Hillcrest Rd, Francis Creek, E 🅕 Citgo/Subway/dsl, Marathon/diner/dsl
154	US 10 W, WI 310, Two Rivers, to Appleton, E 🅕 Mobil, 🅞 H, W 🅕 Cenex
153mm	Manitowoc River
152	US 10 E, WI 42 N, rd JJ, Manitowoc, E 🅕 TimeOut Grill, 🅞 antiques, maritime museum

Copyright 2012 - The Next Exit®

INTERSTATE 43 CONT'D

MANITOWAC

N
S

MILWAUKEE

WI

Exit	Services
149	US 151, WI 42 S, Manitowoc, E BP, Exxon, KwikTrip/dsl, Mobil/dsl/24hr, Shell/dsl/24hr, A&W, Applebee's, Arby's, Burger King, Charcoal Grill, China Buffet, Country Kitchen, Cousins Subs, Culver's, DQ, 4 Seasons Rest., Jimmy John's, McDonald's, Papa Murphy's, Penguin Drive-In, Perkins, Ponderosa, Starbucks, Taco Bell, Wendy's, Birch Creek Inn, Comfort Inn, Holiday Inn, Super 8, H, Aldi Foods, AutoZone, Buick/Cadillac/Chevrolet/GMC, Chrysler/Dodge/Jeep, Copps Foods, $Tree, Family$, Festival Foods, Hobby Lobby, Kohl's, Lowe's Whse, PetCo, Radio Shack, ShopKO, Tires+, Walmart/Subway, museum, USPO, vet, W BP/McDonald's/24hr, Subway, AmericInn, Harley-Davidson, Menards
144	rd C, Newton, E Mobil/dsl, antiques
142mm	weigh sta sb,
137	rd XX, Cleveland, E Citgo/PJ's Grille/dsl, Cleveland Family Rest., Wagner's RV Ctr
128	WI 42, Howards Grove, E BP/dsl/24hr, Culver's, Hardee's, Harry's Diner, Shuff's Rest, TX Roadhouse, Comfort Inn, Gander Mtn, Jo-Ann Fabrics, Pomp's Tire, W Citgo/Cousins Subs/dsl, Menards, Walmart
126	WI 23, Sheboygan, E BP, Applebee's, Cousins Subs, Culver's, McDonald's, New China, Pizza Hut/Taco Bell, Quizno's, La Quinta, H, Aldi Foods, Batteries+, BigLots, Firestone/auto, Ford/Lincoln/Mercury, Goodyear/auto, Hobby Lobby, Honda/Mazda/Toyota, Hyundai, Kia, Kohl's, Sears/auto, ShopKO, Subaru, W Days Inn
123	WI 28, rd A, Sheboygan, E Citgo/dsl/24hr, Mobil/McDonald's/dsl, Coldstone Creamery, Jimmy John's, Perkins, Starbucks, Wendy's, AmericInn, Holiday Inn Express, Harley-Davidson/Cruisers Burgers, Walmart, W Arby's, Century Buffet, Chili's, Best Buy, $Tree, Home Depot, Michael's, Petsmart, Radio Shack, Target, TJ Maxx
120	rds OK, V, Sheboygan, E Citgo/dsl, Judi's Rest., Sleep Inn, to Kohler-Andrae SP, camping, 1 mi W Horn's RV Ctr
116	rd AA, Foster Rd, Oostburg, 1 mi W Pizza Ranch, Subway
113	WI 32 N, rd LL, Cedar Grove, W Citgo/dsl/repair, Mobil, Renew/e-85, Country Grove Rest, Cousins Subs, Lakeview Motel
107	rd D, Belgium, E Lake Church Inn, Harrington Beach SP, W BP/DQ/dsl/24hr, How-Dea Trkstp/dsl/scales, Mobil/McDonald's/dsl/24hr, Bic's Place, Curley's Rest., Hobo's Korner Kitchen, Subway, Regency Inn, NAPA, repair, USPO
100	WI 32 S, WI 84 W, Port Washington, E Citgo/dsl, Mobil, Arby's, McDonald's, Pizza Hut, Subway,

Exit	Services
100	Continued Country Inn&Suites, Holiday Inn, Allen-Edmonds Shoes, Century Foods, Goodyear/auto, Sentry Foods, ShopKO, True Value, W Nisleit's Country Rest.
97	(from nb, exits left), WI 57, Fredonia
96	WI 33, to Saukville, E Citgo, Mobil/dsl/24hr, Culver's, KFC/LJ Silver, Buick/Cadillac/Chevrolet, Dodge, Ford/Lincoln/Mercury, Pick'n Save Foods, Piggly Wiggly, Walgreens, Walmart/drug, W Exxon/McDonald's, DQ, Domino's, Lam's Chinese, Papa Murphy's, Quizno's, Subway, Taco Bell, Super 8, Curves, repair/tires
93	WI 32 N, WI 57 S, Grafton, 1-2 mi E Citgo, Dairy House Rest., Mamma Mia's Cafe, Pied Piper Rest., Smith Bros Fish (4mi), Best Western, Holiday Inn, W Flannery's Cafe
92	WI 60, rd Q, Grafton, E GhostTown Rest., Hampton Inn, W Citgo/DQ/dsl, Charcoal Grill, Noodles&Co, Qdoba, Quizno's, Starbucks, Subway, Baymont Inn, H, AT&T, Best Buy, Costco/gas, Home Depot, Kohl's, Michael's, Petsmart, Target, vet
89	rd C, Cedarburg, W Mobil/dsl, Cedar Crk Settlement Café (6mi), StageCoach Inn, Washington House Inn, H
85	WI 57 S, WI 167 W, Mequon Rd, W Citgo/dsl, Mobil/24hr, Casa Grande Mexican, Caribou Coffee, Chancery Rest., Cousins Subs, Culver's, DQ, Hong Palace Chinese, Jimmy John's, McDonald's, Panera Bread, Papa Murphy's, Starbucks, Subway, Best Western, Chalet Motel, H, Ace Harware, Kohl's, Office Depot, Pick'n Save Foods, Sendik's Foods, Walgreens, vet
83	rd W, Port Washington Rd (from nb only)
82b a	WI 32 S, WI 100, Brown Deer Rd, E

[Map of Wisconsin showing interstate highways including I-94, I-90, I-39, I-43 with cities: Superior, Chippewa Falls, Eau Claire, Menomonie, Wausau, Marshfield, Stevens Point, Green Bay, De Pere, Appleton, Kaukauna, Menominee, Marinette, Two Rivers, Manitowoc, Oshkosh, Sheboygan, Fond Du Lac, La Crosse, Beaver Dam, West Bend, Waukesha, Milwaukee, West Allis, Madison, Monroe, Janesville, Beloit, Racine, Kenosha]

N ↕ S

WI

INTERSTATE 43 CONT'D	
Exit	**Services**
82b a	Continued BP/24hr, Sendik's/dsl, 🍴 Benji's Deli, Cold Stone, Jimmy John's, La Paisa Mexican, Max Field's Pancakes, McDonald's, Noodles&Co, Pizza Hut, Qdoba, Spring Garden Chinese, Starbucks, Subway, Toppers Pizza, ⊡ Best Buy, CVS Drug, GNC, Land's Inlet, Walgreens
80	Good Hope Rd, E 🗭 BP, 🍴 Jimmy John's, King's Wok, Nick-n-Willy's Pizza, Samurai Japanese, Stonecreek Coffee, 🛏 Radisson, Residence Inn, ⊡ Pick'n Save Foods, to Cardinal Stritch U
78	Silver Spring Dr, E 🗭 BP, Citgo, 🍴 Applebee's, BD Mongolian, Boston Mkt, Bravo Italian, Burger King, CA Pizza Kitchen, Carabou Coffee, Cheesecake Factory, Cousins Subs, 5 Guys Burgers, Food Court, Gyro Palace, Kopps, McDonald's, Panera Bread, Perkins, Pizza Hut, Qdoba, Quizno's, Subway, Taco Bell, 🛏 La Quinta, Super 8, ⊡ AT&T, Barnes&Noble, Batteries+, Cadillac, Goodyear/auto, Kohl's, Radio Shack, Sears/auto, Trader Joe's, Walgreens, mall, USPO, W other 🅗
77b a	(from nb), E 🍴 Anchorage Rest., 🍴 Solly's Grill, 🛏 Hilton
76b a	WI 57, WI 190, Green Bay Ave, E 🍴 Anchorage Rest, 🛏 Hilton, ⊡ Home Depot, W 🗭 Citgo, 🍴 Burger King, ⊡ Jaguar/Volvo
75	Atkinson Ave, Keefe Ave, E 🗭 Mobil, W 🗭 BP, Citgo/dsl
74	Locust St
73c	North Ave (rom sb), E 🍴 Wendy's, W 🍴 McDonald's
73a	WI 145 E, 4th St (exits left from sb), Broadway, downtown
72c	Wells St, E 🛏 Hilton, ⊡ 🅗, Civic Ctr, museum
72b	(from sb), I-94 W, to Madison
72a	(310c from nb, exits left from sb), I-794 E, I-94 W to Madison, to Lakefront, downtown
311	WI 59, National Ave, 6th St, downtown
312a	Lapham Blvd, Mitchell St, W 🗭 Shell
312b	(from nb), Becher St, Lincoln Ave
314a	Holt Ave, E 🗭 Andy's/dsl, 🍴 Applebee's, Arby's, China King, Little Caesars, Quizno's, Starbucks, Subway, Wendy's, ⊡ $General, Home Depot, Pick'n Save Foods, Sentry Foods, Target, vet, W 🅗, to Alverno Coll
314b	Howard Ave
10b	(316 from sb), I-94 S to Chicago 🛈
9b a	US 41, 27th St, E 🗭 BP, Citgo, Clark, 🍴 Arby's, Burger King, Chancery Rest., Famous Dave's, Pizza Hut, Rusty Skillet Rest., Subway, 🛏 Suburban Motel, ⊡ AutoZone, Carquest, Curves, K-Mart, Subaru, Target, USPO, Walgreens, W 🍴 Boston Mkt, DQ, Denny's, Los Burritos Tapatios, McDonald's, Rich's Cakes, Wong's Wok, Zebb's Rest., 🛏 🅗ity Inn, Rodeway Inn, ⊡ 🅗, AAA, Advance Parts, Chevrolet, CVS Drug, $Tree, Firestone/auto, Ford, Goodyear/auto, GMC/Hyundai, Kohl's, Michael's, Pick'n Save Foods, Sav-a-Lot Foods
8a	WI 36, Loomis Rd, E 🗭 BP, Citgo, 🍴 Los Mariachi's, ⊡ Aldi Foods, Walgreens, W 🍴 George Webb Rest, ⊡ to Alverno Coll
7	60th St, E 🗭 Speedway/dsl, 🍴 Subway, Wendt's Grille, ⊡ Harley-Davidson, W 🗭 Speedway
5b	76th St (from sb, no EZ return), E 🗭 Speedway/dsl, 🍴

MILWAUKEE

5b	Continued Applebee's, Bakers Square, Burger King, Carrabba's Italian, Champ's Grill, Cousins Subs, George Webb Rest, Hooters, Jimmy John's, Kopp's Burgers, Kyoto Japanese, McDonald's, Noodles&Co, Old Country Buffet, Olive Garden, Outback Steaks, Qdoba, Red Lobster, Ruby Tuesday, TGIFriday's, Topper's Pizza, Wendy's, ⊡ AT&T, Barnes&Noble, Best Buy, Breadsmith, $Tree, Firestone/auto, Isuzu, Jo-Ann Fabrics, Office Depot, PetCo, Sears/auto, Tuesday Morning, Valvoline, Verizon, Vitamin Shoppe, W 🍴 Arby's, Pizza Hut, Ponderosa, Popeye's, ⊡ Pick'n Save Foods, TJ Maxx, Walgreens, USPO
5a	WI 24 W, Forest Home Ave, E 🗭 Citgo, ⊡ Boerner Botanical Gardens
61	(4 from sb), I-894/US 45 N, I-43/US 45 S
60	US 45 S, WI 100, 108th St (exits left from sb), E 🗭 BP, Citgo, Marathon, Mobil, 🍴 A&W, Amore Italian, Baskin-Robbins, Cousins Subs, Fortune Chinese, George Webb Rest, McDonald's, Open Flame Grill, Pizza Hut, Taco Bell, ⊡ AutoZone, $Tree, K-Mart, Radio Shack, Sentry Foods, vet, W 🗭 Phillips 66, 🍴 Forum Rest., McDonald's, Omega Custard, Organ Piper Pizza, ⊡ Aldi Foods, Badger Transmissions, Cabela's, $Daze, Goodyear, NAPA, Walgreens, Walmart/drug, vet
59	WI 100, Layton Ave (from nb, exits left), Hales Corner, W 🗭 BP, same as 60
57	Moorland Rd, E 🗭 Mobil/dsl, 🍴 Applebee's, Stonefire Pizza Co, TX Roadhouse, 🛏 La Quinta, W 🗭 Speedway/dsl/24hr, 🍴 Buffalo Wild Wings, Quizno's, Passport Grill, 🛏 Holiday Inn Express, ⊡ Michael's, Target
54	rd Y, Racine Ave, 1-2 mi E 🗭 Citgo/dsl, KwikTrip, ⊡ Culver's, Cousins Subs, McDonald's
50	WI 164, Big Bend, W 🗭 Citgo/dsl, 🍴 Coach House Grill, Long Neck's Rest., McDonald's
44mm	Fox River
43	WI 83, Mukwonago, E 🗭 BP/dsl, ⊡ Home Depot, Walmart, W 🗭 Citgo, 🍴 Antigua Real Cafe, Boneyard Grill, Chen's Kitchen, DQ, Dominos, Imperial House Chinese, Mario's, Pastime Grille, Taco Bell, 🛏 Sleep Inn
38	WI 20, East Troy, W 🗭 BP, 🔲/Road Ranger/Subway/dsl/24hr, Shell/McDonald's, 🍴 Burger King, Roma's Ristorante, ⊡ Carquest, Chrysler/Dodge/Jeep, $General
36	WI 120, East Troy, E 🛏 Alpine Valley Resort, W 🛏 Country Inn&Suites
33	Bowers Rd, E to Alpine Valley Music Theatre
32mm	**rest area both lanes, full** 🦽 **facilities,** 🔲, 🚻, **litter barrels, vending, petwalk**
29	WI 11, Elkhorn, fairgrounds
27b a	US 12, to Lake Geneva, E 🅗
25	WI 67, Elkhorn, E 🗭 BP/dsl, 🛏 AmericInn, ⊡ Buick/Chevrolet/GMC, Chrysler/Dodge/Jeep, vet, W 🗭 Speedway/dsl/24hr, 🍴 Burger King, Subway, 🛏 Hampton Inn (2mi), ⊡ Dehaan Auto/RV Ctr
21	WI 50, Delavan, E 🗭 Shell/dsl/24hr, 🍴 Brodie's Beef, Chili's, China 1, Culvers, Domino's, Panera Bread, Papa Murphy's, Quizno's, Starbucks, Subway, Yoshi Japanese, ⊡ Aldi Foods, AT&T, F&F Tires, Greyhound Dog-Track, Kohl's, Lowe's Whse, Petsmart, Radio Shack, Staples, Walmart W 🗭 Mobil/24hr, Speedway/dsl, 🍴 Cousins Subs, KFC, McDonald's, Perkins, Pizza Hut,

DELAVAN

🛢️ = gas 🍴 = food 🛏️ = lodging 🅾️ = other

WI

INTERSTATE 43 CONT'D

Exit	Services
21	Continued
	Taco Bell, Wendy's, 🛏️ Comfort Suites, Super 8, 🅾️ Ace Hardware, AutoZone, Cadillac/Chevrolet, $Tree, Ford/Lincoln/Mercury, GNC, NAPA, Piggly Wiggly, ShopKO, Walgreens
17	rd X, Delavan, Darien, **W** 🍴 BP
15	US 14, Darien, **E** 🛢️ Mobil/dsl, 🍴 West Wind Diner
6	WI 140, Clinton, **E** 🛢️ Citgo/Subway/dsl, 🅾️ Ford
2	rd X, Hart Rd, **E** 🍴 Butterfly Fine Dining
1b a	I-90, E to Chicago, W to Madison, **S** 🛢️ BP, Mobil/McDonald's, 🛢️/Taco Bell/dsl/scales/24hr, Shell, Speedway/dsl, 🍴 Applebee's, Arby's, Asia Buffet, Atlanta Bread, Burger King, Culver's, Jimmy John's, Little Caesar's, Papa Murphy's, Road Dawg Rest, Starbucks, Subway, Wendy's, 🛏️ Comfort Inn, EconoLodge, Fairfield Inn, Holiday Inn Express, Rodeway Inn, 🅾️ Aldi Foods, Buick/GMC, Cadillac/Chevrolet, $Tree, GNC, Menards, NTB, O'Reilly Parts, Radio Shack, Staples, Verizon, Walmart, I-43 begins/ends on I-90, exit 185 in Beloit.

INTERSTATE 90

Exit	Services
187mm	I-90 & I-39 run together nb., Wisconsin/Illinois state line
187mm	**Welcome Ctr wb, full ♿ facilities, info, 🍴, 🛏️, litter barrels, vending, petwalk**
185b	I-43 N, to Milwaukee
185a	WI 81, Beloit, **S** 🛢️ BP, Mobil/McDonald's, 🛢️/Taco Bell/dsl/scales/24hr, Shell, Speedway/dsl, 🍴 Applebee's, Arby's, Asia Buffet, Atlanta Bread, Burger King, Culver's, Jimmy John's, Little Caesar's, Papa Murphy's, Road Dawg Rest, Starbucks, Subway, Wendy's, 🛏️ Comfort Inn, EconoLodge, Fairfield Inn, Holiday Inn Express, Rodeway Inn, 🅾️ Aldi Foods, Buick/GMC, Cadillac/Chevrolet, $Tree, GNC, Menards, NTB, O'Reilly Parts, Radio Shack, Staples, Verizon, Walmart
183	Shopiere Rd, rd S, to Shopiere, **S** 🛢️ BP/Rollette/dsl/24hr, 🅾️ 🅷, camping, repair
181mm	**weigh sta, wb**
177	WI 11 W, Janesville, **2 mi S** 🛢️ BP, KwikTrip, 🍴 Bobble Heads Grill, El Jardin Mexican, 🅾️ to Blackhawk Tec Coll, Rock Co 😀
175b a	WI 11 E, Janesville, to Delavan, **N** 🛢️ BP/Subway/dsl/24hr, 🍴 Denny's, 🛏️ Baymont Inn, 🅾️ 🅷, **S** 🛢️ BP, Mobil, 🍴 DQ, 🛏️ Lannon Stone Motel, 🅾️ city park
171c b	US 14, WI 26, Janesville, **N** 🛢️ TA/Mobil/Wendy's/dsl/scales/24hr, 🍴 Coldstone, Cozumel Mexican, Fuddruckers, IHOP, Old Country Buffet, Starbucks, Subway, TX Roadhouse, 🛏️ Holiday Inn Express, Microtel, 🅾️ Best Buy, Gander Mtn, GNC, Home Depot, Michael's, NTB, Old Navy, PetCo, Staples, TJ Maxx, **S** 🛢️ Citgo, Exxon, Kwik Trip/dsl/24hr, 🍴 Applebee's, Arby's, Buffalo Wild Wings, Burger King, ChuckeCheese, Cousin's Subs, Culver's, Famous Dave's, Fazoli's, Fuji Steaks, Ground Round, Hacienda Real, Hardee's, Hooters, Jimmy John's, KFC, La Tolteca Mexican, McDonald's, Noodles&Co, Olive Garden, Papa Murphy's, Peking Chinese, Perkins, Pizza Hut, Prime Quarter Steaks, Red Robin, Subway, Taco Bell, Taco John's, World Buffet, 🛏️ EconoLodge, Super 8, 🅾️ 🅷, Aldi Foods, AutoZone, CarQuest, $Tree, F&F, Ford/Lincoln/Mercury, Harley-Davidson, Hobby

Exit	Services
171c b	Continued
	Lobby, JC Penney, KIA, Kohl's, K-Mart, Menards, O'Reilly Parts, Sears/auto, ShopKO, Subaru, Target, Toyota, Verizon, mall, USPO
171a	WI 26, **N** 🛢️ BP/dsl, Phillips 66/dsl, 🍴 Cracker Barrel, 🛏️ Best Western/rest., Hampton Inn, Motel 6, 🅾️ Chrysler/Dodge/Jeep, Sam's Club, VW, Walmart, Walgreens, **S** same as 171c b
168mm	**rest area eb, full ♿ facilities, 🍴, 🛏️, litter barrels, vending, petwalk**
163.5mm	Rock River
163	WI 59, Edgerton, to Milton, **N** 🛢️ Mobil/Subway/dsl, Shell/Dunkin Donuts/Taco John's, 🍴 Culver's, McDonald's, WI Cheese Store, 🛏️ Comfort Inn, 🅾️ marina
160	US 51S, WI 73, WI 106, Oaklawn Academy, to Deerfield, **N** 🅾️ Hickory Hills Camping, **S** 🛢️ BP/dsl/scales/24hr/@, 🅾️ 🅷
156	US 51N, to Stoughton, **S** 🛏️ Coachman's Inn/rest., 🅷
147	rd N, Cottage Grove, to Stoughton, **S** 🛢️ BP/Arby's/24hr, Road Ranger/🛢️/Subway/dsl/scales, 🅾️ Lake Kegonsa SP, fireworks
146mm	**weigh sta eb**
142b a	(142a exits left from wb), US 12, US 18, Madison, to Cambridge, **N** 🛢️ BP/dsl, 🍴 Roadhouse Rest, 🛏️ Best Value Inn, Magnuson Grand Hotel, 🅾️ Harley-Davidson, **S** 🛢️ Cenex/dsl, Phillips 66/Arby's/dsl, Shell, 🍴 Culver's, Denny's, Quiznos, 🛏️ Days Inn, Sleep Inn, 🅾️ 🅷, Menards, UWI
138a	I-94, E to Milwaukee, W to La Crosse, **I-90 W and I-94 W run together for 93 miles, (exits left from EB)**
138b	WI 30, Madison, **S** 😀
135c b	US 151, Madison, **N** 🛢️ BP, 🍴 Erin's Cafe, Happy Wok, Subway, Uno, 🛏️ Courtyard, Fairfield Inn, La Quinta, Staybridge Suites, 🅾️ Buick/GMC, Chevrolet, Chrysler/Dodge/Jeep, Ford/KIA, Hyundai, Nissan, Toyota/Scion
135a	US 151, Madison, **S** 🛢️ BP/24hr, Citgo, Mobil, Shell, 🍴 Applebee's, Arby's, BD Mongolian, Buffalo Wild Wings, Carlos O'Kelly's, Chili's, Chipotle Mexican, Cracker Barrel, Culver's, Denny's, Emperial Garden, Fazoli's, Hardee's, Hooters, IHOP, Jimmy John's, KFC, La Bamba, McDonald's, Milio's, Noodles&Co, Old Country Buffet, Olive Garden, Outback Steaks, Oysy Seafood Buffet, Panera Bread, Perkins, Pizza Hut, Potbelly, Qdoba, Red Lobster, Red Robin, Rocky's Pizza, Schlotzsky's, Subway, Takumi Japanese, TGIFriday's, Tumbleweed Grill, TX Roadhouse, Wendy's, 🛏️ Baymont Inn, Best Western, Comfort Inn, Courtyard, Crowne Plaza Hotel/rest., EconoLodge, Excel Inn, Hampton Inn, Howard Johnson, Microtel, Motel 6, Red Roof Inn, Residence Inn,

Map of Wisconsin showing cities including Hixton, Stevens Point, Amherst, De Pere, Green Bay, Denmark, Millston, Plainfield, Appleton, Sparta, Tomah, Richford, Oshkosh, New Lisbon, Fond du Lac, Plymouth, La Valle, Dekorra, Baraboo, West Bend, Watertown, Madison, Menomonee Falls, New Berlin, Milwaukee, Edgerton, Caledonia, Janesville, Dubuque, Beloit — with Interstate markers 90, 39, 94, 43.

WI

Left margin (I-43): **N ↕ S**, **B E L O I T**, **E ↕ W**, **J A N E S V I L L E**

Right margin: **M A D I S O N**

INTERSTATE 90 CONT'D

Exit	Services
135a	Continued
	Rodeway Inn, Super 8, URGENT CARE, Aldi Foods, AT&T, Barnes&Noble, Best Buy, Dick's, $Tree, Firestone/auto, Gander Mtn, Home Depot, Hy-Vee Foods, JC Penney, JoAnn Fabrics, Kohl's, Marshall's, Menards, Office Depot, Old Navy, Petsmart, Savers, Sears/auto, ShopKO, Tuesday Morning, Verizon, city park, mall, st patrol, vet
132	US 51, Madison, De Forest, N Shell/Pinecone Rest/dsl/24hr, Cousins Subs, Camping World RV Ctr, Gander Mtn, S TA/Mobil/Subway/Taco Bell/dsl/scales/24hr/@, Economy Motel, Goodyear, Peterbilt, Freightliner/GMC/Volvo/White, WI RV World, camping
131	WI 19, Waunakee, N Kwik Trip, Mobil/dsl, Speedway/dsl, A&W, McDonald's, Rodeside Grill, Days Inn, Super 8, Mousehouse Cheesehaus, Kenworth Trucks, Truckwash, fireworks, S Country Inn&Suites (4mi)
126	rd V, De Forest, to Dane, N BP, Phillips 66/Arby's/dsl, Burger King, Culver's, McDonald's, Subway, Holiday Inn Express, Cheese Chalet, KOA, S Citgo, Comfort Inn, dsl repair
119	WI 60, Arlington, to Lodi, S Mobil/Cousins Subs/dsl, A&W, Rococo's Pizza, Best Western
115	rd CS, Poynette, to Lake Wisconsin, N BP/dsl, McDonald's, Subway, Smokey Hollow Camping, dsl truck/trailer repair, motel, trout fishing
113mm	**rest area both lanes, full facilities, , litter barrels, vending, petwalk**
111mm	Wisconsin River
108b a	I-39 N, WI 78, to US 51 N, Portage, N , to WI Dells, S BP, Petro/DQ/Subway/dsl/24hr/@, Comfort Suites, Days Inn, Devil's Head Resort/Conv Ctr, Blue Beacon
106mm	Baraboo River
106	WI 33, Portage, N , S BP, Kamp Dakota, SkyHigh Camping, to Cascade Mtn Ski Area, Devil's Lake SP, Circus World Museum, Wayside Park, motel
92	US 12, to Baraboo, N BP/dsl, Exxon, Mobil/Dunkin Donuts/dsl/24hr, Sinclair/Subway/dsl, Buffalo Phil's Grille, Burger King, Cracker Barrel, Cheese Factory Rest, Culver's, Damon's, Denny's, Domino's, Famous Dave's BBQ, Field's Steaks, Marley's Rest., Mark's Rest, McDonald's, Monk's Grill, Ponderosa, R Place Italian, Sarento's Italian, Wintergreen Grill, Uno, Alakai Hotel, Country Squire Motel, Dell Creek Motel, Grand Marquis Inn, Great Wolf Lodge, Holiday Motel, Holiday Inn Express, Kalahari Resort, Lake Delton Motel, Ramada, Wilderness Hotel, Wintergreen Hotel, URGENT CARE, Broadway Dinner Theater, Kalahari Conv Ctr, Mkt Square Cheese, Tanger Outlets Famous Brands, museum, S Motel 6, , Scenic Traveler RV Ctr, Jellystone Camping, Red Oak Camping, Mirror Lake SP
89	WI 23, Lake Delton, N Phillips 66, Shell/dsl, Brathouse Grill, Denny's Diner, Howie's Rest., KFC, Moosejaw Pizza, EconoLodge, Hilton Garden, Kings Inn, Malibu Inn, Olympia Motel, Crystal Grand Music Theatre, Springbrook Camping, Jellystone Camping, USPO, S McDonald's, Home Depot, Kohl's, Walmart/Subway, Country Roads RV Park

Exit	Services
87	WI 13, Wisconsin Dells, N Citgo, Mobil/Arby's/dsl, Shell, Applebee's, Bunyan's Rest., Burger King, Coldstone, Country Kitchen, Culver's, Denny's, IHOP, Jimmy John's, McDonald's, Mexicali Rose Rest., Perkins, Starbucks, Taco Bell, Wendy's, AmericInn, Best Western, Comfort Inn, Days Inn, Dells Island Resort, Polynesian Hotel, Super 8, KOA, Sherwood Forest Camping, Walgreens, golf, waterpark, info
85	US 12, WI 16, Wisconsin Dells, **0-3 mi** N Crabby's Sea Culver's, Starbucks, Days Inn, Mayflower Motel, American World RV Park/Hotel, KOA, Sherwood Forest Camping, Standing Rock Camping, to Rocky Arbor SP, S BP, Piccadilly's, Arrowhead Camping, Edge-O-the-Dell RV Camping, Summer Breeze Resort
79	rd HH, Lyndon Sta, S BP/Subway/dsl/24hr
76mm	**rest area wb, full facilities, , , litter barrels, vending, petwalk**
74mm	**rest area eb, full facilities, , , litter barrels, vending, petwalk**
69	WI 82, Mauston, N Mauston TP/BP/Taco Bell/24hr, /Wendy's/dsl/scales/24hr, Shell/24hr, China Buffet, Best Western Oasis, Country Inn, Super 8, Carr Valley Cheese, to Buckhorn SP, S KwikTrip/Hearty Platter Rest/dsl/scales/24hr, Mobil, Culver's, Garden Valley Rest., McDonald's, Pizza Hut, Roman Castle Rest., Subway, Alaskan Inn, Best Value Inn, , Buckhorn SP, Buick/Chevrolet, $General, Family$, Festival Foods, K-Mart, Walgreens, vet
61	WI 80, New Lisbon, to Necedah, N Mobil/A&W/Subway/dsl/scales/24hr, Edge O' the Woods Motel, Travelers Inn, Buckhorn SP, Chrysler/Jeep, Ford, fireworks, S KwikTrip/24hr, True Value, Elroy-Sparta ST Tr, city park, USPO
55	rd C, Camp Douglas, N wayside, to Camp Williams, Volk Field, S BP/dsl, Mobil/Subway/dsl, German Haus Rest., K&K Motel, to Mill Bluff SP
49mm	**weigh sta both lanes**
48	rd PP, Oakdale, N Road Ranger//Subway/dsl/scales/24hr, Granger's Camping, KOA, truck/car wash, antiques, S Love's/Hardee's/dsl/scales/24hr, Mill Bluff SP, repair
45	I-94 W, to St Paul
	I-90 E and I-94 E run together for 93 miles
43	US 12, WI 16, Tomah, N BP, KwikTrip/dsl/24hr, Burnstadt's Café, DQ, Daybreak Inn, Rest Well Motel, , Burnstadt's Mkt, vet
41	WI 131, Tomah, to Wilton, N BP, Mobil/dsl, KwikTrip/dsl/24hr, Burnstadts Cafe, Daybreak Inn, vet, S st patrol
28	WI 16, Sparta, Ft McCoy, N BP/diner/dsl/scales, Kwiktrip/dsl, Best Western,
25	WI 27, Sparta, to Melvina, N Casey's, Cenex/dsl, KwikTrip/dsl, Mobil/Taco Bell, Shell/dsl, Burger King, Culver's, DQ, KFC, McDonald's, Pizza Hut, Subway, Country Inn, Super 8, , Buick/Chevrolet, $General, Family$, Ford/Mercury, O'Reilly Parts, Piggly Wiggly, Walgreens, Walmart, S camping
22mm	**rest area wb, full facilities, , , litter barrels, vending, petwalk**
20mm	**rest area eb, full facilities, , , litter barrels, vending, petwalk**

TOMAH

INTERSTATE 90 CONT'D

Exit	Services
15	WI 162, Bangor, to Coon Valley, **N** 🅖, **S** 🅞 Chevrolet
12	rd C, W Salem, **N** 🅖 Cenex/cafe/dsl/24hr, 🅞 Coulee Region RV Ctr, NAPA, Neshonoc Camping, **S** 🅖 BP/Quiznos/dsl, 🛏 AmericInn
10mm	weigh sta eb
5	WI 16, La Crosse, **N** 🍴 Buffalo Wild Wings, Coldstone, Manny's Mexican, Outback Steaks, Quiznos, 🛏 Baymont Inn, Hampton Inn, Microtel, 🅞 Aldi Foods, $Tree, Freightliner, Home Depot, Walmart/Subway, Woodman's Foods/gas/lube, **S** 🅖 Kwik Trip/dsl/24hr, 🍴 Burracho's Mexican Grill, Carlos O'Kelly's, ChuckeCheese, Culver's, Fazoli's, Jimmy John's, McDonald's, Hong Kong Buffet, Old Country Buffet, Olive Garden, Perkins, Starbucks, TGIFriday's, 🛏 Holiday Inn Express, 🅞 H, Barnes&Noble, Best Buy, F&F, Ford/Lincoln/Mercury, Hobby Lobby, JC Penney, Kohl's, Macy's, Michael's, Sears/auto, ShopKO, Target, Walgreens, mall
4	US 53 N, WI 16, to WI 157, La Crosse, **N** 🅞 Harley-Davidson, **S** 🅖 Kwik Trip, TO, 🍴 Applebee's, Burger King, Caribou Coffee, China Inn, El Charro Mexican, Cousins Subs, Famous Dave's BBQ, Grizzly's Rest, Panera Bread, Papa Murphy's, Red Lobster, Rococo's Pizza, Subway, Taco Bell, Wendy's, 🛏 Comfort Inn, 🅞 H, AT&T, Festival Food/24hr, Gander Mtn, GNC, Goodyear/auto, Hancock Fabrics, Office Depot, Old Navy, PetCo, Petsmart, Sam's Club, Tires+, TJ Maxx, Verizon, La Crosse River St Trail
3	US 53 S, WI 35, to La Crosse, **S** 🅖 Citgo, Kwik Trip, 🍴 Burger King, Coney Island, Edwardo's Pizza, Hardee's, KFC, La Crosse Rest., McDonald's, North Country Steaks, Perkins, Pizza Hut, Subway, 🛏 Best Value Inn, Best Western, Brookstone Inn, EconoLodge, Howard Johnson, Settle Inn, Super 8, 🅞 ShopKO, U-Haul, Walgreens, to Great River St Trail, Viterbo Coll
2.5mm	Black River
2	rd B, French Island, **N** 🅞🖼, **S** 🅖 BP/dsl, Kwik Trip, 🛏 Days Hotel/rest, 🅞 IGA Foods
1mm	**Welcome Ctr eb, full** ♿ **facilities, info,** 🚻, 🖼, **litter barrels, vending, petwalk**
0mm	Wisconsin/Minnesota state line, Mississippi River

INTERSTATE 94

Exit	Services
349mm	Wisconsin/Illinois state line, **weigh sta nb**
347	WI 165, rd Q, Lakeview Pkwy, **E** 🅖 BP/dsl, 🍴 Chancery Rest., Culver's, McDonald's, Quiznos, 🛏 Radisson, 🅞 Old Navy, Prime Outlets/famous brands, **Welcome Ctr, full facilities**
345	rd C
345mm	Des Plaines River
344	WI 50, Lake Geneva, to Kenosha, **E** 🍴 Citgo/dsl, Shell/dsl, Woodman's/gas, 🍴 Buffalo Wild Wings, Nick-n-Willy's Pizza, Noodles&Co, Perkins, Pizza Hut, Quiznos, Starbucks, TX Roadhouse, White Castle, 🛏 La Quinta, Super 8, 🅞 H, Best Buy, Gander Mtn, Walgreens, **W** 🅖 BP, Speedway/dsl, 🍴 Arby's, Birchwood Grill, Cracker Barrel, KFC, McDonald's, Pheonix Rest., Taco Bell, Wendy's, 🛏 Best Western, Comfort Suites, Country Inn&Suites, Value Inn, 🅞 BratStop Cheese Store, CarMax, Chevrolet, Honda, Toyota/Scion

Exit	Services
342	WI 158, to Kenosha, **E** Harley-Davidson, **W** antiques
340	WI 142, rd S, to Kenosha, **E** 🅖 Kenosha TP/BP/Subway/dsl/E85/LP/scales/24hr, Mobil/dsl, 🅞 H, **W** 🍴 Mars Cheese Castle Rest., 🛏 Oasis Inn, 🅞 to Bong RA
339	rd E
337	rd KR, to Mt Pleasant, **W** 🍴 Apple Holler Rest.
335	WI 11, to Mt. Pleasant, Burlington, to Racine
333	WI 20, Waterford, to Racine, **E** 🅖 KwikTrip/dsl/24hr, Shell/Cousins Subs/dsl, 🍴 Burger King, McDonald's, 🛏 Holiday Inn Express, Ramada Ltd, 🅞 H, **W** 🅖 Citgo/Wendy's/dsl/24hr, Petro/Mobil/Iron Skillet/dsl/scales/24hr/@, 🍴 Culver's, Spokes Rest., Subway, 🛏 Grandview Inn, 🅞 Burlington RV Ctr, visitor info
329	rd K, Thompsonville, to Racine, **E** 🅖 🖼/Arby's/Subway/dsl/scales/24hr, **W** 🍴 A&W, 🅞 dsl repair
328mm	**weigh sta eb**
327	rd G, **W** fireworks
326	7 Mile Rd, **E** 🅖 BP/24hr, Mobil/dsl/24hr, 🅞 Jellystone Park, **W** 🅞 antiques
325	WI 241 N (from wb), to 27th St
322	WI 100, to Ryan Rd, **E** 🅖 KwikTrip/dsl, 🍴 McDonald's, Wendy's, 🅞 dsl repair, **W** 🅖 Loves/Denny's/dsl/LP/scales/RV dump/24hr, Mobil, 🖼/Subway/dsl/LP/scales/24hr, Shell/A&W/KFC/dsl, 🍴 Arby's, Cousins Subs, Perkins, Starbucks, Yen Hwa Chinese, 🛏 Value Inn, 🅞 Blue Beacon, Freightliner/repair, Pick'n Save, Walgreens
320	rd BB, Rawson Ave, **E** 🅖 BP/24hr, Mobil, 🍴 Applebee's, Burger King, 🛏 La Quinta
319	rd ZZ, College Ave, **E** 🅖 Shell/Subway, Speedway/dsl, 🍴 Branded Steer Rest., Houlihan's, McDonald's, 🛏 Candlewood Suites, Comfort Suites, Country Inn&Suites, Crowne Plaza, Days Inn, EconoLodge, Fairfield Inn, Hampton Inn, Holiday Inn Express, MainStay Suites, Ramada, Red Roof Inn, **W** 🅖 BP/24hr, FoodMart
318	WI 119, **E** 🖼
317	Layton Ave, **E** 🅖 Andy's/dsl, Clark, 🍴 Burger King, Culver's, IHOP, J-Roberts Porterhouse Steaks, Martino's Rest., Prime Qtr Steaks, Wendy's, 🅞 Checker Parts, **W** 🍴 Spring Garden Rest., 🛏 Howard Johnson
316	I-43 S, I-894 W (I-94 exits left from eb), to Beloit
314b	Howard Ave, to Milwaukee, **W** to Alverno Coll
314a	Holt Ave, **E** 🅖 Andy's/dsl, 🍴 Applebee's, Arby's, China King, Little Caesars, Quiznos, Starbucks, Subway, Wendy's, 🅞 $General, Home Depot, Pick'n Save Foods, Sentry Foods, Target, vet, **W** H, to Alverno Coll
312b a	Becher St, Mitchell St, Lapham Blvd, **W** 🅖 Best Petro

INTERSTATE 94 CONT'D

E ↕ W

Exit	Services
311	WI 59, National Ave, 6th St, downtown
310a	13th St (from eb), E [H]
310b	I-43 N, to Green Bay
310c	I-794 E, E [lodging] Hilton, Holiday Inn, [other] to downtown, Lake Michigan Port of Entry
309b	26th St, 22nd St, Clybourn St, St Paul Ave, N [other] [H], to Marquette U
309a	35th St, N [gas] BP, Speedway, [other] URGENT CARE
308c b	US 41
308a	VA Ctr, N [other] Miller Brewing, S [other] Miller Park
307b	68th-70th St, Hawley Rd
307a	68th-70th St, N 68th St, N [other] Valvoline
306	WI 181, to 84th St, N [H], S [other] Olympic Training Facility
305b	US 45 N, to Fond du Lac, N [H]
305a	I-894 S, US 45 S, to Chicago to [airport]
304b a	WI 100, N [gas] Mobil, OP, Shell/dsl, [food] Caribou Coffee, Cousins Subs, Edwardo's Pizza, Ghengis Khan BBQ, Habanero's Mexican, HoneyBaked Cafe, Jimmy John's, Mo's Irish Grill, Peony Chinese, Qdoba, Starbucks, Taco Bell, [lodging] 40 Winks Inn, Super 8, [other] [H], zoo, S [gas] Mini-Mart 100, Mobil, Speedway/dsl, [food] Culver's, DQ, Fazoli's, McDonald's, Starbucks, Wendy's, [lodging] Days Inn, [other] CarX, O'Reilly Parts, Sam's Club, U-Haul, Walgreens
301b a	Moorland Rd, N [gas] BP, [food] Bakers Square, Bravo Italiano, Chicago Grill, Claim Jumper, Fleming's Rest., McDonald's, Mitchell's Fish Mkt, [lodging] Sheraton, [other] Barnes&Noble, JC Penney, Sears/auto, Walgreens, mall, vet, **N on US 18** [gas] Mobil, [food] Caribou Coffee, Chili's, Fuddrucker's, Hooters, Noodles&Co, Old Country Buffet, Qdoba, Starbucks, Stir Crazy, TGIFriday's, [lodging] Courtyard, TownePlace Suites, [other] CVS Drug, Fresh Mkt Foods, Goodyear/auto, Jo-Ann Fabrics, Metro Mkt, Michael's, Office Depot, PetCo, Petsmart, SteinMart, TJ Maxx, World Mkt, S [food] Champp's Grill, Charcoal Grill, Maxwell's Rest., Panera Bread, Outback Steaks, [lodging] Best Western Midway, Brookfield Suites, Country Inn&Suites, Residence Inn, [other] Pick'n Save Foods, Walgreens, golf
297	US 18, rd JJ, Blue Mound Rd, Barker Rd, **0-2 mi N** [gas] BP/24hr, Clark, [food] Applebee's, BoneFish Grill, Boston Mkt, Brookfield Rest., Carrabba's, ChuckeCheese, Cousin's Subs, HoneyBaked Ham, Jose's Mexican, KFC, Kopp's Custard, McDonald's, Melting Pot, Olive Garden, Perkins, Subway, [lodging] DoubleTree, Hampton Inn, Homestead Suites, La Quinta, Motel 6, Quality Inn, [other] Acura, Advance Parts, Aldi Foods, Best Buy, K-Mart, Lexus/Mazda/VW, S [gas] Clark, F&F/dsl, PDQ, [food] Albanese's Italian, Arby's, Burger King, Cousin's Subs, Famous Dave's BBQ, McDonald's, Milio's, Oscar's Rest, Papa Murphy's, Sonic, Starbucks, Taco Bell, TX Roadhouse, Topper's Pizza, Wendy's, [lodging] Extended Stay America, Ramada Ltd, Super 8, [other] AT&T, Cadillac/GMC, CarMax, CarX, Chevrolet, Firestone/auto, Ford/Lincoln/Mercury, Gander Mtn, Home Depot, Honda, Hyundai, Infiniti/Porsche, KIA, Kohl's, Land Rover, Maserati, Menards, Mercedes, Nissan, Pick'n Save Foods, Sam's Club, Target, Tires+, Volvo, Walgreens, st patrol
295	rd F, to WI 74, Waukesha, N [gas] KwikTrip, [food] Jimmy John's, [lodging] Marriott, S [other] [H], to Carroll Coll
294	WI 164, rd J S, to Waukesha, N [gas] Mobil, [food] Machine Shed Rest., Thunder Bay Grille, [lodging] Comfort Suites,

WAUKESHA

Exit	Services
294	Continued Radisson, S [other] Expo Ctr, Peterbilt
293c	WI 16 W, Pewaukee (from wb), N [other] GE Plant
293b a	rd T, Wausheka, Pewaukee, S [gas] Mobil, KwikTrip, [food] Arby's, Canyon City Wood Grill, Caribou Coffee, Cousins Subs, Culver's, Denny's, Garibaldi Mexican, McDonald's, Mr. Wok, Papa Murphy's, Peking House, Qdoba, Rococo's Pizza, Spring City Rest., Subway, Taco Amigo, Topper's Pizza, Weissgerber's Gasthaus Rest., Wendy's, [lodging] Best Western, [other] AutoZone, CVS Drug, $Tree, Firestone/auto, GNC, Goodharvest Mkt, Jo-Ann Fabrics, Office Depot, Pick'n Save Foods, Radio Shack, Walgreens
291	rd G, N [lodging] Country Springs Inn, S [gas] BP
290	rd SS
287	WI 83, Hartland, to Wales, N [food] Applebee's, Emperor's Kitchen, 5 Guys Burgers, Hardee's, McDonald's, Noodles&Co, Panera Bread, Perkins, Qdoba, Starbucks, Water St Brewery/rest., [lodging] Country Pride Inn, Holiday Inn Express, [other] Amish Barn Gifts, Best Buy, GNC, Kohl's, Marshall's, Radio Shack, Sentry Foods, Verizon, Walgreens, S [gas] BP/dsl/24hr, PDQ/dsl/24hr, [food] Burger King, Coldstone, Delafield Bewhaus, DQ, Jimmy John's, Marty's Pizza, Pacific Asian Bistro, Pizza Hut, StoneCreek Coffee, Subway, [lodging] La Quinta, [other] Ace Hardware, $Tree, Home Depot, PetCo, Target, Tires+, Walmart, vet
285	rd C, Delafield, N [gas] BP, Mobil/deli, [lodging] Delafield Hotel, [other] to St John's Military Academy, S [other] to Kettle Moraine SF
283	rd P, to Sawyer Rd (from wb, no re-entry)
282	WI 67, Dousman, to Oconomowoc, **0-2 mi N** [gas] BP, KwikTrip/dsl, [food] Chili's, Cousins Subs, Culver's, Nick-N-Willy's Pizza, Pizza Hut, Quiznos, Rococo's Pizza, Schlotzsky's, Starbucks, Stone Creek Coffee, Subway, [lodging] Hilton Garden, Olympia Resort, [other] URGENT CARE, Ace Hardware, Aldi Foods, AT&T, Brennan's Mkt, K-Mart, Pick'n Save, Radio Shack, Walgreens, S [lodging] Staybridge Suites, [other] [H], Harley-Davidson, vet, to Kettle Morraine SF (8mi), Old World WI HS (13mi)
277	Willow Glen Rd (from eb, no return)
275	rd F, Ixonia, to Sullivan, N [gas] BP/dsl, [other] Concord Gen Store, S camping
267	WI 26, Johnson Creek, to Watertown, N [gas] BP/McDonald's/dsl, Shell/dsl/rest./scales/24hr, [food] Arby's, Hwy Harry's Cafe, [lodging] Days Inn, JC Plaza Hotel, [other] Goodyear/auto, Johnson Creek Outlet Ctr/famous brands, Old Navy, S [gas] KwikTrip/dsl, [food] Culver's, Subway, [other] [H], Kohl's, Menards, to Aztalan SP
266mm	Rock River
264mm	**rest area wb, full [handicapped] facilities, [phone], [picnic], litter barrels, vending, petwalk**
263mm	Crawfish River
261mm	**rest area eb, full [handicapped] facilities, [phone], [picnic], litter barrels, vending, petwalk**
259	WI 89, Lake Mills, to Waterloo, N [gas] Citgo/dsl/24hr, [lodging] Best Value Inn, [other] truck repair, S [gas] BP/dsl/E85/24hr, KwikTrip/dsl/24hr, [food] Jimmy John's, McDonald's, Pizza Pit, Subway, [lodging] Pyramid Motel/RV park, [other] URGENT CARE, Ace Hardware, Buick/Chevrolet, Walgreens, to Aztalan SP
250	WI 73, Deerfield, to Marshall

MADISON

WI

WI

INTERSTATE 94 CONT'D

Exit	Services
244	rd N, Sun Prairie, Cottage Grove, **N** 🅿 KwikTrip, **S** 🅿 BP, 🍴 Arby's, Subway
240	I-90 E.
	I-94 and I-90 run together 93 miles. See Interstate 90, exits 48-138.
147	I-90 W, to La Crosse
143	US 12, WI 21, Tomah, **N** 🅿 Mobil/dsl, 🍴 A&W/LJ Silver, 4Star Rest., Perkins, 🏠 AmericInn, Holiday Inn, Microtel, Super 8, 🅾 Humbird Cheese/gifts, truckwash, **S** 🅿 BP, KwikTrip/rest./dsl/scales/24hr, 🍴 Arby's, China Buffet, Culver's, Ground Round, KFC, McDonald's, Pizza Hut, Subway, Taco Bell, 🏠 Comfort Inn, Cranberry Suites, EconoLodge, Hampton Inn, 🅾 🅷, Advance Parts, Aldi Foods, $Tree, U-Haul, Walmart, to Ft McCoy (9mi), **S on US 12** 🍴 Burger King, 🅾 Ace Hardware, Buick/Chevrolet, Chrysler/Dodge/Jeep, Curves, Firestone/auto, Ford, O'Reilly Parts, Radio Shack
135	rd EW, Warrens, **N** 🅿 Cenex, 🏠 3 Bears Resort, 🅾 Jellystone Camping, **S** 🍴 Bog Rest.
128	rd O, Millston, **N** 🅾 Black River SF, camping, **S** 🅿 Cenex/dsl, 🅾 USPO
123mm	**rest area/scenic view both lanes, full 🅿 facilities, 🅲, 🚻, litter barrels, vending, petwalk**
116	WI 54, **N** 🅿 Cenex/Subway/Taco Johns/dsl/LP, 🍴 Perkins, 🏠 Best Western Arrowhead/rest., Comfort Inn, Super 8, 🅾 Black River RA, Parkland Camp, casino, **S** 🅿 ⓕFLYING J/Denny's/dsl/24hr/@, KwikTrip/dsl, 🍴 Burger King, Culver's, McDonald's, Oriental Kitchen, Pizza Hut, Subway, 🏠 Days Inn, 🅾 Buick/Chevrolet/GMC, $General, Walmart
115mm	Black River
115	US 12, Black River Falls, to Merrillan, **S** 🅿 BP, Holiday/dsl, 🍴 Hardee's, KFC, Subway, Sunrise Rest., 🅾 🅷, Ace Hardware, Harley-Davidson, NAPA, vet
105	to WI 95, Hixton, to Alma Center, **N** 🏠 Motel 95/campground, 🅾 KOA (3mi), **S** 🅿 Cenex/dsl, Clark/dsl/24hr, 🍴 Timber Valley Rest., 🅾 city park
98	WI 121, Northfield, Pigeon Falls, to Alma Center, **S** 🅿 Cenex/dsl, 🍴 DeeDee's Diner, Northfield Cafe
88	US 10, Osseo, to Fairchild, **N** 🅿 BP/DQ, Mobil/dsl, Shell/Elderberry's/dsl/scales, 🍴 Hardee's, Moe's Diner, 🏠 10-7 Inn, Super 8, 🅾 Chevrolet, Ford, Stoney Cr RV Park, **S** 🅿 Speedway/dsl, 🍴 McDonald's, Subway, Taco John's, 🏠 Osseo Inn, 🅾 🅷, Family$
81	rd HH, rd KK, Foster, **S** 🅿 BP/dsl/LP, 🍴 Foster Cheesehaus
70	US 53, Eau Claire, **N off Golf Rd** 🅿 Mobil/dsl, 🍴 A&W, Applebee's, Asia Palace, Buffalo Wild Wings, Burracho's Mexican, Coldstone, Culver's, Fazoli's, Grizzly's Grill, Jade Garden, Manny's Grill, McDonald's, Noodles&Co, Olive Garden, Panera Bread, TX Roadhouse, TGIFriday's, 🏠 Country Inn&Suites, Grandstay, Heartland Inn, 🅾 Aldi Foods, AT&T, Best Buy, JC Penney, Jo-Ann Fabrics, Kohl's, Macy's, Menards, Michael's, Office Depot, PetCo, Petsmart, Sam's Club, Scheel's Sports, Sears/auto, Target, TJ Maxx, Verizon, Walmart/Subway, Younkers, mall, **S** 🅾 Gander Mtn, st police
68	WI 93, to Eleva, **N** 🅿 BP, Holiday, KwikTrip/dsl, 🍴 Burger King, DQ, Quiznos, Red Robin, 🏠 EconoLodge, 🅾 BigLots, Chrysler/Dodge/Jeep, Festival Foods,

Exit	Services
68	**Continued** Firestone/auto, Goodyear/auto, NAPA, Nissan, Subaru, Suzuki, US RV Ctr, transmissions, vet, **S** 🅿 Holiday/dsl, 🅾 Audi/VW, Ford/Lincoln/Mercury, Honda, Hyundai, KIA
65	WI 37, WI 85, Eau Claire, to Mondovi, **N** 🅿 BP, Exxon, Holiday/dsl, KwikTrip/dsl, 🍴 Arby's, China Buffet, Godfather's Pizza, Green Mill Rest., Hardee's, Jimmy John's, McDonald's, Pizza Hut, Randy's Rest., Red Lobster, Sonic, Starbucks, Subway, Taco Bell, Wendy's, 🏠 Best Value Inn, Best Western, Comfort Inn, Country Hearth Inn, Days Inn/rest., Hampton Inn, Highlander Inn, Holiday Inn/rest., Super 8, 🅾 🅷, Castle Foods, Radio Shack, ShopKo, Toyota/Scion, Walgreens
64mm	Chippewa River
59	to US 12, rd EE, to Eau Claire, **N** 🅿 Holiday/Burger King/dsl/24hr, Holiday/Subway/dsl/24hr, 🍴 Dana's Grill, Exit 59 Rest., McDonald's, 🏠 AmericInn, Days Inn, Knights Inn, 🅾 🅷, Freightliner, Mack/Volvo Trucks, Peterbilt, auto repair/towing, **S** 🅾 US RV Ctr, dsl repair
52	US 12, WI 29, WI 40, Elk Mound, to Chippewa Falls, **S** 🅿 U-Fuel/E85
49mm	weigh sta wb
45	rd B, Menomonie, **N** 🅿 Cenex/Subway/dsl/scales/24hr, **S** 🅿 KwikTrip/dsl/scales/24hr, 🍴 Around The Clock/24hr, 🏠 Quality Inn, 🅾 🅷, AOK RV Ctr, Kenworth, Walmart Dist Ctr, dsl repair, truckwash
44mm	Red Cedar River
43mm	**rest areas both lanes, full 🅿 facilities, 🅲, 🚻, litter barrels, vending, petwalk, weather info**
41	WI 25, Menomonie, **N** 🅿 Cenex/E85, 🍴 Applebee's, Caribou Coffee, China Buffet, Los Cabos Mexican, Pizza Hut, Subway, 🅾 🅷, Aldi Foods, AT&T, $Tree, Radio Shack, Walmart, Twin Springs Camping, **S** 🅿 F&F/dsl, Holiday, SA/dsl, 🍴 Arby's, Jimmy John's, McDonald's, Perkins, Sparx Rest., Taco Bell, Taco John's, Wendy's, 🏠 AmericInn, Country Inn&Suites, EconoLodge, Motel 6, Super 8, 🅾 Advance Parts, Chevrolet, Chrysler/Dodge/Jeep, K-Mart, Mkt Place Foods, O'Reilly Parts, Walgreens, to Red Cedar St Tr
32	rd Q, to Knapp
28	WI 128, Wilson, Elmwood, to Glenwood City, **N** 🅿 KwikTrip/rest./dsl/24hr, **S** 🅾 Eau Galle RA, camping, dsl repair
24	rd B, to Baldwin, **N** 🅿 BP, 🏠 Woodville Motel, **S** 🅾 Eau Galle RA, camping
19	US 63, Baldwin, to Ellsworth, **N** 🅿 Freedom/dsl, KwikTrip/Subway/dsl, 🍴 A&W, DQ, Hardee's, McDonald's, 🏠 AmericInn, 🅾 🅷, **S** 🅿 Mobil/rest./dsl, 🏠 Super 8,

T O M A H

E → W

E A U   C L A I R E

M E N O M O N I E

INTERSTATE 94 CONT'D

Exit	Services
19	Continued 🔲 fireworks
16	rd T, Hammond
10	WI 65, Roberts, to New Richmond, **2 mi N** 🛢 BP/dsl, 🍴 Barn Board Rest.
8mm	**weigh sta eb**
4	US 12, rd U, Somerset, **N** 🛢 BP/dsl, TA/Country Pride/ dsl/scales/24hr/@, 🍴 Rich's Eatery, 🛏 Best Value Inn, 🔲 vet, to Willow River SP, **S** 🔲 Curves
3	WI 35 S, to River Falls, U of WI River Falls
2	rd F, Carmichael Rd, Hudson, **N** 🛢 BP/repair, Freedom/ dsl, Holiday/dsl, 🍴 Applebee's, Caribou Coffee, Cousins Subs, Culver's, KFC, La Fiesta Mexicana,

HUDSON

2	Continued Papa Murphy's, Taco John's, 🛏 Royal Inn, 🔲 Family Fresh Foods, GNC, Radio Shack, Target, repair, **S** 🛢 F&F/dsl, Holiday, KwikTrip/dsl, Shell, 🍴 Arby's, Buffalo Wild Wings, Burger King, Chipotle Mexican, Denny's, Green Mill Rest., McDonald's, Pizza Hut, Perkins, Starbucks, Subway, Taco Bell, Wendy's, 🛏 Best Western, Fairfield Inn, Holiday Inn Express, Quality Inn, Super 8, 🔲 ⒽAldi Foods, Chevrolet/GMC, Chrysler/Dodge/ Jeep, County Mkt Foods, Ford/Mercury, Home Depot, Menards, NAPA, O'Reilly Parts, TireProz, Tires+, Verizon, Walmart, USPO, to Kinnickinnic SP
1	WI 35 N, Hudson, **1 mi N** 🛢 Freedom/dsl, Holiday, 🍴 DQ
0mm	Wisconsin/Minnesota state line, St Croix River

WYOMING

INTERSTATE 25

Exit	Services
300	I-90, E to Gillette, W to Billings. I-25 begins/ends on I-90, exit 56.
299	US 16, Buffalo, **E** 🛢 Cenex, Exxon/dsl, Maverik/dsl, 🍴 Winchester Steaks, 🛏 Comfort Inn, Hampton Inn, Holiday Inn Express, Motel 6, 🔲 Bighorn Tire, Deer Park Camping, NAPA, vet, **W** 🛢 Bighorn/Shell/dsl/24hr, Cenex/rest/dsl/24hr, 🍴 Bozeman Tr Steaks, Dash Inn Rest., Hardee's, McDonald's, Pizza Hut, Sub Shop, Subway, Taco John's, 🛏 Best Western Crossroads, EconoLodge, WYO Motel, Super 8, 🔲 Ⓗ Ace Hardware, Family$, Indian RV Camp, Verizon
298	US 87, Buffalo, **W** Nat Hist Dist Info
291	Trabing Rd
280	Middle Fork Rd
274mm	parking area both lanes, litter barrels
265	Reno Rd
254	Kaycee, **E** 🛢 Exxon/dsl, 🍴 Country Inn Diner, Invasion Rest., 🛏 Cassidy Inn Motel, Siesta Motel, 🔲 Kaycee Gen. Store, NAPA Repair, Powder River RV Park, USPO, museum, **W rest area both lanes, full** ♿ **facilities,** 🚽, 🚮, **litter barrels, petwalk,** 🛢 Sinclair/dsl/LP/motel, 🔲 KC RV Park
249	TTT Rd
246	Powder River Rd
235	Tisdale Mtn Rd
227	WY 387 N, Midwest, Edgerton, **E** Oil Field Museum
223	no services
219mm	parking area both lanes, litter barrels
216	Ranch Rd
210	Horse Ranch Creek Rd, Midwest, Edgerton
197	Ormsby Rd
191	Wardwell Rd, to Bar Nunn, **W** 🛢 Loaf'N Jug/dsl, 🔲 KOA
189	US 20, US 26 W, to Shoshone Port of Entry, 🖂
188b	WY 220, Poplar St, **E** 🍴 El Jarro Mexican, Sideline BBQ, 🛏 Best Western, Hampton Inn, Hilton Garden, La Quinta, Motel 6, Quality Inn, **W** 🛢 Exxon, 🍴 Burger King, Casper's Rest., DQ, 🔲 Harley-Davidson, to Ft Casper HS
188a	Center St, Casper, **E** 🛢 Conoco/dsl, Shell/dsl, 🍴 Poor Boys Steaks, Taco John's, 🛏 National 9 Inn, Ramada,

BUFFALO   N ↕ S   CASPER

188a	Continued Showboat Motel, **W** 🛏 Days Inn, Parkway Plaza Motel, 🔲 USPO
187	McKinley St, Casper, **E** 🛢 Loaf'N Jug/dsl, 🛏 Ranch House Motel, 🔲 repair/transmissons
186	US 20, US 26, US 87, Yellowstone St, **E** 🔲 Audi/VW, Porsche, dsl repair, **W** 🛢 Exxon, 🔲 Ⓗ Chevrolet/Subaru, O'Reilly Parts, Toyota
185	WY 258, Wyoming Blvd, E Casper, **E** 🛢 Kum&Go/dsl, Loaf'n Jug/dsl, 🍴 Applebee's, IHOP, Outback Steaks, 🛏 C'mon Inn, Comfort Inn, Shilo Inn, Super 8, 🔲 Smith RV Ctr, RV camping, **W** 🛢 Exxon/dsl, ⚡FLYING J/Conoco/Subway/dsl/LP/scales/24hr, Loaf'n Jug, 🍴 Arby's, Burger King, DQ, Hardee's, HomeTown Buffet, KFC/LJ Silver, McDonald's, Mongolian Grill, Old Chicago Grill, Olive Garden, On The Border, Perkins, Pizza Hut, Sanford's Cafe, Starbucks, Taco Bell, Taco John's, Village Inn, Wendy's, 🛏 Coutyard, 1st Interstate Motel, Holiday Inn Express, 🔲 AutoZone, Best Buy, Home Depot, JC Penney, K-Mart, Macy's, PetCo, Plains Tire, Safeway Foods/gas, Sam's Club/gas, Sears/auto, Staples, Target, Verizon, Walgreens, Walmart, to Oregon Tr, mall
182	WY 253, Brooks Rd, Hat Six Rd, **E** 🛢 Sinclair/Chesterfried/Lou's Rest/dsl, 🛏 Sleep Inn, 🔲 to Wilkins SP, **W** 🍴 Firerock Rest., 🛏 Holiday Inn, Mainstay Suites, 🔲 Ⓗ Buick/Cadillac/GMC, Chrysler/Dodge/Jeep, Menards
171mm	parking area both lanes, litter barrels
165	Glenrock, same as 160
160	US 87, US 20, US 26, E Glenrock, **E** 🛏 All American Inn, Hotel Higgins B&B, Paisley Shawl, 🔲 Deer Creek Village Camping, to Johnston Power Plant
156	Bixby Rd
154	Barber Rd
153mm	parking area both lanes, litter barrels
151	Natural Bridge
150	Inez Rd
146	La Prele Rd
140	WY 59, Douglas, **E** 🛢 Conoco/Subway/dsl, Maverik/dsl, 🍴 Arby's, La Costa Mexican, McDonald's, Taco John's, 🛏 Best Western, Holiday Inn Express, Sleep Inn, Super 8, 🔲 Ⓗ Chrysler/Dodge/Jeep, Ford, KOA, Lone Tree Village RV Park, Pioneer Museum, WY St Fair,

CASPER   DOUGLAS

WI / WY

D O U G L A S N ↑↓ S	**INTERSTATE 25 CONT'D**

INTERSTATE 25 CONT'D

Exit	Services
140	Continued city park
135	US 20, US 26, US 87, Douglas, E 📳 Sinclair/dsl/rest., 🛏 1st Interstate Inn, Motel 6, 🅾 auto repair, **1-2 mi** E 📳 Loaf'n Jug, Sinclair/dsl, 🍴 4 Seasons Chinese, KFC, Pizza Hut, Plains Trading Post Rest., Taco Bell, Village Inn, 🛏 4 Winds Motel, 🅾 H, Douglas Hardware, Family$, Frontier Drug, O'Reilly Parts, Pamida, Radio Shack, Safeway Foods
129mm	parking area both lanes
126	US 18, US 20 E, Orin, E Orin Jct **Rest Area both lanes, full** 🦽 **facilities,** 🚻s, 🚮, **litter barrels, petwalk, RV dump,** 📳 Sinclair/Orin Jct Trkstp/dsl/café
125mm	N Platte River
111	Glendo, E 📳 Sinclair/dsl, 🍴 Glendo Marina Café, 🛏 Howard's Motel, 🅾 to Glendo SP, Glendo Lakeside RV camping
104	to Middle Bear
100	Cassa Rd
94	El Rancho Rd
92	US 26 E, Dwyer, E **rest area both lanes, full** 🦽 **facilities,** 🚮, **litter barrel, petwalk, RV dump to Guernsey SP, Ft Laramie NHS**
87	Johnson Rd
84	Laramie River Rd
84mm	Laramie River
80	US 87, Laramie Power Sta, Wheatland, Laramie Power Sta, E 📳 Sinclair/A&W/Chester's/dsl, 🍴 Pizza Hut, 🛏 Best Western, Super 8, 🅾 Buick/Cadillac/Chevrolet, CarQuest, Chrysler/Dodge/Jeep, Family$, Ford/Mercury, Pamida/drug, Safeway Foods, Arrowhead RV Park, same as 78
78	US 87, Wheatland, E 📳 Cenex/dsl, Maverik/dsl, Shell/

	C H E Y E N N E

Exit	Services
78	Continued dsl, 🍴 Arby's, Burger King, Subway, Taco John's, Wheatland Rest., 🛏 Motel 6, Vimbo's Motel/rest., West Winds Motel, 🅾 H, Wheatland Country Store, visitors ctr, W 📳 Exxon/dsl, Pitstop/dsl, 🅾 Radio Shack, Mtn View RV Park
73	WY 34 W, to Laramie
70	Bordeaux Rd
68	Antelope Rd
66	Hunton Rd
65.5mm	parking area both lanes, litter barrels
65	Slater Rd
64mm	Richeau Creek
57	TY Basin Rd, Chugwater
54	Lp 25, Chugwater, E 📳 Sinclair/dsl, 🛏 Buffalo Lodge/ Grill, 🅾 RV camping, **rest area both lanes, full** 🦽 **facilities,** 🚻, 🚮, **litter barrels, petwalk, RV dump**
47	Bear Creek Rd
39	Little Bear Community
36mm	Little Bear Creek
34	Nimmo Rd
33mm	Horse Creek
29	Whitaker Rd
25	ranch exit
21	Ridley Rd
17	US 85 N, to Torrington, W 🍴 Little Bear Rest. (2mi)
16	WY 211, Horse Creek Rd
13	Vandehei Ave, E 📳 Loaf'n Jug/Subway, 🍴 Silvermine Subs, W 📳 Shamrock/dsl
12	Central Ave, Cheyenne, E 📳 Exxon/dsl, 🛏 Rodeway Inn, 🅾 H, Frontier Days Park, museum, E **on Yellow- stone Rd** 📳 Loaf'n Jug, 🍴 Arby's, Godfather's, Great Harvest Bread, McDonald's, Pizza Hut, Subway, Taco John's, 🅾 Albertsons, Big O Tire
11b	Warren AFB, Gate 1, Randall Ave, E 🅾 to WY St Capi- tol, museum

= gas   = food   = lodging   = other   Copyright 2012 - The Next Exit®

INTERSTATE 25 CONT'D

Exit	Services
10b d	Warren AFB, Gate 2, Missile Dr, WY 210, HappyJack Rd, W ⊙ to Curt Gowdy SP
9	US 30, W Lincolnway, Cheyenne, E Exxon/Crossroads Cafe/dsl, Denny's, Outback Steaks, Village Inn, Candlewood Suites, Days Inn, Express Inn, Hampton Inn, Holiday Inn Express, La Quinta, Luxury Inn, Microtel, Motel 6, Super 8, ⊙ Buick/Cadillac/GMC, Chevrolet, Ford/Lincoln/Mercury, Home Depot, Honda, Hyundai, Mazda, Nissan, Subaru, Toyota, W Little America/Sinclair/dsl/rest./motel/@
8d b	I-80, E to Omaha, W to Laramie
7	WY 212, College Dr, E Loves/Wendy's/dsl/scales/24hr/@, Shamrock/Subway/dsl/24hr, Arby's, ⊙ A-B RV Park (2mi), Bailey Tire, Truck Repair, W **WY Info Ctr/ rest area both lanes, full** facilities, , , **litter barrels, petwalk**, FLYING J/Denny's/dsl/LP/scales/24hr/@, McDonald's, Comfort Inn
6.5mm	Port of Entry, nb
2	Terry Ranch Rd, **2 mi E** Terry Bison Ranch RV camping
0mm	Wyoming/Colorado state line

INTERSTATE 80

Exit	Services
402mm	Wyoming/Nebraska State line
401	WY 215, Pine Bluffs, N Cenex/A&W/dsl/24hr/@, Conoco/Subway/dsl, Race Track/rest./dsl, Sinclair/dsl, Rikachee's Cafe, Gator's Motel, ⊙ NAPA, USPO, Pine Bluff RV Park, S **Welcome Ctr/rest area both lanes, full** facilities, **info**, , **playground, nature trail**, , **litter barrels, petwalk**
391	Egbert
386	WY 213, WY 214, Burns, N Antelope Trkstp/dsl/cafe
377	WY 217, Hillsdale, N TA/Burger King/Taco Bell/dsl/scales/24hr/@, ⊙ Wyo RV Camping
372mm	Port of Entry wb, truck insp
370	US 30 W, Archer, N Sapp Bros/Spirit/T-Joe's Rest./dsl/scales/24hr/@, ⊙ fireworks, repair, RV park
367	Campstool Rd, N /Subway/dsl/scales/24hr, Sleep Inn, ⊙ KOA (seasonal), S ⊙ to Wyoming Hereford Ranch
364	WY 212, to E Lincolnway, Cheyenne, **1-2 mi N on Lincoln way** Exxon, Loaf'n Jug/Subway, Valero, Burger King, IHOP, KFC, McDonald's, Shari's Rest., Subway, Taco Bell, Wendy's, ⊙ , AutoZone, BigLots, Big O Tire, $Tree, Family$, Harley-Davidson, Hobby Lobby, Sierra Trading Post, Walgreens, S ⊙ AB Camping (4mi), Peterbilt
362	US 85, I-180, to Central Ave, Cheyenne, Greeley, **1 mi N** Kum&Go/dsl, Sinclair, Arby's, Carls' Jr, Guadalajara Mexican, Hacienda Mexican, Jimmy John's, Papa John's, Quiznos, Village Inn, ⊙ CarQuest, museum, st capitol, S Exxon/Domino's/dsl, Shamrock/dsl, Burger King, Taco John's, Little Caesar's, Pizza Hut, Sonic, Subway, Holiday Inn, Roundup Motel, SpringHill Suites, ⊙ , Family$, Safeway Foods/gas, RV camping, transmissions
359c a	I-25, US 87, N to Casper, S to Denver
358	US 30, W Lincolnway, Cheyenne, N Exxon/dsl/24hr, Little America/Sinclair/dsl/motel/@, Denny's, Outback Steaks, Pizza Inn, Village Inn, Days Inn,

358	Continued EconoLodge, Express Inn, Hampton Inn, Hitching Post Inn, Holiday Inn Express, La Quinta, Luxury Inn, Motel 6, Super 8, ⊙ , Chevrolet, Home Depot, Honda
357	Wy 222, Roundtop Rd
348	Otto Rd
345	Warren Rd, N truck parking
342	Harriman Rd
341mm	parking area both lanes
339	Remount Rd
335	Buford, S Buford Trading Post/Cenex/dsl/24hr
333mm	point of interest, parking area both lanes
329	Vedeauwoo Rd, N camping, S to Ames Monument, Nat Forest RA
323	WY 210, Happy Jack Rd, **N rest area both lanes, full** facilities, , , **litter barrels, petwalk, Lincoln Monument, elev. 8640**, to Curt Gowdy SP
322mm	chain up area both lanes
316	US 30 W, Grand Ave, Laramie, **0-2 mi N** Exxon, Loaf'N Jug, Applebee's, Arby's, Bailey's Rest., Burger King, Carl's Jr, Chili's, Godfather's Pizza, Hong Kong Buffet, Jimmy John's, McAlister's Deli, McDonald's, Papa Murphy's, Perkins, Quizno's, Sonic, Subway, Taco Bell, Taco John's, Village Inn, Wendy's, Winger's, AmericInn, Comfort Inn, Hampton Inn, Hilton Garden, Holiday Inn, ⊙ , Albertsons/Osco/gas, Buick/Cadillac/Chevrolet/GMC, $Tree, Ford/Lincoln/Mercury, Staples, Toyota, Walmart, conf. ctr, to UW
313	US 287, to 3rd St, Laramie, Port of Entry, N Gas-o-Mat, Loaf'N Jug, Exxon, Phillips 66/dsl, Shell/dsl, Chuck Wagon Rest., Corona Village Mexican, Great Wall Chinese, 1st Inn Gold, Motel 8, Sunset Inn, ⊙ , Laramie Plains Museum, NAPA, Nissan, USPO, S Motel 6, Ramada Inn
312mm	Laramie River
311	WY 130, WY 230, Snowy Range Rd, Laramie, S Conoco/dsl, Phillips 66/dsl, Sinclair/dsl/LP, McDonald's, Subway, Best Value Inn, Howard Johnson, to Snowy Range Ski Area, WY Terr Park
310	Curtis St, Laramie, N /Wendy's/dsl/scales/24hr, Shamrock/café/dsl, Best Western, Days Inn, EconoLodge, Super 8, ⊙ , KOA, repair/tires, S Petro/Iron Skillet/dsl/scales/24hr/@, Blue Beacon, Fairfield Inn, Quality Inn
307mm	parking area both lanes, litter barrels
297	WY 12, Herrick Lane
290	Quealy Dome Rd, S A&C Truckstop/dsl
279	Cooper Cove Rd
272mm	Rock Creek
272	WY 13, to Arlington, N gas, RV camping
267	Wagonhound Rd, S **rest area both lanes, full** facilities, , , **litter barrels, petwalk**
262mm	parking area both lanes
260	CR 402
259mm	Medicine Bow River, E Fork
257mm	Medicine Bow River
255	WY 72, Elk Mtn, to Hanna, N Conoco/dsl, S Elk Mtn Hotel/rest
238	Peterson Rd
235	WY 130, S US 30/87, N Shell/Cafe/dsl
229mm	N Platte River
228	Ft Steele HS, **N rest area both lanes, full** facilities, , , **litter barrels, petwalk**

CHEYENNE ← N S → ← E W → **CHEYENNE**

LARAMIE

WY

WY

INTERSTATE 80 CONT'D

Exit	Services
221	E Sinclair, N 📶 Phillips 66/rest/dsl/24hr, 🅾 to Seminoe SP, camping
219	W Sinclair, N 🅾 to Seminoe SP, camping
215	Cedar St, Rawlins, N 📶 Conoco/dsl, Phillips 66/dsl, Shell/KFC/Taco Bell/dsl, Sinclair, 🍴 China House, McDonald's, Pizza Hut, Subway, Taco John's, 🛏 Comfort Inn, Days Inn, 1st Choice Inn, Hampton Inn, Holiday Inn Express, Quality Inn, OakTree Inn, The Key Motel, 🅾 Alco, Buick/Chevrolet/GMC, CarQuest, Checker Parts, Chrysler/Dodge/Jeep, City Mkt Food/gas, Do-It Hardware, Firestone/auto, Pamida, TDS Tire, museum, Frontier Prison NHS, to Yellowstone/Teton NP
214	Higley Blvd, Rawlins, N 🛏 Microtel, 🅾 KOA, S 📶 TA/Shell/Subway/dsl/scales/24hr/@, 🛏 Best Value Inn
211	WY 789, to US 287 N, Spruce St, Rawlins, N 📶 Conoco/dsl, Exxon/dsl, Loaf'n Jug, Phillips 66/dsl, Sinclair/dsl, 🍴 Cappy's Rest., 🛏 Best Western, Budget Inn, EconoLodge, Express Inn, Knights Inn, La Bella, Super 8, Sunset Motel, Travelodge, 🅾 Ⓗ, Family$, Ford/Lincoln/Mercury, Golden Eagle RV Park, RV World Camping, V1/LP
209	Johnson Rd, N 📶 FLYING J/Denny's/dsl/LP/scales/24hr
206	Hadsell Rd (no return)
205.5mm	continental divide, elev 7000
204	Knobs Rd
201	Daley Rd
196	Riner Rd
190mm	parking area wb, litter barrels
189mm	parking area eb, 🛏, litter barrels
187	WY 789, Creston, Baggs Rd
184	Continental Divide Rd
173	Wamsutter, N 📶 Loves/Chester's/Subway/dsl/24hr/@, S 📶 Conoco/dsl/repair/café/24hr, Phillips 66/dsl, 🍴 Broadway Café, 🛏 Wamsutter Motel
165	Red Desert
158	Tipton Rd continental divide, elev 6930
156	GL Rd
154	BLM Rd
152	Bar X Rd
150	Table Rock Rd
146	Patrick Draw Rd
144mm	rest area both lanes, full ♿ facilities, 🚻, 🛏, litter barrels, petwalk
143mm	parking area both lanes, litter barrels
142	Bitter Creek Rd
139	Red Hill Rd
136	Black Butte Rd
133mm	parking area both lanes
130	Point of Rocks, N 📶 Conoco/dsl, 🅾 RV Park
122	WY 371, to Superior
111	Airport Rd, Baxter Rd, S 🍴
107	Pilot Butte Ave, Rock Springs, S 📶 Kum&Go, Mobil/dsl, 🍴 Pizza Hut, 🛏 Sands Inn/cafe, Springs Motel
104	US 191 N, Elk St, Rock Springs, N 📶 Conoco/dsl, Exxon, FLYING J/Denny's/dsl/LP/24hr, Kum&Go/gas, Phillips 66/dsl, Sinclair, Texaco/Burger King/dsl, 🍴 McDonald's, Renegade Rest., Santa Fe SW Grill, Taco Time, 🛏 Best Western, EconoLodge/rest., 🅾 Buick/GMC,

Exit	Services
104	Continued truck repair, to Teton/Yellowstone Nat Parks via US 191, S 📶 Exxon/dsl, 🛏 Days Inn
103	College Dr, Rock Springs, S 📶 Loaf'n Jug/dsl/24hr, 🍴 Domino's 🅾 Ⓗ, W WY Coll
102	WY 430, Dewar Dr, Rock Springs, N 📶 Exxon, Loaf'N Jug, Sinclair/dsl, 🍴 Applebee's, China King, KFC/LJ Silver, Taco Time, 🛏 Best Value Inn, Comfort Inn La Quinta, Motel 6, 🅾 Cadillac/Chevrolet, Chrysler/Dodge, $Tree, Harley-Davidson, Herberger's, Home Depot, JC Penney, K-Mart, Smith's Foods, S 📶 Kum&Go, Loaf'N Jug, Mirastar/dsl, Mobil, 🍴 Arby's, Bonsai Chinese, Burger King, Golden Corral, IHOP, McDonald's, Pizza Hut, Quizno's, Sonic, Starbucks, Subway, Taco Bell, Village Inn, Wendy's, Wiki Hawaiian BBQ, Winger's, Wonderful House Chinese, 🛏 Budget Host, Hampton Inn, Holiday Inn, Holiday Inn Express, Homewood Suites, Motel 8, Quality Inn, Super 8, Wingate Inn, 🅾 Ⓗ, Albertsons/Sav-on, AutoZone, Big O Tire, Checker Parts, Curves, Ford/Lincoln/Mercury, Hastings Books, NAPA, Nissan, Radio Shack, Staples, Walgreens, Walmart
99	US 191 S, E Flaming Gorge Rd, N 🅾 KOA (1mi), S 📶 Sinclair/dsl/rest./24hr/@, 🍴 Ted's Rest., 🅾 fireworks, transmissions
94mm	Kissing Rock
91	US 30, to WY 530, Green River, **2 mi** S 📶 Gasamat, Loaf'N Jug, 🍴 Arctic Circle, Don Pedro's Mexican, McDonald's, Pizza Hut, Subway, Taco Time, 🛏 Coachman Inn, Mustang Inn, Super 8, 🅾 Expedition NHS, to Flaming Gorge NRA, same as 89
89	US 30, Green River, S 📶 Exxon/dsl, Sinclair/dsl, 🍴 Penny's Diner, Pizza Hut, 🛏 Hampton Inn, OakTree Inn, Super 8, Western Inn, 🅾 Adam's RV Service, Tex's RV Camp, to Flaming Gorge NRA
87.5mm	Green River
85	Covered Wagon Rd, S 🅾 Adams RV parts/service, Tex's Travel Camp
83	WY 372, La Barge Rd, N to Fontenelle Dam
78	(from wb)
77mm	Blacks Fork River
72	Westvaco Rd
71mm	parking area both lanes
68	Little America, N 📶 Sinclair/Little America Hotel/rest./dsl/24hr/@, 🅾 RV camping
66	US 30 W, to Teton, Yellowstone, Fossil Butte NM, Kemmerer
61	Cedar Mt Rd, to Granger
60mm	parking area both lanes, litter barrels
54mm	parking area eb, litter barrels

WY Map

Casper, Evansville, Glenrock, Douglas, Glendo, Guernsey, Bairoll, Garrett, Wheatland, Hanna, Medicine Bow, Yoder, Rawlins, Sinclair, Elk Mountain, Chugwater, Saratoga, Laramie, Centennial, Cheyenne, Encampment, Jelm, 25, 80

INTERSTATE 80 CONT'D

Exit	Services
53	Church Butte Rd
49mm	parking area wb, litter barrels
48	Lp 80, Lyman, Ft Bridger, Hist Ft Bridger
45mm	Blacks Fork River
41	WY 413, Lyman, **N** ⛽ Gas'n Go/cafe/dsl, **S** rest area both lanes, full ♿ facilities, 🅲, 🚻, litter barrels, petwalk, 🍴 Taco Time, 🅾 Gateway Inn (2mi), KOA (1mi)
39	WY 412, WY 414, to Carter, Mountain View
34	Lp 80, to Ft Bridger, **S** 🏨 Wagon Wheel Motel, 🅾 Ft Bridger RV Camp, Ft Bridger NHS, to Flaming Gorge NRA
33.5mm	parking area eb, litter barrels
33	Union Rd
30	Bigelow Rd, **N** ⛽ TA/Tesoro/Burger King/Taco Bell/Fork In the Road/dsl/scales/24hr/@, **S** fireworks
28	French Rd
28mm	French Rd, parking area both lanes
24	Leroy Rd
23	Bar Hat Rd
21	Coal Rd
18	US 189 N, to Kemmerer, to Nat Parks, Fossil Butte NM
15	Guild Rd (from eb)
14mm	parking area both lanes
13	Divide Rd
10	Painter Rd, to Eagle Rock Ski Area, to Eagle Rock Ski Area
6	US 189, Bear River Dr, Evanston, **N** ⛽ ▨▨▨/Subway/dsl/scales/24hr, Sinclair/dsl, 🍴 Bear Town Rest., Don Pedro Mexican, 🏨 Best Value Inn, Motel 6, Prairie Inn, Vagabond Motel, 🅾 Bear River RV Park, Wyo Downs Racetrack, repair/tires, **S** Welcome Ctr both lanes, full ♿ facilities, 🅲, 🚻, litter barrels, petwalk, RV dump (seasonal), playground, Bear River SP
5	WY 89, Evanston, **N** ⛽ Chevron/Taco Time/dsl, Maverik/dsl, 🍴 Arby's, DragonWall Chinese, McDonald's, Papa Murphy's, Subway, Wendy's, 🏨 EconoLodge, 🅾 🅷, AutoZone, Buick/Chevrolet, $Tree, Family$, Jiffy Lube, Murdoch's, NAPA, Verizon, Walmart/Subway, **S** WY St 🅷
3	US 189, Harrison Dr, Evanston, **N** ⛽ Chevron/dsl, ⬥FLYING J/Subway/dsl/scales/24hr, Gasamat, Sinclair, 🍴 JB's, Lotty's Rest., Wally's Burgers, 🏨 Best Western/rest., Comfort Inn, Days Inn, Hampton Inn, HighCountry Inn, HillCrest Motel, Holiday Inn Express, Howard Johnson, Super 8, 🅾 Cadillac/GMC, Chrysler/Jeep, USPO, **S** 🍴 KFC/Taco Bell, 🅾 🅷, fireworks
.5mm	**Port of Entry eb, weigh sta wb**
0mm	Wyoming/Utah state line

INTERSTATE 90

Exit	Services
207mm	Wyoming/South Dakota state line
205	Beulah, **N** ⛽ Shell/dsl/LP, 🍴 Buffalo Jump Rest., 🏨 The Mill, 🅾 Sand Creek Camping, USPO, **S** Ranch A NHP (5mi)
204.5mm	Sand Creek
199	WY 111, to Aladdin, **N** welcome ctr rest area (both directions), full ♿ facilities, 🚻, litter barrels, 🅲, petwalk, 🅾 Red Water Creek RV Park, to Devil's Tower NM, to Vore Buffalo Jump NHP
191	Moskee Rd
189	US 14 W, Sundance, **N** ⛽ Conoco/dsl/24hr, 🏨 Best Western, 🅾 🅷, Mt View Camping, to Devil's Tower NM,

---

189	Continued museum, **S** rest area both lanes, **full** ♿ **facilities**, info, 🅲, 🚻, litter barrels, playground, petwalk, RV dump, **port of entry/weigh sta**
187	WY 585, Sundance, **N** ⛽ Fresh Start/dsl, Sinclair/dsl, 🍴 Aro Rest., Subway, 🏨 Bear Lodge, Best Western, Budget Host Arrowhead, Pineview Motel, Rodeway Inn, 🅾 🅷, Decker's Foods, NAPA, to Devil's Tower
185	to WY 116, to Sundance, **S** ⛽ Conoco/dsl/service, **2 mi** same as 187
178	Coal Divide Rd
177mm	parking area both lanes
172	Inyan Kara Rd
171mm	parking area eb, litter barrels
165	Pine Ridge Rd, to Pine Haven, **N** Cedar Ridge RV Park (10mi), to Keyhole SP
163mm	parking area both lanes
160	Wind Creek Rd
154	US 14, US 16, **S** ⛽ Cenex/dsl, 🍴 Donna's Diner, Subway, 🏨 Cozy Motel, Moorcourt Motel, Rangerland Motel/RV Park, Wyo Motel, 🅾 Diehl's Foods/gas, USPO, museum, city park
153	US 16 E, US 14, W Moorcroft, **N** rest area both lanes, full ♿ facilities, 🅲, 🚻, litter barrels, petwalk, **S** same as 154
152mm	Belle Fourche River
141	Rozet
138mm	parking area both lanes
132	Wyodak Rd
129	Garner Lake Rd, **S** 🏨 Settle Inn, 🅾 Crazy Woman Camping, Harley-Davidson, High Plains Camping, auto repair
128	US 14, US 16, Gillette, Port of Entry, **N** ⛽ Conoco, Kum&Go, Maverik/dsl, 🍴 Mona's American/Mexican, Taco John's, Village Inn, 🏨 Howard Johnson, Mustang Motel, National 9 Inn, Smart Choice Inn, 🅾 Crazy Woman Camping (2mi), East Side RV Ctr, **S** 🏨 Settle Inn, 🅾 High Plains Camping
126	WY 59, Gillette, **N** ⛽ Cenex/dsl, Conoco/dsl, Loaf'N Jug, 🍴 China King Buffet, Hardee's, Maria's Mexican, McDonald's, Pokey's BBQ, Prime Rib Rest., Starbucks, Subway, 🏨 Best Value Inn, 🅾 Family$, Radio Shack, Smith's Foods, Tire Factory, city park, **S** ⛽ Exxon, ⬥FLYING J/dsl/24hr, Loaf'N Jug, 🍴 A&W/LJ Silver, Applebee's, Arby's, Aztec Buffet, Burger King, DQ, Goodtimes Grill/Taco John's, Great Wall Chinese, KFC, Papa Murphy's, Perkins/24hr, Pizza Hut, Quiznos, Taco Bell, Wendy's, 🏨 Candlewood Suites, Clarion, Country Inn&Suites, Days Inn, Fairfield Inn, Holiday Inn Express, Wingate Inn, 🅾 URGENT CARE, Ace Hardware, Albertson's, Big O Tire, $Tree, Goodyear/auto, Hastings Books, Home Depot, K-Mart, Office Depot, O'Reilly Parts, Osco Drug, Tire-O-Rama, Verizon, Walgreens, Walmart/Subway, city park
124	WY 50, Gillette, **N** ⛽ Conoco/dsl/24hr, Shell/Burger King/dsl, 🍴 Granny's Kitchen, Hong Kong Rest., Los Compadres Mexican, Pizza Hut, Subway, 🏨 Best Western/rest., Budget Inn, Comfort Inn, Hampton Inn, Motel 6, Super 8, 🅾 🅷, Don's Foods, **S** ⛽ Kum&Go/dsl, 🅾 Bighorn Tire, Buick/Chevrolet/GMC, Chrysler/Dodge/Jeep
116	Force Rd
113	Wild Horse Creek Rd
110mm	no services
106	Kingsbury Rd
102	Barber Creek Rd

INTERSTATE 90

E ↕ **W**
BUFFALO

Exit	Services
91	Dead Horse Creek Rd
89mm	Powder River
88	Powder River Rd, **N** 🅖 RV Park, rest area both lanes, full ♿ facilities, 🅒, 🚻, litter barrels, petwalk
82	Indian Creek Rd
77	Schoonover Rd
73.5mm	Crazy Woman Creek
73	Crazy Woman Creek Rd
69	Dry Creek Rd
68.5mm	parking area both lanes, litter barrels (wb only)
65	Red Hills Rd, Tipperary Rd
60mm	parking area both lanes, litter barrels
58	US 16, to Ucross, Buffalo, **0-3 mi S** 🅖 Cenex/rest/dsl/24hr, Maverik/dsl, Shell/dsl/24hr, 🍴 Bozeman Tr Steaks, Dash Inn Rest., Hardee's, McDonald's, Pizza Hut, Sub Shop, Subway, Taco John's, Winchester Steaks, 🛏 Best Western Crossroads, Comfort Inn, EconoLodge, Hampton Inn, Holiday Inn Express, Motel 6, Super 8, WYO Motel, 🅞 Ⓗ, Ace Hardware, Bighorn Tire, Deer Park Camping, Family$, Indian RV Camp, NAPA, Twin Creeks Verizon, Nat Hist Dist, vet
56b	I-25 S, US 87 S, to Buffalo
56a	25 Bus, 90 Bus, to Buffalo, services 2mi S (from eb)
53	Rock Creek Rd
51	Lake DeSmet, **1 mi N** Lake Stop gas/motel/cafe, Lake De Smet RV park
47	Shell Creek Rd
44	US 87 N, Piney Creek Rd, to Story, Banner, **N** 🅞 Ft Phil Kearney, museum, **5 mi S** Wagon Box Cabins/Rest.
39mm	scenic turnout wb
37	Prairie Dog Creek Rd, to Story
33	Meade Creek Rd, to Big Horn

S
H
E
R
I
D
A
N

31mm	parking area eb
25	US 14 E, Sheridan, **N** 🛏 Quality Inn, 🅞 Dalton's RV Ctr, **S** 🅖 Exxon/dsl, Holiday, Loaf'n Jug/dsl, Maverik/dsl, 🍴 Arby's, Burger King, Goodtimes/Taco John's, JB's, Los Agaves, Ole's Pizza, Papa Murphy's, Perkins/24hr, Starbucks, Subway, Taco Bell, Wendy's, 🛏 Candlewood Suites, Days Inn, Holiday Inn, Mill Inn, Parkway Motel, 🅞 Ace Hardware, Albertsons/Osco Drug, Buick/Cadillac/GMC, $Tree, Firestone, Ford/Lincoln/Mercury, Goodyear, Home Depot, Jeep, NAPA, O'Reilly Parts, Tire-Rama, Toyota, Walgreens, Walmart, 🛒, mall, to Hist Dist, Sheridan Coll, vet
23	WY 336, 5th St, Sheridan, **N** 🅖 Rock Stop/Subway/dsl, 🛏 Wingate Inn, rest area both lanes, full ♿ facilities, info, 🅒, 🚻, litter barrels, petwalk, RV dump, **1-2 mi S** 🅖 Cenex, Holiday/dsl, 🍴 DQ, Olivia's Kitchen, Pablo's Mexican, Quizno's, 🛏 Alamo Motel, Best Value Inn, Best Western, Hampton Inn, Motel 6, Sheridan Inn, 🅞 Ⓗ, Honda, Peter D's RV Park, Sheridan Cty Museum, park, radiators
20	Main St, Sheridan, **S** 🅖 Exxon/dsl/scales/24hr, Gas A Mat/dsl, Maverik, Shell/dsl, 🍴 Country Kitchen, Domino's, Little Ceasar's, McDonald's, Pizza Hut, 🛏 Aspen Inn, Bramble Motel, Budget Host, Stage Stop Motel, Sundown Motel, Super 8, Super Saver Motel, Trails End Motel/rest., 🅞 Ⓗ, K-Mart, Peerless Tires
16	to Decker, Montana, port of entry
15mm	Tongue River
14	Acme Rd
9	US 14 W, Ranchester, **1mi S** 🅖 Big Country Oil/dsl, 🅞 Western Motel, 🅞 Foothills Campground, Lazy R Campground, to Yellowstone, Teton NPs, Conner Bfd NHS, Ski Area
1	Parkman
0mm	Wyoming/Montana state line

WY

Assist A Fellow Traveler with...

Published annually,
the Next EXIT ®
provides the best
USA Interstate Highway Information available.
Use this form to order another copy of
the Next EXIT®
for yourself or someone special.